A GUIDE BOOK OF
UNITED STATES COINS
MEGA RED™
5TH EDITION

George Washington was president of the United States when the
first U.S. Mint was established in Philadelphia, Pennsylvania, in 1792.

THE OFFICIAL RED BOOK®

A GUIDE BOOK OF
UNITED STATES COINS
MEGA RED™
5ᵀᴴ EDITION

R.S. YEOMAN

SENIOR EDITOR, **Q. DAVID BOWERS**
VALUATIONS EDITOR **JEFF GARRETT**
EDITOR EMERITUS **KENNETH BRESSETT**

A Fully Illustrated Catalog of Useful Information on Colonial and Federal Coinage, 1616 to Date, With Detailed Photographs to Identify Your Coins and Retail Valuation Charts Indicating How Much They're Worth. Plus Illustrated Grading Instructions With Enlarged Images to Determine Your Coins' Conditions. Insider Tips on Treasures Waiting to be Discovered in Your Pocket Change; Advice on Smart Collecting; and More. Based on the Expertise of More Than 100 Professional Coin Dealers and Researchers. Also Featuring Entertaining Stories, Amazing Essays, and Astounding Facts and Figures About All Manner of Rare and Historical Coins of the United States of America.

A Guide Book of United States Coins™, Deluxe Edition
THE OFFICIAL RED BOOK OF UNITED STATES COINS™

THE OFFICIAL RED BOOK, MEGA RED, and
THE OFFICIAL RED BOOK OF UNITED STATES COINS
are trademarks of Whitman Publishing, LLC.

ISBN: 0794847056
Printed in the United States of America.

Collect all the books in the Bowers Series. *A Guide Book of Morgan Silver Dollars* • *A Guide Book of Double Eagle Gold Coins* • *A Guide Book of United States Type Coins* • *A Guide Book of Modern United States Proof Coin Sets* • *A Guide Book of Shield and Liberty Head Nickels* • *A Guide Book of Flying Eagle and Indian Head Cents* • *A Guide Book of Washington and State Quarters* • *A Guide Book of Buffalo and Jefferson Nickels* • *A Guide Book of Lincoln Cents* • *A Guide Book of United States Commemorative Coins* • *A Guide Book of United States Tokens and Medals* • *A Guide Book of Gold Dollars* • *A Guide Book of Peace Dollars* • *A Guide Book of the Official Red Book of United States Coins* • *A Guide Book of Franklin and Kennedy Half Dollars* • *A Guide Book of Civil War Tokens* • *A Guide Book of Hard Times Tokens* • *A Guide Book of Mercury Dimes, Standing Liberty Quarters, and Liberty Walking Half Dollars* • *A Guide Book of Half Cents and Large Cents* • *A Guide Book of Barber Silver Coins* • *A Guide Book of Liberty Seated Silver Coins* • *A Guide Book of Modern U.S. Dollar Coins* • *A Guide Book of the United States Mint* • *A Guide Book of Gold Eagle Coins*.

For a complete listing of numismatic reference books, supplies, and storage products, visit Whitman Publishing online at www.whitman.com.

If you enjoy U.S. and related coins, join the American Numismatic Association. Visit the ANA online at www.money.org.

WHITMAN™

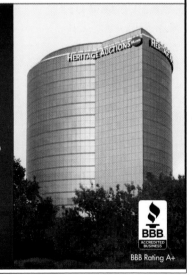

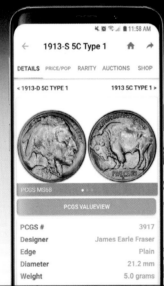

CONTENTS

CONTENTS

CREDITS AND ACKNOWLEDGMENTS

CONTRIBUTORS TO THE FIFTH MEGA RED

Senior Editor: Q. David Bowers. *Valuations Editor:* Jeff Garrett. *Editor Emeritus:* Kenneth Bressett.
Special Consultants: Philip Bressett, Maxwell Gregory, Robert Rhue, Troy Thoreson, Ben Todd, Jake Walker

The following coin dealers and collectors have contributed pricing information to this edition:

Gary Adkins	Mike Fuljenz	Donald H. Kagin	Maurice Rosen
Buddy Alleva	Dennis M. Gillio	Jim Koenings	Gerald R. Scherer Jr.
Mitchell Battino	Ronald J. Gillio	Julian M. Leidman	Harry Schultz
Lee J. Bellisario	Rusty Goe	Denis W. Loring	Jeff Shevlin
William Bugert	Kenneth M. Goldman	Dwight N. Manley	Roger Siboni
H. Robert Campbell	Thomas Hallenbeck	Syd Martin	James Simek
Elizabeth Coggan	James Halperin	David McCarthy	David M. Sundman
Gary and Alan Cohen	Stephen Hayden	Lee S. Minshull	Barry Sunshine
Stephen M. Cohen	Brian Hendelson	Charles Morgan	Anthony Terranova
Steve Contursi	John W. Highfill	Paul Nugget	Troy Thoreson
Adam Crum	Brian Hodge	Mike Orlando	Frank VanValen
Steven Ellsworth	Jack Howes	Joseph Parrella	Fred Weinberg
Gerry Fortin	Steve Ivy	Robert M. Paul	Mark S. Yaffe
Pierre Fricke	Amandeep Jassal	Robert Rhue	
John Frost	Joseph Jones	Steve Roach	

Special credit is due to the following for contributions to the *Guide Book of United States Coins, Deluxe Edition*: Gary Adkins, David W. Akers, John Albanese, David Allison, Jeff Ambio, the American Numismatic Society, Marc Banks, Mitchell Battino, Jack Beymer, Doug Bird, Jon Alan Boka, Mark Borckardt, Q. David Bowers, Kenneth Bressett, Nicholas P. Brown, Roger W. Burdette, David J. Camire, Julia Casey, Fonda Chase, Elizabeth Coggan, Greg Cohen, Ray Czahor, John W. Dannreuther, Beth Deisher, Dan Demeo, Richard Doty, Bill Eckberg, Michael Fahey, David Fanning, Bill Fivaz, Pierre Fricke, Jeff Garrett, Ira Goldberg, Lawrence Goldberg, Ken Goldman, J.R. Grellman Jr., Ron Guth, James Halperin, Greg Hannigan, Phil Hinkelman, Daniel W. Holmes Jr., Gwyn Huston, Walter Husak, Tom Hyland, Wayne Imbrogno, Steve Ivy, R.W. Julian, Brad Karoleff, David W. Lange, Julian Leidman, Jon Lerner, Denis W. Loring, John Lusk, Ron Manley, J.P. Martin, Jim Matthews, Chris Victor-McCawley, Jim McGuigan, Jack McNamara, Harry Miller, Paul Minshull, Scott Mitchell, Charles Moore, Dan Moore, Jim Neiswinter, Eric P. Newman, Numismatic Guaranty Corporation of America (NGC), Joel J. Orosz, John M. Pack, D. Brent Pogue, Michael Printz, Jim Reardon, Tom Reynolds, Harry Salyards, Louis Scuderi, Thomas Serfass, Neil Shafer, Michael Sherrill, Jeff Shevlin, Craig Sholley, the Smithsonian Institution, Rick Snow, Max Spiegel, Lawrence R. Stack, David M. Sundman, Barry Sunshine, David Sunshine, James Taylor, Saul Teichman, R. Tettenhorst, Scott Travers, Rich Uhrich, the United States Mint, Frank Van Valen, Alan V. Weinberg, Fred Weinberg, Ken and Stephanie Westover, James Wiles, Ray Williams, Doug Winter, David Wnuck, and Winston Zack.

Special credit is due to the following for service and data in the 2020 regular edition of the *Guide Book of United States Coins*: Frank J. Colletti, Charles Davis, David Fanning, George F. Kolbe, Christopher McDowell, and P. Scott Rubin.

Special credit is due to the following for service in past editions: David Akers, John Albanese, Lyman Allen, Jeff Ambio, Michael Aron, Philip E. Benedetti, Richard A. Bagg, Jack Beymer, George Blenker, Walter Breen, John Burns, Jason Carter, Marc Crane, Silvano DiGenova, Cynthia Roden Doty, Ken Duncan, Bob Entlich, John Feigenbaum, George Fitzgerald, Dennis Forgue, Harry Forman, George Fuld, Henry Garrett, William Gay, Harry Gittelson, J.R. Grellman, Ron Guth, John Hamrick, Gene L. Henry, Karl D. Hirtzinger, Michael Hodder, John L. Howes, Robert Jacobs, James J. Jelinski, Larry Johnson, A.M. Kagin, Stanley Kesselman, Jerry Kimmel, Mike Kliman, Paul Koppenhaver, Robert B. Lecce, Ed Leventhal, Stuart Levine, Kevin Lipton, Arnold Margolis, David McCarthy, Chris McCawley, Glenn Miller, Charles Morgan, Richard Nachbar, Casey Noxon, Paul Nugget, John M. Pack, William P. Paul, Thomas Payne, Beth Piper, Doug Plasencia, Andrew Pollock III, John Porter, Mike Ringo, Cherie Schoeps, J.S. Schreiber, Hugh Sconyers, Robert Shaw, Arlie Slabaugh, Thomas Smith, William Spencer, Paul Spiegel, Lawrence R. Stack, Maurice Storck Sr., Charles Surasky, Anthony J. Swiatek, Steve Tanenbaum, Mark Van Winkle, Russell Vaughn, Douglas Winter, and Mark Yaffe.

Special photo credits are due to the following: Al Adams, the American Numismatic Association, Angel Dee's Coins and Collectibles, the Architect of the Capitol (Washington, D.C.), Douglas F. Bird, Karen Bridges, Michael Bugeja, Civil War Token Society, Steve Contursi, Tom Denly, Bill Fivaz, Ira & Larry Goldberg Coins & Collectibles, Kenneth Goldman, Colin Gullberg, Isaiah Hageman, Steve Hayden, the estate of Bernard Heller, Heritage Auctions (www.ha.com), Rich Licato, Littleton Coin Co., Tom Mulvaney, Numismatic Guaranty Corporation of America (NGC), PCGS, Doug Plasencia, D. Brent Pogue, Jon Potts, Jim Pruitt, David Reimer, Sarasota Rare Coin Gallery, John Scanlon, Jeff Shevlin, Bob Simpson, Pete Smith, the Smithsonian Institution, Spectrum, Stack's Bowers Galleries, J.T. Stanton, Richard Stinchcomb, Barry Sunshine, Superior Galleries, Steve Tannenbaum, and the United States Mint.

HOW TO USE THIS BOOK

Numismatics, in its purest sense, is the study of items used as money. Today in the United States, as around the world, the term embraces the activities of a diverse community of hobbyists, historians, researchers, museum curators, and others who collect and study coins, tokens, paper money, and similar objects.

Since 1946 the *Guide Book of United States Coins* has served this community as the preeminent annual reference for coin specifications, mintages, values, photographs, and other information important to collectors and students. With more than 23 million copies in print since the first edition, the *Guide Book* (commonly known as the "Red Book") is well established as the most popular reference in numismatics—not to mention one of the best-selling nonfiction books in the history of American publishing. (In 1964 the 18th edition of the Red Book ranked number 5 on the national sales lists, at 1.2 million copies—higher than Dale Carnegie's *How to Win Friends and Influence People* at number 6, and John F. Kennedy's *Profiles in Courage* at number 9.)

Building on this strong foundation, the Deluxe Edition of the *Guide Book of United States Coins* is an expanded and enlarged volume intended to serve not only beginning collectors, but also intermediate to advanced coin collectors, professional coin dealers and auctioneers, researchers, and investors. It features more photographs, detailed higher-grade valuations, additional listings of die varieties and rare early Proof coins, certified-coin population data, auction records, and other resources that provide a wealth of information on every coin type ever made by the U.S. Mint. The Deluxe Edition also expands on the regular edition's coverage of collectible die varieties, with close-up photographs, valuations, and chart notes. It is a handy single-source guide that educates its users in auction and certification trends, retail valuations, and similar aspects of the marketplace.

Like the regular-edition Red Book, the Deluxe Edition includes information on colonial and early American coins and tokens as well as all federal series (copper half cents through gold double eagles). It also covers private and territorial gold pieces; Hard Times tokens; Civil War tokens; Confederate coins; Hawaiian, Puerto Rican, and Philippine coins; Alaskan tokens; misstrikes and errors; numismatic books; Proof and Mint sets; commemorative coins from 1892 to date; silver, gold, and platinum bullion coins; and other topics.

Readers of the *Guide Book of United States Coins, Deluxe Edition,* benefit from the following useful information.

The "Red Book" has become a popular collectible itself, with fans striving to acquire one of each edition dating back to number 1, published in November 1946 with a 1947 cover date. Rare early volumes can be worth $1,000 or more.

R.S. Yeoman, author of the original *Guide Book of United States Coins,* examining press proofs in 1969.

DENOMINATION INTRODUCTIONS

Each coinage denomination is discussed first in an overview of its history, major design types and subtypes, and general collectability by type. (The dollar denomination is divided into silver dollars, trade dollars, and modern dollars.) A second essay gives collectors a more in-depth analysis of specializing in that denomination. *These sections encapsulate decades of numismatic research and market observation, and they should be read in conjunction with the charts, photographs, and other information that follow.*

TYPE-BY-TYPE STUDIES

Within each denomination, each major coin type is laid out in chronological order. As in the regular-edition Red Book, the type's designer and its specifications (weight, composition, diameter, edge treatment, and production facilities) are given. Coinage designs are pictured at actual size except commemorative designs, which are standardized (one Mint State example and one Proof example, when available). Each type section includes summary text on the type's history; aspects of its striking, sharpness, and related characteristics; and its market availability. In-depth grading instructions, with enlarged illustrations, show how to grade each coin type, covering circulation strikes as well as Proofs.

CHARTS

The data charts include these elements:

	Mintage	Cert	Avg	%MS	G-4	VG-8	F-12	VF-20	EF-40	AU-50	MS-60 PF-60	MS-63 PF-63	MS-65 PF-65
1840, Medium Letters (b)	(c)	47	40.0	15%	$140	$190	$275	$450	$800	$1,600	$3,750	$7,750	$23,500
Auctions: $2,233, MS-62, February 2015; $1,028, AU-58, January 2015; $259, EF-45, May 2015; $188, VF-30, September 2015													
1840, Small Letters, Proof	4–8	7	64.0										$100,000
Auctions: $30,550, PF-63, November 2013													
1840-O	855,100	130	49.0	27%	$42	$55	$70	$115	$190	$400	$900	$3,500	
Auctions: $2,350, MS-62, January 2015; $1,410, MS-60, June 2015; $212, EF-45, June 2015; $141, VF-30, June 2015													
1841	310,000	75	54.8	32%	$42	$60	$95	$150	$275	$450	$1,400	$2,800	$9,000
Auctions: $11,750, MS-65, May 2015; $4,230, MS-64, January 2015; $857, AU-58, June 2015; $364, EF-45, August 2015													
1841, Proof	4–8	6	64.5								$20,000	$45,000	$85,000
Auctions: $30,550, PF-64, September 2013													

b. The 1840, Medium Letters, half dollars were struck at the New Orleans Mint from a reverse die of the previous style, without mintmark. **c.** Included in circulation-strike 1840, Small Letters, mintage figure. **d.** Included in 1842, Medium Date, mintage figure.

Mintages. Mintage data is compiled from official Mint records whenever possible, and in other cases from more than 70 years of active numismatic research. In instances where the Mint's early records are in question or have been proven faulty, the official numbers are provided and further information is given in chart notes. For some early Proof coins for which no official mintage records exist, an estimated mintage, or the number of coins known in collections, is given. For modern issues (usually those minted within the past five years), the Mint has released production and/or sales numbers that are not yet officially finalized; these are given in italics.

Note that Mint reports are not always reliable for estimating the rarities of coins. In the early years of the Mint, coinage dies of previous years often were used until they became worn or broken. Certain reported quantities, particularly for gold and silver coins, cover the number of pieces struck and make no indication of the quantity that actually reached circulation. Many issues were deposited in the Treasury as backing for paper currency and later were melted without ever being released to the public.

Gold coins struck before August 1, 1834, are rare today because from 1821 onward (and at times before 1821) the gold in the coins was worth more than their face values, so they were struck as bullion and traded at a premium. Many were exported and melted for their precious-metal value.

Mintage figures shown for 1964 through 1966 are for coins bearing those dates. Some of these coins were struck in more than one year and at various mints, both with and without mintmarks. In recent years, mintage figures reported by the Mint have been revised several times and precise amounts remain uncertain.

Mintage figures shown in italics are estimates based on the most accurate information available. Numismatic research is constantly ongoing, and listed figures are sometimes revised, when new information becomes available.

Certified Populations. For each coin of a particular date and mint, a summary is provided of (1) the number of coins certified, (2) the average grade, on the standard 1–70 scale, of those coins graded, and (3) for circulation-strike coins, the percentage certified in Mint State.

These summaries provide the collector and investor with working data useful in comparing coins offered for sale or bid.

Certified population data is provided courtesy of Numismatic Guaranty Corporation of America (NGC), one of the nation's leading professional third-party grading firms.

It should be noted that for most coins, especially rare dates and varieties, the number certified actually represents the quantity of *submissions*, rather than the number of individual coins submitted. For example, a particular 1801 silver dollar that is submitted for certification five times would be counted the same as five individual coins. Such resubmissions can sometimes result in numbers close to or higher than a coin's entire surviving mintage.

Note, too, that the grade number assigned to a "slabbed" (graded and encapsulated) coin does not tell anything about the strength of that particular coin's strike, the quality of its planchet, whether it has been cleaned or dipped, or its overall eye appeal. Such factors are important to a coin's value. Two rare coins of the same date and variety, each with the same amount of surface wear and graded, for example, MS-63, will find different values in the marketplace if one is eye-pleasing and well struck, and the other is dull and poorly struck.

Valuations. Coin values shown in the Deluxe Edition are retail prices compiled from data and market observations provided by active coin dealers, auctioneers, and other qualified observers, under the direction and analysis of Valuations Editor Jeff Garrett and Senior Editor Kenneth Bressett and their consultants. In this guide book, values from under $1 up to several hundred dollars are for "raw" coins—that is, coins that have *not* been graded and encapsulated by a professional third-party grading service. Values near or above $500 reflect typical auction and retail prices seen for professionally certified coins. The valuations of professionally certified coins often are higher than what collectors normally pay for non-certified ("raw") coins. Values of certified coins may vary widely, depending on the grading service.

The coin market is so active in some categories that values can readily change after publication. Values are shown as a guide and are not intended to serve as a price list for any dealer's stock. A dash appearing in a valuations column indicates that coins in that grade exist even though there are no current retail or auction records for them. The dash does not necessarily mean that such coins are exceedingly rare. Italicized numbers indicate unsettled or speculative (estimated) values. A number of listings of rare coins lack valuations or dashes in certain grades, indicating that they are not available, or not believed to exist, in those grades. Proof coins are usually not shown with values in circulated grades.

For wholesale pricing, the *Handbook of United States Coins* (popularly called the Blue Book, and published since 1942), by R.S. Yeoman, contains average prices dealers nationwide will pay for U.S. coins. It is obtainable through most coin dealers, hobby shops, bookstores, and the Internet.

Auction Records. Multiple recent auction records are provided for nearly every coin (some exceptions being coins that are too common to sell individually at auction). Each record indicates:

    the price paid for the coin (including any fees)

    the grade of the coin

    the date (month and year) of the auction

This combination of auction data gives valuable market information for each coin. It also serves as a springboard for further research. Many auction firms have online archives of coins sold, or else their auction catalogs can be studied using the information provided.

Chart notes. Additional information is provided for certain coins in chart notes. Historical background, die-variety diagnostics, notable market conditions, and other specific details are intended to further guide the collector and investor.

Abbreviations. These are some of the abbreviations you'll find in the charts.

    %MS—Percentage of coins certified in Mint State

    Avg—Average grade (on a 1–70 scale)

    BN—Brown; descriptive of the coloration or toning on certain copper coins

    Cam—Cameo

    Cert—Certified population

    DblDie—Doubled Die

    DCam—Deep Cameo

    DMPL—Deep Mirror Prooflike

    D/S—D Over S; a slash between words or letters represents an overdate or overmintmark

    Dt—Date

    Ex.—Extremely

    FB—Full Bands

    FBL—Full Bell Lines

    FH—Full Head

    FS—Full Steps

    FT—Full Torch

    Horiz—Horizontal

    Inv—Inverted

    Knbd—Knobbed-Top

    Lg—Large

    Ltrd—Lettered

    Ltrs—Letters

    Med—Medium

    Mintmk—Mintmark

    Obv—Obverse

    QuintDie—Quintupled Die

RB—Red and brown; descriptive of the mixture of mint red and brown coloration or toning on a copper coin

RD—Red; descriptive of the mint red color on an untoned copper coin

Rev—Reverse

RPD—Repunched Date

RPM—Repunched Mintmark

Sm—Small

SMS—Special Mint Set

Sq—Square

TransRev—Transitional Reverse

TripDie—Tripled Die

UCam—Ultra Cameo

Var—Variety

2019 COIN MARKET REPORT

by Valuations Editor Jeff Garrett

There are millions of coin collectors in the United States, but the hobby is not immune to the laws of supply and demand. The supply imbalance of the last few years has probably had a greater impact on rare-coin prices than any other factor. Nearly all would agree that the number of collectors who are actively involved in the hobby has been flat or somewhat diminished in recent years. Some longtime observers of numismatics blame aging demographics. Others feel that social media and everything "Internet" has diverted attention that would otherwise be spent on collecting. Numismatics is not alone in these concerns, as nearly all other established hobby fields are feeling the same waves of change. Numismatics has actually fared much better than some fields, such as stamp collecting and antiques.

With the demand side of the equation being flat or in decline, the last few years has been challenging from the standpoint of supply entering the market. In the last three to five years many major, lifelong collections (of D. Brent Pogue, Eric Newman, Henry P. Kendall, and others) were offered for sale in unreserved public auctions. Some of these collections had been off the market for generations. Others were collections that had been formed more recently, but were still incredibly impressive and impactful on the market.

Many of these sales contained amazing collections of colonial and early American coinage. Early American coinage is one of my favorite areas of the market, and one that is covered here and in *A Guide Book of United States Coins* (the regular-edition *Red Book*). Many hobbyists view the collecting of colonial American coinage as a more advanced pursuit of numismatics. The number of collectors is much more limited than for series such as Morgan silver dollars. The above-mentioned collections overwhelmed the demand for many sections of colonial coinage. Prices for many popular early American coins slipped as a result. A high-grade classic Massachusetts New England "NE" shilling (1652) which normally would be seen at auction every several years, was offered multiple times, each time at lower prices. The 2015 *Red Book* price of $350,000 for an Extremely Fine example dropped to $225,000 in the 2019 edition (published in 2018). At the same time the market for affordable colonial and early American coins such as state coppers of the 1780s and Fugio cents remains strong.

The same scenario has also played out in recent years in the field of early United States copper coinage. Quite a few major collections of early copper half cents and cents have been sold, and new major buyers have not arrived in numbers to match those bidding high prices 10 to 20 years ago. It has been reported to me that top-quality coins are still in strong demand, but lesser-quality, *rare* Sheldon varieties have fallen in price. As mentioned above with colonial coinage, the thinner market participation and increased supply have adversely affected the market for higher-grade expensive varieties of early copper coinage.

Some other areas of the market were better able to absorb the quantity of material being offered for sale in these major actions. Early silver and gold coins from 1794 to the 1830s have fared quite well and in some cases price increases have been reported. Some of the finest early coins in existence have been sold in the last few years. These were mostly from the collection of D. Brent Pogue. Prices for some of these coins far exceeded expectations and were once again a reminder that collectors will show up in force when "once in a lifetime" opportunities present themselves. Other collections of high-quality early federal silver and gold coinage did extremely well in the last few years as well.

One of my biggest observations of the last several years has been the active participation of serious collectors and the diminished buying of rare-coin speculators and investors. Every seasoned collector hopes their expenditure in rare coins will one day prove to be a solid investment, but it is not the primary or driving force in their buying decisions. Collectors love the history and romance numismatics has to offer and many will be active for long periods of time, if not a lifetime. Investors are interested in short-term gains or portable wealth the hobby may provide.

The interest of investors in numismatics has a long and complicated history, but is usually punctuated by sharp rises and crashes. Investors are usually drawn to the hobby by headline events, such as soaring bullion prices or financial panics such as in 2008 and 2009. Inevitably, these unsophisticated buyers soon lose interest and, most likely, a portion of their investment. Serious collector demand is much better for long term health of the hobby.

The domination of collectors has had another interesting and significant impact on numismatics. Collectors are much more quality-conscious than investors. When I mention quality, I am not talking about those who only buy the finest known examples of a particular series. Serious collectors want coins that look good and are exceptional for the grade. This can mean a Very Fine Draped Bust silver dollar that has normal wear, but is free of cleaning, scratches, nicks, or dark toning. The same can be said for nearly every series of United States coinage. It also translates to every grade from Poor 1 to MS-70. Simply put, collectors are demanding quality within a grade and are willing to pay for it. A quick study of the auction results of any major auction demonstrates this new demand for coins with great eye appeal. Coins of the same grade but softly struck or without eye appeal often sell at auction for much different prices—sometime as much as 50 percent difference.

There has been much discussion among experts, collectors, dealers, and the grading companies themselves about evolving grading standards. No one really argues the fact that grading standards of 30 years ago have changed. This is clearly seen when some coins graded 25 to 30 years ago by NGC or PCGS sell at auction. They frequently bring substantial premiums over coins that have earned the same grades more recently. It's a complicated subject with thousands of variables. The fact that *Photograde* and the Official ANA Grading Standards have been slowly abandoned by many buyers, sellers, and graders over the years should really come as no surprise. Coin dealers for decades have spent millions resubmitting high-end coins hoping for the next higher grade. This is understandable, considering the huge price jumps for many coins from one grade to the next. In a way this has been win-win for the owners of coins, and for the third-party grading firms it is much more profitable to grade a coin several times than just once.

Over time, the result has been a noticeable shift as the standards in effect in the 1980s were left behind. Time also created a learning curve for the grading companies. Over the decades they have seen nearly every coin in the book, and then some. This increased knowledge has also led to changes in rare-coin grading. When grading becomes too liberal, prices for those products drop in the open market.

This has been the case in the last few years for various segments of the market. Silver dollars and twentieth-century gold coins are just a couple of examples. In some instances what was MS-65 per the old 1980s standards and very rare in PCGS and NGC population reports is now MS-66 or better. This has caused a drop in the price of some more recently graded coins. The price drops becomes understandable as a result of changing grading, not of a changing market.

Understanding grading is one of the most important tasks for anyone who wants to be a successful collector. When purchasing coins, it is important to understand grading for the series you collect. As has always been the case, you should "buy the coin and not the holder."

The above-mentioned buyer emphasis on quality makes the task of pricing coins for *Mega Red* and the *Red Book* or any other price guide quite difficult. For now, prices are for the theoretical "average" examples of a given series or individual coin. In the future, there may be a need to express prices in terms of price ranges given for the sake of accuracy. In the meantime, collectors are encouraged to do careful price research when making a major buying decision. Whitman Publishing offers an amazing number of research tools for collectors, including a specialty book on nearly every facet of numismatics.

In addition to the many books focusing on segments of numismatics, there are also dozens of great specialized numismatic organizations for collectors of a particular series. One of my favorites is the Liberty Seated Collectors Club (www.LSCCweb.org), which has been very active in recent decades. Members of this club, and many others, share their collective knowledge with each other and offer tremendous research information. Liberty Seated coinage has been in strong demand in recent years, in no small part due to the efforts of this fine organization. The American Numismatic Association (ANA) has a list of most specialty membership clubs listed on its web site, www.money.org.

I have been very involved in the ANA for many years, including serving as president from 2015 to 2017. One of my biggest goals as president was to greatly increase membership in the organization. After two years of trying every idea that the board and I could think of, a small increase was the best we could muster. Other hobby organizations have seen dropping membership numbers, so a small increase has been seen as a victory. Membership numbers are important not only for the health of the ANA, but for the health of the hobby in general. The ANA has a long history of creating serious collectors and dealers (including me). Its offering of educational material for all levels of numismatics is unmatched. The organization is also the premier advocate for Young Numismatists in the country. The future of numismatics is not guaranteed, and organizations such as the ANA are among the best things going for our hobby.

The ANA is valuable for educating collectors once they have been exposed to the hobby. One of the challenges has been to get people interested in the hobby in the first place. The last great general introduction in numismatics occurred in 1999 when the State quarters program was introduced nationwide. Millions of new individuals began a collection of State quarters for face value or at a small premium if bought from a dealer, and substantial numbers graduated to more advanced interest in numismatics. Modern coins have been a wonderful "gateway" into more serious numismatics for millions of collectors. It has been estimated that more people now collect American Silver Eagles than Morgan and Peace silver dollars. The "golden dollars" from the 2000 Sacagawea to date, through several series, have been widely popular. That is understandable, as a complete set is much more affordable for the more modern version of American silver dollars.

Modern coins are not without their detractors, and there has been much debate in recent years about the pros and cons of the aftermarket value of modern U.S. Mint products. The biggest negative from most people's perspective has been the amount of money that flows from the hobby when the U.S. Mint releases its next big thing. Many feel this is money that collectors could or should be spending on vintage U.S. coinage. Others feel the flow of new collectors drawn to the hobby by mass-market advertising of the products outweighs the negatives.

Another major force in recent years for American numismatics has been the tremendous interest in set-registry collecting. Set registries have been created by PCGS and NGC for collectors to compete with one another building sets. There are tens of thousands of sets registered, with collectors around the world competing with one another. This competition has greatly skewed the prices for many finest-known examples of coins, with collectors willing to pay sometimes irrational (in my opinion) prices for pieces that are common and inexpensive in, say, MS-65 Gem grade, but for which only a few have been graded close to MS-70, that will give them a leg up on their rivals.

Set-registry collecting has had a huge impact on prices in recent years for coins at the top of the grading range. This competition is not without risks, however. It has not been uncommon for a coin to sell for a huge price when there has only been one example at the top end of the population report. The risk comes when another, or more than one, example receives the same grade. The once nearly unobtainable now becomes more readily available and prices drop—sometime considerably. This has been the case in recent years for many twentieth-century series such as Lincoln cents, Jefferson nickels, and so on.

Morgan and Peace dollars have also seen substantial drops at the high end of the market. This has been caused by increased supply and more emphasis on quality within the grade range, and many other factors, including, for example, yesteryear's MS-65 coins now grading 66 or 67. There are exceptions and when amazing examples of varieties that are key in any grades (1889-CC, 1893-S, 1934-S, and the like) cross the auction block, or are offered privately, new price records are not uncommon. Beautifully toned Morgan silver dollars continue to stun me when I review prices realized after a major sale.

One of the biggest stories of the last few years in American numismatics has been the crash of premiums paid for bullion-related classic United States gold coins. Many American double eagles now trade for just a few percent above melt when offered for sale. These coins now sell at the lowest premium to melt in my 45 years as a professional numismatist. This situation is deeply rooted in the supply-and-demand story for numismatics. There is simply not enough *numismatic* demand for the amount of coins now on the market. Some attribute this lack of demand for vintage U.S. gold coins to the rise in popularity of American Gold Eagles. U.S. double eagles contain .9675 ounce of gold and many hard-money investors prefer the exactly 1 ounce of precious metal that American Gold Eagles offer. Another concern is that many of today's investors can simply buy a gold ETF (electronic traded fund) with little effort. For decades, United States gold coins which had been sent overseas in the nineteenth and twentieth centuries have been slowly flowing back into this country. The pace of this repatriation has increased in recent years and the supply has overwhelmed numismatic demand. The good news: premiums can't get any lower!

Another fascinating aspect of the rare-coin market in the last few years has been the increase activity of mega-collectors. At least three or four individuals have spent more than $100 million on their coin collections in recent years. One collector has quite publicly stated his desire to build the best collection of United States coins ever assembled. Another collector from the tech world is trying to assemble a complete set of every coin ever struck worldwide!

These so-called mega-collectors are not just buying million-dollar coins. They are actively building sets of United States, world, and ancient coins. They want the finest pieces available and will spend to get them. These collectors have been very fortunate in the last several years as quite a few legacy collections have been offered at auction.

The question is, why have they invested so heavily into the "hobby of kings," numismatics? After speaking with one of these collectors, and others who know them, I see one common motivator is a love of history. All seem to really appreciate the tangible links to history that numismatics provides. Whether it is a coin issued by Alexander the Great, or a coin that had the personal involvement of Thomas Jefferson or George Washington, the historical aspect provides a strong magnet of interest. Rare coins are closely tied to many of the most important historical milestones of our country. Also, the financial history of our nation is closely reflected in these artifacts, which for obvious reasons is of interest to the extremely wealthy.

There is also little doubt that these individuals think rare coins are an underpriced asset class. It would be hard to imagine anyone spending these huge sums on rare coins unless they thought it was a good investment. They may be buying the coins due to a love of history, but, like all serious collectors, they hope their financial commitment to the hobby will prove to one day yield a great return on investment.

There is ample reason to think many rare coins are underpriced at current levels. Truly great coins sell for millions of dollars, but truly great works of art sells for hundreds of millions. One super-rich collector stated that he could purchase a world-class coin collection, but a world-class art collection is beyond the reach of even the average billionaire. It's an interesting perspective that only the super-rich would ponder.

I believe that one of the biggest factors in the interest in rare coins of the super-rich has been the incredible increases in net worth among the wealthy. The stock market, real estate, and business in general are at all-time highs in many cases. One wealthy collector stated to me that he was selling assets that he thought were over-priced and buying assets that he thought were underpriced—including rare coins.

As incredible as at seems, these collectors also like competing with one another for having the best sets in the set-registry programs. One collector's stated goal is to surpass Louis E. Eliasberg Sr.'s role as the builder of the number one American collection of all time. This is ambitious to say the least, but there is little doubt to his commitment. These serious collectors love the competition and recognition that set-registry collecting provides.

The average collector may think this has little to do with their collecting activity, but as stated above, it's always good to observe the activity of "smart money." The gigantic sums these collectors have infused into the hobby in recent years have impacted nearly every part of the rare-coin market. Many observers wonder how the rare-coin market would look if these folks had not fallen in love with coins.

Even with the incredible sums of money entering the market via the above-mentioned billionaires, apparently a rising tide does *not* lift all ships. Large portions of the market for United States coins have slipped in price for the last several years. Prices for many commonly collected series are at levels last seen in the 1980s. These include selected silver and gold classic commemorative coins, Mint State and Proof type coins, Morgan and Peace silver dollars, and many more. These series have historically been the target of rare-coin investors. The lack of investor interest in numismatics, changing grading standards, and the oversupply have continued to depress prices for these staples of the hobby.

I hasten to mention that many specialty areas are quite healthy, especially in the demand for circulated coins. Most collectors of Liberty Seated and Barber coins seek examples graded from VF to EF or so, enabling them to build extensive collections rather than just owning a handful of expensive Gems. Tokens and medals are doing just fine in a small milieu of fewer than 2,000 collectors who belong to the specialist societies.

One of the most important bellwether events each year for numismatics is the annual American Numismatic Association World's Fair of Money. The 2018 show was held in the City of Brotherly Love, Philadelphia. Nearly everyone who planned to attend the event was excited that the convention would be held in a major East Coast city. Philadelphia is an ideal location from the standpoint of how many collectors live within a 500-mile radius. The convention center and its labor-union rules presented considerable challenges, but in the end the outstanding attendance and participation of active collectors won the day.

There was considerable buzz and excitement from the start to the finish. The Whitman Publishing booth saw record numbers of collectors buying the latest numismatic books. Collectors lined up to meet legends of the hobby including Q. David Bowers and Kenneth Bressett, and have them sign copies of their many numismatic publications. The bourse floor was alive with activity and those with inventory reported brisk business. Most of the educational events were well attended, proving that numismatic education is alive and well.

There are constant media articles and editorials about the decline of coin shows in the United States. Most point out that collectors can stay at home and buy coins on the Internet. This may be true, but my observation is that several well-run shows still draw big crowds. Collectors enjoy the opportunity to see coins in person, and to meet experts in the series they collect. Coin collecting is considerably more enjoyable for those who have the chance to establish relationships with others with the same interest. Many of my closet friends are ones that I met decades ago on the bourse floor.

In summary, the rare-coin market is vibrant and healthy, but not all segments are doing well. If you believe in being a contrarian, looking for opportunity where others see failure, the rare-coin market currently offers a lot of opportunities. As mentioned above, some worry about the distraction of social media and the Internet. In the long run, however, these may be the savior of our hobby as numismatic leaders search for ways to harness these powerful tools. I believe that the hobby is well positioned for tremendous success in coming years.

COLLECTING U.S. COINS

Coins are meant to be enjoyed. This can be done by learning, going slowly, and becoming familiar with the many aspects of American numismatics. The following sections include an inside view of authenticity, cleaning, conservation, and more—elements that are known to most experienced professionals and long-time collectors.

In just about every other field of collectibles, prints, antiques, art, and related items there are problems with counterfeiting, cleaning, alterations, and the like. Fakes are so common in art that some dealers and auction houses now find it nearly impossible to have an impartial expert guarantee authenticity, as so many lawsuits against them have been filed by owners of paintings. In automobiles there are counterfeit classic cars made from a combination of old and new parts. Many other instances could be cited. And yet, art is popular to collect, classic cars ditto. In every field, caution and expertise are needed.

As a reader of *Mega Red* you know what leading dealers and other experts know. Knowledge is more readily available in numismatics than in many other collectible fields. Indeed, knowledge is the key to enjoyment.

The inside view you will get of some of the challenges contains elements rarely present in sales presentations, investment programs, and the like, for fear that knowledge of negative things can influence buyers to turn elsewhere. Over a long period of years the Whitman Publishing staff and key consultants have learned just the opposite: the more knowledge someone has, the more confident they are and the longer they will be immersed in numismatics. Indeed, countless informed people have made coins and related numismatic areas an integral part of their lives.

Carefully building a fine collection of coins by studying their art, history, and romance and by buying carefully can add a lot to the enjoyment of life. The vast majority of *experienced* numismatists active today were active a decade ago.

Eric P. Newman, who began collecting at the age of 11 years, maintained his interest to the time of his passing at 106. Emery May Holden Norweb began her interest as a pre-teenager when she attributed Massachusetts silver coins for her father, using *Early American Coins*, published in 1875. She collected for the rest of her life and was a member of the American Numismatic Association for more than 70 years. Harry W. Bass Jr. (1927–1998), entrepreneur oil man and founder of the Beaver Creek ski resort, discovered rare coins in 1976 and by the time of his passing built one of the finest collections ever.

Others still living have focused their energy and received enjoyment from the history and lore of numismatics.

A great numismatic future awaits you!

A SEMINAR IN THE GRADING OF COINS

Grading is an art, not a science.

Repeat: Grading is an art, not a science.

Welcome to a "seminar" on the subject, giving information on various elements of one of the most important considerations when buying or selling coins.

COIN PRODUCTION AND STORAGE AND ITS EFFECTS ON MINT STATE GRADES

The grading of a coin is dependent on the amount of *wear* it has received. A mint-fresh coin, like new, is called Mint State. (Until recent generations the term "Uncirculated" was used most of the time, and Mint State rarely.) When struck, the typical coin was ejected mechanically from the press and dropped into a bin or hopper. Mixed with other coins, it was run through a mechanical counting device and then in most instances put into a cloth bag. A bag of silver dollars contained 1,000 coins; in the twentieth century a bag of Lincoln cents contained $50 face value (5,000 coins). Morgan silver dollars minted from 1878 to 1904 and later in 1921 were mostly stored in vaults. Hundreds of millions more were minted than could be used in commerce, so they were stored in Treasury and bank vaults. In Treasury vaults the bags were opened and mechanically counted at intervals, such as after a change in the presidential administration. In their day, before 1934, gold coins were made and bagged the same way. In no instance did any of the mints spend even the slightest effort to create mark-free circulating coins for numismatists.

As a result, a Mint State coin today can have nicks, minor scratches, and other defects and can thus be "low end," even though just taken from an original bag. Many other coins received light handling and can be nearly mark-free.

A WORD OF CAUTION REGARDING CERTIFIED MINT STATE COINS

Today as you read these words, certified grading services have endeavored to separate low-end and high-end Mint State coins into 21 categories using numbers adapted (but not copied from) the Sheldon Scale published in 1949 in *Early American Cents.* According to certain third-party grading (TPG) services, the lowest Mint State is MS-60, proceeding in single digits up to the highest grade of MS-70, representing absolute perfection. In the twenty-first century the TPG added + marks, indicating better than average quality, after all grades from 60 to 69 (not to 70, as a coin cannot be better than perfect). This gives MS-60, MS-60+, MS-61, MS-61+, and so on, for a total of 21 different Mint State grades.

There is no way that such precise designations can be assigned in a way that can be consistently and accurately replicated. Grading strives to be scientific but is subjective and open to interpretation. There are no published written standards or photographic images to guide a buyer of a coin graded by Professional Coin Grading Service (PCGS) or Numismatic Guaranty Corporation (NGC) to understand how, for example, MS-65+ is defined and differentiated from MS-65 or MS-66. Moreover, if, say, 10 professionally graded Mint State coins with regular number and also + designations were taken from their holders and sent back for regrading, they most likely would not all be replicated in the exact same grades.

Both PCGS and NGC have population reports that list the number of "certification events" for each coin in each grade over the years. Such certification data must be studied and interpreted carefully. For example, a data point of 120 Mercury dimes, 1916-D, graded MS-66 might represent that 120 such coins were submitted for grading. However, it's more likely there were only 20 or 30 coins submitted, four to six times each, with their owners hoping to attain higher grades.

If at, say, MS-68 there are only three coins graded and none higher, it will be nicknamed "top pop" or top of the population. Both PCGS and NGC sponsor and maintain registry-set competitions. These are online competitions that register who has the best set of, for example, Peace silver dollars in PCGS holders or NGC holders. There is no crossover, so if the highest NGC grade for a particular date is MS-68 and PCGS has graded a 68+ this counts for the PCGS registry-set competition but has no relevance to someone being an NGC winner.

When it comes to market values, an uninformed collector might assume that the fewer coins have been certified for a particular date or variety in a particular grade, the more valuable it is. However, in many instances that is false security.

On September 6, 2018, these mid-range Morgan silver dollar listings (there were many higher) were posted by PCGS for the 1881-S dollar, one of the more common issues of that series:

1881-S $1

MS-64	107,787 coins
MS-64+	1,919 coins

This might lead a buyer to think that an MS-64+ coin is far rarer than a regular MS-64. The truth is that MS-64+ is a fairly recently developed designation, and tens of thousands of regular MS-64 coins were certified before the + was used. In actuality, MS-64+, a popular twenty-first-century grade, may or may not be *slightly* rarer and only slightly more valuable.

Let us explore the 1886-O, a Morgan dollar that is common in worn grades but rare in high Mint State levels. Here are the highest-graded PCGS coins, and their current prices in the fifth edition of *Mega Red*:

1886-O $1

MS-63	595 coins	$2,700
MS-63+	28 coins	
MS-64	242 coins	9,000
MS-64+	24 coins	
MS-6	52 coins	150,000
MS-65+	1 coin	

As Mint State levels are not precisely defined and as "gradeflation" (defined below) has been endemic since the early 1990s, a smart buyer seeking a high-grade 1886-O Morgan dollar, and being able to afford one, would likely opt to examine several certified MS-64 coins and buy a high-end one at the MS-64 price rather than an average MS-65 at the MS-65 price. Whitman Publishing calls MS-64, in this case study, the coin's Optimum Collecting Grade (OCG). A well-informed buyer would consider it to be a good value for the price paid.

CIRCULATED GRADES

After a coin is taken from a bag or roll or other holder and placed into circulation it begins to acquire wear. This takes the form of friction on the higher parts (which can also be found on some carefully graded low-end Mint State coins), and this is *definitive* loss of luster in the fields. On the obverse of a coin with a Liberty Head, this luster begins to be removed from the fields to the left and right. On some designs that are intricate the motifs protect the fields, so for example the luster can start disappearing from the obverse while it remains more intact on the reverse.

With circulation wear a coin's grade moves from Mint State down to About Uncirculated (AU), then with further wear to Extremely Fine (EF), then down to Very Fine (VF), then Fine, Very Good (VG), Good (G), About Good (AG), Fair, and Poor.

THE SHELDON GRADING SCALE

Dr. William H. Sheldon, the originator of the numbering system proposed in 1949, laid out a simple grading arrangement. He applied it to early U.S. copper coins.

Basal State 1

Fair-2

Very Fair 3

Good 4

Fine 12

Very Fine 20

Extremely Fine 40

About Uncirculated 50

Mint State 60, 65, and 70

This was understandable enough to most specialists at the time. MS-70 or perfection was unusable, so for practical purposes that was satisfactory to all involved. When I first discovered numismatics at the age of 13 in 1952 most grading was by adjectives, but the Sheldon system was used for early cents and some other early coppers. Uncirculated was simply Uncirculated.

On November 12, 1957, Stack's sold the Empire Collection, one of the finest cabinets of American coins from colonials to silver dollars ever to cross the auction block. The firm was a leader in the auction business, was highly respected, and had a clientele that included most of the leading buyers. Here are some descriptions reflecting the *simplicity* of grading in effect at that time—adjectives with an occasional descriptor to clarify:

Half cent: 1828 The 13 star variety. Uncirculated. Brown but has some handling marks.

Cent: 1877 About Uncirculated. Chocolate brown.

Cent: 1909-S V.D.B. Lincoln. Brilliant Uncirculated, red.

Silver three cents: 1851 Uncirculated.

Nickel: 1885 Brilliant Proof.

Nickel: 1926-D Uncirculated, weak strike.

Dime: 1892-O Brilliant Uncirculated.

Quarter: 1901-S Perfect Brilliant Uncirculated Gem.

Half dollar: 1923-S Brilliant Uncirculated, however weakly struck.

Silver dollar: 1895 Brilliant Proof. Superb.

CHERRYPICKING FOR QUALITY

Not long after the Empire Sale I went to visit Arthur W. Conn, one of the largest advertisers in *The Numismatic Scrapbook Magazine*, at the office in his home in Melrose, Massachusetts. He specialized in commemorative coins and had each type in 2x2-inch paper envelopes in its own box. He had dozens of 1900 Lafayette dollars, each marked "Unc." and each priced the same. He offered me the usual typical dealer's discount. I went through his Lafayettes and picked out nearly a dozen that were almost perfect. I did the same with others.

Cherrypicking for quality was practiced by many collectors at the time. Both Emery May Holden Norweb and John J. Pittman, fine customers of mine at the time, would look through dealers' stocks and only buy top-level Uncirculated and Proof coins. These cost no more than less pristine examples.

This changed after the rare-coin boom that started in 1960. In 1970 James F. Ruddy published *Photograde*, which became a sensation. Later in the decade Abe Kosoff (data gathering), Kenneth Bressett (descriptions describing each grade number), and I (introductory narrative) created the *Official American Numismatic Association Grading Standards for United States Coins*. This was adopted by the ANA board of governors and published as a book. The American Numismatic Association Certification Service was set up in Colorado Springs to grade coins for a fee and return each with a certificate and photograph.

Both books were widely used. Responding to pressure from dealers (in particular) the ANA kept adding intermediate grades, including 11 grades from MS-60 to 70. In 1986 PCGS was formed, followed by NGC in 1987 and dozens of other third-party grading firms ("third party" meaning they are neither the owner nor the prospective buyer of graded coins). Later, most faded.

Coins graded by PCGS and NGC in the 1980s that still survive in their original holders are found to be very conservatively graded by today's market-accepted standards.

GRADEFLATION

Established standards notwithstanding, grading was anybody's game even in the 1980s and beyond. Gradeflation became endemic. Coins graded AU-55 and AU-58, if removed from their holders and resubmitted for certification later, might the next time around be graded as MS-60 to MS-62 or even 63. Grades of MS-65 were not common in the late 1980s, and there were very, very few higher in the population reports. Later they became as common as fleas on a stray dog. Anyone who in 1990 was proud of his MS-65 Red 1909-S V.D.B. cent and considered it to be top of the line became increasingly befuddled as coins not as nice were graded higher.

By definition a Mint State coin cannot have wear from circulation. Never mind—nearly all early gold coins certified today as MS-60 to MS-62 show *wear* in the fields, this being just one of many examples of "relaxed" application of the grading standards. An 1853 double eagle graded AU-58 and sold by Christie's in 1999 was sent to the same grading service a few days after the sale and was returned as MS-62. Magically, the coin had become Mint State. And so have thousands of others.

Circulated coins have undergone gradeflation as well. By *Photograde* and *Official ANA Standards* an Indian Head cent in VG-8 grade can have several letters in LIBERTY missing. For VF-20 all letters have to be full and *sharp*. A survey taken in 2018 of more than 100 Indian Head cents certified as VF-20 by the leading services showed *many* with some letters in LIBERTY *missing*, never mind full.

It used to be that a grading service could say "This is our interpretation of the standards." However, there is no way that a circulated 1807 $5 gold coin can be called Mint State by traditional standards or an 1877 Indian Head cent with letters in LIBERTY missing can be called VF-20.

In a phrase, *there are no widely accepted, definable, and strictly applied grading standards for United States coins today.*

STRATEGY FOR THE INFORMED BUYER

Good news for the educated, intelligent buyer: If you are a collector of rare books you can buy with confidence from dealers and auction houses that basically use these definitions: Mint (as new or close; if original dustjacket is present, that should be noted); Very Fine or Extremely Fine (a nice used copy without tears, stains, writing, or other problems); Reading copy (a book that has problems, is marked up, etc.).

Further good news for numismatists: You can follow in the footsteps of generations of earlier connoisseurs and examine multiple coins and pick one that is high end at no extra cost. As to value, this will require some homework. Basic references such as the *Guide Book of United States Coins*, the *Coin Dealer Newsletter*, *Coin World*, *Numismatic News*, and others list many prices These are not consistent with each other but do give approximate values.

Before long you will able to cherrypick for high-end coins by instinct. I have collected 1785–1788 Vermont copper coins for a long time and wrote a book on them. There are some I would like to upgrade, such as my 1785 Vermont IMMUNE COLUMBIA muling. I would like a nice VF or EF. If offered one I will not care if it is certified, or, if it is, what grade has been assigned. I will look at the coin itself to see if it is pleasing in all respects. *Nearly all* advanced collectors of colonial coins, early copper coins, tokens, medals, foreign coins, and ancient coins are not the slightest bit interested in or concerned with minute differences in grading.

Buying coins from common to rare today does require study if you want to build a choice collection. Probably fewer than 10 percent of buyers care about this, so you are in the minority. You will also be able to cherrypick for quality at no extra price, if you know what to look for. The other 90 percent won't know about this.

Enjoy the pursuit!

RARE COINS AS AN INVESTMENT

The rare-coin market combines some aspects of commodity trading with peculiarities seen more often among markets such as those for fine art, real estate, cut gemstones, and similar investments and collectibles. Armed with knowledge and experience, a seasoned investor can have a very rewarding experience buying and selling rare coins. An uneducated investor can just as easily see substantial losses and many if not most do.

The "History of Coins in America" section that follows this gives many specifics concerning success or lack thereof. Success stories are very inspirational, but each includes knowledge, care, and patience. Today in the twilight of the second decade of the twenty-first century there are many opportunities.

The regular edition of the *Guide Book of United States Coins* includes this bit of guidance, which bears repeating here: "The best advice given to anyone considering investing in rare coins is to use common sense."

Any collector with common sense would think twice about buying a silver dollar at a flea market for less than half of its *Red Book* or *Mega Red* value. A common-sense collector who is offered a $1,000 coin from an "unsearched estate," or from a non-specialist who claims to know nothing of its provenance, would refuse it at $500—at least until a diligent examination was possible, and only with an iron-clad return policy and guarantee of authenticity.

Profitable investment requires careful selection of one or several names from the large membership list of qualified dealers such as those who belong to the Professional Numismatists Guild (www.PNG-dealers.org) and/or the International Association of Professional Numismatists (www.iapn-coins.org) and *your* careful personal attention. Very, very few significant success stories involve advisors whose clients are not themselves numismatically knowledgeable.

ASPECTS OF AUTHENTICITY

In the marketplace there are many counterfeit coins, or coins that have been altered so that they appear to be something other than what they really are. Many of these are sold by vendors who are not aware of their false nature. Others are deliberately, fraudulently sold. If a coin is found to be counterfeit, getting your money back may be difficult or impossible. Exceptions are coins certified by third-party grading services that have guaranteed authenticity.

Authenticity refers only to a coin being genuine and struck at the place and in the era as expected. As an example, a rare 1893-S Morgan dollar is expected to be a coin made by the San Francisco Mint in the year 1893. A 1916-D Mercury dime is expected to be a coin made at the Denver Mint in the year 1916. A one-ounce 2011-W American Gold Eagle is expected to be a one-ounce .9167 fine gold coin struck at the West Point Mint in the year 2011.

Authenticity does not refer to the grade of a coin, such as to whether it is MS-63 or MS-65, or to the character of its surface (i.e., whether it is Mint State, prooflike, or Proof). Authenticity refers only to originality.

Your risk of purchasing a spurious coin can be minimized if you are aware of certain factors. If a coin is priced significantly below market value, beware. If the seller will not give in writing a guarantee of authenticity, beware. If the seller is not a recognized professional numismatist, such as being a member of the Professional Numismatists Guild, at least be careful (many fine dealers do not belong to this group).

FALSE COINS

False coins can include these:

Struck copies from false dies. Many are crude, but in modern generations there have been a lot of fakes that almost defy detection. Many have come from China and include coins from common to rare as well as American Silver and Gold Eagles. Beth Deisher, former editor of *Coin World*, is working with the Anti-Counterfeiting Educational Foundation's Anti-Counterfeiting Task Force to combat these. EAC (Early American Coppers) is doing research as well, led by Jack Young.

Electrotypes made by using a genuine coin to create molds of the obverse and reverse and then electrodepositing metal into each mold. The two pieces are then smoothed and joined together. Most can be detected by a microscopic seam on the edge. Many rare copper half cents and cents, early medals, and other issues have been electrotyped. Both the British Museum and the American Numismatic Society furnished electrotypes years ago to collectors to have for display, these being offered openly as such.

Alterations are made by adding a mintmark to a Philadelphia Mint coin, reengraving a date to change it to another year, or changing another feature. One researcher reported that in the late 1950s more than half of the "1916-D" Mercury dimes seen at a leading convention had added D mintmarks. At a convention in 2018 I was shown a "1934-S" dollar with an added S. Many alterations can often be detected by examination under a high-power stereomicroscope.

Coins of the wrong weight. Silver and gold coins if in Mint State should conform to their authorized weights. Worn coins can show a slight reduction. Any off-weight coins should be viewed with suspicion.

Replicas of colonial and other coins have been made in quantity and sold as souvenirs including at historical sites maintained by the Department of the Interior. Many of these have changed hands to new owners not aware of their status. Some are marked COPY, but not all are, and some have had that word removed.

SURFACE ALTERATIONS OF GENUINE COINS

For genuine coins there are other elements that can decrease value.

Whizzing, or the treatment of the surface of a coin with a high-speed polishing wire brush, can give false luster. This problem was endemic in the late nineteenth century and the American Numismatic Association and others took action that nearly eliminated whizzing and forced the closing of a "factory" that produced such coins. Today, newly whizzed coins are rare, but some older ones linger in the marketplace.

The alteration of a coin's surface can be done by plugging a hole, removing stamped initials or cuts, strengthening the hair details of Miss Liberty, etching to remove wear, or other doctoring. Such actions might improve a damaged or worn coin's visual appeal, but they are detectable, and will nearly always decrease rather than increase its value.

Cyanide, a lethal chemical, if applied to a silver coin will remove friction and a give an acceptable grainy surface. Decades ago James F. Kelly, a leading Ohio dealer, demonstrated this to me. A generation earlier, on June 24, 1922, J. Sanford Saltus, a well-to-do numismatist and benefactor of the American Numismatic Society, died while using cyanide to clean ancient silver coins (a tragedy widely reported at the time).

RECOMMENDATIONS AND CAVEATS

Buying coins from a trusted source is the best way to ensure authenticity, as many of the most obvious fakes (as described above) are recognized and not sold by reputable professionals and firms. However, even the most experienced expert can be fooled.

The UCC (Uniform Commercial Code) and various state regulations limit the time in which the buyer of a false coin has recourse against the seller, statutes of limitations.

As of press time certain elements of the guarantees of authenticity of *American coins* offered by several third-party grading firms are *excerpted* below. For *complete* information consult their web sites; this is extremely important. Guarantees for foreign and ancient coins can be much different. Guarantee provisions can be very complex, and herein we only give partial information.

Also be aware that the provisions of guarantees can change from time to time. Certain coins are excluded from guarantees, examples being private and territorial gold coins that were considered genuine in the twentieth century but for which research has found them to be fakes. Restrike vs. original status is not covered as well. Guarantees do not include obvious typographical errors made on the holders, such as the wrong date or mintmark or attribution. Guarantees involving *grading* can be widely different.

> **Professional Coin Grading Service (PCGS):** If a coin certified by PCGS is felt to be counterfeit and if PCGS agrees that it is, current market value as determined by PCGS will be paid, but PCGS will then own the coin. Or the coin will be returned and PCGS will pay the difference between the buyer's cost and the market value.

> **Numismatic Guaranty Corporation (NGC):** If a coin certified by NGC is felt to be counterfeit and if NGC agrees that it is, NGC will pay the lesser of the fair market price as determined by NGC or the price the owner paid. NGC can elect to retain the coin and replace it with a genuine example in the same assigned grade.

> **ANACS (years ago known as the American Numismatic Association Certification Service when it was owned by the ANA; later sold several times and known today as ANACS, with no affiliation with the ANA):** The guarantee applies only to coins certified by ANACS since January 1, 2008, the inception of current ownership. ANACS will purchase the coin at the fair market value as determined by ANACS or will pay the difference between that and the owner's original cost.

Most leading collectors and dealers today agree that buying a coin certified for its authenticity is the best protection against counterfeits and altered coins. Other services than PCGS, NGC, and ANACS offer guarantees and their guarantees should be checked if you are offered their coins. The counter to this is that it can be expensive to have modern coins and coins of low value certified, and their bulk adds to challenges of how to store and enjoy them.

To the above, Beth Deisher has contributed the following.

CHINESE COUNTERFEITS
by Beth Deisher

The use of the steam-powered coin press at the Philadelphia Mint in 1836 and the introduction of the French portrait lathe in its die-making process elevated coin manufacturing to a new level. For more than 170 years after, counterfeiters rarely had access to the die-making equipment or production presses necessary for large-scale counterfeit-coin production.

However, the landscape changed dramatically in the early years of the twenty-first century. By 2005 most sovereign mints around the world had begun embracing computer technology and robotics in their die-making and coin-production processes. It was not a matter of simply installing and adapting modern manufacturing methods. Rather, competition—especially in the commemorative coin sector—demanded cost-effective manufacturing and innovative features in design and metallurgy.

The U.S. Mint, content to produce its two lowest circulating-denomination coins at a loss, was directed by Congress to look for lower-cost alloys for the cent and five-cent coins. Also, increasingly innovative commemorative coins on the world stage led to questions of why the United States could not produce equally interesting and visually attractive coins.

The search for both efficiency and innovation led to the U.S. Mint's transition in 2008 to digital technology in its die-making operation, producing both never-before-experienced efficiencies and precision. During the same period, the Mint moved to increase use of computer-controlled processes and robotics throughout its manufacturing and packaging operations.

Ironically, rather than making counterfeiting more difficult, the transition to computers and digital technology opened new doors of opportunity for counterfeits. That is primarily due to rapid leaps in technology and knowledge of how to use it that have spread throughout the world at levels unprecedented in human history. The same is true for the accessibility to computer hardware and production equipment used in the various stages of coin production. Costs and availability are no longer a barrier to entry for counterfeiters.

For example, software programs used by designers and engravers at government mints are commercially available and easily acquired. Computer-savvy operators can bypass years of training and experience by simply scanning high-resolution digital images and manipulating them to produce the desired product. Equipment to laser-cut master dies can be purchased at manufacturers' trade shows. The same is true for each step of the coining process, from blanking, to burnishing, to metal-plating, to producing the finished coin.

During 2007 and 2008, it became apparent to the numismatic community that the numbers of counterfeit coins in the American marketplace were increasing at a rapid pace. Specialists in early American copper coins, trade dollars, and Morgan dollars were among the first to sound the alarm.

The weekly Coin World joined the New York Times in a year-long investigation, resulting in Coin World's publication of a series in December 2008 that revealed more than 100 thriving coin-counterfeiting operations in China. Most were small, cottage-type operations. The largest, owned by a 26-year-old entrepreneur, relied on vintage 1870s U.S. coin presses salvaged from "scrap metal" sold by the Chinese government. (The U.S. government in the 1920s sold old coining presses to China, which after using stored them in the 1950s and had recently sold them as scrap.)

The proprietor of this operation claimed in 2008 that he had the capacity to produce 100,000 coins a month, most of which were older Chinese coin types and sold in China. However, he was expanding a new line of counterfeit United States coins and selling about 1,000 per month in the United States via eBay. His business plan called for locating and establishing "wholesale" buyers in the United States who would buy in bulk and help him to identify the most popular sellers. Most of his "replica" coins could be identified because he used iron-based planchets plated with silver or with the proper alloy to match the authentic coin. He accepted orders for counterfeits that were themselves made of 90 percent silver and gold, but for those pieces his prices reflected the higher-quality planchets. They constituted a very small portion of his business.

By 2018, dozens of Chinese counterfeiters were claiming production capacities of up to 500,000 per month of highly sophisticated and dangerous gold and silver counterfeits of various types of United States coins. They proudly show on their web sites images taken within their modern manufacturing facilities of lines of coin presses in operation. They brag of their extensive use of digital technology, including lasers and 3-D printing. And they also assure fast delivery, less than a week, depending on payment arrangements.

A prime factor in the accelerating growth of Chinese coin counterfeiters is their ability to market their wares worldwide via Alibaba, the e-commerce company that in 1999 entered the marketplace to connect Chinese manufacturers with overseas buyers. In April 2016 Alibaba.com became the world's largest retailer and one of the largest Internet companies, reaching into 200 countries.

Leaders from throughout the numismatic community in the United States, recognizing the danger and urgency of the threat posed by the growing numbers of highly deceptive counterfeit coins entering the marketplace, came together in January 2017 to create the Anti-Counterfeiting Task Force (ACTF) under the authority of the Industry Council for Tangible Assets (ICTA).

To tackle the seemingly overwhelming situation, the task force determined that its top priority must be to educate law-enforcement authorities and policy makers about the rising threat of counterfeiting. Simultaneously, it sought to mobilize law enforcement to attack counterfeiters where they are most vulnerable. Equally important, the ACTF has committed to assisting law enforcement with expertise and other resources in the investigation and prosecution of counterfeiters and those involved at all levels of their distribution networks.

The task force's mission and programs support all who work in and who earn their livings from businesses related to the numismatic, bullion, and circulating coins. Equally important is protecting collectors and investors who fall victim to counterfeiters. Above all, the task force seeks to ensure that decades of consumer confidence are not eroded by the increasing threat posed by the counterfeiters.

As a part of its education mission, the task force presents anti-counterfeiting educational seminars and forums at major coin shows and is developing guidelines for both collectors and dealers on how to deal with counterfeit coins and fake bullion bars encountered in the marketplace. Among the most important is an understanding of individual responsibilities.

U.S. COUNTERFEITING LAWS AND COMPLIANCE

It is a federal crime to knowingly possess, buy, sell, or import into the United States counterfeit coins or precious metals bars (U.S. Code, Title 18, Part I, Chapter 25, Sections 485 through 492). There are no exceptions for possessing counterfeit coins for "educational" purposes.

Many collectors and coin dealers mistakenly believe they have a special dispensation to keep a "reference collection" of counterfeits. While such has been longstanding practice in the hobby, be aware such "reference collections" could be confiscated and you could be charged with federal crimes punishable by fines and sentences ranging from to 5 to 15 years in federal prison. Also, don't get caught up in purchasing so-called "replica" coins online from a seller in a foreign country because you are curious as to how deceptive they may be. Knowingly importing counterfeit coins into the United States is a federal crime punishable by up to 15 years in federal prison.

Many sellers, especially from China, sell "replica" United States and other nation's coins in China and via online companies such as Alibaba.com, AliExpress.com, Wish.com, TopHatter.com, and eBay.com. It is likely that many Internet sites are not aware that vendors are selling false coins. In America eBay takes steps to cancel proven sellers of counterfeits, but many have slipped through.

While China licenses factories located in China to manufacture replicas of virtually every name-brand product in the market, the Chinese government does not recognize international copyright or trademark laws. Neither does it recognize the United States Hobby Protection law (U.S. Code, Title 15, Chapter 48, Sections 2101 through 2106), which requires the word COPY to be stamped on all replicas of coins and numismatic items (coins, precious-metal bars, precious-metal rounds, medals, and paper money). The Hobby Protection law was amended and expanded in 2014 to include replica encapsulation holders of coin and paper-money grading services as well as replica certificates and packaging of numismatic products.

Once a replica numismatic item that is not marked in compliance with the U.S. Hobby Protection law enters the United States, it becomes a counterfeit and anyone knowingly selling, buying, or importing is subject to U.S. federal counterfeiting laws as well as to the Hobby Protection law.

If you have reason to question the authenticity of a coin or numismatic item you are interested in purchasing, the best strategy is to insist that the purchase be contingent upon the coin being certified as genuine by one of the leading third-party grading services that backs its certification with a guarantee, as recommended in the preceding text. It is much easier to buy a guaranteed-authentic coin to begin with, even at a higher price, than to buy a "bargain" fake for which you will either take a complete loss or expend a lot of time and energy seeking compensation.

If you purchase a coin or numismatic item online via eBay and later find that it is counterfeit, eBay has a process for returning the item to the seller and getting a refund. Reputable dealers do not knowingly buy or sell counterfeits. If a highly deceptive counterfeit gets past a reputable dealer and he sells it to you, upon being presented with the evidence that the coin or item is counterfeit, he will refund your money and likely take possession of the fake in order to remove it from the marketplace.

Once a coin or other numismatic item is determined to be counterfeit, whoever is in possession of it—dealer or collector—has a legal responsibility to turn it over to the U.S. Secret Service. To locate your nearest U.S. Secret Service Field Office, go online to https://www.secretservice.gov/contact/field-offices. Enter your city and state or your zip code and click "Go." The Secret Service is the final repository for all counterfeits. Counterfeit items may be turned over to the Secret Service directly or through some local police, but ultimately, they end up with the Secret Service.

If you are a victim and have unwittingly purchased counterfeit coins or other numismatic items, your local police or sheriff may your best choice for reporting the incident. (The U.S. Secret Service is not set up to respond to all incidents.) Depending on the state in which you reside or in which the incident occurs, local and state law-enforcement officers may investigate counterfeiting as criminal fraudulent activity.

The task force and its work are funded entirely through donations to the Anti-Counterfeiting Educational Foundation, which in 2018 received IRS approval as a 501(c)(3) non-profit and designation as a public charity. Tax deductible donations should be mailed to David Crenshaw, P.O. Box 237 Dacula, GA 30019 or can contributed online at https://www.ictaonline.org/actf.

CLEANING, CONSERVATION, AND PRESERVATION

TONING ON COINS

Silver coins left in the atmosphere, especially in air that contains traces of sulfur (as from a furnace), will tone, sometimes attractively. Slow toning such as this is often described as *natural*. Cardboard album pages that contain sulfur, such as the National pages once marketed by Wayte Raymond, tend to give light rainbow toning from the edge of a coin inward, often imparting great beauty and, in today's marketplace, additional value.

In contrast, fast toning such as by deliberately applied heat and chemicals is often called *artificial*. Vast quantities of artificially toned coins have been encapsulated by the third-party grading services, but many others, even of similar appearance, have been sent back ungraded and marked "artificial toning." There are no rules. One leading dealer simply sends such coins to another grading firm and, often, they are returned graded, with no negative comment.

Toned silver coins enjoy a wide market. The exact definition of "artificial" has eluded definition. Silver coins placed in old National holders (with sulfur content in the cardboard) and heated slightly over a period of time can develop beautiful iridescent toning. Morgan silver dollars in original bags were often toned on one side—the side that contacted the canvas. In the 1960s no specialists had ever seen or heard of a coin with vivid rainbow toning on *both* sides. Today these are common. Some of this toning is accomplished by heat and chemicals.

Just as coins can be artificially toned, they can also be deliberately brightened. As described above, a silver coin if left in the atmosphere will gain toning over a period of time. Ancient silver coins found in hoards are routinely brightened by collectors using various processes, a practice well accepted in numismatics. Old silver American coins with the exception of long-stored silver dollars in bags have all gained toning to one degree or another. Sometimes the toning is dark gray or brown and other times it is attractively lightly iridescent. Such coins can be brightened by dipping into a liquid made for silverware, and other products. If no friction is used and coins are rinsed in cold water afterward, there is no numismatic problem. Every Capped Bust or Liberty Seated coin that is fully brilliant today has been dipped. (However, "dipped" is a nasty word within the hobby community, with an implication of dishonest or deceptive alteration, and is hardly ever used.)

Dipped copper coins become bright, but often of unnatural color. Such pieces tend to retone, often with spots. *Never dip a copper coin.* If a coin has been dipped it can often be restored by rubbing it lightly with powdered sulfur, then wiping it with mineral oil. A related process is described by Dr. William H. Sheldon in *Early American Cents.* Lightly rubbing a toned copper coin with a camel's-hair brush has been practiced for generations by collectors and museum staff (the American Numismatic Society being an example).

Grime on gold coins can be removed by acetone or ammonia without disturbing any original mint luster that may be present. The latter chemical may lighten the surface, as will the use of silver dip. Continued use of silver dip will microscopically etch the surface and in time lower the grade.

I received a brilliant Proof silver medal a few years ago and opened it from its packaging, but a visitor was about to enter the office, so I carefully placed in it the top drawer of a Conant Ball oak side table recently received. I forgot about it. About a month later I found it. The down-side was lightly toned the most gorgeous light blue I had ever seen. Was this natural toning or was it artificial?

As can be seen, the nature of toning is in the eye of the beholder. Refunds are not likely to be given if you have a certified coin and you and others consider it to be artificially toned (whatever that means).

CLEANING VS. CONSERVATION

In February 1901 in *The Numismatist* Augustus G. Heaton gave this good advice:

> Coins of all metals require the greatest care. They should be handled with clean fingers only by the edge, should not rest on colored material of any kind or on wood not thoroughly seasoned, or come in any contact with rubber bands and should be kept in a dry place and never exposed to dust, dandruff, damp or foul air or even human breath. All these influences will in time discolor them and much impair their value. Attempts at cleaning are also very dangerous to fine coins. Uncirculated pieces or Proofs

should be let alone. If really soiled or dirty, copper coins may be put in olive oil a while and then wiped (not rubbed) dry with a soft rag, and silver coins may be carefully washed, using a mild soap, but all methods of polishing are abhorrent and have made many coins worthless.

This brings up the subject of conservation, or the improvement of the appearance of a coin. And what defines a "cleaned" coin? Nearly all other hobbies have conservation as an essential activity. The Smithsonian Institution conserves many things (including the original Star Spangled Banner). The National Archives as well as dealers and collectors conserve documents and other items by removing stains, repairing folds and tears, and the like. Art is routinely cleaned and brightened. Antique furniture is improved. In numismatics, the filling of holes, removal of scratches, and similar actions, are not envisioned as being good practice, but many coins with "environmental damage," "cleaning," etc., would benefit from some conservation.

Bill Fivaz, longtime numismatist and author, says this: "When someone asks me the difference between conservation and cleaning, I tell them that in my opinion when you conserve a coin you are not altering the *original surface* of that coin. If there was original luster, there still should be original luster, etc. If you clean a coin the original surface(s) are altered in some way, affecting the luster, etc."

In general, the use of friction, such as rubbing a coin with baking soda under the pressure of a fingertip, will cause minute hairlines. Using silver polish or paste will leave many hairlines that cannot be removed. Such use was once recommended, including in pages of *The Numismatist*. As a result, more than 95 percent of all nineteenth-century and early twentieth-century mirror Proof coins have hairlines. Were it not so, all would be in ultra-high grades.

In *The Numismatist*, August 1903, Farran Zerbe told of visiting the Mint Cabinet collection in Philadelphia:

> I found many of the silver Proof coins of late years partially covered with a white coating. On inquiry I learned that an overzealous attendant during the last vacation months when the numismatic room was closed took it on himself to clean the tarnished coins, purchase some metal polish at a department store, and proceeded with his cleaning operation. Later a coating of white appeared on the coins, which was now slowly disappearing. I expressed my displeasure at this improper treatment of Proof coins, and the custodian explained, "that is nothing. I have been here eight years and they have been cleaned three or four times in my time."

Zerbe speculated that should this cleaning continue, in the future one would have nothing left except plain planchets and badly worn coins!

We cannot undo the past, but in the future all numismatists should refrain from *cleaning* coins.

The above said, many coins can be professionally conserved to improve their appearance and value. The National Conservation Service (NCS) branch of NGC does this for a fee. Researcher Bob Evans used chemicals and scientific procedures to remove stain, rust, and discoloration from gold coins and ingots from the SS *Central America* treasure without altering the original surfaces.

Some basic conservation of coins can be done at home. In any and all instances, experiment with common coins of low value before working with expensive ones. Also, this information reflects what many others have done with success, but there is no inference or guarantee that it will work for you. *You are on your own*.

Examples of household solutions include:

> *Acetone*, a chemical that must be used with adequate ventilation and away from flames, will remove PVC contamination, varnish, and other substances. A coin bathed in acetone should be lightly dried by touching with a pledge of cotton or a swab. Avoid friction.

Ammonia is ideal for removing vault grime from silver and gold coins. It will often discolor copper coins, so should not be used with copper. It will also slightly lighten the color of gold.

Plain soap and water will often remove dirt.

CARE OF YOUR COINS AND COLLECTION

Coins require care in order to preserve them in the condition in which they were acquired.

Coins not in holders should always be handled carefully, by the edge. Avoid talking when handling a coin, as bits of moisture may fall on it and in time develop into black spots. Hold coins over a soft surface such as cloth or a pad.

Except on rare occasions with another knowledgeable collector or dealer, do not let anyone handle your valuable coins.

Keep coins in a dry place and avoid heat. Both of these cautions are very important. Dampness can facilitate spotting and corrosion. Heat can facilitate corrosion and change the color of a coin. Keep coins protected in a holder of some kind, not in the open air. Coastal areas often have microscopic salt particles in the air that can discolor copper coins in particular.

Effective holders include 2x2-inch paper envelopes with flaps; indeed these were the way that nearly all coins were stored prior to 1930. Many still are. Some specialists in colonial and early copper coins add a small cotton-lined inner envelope.

Albums and folders made specifically to hold coins are convenient. All old ones and many new ones contain traces of sulfur that over time can cause copper coins in particular to tone. 2x2-inch cardboard holders with clear Mylar® interiors, stapled (carefully) at the edges, are a very effective way to store coins and study them at the same time. These require little space for storage.

Airtight plastic holders are very effective, but the small amount of air within can cause toning on copper coins and even spotting. For this reason the leading third-party certification services do not guarantee that copper will not change color or develop spots within their slabs.

PVC (polyvinyl chloride) envelopes must be avoided completely as they will deposit "goo" on the surface of copper and nickel coins and often will cause corrosions. For silver coins there will be goo but no corrosion. Gold coins are usually not affected by PVC. Envelopes made with PVC are clear and supple, durable, not brittle; this is what makes them attractive, and convenient for short-term storage. However, the irreversible nature of the damage the chemical causes over time makes it unacceptable.

The careful application of clear fingernail polish to brilliant Mint State copper coins will usually preserve the color perfectly. The polish can be removed instantly with acetone. This is an effective but little-used method of benefit for coins in folders and albums.

Each of the basic metals of federal coinage has its own characteristics:

Copper or *bronze* as used for cents, two-cent pieces, and some patterns is a very chemically active. Such coins should be kept away from heat, moisture, sunlight, and exposure to open air.

Silver is less sensitive but will tone, sometimes attractively, when exposed to heat or sulfur. It is best to keep silver coins away from such elements.

Gold is inert. Over a period of time, such as when stored in bulk in bank vaults, they will develop grime. This can be easily removed with acetone (with great care as the vapors should not be breathed or near flame) or alcohol. As noted above, ammonia can be used as well but will slightly lighten the color.

Security is an important aspect of coin preservation. For this reason many numismatists collect in private and do not want their names published, including when they sell their coins. Others, with care, will keep numismatists informed. It is not good practice to discuss coin values with non-collecting friends or the general public, as tales are often multiplied and could put you and your coins in danger.

The best protection is to keep coins in a safe deposit box in a local or regional bank. The facility should be checked to be sure it is never subject to flooding. It is good practice to select boxes or a vault a foot or two above the floor level.

Today photography and scanning are very sophisticated, and images of coins, tokens, medals, and paper money are often sharper than the pieces are themselves when examined under low magnification. Images of your collection can easily be stored on a personal computer or even an iPhone.

It is good practice to keep an inventory of your coins and to preserve original invoices. It is also good practice, if relationships and circumstances permit, to share the information with your immediate family so they will be aware in case for some reason you become incapacitated. If you have a trusted dealer or other advisor make him or her known to your family. This advisor should be reviewed from time to time.

More advice on security, storage, conservation, toning, and other important topics can be found in the *Whitman Guide to Coin Collecting* (Bressett), *Cash In Your Coins: Selling the Rare Coins You've Inherited* (Deisher), *Grading Coins by Photographs* (Bowers), and other Whitman Publishing books.

THE HISTORY OF COINS IN AMERICA, 1607 TO DATE

*This introduction to U.S. coins is the work of Whitman Publishing numismatic director (and **Mega Red** senior editor) Q. David Bowers.*

Settlers in America from the Jamestown Colony in 1607 and the landing of the Pilgrims in Plymouth in 1620, continuing with immigrants from many lands, were mostly of European stock.[1] The New World promised land for settlement and the pursuit of hunting and agriculture for most. For others such as settlers in what became Pennsylvania and Rhode Island, religious freedom prompted their settling on the far side of the Atlantic Ocean.

An NE (New England) shilling from the first coinage series struck in what is now the United States, by the Massachusetts Bay Colony in 1652.

The landing of the Pilgrims in the New World in 1620. In time the emigrants founded the Massachusetts Bay Colony.

During most of the seventeenth century, the first century of permanent North American colonization by Europeans, coins were scarce. To fill the demand for media of exchange many commodities and commercial products were used. In Maryland and Virginia tobacco, powder, and shot traded at set rates. As an example, on March 4, 1635, the Massachusetts General Court adopted legislation that provided: "It is likewise ordered

Cattle served as currency in certain areas of colonial America as did other perishable goods such as agricultural products.

that musket bullets of a full bore shall pass currently for a farthing apiece, provided that no man be compelled to take above XII [one shilling] at a time in them."

In the early days in some colonies grain (a general term for corn, peas, and wheat), oat meal, cattle, furs, and fish were also used in payment of debt. Each of these had a utility value. Tobacco could be smoked, or if the recipient did not indulge, a neighbor might. Fish could be eaten, fur could be made into caps and clothing. Such commodities were often referred to as "country pay," or barter items.

In New Hampshire dried and salted fish, lumber, and agricultural products saw service as currency as did gunpowder and cattle. Citizens of the Carolinas often used tobacco, corn, peas, rice, and even pine tar for the same purpose. In New York beaver skins were sometimes specified as payment in contracts. Each of these things required effort to find or produce. Accordingly, the market could not be disturbed by an unexpected flood of animal skins or musket balls. This is the labor theory of value, originally developed by Adam Smith (and later extensively expanded by Karl Marx). Counterfeiting was not a problem. Unfortunately, tobacco depreciated so badly from overproduction in Virginia that, in 1640 (21 years after tobacco was made the official currency), all the "bad" and half the "good" was ordered burned. This was not successful in decreasing the flood of tobacco on the market, so in 1666 both Virginia and Maryland banned the planting of tobacco entirely for a year. Prices in 1683 were so low from overproduction that there were riots when Virginia refused to order another one-year ban. Beaver skins fluctuated also.

In the meantime and since the earliest days gold and silver coins of all nations were accepted in normal dealings by the colonists who in turn used them to purchase imported goods. English silver coins were familiar and desirable, but of equal value were the German thalers, Dutch silver Lyon (lion) dollars and gold ducats, French louis, and of course, the ever-present gold doubloons and silver pieces-of-eight and their fractions from Spain as well as mints from Mexico to South America. English copper coins served the need for small change, but even these were scarce and rarely adequate for commercial needs.

On November 15, 1637, the Massachusetts General Court ordered that particular shell beads called wampum (shortened from the Algonquin *wampumpeage*, or "white beads") should pass at six per penny for any sum under 12 pence. From that year to 1661, Indian wampum became a standard medium of exchange for trade with the Native Americans. Strings of wampum were highly coveted and could be exchanged for furs. Six white beads or three blue beads equaled one English penny. All financial records were kept in the traditional English pounds, shillings, and pence, but debts and taxes were often paid in corn, beaver, peas, or whatever foreign coins were available.

A Dutch silver Lyon dollar of 1589 representative of many European crown- or dollar-size coins in circulation in America in the early years of colonization.

Harvard College was founded in 1636. Tuition of £1 6s 8d could be paid several ways, including by about 1,900 beads of white whelk and blue (purple) quahog wampum. On October 7, 1640, the General Court directed that white wampum should pass at four per penny and blue at two per penny, with no more than 12 pence worth to be used at one time unless the receiver desired more. Wampum had its problems, for it developed that similar glass beads could be made cheaply in factories, and wampum of quahog clam shells counterfeited from seashells. What had become an accepted medium of exchange among Indians became devalued when interfered with by white settlers.

Although country pay faded in the early 19th century and was largely replaced in cities and larger settlements by coins, the barter system endured. There are many nineteenth-century accounts of businesses in rural areas of America taking goods and services in trade for merchandise.[2]

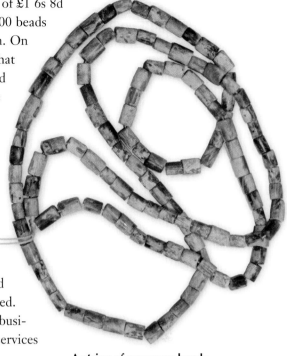

A string of wampum beads.

COINS USED IN THE COLONIES

Prior to establishment of the United States Mint in Philadelphia in 1792 and its subsequent production of coinage for circulation in 1793, metallic money in the American colonies came in many forms. Foreign coins comprised a wide variety of copper, silver, and gold issues from Spanish America, England, Portugal, Holland, France, Germany, and elsewhere. Many of these were made legal tender by federal law.

As a general rule, in the eighteenth century copper coins used for small change were apt to be British. Silver and gold issues, used in larger transactions, were typically struck by Spanish-American mints in Mexico (in particular), Chile, Peru, and elsewhere. These were denominated in reales (sometimes given as *reals*), with eight reales equaling a Spanish dollar. Gold coins were reckoned in escudos, with 8 escudos equaling a gold doubloon, worth about 16 Spanish dollars. Deeds, contracts, and other documents involving money were usually drawn in English or Spanish money. Brazilian gold coins were important as well as were scattered other European issues.

The popular Spanish milled dollar, or eight-reales piece, was divided into eighths or bits, the one-real worth 12-1/2¢. From this, the term "two bits" for a 25¢ coin passed into the modern idiom.

Indeed, long after the Philadelphia Mint and its several branches were in operation, most silver coins in circulation in the United States were still the Spanish-American types. In New York City, Boston, or Philadelphia in the 1850s, silver two-reales coins were much more common than federal Liberty Seated coins. From 1821 until August 1834 there were no United States gold coins in circulation as the value of that metal had risen to the point that it cost more than face value to mint a $5 gold coin.

1745 Peru eight escudos or doubloon, one of many issues of Spanish-American gold coins that facilitated trade in early America.

These continued to be struck to the order of those who deposited sufficient gold to make them. After they were delivered, the coins were used in international trade where the face value made no difference. A $5 gold coin containing, for example, $5.05 worth of precious metal would be valued at $5.05 at a destination such as London, Paris, or Vienna. In the meantime, Spanish-American doubloons and other gold coins were widely used.

Spanish-American two-reales coins were the most plentiful silver coins in day-to-day commerce into the 1850s, by which time most were worn nearly smooth, as was this 1781 Mexico City Mint coin counterstamped in the 1850s in New York City to advertise a hair product.

Selected foreign silver and gold coins remained legal tender until after the Act of February 21, 1857, mandated their retirement. An extension was granted for two years, then another for six months, making them useful in commerce well into the year 1859. In 1857 the Treasury began large-scale redemption of foreign silver and gold issues, exchanging them for federal coins.

It was difficult, if not impossible, for the average merchant or banker to know the exchange value of an eight-escudo gold doubloon from Mexico, as compared to one from Peru or Chile, or to figure the trade worth of a French silver five-franc coin. Exchange-rate tables published in newspapers and almanacs were a help as were charts and publications known as cambists. Most city newspapers had a "prices current" column giving values of popular gold and silver coins as well as market values for commodities. A wide class of publications known as counterfeit detectors and bank-note reporters developed. These told the value of paper money in particular (in addition to endeavoring to identify counterfeits), but often gave exchange values for foreign coins.

Beyond that, values of coins varied from colony to colony. A Mexican doubloon had one value in New York City and a slightly different value in Charleston.

From time to time paper currency issues were produced by the various colonies, the earliest being the issue of Massachusetts dated December 10, 1690, on the old calendar (in which the year began on March 25). Because of this, other Massachusetts bills dated "February 3, 1690" were printed before March 25, 1691, as authorized by the "order of February 3, 1690/91," the double date used by historians to explain this transitional period. Although dated earlier, the February 3, 1690, bills were actually printed later than the December 10, 1690, currency. Confusing? Under the old Julian calendar in use in Protestant England before 1752, New Year's Day came on March 25. The day before March 25, 1691, was thus March 24, 1690, in the old calendar. In 1752, England and her American colonies changed to the Gregorian calendar and to adjust for doing so dropped 11 days from the month of September. To make the conversion beginning in 1752, the year 1751 was a "short" year beginning

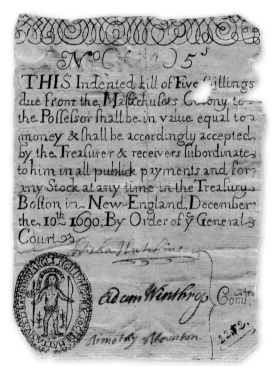

A December 10, 1690, 5-shilling note of Massachusetts, the first paper money printed in North America.

March 25, 1751, and ending December 31. Thus today we celebrate Benjamin Franklin's birthday on January 17 (1706) but the old-style date was January 6 (1705). Looking back from today, we use the double date to correct the Julian year to Gregorian but usually ignore the 11 days. The double date was not used in the eighteenth century.

Paper issues printed for colonial monies of account usually were reckoned in British pounds, shillings, and pence, or in Spanish dollars. For example, an early note of Pennsylvania bore the inscription: "This bill shall pass current for five shillings within the Province of Pennsylvania according to an Act of Assembly made in the 31st year of the reign of King George II. Dated May 20, 1758."

A note of Delaware was inscribed: "This indented bill shall pass current for Fifteen Shillings within the Government of the Counties of New Castle, Kent, Sussex on Delaware, according to an Act of Assembly of the said Government made in the 32nd Year of the Reign of our Sovereign Lord King George II. Dated the 1st Day of June, 1759."

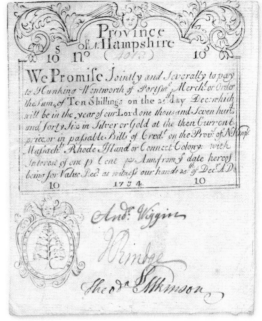

A New Hampshire 10-shilling note of 1734. Most colonial bills traded within the colonies that issued them and were not accepted in distant places.

When the first issues of the Continental Congress appeared in 1775 they specified payment in Spanish coins. For example, a typical note reads: "This Bill entitles the Bearer to receive EIGHT Spanish milled DOLLARS, or the Value thereof in Gold or Silver, according to the Resolutions of the CONGRESS, held at Philadelphia the 10th of May, 1775."

Paper money of various kinds, issued in large amounts during the eighteenth century, was often viewed with distrust. Counterfeiting was rife, notes or bills good in one area were often valueless or deeply depreciated in another, and many other problems surfaced. Bills were often altered by removing one denomination and inking in a higher value. Counterfeits were made by various processes, including carefully drawing notes by hand as well as the more expedient making of a false printing plate. Because of counterfeits, official designs were often changed at short intervals, at which time earlier currency was called in, inspected for genuineness, and exchanged for the new. Very few people could tell counterfeits from the genuine, some of which were so clever that numismatists today need to look for secret privy marks and other signs. Despite the warning "To Counterfeit Is Death" printed on many notes, the game continued. In practice, very few makers of false notes were ever executed, as juries were reluctant to apply the ultimate penalty.

Moreover, much paper money became devalued. It took ever-increasing amounts of paper to buy a given item. Such currency generally stayed within the colony of issue, or, if taken across borders, was apt to sell at a deep discount. Older paper money of higher value was often referred to as "old tenor," as were earlier coins of higher weight. The quality and acceptance of paper varied from colony to colony—with some keeping tighter rein than others.

Making matters even more difficult, the value of a given note varied from colony to colony, much more so than changing values of silver and gold coins for paper had no intrinsic or melt-down worth.

The saying, "never keep a paper dollar in your pocket till tomorrow," popularized by Aaron White in a token he issued in 1857, was just as applicable in colonial days. A citizen holding Spanish coins worth five pounds and an equivalent amount of paper money with the same value would nearly always spend the paper money first.

Continental currency was authorized by the Continental Congress and was issued in five series with 11 different authorization dates, in denominations from fractions of a dollar up to, eventually, $80. Although these notes were payable in Spanish milled dollars, as related above, the federal treasury was empty. Accordingly, the bills depreciated rapidly from their first issue in 1775 to the last in 1779. In January 1777 it took $105 in Continental paper money to buy $100 in Spanish

A February 17, 1776, $8 Continental currency note. Each bill was signed by hand.

silver dollars at an exchange office. By February 1781 it took $7,500! After this time, the bills became virtually worthless. Some smart speculators made a market in them and were rewarded when on August 4, 1790, Congress passed an act providing that Continental currency would be received at the Treasury until September 1, 1791, at the rate of $100 in bills to $1 in silver or gold coins. Among those profiting on a large scale seems to have been "Lord" Timothy Dexter, a wealthy entrepreneur in Newburyport, Massachusetts, who decorated his front lawn with statues of prominent historical figures.

The Act of May 8, 1792, extended the redemption period of March 7, 1792, after which time the bills were repudiated, the status they retain today, although in all instances a well-preserved note has a numismatic value higher than its face value. Later paper-money issues of the various states, similar in design to certain Continental notes, were guaranteed by the state governments. It is an arguable point as to the legal-tender status today of signed, unredeemed bills. Again, that problem is solved by their numismatic worth.

In April 1782 the Commonwealth of Pennsylvania affirmed the charter of the Bank of North America, the first such institution authorized by a state, although banks and money-exchange offices were hardly new. Soon the bank issued paper money with its imprint, redeemable in specie (gold and silver

coins) at its office. This set the pace for more than 3,000 banks to gain state charters and issue paper money from that time until the mid-1860s. In addition many private notes were issued by merchants and towns, particularly in times of economic stress, such as after the War of 1812 and following the Panic of 1837.

The failure of Continental notes had warned the public, and it was thought that federal paper money would be questioned.

Front of the mansion of "Lord" Timothy Dexter on High Street in Newburyport, Massachusetts. He speculated in Continental currency. The building (without statues) still stands today.

As it developed, bills of banks ranged from worthless to fully redeemable in gold or silver, depending on the reputation and capital of the institution involved. It was not until 1861 that the federal government again issued currency in quantity for public use. During the entire colonial era, and extending well into the mid-nineteenth century, gold and silver coins were always preferable to paper money. Anyone with a $5 gold coin and a $5 bill would spend the bill first.

EUROPEAN COINAGE FOR AMERICA

In the eighteenth century, as part of the flood of European coins brought to America, such low-denomination coins as Mark Newby farthings and half-pence featuring St. Patrick and British coppers were used here, although they were not made specifically for this side of the Atlantic, nor did they bear any inscriptions relating to the colonies. Mark Newby's coppers were legal tender for a time in West Jersey (largely today's New Jersey), but no such mantle was ever placed on other English or Irish coppers. The legislature of the colony made them legal tender.

Various coins were produced in England for specific distribution in America.

In 1688, Richard Holt, a British entrepreneur, caused a quantity of 1/24th-real tin coins to be made for the American plantations, but these never reached circulation this side of the Atlantic.

For Maryland, Cecil Calvert, the second Lord Baltimore, caused a series of silver coins ranging from the groat (fourpence) to the shilling to be struck. He also had struck a copper denarium or penny.

William Wood, under a royal patent, produced the distinctive Rosa Americana issues, these in addition to his Hibernia coppers made for circulation in Ireland, but some found their way to America. To the coins in circulation were added coins and tokens of private issuers.

St. Patrick halfpennies (illustrated here) and farthings made for circulation in Ireland were imported to West Jersey in America and declared legal tender.

Copper halfpence for Virginia were struck at the Tower Mint in London in 1773 and shipped to that colony.

Mention is made of the brass pieces produced in England circa 1616 for the Sommer Islands (Bermuda). At the time these were under the authority of the Virginia Company, but that division was separate from the colony on the American mainland. The authorization provided that these little coins, each depicting a wild hog, only be used on those islands. These are detailed in the present text by "numismatic tradition" although they are not part of coinage made for land that later became the United States. The main "currency" of the Sommer Islands during that time was tobacco.

Silver sixpence struck in England for circulation in the colony of Maryland.

Curiously, the many other issues that were legal tender on this side of the Atlantic—various foreign gold and silver issues—are *not* collected as part of the American colonial series. Many are of significant related interest, however. Extensive collections could be made of Spanish-American dollars and their fractional parts, as these were the main coins in American circulation in the eighteenth and early nineteenth centuries, and were given legal-tender status.

Rosa Americana coins intended for circulation in America were made under contract by William Wood beginning in 1722. Shown is a 1722 penny.

Halfpence for circulation in America were made in London and circulated widely.

EARLY COINAGE IN AMERICA

It was not until 1652, during the reign of Oliver Cromwell, three years after King Charles was removed from the British throne, that the Massachusetts Bay Colony faced and attempted to correct the shortage of circulating coins. A mint was established in Boston to provide a coinage that could be used to satisfy local needs and to counteract debased-alloy Spanish-American silver coins. The coins that were made at that historic facility were produced over the next 30 years in defiance of British law. The date 1652 was continued in use on them by convention, representing the date of authorization by the colony. Designs included the NE (New England), Willow Tree, Oak Tree, and Pine Tree motifs.

In Simsbury, Connecticut, in 1737, Dr. Samuel Higley struck copper threepence pieces made from metal taken from local mines, a coinage that was continued after his death the same year. The first issues were denominated as three pence. Objection arose among locals who disputed the value of the tokens, and later varieties said VALUE ME AS YOU PLEASE. Today all such coins are very rare.

In 1783, John Chalmers, an Annapolis, Maryland, silversmith, issued his own high-quality coins that were readily accepted in regional commerce. The dies were made by Thomas Sparrow, who also engraved plates for bank notes.

After the Declaration of Independence made the case for American freedom from British rule, the first of the emerging states to consider the subject of coinage was New Hampshire. The State House of

The 1652 Pine Tree shilling is perhaps the most famous American colonial coin. Nathaniel Hawthorne once wrote a story about it.

Higley coppers were struck in Simsbury, Connecticut, in 1737 and 1739. This early issue is lettered THE VALUE OF THREE PENCE.

Representatives authorized a limited quantity of pure-copper coins. Silversmith William Moulton was empowered to make them; he prepared cast patterns featuring a pine tree and a harp, and the date 1776. Historians believe these patterns were not accepted by the public, and few of them entered circulation. Still, they marked the beginning of a new period in American money.

During the pre-federal period each die was made of distinctive character, so the finished coins would indicate the authority of the issuer and be familiar as to value. By the time that state coinage commenced in 1785 (by Connecticut and Vermont) the most familiar foreign copper coins in circulation were British halfpence. These depicted the king on the obverse and the seated figure of Britannia, the personification of Great Britain, on the reverse. It was logical that Connecticut and Vermont (beginning in 1786, after its "landscape" coinage) placed a portrait on the one side of their coins and a seated figure on the other. Such motifs gave instant familiarity and credibility to new issues and implied that they were worth as much as a British halfpenny.

Other coppers of the 1780s had IMMUNIS COLUMBIA, NON VI VIRTUTE VICI, E PLURIBUS UNUM, LIBER NATUS LIBER-TATEM DEFENDO, and other Latinized inscriptions, the meanings of which were probably unknown to the majority of the overall population. INDE ET LIB on the reverse of Connecticut and Vermont coppers meant "Independence and liberty," from Latin, later also related to 'Indépendence Et Liberté" used on certain French coins of the nineteenth century.

1783 silver shilling made in Annapolis, Maryland, by silversmith John Chalmers. Two birds compete for a worm, while behind a fence a dangerous snake (an allegory for Britain) lurks unnoticed amidst their squabble.

British halfpence and counterfeits thereof were the most often seen copper coins in circulation in the United States in the late eighteenth century. Shown is a genuine 1771 halfpenny.

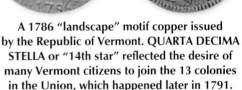

A 1786 "landscape" motif copper issued by the Republic of Vermont. QUARTA DECIMA STELLA or "14th star" reflected the desire of many Vermont citizens to join the 13 colonies in the Union, which happened later in 1791.

To facilitate their use in commerce the design of Vermont coppers was changed to the portrait of King George III and the figure of Britannia, now with Vermont-related legends translating to "By the Authority of Vermont" and "Independence and Liberty."

Copper coins for Connecticut were struck under contract from 1785 to 1788 and circulated widely. Most bore portraits of King George II or, as seen here, III.

TOWARD A FEDERAL COINAGE

Fugio coppers, struck under the authority of Congress under contract with the Connecticut mint, made their appearance in 1788, but were back-dated 1787, and used a sundial motif earlier found on certain Continental paper-money issues. Taken together, these diverse coinages and others are often referred to as "colonials" by numismatists today. As to when the colonial era ended can be debated. The Declaration of Independence, dated July 4, 1776, proclaimed that the colonies were henceforth independent. Therefore, they were no longer colonies. The Battle of Yorktown, 1781, marked the end of the war. The Treaty of Paris, signed in 1783, resulted in all countries, including Britain, recognizing the independence of the United States of America.

The 1787 Fugio copper cent.

In 1782 Robert Morris, the Confederation's superintendent of finance, proposed to Congress a curious money system of 1,440 "units" making up a dollar. This was calculated to figure (to the smallest fraction) into the many different valuations of the Spanish dollar, which varied throughout the states. Thomas Jefferson favored a simpler dollar unit and a decimal system. "The most easy ratio of multiplication and division is that of ten," he noted in 1784. George Washington referred to the decimal system as "a measure, which in my opinion has become indispensably necessary."

In 1783 Morris submitted to Congress a series of patterns, designed by Benjamin Dudley, as a proposal along the decimal line. The largest piece, with a denomination of 1,000 "units" (each unit being a quarter grain of silver), he called a *mark*. The 500-unit piece was a *quint* and the 100-unit a *bit*. These silver patterns were proposed along with a copper 5-unit piece. The system never went beyond the experimental stage.

Silver 1783 pattern for 1,000 units or one mark.

Actual statehood commenced when the various former colonies ratified the United States Constitution. Delaware was the first in 1787. Complicating the discussion is the issuance of paper money by the Continental Congress in the late 1770s, specifically marked "United States."

Coins and tokens of George Washington, mostly struck in England from 1783 through the mid-1790s, are often collected with colonial issues and are included herein.

In *American Gold and Silver: U.S. Mint Collector and Investor Coins and Medals, Bicentennial to Date*, numismatist Dennis Tucker quoted Benjamin Franklin: "There are three faithful friends: An old wife, an old dog, and ready money." Tucker went on to note:

> For many decades, Americans considered the best kinds of ready money to be *silver* and *gold*, prized above copper, paper currency, credit, and other financial instruments. As treasured as they were, in many periods of our nation's history silver and gold coins were the most difficult to obtain and keep.
>
> Britain's colonies in North America, unlike most of Spain's in Mexico and Central and South America, never were significant sources of native gold and silver. The British would have to mine their New World treasure not with pick axes and shovels, but with trade and commercial policy. Tariffs and other

regulations were designed to give every advantage to British producers, and America's colonists were forced into the dependent status of consumers. The effect was a draining of capital, and in particular silver and gold coins, from the New World back to the Old.

The advent of extensive federal coinage beginning with the Philadelphia Mint in 1792 was intended to help solve that.

FEDERAL COINAGE IN THE EARLY YEARS

By the late 1780s the individual states had ceased to issue their own coins and paper money. The sinews of commerce were secured by foreign silver and gold coins authorized as legal tender by Congress (the authorization of most did not expire until 1860, as noted earlier). Dominating the activity were coins of Spanish America, with those from the Mexico City Mint being the most prevalent. Coins of Great Britain, France, the Netherlands, and certain other European countries were legal tender as well. Joining the legitimate silver and copper issues was a flood of copper coins, mostly genuine and counterfeit British halfpence that had no legal-tender status but were widely accepted in commerce. The value of such coppers in quantity fluctuated, and in the late 1790s there had been a deep depression. However, the coins singly and in small groups continued to pass readily.

Alexander Hamilton.

In planning for a federal coinage Alexander Hamilton, who would become the nation's first secretary of the Treasury, agreed fundamentally with the decimal concept and urged that gold and silver be used in the nation's standard money. On March 3, 1791—during George Washington's first presidential term—Congress authorized the president to hire artists and acquire machinery for coinage in order to establish a federal mint. Some initial steps were taken, and that October, in his annual address, Washington stated, "The disorders in the existing currency, and especially the scarcity of small change, a scarcity so peculiarly distressing to the poorer classes, strongly recommend the carrying into immediate effect the resolution already entered into concerning the establishment of a mint."

Philadelphia in the 1790s, when it was the seat of the United States government.

Five months later, the Mint Act of April 2, 1792, provided that "the money of account of the United States should be expressed in dollars or units, dismes or tenths, cents or hundredths, and milles or thousandths; a disme being the tenth part of a dollar, a cent the hundredth part of a dollar, a mille the thousandth part of a dollar. . . ." The Mint Act also established the metal content of the coins, and their imagery; identified the "seat of government," Philadelphia, as the site of the new mint; and guaranteed that silver and gold would be made into coins free of charge to those who brought the metal in.

> The latter provision would save the Mint from having to source its own raw gold and silver. It also offered banks, merchants, and others a way to transform bullion and miscellaneous foreign specie into official, spendable U.S. coins, and thereby inject larger-denomination coins into commerce. (The conversion, while convenient, was not automatic; refining and coining took time. Alternately, one could deliver bullion to the Mint and exchange it immediately for equivalent U.S. coins, with one-half of 1 percent deducted for expenses.) The act also provided for a coinage of copper small-change coins.[3]

Copper coinage was extremely important for the early Mint. There was no profit to be made on coining silver and gold, but copper half cents and cents yielded any profit that could be made between the cost of copper stock and the face value of the coins. It was more expedient to coin a single cent than two half cents, with the result that cents were made in large quantities as compared to sporadic lower quantities for half cents.

The coins specified in the Mint Act of 1792 included these:

Denomination	Value	Fineness	Denomination	Value	Fineness
eagle	$10.00	91.7% pure gold (22k)	quarter dollar	$0.25	89.2% pure silver
half eagle	$5.00	91.7% pure gold (22k)	disme	$0.10	89.2% pure silver
quarter eagle	$2.50	91.7% pure gold (22k)	half disme	$0.05	89.2% pure silver
dollar	$1.00	89.2% pure silver	cent	$0.01	100% pure copper
half dollar	$0.50	89.2% pure silver	half cent	$0.005	100% pure copper

COINAGE OF THE 1790s

On July 31, 1792, the cornerstone was laid for the Philadelphia Mint, the second building created by the United States government (the first was a lighthouse). In attendance were President George Washington, Mint Director David Rittenhouse, and others. At the time Rittenhouse, a maker of clocks and scientific apparatus, was one of the Americans most skilled in mechanics and was an ideal choice. Philadelphia was the seat of the federal government, and the president resided just a short walk away.

By that time there was a coining press and some other equipment on hand, stored in an old carriage house on Sixth Street, above Chestnut, owned by John Harper, a saw maker and mechanic. Thomas Jefferson, in his Memorandum Book July 11, 1792, entry, noted that he took $75 in silver to the Mint to be coined. His July 13, 1792, entry records receiving 1,500 half dismes from the Mint. In the autumn the Mint was in operation, and additional silver half dismes were produced.

Dr. David Rittenhouse, the first director of the Philadelphia Mint.

In December some pattern one-cent pieces and other proposals were made. Dies for some early patterns were made by Robert Birch, and Joseph Wright created a quarter-dollar pattern.

Copper one-cent pieces were first made for circulation in February 1793. The earliest versions had a head of Miss Liberty on the obverse and a chain of 15 links on the reverse, one for each state (by this time Vermont had joined the Union, in 1791, and Kentucky in 1792). To some the design was less than pleasing. One newspaper account described Miss Liberty as being "in a fright," and the chain on the reverse as an ill omen for a land of freedom. The motif was changed to a different face of Miss Liberty, and, on the reverse, a wreath. That summer, copper half cents were made for the first time. Some early dies were made by Joseph Wright (who died of yellow fever that September), and possibly by Henry Voigt, an engraver on the Mint staff. In the autumn Robert Scot, a British immigrant who was important as a local maker of copper plates for bank-notes, maps, and illustrations, was hired as engraver. In the first year the fledgling Mint struck 35,334 half cents and 111,512 cents, a creditable output. Sources of copper were erratic and problematical and ranged from new sheets to old roofing, some acquired through local advertisements.

On October 15, 1794, the first silver dollars were struck for circulation, comprising 1,578 coins that were found satisfactory and some others with defects that were held back for recoinage of the metal. Half dollars were also struck in the autumn. Dies dated 1794 for the half dime were made, but were not used until 1795. It was not until 1795 that a press of sufficient size to strike dollars properly was installed. These were of the Flowing Hair design from dies by Robert Scot.

1792 half dismes were first struck in July of that year, the first circulating coinage minted by the federal government.

A view of the first Mint as envisioned by painter Edwin Lamasure in 1914. The front structure was two joined buildings that had earlier served as a brewery and for other purposes. The rear buildings are depicted with some artistic license on Lamasure's part. This facility was used through the year 1832.

The first cents struck for circulation at the Mint were made in March 1793 and depicted Miss Liberty on the obverse and a chain of 15 links on the reverse. On the first die the abbreviation AMERI. was used on the reverse.

David Rittenhouse, in poor health, resigned as Mint director in June 1795 and was replaced by Henry William de Saussure, who served only to the following November. Replacing him in in the same month was Elias Boudinot, who remained in the post until July 1805.

The Draped Bust design was introduced on the dollar in autumn 1795 and was later used on half cents (starting in 1800) and on cents and other silver coins (1796). This was from a portrait of socialite Mrs. William Bingham drawn by Gilbert Stuart.

In July of 1795 the first federal gold coins, half eagles ($5 gold pieces), were delivered, soon followed by eagles ($10), the largest denomination. Designs changed and evolved over the years. It was general practice to have copper coins bear one common design, silver coins another standard motif, and gold coins to share still another, although sometimes there was overlapping. The Draped Bust obverse was first used on silver coins of 1795 as noted, while gold coins of that and succeeding years into the next century depicted Miss Liberty wearing a conical cloth cap.

In 1796 the first silver dimes and quarter dollars were struck and also the first quarter eagles ($2.50 gold coins), completing all of the denominations authorized by the 1792 Mint Act. While half cents and cents were struck for the account and profit of the Mint, silver and gold coins were made only on the request of depositors of such precious metals. This was usually deposited in the form of foreign coins, but sometimes in other forms, including worn-out utensils and old ornaments.

In the early days dies for all denominations were cut by hand, with separate punches used to add numerals, letters, stars, and devices such as eagles and Liberty heads. No two dies were ever precisely alike, creating a wide panorama of varieties usually differing from each other slightly. However, more than just a few had interesting errors or blunders, such as having a word spelled as IINITED instead of UNITED, or having a fraction read 1/000, which is mathematically meaningless, instead of 1/100. While 13 stars, or one for each of the original colonies, has been the standard count on federal silver and gold coins up to the modern day, some of 1796 were given 15 stars, representing the current number of states

The first silver dollars were of the Flowing Hair type and were struck in one day on October 15, 1794.

The Draped Bust design was first used on silver dollars in 1795 and was later the motif on other copper and silver coins.

Half eagles first made in July 1795 were the first federal gold coins.

A famous reverse die for an 1801 cent had three errors: the left stem at the bottom of the wreath was missing, UNITED was spelled as IINITED, and the fraction was a meaningless 1/000 instead of 1/100.

in the Union. Tennessee joined in this year, raising the count to 16, and some coins were made with this number of stars. Soon, the idea was abandoned, and 13 became the standard.

During the 1790s continuing into the new century epidemics of yellow fever swept Philadelphia on several occasions, resulting in many deaths (including of engraver Joseph Wright in 1793). The Mint was closed during these periods and the dies stored in the vaults of a local bank. The Bank of America and the Bank of Pennsylvania were especially important in the early years of the Mint and made deposits of foreign gold and silver coins and received quantities of newly made federal issues.

Most dies of the era continued to be made by Robert Scot, with the assistance in earlier years of Henry Voigt and John Smith Gardner. Copper cents in circulation were augmented by many private tokens imported from England, mostly notably those bearing the advertisement of Talbot, Allum & Lee, New York City mer-

An engraver at the Philadelphia Mint. (Concept by Marcia Davis, 1984)

chants in the India trade. In the spring of 1795 about 52,000 of them were bought by the Mint, and planchets for half cents were cut from them. Later, an arrangement was made for Boulton & Watt in Birmingham, England, to supply ready-made copper planchets, a practice that was maintained until the War of 1812. There were some schedule problems in 1799 that resulted in a smaller coinage of cents that year; no half cents were made in 1798 or 1799. In 1800 Johann (John) Matthias Reich was hired on contract to make medals, thus assisting engraver Robert Scot.

"Despite the Mint's best efforts in its early years, its coinage remained scarce in circulation. Gold and silver in particular were rarely seen in commerce, but the problem extended to small change, as well. By 1799 only about $50,000 worth of copper cents and half cents had been pumped into the economy—roughly one coin for every citizen, not nearly enough for the nation's day-to-day business."[4] Filling the void, earlier tokens and coins of the colonies and states continued to circulate. Silver and gold coins were seldom seen in commerce, except in large cities. Many if not most silver dollars and gold $10 eagles were used in the export trade and never returned.

Legal-tender silver and gold coins of European and Central and South American countries continued to fill nearly all of the need for large denominations in circulation. The Spanish-American silver 8-reales, dollar sized, was the world's most popular trade coin. Vast quantities were purchased by American merchants and exported in exchange for goods. Whaling and merchant ships headed to the Pacific and Far East carried thousands of these coins as they were accepted at all foreign ports. A common arrangement for security was to store thousands of coins in a compartment near the captain's stateroom.

Despite the output of the Philadelphia Mint the Spanish-American 8-reales or piece-of-eight coin dominated domestic as well as world commerce well into the early nineteenth century. Shown is a 1761 Mexico City Mint 8-reales.

THE EARLY NINETEENTH CENTURY

At the beginning of the nineteenth century, officially 1801, these coins were being struck: cent, half dime, dime, and silver dollar, each with the Draped Bust obverse, and $5 and $10 gold of the Capped Bust motif. Yellow fever continued to be a problem, resulting in Mint closings. Another problem was the opposition of certain members of Congress to the Mint itself, and several proposals were made to close it and have coinage done under private contract. Those situations were resolved and the Mint continued operations.

Robert Maskell Patterson was appointed Mint director by President Thomas Jefferson on January 1, 1806. He served until July 1834, the longest tenure of anyone ever holding the office.

In 1806 John Reich was given a position on the Mint staff as assistant engraver. He created a version of Miss Liberty in a floppy mob cap, called the Capped Bust motif. This was first used on half dollars and half eagles of 1807 and later on the cent

Elias Boudinot, Mint director from 1795 to 1805.

(1808), half cent (1809), half dime (1829), dime (1809), and quarter (1815). Today, Capped Bust half dollars, made in large quantities, are especially popular with numismatists. Reich also redesigned the reverses of silver and gold coins to incorporate a perched eagle holding arrows and an olive branch.

America was prosperous from the early 1790s until 1808, when the effects of Thomas Jefferson's 1807 Embargo Act were felt. By that time the French, then the British, had seized many American ships on the high seas, the British often kidnapping our sailors and forcing them to serve on their ships. The Embargo Act prohibited nearly all trade with foreign ports, in effect freezing the economy of most coastal cities. Many businesses failed, and other hardships were experienced. The War of 1812 created more chaos. The United States Navy was not strong, and to help fight the enemy, the government gave letters of

The Capped Bust design by John Reich was introduced on the 1807 half dollar (as shown) and half eagle and was used on certain coins as late as 1838.

Robert M. Patterson served as Mint director from 1806 to 1834.

marque, as they were called, to the captains of and owners of ships. They then engaged in privateering under the American flag, capturing whatever enemy prizes they could find and taking the ships to ports where they and their contents were sold at auction—with the money divided among the ship crews and owners. This was a rich undertaking for many, and more than a few family fortunes in Portsmouth, Baltimore, and other cities were augmented in this manner.

The monetary situation in the United States was tumultuous. The supply of copper planchets from England was exhausted in 1814, and no copper coins were made in 1815. Deposits of silver and gold coins were small, and relatively few coins of these metals were struck in mid-decade. In 1816 only copper cents were made.

In a famous battle at sea in the War of 1812 the USS *Constitution* vanquished the HMS *Guerriere*. (Anton Otto Fischer)

Gold and silver coins were in circulation in some periods in the 1810s, then one or another of these metals would rise in value, and many coins would disappear. Meanwhile, a flood of paper bills was issued by banks, merchants, and others.

John Reich left the Mint in 1817 to pursue other opportunities. Engraving was primarily continued by Robert Scot, in service since 1793, but his eyesight was failing. There were no new designs to be created for the next several years, and the design hubs and punches on hand remained in use for new dies. Economic times were difficult in 1818 and 1819, what would be called a recessionary period by later economists.

By this time only a few dozen collectors and museums pursued the art and history of numismatics. In coming years their numbers would increase.

The 1816 cent of the new Matron Head design was the only federal coinage of this year.

A $1 note issued by the Owl Creek Bank of Mount Vernon, Ohio, in 1816, a time of monetary crisis.

THE 1820s AND 1830s

The financial matters improved in the 1820s, in part spawning the creation historical societies, athenaeums, and libraries that often included coins in their holdings and exhibits.

The first professional numismatist in the United States seems to have been John Allan, born in Scotland. In 1820 he was just one of three American subscribers to Mudie's set of National Medals, published in England. Philip Hone, a wealthy New Yorker who served as mayor of the city in 1826, is known to have been an active coin collector in New York City circa 1822–1827.[5] The private collection of Benjamin H. Watkins, auctioned in Salem, Massachusetts, on June 12 and 13, 1828, is thought to be the first significant cataloged sale of coins in the United States, although the descriptions were poor by later standards.

In the meantime the international price of gold rose in relation to silver, and gold coins became worth more in melt value than face value. Large quantities were coined to the order of depositors who shipped them overseas, where they were received on the basis of weight, with the stamped value being of no importance. In the United States anyone desiring gold coins had to pay a premium for them to a money broker or exchange office. There were no federal gold coins in domestic circulation after 1820. Mintages of half eagles were nearly all to the order of merchants and others who exported them to Europe, where they were melted.

Robert Scot continued as engraver at the Mint until his death on November 3, 1823. William Kneass, a local engraver of copper plates for bank notes and other items, was appointed engraver in 1824. Christian Gobrecht, who did some contract work in the 1820s, hoped to be appointed but was not considered. Beginning about this year Adam Eckfeldt and perhaps one or two others working at the Philadelphia Mint began saving current coinage.[6] It is said that copper cents and other items were kept on hand for sale or exchange with interested collectors. Interesting rare coins were

From 1821 to June 1834 all newly minted federal gold coins such as this half eagle cost more than face value to make. Depositors were charged a premium for them. Nearly all were shipped overseas and melted for bullion value, as the face value made no difference.

picked out of incoming deposits and saved. Many old dies were still at the Mint, and on occasion restrikes would be made to supply pieces needed by collectors. No records were kept of such activities, and today we can only speculate as to what occurred.

On July 4, 1829, the cornerstone was laid for a new Philadelphia Mint building. For the occasion, half dimes of the Capped Bust type were struck for the first time, there having been no coinage of this denomination since 1805.

Andrew Jackson, elected president in 1828, took office on March 4, 1829. The first Bank of the United States had operated from 1791 to 1811, after which its 20-year charter was not renewed. The second Bank of the United States was chartered in 1816, to operate until 1836. This bank was mainly owned by private stockholders, although the government had a significant interest. It had many branches in the East and Midwest and issued paper money. Great resistance to it was made by the politicians of many states whose state-chartered banks felt it was unfair competition.

Jackson disliked the bank and resolved to veto any charter extension. His opponents in Congress passed a bill well in advance, in 1830, to assure that renewal would take place in 1836. Jackson kept his word, and in the 1830s the bank wound down its operations to the point that most activity ended in 1835. This was the great political issue of the era. From that time onward, politicians, newspapers, and others were largely divided into two groups: pro-Jackson and anti-Jackson. As if that was not enough, John C. Calhoun, senator from South Carolina, frequently suggested that South Carolina withdraw from the Union, and other Southern states do so as well, as the commercial interests of the South (cotton, tobacco, and other agricultural products) were so different from those of the North (manufacturing, banking, etc.). In particular, high tariffs had diminished exports of cotton, to the detriment of the South, while restricting imports from Europe and thus bringing great prosperity to factories in the North.

The charter to renew the second Bank of the United States was vetoed by President Andrew Jackson in 1830, after which the institution wound down its business, closing in 1836.

Extensive gold strikes were made in Georgia and North Carolina in the 1820s, the first time that significant quantities of that metal were discovered in the United States. In 1830 Templeton Reid issued his own $2.50, $5, and $10 gold coins, and in Rutherfordton, North Carolina, Christopher Bechtler and his family operated a private mint that would remain in business until the early 1850s and would make $1, $2.50, and $5 coins. In 1833 the new Philadelphia Mint went into operation and would remain the center of coinage activity until 1901.

A $2.50 gold coin minted by Templeton Reid in Georgia following the most important gold strike to that date on United States soil.

Prosperity continued apace, aided by the enthusiasm for building canals and railroads, the opening up of new lands in the West and making them easy to buy, and a general atmosphere of well-being. The age of steam was beginning in a large way and would soon revolutionize industrial America.

The second Philadelphia Mint operated from 1833 to 1901.

The Act of June 28, 1834, reduced the amount of gold in coins, and the lightweight issues made beginning in August of that year circulated readily. Gold had not been seen in domestic commerce since 1820.

The expansion of America and continuing prosperity brought an increased need for coinage. In 1835 Congress authorized the opening of three branch mints. Each was opened for business several years later in 1838.

The New Orleans Mint was located near the mouth of the Mississippi River, the gateway to inland commerce. Mints at Charlotte, North Carolina, and Dahlonega, Georgia, were in gold-mining regions and provided convenient facilities for converting bullion to coins. The alternative would have been to ship it to distant Philadelphia. The mintmarks O, C, and D were added to each coin to signify their origin.

In August 1835, Chief Engraver Kneass was paralyzed by a stroke. In the next month Christian Gobrecht, a Philadelphia engraver of bank-notes, book plates, and other items, and an inventor, was hired as second engraver. A man of formidable artistic ability, Gobrecht did not want to be called "assistant," and thus the "second" in his title. As it turned out, he did most of the engraving work from that point onward, although Kneass retained the primary engravership until his death in 1840.

The New Orleans Mint operated from 1838 to 1861 and again from 1879 to 1909 and produced silver and gold coins. The facility houses a museum today.

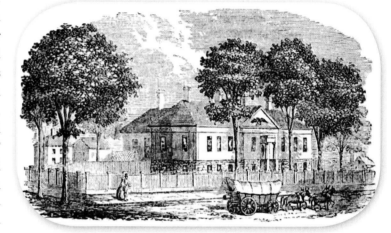

The Charlotte Mint coined gold from 1838 to 1861. Today the building, disassembled and moved to a park, is the Charlotte Art Museum.

The Dahlonega Mint produced gold coins from 1838 to 1861. The building burned in 1878. Today the Dahlonega Gold Museum Historic Site, housed in the historic Old Lumpkin County Courthouse, celebrates the region's importance in mining and private gold coinage.

An 1838-C quarter eagle, with Charlotte's C mintmark above the date.

Coinage presses were operated by hand. In 1836 steam power was introduced and in 1837 would be used on all presses for circulating coinage. Proofs made for collectors continued to be made on hand-operated equipment. Called "master coins" in the early days, Proofs would become increasingly important at the Mint, to the point in later years some coins were struck only in that format for collectors, and none for circulation (the earliest example may be the 1827 quarter dollar, for which information is incomplete, or may be the 1804 silver dollar, made in 1834 and backdated 20 years).

Prosperity continued in America through 1836, the year that the Bank of the United States charter expired. Speculation in real estate in the prairie beyond Pennsylvania was wildly out of control. Vast tracts were purchased through cred-

An early steam-powered knuckle-action coining press made for the Philadelphia Mint by a local manufacturer.

its and drafts, paper money of depreciated or uncertain value, and promissory notes. This set the scene for Andrew Jackson's Specie Circular, July 11, 1836, one of the most pivotal documents in American financial history. This decree mandated that lands be paid for in gold and silver coins, instead of paper money and credits, that buyers be bona-fide residents or settlers, and that the amount of acreage be restricted for each purchaser. Very few buyers of land had silver half dollars or gold half eagles, and speculation came to an abrupt halt. Loans were called, but debtors could not pay. By early 1837 there was a chill in the American economy, and European bankers, who held many investments, were becoming concerned.

In the same year, 1836, the Liberty Seated design made its debut on the silver dollar, the first of this denomination coined for circulation since 1804. By 1839 it was used on all silver denominations.

After the charter of the second Bank of the United States expired, many banks were formed with reckless abandon. The bank-note companies in New York and Philadelphia were eager to print as many bills as they could sell, with little notice taken as to whether the banks were chartered or legitimately established. The system of banks issuing large amounts of paper money worked perfectly fine in the heady days of 1835 and 1836. However, in early 1837 many people became wary of banks, and sought to redeem bills for gold and silver. It was quickly learned that while some banks could redeem a small percentage of their currency, no bank was able to exchange for all. On May 10, 1837, specie payments were suspended by most Eastern banks, and within weeks most banks in the South and West also stopped paying out coins.

A Liberty Seated half dime of 1837, the first year of use on this denomination as well as the dime. The motif first appeared on dollars of 1836 and later on quarters starting in 1838 and half dollars in 1839.

Soon, silver and gold coins disappeared completely from circulation, although copper cents remained. To facilitate commerce, countless cent-size Hard Times tokens (as we call them today) were issued, in a wide variety of designs, including advertisements for merchants, caricatures and comments about Jackson and his veto of the Bank of the United States, and more.

In 1837 coins became scarce and many Hard Times tokens were privately issued, such as this one mentioning the suspension of specie payments.

In June 1838 the Mint Cabinet was authorized by Congress—a display of American coins old and new, together with foreign and ancient coins and medals, and mineral specimens and ores. While a few coins were purchased, the main source of supply continued to be the extraction of interesting pieces from deposits made at the Mint. Veteran Mint employee Adam Eckfeldt supplied details of Mint history to interested visitors. Numismatics was becoming increasingly important, and there were at least several hundred serious collectors in America.

THE 1840s TO THE CIVIL WAR

By the early 1840s, Jacob Reese Eckfeldt and William DuBois were curators of the pieces on display in the Mint Cabinet. In 1842 a book by these two men, *A Manual of Gold and Silver Coins of All Nations*, was published by the Mint. The text did not contain numismatic text or comments of use to collectors, but dealt with the weights and designations of coins in these metals. The main audiences were banks and counting houses.

The gold districts of North Carolina and Georgia continued to supply the Charlotte and Dahlonega mints. The Bechtler family in North Carolina, which had begun producing $1, $2.50, and $5 gold coins from regional metal since the early 1830s, continued in business without interference from the Treasury Department, seemingly as their coins were of full weight and value and helped with commerce in the Southeast.

By 1844 the Hard Times era had ended, and American commerce was flourishing. Railroad stocks led the securities market. Year by year, towns and cities throughout the East and Midwest were connected. Many new lines were formed, many of which had banking support. Some even issued paper money. Meanwhile, canals, so important earlier, were fading from the scene with many old waterways and new projects abandoned. The Erie Canal connecting the Hudson River with Lake Erie remained important. On inland waterways and on the high seas sidewheel steamships carried most of the maritime passenger traffic and much cargo. Sailing vessels were still important on routes in which speed was important. In the 1850s fast-sailing clipper ships became important in long-distance freight.

In 1844 Christian Gobrecht, engraver at the Mint since autumn 1835 and responsible for the Liberty Seated design and other motifs, passed away. James B. Longacre, a highly accomplished engraver in the field of portraits and bank notes, was

Commerce on the Erie Canal.

Railroads were the growth industry of the 1840s and 1850s.

appointed in his place. He would serve until his death on January 1, 1869. During his tenure he would create many designs for pattern and regular coinage. Interest in numismatics moved another step forward in 1846 with William DuBois's 138-page *Pledges of History*, a carefully prepared volume describing coins and other items in the Mint Cabinet. The War with Mexico in 1846 and 1847 resulted in victory for the United States. As had been the case with earlier wars, medals were struck to commemorate leaders and battles. The West was expanding in population, most notably by emigrants on the Oregon Trail.

America changed dramatically following the discovery of a gleaming flake of gold in California in the tail race at Sutter's Mill, on the American River, January 24, 1848. This ignited the California Gold Rush, the travel westward of Forty Niners the following year, and the establishment of California as a state in 1850. This transformed the boundaries and encouraged settlement more than any other single event in American history. Now, the country extended from sea to shining sea.

The vast discoveries of precious metal engendered the establishment of several private mints in San Francisco, Sacramento, and elsewhere in 1849 and 1850. Large quantities of gold were sent to the East for coinage, usually by sidewheel steamship from San Francisco to Panama, then across land for about 48 miles, then connecting to another ship on the Atlantic side at the port of Aspinwall (today's Colón).

The dramatic influx of gold resulted in the Act of March 3, 1849, which introduced two new denominations—the gold dollar and $20 double eagle. The unprecedented quantity of new gold upset the traditional ratio

Sutter's Mill on the American River, the site of the first large-scale discovery of gold in California.

In 1849 the U.S. Mint introduced the gold dollar to facilitate the coining of gold arriving from California.

of 1 ounce of gold being equal to about 15.5 ounces of silver. Silver became relatively rarer than before, causing federal silver coins in circulation to increase in value to the point at which, by December 1849, they could be melted down to yield more in bullion value than face value. Nearly all disappeared from circulation. The situation would become even more acute.

The first California private gold coins were issued by Norris, Grieg, and Norris in Benecia City with the imprint of San Francisco.

In California beginning in spring 1849 and continuing through 1855 more than a dozen private companies and banks issued their own gold coins of varied design. Although these were not official legal tender they passed readily in commerce. From 1851 to 1853 Augustus Humbert, appointed by the Treasury Department as the official United States assayer of gold in California, supervised the striking of gold coins of denominations from $10 to $50, including at the United States Assay Office of Gold, the activity being conducted by arrangement and under the aegis of Moffat & Company, a firm which separately issued its own coins.

Octagonal $50 gold coins called slugs were issued under the supervision of Augustus Humbert in 1851 (as shown here) and 1852.

In 1850 the California state constitution was adopted. It forbid the use of paper money at face value in the channels of commerce. Only coins had legal-tender value. This would have important implications in the following decade of the 1860s.

In the early 1850s there was the strange situation that in the channels of commerce in the East and Midwest, Liberty Seated coins were nowhere to be seen as they had been gathered by hoarders and speculators in silver metal, and their place was nearly completely taken by Spanish-American silver coins, with the 2-reales coin being the denomination most often seen.

In 1850 double eagles were introduced and were struck at the Philadelphia and New Orleans mints. These coins became exceedingly popular, and during the next 75 years, more value was minted in this denomination than of all other United States gold coins combined.

Placer Operations at Foster's Bar, an 1851 oil by Ernest Narjot, depicted gold mining on the American River east of Sacramento. (Bancroft Library)

In 1850 Jacob Reese Eckfeldt and William DuBois, continuing assayers at the Mint and keepers of the Mint Cabinet, published a small book of 61 pages, *New Varieties of Gold and Silver Coins, Counterfeit Coins, Bullion with Mint Values.* Included was information on gold coins privately minted in California. This work was also issued in modified form in 1851 and 1852. The two later versions also included the text of DuBois's 1846 *Pledges of History* work, the latter being out of print at the time.

The first truly important American auction sale featuring rare coins was that of the late Dr. Lewis Roper, a Philadelphia physician who had gone west to seek his fortune in the gold fields, but died of cholera at sea off of Panama on his return voyage in 1850. The coins were offered on February 20, 1851, in the sale room of Moses Thomas & Son, Philadelphia, a popular location for the sale of antiques, books, and other items.

In 1851 with Liberty Seated coins still absent from circulation the silver three-cent piece, or *trime*, was issued. Of 75 percent silver and 25 percent copper (instead of the standard 90:10 ratio), these coins were not profitable to melt, and thus they circulated in commerce at a time when other federal silver coins were being hoarded or melted.

In 1852 *Uncle Tom's Cabin*, a novel by Harriet Beecher Stowe describing the life of slaves on Southern plantations, was published. By decade's end it was the best-selling novel in American history. Perhaps more than any other single factor the book influenced millions of Americans, mostly in the North, to condemn slavery and campaign for abolition. Relations of Northern politicians with those in the South worsened, with the result that the presidential administrations of Franklin Pierce (1853–1857) and James Buchanan (1857–1861) would be viewed as by historians as two of the most ineffective in American history. Each attempted to please both the North and South, to the dissatisfaction of all.

The silver coinage problem ended with the implementation of the Act of February 21, 1853, in which the authorized weights of the silver half dime, dime, quarter, and half dollar were reduced. Coins made under the new standard had arrowheads added to each side of the date to distinguish them. These lightweight coins circulated, thus ending the money problems that had plagued the market since 1850. The Liberty Seated dollar weight was unchanged and those coins remained available for bullion value, or more than face value, for those who acquired them for export, in which transactions the imprinted face value made no difference.

The three-cent piece or trime was introduced in 1851. With a silver content of only 75 percent (unlike the 90 percent of other denominations) it had less than face value in metal and was not attractive to speculators.

Slaves at work in a cotton field under the gaze of the plantation owner and his family. (Vignette from a bank note of the Farmers Banking Association, Demopolis, Alabama)

In 1853 the Treasury Department acquired the building and facilities of private coiner Moffat & Company and its associates and remodeled it to become the San Francisco Mint. It opened in March 1854 and commenced striking coins with S mintmarks. Commercial connections between the Atlantic and Pacific coasts were mainly by ship, interrupted by a land crossing at Panama or, less often, Nicaragua, or entirely by sea, around the tip of South America. In the same year the new $3 gold denom-

An 1853 quarter dollar with arrows at the date to indicate reduced silver content.

ination was introduced at the Philadelphia, Dahlonega, and Charlotte mints, but this met with only a lukewarm reception, as the value was too close to the long-established $2.50 quarter eagle. Over the years the mintage figures declined, and in 1889 it was discontinued.

The American economy was enjoying a new era of prosperity brought on by the gold excitement, the continued expansion of railroads (their shares dominated the stock exchanges), and excellent business conditions everywhere. Land investment and speculation was back in vogue, and real-estate agents were literally doing a land-office business in what was by then known as the Midwest, the term *West* being descriptive of the Rocky Mountains to the Pacific shore.

The Mint had been experimenting since 1850 with ways to reduce the size and weight of the large-diameter one-cent piece, to increase profits. The price of copper had been rising. In 1856, Engraver Longacre created a cent which was proposed for adoption. The obverse featured a flying eagle (adapted from the reverse of Gobrecht's silver dollar of 1836), and the reverse used an "agricultural wreath" from the $3 gold coin of 1854. An estimated 800 to 1,000 coins were struck in late 1856 and early 1857, all dated 1856, and sent to congressmen, newspaper editors, and others to acquaint them with the new design.

The Philadelphia Mint remained the primary facility for federal coinage. The director of the Mint had his office there

The San Francisco Mint as depicted in *Hutchings' California Magazine.* This facility operated until 1874 when it was replaced by a new structure.

and supervised the operations of the branches at Charlotte, Dahlonega, New Orleans, and San Francisco. Coins in circulation or currently being minted included the copper half cent and cent, the silver three-cents, half dime, dime, quarter dollar, half dollar, and dollar, and the gold $1, $2.50, $3, $5, $10, and $20. Gold from California was still arriving in quantity, although the peak year was 1853.

The Act of February 21, 1857, abolished the copper half cent and cent and mandated other changes, including the planned expiration of the legal-tender privilege for certain foreign silver and gold coins. New cents of the Flying Eagle design, of smaller diameter and made of copper-nickel, soon began rolling off the presses. On May 25, the first small cents were available to the public in exchange for old coppers and Spanish silver.

A gold ingot issued by the assaying firm of Harris & Marchand in Sacramento. Such ingots facilitated the shipment of gold in quantity.

The passion for coin collecting spread rapidly, with numismatologists, as they were called, seeking rare early cents such as 1793 and 1799, while noticing other interesting old coins as well. Within several years important reference books would be published on coins, dealers would set up shop in major cities, and coin auctions would be held frequently. Thus was born an active market for rare coins, tokens, and medals. The *Historical Magazine* was launched in January 1857 and went on to include many articles about coins, including, in August, the first installment of "The First Coinage of America," by Jeremiah Colburn, who in the same year wrote articles about old copper cents for the Boston *Evening Transcript*. In New York City, Augustus B. Sage and Charles I. Bushnell engaged in a lively debate about rare coins in the pages of the *New-York Dispatch*. In the autumn the first issue of *Norton's Literary Letter*, mostly about books, but with much information on coins, was welcomed by collectors. Thus was born a new market with many thousands of numismatists participating.

The economy had enjoyed good times since 1844 and the passing of the Hard Times era. That changed on August 24, 1857, when the Ohio Life Insurance & Trust Company failed. With offices in Cincinnati and New York, it had been a big player in loans, credit, and the processing of paper relating to real estate. By then there had been some shivers in the money market, and some people were apprehensive concerning seemingly unwise investments, but little was said. On the same day the Mechanics Banking Association suspended specie payments. Fear spread, and those holding stocks and investment paper rushed to cash it in at current rates, but found few buyers. Within days, several stock brokers and money dealers failed. This was disturbing but exciting news, and papers in major cities lost no time printing "scare" headlines, which sold more papers, but also helped spread fear. In a domino effect, one failure created another, and soon the Panic of 1857 was underway. In October all of the banks in New York City suspended specie payments, except for the Chemical Bank. Unlike previous economic disturbances, the Panic of 1857 had little effect on the production of federal coinage.

On January 1, 1858, the Philadelphia Numismatic Society was formed, becoming the first such group in the United States. In March, teenaged Augustus B. Sage and friends founded the American Numismatic Society in New York City. By late summer 1858 there were nearly a dozen coin dealers active in the United States, including, in New York City alone, the venerable John Allan, and at least three young men: Augustus Sage, Henry Bogert, and John Curtis. In the same year the first important American numismatic book was published, *An Historical Account of American Coinage*, by John H. Hickcox. The slim volume included 151 numbered pages plus five pages of illustrations by John Gavit, a well-known engraver of bank note plates. Hickcox had spent some time in research and had contacted historical societies and several numismatists as well as Mint Director James Ross Snowden. Only 200 regular copies were printed, and these were mostly sent to libraries and historical societies. For collectors there was no single readily available source for information, and many still sought the elusive copper cent of 1815, not realizing that none were minted that year.

The issuance of medalets depicting historical events achieved wide popularity in 1858 and 1859 with the creation of hundreds of different privately minted varieties, most in copper and about 32 mm diameter.

Proof coins became popular in 1858, and an estimated 210 sets of silver denominations were sold, plus a larger number of coppernickel Flying Eagle cents. Proof gold coins were available singly, and the dollar was the most popular denomination in this metal, probably with a sale of a few dozen or so.

A copper medalet depicting Charles I. Bushnell, one of America's most prominent numismatists in 1859. (Augustus Sage's Numismatic Gallery No. 1)

In the meantime James Ross Snowden, Mint director since 1853, was receiving continuous requests for restrikes of earlier coins (heretofore usually granted) and new patterns. Snowden was a numismatist and decided to vastly expand the Mint Cabinet's holding of George Washington–related tokens and medals. He offered to exchange restrikes and rarities for needed pieces. In the spring of 1859 the coining of special coins went "underground," no information was released, and *The Nation*, a popular journal, later estimated that by 1860 Mint officials had pocketed at least $60,000 secretly and without benefit to the government. This largesse would continue unabated until the summer of 1885.

In a way numismatists can be grateful for this illegal activity, for probably at least 90 percent of the nineteenth-century pattern coins in existence today were produced secretly! The logic of this can be contemplated.

Meanwhile, coin auctions became more frequent, and in 1859 dealer Sage cataloged four sales in New York City, more than any other professional. In Philadelphia, Edward Cogan and William K. Idler became important in the coin trade. Henry Cook bought and sold coins in Boston, another shop was open in Baltimore, and a few more were scattered here and there. The first really large and impressive book for coin collectors was published that year, the *American Numismatical Manual*, by Dr. Montroville W. Dickeson.

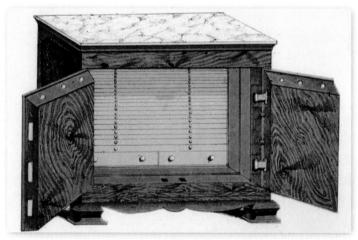

A wooden cabinet with sliding drawers was the standard way to store and display a rare-coin collection, as seen in this 1859 illustration in the *American Numismatical Manual*.

THE 1860s AND THE CIVIL WAR

In 1860 and 1861 in Denver the banking firm of Clark, Gruber & Co., headquartered in Leavenworth, Kansas, set up a private mint and bank, and coined $2.50, $5, $10, and $20 gold pieces from local bullion. The district was in the middle of the "Pikes Peak or Bust" gold boom. Such coins were also made in 1861.

The swelling number of incoming enthusiasts electrified the coin market. Most in demand were the old copper cents, but the hottest area in terms of rapid price appreciation was the specialty of Washington pieces. Collectors scrambled to buy them in competition with Director Snowden. Prices multiplied, and specimens were hard to find.

The Clark, Gruber & Co. bank and mint in Denver in 1861. In 1862 the facility
was acquired by the Treasury Department. It was renamed the Denver
Mint but functioned only as an assay office and did not produce coins.

The 1860 presidential election fielded four candidates: Abraham Lincoln, Republican Party from Illinois; John C. Breckinridge, Southern Democratic Party from Kentucky; John C. Bell, Constitution Union Party from Tennessee; and Stephen A. Douglas, Northern Democratic Party from Illinois. In the November contest Lincoln, who campaigned as a staunch abolitionist, won by a landslide. This prompted South Carolina to secede from the Union on December 20, followed by six other Southern states in short order. These formed the Confederate States of America (CSA) in January 1861, with its capital in Montgomery, Alabama (moved later in the year to Richmond, Virginia).

An 1860 Lincoln token for the presidential campaign.

$1000 note printed for the Confederate States of America by the
National Bank Note Company, New York City, in March 1861.

At first, many in the Confederacy hoped to have favorable relations with the Union as a separate nation and trading partner. The first CSA issues of paper money and the first bonds were printed to its order by the National Bank Note and American Bank Note companies in New York City. Lincoln was inaugurated on March 4, 1861. Relations deteriorated. In the second week of April CSA forces at Fort Moultrie on the shore of Charleston Harbor bombarded and destroyed federal Fort Sumter, but allowed the men there to escape under a white flag to board a steamship for the North.

The War of the Rebellion, later generally called the Civil War (or, in the South, the War of Northern Aggression), began. The Northerners or Yankees perceived this as a quick win—the mighty industrial North against the primarily agricultural South. President Lincoln called for 90-day enlistments, by which time it was thought the war would certainly be over. Reality proved otherwise, and it was not until late July that the first important battle took place, at Bull Run in Manassas, Virginia, not far from the Union capital of Washington, D.C. To the surprise of the North, the Confederate troops won.

Under the Act of July 17, 1861, the Treasury Department issued $50,000,000 in Demand Notes, the first widely circulated paper money since Revolutionary times. To facilitate their acceptance, they could be exchanged at par for gold coins. Additional Demand Notes were authorized in February 1862. The story of federal paper money from this point onward is extensive and complex, beyond the purview of *Mega Red*, although scattered mentions are included here.

Meanwhile, in the Confederate States of America, coins all but disappeared. The Confederacy contemplated issuing a new series of half dollars with a unique design, but the coinage amounted to only four patterns. The *Richmond Enquirer*, December 31, 1861, reported that entrepreneurs were paying 30 to 50 percent premium in paper money to buy silver and gold coins: "The present price of specie will be hereafter quoted through all time as a damning stigma upon the character of Southern merchants." By that time Confederate paper money circulated widely through the region. Such bills continued to be issued into 1864 and steadily depreciated in value.

The bombardment of federal Fort Sumter in the harbor of Charleston, South Carolina on April 12, 1861, by cannon at Fort Moultrie on the shore.

By December 1861 the war was not going well for either side. In the North, citizens became apprehensive and began to hoard gold and silver. By early 1862, such coins were worth a small premium in terms of paper money, the latter being in the form of bills issued by banks. Things went from bad to worse after the Act of February 25, 1862, authorized the issue of a new series of paper money, Legal Tender notes, not redeemable in coins, but only exchangeable for other paper money.

Jefferson Davis, president of the Confederate States of America. (portrait by Mathew Brady)

General Robert E. Lee, commander of the Confederate forces.

Union soldiers taking a break.

The Confederate ironclad CSS *Merrimac* (center) and the Union USS *Monitor,* in the first battle of ironclad ships, off of Norfolk, Virginia, ended in a draw but revolutionized naval warfare.

Legal Tender Notes authorized in early 1862 were exchangeable at par only for other bank notes and not for gold or silver coins. The monetary system became disruptive.

Coin hoarding increased, and by summer 1862 no silver or gold coins were to be seen anywhere in circulation in the East or Midwest. Money brokers conducted a lively exchange business with investors and speculators, and daily prices were quoted for silver and gold coins. Proof coins continued to be minted for collectors, but the Philadelphia Mint would not accept Legal Tender notes at par for them. Instead, numismatists had to go to money brokers and buy regular coins for a premium, then send these coins to the Mint, with extra coins for the proofing charge, to obtain such sets. As a result mintages were low.

On the West Coast it was a different monetary story from the scenario in the East. The California State Legislature had made the use of paper money *illegal* in commerce, beginning in 1850. When the federal government started sending Legal Tender and other notes to the West, such as to pay soldiers and government employees, these bills were accepted only at a deep discount. "Hard money" in the form of silver and gold coins continued to trade there at face value during the conflict, continuing into the 1870s.

By the second week of July, 1862, even one-cent pieces were hoarded in the East and Midwest.

Postage Currency notes with stamp designs, 5 cents to 50 cents, were issued by the Treasury in the summer of 1862 at a time when no coins were in circulation.

More than 30 merchants issued encased postage stamps beginning in the summer of 1862, using stamps from 1¢ to 90¢ values.

To facilitate commerce, a flood of paper scrip notes (3¢, 5¢, 10¢, and 25¢ were the most popular denominations) and even postage stamps was used as money. John Gault patented his encased postage stamps, with a regular stamp, from 1¢ to 90¢, mounted behind clear mica in a brass case—intended to be durable in circulation. Soon a flood of federal Postage Currency notes appeared, followed by Fractional Currency, eventually swelling to many millions of dollars in 3¢, 5¢, 10¢, 15¢, 25¢, and 50¢ denominations. Legal Tender notes rolled off the printing presses, and a new series of National Bank notes appeared.

Civil War tokens of bronze and brass were issued by the millions. Dates range from 1861 to 1864 but most bear the year 1863. These featured many different motifs, ranging from historical portraits to war heroes and scenes, to advertisements for more than 900 stores and services. Sutlers—licensed merchants who mostly traveled with the troops—issued tokens as well. At the very outset these became popular with numismatists and have remained a popular specialty ever since.

In 1862 the United States government purchased the private mint of Clark, Gruber & Co. and designated it as the Denver Mint in its reports for the next several decades, but no coins were struck there. Years later in 1906 another Denver Mint was opened and was the first facility there to make coins.

The Act of April 22, 1864, provided that bronze alloy be used for cents and the new two-cent denomination, and it made the cent legal tender up to the amount of 10¢ and the two-cent piece legal tender up to 20¢. Thus, for the first time, coins other than silver or gold became legal tender in the United States. It is a curious fact that the old copper half cents and cents (of 1793–1857) were not legal tender, and anyone had the right to refuse them in payment for debts. The motto IN GOD WE TRUST was employed on the two-cent piece, the first use of this for circulating coins. Later, it would be added to most other coins. After the spring of 1864 federal cents returned to circulation, including millions of hoarded pieces.

A Civil War token issued by Sherwood & Hopson, Utica, New York.

In July 1864 in the East it took $285 in Legal Tender bills to buy $100 in gold coins from a money broker or exchange office, the all-time high for the Civil War period.[7] On the West Coast the situation was the opposite: coins were plentiful in stores, banks, and elsewhere; paper bills brought from the East remained illegal in commerce, but could be bought or sold to money brokers at a discount deep enough to equal the premium on gold and silver coins in the East. If at a particular time it took $285 in Legal Tender notes to buy $100 in gold coins in New York, then in San Francisco anyone with $100 in gold coins could go to an exchange dealer and buy $285 in Legal Tender notes.

A token issued by Harvey Lewis, sutler to the 23rd Massachusetts regiment.

Silver and gold coins were anticipated to soon return to circulation when the Civil War ended in April 1865. However, the public remained wary of all of the paper bills in commerce, and silver and gold remained at a premium. It was not until years later, in April 1876, that silver coins were again exchangeable at par with paper, and not until December 1879 that gold and paper were equal. By those times in the 1870s a generation of children had grown into adulthood without seeing a single silver or gold coin in circulation!

In the meantime in the 1860s numismatics prospered. On February 22, 1860, the Washington Cabinet was opened at the Mint and featured the vastly

In 1864 the two-cent piece was introduced, the first circulating coin to have the motto IN GOD WE TRUST. These did not prove to be popular and were discontinued in 1873.

In 1869 Ebenezer Locke Mason Jr., a prominent coin dealer in Philadelphia, published *Mason's Photographic Gallery of the Coin Collectors of the United States.*

expanded display gathered by Director James Ross Snowden. Auctions became a regular feature in the 1860s, and dozens of important sales were conducted by W. Elliot Woodward, Edward D. Cogan, and others. Usually, the sales were held in commercial auction rooms and conducted by a professional auctioneer, not the writer of the catalog. Such auction firms usually sold other things as well, including books, art, and furniture.

In 1866 the first regularly issued coin magazine, the *American Journal of Numismatics*, was published by the American Numismatic and Archaeological Society, successor in 1864 to the short-lived 1858–1859 American Numismatic Society. In the same decade Ebenezer Locke Mason Jr., a Philadelphia coin dealer, issued his own combined news magazine and price list. There were no grading standards and no single source to learn coin mintages and market prices. Accordingly, it devolved upon every successful collector and dealer to spend time to learn the intricacies of the hobby. This resulted in deep bonding with numismatics, and most serious numismatists remained in the field for many years.

In 1865 the nickel three-cent piece was introduced to facilitate commerce, as silver coins were still being hoarded.

The nickel five-cent piece made its debut in the summer of 1865 and largely replaced the three-cent piece. The larger denomination proved to be popular and has been made nearly continuously ever since.

THE 1870s AND 1880s

The Carson City Mint was opened in Nevada 1870 to coin silver and gold from Virginia City and the Comstock Lode. Each coin bore a CC mintmark. The facility produced silver and gold coins through 1885 and again from 1889 to 1893. The career of the mint was somewhat checkered—interlaced with politics. Much silver and gold was shipped from Virginia City to the distant San Francisco Mint instead of 15 miles away to the Carson City Mint. Today the Nevada State Museum is housed there. CC-mintmark coins are especially highly prized by numismatists.

In the 1870s the prices of most coins, tokens, and medals rose steadily, although Washington pieces, once the darlings of the market, fell from favor. Changes were in the wind, and among many other provisions, the Coinage Act of 1873 abolished the two-cent piece, silver three-cent piece, and half dime, provided for the new trade dollar denomination, and slightly increased the authorized weights of dimes, quarter dollars, and half dollars

The Carson City Mint.

(which subsequently were made with arrowheads at the date to indicate the different standard). The standard silver dollar was not treated in the act, and this denomination therefore lapsed.

Soon, there was a popular outcry that the act was unfavorable to silver-mining interests and citizens of Western states, and the legislation became known as the "Crime of '73." Some politicians said that the act was rushed through passage, they did not have time to study it, did not realize the standard dollar would be discontinued,

The Gould & Curry mine and mill in Virginia City, the largest producer of silver and gold in the Comstock Lode.

did not like the idea of the gold dollar becoming important by this default, would not have voted for it if they had been aware of its implications, etc. However, the *Congressional Record* shows very clearly that Western legislators studied and debated the bill at length before its passage. Later historians have been largely unaware of this.

In 1874 the San Francisco Mint was relocated to a new facility that would remain in operation until 1937. Modern equipment and the latest amenities were put in place. The cornerstone was laid in 1870 and included examples of the coinage of that year. Of the 1870-S half dime and $3 gold coin only one example of each is known today and of the 1870-S silver dollar only about a dozen.

In 1875 a new denomination, the 20-cent piece, was introduced with the expectation that it would be useful in the West, but the public confused the coins with quarter dollars, and in 1876 the mintage was sharply decreased. Only Proofs were made for collectors in 1877 and 1878, after which production was discontinued.

During the decade the price of silver declined on world markets. In the United States, increasing production in Nevada plus new discoveries,

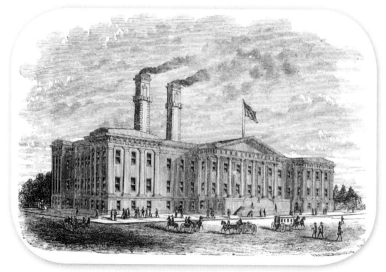

The second San Francisco Mint opened in 1874.

An 1875-S 20-cent piece.

including in the Leadville, Colorado, district, resulted in a glut of the metal. Free Silverites, as pro-silver advocates were called, pressured politicians to abandon gold and institute silver as the dominant coinage metal. From the late 1870s onward this was the overwhelming political question in America, and it remained so until the presidential election of 1896.

After about April 20, 1876, the price of silver coins reached parity with Silver Certificates and other paper money. Citizens, exchange brokers, and banks who had been hoarding quantities of coins since 1862 turned them loose, resulting in a large glut of coins from half dimes to half dollars flooding circulation. Because of this, most mintages of quarters and half dollars dropped to low levels through the end of the Liberty Seated design in 1891.

A notable political boondoggle to support the sagging market for silver bullion, the Bland-Allison Act of February 28, 1878, directed the government to purchase millions of ounces of silver each year and coin the metal into dollars. The talents of assistant engraver George T. Morgan were tapped for the design, based on an 1877 pattern half dollar. Hundreds of millions of these dollars were made through 1921 and mainly stored in bank vaults. Today, Morgan silver dollars are the most popular nineteenth-century coins from a numismatic viewpoint, from the later release of millions of coins.

In December 1879 the value of gold coins achieved parity with Legal Tender Notes on the markets, and long-stored gold coins came out of hiding and were once again seen in commerce. By this time the public had good faith in paper money with the result that the widespread use of gold in everyday transactions was mainly confined to the Western states.

The new 1878 Morgan silver dollar.

A great speculation arose in gold dollars. All available supplies were bought, and the market price rose to a modest premium. New pieces produced at the Philadelphia Mint yielded instant profits for those who were lucky enough to obtain and resell them. Investment interest in gold dollars continued for the rest of the decade. As a result in today's market Mint State gold dollars of 1879 to 1889 are plentiful in relation to their low mintages, while most earlier dates are rare in this state of preservation. At the same time a "bubble" rose in the market for Proof silver trade dollars, a denomination that had not been made in circulation-strike form after early 1878. Speculators scrambled to order 1879 Proofs from the Mint, and the production jumped up to 1,541 pieces (as compared to only 900 Proofs in 1878). The excitement continued, and in 1880 the Mint set a record of 1,987 Proofs. The passion faded, and in 1881 just 960 Proofs were struck.

The New Orleans Mint, closed since early 1861, was refurbished in 1878 and reopened for business in 1879. Silver and gold coins would be made there until 1909, after which time the building was used for other purposes. Today it houses a museum.

In January 1883 the new Liberty Head nickel without CENTS on the reverse created a nationwide sensation. Sharpers gold-plated them and passed them off as $5 gold coins. It was stated in many newspaper articles that the Mint had made a terrible mistake and would be recalling all examples, after which they would have great value. Excitement prevailed, and thousands of newcomers entered the hobby. In the meantime, the coins

The first 1883 Liberty Head nickels had the denomination expressed only by the letter V, prompting some sharpers to gold-plate them and pass them as $5 gold coins.

never did become rare, as many were minted and large quantities were saved. Still, the craze was good for the hobby, as countless thousands of citizens went from the new nickels to collect other coins.

The market went into overdrive. Many dealers opened up shops, several issued their own magazines (Ed Frossard's *Numisma* and Scott Stamp & Coin Company's *Coin Collector's Journal* notable among them), and the field of auction catalogers grew as well. John W. Haseltine and the Chapman brothers (S. Hudson and Henry) created many memorable sales, with the 1882 Bushnell Collection by the Chapmans being the most exciting auction event of the decade.

T. Harrison Garrett, of Baltimore, and Lorin G. Parmelee, of Boston, became known as super-collectors, snatching up rarities. Rare coins furnished fodder for newspapers, and metropolitan dailies carried many accounts of rare 1804 silver dollars being sold at auction, or old Massachusetts Pine Tree shillings being found buried in the ground, and more. All during this scenario, the prices of scarce and rare early United States coins continued to rise. During the 1880s a dozen or more newspapers devoted to collecting coins, stamps, Indian relics, and other things were published, often with news on multiple fields of interest.

In 1888 *The Numismatist* began publication under the auspices of Dr. George F. Heath, a Monroe, Michigan, physician who was a deeply knowledgeable collector and a skilled writer. It has endured and today is the official publication of the American Numismatic Association, as it has been for many years.

The Coinage Act of 1889 discontinued the nickel three-cent piece and the gold $1 and $3.

The decade of the 1880s had been a golden era for many activities. More county and other history books were published than in any such period before, railroad and ocean-travel facilities were more elegant than ever, and the outlook was rosier than it had been in a long time. In the Midwest many towns rose from the land as boulevards, buildings, rail lines, and other construction took place.

Things changed. Late in the decade storm clouds rose on the economic horizon, mainly due to over-speculation in land and buildings in the prairie states. Bonds to furnish large-scale expansion had been issued at interest rates of 8 to 10 percent, several points more than comparable securities issued in the East paid. Large amounts of money flowed into Iowa, Nebraska, and other states. Then came reality. Municipalities and others were not able to maintain interest payments and there were many bankruptcies.

THE 1890s INTO THE 1900s

By 1890 there were coin dealers in most cities in the eastern part of the United States, with Boston, New York City, and Philadelphia the central points of activity. J.W. Scott. W. Elliot Woodward, the auction firm of Bangs, Merwin & Co., the Chapman brothers, John Haseltine, Lyman H. Low, Ed. Frossard, and Charles Steigerwalt were among the leading professionals of the day. In 1890 New York Coin & Stamp Co. conducted the sale of the Lorin G. Parmelee Collection, the second finest cabinet (after T. Harrison Garrett's) in private hands in America. Results were mixed, and Parmelee, hardly a motivated seller, bought many of the rarities back. The coin market was entering a chilly period as was the national economy. Difficult times lay ahead.

In November 1891 in Chicago the American Numismatic Association (ANA) was formed, thus providing a common meeting place for the exchange of ideas and values among collectors from all parts of the United States and elsewhere. Beginners and amateurs were encouraged to join, while some other societies preferred numismatists with experience. Charles E. Barber's Liberty Head silver dime, quarter, and half dollar, called "Barber coins" today, were first issued in 1892. Public and numismatic interest was lukewarm.

An 1894 proposal for the American Numismatic Association seal, and one later adopted.

An 1892-O Barber dime. Dimes, quarters, and half dollars designed by Chief Engraver Charles E. Barber were introduced in this year and remained in use until 1916 for the dime and quarter and 1915 for the half dollar.

The 1892 Columbian souvenir half dollar, as it was called, was produced in the year before the World's Columbian Exposition opened to the public. This was the first United States commemorative coin.

The World's Columbian Exposition was planned to open in Chicago in 1892 to celebrate the 400th anniversary of Christopher Columbus's landing in the New World. Progress was slower than anticipated, and it did not open to the public until 1893. Attractions included dozens of impressive buildings, the gigantic Ferris Wheel, and extensive exhibits of art, culture, and industry. America's first commemorative coins were issued for this event, initiating a numismatic specialty that eventually included hundreds of varieties and remains dynamic to the present day.

To this point numismatists had little interest in collecting coins by mintmark varieties. Whether a coin had an S, D, or other letter was of no importance. It was just the date of the coin that mattered. This began to change in 1893 when Augustus G. Heaton, a professional artist by trade and a numismatist by avocation, published a treatise on coins from the United States branch mints. In time such branch-mint rarities as the 1894-S dime and 1876-CC twenty-cent piece attracted notice. Interest in mintmarked gold coins developed much more slowly and did not become widely popular until decades later in the 1930s.

Speculation in prairie lands, unwise loans, and unbridled growth of the 1880s came together in the Panic of 1893. Times were difficult, many banks failed, and there was political unrest. Participants in the Free Silver movement, a political philosophy which had been gaining adherents since the 1870s, became especially vocal. It was felt by this faction that reliance on gold was hindering national growth and prosperity, and that American coinage and international trade should be based on silver, a metal in oversupply.

The government policy of coining large amounts of silver into dollar coins was part of the "Silver Question," the pivotal political debate of the era. As the poor economic climate continued, the supply of gold coins in the United States Treasury fell to $41 million due to large exports of double eagles. Foreign interests were fearful that the Silverites would convince the government to allow overseas debts to be paid in silver dollars (the intrinsic worth of which kept declining and were worth about 48 cents each) and demanded gold. Banker J.P. Morgan and his associates stepped in to augment the gold reserves, one of the most embarrassing points in American financial history.

Silver, in oversupply in relation to the market, continued to be produced in large quantities. Shown are silver ingots at the American Smelter in Leadville, Colorado, in 1893.

Several conventions were staged by advocates of free and unlimited coinage of silver to support the diminishing market. In an 1895 cartoon, "turtles" of silver dollars, marked "Real Value 50 Cents," are about to plunge into financial oblivion over a waterfall—suggesting what might happen to the American economy if such practice was continued. The presidential election of 1896 focused on silver and pitted Democrat William Jennings Bryan against Republican William McKinley. Bryan's "Cross of Gold" speech electrified the nation and gave momentum to the Free Silver movement and "easy money," promising Midwesterners and others in distress the ability to pay their debts more readily. McKinley won, and the silver movement faded sharply, although remnants lingered into the new century. Bryan ran for president on the Democratic ticket in 1900 and 1908 and lost both times.

In the 1890s gold strikes in the Cripple Creek District of Colorado starting early in the decade, followed by the Klondike Gold Rush of the late 1890s, yielded vast quantities of precious metals, much of which were coined into double eagles at the San Francisco Mint. Both events electrified the country with tales of adventures and fortunes and newspaper coverage knew no limits.

The discovery in the early 1890s of gold-bearing calaverite and telluride ore in the Cripple Creek District on the west side of Pikes Peak created a great rush that resulted in a population of more than 100,000 people by the turn of the century. An estimated $400 million in gold was extracted in an era in which the metal was worth $20.67 per ounce. The Cripple Creek District included Victor, Altman, and other communities. Shown is the panorama in 1895.

The Portland Mine on Battle Mountain, Victor, in 1896, the largest mine in the Cripple Creek District.

Main Street in Dawson City in 1898, the largest settlement in the Klondike district.

The Klondike on the Yukon River in British Columbia and Alaska yielded large amounts of gold late in the 1890s, much of which went to the San Francisco Mint to be coined into double eagles. Shown are adventurers in Chilkoot Pass, above Skagway, Alaska, on the way to the gold district.

In 1901 the third Philadelphia Mint was opened and would remain in use until 1966. All equipment and facilities were state of the art. The engraving and die-making departments continued to be centered there and served the branch mints.

In September of the same year President William McKinley was assassinated while attending the Pan-American Exposition in Buffalo, New York. Vice President Theodore Roosevelt succeeded him in the post.

In 1903 the United States began minting coins specifically for the Philippines, which had been a U.S. possession since the conclusion of the Spanish-American War in 1898. The coins featured the name UNITED STATES OF AMERICA and also the Spanish name FILIPINAS, along with designs by Filipino artist Melecio Figueroa.

The new Philadelphia Mint opened in 1901.

A silver peso minted for the Philippines under U.S. administration.

The Main Coining Room in the new Mint, with rows of electrically driven presses.

In 1904 the Louisiana Purchase Exposition opened in St. Louis. In connection with it two varieties of 1903 gold dollars were minted, the first U.S. commemoratives in that metal.

In 1906 the new Denver Mint opened for business and struck silver and gold coins. It was not until 1911 that copper coins were made there. Its coins bore a D mintmark, a letter that had been used earlier by the Dahlonega Mint from 1838 to 1861.

In April 1906 San Francisco was ravaged by a strong earthquake followed by a fire that leveled most of the commercial district of the city. The Mint was the only building remaining intact in its area and served as a headquarters for relief efforts as well as financial activity.

In 1904 President Roosevelt visited the Smithsonian Institution, a short distance from the White House, and was impressed with the beautiful artistry of ancient Greek coins on display. Not long afterward he determined to make American coins more attractive than ever before, replacing the current designs. He tapped Augustus Saint-Gaudens, America's most famous sculptor, to redesign the entire coinage spectrum from the cent to the double eagle. The artist's first effort was the $20 coin, the new design being in medallic high relief and the 1907 date in Roman numerals as MCMVII. On the obverse was *Victory* holding a palm branch, and on the reverse was a flying eagle. The sculptor redesigned he $10 eagle with an

The Denver Mint with the Colorado State Capitol in the distance. The facility was greatly expanded in 1937 and remains in use today.

Looking toward Market Street in San Francisco after the earthquake of April 18, 1906, with the fire beginning to consume most of the city.

After the fire the San Francisco Mint was the only building that remained standing. It served as a relief center and also assisted with banking.

Indian Head. Saint-Gaudens passed away in August 1907. The redesign of coinage by artists in the private sector was continued in later years with all other denominations.

The high relief of the MCMVII $20 caused production problems, and Chief Engraver Charles E. Barber changed the design to low relief and the date to regular numerals. Only 12,367 of the MCMVII coins were made, but they were so popular with the public and with numismatists that enough were saved that about half the mintage survives today.

In the same year the $2.50 and $5 gold coins were redesigned by Bela Lyon Pratt, with a recessed relief design. This met with uniformly negative reaction by collectors and dealers as expressed in pages of *The Numismatist.* Starting with each of the four gold denominations in 1908 the Sand Blast Proof finish took the place of the mirror style used in earlier years. These new Proofs were unpopular with collectors, and in the next year Satin Finish Proofs succeeded them. These also generated complaints, and in 1911 the Sand Blast Proofs were resumed, to continue in the gold series to 1915.

The MCMVII (1907) High Relief double eagle by Augustus Saint-Gaudens.

In 1908 Indian Head cents were struck at the San Francisco Mint, the first branch-mint coinage of a minor (non–precious metal) denomination. In the same year the American Numismatic Society ("and Archaeological" having been dropped from its name) moved into a handsome new stone building, largely financed by Archer M. Huntington (stepson of railroad magnate Collis P. Huntington), on Audubon Terrace, Morningside Heights, New York City. An additional gift from Huntington added an adjacent matching building in the early 1930s.

The 1907 Indian Head $10 by Saint-Gaudens.

The 1908 $2.50 designed by Bela Lyon Pratt. $5 coins were made with the same motif.

In August 1909 the new Lincoln design for the cent was issued, created by Victor D. Brenner, a sculptor and medalist of renown. It the latest in the series of motifs designed by artists in the private sector. The first issues had the initials V.D.B. on the reverse, but a controversy arose, and they were soon removed, by which time 27,995,000 had been made at the Philadelphia Mint. Only 484,000 were made of the San Francisco issue (1909-S V.D.B.), creating a numismatic rarity. Proofs for collectors were in the Matte style, not much different from circulation strikes upon quick glance, and were not popular.

The 1909-S V.D.B. Lincoln cent became the key to the series and remains a numismatic favorite today.

The rare-coin market had been very strong during the decade, with steady rises in the number of collectors and in values. Collecting coins by mintmarks had not become widely popular yet, but the 1909-S V.D.B. cent, which quickly went up in value to 5¢, then 10¢, then higher, prompted many more numismatists to pay attention to branch-mint issues.

The decade saw many innovations and expansions including the vastly increased popularity of the automobile and the dawn of the age of aviation. Prosperity was the order of the era, and the difficulties of the 1890s were largely forgotten.

Orville Wright and the first powered heavier-than-air craft at Kill Devil Hill on December 17, 1903, inaugurating the aviation age.

By 1910, automobiles were a familiar sight all across America. Shown is a Hupmobile of that year.

THE 1910s AND 1920s

In 1912 the first branch-mint nickel coins were struck at the Denver and San Francisco mints. This was the last year of the Liberty Head design (although a few 1913 coins were privately made the next year). In 1913 the Buffalo or Indian Head five-cent piece, by sculptor James Earle Fraser, was released and achieved wide popularity.

To observe the opening of the Panama Canal (in 1914) and the rebirth of the city after the fire and earthquake of 1906, the Panama-Pacific Exposition in San Francisco offered a grand "city" of elegant buildings with many displays and attractions. Coin dealer Farran Zerbe had charge of selling commemorative coins of the half dollar, gold dollar, $2.50, and two varieties of the $50 denominations. The American Numismatic Association held its annual convention in the same city this year, but attendance was very low, due in part to the unpopularity of Zerbe and certain questionable actions he had with the ANA earlier when he served as president (such as rigging an election).

Production of Sand Blast Proof gold coins ended in 1915, and 1916 was the last year for Matte Proof cents and nickels. These finishes were very unpopular with collectors, who preferred the older style "brilliant" or "mirror" field type. Protests to no avail had been made to the Mint by the New York Numismatic Club and others. It was not until 1936 that Proof coins, then of the popular mirror finish, were again available to collectors.

In 1916 the denominations of silver coins then being struck were given new designs, much to the enthusiasm and acclamation not only of the numismatic community but of the public as well. The new "Mercury" or Winged Liberty Head dime was created by Adolph A. Weinman, the Standing Liberty quarter dollar by Hermon A. MacNeil, and the Liberty Walking half dollar by Weinman. The 1916-D dime and the 1916 Standing Liberty quarter became rarities due to their low mintages.

The World War had been raging in Europe since August 1914. In 1916 many Americans joined the English and French and other forces opposing the German troops of Kaiser Wilhelm II and his allies.

In 1913 the Buffalo nickel, as it came to be called, was introduced with a design by sculptor James Earle Fraser. The obverse depicted a Native American and the reverse a bison. The motif was continued through 1938.

The 1916 Winged Liberty Head or "Mercury" dime by Adolph A. Weinman.

The 1916 Standing Liberty quarter by Hermon A. MacNeil.

The 1916 Walking Liberty half dollar by Adolph A. Weinman.

This was on a voluntary basis, such as service with the Red Cross and the airborne Lafayette Escadrille. In 1917 the United States declared war and many soldiers, sailors, and aviators volunteered for service. Liberty Bond campaigns were conducted across the land. Truce finally took place on November 11, 1918. The terms the victorious allies demanded of the Germans were very harsh, creating much turmoil during the next 15 years, including runaway inflation, which led to the rise of Adolph Hitler and the Nazi party in the early 1930s.

The war brought great prosperity to American industries supplying munitions, equipment, and other necessities of combat. Coin mintages reached record highs. The good times did not last, and from 1921 into 1923 the American economy took a nap. Coin mintages dropped precipitately. In 1922 no nickels, dimes, quarters, or regular-issue half dollars were made (although within the latter denomination there were some commemoratives).

In 1918 the Pittman Act resulted in the melting of 270,232,722 silver dollars in Treasury storage, to supply bullion to England to ship to India. None had been minted since 1904, and the denomination was believed to have been discontinued. At the Mint the models and master dies had been destroyed in 1910.

A Liberty Loan poster for the World War, 1917, designed by Howard Chandler Christy.

In February 1918 the Philippine Legislature passed an appropriations bill for construction of machinery for a new mint. The Philippines in that era was still under the administration of the United States, but moving steadily toward independence. The Manila Mint opened on July 15, 1920. Earlier U.S./Philippine coins had been struck in Philadelphia, San Francisco, and Denver. Now the islands had a domestic source for coinage, which would continue to operate until the Japanese military invaded in 1941.

In 1921 the Treasury gave a hurry-up call to mint more silver dollars to provide backing for Silver Certificates. The old Morgan design was remodeled slightly, and more than 85 million new dollars were struck at the Philadelphia, Denver, and San Francisco mints. The Treasury hoped for a new design, but that was not ready until December 1921, when 1,006,473 coins of the Peace design by sculptor Anthony de Francisci were struck. The Peace dollar design was continued to 1928 and again in 1934 and 1935.

Florida experienced a wild boom in real estate in 1924 and 1925, but the end came soon, in 1926. Acres of vacant home lots were left in planned communities. Not to worry, as overall the American economy experienced boom times—the "Roaring Twenties." Many skyscrapers were built in cities, luxury automobiles were all the rage, mansions were constructed—an era epitomized by novelist F. Scott Fitzgerald in *The Great Gatsby* and in a later retrospective history, *Only Yesterday*, by Frederick Lewis Allen. Riding along with the crest, in the next several years, rare books, art, and common stocks became investment sensations.

An official commemorative medal popularly known as the "Wilson Dollar" was struck to celebrate the 1920 opening of the Manila Mint.

The rare-coin market did not participate in the boom economy and remained very quiet. New York City dealer Thomas L. Elder lamented that the great collectors of yesteryear had not been replaced by a new generation of moneyed buyers. This had a bright side, in a way. When other markets collapsed in 1929, coins held their values fairly well. Several wealthy people who were hurt by the economic conditions of the early 1930s found comfort in the value of their coin collections—Waldo C. Newcomer of Baltimore being one. Great numismatic rarities sold slowly, but not at significant discounts.

In 1929 small-size bills replaced the large-size federal paper money in use since 1861.

Architect's illustration of the Empire State Building in New York City. Envisioned and designed during the late 1920s, it was built on the site of the first Waldorf-Astoria Hotel and opened in 1931. The top featured a mooring mast for passenger zeppelins but was never used for that purpose.

The Peace design silver dollar designed by Anthony de Francisci was first issued in 1921. With the design modified to lower relief, the motif continued in use through 1935.

THE 1930s AND THE DEPRESSION ERA

In the early 1930s the rare-coin market continued on a consistent basis. The only notable bankruptcy was the firm of Guttag Brothers, leading coin dealers in the 1920s whose main business was investment securities. In 1929 they moved into their new multi-story building in New York City. The business ran into trouble early that year and collapsed in early 1930, sustaining a loss reported as $9 million. In contrast other leading dealers such as B. Max Mehl in Texas, who had been prominent since the early 1900s, Thomas L. Elder, Wayte Raymond, John Macallister, and others continued to be profitable. Coin prices softened, as noted, but demand remained fairly strong.

Franklin D. Roosevelt entered the presidential race in 1932, running against incumbent Herbert Hoover. The latter promised that "recovery is just around the corner," but economic conditions worsened. Roosevelt promised the "New Deal," a change in policies. In November he won in a landslide. Inaugurated on March 4, 1933, he set about creating many new programs. He prohibited the further issuance of gold coins by the Treasury, although mintage of $10 and $20 gold coins continued for a while. Next came the demand that all citizens turn in gold coins, those of numismatic value and a small allowance per person excepted. In January 1934 America

The $10 and $20 denominations were the only gold coins struck in 1933.

abandoned the gold standard, resulting in runaway inflation of the prices of goods and services, particularly starting in the late 1930s when the Depression wound down.

The change in gold regulations had a dramatic effect on the numismatic market. All of a sudden collectors who had not paid much attention to gold coins set about forming sets and collections. Floyd Starr of Philadelphia and Louis E. Eliasberg of Baltimore were among the best known. Thomas L. Elder issued a premium guide he sent to bank tellers and others advising that many varieties of gold coins turned in to banks by the public had significant numismatic value. Countless thousands of scarce and rare coins were thus saved from destruction.

In New York City in 1933 Morton and Joseph Stack relocated from Wheeling, West Virginia, to set up a rare-coin dealership that soon expanded by leaps and bounds. In 1935 the firm held its first auction. In the meantime Thomas L. Elder and Wayte Raymond held many public auctions, and in Fort Worth, Texas, B. Max Mehl turned out a stream of mail auctions. He also published the *Star Rare Coin Encyclopedia* with buying prices, suggesting that treasures such as a 1913 Liberty Head nickel might be found in pocket change.

As curious as the scenario may seem to an economist or historian without numismatic knowledge, the 1930s saw the greatest market boom in coin-collecting history!

In the early 1930s the Scott Stamp & Coin Company under the direction of Wayte Raymond published the National line of cardboard coin-album pages. These had openings faced on the front and back with cellulose acetate slides, permitting coins to be easily stored and the obverse and reverse to be viewed. Dates and mintages were printed below each opening. This revolutionized numismatics. Now, instead of storing coins in wooden cabinets with trays, collectors could house them in convenient pages that fit into a notebook binder, and could examine the coins from both sides.

The race was on! In the depth of the Depression the hope was held to find in pocket change many coins that had numismatic value, such as the 1877 and 1909-S Indian Head cents, 1909-S V.D.B. and 1914-D Lincoln cents, and many others. The recently issued 1931-S cent with a low mintage of 866,000 coins created excitement, and nearly all were bought by dealers and collectors. Barber dimes, quarters, and half dollars could be found dating back to 1892, usually in About Good or Good grades, well-worn but exciting to collect and enjoy as hole after hole was filled in albums.

Helping matters was that hobbies were all the rage during this era. Crossword puzzles, games, hunting and fishing, and other pursuits drew many new participants. Many towns had shops that sold or rented jigsaw puzzles. Collecting scenic postcards achieved unprecedented popularity.

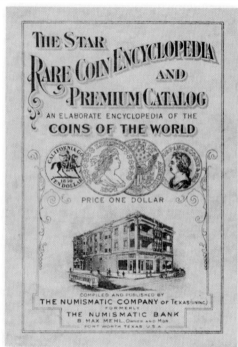

The *Star Rare Coin Encyclopedia* published by B. Max Mehl offered premiums for rare coins, including certain issues in circulation. In the 1930s the book was promoted by print advertising as well as a weekly radio program.

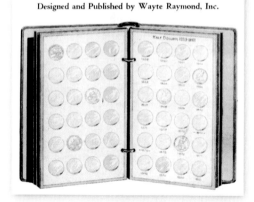

The National Coin Album line published by Scott Stamp & Coin Company, later by Wayte Raymond, Inc., did much to popularize the collecting of coins by dates and mintmarks.

Meanwhile in 1932 the new Washington quarter design by John Flanagan replaced the Standing Liberty motif in use since 1916 (excepting 1922 and 1931). It was intended as a circulating commemorative coin to honor the 200th anniversary of Washington's February 22, 1732, birth, but the Treasury Department decided to continue it as a regular design. Due to economic conditions, relatively few 1932 coins were saved by the general public and not many by numismatists either.

J.K. Post of Neenah, Wisconsin, in 1934 launched the Penny Collector board, a cardboard sheet with openings for each date and mintmark of Lincoln cent from 1909 to date. Western Publishing of Racine, Wisconsin, acquired the product and expanded it to include the Whitman line of boards and, in time, folders and albums.

While the preceding innovations were still in progress the commemorative-coin boom came next. This was launched by one man, Frank Dunn of Lexington, Kentucky, who was in charge of ordering and selling half dollars for the Boone Bicentennial in 1934. From his second-floor office in the Phoenix Hotel he sold 10,000 pieces for $1.60 each. At the time such coins could be ordered by various commissions (some of which were very questionable) who persuaded Congress to pass authorization. Coins were sent to the commissions for face value plus a small charge. The commissions were in charge of setting prices and policies—like coining your own money!

The year 1935 began in a normal way when 10,010 Boone halves were struck in Philadelphia in March and 5,005 each at the Denver and San Francisco mints in May. These were dated 1935 on the reverse of the coin, representing the issue date. Philadelphia coins were offered for $1.10 each, and $1.50 was charged for each Denver and San Francisco coin. A 1935 Boone set of three coins cost a total of $4.10. So far the only problem was that it was no longer the bicentennial of Boone's birthday, and there was no reason to continue celebrating a 1934 anniversary in 1935.[8]

Unexpectedly, in October 1935 at the Philadelphia Mint 10,008 more 1935-dated Boone half dollars were made but with the addition of 1934 / PIONEER YEAR in small numerals on the right side of the reverse. No excitement here, but why create the variety? Then came excitement that knew no bounds. In November the Denver and San Francisco mints produced the very small quantity of just 2,003 and 2,004, respectively, of the modified design. News releases calling attention to the rare issues were sent

A 1932-S
Washington quarter.

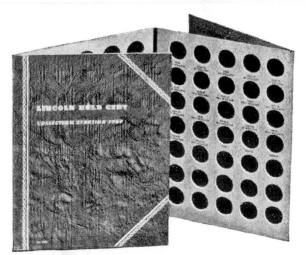

WHITMAN PUBLISHING CO.

Whitman Publishing entered the coin-supply business in 1934 and soon offered a line of boards, later followed by folders, as seen here. More people entered numismatics through the use of Lincoln cent folders than by any other method.

out by Dunn. New York City newspapers, among others, carried the information that a pair of low-mintage Boone half dollars had been created at the Denver and San Francisco mints and could be ordered for $3.70 by sending remittances to Dunn. This equaled $1.85 per coin—a truly affordable rarity. These were also advertised in *The Numismatist*. As might be expected for such an incredibly low mintage, orders rushed in. Not so fast! There was a problem. So far as is known (per research conducted years ago by Lee F. Hewitt) *everyone* who ordered received a "Sorry, sold out" letter. No exceptions! Dunn said that they had all been sold to those who had read newspaper accounts.

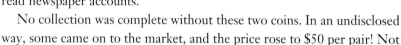

Detail of the reverse of the 1935-S Boone Bicentennial half dollar with small 1934, of which 2,000 were offered.

No collection was complete without these two coins. In an undisclosed way, some came on to the market, and the price rose to $50 per pair! Not long afterward it was discovered that most of the coins had been retained by Dunn! He was accused of fraud, and transferred many assets to his wife. However, he was never prosecuted, and he continued selling three-coin Boone sets yearly through 1938!

Thus was set the scene for much excitement, with the details of various issues being given later in this book. Many abuses took place. In late 1936, after *dozens* of new varieties had been introduced in that year, the market cooled. In 1939 Congress ended the largess by prohibiting further issues.

After the commemorative slump of late 1936 the overall coin market remained robust. A new monthly publication, *The Numismatic Scrapbook*, was launched by Lee F. Hewitt. Unlike *The Numismatist*, the *Scrapbook* emphasized the human interest side of numismatics rather than technical points and history. Reports of rare coins found in circulation, collector and dealer activities, and such make up most of the content. Quickly, it gained the largest subscription base of any numismatic publications. In the meantime *Hobbies* magazine had a monthly coin section.

In 1937 the third San Francisco Mint opened, replacing the facility in use since 1974. The building, with modernization in the intervening years, is still in use today.

In the same year the Federal Bullion Depository opened on the grounds of the Fort Knox military base in Kentucky. Double eagles and other federal gold coins dating back many years that had been stored in the Philadelphia Mint were melted and the metal was cast into gold ingots and shipped to Fort Knox. During this procedure some Mint employees substituted common-date $20 and other coins for those scheduled for melting, thus rescuing them for numismatic posterity. New York City dealers of the era eagerly purchased most of these coins, including 1933 $10 and $20 issues.

The third San Francisco Mint opened in 1937 on a prominent site overlooking the city.

The Federal Bullion Depository at Fort Knox, Kentucky.

In 1938 Felix O. Schlag entered a nationwide competition of about 300 artists vying to create a new design to replace the Buffalo nickel. His design won, and the obverse was selected. His reverse was considerably modified at the Mint.

In 1939 Nazi Germany went to war and overran Czechoslovakia. Other countries fell to the Nazis. Once again, American industries rose to supply forces opposing the Germans. The Depression ended, and the economy recovered, to go on to new highs.

The B-17 Flying Fortress bomber was developed in the 1930s and saw extensive use in Europe during World War II, especially with the 8th Air Force.

The Jefferson nickel was introduced in 1938. Revised versions are still coined today.

THE 1940s AND 1950s

In Europe World War II, as it was called, expanded as Adolf Hitler's Nazi troops overran France, Holland, Belgium, and other countries, meanwhile persecuting Jews, religious figures, and others, sending many to confinement and eventual death in concentration camps. Those who were fortunate fled, many finding asylum in America, including scientist Albert Einstein and professional numismatist Hans M.F. Schulman (whose other family members in Amsterdam perished). The Battle of Britain took place in 1940 with German bombers laying waste to large portions of London and with destruction in other areas (such as the famous cathedral in Coventry). America rushed to help with the Lend-Lease Act providing ships, exports of munitions, and more, including American men and women volunteers.

The United States officially entered the war after the "day of infamy," so called for Japan's unprovoked surprise attack on Pearl Harbor on December 7, 1941. War was also declared against other members of the Axis Powers—Germany and Italy (under dictator Benito Mussolini). In the Pacific Theater, more than a quarter million Filipino volunteers joined the American armed forces to fight off the Japanese. Then followed four more years of domestic and worldwide sacrifices, the details of which are well-known and beyond the scope of the present text.

After Proof sets were sold in 1942, production was stopped so as not to detract from the Mint's activity in providing record quantities of coins for circulation. To save copper, Lincoln cents were made of zinc-coated steel in 1943. The coins quickly tarnished and spotted, and bronze was resumed

In 1943 Lincoln cents were made of zinc-coated steel while copper was directed toward the war effort.

in 1944. The alloy of five-cent pieces was changed to eliminate nickel and to make silver the main metal, a policy continued through 1945.

By 1943 cash was plentiful, but consumer goods were scarce. Inflation was everywhere, despite federal efforts to control it. On September 10 and 11, 1943, New York City dealer Abe Kosoff conducted an auction of the Michael F. Higgy Collection. A bidding frenzy took place, and many coins sold for 5 to 10 times their pre-sale estimates! From that point, prices went onward and upward all across the market. Common-date double eagles were in particular demand, a place to put extra money, and sold for about $65 each.

In 1944 and 1945, the San Francisco, Denver, and Philadelphia mints were used to produce coins for the Philippines. These were then brought over by American military transport to aid commerce during the liberation of the islands from Japanese control.

In November 1946 *A Guide Book of United States Coins*, written by Richard S. Yeo (under the pen name of "R.S. Yeoman") with the technical assistance of Stuart Mosher, was published with a 1947 cover date. It went on to be published annually, selling tens of millions of copies over the ensuing decades. Although World War II was over, consumer goods were still scarce. There was much uncertainty as to the future of the economy—would it be booming, or would it bust? The rare-coin market continued to be a refuge for spare cash.

President Franklin D. Roosevelt, in office since 1933, died of natural causes while at Warm Springs, Georgia, in early 1945. The Treasury decided to honor him by changing the Mercury dime to his portrait as modeled by Chief Engraver John R. Sinnock. The 10-cent denomination was chosen because Roosevelt, stricken with a paralytic illness as young man, was the spokesperson for many years for the March of Dimes, a non-profit organization that raised money to combat polio (this was finally accomplished in 1955 with the vaccine of Dr. Jonas Salk).

Before long the coin market went into a slump. By 1947 consumer goods were becoming widely available. Money went to buy appliances,

A World War II centavo of the Philippines, minted in the United States.

In 1946 Whitman Publishing launched *A Guide Book of United States Coins* with the cover date of 1947. It went on to become the best-selling book in numismatic history.

The Roosevelt dime made its debut in 1946.

new homes springing up in vast developments, and other goods, and automobiles were beginning to be available. In this year and in 1948, prices of coins dropped across the board. Common-date double eagles that sold for $65 during the war now wholesaled below $40. Convention attendance dwindled. In retrospect, if there was ever a good time to *buy* coins in the postwar era it was now!

Levittown, New York, in 1947, one of many communities and developments that sprung up to provide affordable housing for returning veterans and other buyers.

The very bottom was probably in early 1949.

Not related to market prices at all, but in terms of numismatic history, 1949 is one of the most memorable years for it saw the publication of *Early American Cents*, by Dr. William H. Sheldon. The author, a psychologist and medical professor, billed himself as a scientist with the ability to analyze and make changes. With an office at Columbia University he had developed a new version of somatotypology by classifying people as *endomorphic*, *mesomorphic*, and *ectomorphic*, based on many photographs and measurements of nude figures taken at Ivy League schools. (Today, this is dismissed as pseudo-science.) In numismatics he was a grand figure and respected for his knowledge.

For years the grading of coins was a problem, with no firmly established and globally recognized standards, and establishing market values involved a lot of guesswork. In the August 1949 issue of *The Numismatist* Abe Kosoff, one of America's leading coin dealers, told about Sheldon's forthcoming book, *Early American Cents*:

> Now comes one book that is complete within itself and is not only a list—it is a new treatment of the series. Order and system were applied to the identification, grading, and valuing of every known variety of early cent. Reference to the plates and tables makes it simple for even a novice to accurately identify and appraise the value of any of the early copper cents.

Guesswork was now replaced by science! His grading system, discussed earlier in the present text, was expanded beyond early cents to include coins in all series. (Unfortunately today it is in confusion.)

B. Max Mehl's sale of April 26, 1949, the Dr. Charles W. Green Collection, billed as the greatest gold coin sale ever held, broke price records left and right. Among the greatest rarities was a 1926-S double eagle, of which only three were said to be known. It realized $1,525, or more than double expectations.

All bets were off, and the room was up for grabs. All of a sudden, many collectors who had been inactive during the slump jumped back into the market with vigor. The

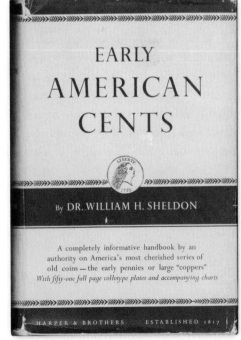

Early American Cents by William H. Sheldon, published in 1949, contained a market value and grading system that in time completely transformed American numismatics.

market became dynamic—more so than ever before when considered on a widespread basis from colonial coinage onward.

Secretly, James F. Kelly, a prominent Dayton, Ohio, dealer, had enlisted Paul Wittlin, a professional numismatist from California, to go to Europe and investigate reports of hoards of American gold coins shipped there before 1933, with some said to be intact. Wittlin struck gold—literally and figuratively—in bank vaults, primarily in Switzerland. Success attended his efforts. Surprisingly, banks in France also yielded many coins, especially dou-

In 1949 it was thought that only three examples existed of the 1926-S double eagle. This led to a treasure hunt in Europe and elsewhere to find coins shipped to foreign banks and governments earlier in the century. Today several hundred 1926-S $20 coins are known.

ble eagles that had been kept "underground" during the war. The rare became common. This set the scene for a broad and enthusiastic market in double eagles which exists to the present day.

In the 1950s thousands of newcomers entered the market and, following the tradition of years earlier, bought blue Whitman folders, and started looking for treasures in pocket change—the 1909-S V.D.B. cent, 1916-D dime, and 1916 Standing Liberty quarter being targets. Some Indian Head cents and Liberty Head nickels were in circulation, and there were many Barber silver coins, particularly half dollars.

Bank-wrapped rolls, gold coins, copper coins, and just about all other federal series were in unprecedented demand. The Philadelphia Mint, which had stopped making Proofs in 1942, resumed the tradition in 1950 and produced 51,386 Proof sets. In 1950 the Denver Mint produced only 2,630,030 nickels—the smallest nickel five-cent piece coinage since 1931. When the mintage figures were released, excitement prevailed! These and the new Proofs gave a further boost to the market.

In 1951, 57,500 Proof sets were made. As production climbed year by year there began to be considerable interest in Proof sets from an investment viewpoint. In this decade buy and sell prices were posted of these and for bank-wrapped rolls of modern circulation coins.

The Franklin half dollars introduced in 1948 remained the standard design through 1963.

In Iola, Wisconsin, in 1952, Chet Krause started *Numismatic News* as a monthly publication devoted to classified advertisements. In time the emphasis changed, and news articles and announcements were carried. Later, in the early 1960s, it went to a weekly. Krause Publications, as it became called, included Cliff Mishler as a key executive. The parent company became one of America's most important publishers of magazines and reference books in many hobby and sports areas, one of the largest in the world.

Beginning with the 1952 ANA Convention sale (the work of a combination of four dealers with different specialties), the New Netherlands Coin Co. of New York City, owned by Charles M. Wormser (business manager) and John J. Ford Jr. (numismatic expert), with Walter Breen as a key employee, produced catalogs with extremely detailed descriptions. Coins came to life, the New Netherlands sales had an almost cult following, and the combination of salesmanship, history, market and coin-collecting gossip and remarks, and detailed descriptions of the offered pieces initiated a new trend. This methodology was later adopted by several other auction firms. In the meantime most retail sales were through shops, price lists, and advertisements.

In 1954 a Proof set of 1936 had a market value of $100, increasing to $300 in 1955, onward and upward to $500, then to $600. At several large coin shows, Cincinnati dealer Sol Kaplan posted "bid" and "ask" prices for sets from 1936 to 1942, and 1950 to date, and prices sometimes changed hourly. A 1956 Proof set, available from the Mint that year for $2.10, was worth $2.50 to those who did not want to wait for sets to arrive in the mail. In that year a record 669,384 sets were struck, nearly doubling the preceding year's total and exceeding by more than a dozen times the number struck six years earlier in 1950. In 1957 the market for Proof sets crashed. The 1936 set dropped all the way back to $300, with scarcely a buyer in sight. Latecomers to the market racked up large losses, and many left in a hurry—perhaps muttering that coin investment was for gullible people only. While the market for Proof sets busted in 1957, time healed the wounds, recovery took place in succeeding years, and today a gem 1936 Proof set is worth well into five figures!

In the meantime, anyone who diversified their holdings did well—as large copper cents, silver dollars, paper money, territorial gold, and Liberty Head nickels, along with just about everything else, continued to rise in price. Many records were set. In the autumn of 1957 in Stack's Empire Sale a rare 1894-S dime sold for an amazing $4,750, an event publicized in newspapers nationwide. The coin was later acquired by Emery May Holden Norweb, a leading collector of the era.

An 1894-S dime, one of only 24 minted and of only 10 or so known today.

The Professional Numismatists Guild, formally organized in 1955, would go on to become America's leading organization of dealers in numismatic items. The Guild (online today at www.PNGdealers.org) has helped with many educational, authentication, and other matters of interest to the collecting community.

In 1955 the San Francisco Mint struck only cents and dimes, after which the Treasury Department stated that coinage there would end and it would become known as the San Francisco Assay Office. That changed in the 1960s when it again was designed as a mint, and was kept busy striking coins.

In 1955 at the Philadelphia Mint an obverse die was impressed twice, slightly off-register, by a hub die. The result was that the date was blurred and appeared as 11995555. Your editor inquired at the Philadelphia Mint and learned that, on a particular day in 1955, several presses were coining cents, dumping the coins into a box where they were then collected and mixed with the cents from other coining presses. Late in the afternoon, a Mint inspector noticed the bizarre doubled cents and removed the offending die. By that time, somewhat more than 40,000 cents had been produced, about 24,000 of which had been mixed with normal cents from other presses. The decision was made to destroy the cents still in the box, and to release into circulation the 24,000 or so pieces that were mixed with other cents. The Mint had no reason to believe that these would attract attention or have value with collectors. They were simply viewed as defective coins. It is likely that about 3,000 to 4,000 1955 Doubled Die cents exist. This variety launched in a large way the numismatic passion, today dynamic, for unusual die errors and varieties. *The Cherrypickers' Guide to Rare Die Varieties of United States Coins*, published in staggered multiple volumes covering half cents through gold, commemoratives, and bullion, is the main guide.

The obverse of the 1955 Doubled Die Lincoln cent.

Coin collecting in the 1950s was becoming an increasingly popular pastime, conventions enjoyed record attendance (the 1955 ANA show in

Omaha totaled an unprecedented 49 dealers and 510 total registrants), and dealers enjoyed excellent business as well. Proof sets, bank-wrapped rolls of Mint State coins, and commemoratives were especially popular with investors, as they were easy to understand—quite unlike esoteric colonial or pattern coins.

The 1959 cent introduced the Lincoln Memorial reverse by Frank Gasparro, an engraver at the Mint.

Without earlier notice to the numismatic periodicals—the *Numismatic Scrapbook Magazine*, *The Numismatist*, and *Numismatic News*—the Treasury Department announced in December 1958 that the traditional wheat-ears reverse of the Lincoln cent in use since 1958 would be replaced by the Lincoln Memorial design in 1959. The new motif by Frank Gasparro drew mixed reviews, with numismatic writer Don Taxay saying that it looked like a trolley car. The design was continued through 2008.

1958 and 1959 were good years for the collector, investor-speculator, and dealer alike. Interest in early coins expanded, and colonial coins, copper cents and half cents, Capped Bust half dollars, and other series attracted many specialists, in time generating new reference books. Thousands of citizens took up the pursuit of numismatics, usually starting by filling in holes in blue Whitman folders. Coin clubs with monthly meetings expanded. Many regional associations were formed while others expanded. A short list includes the Central States Numismatic Association, Empire State Numismatic Association, Florida United Numismatists, Mid-Atlantic Numismatic Association, New England Numismatic Association, Penn-Ohio Coin Clubs, and Southern California Numismatic Association.

The Rittenhouse Society was organized in the late 1950s as an organization of young numismatic researchers (including Q. David Bowers, Kenneth Bressett, Walter Breen, George Fuld, Ken Rendell, and others). It would continue as an honorary society to the present day, with its original age limitation for membership removed.

Coin shows varied in attendance. The most dynamic American Numismatic Association convention for me was in 1957 with a line of five to ten people waiting their turn to examine coins. The slowest was a Penn-Ohio show in Akron in which neither I nor neighboring dealer William Fox Steinberg sold even a single coin, so each agreed to buy $300 worth from the other.

By 1959 the market was very strong in all areas from colonial coins to private and territorial gold and all series in between.

THE 1960s AND 1970s

1960 was a watershed year in the coin market, leaving behind the older scenario of collectors and dealers, plus a limited number of investors, participating in a relatively small market. *Coin World* was launched by the Sidney Printing and Publishing Co. (now Amos Media), an entrepreneurial company that sought to establish a weekly paper in a hobby field. The choice was narrowed to antiques, bowling, and coins, with the latter winning out.

Coin World became an instant success, fueled greatly by the nationwide publicity given to the 1960 Small Date Lincoln cents. Television and newspaper coverage reported on lucky people getting $50 bags of these new cents and selling them for $10,000 to $12,000 each. To put matters in perspective, in 1960 $12,000 was about twice the price of a new Cadillac Seville convertible, one of America's most popular top-of-the-line automobiles. The cost of the average American home was $11,900. Within this year the coin market probably doubled or tripled the number of participants.

Fueled by the launch of *Coin World* in 1960 and the excitement of the Small Date Lincoln cents of that year, the coin market took off like a rocket. Hundreds of thousands of new participants entered, and the circulation of *Coin World* alone crossed the 150,000 mark at one time, with D. Wayne ("Dick") Johnson as founding editor, soon followed in the post by Margo Russell (who went on to nearly 25 years of service). The *Coin World* "Trends" column, conducted by James F. Kelly, gave coin-market prices on a *weekly* basis—the first time ever. Teletype systems linked several hundred dealers by 1962–1963, and at one time the Professional Numismatists Guild even had its own network. Dealers posted bid and ask prices as well as market news and lots of gossip, printed out by noisy, clacking keys on rolls of yellow paper. To many, this was like the stock exchange—instant price information from Chicago could be printed out in New York or Los Angeles.

The Coin Dealer Newsletter was started in 1963, listing bid and ask prices for rolls, Proof sets, and other items, using Teletype data as a basis. The great silver dollar bonanza of 1962 to 1964 added more excitement. Leading the market activity were bank-wrapped rolls of coins (with the 1950-D nickel being the hottest item of all, a 40-coin roll rising during the period from below $200 to over $1,200), Proof sets 1936 to date, common-date gold coins

The first issue of *Coin World*, April 21, 1960.

(owning a common-date Mint State double eagle for less than $50 was very exciting), 1,000-coin bags of silver dollars, and more. The Coin and Currency Institute featured its new "Library of Coins" albums, more compact and attractive than any on the market at the time. Many interesting and attractive holders and albums were produced by others.

Many traditional market areas such as tokens, medals, colonials, copper half cents and cents, paper money, and just about any other area requiring study and knowledge, were ignored by investors and speculators not interested in numismatic art, science, and history. At the same time the interest in such specialties was growing, surely but slowly, aided by an unprecedented interest in numismatic history, tradition, and die varieties, and with special-interest groups adding to the growing excitement. The Token and Medal Society, Civil War Token Society, Early American Coppers, Liberty Seated Collectors Club, and other groups formed during the decade went on to become very important to the hobby.

The *Colonial Newsletter* was established in 1960 by Alfred D. Hoch, of Lexington, Massachusetts, to "provide in permanent form an exchange of information, opinions and discoveries concerning early American numismatics." Later in the decade the editorship passed to Jim Spilman, a true rocket scientist (he worked at the NASA facility in Huntsville, Alabama). From that time to the present, under several editors, the publication became the standard source for research on colonial and early American coins. Today under editor Christopher McDowell it is known as the *Journal of Early American Numismatics* and is published by the American Numismatic Society. Early American Coppers launched *Penny-Wise* under the editorship of Warren Lapp, in time succeeded by Harry Salyards, both medical doctors. Other specialized societies attracted editors and members of a generally high degree of education and intellectual curiosity. Most have remained in numismatics for their entire lives.

Large (top) and small dates on 1960 Philadelphia Mint Lincoln cents. The Small Date cents were perceived as rarities and created nationwide attention.

In November 1962 a long-sealed (since 1929) vault at the Philadelphia Mint was opened in order to tap reserves of silver dollars, popular for banks to pay out during the holiday season. A few hundred 1,000-coin bags of sparkling new 1903-O Morgan dollars were casually given out, this being the rarest and most famous of all coins in the series—so rare that it was estimated that no more than a dozen or two Mint State coins existed! The 1903-O listed for $1,500 in the *Red Book*, the top price level. This was like finding money in the streets, a nationwide silver rush occurred, and several hundred million silver dollars were paid out from Treasury and bank vaults.

In Washington at the Treasury Building people formed long lines with wheelbarrows and sacks for silver dollars to wait their turn to get coins from the Cash Room. Coins had been stored there for generations, including large quantities of dollars brought from the closed Carson City Mint in 1911.

Finally, in March 1964, the supply ran out, at which time the Treasury took stock of its remaining pieces and found about 3,000,000 CC dollars on hand—Mint State, low-mintage issues that were later auctioned over a period of time. This dollar bonanza inspired tens of thousands of people to discover numismatics and become serious collectors, while hundreds of thousands more developed a casual interest—perhaps setting aside a few dozen or even a bag or two of dollars.

Prior to November 1962 the 1903-O was considered to be the rarest Morgan silver dollar in Mint State. Most dealers had never seen or handled one.

About the same time the Kennedy half dollar made its debut. After the assassination of President John F. Kennedy in November 1963, the Treasury

The United States Treasury in Washington, D.C.

One of the Treasury Building silver dollar vaults as photographed in 1904.

abandoned the Benjamin Franklin motif and replaced it with a Kennedy portrait made by Chief Engraver Gilroy Roberts and a Heraldic Eagle reverse by Frank Gasparro, an assistant engraver on the Mint staff. Not long afterward Roberts resigned to take a position with the Franklin Mint, a private coiner of medals, and Gasparro became chief engraver, a position he held until his resignation in 1982.

In 1965 the coin-investment market, mostly driven by speculators with little interest in the hobby of coin collecting, ran out of new players. Rolls of 1950-D nickels seem to have stopped in their tracks at the $1,200 level or so, and holders of quantity could find few buyers at this figure. Rolls, Proof sets, 1960 Small Date Lincoln cents, and the number of subscribers to coin newspapers and magazines slumped. In the meantime, other areas that did not participate in the investment boom were doing just fine—colonials, paper money, early copper, and more. Silver dollars continued their popularity as the majority of the nearly 125 different dates and mintmarks of Morgan and Peace dollars could be obtained in Mint State for just a few dollars up to $50. It was realized that the vaults were empty, and there would be no more "surprise" bags of rarities coming on the market. Many dealers set up as to specialize in these coins.

The Kennedy half dollar was released in March 1964.

One of the most dramatic changes in both coin production and in numismatics took place in 1965. The price of silver rose on international markets, and in that year the Treasury Department abandoned this traditional metal for use in the dime and quarter, and created a reduced-silver version of the half dollar (until 1970). New copper-nickel–clad metal compositions were used instead. The price of silver continued to rise, and all silver coins in circulation became worth more than face value—and profitable to melt down, a repeat of the 1850 to 1853 situation in American history. Copper-nickel coins have remained standard for circulation since.

Within a short time most silver coins disappeared from circulation. No longer was it possible to fill a folder or album with Mercury and Roosevelt dimes, Standing Liberty and Washington quarters, or Walking Liberty and Franklin half dollars, as no more were to be found in change. The idea of finding a 1916-D or 1942, 2 Over 1, dime or a 1932-D or -S quarter "treasure" in pocket change was gone forever. Henceforth, coins had to be purchased from dealers or found here and there by chance.

For some illogical reason, as silver coins were quickly withdrawn from circulation the general public decided to hoard cents and nickels. These became scarce in circulation, and some stores offered to pay a premium for quantities of "pennies"! Mint Director Eva Adams blamed this on coin collectors, and "punished" them by removing mintmarks from branch-mint (Denver) coins and also discontinuing the making of Proof sets. Later, Miss Adams "got religion," realized it was really the fault of the general public, became interested in numismatics, and actually sought and was elected to the office of governor of the American Numismatic Association.

In 1968, Proof sets were again made available for collectors. For the first time they were struck at the San Francisco Mint and bore S mintmarks. Interest in collecting and investing in coins entered a new period of growth. Investors had been absent from the market for several years. In 1969 and 1970 and again in 1973 and 1974 the stock market was weak—at a period when the coin market exhibited great strength, making coins all the more attractive as an alternate investment. In particular, gold was a hot item.

A 1968-S Proof cent, the first Proof of this denomination ever to bear an S mintmark.

Silver dollars had not been issued for circulation since 1935. The Treasury decided that a new issue of dollars would be desirable, now of copper-nickel metal. These would find use on gaming tables but, much more importantly, as a substitute for the paper dollar. Paper bills lasted only about 18 months in circulation while a metal dollar was expected to be used for 20 years or more. The Eisenhower dollar designed by Chief Engraver Frank Gasparro was introduced in 1971. While collectors were enthu-

A 1971-S Eisenhower dollar, designed by Frank Gasparro, a Proof from the set of this year.

siastic, the coins found little use in commerce and were discontinued in 1978. In 1979 a new mini-dollar was introduced, again by Gasparro, this time with the portrait of Susan B. Anthony. It was hoped that at last the public would use them due to their convenient small size. The relatively few used in circulation were often confused with quarters of just slightly smaller size. These coins were discontinued in 1981, followed by a curious additional coinage of the same design in 1999.

The government provisions of 1933 and 1934 prohibiting citizens from holding non-numismatic gold coins (and a small personal allowance) did not include Proofs of various countries, and an exception was made for modern Krugerrands from South Africa, first minted in 1967. Pegged at $35 per ounce, gold had remained at this level for decades, until the 1960s, when it began going upward. In the early 1970s, the price of gold bullion continued to rise steadily. In America where investors could not buy bulk, they could and did buy quantities of Krugerrands. In 1974 there was great excitement as the restriction was to end on December 31. The prices of common gold coins escalated. The price of bulk gold varied.

In 1975 there was not much joy in the coin market. Many dealers had been caught up, and profitably so, in the boom market for Krugerrands, double eagles, and other gold-coin investments, and, to the public "coin investment" was still a bad term, with memories of the boom-and-bust of the early 1960s. Even serious collectors pulled in their horns, with the result that many fine-quality coins, including such things as Proof gold, slumped during this time.

The 1776–1976 Bicentennial coins, which would have been as hot as a pistol in normal "up" periods of the investment cycle, laid an egg, and the Mint had a hard time pushing Proofs and special strikings out the door—and had a supply on hand for several years afterward. Serious collectors and alert investors with a contrarian turn of mind bought quietly during this period, and were to reap great profits later. Harry W. Bass Jr., who later formed one of the greatest coin collections ever, began his numismatic interest this year.

In 1978 and 1979 there was a mad rush to speculate in silver and gold bullion, sparked by the Hunt brothers, wealthy Texans seeking to buy all the silver and silver futures they could. Coin dealers who had shops and stores bought large quantities of worn silver coins, tableware, and other items, as well as scrap silver and gold jewelry, to make profits by selling to refiners. Many profited handsomely and used their gains to buy trophy coins and rarities in the coin market, which was as hot as a firecracker. Runaway inflation in the

Numismatists found artistic fault with the Bicentennial half dollar and dollar, but the quarter dollar, shown here, was widely acclaimed. The market was in the doldrums and many fewer coins were distributed than had been hoped.

American economy and high interest rates made homes and other items less affordable than before, prompting many people to invest in tangible assets, hoping to yield more than bank interest. The first of four sessions of the Garrett Collection was auctioned by Bowers and Ruddy Galleries in November 1979 and set many records.

The 1960s and 1970s also saw vast changes in American society, including the gaining of improved civil rights by African-Americans and others, the popularization of passenger-jet aircraft that facilitated travel to foreign countries, and the space race between the United States and the Soviet Union. With the assassination of President John F. Kennedy in 1963, the resignation of President Richard M. Nixon in 1974, the election of former movie actor Ronald Reagan as president in 1979, and other events it was a time to remember. That was done and in spades by books and articles written by many people who had served in the White House and elsewhere in

A uniform patch for the Apollo 11 mission that on July 20, 1969, achieved the first landing of humans on the Moon. Adaptations of this insignia were used on several coin types.

government. Detroit was still the epicenter of the automobile industry with Cadillac and Lincoln being the favorite marques for those who wanted an expensive vehicle. Volvo, Volkswagen, Toyota, Honda, Citroen, Mercedes, and other foreign makes were mostly in the shadows, but expanding rapidly. The Volkswagen "beetle" was the car of choice for many who desired transportation at low cost.

The Boeing 707 revolutionized air travel in the 1960s and was joined by the much larger 747 jumbo jet in the early 1970s.

The American Numismatic Association underwent transition as well. In the early 1960s members of the Professional Numismatist Guild and others in the field raised donations to build a permanent headquarters for the ANA. In 1965 the Home and Headquarters Committee interviewed representatives from cities desiring to be the location. In early 1965 Chairman Charles Johnson reported that one or more of the three committeemen had visited most of the 16 locations from which bids were received prior to February 1. For the record, the cities offering free sites or other inducements for the headquarters were Abilene, Kansas; Amarillo, Texas; Canton, Ohio; Colorado Springs, Colorado; Dubuque, Iowa; Evansville, Indiana; Kansas City, Missouri; Linton, Indiana; Oklahoma City, Oklahoma; Omaha, Nebraska; Prairie du Chien, Wisconsin; Salina, Kansas; Stafford, Virginia; Texarkana, Arkansas; Wichita, Kansas; and Yuma, Arizona. Evanston, Illinois; Minneapolis, Minnesota; and Philadelphia, Pennsylvania, contacted the committee but did not make firm offers.

Omaha was selected as the preferred site, with Colorado Springs, Oklahoma City, and Kansas City following in that order. This was reconsidered, and not long afterward the committee started negotiations for an ANA site at Colorado Springs. Satisfactory progress was being made for a site offered the Association on the campus of Colorado College. The site included in excess of 30,000 square feet of choice space and was offered on a 99-year lease at $1 annual rental. The proposed agreement included an option for renewal of the lease prior to its expiration. This was finalized, and the Home and Headquarters had its dedication on June 10, 1967.

During most of the period Edward C. Rochette was executive director.

In the late 1970s dealer Abe Kosoff was commissioned to set up what was published as *The Official ANA Grading Standards for United States Coins*. Kenneth Bressett, by that time editor of *A Guide Book of*

United States Coins, was tapped to write the grade descriptions and Q. David Bowers the general narrative. The American Numismatic Authentication Service (ANACS) was set up to examine coins for a fee and determine their authenticity or lack thereof. Soon, this evolved into the grading of coins as well. Each coin was assigned a separate grade for the obverse and reverse in accordance with the official standards. It is a matter of fact that each side can be different. Most Morgan silver dollars 1878 to 1921 are a point or two less on the obverse than on the reverse, as the head of Liberty on the obverse is in high relief and is more prone to receiving marks and wear. In the interest of simplification, this was later changed throughout the hobby to a single grade reflecting the average of both sides.

THE 1980s AND 1990s

Going into 1980 the coin market was still riding a crest. The price of bullion gold peaked at $873 an ounce in January 1980. The price of silver topped out at $50.35 per ounce on January 18. On the same day Allen Harriman, editor of the *Coin Dealer Newsletter*, said this: "With both silver and gold bullion soaring into new uncharted ranges, trading in many areas of the coin market becomes more uncertain each day—if not each hour! Most strongly affected, of course, is the bullion-related material. . . ." In early 1980 a longtime client, Dr. Collier, told me that he had been offered $15,000 *per coin* for the set of Barber Proof half dollars, 1892–1915, purchased from me a few years earlier for less than $2,000 per coin. In

March 1980, some say even during the Central States convention itself, the speculation-driven market for rare coins collapsed, and the prices of many "investment grade" coins (generally, MS-65 and Proof-65 or finer silver and gold coins) fell sharply. Many other areas of numismatics, such

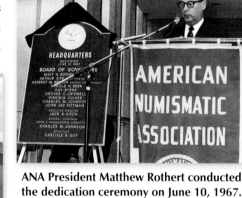

ANA President Matthew Rothert conducted the dedication ceremony on June 10, 1967. The officers and others are listed to the left. One success led to another, the ANA grew and prospered, and in 1982 a second story was added to the building, dedicated on June 10 (15th anniversary of the first event).

The expanded ANA headquarters in 1982.

The plaque for the 1982 dedication.   The American Numismatic Association headquarters building in 1967.

as copper coins, tokens, medals, etc., were not affected. Allen Harriman reported on March 21: "This week's unprecedented drop in the price of both silver and gold bullion has as yet had little or no effect on the numismatic market. In fact, plus signs are very liberally scattered across virtually all of the various pricing charts onceagain this week. . . ." Not helping matters was a nationwide recession that year in which the GDP (Gross Domestic Product) lost 2.2 percent followed the next year by a 2.6 percent loss.

That did not hold, and most series that were the darlings of speculators dropped sharply in price. The *investment market* for coins was in a blue funk for the next several years. In the meantime, scarce and rare Capped Bust and Liberty Seated silver coins, large copper cents, colonials, Charlotte and Dahlonega mint gold, and other collector-oriented series continued to play to a solid market. Established dealers in rare coins persevered and expanded as the decade progressed, and most auctions were very successful. Much dealer-to-dealer business was conducted on Teletype machines.

A perspective on what happened was given by David Hall in the Monthly Summary of the *Coin Dealer Newsletter*, January 1981 (excerpted):

> January 1 to April 17, 1980: dealers called it "stone heat" as prices went up virtually across-the-board every week! At coin shows, choice material was trading 30%, 40%, even 50% over CDN bid/ask levels. At auctions it wasn't unusual for coins to sell for double bid and then some! During the first four months of 1980, bid levels for choice Proof and choice Brilliant Uncirculated type coins increased over 100%! And MS-65 gold bid levels increased over 50%. CDN summary bids increased an average 86.9% for Buffalo nickels, 66.6% for Mercury dimes, 88.5% for Standing Liberty quarters and 75.6% for Walking Liberty half dollars. Though substantial, the 30% average price gain for MS-65 Morgan and Peace dollars was overshadowed by the explosive gains in other areas. Never before had coin prices increased so quickly!

> The prices realized by the coins sold by Bowers and Ruddy Galleries as "Part II" of the Garrett Sale in late March gives us a perfect example of the true hysteria of the "stone heat" market. The total price realized at that sale was in excess of $11 million. The average price per lot was an incredible $20,526! Twenty single coins sold in excess of $100,000 each.

> "Black Friday": The April 1980 Central States Numismatic Society convention was like no other coin show in history. At that show the four-year bull market literally "stopped on a dime." In retrospect, undoubtedly there were several reasons for the sudden slowdown. Dealers had become very sloppy with their purchase policies and many dealers were financially overextended. Bullion prices were crashing. Interest rates had soared to 20%. And those huge Garrett Sale payments were due on April 18th. In looking back, it's also evident that there were rumblings of a market slowdown, subtle hints if you will, in the weeks preceding the Central States Show. However, no one expected it to happen when it did and every dealer I know was stunned at how incredibly sudden and incredibly hard the brakes came on. If you weren't there, it may be hard to comprehend, but I was there and believe me on April 17th it was business as usual and on April 18th no one would even look at coins!

> April 19 to October 17 1980: For six months the rare coin market went through a period of sluggish activity and declining prices. At first, there were no buyers at *any* price, but, as prices continued to drop and dealer cash positions improved, the market began to firm up. Coins began to trade at 20% or 30% or 40% below bid. By mid-October many issues were again trading in the bid/ask range—or slightly below—with a lot of Teletype "bargain hunting" bids (in the 5% to 15% under bid range) for commemoratives, early Proof sets, Walking Liberty rolls, cheaper type coins, etc. It's important to note that this is an overview of the entire market and not all series followed the general pattern. For example, Morgan and Peace dollars started heating up after the rest of the market fell flat.

As a reader of *Mega Red* you can study much market information such as the above that has been largely forgotten.

The market recovered, and today just about all coins are worth more than they were in April 1980. As to the Garrett Collection, it was cataloged by me and my staff. This was an old-time holding started in 1864 by T. Harrison Garrett, scion of the family that controlled the Baltimore & Ohio Railroad. Items that were hot investment items in 1980 comprised only a tiny part of that collection. By the fourth sale in 1981 the Garrett Collection, appraised at $8.9 million, yielded $25 million. Today the collection would probably sell for more than $100 million.

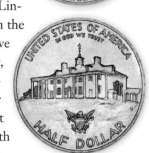

Due to rising copper prices the Mint in 1982 changed the composition of Lincoln cents from bronze to copper-coated zinc, the standard still used today. In the same year the Treasury Department resumed the issuance of commemorative coins, the first since 1954. The Washington commemorative half dollar, designed by Chief Engraver Elizabeth Jones, recent successor to Frank Gasparro, accompanied by publicity and enthusiasm generated by Mint director Donna Pope, was issued to observe the 250th anniversary of the birth of our first president. The pieces, made with Proof finish by the San Francisco Mint and with Mint State finish by the Denver Mint, were very well received, and within a year or so most were sold. This set the scene for hundreds of later commemoratives, production of which continues to be important today. During the decade the Marketing Department of the Mint was expanded, put new policies in place, and became more interactive with the numismatic community than ever before.

The first commemorative coin issued since 1954 was the 1982 half dollar observing the 250th anniversary of George Washington's birth.

The United States Silver Bullion Depository, often referred to as the West Point Bullion Depository and today as the West Point Mint, officially opened on June 13, 1938. Its purpose was to store silver bullion, while at Fort Knox, Kentucky, the recently opened building stored most of the nation's gold reserve. In 1980, Lincoln cents were made at the Depository. Lacking mintmarks, they appeared similar to Philadelphia coins.

In the same year the facility began striking gold pieces for the American Arts Commemorative Series gold medallion program. Produced were half-ounce and one-ounce gold medals depicting famous American painters, writers, performers, and other artists. Marketing was encumbered by frequent changes of price in step with bullion values and a complex procedure to order. The program went through its legislated run, ending in 1984, and wasn't renewed. "In hindsight," writes Dennis Tucker in *American Gold and Silver: U.S. Mint Collector and Investor Coins and Medals, Bicentennial to Date*, "it might be tempting to label the American Arts initiative a failure. . . . But the American Arts medals were a crucial part of the nation's learning curve, and seen in this light the program was if not entirely *successful*, certainly *important*. Congress and the Treasury Department were feeling their way toward what would become the world's best-selling gold-bullion series."

A 1980 one-ounce gold American Arts Gold Medallion depicting artist Grant Wood.

Beginning in 1984, the W mintmark was first used on coins—$10 gold commemoratives for the Olympic Games. Since that time many W-mintmarked coins have been struck there.

The 1984-W commemorative $10 gold piece made the first use of the W mintmark on a legal-tender coin.

When it came to grading, many dealers felt that the main Mint State grades of 60, 63, 65, 67, and 70 were not enough. Many advertisers used plus marks, such as MS-65++. The *Coin Dealer Newsletter* reported this on July 4, 1986:

> This past weekend, the ANA Board of Governors met, debated, and unanimously accepted the 11 point grading scale—MS-60, 61, 62 . . . 70. Originally intended to discuss the feasibility of the MS-64 grade, the ANA Governors showed their leadership in the hobby by going the whole route and accepting all 11 grades. They felt this was a necessary action for the future as well as today. MS-64 has been used for the last couple of years in the marketplace and eventually all in-between grades will be followed. By accepting the new system, the ANA is looking to the future when grading can, at least in terminology, be standardized. There will probably always be debates over how a coin grades, but at least now, the industry will be talking the same language—numerals.

As it developed the 11-point scale would be defined but not consistently applied.

Investing in gold and silver bullion became very important. The market fall in 1980 was history, and in 1986 there were many new players buying Krugerrands, Canadian Maple Leafs, common-date double eagles, and other coins. The U.S. Mint entered the field with its own bullion coins—the American Eagle made in one-ounce silver and tenth-ounce to one-ounce gold formats. The date for the American Silver Eagle was 1986 but for the American Gold Eagle it was in Roman numerals the first year, MCM-LXXXVI, later changed to Arabic for each year. Bullion strikes were produced for mass sale and Proofs for collectors. The 1995-W Proof American Silver Eagle was a special issue sold at a premium and set the stage for many "special" Proof coins and West Point coins that would be made in various series in the twenty-first century, new varieties that met with mixed reviews from buyers. The basic program was an immediate success and continues as such to the present day.

In 1986 David Hall and a group of dealer associates formed the Professional Coin Grading Service (PCGS), which offered for a fee to receive coins, give an opinion of grade via several experts, and sonically seal the coin in a hard plastic holder, which became known as a "slab." In 1987 John Albanese, earlier with PCGS, established the Numismatic Guaranty Corporation of America (NGC), which also became spectacularly successful. Other services were founded, and some enjoyed niches in the marketplace. ANACS with its paper certificates and photographs faded in importance and was later sold by the ANA, eventually reestablishing itself among the most popular professional certification services.

1986 American Silver Eagle.

Certified grading did wonders for the investment market as sellers found that newcomers to numismatics would readily buy coins in holders and not worry about the grade. An ugly or poorly struck coin that might be virtually unsaleable except at a deep discount now could be readily sold for the full "bid" price. This made many ugly ducklings marketable. It was further beneficial to dealers in that clients rarely returned coins certified by a third-party grading service.

MCMLXXXVI (1986) American Gold Eagle.

The market for so-called investment-grade coins, 65 and higher, rose sharply as a part of the largely unquestioned numbers applied by grading services. *The Coin Dealer Newsletter* in April 1988 included this:

> The past two years have seen a growing interest, by the public, in certified coins. Experienced business entrepreneurs learned in the early stages of their training "to give the public what they want." Therefore, there has also been an increase in the marketing of certified coins, so much so, that the year 1987 may be remembered as the year of "overkill."

The CDN added that the public remained confused as to why different services would grade the same coin differently. Not making matters simpler, "there have been significant grading changes."

Several mutual funds were formed to simplify the buying of coins, including one by Merrill Lynch (it was later dissolved and participants reimbursed).

The market for investment coins reached a high in 1989 and early 1990, at which time commemoratives (most of which in the market are in Mint State) and related coins were trading to speculators (or the more popular term, investors) at prices far beyond what any seasoned collector would pay. Finally, the runaway train ran out of steam, and in early 1990 few investors wanted to get on board. The market crashed, and prices fell back to basic or foundational levels reflecting collector demand. Today, as you read these words in *Mega Red*, if you check the *Coin Dealer Newsletter* prices of early 1989 you will see that *most* MS-65 and higher commemorative silver coins and countless other high-grade speculators' favorites are far cheaper now than they were then.[9] Hardly anything about this crash has been mentioned in numismatic magazines and newspapers.

A 1926 Sesquicentennial of American Independence commemorative half dollar in MS-65 had a market value of $14,500 in the spring of 1990. Years later in the 2019 edition of *A Guide Book of United States Coins* it was listed as $600.

Most but hardly all areas of the market recovered as the years progressed. Along the way the interest in specialties increased. Although many 1989 investments were great disasters, most high-grade federal coins have increased in value since that time, and many high-level Mint State coins of the mid-nineteenth century and earlier have multiplied in price.

In June 1989 Edward C. Rochette retired from 20 years of service as the executive vice president (term for what is known as the executive director today) of the American Numismatic Association. Under his leadership the association had grown and prospered as never before. He went on to serve the ANA in other roles including as president and as interim executive director when changes were being made.

In 1990 the World Wide Web was initiated, but few people paid attention to the news.

The market regained strength by 1996 when the second part of the Louis E. Eliasberg Collection crossed the auction block. A Gem Proof 1913 Liberty Head nickel sold for $1,485,000, the first time in world numismatic history that any coin sold for more than a million dollars.

In 1997 the price of gold tumbled. On November 27 an ounce fell to $295.95, its lowest price since March 1985. In numismatic circles the precious metal remained popular and more than a few dealers based their marketing programs

The Eliasberg 1913 Liberty Head nickel, the finest of five known specimens.

on rosy expectations (which in time proved to be correct). In that year the Mint began making platinum bullion coins for collectors and investors. With mixed results these have been continued to the present day.

In 1999 the State quarter program was launched. It was one of the most dramatic programs ever instituted by the Treasury Department, largely based on congressional testimony given by Harvey Stack of Stack's, New York City. Five different states would be honored each year, in the order in which they ratified the Constitution, the first being Delaware. The program was planned to continue for ten years, until all states had been covered. The plan called for designs to be created within the individual states, by artists, members of the public, and others who were to submit ideas, to be reviewed and then finalized by the governors of the states. The eventual result was fifty different designs, no two alike, which delighted numismatists who gave many reviews and opinions concerning the beauty or lack thereof.

Each of the quarters had a special launch ceremony covered with fanfare. Great excitement prevailed from beginning to end, and much was done for the entire numismatic hobby, with books published about the coins, and folders, albums, maps, and other holders and display cases made for eager collectors.

In the same year the euro became the standard currency of many European nations.

New hobby organizations formed after the 1960s included the Colonial Coin Collectors Club and the John Reich Collectors Society. The older specialized groups continued to do well, publishing new research and encouraging new collectors.

As time went on, writers in the popular numismatic press told of gradeflation, or the assigning of higher numbers by certification services than given to the same coins earlier, a subject detailed elsewhere in this book. By the last year of the twentieth century, 2000, the hobby was quite strong in most areas. Personal computers were gaining in popularity, and by this time there were many numismatic applications. Chat rooms and message boards were set up and provided many exchanges as well as instant information.

The American Numismatic Association remained the leading worldwide organization of numismatists and had slightly more than 30,000 paid members. In the United States the American Numismatic Society in New York City was a smaller group mostly devoted to advanced collectors and research. Its Coinage of the America Conference programs were held yearly with leading presenters discussing and displaying coins, tokens, and medals of the Western Hemisphere, followed by a reference book. This illustrious series ran into the early twenty-first century, after which time most conferences related to ancient coins. Across the nation several hundred local and regional coin clubs met monthly.

The 1999-P Delaware quarter, the first in the State quarter program.

The American Numismatic Association headquarters in Colorado Springs on the campus of Colorado College.

An 1807 Capped Bust half dollar, designed by John Reich.

2000 TO DATE

The years from 2000 to date including the official start of the twenty-first century in 2001 have seen countless changes and events on the national and international scenes. A short list includes the Y2K monetary excitement of 2000, the NASDAQ stock-market crash, the World Trade Center disaster and its vast effects on security and travel, CDs and DVDs, presidential administrations from the end of Bill Clinton to the beginning of Donald Trump, Enron, artificial intelligence, home theaters, space shuttles, federal budget, interest rates, LGBTQ, the rebirth of Apple, iPhones and other electronic devices, electronic credit and bill paying, domestic shootings, robots, Uber and Lyft, racial equality, the securities market and the rise and fall of various companies and industries, nanotechnology, video streaming, the fighting of multiple wars in countries that do not like America, global warming, self-driving cars, weather and natural disasters, and more.

The present chapter is nearly completely devoted to numismatics, and readers are referred to other sources for details concerning the above. The year 2000 began with a healthy, indeed dynamic rare-coin market mainly driven by speculator interest in coins common and rare certified in ultra-high grades. More broadly spread, and on a much more permanent basis, was well-studied *collector* interest in copper, silver, and gold coins.

The year started with the launch of the first "golden dollar," a mini-dollar in manganese-brass alloy. The obverse design featured Sacagawea, a translator who traveled with the Lewis and Clark expedition in the upper reaches of the Missouri River, carrying her baby, Pomp. The design was by artist Glenna Goodacre. The reverse depicted a flying eagle by Mint engraver Thomas D. Rogers Sr.

The Sacagawea "golden dollar" was launched in 2000 and proved to be a numismatic favorite. Circulation strikes were made at the Philadelphia and Denver mints. Proofs (as shown) were struck in San Francisco.

The Mint was eager to promote public interest and acceptance of the new dollar. It arranged with General Mills, Inc., the Minneapolis manufacturer of cereals and other foods, to supply 5,500 coins struck in late summer or early autumn 1999 with a 2000-P obverse and the prototype reverse. The difference in the reverse details was not disclosed to the numismatic community at the time. General Mills advertised a "treasure hunt"—one in every 2,000 boxes of Cheerios would contain a new Sacagawea dollar, not yet in general release, and a 2000-dated Lincoln cent. "The only place to get either coin is in a box of Cheerios." Further, one box in every 4,400 had a certificate redeemable for 100 Sacagawea dollars (finders who redeemed them received the dollars with the later-type reverse). It was not until February 2005 that the differences distinguishing this variety was noticed by a numismatist and publicized. The first one auctioned sold for nearly $35,000. More were found, and today somewhat more than 100 have been identified.[10]

Detail of the tail feathers with cross-vanes used only on the rare 2000-P "Cheerios" dollar, the "poster rarity" of the turn of the century.

In August 2000 the ANA World's Fair of Money convention was held in Philadelphia and drew more than 20,000 attendees, an all-time record.[11] Across the front of the bourse area the California Gold Marketing Group set up the 50-foot-wide Ship of Gold display. This was a reproduction of the *SS Central America*, the treasure-laden ship that sank on September 12,

The regular reverse with plain tail feathers (no vanes), as used on all regular Sacagawea dollars 2000 to 2008.

1857, and from which the Columbus-America Discovery Group recovered gold coins and ingots in the late 1980s. Shown were many items recovered, and a mini-theater projected films of the find. A program by treasure-finding scientist Bob Evans had an attendance of more than 400 visitors. Marketing of the treasure had begun in 1999 and continued for several years, by which time about $100 million was realized. The treasure and its publicity electrified the market and were called by *Coin World* "the story of the year."

How many people collect coins? How many are serious numismatists? Beth Deisher, editor of *Coin World*, provided comments on this in the issue of March 12, 2001. She suggested that most numismatists and related organizations define a collector as "one who spends time and money to systematically gather coins for the purpose of forming a collection. Using that definition, we can begin to build a total that has some facts behind it." She suggested that about 450,000 people were serious about numismatics but noted that the United States Mint had 1,800,000 names on its mailing list.[12] Further, "The U.S. Mint reports that its marketing surveys show that up to 110 million adults are actively collecting the State quarters."

As to how many people in 2001 went beyond collecting State quarters and modern Mint products and were serious enough to spend, say, $500 to $1,000 each year on Morgan dollars, Indian Head cents, colonial copper coins, and the like, and to attend coin shows and bid in auctions, your editor's guess is about 250,000. That would have been a solid base for any collecting hobby that involves art, history, romance, and methodology of acquisition.

More than 7,400 mint-fresh 1857-S double eagles have been recovered from the wreck of the *Central America*.

The numismatic collection of the late Harry W. Bass Jr., one of the finest ever formed, was sold at auction in several sales beginning in 1999. Christine Karstedt and Q. David Bowers worked with the Bass and Calhoun families in Dallas as they created the Bass Gallery at American Numismatic Association headquarters in Colorado Springs.

The SS *Central America* sidewheel steamship was in service to and from Panama and New York City in 1857. (*Frank Leslie's Illustrated Newspaper*, September 26, 1857)

A small part of the Harry W. Bass, Jr. Gallery at ANA headquarters in Colorado Springs.

The formation of registry sets, a collecting concept pioneered by PCGS and picked up by NGC, went into high gear. The challenge was to have the highest-graded coin or set of coins certified. In *COINage*, April 2003, editor Ed Reiter reported:

> Recently, one of these "modern rarities" brought $39,100 at an auction at the Florida United Numismatists convention in Orlando. The coin was a 1963 Lincoln cent graded Proof-70 Deep Cameo by the Professional Coin Grading Service (PCGS). It is said to be the only Proof Lincoln cent of that date ever to receive a perfect grade from one of the leading coin-certification services.[13]

Registry set participation would eventually involve more than 10,000 people at the various services and would be responsible in coming years for many coins that are common in, say, MS-65 grade and priced at below $10 to sell for thousands of dollars in ultra-grades. Sets have contributed much to the strength of the market in recent years. Multiple losses have occurred when an ultra-grade coin that was once rare "becomes common" when more are certified. All of this part of numismatics, and the key is to become as informed as possible before buying.

To this must be added the reality than in many older series such as colonials and early nineteenth-century copper, silver, and gold coins, coins from Good-4 to Mint State (never mind non-existent ultra-high grades) have enjoyed a strong market as well.

A renaissance in numismatic research and publishing was kindled in the early 2000s under the management and inspiration of Anderson Press. By 2003 Whitman Coin Products, after many years as a division of Western Publishing Company in its hometown of Racine, Wisconsin, and after later sales to various other firms, was operated by St. Martin's Press in New York City. Whitman had continued to publish the *Red Book* (its guide to retail coin prices) and the *Blue Book* (its guide to wholesale coin prices) under the editorial direction of Kenneth Bressett, but in recent years had done little in the way of new titles. This changed dramatically when H.E. Harris & Co., an Anderson Press company, bought Whitman from St. Martin's. Under new management and ownership, the combined firm took the name of the present-day Whitman Publishing, LLC. Since then Whitman has published more than 300 new books for collectors, investors, and researchers, including more than two dozen volumes in the Bowers Series (on various U.S. coin types, denominations, and related subjects); the *Cherrypickers' Guide to Rare Die Varieties of United States Coins*; the "100 Greatest" library of books; and many others ranging from 96-page monographs to multiple-volume encyclopedias, and the present 1,504-page *Mega Red*. These books cover American and world coins, ancient coins, paper currency, medals, tokens, bullion, and other numismatic and historical topics. Whitman has also dramatically increased its line of folders, albums, display cases, magnifiers, and other storage, display, and research products for collectors.

Whitman purchased the Baltimore Coin and Currency Convention and rebranded it as the Whitman Coin & Collectibles Expo, expanding the show and adding new features, with three events held annually in Baltimore. The company has supported many hobby organizations and programs, funding the ANA's annual Young Numismatists literary competition, sponsoring the Rittenhouse Society's annual breakfast, donating books and collector supplies to the Boy Scouts of America and other groups, assisting Women In Numismatics (www.womeninnumismatics.com), and facilitating communications and cooperation among researchers, specialty groups, museums, archives, government agencies, and others.

In 2003 the United States Mint implemented the novel Artistic Infusion Program, an effort to bring the talents of private-sector artists under the wing of the government. Eighteen "master" designers and six "associate" designers were selected from applications received, to create motifs for American coins and medals. By this time State quarters at the rate of five per year plus new medals put pressure on the Engraving Department. The program worked out well, and over the years various early artists departed and new ones were selected. The AIP has injected new artistry and creativity into American coinage and medal design.

Also in 2003, the Citizens Coinage Advisory Committee (www.CCAC.gov) was established by Act of Congress to advise the secretary of the Treasury on themes and design proposals for circulating coinage, bullion coins, Congressional Gold Medals, and national and other medals.

The Whitman Publishing exhibit at a Whitman Coin & Collectibles Expo in Baltimore, an event held three times a year.

In 2004 the American Numismatic Society relocated from its two stone bank-like buildings on Audubon Terrace in New York City, its home since 1908, to a multi-story structure at 140 William Street in the Financial District that included the expansive Harry W. Bass Jr. Memorial Library. The new building was sold at a handsome profit, and the ANS later moved to leased quarters on the 11th floor of the former New York Tribune printing plant on Varick Street.

In 2004 and 2005 Westward Journey nickel five-cent pieces were made at the mints to honor the Lewis and Clark expedition. Beyond the coins themselves, special sets including medals were marketed, not to the pleasure of some collectors who believed that coin issues should be simple and straightforward.[14] The portrait of President Thomas Jefferson was changed in 2005 from that created in 1938.

A reflection of the market was given by Mike Gumpel in *COINage*, January 2005 (excerpted):

> This past year saw the strength of the rare-coin market continue at a faster pace than the previous year while broadening at the same time. 2003 was a great year for collector coins, especially rare and better dates, and also a great year for more modern pieces in super-high grades. 2004 continued to be even better in those two areas, but the health of the market moved in several other sections also. Key date coins of Bust, Seated and Barber series all saw surprising demand. Common date, high-grade Barber coins; commems; common and rare date gold; circulated type coins; bullion-related coins, and just about everything was more in demand in 2004 than the previous years. Things like a weaker dollar overseas helped by influencing the advancing price of gold. A lackluster Wall Street also helped, as a number of investors decided to invest outside of the stock market with some of that money going into rare coins.

The *Coin Dealer Newsletter*, January 21, 2005, reported that at the recent Florida United Numismatists Convention many dealers lowered their "bid" and other prices as money was scarce for some, and there were auction expenses and other bills to be paid.

Year in and year out market commentaries appeared in the various numismatic magazines. Coverage of the same events often varied widely. Many shows routinely issued news releases saying that activity was

The two reverse designs for the 2004 Westward Journey nickels and the shared obverse.

**The two reverse designs for the 2005 Westward Journey nickels
and the shared obverse with a revised portrait of Jefferson.**

robust, although some were slow. Meanwhile, the Internet took away much business that formerly took place at conventions, and onerous security procedures at airports deterred some collectors from traveling.

At the same time grading became increasingly difficult to figure out. In *Penny-Wise*, journal of the Early American Coppers group, editor Harry Salyards commented that certified grades on large copper cents were often far higher than the grades assigned by longtime specialists who belonged to EAC. "For years, it has been recognized that the slabbed '62' may be an EAC '45,' or the slabbed '50' an EAC '30.'" This led to a new practice of auction listings giving both the EAC and certified grades. With accompanying pictures buyers were able to bid confidently.

The Mint reported in early 2005 that sales of platinum coins were sagging. The program had never caught on with enthusiasm, and a redesign of the series was being considered. High prices were a deterrent to buying, but for the Mint the coins produced a nice profit.[15]

Around this time increased numbers of sophisticated Chinese counterfeits of United States coins began appearing in quantity on the market, including on eBay.[16] Buying coins that were professionally certified as authentic became a necessity for many advanced collectors.

In 2005 the Mint announced that "Satin Finish" would be available on circulating coins included in Mint sets sold to collectors. In *Coin World*, May 23, 2005, editor Beth Deisher asked if this meant that coin albums needed to be redesigned to accommodate two versions of current circulating coins. Increasingly the Mint offered various packaging opinions and special finishes rather than single coins.

The ANA World's Fair of Money held in San Francisco in July 2005 was reported as one of the slowest such events in recent years and nearly all reports were negative. The reasons suggested were that a 300-mile circle drawn around the city was 50 percent ocean and in the land part there lived only a tiny percentage of ANA members, that parking cost $15 to $20 per day, and that the show was held on two floors, not well marked so that some visitors were not aware that there were two large separate levels of activities.[17] The ANA also held smaller shows at other times of the year. Convention scheduling caused great debate among members. Some thought it a good idea to constantly move events around the country so that various regions, even with low populations, would be represented, and others suggested that they be held only in large cities such as Chicago that had easy air connections.

The United States Mint regularly sets up displays at coin conventions. This one with information on the Westward Journey nickels was on view at the 2015 ANA convention. Many images of proposed 2006 nickels, none of which ever reached reality, were shown.

For a number of years Solomon Brothers, a leading Wall Street securities firm, published the results of rare-coin investment along with other fields. The "basket" of coins contributed by Stack's included these 20 coins:

1794 half cent, EF; 1873 two-cent piece, Brilliant Proof; 1866 nickel, Brilliant Proof; 1862 three-cent silver, Mint State; 1862 half dime, Mint State; 1807 dime, Mint State; 1866 dime, Mint State; 1876 20-cent piece, Mint State; 1873 With Arrows quarter, Mint State; 1886 quarter, Mint State; 1916 Standing Liberty quarter, Mint State; 1815, 5 Over 2, half dollar, Mint State; 1834 half dollar, Mint State; 1855-O half dollar, Mint State; 1921 half dollar, Mint State; 1795 Draped Bust dollar, Mint State; 1847 dollar, Mint State; 1884-S dollar, Mint State; 1881 trade dollar, Brilliant Proof; and 1928 Hawaiian commemorative half dollar, Mint State.

The index did not include colonials or gold coins. It did provide a bellwether of prices. David L. Ganz reported this in *Numismatic News*, March 7, 2006:

> Over a 67-year period of time, 1938 to 2005, rare coins increased an average of 13.56 percent, compared to 8.39 percent for the Dow Jones Industrial Average. Both the Dow Jones and the index compilation for rare coins use a market-basket approach, measuring selected coins designed to represent the whole marketplace, and selected stocks that are broadly representative of the industrial sector of the American economy.
>
> Components of the Dow Jones have changed during the period (though the results have not); the coin list is static. Dow Jones statistics are calculated daily, and based on actual components and prices published in many periodicals. The coin list was first compiled by Solomon Brothers going back to 1978, and carried through 1990, and was always done on an annualized basis [later it was done semi-annually].

In late 2006 extending to August 19, 2007, the American Museum of Natural History in New York City mounted a large exhibit, "Gold." The display included coins from ancient times to present, mostly on loan from the American Numismatic Society, and ingots and coins from the *SS Central America*, among many other sections.

On January 2, 2007, in *Coin World* market analyst Mark Ferguson discussed certified coins, including this:

Theoretically, there is very little difference between a coin grading Proof or Mint State 69 in comparison to the same design coin grading a perfect Proof or Mint State 70. In fact, a loupe is often required to find the minute blemishes in a 69-graded coin that keep it from a perfect grade. To the naked eye, these coins should look virtually identical. So, why are there wide variations in prices between these two grades, and even for the same grades? The answer partially lies in people's preferences for coins endorsed as "perfect" by third-party grading services. . . .

What we know about the coin in terms of rarity and availability is still evolving, resulting in vast price variations at this time. . . .

The American Museum of Natural History mounted the spectacular "Gold" exhibit in 2006 and 2007, advertised on banners in the city, including on the front of the museum.

At the time the American Numismatic Association was in a growth stage and had about 32,000 members. Overall attendance at auctions and conventions declined in the early 2000s as buying and selling via the Internet was much more comfortable and convenient. The association had proposed to establish a numismatic museum in Washington, D.C., but that was scrapped in October 2007. Such would have been redundant in any event, as the National Numismatic Collection at the Museum of American History building of the Smithsonian Institution, with curators Dr. Vladimir Clain-Stefanelli and his wife Elvira, succeeded by Dr. Richard Doty, had extensive exhibits of coins, tokens, medals, and paper money from all eras. Collectors and researchers were warmly welcomed and many special events were held.

In 2007 the Mint issued a Proof $20 gold coin of the Saint-Gaudens design with the date as MMVII on the 100th anniversary of the original MCMVII (1907) issue, much to the acclaim of the numismatic community. It was of smaller diameter than the 1907 original but was thicker, thus maintaining the same weight. During this era Mint Director Edmund C. Moy was very involved in numismatic activities and was a regular attendee of major coin conventions.

In 2007 the Presidential series of "golden dollars" was introduced, overlapping slightly with the Sacagawea dollar series that ended in 2008. Presidents were featured from George Washington onward, living presidents excluded. The obverse designs featured a portrait (by various artists) and the reverse the Statue of Liberty (by Mint sculptor-engraver Don Everhart).

The Presidential series of "golden dollars" was introduced in 2007 with the dates and mintmarks on the edge, a curious change.

In 2009 the Sacagawea obverse was continued in a new series with Native American reverse motifs. Both of these new series had a major numismatic liability, according to nearly everyone: the dates and mintmarks were placed on the *edges* of the coins, where they could not be seen in holders or albums! Other new series included 24-karat American Buffalo gold bullion coins and First Spouse coins. It cost more than $20,000 in Mint-issue prices to keep current with every legal-tender coin variety produced in a given year. Sales of platinum coins continued to fall below Mint expectations and there was discussion as to what to do, such as changing the designs.

The State quarter program wound down in 2008, after which in one year six quarters for the District of Columbia and U.S. territories were made, followed in 2010 by the new America the Beautiful quarters. The latter program features national parks, national historic sites, wildernesses, forests, and other "national" locations. In connection with these a parallel series of five-ounce silver bullion coins is being produced.

In 2009 the golden dollar was continued, now with a *dateless* obverse, combined with a yearly change of reverse in the Native American series. Dates and mintmarks were placed on the edge.

The 2008 ANA World's Fair of Money had a registered attendance of 9,717, including dealers and their helpers. The American economy was entering a recession, with the second week in October being the worst week in the 112-year history of the Dow-Jones Industrial Average, but this and the collapse of several major Wall Street firms had no measurable effect on the numismatic market.

Conventions were increasingly becoming "virtual" with no in-person attendance necessary. In 2008 American Numismatic Rarities held the sale of the Dice-Hicks Collection. A shareholder in the company called (on a cell phone of course) to check on progress. "How many people are attending?" I replied, "There were nine, but one went to the rest room, so now there are eight." Even with such a light crowd, the sale brought three times its estimate because nearly all of the bidders participated in real time on the Internet.

It is not unusual for a leading auction company to hold a public sale at a large convention and have fewer than a dozen people in attendance while at the same time setting many records. Bidders participate from all over the world from the comfort and convenience of their homes and offices.

Despite repeated predictions that "pennies" were no longer needed in commerce, the Mint continued to turn out billions, including four commemorative reverse designs in 2009 observing the bicentennial of Abraham Lincoln's 1809 birth. At this time the recession resulted in erratic distribution through the Federal Reserve Banks and less public interest than might have been the case in good times.

In 2010 the Union Shield design (by AIP artist Lyndall Bass, modeled by Mint medallic sculptor Joseph Menna) became the cent's new reverse motif.

In "Making the Grade" in *Numismatic News*, December 22, 2009, F. Michael Fazzari, longtime professional grader and columnist, discussed the fact that many coins called About Uncirculated–55 and 58 earlier were now being certified as Mint State. Many coins jumped five to seven or eight grade points higher over time, although the coins themselves did not change. Mint State and Proof coins saw gradeflation as well—for example, an 1804 dollar jumping from EF-45 to Proof-62.

In 2009 the price of gold bullion ranged from a low of $810.00 per ounce on January 15 to a high of $1,212.50 on December 2. American Eagle silver and gold issues remained very popular. In 2010 the year started on a high note with nearly 10,000 hobbyists attending the Florida United Numismatists convention in Orlando. Meanwhile, the ANA was striving to increase attendance at the World's Fair of Money show, and the board of governors voted to let the Professional Numismatists Guild have a pre-show day (which had been done in some earlier years). The Whitman Coin & Collectibles Expo conventions in Baltimore remained a strong drawing card three times a year—March, June, and November. On the West Coast the Long Beach shows were popular. Regional conventions were held by some clubs. Early American Coppers had its own stand-alone gathering each year, complete with "happenings" in which members shared particular coin types or years and compared them with others.

The four reverse designs used on Lincoln cents in 2009.

With increased hassles in air transportation (long security lines, extra charges for baggage, reduced comfort and amenities on board) more and more people were "attending" conventions in virtual reality. In the meantime the number of coin shops in America was smaller than ever. In 1963 Chester L. Krause told the editor that he estimated there were at least 6,000 walk-in coin, hobby, and other shops offering displays of coins for sale.

A 2010-D cent with the new reverse adopted as standard that year.

How should Abraham Lincoln be depicted on new coinage? Here are proposals studied by the CCAC for the obverse of the proposed 2009 Lincoln bicentennial commemorative dollar. Many choices!

Throughout this era the Citizens Coinage Advisory Committee met several times a year at the U.S. Mint's executive offices in Washington, D.C., and at other venues. Proposed coinage and medallic designs were reviewed and discussed in depth. For example, on March 23, 2010, the CCAC overwhelmingly and enthusiastically endorsed a motif featuring a modern woman as Justice on the reverse of the Proof platinum series that year. The committee in its two-hour session had a prolonged discussion on the lack of interest by *collectors* in these and other non-circulating coins.[18]

In 2007 Mint Director Edmund C. Moy stated, "I want and intend to spark a neo-renaissance of coin design and achieve a new level of design excellence that will be sustained long after my term expires." Advances were made but overall this did not happen. "We are getting pictorial decorative art," said CCAC member Donald Scarinci. "We aren't getting anything bold or inspiring or new or innovative. The only time those four words get used are in Director (Ed) Moy's speeches. And the speeches have no bearing with reality."[19]

Elsewhere in Mint news it was noted that its customer mailing list had slipped below one million names in recent months. Apart from the CCAC quite a few people wondered why the Mint kept using early twentieth-century motifs instead of creating new classics. However, the recycled early-twentieth-century designs of James Earle Fraser (1913 Buffalo nickel)

The obverse of the 2010 Lincoln Presidential dollar, as chosen by the secretary of the Treasury. An attractive portrait?

**Mint Director Edmund C. Moy at a launch
ceremony for the John Adams Presidential dollar.**

and Adolph A. Weinman (1916 Walking Liberty half dollar) were considered by many numismatists to be the most beautiful designs used by the Mint in the early twenty-first century.

In the marketplace PCGS and NGC "officially" recognized adding + signs to grades. "Secure plus" and "star" additions were also used. More logical than any of this, the Certified Acceptance Corporation (CAC) led by John Albanese did not grade coins at all, but viewed coins graded by others and gave them a green sticker if they were high-end or attractive.[20]

There was not much of an aftermarket for modern Mint commemoratives, and dealers were often paying just melt value or slightly less in the secondary market. Hobbyists who were building collections and desired to buy coins for little more than melt value had a great opportunity, commented editor Steve Roach in *Coin World*, March 7, 2011. He observed that 38 varieties of commemorative silver dollars were thus available.

That situation did not change in later years. Of course, this strategy was and is not risk-free from a resale viewpoint. On April 25, 2001, the closing price of silver was $48.70, its highest in 31 years. Anyone who bought silver dollars at bullion value then would have lost money. In late February 2019, an ounce of silver was $16.

The market price of silver and gold bullion only affects certain common coins for which the bullion price is a component. This includes worn common-date Morgan and Peace silver dollars, common-date double eagles, pre-1965 common silver coins, etc. It has no impact on the vast majority of collectible coins. It is not important to the value of scarce and rare coins. The melt value of a Liberty Seated quarter or a gold dollar is irrelevant. Probably the best advice concerning modern commemoratives is to acquire one each for your collection, as in terms of the overall value of your holdings variations in metal prices will have little effect.

It was reported that Presidential dollars had proved to be a dud with regard to public acceptance, and with many numismatists they achieved low marks as well. In the three and a half years since the program started, 1,252,000,000 unwanted coins were placed in Treasury storage, and $650,000 was to be spent at the Federal Reserve Bank of Dallas to store them, with the expectation that there would be two billion coins by the time the program ended.[21] The main reason for this seemingly illogical

The price of a common 1884 Morgan dollar in Very Fine grade varies with the value of silver metal as a commodity.

The ANA Hall of Fame Gallery.

situation is that the Treasury booked a handsome profit on each coin—the difference between the low cost of metal and coinage and the face value—a fact rarely discussed.

As to numismatics, in 2011 it cost $23,500 for a completist to buy every 2011 coin variety offered by the Mint, a figure that did not include every packaging option.[22]

In 2011 the Hall of Fame Gallery was opened in the indoor atrium at American Numismatic Association headquarters in Colorado Springs. Each honoree has a special plaque with a portrait and about 100 words of biographical information.[23] At the World's Fair of Money held by the ANA in Rosemont, Illinois, in August the price of gold was $1,913 per ounce on the commodities market, and common-date double eagles in worn grades started at over $2,000. This enthusiasm spurred record sales volume of gold coins at the show. In November the price of an ounce of gold fell (below $1,700), as did the desire for common-date double eagles.[24]

In my "Joys of Collecting" column in *Coin World* on August 1, 2011, I stated, "Today, certified coins, electronic sources and more make it possible for anyone to be a coin dealer. No knowledge or experience is needed." A reader wrote in, "I look forward to and expect an apology from Q. David Bowers."

I am reminded of a telemarketer who called and upon questioning revealed he had never heard of the Professional Numismatists Guild.

In 2010 Edmund Moy announced his resignation as director of the Mint, effective January 2011. No successor was immediately appointed. Several deputy directors filled the leadership position as acting director or principal deputy director over the next few years. Deputy Director Richard Peterson acted as director for a time. Rhett Jeppson served as principal deputy director, and David Motl and Dave Croft were acting deputy directors in turn, by dint of their positions as senior career officials within the Mint management structure. Finally in 2017 David J. Ryder, who had served as Mint director in 1992 and 1993, was nominated to again take the post of director. He was confirmed by the Senate in March 2018.

There has been no presidentially appointed and Senate-confirmed chief engraver at the Mint since the highly accomplished Elizabeth Jones, successor to Frank Gasparro, resigned in 1991. The position of chief engraver, which had started under Director David Rittenhouse in the 1790s, remained vacant for several years. Then it was officially abolished in an organizational restructuring in 1996. In 2006 John Mercanti, who had worked as a sculptor-engraver at the Mint since 1974, was elevated to the new position of supervisory design and master tooling development specialist. In 2009 Director Moy under his own authority named Mercanti chief engraver. After Mercanti retired in 2010, the position of chief engraver was vacant until early 2019, when medallic sculptor Joseph Menna, of the Mint's Philadelphia staff, was named to the office.

In 2010 the Mint decided to discontinue most launch ceremonies for the America the Beautiful quarters. Public interest had reached a low, and the cost of sending Mint officials to distant locations was not effective. Launches were resumed later. Tom Jurkowsky, the Mint's director of corporate communications, working with Deputy Director Richard Peterson, interfaced with the numismatic community and helped with much research, including for multiple Whitman Publishing projects.

Mint products for numismatists such as Reverse Proofs and special issues with W mintmarks drew mixed reviews, and the continued placement of dates and mintmarks on the edge of dollars remained unfortunate. The Presidential dollars program received few glowing comments. The Sacagawea and Native American dollars earned complimentary notices and were and are well liked for their designs.

In 2013, the American Numismatic Association appointed Kimberly Kiick to the post of executive director. Kiick had been hired by the ANA in 1982 and over the years gained experience in many posts, starting as receptionist, progressing to senior manager and director of operations.

Chinese counterfeits continued to plague the hobby. These extended to coins such as common Morgan dollars in grades of Extremely Fine and About Uncirculated as well as to common large copper cents and other coins. Gold ingots and American Gold Eagles were faked and fooled many people. One American importer offered Eagles at a third of bullion value. It became a dangerous procedure to buy gold coins and ingots and store them without having them examined or assayed. Beth Deisher, who retired from *Coin World* in 2012, held seminars on the subject. Leading third-party grading services guaranteed authenticity, making the premium for encapsulation a worthwhile precaution for many buyers.

In the market for rare and expensive federal coins, certification was the rule, not the exception. In the marketplace certified coins attracted many buyers and bidders who lacked experience and would not otherwise participate. CAC stickers became more popular than ever for selected rarities.

In 2014 on the 50th anniversary of the Kennedy half dollar the Mint struck Proof dual-dated 1964–2014 coins in gold. Distribution began on August 4, including at the World's Fair of Money in Chicago, for the issue price of $1,240. Some enterprising dealers hired several hundred unemployed individuals to wait in line in a queue extending out the doors, to buy sets that were limited, in the process causing

Mint Deputy Director Richard Peterson emcees the 2013 White Mountain New Hampshire quarter dollar launch.

a great distraction and inconvenience. The first set acquired at the show was sold by the buyer for $6,240, then certified as the first by PCGS and resold for $100,000 to a buyer who had been purchasing other coins on a TV marketing program.[25] The coins met with a warm reception by the numismatic community. Several other variations of the anniversary coin were made, including a Reverse Proof from West Point and an "enhanced" Uncirculated coin from San Francisco, 13 different varieties in all.[26]

The 1964–2014 gold
Proof Kennedy half dollar.

In 2014 Bob Evans, the scientist who led the earlier discovery of the long-lost *SS Central America*, returned to the site off of the coast of North Carolina in a new expedition. The recovery of gold coins, ingots, and other items was substantial, in the tens of millions of dollars in numismatic value, but much less than the first find.

Several important collections were marketed in this era, including selections from the cabinets of Eugene Gardner, Donald Partrick, Eric P. Newman, D. Brent Pogue, and Bernard Edison, each one playing to a wide audience with strong bidding and many record prices. However, the overall prices for many series were lower as supply in the marketplace exceeded numismatic demand. (See Jeff Garrett's 2019 Market Report herein for more information.)

In 2016 the Mint issued tribute coins of the 1916 dime, quarter, and half dollar, in gold with a 2016 date. This time, sales were orderly. These coins, like the 2014 Kennedy gold half dollar, were well received.

One of 45 gold ingots recovered
from the SS *Central America* in
2014, adding to the over 400
recovered in the 1980s.

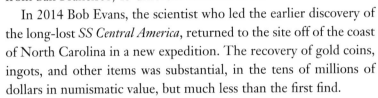

The three different gold denominations struck in 2016 on the 100th
anniversary of the release of the silver coins of the same motifs in 1916.

The American Liberty series of $100 denomination one-ounce gold coins was launched in 2015. Shown are the 2017 obverse, designed by Justin Kunz and sculpted by Phebe Hemphill; and reverse, designed by Chris Costello and sculpted by Michael Gaudioso.

A 2017 American Palladium Eagle with imprinted value of $25, much lower than its bullion value. Apparently Congress felt the best choice for a design was not to tap the current Mint Engraving Department staff but to resurrect the Mercury dime motif created by Adolph A. Weinman in 1916, and a high-relief version of his 1907 American Institute of Architects gold medal reverse.

In 2008 Representative Michael Castle, longtime congressional friend of numismatists and the legislator who facilitated the 1999 and later special quarter issues, introduced a bill for palladium coins. That gained no traction, but years later in 2017 Eagles were made in that metal. Comments concerning palladium coins as well as platinum coins were mixed among numismatists.[27] Neither metal had anything to do with regular American circulating coins (although in 1815 an experimental platinum half dollar had been struck from regular dies). As to whether coins in either metal appealed more to numismatists or to speculators in bullion metal was debatable.

In the twenty-first century the Internet and computer have wrought major structural changes in the market. Today as you read these words, a large percentage of the membership of the American Numismatic Association, about 25,000 people, receive *The Numismatist* in virtual form on the Internet. *Coin World* and other magazines are far thinner than they were a generation ago as most dealers no longer list coins for sale in print. The Internet is faster, and cheaper, and allows instant transactions.

In recent years many sales of scarce and rare coins that might have been made privately by dealers to clients have been consigned to public auction instead. On eBay an unprecedented number of rarities from different vendors can be found, some of questioned authenticity. This has resulted in a rearrangement of retail practices that were in effect a generation ago.

Books in print remain important (*Mega Red* has had record sales), but information on the Internet offers competition to traditional numismatic publishing.

Instant communications bring the world of numismatics to everyone, even on cell phones when traveling. More data are available than ever before. On the negative side, anyone collecting a popular coin series such as Morgan dollars and who has a modest budget can complete most of their collection on the Internet in a day—and with the coin budget exhausted, the fun of months or years of measured collecting might not lie ahead. On the other hand, for tokens, medals, die varieties, and other specialties, many items are inexpensive. A budget of $10,000 can build a memorable display in certain token, medal, and die variety series. Many modern series are very affordable in, say, MS-65 or Gem Mint State—such as modern dollars, Eisenhower to date, State quarters, and America the Beautiful quarters. Current Mint products such as commemoratives, Proofs, and modern medals are interesting to own and contemplate, with many beautiful and historic designs.

A working library of interesting and useful numismatic books can be a treasure and resource. As an example, it is enjoyable to read about numismatic treasures from hoards to shipwrecks without owning any of the coins. The Newman Numismatic Portal on the Internet, coordinated by Leonard Augsburger, provides free and unlimited access to thousands of magazines, newspapers, price lists, auction catalogs, and other material, an unprecedented incredible asset for research, effectively taking the place of a library that would require a lifetime and hundreds of thousands of dollars to form—and even then it would not match the NNP. The Internet is a gateway to explore many numismatic side roads and to gain knowledge on any coin or series.

As has always been true, a collecting instinct is needed to be a longtime numismatist and an intellectual curiosity is essential to keep exploring the endless byways of numismatics to discover new things. In 2018 the number of leading buyers building large collections was greater than ever before in numismatic history. The hobby is alive and well. At Whitman Publishing all of us are enthusiastic about the future.

Colonial Issues

FOREIGN COINS IN THE COLONIES

Money had a rich history in America prior to the advent of the United States' national coinage in 1793. When coins tumbled off the presses from the first Philadelphia Mint the country was much more accustomed to coins from other lands. Prior to 1652 there was no local coinage and the only money in circulation was whatever came here from Europe through trade or travel. People were content to use currency, both old and new, whose value was based more on the metal content than on the issuer's reliability. Foreign money in America during the colonial period had become so embedded that it continued to be accepted as legal tender until discontinued by the Coinage Act of February 21, 1857. Coins of this era are so fundamental to American numismatics that every collection should include at least a sampling.

From the very beginning of commerce in America "hard money" was needed for trade with overseas nations. The largest quantity of coinage consisted of English crowns, shillings, and pence, and Spanish and Spanish-American silver pieces of eight, all of which circulated throughout colonial settlements until being sent back to England for critically needed supplies. Additional quantities of coins came from trading furs, lumber, and other exports that provided a limited but much needed supply of hard currency. Of equal importance to commerce were similar coins of other European countries. The large silver Dutch *leeuwendaalder* (Lyon or Lion dollar) and French *écu* saw extensive circulation, as did the Brazilian gold *peças*. Some New York bills of 1709 were even denominated in Lyon dollars. Distinguishing between the relative values of the multitude of different foreign currencies was not a simple task. To facilitate conversions, books and tables showed comparison prices for each currency.

The most familiar currency in Colonial America was the Spanish-American piece of eight, the Dutch Lion Dollar, and Native American wampum.

The popular Spanish-American silver eight reales, Pillar dollar, or piece of eight, which was a radical departure from denominations in terms of English pounds, shillings, and pence, became a model for the American silver dollar, and its fractional parts morphed into the half-dollar and quarter-dollar coins that are now considered decimal fractions of the dollar. The American quarter dollar, which was similar in size and value to the Spanish two-real coin, took on the nickname "two bits"—a moniker that remains today. Similarly, the American one-cent coin has never totally lost its association with the English penny, and is still called that by anyone indifferent to numismatic accuracy.

Coins, tokens, paper money, and promissory notes were not the only media of exchange used during the early formation of the country. Many day-to-day transactions were carried on by barter and credit. Mixed into this financial morass were local trade items such as native wampum, hides, household goods, and tools. Records were kept in the traditional English pounds, shillings, and pence, but debts and taxes were paid in corn, beaver pelts, or money—money being whatever foreign coins were available. The terms "country pay" or "corn" referred to a number of different kinds of grain or even peas. Standard exchange rates were established and country pay was lawfully received at the colonial treasury for taxes.

Beyond these pre-federal considerations are the many kinds of private and state issues of coins and tokens that permeate the colonial period from 1616 to 1776. These are items that catch the attention and imagination of everyone interested in the history and development of early America. Yet, despite their enormous historical importance, forming a basic collection of such items is not nearly as daunting as one might expect.

The coins and tokens described in the next three sections of this book are fundamentally a major-type listing of the metallic money used throughout the pre-federal period. Many collectors use this as a guide to forming a basic set of these pieces. It is not encyclopedic in its scope. Beyond the basic types are numerous sub-varieties of some of the issues, and a wider range of European coins. Some collectors aim for the finest possible condition, while others find great enjoyment in pieces that saw actual circulation and use during the formative days of the country. There are no rules about how or what to collect other than to enjoy owning a genuine piece of early American history.

SPANISH-AMERICAN COINAGE IN THE NEW WORLD

Values shown for these silver coins are for the most common dates and mintmarked pieces of each issue. Similar pieces were struck at Spanish-American mints in Bolivia, Chile, Colombia, Guatemala, Mexico, Panama, and Santo Domingo.

COB COINAGE – KING PHILIP II (1556–1598) TO KING CHARLES III (1760–1772)

| 1 real cob of Mexico from the reign of Philip III | 1668 2 reales cob struck in Potosi, from the reign of Charles II |

	VG	F	VF	EF
Cob Type, 1/2 Real (1556–1773)	$30	$70	$125	$400
Cob Type, 1 Real (1556–1773)	$40	$100	$175	$425
Cob Type, 2 Reales (1556–1773)	$75	$160	$250	$650
Cob Type, 4 Reales (1556–1773)	$110	$250	$300	$800
Cob Type, 8 Reales (1556–1773)	$150	$300	$500	$900

Values are for coins with partial or missing dates. Fully dated coins are valued much higher. Some cobs were also issued beyond these dates and until as late as 1773 in Bolivia.

PILLAR TYPE – KING PHILIP V (1732–1747), KING FERDINAND VI (1747–1760), AND KING CHARLES III (1760–1772)

1734 8 reales Pillar dollar from the reign of Philip V.

1761 2 reales "pistareen" from the reign of Charles III

	VG	F	VF	EF
Pillar Type, 1/2 Real (1732–1772)	$20	$35	$75	$150
Pillar Type, 1 Real (1732–1772)	$30	$50	$80	$175
Pillar Type, 2 Reales (1732–1772)	$40	$65	$120	$300
Pillar Type, 4 Reales (1732–1772)	$150	$375	$675	$900
Pillar Type, 8 Reales (1732–1772)	$120	$200	$450	$675
Spanish 2 Reales "pistareen" (1716–1771)	$20	$35	$60	$120

BUST TYPE – KING CHARLES III (1772–1789), KING CHARLES IV (1789–1808), AND KING FERDINAND VII (1808–1825)

1807 8 reales Bust dollar from the reign of Charles IV.

	VG	F	VF	EF
Bust Type, 1/2 Real (1772–1825)	$10	$15	$35	$100
Bust Type, 1 Real (1772–1825)	$20	$35	$50	$120
Bust Type, 2 Reales (1772–1825)	$25	$50	$75	$180
Bust Type, 4 Reales (1772–1825)	$100	$250	$475	$800
Bust Type, 8 Reales (1772–1825)	$40	$70	$100	$220

The New World began its first coinage in 1536 in Mexico City. By 1732 the first round coins were made and the columnario. or Pillar coinage, became the coin of trade internationally. In 1772 the Bust dollars with the effigy of the king of Spain were placed in circulation. These coins and the Republican style of later Latin American countries circulated legally in the United States until 1857. Parallel issues of Spanish-American gold coins were made during this period. They saw extensive use for international trade and somewhat lesser use in domestic transactions in America. The Spanish silver pistareen was also a popular and convenient coin in circulation.

TYPICAL WORLD COINAGE USED IN COLONIAL AMERICA
NETHERLANDS SILVER COINAGE, 1601–1693

1640 1/2 Leeuwendaalder.

	VG	F	VF	EF
Netherlands, 1/2 Leeuwendaalder (1601–1653)	$60	$120	$300	$800
Netherlands, Leeuwendaalder "Lion Dollar" (1601–1693)	$70	$150	$275	$700

FRENCH SILVER COINAGE OF KING LOUIS XV (1715–1774) AND KING LOUIS XVI (1774–1792)

1791 écu from the reign of Louis XVI.

	VG	F	VF	EF
France, 1/2 Écu (1715–1792)	$25	$80	$150	$325
France, Écu (1715–1792)	$40	$100	$225	$375

See additional listings of French coins authorized for use in North America on pages 141–144.

BRITISH SILVER COINAGE OF KING CHARLES I (1625–1649) TO KING GEORGE III (1760–1820)

1639 6 pence from the reign of Charles I.   1787 shilling from the reign of George III.

	VG	F	VF	EF
England, Threepence (1625–1786)	$15	$25	$60	$90
England, Sixpence (1625–1787)	$20	$35	$80	$100
England, Shilling (1625–1787)	$35	$50	$100	$200
England, Half Crown (1625–1750)	$90	$160	$350	$600
England, Crown (1625–1730)	$200	$450	$800	$1,200

English copper coins and their imitations circulated extensively in early America and are described on pages 157–159.

Other items frequently used as money in early America included cut fractions of various silver coins. These were cut by private individuals. The quarter 8-reales coin was "two bits." Worn and cut portions of coins usually passed for change according to their weight.

BRITISH NEW WORLD ISSUES

SOMMER ISLANDS (BERMUDA)

This coinage, the first struck for the English colonies in the New World, was issued circa 1616. The coins were known as *Hogge Money* or *Hoggies*, from the wild hogs depicted on their obverses.

The Sommer Islands, as Bermuda was known at the time, were under the jurisdiction of the Virginia Company, a joint-stock mercantile venture formed under a British royal patent and headquartered in London. (This venture was actually undertaken by two companies: the Virginia Company of Plymouth, for what is now New England; and the Virginia Company of London, for the American South.)

English government of the islands had started a few years before the coins were issued—by accident! In 1609 Admiral Sir George Somers led a fleet bound from England to the New World, laden with relief supplies for the Virginia settlement of Jamestown. Somers and his ship were separated from the rest of the fleet in a strong storm, and they ran onto the reefs of the Bermuda Islands, some 700 miles from Virginia. (The islands were named for Juan de Bermúdez, who is believed to have stopped there some hundred years earlier.) For ten months Somers and his party were able to live on wild hogs and birds, local plants, and fish, building houses and a church. During this time they also constructed two small ships, in which, in May 1610, most of the shipwrecked colonists continued their interrupted journey to Virginia.

Bermuda became a separate entity of the Virginia Company of London, from November 1612 until June 29, 1615, when "the Governour and Company of the City of London for the Plantacon of the Somer Islands" (often called the Bermuda Company by historians) was officially incorporated under royal charter. This incorporation granted the right of coinage. The coins did not arrive in the islands until May 16, 1616, at the earliest, a year after Bermuda was under its new charter.

The pieces were struck on thin planchets of brass or copper, lightly silvered, in four denominations: shilling, sixpence, threepence, and twopence, each indicated by Roman numerals. A wild hog is the main device and appears on the obverse side of each coin. SOMMER ISLANDS is inscribed (misspelling both the English admiral's name and the corporation's) within beaded circles on the larger denominations. The reverse shows a full-rigged galleon, or carrack, with the flag of St. George on each of four masts. Many examples of these coins show signs of oxidation or pitting.

"In an era when British silver shillings and fractions traded in commerce based on their intrinsic value," writes Q. David Bowers, "the Bermuda pieces were tokens of little value, a fiat currency that circulated in the manner that paper money would later be used worldwide—good as long as both parties had confidence in the value. As might be expected, these coins had little or no trade value other than within the islands, where they were mostly used at the company storehouse, exchanged for supplies" (*Whitman Encyclopedia of Colonial and Early American Coins*).

These coins of Bermuda did not circulate in North America, but they have traditionally been considered part of early "American" coinage. Sylvester S. Crosby, writing in his 1875 masterwork *Early Coins of America*, insisted that the Bermuda coins laid claim to being "the first ever struck for the English colonies in America," this despite the fact that the islands were not a part of the Virginia colony proper. The regular edition of the *Guide Book of United States Coins* has included them in its pre-federal coverage since the first edition, published in 1946.

Twopence   Threepence

Sixpence Obverse   Large Portholes Reverse   Small Portholes Reverse

Shilling Obverse   Small Sail Reverse   Large Sail Reverse

	AG	G	VG	F	VF	EF
Twopence, Large Star Between Legs	$4,500	$10,000	$15,000	$20,000	$40,000	$65,000
Twopence, Small Star Between Legs	$4,500	$10,000	$15,000	$20,000	$40,000	$65,000
Threepence	—	—	$35,000	$65,000	$90,000	—
Sixpence, Small Portholes	$3,500	$7,500	$10,000	$20,000	$40,000	$65,000
Sixpence, Large Portholes	$3,750	$10,000	$15,000	$20,000	$55,000	$80,000
Shilling, Small Sail	$4,750	$6,500	$10,000	$30,000	$55,000	$75,000
Shilling, Large Sail	$8,000	$15,000	$40,000	$70,000	$90,000	—

MASSACHUSETTS
"NEW ENGLAND" COINAGE (1652)

The earliest authorized medium of exchange in the New England settlements was wampum. The General Court of Massachusetts in 1637 ordered "that wampamege should passe at 6 a penny for any sume under 12 d." Wampum consisted of shells of various colors, ground to the size of kernels of corn. A hole was drilled through each piece so it could be strung on a leather thong for convenience and adornment.

Corn, pelts, and bullets were frequently used in lieu of coins, which were rarely available. Silver and gold coins brought over from England, Holland, and other countries tended to flow back across the Atlantic to purchase needed supplies. The colonists, thus left to their own resources, traded with the friendly Native Americans in kind. In 1661 the law making wampum legal tender was repealed.

Agitation for a standard coinage reached its height in 1651. England, recovering from a civil war between the Puritans and Royalists, ignored the colonists, who took matters into their own hands in 1652.

The Massachusetts General Court in 1652 ordered the first metallic currency—the New England silver threepence, sixpence, and shilling—to be struck in the English Americas (the Spaniards had established a mint in Mexico City in 1535). Silver bullion was procured principally in the form of mixed coinage from the West Indies. The mint was located in Boston, and John Hull was appointed mintmaster; his assistant was Robert Sanderson (or Saunderson). At first, Hull received as compensation one shilling threepence for every 20 shillings coined. This fee was adjusted several times during his term as mintmaster.

The planchets of the New England coins were struck with prepared punches twice (once for the obverse, and once for the reverse). First the letters NE were stamped, and then on the other side the numerical denomination of III, VI, or XII was added.

These are called "NE coins" today.

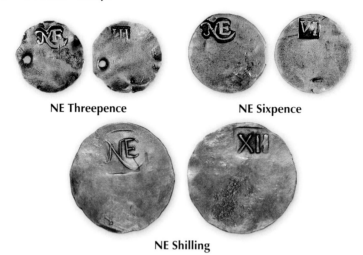

NE Threepence   NE Sixpence

NE Shilling

Early American coins in conditions better than those listed are rare and are consequently valued much higher.

	G	VG	F	VF	EF	AU
NE Threepence (a)				—		
NE Sixpence (b)	$45,000	$75,000	$115,000	$200,000	$325,000	$600,000
NE Shilling	$50,000	$75,000	$100,000	$140,000	$180,000	$250,000

a. Unique. b. 8 examples are known.

WILLOW TREE COINAGE (1653–1660)

The simplicity of the designs on the NE coins invited counterfeiting, and clipping or shaving of the edges by charlatans who sought to snip a little bit of metal from a lot of coins and thereby accumulate a pile of silver. Therefore, they were soon replaced by the Willow Tree series.

All of the Willow Tree coins bore the date 1652, when Oliver Cromwell was in power in Britain, after the English civil war and during the Interregnum government. In fact they were minted from 1653 to 1660. The date 1652 may have been used simply because this was the year the coinage was authorized. Output increased over the years, and the coins were plentiful in circulation.

These pieces, like all early American coins, were produced from handmade dies that are often individually distinctive. The tree in the design is known as a "willow" not from any official legislative records, and certainly not from lifelike resemblance to an actual willow tree, but from terminology dating from 1867 in an auction catalog of the Joseph Mickley Collection. To make the coins, a worker likely placed a silver planchet into a rocker press, which forced a curved upper die against a curved or flat bottom die. This would explain the slight elongation and gentle bend of many Willow Tree coins.

NEW ENGLAND is spelled out, instead of being abbreviated, as on the earlier NE coinage.

Among the four classes of Massachusetts silver coins—NE, Willow Tree, Oak Tree, and Pine Tree— the Willow Tree pieces are far and away the rarest today. The die varieties that can be found and identified are of interest to collectors who value each according to individual rarity. Values shown for type coins are for the most frequently seen die variety.

Threepence

Sixpence

Shilling

	G	VG	F	VF	EF
1652 Willow Tree Threepence (a)	—	—	—		
Auctions: $587,500, VF, March 2015					
1652 Willow Tree Sixpence (b)	$20,000	$35,000	$70,000	$125,000	$250,000
Auctions: $253,000, Unc., November 2005					
1652 Willow Tree Shilling	$20,000	$35,000	$60,000	$120,000	$200,000
Auctions: $276,000, EF, November 2005					

a. 3 examples are known. **b.** 14 examples are known.

OAK TREE COINAGE (1660–1667)

The Oak Tree coins of Massachusetts were struck from 1660 to 1667, following the Willow Tree coinage. The 1662-dated twopence of this type was the only coin of the Willow Tree, Oak Tree, and Pine Tree series that did not bear the date 1652. Numismatists are divided on whether the twopence date of 1662 is an error, or a deliberate use of the year that the new denomination was authorized.

The obverse of these coins features a tree traditionally described by numismatists as an oak tree. Although it is deciduous, it does not closely resemble a specific species. On the reverse, NEW ENGLAND is spelled out, surrounding the date and denomination.

In 1660 the Commonwealth of England was dissolved and the British monarchy was restored under King Charles II. At the time, following longstanding tradition and law, the right to produce coins was considered to be a royal sovereign prerogative. Sylvester Crosby in *Early Coins of America* suggested that during the Massachusetts silver coinage period, numerous tributes—including ship masts, 3,000 codfish, and other material items—were sent to the king to placate him and postpone any action on the Massachusetts coinage question. As with many situations involving early American coinage, facts are scarce.

As with other types of Massachusetts silver, a number of die varieties of Oak Tree coinage can be collected and studied. In the marketplace they are seen far more often than are the two earlier types. They are valued according to their individual rarity. Values shown here are for the most frequently seen die varieties.

Twopence

Threepence

Sixpence

Shilling

	G	VG	F	VF	EF	AU	Unc.
1662 Oak Tree Twopence, Small 2	$600	$1,000	$1,500	$2,700	$5,000	$7,500	$12,000
1662 Oak Tree Twopence, Large 2	$600	$1,000	$1,500	$2,700	$5,000	$7,500	$12,000
1652 Oak Tree Threepence, No IN on Obverse	$725	$1,100	$2,600	$6,000	$11,000	$17,000	—
1652 Oak Tree Threepence, IN on Obverse	$725	$1,100	$2,800	$6,500	$13,000	$21,000	$50,000
1652 Oak Tree Sixpence, IN on Reverse	$800	$1,300	$2,800	$6,500	$13,000	$18,000	$40,000
1652 Oak Tree Sixpence, IN on Obverse	$800	$1,300	$3,200	$6,500	$12,000	$16,000	$35,000
1652 Oak Tree Shilling, IN at Left	$750	$1,250	$2,500	$6,000	$9,000	$15,000	$30,000
1652 Oak Tree Shilling, IN at Bottom	$750	$1,250	$2,500	$6,000	$9,000	$15,000	$30,000
1652 Oak Tree Shilling, ANDO	$900	$1,700	$3,500	$8,000	$13,000	$18,000	$40,000
1652 Oak Tree Shilling, Spiny Tree	$750	$1,250	$3,250	$7,000	$12,000	$20,000	$40,000

PINE TREE COINAGE (1667–1682)

The first Pine Tree coins were minted on the same-size planchets as the Oak Tree pieces, in denominations of threepence, sixpence, and shilling. Subsequent issues of the shilling were narrower in diameter and thicker. Large Planchet shillings ranged from 27 to 31 mm in diameter; Small Planchet shillings ranged from 22 to 26 mm in diameter.

The design of the Pine Tree coins borrowed from the flag of the Massachusetts Bay Colony, which featured a pine tree. On the reverse, NEW ENGLAND is spelled out, surrounding the date and a Roman numeral indicating the denomination (III, VI, or XII).

Large quantities of Pine Tree coins were minted. The coinage was abandoned in 1682. A proposal to renew coinage in 1686 was rejected by the General Court of Massachusetts.

As with other types of Massachusetts silver, a number of die varieties of Pine Tree coins are available for collecting and study. In the marketplace, they are valued according to their individual rarity. Values shown here are for the most often seen die varieties.

Threepence

Sixpence

Shilling, Large Planchet (1667–1674)   Shilling, Small Planchet (1675–1682)

	G	VG	F	VF	EF	AU	Unc.
1652 Threepence, Pellets at Trunk	$550	$800	$1,500	$3,000	$5,500	$9,000	$20,000
1652 Threepence, Without Pellets	$550	$800	$1,500	$3,000	$5,500	$9,000	$20,000
1652 Sixpence, Pellets at Trunk	$600	$925	$1,600	$3,200	$5,500	$9,000	$20,000
1652 Sixpence, Without Pellets	$600	$925	$1,600	$3,200	$5,500	$9,000	$20,000
1652 Shilling, Large Planchet (27–31 mm)							
Pellets at Trunk	$700	$1,100	$2,400	$5,000	$8,000	$13,000	$25,000
Without Pellets at Trunk	$700	$1,000	$2,300	$4,750	$8,000	$13,000	$25,000
No H in MASATUSETS	$800	$1,400	$2,700	$6,500	$12,000	$18,000	—
Ligatured NE in Legend	$700	$1,100	$2,400	$5,000	$8,000	$12,000	$25,000
1652 Shilling, Small Planchet (22–26 mm)	$600	$925	$2,200	$3,000	$5,000	$20,000	$25,000

MARYLAND

LORD BALTIMORE COINAGE

Cecil Calvert, the second Lord Baltimore, inherited from his father nearly absolute control over Maryland. Calvert believed he had the right to coin money for the colony, and in 1659 he ordered shillings, sixpences, and groats (four-penny pieces) from the Royal Mint in London and shipped samples to Maryland, to his brother Philip, who was then his secretary for the colony. Calvert's right to strike coins was upheld by Oliver Cromwell's government. The whole issue was small, and while his coins did circulate in Maryland at first, by 1700 they had largely disappeared from commerce.

Calvert's coins bear his portrait on the obverse, with a Latin legend calling him "Lord of Mary's Land." The reverses of the larger denominations bear his family coat of arms and the denomination in Roman numerals. There are several die varieties of each. Some of these coins are found holed and repaired. The copper penny, or denarium, is the rarest denomination, with only nine reported specimens, including some found in recent times by detectorists using electronic devices.

The silver groats (fourpence), sixpence, and shillings were used extensively in commerce, and today most examples show considerable wear. Typical grades include VG, Fine, and VF, often with surface marks or damage. Those graded AU or higher are major rarities. The silver pieces have an engrailed edge.

Penny (Denarium)	Fourpence (Groat)	Sixpence	Shilling

	G	VG	F	VF	EF	AU
Denarium copper (a)	—	—	$75,000	$125,000	$150,000	—
	Auctions: $241,500, AU, May 2004					
Fourpence	$4,000	$7,000	$13,000	$25,000	$35,000	$50,000
Fourpence, Small Bust			*(unique)*			—
	Auctions: $111,000, AU, January 2015					
Sixpence	$1,700	$2,500	$5,000	$7,500	$11,000	$20,000
Shilling	$2,500	$4,500	$6,500	$12,000	$17,000	$32,000

a. Extremely rare.

NEW JERSEY
ST. PATRICK OR MARK NEWBY COINAGE

Mark Newby was a shopkeeper in Dublin, Ireland, in the 1670s and came to America in November 1681, settling in West Jersey (today's New Jersey). He brought with him a quantity of copper pieces, of two sizes, believed by numismatists to have been struck in Dublin circa 1663 to 1672. These are known as *St. Patrick coppers.* (Alternatively, they may have been struck for circulation in Ireland by Pierre Blondeau to fill an order made by the duke of Ormonde, but this has not been confirmed.) The larger-sized piece, called by collectors a *halfpenny,* bears the arms of the City of Dublin on the shield on the reverse. The smaller-sized piece, called a *farthing,* does not. Although neither bears a denomination, these are designations traditionally assigned by numismatists. Both sizes have reeded edges.

Newby became a member of the legislature of West Jersey, and under his influence the St. Patrick coinage was made legal tender by the General Assembly of New Jersey in May 1682. The legislature did not specify which size piece could circulate, only that the coin was to be worth a halfpenny in trade and that no one would be obliged to accept more than five shillings' worth (120 coins) in one payment. Some numismatists believe the larger-size coin was intended. However, many more farthing-size pieces are known than halfpennies, and numerous coins of the farthing size have been excavated by detectorists in New Jersey, while none of the larger coins have been found this way. Most numismatists believe that the smaller-sized piece was the one authorized as legal tender. Copper coins often circulated in the colonies at twice what they would have been worth in England.

The obverses show King David crowned, kneeling and playing a harp. The legend FLOREAT REX ("May the King Prosper") is separated by a crown. The reverse side of the halfpence shows St. Patrick with a crozier in his left hand and a trefoil in his right, and surrounded by people. At his left side is a shield. The legend is ECCE GREX ("Behold the Flock"). The farthing reverse shows St. Patrick driving away serpents and a dragon as he holds a metropolitan cross in his left hand. The legend reads QUIESCAT PLEBS ("May the People Be at Ease").

The decorative brass insert found on the coinage, usually over the crown on the obverse, was put there to make counterfeiting more difficult. On some pieces this decoration has been removed or does not show. Numerous die variations exist (more than 140 of the smaller coins, and 9 of the larger). The silver strikings, and a unique gold piece, were not authorized as legal tender, although many of the silver coins are heavily worn, suggesting that they were passed many times from hand to hand in commerce, perhaps at the value of a shilling.

St. Patrick "Farthing"   St. Patrick "Halfpenny"

	G	VG	F	VF	EF	AU
St. Patrick "Farthing"	$200	$400	$600	$2,000	$4,000	$15,000
Similar, Halo Around Saint's Head	$1,000	$2,500	$7,000	$18,000	$45,000	—
Similar, No C in QUIESCAT	$1,000	$5,000	$10,000	$20,000	—	—
St. Patrick "Farthing," Silver	$1,800	$3,000	$7,500	$15,000	$22,000	$36,000
St. Patrick "Farthing," Gold (a)						—
	Auctions: $184,000, AU, January 2005					
St. Patrick "Halfpenny"	$350	$600	$800	$2,200	$9,500	$20,000

a. Unique.

COINAGE AUTHORIZED BY BRITISH ROYAL PATENT

AMERICAN PLANTATIONS COINS (1688)

These tokens, struck in nearly pure tin, were the first royally authorized coinage for the British colonies in America. They were made under a franchise granted in August 1688 to Richard Holt, an agent for the owners of several tin mines. Holt proposed that the new issues be made with a Spanish monetary designation to increase their acceptance in the channels of American commerce, where Spanish-American coins were often seen. Thus the tokens are denominated as 1/24 part of a Spanish real.

The obverse shows an equestrian portrait of King James II in armor and flowing garments. The reverse features four heraldic shields (English, Scottish, French, and Irish) connected by chains. The edge is decorated with dots.

Numismatist Eric P. Newman has identified seven different obverse dies and an equal number of reverse dies. Most American Plantation tokens show black oxidation of the tin. Bright, unblemished original specimens are more valuable. (Around 1828 a London coin dealer acquired the original dies and arranged for restrikes to be made for sale. In high grades these pieces are seen more frequently in the marketplace than are originals. They are valuable but worth less than original strikes.)

	G	VG	F	VF	EF	AU	Unc.
(1688) James II Plantation 1/24 Real coinage							
1/24 Part Real	$225	$400	$900	$1,800	$2,700	$7,500	$10,000
1/24 Part Real, ET. HB. REX	$275	$400	$900	$2,000	$3,000	$8,000	$10,000
1/24 Part Real, Sidewise 4 in 24	$425	$1,000	$2,000	$5,000	$7,500	$10,000	$20,000
1/24 Part Real, Arms Transposed	$675	$1,750	$2,900	$7,000	$13,000	$19,000	—
1/24 Part Real, Restrike	$100	$150	$250	$450	$700	$900	$2,000

COINAGE OF WILLIAM WOOD (1722–1733)

William Wood, an English metallurgist, experimented with the production of several pattern coins (of halfpenny, penny, and twopence size) in 1717. In 1722 he was granted royal patents to mint coins for America and Ireland. At the time his productions were largely unpopular as money, but later generations of coin collectors have sought his Rosa Americana coins for their connections to colonial America. The Hibernia coins are similar in some respects; they have no connection with America but are sought as companion pieces.

ROSA AMERICANA COINS (1722–1723, 1733)

On July 12, 1722, William Wood obtained a patent from King George I to make coins for the American colonies. At the time the colonies were facing a serious shortage of circulating coins.

The first pieces Wood struck were undated. Later issues bear the dates 1722, 1723, 1724, and 1733. The Rosa Americana pieces were issued in three denominations—half penny, penny, and twopence—and were intended for America. This type had a fully bloomed rose on the reverse with the words ROSA AMERICANA UTILE DULCI ("American Rose—Useful and Sweet").

The obverse, common to both Rosa Americana and Hibernia pieces, shows the head of George I and the legend GEORGIUS D:G MAG: BRI: FRA: ET. HIB: REX ("George, by the Grace of God, King of Great Britain, France, and Ireland") or abbreviations thereof.

Despite Wood's best efforts, these Rosa Americana coins circulated in the colonies only to a limited extent. They eventually did see use as money, but it was back in England, and likely at values lower than their assigned denominations. (Each was about half the weight of its English counterpart coin.)

The 1733 twopence is a pattern that bears the bust of King George II facing to the left. It was issued by the successors to the original coinage patent, as William Wood had died in 1730.

The coins are made of a brass composition of copper and zinc (sometimes mistakenly referred to as *Bath metal*, an alloy proposed by Wood that would have also included a minute portion of silver). Planchet quality is often rough and porous because the blanks were heated prior to striking. Edges often show file marks.

	VG	F	VF	EF	AU	Unc.
(No date) Twopence, Motto in Ribbon *(illustrated)*	$200	$400	$700	$1,000	$2,500	$5,300
(No date) Twopence, Motto Without Ribbon (a)		—	—	—		

a. 3 examples are known.

	VG	F	VF	EF	AU	Unc.
1722 Halfpenny, VTILE DVLCI	$900	$2,000	$3,500	$6,250	$10,000	
1722 Halfpenny, D.G.REX ROSA AMERI. UTILE DULCI	$150	$200	$400	$750	$1,200	$3,200
1722 Halfpenny, DEI GRATIA REX UTILE DULCI	$150	$200	$400	$700	$1,100	$2,700

	VG	F	VF	EF	AU	Unc.
1722 Penny, GEORGIVS			$12,000	$17,500	$22,500	$30,000
1722 Penny, VTILE DVLCI	$170	$300	$700	$1,100	$2,500	$6,000
1722 Penny, UTILE DULCI	$150	$200	$300	$600	$1,200	$2,500

	VG	F	VF	EF	AU	Unc.
1722 Twopence, Period After REX	$175	$300	$600	$1,100	$1,800	$3,500
1722 Twopence, No Period After REX	$175	$300	$600	$1,100	$1,800	$3,500

	VG	F	VF	EF	AU	Unc.
1723 Halfpenny, Uncrowned Rose	$1,000	$1,800	$3,600	$5,500	$8,500	$12,500
1723 Halfpenny, Crowned Rose	$125	$200	$375	$600	$1,250	$2,700

	VG	F	VF	EF	AU	Unc.
1723 Penny *(illustrated)*	$100	$125	$275	$500	$800	$2,000
1723 Twopence	$150	$250	$350	$700	$1,200	$2,400

	EF	AU	Unc.
1724, 4 Over 3 Penny (pattern), DEI GRATIA		$20,000	$27,500
1724, 4 Over 3 Penny (pattern), D GRATIA	$8,750	$20,000	$31,000
(Undated) (1724) Penny, ROSA: SINE: SPINA. (a)	$18,000	$25,000	$31,200

a. 5 examples are known.

1724 Twopence (pattern)
Auctions: $25,300, Choice AU, May 2005

1733 Twopence (pattern), Proof

	Auctions: $63,250, Gem PF, May 2005

WOOD'S HIBERNIA COINAGE (1722–1724)

Around the same time that his royal patent was granted to strike the Rosa Americana coins for the American colonies, William Wood received a franchise to produce copper coins for circulation in Ireland. This was ratified on July 22, 1722. The resulting coins, likely struck in Bristol, England, featured a portrait of King George and, on the reverse, a seated figure with a harp and the word HIBERNIA. Their edges are plain. Denominations struck were farthing and halfpenny, with dates of 1722, 1723, and 1724. These Hibernia coins were unpopular in Ireland and faced vocal public criticism, including from satirist Jonathan Swift. "It was asserted that the issues for Ireland were produced without Irish advice or consent, that the arrangements were made in secret and for the private profit of Wood, and that the pieces were seriously underweight" (*Whitman Encyclopedia of Colonial and Early American Coins*). As a result, King George reduced the number of coins allowed by Wood's patent, and the franchise was retired completely in 1725 in exchange for Wood receiving a £24,000 pension over eight years. Some of the unpopular Hibernia coins, meanwhile, may have been sent to the American colonies to circulate as small change. Their popularity with American numismatists stems from the similarity of their obverses to those in the Rosa Americana series.

Numerous varieties exist.

1722, Hibernia Farthing	1722, Hibernia Halfpenny, First Type	1722, Hibernia Halfpenny, Second Type	1723, 3 Over 2, Halfpenny

1724, Hibernia Farthing   1724, Hibernia Halfpenny

	G	VG	F	VF	EF	AU	Unc.
1722 Farthing, D: G: REX	$500	$1,000	$2,000	$3,000	$4,000	$8,500	$16,000
1722 Halfpenny, D: G: REX, Rocks at Right (pattern)	—	—	$5,000	$8,000	$12,000	$20,000	$40,000
1722 Halfpenny, First Type, Harp at Left	$50	$80	$125	$250	$450	$700	$1,400
1722 Halfpenny, Second Type, Harp at Right	$45	$70	$100	$200	$400	$700	$1,200
1722 Halfpenny, Second Type, DEII (blunder)	$80	$150	$375	$800	$1,400	$1,800	$3,000
1723 Farthing, D.G.REX	$125	$300	$400	$700	$1,800	$2,000	$3,000
1723 Farthing, DEI. GRATIA. REX	$25	$50	$80	$125	$225	$400	$600
1723 Farthing (silver pattern)	$400	$600	$1,200	$2,500	$4,000	$5,000	$9,000
1723 Halfpenny, 3 Over 2 (a)	$40	$60	$125	$350	$500	$900	$1,750
1723 Halfpenny	$25	$45	$75	$125	$250	$375	$700
1723 Halfpenny (silver pattern)			—	—	—	—	—
1724 Farthing	$50	$125	$200	$600	$1,250	$1,450	$3,600
1724 Halfpenny	$45	$100	$150	$350	$600	$900	$2,000
1724 Halfpenny, DEI Above Head					—	—	

a. Varieties exist.

VIRGINIA HALFPENNIES (1773–1774)

In 1773 the British Crown authorized coinage of copper halfpennies for the colony of Virginia, not to exceed 25 tons' weight. "This was the first and only colonial coinage authorized and produced in Britain for use in an American colony, thereby giving the Virginia pieces the unique claim of being the only true American colonial coinage" (*Whitman Encyclopedia of Colonial and Early American Coins*). The designs included a laurelled portrait of King George III and the royal coat of arms of the House of Hanover. The coins were struck at the Tower Mint in London. Their edges are plain.

Most Mint State pieces available to collectors today are from a hoard of some 5,000 or more of the halfpennies held by Colonel Mendes I. Cohen of Baltimore, Maryland, in the 1800s. Cohen came from a prominent banking family. His cache was dispersed slowly and carefully from 1875 until 1929, as the coins passed from his estate to his nieces and nephews. Eventually the remaining coins, numbering approximately 2,200, the property of Bertha Cohen, were dispersed in one lot in Baltimore. These pieces gradually filtered out, in groups and individually, into the wider numismatic marketplace.

The Proof patterns that were struck on a large planchet with a wide milled border are often referred to as pennies. The silver pieces dated 1774 are referred to as shillings, but they may have been patterns or trials for a halfpenny or a guinea.

Red Uncirculated pieces without spots are worth considerably more.

	G	VG	F	VF	EF	AU	Unc.
1773 Halfpenny, Period After GEORGIVS	$25	$50	$100	$150	$350	$500	$1,100
1773 Halfpenny, No Period After GEORGIVS	$35	$75	$140	$200	$400	$500	$1,100

1773, "Penny" 1774, "Shilling"

	PF
1773 "Penny"	$27,000
1774 "Shilling" (a)	*$110,000*

a. 6 examples are known.

EARLY AMERICAN AND RELATED TOKENS

ELEPHANT TOKENS (CA. 1672–1694)

LONDON ELEPHANT TOKENS

The London Elephant tokens were struck in London circa 1672 to 1694. Although they were undated, two examples are known to have been struck over 1672 British halfpennies. Most were struck in copper, but one was made of brass. Their legend, GOD PRESERVE LONDON, may have been a general plea for divine aid and not a specific reference to the outbreak of plague in 1665 or the great fire of 1666.

These pieces were not struck for the colonies, and they probably did not circulate widely in America, although a few may have been carried there by colonists. They are associated, through a shared obverse die, with the 1694 Carolina and New England Elephant tokens. They have a plain edge but often show the cutting marks from planchet preparation.

	VG	F	VF	EF	AU	Unc.
(1694) Halfpenny, GOD PRESERVE LONDON, Thick Planchet ‡	$350	$600	$900	$1,300	$2,000	$3,200
(1694) Halfpenny, GOD PRESERVE LONDON, Thin Planchet ‡	$550	$1,000	$1,800	$2,500	$4,000	$12,000
Similar, Brass ‡ (a)					—	
(1694) Halfpenny, GOD PRESERVE LONDON, Diagonals in Center of Shield ‡	$700	$1,800	$4,000	$7,500	$15,000	$30,000
(1694) Halfpenny, Similar, Sword in Second Quarter of Shield ‡	—	—	$20,000	—	—	—
(1694) Halfpenny, LON DON ‡	$1,000	$2,000	$3,500	$7,500	$15,000	$24,000

‡ All Elephant Tokens are ranked in the *100 Greatest American Medals and Tokens,* as a single entry. **a.** Unique.

CAROLINA ELEPHANT TOKENS

Although no law is known authorizing coinage for Carolina, two very interesting pieces known as Elephant tokens were made with the date 1694. These copper tokens are of halfpenny denomination. The reverse reads GOD PRESERVE CAROLINA AND THE LORDS PROPRIETERS 1694.

The second and more readily available variety has the last word spelled PROPRIETORS. The correction was made on the original die, for the E shows plainly beneath the O. On the second variety the elephant's tusks nearly touch the milling.

The Carolina pieces were probably struck in England and perhaps intended as advertising to heighten interest in the Carolina Plantation. Another theory suggests they may have been related to or made for the Carolina coffee house in London.

	VG	F	VF	EF	AU	Unc.
1694 PROPRIETERS ‡	$10,000	$30,000	$50,000	$60,000	$80,000	$125,000
1694 PROPRIETORS, O Over E ‡	$6,500	$11,000	$20,000	$40,000	$65,000	$100,000

‡ All Elephant Tokens are ranked in the *100 Greatest American Medals and Tokens*, as a single entry.

NEW ENGLAND ELEPHANT TOKENS

Like the Carolina tokens, the New England Elephant tokens are believed to have been struck in England, possibly as promotional pieces to increase interest in the American colonies, or perhaps related to the New England coffee house in London

	VG	F	VF	EF	AU
1694 NEW ENGLAND ‡	$140,000	$160,000	$180,000	$220,000	—

‡ All Elephant Tokens are ranked in the *100 Greatest American Medals and Tokens*, as a single entry.

NEW YORKE IN AMERICA TOKENS (1660S OR 1670S)

The New Yorke in America tokens are farthing or halfpenny tokens intended for New York, issued by Francis Lovelace, who was governor from 1668 until 1673. The tokens use the older spelling with a final "e" (YORKE), which predominated before 1710. The obverse shows Cupid pursuing the loveless butterfly-winged Psyche—a rebus on the name Lovelace. The reverse shows a heraldic eagle, identical to the one displayed in fesse, raguly (i.e., on a crenellated bar) on the Lovelace coat of arms. In weight, fabric, and die axis the tokens are similar to certain 1670 farthing tokens of Bristol, England, where they may have been struck. There is no evidence that any of these pieces ever circulated in America. Fewer than two dozen are believed to now exist.

	VG	F	VF	EF
(Undated) Brass or Copper ‡	$10,000	$18,000	$30,000	$60,000
(Undated) Pewter ‡	$10,000	$23,000	$33,000	$72,500

‡ All New Yorke in America Tokens are ranked in the *100 Greatest American Medals and Tokens*, as a single entry.

GLOUCESTER TOKENS (1714)

Sylvester S. Crosby, in his book *The Early Coins of America*, stated that these tokens appear to have been intended as a pattern for a shilling—a private coinage by Richard Dawson of Gloucester (county), Virginia. The only specimens known are struck in brass, although the denomination XII indicates that a silver coinage (one shilling) may have been planned. The building depicted on the obverse may represent some public building, possibly the courthouse.

Although neither of the two known examples shows the full legends, combining the pieces shows GLOVCESTER COVRTHOVSE VIRGINIA / RIGHAVLT DAWSON. ANNO.DOM. 1714. This recent discovery has provided a new interpretation of the legends, as a Righault family once owned land near the Gloucester courthouse. A similar, but somewhat smaller, piece possibly dated 1715 exists. The condition of this unique piece is too poor for positive attribution.

	F
1714 Shilling, brass ‡ (a)	$120,000

‡ Ranked in the *100 Greatest American Medals and Tokens*. **a.** 2 examples are known.

HIGLEY OR GRANBY COPPERS (1737–1739)

Dr. Samuel Higley owned a private copper mine near Granby, Connecticut, in an area known for many such operations. Higley was a medical doctor, with a degree from Yale College, who also practiced blacksmithing and experimented in metallurgy. He worked his mine as a private individual, extracting particularly rich copper, smelting it, and shipping much of it to England. He also made his own dies for plain-edged pure-copper "coins" that he issued.

Legend has it that a drink in the local tavern cost three pence, and that Higley paid his bar tabs with his own privately minted coins, denominated as they were with the legend THE VALUE OF THREEPENCE. When his supply of such coppers exceeded the local demand, neighbors complained that they were not worth the denomination stated, and Higley changed the legends to read VALUE ME AS YOU PLEASE and I AM GOOD COPPER (but kept the Roman numeral III on the obverse).

After Samuel Higley's death in May 1737 his older brother John continued his coinage.

The Higley coppers were never officially authorized. There were seven obverse and four reverse dies. All are rare. Electrotypes and cast copies exist.

	AG	G	VG	F	VF
1737 THE VALVE OF THREE PENCE, CONNECTICVT, 3 Hammers ‡	$12,000	$18,000	$30,000	$50,000	$100,000
1737 THE VALVE OF THREE PENCE, I AM GOOD COPPER, 3 Hammers ‡ (a)	—	$35,000	$50,000	$80,000	$175,000
1737 VALUE ME AS YOU PLEASE, I AM GOOD COPPER, 3 Hammers ‡	$12,000	$18,000	$30,000	$50,000	$100,000
1737 VALVE • ME • AS • YOU • PLEASE, I • AM • GOOD • COPPER, 3 Hammers ‡ (a)			$75,000		
(1737) VALUE • ME • AS • YOU • PLEASE, J • CUT • MY • WAY • THROUGH, Broad Axe ‡	$12,000	$18,000	$30,000	$50,000	$100,000
(1737) THE • WHEELE • GOES • ROUND, Reverse as Above (b) ‡					$376,000
1739 VALUE • ME • AS • YOU • PLEASE, J • CUT • MY • WAY • THROUGH, Broad Axe ‡	$15,000	$20,000	$37,500	$60,000	$125,000

‡ All Higley Coppers are ranked in the *100 Greatest American Medals and Tokens*, as a single entry. **a.** This issue has the CONNECTICVT reverse. 3 examples are known. **b.** Unique.

HIBERNIA–VOCE POPULI COINS

These coins, struck in the year 1760, were prepared by Roche, of King Street, Dublin, who was at that time engaged in the manufacture of buttons for the army. Like other Irish tokens, some could have found their way to colonial America and possibly circulated in the colonies with numerous other counterfeit halfpence and "bungtown tokens." There is no evidence to prove that Voce Populi pieces, which bear the legend HIBERNIA (Ireland) on the reverse, ever circulated in North America. Sylvester S. Crosby did not include them in *The Early Coins of America*, 1875. Nor were they covered in Wayte Raymond's *Standard Catalogue of United States Coins* (until Walter Breen revised the section on colonial coins in 1954, after which they were "adopted" by mainstream collectors). Various theories exist regarding the identity of the bust portrait on the obverse, ranging from kings and pretenders to the British throne, to the provost of Dublin College.

There are two distinct issues. Coins from the first, with a "short bust" on the obverse, ranged in weight from 87 to 120 grains. Those from the second, with a "long bust" on the obverse, ranged in weight from 129 to 154 grains. Most of the "long bust" varieties have the letter P on the obverse. None of the "short bust" varieties bear the letter P, and, judging from their weight, they may have been contemporary counterfeits.

Farthing, Large Letters

Halfpenny

Halfpenny, VOOE POPULI

Halfpenny, P in Front of Face

	G	VG	F	VF	EF	AU	Unc.
1760 Farthing, Large Letters	$200	$300	$500	$1,250	$2,000	$3,000	$5,500
1760 Farthing, Small Letters			$8,000	$10,000	$15,000	$20,000	$25,000
1760 Halfpenny	$80	$110	$180	$300	$500	$700	$1,250
1760 Halfpenny, VOOE POPULI	$90	$150	$200	$400	$550	$1,000	$3,000
1760 Halfpenny, P Below Bust	$110	$200	$300	$600	$900	$1,600	$4,500
1760 Halfpenny, P in Front of Face	$90	$175	$250	$500	$800	$1,400	$4,000

Pitt Tokens (ca. 1769)

William Pitt the Elder, the British statesman who endeared himself to America, is the subject of these brass or copper pieces, probably intended as commemorative medalets. The so-called halfpenny (the larger of the type's two sizes) served as currency during a shortage of regular coinage. The farthing-size tokens are rare.

The reverse legend (THANKS TO THE FRIENDS OF LIBERTY AND TRADE) refers to Pitt's criticism of the Crown's taxation of the American colonies, and his efforts to have the Stamp Act of March 22, 1765, repealed in 1766. The obverse bears a portrait and the legends THE RESTORER OF COMMERCE and NO STAMPS.

"Little is known concerning the circumstances of issue. Robert Vlack suggests that the pieces may have been designed by Paul Revere. Striking may have been accomplished around 1769 by James Smither (or Smithers) of Philadelphia" (*Whitman Encyclopedia of Colonial and Early American Coins*).

Farthing   Halfpenny

	G	VG	F	VF	EF	AU	Unc.
1766 Farthing ‡	$2,500	$5,000	$10,000	$22,000	$30,000	$50,000	
1766 Halfpenny ‡	$300	$450	$650	$1,100	$1,700	$2,700	$9,000
1766 Halfpenny, silvered ‡				$1,600	$3,500	$5,000	$12,000

‡ All Pitt Tokens are ranked in the *100 Greatest American Medals and Tokens*, as a single entry.

Rhode Island Ship Medals (ca. 1779)

The circumstances of the issue of these medals (or tokens) are mysterious. They were largely unknown to American coin collectors until 1864, when a specimen was offered in W. Elliot Woodward's sale of the Seavey Collection. It sold for $40—a remarkable price at the time.

The obverse shows the flagship of British admiral Lord Richard Howe at anchor, while the reverse depicts the American retreat from Rhode Island in 1778. The inscriptions show that the coin was meant for a Dutch-speaking audience. The word *vlugtende* ("fleeing") appears on the earlier issues below Howe's flagship—an engraving error. After a limited number of pieces were struck with this word, it was removed on all but two surviving examples by adding a wreath over the word on the dies or physically obliterating the word by grinding it off. It is believed the medal was struck in Holland as a jetton, but some think it was struck in England as a propaganda piece. Specimens are known in brass, pewter, and with a silvered (actually tin) wash.

Rhode Island Ship Medal (1778–1779)   Legend "vlugtende"   Wreath Below Ship
                                             Below Ship

	VF	EF	AU	Unc.
With "vlugtende" (fleeing) Below Ship, Brass ‡		$90,000		
Wreath Below Ship, Brass ‡	$1,000	$1,750	$2,700	$5,000
Without Wreath Below Ship, Brass ‡	$900	$1,700	$2,700	$5,000
Similar, Pewter ‡	$3,500	$5,500	$8,000	$15,000

‡ All Rhode Island Ship Tokens are ranked in the *100 Greatest American Medals and Tokens*, as a single entry.

JOHN CHALMERS ISSUES (1783)

John Chalmers, a Maryland goldsmith and silversmith, struck a series of silver tokens of his own design in Annapolis in 1783. The dies were by Thomas Sparrow, another silversmith in the town. The shortage of change in circulation and the refusal of the American people to use underweight cut Spanish coins prompted the issuance of these pieces. (Fraudsters would attempt to cut five "quarters" or nine or ten "eighths" out of one Spanish silver dollar, thereby realizing a proportional profit when they were all spent.)

On the Chalmers threepence and shilling obverses, two clasped hands are shown, perhaps symbolizing unity of the several states; the reverse of the threepence has a branch encircled by a wreath. A star within a wreath is on the obverse of the sixpence, with hands clasped upon a cross utilized as the reverse type. On this denomination, the designer's initials TS (for Thomas Sparrow) can be found in the crescents that terminate the horizontal arms of the cross. The reverse of the more common shilling varieties displays two doves competing for a worm underneath a hedge and a snake. The symbolic message is thought to have been against the danger of squabbling with brethren over low-value stakes while a dangerous mutual enemy lurked nearby. The edges of these tokens are crudely reeded. There are only a few known examples of the shilling type with 13 interlinked rings, from which a liberty cap on a pole arises.

Threepence	Sixpence, Small Date	Sixpence, Large Date

Shilling, Birds, Short Worm	Shilling, Rings

	VG	F	VF	EF	AU
1783 Threepence	$2,000	$4,000	$8,000	$18,000	$32,500
1783 Sixpence, Small Date	$3,500	$7,500	$19,000	$32,000	$65,000
1783 Sixpence, Large Date	$2,600	$6,000	$15,000	$30,000	$60,000
1783 Shilling, Birds, Long Worm	$1,100	$2,000	$5,000	$9,000	$18,000
1783 Shilling, Birds, Short Worm *(illustrated)*	$1,100	$2,000	$5,000	$8,000	$16,000
1783 Shilling, Rings (a)	*$50,000*	*$100,000*	*$200,000*	—	—

a. 5 examples are known.

FRENCH NEW WORLD ISSUES

None of the coins of the French regime relate specifically to territories that later became part of the United States. They were all general issues for the French colonies of the New World. The coinage of 1670 was authorized by an edict of King Louis XIV dated February 19, 1670, for use in New France,

Acadia, the French settlements in Newfoundland, and the French West Indies. The copper coinage of 1717 to 1722 was authorized by edicts of 1716 and 1721 for use in New France, Louisiana, and the French West Indies.

COINAGE OF 1670

The coinage of 1670 consisted of silver 5 and 15 sols and copper 2 deniers (or "doubles"). A total of 200,000 of the 5 sols and 40,000 of the 15 sols was struck at Paris. Nantes was to have coined the copper, but did not; the reasons for this may never be known, since the archives of the Nantes Mint before 1700 were destroyed. The only known specimen is a pattern struck at Paris. The silver coins were raised in value by a third in 1672 to keep them circulating, but in vain. They rapidly disappeared, and by 1680 none were to be seen. Later they were restored to their original values. This rare issue should not be confused with the common 1670-A 1/12 écu with reverse legend SIT. NOMEN. DOMINI. BENEDICTUM.

The 1670-A double de l'Amerique Françoise was struck at the Paris Mint along with the 5- and 15-sols denominations of the same date. All three were intended to circulate in France's North American colonies. Probably due to an engraving error, very few 1670-A doubles were actually struck. Today, only one is known to survive.

Copper Double   **Silver 5 Sols**

	VG	F	VF	EF	Unc.
1670-A Copper Double (a)			$225,000		
1670-A 5 Sols	$1,000	$2,000	$3,000	$4,000	$10,000
1670-A 15 Sols	$13,000	$32,000	$75,000	$125,000	—

a. Unique.

COINAGE OF 1717–1720

The copper 6 and 12 deniers of 1717 were authorized by an edict of King Louis XV (by order of the six-year-old king's regent, the duke of Orléans) dated December 1716, to be struck at Perpignan (mintmark Q). The order could not be carried out, for the supply of copper was too brassy, and only a few pieces were coined. The issues of 1720, which were struck at multiple mints, are popularly collected for their association with the John Law "Mississippi Bubble" venture.

1720 6 Deniers

1717-Q 12 Deniers

1720 20 Sols

	F	VF	EF
1717-Q 6 Deniers, No Crowned Arms on Reverse (a)			—
1717-Q 12 Deniers, No Crowned Arms on Reverse			—
1720 Liard, Crowned Arms on Reverse, Copper	$350	$500	$900
1720 6 Deniers, Crowned Arms on Reverse, Copper	$550	$900	$1,750
1720 12 Deniers, Crowned Arms on Reverse, Copper	$400	$750	$1,500
1720 20 Sols, Silver	$375	$700	$1,500

a. Extremely rare.

BILLON COINAGE OF 1709–1760

The French colonial coins of 30 deniers were called *mousquetaires* because of the outlined cross on their reverse, evocative of the design on the short coats worn by French musketeers. These coins were produced at Metz and Lyon. The 15 deniers was coined only at Metz. The sou marque and the half sou were coined at almost every French mint, those of Paris being most common. The half sou of 1740 is the only commonly available date. Specimens of the sou marque dated after 1760 were not used in North America. A unique specimen of the 1712-AA 30 deniers is known in the size and weight of the 15-denier coins.

30 Deniers "Mousquetaire"

Sou Marque (24 Deniers)

	VG	F	VF	EF	AU	Unc.
1711–1713-AA 15 Deniers	$150	$300	$500	$1,000	$1,750	$4,000
1709–1713-AA 30 Deniers	$75	$100	$250	$400	$675	$1,500
1709–1713-D 30 Deniers	$75	$100	$250	$400	$675	$1,500
1738–1748 Half Sou Marque, various mints	$60	$100	$200	$350	$575	$1,200
1738–1760 Sou Marque, various mints	$50	$80	$125	$175	$300	$500

COINAGE OF 1721–1722

The copper coinage of 1721 and 1722 was authorized by an edict of King Louis XV dated June 1721. The coins were struck on copper blanks imported from Sweden. Rouen and La Rochelle struck pieces of nine deniers (one sou) in 1721 and 1722. New France received 534,000 pieces, mostly from the mint of La Rochelle, but only 8,180 were put into circulation, as the colonists disliked copper. In 1726 the rest of the issue was sent back to France.

In American coin catalogs of the 1800s, these coins were often called "Louisiana coppers."

	VG	F	VF	EF
1721-B (Rouen)	$500	$1,000	$3,500	$10,000
1721-H (La Rochelle)	$100	$175	$1,000	$2,500
1722-H	$100	$175	$1,000	$2,500
1722-H, 2 Over 1	$175	$275	$1,200	$4,000

FRENCH COLONIES IN GENERAL (1767)

These copper coins were produced for use in the French colonies and only unofficially circulated in Louisiana along with other foreign coins and tokens. Most were counterstamped RF (République Française) for use in the West Indies. The mintmark A signifies the Paris Mint. The edge is decorated with a double row of dots.

	VG	VF	EF	AU
1767 French Colonies, Sou	$120	$250	$600	$1,400
1767 French Colonies, Sou, counterstamped RF	$100	$200	$250	$600

Post-Colonial Issues

The coins explored in this section are classified as "post-colonial" because they came after the colonial period (some during the early months of rebellion; most after the official declaration of independence) but before the first federal Mint was established in Philadelphia in 1792.

Early American coins were produced from hand-engraved dies, which are often individually distinctive. For many types, the great number of die varieties that can be found and identified are of interest to collectors who value each according to its individual rarity. Values shown for type coins in this section are for the most common die variety of each.

SPECULATIVE ISSUES, TOKENS, AND PATTERNS

NOVA CONSTELLATIO COPPERS (1783–1786)

The Nova Constellatio coppers, dated 1783 and 1785 and without denomination, were struck in fairly large quantities in Birmingham, England, and were shipped to New York where they entered circulation. Apparently they resulted from a private coinage venture undertaken by Constable, Rucker & Co., a trading business formed by William Constable, John Rucker, Robert Morris, and Gouverneur Morris as equal partners. The designs and legends were copied from the denominated patterns dated 1783 made in Philadelphia (see page 181). A few additional coppers dated 1786 were made by an inferior diesinker.

"The Nova Constellatio coppers were well received and saw extensive use in commerce, as evidenced by the wear seen on typically specimens today," writes Q. David Bowers in the *Whitman Encyclopedia of Colonial and Early American Coins*. "Later, they were devalued, and many were used as undertypes (planchets) for Connecticut and, to a lesser extent, New Jersey and Vermont coppers."

1783, CONSTELLATIO,
Pointed Rays, Small U.S.

1783, CONSTELLATIO
Pointed Rays, Large U.S.

	VG	F	VF	EF	AU	Unc.
1783, CONSTELLATIO, Pointed Rays, Small U.S.	$100	$200	$375	$750	$1,300	$3,000
1783, CONSTELLATIO, Pointed Rays, Large U.S.	$100	$500	$750	$2,000	$4,500	$10,000

1783, CONSTELATIO, Blunt Rays

1785, CONSTELATIO, Blunt Rays   **1785, CONSTELLATIO, Pointed Rays**

	VG	F	VF	EF	AU	Unc.
1783, CONSTELATIO, Blunt Rays	$100	$225	$550	$1,000	$2,500	$7,000
1785, CONSTELATIO, Blunt Rays	$100	$225	$550	$1,000	$2,500	$6,000
1785, CONSTELLATIO, Pointed Rays	$100	$200	$375	$750	$1,300	$3,000
1785, Similar, Small, Close Date	$300	$500	$1,800	$3,500	$5,500	$15,000
1786, Similar, Small Date	$2,500	$5,000	$7,500	$15,000		

IMMUNE COLUMBIA PIECES (1785)

These pieces are considered private or unofficial coins. No laws describing them are known. There are several types bearing the seated figure of Justice. These pieces are stylistically related to the Nova Constellatio coppers, with the Immune Columbia motif with liberty cap and scale replacing the LIBERTAS and JUSTITIA design.

1785, Silver, 13 Stars   **1785, Pointed Rays, CONSTELLATIO**

	F	VF	EF
1785, Copper, 13 Stars	$15,000	$27,000	$45,000
1785, Silver, 13 Stars	$25,000	$50,000	$75,000
1785, Pointed Rays, CONSTELLATIO, Extra Star in Reverse Legend, Copper	$15,000	$27,000	$45,000
1785, Pointed Rays, CONSTELLATIO, Gold (a)			—
1785, Blunt Rays, CONSTELLATIO, Copper (b)		$50,000	—

Note: The gold specimen in the National Numismatic Collection (now maintained by the Smithsonian) was acquired in 1843 from collector Matthew A. Stickney in exchange for an 1804 dollar. **a.** Unique. **b.** 2 examples are known.

1785, George III Obverse

	G	VG	F	VF
1785, George III Obverse	$5,500	$8,500	$11,000	$18,000
1785, VERMON AUCTORI Obverse, IMMUNE COLUMBIA	$6,000	$10,000	$15,000	$30,000

1787, IMMUNIS COLUMBIA, Eagle Reverse

	VG	F	VF	EF	AU	Unc.
1787, IMMUNIS COLUMBIA, Eagle Reverse	$600	$1,000	$3,000	$4,500	$8,000	$17,500

Note: Believed to be a prototype for federal coinage; some were coined after 1787.

CONFEDERATIO AND RELATED TOKENS

The Confederatio and associated pieces are believed to be proposed designs for America's early federal coinage. The 1785, Inimica Tyrannis America, variety may owe its design to a sketch by Thomas Jefferson. In all, 12 dies were presumed struck in 13 combinations. No one knows for certain who made these pieces. The combination with a standard reverse die for a 1786 New Jersey copper is especially puzzling. They were all made in small quantities and were circulated. Research is ongoing.

America   Americana   Washington

Immunis   Eagle   Libertas et Justitia

Large Circle   Small Circle   Pattern Shield

The 1786, Immunis Columbia, with scrawny-eagle reverse is a related piece probably made by a different engraver or mint.

	VG	F	VF	EF	AU
1785 Inimica Tyrannis America, Large Circle (a,b)	$40,000	$70,000	$100,000	$150,000	$225,000
1785 Inimica Tyrannis Americana, Small Circle (c,d)	$30,000	$40,000	$50,000	$125,000	$200,000
1785 Inimica Tyrannis Americana, Large Circle, Silver (b,e)		50,000 (f)			
1785 Gen. Washington, Large Circle (g,h)	$50,000	$75,000	$125,000	$250,000	
1786 Gen. Washington, Eagle (i,j)		$40,000			
(No Date) Gen. Washington, Pattern Shield (k,l)		$75,000	$100,000		$300,000
1786 Immunis, Pattern Shield (m,n)		$25,000	$50,000	$100,000	$125,000
1786 Immunis, 1785 Large Circle (o,j)					$100,000
1786 Eagle, Pattern Shield (p,e)					$200,000
1786 Eagle, 1785 Large Circle (q,j)		$50,000	$85,000		
1785 Libertas et Justitia, 1785 Large Circle (r,e)	$25,000				
1785 Small Circle, 1787 Excelsior Eagle (s,j)		$35,000			
1786 Immunis Columbia, Scrawny Eagle (l)			$50,000	$90,000	

a. America obverse, Large Circle reverse. **b.** 7 examples are known. **c.** Americana obverse, Small Circle reverse. **d.** 9 examples are known. **e.** 1 example is known. **f.** Damaged. **g.** Washington obverse, Large Circle reverse. **h.** 6 examples are known. **i.** Washington obverse, Eagle reverse. **j.** 2 examples are known. **k.** Washington obverse, Pattern Shield reverse. **l.** 3 examples are known. **m.** Immunis obverse, Pattern Shield reverse. **n.** 17 examples are known. **o.** Immunis obverse, Large Circle reverse. **p.** Eagle obverse, Pattern Shield reverse. **q.** Eagle obverse, Large Circle reverse. **r.** Libertas et Justitia obverse, Large Circle reverse. **s.** Small Circle obverse, 1787 Excelsior Eagle reverse. Image of the 1787 Excelsior eagle (facing right) is on page 156.

COINAGE OF THE STATES

NEW HAMPSHIRE (1776)

New Hampshire was the first of the states to consider the subject of coinage following the Declaration of Independence. On March 13, 1776, by which time the colonies were in rebellion but had not yet formally declared their independence, the New Hampshire House of Representatives established a committee to consider the minting of copper coins. The committee recommended such coinage as a way to facilitate small commercial transactions.

William Moulton was empowered to make a limited quantity of coins of pure copper authorized by the State House of Representatives in 1776. Although cast patterns were prepared, it is believed that they were not approved. Little of the proposed coinage was ever actually circulated.

Other purported patterns are of doubtful origin. These include a unique engraved piece and a rare struck piece with large initials WM on the reverse.

		G
1776 New Hampshire Copper		$100,000
	Auctions: $172,500, VG-10, March 2012	

MASSACHUSETTS

MASSACHUSETTS UNOFFICIAL COPPERS (1776)

Presumably, in 1776, the year the colonies proclaimed their independence from Britain, three types of Massachusetts coppers were created. Very little is known about their origins or the circumstances of their production. Numismatic historians deduced them to be patterns until recent scholarship cast doubt on their authenticity as coppers of the Revolutionary War era.

The obverse of one of these coppers has a crude pine tree with "1d LM" at its base and the legend MASSACHUSETTS STATE. The reverse has a figure probably intended to represent the Goddess of Liberty, seated on a globe and holding a liberty cap and staff. A dog sits at her feet. The legend LIBERTY AND VIRTUE surrounds the figure, and the date 1776 is situated beneath.

Sylvester S. Crosby, writing in 1875 in *The Early Coins of America*, traced the provenance of this unique copper back to a grocer who sold it to a schoolboy around 1852. The grocer was from "the northerly part" of Boston, and he had "found it many years before while excavating on his premises, in the vicinity of Hull or Charter Street."

	VF
1776 Pine Tree Copper (a)	—

a. Unique, in the Massachusetts Historical Society collection.

A similar piece, probably from the same source as the Pine Tree copper, features a Native American standing with a bow on the obverse, with a worn legend that may read PROVINCE OF MASSA or similar. On the reverse is a seated figure and globe, visible partially visible legend (LIBERTATIS), and the date 1776 at bottom. The only known example was overstruck on a 1747 English halfpenny, and is holed.

	VG
1776 Indian Copper (a)	—

a. Unique.

A third Massachusetts piece is sometimes called the *Janus copper*. On the obverse are three heads, facing left, front, and right, with the legend STATE OF MASSA. 1/2 D. The reverse shows the Goddess of Liberty facing right, resting against a globe. The legend is GODDESS LIBERTY 1776.

	F
1776 Halfpenny, 3 Heads on Obverse (a)	—
Auctions: $44,650, Fine, January 2015; $40,000, Fine, November 1979	

a. Unique.

MASSACHUSETTS AUTHORIZED ISSUES (1787–1788)

An "Act for establishing a mint for the coinage of gold, silver and copper" was passed by the Massachusetts General Court on October 17, 1786. The next year, the council directed that the design of the copper coins should incorporate ". . . the figure of an indian with a bow & arrow & a star on one side, with the word 'Commonwealth,' the reverse a spread eagle with the words—'of Massachusetts A. D. 1787'—" (this wording would be slightly different in the final product).

The coinage of Massachusetts copper cents and half cents in 1787 and 1788 was under the direction of Captain Joshua Witherle of Boston. These were the first coins bearing the denomination *cent* as would be later established by Congress. They were produced in large quantities and are fairly plentiful today. The wear seen on many of the Massachusetts cents and half cents indicates that they enjoyed long circulation in commerce. Many varieties exist, the most valuable being that with arrows in the eagle's right talon.

Most of the dies for these coppers were made by Joseph Callender. Jacob Perkins of Newburyport also engraved some of the 1788 dies.

The mint was abandoned early in 1789, in compliance with the newly ratified U.S. Constitution, and because its production was unprofitable.

1787 Half Cent

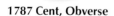

1787 Cent, Obverse

Arrows in Right Talon

Arrows in Left Talon

	G	VG	F	VF	EF	AU	Unc.
1787 Half Cent	$100	$125	$225	$450	$650	$1,300	$3,000
1787 Cent, Arrows in Right Talon	$10,000	$16,000	$25,000	$50,000	$75,000	$100,000	$200,000
1787 Cent, Arrows in Left Talon	$100	$110	$200	$600	$1,250	$2,500	$7,000
1787 Cent, "Horned Eagle" (die break)	$110	$135	$235	$650	$1,300	$3,000	$9,000

1788 Half Cent   **1788 Cent, Period After**
MASSACHUSETTS

	G	VG	F	VF	EF	AU	Unc.
1788 Half Cent	$100	$125	$225	$500	$700	$1,400	$4,500
1788 Cent, Period After MASSACHUSETTS	$100	$110	$200	$600	$1,250	$2,500	$6,000
1788 Cent, No Period After MASSACHUSETTS	$100	$110	$200	$600	$1,200	$2,700	$7,500

CONNECTICUT (1785–1788)

Authority for establishing a mint near New Haven was granted by the state of Connecticut to Samuel Bishop, Joseph Hopkins, James Hillhouse, and John Goodrich in October 1785. They had petitioned the state's General Assembly for this right, noting the public need—small coins were scarce in circulation and many of those seen were counterfeits. Under the Assembly's grant, the four minters would pay the state's treasury an amount equal to 5 percent of the copper coins they produced. To make a profit, the minters would deduct this royalty, plus their other expenses (including materials, labor, and distribution), from the face value of the coins they struck.

Available records indicate that most of the Connecticut coppers were coined under a subcontract, by Samuel Broome and Jeremiah Platt, former New York merchants. Abel Buell was probably the principal diesinker. Many others were struck by Machin's Mills in Newburgh, New York, and were not authorized by Connecticut. These are as highly prized by collectors as are regular issues.

The Connecticut coppers were often struck crudely and on imperfect planchets. Numerous die varieties exist; over the years, collectors have given many of them distinctive nicknames.

1785 Copper, Bust Facing Left   **1785 Copper, Bust Facing Right**

1785 Copper, African Head

	G	VG	F	VF	EF	AU
1785 Copper, Bust Facing Left	$150	$250	$500	$1,500	$3,600	$8,000
1785 Copper, Bust Facing Right	$35	$60	$125	$475	$1,300	$3,500
1785 Copper, African Head	$70	$120	$400	$1,100	$3,000	$8,000

1786 Copper, ETLIB INDE

1786 Copper, Large Head Facing Right

1786 Copper, Mailed Bust Facing Left

1786 Copper, Draped Bust

1786 Copper, Mailed Bust Facing Left, Hercules Head

	G	VG	F	VF	EF	AU
1786 Copper, ETLIB INDE	$70	$140	$325	$850	$2,500	$7,000
1786 Copper, Large Head Facing Right	$250	$500	$1,500	$4,600	$10,000	
1786 Copper, Mailed Bust Facing Left	$40	$75	$140	$400	$800	$220
1786 Copper, Draped Bust	$75	$150	$400	$1,000	$2,200	$5,000
1786 Copper, Mailed Bust Facing Left, Hercules Head	$110	$200	$450	$1,500	$4,000	

1787 Copper, Small Head Facing Right, ETLIB INDE

1787 Copper, Muttonhead Variety, Topless Liberty

	G	VG	F	VF	EF	AU
1787 Copper, Small Head Facing Right, ETLIB INDE	$90	$150	$300	$1,300	$3,000	$5,500
1787 Copper, Liberty Seated Facing Right (a)		—				
1787, Mailed Bust Facing Right, INDE ET LIB	$100	$180	$400	$2,200	$5,000	
1787 Copper, Muttonhead	$100	$180	$400	$1,700	$4,000	$7,500

a. 2 examples are known.

1787 Copper, Mailed Bust Facing Left

1787 Copper, Laughing Head

1787 Copper, Reverse

	G	VG	F	VF	EF	AU
1787 Copper, Mailed Bust Facing Left	$40	$65	$120	$350	$900	$2,200
1787 Copper, Mailed Bust Facing Left, Laughing Head	$50	$100	$200	$500	$900	$2,000

**1787 Copper,
Horned Bust**

	G	VG	F	VF	EF	AU
1787 Copper, Mailed Bust Facing Left, Horned Bust	$40	$65	$120	$375	$600	$1,300
1787 Copper, Mailed Bust Facing Left, Hercules Head *(see 1786 for illustration)*	$400	$700	$1,700	$3,500	$7,000	—
1787 Copper, Mailed Bust Facing Left, Dated 1787 Over 1877	$80	$180	$600	$1,400	$4,200	—
1787 Copper, Mailed Bust Facing Left, 1787 Over 88	$175	$235	$600	$1,500	$4,500	—
1787 Copper, Mailed Bust Facing Left, CONNECT, INDE	$50	$125	$200	$500	$1,200	$2,500
1787 Copper, Mailed Bust Facing Left, CONNECT, INDL	$375	$700	$1,500	$3,000	$6,500	

1787 Copper, Draped Bust Facing Left

	G	VG	F	VF	EF	AU
1787 Copper, Draped Bust Facing Left	$30	$50	$80	$200	$450	$900
1787 Copper, Draped Bust Facing Left, AUCIORI	$40	$65	$100	$300	$700	$1,300
1787 Copper, Draped Bust Facing Left, AUCTOPI	$45	$75	$140	$400	$1,000	$1,800
1787 Copper, Draped Bust Facing Left, AUCTOBI	$45	$75	$140	$400	$1,200	$1,700
1787 Copper, Draped Bust Facing Left, CONNFC	$40	$60	$100	$350	$700	$1,300
1787 Copper, Draped Bust Facing Left, CONNLC	$75	$150	$250	$700	$2,500	—
1787 Copper, Draped Bust Facing Left, FNDE	$40	$65	$150	$400	$1,300	$2,400
1787 Copper, Draped Bust Facing Left, ETLIR	$40	$60	$125	$300	$800	$1,400
1787 Copper, Draped Bust Facing Left, ETIIB	$40	$60	$125	$300	$800	$1,400
1787 Copper, GEORGIVS III Obverse, INDE•ET Reverse	$1,500	$3,250	$4,000	—	—	—

1788 Copper, Mailed Bust Facing Right

	G	VG	F	VF	EF	AU
1788 Copper, Mailed Bust Facing Right	$40	$80	$150	$450	$1,100	$2,000
1788 Copper, GEORGIVS III Obverse *(Reverse as Above)*	$100	$210	$500	$1,400	$2,800	—
1788 Copper, Small Head *(see 1787 for illustration)*	$1,500	$3,750	$4,500	$11,000	$20,000	—

1788 Copper, Mailed Bust Facing Left		1788 Copper, Draped Bust Facing Left	

	G	VG	F	VF	EF	AU
1788 Copper, Mailed Bust Facing Left	$45	$70	$175	$300	$900	$1,800
1788 Copper, Mailed Bust Facing Left, CONNLC	$55	$130	$200	$500	$1,500	$2,800
1788 Copper, Draped Bust Facing Left	$45	$70	$175	$300	$900	$1,800
1788 Copper, Draped Bust Facing Left, CONNLC	$85	$200	$350	$800	$2,000	$3,000
1788 Copper, Draped Bust Facing Left, INDL ET LIB	$80	$140	$250	$700	$1,800	$3,400

NEW YORK AND RELATED ISSUES (1780s)

No official state coinage for New York is known to have been authorized. However, a number of issues in copper and gold were made relating to the state, by a variety of different issuers.

BRASHER DOUBLOONS (1786–1787)

Among the most famous early American pieces coined before establishment of the U.S. Mint at Philadelphia were those produced by the well-known New York City silversmith, goldsmith, and jeweler Ephraim Brasher, who was a neighbor and friend of George Washington's when that city was the seat of the federal government.

The gold pieces Brasher made weighed about 408 grains and were valued at $15 in New York currency. They were approximately equal to the Spanish doubloon, which was equal to 16 Spanish dollars.

Pieces known as *Lima Style doubloons* were dated 1742, but it is almost certain that they were produced in 1786, and were the first efforts of Brasher to make a circulating coin for regional use. Neither of the two known specimens shows the full legends; but weight, gold content, and hallmark are all identical to those for the 1787-dated Brasher coins. An analogous cast imitation Lima style doubloon dated 1735 bears a hallmark attributed to Standish Barry of Baltimore, Maryland, circa 1787.

The design used on the 1787 Brasher doubloon features an eagle on one side and the arms of New York on the other. In addition to his impressed hallmark, Brasher's name appears in small letters on each of his coins. The unique 1787 gold half doubloon is struck from doubloon dies on an undersized planchet that weighs half as much as the larger coins. It is in the National Numismatic Collection in the Smithsonian Institution.

It is uncertain why Brasher produced these pieces. He may have produced them for his own account, charging a nominal fee to convert metal into coin. He was later commissioned by the government to test and verify other gold coins then in circulation. His hallmark EB was punched on each coin as evidence of his testing and its value. In some cases the foreign coins were weight-adjusted by clipping.

		EF
"1742" (1786) Lima Style gold doubloon (a)		$700,000
	Auctions: $690,000, EF-40, January 2005	

a. 2 examples are known.

		EF
1787 New York gold doubloon, EB on Breast		*$5,000,000*
	Auctions: $2,990,000, EF-45, January 2005	
1787 New York gold doubloon, EB on Wing		*$4,000,000*
	Auctions: $4,582,500, MS-63, January 2014	
1787 New York gold half doubloon (a)		—
Various foreign gold coins with Brasher's EB hallmark		*$5,000–$20,000*

a. Unique, in the Smithsonian Collection.

NEW YORK COPPER COINAGE

Several individuals petitioned the New York Legislature in early 1787 for the right to coin copper for the state, but a coinage was never authorized. Instead, a law was passed to regulate the copper coins already in use. Nevertheless, various unauthorized copper pieces were made privately and issued within the state.

One private mint known as Machin's Mills was organized by Captain Thomas Machin, a distinguished veteran of the Revolutionary War, and situated at the outlet of Orange Pond near Newburgh, New York. Shortly after this mint was formed, on April 18, 1787, it was merged with the Rupert, Vermont, mint operated by Reuben Harmon Jr., who held a coinage grant from the Republic of Vermont. The combined partnership agreed to conduct their business in New York, Vermont, Connecticut, or elsewhere if they could benefit by it (though their only known operation was the one at Newburgh).

The operations at Machin's Mills were conducted in secret and were looked upon with suspicion by the local residents. They minted several varieties of imitation George III halfpence, as well as counterfeit coppers of Connecticut and New Jersey. Only their Vermont coppers had official status.

Mints located in or near New York City were operated by John Bailey and Ephraim Brasher. They had petitioned the legislature on February 12, 1787, for a franchise to coin copper. The extent of their partnership, if any, and details of their operation are unknown. Studies of the state coinage show that they produced primarily the EXCELSIOR and NOVA EBORAC pieces of New York, and possibly the "running fox" New Jersey coppers.

Believed to be the bust of George Washington.

	G	VG	F	VF	EF	AU
1786, NON VI VIRTUTE VICI	$6,000	$10,000	$20,000	$40,000	$67,500	$100,000

1787 EXCELSIOR Copper, Large Eagle on Obverse

1787 EXCELSIOR Copper, Eagle on Globe Facing Left

	G	VG	F	VF	EF
1787 EXCELSIOR Copper, Eagle on Globe Facing Right	$2,750	$4,000	$8,500	$25,000	$60,000
1787 EXCELSIOR Copper, Eagle on Globe Facing Left	$2,750	$3,500	$8,000	$18,000	$40,000
1787 EXCELSIOR Copper, Large Eagle on Obverse, Arrows and Branch Transposed	$4,100	$6,750	$18,000	$35,000	$70,000

1787, George Clinton

1787, Indian and New York Arms

1787, Indian and Eagle on Globe

1787, Indian and George III Reverse

	G	VG	F	VF	EF
1787, George Clinton	$10,000	$20,000	$50,000	$75,000	$150,000
1787, Indian and New York Arms	$10,000	$18,000	$40,000	$65,000	$125,000
1787, Indian and Eagle on Globe	$10,000	$18,000	$40,000	$65,000	$125,000
1787, Indian and George III Reverse (a)		—			

a. 4 examples are known.

BRITISH COPPER COINS AND THEIR IMITATIONS
(INCLUDING MACHIN'S MILLS AND OTHER UNDERWEIGHT COINAGE OF 1786–1789)

The most common copper coin used for small transactions in early America was the British halfpenny. Wide acceptance and the non–legal-tender status of these copper coins made them a prime choice for unauthorized reproduction by private individuals.

Many such counterfeits were created in America by striking from locally made dies, or by casting or other crude methods. Some were made in England and imported into this country. Pieces dated 1781 and 1785 seem to have been made specifically for this purpose, while others were circulated in both countries.

Genuine regal British halfpence and farthings minted in London and dated 1749 are of special interest to collectors because they were specifically sent to the North American colonies as reimbursement for participation in the expedition against Cape Breton, and circulated extensively throughout New England.

Genuine British halfpenny coppers of both George II (dated 1729–1754) and George III (dated 1770–1775) show finely detailed features within a border of close denticles; the 1 in the date looks like a J. They are boldly struck on good-quality planchets. Their weight is approximately 9.5 grams; their diameter, 29 mm.

British-made lightweight imitation halfpence are generally smaller in diameter and thickness, and weigh less than genuine pieces. Details are crudely engraved or sometimes incomplete. Inscriptions may be misspelled. Planchet quality may be poor.

	G	VG	F	VF	EF
1749, George II British farthing	$20	$40	$75	$175	$250
1749, George II British halfpenny	$25	$50	$100	$200	$300
1770–1775, George III British halfpenny (a)	$15	$20	$50	$100	$250
1770–1775, British imitation halfpenny (a)	$15	$20	$25	$100	$250

a. Values shown are for the most common variety. Rare pieces are sometimes worth significantly more.

During the era of American state coinage, New York diemaker James F. Atlee and/or other coiners minted unauthorized, lightweight, imitation British halfpence. These American-made false coins have the same or similar devices, legends, and, in some cases, dates as genuine regal halfpence, but they contain less copper. Their details are often poorly rendered or missing. Identification of American-made imitations has been confirmed by identifying certain punch marks (such as letters and numerals) and matching them to the distinct punch marks of known engravers.

There are four distinct groups of these halfpence, all linked to the regular state coinage. The first group was probably struck in New York City prior to 1786. The second group was minted in New York City in association with John Bailey and Ephraim Brasher during the first half of 1787. The third group was struck at Machin's Mills during the second half of 1787 and into 1788 or later. A fourth group, made by the Machin's Mills coiners, consists of pieces made from dies that were muled with false dies of the state coinages of Connecticut, Vermont, and New York. Pieces with very crude designs and other dates are believed to have been struck elsewhere in New England.

GEORGIVS/BRITANNIA
"MACHIN'S MILLS" COPPER HALFPENNIES MADE IN AMERICA

Dates used on these pieces were often "evasive," as numismatists describe them today. They include dates not used on genuine pieces and, sometimes, variations in spelling. They are as follows: 1771, 1772, 1774, 1775, and 1776 for the first group; 1747 and 1787 for the second group; and 1776, 1778, 1787, and 1788 for the third group. Pieces generally attributed to James Atlee can be identified by a single outline in the crosses (British Union) of Britannia's shield and large triangular denticles along the coin circumference. The more-valuable American-made pieces are not to be confused with the similar English-made George III counterfeits (some of which have identical dates), or with genuine British half-pence dated 1770 to 1775.

Group I coins dated 1771, 1772, 1774, 1775, and 1776 have distinctive bold designs but lack the fine details of the original coins. Planchets are generally of high quality.

Group II coins dated 1747 and 1787 are generally poorly made. The 1 in the date is not J-shaped, and the denticles are of various sizes. There are no outlines to the stripes in the shield.

Group III coins dated 1776, 1778, 1787, and 1788, struck at Machin's Mills in Newburgh, New York, are similar to coins of Group II, with their triangular-shaped denticles. Most have large dates and berries in the obverse wreath.

	AG	G	VG	F	VF	EF	AU
1747, GEORGIVS II. Group II	$125	$250	$400	$700	$2,500	$5,500	$15,000
1771, GEORGIVS III. Group I	$70	$100	$220	$325	$1,000	$2,500	$5,000
1772, GEORGIVS III. Group I	$80	$150	$250	$500	$1,300	$2,700	$5,500
1772, GEORGIUS III. Group I	$85	$200	$300	$750	$2,300	$4,500	—
1774, GEORGIVS III. Group I	$40	$80	$100	$225	$700	$2,200	$4,000
1774, GEORGIUS III. Group I	$80	$150	$225	$400	$1,750	$3,750	—
1775, GEORGIVS III. Group I	$35	$70	$100	$225	$700	$1,800	$4,000
1776, GEORGIVS III. Group III	$155	$300	$450	$850	$2,200	$7,000	—
1776, GEORCIVS III, Small Date	$1,000	$2,000	$4,500	$9,000	$18,000	$25,000	$35,000
1778, GEORGIVS III. Group III	$40	$70	$125	$275	$700	$2,000	$3,200
1784, GEORGIVS III	$200	$400	$800	$1,500	$2,500	$3,500	$6,000
1787, GEORGIVS III. Group II	$30	$75	$100	$200	$600	$1,200	$2,500
1787, GEORGIVS III. Group III	$30	$75	$100	$200	$600	$1,200	$2,500
1788, GEORGIVS III. Group III	$30	$75	$100	$200	$600	$1,200	$2,800

Note: Values shown are for the most common varieties in each category. Rare pieces can be worth significantly more. Also see related George III combinations under Connecticut, Vermont, and New York.

The muled coins of Group IV are listed separately with the Immune Columbia pieces and with the coins of Connecticut, Vermont, and New York. Other imitation coppers made by unidentified American makers are generally very crude and exceedingly rare. Cast copies of British coins probably circulated along with the imitations without being questioned. Counterfeits of silver Spanish-American coins and Massachusetts tree coins may have also been coined by American minters.

NOVA EBORAC COINAGE FOR NEW YORK

An extensive issue of 1787-dated copper coins appeared, each with a bust on the obverse surrounded by NOVA EBORAC ("New York"). The reverse showed a seated goddess with a sprig in one hand and a liberty cap on a pole in the other hand, with the legend VIRT. ET. LIB. ("Virtue and Liberty") surrounding, and the date 1787 below. The letter punches used on this issue are identical to those used on the Brasher doubloon die. It is likely that John Bailey and Ephraim Brasher operated a minting shop in New York City and produced these and possibly other issues.

1787, NOVA EBORAC, Reverse: Seated Figure Facing Right

1787, NOVA EBORAC, Reverse: Seated Figure Facing Left

1787, NOVA EBORAC, Small Head

1787, NOVA EBORAC, Large Head

	AG	G	F	VF	EF	AU
1787, NOVA EBORAC, Seated Figure Facing Right	$50	$110	$300	$700	$1,200	$2,000
1787, NOVA EBORAC, Seated Figure Facing Left	$50	$100	$250	$600	$1,000	$1,500
1787, NOVA EBORAC, Small Head	$1,700	$4,000	$13,000	$25,000		
1787, NOVA EBORAC, Large Head	$500	$900	$2,000	$5,250	$8,500	

NEW JERSEY (1786–1788)

On June 1, 1786, the New Jersey General Assembly granted to businessman and investor Thomas Goadsby, silversmith and assayer Albion Cox, and minter Walter Mould authority to coin three million coppers weighing six pennyweight and six grains (150 grains total, or 9.72 grams) apiece, to be completed by June 1788, on condition that they deliver to the state treasurer "one Tenth Part of the full Sum they shall strike." These coppers were to pass current at 15 to the shilling. Revolutionary War hero and New Jersey state legislator Matthias Ogden also played a significant financial and political role in the operation.

In an undertaking of this kind, the contractors purchased the metal and assumed all expenses of coining. The difference between these expenses and the total face value of the coins issued represented their profit.

Later, Goadsby and Cox asked authority to coin two-thirds of the total independently of Mould. Their petition was granted November 22, 1786. Mould was known to have produced his coins at Morristown, while Cox and Goadsby operated in Rahway. Coins with a diameter of 30 mm or more are generally considered Morristown products. Coins were also minted in Elizabethtown by Ogden and, without authority, by Machin's Mills.

The obverse shows design elements of the state seal, a horse's head with plow, and the legend NOVA CÆSAREA (New Jersey). The reverse has a United States shield and, for the first time on a coin, the legend E PLURIBUS UNUM (One Composed of Many). More than 140 varieties exist. The majority have the horse's head facing to the right; however, three of the 1788 date show the head facing left. Other variations have a sprig beneath the head, branches below the shield, stars, cinquefoils, a running fox, and other ornaments.

1786, Date Under
Plow Beam

1786, Date Under
Plow, No Coulter

1786 and 1787,
Pattern Shield

	AG	G	F	VF	EF
1786, Date Under Plow Beam			$85,000	$125,000	$200,000
1786, Date Under Plow, No Coulter	$500	$900	$3,000	$7,000	$15,000
1787, Pattern Shield (a)	$400	$700	$1,750	$3,000	$7,500

a. The so-called Pattern Shield reverse was also used on several speculative patterns. See page 147.

1786, Straight
Plow Beam,
Protruding Tongue

1786, Wide Shield

1786, Curved Plow
Beam, Bridle Variety

	AG	G	F	VF	EF	AU
1786, Straight Plow Beam (common varieties)	$25	$55	$175	$500	$800	$1,250
1786, Curved Plow Beam (common varieties)	$25	$55	$175	$500	$875	$1,500
1786, Protruding Tongue	$30	$70	$235	$600	$1,600	$4,000
1786, Wide Shield	$30	$75	$240	$650	$1,800	$4,500
1786, Bridle variety	$30	$75	$240	$650	$1,800	$4,500

1787, PLURIBS Error

**1787, Second U Over S
in PLURIBUS**

1787, PLURIRUS Error

	AG	G	F	VF	EF	AU
1786, PLUKIBUS error	$30	$75	$250	$450	$1,700	$4,500
1787, PLURIBS error	$40	$125	$500	$1,600	$3,500	$9,000
1787, Second U Over S in PLURIBUS	$40	$160	$470	$1,000	$2,700	$5,000
1787, PLURIRUS error	$40	$160	$470	$1,100	$3,000	$5,000

**1787, Sprig
Above Plow**

**1787, WM
Above Plow**

1787, Hidden WM

	AG	G	F	VF	EF	AU
1787, Sprig Above Plow (common varieties)	$25	$65	$220	$650	$1,100	$2,500
1787, No Sprig Above Plow (common varieties)	$25	$65	$220	$550	$900	$1,800
1787, WM Above Plow (a)				—		
1787, Hidden WM in Sprig	$35	$75	$225	$750	$2,200	$4,500

a. Unique.

1787, 1787 Over 1887

1787, Camel Head

1787, Serpent Head

	AG	G	F	VF	EF	AU
1787, 1787 Over 1887	$200	$600	$3,000	$6,000	$15,000	—
1787, Camel Head (snout in high relief)	$30	$60	$200	$650	$900	$1,800
1787, Serpent Head	$35	$85	$400	$1,300	$3,200	$6,000
1787, Goiter Variety	$40	$75	$500	$1,200	$1,800	$4,500

**1788, Running
Fox Before Legend**

**1788, Indistinct
Coulter**

**1788, Running
Fox After Legend**

1788, Braided Mane

**1788, Horse's
Head Facing Left**

	AG	G	F	VF	EF	AU
1788, Horse's Head Facing Right, several varieties	$25	$60	$175	$550	$900	$2,000
1788, Horse's Head Facing Right, Running Fox Before Legend	$75	$150	$550	$2,000	$4,000	$9,000
1788, Similar, Indistinct Coulter	$150	$650	$2,500	$6,500	$15,000	—
1788, Horse's Head Facing Right, Running Fox After Legend			$50,000	$75,000	—	
1788, Braided Mane	$50	$300	$1,200	$3,800	$7,500	$13,000
1788, Horse's Head Facing Left	$175	$450	$1,500	$4,750	$12,000	$25,000

REPUBLIC OF VERMONT (1785–1788)

The Republic of Vermont was not formally part of the Union in the 1780s. However, it considered itself American and allied with the original 13 colonies, having declared independence from Britain in January 1777 and having fought in the Revolutionary War. After the war Vermont sought political connection with the United States. Territorial disagreements with New York delayed its entry into the Union, but this was finally accomplished in 1791, when it was admitted as the 14th state. In the meantime, Vermont had already embarked on its own experiments in local coinage.

Reuben Harmon Jr., a storekeeper and entrepreneur of Rupert, Vermont, was granted permission by the Vermont House of Representatives to coin copper pieces for a period of two years beginning July 1, 1785. The well-known Vermont "Landscape" coppers were first produced in that year. The franchise was extended for eight years in 1786.

Harmon's mint was located in the northeast corner of Rupert near a stream known as Millbrook. Colonel William Coley, a New York goldsmith, made the first dies. Some of the late issues were made near Newburgh, New York, by the Machin's Mills coiners.

Most coppers made in Vermont were struck on poor and defective planchets. These included the landscape and Draped Bust Left varieties. Well-struck coins on smooth, full planchets command higher prices. Later pieces made at Machin's Mills are on high-quality planchets but usually have areas of weak striking.

1785, IMMUNE COLUMBIA

1785, VERMONTS   **1785, Reverse**   **1785, VERMONTIS**

1786, VERMONTENSIUM   **1786, Baby Head**

1786, Bust Left   **1786, Reverse**   **1787, Reverse**

	AG	G	VG	F	VF	EF	AU
1785, IMMUNE COLUMBIA	$4,000	$6,000	$10,000	$15,000	$30,000	$50,000	$75,000
1785, VERMONTS	$150	$275	$450	$700	$2,400	$5,000	$12,000
1785, VERMONTIS	$175	$325	$600	$1,300	$4,250	$12,000	$20,000
1786, VERMONTENSIUM	$110	$200	$350	$500	$1,350	$3,200	$7,500
1786, Baby Head	$150	$275	$400	$1,000	$2,500	$7,500	$20,000
1786, Bust Left	$80	$125	$250	$600	$2,200	$3,600	—
1787, Bust Left			$10,000	$20,000	$35,000	—	

1787, BRITANNIA

	AG	G	VG	F	VF	EF	AU
1787, BRITANNIA (a)	$45	$90	$120	$200	$400	$850	$1,800

a. The reverse of this coin is always weak.

1787, 1788, Bust Right (Several Varieties)

	AG	G	VG	F	VF	EF	AU
1787, Bust Right, several varieties	$60	$110	$150	$250	$800	$2,000	$3,500
1788, Bust Right, several varieties	$50	$90	$120	$225	$500	$1,250	$2,500
1788, Backward C in AUCTORI		$4,750	$8,000	$17,500	$40,000	$75,000	
1788, *ET LIB* *INDE	$175	$300	$550	$1,250	$4,000	$10,000	$15,000

1788, GEORGIVS III REX / INDE+ ET•LIB+

	AG	G	VG	F	VF	EF	AU
1788, GEORGIVS III REX (a)	$300	$500	$900	$2,200	$4,500	$11,000	

a. This piece should not be confused with the common English halfpence with similar design and reverse legend BRITANNIA.

PRIVATE TOKENS AFTER CONFEDERATION

The formal ratification of the Articles of Confederation—the document signed amongst the original 13 colonies, which established the United States of America as a confederation of sovereign states and served as its first constitution—was accomplished in early 1781. A number of private coinages sprang up after confederation, intended to facilitate local commerce. These were not the products of the federal government, but were tokens issued by businesses and other private concerns.

NORTH AMERICAN TOKENS (DATED 1781)

These tokens were struck in Dublin, Ireland. The obverse shows the seated figure of Hibernia, the personification of Ireland, facing left. The date of issue is believed to have been much later than that shown on the token (1781). Like many Irish tokens, this issue found its way to America in limited quantities and was accepted in commerce near the Canadian border.

	VG	F	VF	EF	AU
1781, Copper or Brass	$60	$100	$200	$600	$1,500

Bar Coppers (ca. 1785)

The Bar coppers are undated and of uncertain origin. They have 13 parallel and unconnected bars on one side. On the other side is the large roman-letter USA monogram. The design is virtually identical to that used on a Continental Army uniform button.

The significance of the design is clearly defined by its extreme simplicity. The separate 13 states (bars) unite into a single entity as symbolized by the interlocking letters (USA).

These pieces are believed to have first circulated in New York during November 1785, as mentioned in a report in the *New Jersey Gazette* of November 12, 1785. They may have been made in England. Although they are scarce, examples enter the marketplace with regularity, and nearly all are in higher grades.

John Adams Bolen (1826–1907), a numismatist and a master diesinker in Springfield, Massachusetts, struck copies of the Bar copper around 1862. On these copies, the letter A passes under, instead of over, the S. Bolen's intent was not to deceive, and he advertised his copies plainly as reproductions. But his skills were such that W. Elliot Woodward, a leading auctioneer of tokens and medals in the 1860s, vacillated between selling Bolen's copies and describing them as "dangerous counterfeits." Bolen copies of the Bar copper are highly collectible in their own right, but they are less valuable than the originals.

	G	VG	F	VF	EF	AU	Unc.
(Undated) (Circa 1785) Bar Copper ‡	$500	$1,800	$3,000	$6,000	$8,000	$11,000	$25,000

‡ Ranked in the *100 Greatest American Medals and Tokens*.

Auctori Plebis Tokens (1787)

These tokens are sometimes included with the coins of Connecticut, as they greatly resemble issues of that state. (The obverse features a draped male bust, possibly King George II, wearing laurels and facing left.) They were struck in England by an unknown maker, possibly for use in America.

	G	VG	F	VF	EF	AU	Unc.
1787, AUCTORI PLEBIS	$90	$110	$225	$450	$800	$1,400	$7,500

Mott Store Cards (Dated 1789)

These 19th-century store cards have long been included in Early American coin collections because of the date they bear (1789). Most scholars believe these were produced no earlier than 1807 (and possibly in the Hard Times era of the late 1830s) as commemoratives of the founding of the Mott Company, and served as business cards. The firm, operated by Jordan Mott, was located at 240 Water Street, a fashionable section of New York at that time.

The obverse of the token features an eagle with wings spread and an American shield as a breastplate. The eagle holds an olive branch and arrows in his talons. Above is the date 1789, and around the rim is the legend CLOCKS, WATCHES, JEWELRY, SILVERWARE, CHRONOMETERS. The reverse of the token features a regulator clock with the legend MOTT'S N.Y. IMPORTERS, DEALERS, MANUFACTURERS OF GOLD & SILVER WARES.

	VG	F	VF	EF	AU	Unc.
"1789," Mott Token, Thick Planchet	$80	$175	$300	$400	$500	$1,000
"1789," Mott Token, Thin Planchet	$80	$200	$350	$600	$1,200	$2,200
"1789," Mott Token, Entire Edge Engrailed	$80	$300	$450	$900	$1,400	$3,000

STANDISH BARRY THREEPENCE (1790)

Standish Barry, of Baltimore, was a watch- and clockmaker, an engraver, and, later, a silversmith. In 1790 he circulated a silver threepence of his own fabrication. The tokens are believed to have been an advertising venture at a time when small change was scarce. The precise date on this piece may indicate that Barry intended to commemorate Independence Day, but there are no records to prove this. The head on the obverse is probably that of James Calhoun, who was active in Baltimore politics in the 1790s. The legend BALTIMORE TOWN JULY 4, 90, appears in the border. An enigmatic gold doubloon is also attributed to Barry (see page 151).

Nearly all examples of the silver threepence show significant wear, suggesting that they circulated for a long time.

	VG	F	VF	EF	AU
1790 Threepence	$10,000	$22,500	$50,000	$80,000	$110,000

ALBANY CHURCH PENNIES (1790)

The First Presbyterian Church of Albany, New York, authorized an issue of 1,000 copper uniface tokens in 1790. These passed at 12 to a shilling. They were used to encourage parishioner donations (at that time, there was a scarcity of small change in circulation). They were also intended to stop contributions of worn and counterfeit coppers (in the words of the church elders' resolution, "in order to add respect to the weekly collections"). Two varieties were made, one with the addition of a large D (the abbreviation for *denarium*, or penny, in the British monetary system) above the word CHURCH. All are rare, with fewer than a dozen of each variety known.

	VG	F	VF	EF
(Undated) (1790) **Without D** ‡	$10,000	$15,000	$30,000	$50,000
(Undated) (1790) **With D Added** ‡	$10,000	$15,000	$30,000	$50,000

‡ Both Albany Church Penny varieties are ranked in the *100 Greatest American Medals and Tokens,* as a single entry.

KENTUCKY TOKENS (CA. 1792–1794)

These tokens were struck in England circa 1792 to 1794. Their obverse legend reads UNANIMITY IS THE STRENGTH OF SOCIETY; the central motif is a hand holding a scroll with the inscription OUR CAUSE IS JUST. The reverse shows a pyramid of 15 starbursts surrounded by rays. Each star in the triangle represents a state, identified by its initial letter. These pieces are usually called *Kentucky cents* or *Kentucky tokens* because the letter K (for Kentucky) happens to be at the top. Some of the edges are plain; others are milled with a diagonal reeding; and some have edge lettering that reads PAYABLE IN LANCASTER LONDON OR BRISTOL, PAYABLE AT BEDWORTH NUNEATON OR HINKLEY, or PAYABLE AT I. FIELDING, etc.

These are not known to have circulated in America. Rather, they were made as produced as collectibles, popular among English numismatists and others at the time. Likely more than 1,000 Kentucky tokens are in the hands of numismatists today.

	VF	EF	AU	Unc.
(1792–1794) Copper, Plain Edge	$185	$275	$450	$850
(1792–1794) Copper, Engrailed Edge	$500	$800	$1,200	$2,000
(1792–1794) Copper, Lettered Edge, PAYABLE AT BEDWORTH, etc.	—	—	—	—
(1792–1794) Copper, Lettered Edge, PAYABLE IN LANCASTER, etc.	$250	$350	$550	$1,200
(1792–1794) Copper, Lettered Edge, PAYABLE AT I. FIELDING, etc.	—	—	—	—

FRANKLIN PRESS TOKENS (1794)

These were English tradesman's tokens of the kind collected by English numismatists in the late 1700s and early 1800s. (As a group, they were popularly called Conder tokens, after James Conder, the man who first cataloged them for collectors.) The Franklin Press tokens did not circulate as money in America, but, being associated with a London shop where Benjamin Franklin once worked, they have long been included in American coin collections.

The obverse features a wood-frame printing press of the style that Benjamin Franklin would have operated by hand as a printer in England in 1725. He had left Philadelphia at the age of 18 to buy printing supplies in London and look for work. Around the central design is the legend SIC ORITOR DOCTRINA SURGETQUE LIBERTAS ("Thus Learning Advances and Liberty Grows"), and below is the date, 1794. The reverse legend reads PAYABLE AT THE FRANKLIN PRESS LONDON.

Most are plain-edged, but rare lettered-edge varieties exist, as well as a unique piece with a diagonally reeded edge.

	VG	VF	EF	AU	Unc.
1794 Franklin Press Token	$100	$250	$350	$550	$1,000
Similar, Edge Reads AN ASYLUM FOR THE OPPRESS'D OF ALL NATIONS	*(unique)*				
Similar, Edge Diagonally Reeded	*(unique)*				

Talbot, Allum & Lee Cents (1794–1795)

Talbot, Allum & Lee was a firm of importers engaged in the India trade and located at 241 Pearl Street, New York. It placed a large quantity of English-made coppers in circulation during 1794 and 1795.

ONE CENT appears on the 1794 issue, and the legend PAYABLE AT THE STORE OF on the edge. The denomination is not found on the 1795 reverse but the edge legend was changed to read WE PROMISE TO PAY THE BEARER ONE CENT. Rare plain-edged specimens of both dates exist. Exceptional pieces have edges ornamented or with lettering CAMBRIDGE BEDFORD AND HUNTINGDON.X.X.

It is estimated that more than 200,000 of these tokens were minted, though no original records have been located. Varieties and mulings are known; the values shown here are for the most common types.

Many undistributed tokens were sold to the Philadelphia Mint in a time of copper shortage. These were cut down and used by the Mint as planchets for coining 1795 and 1797 half cents.

1794 Cent, With NEW YORK   1795 Cent

	VG	F	VF	EF	AU	Unc.
1794 Cent, With NEW YORK ‡	$65	$80	$225	$350	$500	$1,400
1794 Cent, Without NEW YORK ‡	$500	$850	$2,500	$3,500	$6,500	$8,500
1795 Cent ‡	$60	$80	$200	$300	$400	$800

‡ All Talbot, Allum & Lee cents are ranked in the *100 Greatest American Medals and Tokens*, as a single entry.

Myddelton Tokens (1796)

Philip Parry Price Myddelton was an Englishman who bought land in America after the Revolutionary War. He hoped to begin a vibrant farming community along the Ohio River and entice English craftsmen and workers to move there. To this end he contracted the design of a promotional token and had examples made in copper and silver. These tokens were struck at the Soho Mint of Boulton and Watt near Birmingham, England. Although their obverse legend reads BRITISH SETTLEMENT KENTUCKY, and Myddelton planned to order large quantities of the copper version for shipment to the United States, they were never actually issued for circulation in Kentucky. The entrepreneur was arrested in August 1796 and convicted in London for the crime of convincing hundreds of workers to leave England for America. He was jailed in Newgate prison for three and a half years, which ended his Kentucky plans.

The obverse of Myddelton's token shows Hope presenting two "little genii" (his description) to the goddess Liberty. She welcomes them with an open hand. At her feet is a flourishing sapling and a cornucopia representing America's bounty, and she holds a pole with a liberty cap. On the reverse, seated Britannia leans wearily on a downward-pointing spear, looking at the broken scale and fasces—symbols of unity, justice, and liberty—scattered at her feet.

Sylvester S. Crosby, in *The Early Coins of America*, remarked that "In beauty of design and execution, the tokens are unsurpassed by any piece issued for American circulation."

	PF
1796, Proof, Copper ‡	$20,000
1796, Proof, Silver ‡	$25,000

‡ Both Myddelton Token varieties are ranked in the *100 Greatest American Medals and Tokens,* as a single entry.

COPPER COMPANY OF UPPER CANADA TOKENS (EARLY 1800s)

These pieces were struck some time in the early 1800s. The obverse is the same as that of the Myddelton token. The new reverse refers to a Canadian firm, the Copper Company of Upper Canada, with the denomination ONE HALF PENNY. These tokens may have been made for numismatic purposes (for sale to collectors), or as part of the coiner's samples. Their maker is unknown. Restrikes were made in England in the 1890s.

	PF
1796, Proof, Copper	$7,000

CASTORLAND MEDALS (1796)

These medals, or "jetons," are dated 1796 and allude to a proposed French settlement known as Castorland. This was to be located on the Black River, in northern New York, not far from the Canadian border. Peter Chassanis of Paris had acquired land that he and others intended to parcel into large farms, with Chassanis heading the settlement's government, two commissaries residing at its seat, Castorville, and four commissaries headquartered in Paris. The medals were to be given as payment ("in recognition of the care which they may bestow upon the common concerns") to the Parisian directors of the colonizing company for their attendance at board meetings.

Some 20 French families, many of them aristocratic refugees from the French Revolution, moved to the settlement between 1796 and 1800. Challenges including sickness, harsh northern New York winters, loss of livestock, and theft of finances proved too much for the company, and Castorland was dissolved in 1814. Many of the surviving settlers moved to more prosperous American communities or returned to Europe.

The obverse of the Castorland medal features a profile portrait of the ancient goddess Sybele, associated with mountains, town and city walls, fertile nature, and wild animals. She wears a *corona muralis* ("walled crown"), laurels, and a draped head covering. The legend reads FRANCO-AMERICANA COLONIA, with CASTORLAND 1796 below. On the reverse the goddess Ceres, patroness of agriculture, stands at a maple with a sap drill while the tree's bounty flows into a waiting bucket. Ceres holds a cornucopia; at her feet are a sickle and a sheaf of wheat. A beaver at the bottom of the reverse further symbolizes Castorland and its resources (*castor* is French for "beaver," an animal crucial to the very profitable North American fur trade in the early 1800s). The legend, in Latin, is SALVE MAGNA PARENS FRUGUM—"Hail, Great Mother of Crops" (from Virgil).

Copy dies of the Castorland medal are still available and have been used at the Paris Mint for restriking throughout the years. Restrikes have a more modern look than originals; their metallic content (in French) is impressed on the edge: ARGENT (silver), CUIVRE (copper), or OR (gold).

	EF	AU	Unc.
1796, Original, Silver (reeded edge, unbroken dies) ‡	$3,000	$4,500	$7,500
1796, Original, Silver (reverse rusted and broken) ‡	$300	$600	$1,500
1796, Original, Bronze (reverse rusted and broken) ‡	$200	$300	$700
(1796) Undated, Restrike, Silver (Paris Mint edge marks) ‡		$30	$70
(1796) Undated, Restrike, Bronze (Paris Mint edge marks) ‡		$20	$40

‡ All Castorland Token varieties are ranked in the *100 Greatest American Medals and Tokens*, as a single entry.

THEATRE AT NEW YORK TOKENS (CA. 1798)

These penny tokens were issued by Skidmore of London and illustrate the New Theatre (later known as the Park Theatre) in Manhattan, as it appeared circa 1797. The theater was New York City's attempt at a prestigious new level of entertainment, as the famous John Street Theatre (the "Birthplace of American Theater") was suffering from poor management and physical decay in the 1790s. The building's cornerstone was laid on May 5, 1795, and the theater opened on January 29, 1798, with a presentation of entertainments including Shakespeare's *As You Like It*.

The obverse of this copper token features a view of the playhouse building with the legend THE THEATRE AT NEW YORK AMERICA. The reverse shows an allegorical scene of a cornucopia on a dock, with bales, an anchor, and sailing ships. The legend reads MAY COMMERCE FLOURISH. The edge is marked I PROMISE TO PAY ON DEMAND THE BEARER ONE PENNY.

All known examples are struck in copper and have a Proof finish. They were made for collectors, not for use as advertising. Today examples are scarce, with about 20 known.

	EF
	PF
Penny, THE THEATRE AT NEW YORK AMERICA	—
Penny, THE THEATRE AT NEW YORK AMERICA, Proof ‡	$25,000

‡ Ranked in the *100 Greatest American Medals and Tokens*, as a single entry.

NEW SPAIN (TEXAS) JOLA TOKENS (1817–1818)

In 1817 the Spanish governor of Texas, Colonel Manuel Pardo, authorized Manuel Barrera to produce 8,000 copper coins known as jolas. These crudely made pieces show the denomination 1/2 [real], the maker's initials and the date on the obverse, and a five-pointed star on the reverse.

The 1817 coins were withdrawn from circulation the following year and replaced by a similar issue of 8,000 pieces. These bear the date 1818 and the initials, JAG, of the maker, José Antonio de la Garza. Several varieties of each issue are known. All are rare.

	F	VF	EF
1817 1/2 Real	$10,000	$25,000	$50,000
1818 1/2 Real, Large or Small Size ‡	$15,000	$25,000	$50,000

‡ Ranked in the *100 Greatest American Medals and Tokens*.

NORTH WEST COMPANY TOKENS (1820)

These tokens were probably valued at one beaver skin and struck in Birmingham, England, in 1820 by John Walker & Co. All but two known specimens are holed. Most have been found in Oregon in the region of the Columbia and Umpqua river valleys. They feature a portrait of King George IV on the obverse, with the legend TOKEN and the date 1820. The reverse shows a beaver in the wild, with the legend NORTH WEST COMPANY.

Holed Brass Token

James A. Haxby, in the *Guide Book of Canadian Coins and Tokens*, writes, "The pieces actually issued for circulation were pierced at the top for suspension or stringing. Unholed copper strikes are known with plain or engrailed edge and are very rare. A number of pieces have been found buried in western Canada and as far south as central Oregon."

Unholed Copper Token

	AG	G	VG	F	VF
1820, Copper or Brass, holed ‡	$375	$800	$2,000	$3,700	$8,000
1820, Copper, unholed, plain or engrailed edge ‡	—	—	—	—	—

‡ All North West Company Token varieties are ranked in the *100 Greatest American Medals and Tokens*, as a single entry.

WASHINGTON PIECES

Medals, tokens, and coinage proposals in this interesting series dated from 1783 to 1795 bear the portrait of George Washington. The likenesses in most instances were faithfully reproduced and were designed to honor the first president. Many of these pieces were of English origin and, although dated 1783, probably were made in the 1820s or later.

The legends generally signify a strong unity among the states and the marked display of patriotism that pervaded the new nation during that period. We find among some of these tokens an employment of what were soon to become the nation's official coin devices, namely, the American eagle, the United States shield, and stars. The denomination ONE CENT is used in several instances, while on some of the English pieces HALFPENNY will be found. Several of these pieces were private patterns for proposed coinage contracts.

GEORGIVS TRIUMPHO TOKENS

Although the head shown on these tokens bears a strong resemblance to that on some coins of King George III, many collectors consider the Georgivs Triumpho ("Triumphant George") tokens a commemorative of America's victory in the Revolutionary War.

The reverse side shows the Goddess of Liberty behind a framework of 13 bars and fleurs-de-lis. Holding an olive branch in her right hand and staff of liberty in her left, she is partially encircled by the words VOCE POPOLI ("By the Voice of the People") 1783. An example is known used as an undertype for a 1787 New Jersey copper.

	VG	F	VF	EF	AU	Unc.
1783, GEORGIVS TRIUMPHO	$110	$225	$500	$700	$1,000	$6,000

WASHINGTON PORTRAIT PIECES (1780S TO EARLY 1800S)

Military Bust. "The 1783-dated Washington Military Bust coppers bear a portrait, adapted (with a different perspective on the coin and a wreath added to the head) from a painting by Edward Savage," writes Q. David Bowers in the *Whitman Encyclopedia of Colonial and Early American Coins*. "These seem to have circulated in England as well as America. . . . Many varieties exist, but they are not well known outside of a circle of specialists. Accordingly, the opportunity exists to acquire rare die combinations for little premium over a regular issue."

The reverse features a seated female figure holding an olive branch and a pole topped by a liberty cap. Values shown are for the most common varieties.

1783, Large Military Bust, Point of Bust Close to W

1783, Small Military Bust

	F	VF	EF	AU	Unc.
1783, Large Military Bust	$75	$160	$350	$500	$1,600
1783, Small Military Bust, Plain Edge	$80	$175	$350	$650	$1,800
1783, Small Military Bust, Engrailed Edge	$100	$200	$550	$1,000	$2,200

Draped Bust. Draped Bust coppers dated 1783 depict Washington with the top of a toga draped over his shoulder. One variety includes a button at the folds in front of the toga. Another variety has no button, and has the initial "I" (for Ingram) in the toga, above the right side of the numeral 3 in the date. Both varieties feature a similar reverse design with a female figure seated on a rock, holding an olive branch and a pole surmounted by a liberty cap.

1783, Draped Bust, No Button   **With Button**

	F	VF	EF	AU	Unc.
1783, Draped Bust, No Button *(illustrated)*	$80	$160	$300	$500	$1,500
1783, Draped Bust, With Button (on Drapery at Neck)	$125	$225	$350	$700	$3,200
1783, Draped Bust, Copper Restrike, Plain Edge, Proof	$125	$225	$350	$700	$900
1783, Draped Bust, Copper Restrike, Engrailed Edge, Proof					$750
1783, Draped Bust, Silver Restrike, Engrailed Edge, Proof					$5,000

Unity States. The 1783-dated coppers with the legend UNITY STATES OF AMERICA were likely coined in the early 1800s at the Soho Mint in Birmingham, England. The obverse features a portrait of Washington in a toga and wearing laurels. The reverse is a copy of the wreath design on the copper cent produced by the Philadelphia Mint from 1796 to 1807, with UNITED spelled UNITY, perhaps as a way to evade charges of counterfeiting.

Despite the American denomination of this piece, they likely circulated in England (at the value of a halfpenny), as reflected by examples being found there in quantity in later years. They were imported into the United States as well, for use as a cent, and are mentioned in several counterfeit-detector publications in the 1850s.

1783, Unity States

	VG	VF	EF	AU	Unc.
1783, UNITY STATES	$100	$200	$325	$550	$1,400

Double Head. Although the Washington Double Head cents are undated, some numismatists assign them a date of 1783, given their resemblance to the Military Bust coppers that bear that date (even though those were probably struck years later). They were likely struck in Birmingham, England, by Edward Thomason sometime in the 1820s or later. They were made in England, as evidenced by many having been found there, but long after the Conder token era. They are denominated ONE CENT and, when exported to the United States, circulated along with Hard Times tokens of the 1830s.

Undated Double-Head Cent

	F	VF	EF	AU	Unc.
(Undated) Double-Head Cent	$100	$250	$425	$650	$2,200

Ugly Head. The so-called Ugly Head token is a medalet struck in copper and white-metal varieties, possibly satirical, and presumably of American origin. The token's legend reads WASHINGTON THE GREAT D.G. The abbreviation "D.G." on English coins stands for Dei Gratia ("By the Grace of God"), and the portrait appears to be wigless and possibly toothless, leading some numismatists to opine that the token is a satire on George Washington. Bowers notes that the token's date, 1784, has no particular significance in Washington's life. By that year the American Revolution was over and the general had retired his commission as commander-in-chief of the Continental Army. He would not assume the presidency until 1789. The reverse of the token features a design of linked rings with abbreviations for the British colonies, reminiscent of the 1776 Continental dollar.

1784, Ugly Head

	VF	EF
1784, Ugly Head, Copper	$50,000	$75,000
Auctions: $20,000, Crude Good, December 1983		
1784, Ugly Head, Pewter		*(unique)*

Small and Large Eagle. Small Eagle and Large Eagle one-cent tokens dated 1791 were made in Birmingham, England, sponsored by merchants W. and Alex Walker of that city as proposals for official American coinage. Bowers writes in the *Whitman Encyclopedia of Colonial and Early American Coins* that the Walker firm "shipped a cask filled with these cents, estimated to be about 2,500 Large Eagle and 1,500 Small Eagle coins, to Thomas Ketland & Sons, a Philadelphia contact, to be distributed to legislators. The depiction of Washington was contrary to the president's own desires, who felt that having his image on coins would appear to have the 'stamp of royalty.'"

1791 Cent, Small Eagle Reverse, Edge Lettered UNITED STATES OF AMERICA

1791 Cent, Large Eagle Reverse

	VG	F	VF	EF	AU	Unc.
1791 Cent, Small Eagle (Date on Reverse)		$475	$650	$800	$1,200	$2,750
1791 Cent, Large Eagle (Date on Obverse)	$150	$350	$550	$750	$1,100	$2,400

Liverpool. The Liverpool Halfpenny tokens were most likely made around 1793. They were intended for circulation as small change in England, although numismatists of the time also sought them for their collections. The obverse shows a uniformed bust of George Washington, as used on the Large Eagle one-cent tokens of 1791. The reverse features a sailing ship and the legend LIVERPOOL HALFPENNY, a design used on various English Conder tokens.

1791 Liverpool Halfpenny

	VG	F	VF	EF	AU	Unc.
1791 Liverpool Halfpenny, Lettered Edge	$700	$900	$1,500	$2,000	$3,200	—

1792. An extensive series of 1792-dated Washington pieces was produced in many varieties, bearing no denomination. These apparently were made in England, and were collected by numismatists in addition to circulating as coinage substitutes in America.

1792 Cent, Eagle with 13 Stars Reverse

	VG	F	VF	EF
1792, WASHINGTON PRESIDENT, Eagle With 13 Stars Reverse				
PRESIDENT at Side of Bust, Copper				—
PRESIDENT, Silver			$125,000	—
PRESIDENT, Gold (a)			—	
PRESIDENT Extends Below Bust, Copper (a)				$125,000

a. Unique.

1792, WASHINGTON PRESIDENT

Legend Reverse

	VG	F	VF	EF
1792, WASHINGTON PRESIDENT, Legend on Reverse				
Plain Edge, Copper	$2,750	$7,500	$18,000	$50,000
Lettered Edge, Copper	—	—	—	—

(1792) Undated,
WASHINGTON
BORN VIRGINIA

	VG	F	VF	EF
(1792) Undated, WASHINGTON BORN VIRGINIA, Eagle With 13 Stars Reverse *(reverse illustrated on previous page)*, Copper ‡ (a)		—		
(1792) Undated, WASHINGTON BORN VIRGINIA, Legend on Reverse				
Copper ‡	$1,000	$1,500	$3,000	$5,000
Copper, Edge Lettered UNITED STATES OF AMERICA *(1 known)* ‡				
Silver ‡	—	—	—	—

‡ All WASHINGTON BORN VIRGINIA copper pieces are ranked in the *100 Greatest American Medals and Tokens*, as a single entry.
a. 3 examples are known.

Peter Getz. Dies engraved by silversmith, mechanic, and inventor Peter Getz of Lancaster, Pennsylvania, are believed to have been made to produce a half dollar and a cent as a proposal to Congress for a private contract coinage before the Philadelphia Mint became a reality. These feature George Washington, in a military bust portrait, and a heraldic eagle.

1792, Small Eagle Reverse   Large Eagle Reverse

	VG	F	VF	EF	AU	Unc.
1792, Small Eagle, Silver	—	—	—	$175,000		
	Auctions: $241,500, AU, May 2004					
1792, Small Eagle, Copper	$6,000	$12,000	$30,000	$50,000	$75,000	$150,000
	Auctions: $299,000, MS-64 BN, November 2006					
1792, Small Eagle, Ornamented Edge (Circles and Squares), Copper	—	—	—	$150,000		
	Auctions: $207,000, AU, November 2006					
1792, Small Eagle, Ornamented Edge, Silver (a)	—	—	$100,000	$175,000		
	Auctions: $391,000, Gem BU PL, May 2004					
1792, Large Eagle, Silver			—	—		
	Auctions: $34,500, EF, May 2004					

a. 4 examples are known.

Roman Head. The 1792-dated Roman Head cents show Washington in the style of an ancient Roman dignitary. These copper pieces were struck in England for collectors, as opposed to being intended for circulation. Their edge is lettered UNITED STATES OF AMERICA.

1792 Cent, Roman Head

	PF
1792 Cent, Roman Head, Lettered Edge UNITED STATES OF AMERICA, Proof	$90,000

Ship Halfpenny. The 1793 Ship Halfpenny tokens were struck from an overdated (3 Over 2) reverse die. These copper pieces were intended for collectors, but nearly all of them ended up in circulation in England. The more common lettered-edge variety reads PAYABLE IN ANGLESEY LONDON OR LIVERPOOL.

1793 Ship Halfpenny

	VG	F	VF	EF	AU	Unc.
1793 Ship Halfpenny, Lettered Edge	$100	$200	$400	$600	$850	$3,250
1793 Ship Halfpenny, Plain Edge (a)			—	—		

a. Rare.

1795 Copper. Copper tokens dated 1795 were made in large quantities as promotional pieces for the London firm of Clark & Harris, dealers in stoves and fireplace grates. The die work is attributed to Thomas Wyon, and numismatists believe the pieces were struck in Birmingham, England, for circulation in the British Isles (although collectors saved them as well).

The obverse features a right-facing portrait of George Washington in military uniform. Two varieties exist, Small Buttons and Large Buttons (describing the coats on his frock). The legend reads G. WASHINGTON: THE FIRM FRIEND TO PEACE & HUMANITY.

The reverse shows a fireplace with a coal grate, with legends PAYABLE BY CLARK & HARRIS 13. WORMWOOD St. BISHOPSGATE and LONDON 1795.

Most have a diagonally reeded edge, although some are edge-lettered as PAYABLE AT LONDON LIVERPOOL OR BRISTOL.

1795, Large Buttons   **1795, Small Buttons**

	F	VF	EF	AU	Unc.
1795, Large Buttons, Lettered Edge	$180	$350	$700	$1,500	$2,200
1795, Large Buttons, Reeded Edge	$80	$175	$300	$400	$700
1795, Small Buttons, Reeded Edge	$80	$200	$400	$650	$1,750

Liberty and Security. The Liberty and Security halfpenny and penny tokens were made in England in 1795 as collectibles, although the halfpence also circulated widely there as small change. Their designs consist of a portrait of George Washington, identified by name, and a heraldic eagle surmounting a stylized American shield, holding a sprig of olive and several arrows. Some of their edges are plain, and some are lettered with various phrases such as AN ASYLUM FOR THE OPPRESS'D OF ALL NATIONS and BIRMINGHAM REDRUTH & SWANSEA.

Varieties exist in copper and white metal, and with mulings of different reverses.

The common name of this series derives from the reverse legend, LIBERTY AND SECURITY.

1795, Liberty and Security Halfpenny

	F	VF	EF	AU	Unc.
1795 Halfpenny, Plain Edge	$110	$200	$500	$850	$2,650
1795 Halfpenny, LONDON Edge	$100	$210	$500	$700	$2,500
1795 Halfpenny, BIRMINGHAM Edge	$125	$250	$500	$900	$2,500
1795 Halfpenny, ASYLUM Edge	$200	$400	$1,000	$1,700	$4,500
1795 Penny, ASYLUM Edge	$2,500	$7,500	$10,000	$15,000	$25,000

(1795) Undated, Liberty and Security Penny, ASYLUM Edge

	F	VF	EF	AU	Unc.
(1795) Undated, Liberty and Security Penny	$275	$450	$650	$1,150	$2,250
Same, Corded Outer Rims	$600	$1,000	$2,500	$5,000	$7,500

North Wales. "The undated North Wales halfpenny issues, believed to have been struck in England in the early 1790s (usually listed as 1795, although this may be two or three years after they were coined), are part of the 'evasion halfpence' series. Accordingly, unlike Conder tokens, they were not created for collectors. None are known to have survived with sharp features and in high grades, as is characteristic of cabinet pieces" (*Whitman Encyclopedia of Colonial and Early American Coins*).

(1795) Undated, NORTH WALES Halfpenny

	G	F	VF	EF	AU
(1795) Undated, NORTH WALES Halfpenny	$90	$200	$500	$750	$1,000
(1795) Undated, Lettered Edge	$450	$1,200	$4,000	$6,000	$7,500
(1795) Undated, Two Stars at Each Side of Harp	$2,200	$7,500	$13,500		

Success Tokens. Small and large types exist of these mysterious pieces of unknown date and purpose. Today known as Success tokens, they may have been souvenirs, perhaps struck to commemorate George Washington's second inauguration (March 1793), or 19th-century gaming tokens. They were struck in copper or brass and most likely were made in the mid-1800s. Specimens with original silvering are rare and are valued 20% to 50% higher than others. Varieties exist.

(Undated) SUCCESS Token, Large

(Undated) SUCCESS Token, Small

	F	VF	EF	AU	Unc.
(Undated) SUCCESS Token, Large, Plain or Reeded Edge	$250	$450	$750	$1,400	$2,750
(Undated) SUCCESS Token, Small, Plain or Reeded Edge	$300	$500	$800	$1,500	$3,200

Contract Issues and Patterns

CONTINENTAL CURRENCY (1776)

The Continental Currency dollars (as they are known to numismatists) were made to serve in lieu of a paper dollar, but the exact nature of their monetary role is still unclear. They were the first dollar-sized coins ever attributed to the United States. One obverse die was engraved by someone whose initials were E.G. (thought to be Elisha Gallaudet) and is marked EG FECIT ("EG Made It"). Studies of the coinage show that there may have been two separate emissions made at different mints, one in New York City. The link design on the reverse was suggested by Benjamin Franklin and represents the former colonies.

Varieties result from differences in the spelling of the word CURRENCY and the addition of EG FECIT on the obverse. These coins were struck in pewter, brass, and silver. Pewter pieces served as a dollar, taking the place of a Continental Currency paper note. Brass and silver pieces may have been experimental or patterns. The typical grade encountered for a pewter coin is VF to AU. Examples in original bright Uncirculated condition are worth a strong premium.

Numerous copies and replicas of these coins have been made over the years. Authentication is recommended for all pieces.

| | | CURRENCY | | CURENCY | |

	G	F	VF	EF	AU	Unc.
1776 CURENCY, Pewter † (a)	$7,750	$12,000	$24,000	$36,000	$50,000	$75,000
1776 CURENCY, Brass † (a)	$25,000	$35,000	$65,000	$115,000	$220,000	—
Auctions: $299,000, MS-63, July 2009						
1776 CURENCY, Silver † (b)			1,527,000			
Auctions: $1,410,000, MS-63, May 2014; $1,527,500, MS-62, January 2015; $1,527,500, EF-40, January 2015						
1776 CURRENCY, Pewter †	$8,000	$13,000	$25,000	$37,500	$52,500	$80,000
1776 CURRENCY, EG FECIT, Pewter †	$8,500	$15,000	$27,500	$40,000	$55,000	$85,000
Auctions: $546,250, MS-67, January 2012						

† All varieties of Continental Currency dollars are ranked in the *100 Greatest U.S. Coins* (fourth edition), as a single entry. **a.** 2 varieties. **b.** 2 examples are known.

	G	F	VF	EF	AU	Unc.
1776 CURRENCY, EG FECIT, Silver † (b)		—	—	—	—	$1,500,000
Auctions: $1,410,000, MS-63, May 2014						
1776 CURRENCEY, Pewter †	—	—	$65,000		$175,000	—
1776 CURRENCY, Pewter, Ornamented Date † (c)				$276,000	$329,000	
Auctions: $276,000, EF-45, July 2009						

† All varieties of Continental Currency dollars are ranked in the *100 Greatest U.S. Coins* (fourth edition), as a single entry. **b.** 2 examples are known. **c.** 3 examples are known.

NOVA CONSTELLATIO PATTERNS (1783)

These Nova Constellatio pieces represent the first official patterns for a coinage of the United States. They were designed by Benjamin Dudley for Gouverneur Morris to carry out his ideas for a decimal coinage system. The 1,000-unit coin is a mark, the 500 a quint. These denominations, together with the small 100-unit piece, were designed to fit in with the many different values for foreign coins that constituted money in America at the time. These pattern pieces represent the first attempt at a decimal ratio, and were the forerunners of our present system of money values. Neither the proposed denominations nor the coins advanced beyond the pattern stage. These unique pieces are all dated 1783. There are two types of the quint. The copper "five" was first brought to the attention of collectors in 1980. Electrotype and cast copies exist.

5 Units

Quint, Plain Obverse **Quint, Legend on Obverse** **Quint Reverse**

Bit (100 Units)

Mark

1783 (Five) "5," Copper	*(unique)*
1783 (Bit) "100," Silver, Decorated Edge	*(2 known)*
Auctions: $97,500, Unc., November 1979	
1783 (Bit) "100," Silver, Plain Edge	*(unique)*
Auctions: $705,000, AU-55, May 2014	
1783 (Quint) "500," Silver, Plain Obverse	*(unique)*
Auctions: $1,175,000, AU-53, April 2013	
1783 (Quint) "500," Silver, Legend on Obverse	*(unique)*
Auctions: $165,000, Unc., November 1979	
1783 (Mark) "1000," Silver	*(unique)*
Auctions: $190,000, Unc., November 1979	

FUGIO COPPERS (1787)

The first coins issued under U.S. authority for which contract information is known today were the Fugio pieces, which were valued at one cent each. They were made under contract with James Jarvis, owner of a a controlling interest in the Connecticut mint, which was then striking Connecticut coppers in New Haven. Jarvis obtained the federal contract with a $10,000 bribe to Col. William Duer, then head of the Board of Treasury. The contract called for Jarvis to deliver 345 tons of copper coins to the federal government. Congress, which was ignorant of the bribe, directed on July 7, 1787, "that the Board of Treasury direct the contractor for the copper coinage to stamp on one side of each piece the following device, viz: thirteen circles linked together, a small circle in the middle, with the words 'United States,' around it; and in the centre, the words 'We are one'; on the other side of the same piece the following device, viz: a dial with the hours expressed on the face of it; a meridian sun above on one side of which is the word 'Fugio,' ["time flies"] and on the other the year in figures '1787,' below the dial, the words 'Mind Your Business.'"

Jarvis was only able to mint 11,910 pounds of Fugios (equal to around 554,741 coins). Not all of these were shipped to the government, which cancelled the contract for failure to meet the delivery schedule.

All Fugios were minted in 1788 and back-dated 1787. The dies were engraved by Abel Buell.

1787, WITH POINTED RAYS

The 1787, With Pointed Rays, was later replaced by the With Club Rays variety.

American Congress Pattern

Cross After Date

Label With Raised Rims

	G	VG	F	VF	EF	AU	Unc.
Obverse Cross After Date, No Cinquefoils							
Reverse Rays and AMERICAN CONGRESS †				—	$300,000	$425,000	
Reverse Label with Raised Rims † (a)			$14,000	$20,000	$35,000		
Reverse STATES UNITED †	$300	$650	$1,100	$2,700	$6,500	$13,000	—
Reverse UNITED STATES †	$275	$500	$900	$2,200	$5,000	$10,000	—

† All non-restrike Fugio Coppers are ranked in the *100 Greatest U.S. Coins* (fourth edition), as a single entry. **a.** Extremely rare.

Cinquefoil After Date
These types, with pointed rays, have regular obverses punctuated with four cinquefoils (five-leafed ornaments).

	G	VG	F	VF	EF	AU	Unc.
STATES UNITED at Sides of Circle, Cinquefoils on Label †	$150	$350	$500	$850	$1,400	$1,800	$3,500
STATES UNITED, 1 Over Horizontal 1 †	$225	$450	$1,000	$4,000	$9,000		
UNITED STATES, 1 Over Horizontal 1 †	$200	$400	$900	$3,500	$8,000		
UNITED STATES at Sides of Circle †	$150	$350	$500	$850	$1,600	$1,900	$4,000
STATES UNITED, Label With Raised Rims, Large Letters in WE ARE ONE †	$200	$400	$700	$2,000	$4,000	$8,500	$20,000
STATES UNITED, 8-Pointed Star on Label †	$200	$400	$600	$1,100	$2,000	$3,600	$9,000
UNITED Above, STATES Below †	$850	$1,750	$3,750	$9,000	$12,500	$19,500	$27,500

† All non-restrike Fugio Coppers are ranked in the *100 Greatest U.S. Coins* (fourth edition), as a single entry.

1787, WITH CLUB RAYS

The 1787, With Club Rays, is differentiated between concave and convex ends.

Rounded Ends   **Concave Ends**

	G	VG	F	VF	EF	AU
Club Rays, Rounded Ends †	$200	$400	$800	$1,400	$2,600	$5,000
Club Rays, Concave Ends to Rays, FUCIO (C instead of G) † (a)	$1,750	$3,750	$8,000	$24,000	$35,000	
Club Rays, Concave Ends, FUGIO, UNITED STATES †	$2,200	$5,000	$10,000	$30,000	$40,000	$90,000
Club Rays, Similar, STATES UNITED Reverse †		—	—		—	—

† All non-restrike Fugio Coppers are ranked in the *100 Greatest U.S. Coins* (fourth edition), as a single entry. **a.** Extremely rare.

The so-called New Haven "restrikes" were made for Horatio N. Rust from dies recreated in 1859. These are distinguished by narrow rings on the reverse. At the time the fanciful story was given that teenaged C. Wyllys Betts discovered original dies in 1858 on the site of the Broome & Platt store in New Haven, where the original coins had been made.

New Haven Restrike.
Note narrow rings.

	EF	AU	Unc.
New Haven restrike, Gold (a)		—	—
New Haven restrike, Silver	$3,200	$4,750	$7,500
New Haven restrike, Copper or Brass	$500	$600	$900

a. 2 examples are known.

1792 PROPOSED COINAGE

Some members of the House of Representatives favored a depiction of the president's head on the obverse of each federal coin; others considered the idea an inappropriately monarchical practice. George Washington himself is believed to have expressed disapproval of the use of his portrait on American coins. The majority considered a figure emblematic of Liberty more appropriate, and the Senate finally concurred in this opinion. Robert Birch was an engraver employed to design proposed devices for American coins. He, perhaps together with others, engraved the dies for the disme and half disme. He also cut the dies for the large copper patterns known today as *Birch cents*. Most 1792 half dismes circulated and were considered to be official coinage, rather than patterns; they are summarized here and discussed in more detail under "Half Dismes."

1792 SILVER CENTER CENT

The dies for the 1792 cent with a silver center may have been cut by Henry Voigt. The coins are copper with a silver plug in the center. The idea was to create a coin with an intrinsic or melt-down value of a cent, but of smaller diameter than if it were made entirely of copper. On the obverse is a right-facing portrait of Miss Liberty, the legend LIBERTY PARENT OF SCIENCE & INDUSTRY, and the date 1792.

	F	VF	EF	AU
Cent, Silver Center † (a)	$200,000	$275,000	$350,000	$600,000
Auctions: $1,997,500, MS-64, August 2014; $1,410,000, MS-63BN+, May 2014; $705,000, MS-61+, September 2014				
Cent, Without Silver Center (b)	$250,000	$375,000	$475,000	$650,000
Auctions: $603,750, VF-30, January 2008				

† Ranked in the *100 Greatest U.S. Coins* (fourth edition). **a.** 14 examples are known, including one unique specimen without plug. **b.** Six or 7 examples are known.

1792 BIRCH CENT

On the large-diameter copper Birch cent, the portrait of Miss Liberty is "bright-eyed and almost smiling," as described in *United States Pattern Coins*. The legend LIBERTY PARENT OF SCIENCE & INDUSTRY surrounds the portrait. BIRCH is lettered on the truncation of her neck, for the engraver. On the reverse is a ribbon-tied wreath with the legend UNITED STATES OF AMERICA and the denomination in fractional terms of a dollar: 1/100. The edge of some examples is lettered TO BE ESTEEMED BE USEFUL (with punctuating stars).

G★W.PT.

	F	VF	EF
Copper, Lettered Edge, TO BE ESTEEMED * BE USEFUL* † (a)	$225,000	$550,000	$675,000
Auctions: $564,000, MS-61, January 2015			
Copper, Plain Edge † (b)		$700,000	
Copper, Lettered Edge, TO BE ESTEEMED BE USEFUL * † (b)		—	
Auctions: $2,585,000, MS-65H, January 2015			
White Metal, G★W.PT. (George Washington President) Below Wreath † (c)		—	

† All varieties of 1792 Birch Cents are ranked in the *100 Greatest U.S. Coins* (fourth edition), as a single entry. **a.** Six or seven examples are known. **b.** Two examples are known. **c.** Unique.

1792 HALF DISME

About 1,500 silver half dismes were struck in mid-August 1792 in the shop of John Harper, using equipment ordered for the Philadelphia Mint (the foundation stones of which would be laid on July 31). Nearly all were placed into circulation. In his annual address that autumn, President George Washington noted that these had been so distributed. Their obverse design is a portrait of Miss Liberty similar to the Birch cent's, but facing left. Its legend is abbreviated as LIB. PAR. OF SCIENCE & INDUSTRY. The reverse shows an eagle in flight, with UNI. STATES OF AMERICA around the top, and HALF DISME below.

	Mintage	AG	G	VG	F	VF	EF	AU	Unc.
Silver †	1,500	$9,500	$22,000	$27,500	$40,000	$80,000	$110,000	$175,000	$300,000
	Auctions: $1,292,500, SP-67, August 2014								

† Ranked in the *100 Greatest U.S. Coins* (fourth edition).

1792 DISME

The 1792 pattern disme occurs in one silver variety and two copper varieties (plain-edged and the more readily available reeded-edge). The obverse legend is abbreviated as LIBERTY PARENT OF SCIENCE & INDUST., with the date 1792 below Miss Liberty's neck. The reverse features an eagle in flight, different in design from that of the half disme, with UNITED STATES OF AMERICA around the top of the coin and the denomination, DISME, below.

	F	EF	AU	Unc.
Silver † (a)	$300,000	$450,000	$850,000	
	Auctions: $998,750, AU-50, January 2015			
Copper *(illustrated)* † (b)	$135,000	$225,000	$450,000	$950,000
	Auctions: $1,057,500, MS-64, January 2015			

† Both 1792 Disme Pattern varieties are ranked in the *100 Greatest U.S. Coins* (fourth edition), as a single entry. **a.** 3 examples are known. **b.** Approximately 15 examples are known.

1792 QUARTER DOLLAR

Little is known of this pattern coin's origins, except that it was added to the Mint Cabinet by Chief Coiner Adam Eckfeldt. In the 19th century it was often called a "cent," but the eagle design is more appropriate for a silver or gold issue than a copper. It is commonly called a "quarter" today. Unique uniface trials of the obverse and reverse also exist.

	EF
1792, Copper *(illustrated)* † (a)	$750,000
Auctions: $2,232,500, MS-63, January 2015	
1792, White Metal † (b)	$325,000

† Both 1792 Quarter Dollar Pattern varieties are ranked in the *100 Greatest U.S. Coins* (fourth edition), as a single entry. **a.** 2 examples are known. **b.** 4 examples are known.

THE LIBERTAS AMERICANA MEDAL (1782)

The Liberty Cap coinage of the fledgling United States was inspired by the famous Libertas Americana medal, whose dies were engraved by Augustin Dupré in Paris in 1782 from a concept and mottoes proposed by Benjamin Franklin. To Franklin (then U.S. minister to France), the infant Hercules symbolized America, strangling two serpents representing the British armies at Saratoga and Yorktown. Minerva, with shield and spear, symbolized France as America's ally, keeping the British Lion at bay. Franklin presented gold examples of the medal to the French king and queen and silver strikings to their ministers, "as a monumental acknowledgment, which may go down to future ages, of the obligations we are under to this nation."

Between 100 and 125 original copper medals exist, and two dozen or more silver; the location of the two gold medals is unknown. Over the years the Paris Mint has issued additional medals that are appreciated and collected at a fraction of the cost for originals.

	PF-50	PF-60	PF-63	PF-65
Libertas Americana medal, Proof, Copper ‡ (a)	$10,000	$15,000	$27,500	$50,000
Libertas Americana medal, Proof, Silver ‡ (b)	$60,000	$100,000	$175,000	$300,000

‡ Both Libertas Americana varieties are ranked in the *100 Greatest American Medals and Tokens*, as a single entry. **a.** 100 to 125 examples are known. **b.** At least 24 examples are known.

Half Cents
1793–1857

AN OVERVIEW OF HALF CENTS

Building a type set of the six different major designs in the half cent series can be a challenging and rewarding pursuit. The first design, with Liberty Head facing left with pole and cap, minted only in 1793, is scarce in all grades and will be the most difficult to locate. However, hundreds exist of this American classic, and many are fairly attractive.

The second type, with a *large* Liberty Head facing right with pole and cap, made only in 1794, is scarce with good eye appeal. Most are dark and rough. The next type, the *small* Liberty Head facing right, with pole and cap, is scarce, but enough are on the market that a collector can find a specimen without difficulty.

The Draped Bust half cents, struck from 1800 to 1808, are easily available as a type, including in higher grades. The Classic Head (1809–1836) and Braided Hair (1840–1857) are plentiful as types.

For the earlier half cent types there is ample opportunity for connoisseurship, for quality often varies widely, and every coin is apt to have a different appearance and "personality," even within the same grade.

FOR THE COLLECTOR AND INVESTOR: HALF CENTS AS A SPECIALTY

Collecting half cents by dates and major varieties has been a popular niche specialty for a long time. Some key issues in the series are the 1793; 1796, With Pole to Cap; 1796, Without Pole to Cap, (the most famous of all the rarities); 1802, 2 Over 0, With Reverse of 1800, (a single leaf at each side of the wreath apex, rare but somewhat obscure); 1831; and the Proof-only issues of 1836, 1840 through 1848, Small Date, and 1852.

As there are so many Proof varieties, and each of these is rare as well as expensive, many collectors opt to acquire only the circulation strikes. However, the Proofs are not nearly as expensive as one might think, probably because with so many different dates and varieties needed to complete a Proof collection, the prospect is daunting to many buyers. Proofs of most dates are available in both original and restrike forms. Although this rule is not without exceptions, the original strikings of the 1840–1848 and 1849, Small Date, half cents are usually described as having the Large Berries reverse, while restrikes are of the Small Berries reverse (within the Small Berries issues there are two dies—one with diagonal die striae below RICA, and the other with doubling at the ribbon wreath). Assembling Proofs by reverse varieties is a somewhat esoteric pursuit.

For an exhaustive study of die varieties of circulation strikes and Proofs, *Walter Breen's Encyclopedia of United States Half Cents, 1793–1857*, is definitive. Roger S. Cohen Jr.'s study, *American Half Cents, The "Little Half Sisters,"* gives detailed information on circulation strikes, but omits Proofs.

Die varieties are especially abundant among half cents of the first several types, 1793 to 1808. The year 1804 offers a panorama of dies, some of which have been studied as to die states, referring to the progression of use of a die as it develops wear, cracks, etc. Varieties of 1795 exist with and without the pole to the liberty cap, the Without Pole half cents being the result of a die being relapped (reground to dress the surface), during which process the pole was removed. On the other hand, the 1796, Without Pole, half cent was the result of a die-engraving error—the diecutter forgot to add it. Some half cents of 1795 and 1797 were struck on planchets cut from copper tokens issued by the New York City firm of Talbot, Allum & Lee. Upon close inspection, some of the design details of the tokens can still be seen.

One curious and readily available variety of the 1828 half cent has 12 stars instead of the standard 13. However, in choice Mint State the 12-stars issue becomes a rarity, for, unlike the 13-stars issue, none were ever found in hoards.

The Early American Coppers Club is a special-interest group emphasizing copper half cents and large cents. Its journal, *Penny-Wise*, provides much research, social, and collecting news and information.

LIBERTY CAP, HEAD FACING LEFT (1793)

Designer: *Henry Voigt.* **Weight:** *6.74 grams.* **Composition:** *Copper.* **Diameter:** *21.2 to 24.6 mm.*
Edge: *Lettered TWO HUNDRED FOR A DOLLAR.* **Mint:** *Philadelphia.*

Bowers-Whitman–4,
Cohen-4, Breen-4.

History. Among U.S. coinage, the Liberty Cap, Head Facing Left, design belongs to the small class of one-year-only types. Its design was inspired by Augustin Dupré's Libertas Americana medal. The Liberty Cap dies are often credited to Joseph Wright, who also cut the dies for the related cent, but they were more likely done by Henry Voigt.

Striking and Sharpness. Good-quality copper was used in these half cents, so they are often found light brown and on fairly smooth planchets. Unlike in later types, the borders on both sides are raised beads; certain of these beads can be weak, though this is not the norm. Some varieties are lightly defined at HALF CENT on the reverse, due to a combination of striking and shallow depth of letters in the die. This feature cannot be used in assigning a grade, as in lower grades (up to and including VG-8) these words may be completely missing.

Availability. Most half cents of 1793 are AG-3 to F-12. EF and AU examples are rare, and MS very rare (most being MS–60 to 63). Market grading is often liberal. Early American Coppers Club (EAC) "raw" grades often are lower than those of the certification services.

GRADING STANDARDS

MS-60 to 65 (Mint State). *Obverse:* In the lower ranges, MS–60 and 61, some light abrasions can be seen on the higher areas of the portrait. Luster in the field is incomplete, particularly in the center of the open areas. At the MS-63 level, luster should be complete, with no abrasions evident. In higher levels, the luster is deeper, and some original mint color may be seen. *Reverse:* In the lower ranges some abrasions are seen on the higher

1793; Bowers-Whitman–3, Cohen-3,
Breen-3. Graded MS-60BN.

areas of the leaves. Generally, luster is complete in all ranges, as the open areas are protected by the lettering and wreath. Otherwise, the same comments apply as for the obverse.

Illustrated coin: Well struck and nicely centered on the planchet, this example shows no sign of wear. Its color is a rich orange-brown overall, with a bit of darker gray-brown on the lower-right edge and field of the obverse. The faint roughness on the obverse is a flaw of the original planchet, and is not related to wear.

AU-50, 53, 55, 58 (About Uncirculated).

Obverse: Friction is seen on the higher parts, particularly on the rounded cheek and on the higher strands of the hair. Friction and scattered marks are in the field, ranging from extensive at AU-50 to minimal at AU-58. Luster may be seen in protected areas, minimal at AU-50, but sometimes extensive on an AU-58 coin. Border beads, if well struck, are separate and boldly defined. *Reverse:* Friction

1793; BW-3, C-3, B-3. Graded AU-58.

is seen on the higher wreath leaves and (not as easy to discern) on the letters. The fields, protected by the designs, show friction, but not as noticeably as on the obverse. At AU–55 and 58 little if any friction is seen. The reverse may have original luster, toned brown, minimal on lower About Uncirculated grades, sometimes extensive at AU-58. Border beads, if well struck, are separate and boldly defined. Grading at the About Uncirculated level is mainly done by viewing the obverse.

Illustrated coin: Two tiny rim bruises can be seen, and some nicks can be seen as well under low magnification, none of which immediately draw the eye. This coin is about as good as can be found in this grade, as many examples of the date are porous.

EF-40, 45 (Extremely Fine).

Obverse: Wear is seen on the portrait overall, with reduction or elimination of some separation of hair strands on the highest part. The cheek is ever so slightly flat on the highest part. Some leaves will retain some detail, especially where they join the stems. Luster is minimal or non-existent at EF-40 and may survive in traces in protected areas at EF-45. *Reverse:* Wear is seen on the highest wreath and rib-

1793; BW-3, C-3, B-3. Graded EF-45.

bon areas and the letters. Luster is minimal, but likely more noticeable than on the obverse, as the fields are protected by the designs and lettering.

Illustrated coin: The devices are crisp for the grade. Note the glossy golden-tan surfaces and the lack of meaningful contact marks.

VF-20, 30 (Very Fine). *Obverse:* Wear on the portrait has reduced the hair detail to indistinct or flat at the center on a VF-20 coin, with slightly more detail at VF-30. The thin, horizontal (more or less) ribbon near the top of the hair is distinct. The border beads are blended together, with many blurred or missing. No luster is seen. *Reverse:* The leaf details are nearly completely worn away at VF-20, and with slight detail at

1793; BW-3, C-3, B-3. Graded VF-30.

VF-30. The border beads are blended together, with many indistinct. Some berries in the sprays may be worn away, depending on the strike (on strong strikes they can be seen down into Very Good and Good grades). No luster is seen. HALF CENT may be weak, but is fully readable, on certain coins (such as BW-1, C-1, B-1) in which this feature was shallowly cut into the dies.

Illustrated coin: A small planchet crack at 8 o'clock on the obverse rim appears as struck. This planchet crack explains the softness of detail at the borders both in that area at 10 o'clock on the reverse.

F-12, 15 (Fine). *Obverse:* The hair details are mostly worn away, with about one-third visible, mainly at the edges. Border beads are weak or worn away in areas. F-15 shows slightly more detail. *Reverse:* The wreath leaves are worn flat, but their edges are distinct. HALF CENT may be missing on 1793 (Bowers-Whitman–1)—also true of lower grades given below. Border beads are weak or worn away in areas. F-15 shows slightly more detail.

1793; BW-3, C-3, B-3. Graded F-15.

Illustrated coin: Under magnification the surfaces are seen to be lightly porous.

VG-8, 10 (Very Good). *Obverse:* The portrait is well worn, although the eye can be seen, and the hair tips at the right show separation. Border beads are worn away, and the border blends into the field in most if not all of the periphery. LIBERTY and 1793 are bold. VG-10, not an official ANA grading designation, is sometimes applied to especially nice Very Good coins. *Reverse:* The wreath, bow, and lettering are seen in outline

1793; BW-4, C-4, B-4. Graded VG-8.

form, and some leaves and letters may be indistinct in parts. Border beads are worn away, and the border blends into the field in most if not all of the periphery.

Illustrated coin: The scratch from the E of LIBERTY to the base of the cap behind Liberty's head is less evident at the coin's unmagnified size.

G-4, 6 (Good). *Obverse:* The portrait is worn smooth and is seen only in outline form, although the eye position can be discerned. LIBERTY and 1793 are complete, although the date may be weak. *Reverse:* Extensive wear is seen overall. From half to two-thirds of the letters in UNITED STATES OF AMERICA and the fraction numerals are worn away. The reverse shows more evidence of wear than does the obverse,

1793; BW-2, C-2, B-2. Graded G-6.

and is key in assigning this grade. G-6 is often assigned to finer examples in this category.

AG-3 (About Good). *Obverse:* Wear is more extensive than on the preceding. The portrait is visible only in outline. LIBERTY is weak but usually fully discernible. 1793 is weak, and the bottoms of the digits may be worn away. *Reverse:* Parts of the wreath are visible in outline form, and all but a few letters are gone. Grading of AG-3 is usually done by the reverse.

1793; BW-3, C-3, B-3. Graded AG-3.

Fair-2 (Fair). *Obverse:* Worn nearly smooth. Date is partly visible, not necessarily clearly. Head of Miss Liberty is in outline form. Some letters of LIBERTY are discernible. *Reverse:* Worn nearly smooth. Peripheral letters are nearly all gone, with only vestiges remaining. Wreath is in outline form. HALF CENT ranges from readable to missing (the latter on certain die varieties as struck).

1793; BW-2, C-2, B-2. Graded Fair-2.

	Mintage	Cert	Avg	%MS	AG-3	G-4	VG-8	F-12	VF-20	EF-40	AU-50	MS-60BN	MS-63BN
1793	35,334	168	31.1	8%	$2,500	$3,500	$5,500	$9,000	$14,000	$22,500	$27,500	$60,000	$95,000
	Auctions: $176,250, MS-64, February 2016; $47,000, MS-62, November 2016; $1,528, G-4, August 2016												

LIBERTY CAP, HEAD FACING RIGHT (1794–1797)

Designer: *1794—Robert Scot; 1795–1797—Possibly Scot, John Smith Gardner, or other.*
Weight: *1794, thick planchet—6.74 grams; 1795–1797—5.44 grams.* **Composition:** *Copper.*
Diameter: *23.5 mm.* **Edge:** *1794, some of 1795, some of 1797—Lettered TWO HUNDRED FOR A DOLLAR; 1795, 1796, most of 1797—Plain; some of 1797—Gripped.* **Mint:** *Philadelphia.*

1795, Lettered Edge,
With Pole; BW-1, C-1, B-1.

History. The design of the half cent changed in 1794 to a depiction, by Robert Scot, of Miss Liberty facing right. A smaller-headed portrait was used from 1795 on.

Striking and Sharpness. Half cents of 1794 usually are dark, with rough surfaces, and of low aesthetic quality. Most 1795's are on high-quality planchets, smooth and attractive, this being truer of the later plain-edge type than the early thick-planchet issue. Striking can be weak in areas. Often the denticles are incomplete on one or both sides. Many Small Head coins, particularly of 1795 to 1797, have very little detail on the hair, even in higher grades. Half cents of 1796 vary in quality; higher-grade pieces are usually attractive. Half cents of 1797 are usually seen in low grades and on poor planchets; striking varies widely, but is usually weak in areas. Denticles can be weak or can be prominent in various circulated grades, down to the lowest; on certain varieties of 1795 they are prominent even on well-worn coins. Grades must be assigned carefully, and expertise is recommended—combining knowledge of a given die variety and its relief or sharpness in the die, with observations of actual circulation wear. Grades of certified coins can vary widely in their interpretations.

Availability. As a general type, this issue is scarce, but available. Most are in lower grades, but VF and EF coins appear in the market with regularity.

GRADING STANDARDS

MS-60 to 70 (Mint State). *Obverse:* On MS–60 and 61 coins there are some traces of abrasion on the higher areas of the portrait. Luster in the field is incomplete, particularly in the center of the open areas. At MS-63, luster should be complete, and no abrasion is evident. At higher levels, the luster is deeper, and some original mint color may be seen. At MS-65 there are some scattered contact marks and possibly some traces of finger-

1794; BW-9, C-9, B-9. Graded MS-65.

prints or discoloration, but these should be minimal and not at all distracting. Above MS-65, a coin should approach perfection. *Reverse:* In the lower ranges some abrasions are seen on the higher areas of the leaves. Generally, luster is complete in all ranges, as the open areas are protected by the lettering and wreath. Otherwise, the same comments apply as for the obverse.

Illustrated coin: A spectacular coin of a year seldom seen in Mint State. Both sides have rich, brown surfaces. On the obverse the luster is light, while on the reverse it is not as noticeable. Note that the obverse die is in very high relief and of the Large Head style, while the reverse is in shallower relief.

AU-50, 53, 55, 58 (About Uncirculated).
Obverse: Friction is seen on the higher parts, particularly the center of the portrait. Friction and scattered marks are in the field, ranging from extensive at AU-50 to minimal at AU-58. To reiterate: knowledge of the die variety is important. For certain shallow-relief dies (such as those of 1797) an About Uncirculated coin may appear to be in a lower grade. Luster may be seen in protected

1794; BW-1a, C-1a, B-1a. Graded AU-50.

areas, minimal at AU-50, but sometimes extensive on an AU-58 coin. *Reverse:* Friction is seen on the higher wreath leaves and (not as easy to discern) on the letters. The fields, protected by the designs, show friction, but not as noticeably as on the obverse. At AU–55 and 58 little if any friction is seen. The reverse may have original luster, toned brown, minimal on lower About Uncirculated grades, sometimes extensive on higher. Grading at the About Uncirculated level is mainly done by viewing the obverse.

Illustrated coin: Note faint ruddy highlights in the protected areas. The devices are boldly impressed. On this variety the 179 in the date was punched low into the die, partly effaced, then repunched in a higher position. On the reverse, a natural planchet fissure, small and as struck, runs from the rim through the M of AMERICA, and a smaller fissure runs from the rim to the E of AMERICA.

EF-40, 45 (Extremely Fine). *Obverse:*
Wear is seen on the portrait overall, with some reduction or elimination of the separation of hair strands on the highest part. This varies by die variety, as some are better delineated than others. The cheek shows light wear. Luster is minimal or nonexistent at EF-40, and may survive in traces in protected areas (such as between the letters) at EF-45. *Reverse:* Wear is seen on the highest wreath and ribbon areas and the letters. Luster is minimal, but likely

1795, Pole to Cap, Lettered Edge; BW-1, C-1, B-1. Graded EF-45.

more noticeable than on the obverse, as the fields are protected by the designs and lettering. Sharpness will vary depending on the die variety. Expect certain issues of 1794 and 1797 to be lighter.

Illustrated coin: This coin has bold details and excellent centering.

VF-20, 30 (Very Fine). Obverse: Wear on the portrait has reduced the hair detail to indistinct or flat at the center. The border denticles are blended together, with many indistinct. No luster is seen. Again, knowing details of the die variety is important. A VF–20 or 30 1797 is very different in appearance from a 1794, Large Head, in the same grade. *Reverse:* The leaf details are nearly completely worn away at VF-20, with slight

1797; BW-2, C-2. Graded VF-30.

detail at VF-30. The border denticles are blended together, with many indistinct. No luster is seen. The sharpness of details depends on the die variety. Half cents of 1797 require special care in their study.

Illustrated coin: Minor roughness is apparent at the center of both sides, undoubtedly a trace of microporosity from the blank planchet, although the devices are overall bold from a well executed strike.

F-12, 15 (Fine). *Obverse:* The hair details are mostly worn away, with about one-third visible, mainly at the edges. Border denticles are weak or worn away in areas. F-15 shows slightly more detail. *Reverse:* The wreath leaves are worn flat, but their edges are distinct. Border denticles are weak or worn away in areas. F-15 shows slightly more detail.

Illustrated coin: This late-die-state variety has a noticeable die crack in the E of UNITED.

1794, High-Relief Head; BW-7, C-7, B-7. Graded F-15.

VG-8, 10 (Very Good). *Obverse:* The portrait is well worn, although the eye can be seen, and the hair tips at the left show separation. Border denticles are worn away on some issues (not as much for 1795 coins), and the border blends into the field in most if not all of the periphery. LIBERTY and the date are bold. VG-10, not an official ANA grading designation, is sometimes applied to especially nice Very Good coins. *Reverse:* The

1794, High Relief Head; BW-9, C-9, B-9. Graded VG-8.

wreath, bow, and lettering are seen in outline form, and some leaves and letters may be indistinct in parts. Border denticles are worn away, and the border blends into the field in most if not all of the periphery. In certain die varieties and die states, especially of 1797, some letters may be very weak or missing.

Illustrated coin: This coin exhibits roughness in the fields, but the same does not apply to the devices.

G-4, 6 (Good). *Obverse:* The portrait is worn smooth and is seen only in outline form, although the eye position can be discerned. LIBERTY and the date are complete, although the date may be weak. Denticles are gone on some, but not all, die varieties. *Reverse:* Extensive wear is seen overall. From half to two-thirds of the letters in UNITED STATES OF AMERICA, and the fraction numerals, are worn away. Certain shallow-relief dies

1794; BW-2a, C-2a, B-2a. Graded G-4.

may have letters missing. G-6 is often assigned to finer examples in this category.

Illustrated coin: On this coin the surfaces are heavily worn, yet with considerable boldness of detail remaining on the obverse.

AG-3 (About Good). *Obverse:* Wear is more extensive than on the preceding. The portrait is visible only in outline. LIBERTY is weak but usually fully discernible. The date is weak, and the bottoms of the digits may be worn away. *Reverse:* Parts of the wreath are visible in outline form, and all but a few letters are gone. Grading of AG-3 is usually done by the reverse, as the obverse typically appears to be in a slightly higher grade. If split grading were used, more than just a few half cents of this type could be designated as G-4 / AG-3 or even G-6 / AG-3.

1795, Plain Edge, Punctuated Date;
BW-5, C-4, B-4. Graded AG-3.

1794, Normal Head

1794, High-Relief Head

1795, With Pole

1795, No Pole

1795, Punctuated Date

	Mintage	Cert	Avg	%MS	AG-3	G-4	VG-8	F-12	VF-20	EF-40	AU-50	MS-60BN	MS-63BN
1794, All kinds	81,600												
1794, Normal Head		37	32.1	8%	$450	$575	$850	$1,800	$2,500	$5,000	$12,000	$25,000	$55,000
Auctions: $88,125, MS-63BN, April 2014													
1794, High-Relief Head		15	34.3	0%	$475	$600	$975	$1,850	$3,200	$6,200	$14,500	$27,500	$65,000
Auctions: $1,586, VF-20, October 2013													
1795, All kinds	139,690												
1795, Lettered Edge, With Pole		59	31.8	12%	$325	$600	$825	$1,350	$2,500	$6,000	$12,000	$17,000	$45,000
Auctions: $3,525, EF-40, September 2013; $2,820, VF-30, March 2015													
1795, Lettered Edge, Punctuated Date		6	17	0%	$350	$675	$875	$1,600	$3,000	$7,000	$13,500	$25,000	$55,000
Auctions: $12,925, AU-55, August 2013													
1795, Plain Edge, Punctuated Date		7	29.7	14%	$275	$550	$725	$1,250	$2,350	$5,500	$9,500	$15,000	$45,000
Auctions: $1,501, VF-20, August 2011													
1795, Plain Edge, No Pole (a)		34	28.5	0%	$220	$500	$675	$1,250	$2,000	$4,750	$8,500	$14,000	$25,000
Auctions: $7,638, AU-55, June 2014													

| | | 1796, "Dr. Edwards" Copy | | | 1797, 1 Above 1 | | | 1797, Low Head |

	Mintage	Cert	Avg	%MS	AG-3	G-4	VG-8	F-12	VF-20	EF-40	AU-50	MS-60BN	MS-63BN
1796, With Pole † (b)	1,390	22	38.6	45%	$10,500	$20,000	$27,500	$37,500	$55,000	$75,000	$95,000	$165,000	
Auctions: $76,375, EF-40, August 2013													
1796, No Pole †	(c)	1	62	100%	$22,500	$37,500	$55,000	$105,000	$150,000	$225,000	$300,000	$450,000	
Auctions: $891,250, MS-65BN, January 2014; $382, VG-8, September 2013													
1797, All kinds	127,840												
1797, 1 Above 1, Plain Edge		64	25.2	3%	$250	$500	$650	$1,100	$1,800	$4,000	$6,500	$15,000	
Auctions: $7,931, AU, March 2014													
1797, Plain Edge, Low Head		6	11.7	0%	$350	$575	$975	$2,250	$4,500	$14,000	—		
Auctions: $1,495, VG-10, February 2012													
1797, Plain Edge		65	21.8	5%	$275	$500	$750	$1,250	$3,500	$6,000	$8,500	$16,000	
Auctions: $3,055, AU-50, April 2013; $823, F-12, August 2015; $400, VG-8, September 2015; $505, G-6, January 2015													
1797, Lettered Edge		4	14.3	0%	$700	$1,400	$2,750	$7,000	$16,000	$50,000	$77,500		
Auctions: $7,638, VG-10, November 2013; $3,995, VG-10, March 2016													
1797, Gripped Edge		0	n/a		$20,000	$45,000	$75,000	$145,000	—	—	—		
Auctions: $195,500, G-6, September 2011													

† Both 1796 half cent varieties are ranked in the *100 Greatest U.S. Coins* (fourth edition), as a single entry. **a.** Many of this date/variety were struck on cut-down cents (coins that had been rejected for circulation by Mint workers), or on planchets cut from English-made Talbot, Allum & Lee tokens (see the *Whitman Encyclopedia of Colonial and Early American Coins*). **b.** The deceptive "Dr. Edwards" struck copy of this coin has a different head and larger letters, as pictured. **c.** Included in 1796, With Pole, mintage figure.

DRAPED BUST (1800–1808)

Designer: *Robert Scot.* **Weight:** *5.44 grams.* **Composition:** *Copper.*
Diameter: *23.5 mm.* **Edge:** *Plain.* **Mint:** *Philadelphia.*

1804, Crosslet 4, Stems to Wreath;
BW-9, C-10, B-9.

History. By the turn of the century the Draped Bust design was already familiar to Americans from its use on cents and silver coins. The motif was introduced to the half cent in 1800, and was used through 1808.

Striking and Sharpness. Striking varies. Weakness is often seen at the center of the obverse and on the wreath leaves on the reverse. Planchet quality is often porous and dark for 1802, 1803, 1807, and 1808 due to the copper stock used.

Availability. As a type, Draped Bust half cents are available in any grade desired, up to and including Mint State, the latter usually dated 1806 (occasionally 1800 and, less often, 1804). The year 1804 includes many different die varieties and die states. Apart from aspects of strike, cherrypicking for planchet quality is essential for 1802, 1803, 1807, and 1808.

GRADING STANDARDS

MS-60 to 70 (Mint State). *Obverse:* In the lower grades, MS-60 and 61, some slight abrasions can be seen on the higher areas of the portrait. Luster in the field is incomplete, particularly in the center of the open areas, which on this type are very extensive. At the MS-63 level, luster should be nearly complete, and no abrasions evident. In higher levels, the luster is complete and deeper and some original mint color may be seen. MS-64

1800; BW-1, C-1, B-1. Graded MS-62.

coins may have some slight discoloration or scattered contact marks. A well-graded MS-65 or higher coin has full, rich luster; no marks visible except under magnification; and a blend of brown toning or nicely mixed (not stained or blotchy) mint color and natural brown toning. *Reverse:* In the lower Mint State ranges some abrasions are seen on the higher areas of the leaves. Generally, luster is complete in all ranges, as the open areas are protected by the lettering and wreath. Sharpness of the leaves can vary by die variety, so check this aspect. Otherwise, the same comments apply as for the obverse.

AU-50, 53, 55, 58 (About Uncirculated). *Obverse:* Friction is seen on the higher parts, particularly the hair of Miss Liberty. Friction and scattered marks are in the field, ranging from extensive at AU-50 to minimal at AU-58. Luster may be seen in protected areas, minimal at AU-50, with more at AU-58. At AU-58 the field may retain some luster, as well. In all instances, the luster is lesser in area and in "depth" than on the reverse of this type.

1800; BW-1, C-1, B-1. Graded AU-58.

Reverse: Friction is evident on the higher wreath leaves and (not as easy to discern) on the letters. Again, the die variety should be checked. The fields, protected by the designs, show friction, but not as noticeably as on the obverse. At AU-55 and 58, little if any friction is seen. The reverse may have original luster, toned brown, minimal on lower About Uncirculated grades, often extensive at AU-58.

    Illustrated coin: The motifs are very boldly rendered, except for partial weakness on the lower obverse and OF on the upper reverse, which is virtually missing due to the late die state.

EF-40, 45 (Extremely Fine). *Obverse:* Wear is seen on the portrait overall, with reduction or elimination of some separation of hair strands on the highest part. The cheek shows light wear. Luster is minimal or non-existent at EF-40, and may survive among the letters of LIBERTY at EF-45. *Reverse:* Wear is seen on the highest wreath and ribbon areas, and the letters. Luster is minimal, but likely more noticeable than on the obverse, as the fields are protected by the designs and lettering.

1800; BW-1, C-1, B-1. Graded EF-40.

VF-20, 30 (Very Fine). *Obverse:* Wear on the portrait has reduced the hair detail to indistinct or flat at the center. The border denticles are blended together, with many indistinct. No luster is seen. *Reverse:* The leaf details are nearly completely worn away at VF-20, and with slight detail at VF-30. The border denticles are blended together, with many indistinct. No luster is seen.

Illustrated coin: Struck from a later die state, the reverse shows a bisecting die crack.

1803; BW-1, C-1, B-1. Graded VF-20.

F-12, 15 (Fine). *Obverse:* The hair details are mostly worn away, with about one-third visible, mainly at the edges. Border denticles are weak or worn away in areas. F-15 shows slightly more detail. *Reverse:* The wreath leaves are worn flat, but their edges are distinct. HALF CENT may be missing on weakly struck varieties (also true of lower grades given below). Border denticles are weak or worn away in areas. F-15 shows slightly more detail.

1804, "Spiked Chin"; BW-5, C-8, B-7. Graded F-15.

Illustrated coin: This is the "Spiked Chin" variety, so called because of a thorn-like projection from the chin. The variety does not affect the grade.

VG-8, 10 (Very Good). *Obverse:* The portrait is well worn, although the eye can be seen, as can hints of hair detail (some at the left shows separation). Curls now appear as mostly solid blobs. Border denticles are worn away on most varieties, and the rim, although usually present, begins to blend into the field. LIBERTY and the date are bold. VG-10, not an official ANA grading designation, is sometimes applied to especially nice Very Good coins. *Reverse:* The wreath, bow, and letter-

1804, Plain 4, Stems to Wreath; BW-12, C-11, B-12. Graded VG-10.

ing are seen in outline form, and some leaves and letters may be indistinct in parts. The border may blend into the field on some of the periphery.

Illustrated coin: This coin is has many scratches, which detract from overall eye appeal.

G-4, 6 (Good). *Obverse:* The portrait is worn smooth and is seen only in outline form, although the eye position can be discerned. LIBERTY and the date are complete, although the date may be weak. The border blends into the field more extensively than on the preceding, but significant areas are still seen. *Reverse:* Extensive wear is seen overall. From one-half to two-thirds of the letters in UNITED STATES OF AMERICA and the

1808, 8 Over 7; BW-2, C-2, B-2. Graded G-4.

fraction numerals are worn away. G-6 is often assigned to finer examples in this category.

Illustrated coin: A slightly off-center strike has allowed areas of heavier wear to creep in near the borders. There are many noticeable scratches on the obverse.

AG-3 (About Good). *Obverse:* Wear is more extensive than on the preceding. The portrait is visible only in outline. LIBERTY is weak but usually discernible. The date is weak, and the bottoms of the digits may be worn away, but must be identifiable. *Reverse:* Parts of the wreath are visible in outline form, and all but a few letters are gone.

1802, 2 Over 0; BW-2, C-2, B-2. Graded AG-3.

1st Reverse
(Style of 1800)

2nd Reverse
(Style of 1802)

1803, Normally Spaced 3

1803, Widely Spaced 3

1804, Plain 4

1804, Crosslet 4

Stems to Wreath

Stemless Wreath

1804, "Spiked Chin"

	Mintage	Cert	Avg	%MS	AG-3	G-4	VG-8	F-12	VF-20	EF-40	AU-50	MS-60BN	MS-63BN
1800	202,908	222	43.2	29%	$55	$110	$150	$175	$300	$700	$1,000	$2,250	$4,000
Auctions: $282, VF-35, May 2015; $329, VF-25, January 2015; $4,113, VF-20, June 2013													
1802, 2 Over 0, Reverse of 1800	(a)	2	2	0%	$10,000	$22,000	$35,000	$55,000	$75,000	$95,000	—		
Auctions: $35,938, VG-8, April 2009; $4,935, AG-0, March 2016													
1802, 2 Over 0, Reverse of 1802	20,266	46	9.2	0%	$475	$1,000	$2,250	$4,750	$12,500	$25,000	—		
Auctions: $4,406, F-12, February 2013; $940, G-6, June 2015; $940, G-6, March 2016; $940, G-6, August 2016; $960, G-6, January 2018													
1803	(b)	219	28.7	8%	$45	$95	$120	$175	$325	$950	$1,500	$3,250	$7,000
Auctions: $646, VF-35, August 2015; $376, VF-25, June 2015; $235, VF-30, February 2015; $153, VG-8, February 2015; $79, G-4, March 2018													
1803, Widely Spaced 3	92,000	24	32.5	8%	$50	$100	$135	$185	$325	$950	$1,500	$3,500	$7,500
Auctions: $1,840, AU-55, April 2012													
1804, All kinds	1,055,312												
1804, Plain 4, Stems to Wreath		12	30.8	0%	$40	$100	$125	$200	$475	$1,300	$2,200	$4,000	
Auctions: $4,994, AU-58, October 2013; $1,410, EF-45, March 2016; $823, VF-30, August 2015													
1804, Plain 4, Stemless Wreath		215	43	16%	$40	$85	$125	$145	$225	$385	$675	$1,300	$2,800
Auctions: $940, AU-58, June 2015; $646, AU-55, October 2015; $588, AU-55, August 2015; $259, AU-50, May 2015													
1804, Crosslet 4, Stemless		57	54.8	46%	$40	$85	$125	$145	$225	$385	$675	$1,300	$2,800
Auctions: $5,141, MS-64BN, September 2013; $376, EF-40, January 2015													
1804, Crosslet 4, Stems		119	44.5	16%	$40	$85	$125	$145	$225	$400	$675	$1,300	$2,800
Auctions: $705, AU-55, March 2015; $470, EF-45, October 2015; $364, EF-40, April 2015; $282, VF-35, August 2015													
1804, "Spiked Chin"		403	42.7	12%	$40	$95	$125	$225	$350	$600	$950	$2,000	$3,500
Auctions: $764, AU-53BN, September 2015; $646, AU-50, February 2015; $423, EF-45, June 2015; $247, EF-40, July 2015													

a. Included in 1800 mintage figure. **b.** Included in 1802, 2 Over 0, Second Reverse, mintage figure.

1805, Medium 5

1805, Small 5

1805, Large 5

1806, Small 6

1806, Large 6

1808, Normal Date

1808, 8 Over 7

	Mintage	Cert	Avg	%MS	AG-3	G-4	VG-8	F-12	VF-20	EF-40	AU-50	MS-60BN	MS-63BN
1805, All kinds	814,464												
1805, Medium 5, Stemless		52	37.8	12%	$40	$85	$125	$145	$225	$400	$750	$1,350	$3,000
Auctions: $4,113, MS-64BN, April 2014; $517, EF-45, January 2015; $447, EF-40, January 2015													
1805, Small 5, Stems		8	13.1	0%	$500	$1,000	$1,600	$4,000	$8,000	$17,000	$50,000		
Auctions: $1,116, VG-8, August 2015; $1,175, G-6, March 2016													
1805, Large 5, Stems		32	33.3	0%	$40	$85	$125	$145	$225	$425	$850	$1,700	$3,750
Auctions: $1,293, AU-55, July 2015; $353, VF-35, June 2015; $223, VF-30, July 2015													
1806, All kinds	356,000												
1806, Small 6, Stems		20	29.7	0%	$100	$235	$425	$750	$1,650	$3,500	$9,000	$12,500	
Auctions: $646, F-15, September 2016; $505, F-12, July 2016; $400, VG-10, March 2016; $188, G-6, August 2016													
1806, Small 6, Stemless		167	41.7	13%	$40	$85	$125	$145	$175	$325	$675	$1,200	$2,900
Auctions: $823, AU-58, January 2015; $564, AU-50, September 2015; $517, AU-50, August 2015; $329, EF-45, February 2015													
1806, Large 6, Stems		96	48.7	39%	$40	$85	$125	$145	$175	$325	$675	$1,200	$2,900
Auctions: $5,581, MS-63RB, June 2014; $780, AU-55, April 2018													
1807	476,000	299	35.9	6%	$40	$85	$125	$145	$200	$500	$1,000	$2,000	$3,750
Auctions: $1,175, AU-58, February 2013; $212, VF-20, May 2015													
1808, All kinds	400,000												
1808, Normal Date		159	28.5	3%	$40	$85	$125	$145	$220	$525	$1,300	$2,500	$5,000
Auctions: $823, AU-50, June 2014; $447, EF-45, January 2015; $200, VF-25, June 2015; $660, EF-45, January 2018													
1808, 8 Over 7		49	18.9	0%	$80	$150	$350	$750	$2,000	$4,000	$10,000		
Auctions: $2,585, EF-40, April 2013													

CLASSIC HEAD (1809–1836)

Designer: *John Reich.* **Weight:** *5.44 grams.* **Composition:** *Copper.*
Diameter: *23.5 mm.* **Edge:** *Plain.* **Mint:** *Philadelphia.*

Circulation Strike
1833; BW-1.

Proof
1836; BW-1.

History. The Classic Head design (by Mint engraver John Reich) made its first appearance on the half cent in 1809, a year after it was adopted for the one-cent coin. A very similar motif of Miss Liberty was used on the quarter eagles and half eagles of the 1830s.

Striking and Sharpness. Coins of 1809 to 1811 usually have areas of light or incomplete striking. Grading coins of the early years requires special care and expertise. Sometimes coins as high as MS appear "blurry" in areas, due to the dies and striking. Those of later years are often found well struck and are easier to grade. Areas to check include the denticles and rims on both sides, the star centers and hair detail on the obverse, and the leaf detail on the reverse.

Availability. As a type this issue is found easily enough, although 1811 is scarce and 1831 and 1836 are notable rarities. MS coins from old hoards exist for certain of the later dates, particularly 1828, 1833, and 1835, but often have spotting, and many seen in the marketplace are cleaned or recolored. Care is advised. Although 1809–1811 half cents are often seen with extensive wear, those of the 1820s and 1830s are not often seen less than VF, as they did not circulate extensively.

GRADING STANDARDS

MS-60 to 70 (Mint State). *Obverse:* In the lower grades, MS–60 and 61, some slight abrasions can be seen on the portrait, most evident on the cheek, as the hair details are complex on this type. Luster in the field is complete or nearly complete. At MS-63, luster should be complete, and no abrasions are evident. In higher levels, the luster is complete and deeper, and some original mint color may be seen. MS-64 coins may have

1810; BW-1, C-1, B-1. Graded MS-64BN.

some slight discoloration or scattered contact marks. A well-graded MS-65 or higher coin has full, rich luster, with no marks visible except under magnification, and has a nice blend of brown toning or nicely mixed (not stained or blotchy) mint color and natural brown toning. Coins dated 1809 to 1811 may exhibit significant weakness of details due to striking (and/or, in the case of most 1811's, porous planchet stock). *Reverse:* In the lower Mint State grades, some abrasions are seen on the higher areas of the leaves. Mint luster is complete in all Mint State grades, as the open areas are protected by the lettering and wreath. Sharpness of the leaves can vary by die variety, so check this aspect. Otherwise, the same comments apply as for the obverse. Coins dated 1809 to 1811 may exhibit significant weakness of details due to striking (and/or, in the case of most 1811's, porous planchet stock).

Illustrated coin: Some surface marks on the coin holder obscure the reverse, but no such marks mar the surface of this sharply struck coin.

AU-50, 53, 55, 58 (About Uncirculated). *Obverse:* Friction is seen on the higher parts, particularly the cheek and hair (under magnification) of Miss Liberty. Friction and scattered marks are in the field, ranging from extensive at AU-50 to minimal at AU-58. Luster may be seen in protected areas, minimal at the AU-50 level, with more showing at AU-58. At AU-58 the field may retain some luster as well. *Reverse:* Friction is seen on the

1828, 12 Stars; BW-3, C-2, B-3. Graded AU-58.

higher wreath leaves and (not as easy to discern) on the letters. Again, half cents of 1809 to 1811 require special attention. The fields, protected by the designs, show friction, but not as noticeably as on the obverse. At AU–55 and 58, little if any friction is seen. The reverse may have original luster, toned brown, minimal on lower About Uncirculated grades, often extensive at AU-58.

EF-40, 45 (Extremely Fine). *Obverse:* Wear is seen on the portrait overall, with reduction or elimination of some separation of hair strands. The cheek shows light wear. Luster is minimal or nonexistent at EF-40 but may survive among the letters of LIBERTY at EF-45. *Reverse:* Wear is seen on the highest wreath and ribbon areas and the letters. Luster is minimal, but likely more noticeable than on the obverse, as the fields are protected by the designs and lettering.

1831, Original; BW-1, C-1, B-1. Graded EF-45.

VF-20, 30 (Very Fine). *Obverse:* Wear on the portrait has reduced the hair detail, but much can still be seen (in this respect the present type differs dramatically from earlier types). *Reverse:* The wreath details, except for the edges of the leaves, are worn away at VF-20, and have slightly more detail at VF-30.

Illustrated coin: This coin is lightly struck at the left-reverse border, despite overall bold striking elsewhere.

1811, Close Date; BW-3, C-3, B-2. Graded VF-30.

F-12, 15 (Fine). *Obverse:* The hair details are fewer than at the preceding level, but many are still present. Stars have flat centers. F-15 shows slightly more detail. *Reverse:* The wreath leaves are worn flat, but their edges are distinct. F-15 shows slightly more detail.

1809, Normal Date. Graded F-15.

VG-8, 10 (Very Good). *Obverse:* The portrait is well worn, although the eye and ear can be seen, as can some hair detail. The border is well defined in most areas. *Reverse:* The wreath, bow, and lettering are seen in outline form, and some leaves and letters may be indistinct in parts. The border is well defined in most areas.

1809, 9 Over Inverted 9; BW-6, C-5, B-5. Graded VG-10.

G-4, 6 (Good). *Obverse:* The portrait is worn smooth and is seen only in outline form. Much of LIBERTY on the headband is readable, but the letters are weak. The stars are bold in outline. Much of the rim can be discerned. *Reverse:* Extensive wear is seen overall. Lettering in UNITED STATES OF AMERICA ranges from weak but complete (although the ANA grading guidelines allow for only half to be readable; the ANA text

1811; BW-1, C-1, B-1. Graded G-6.

illustrates the words in full) to having perhaps a third of the letters missing. HALF CENT is usually bold.

Illustrated coin: While ultimately well-preserved for the grade, this coin is a bit rough in texture, with light pitting and traces of old, inactive surface build up.

AG-3 (About Good). *Obverse:* Wear is more extensive than on the preceding. The portrait is visible only in outline. A few letters of LIBERTY are discernible in the headband. The stars are weak or worn away on their outer edges. The date is light. *Reverse:* The wreath is visible in outline form. Most or even all of UNITED STATES OF AMERICA is worn away. HALF CENT is usually readable.

1811; BW-1, C-1, B-1. Graded AG-3.

PF-60 to 70 (Proof). Proofs were struck of various years in the 1820s and 1830s, with 1831 and 1836 being great rarities (these dates were also restruck at the Mint circa 1859 and later). Some prooflike circulation strikes (especially of the 1833 date) have been certified as Proofs. Except for the years 1831 and 1836, for which Proofs are unequivocal, careful study is advised when contemplating the purchase of a coin described as Proof.

1831, First Restrike; BW-1a, C-PR-2, B-2. Graded PF-66BN.

Blotchy and recolored Proofs are often seen, but hardly ever described as such. Probably fewer than 25 of the Proofs of this type are truly pristine—without one problem or another. *Obverse and Reverse:* Proofs that are extensively hairlined or have dull surfaces, this being characteristic of many issues (1831 and 1836 usually excepted), are graded PF–60 to 62 or 63. This includes artificially toned and recolored coins, a secret that isn't really secret among knowledgeable collectors and dealers, but is rarely described in print. To qualify as PF-65 or higher, hairlines should be microscopic, and there should be no trace of friction. Surfaces should be prooflike or, better, fully mirrored, without dullness.

Illustrated coin: Note the traces of mint red throughout and the blue iridescence of the reverse. The reverse die is severely cracked from the F in OF to the T of UNITED.

1809, Normal Date

1809, Small 0 Inside 0

1809, 9 Over Inverted 9

1811, Wide Date

1811, Close Date

1828, 13 Stars

1828, 12 Stars

	Mintage	Cert	Avg	%MS	G-4	VG-8	F-12	VF-20	EF-40	AU-50	MS-60BN	MS-63BN	MS-63RB
1809, All kinds	1,154,572												
1809, Normal Date		427	44	22%	$55	$95	$115	$125	$150	$300	$850	$1,500	$2,000
Auctions: $588, MS-61BN, June 2015; $823, AU-58, January 2015; $388, AU-55, March 2015; $176, AU-50, January 2015													
1809, Small o Inside 0		16	36.8	0%	$65	$85	$135	$160	$450	$900	$1,400	$5,000	
Auctions: $55, G-4, January 2013													
1809, 9 Over Inverted 9 (a)		238	49.6	18%	$65	$85	$125	$150	$375	$750	$1,300	$2,200	$3,000
Auctions: $1,116, AU-58, June 2015; $423, AU-50, January 2015; $306, EF-45, September 2015; $200, VF-30, May 2015													
1810	215,000	104	40.1	17%	$70	$100	$150	$270	$575	$1,000	$2,000	$3,200	$6,750
Auctions: $2,800, MS-63BN, April 2014; $376, VF-30, May 2015													
1811, All kinds	63,140												
1811, Wide Date		6	24.5	0%	$450	$850	$1,900	$2,750	$6,500	$10,000	$30,000	$75,000	
Auctions: $764, VF-20, December 2015; $494, VF-20, August 2016; $1,050, F-12, February 2018													
1811, Close Date		9	21.4	0%	$400	$725	$1,750	$2,500	$6,500	$10,000	$30,000	$75,000	
Auctions: $26,450, AU-50, September 2011; $1,050, F-12, February 2018													
1811, Reverse of 1802, Unofficial Restrike (b)		5	63.8	100%					—	—	$16,000	$20,000	$25,000
Auctions: $23,000, MS-64BN, September 2008													
1825	63,000	296	47.4	22%	$55	$90	$100	$115	$200	$325	$900	$1,800	$3,000
Auctions: $529, MS-61BN, June 2015; $564, AU-55, May 2015; $282, AU-55, January 2015; $259, EF-45, June 2015													
1826	234,000	383	48.2	27%	$55	$90	$100	$115	$150	$300	$600	$1,000	$1,300
Auctions: $999, MS-63BN, August 2015; $764, MS-62BN, September 2015; $306, MS-61BN, May 2015; $165, EF-45, August 2015													
1828, All kinds	606,000												
1828, 13 Stars		139	49.2	37%	$50	$90	$100	$115	$120	$225	$350	$600	$1,000
Auctions: $1,028, MS-64RB, January 2015; $999, MS-64BN, January 2015; $590, MS-63BN, February 2015; $309, MS-62BN, September 2015													
1828, 12 Stars		221	50.3	25%	$50	$90	$115	$120	$250	$425	$1,300	$1,850	$3,500
Auctions: $2,468, MS-63BN, February 2014													
1829	487,000	376	50.6	43%	$50	$90	$100	$115	$140	$220	$400	$700	$1,100
Auctions: $482, MS-63BN, February 2015; $764, MS-61BN, June 2015; $517, AU-58, September 2015; $235, AU-53, September 2015													

a. Traditionally called 9 Over Inverted 9, but recent research shows it not to have an inverted digit. **b.** This coin is extremely rare.

1831, Proof, Restrike	Reverse of 1831–1836	Reverse of 1840–1857

	Mintage	Cert	Avg	%MS	VG-8	F-12	VF-20	EF-40	AU-50	MS-60BN	MS-63BN PF-60BN	MS-63RB PF-63BN	MS-65RB PF-65BN
1831, Original (a)		6	52	50%					$50,000	$75,000			
Auctions: No auction records available.													
1831, Original, Proof (b)	2,200	5	53.4								$85,000	$125,000	
Auctions: $57,281, PF-60BN, January 2014													
1831, Restrike, Large Berries, Proof (Reverse of 1836)	25–35	9	65.7								$10,000	$15,000	$25,000
Auctions: $47,000, PF-65RB, February 2014													
1831, Restrike, Small Berries, Proof (Reverse of 1840–1857)	10–15	0	n/a								$14,000	$21,500	$40,000
Auctions: $63,250, PF-66BN, July 2009													
1832 (c)	51,000	467	52	36%	$65	$90	$110	$125	$200	$325	$475	$875	$4,000
Auctions: $999, MS-64BN, June 2015; $306, MS-62BN, January 2015; $282, MS-61BN, May 2015; $259, AU-58, August 2015													
1832, Proof	10–15	1	64								$7,000	$10,000	$17,500
Auctions: $44,063, PF-64BN, January 2014													
1833 (c)	103,000	669	57.2	62%	$65	$90	$110	$125	$200	$325	$450	$750	$3,500
Auctions: $940, MS-64BN, February 2015; $823, MS-64BN, June 2015; $410, MS-63BN, May 2015; $212, AU-58, January 2015													
1833, Proof	25–35	14	64.1								$5,000	$6,000	$10,500
Auctions: $11,163, PF-65BN, March 2013													
1834 (c)	141,000	679	55.1	48%	$65	$90	$110	$125	$200	$300	$450	$750	$3,500
Auctions: $541, MS-64BN, January 2015; $423, MS-63BN, September 2015; $353, MS-62BN, March 2015; $259, AU-58, January 2015													
1834, Proof	25–35	13	64.8								$5,000	$6,000	$11,000
Auctions: $18,800, PF-64RB, August 2013													
1835 (c)	398,000	1,291	54.5	52%	$65	$85	$110	$125	$200	$325	$450	$750	$3,500
Auctions: $823, MS-64BN, August 2015; $646, MS-64, March 2015; $353, MS-63BN, May 2015; $329, MS-62BN, April 2015													
1835, Proof	15–20	2	64								$5,000	$6,000	$10,500
Auctions: $11,163, PF-64RB, January 2014													
1836, Original, Proof	140–240	13	63.8								$6,000	$8,000	$12,500
Auctions: $12,925, PF-64BN, April 2013													
1836, Restrike, Proof (Reverse of 1840–1857)	8–15	2	64.5								$9,000	$17,000	$30,000
Auctions: No auction records available.													

a. Circulation strike. **b.** Beware of altered date. **c.** The figures given here are thought to be correct, although Mint records report these quantities for 1833 through 1836 rather than 1832 through 1835.

1837 "HALF CENT" TOKEN

The last circulation-strike half cents of the Classic Head design were minted in 1835, and Proofs of the series were made in 1836 (see next section). No half cents of any format were minted in 1837, 1838, or 1839—it would be 1840 before the denomination started up again, with the Braided Hair type.

To help fill that gap for date-by-date collectors, in the 1930s Wayte Raymond included in his "National" brand of coin albums a slot for a half cent–sized Hard Times token dated 1837. The token had been privately struck in the thousands as a supply of small change in the midst of the country's financial stagnation of the 1830s and early 1840s. It joined several hundred types of larger, cent-sized copper tokens, all privately manufactured and put into circulation by enterprising businesspeople, as substitutes for the federal government's half cents and large cents that were no longer circulating in any quantity.

Raymond's dignifying of the 1837 token brought about a new numismatic tradition. Half-cent collectors began to include the token—despite its not being official federal coinage—in their collections, and today the "Half Cent Worth of Pure Copper" is often found among their treasured coins.

	G-4	VG-8	F-12	VF-20	EF-40	AU-50	MS-60
1837 Token *(not a coin)*	$45	$65	$75	$110	$200	$375	$700

BRAIDED HAIR (1840–1857)

Designer: *Christian Gobrecht.* **Weight:** *5.44 grams.* **Composition:** *Copper.*
Diameter: *23 mm.* **Edge:** *Plain.* **Mint:** *Philadelphia.*

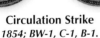

Circulation Strike	Proof
1854; BW-1, C-1, B-1.	1843; BW-1c, C-SR-13, B-3.

History. The Braided Hair half cent debuted in 1840, a year after the same design was introduced on copper cents. There was scant commercial demand for this denomination, so only Proofs were struck from 1840 to 1848 and in 1852. (In 1849–1851 and 1853–1857 both Proofs and circulation strikes were made.) Ultimately the half cent was discontinued by the Act of February 21, 1857. After that point the coins were rapidly withdrawn from circulation, and by 1860 virtually all had disappeared from commerce.

Striking and Sharpness. Many if not most Braided Hair half cents are well struck, and nearly all are on good planchet stock. Check these points for sharpness: the denticles on both sides; the star centers and hair detail on the obverse; and the leaf detail on the reverse.

Availability. Because Braided Hair half cents were not struck for circulation until 1849 and they did not circulate after the 1850s, they never acquired extensive wear. Most coins grade EF-40 and finer. Lower grades are sometimes seen, but are not in demand.

GRADING STANDARDS

MS–60 to 70 (Mint State). *Obverse:* In the lower Mint State grades, MS–60 and 61, some slight abrasion can be seen on the portrait, most evidently on the cheek. Check the tip of the coronet as well. Luster in the field is complete, or nearly so. At MS–63, luster should be complete, and no abrasions evident. At higher levels, the luster is complete and deeper, and some original mint color may be seen. Mint frost on this type is usually

1849, Large Date; BW-3, C-1, B-4. Graded MS-63BN.

deep, sometimes satiny, but hardly ever prooflike. MS-64 coins may have some slight discoloration or scattered contact marks. A well-graded MS-65 or higher coin has full, rich luster; no contact marks visible except under magnification; and a nice blend of brown toning or nicely mixed (not stained or blotchy) mint color and natural brown toning. The late Walter Breen stated that he had never seen an 1853 (common date) half cent with extensive original mint color, but these are plentiful with brown-toned surfaces. *Reverse:* In the lower Mint State grades some abrasions are seen on the higher areas of the leaves. Mint luster is complete in all Mint State grades, as the open areas are protected by the lettering and wreath.

AU-50, 53, 55, 58 (About Uncirculated). *Obverse:* Wear is evident on the cheek, the hair above the forehead, and the tip of the coronet. Friction is evident in the field. At AU-58, luster may be present except in the center of the fields. As the grades go down to AU-50, wear is more evident on the portrait. Wear is seen on the stars, but is not as easy to discern as it is elsewhere. At AU-50 there is either no luster or only traces of luster close

1849, Large Date; BW-3, C-1, B-4. Graded AU-50.

to the letters and devices. *Reverse:* Wear is most evident on the highest areas of the leaves and the ribbon bow. Luster is present in the fields. As the grades go downward from AU–58 to 50, wear increases and luster decreases. At the AU-50 level there is either no luster or traces of luster close to the letters and devices.

   Illustrated coin: This coin shows Full Details on both sides, and has eye-pleasing, light-brown surfaces.

EF-40, 45 (Extremely Fine). *Obverse:* Wear is more extensive on the portrait, including the cheek, hair, and coronet. The star centers are worn down slightly. Traces of luster are minimal, if at all existent. *Reverse:* The centers of the leaves are well worn, with detail visible only near the edges of the leaves and nearby, with the higher parts worn flat. Letters show significant wear. Luster, if present, is minimal.

1853; BW-1, C-1, B-1. Graded EF-40.

VF-20, 30 (Very Fine). *Obverse:* Wear is more extensive than at the preceding levels. Some of the strands of hair are fused together. The center radials of the stars are worn nearly completely away. *Reverse:* The leaves show more extensive wear, with details visible at the edges, and only minimally and not on all leaves. The lettering shows smooth, even wear.

The Braided Hair half cent is seldom collected in grades lower than VF-20.

1849, Large Date; BW-3, C-1, B-4. Graded VF-30.

PF-60 to 70 (Proof). For the issues of 1840 to 1848, the 1849, Small Date, and the issues of 1852, only Proofs were made, without related examples for circulation. All were restruck at the Mint. Generally, the quality of these Proofs is very good, with excellent striking of details and nice planchet quality. *Obverse and Reverse:* Superb gems at PF–65 and 66 show hairlines only under high magnification, and at PF-67 none are seen. The

1843, First Restrike; BW-2, C-SR-5, B-2. PF-64RB.

fields are deeply mirrorlike. There is no evidence of friction. At lower levels, hairlines increase, with a profusion at PF–60 to 62 (and also a general dullness of the fields). Typical color for an undipped coin ranges from light or iridescent brown to brown with some traces of mint color. Except for issues in the 1850s, Proofs are nearly always BN or, less often, RB. The rare Proofs of the 1840s are sometimes seen with light wear and can be classified according to the About Uncirculated and Extremely Fine comments above, except in place of "luster" read "Proof surface."

Illustrated coin: Overall this coin's surfaces are smooth, and the dominant sandy-olive patina belies semi reflective tendencies in the fields and gold, apricot and lilac undertones when viewed under direct light.

Large Berries (Original Strike)	Small Berries (Restrike)

	Mintage	Cert	Avg	%MS	VG-8	F-12	VF-20	EF-40	AU-50	MS-60BN / PF-60BN	MS-63BN / PF-63BN	MS-63RB	MS-65RB / PF-65BN
1840, Original, Proof	125–150	11	63.8							$5,350	$6,500		$10,000
Auctions: $7,475, PF-62BN, August 2006													
1840, Restrike, Proof	21–25	7	64.4							$5,350	$6,500		$9,250
Auctions: $25,850, PF-65RB, June 2014													
1841, Original, Proof	150–250	19	64.2							$4,500	$5,500		$10,000
Auctions: $21,150, PF-65BN, September 2013; $4,700, PF-58, September 2015; $2,400, PF-40, February 2018													
1841, Restrike, Proof	15–19	8	64.6							$4,500	$5,500		$8,750
Auctions: $8,625, PF-66BN, June 2008													

1849, Small Date
(Proof Only)

1849, Large Date

	Mintage	Cert	Avg	%MS	VG-8	F-12	VF-20	EF-40	AU-50	MS-60BN	MS-63BN PF-60BN	MS-63RB PF-63BN	MS-65RB PF-65BN
1842, Original, Proof	120–180	6	63.5								$5,500	$7,000	$10,000
Auctions: $15,275, PF-64BN, February 2014; $12,925, PF-64, January 2015													
1842, Restrike, Proof	35–45	10	64.7								$4,500	$5,500	$8,750
Auctions: $20,700, PF-65RB, April 2010													
1843, Original, Proof	125–200	6	62.7								$4,500	$5,500	$10,000
Auctions: $73,438, PF-65RD, April 2014													
1843, Restrike, Proof	37–44	7	64.7								$4,750	$5,700	$8,750
Auctions: $9,988, PF-64BN, February 2014													
1844, Original, Proof	120–180	9	62.9								$5,000	$6,000	$12,500
Auctions: $4,888, PF-50, May 2008													
1844, Restrike, Proof	21–26	2	65.5								$4,750	$5,750	$8,750
Auctions: $1,777, PF, February 2014													
1845, Original, Proof	110–170	3	65								$5,000	$6,000	$15,000
Auctions: $23,500, PF-64BN, April 2013													
1845, Restrike, Proof	20–24	9	64.4								$4,500	$5,400	$9,000
Auctions: $9,200, PF-65BN, October 2011													
1846, Original, Proof	125–200	8	64								$5,000	$6,000	$12,500
Auctions: $21,150, PF-64BN, January 2014													
1846, Restrike, Proof	19–24	8	65								$4,750	$5,750	$8,750
Auctions: $23,630, PF-66BN, June 2014; $15,275, PF-66BN, October 2015													
1847, Original, Proof	200–300	10	64.4								$5,000	$6,000	$12,500
Auctions: $5,288, PF-63BN, January 2014													
1847, Restrike, Proof	33–44	15	64.7								$4,500	$5,500	$8,500
Auctions: $15,275, PF-66BN, January 2014													
1848, Original, Proof	150–225	3	64.3								$5,500	$6,250	$15,000
Auctions: $10,350, PF-64RB, September 2003													
1848, Restrike, Proof	40–47	12	64.5								$4,500	$5,600	$8,500
Auctions: $6,169, PF-64BN, February 2014													
1849, Large Date	39,864	297	57.6	60%	$60	$75	$90	$150	$240	$500	$700	$900	$2,700
Auctions: $517, MS-63, August 2016; $353, AU-58, June 2016; $176, AU-55, October 2016; $336, AU-55, February 2018													
1849, Original, Small Date, Proof	70–90	4	59								$4,500	$5,500	$10,000
Auctions: $8,813, PF-64RB, April 2014													
1849, Restrike, Small Date, Proof	30–36	4	64.3								$5,000	$5,750	$9,750
Auctions: $7,344, PF-64BN, January 2014													
1850	39,812	278	56.9	53%	$60	$75	$125	$175	$275	$600	$800	$1,050	$3,000
Auctions: $7,210, MS-65, February 2016; $1,998, MS-64, July 2015; $517, AU-55, March 2016; $528, AU-55, January 2018													
1850, Proof	10–20	9	62.7								$5,000	$7,000	$13,000
Auctions: $17,625, PF-64, May 2015; $5,875, PF-63BN, January 2014													
1851	147,672	829	57.8	60%	$60	$75	$90	$115	$175	$275	$550	$650	$2,000
Auctions: $1,175, MS-64RB, October 2015; $705, MS-64BN, August 2015; $441, MS-64, March 2015; $447, MS-63BN, January 2015													
1851, Proof	10–20	0	n/a								$7,000	$8,000	$20,000
Auctions: No auction records available.													

	Mintage	Cert	Avg	%MS	VG-8	F-12	VF-20	EF-40	AU-50	MS-60BN	MS-63BN	MS-63RB	MS-65RB
											PF-60BN	PF-63BN	PF-65BN
1852, Original, Proof	*225–325*	0	n/a									—	
Auctions: No auction records available.													
1852, Restrike, Proof	*110–140*	33	64.3								$4,000	$6,000	$9,000
Auctions: $6,463, PF, August 2013													
1853	129,694	1,027	60.4	76%	$60	$75	$90	$115	$175	$275	$550	$650	$1,700
Auctions: $940, MS-65BN, September 2015; $646, MS-64BN, August 2015; $329, MS-63BN, May 2015; $223, MS-61BN, May 2015													
1854	55,358	758	61	80%	$60	$75	$90	$115	$165	$275	$550	$650	$1,700
Auctions: $1,410, MS-65BN, August 2015; $541, MS-63RB, June 2015; $230, MS-62BN, September 2015; $161, MS-60, May 2015													
1854, Proof	*10–20*	4	64.3								$3,500	$4,500	$8,000
Auctions: $7,931, PF-65RB, February 2014; $7,344, PF-65RB, January 2015													
1855	56,500	1,066	61.7	85%	$60	$75	$90	$100	$165	$275	$550	$650	$1,600
Auctions: $940, MS-65BN, January 2015; $494, MS-64BN, September 2015; $376, MS-63BN, September 2015													
1855, Proof	*40–60*	19	64.2								$3,500	$4,500	$8,000
Auctions: $5,750, PF-64BN, August 2011													
1856	40,430	404	59.6	71%	$60	$75	$90	$125	$185	$275	$575	$675	$2,000
Auctions: $400, MS-63BN, August 2015; $306, MS-63BN, May 2015; $294, MS-63BN, June 2015; $153, AU-55, May 2015													
1856, Proof	*50–75*	20	64.3								$3,500	$4,500	$8,000
Auctions: $7,050, PF-65BN, January 2015; $8,519, PF, February 2014													
1857	35,180	629	60.2	77%	$95	$115	$130	$185	$260	$400	$650	$750	$2,500
Auctions: $823, MS-64BN, October 2015; $541, MS-63BN, July 2015; $376, MS-62BN, May 2015; $720, MS-63RB, April 2018													
1857, Proof	*75–100*	37	63.9								$3,500	$4,500	$8,000
Auctions: $14,100, PF-66RB, June 2014; $4,465, PF-64BN, January 2015													

Large Cents
1793–1857

AN OVERVIEW OF LARGE CENTS

Collecting one each of the major types of 1793–1857 copper cents can be a fascinating challenge. Early varieties were struck from hand-engraved dies, often on copper planchets of uncertain quality. It was not until 1836 that steam power was used to run coining presses at the Mint. All earlier issues were made by hand, by two men tugging on the weighted lever arm of a small screw-type press. As might be expected, this resulted in many variations in striking quality.

The first cents of 1793, the Chain varieties, are found with two major differences: AMERI. on the reverse, and the later version with AMERICA spelled out in full. These early issues have been highly desired from the beginning days of the numismatic hobby in America, and remain in the limelight today.

Wreath cents of 1793 occur with the edge displaying a vine and bars motif and also with lettering ONE HUNDRED FOR A DOLLAR. Liberty Cap cents of the 1793–1796 years have lettered edges (ONE HUNDRED FOR A DOLLAR) used in 1793, 1794, and part of 1795, and plain edges for most 1795 coins and all of 1796.

The Draped Bust type commenced partway through 1796 and was continued through 1807. This span includes the notably rare 1799, 9 Over 8, overdate and the 1799 as well as the somewhat rare 1804. Many interesting die varieties occur in this type, particularly with regard to errors on the reverse. The Classic Head cent, designed by John Reich, was introduced in 1808, and was continued through 1814. In 1815 no cents of this date were produced. Then in 1816 the Matron Head commenced, a new motif with a new reverse as well. With modifications this was continued through 1839, in which year the Braided Hair design by Christian Gobrecht made its appearance. Large cents were made continually through January 1857 and then discontinued.

FOR THE COLLECTOR AND INVESTOR: LARGE CENTS AS A SPECIALTY

For the enjoyment of copper cents 1793–1857 it is possible to go far beyond a type set. Today, varieties of the 1793–1814 cents are generally collected by Sheldon numbers (S-1, S-2, etc.), given first in *Early American Cents* and, later, in its revision, *Penny Whimsy*. Building upon this foundation, *Walter Breen's Encyclopedia of Early United States Large Cents, 1793–1814*, gives more information on this date range than available in any other single source.

Among dates and major varieties in the early range of the series, the 1793 issues Chain AMERI., Chain AMERICA, Wreath, and Liberty Cap, the 1799 (far and away the rarest date in the series), and the 1804 are key issues, each a part of an extensive series of more than 300 die varieties through and including 1814.

The most popular way to collect large cents is by basic varieties, mainly dates, overdates, and major varieties. Sometimes, a particular date is selected as a specialty for collecting die varieties by Sheldon numbers.

Generally, grades from Good to VF are popular objectives for the early series from 1793 to 1814, and for some varieties no better coins exist. EF, AU, and Mint State coins are available and are more likely to be sought by collectors of basic dates and major varieties, rather than by specialists seeing long runs of Sheldon numbers. Type-set collectors are also important in the market for high-grade pieces, where sights can be set high as there are fewer varieties to obtain. Accordingly, as a type-set collector one may aspire to own an AU or Mint State cent of the 1796–1807 Draped Bust type. However, for a specialist in die varieties, who wants to acquire more than 100 different specimens from this date range, such high grades might not be feasible to acquire.

Collecting cents of the later dates by basic varieties is an interesting pursuit, and one that is quite attainable in such grades as EF, AU, or even MS-60, most dates after the 1820s being readily available for relatively inexpensive prices. Key issues among 1816–1857 cents include 1823, 3 Over 2; 1823; 1824, 4 Over 2; 1839, 9 Over 6; and a few others. Collecting Braided Hair cents toward the end of the series, 1839 to 1857, is least expensive of all, and most major varieties can be obtained in such grades as MS–60 to 63, with lustrous brown surfaces, for reasonable figures.

FLOWING HAIR, CHAIN REVERSE (1793)

Designer: *Henry Voigt.* **Weight:** *13.48 grams.* **Composition:** *Copper.*
Diameter: *Average 26 to 27 mm.* **Edge:** *Vine and bars design.* **Mint:** *Philadelphia.*

Chain AMERI. Reverse
1793; Bowers-Whitman–1, Sheldon-1, Breen-1.

Chain AMERICA Reverse

Vine-and-Bars Edge

History. The first U.S. cents intended for circulation were struck at the Mint in Philadelphia from February 27 through March 12, 1793. These were of the Flowing Hair design, with a Chain reverse. Several varieties were struck, today these can be attributed by Bowers-Whitman numbers or Sheldon numbers. The first, or Bowers-Whitman–1, Sheldon-1, had AMERICA abbreviated as AMERI. A contemporary account noted that Miss Liberty appeared to be "in a fright," and that the chain motif on the reverse, 15 links intended to symbolize unity of the states in the Union, was an "ill omen" for a land of liberty; accordingly, the design was used for only a short time. The rims on both sides are raised, without denticles or beads.

Striking and Sharpness. The details of Miss Liberty's hair are often indistinct or missing, including on many higher-grade specimens. For all grades and varieties, the reverse is significantly sharper than the obverse. The portrait of Miss Liberty is shallow and is often weak, especially on the BW-1, S-1, variety (which is often missing the date). Note that early copper coins of all kinds may exhibit "tooling" (engraving done outside the Mint in order to simulate details that were worn away or weakly struck to begin with). Also, these old coppers have sometimes been burnished to smooth out areas of porosity. These alterations are considered to be damage, and they significantly decrease a coin's value.

Availability. Demand is higher than supply for all varieties, with fewer than 1,000 or so examples surviving today. Most are in lower grades, from Fair-2 to VG-8. Even heavily worn coins (still identifiable by the chain device) are highly collectible. VF and EF coins are few and far between, and AU and MS are very rare.

GRADING STANDARDS

MS-60 to 70 (Mint State). *Obverse:* In the lower Mint State grades, MS–60 and 61, some slight abrasions can be seen on the higher areas of the portrait. The large open field shows light contact marks and perhaps a few nicks. At MS-63 the luster should be complete, although some very light abrasions or contact marks may be seen on the portrait. At MS-64 or higher—a nearly impossible level for a Chain cent—there is no sign of abrasion anywhere. Mint color is not extensive on any known Mint State coin,

1793; Bowers-Whitman–4, Sheldon-3, Breen-4. Graded MS-66BN.

but traces of red-orange are sometimes seen around the rim and devices on both sides. *Reverse:* In the lower Mint State grades some abrasions are seen on the chain links. There is some abrasion in the field. At MS-63, luster should be unbroken. Some abrasion and minor contact marks may be evident. In still higher grades, luster is deep and there is no sign of abrasion.

Illustrated coin: This coin is sharply struck with full hair detail. It is the Cleneay-Jackman-Ryder specimen mentioned in Sheldon's *Penny Whimsy* as the unrivalled, finest-known example of this variety.

AU-50, 53, 55, 58 (About Uncirculated). *Obverse:* Light wear is seen on the highest areas of the portrait. Some luster is seen in the large open fields at the AU-58 level, less at AU-55, and little if any for AU–53 and 50. Scattered marks are normal and are most evident in the field. At higher levels, some vestiges of luster may be seen among the letters, numerals, and between the hair tips. *Reverse:* Light wear is most evident on the chain, as

1793; BW-4, S-3, B-4. Graded AU-53.

this is the most prominent feature. The letters show wear, but not as extensive. Luster may be seen at the 58 and 55 levels, usually slightly more on the reverse than on the obverse. Generally, the reverse grades higher than the obverse, usually by a step, such as an AU-50 obverse and an AU-53 reverse (such a coin would be listed as the lower of the two, or AU-50).

EF-40, 45 (Extremely Fine). *Obverse:* The center of the portrait is well worn, with the hair visible only in thick strands, although extensive detail remains in the hair tips at the left. No luster is seen. Contact marks are normal in the large expanse of open field, but should be mentioned if they are distracting. *Reverse:* The chain is bold and shows light wear. Other features show wear, as well— more extensive in appearance, as the relief is

1793; BW-4, S-3, B-4. Graded EF-45.

lower. The fields show some friction, but not as much as on the obverse.

VF-20, 30 (Very Fine). *Obverse:* More wear is seen on the portrait, with perhaps half or slightly more of the hair detail showing, mostly near the left edge of the hair. The ear usually is visible (but might not be, depending on the sharpness of strike). The letters in LIBERTY show wear. The rim remains bold (more so than on the reverse). *Reverse:* The chain shows more wear than on the preceding, but is still bold. Other features show more wear and may be weak in areas. The rim may be weak in areas.

1793; BW-5, S-4, B-5. Graded VF-30.

F-12, 15 (Fine). *Obverse:* The hair details are mostly worn away, with about one-third visible, that being on the left. The rim is distinct on most examples. The bottoms of the date digits are weak or possibly worn away. *Reverse:* The chain is bold, as is the lettering within the chain. Lettering around the border shows extensive wear, but is complete. The rim may be flat in areas.

Illustrated coin: The surface is generally smooth and even under close scrutiny reveals only minor roughness. Note the shallow reverse rim bruise outside the letters AM in AMERICA and some mild encrustation around the letter C in CENT and the nearby chain links.

1793; BW-5, S-4, B-5. Graded F-15.

VG-8, 10 (Very Good). *Obverse:* The portrait is well worn, although Miss Liberty's eye remains bold. Hair detail is gone at the center, but is evident at the left edge of the portrait. LIBERTY is always readable, but may be faded or partly missing on shallow strikes. The date is well worn, with the bottom of the numerals missing (published standards vary on this point, and it used to be the case that a full date was mandatory). *Reverse:* The chain remains bold, and the center letters are all readable. Border letters may be weak or incomplete. The rim is smooth in most areas.

1793; BW-4, S-3, B-4. Graded VG-10.

Illustrated coin: The coin is smooth in appearance with the worn areas showing lighter copper, while the fields have trace roughness and the classic black olive texture. Note the planchet flaw right of ONE, which appears as a void in the metal.

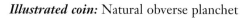

G-4, 6 (Good). *Obverse:* The portrait is worn smooth and is seen only in outline form, although the eye position can be discerned. LIBERTY may be weak. The date is weak, but the tops of the numerals can be discerned. *Reverse:* The chain is fully visible in outline form. Central lettering is mostly or completely readable, but light. Peripheral lettering is mostly worn away.

1793; BW-1, S-1, B-1. Graded G-4.

Illustrated coin: Natural obverse planchet flaws, as struck, can be seen both at 12 o'clock on the rim and above and to the left of the date, with other faint fissuring seen on the reverse under low magnification.

AG-3 (About Good). *Obverse:* The portrait is visible as an outline. LIBERTY and the date are mostly or even completely worn away. Contact marks may be extensive. *Reverse:* The chain is fully visible in outline form. Traces of the central letters—or, on better strikes, nearly all of the letters—can be seen. Around the border all letters are worn away.

1793; BW-5, S-4, B-5. Graded AG-3.

	Mintage	Cert	Avg	%MS	AG-3	G-4	VG-8	F-12	VF-20	EF-40	AU-50	MS-60
1793, Chain, All kinds †	36,103											
1793, AMERI. in Legend †		37	22.9	5%	$5,500	$11,000	$18,500	$28,000	$45,000	$85,000	$175,000	$300,000
	Auctions: $25,850, F-12, August 2016; $18,800, F-12, August 2015; $3,173, Fair-2, March 2015											
1793, AMERICA, Periods †		17	21.8	0%	$4,750	$7,750	$15,000	$21,000	$37,500	$65,000	$120,000	$225,000
	Auctions: $22,325, AU-50, September 2013											
1793, AMERICA, No Periods †		136	21.4	4%	$4,750	$7,500	$14,000	$19,500	$32,000	$60,000	$100,000	$180,000
	Auctions: $998,750, MS-65BN, January 2013											

† All varieties of 1793 Flowing Hair, Chair Reverse Large Cents are ranked in the *100 Greatest U.S. Coins* (fourth edition), as a single entry.

FLOWING HAIR, WREATH REVERSE (1793)

Designer: *Henry Voigt.* **Weight:** *13.48 grams.* **Composition:** *Copper.*
Diameter: *26 to 28 mm.* **Edge:** *Vine and bars design, or lettered ONE HUNDRED FOR A DOLLAR followed by either a single or a double leaf.* **Mint:** *Philadelphia.*

1793, Wreath Type, Vine and Bars Edge; BW-11, S-5, B-6.

Vine-and-Bars Edge

Lettered Edge
(ONE HUNDRED FOR A DOLLAR)

History. Between April 9 and July 17, 1793, the U.S. Mint struck and delivered 63,353 large copper cents. Most of these, and perhaps all, were of the Wreath type, although records do not specify when the design types were changed that year. The Wreath cent was named for the new reverse style. Both sides have raised beads at the border, similar to the style used on 1793 half cents.

Striking and Sharpness. These cents usually are fairly well struck, although high-grade pieces often exhibit some weakness on the highest hair tresses and on the leaf details. (On lower-grade pieces these areas are worn, so the point is moot.) Planchet quality varies widely, from smooth, glossy brown to dark and porous. The lettered-edge cents are often seen on defective planchets. Consult Sheldon's *Penny Whimsy (1793–1814)* and photographs to learn the characteristics of certain varieties. The borders have raised beads; on high-grade pieces these are usually very distinct, but they blend together on lower-grade coins and can sometimes be indistinct. The beads are not as prominent as those later used on the 1793 Liberty Cap cents.

Availability. At least several thousand examples exist of the different varieties of the type. Most are in lower grades, from AG-3 to VG-8, although Fine and VF pieces are encountered with regularity. Choice EF, AU, and finer coins see high demand. Some in MS have been billed as "specimen" or "presentation" coins, although this is supposition, as no records exist.

GRADING STANDARDS

MS-60 to 70 (Mint State). *Obverse:* On MS–60 and 61 coins there are some traces of abrasion on the higher areas of the portrait, most particularly the hair. As this area can be lightly struck, careful inspection is needed for evaluation, not as much in Mint State (as other features come into play), but in higher circulated grades. Luster in the field is incomplete at lower Mint State levels, but should be in generous quantity. At MS-63, luster should

1793; BW-12, S-6, B-7. Graded MS-66.

be complete, and no abrasion evident. At higher levels, the luster is deeper, and some original mint color may be seen. At MS-65 there might be some scattered contact marks and possibly bare traces of fingerprints or discoloration. Above MS-65, a coin should approach perfection. A Mint State 1793 Wreath cent is an object of rare beauty. *Reverse:* In the lower Mint State grades some abrasion is seen on the higher areas of the leaves. Generally, luster is complete in all grades, as the open areas are protected by the lettering and wreath. In many ways, the grading guidelines for this type follow those of the 1793 half cent—also with sprays of berries (not seen elsewhere in the series).

Illustrated coin: Remarkably, this coin displays some original Mint orange.

AU-50, 53, 55, 58 (About Uncirculated).
Obverse: Friction is seen on the highest areas of the hair (which may also be lightly struck) and the cheek. Some scattered marks are normal in the field, ranging from more extensive at AU-50 to minimal at AU-58. *Reverse:* Friction is seen on the higher wreath leaves and (not as easy to discern) on the letters. The fields, protected by the designs (including sprays of berries at the center), show fric-

1793; BW-23, S-11c, B-16c. Graded AU-50.

tion, but not as noticeably as on the obverse. At AU–55 and 58, little if any friction is seen. Border beads, if well struck, are separate and boldly defined.

Illustrated coin: Note the clash marks on the obverse indicative of a late die state. Significant portions of the reverse wreath are clashed in the field from Liberty's nose to the base of the throat, below the bust around the leaf cluster, and between some of the strands of hair at the back of Liberty's head. Additionally, the letters MERICA in the word AMERICA are clashed in the right-obverse field, the letters becoming bolder toward the end of that word.

EF-40, 45 (Extremely Fine). *Obverse:* More extensive wear is seen on the high parts of the hair, creating mostly a solid mass (without detail of strands) of varying width in the area immediately to the left of the face. The cheek shows light wear. Luster is minimal or nonexistent at EF-40, and may survive in traces in protected areas (such as between the letters) at EF-45. *Reverse:* Wear is seen on the highest wreath and ribbon areas, and

1793; BW-17, S-9, B-12. Graded EF-40.

the letters. Luster is minimal, but likely more noticeable than on the obverse, as the fields are protected by the designs and lettering. Some of the beads blend together.

VF-20, 30 (Very Fine). *Obverse:* Wear on the hair is more extensive, and varies depending on the die variety and sharpness of strike. The ANA grading standards suggest that two-thirds of the hair is visible, which in practice can be said to be "more or less." More beads are blended together, but the extent of this blending depends on the striking and variety. Certain parts of the rim are smooth, with beads scarcely visible at all. No

1793; BW-12, S-6, B-7. Graded VF-25.

luster is seen. The date, LIBERTY, and hair ends are bold. *Reverse:* The leaf details are nearly completely worn away at VF-20, with slight detail at VF-30. The border beads are blended together, with many indistinct. Some berries in the sprays are light, but nearly all remain distinct. No luster is seen.

Illustrated coin: The surfaces are a bit rough overall with a few areas also revealing slight verdigris.

F-12, 15 (Fine). *Obverse:* The hair details are mostly worn away, with about one-third visible, mainly at the edges. The ANA grading standards suggest that half of the details are visible, seemingly applying to the total area of the hair. However, the visible part, at the left, also includes intermittent areas of the field. Beads are weak or worn away in areas. F-15 shows slightly more detail. By this grade, scattered light scratches, noticeable contact marks,

1793; BW-17, S-9, B-12. Graded F-12.

and the like are the rule, not the exception. These are not mentioned at all on holders and are often overlooked elsewhere, except in some auction catalogs and price lists. Such marks are implicit for coins in lower grades, and light porosity or granularity is common as well. *Reverse:* The wreath leaves are worn flat, but their edges are distinct. Border beads are weak or worn away in areas. F-15 shows slightly more detail.

Illustrated coin: Despite slight pock-marking on the obverse and scattered rim bruises, this coin features strong definition for an F-12 piece.

VG-8, 10 (Very Good). *Obverse:* The hair is well worn toward the face. Details at the left are mostly blended together in thick strands. The eye, nose, and lips often remain well defined. Border beads are completely gone, or just seen in traces, and part of the rim blends into the field. LIBERTY may be slightly weak. The 1793 date is fully visible, although there may be some lightness. Scattered marks are more common than on

1793; BW-23, S-11c, B-16c. Graded VG-8.

higher grades. *Reverse:* The wreath, bow, and lettering are seen in outline form, and some leaves and letters may be indistinct in parts. Most of the berries remain visible, but weak. Border beads are worn away, and the border blends into the field in most if not all of the periphery.

G-4, 6 (Good). *Obverse:* The hair is worn smooth except for the thick tresses at the left. The eye, nose, and lips show some detail. LIBERTY is weak, with some letters missing. The date is discernible, although partially worn away. The sprig above the date is usually prominent. The border completely blends into the field. *Reverse:* Extensive overall wear. The wreath is seen in outline form, with some areas weak. Usually ONE CENT remains

1793; BW-12, S-6, B-7. Graded G-4.

readable at the center. The border letters and fraction show extensive wear, with some letters very weak or even missing, although most should be discernible. Dark or porous coins may have more details on both sides in an effort to compensate for the roughness. Marks, edge bumps, and so on are normal.

Illustrated coin: Note minor surface roughness. Definition in the major devices is strong for this grade.

AG-3 (About Good). *Obverse:* Wear is more extensive than on the preceding. The eye, nose, and lips may still be discernible, and the sprig above the date can usually be seen. LIBERTY may be very weak or even missing. The date is gone, or just a trace will remain. *Reverse:* Parts of the wreath are visible in outline form. ONE CENT might be readable, but this is not a requirement. Most border letters are gone. If a coin is dark or porous

1793; BW-18, S-8, B-13. Graded AG-3.

it may be graded AG-3 and may be sharper than just described, with the porosity accounting for the lower grade.

Regular Sprig

Strawberry Leaf

	Mintage	Cert	Avg	%MS	AG-3	G-4	VG-8	F-12	VF-20	EF-40	AU-50	MS-60BN	MS-63BN
1793, Wreath, All kinds	63,353												
1793, Vine/Bars Edge		210	31.3	12%	$1,600	$3,250	$4,700	$7,500	$13,000	$21,000	$35,000	$55,000	$100,000
	Auctions: $176,250, MS-65BN, June 2015; $44,650, AU-55, August 2015; $8,813, VF-25, October 2016; $1,560, AG-3, February 2018												
1793, Lettered Edge		46	21.0	4%	$1,800	$3,500	$5,000	$8,500	$15,000	$27,500	$36,000	$80,000	$125,000
	Auctions: $18,800, F-15, January 2014; $4,935, F-15, March 2016; $646, VG-8, December 2015												
1793, Strawberry Leaf †	(a)	1	12.0	0%	$250,000	$300,000	$375,000	$750,000					
	Auctions: $381,875, G-4, January 2014												

† Ranked in the *100 Greatest U.S. Coins* (fourth edition). **a.** 4 examples are known.

LIBERTY CAP (1793–1796)

Designer: *1793–1795, thick planchet—Probably Joseph Wright; 1795–1796, thin planchet—John Smith Gardner.* **Weight:** *1793–1795, thick planchet—13.48 grams; 1795–1796, thin planchet—10.89 grams.* **Composition:** *Copper.* **Diameter:** *Average 29 mm.* **Edge:** *1793–1795, thick planchet—Lettered ONE HUNDRED FOR A DOLLAR; 1795–1796, thin planchet—Plain.* **Mint:** *Philadelphia.*

1794, Thick Hair, Close Date, Short Right Stem; BW-80, S-61, B-53.

Lettered Edge (1793–1795)

Reeded Edge (1795)

History. The Liberty Cap design was created in the summer of 1793 by artist and engraver Joseph Wright, who is also believed by some to have designed the 1793 half cent. On the cent, Miss Liberty faces to the right, rather than to the left (as on the half cent). Liberty Cap cents of 1793 have raised beaded borders. Other issues have denticles. Cents of 1794 and some of 1795 are on thick planchets with the edge lettered ONE HUNDRED FOR A DOLLAR, while those made later in 1795, and in 1796, are on thinner planchets and have a plain edge.

Striking and Sharpness. The depth of relief and striking characteristics vary widely, depending on the variety. Points to check are the details of the hair on Miss Liberty, the leaf details on the wreath, and the denticles on both sides. Generally, the earlier, thick-planchet issues are better strikes than are the thin-planchet coins. Plain-edge 1795 cents often have low or shallow rims. To determine the difference between lightness caused by shallow dies and lightness caused by wear, study the characteristics of the die variety involved (see in particular the reverses of 1793, BW-27, S-13, and 1793, BW-28 / BW-29, S-15 / S-12).

Availability. Cents of this type are readily available, although those of 1793 are rare and in great demand, and certain die varieties of the other dates are rare and can command high prices. Typical grades range from AG upward to Fine, VF, and, less often, EF. Attractive AU and MS coins are elusive, and when found are usually dated 1795, the thin planchet variety.

GRADING STANDARDS

MS-60 to 70 (Mint State). *Obverse:* On MS–60 and 61 coins there are some traces of abrasion on the higher areas of the portrait. Luster is incomplete, particularly in the field. At MS-63, luster should be complete, and no abrasion evident. At higher levels, the luster is deeper, and some original mint color may be seen on some examples. At the MS-65 level there may be some scattered contact marks and

1794; BW-12, S-22, B-6. Graded MS-62BN.

possibly some traces of fingerprints or discoloration, but these should be very minimal and not at all distracting. Generally, Liberty Cap cents of 1793 (in particular) and 1794 are harder to find with strong eye appeal than are those of 1795 and 1796. Mint State coins of 1795 often have satiny luster. Above MS-65, a coin should approach perfection, especially if dated 1795 or 1796. Certified Mint State cents can vary in their strictness of interpretation. *Reverse:* In the lower Mint State grades some abrasion is seen on the higher areas of the leaves. Generally, luster is complete in all grades, as the open areas are protected by the lettering and wreath. Often on this type the reverse is shallower than the obverse and has a lower rim.

Illustrated coin: Boldly struck on both the obverse and reverse, with strong hair separation evident on Liberty and some evidence of a central vein on each leaf. Note the small toning speck under the L of LIBERTY.

AU-50, 53, 55, 58 (About Uncirculated). *Obverse:* Very light wear is evident on the highest parts of the hair above and to the left of the ear. Friction is seen on the cheek and the liberty cap. Coins at this level are usually on smooth planchets and have nice eye appeal. Color is very important. Dark and porous coins are relegated to lower grades, even if AU-level sharpness is present. *Reverse:*

1794; BW-98, S-71, B-63. Graded AU-50.

Very light wear is evident on the higher parts of the leaves and the ribbon, and, to a lesser extent, on the lettering. The reverse may have original luster, toned brown, varying from minimal (at lower About Uncirculated grades) to extensive. Grading at the About Uncirculated level is mainly done by viewing the obverse, as many reverses are inherently shallow due to lower-relief dies.

Illustrated coin: Note the rough patch on and below Liberty's cap.

EF-40, 45 (Extremely Fine). *Obverse:* The center of the coin shows wear or a small, flat area, for most dies. Other hair details are strong. Luster is minimal or nonexistent at EF-40, and may survive in traces in protected areas (such as between the letters) at EF-45. *Reverse:* Wear is seen on the highest wreath and ribbon areas and the letters. Luster is minimal, but likely more noticeable than on the

1794; BW-18, S-28, B-10. Graded EF-40.

obverse, as the fields are protected by the designs and lettering. Sharpness varies depending on the die variety but is generally shallower than on the obverse, this being particularly true for many 1795 cents.

VF-20, 30 (Very Fine). *Obverse:* Wear on the portrait has reduced the hair detail to indistinct or flat at the center, and on most varieties the individual strands at the left edge are blended together. One rule does not fit all. The ANA grading standards suggest that 75% of the hair shows, while PCGS suggests 30% to 70% on varieties struck from higher-relief dies, and less than 50% for others. Examples such as this reflect the artistic, rather than sci-

1794, Head of 1794; BW-74, S-57, B-55. Graded VF-30.

entific, nature of grading. *Reverse:* The leaf details are nearly completely worn away at VF-20, and with slight detail at VF-30. Some border letters may be weak, and ditto for the central letters (on later varieties of this type). The border denticles are blended together with many indistinct. No luster is seen. The sharpness of details depends on the die variety.

F-12, 15 (Fine). *Obverse:* The hair details are mostly worn away, with about one-third visible, mainly at the lower edges. Border denticles are weak or worn away in areas, depending on the height of the rim when the coin was struck. F-15 shows slightly more detail. *Reverse:* The wreath leaves are worn flat, but their edges are distinct. Border denticles are weak or worn away in areas. F-15 shows slightly more detail. At this level and

1794, Head of 1794; BW-98, S-71, B-63. Graded F-15.

lower, planchet darkness and light porosity are common, as are scattered marks.

VG-8, 10 (Very Good). *Obverse:* The hair is more worn than on the preceding, with detail present only in the lower areas. Detail can differ, and widely, depending on the dies. Border denticles are worn away on some issues (not as much for 1793 and 1794 coins), and the border will blend into the field in areas in which the rim was low to begin with, or in areas struck slightly off center. LIBERTY and the date are bold. VG-10 is sometimes applied

1796; BW-1, S-91, B-1. Graded VG-8.

to especially nice Very Good coins. *Reverse:* The wreath, bow, and lettering are seen in outline form, and some leaves and letters may be indistinct in parts. Border denticles are worn away, and the border blends into the field in most if not all of the periphery. In certain die varieties and die states, especially of 1797, some letters may be very weak, or missing.

G-4, 6 (Good). *Obverse:* The portrait is worn smooth and is seen only in outline form, although the eye and nose can be discerned. LIBERTY and the date are complete, although the date may be weak. Denticles are gone on varieties struck with low or shallow rims. *Reverse:* Extensive wear is seen overall. From half to two-thirds of the letters in UNITED STATES OF AMERICA and the fraction numerals are worn away. Certain

1794, Starred Reverse; BW-59, S-48, B-38. Graded G-4.

shallow-relief dies may have letters missing. G-6 is often assigned to finer examples in this category. Darkness, porosity, and marks characterize many coins.

Illustrated coin: This coin is an example of the highly sought 1794, Starred Reverse, variety.

AG-3 (About Good). *Obverse:* Wear is more extensive than on the preceding. The portrait is visible only in outline. LIBERTY will typically have some letters worn away. The date is weak, but discernible. *Reverse:* Parts of the wreath are visible in outline form, and all but a few letters are gone. Grading of AG-3 is usually done by the reverse, as the obverse typically appears to be in a slightly higher grade.

1794, Starred Reverse; BW-59, S-48, B-38. Graded AG-3.

Illustrated coin: This coin is closer to G-4 on the obverse, but weak on the reverse, prompting a more conservative grade. While the reverse is worn nearly smooth, almost a third of the stars at the denticles, which mark this cent as a 1794, Starred Reverse, are visible.

Head of 1793 (1793–1794)
Head in high, rounded relief.

Head of 1794 (1794)
Well-defined hair; hook on lowest curl.

Beaded Border (1793)

Denticle Border (1794–1796)

	Mintage	Cert	Avg	%MS	AG-3	G-4	VG-8	F-12	VF-20	EF-40	AU-50	MS-60BN	MS-63BN
1793, Liberty Cap	11,056	29	12.6	0%	$9,000	$14,000	$20,000	$26,000	$50,000	$120,000	$240,000		
	Auctions: $21,150, F-12, July 2015; $19,389, VG-10, August 2016; $3,760, VG-8, January 2015; $5,875, AG-3, March 2016												

1794, Normal Reverse

1794, Starred Reverse

Head of 1795 (1794–1796)
Head in low relief;
no hook on lowest curl.

1795, "Jefferson Head"

	Mintage	Cert	Avg	%MS	AG-3	G-4	VG-8	F-12	VF-20	EF-40	AU-50	MS-60BN	MS-63BN
1794, All kinds	918,521												
1794, Head of 1793		21	18.1	14%	$800	$1,600	$3,500	$5,000	$12,000	$25,000	$45,000	$100,000	$200,000
	Auctions: $881,250, MS-64BN, January 2013												
1794, Head of 1794		331	31.5	4%	$275	$425	$700	$1,250	$2,300	$4,500	$9,500	$14,000	$30,000
	Auctions: $12,925, AU-55, June 2015; $9,988, AU-55, June 2015; $8,813, EF-45, June 2015; $2,468, VF-35, August 2015												
1794, Head in Low Relief		0	n/a		$250	$400	$650	$1,200	$2,100	$4,250	$9,000	$13,000	$27,500
	Auctions: No auction records available.												
1794, Exact Head of 1795 (a)		60	31.2	7%	$300	$475	$750	$1,350	$2,750	$5,750	$8,500	$25,000	$45,000
	Auctions: $329, VF-20, July 2015; $447, F-15, July 2015; $376, F-12, November 2015; $4,560, VG-10, January 2018												
1794, Starred Reverse †		9	12.9	0%	$14,500	$18,500	$25,000	$50,000	$90,000	$225,000	$700,000		
	Auctions: $99,875, VF-25, May 2015; $15,275, AG-3, October 2013												
1794, No Fraction Bar		7	33.3	29%	$300	$500	$850	$1,500	$3,000	$6,500	$15,000	$40,000	$75,000
	Auctions: $381,875, MS-64BN, January 2014												
1795, Lettered Edge	37,000	70	26.4	11%	$275	$500	$900	$1,250	$2,750	$5,500	$8,500	$14,000	$27,500
	Auctions: $79,313, MS-65BN, April 2013; $1,140, VG-10, February 2018												
1795, Plain Edge	501,500	288	24.8	11%	$200	$375	$600	$1,000	$1,800	$3,300	$6,000	$8,500	$20,000
	Auctions: $21,150, MS-63BN, April 2013; $548, G-6, July 2015; $780, F-12, January 2018												
1795, Reeded Edge	(b)	0	n/a		$125,000	$275,000	$550,000	$900,000					
	Auctions: $646,250, VG-10, January 2014												
1795, "Jefferson Head" (c)		1	10.0	0%	$11,000	$25,000	$37,500	$55,000	$125,000	$250,000			
	Auctions: $184,000, VF-25, March 2012												
1795, "Jefferson Head," Lettered Edge (c)	(d)	0	n/a			—	$55,000	$90,000	$200,000				
	Auctions: No auction records available.												
1796, Liberty Cap	109,825	173	22.4	9%	$300	$475	$850	$1,750	$3,500	$7,000	$12,500	$30,000	$37,500
	Auctions: $141,000, MS-64RB, January 2014; $400, AG-3, February 2015; $376, AG-3, May 2015												

† Ranked in the *100 Greatest U.S. Coins* (fourth edition). **a.** The 1794 coin with Head of 1795 has a hooked curl but is in low relief. **b.** 9 examples are known. **c.** The "Jefferson Head" is not a regular Mint issue, but a design struck privately in an attempt to win a federal coinage contract. **d.** 3 examples are known.

DRAPED BUST (1796–1807)

Designer: *Robert Scot.* **Weight:** *10.89 grams.* **Composition:** *Copper.*
Diameter: *Average 29 mm.* **Edge:** *Plain.* **Mint:** *Philadelphia.*

1797, Reverse of 1795, Gripped Edge;
BW-3b, S-121b, B-3b.

History. The Draped Bust cent made its debut in 1796, following a coinage of Liberty Cap cents the same year. The motif, from a drawing by Gilbert Stuart, was first employed on certain silver dollars of 1795. (Its use on half cents did not take place until later, in 1800.) In 1798 Miss Liberty's head was slightly modified in design.

Striking and Sharpness. Most Draped Bust cents were struck on high-quality planchets. (This high planchet quality is less predictable for varieties of 1796, and almost never present for those of 1799 and 1800.) Detail sharpness differs by die variety. Weakness, when present, is usually on the hair behind the forehead, on the leaves in the upper part of the wreath, and among the denticles. However, a weak strike can show up in other areas as well. Many if not most Draped Bust cents are imperfectly centered, with the result that denticles can be bold on one side of a coin and light or even missing on the opposite side; this can occur on obverse as well as reverse. Typically this does not affect value. Certain Draped Bust cents of 1796 have semi-prooflike surfaces. Those of 1799 often have rough or porous surfaces and are found in lower grades.

Availability. As a type, Draped Bust cents are readily available, although the 1799, 9 Over 8, and 1799 are the keys to the series, and the 1804 is elusive. A different scenario evolves when considering engraving errors, repunched dates, and recut letters and numerals; many of these varieties are very difficult to locate. The eye appeal of these rarities usually is below par. Other years are generally available in high grades, VF and finer, well struck (except for some reverse leaves, in instances), on high-quality planchets, and with excellent eye appeal. Dark and porous coins are plentiful among coins graded below VF. True MS coins tend to be MS–60 to 63, when found.

GRADING STANDARDS

MS-60 to 70 (Mint State). *Obverse:* In the lower Mint State grades, MS–60 and 61, some slight abrasion can be seen on the higher areas of the portrait, especially the cheek, and the hair behind the forehead. Luster in the field is incomplete, particularly in the center of the open areas, which on this type are very open, especially at the right. At MS-63, luster should be nearly complete, and no abrasions evident. In higher levels, the lus-

1803, Small Date, Large Fraction;
BW-12, S-258, B-17. Graded MS-63BN.

ter is complete and deeper, and some original mint color should be seen. MS-64 coins may have some slight discoloration or scattered contact marks. A well-graded MS-65 or higher coin will have full, rich luster; no marks visible except under magnification; and a nice blend of brown toning or nicely mixed (not stained or blotchy) mint color and natural brown toning. *Reverse:* In the lower Mint State ranges some abrasions are seen on the higher areas of the leaves. Generally, luster is complete in all Mint State ranges, as the open areas are protected by the lettering and wreath. Sharpness of the leaves can vary by die variety, so check this aspect. Otherwise, the same comments apply as for the obverse.

Illustrated coin: This example is quite attractive despite the scratch on Liberty's bust and another through the D of UNITED. However, the left side of the reverse has toned differently from the rest of the coin's surfaces.

AU-50, 53, 55, 58 (About Uncirculated).

Obverse: Friction is seen on the higher parts, particularly the hair of Miss Liberty and the cheek. Friction and scattered marks are in the field, ranging from more extensive at AU-50 to minimal at AU-58. Luster may be seen in protected areas, minimal at AU-50, more visible at AU-58. At AU-58 the field may retain some luster, as well. In many instances, the luster is smaller in area and lesser in "depth"

1803, Small Date, Large Fraction; BW-12, S-258, B-17. Graded AU-58.

than on the reverse of this type. Cents of this type can be very beautiful in About Uncirculated. *Reverse:* Friction is seen on the higher wreath leaves and (not as easy to discern) on the letters. Again, the die variety should be checked. The fields, though protected by the designs, show friction, but not as noticeably as on the obverse. At AU–55 and 58, little if any friction is seen. The reverse may have original luster, toned brown, minimal on lower About Uncirculated grades, often extensive at the AU-58 level. General rules for cents follow the half cents of the same type.

Illustrated coin: Note the die crack arcing through the lower-left obverse. This crack was also on the preceding coin, but is more noticeable here.

EF-40, 45 (Extremely Fine). *Obverse:* Wear

is seen on the portrait overall, with reduction or elimination of some separation of hair strands on the highest part. By the standards of the Early American Coppers society, if the "spit curl" in front of Liberty's ear is missing, the coin is not EF. The cheek shows more wear than on higher grades, and the drapery covering the bosom is lightly worn on the higher areas. Often weakness in the separa-

1804, Original; BW-1, S-266, B-1. Graded EF-40.

tion of the drapery lines can be attributed to weakness in striking. Luster is minimal or nonexistent at EF-40, and may survive in amongst the letters of LIBERTY at EF-45. *Reverse:* Wear is seen on the highest wreath and ribbon areas, and on the letters. Luster is minimal, but likely more noticeable than on the obverse, as the fields are protected by the designs and lettering. The ANA grading standards state that at EF-45 nearly all of the "ribbing" (veins) in the leaves is visible, and that at EF-40 about 75% is sharp. In practice, striking plays a part as well, and some leaves may be weak even in higher grades.

Illustrated coin: This coin features a few small patches of porosity.

VF-20, 30 (Very Fine). *Obverse:* Wear on the portrait has reduced the hair detail further, especially to the left of the forehead. The rolling curls are solid or flat on their highest areas, as well as by the ribbon behind the hair. The border denticles are blended together, with many indistinct. No luster is seen. *Reverse:* The leaf details are nearly completely worn away at VF-20, and with slight detail at VF-30. The ANA grading

1805; BW-1, S-267, B-1. Graded VF-35.

standards are a bit stricter: 30% remaining at VF-20 and 50% at VF-30. In the marketplace, fewer details can be seen on most certified coins at these levels. The border denticles are blended together with many indistinct. No luster is seen.

F-12, 15 (Fine). *Obverse:* Many hair details are worn away, with perhaps one-half to one-third visible, mainly at the edges and behind the shoulder. Border denticles are weak or worn away in areas. F-15 shows slightly more detail. Porosity and scattered marks become increasingly common at this level and lower. *Reverse:* The wreath leaves are worn flat, but their edges are distinct. Little if anything remains of leaf vein details. Border denticles

1807, 7 Over 6; BW-2, S-273, B-3. Graded F-12.

are weak or worn away in areas. F-15 shows slightly more detail.

Illustrated coin: There are several distracting contact marks on the obverse of this coin. Note the 6 visible under the 7 in the date.

VG-8, 10 (Very Good). *Obverse:* The portrait is well worn, although the eye can be seen, as can hints of hair detail. Some hair at the left shows separation. Curls now appear as mostly solid blobs. Border denticles are worn away on most varieties, and the rim, although usually present, begins to blend into the field. LIBERTY and the date are bold in most areas, with some lightness toward the rim. VG-10 is sometimes applied to espe-

1807, Large Fraction. Graded VG-8.

cially nice Very Good coins. *Reverse:* The wreath, bow, and lettering are seen in outline form, and some leaves and letters may be indistinct in parts. The border may blend into the field on some of the periphery. The strength of the letters is dependent to an extent on the specific die variety.

G-4, 6 (Good). *Obverse:* The portrait is worn smooth and is seen only in outline form, although the eye position can be discerned and some curls can be made out. LIBERTY is readable, but the tops of the letters may fade away. The date is clearly readable, but the lower part of the numerals may be very weak or worn away. The border will blend into the field more extensively than on the preceding, but significant areas will still be seen. *Reverse:*

1799, 9 Over 8; BW-2, S-188, B-2. Graded G-6.

Extensive wear is seen overall. From one-half to two-thirds of the letters in UNITED STATES OF AMERICA and the fraction numerals are worn away. On most varieties, ONE CENT is fairly strong. G-6 is often assigned to finer examples in this category.

   Illustrated coin: This coin shows evidence of a past cleaning, but it has retoned.

AG-3 (About Good). *Obverse:* Wear is more extensive than on the preceding. The portrait is visible only in outline. LIBERTY is weak, partially worn away, but usually discernible. The date is weak, and the bottoms of the digits may be worn away, but must be identifiable. *Reverse:* Parts of the wreath are visible in outline form, and all but a few letters are gone. ONE CENT is usually mostly or completely discernible, depending on the variety.

1796, Reverse of 1797; BW-53, S-100, B-24. Graded AG-3.

   Illustrated coin: Early American Coppers has graded this same coin at Good.

Reverse of 1794 (1794–1796)
*Note double leaf at top right;
14–16 leaves on left,
16–18 leaves on right.*

Reverse of 1795 (1795–1798)
*Note single leaf at top right;
17–21 leaves on left,
16–20 leaves on right.*

Reverse of 1797 (1796–1807)
*Note double leaf at top right; 16
leaves on left, 19 leaves on right.*

1796, LIHERTY Error

1797, Wreath With Stems

1797, Stemless Wreath

Style 1 Hair
Found on all coins of 1796 and 1797, many 1798 varieties, and 1800, 1800 Over 1798.

Style 2 Hair
Found on coins of 1798–1807. Note the extra curl near shoulders.

1798, 8 Over 7

	Mintage	Cert	Avg	%MS	AG-3	G-4	VG-8	F-12	VF-20	EF-40	AU-50	MS-60BN	MS-63BN
1796, Draped Bust, All kinds	363,375												
1796, Reverse of 1794		36	14.3	0%	$275	$425	$700	$1,500	$2,750	$6,250	$12,500	$18,000	$27,500
Auctions: $11,750, AU-53, January 2014													
1796, Reverse of 1795		23	21.8	4%	$225	$375	$600	$1,150	$3,000	$6,500	$13,000	$19,500	$30,000
Auctions: $20,563, AU-58, January 2014; $764, G-6, October 2015; $646, G-6, October 2015													
1796, Reverse of 1797		25	18.8	12%	$200	$350	$500	$1,000	$2,250	$4,500	$6,750	$9,000	$14,000
Auctions: $28,200, MS-64BN, April 2013													
1796, LIHERTY Error		16	23.3	6%	$450	$850	$1,600	$3,500	$6,000	$14,000	$40,000	$60,000	$85,000
Auctions: $2,350, VF-20, August 2013; $1,704, VG-10, March 2015													
1796, Stemless Reverse	(a)	0	n/a			$25,000							
Auctions: No auction records available.													
1797, All kinds	897,510												
1797, Gripped Edge, 1795-Style Reverse		19	19.7	0%	$130	$225	$400	$750	$1,500	$3,700	$10,000	$26,000	
Auctions: $1,351, VG-8, March 2013													
1797, Plain Edge, 1795-Style Reverse		13	11.9	0%	$150	$275	$500	$1,200	$2,500	$4,500	$12,000	$26,500	
Auctions: $940, EF-40, June 2014													
1797, 1797 Reverse, With Stems		235	30.3	16%	$100	$200	$300	$650	$1,400	$2,400	$4,400	$6,500	$12,000
Auctions: $41,125, MS-65RB, January 2013; $2,350, EF-45, March 2015; $999, F-15, June 2015; $129, F-12, March 2015													
1797, 1797 Reverse, Stemless		28	22.8	4%	$125	$275	$650	$1,400	$3,000	$7,000	$13,000	$60,000	
Auctions: $1,645, VF-25, January 2014; $720, VG-10, March 2018													
1798, All kinds	1,841,745												
1798, 8 Over 7		21	24.6	5%	$200	$375	$650	$1,500	$3,500	$8,000	$16,500		
Auctions: $14,688, AU-58, February 2013													
1798, Reverse of 1796		11	17.1	0%	$250	$500	$1,250	$3,000	$5,500	$11,000	$23,000	$32,000	$50,000
Auctions: $3,290, VF-20, September 2013													
1798, Style 1 Hair		95	22.3	1%	$95	$150	$250	$450	$800	$2,200	$5,000	$11,000	$19,000
Auctions: $494, EF-40, June 2015; $494, VF-20, May 2015; $494, F-12, January 2015; $132, G-6, March 2018													
1798, Style 2 Hair		235	29.2	3%	$80	$130	$225	$400	$600	$1,800	$3,500	$9,000	$17,500
Auctions: $823, VF-30, August 2015; $940, VF-25, June 2015; $541, VF-20, January 2015; $1,020, VF-30, February 2018													

a. 3 examples are known.

1799, 9 Over 8   **1799, Normal Date**

1800, 1800 Over 1798   **1800, 80 Over 79**   **1800, Normal Date**

1801, Normal Reverse   **1801, 3 Errors: 1/000,**   **1801, Fraction 1/000**   **1801, 1/100 Over 1/000**
                           One Stem, and IINITED

	Mintage	Cert	Avg	%MS	AG-3	G-4	VG-8	F-12	VF-20	EF-40	AU-50	MS-60BN	MS-63BN
1799, 9 Over 8	(b)	9	7.8	0%	$4,000	$7,000	$11,500	$24,000	$40,000	$135,000	$325,000	$750,000	
	Auctions: $70,500, VF-25, January 2014; $1,293, AG-3, March 2016												
1799, Normal Date	(b)	48	11.4	2%	$2,750	$4,500	$8,000	$14,500	$30,000	$95,000	$225,000	$500,000	
	Auctions: $30,550, AU-58, May 2016; $99,875, VF-35, January 2013; $32,900, VF-30, March 2015												
1800, All kinds	2,822,175												
1800, 1800 Over 1798, Style 1 Hair		27	24.9	4%	$65	$130	$250	$550	$1,400	$3,850	$7,000	$10,000	$14,000
	Auctions: $2,585, G-6, January 2014												
1800, 80 Over 79, Style 2 Hair		63	22.8	6%	$65	$125	$200	$400	$1,000	$2,500	$4,000	$8,000	$25,000
	Auctions: $19,388, MS-62BN, June 2014; $288, VG-10, March 2018												
1800, Normal Date		152	24.1	9%	$65	$125	$160	$325	$800	$2,000	$3,500	$6,500	$14,000
	Auctions: $70,500, MS-65BN, January 2013; $1,058, VF-25, June 2015; $705, VF-20, October 2015												
1801, All kinds	1,362,837												
1801, Normal Reverse		150	22.6	5%	$60	$95	$125	$250	$600	$1,500	$3,000	$7,500	$14,500
	Auctions: $1,645, EF-40, February 2015; $112, VF-20, July 2015; $494, F-12, August 2015; $282, VG-10, July 2015												
1801, 3 Errors: 1/000, One Stem, and IINITED		27	18.1	7%	$125	$225	$475	$1,100	$3,000	$7,750	$14,000	$35,000	$115,000
	Auctions: $3,525, EF-40, August 2013; $2,400, VG-10, February 2018												
1801, Fraction 1/000		46	21.6	4%	$85	$125	$225	$425	$850	$3,500	$4,800	$9,000	$22,000
	Auctions: $4,406, EF-40, January 2014												
1801, 1/100 Over 1/000		10	21.3	10%	$85	$125	$275	$575	$1,200	$4,500	$9,000	$30,000	$55,000
	Auctions: $1,528, EF-45, January 2014												

b. Included in 1798, All kinds, mintage figure.

1802, Normal Reverse

1802, Fraction 1/000

1802, Stemless Wreath

1803, Small Date

1803, Large Date

*Note that Small Date varieties have a
blunt 1 in the date, and Large Date varieties
have a pointed 1 and noticeably larger 3.*

1803, Small Fraction

1803, Large Fraction

1803, 1/100 Over 1/000

1803, Stemless Wreath

	Mintage	Cert	Avg	%MS	AG-3	G-4	VG-8	F-12	VF-20	EF-40	AU-50	MS-60BN	MS-63BN
1802, All kinds	3,435,100												
1802, Normal Reverse		470	29.1	3%	$75	$100	$125	$250	$500	$1,200	$2,500	$4,500	$11,000
Auctions: $1,058, AU-50, January 2015; $881, EF-40, January 2015; $705, VF-35, January 2015; $617, VF-30, June 2015													
1802, Fraction 1/000		26	33.7	15%	$75	$125	$200	$375	$650	$1,750	$4,800	$7,250	$17,000
Auctions: $11,163, AU-55, January 2014													
1802, Stemless Wreath		49	29.8	4%	$65	$100	$135	$250	$550	$1,300	$2,750	$4,000	$12,000
Auctions: $2,938, AU-55, October 2013; $646, VF-25, January 2015; $470, VF-25, September 2015; $447, VF-25, August 2015													
1803, All kinds	3,131,691												
1803, Small Date, Small Fraction		177	30.0	6%	$65	$85	$125	$250	$500	$1,200	$2,500	$5,500	$11,000
Auctions: $423, EF-40, November 2015; $646, VF-30, July 2015; $541, VF-30, September 2015; $259, F-12, September 2015													
1803, Small Date, Large Fraction		105	31.1	9%	$65	$85	$130	$250	$500	$1,100	$2,250	$4,500	$9,000
Auctions: $18,800, MS-64BN, January 2014; $840, EF-40, April 2018													
1803, Large Date, Small Fraction		3	12.0	0%	$4,500	$7,500	$13,000	$24,000	$40,000	$120,000			
Auctions: $15,275, VF-20, January 2014													
1803, Large Date, Large Fraction		6	45.0	17%	$160	$265	$500	$900	$2,200	$3,700	$8,500		
Auctions: $353, VF-20, August 2013													
1803, 1/100 Over 1/000		18	25.9	6%	$75	$150	$250	$475	$950	$2,250	$4,000	$12,000	$25,000
Auctions: $2,820, EF-45, September 2013													
1803, Stemless Wreath		16	28.4	13%	$65	$125	$150	$325	$800	$1,800	$4,000	$10,000	$20,000
Auctions: $8,225, AU-58, January 2014; $180, VG-8, March 2018													

1804, Broken Dies
Bowers-Whitman–1c, Sheldon-266c.

Unofficial 1804 "Restrike"
Bowers-Whitman–3, Breen-1761, Pollock-6050.

Small 1807, 7 Over 6, Blunt 1

Large 1807, 7 Over 6, Pointed 1

1807, Small Fraction

1807, Large Fraction

1807, "Comet" Variety
Note the die break behind Miss Liberty's head.

	Mintage	Cert	Avg	%MS	AG-3	G-4	VG-8	F-12	VF-20	EF-40	AU-50	MS-60BN	MS-63BN
1804 (c)	96,500	111	14.0	0%	$1,100	$2,300	$3,500	$5,500	$9,500	$17,000	$40,000	$300,000	$650,000
Auctions: $223,250, AU-55, January 2013; $780, Fair 2, January 2018													
1804, Unofficial Restrike of 1860 (d)		89	61.1	87%						$1,000	$1,100	$1,200	$1,500
Auctions: $489, AU-55, August 2011													
1805	941,116	162	35.5	10%	$60	$85	$115	$225	$500	$1,200	$2,750	$5,250	$16,000
Auctions: $940, VF-35, January 2015; $447, VF-20, February 2015; $376, VF-20, May 2015; $129, VG-10, May 2015													
1806	348,000	93	28.4	9%	$75	$125	$180	$400	$700	$2,000	$3,250	$8,500	$28,000
Auctions: $3,819, AU-50, February 2013													

c. All genuine 1804 cents have a crosslet 4 in the date and a large fraction. The 0 in the date is in line with the O in OF on the reverse.
d. Discarded Mint dies were used, circa 1860, to create "restrikes" (actually novodels or fantasies) of the scarce 1804 cent for collectors. These combine two unrelated dies: an altered 1803 die was used for the obverse, and a die of the 1820 cent for the reverse. The resulting coins cannot be confused with genuine 1804 cents.

	Mintage	Cert	Avg	%MS	AG-3	G-4	VG-8	F-12	VF-20	EF-40	AU-50	MS-60BN	MS-63BN
1807, All kinds	829,221												
1807, Small 1807, 7 Over 6, Blunt 1		6	15.3	0%	$1,500	$3,250	$5,000	$9,500	$20,000	$45,000	$150,000		
Auctions: $2,585, F-15, January 2014													
1807, Large 1807, 7 Over 6, Pointed 1		95	23.7	7%	$65	$100	$225	$450	$700	$1,500	$3,500	$10,000	$23,500
Auctions: $70,500, MS-65BN, April 2014; $764, VF-25, January 2015													
1807, Small Fraction		7	11.4	0%	$55	$100	$200	$400	$750	$2,500	$4,000	$8,500	$22,500
Auctions: $1,763, AU-50, August 2013													
1807, Large Fraction		34	19.6	0%	$55	$100	$200	$350	$550	$1,250	$2,300	$4,600	$16,500
Auctions: $5,750, AU-58, August 2011; $541, VF-25, October 2015; $306, F-12, June 2015; $89, G-6, March 2018													
1807, "Comet" Variety		30	29.5	17%	$85	$175	$300	$550	$1,200	$2,850	$5,500	$13,000	$26,000
Auctions: $27,600, MS-61BN, February 2012													

CLASSIC HEAD (1808–1814)

Designer: *John Reich.* **Weight:** *10.89 grams.* **Composition:** *Copper.*
Diameter: *Average 29 mm.* **Edge:** *Plain.* **Mint:** *Philadelphia.*

1808; BW-1, S-277, B-1.

History. The Classic Head design, by U.S. Mint assistant engraver John Reich, debuted in 1808. This cent type was minted through 1814. The quality of the coins' copper was poor during the War of 1812; the hostilities had ended the importation of high-quality planchets from England.

Striking and Sharpness. Striking sharpness varies, but often is poor. The cents of 1809 are notorious for having obverses much weaker than their reverses. Points to look for include sharpness of the denticles (which are often mushy, and in *most* instances inconsistent), star centers (a key area), hair details, and leaf details. Classic Head cents often are dark and porous due to the copper stock used.

Availability. Examples are readily available in grades from well worn to VF and EF, although overall quality often leaves much to be desired. AU and MS coins are elusive. Grading numbers do not mean much, as a connoisseur might prefer a high-quality EF-45 to a poorly struck MS-63. Overall eye appeal of obverse and reverse is often sub-par, a characteristic of this type.

GRADING STANDARDS

MS-60 to 70 (Mint State). *Obverse:* In the lower Mint State grades, MS-60 and 61, some slight abrasions can be seen on the portrait, most evidently on the cheek, as the hair details are complex on this type. Luster in the field is complete or nearly complete; the field is not as open on this type as on the Draped Bust issues. At MS-63, luster should be complete, and no abrasion evident. In higher levels, the luster is complete and deeper, and some orig-

1812, Large Date; BW-1, S-288, B-3. Graded MS-64BN.

inal mint color may be seen. MS-64 coins may have some slight discoloration or scattered contact marks. A well-graded MS-65 or higher coin will have full, rich luster; no marks visible except under magnification; and a nice blend of brown toning or nicely mixed (not stained or blotchy) mint color and natural brown toning. Incomplete striking of some details, especially the obverse stars, is the rule. *Reverse:* In the lower Mint State grades, some abrasion is seen on the higher areas of the leaves. Mint luster is complete in all Mint State grades, as the open areas are protected by the lettering and wreath. Sharpness of the leaves can vary by die variety, so check this aspect. Otherwise, the same comments apply as for the obverse.

Illustrated coin: The central devices are sharply struck and well preserved though obverse stars 1 through 5 are somewhat flat, as is virtually always seen on this type, and the reverse denticles from 8 o'clock to 11 o'clock are soft, which is also typical. This is one of the highest-graded Classic Head cents in existence.

AU-50, 53, 55, 58 (About Uncirculated). *Obverse:* Friction is seen on the higher parts, particularly the cheek. The hair will have friction and light wear, but will not be as obvious. Friction and scattered marks are in the field, ranging from more extensive at AU-50 to minimal at AU-58. Luster may be seen in protected areas, minimal at AU-50, but more visible at AU-58. At AU-58 the open field may retain some luster, as well.

1812, Large Date; BW-2, S-289, B-4. Graded AU-58.

Reverse: Friction is seen on the higher wreath leaves and on the letters. Fields, protected by the designs, show less friction. At the AU–55 and 58 levels little if any friction is seen. The reverse may have original luster, toned brown, minimal on lower About Uncirculated grades, often extensive at AU-58.

EF-40, 45 (Extremely Fine). *Obverse:* Wear is seen on the portrait overall, but most hair detail will still be present. The cheek shows light wear. Luster is minimal or nonexistent at EF-40, and may survive in among the letters of LIBERTY at EF-45. *Reverse:* Wear is seen on the highest wreath and ribbon areas and the letters. Leaf veins are visible except in the highest areas. Luster is minimal, but likely more noticeable than on the obverse, as the fields are protected by the designs and lettering.

1809; BW-1, S-280, B-1. Graded EF-40.

VF-20, 30 (Very Fine). *Obverse:* Wear on the portrait has reduced the hair detail, especially on the area to the right of the cheek and neck, but much can still be seen. *Reverse:* The wreath details, except for the edges of the leaves and certain of the tips (on leaves in lower relief), are worn away at VF-20, and with slightly more detail at VF-30.

1812, Large Date; BW-2, S-289, B-4. Graded VF-25.

F-12, 15 (Fine). *Obverse:* The hair details are fewer than on the preceding, but many are still present. The central hair curl is visible. Stars have flat centers. F-15 shows slightly more detail. The portrait on this type held up well to wear. *Reverse:* The higher areas of wreath leaves are worn flat, but their edges are distinct. F-15 shows slightly more detail.

Illustrated coin: This is a dark and somewhat porous example of what is considered to be the key issue of the Classic Head type.

1809; BW-1, S-280, B-1. Graded F-15.

VG-8, 10 (Very Good). *Obverse:* The portrait is well worn, although the eye and ear can be seen clearly. The hair is mostly blended, but some slight separation can be seen in areas. The border is raised in most or all areas. *Reverse:* The wreath is more worn than on the preceding grade, but there will still be some detail on the leaves. On most coins, ONE CENT is bold. Border letters are light or weak but are fully readable. The border is well defined in most areas.

1808. Graded VG-8.

G-4, 6 (Good). *Obverse:* The portrait is worn smooth and is seen only in outline form. Much or even all of LIBERTY on the headband is readable, but the letters are weak. The stars are weak, only in outline form, and several may be scarcely discernible. *Reverse:* Extensive wear is seen overall. Lettering in UNITED STATES OF AMERICA is weak, but completely discernible. The wreath is in outline, but still fairly bold, and ONE CENT is usually strong.

1808; BW-1, S-277, B-1. Graded G-6.

AG-3 (About Good). *Obverse:* Wear is more extensive than on the preceding. The portrait is visible only in outline. Most letters of LIBERTY are discernible, as this feature is in low relief. The stars are weak or worn away on their outer edges, and the date is light. *Reverse:* The wreath is visible in outline form but remains fairly strong. Most or even all of UNITED STATES OF AMERICA is worn away. ONE CENT is usually easily readable.

1808; BW-2, S-278, B-2. Graded AG-3.

| 1810, 10 Over 09 | 1810, Normal Date |

| 1811, Last 1 Over 0 | 1811, Normal Date |

| 1812, Small Date | 1812, Large Date |

| 1814, Plain 4 | 1814, Crosslet 4 |

	Mintage	Cert	Avg	%MS	AG-3	G-4	VG-8	F-12	VF-20	EF-40	AU-50	MS-60BN	MS-63BN
1808	1,007,000	144	32.0	14%	$65	$115	$235	$550	$1,100	$2,200	$4,000	$10,000	$17,500
	Auctions: $25,850, MS-64BN, January 2013; $400, F-12, May 2015; $69, F-12, April 2015												
1809	222,867	77	28.1	9%	$150	$235	$500	$850	$1,700	$3,600	$5,000	$11,500	$28,000
	Auctions: $28,200, MS-63BN, January 2013; $754, F-12, January 2015; $376, G-4, May 2015												
1810, All kinds	1,458,500												
1810, 10 Over 09		57	27.7	9%	$65	$110	$225	$550	$1,000	$2,000	$3,600	$9,500	$15,000
	Auctions: $10,575, AU-55, April 2013												
1810, Normal Date		147	31.3	13%	$60	$100	$200	$450	$900	$1,900	$3,300	$9,000	$15,000
	Auctions: $32,900, MS-64BN, January 2014; $376, EF-40, January 2015; $1,234, VF-35, January 2015; $940, VF-20, July 2015												
1811, All kinds	218,025												
1811, Last 1 Over 0		32	23.6	9%	$165	$275	$400	$900	$2,100	$6,000	$12,500	$35,000	$60,000
	Auctions: $2,585, VF-25, March 2015; $1,410, VF-20, August 2016; $764, VG-10, August 2015												
1811, Normal Date		91	27.5	12%	$110	$200	$300	$650	$1,350	$2,800	$5,000	$9,500	$20,000
	Auctions: $23,500, MS-64BN, January 2013; $336, VG-10, March 2018												
1812, All kinds	1,075,500												
1812, Small Date		37	30.1	5%	$60	$100	$200	$450	$900	$1,900	$3,300	$7,000	$13,500
	Auctions: $44,063, MS-65RB, June 2014; $881, VF-30, August 2015; $94, F-12, March 2015; $153, VG-8, June 2015												
1812, Large Date		33	32.3	9%	$60	$100	$200	$450	$900	$1,900	$3,300	$7,000	$13,500
	Auctions: $3,819, AU-55, January 2014												
1813	418,000	198	35.1	10%	$70	$125	$275	$500	$900	$2,300	$4,200	$9,000	$15,000
	Auctions: $211,500, MS-65BN, January 2013; $940, AU-50, January 2015; $1,880, EF-40, March 2015; $1,116, VF-20, August 2015												
1814, All kinds	357,830												
1814, Plain 4		151	21.9	5%	$60	$100	$200	$400	$700	$1,700	$3,000	$6,000	$12,500
	Auctions: $47,000, MS-65BN, April 2014; $223, VG-10, May 2015; $129, G-6, April 2015; $74, G-4, April 2015												
1814, Crosslet 4		117	26.0	12%	$60	$100	$200	$400	$700	$1,700	$3,000	$6,000	$12,500
	Auctions: $1,028, VF-30, February 2015; $376, VF-20, November 2015; $188, VF-20, May 2015; $259, VG-10, May 2015												

MATRON HEAD (1816–1839)

Designer: *1816–1835, Matron Head—Possibly Robert Scot or John Birch;*
1835–1839, Matron Head Modified—Christian Gobrecht. **Weight:** *10.89 grams.*
Composition: *Copper.* **Diameter:** *1816–1835, Matron Head—28 to 29 mm;*
1835–1839, Matron Head Modified—27.5 mm. **Edge:** *Plain.* **Mint:** *Philadelphia.*

Matron Head (1816–1835),
Circulation Strike
1827; Newcomb-5.

Matron Head, Proof
1831; Newcomb-10.

Matron Head Modified (1835–1839),
Circulation Strike
1835; Newcomb-8.

Matron Head Modified, Proof
1837; Newcomb-9.

History. The term *Matron Head* describes cents of 1816 to 1835 (none were struck in 1815). Engraver Christian Gobrecht experimented with various "Matron Head Modified" portraits in the later 1830s.

Striking and Sharpness. Planchet quality is generally very good for Liberty Head cents. Color tends to be lighter on coins of the 1830s than on earlier dates. Striking can vary. Points to check include the obverse stars (in particular), the highest hair details, and the leaves on the reverse. Denticles can range from sharp to weak, and centering is often irregular. The reverse design is essentially the same as that used on the Classic Head of 1808 to 1814, and can be graded the same way. This motif stood up to circulation particularly well.

Availability. As a type, Liberty Head cents are easily available. The scarcest date by far is 1823 (and the related 1823, 3 Over 2, overdate). Cents of 1816 to 1820 (particularly 1818 and 1820) are readily available in MS. Other MS coins are generally scarce, although those of the 1830s are more readily available than those of the teens and 1820s. Circulated examples exist in approximate relationship to their mint-ages. Planchet quality and striking sharpness vary in all grades.

GRADING STANDARDS

MS-60 to 70 (Mint State). *Obverse:* In the lower Mint State grades, MS–60 and 61, some slight abrasions can be seen on the portrait, most evidently on the cheek, which on this type is very prominent. Higher areas of the hair can be checked, particularly the top and back of Liberty's head, but do not confuse with lightness of strike. Luster in the

1817; N-2. Graded MS-63BN.

field is complete or nearly complete. At MS-63, luster should be complete, and no abrasion is evident.

In higher levels, the luster is complete and deeper, and some original mint color may be seen. MS-64 coins may have some minimal discoloration or scattered contact marks. A well-graded MS-65 or higher coin will have full, rich luster; no marks visible except under magnification; and a nice blend of brown toning or nicely mixed mint color and natural brown toning. Randall Hoard coins of the 1816 to 1820 years usually have much mint red and some black spotting. *Reverse:* In the lower Mint State grades some abrasion is seen on the higher areas of the leaves. Mint luster is complete in all Mint State grades, as the open areas are protected by the lettering and wreath. Sharpness of the leaves can vary by die variety, so check this aspect. Otherwise, the same comments apply as for the obverse.

Illustrated coin: Note the reverse die break running from NI of UNITED to OF A in OF AMERICA.

AU-50, 53, 55, 58 (About Uncirculated).

Obverse: Friction is seen on the higher parts, particularly the cheek. The hair has friction and light wear, usually most notable in the general area above BER of LIBERTY. Friction and scattered marks are in the field, ranging from extensive at AU-50 to minimal at AU-58. Luster may be seen in protected areas, minimal at the AU-50 level, more visible at AU-58. At AU-58 the field may retain some luster as well.

1820, 20 Over 19; N-10. Graded AU-58.

Reverse: Friction is seen on the higher wreath leaves and on the letters. Fields, protected by the designs, show friction. At the AU–55 and 58 levels little if any friction is seen. The reverse may have original luster, toned brown, minimal on lower About Uncirculated grades, often extensive at AU-58.

Illustrated coin: Flecks of darker patination spot both sides, but are particularly evident on the obverse.

EF-40, 45 (Extremely Fine).

Obverse: Wear is seen on the portrait overall, but most hair detail is still present, except in higher areas. The cheek shows light wear. Luster is minimal or nonexistent at EF-40, and may survive in among the letters of LIBERTY at EF-45. *Reverse:* Wear is seen on the highest wreath and ribbon areas, and on the letters. Leaf veins are visible except in the highest areas. Luster is minimal, but likely more noticeable

1816. Graded EF-45.

than on the obverse, as the fields are protected by the designs and lettering.

VF-20, 30 (Very Fine).

Obverse: Wear on the portrait has reduced the hair detail, especially on the area to the right of the cheek and neck, but much can still be seen. *Reverse:* The wreath details, except for the edges of the leaves and certain of the tips (on leaves in lower relief), are worn away at VF-20, and with slightly more detail at VF-30.

1823; N2. Graded VF-20.

F-12, 15 (Fine). *Obverse:* The hair details are fewer than on the preceding, but still many are present. Wear is extensive above and below the LIBERTY coronet, with the area from the forehead to the coronet worn flat. Stars have flat centers. F-15 shows slightly more detail. *Reverse:* The higher areas of wreath leaves are worn flat, but their edges are distinct. F-15 shows slightly more detail.

1816. Graded F-15.

VG-8, 10 (Very Good). *Obverse:* The portrait is well worn, although the eye and ear can be seen clearly. The hair is mostly blended, but some slight separation can be seen in lower areas. The border is raised in most or all areas. *Reverse:* The wreath is more worn than on the preceding, but still there is some detail on the leaves. On most coins, ONE CENT is bold. Border letters are light or weak but are fully readable. The border is well defined in most areas.

1831, Large Letters; N-9. Graded VG-8.

    Illustrated coin: A die break caused the internal cud which connects stars 3 through 5, and that broken die would have been retired shortly after striking this piece.

G-4, 6 (Good). *Obverse:* The portrait is worn smooth and is seen only in outline form. Much or even all of LIBERTY on the headband is readable, but the letters are weak, and L may be missing. The stars are weak. The rim is usually discernible all around. *Reverse:* Extensive wear is seen overall. Lettering in UNITED STATES OF AMERICA is weak, but completely discernible. The wreath is in outline, but still fairly bold, and ONE CENT

1830; N-9. Graded G-4.

is usually strong. The rim is usually faded into the field in many areas (depending on the die variety).

    Illustrated coin: Note the lovely golden brown and rose surfaces.

AG-3 (About Good). *Obverse:* Wear is more extensive than on the preceding. The portrait is visible only in outline. Most letters of LIBERTY remain discernible in the headband, as this feature is in low relief. The stars are weak or worn away on their outer edges, and the date is light. *Reverse:* The wreath is visible in outline form, but remains fairly strong. Most of UNITED STATES OF AMERICA is worn away. ONE CENT is usually readable, but light.

1818; N-6. Graded AG-3.

PF-60 to 70 (Proof). Proofs were made for cents from 1817 onward. Often, what are called "Proofs" are only partially mirrorlike, and sometimes the striking is casual, e.g., with weakness on certain of the stars. Complicating the situation is the fact that all but one of the same die pairs were also used to make circulation strikes. Many misattributions were made generations ago, some of which have been perpetuated. Except among large-cent

1831, Large Letters; N-9. Graded PF-63BN.

specialists, debate is effectively ended when a certification service seals a coin as a Proof (logic aside). True Proofs with deeply mirrored surfaces are in the small minority. ***Obverse and Reverse:*** Proofs that are extensively hairlined or have dull surfaces, this being characteristic of many issues (exceptions, when found, are usually dated in the 1830s) are graded PF–60 to 62 or 63. Artificially toned and recolored coins may be graded lower. To qualify as PF-65 or higher, hairlines should be microscopic, and there should be no trace of friction. Surfaces should be prooflike or, better, fully mirrored and without dullness.

Illustrated coin: This coin shows high quality for the grade. The surfaces are a light, reddish brown with areas of deep tan and hints of blue, green, gold and violet as well as considerable faded mint red on the reverse. This is one of two known Proof examples for the year.

| | **1817, 13 Stars** | | **1817, 15 Stars** | |

	Mintage	Cert	Avg	%MS	G-4	VG-8	F-12	VF-20	EF-40	AU-50	MS-60BN / PF-63BN	MS-63BN / PF-64BN	MS-65BN / PF-65BN
1816	2,820,982	350	52.2	53%	$25	$35	$50	$110	$250	$400	$600	$900	$3,600
Auctions: $823, MS-63BN, October 2015; $259, AU-50, August 2015; $306, EF-45, April 2015; $69, EF-40, October 2015													
1817, All kinds	3,948,400												
1817, 13 Stars		514	50.0	49%	$25	$35	$50	$100	$200	$350	$450	$800	$2,800
Auctions: $1,293, MS-63BN, January 2015; $1,116, MS-63BN, January 2015; $1,175, MS-62BN, June 2015; $282, MS-60, June 2015													
1817, 15 Stars		48	48.6	23%	$35	$60	$100	$175	$700	$1,200	$2,800	$5,500	$35,000
Auctions: $9,400, VF-20, January 2014; $360, VF-20, April 2018													
1817, Proof	*2–3*	1	63.0								$70,000	$100,000	$150,000
Auctions: $48,300, PF-66, July 2005													
1818	3,167,000	840	56.9	72%	$25	$30	$45	$85	$175	$300	$450	$600	$1,600
Auctions: $823, MS-64BN, September 2015; $764, MS-63RB, June 2015; $541, MS-62BN, October 2015; $494, MS-62BN, June 2015													

1819, 9 Over 8	1819, Large Date	1819, Small Date

1820, 20 Over 19
Note the 1 under the 2.

1820, Large Date
Note the plain-topped 2.

1820, Small Date
Note the curl-topped 2.

	Mintage	Cert	Avg	%MS	G-4	VG-8	F-12	VF-20	EF-40	AU-50	MS-60BN / PF-63BN	MS-63BN / PF-64BN	MS-65BN / PF-65BN
1819, All kinds	2,671,000												
1819, 9 Over 8		121	50.0	38%	$25	$35	$55	$100	$325	$375	$850	$1,300	$4,000
Auctions: $705, AU-58, October 2015; $259, EF-45, September 2015													
1819, Large Date		257	52.5	54%	$25	$30	$45	$85	$175	$300	$550	$950	$3,000
Auctions: $940, MS-63BN, August 2015; $259, AU-55, May 2015; $202, EF-40, September 2015													
1819, Small Date		104	54.5	60%	$25	$30	$45	$85	$200	$350	$550	$1,000	$3,300
Auctions: $1,293, MS-63BN, June 2015; $646, AU-58, October 2015; $282, AU-50, August 2015; $212, EF-40, May 2015													
1819, 9 Over 8, Proof	2–3	1	64.0								$75,000		
Auctions: $32,200, PF-64BN, June 2005													
1820, All kinds	4,407,550												
1820, 20 Over 19		44	40.8	27%	$25	$40	$55	$110	$400	$550	$1,350	$1,600	$4,500
Auctions: $764, AU-55, August 2015													
1820, Large Date		117	56.2	69%	$25	$30	$45	$85	$175	$300	$400	$650	$1,800
Auctions: $1,293, MS-63BN, August 2015; $705, MS-63BN, January 2015; $588, MS-63BN, January 2015; $494, MS-60, September 2015													
1820, Small Date		38	51.3	53%	$25	$40	$120	$180	$500	$950	$1,700	$2,300	$4,500
Auctions: $4,994, MS-64BN, January 2014													
1820, Proof	8–15	3	63.7								$40,000	$50,000	$60,000
Auctions: $46,000, PF-64, November 2008													
1821 (a)	389,000	151	29.7	7%	$45	$60	$190	$400	$1,300	$2,300	$9,000	$20,000	
Auctions: $564, AU-50, January 2015; $494, VF-25, August 2015; $400, VF-20, January 2015; $129, VF-20, May 2015; $312, VF-30, April 2018													
1821, Proof	4–6	3	63.0								$32,500	$40,000	$55,000
Auctions: $35,250, PF-62BN, August 2013													
1822	2,072,339	260	43.0	22%	$30	$40	$55	$150	$425	$700	$1,200	$2,300	$10,000
Auctions: $1,058, AU-58, June 2015; $793, AU-58, February 2015; $494, AU-55, January 2015; $517, AU-50, June 2015													
1822, Proof	4–6	1	62.0								$35,000	$50,000	
Auctions: $25,300, PF-63, March 2004													

a. Wide and closely spaced AMER varieties are valued the same.

1823, 3 Over 2

1824, 4 Over 2

Unofficial 1823 "Restrike"
Newcomb-3, Breen-1823, Pollock-6220.

1826, 6 Over 5

**Date Size, Through 1828
(Large, Narrow Date)**

**Date Size, 1828 and
Later (Small, Wide Date)**

	Mintage	Cert	Avg	%MS	G-4	VG-8	F-12	VF-20	EF-40	AU-50	MS-60BN / PF-63BN	MS-63BN / PF-64BN	MS-65BN / PF-65BN
1823, 3 Over 2	(b)	105	21.2	2%	$115	$250	$600	$1,200	$3,000	$6,500	$20,000	—	
Auctions: $1,645, VF-30, January 2015; $564, F-15, February 2015; $259, VG-10, May 2015; $132, G-6, February 2018													
1823, Normal Date	(b)	62	19.5	3%	$125	$285	$700	$1,650	$4,000	$8,500	$23,000	$30,000	$115,000
Auctions: $3,584, VF-35, January 2014; $900, VF-20, February 2018; $132, G-4, March 2018													
1823, Unofficial Restrike (c)		60	63.3	97%				$450	$550	$925	$1,250	$1,500	$1,750
Auctions: $2,350, MS-64BN, December 2013													
1823, Proof	2–3	1	65.0										$90,000
Auctions: No auction records available.													
1823, 3 Over 2, Proof	5–8	3	64.3								$50,000	$60,000	
Auctions: $47,000, PF-64BN, June 2014													
1824, All kinds	1,262,000												
1824, 4 Over 2		47	34.3	9%	$50	$75	$110	$275	$1,200	$2,500	$6,000	$25,000	
Auctions: $423, VF-25BN, September 2015; $129, VG-10, May 2015; $94, VG-10, June 2015; $99, VG-8, May 2018													
1824, Normal Date		148	39.5	16%	$35	$50	$75	$165	$550	$850	$3,000	$4,600	$13,000
Auctions: $564, EF-45, June 2015; $235, EF-40, January 2015; $259, VF-30, September 2015; $235, VF-30, May 2015													
1825	1,461,100	189	42.8	25%	$30	$40	$60	$150	$450	$750	$1,750	$2,750	$7,500
Auctions: $6,463, MS-64BN, January 2014													
1826, All kinds	1,517,425												
1826, 6 Over 5		19	49.7	42%	$30	$50	$100	$275	$975	$1,500	$2,800	$5,500	$20,000
Auctions: $10,575, MS-62BN, January 2014													
1826, Normal Date		295	45.3	31%	$25	$30	$50	$100	$250	$450	$900	$1,500	$3,100
Auctions: $3,290, MS-64, March 2015; $1,234, AU-58, August 2015; $376, AU-53, September 2015; $329, EF-40, June 2015													
1827	2,357,732	270	41.8	25%	$25	$30	$45	$100	$225	$425	$775	$1,400	$3,250
Auctions: $881, AU-58BN, October 2015; $576, AU-55, March 2015; $376, AU-53, May 2015; $259, EF-45, May 2015													
1827, Proof	5–8	2	64.0								$20,000	$25,000	$40,000
Auctions: $20,125, PF-64, March 2004													
1828, All kinds	2,260,624												
1828, Large Narrow Date		81	50.5	30%	$25	$30	$45	$90	$210	$400	$1,250	$1,750	$4,250
Auctions: $3,672, MS-64, March 2015; $881, AU-58, October 2015; $141, VF-30, January 2015													
1828, Small Wide Date		20	49.1	40%	$30	$35	$50	$190	$275	$650	$1,950	$3,500	$20,000
Auctions: $7,638, MS-64BN, February 2013; $432, EF-45, May 2018													
1828, Proof	2–3	1	65.0										$80,000
Auctions: No auction records available.													

b. Included in 1824, All kinds, mintage figure. **c.** The unofficial 1823 "restrikes" (actually novodels or fantasies) were made at the same time (around 1860) and by the same people as those of 1804. The coins were made from a discarded obverse die of 1823 and an 1813 reverse die—both heavily rusted, producing surface lumps. Most examples have both dies cracked.

Large Letters (1808–1834)
*Note the size and proximity
of individual letters.*

Medium Letters (1829–1837)
*Note the isolation of the
letters, especially of STATES.*

	Mintage	Cert	Avg	%MS	G-4	VG-8	F-12	VF-20	EF-40	AU-50	MS-60BN / PF-63BN	MS-63BN / PF-64BN	MS-65BN / PF-65BN
1829, All kinds	1,414,500												
1829, Large Letters		47	45.6	32%	$25	$30	$45	$110	$200	$385	$650	$1,500	$5,200
Auctions: $646, AU-55, February 2015; $129, VF-25, February 2015													
1829, Medium Letters		17	40.6	18%	$25	$45	$110	$350	$800	$2,500	$6,500	$10,500	$17,000
Auctions: $7,050, AU-58, January 2014													
1829, Proof	2–3	1	64.0								$20,000	$25,000	$40,000
Auctions: $47,000, PF-64RB, January 2014													
1829, Bronzed, Proof	10–15	5	64.6								$18,000	$26,000	$40,000
Auctions: $41,125, PF-65BN, August 2013													
1830, All kinds	1,711,500												
1830, Large Letters		99	47.4	33%	$25	$30	$40	$70	$190	$300	$550	$1,000	$2,700
Auctions: $562, AU-55, August 2015; $646, AU-53, October 2015; $235, EF-40, May 2015; $153, VF-25, May 2015													
1830, Medium Letters		10	29.5	10%	$30	$40	$160	$500	$2,000	$5,000	$14,000	$25,000	$32,000
Auctions: $3,055, EF-40, June 2013													
1830, Proof	2–3	1	64.0								$25,000	$35,000	$65,000
Auctions: $16,500, PF-64, November 1988													
1831, All kinds	3,359,260												
1831, Large Letters		91	52.2	52%	$25	$30	$40	$70	$150	$250	$400	$700	$1,800
Auctions: $212, AU-53, July 2015; $224, AU-50, March 2015													
1831, Medium Letters		46	50.9	41%	$25	$30	$40	$70	$200	$350	$750	$1,600	$3,500
Auctions: $3,290, MS-62BN, January 2014													
1831, Proof	10–20	8	64.1								$14,500	$24,500	$50,000
Auctions: $30,550, PF-65BN, January 2014													
1832, All kinds	2,362,000												
1832, Large Letters		32	54.0	53%	$25	$30	$40	$70	$150	$250	$375	$650	$2,300
Auctions: $3,525, MS-65BN, January 2014; $306, AU-58, June 2015													
1832, Medium Letters		34	56.6	56%	$25	$30	$40	$85	$200	$550	$900	$1,200	$2,900
Auctions: $940, MS-62BN, July 2014													
1832, Proof	2–4	1	64.0								$40,000	$50,000	$65,000
Auctions: No auction records available.													
1833	2,739,000	310	49.3	40%	$25	$30	$40	$70	$150	$250	$375	$750	$2,600
Auctions: $423, AU-58, May 2015; $294, AU-53, May 2015; $223, EF-40, August 2015; $206, EF-40, June 2015													
1833, Proof	**(d)**	0	n/a										
Auctions: No auction records available.													

d. Unique.

1834, Large 8,
Large Stars,
Large Letters
Newcomb-6.

1834, Large 8,
Large Stars,
Medium Letters
Newcomb-5.

1834, Large 8,
Small Stars,
Medium Letters
Newcomb-3.

1834, Small 8,
Large Stars,
Medium Letters
Newcomb-1.

	Mintage	Cert	Avg	%MS	G-4	VG-8	F-12	VF-20	EF-40	AU-50	MS-60BN PF-63BN	MS-63BN PF-64BN	MS-65BN PF-65BN
1834, All kinds	1,855,100												
1834, Large 8, Stars, and Reverse Letters		14	44.4	7%	$25	$35	$75	$200	$550	$1,200	$2,250	$4,000	$8,500
	Auctions: $2,820, AU-58, January 2014												
1834, Large 8 and Stars, Medium Letters		6	52.2	33%	$160	$325	$400	$1,000	$3,500	$6,500	$8,500	$12,000	$22,000
	Auctions: $58,750, MS-65BN, January 2014; $253, AU-50, June 2015; $165, EF-40, January 2015												
1834, Large 8, Small Stars, Medium Letters		38	46.3	29%	$25	$30	$35	$65	$140	$240	$500	$800	$2,000
	Auctions: $1,528, MS-63BN, January 2014; $216, EF-45, April 2018; $240, EF-40, March 2018												
1834, Small 8, Large Stars, Medium Letters		83	53.4	46%	$25	$30	$35	$65	$140	$240	$350	$625	$1,500
	Auctions: $4,994, MS-66BN, January 2014; $823, AU-58, September 2015												
1834, Proof	6–8	4	65.0								$15,000	$21,000	$40,000
	Auctions: $52,875, PF-60BN, January 2014												

1835, Large 8,
Large Stars,
Matron Head

1835, Small 8,
Small Stars,
Matron Head

Medium Letters
(1829–1837)

Small Letters
(1837–1839)

1835,
Matron
Head

1835, Head of 1836

1837
*Note the plain
hair cords.*

1837, Head of 1838
*Note the slim bust
and the beaded hair cords.*

1839, 1839 Over 1836
*Note the closed 9 and
the plain hair cords.*

1839, Silly Head
*Note the prominent lock
of hair at the forehead.*

1839, Booby Head
Note the shoulder tip. Also note the absence of a line under CENT.

	Mintage	Cert	Avg	%MS	G-4	VG-8	F-12	VF-20	EF-40	AU-50	MS-60BN PF-63BN	MS-63BN PF-64BN	MS-65BN PF-65BN
1835, All kinds	3,878,400												
1835, Large 8 and Stars		15	47.2	33%	$25	$30	$35	$75	$225	$400	$750	$1,400	$3,750
Auctions: $16,450, MS-64BN, January 2013													
1835, Small 8 and Stars		51	46.5	29%	$25	$30	$35	$65	$175	$375	$475	$675	$1,750
Auctions: $3,819, MS-63BN, January 2014													
1835, Head of 1836		98	53.6	41%	$25	$30	$35	$55	$125	$250	$350	$550	$1,300
Auctions: $712, MS-62BN, August 2015; $646, AU-58, September 2015; $176, AU-50, October 2015; $106, AU-50, April 2015													
1836	2,111,000	260	51.0	43%	$25	$30	$35	$55	$125	$250	$350	$550	$1,300
Auctions: $881, MS-64BN, January 2015; $447, AU-58, September 2015; $259, AU-55, September 2015; $153, EF-45, August 2015													
1836, Proof	6–8	4	64.0								$15,000	$21,000	$40,000
Auctions: $47,000, PF-63RB, June 2014													
1837, All kinds	5,558,300												
1837, Plain Cord, Medium Letters		164	57.2	62%	$20	$25	$35	$55	$125	$250	$350	$550	$1,200
Auctions: $94, VF-35, February 2015													
1837, Plain Cord, Small Letters		27	53.5	48%	$20	$25	$35	$55	$125	$250	$375	$600	$1,500
Auctions: $411, AU-58, February 2014													
1837, Head of 1838		82	58.1	61%	$20	$25	$35	$50	$110	$200	$325	$500	$1,200
Auctions: $1,116, MS-64BN, January 2015; $646, MS-63BN, August 2015; $306, AU-58, August 2015; $235, AU-53, June 2015													
1837, Proof	8–12	7	64.0								$30,000		
Auctions: $27,025, PF-63BN, January 2014													
1838	6,370,200	990	53.7	52%	$20	$25	$35	$50	$120	$225	$335	$575	$1,325
Auctions: $1,028, MS-64BN, January 2015; $470, MS-63BN, January 2015; $223, AU-58, August 2015; $223, AU-55, May 2015													
1838, Proof	10–20	6	64.3								$14,000	$20,000	$38,000
Auctions: $64,625, PF-64RD, January 2014													
1839, All kinds	3,128,661												
1839, 1839 Over 1836, Plain Cords		64	13.7	0%	$400	$650	$1,400	$3,000	$7,000	$20,000	$65,000	$100,000	$250,000
Auctions: $5,581, VF-35, January 2014; $881, F-12, August 2016; $588, VG-10, September 2016; $564, VG-8, February 2018													
1839, Head of 1838, Beaded Cords		116	52.0	39%	$25	$30	$40	$55	$130	$250	$350	$550	$1,450
Auctions: $1,645, MS-64BN, September 2013; $176, EF-45, February 2015; $141, EF-45, July 2015; $143, VF-35, September 2015													
1839, Silly Head		148	49.6	41%	$25	$35	$45	$75	$200	$400	$850	$1,400	$2,700
Auctions: $12,925, MS-67BN, January 2014; $160, EF-40, July 2015; $1,800, MS-63BN, 2018													
1839, Booby Head		446	53.0	52%	$25	$35	$45	$75	$165	$350	$700	$1,500	$2,800
Auctions: $470, AU-53, August 2015; $329, EF-40, May 2015; $141, VF-35, June 2015; $660, MS-61BN, February 2018													

BRAIDED HAIR (1839–1857)

Designer: *Christian Gobrecht.* **Weight:** *10.89 grams.* **Composition:** *Copper.*
Diameter: *27.5 mm.* **Edge:** *Plain.* **Mint:** *Philadelphia.*

Circulation Strike
1845; N-11.

Proof
1852; N-24.

History. Christian Gobrecht's Braided Hair design was introduced in 1839. It loosely followed the design he had created for the 1838 gold eagle. On issues of 1839 through part of 1843, Miss Liberty's portrait is tilted forward, with the left tip of her neck truncation over the 8 of the date. For most issues of 1843 and all later dates her head is larger and aligned in a more vertical position, and the tip of her neck is over the first digit of the date. The reverse lettering was made larger beginning in 1844. The net result is that cents after 1843 are less delicate in appearance than are those of earlier dates. These coins were made in large quantities, except for their final year. They remained in circulation in the United States until the late 1850s, not long enough to be worn down to very low grades. (Some circulated in the eastern part of Canada through the 1860s, accounting for many of the more worn examples seen today.)

Striking and Sharpness. Sharpness can vary. On the obverse, the star centers can be weak, especially for dates in the 1850s, and, less often, there can be lightness on the front of the coronet and the hair. On the reverse the leaves can be light, but most are well struck. The denticles can be mushy and indistinct on either side, this being particularly true of dates in the early and mid-1850s. Flaky or laminated planchets can be a problem, again among coins of the 1850s, in which tiny pieces of metal fall away from the surface, leaving areas in the field that interrupt the luster on MS coins.

Availability. All dates of Braided Hair cents are readily available, with the 1857 somewhat less so (it was minted in January 1857 in low quantity; seemingly not all were released). The delicate-featured issues of 1839 to 1843 are becoming more difficult to find in EF or finer grades without surface problems. Cents dated in the 1850s are usually seen in VF or higher grades. Certain die varieties attributed by Newcomb numbers can be scarce or rare. For issues in the 1850s the differences can be microscopic, thus limiting their numismatic appeal and making them unattributable unless in high grades. Hoards were found of some dates, particularly 1850 to 1856, making MS coins of these years more readily available than would otherwise be the case. MS-64RD or higher coins with *original* color range from scarce to very rare for dates prior to 1850, but those of the 1850s are seen regularly (except for 1857). Coins below VF-20 are not widely collected and, for many issues, are too worn to attribute by die variety.

GRADING STANDARDS

MS-60 to 70 (Mint State). *Obverse:* In the lower Mint State grades, MS–60 and 61, some slight abrasions can be seen on the portrait, most evidently on the cheek. Check the tip of the coronet and the hair above the ear, as well. Luster in the field is complete or nearly so. At MS-63, luster should be complete, and no abrasion evident. If there is weakness on the hair it is due to light striking, not to wear; this also applies for the stars. In

1840, Large Date; N-7. Graded MS-64BN.

higher levels, the luster is complete and deeper, and some original mint color may be seen. Mint frost on this type is usually deep, sometimes satiny, but hardly ever prooflike. MS-64 coins may have some slight discoloration or scattered contact marks. A well-graded MS-65 or higher coin will have full, rich luster; no marks visible except under magnification; and a nice blend of brown toning or nicely mixed (not stained or blotchy) mint color and natural brown toning. MS-64RD or higher coins with original color range from scarce to very rare for dates prior to 1850, but those of the 1850s are seen regularly (except for 1857). *Reverse:* In the lower Mint State grades some abrasion is seen on the higher areas of the leaves. Mint luster is complete in all Mint State ranges, as the open areas are protected by the lettering and wreath. The quality of the luster is the best way to grade both sides of this type.

Illustrated coin: This coin is a light, golden olive with faint tints of pale green in places, with scattered red spotting on both the obverse and reverse. About half of the stars show their centers, but all of the stars are soft.

AU-50, 53, 55, 58 (About Uncirculated). *Obverse:* Wear is evident on the cheek, the hair above the ear, and the tip of the coronet. Friction is evident in the field. At AU-58, luster may be present except in the center of the fields. As the grade goes down to AU-50, wear becomes more evident on the cheek. Wear is seen on the stars, but is not as easy to discern as it is elsewhere and, in any event, many stars are weakly struck. At AU-50 there

1840, Large Date; N-8. Graded AU-58.

will be either no luster or only traces of luster close to the letters and devices. *Reverse:* Wear is most evident on the highest areas of the leaves and the ribbon bow. Luster is present in the fields. As grade goes down from AU–58 to 50, wear increases and luster decreases. At AU-50 there will be either no luster or just traces close to the letters and devices.

EF-40, 45 (Extremely Fine). *Obverse:* Wear is more extensive on the portrait, including the cheek, the hair above the ear, and the coronet. The star centers are worn down slightly (if they were sharply struck to begin with). Traces of luster are minimal, if at all existent. *Reverse:* The centers of the leaves are well worn, with detail visible only near the edges of the leaves and nearby, with the higher parts worn flat. Letters show significant wear. Luster, if present, is minimal.

1842, Large Date; N-6. Graded EF-45.

VF-20, 30 (Very Fine). *Obverse:* Wear is more extensive than on the preceding. Some of the strands of hair are fused together at the top of the head, above the ear, and on the shoulder. The center radials of the stars are nearly completely worn away. *Reverse:* The leaves show more extensive wear. Details are visible at the leaves' edges only minimally and not on all the leaves. The lettering shows smooth, even wear.

1842, Large Date; N-6. Graded VF-30.

F-12, 15 (Fine). *Obverse:* About two-thirds of the hair detail is visible. Extensive wear is seen below the coronet. On the coronet the beginning of the word LIBERTY shows wear, with L sometimes only partially visible. The hair behind the neck is flat. The stars are flat. *Reverse:* The leaves show more wear and are flat except for the lower areas. The ribbon has very little detail.

The Braided Hair large cent is seldom collected in grades lower than F-12.

1839, 9 Over 6; N-1. Graded F-12.

PF-60 to 70 (Proof). Except for the Proof 1841 cent, Proof Braided Hair cents before 1855 range from rare to very rare. Those from 1855 to 1857 are seen with some frequency. Most later Proofs are well struck and of nice quality, but there are exceptions. Most pieces from this era that have been attributed as Proofs really are such, but beware of deeply toned "Proofs" that are actually prooflike, or circulation strikes with polished fields, and

1841, Small Date; N-1. Graded PF-64RB.

recolored. *Obverse and Reverse:* Superb gems PF–65 and 66 show hairlines only under high magnification, and at PF-67 none are seen. The fields usually are deeply mirrorlike on issues after 1843, sometimes less so on earlier dates of this type. Striking should be sharp, including the stars (unlike the situation for many Proofs of the Matron Head type). There is no evidence of friction. In lower grades, hairlines are more numerous, with a profusion of them at the PF–60 to 62 levels, and there is also a general dullness of the fields. Typical color for an undipped coin ranges from light or iridescent brown to brown with some traces of mint color. Except for issues after 1854, Proofs are nearly always BN or, less often, RB. Prooflike pieces are sometimes offered as Proofs. Beware deeply toned "Proofs" and those that do not have full mirrorlike fields.

Illustrated coin: Early Proofs from this period are scarce to extremely rare. This example retains some mint orange in protected areas, as well as exhibiting hints of lilac and electric blue on the obverse.

Small Letters (1839–1843)

Large Letters (1843–1857)

1840, Large Date

1840, Small Date

**1840, Small Date
Over Large 18**

1842, Small Date

1842, Large Date

	Mintage	Cert	Avg	%MS	G-4	VG-8	F-12	VF-20	EF-40	AU-50	MS-60BN PF-63BN	MS-63BN PF-64BN	MS-65BN PF-65BN
1839	(a)	84	52.1	49%	$30	$45	$70	$100	$210	$440	$800	$1,600	$5,500 (b)
	Auctions: $17,625, MS-65RB, January 2014; $1,293, MS-63BN, January 2015; $176, EF-40, May 2015; $360, AU-50, January 2018												
1840, All kinds	2,462,700												
1840, Large Date		110	55.1	47%	$25	$35	$40	$50	$100	$250	$600	$1,150	$2,300
	Auctions: $14,100, MS-64RD, January 2013												
1840, Small Date		50	55.9	50%	$25	$35	$40	$50	$100	$250	$600	$1,150	$2,300
	Auctions: $541, MS-61BN, August 2015; $259, MS-60, October 2015; $400, AU-58, February 2015												
1840, Small Date Over Large 18		12	42.5	33%	$25	$35	$40	$60	$200	$400	$900	$1,600	$2,600
	Auctions: $16,100, MS-65RB, September 2011												
1840, Proof	*15–20*	7	64.1								$7,000	$10,500	$20,000
	Auctions: $14,100, PF-63RB, January 2014												
1841, Small Date	1,597,367	158	52.7	46%	$25	$40	$60	$90	$135	$300	$800	$1,500	$3,200 (c)
	Auctions: $4,113, MS-66BN, June 2014												
1841, Proof	*30–50*	20	64.3								$6,000	$9,500	$18,500
	Auctions: $21,150, PF-65RB, August 2013												
1842, All kinds	2,383,390												
1842, Small Date		56	51.1	41%	$25	$30	$35	$45	$90	$220	$625	$1,200	$2,700 (d)
	Auctions: $23,500, MS-64RD, January 2014												
1842, Large Date		162	49.3	40%	$25	$30	$35	$45	$90	$200	$550	$1,100	$2,500 (e)
	Auctions: $1,175, MS-63BN, August 2015; $881, MS-63BN, June 2015; $259, AU-55, April 2015; $188, AU-55, June 2015												
1842, Proof	*10–20*	5	64.2								$7,000	$11,000	$20,000
	Auctions: $14,100, PF-64BN, January 2014												

a. Included in 1839, All kinds, mintage figure on page 246. **b.** Value in MS-65RB is $8,000. **c.** Value in MS-65RB is $4,500. **d.** Value in MS-65RB is $4,000. **e.** Value in MS-65RB is $3,300.

1844, 44 Over 81

Head of 1840
("Petite Head," 1839–1843)

Head of 1844
("Mature Head," 1843–1857)

1847, 7 Over "Small 7"

1846, Small Date
Note the squat date
and the closed 6.

1846, Medium Date
Note the medium date
height and the ball-top 6.

1846, Tall Date
Note the vertically
stretched date and
the open-mouthed 6.

1851, 51 Over 81
These are not true
overdates, but are three
of the more spectacular
of several date-punch
blunders of the 1844–
1854 period. The so-called
overdates of 1844 and
1851 each have the date
punched upside down,
then corrected normally.

1855, Upright 5's

1855, Slanting 5's

1855, Knob on Ear

	Mintage	Cert	Avg	%MS	G-4	VG-8	F-12	VF-20	EF-40	AU-50	MS-60BN	MS-63BN	MS-65BN
											PF-63BN	PF-64BN	PF-65BN
1843, All kinds	2,425,342												
1843, Petite Head, Small Letters		194	52.7	54%	$25	$30	$35	$45	$90	$200	$550	$950	$2,500
	Auctions: $1,293, MS-63BN, January 2015; $588, MS-63BN, August 2015; $494, AU-58, August 2015; $376, AU-58, August 2015												
1843, Petite Head, Large Letters		63	52.8	48%	$25	$35	$45	$100	$250	$320	$825	$1,500	$2,300
	Auctions: $4,406, MS-64BN, January 2014												
1843, Mature Head, Large Letters		63	45.2	35%	$25	$30	$35	$45	$150	$275	$550	$900	$2,100
	Auctions: $9,988, MS-64RB, January 2014												
1843, Proof	*10–20*	9	64.4								$7,000	$11,000	$20,000
	Auctions: $25,850, PF-66RB, June 2014												
1844, Normal Date	2,398,752	233	50.9	42%	$25	$30	$35	$40	$90	$200	$550	$1,000	$2,500
	Auctions: $8,225, MS-65BN, January 2014; $940, MS-62BN, June 2015; $141, AU-53, January 2015												
1844, 44 Over 81	(f)	43	43.4	23%	$60	$100	$130	$200	$250	$600	$1,700	$4,000	$7,000
	Auctions: $1,175, MS-60BN, January 2014; $705, AU-50, September 2016; $212, VF-25, August 2015												
1844, Proof	*10–20*	7	64.6								$13,000	$20,000	$30,000
	Auctions: $55,813, PF-65RD, January 2014; $31,725, PF-64, May 2015												
1845	3,894,804	394	52.7	50%	$25	$30	$35	$40	$75	$135	$225	$375	$1,200
	Auctions: $881, MS-64BN, January 2015; $423, MS-63BN, March 2015; $353, MS-62BN, May 2015; $176, AU-53, January 2015												
1845, Proof	*8–12*	5	63.8								$8,000	$15,000	$25,000
	Auctions: $16,450, PF-64BN, April 2013												

f. Included in 1844, Normal Date, mintage figure.

	Mintage	Cert	Avg	%MS	G-4	VG-8	F-12	VF-20	EF-40	AU-50	MS-60BN PF-63BN	MS-63BN PF-64BN	MS-65BN PF-65BN
1846, All kinds	4,120,800												
1846, Small Date		347	50.9	50%	$25	$30	$35	$40	$75	$135	$225	$350	$1,200
Auctions: $494, MS-64BN, February 2015; $329, MS-62BN, February 2015; $129, AU-53, February 2015; $119, AU-50, April 2015													
1846, Medium Date		47	51.7	49%	$25	$30	$35	$40	$85	$150	$250	$400	$1,350
Auctions: $705, MS-61BN, March 2013													
1846, Tall Date		71	45.1	34%	$25	$35	$40	$50	$150	$250	$650	$1,000	$2,000
Auctions: $56, VF-30, September 2011													
1846, Proof	8–12	2	66.0								$8,000	$15,000	$25,000
Auctions: $30,550, PF-65BN, June 2014													
1847	6,183,669	843	54.5	56%	$20	$25	$35	$40	$75	$135	$225	$350	$1,250
Auctions: $646, MS-64BN, August 2015; $881, MS-63BN, August 2015; $188, MS-62BN, June 2015; $223, MS-61BN, September 2015													
1847, 7 Over "Small 7"	(g)	38	50.4	42%	$30	$60	$90	$135	$300	$420	$1,350	$2,000	$5,000
Auctions: $9,694, MS-65BN, January 2014													
1847, Proof	8–12	1	64.0								$8,000	$15,000	$25,000
Auctions: $31,050, PF-65RB, February 2011													
1848	6,415,799	899	53.6	50%	$20	$25	$35	$40	$75	$130	$225	$350	$925
Auctions: $1,175, MS-65BN, January 2015; $223, MS-62BN, January 2015; $259, AU-58, January 2015; $129, AU-55, October 2015													
1848, Proof	15–20	10	64.6								$10,000	$15,000	$25,000
Auctions: $14,100, PF-64BN, August 2013													
1849	4,178,500	492	53.9	49%	$20	$25	$35	$40	$85	$150	$250	$450	$1,200
Auctions: $317, MS-62, March 2015; $259, AU-58, October 2015; $353, AU-50, July 2015; $84, EF-40, May 2015													
1849, Proof	6–10	4	64.3								$8,500	$16,000	$25,000
Auctions: $23,500, PF-65RB, August 2013													
1850	4,426,844	1,096	58.4	71%	$20	$25	$35	$40	$65	$125	$180	$230	$650 (h)
Auctions: $1,058, MS-65BN, January 2015; $376, MS-64BN, January 2015; $286, MS-63BN, February 2015; $259, AU-58, June 2015													
1850, Proof	6–10	4	64.3								$10,000	$20,000	$30,000
Auctions: $19,550, PF-64RB, February 2011													
1851, Normal Date	9,889,707	1,588	56.9	63%	$20	$25	$35	$40	$65	$125	$180	$230	$650 (h)
Auctions: $1,058, MS-65BN, August 2015; $411, MS-64BN, May 2015; $306, MS-64BN, October 2015; $100, AU-50, April 2015													
1851, 51 Over 81	(i)	95	56.7	63%	$30	$50	$80	$120	$200	$375	$575	$1,000	$2,400
Auctions: $1,763, MS-65BN, June 2014; $329, AU-55, May 2015													
1852	5,063,094	1,435	58.8	69%	$20	$25	$35	$40	$65	$125	$180	$230	$635 (j)
Auctions: $881, MS-65BN, October 2015; $764, MS-65BN, January 2015; $353, MS-64BN, January 2015; $129, AU-55, February 2015													
1852, Proof	4–6	1	65.0								$20,000	$45,000	$75,000
Auctions: $47,150, PF-64BN, February 2011; $9,528, PF-64, November 2016; $12,925, PF-62, March 2016													
1853	6,641,131	2,299	58.5	68%	$20	$25	$35	$40	$65	$125	$180	$230	$635 (j)
Auctions: $2,115, MS-65RD, January 2015; $588, MS-64RB, January 2015; $235, MS-63BN, January 2015; $212, MS-62BN, June 2015													
1854	4,236,156	1,277	57.2	60%	$20	$25	$35	$40	$65	$125	$180	$230	$650 (h)
Auctions: $360, MS-64BN, October 2015; $282, MS-63BN, May 2015; $212, MS-62BN, January 2015; $141, AU-58, January 2015													
1854, Proof	4–6	5	64.6								$8,500	$10,000	$15,000
Auctions: $28,200, PF-65RB, June 2014													
1855, All kinds	1,574,829												
1855, Upright 5's		465	56.6	57%	$20	$25	$35	$40	$65	$125	$180	$230	$635 (j)
Auctions: $1,116, MS-65RB, January 2015; $400, MS-64BN, June 2015; $282, MS-63BN, July 2015; $200, MS-62BN, January 2015													
1855, Slanting 5's		129	56.6	53%	$20	$25	$35	$45	$65	$130	$200	$275	$1,250 (k)
Auctions: $353, MS-62BN, November 2015; $200, MS-61BN, June 2015; $141, MS-60, January 2015; $153, AU-53, June 2015													
1855, Slanting 5's, Knob on Ear		164	54.9	40%	$30	$40	$50	$75	$140	$250	$400	$600	$2,150
Auctions: $259, AU-50, July 2015; $153, EF-45, September 2015; $100, EF-40, August 2015													
1855, Proof	15–20	10	64.5								$5,500	$7,000	$10,000
Auctions: $8,050, PF-64RB August 2011													

g. Included in 1847 mintage figure. **h.** Value in MS-65RB is $1,200. **i.** Included in 1851, Normal Date, mintage figure. **j.** Value in MS-65RB is $1,150. **k.** Value in MS-65RB is $2,000.

1856, Upright 5	1856, Slanting 5	1857, Large Date	1857, Small Date

	Mintage	Cert	Avg	%MS	G-4	VG-8	F-12	VF-20	EF-40	AU-50	MS-60BN PF-63BN	MS-63BN PF-64BN	MS-65BN PF-65BN
1856, All kinds	2,690,463												
1856, Upright 5		305	57.6	58%	$20	$25	$35	$40	$65	$130	$200	$270	$675 **(h)**
	Auctions: $725, MS-65BN, January 2015; $705, MS-64RB, January 2015; $482, MS-64BN, January 2015; $165, AU-58, September 2015												
1856, Slanting 5		451	55.8	54%	$20	$25	$35	$40	$65	$130	$200	$270	$675 **(h)**
	Auctions: $999, MS-66BN, June 2015; $764, MS-65BN, February 2015; $259, MS-63BN, February 2015; $223, MS-62BN, February 2015												
1856, Proof	40–60	20	64.7								$5,000	$7,000	$10,000
	Auctions: $25,850, PF-66RB, November 2013												
1857, All kinds	333,546												
1857, Large Date		675	56.6	55%	$60	$110	$150	$175	$225	$300	$400	$750	$1,200
	Auctions: $823, MS-64BN, January 2015; $558, MS-62, March 2015; $141, AU-50, July 2015; $223, EF-45, October 2015												
1857, Small Date		291	54.0	39%	$65	$115	$160	$200	$275	$350	$500	$850	$1,500
	Auctions: $940, MS-64BN, January 2015; $646, MS-63BN, August 2015; $494, MS-62BN, January 2015; $353, AU-55, September 2015												
1857, Large Date, Proof (l)													
1857, Small Date, Proof	15–20	8	65.1								$5,000	$7,000	$10,000
	Auctions: $52,875, PF-65RD, April 2014												

Note: Numismatic anachronisms dated 1868 were struck in nickel and in copper, featuring the large cent design last used in 1857. These likely were quietly and unofficially sold by Mint employees to collectors. They are classified as Judd-610 and 611 in *United States Pattern Coins*. **h.** Value in MS-65RB is $1,200. **l.** The 1857, Large Date, Proof large cent is not known to exist, and will be deleted from the next edition.

THE PASSING OF THE LARGE CENT AND HALF CENT

By 1857 the U.S. Mint's costs for manufacturing and distributing its half cents and large cents had risen so high that Mint Director James Ross Snowden reported that the copper coins "barely paid expenses." Both denominations had become unpopular, and they rarely circulated outside the nation's larger cities. With this pressure, change was on the horizon. The Treasury Department had recent precedent to tinker with coinage sizes and compositions. For several years in the early 1850s the Mint had issued silver coins of reduced weight, as a way to discourage their melting and export (the coins' silver content had been greater than their face values). On the heels of this coinage reform, new legislation in 1857 replaced the large copper cent with a smaller copper-nickel coin of the same value, and terminated the half cent outright.

The coinage legislation of 1857 brought important benefits to the United States. Under its terms, Spanish coins were redeemed for melting at the Mint and exchanged for the new, small cents. The old-fashioned reckoning of business transactions in Spanish *reales* and *medios*, British shillings, and other currencies was (officially, at least) abandoned, and the American decimal system was popularized. Citizens found the new small cent to be convenient, and it quickly became a favored and useful means of retail trade. Tens of millions would be minted before the decade closed.

The hobby of coin collecting experienced a boom when the large cent and half cent passed away. Casual observers set aside the obsolete coins as mementoes of a time gone by, while more experienced collectors sought to assemble collections composed of one of each date. Over the ensuing decades the study and collecting of these old coppers has become more and more specialized while still attracting hobby newcomers. Their devoted enthusiasts appreciate the coins' historical connections and cultural significance.

Small Cents
1856 to Date

AN OVERVIEW OF SMALL CENTS

On May 25, 1857, the U.S. Mint debuted its new small-diameter Flying Eagle cent. Designed by Chief Engraver James B. Longacre, the obverse featured a flying eagle, copied after Christian Gobrecht's silver dollar of 1836. The reverse showed an agricultural wreath enclosing the denomination. Problems developed with striking the pieces up properly, and in 1859 a new type, the Indian Head cent, was introduced. With several variations this design was continued through 1909. In that year the Lincoln cent with Wheat Ears reverse was introduced. The series was continued for many years, until 1959, when the Memorial Reverse type was introduced, continuing the same Lincoln portrait on the obverse. Then in 2009 four different reverses were introduced to commemorate the 200th anniversary of the birth of Abraham Lincoln. In 2010 a new reverse symbolized President Lincoln's preservation of the Union.

Forming a type set of small cents is done easily enough, although the first two issues, the 1857 and 1858 Flying Eagles, as well as the 1859 Indian Head with laurel wreath reverse, can be expensive in higher grades. Striking quality is a consideration for all small cents from 1857 to the end of the Indian Head series in 1909, but enough exist that finding a needle-sharp piece is simply a matter of time. Lincoln cents are easy enough to find sharply struck, though some varieties are more difficult to find this way than others.

FOR THE COLLECTOR AND INVESTOR:
SMALL CENTS AS A SPECIALTY

Flying Eagle and Indian Head cents often are collected together by specialists, who usually aspire to add the pattern 1856 Flying Eagle to the series. Proof Flying Eagle and Indian Head cents form a separate specialty and are widely collected. The Flying Eagle and Indian Cent Collectors Society (www.fly-inclub.org) welcomes aficionados of these series. Its journal, *Longacre's Ledger*, serves as a forum for new discoveries, market information, and the exchange of ideas and research.

One of the foundations of modern American numismatics is the collecting of Lincoln cents, 1909 to date. Collectors have a wide variety of folders, albums, and holders to choose from; these have a tradition dating back to the

This 1857 pattern small cent (J-186) features a proposed head of Liberty, similar to the design that would eventually be used on the nation's nickel three-cent pieces.

1930s, when R.K. Post of Neenah, Wisconsin, launched his "penny boards" (made for him by Whitman Publishing Co., which later acquired the rights), and Wayte Raymond marketed a series of "National" album pages. Today, a search through pocket change might yield coins dating back to 1959, the first year of the Lincoln Memorial reverse, before which date even high-mintage issues are hardly ever seen. A generation ago it was possible to find cents from 1909 onward. However, key issues such as 1909-S V.D.B. (the most famous of all "popular rarities" in the U.S. series), 1914-D, 1924-D, 1926-S, 1931-S, and 1955 Doubled Die Obverse eluded most enthusiasts.

Lincoln cents can be collected casually, or a specialty can be made of them. A dedicated enthusiast may want to secure one each in a grade such as MS-65, also taking care that each is sharply struck. There are quite a few issues, including Denver and San Francisco varieties from about 1916 to the late 1920s, that are plentiful *except* if sharply struck (with full hair detail on the Lincoln portrait, no tiny marks on Lincoln's shoulder, and sharp details and a smooth field on the reverse). Die-variety specialists have dozens of popular doubled dies, overmintmarks, and other varieties to hunt down, using the *Cherrypickers' Guide* as their standard reference. With the Mint's rollout of four new reverse designs in 2009, and another in 2010, the Lincoln cent promises to intrigue another generation of Americans and continue to bring new collectors to the hobby.

FLYING EAGLE (1856–1858)

Designer: *James B. Longacre.* **Weight:** *4.67 grams.* **Composition:** *.880 copper, .120 nickel.*
Diameter: *19 mm.* **Edge:** *Plain.* **Mint:** *Philadelphia.*

Circulation Strike   Proof

History. The nation's large copper cents became increasingly expensive to produce, leading the U.S. Mint to experiment with smaller versions during the 1850s. Finally a new design and format were chosen: the Flying Eagle cent, of smaller diameter and 4.67 grams' weight (compared to nearly 11). Many patterns were made of this design in 1856 (for distribution to interested congressmen), and later restrikes (bearing that same date) were extensive, with the result that many numismatists collect the 1856 cent along with the regular series. Distribution of the new 1857 Flying Eagle cents for circulation commenced on May 25 of that year. Problems resulted from striking the design properly, and the motif was discontinued in 1858. Although attempts were made to create a modified, thinner eagle, the unattractive results were scrapped in favor of an entirely new design. The coins remained in circulation until the early 1900s, by which time any found in pocket change were well worn.

Striking and Sharpness. The heavy wreath on the reverse was opposite in the dies (while in the press) from the head and tail of the eagle on the obverse, and, accordingly, many Flying Eagle cents were weakly struck in these areas. Today, this lightness of strike is most visible at each end of the eagle and on the wreath, particularly the higher areas, and on the vertical separation at the middle of the ribbon knot. Striking weakness is most obvious (especially for novice collectors) on the eagle's tail feathers. Many Flying Eagle cents, however, are quite well struck. A first-class Proof should have a fully and deeply mirrored field on both sides, except for those of 1856, which are usually a combination of mirror-like and grainy in character.

Availability. As a type the Flying Eagle cent is easy to find, although some varieties, such as 1856 and 1858, 8 Over 7, range from scarce to rare. Most are seen in worn grades. In MS, many are in the marketplace, although dipping, cleaning, and recoloring (causing staining and spotting) have eliminated the majority from consideration by connoisseurs. Proof Flying Eagle cents dated 1856 are plentiful, surviving from the quantity of perhaps 2,000 to 2,500 or more restruck in 1859 and later. (Today's collectors do not distinguish, price-wise, between the 1856 originals and restrikes dated 1856.) Proofs of 1857 are very rare. Proofs of 1858 are rare, but are significantly more readily available than for 1857. Some prooflike Mint State coins have been called Proofs. Quality is a challenge for Proofs, and problem-free examples are in the minority.

GRADING STANDARDS

Caveat: These grading standards do not take sharpness of strike into account.

MS-60 to 70 (Mint State). *Obverse:* Contact marks, most obvious in the field, are evident at MS-60, diminishing at MS–61, 62, and higher. The eagle, the feathers of which usually hide marks, shows some evidence of contact as well. At Gem MS-65 or finer there is no trace of friction or rubbing. A few tiny nicks or marks may be seen, but none are obvious. At MS-67 and higher levels the coin will approach perfection. A theoretically perfect MS-70 will

1858; Snow-11. Graded MS-64.

have no marks at all evident, even under a strong magnifier. Although in practice this is not always consistent, at MS-66 and higher there should be no staining or other problems, and the coin should have good eye appeal overall. *Reverse:* Check the higher parts of the wreath for slight abrasions at MS–60 to 62. Otherwise, the above guidelines apply.

Illustrated coin: The surfaces display a healthy satin luster, as well as an iridescent rose and golden-tan patina. The coin is sharply and evenly struck and offers razor-sharp definition.

AU-50, 53, 55, 58 (About Uncirculated). *Obverse:* At AU-50, light wear is seen on the breast of the eagle, the top edge of the closest wing, and, less so, on the head. As both the head and tail tip can be lightly struck, these are not reliable indicators of grade. Luster is present in traces among the letters. At higher About Uncirculated levels the evidence of wear diminishes. An AU-58 coin will have nearly full luster, but friction is seen in the fields, as

1858. Graded AU-53.

are some marks. *Reverse:* At AU-50, light wear is seen on the ribbon bow and the highest areas of the leaves. Some luster is seen (more than on the obverse). Friction is evident, as are some marks, but these will not be as distracting as those on the obverse, as the heavy wreath and lettering are more protective of the reverse field. In higher grades, wear is less, and at AU-58 nearly full luster—or even completely full luster—is seen.

Illustrated coin: The reverse features a large rim cud.

EF-40, 45 (Extremely Fine). *Obverse:* Wear is more extensive, especially on the eagle's breast and the top of the closest wing. Wear will also show on the other wing in the area below OF. Marks may be more extensive in the field. The wear is slightly greater at EF-40 than at EF-45, although in the marketplace these two grades are not clearly differentiated. *Reverse:* More wear shows on the higher areas of the wreath, but most detail

1858, Small Letters. Graded EF-40.

will still be present. There may be tinges of luster in protected areas, more likely at EF-45 than at EF-40.

VF-20, 30 (Very Fine). *Obverse:* Wear is appreciable, with the breast feathers gone over a larger area and with more wear on the wings. The tail shows significant wear, negating the question as to whether it was well struck originally. Marks are more extensive, although across all grades the durable copper-nickel metal resisted heavy marks and cuts; any such should be separately described. Staining and spotting, not related to grade, is

1858, Small Letters. Graded VF-20.

common. Cherrypicking (examining multiple coins, all slabbed at the same grade level, and selecting the finest of them) at this and lower grades will yield nice coins in any given category. *Reverse:* The wreath is worn flat in the higher and medium–relief areas, although some detail is seen in the lower areas close to the field. ONE / CENT may be slightly weak, depending on the quality of the original strike. Marks are fewer than on the obverse.

F-12, 15 (Fine). *Obverse:* The eagle shows extensive wear, with about half of the feathers gone. Some detail is still seen, especially on the underside of the closest wing, above the breast. *Reverse:* Wear is even more extensive, with the wreath nearing flatness, but still with some detail in the lower areas.

1857. Graded F-12.

VG-8, 10 (Very Good). *Obverse:* On the obverse the eagle is clear in outline form, but only a small number of feathers can be discerned, mostly above the breast. Letters and the date show extensive wear but are complete and clear. *Reverse:* The wreath is now mostly an outline, although some lower-relief features can be differentiated. ONE / CENT may be weak (depending on the strike).

1858, Small Letters. Graded VG-10.

G-4, 6 (Good). *Obverse:* The eagle is nearly completely flat, with just a few feathers, if any, discernible. The rim is worn down, making the outer parts of the letters and the lower part of the date slightly weak, but all are readable. *Reverse:* The wreath is basically in outline form, with hardly any detail. ONE / CENT is weak, usually with CENT weakest. The rim is worn down.

1857. Graded G-4.

AG-3 (About Good). *Obverse:* Wear is extensive, but most of the eagle is visible in outline form. The letters are mostly worn away, with vestiges remaining here and there. The date is partially worn away at the bottom, but is distinct and readable. *Reverse:* The wreath is so worn that it cannot be distinguished from the field in areas, usually toward the top. ONE / CENT is mostly gone, but much of CENT can be discerned (unless the coin was a weak strike to begin with).

1857. Graded AG-3.

PF-60 to 70 (Proof). *Obverse and Reverse:* Gem PF-65 coins have very few hairlines, and these are visible only under a strong magnifying glass. At the PF-67 level or higher there should be no evidence of hairlines or friction at all. PF-60 coins can be dull from repeated dipping and cleaning (remember, hairlines on any Proof were caused by cleaning with an abrasive agent; they had no hairlines when struck). At PF-63 the mirrorlike fields should

1858, Large Letters. Graded PF-65.

be attractive, and hairlines should be minimal, best seen when the coin is held at an angle to the light. No rubbing is seen. PF-64 coins are even nicer.

    Illustrated coin: The fields of this coin are highly reflective for a nickel-alloy Proof cent.

1857, Reverse 25¢ Clash
FS-01-1857-901.

1857, Obverse $20 Clash
FS-01-1857-403.

1858, Large Letters

1858, Small Letters

1858, 8 Over 7
FS-01-1858-301.

	Mintage	Cert	Avg	%MS	G-4	VG-8	F-12	VF-20	EF-40	AU-50	MS-60BN / PF-60	MS-63BN / PF-63BN	MS-65 / PF-65BN
1856 † (a)	2,000	0	n/a		$7,000	$7,750	$9,500	$11,000	$13,000	$13,500	$15,000	$20,000	$65,000
Auctions: $32,900, MS-64, April 2013													
1856, Proof	1,500	436	57.8								$14,000	$16,500	$32,500
Auctions: $38,188, PF-65, January 2014; $14,100, PF-63, August 2014; $8,813, PF-62, October 2014													
1857	17,450,000	3,998	51.5	55%	$25	$40	$50	$60	$140	$215	$450	$1,000	$3,500
Auctions: $21,150, MS-66, June 2014; $4,113, MS-65, November 2014; $2,468, MS-64+, November 2014													
1857, Obverse 50¢ Clash (b)	(c)	141	33.5	24%					$225	$450	$800	$1,250	$3,750
Auctions: $3,525, MS-65, October 2014; $5,816, MS-65, October 2013													
1857, Reverse 25¢ Clash ‡‡ (d)	(c)	42	45.1	33%					$250	$500	$1,000	$2,750	$8,500
Auctions: $223, EF-40, July 2014													
1857, Obverse $20 Clash (e)	(c)	21	18.4	0%					$2,500	$6,000	$20,000		
Auctions: $242, F-12, March 2011													
1857, Proof	100	34	63.8								$5,000	$8,000	$25,000
Auctions: $34,075, PF-65, October 2014; $8,813, PF-64, October 2014; $34,075, PF, January 2013													
1858, All kinds	24,600,000												
1858, Large Letters		1,841	46.9	44%	$25	$40	$50	$60	$140	$215	$450	$1,000	$3,500
Auctions: $9,988, MS-66, October 2014; $17,625, MS-66, June 2013; $3,290, MS-65, November 2014; $1,645, MS-64, October 2014													
1858, 8 Over 7 (f)		170	52.6	50%	$75	$100	$200	$400	$850	$1,500	$3,650	$11,000	$50,000
Auctions: $74,025, MS-65, October 2014; $764, AU-55, July 2014; $940, AU-50, January 2015; $504, EF-40, January 2018													
1858, Small Letters		2,053	45.4	38%	$25	$40	$50	$60	$150	$250	$500	$1,150	$3,750
Auctions: $24,675, MS-66, October 2014; $16,450, MS-66, August 2013; $3,525, MS-65, August 2014; $2,233													
1858, Large Letters, Proof	100	35	64.7								$5,000	$8,000	$23,500
Auctions: $20,563, PF-65, October 2014; $8,225, PF-64, October 2014; $28,200, PF, January 2013; $36,000, PF-66, January 2018													
1858, Small Letters, Proof	200	26	64.2								$5,000	$8,000	$23,500
Auctions: $32,900, PF-66, January 2014; $14,100, PF-64, October 2014; $7,638, PF-64, October 2014; $7,200, PF-64, February 2018													

† Ranked in the *100 Greatest U.S. Coins* (fourth edition). ‡‡ Ranked in the *100 Greatest U.S. Error Coins*. **a.** Actually a pattern, but collected along with the regular issue since it shares the same design. See *United States Pattern Coins*, tenth edition. **b.** The obverse die was clashed with the obverse die of a Liberty Seated half dollar. This is most evident through AMERICA. **c.** Included in circulation-strike 1857 mintage figure. **d.** The reverse die was clashed with the reverse die of a Liberty Seated quarter dollar. The outline of the eagle's head is evident above ONE. **e.** The obverse die was clashed with the obverse die of a Liberty Head double eagle. **f.** The flag of the upper-right corner of a 7 can be seen above the second 8 in the date. There is a raised triangular dot in the field above the first 8. Late-die-state specimens are worth considerably less than the values listed, which are for early die states.

INDIAN HEAD (1859–1909)

Variety 1 (Copper-Nickel, Laurel Wreath Reverse, 1859):
Designer: *James B. Longacre.* **Weight:** *4.67 grams.* **Composition:** *.880 copper, .120 nickel.*
Diameter: *19 mm.* **Edge:** *Plain.* **Mint:** *Philadelphia.*

Copper-Nickel, **Laurel Wreath Reverse,** **Without Shield (1859)**	**Copper-Nickel,** **Laurel Wreath Reverse,** **Without Shield, Proof**

Variety 2 (Copper-Nickel, Oak Wreath With Shield, 1860–1864):
Designer: *James B. Longacre.* **Weight:** *4.67 grams.* **Composition:** *.880 copper, .120 nickel.*
Diameter: *19 mm.* **Edge:** *Plain.* **Mint:** *Philadelphia.*

Copper-Nickel, **Oak Wreath Reverse,** **With Shield (1860–1864)**	**Copper-Nickel,** **Oak Wreath Reverse,** **With Shield, Proof**

Variety 3 (Bronze, 1864–1909): **Designer:** *James B. Longacre.*
Weight: *3.11 grams.* **Composition:** *.950 copper, .050 tin and zinc.*
Diameter: *19 mm.* **Edge:** *Plain.* **Mints:** *Philadelphia and San Francisco.*

Bronze, Oak Wreath Reverse, **With Shield (1864–1909)**	**Bronze, Oak Wreath Reverse,** **With Shield, Proof**

History. After nearly a dozen varieties of patterns were made in 1858, in 1859 the Indian Head was adopted as the new motif for the cent. Observers of the time noted the incongruity of placing a Native American war bonnet on a bust which was meant to be both female and classically Greek; designer James B. Longacre's earlier use of a feathered tiara on the Indian Head three-dollar gold piece had been viewed as less strange. The reverse of the 1859 coin illustrates an olive (or laurel) wreath. In 1860 this was changed to a wreath of oak and other leaves with a shield at the apex, a design continued through the end of the series in 1909. From 1859 through spring 1864 cents were struck in copper-nickel, the alloy used earlier for Flying Eagle cents. In 1864 a new bronze alloy was adopted.

Indian Head cents remained in circulation through the 1940s, but by the early 1950s were rarely seen. In the 1930s, when Whitman and other coin boards and folders became widely available, collectors picked many key dates out of circulation. The typical grade for the scarce issues of the 1870s was Good or so, and the 1908-S and 1909-S could be found in VF.

Striking and Sharpness. The strike on Indian Head cents can vary widely. On the obverse the points to check include the details at the tips of the feathers and the diamonds on the ribbon. The diamonds *cannot* be used as a grading marker, and the feather tips can be used only if you have familiarity with how sharp the coin was struck to begin with. In general, the reverse is usually sharper, but check the leaf and shield details. On many bronze cents beginning in the 1870s the bottom of the N of ONE and the tops of the EN of CENT are light, as they were in the dies (this is not factored when grading). Check the denticles on both sides. Generally, copper-nickel cents of the early 1860s are candidates for light striking as are later issues in the bronze format, of the 1890s onward.

Availability. In worn grades Indian Head cents are available in proportion to their mintages, in combination with survival rates being higher for the later issues. (The low-mintage 1909-S was saved in larger quantities than the higher-mintage 1877, as an example.) MS coins survive as a matter of chance, with those of 1878 and before being much scarcer than those of 1879 and later, and some of the 1900s being readily available. Many if not most higher-grade MS coins have been dipped or recolored, unless they are a warm orange-red color with traces of natural brown. The search for quality among bronze cents is particularly challenging. Some tiny toning flecks are to be expected on many coins, and as long as they are microscopic they can often be ignored (except in grades on the far side of MS-65). A set of MS-65 coins in RB or RD can be formed quickly, but a collection with *original* color, sharp strike, and excellent eye appeal may take several years.

During the years these coins were in production, collectors who wanted single pieces each year often bought Proofs. In the late 1930s, many 1878–1909 Proof Indian Head cents began to be released from several estate hoards. These had vivid violet and blue iridescent toning from being stored for decades in tissue paper. They are highly sought-after today.

Proofs. Proof Indian Head cents were made of all dates 1859 to 1909. The 1864 bronze variety with a tiny L (for designer James B. Longacre) on the ribbon is a rarity, with only about two dozen known. Generally, Proofs are sharp strikes until the 1890s, when some can be weak. On bronze coins tiny carbon flecks are typical, but should be microscopic. If larger, avoid, and at PF-65 or higher, avoid as well. The majority of Proofs have been dipped, and many bronze pieces have been retoned. Most undipped coins are either rich brown (can be very attractive) or red and brown. The late John J. Pittman spent 50 years trying to find a Gem Proof 1907 Indian Head cent with brilliant original color! Cherrypicking is the order of the day. Extra value can be found in BN and RB, simply because investors won't buy them; instead, they are drawn to RD coins, most of which have been "improved" (dipped and retoned).

Proofs are generally designated BN if the surfaces are mainly brown or iridescent, or have up to perhaps 30% original mint red-orange color (there is little consistency, within the hobby community, in this determination). RB is the designation if the surface is a mixture of red-orange and brown, best if blended together nicely, but often with patches of mint color among brown areas. RD designates a coin with original (in theory) mint-red orange, always blending to slight natural brown toning unless the coin has been dipped. Likely, any RD coin with even a few hairlines has been cleaned (or at least mishandled) at one time; in most such cases, what appears to be mint-red color is not original. Certification services take no notice of this. For this reason, a connoisseur will prefer a gem BN coin with no hairlines to a PF-65 or 66 RD coin with some hairlines. Proof copper-nickel Indian Head cents of 1859 to 1864 need no letter to indicate color, as their hue derives more from the nickel than the copper. As a general rule, these survive in higher grades and with greater eye appeal, as they stayed "brilliant" (the watchword for most collectors until recent decades) and did not need dipping. Moreover, when such pieces were cleaned and acquired hairlines, they tended to be fewer than on a bronze coin, due to the very hard nature of the copper-nickel alloy.

GRADING STANDARDS

Caveat: These grading standards do not take sharpness of strike into account.

MS-60 to 70 (Mint State). *Obverse:* Contact marks, most obvious in the field, are evident at MS-60, diminishing at MS–61, 62, and higher. This abrasion is most noticeable on copper-nickel cents, for it blends in with the background on bronze issues. The cheek of the Indian and the field show some evidence as well. Typical color is BN, occasionally RB at MS-63 and 64, unless dipped to be RD. At gem MS-65 or finer there is no trace of abra-

1860, Pointed Bust. Graded MS-63.

sion. A few tiny nicks or marks may be seen, but none are obvious. At MS-67 and finer the coin will approach perfection. Check "RD" coins for originality. A theoretically perfect MS-70 will have no marks at all, even under a strong magnifier. Although in practice this is not always consistent, at MS-66 and higher there should be no staining or other problems, and the coin should have good eye appeal overall. *Reverse:* Check the high parts of the wreath for abrasion. Otherwise the above comments apply.

Illustrated coin: The surfaces display satin luster and a lovely pinkish-tan patina.

AU-50, 53, 55, 58 (About Uncirculated). *Obverse:* At AU-50, wear is most noticeable on the hair above the ear, on the central portion of the ribbon, on the curl to the right of the ribbon, and near the feather tips, although the last is not a reliable indicator due to striking. Luster is present, but mostly in protected areas. At AU–53 and 55, wear is less. At AU-58 friction is evident, rather than actual wear. Luster, toned brown, is nearly complete at

1861. Graded AU-55.

AU-58, but may be incomplete in the field. *Reverse:* At AU-50, light wear is seen on the ribbon and the higher-relief areas of the leaves, while the lower areas retain their detail. Some luster may be present in protected areas. At AU-53 and 55, wear is less and luster is more extensive. An AU-58 coin will have nearly full luster and show only light friction.

EF-40, 45 (Extremely Fine). *Obverse:* Wear is more extensive, but all of LIBERTY is very clear. Wear is seen on the hair above and below the ear, on the central portion of the ribbon, and on the feather tips. Overall the coin is bold. Scattered marks are normal for this and lower grades, most often seen on the cheek and in the field. *Reverse:* The higher-relief parts of the leaves and ribbon bow show light wear, but details are sharp in lower areas. Some tiny lines in the vertical stripes in the shield may be blended. Scattered marks may be pres-

1861. Graded EF-45.

ent, but on all grades they are usually fewer on the reverse than on the obverse.

VF-20, 30 (Very Fine). *Obverse:* Wear is more extensive. LIBERTY shows significant wear on BE, but it is sharp overall. Most hair detail is gone. The feather tips show greater wear (the extent of which will depend on the original strike). The ribbon and hair no longer show separation. *Reverse:* Wear is more extensive than at the preceding level, and many tiny vertical lines are fused together. Detail is still good on lower levels of the leaves.

1870, Shallow N. Graded VF-30.

F-12, 15 (Fine). *Obverse:* Traditionally, the word LIBERTY should be fully readable, but weak on the higher letters of LIB. PCGS suggests this is true, but not if a coin was lightly struck. Full or incomplete, well-struck or lightly struck, no matter what the coin, most buyers still want the word to be discernible. Other areas have correspondingly more wear than on the next-higher grade. *Reverse:* The higher areas of the leaves and the bow show

1870. Graded F-15.

wear. The shield shows greater wear than at the preceding level. Overall, the reverse appears to be less worn than the obverse, this being generally true of all circulated grades.

VG-8, 10 (Very Good). *Obverse:* A total of at least three letters in LIBERTY must be visible. This can be a combination of several partial letters. PCGS does not adhere to this rule and suggests that wear on the feathers is a better indicator. The rim may blend into the field in areas, depending on striking. *Reverse:* Wear is even more extensive. Leaves on the left have hardly any detail, while those on the right may have limited detail. The rim is complete.

1870, Bold N. Graded VG-10.

G-4, 6 (Good). *Obverse:* The coin is worn flat, with the portrait visible mostly in outline form, with only slight indication of feathers. Lettering and date are complete. Part of the rim is usually gone. At G-6, the rim is clearer. *Reverse:* The wreath is nearly flat, although some hints of detail may be seen on the right side. All letters are readable, although the inscription is light at the center (on issues from the 1870s onward). The rim is discern-

1877. Graded G-6.

ible all around, but is light in areas. At G-6 the rim is clearly delineated.

   Illustrated coin: The date is actually quite sharp for this grade.

AG-3 (About Good). *Obverse:* Most letters are worn away, as is the rim. The portrait is in outline form. The date is clearly readable, but may be weak or missing at the bottom. *Reverse:* Extensive wear prevails, although the rim will usually be more discernible than on the obverse. Most lettering, or sometimes all, is readable.

1877. Graded AG-3.

PF-60 to 70 (Proof). *Obverse and Reverse:* Gem PF-65 coins will have very few hairlines, and these are visible only under a strong magnifying glass. At any level and color, a Proof with hairlines likely (though not necessarily) has been cleaned. At PF-67 or higher there should be no evidence of hairlines or friction at all. Such a coin is fully original. PF-60 coins can be dull from repeated dipping and cleaning and are often toned iridescent colors. At

1868. Graded PF-64RB.

PF-63 the mirrorlike fields should be attractive, and hairlines should be minimal. These are easiest to see when the coin is held at an angle to the light. No rubbing is seen. PF-64 coins are even nicer.

COPPER-NICKEL COINAGE

1860, Rounded Bust

1860, Pointed Bust

	Mintage	Cert	Avg	%MS	G-4	VG-8	F-12	VF-20	EF-40	AU-50	MS-60BN PF-63BN	MS-63BN PF-64BN	MS-65 PF-65BN
1859	36,400,000	2,317	56.2	59%	$15	$20	$25	$55	$110	$200	$285	$700	$2,800
	Auctions: $23,500, MS-66+, November 2014; $11,750, MS-66, April 2013; $3,966, MS-65, September 2014												
1859, Proof	*800*	189	n/a								$1,650	$2,500	$4,500
	Auctions: $13,513, PF-66Cam, June 2014; $4,700, PF-66, September 2014; $3,173, PF-64, October 2014; $2,585, PF-64, August 2014												
1859, Oak Wreath With Shield, experimental reverse (a)		0	64.4									$1,100	
	Auctions: No auction records available.												
1860, Rounded Bust	20,566,000	1,403	58.1	68%	$10	$15	$20	$35	$70	$110	$185	$250	$1,200
	Auctions: $8,813, MS-66, January 2014; $3,290, MS-66, October 2014; $2,938, MS-66, October 2014; $764, MS-64, December 2014												
1860, Pointed Bust	(b)	167	58.1	70%	$20	$25	$30	$50	$100	$165	$300	$575	$3,500
	Auctions: $32,900, MS-67, February 2014; $7,931, MS-66, October 2014; $2,409, MS-65, August 2014; $1,469, MS-64, July 2014												
1860, Rounded Bust, Proof	*1,000*	57	64.8								$900	$1,850	$3,000	$6,500
	Auctions: $9,989, PF-66, April 2014; $5,875, PF-66, August 2014; $8,813, PF-66, October 2014; $4,137, PF-66, October 2014												

a. 1,000 pieces were made but never released for circulation. b. Included in circulation-strike 1860, Rounded Bust, mintage figure.

1863, Doubled
Die Reverse
FS-01-1863-801.

	Mintage	Cert	Avg	%MS	G-4	VG-8	F-12	VF-20	EF-40	AU-50	MS-60BN / PF-63BN	MS-63BN / PF-64BN	MS-65 / PF-65BN
1861	10,100,000	1,297	55.5	62%	$25	$35	$45	$60	$110	$175	$225	$400	$1,150
Auctions: $14,100, MS-67, October 2014; $4,113, MS-66, February 2014; $2,820, MS-66, September 2014													
1861, Proof	1,000	77	64.1								$1,200	$3,000	$5,500	$15,000
Auctions: $24,675, PF-66, September 2013; $2,585, PF-64, October 2014; $1,763, PF-64, October 2014													
1862	28,075,000	2,126	60.4	78%	$10	$15	$20	$30	$50	$75	$110	$200	$1,000
Auctions: $15,275, MS-67, February 2013; $11,163, MS-67, October 2014; $8,813, MS-67, November 2014													
1862, Proof	550	309	64.6								$850	$1,250	$2,500	$4,000
Auctions: $11,750, PF-67Cam, September 2014; $2,468, PF-66Cam, November 2014; $4,113, PF-66, June 2014													
1863	49,840,000	2,813	60.4	77%	$10	$15	$20	$30	$50	$75	$110	$200	$1,000
Auctions: $3,055, MS-66, August 2014; $1,998, MS-66, November 2014; $2,820, MS-66, August 2013; $969, MS-65, July 2014													
1863, Doubled Die Reverse (c)	(d)	2	62.5	100%					$200	$375	$450	$950	$3,000
Auctions: No auction records available.													
1863, Proof	460	142	64.3								$850	$1,250	$2,500	$4,000
Auctions: $9,988, PF-67Cam, September 2014; $1,998, PF-65Cam, July 2014; $1,058, PF-64Cam, November 2014													
1864, Copper-Nickel	13,740,000	1,658	58.0	71%	$20	$30	$40	$55	$100	$150	$200	$325	$1,300
Auctions: $6,463, MS-66, April 2014; $3,055, MS-66, November 2014; $1,351, MS-65, October 2014; $676, MS-64, July 2014													
1864, Copper-Nickel, Proof	370	153	64.3								$850	$1,450	$2,500	$4,000
Auctions: $8,813, PF-67Cam, September 2014; $12,925, PF-66DCam, July 2014; $1,880, MS-64Cam, August 2014													

c. Strong doubling is evident on the right leaves of the wreath, and, to a lesser degree, on the upper left leaves. d. Included in circulation-strike 1863 mintage figure.

Bronze Coinage

1864, No L   1864, With L

	Mintage	Cert	Avg	%MS	G-4	VG-8	F-12	VF-20	EF-40	AU-50	MS-60BN / PF-63BN	MS-63BN / PF-64RB	MS-65RB / PF-65RD	MS-65RD
1864, Bronze, All kinds	39,233,714													
1864, No L		1,458	59.1	80%	$15	$20	$25	$45	$70	$90	$115	$150	$400	$750
Auctions: $764, MS-66RB, September 2014; $881, MS-65RD, August 2014; $306, MS-64RB, October 2014; $7,050, VF-30, April 2013														
1864, With L		1,688	50.2	44%	$55	$80	$150	$200	$275	$375	$425	$575	$1,750	$4,750
Auctions: $2,115, MS-65RB, May 2013; $1,469, MS-64RD, November 2014; $1,293, MS-64RB, July 2014; $646, MS-62RB														
1864, No L, Proof	150+	120	64.7								$500	$1,750	$9,000	
Auctions: $17,625, PF-67RB, April 2013; $2,585, PF-65RB, November 2014; $2,129, PF-65RB, October 2014; $1,980, PF-65RB, April 2018														
1864, With L, Proof	20+	5	64.4								$20,000	$55,000		
Auctions: $141,000, PF-65RD, September 2013; $45,600, PF-64RB, January 2018														

**1865, Die Gouge
in Headdress**
FS-01-1865-1401.

1865, Doubled Die Reverse
FS-01-1865-1801.

1869, 9 Over 9
FS-01-1869-301.

Shallow N

Bold N

	Mintage	Cert	Avg	%MS	G-4	VG-8	F-12	VF-20	EF-40	AU-50	MS-60BN	MS-63BN PF-63BN	MS-65RB PF-64RB	MS-65RD PF-65RD
1865	35,429,286	1,140	60.2	78%	$15	$20	$25	$30	$45	$65	$90	$150	$750	$1,750
	Auctions: $1,998, MS-66RB, October 2014; $1,998, MS-65RD, March 2013; $270, MS-64BN, October 2014; $165, MS-64BN, September 2014													
1865, Die Gouge in Headdress (a)	**(b)**	0	n/a							$500	$750	$1,200		
	Auctions: No auction records available.													
1865, Doubled Die Reverse	**(b)**	11	41.5	36%					$800	$1,100	$2,200	$5,500		
	Auctions: $1,175, AU-55, April 2013													
1865, Proof	*500+*	154	64.2									$375	$800	$7,500
	Auctions: $14,100, PF-65Cam, August 2014; $15,275, PF-66RD, October 2014; $12,925, PF-65RD, June 2014; $3,055, PF-64RD, October 2014													
1866	9,826,500	1,158	52.7	56%	$50	$65	$80	$100	$190	$250	$275	$380	$1,500	$2,750
	Auctions: $1,087, MS-66BN, September 2014; $3,290, MS-65RD, June 2014; $499, MS-63RB, August 2014; $212, MS-62BN, October 2014													
1866, Proof	*725+*	129	64.5									$400	$600	$5,000
	Auctions: $21,150, PF-66Cam, June 2014; $2,820, PF-65Cam, October 2014; $999, PF-65RB, July 2014; $529, PF-64BN, November 2014													
1867	9,821,000	1,141	51.3	55%	$50	$70	$90	$135	$230	$275	$300	$400	$1,600	$6,500
	Auctions: $6,463, MS-65RD, February 2014; $1,293, MS-65RB, October 2014; $6,756, MS-65RD, October 2014; $780, MS-64RB, April 2018													
1867, Proof	*625+*	193	64.3									$400	$600	$5,000
	Auctions: $3,525, PF-66RB, July 2014; $6,463, PF-66RD, March 2014; $705, PF-64RB, August 2014; $306, PF-63BN, October 2014													
1868	10,266,500	1,109	51.8	56%	$40	$50	$70	$125	$170	$220	$250	$360	$925	$2,500
	Auctions: $1,880, MS-66RB, September 2014; $29,375, MS-66RD, April 2014; $3,525, MS-65RD, October 2014													
1868, Proof	*600+*	131	64.4									$375	$550	$5,000
	Auctions: $17,625, PF-66RD, June 2014; $6,756, PF-65RD, September 2014; $588, PF-63RB, October 2014; $5,040, PF-65RD, January 2018													
1869	6,420,000	1,206	44.0	43%	$85	$120	$235	$335	$445	$550	$600	$700	$1,800	$2,750
	Auctions: $3,290, MS-66RB, August 2013; $1,763, MS-64RB, October 2014; $499, MS-61BN, November 2014; $1,175, MS-60BN, July 2014													
1869, 9 Over 9	**(c)**	461	39.4	32%	$125	$225	$450	$575	$725	$825	$975	$1,200	$2,400	
	Auctions: $4,113, MS-66, March 2015; $1,645, MS-64RB, November 2014; $3,055, MS-64RD, August 2014													
1869, Proof	*600+*	180	64.4									$380	$650	$3,000
	Auctions: $4,847, PF-66Cam, June 2014; $11,750, PF-66RD, October 2014; $1,528, PF-65RB, October 2014; $558, PF-64RB, November 2014													
1870, Shallow N	5,275,000	7	43.7	14%	$80	$100	$220	$320	$400	$500	$550	$900	$1,600	
	Auctions: $1,265, MS-64RB, March 2012													
1870, Bold N	**(d)**	1,081	45.1	43%	$55	$75	$200	$280	$375	$450	$500	$850	$1,300	$4,000
	Auctions: $23,500, MS-66RD, May 2013; $3,819, MS-65RD, October 2014; $1,880, MS-65RB, November 2014; $705, MS-65BN, July 2014													

Note: Cents dated 1869 and earlier have a shallow N in ONE. Those dated 1870, 1871, or 1872 have either shallow N or bold N, except Proofs of 1872, which were struck only with the bold N, not the shallow N. Those dated 1873 to 1876 all have the bold N. Circulation strikes of 1877 have the shallow N, while Proofs have the bold N. **a.** Currently described as a die gouge in the *Cherrypickers' Guide to Rare Die Varieties,* sixth edition, volume I, the curved "gouge" is a mark from the Janvier reducing lathe. **b.** Included in circulation-strike 1865 mintage figure. **c.** Included in circulation-strike 1869 mintage figure. **d.** Included in circulation-strike 1870, Shallow N, mintage figure.

1870, Doubled Die Reverse
FS-01-1870-801.

1873, Close 3

1873, Open 3

1873, Doubled LIBERTY
FS-01-1873-101.

	Mintage	Cert	Avg	%MS	G-4	VG-8	F-12	VF-20	EF-40	AU-50	MS-60BN	MS-63BN	MS-65RB	MS-65RD
												PF-63BN	PF-64RB	PF-65RD
1870, Doubled Die Reverse	(d)	10	56.3	80%					$575	$750	$850	$1,000	$2,500	
Auctions: $1,035, MS-64RB, January 2012														
1870, Shallow N, Proof	1,000+	184	64.0									$425	$525	$1,900
Auctions: $1,380, PF-65RB, April 2012														
1870, Bold N, Proof	(e)	(f)										$325	$725	$2,500
Auctions: $3,173, PF-67RB, August 2014; $10,575, PF-66RD, January 2014; $9,988, PF-66RD, July 2014; $1,528, PF-64RD, November 2014														
1871, Shallow N	3,929,500	2	54.0	0%	$130	$180	$325	$450	$575	$650	$775	$1,000	$2,600	
Auctions: $8,225, MS-66, January 2015; $2,585, MS-63RB, February 2013														
1871, Bold N	(g)	1,190	44.5	41%	$70	$85	$250	$350	$475	$525	$550	$800	$2,350	$7,500
Auctions: $44,063, MS-66RD, January 2014; $999, MS-64BN, November 2014; $999, MS-62BN, October 2014														
1871, Shallow N, Proof	960+	267	64.3									$500	$875	$2,350
Auctions: $7,344, PF-65RD, January 2013														
1871, Bold N, Proof	(h)											$325	$600	$2,500
Auctions: $2,350, PF-65RD, June 2014; $499, PF-65BN, October 2014; $294, PF-62BN, November 2014; $282, PF-60BN, November 2014														
1872, Shallow N	4,042,000	9	35.0	22%	$100	$170	$370	$425	$575	$700	$950	$1,250	$4,500	
Auctions: $764, MS-63, March 2016; $881, AU-55, April 2013														
1872, Bold N	(j)	1,456	41.4	33%	$90	$140	$300	$375	$500	$650	$785	$1,150	$3,750	$10,000
Auctions: $28,200, MS-65RD, June 2014; $3,819, MS-65RB, August 2014; $5,581, MS-64RD, October 2014; $588, AU-58BN, July 2014														
1872, Bold N, Proof (k)	950+	175	64.3									$400	$700	$4,300
Auctions: $7,050, PF-66RD, October 2014; $705, PF-65BN, November 2014; $705, PF-64RB, November 2014; $12,925, PF, October 2013														
1873, All kinds	11,676,500													
1873, Close 3		330	52.9	54%	$25	$35	$65	$125	$185	$235	$410	$550	$2,500	$6,500
Auctions: $6,463, MS-65RD, October 2014; $2,820, MS-65RB, December 2013; $1,293, MS-64RB, October 2014; $793, MS-63RB														
1873, Doubled LIBERTY		134	44.6	34%	$200	$350	$825	$1,750	$2,500	$5,250	$7,500	$13,500	$55,000	
Auctions: $15,275, MS-64, March 2015; $9,988, MS-63RB, October 2014; $7,050, MS-63BN, September 2014														
1873, Open 3		635	52.3	50%	$20	$30	$50	$85	$160	$190	$250	$325	$1,275	$5,000
Auctions: $4,406, MS-65RD, April 2014; $3,819, MS-65RD, October 2014; $470, MS-64RB, November 2014; $470, MS-63RB, July 2014														
1873, Close 3, Proof	1,100+	243	64.2									$265	$550	$2,050
Auctions: $1,293, PF-65RB, April 2013; $589, PF-64RD, October 2014; $470, PF-64RB, October 2014; $1,440, PF-64RD, April 2018														
1874	14,187,500	1,023	56.4	63%	$20	$25	$45	$65	$100	$150	$225	$250	$725	$3,000
Auctions: $1,880, MS-65RD, October 2014; $2,820, MS-65RD, April 2013; $1,116, MS-65RB, October 2014														
1874, Proof	700	176	64.4									$250	$400	$2,500
Auctions: $823, PF-66BN, July 2014; $1,175, PF-65RB, June 2013; $617, PF-64RD, October 2014; $470, PF-64RB, July 2014														

Note: Cents dated 1869 and earlier have a shallow N in ONE. Those dated 1870, 1871, or 1872 have either shallow N or bold N, except Proofs of 1872, which were struck only with the bold N, not the shallow N. Those dated 1873 to 1876 all have the bold N. Circulation strikes of 1877 have the shallow N, while Proofs have the bold N. **d.** Included in circulation-strike 1870, Shallow N, mintage figure. **e.** Included in 1870, Shallow N, Proof, mintage figure. **f.** Included in certified population for 1870, Shallow N, Proof. **g.** Included in circulation-strike 1871, Shallow N, mintage figure. **h.** Included in 1871, Shallow N, Proof, mintage figure. **i.** Included in certified population for 1871, Shallow N, Proof. **j.** Included in 1872, Shallow N, mintage figure. **k.** Proofs of 1872 were struck only with the bold N, not the shallow N.

1875, Dot Reverse
FS-01-1875-801.

1880, Doubled Die Obverse, Reverse Clash
FS-01-1880-101.

1882, Misplaced Date
FS-01-1882-401.

	Mintage	Cert	Avg	%MS	G-4	VG-8	F-12	VF-20	EF-40	AU-50	MS-60BN	MS-63BN	MS-65RB	MS-65RD
												PF-63BN	PF-64RB	PF-65RD
1875	13,528,000	954	55.1	65%	$20	$35	$60	$75	$120	$160	$235	$260	$900	$2,500
	Auctions: $1,763, MS-66RB, July 2014; $5,581, MS-65RD, December 2013; $881, MS-65RB, August 2014; $646, MS-64RB, August 2014													
1875, Dot Reverse (l)	(m)	1	64.0	100%									—	
	Auctions: $700, AU-50BN, April 2012													
1875, Proof	700	183	64.2									$250	$500	$5,400
	Auctions: $8,813, PF-65RD, June 2014; $306, PF-63RB, October 2014; $960, PF-64RD, January 2018													
1876	7,944,000	959	52.5	56%	$35	$40	$70	$135	$225	$240	$300	$390	$1,000	$2,750
	Auctions: $1,998, MS-65RD, October 2014; $1,880, MS-65RD, October 2013; $1,293, MS-65RB, November 2014; $270, MS-62RB, November 2014													
1876, Proof	1,150	220	64.4									$250	$450	$2,250
	Auctions: $15,275, PF-66Cam, January 2014; $2,585, PF-66RD, October 2014; $646, PF-64RD, October 2014; $823, PF-64BN, November 2014													
1877 (n)	852,500	3,470	22.6	10%	$900	$1,100	$1,550	$2,000	$2,500	$3,000	$3,800	$4,500	$15,000	$25,000
	Auctions: $32,900, MS-65RD, August 2014; $14,100, MS-65RB, January 2014; $14,100, MS-65, August 2016													
1877, Proof	900	268	63.7									$3,000	$4,500	$12,000
	Auctions: $9,988, PF-66RD, October 2014; $14,100, PF-66RD, June 2013; $3,525, PF-64RB, October 2014; $3,819, PF-63RB, November 2014													
1878	5,797,500	898	54.1	63%	$35	$45	$60	$110	$200	$275	$325	$380	$950	$2,250
	Auctions: $8,813, MS-66RD, September 2014; $1,645, MS-65RD, October 2013; $881, MS-65RB, August 2014; $388, MS-63RB, October 2014													
1878, Proof	2,350	337	64.2									$235	$450	$1,500
	Auctions: $7,638, PF-66Cam, June 2014; $1,763, PF-65Cam, August 2014; $1,116, PF-65Cam, November 2014; $588, PF-64RD, October 2014													
1879	16,228,000	924	60.6	82%	$8	$12	$20	$40	$70	$80	$90	$140	$425	$1,250
	Auctions: $2,233, MS-65RD, June 2014; $470, MS-65RB, November 2014; $259, MS-64RB, July 2014; $247, MS-63RB, August 2014													
1879, Proof	3,200	385	64.5									$150	$325	$1,200
	Auctions: $11,163, PF-67RD, July 2014; $2,115, PF-66Cam, August 2014; $1,645, PF-66RD, October 2014; $217, PF-64BN, November 2014													
1880	38,961,000	800	62.0	89%	$5	$7	$9	$12	$30	$60	$80	$130	$400	$1,150
	Auctions: $5,288, MS-66RD, June 2014; $940, MS-65RD, September 2014; $441, MS-65RB, November 2014; $129, MS-64BN, November 2014													
1880, Doubled Die Obverse, Reverse Clash (o)	(p)	10	54.8	70%						$390	$750	$1,500	$2,000	
	Auctions: $2,070, MS-65BN, June 2009													
1880, Proof	3,955	422	64.4									$150	$325	$1,200
	Auctions: $8,813, PF-67RD, June 2014; $969, PF-66RB, August 2014; $705, PF-65RD, July 2014; $646, PF-65RB+, July 2014													

Note: Cents dated 1869 and earlier have a shallow N in ONE. Those dated 1870, 1871, or 1872 have either shallow N or bold N, except Proofs of 1872, which were struck only with the bold N, not the shallow N. Those dated 1873 to 1876 all have the bold N. Circulation strikes of 1877 have the shallow N, while Proofs have the bold N. **l.** In 1875 Mint officials suspected a longtime employee was stealing Indian Head cents. They secretly modified a reverse die by making a small gouge in the N in ONE, and then put the die into production one morning. Later that morning the suspect employee was called aside. He was asked to empty his pockets, revealing 33 of the marked cents. At first he insisted his son gave him this pocket change, but when confronted with the secretly marked die, he admitted his guilt. He tendered his resignation, disgraced, after more than 50 years of service to the Mint. The market value for this variety is not yet reliably established. **m.** Included in circulation-strike 1875 mintage figure. **n.** Beware the numerous counterfeits and altered-date 1877 cents. The latter typically are altered from 1875- or 1879-dated cents. **o.** Doubling is visible on the obverse in higher grades, as a very close spread on LIBERTY. The primary diagnostic, though, is the misaligned die clash evident on the reverse, with obvious reeding running from the upper-right leaf tip, through the E of ONE, and down to the very top of the N of CENT. **p.** Included in circulation-strike 1880 mintage figure.

1886, Variety 1
The last feather points between the I and the C in AMERICA.

1886, Variety 2
The last feather points between the C and the A in AMERICA.

1887, Doubled Die Obverse
FS-01-1887-101.

	Mintage	Cert	Avg	%MS	G-4	VG-8	F-12	VF-20	EF-40	AU-50	MS-60BN	MS-63BN	MS-65RB	MS-65RD
												PF-63BN	PF-64RB	PF-65RD
1881	39,208,000	810	62.2	91%	$5	$6	$8	$10	$25	$35	$60	$90	$315	$1,150
Auctions: $1,645, MS-67RB, October 2014; $6,463, MS-66RD, October 2014; $1,528, MS-66RB, August 2014														
1881, Proof	3,575	405	64.6									$150	$325	$1,200
Auctions: $2,115, PF-66RB, November 2014; $1,880, PF-66RD, June 2013; $1,234, PF-65Cam, July 2014; $881, PF-65RB, August 2014														
1882	38,578,000	824	62.5	91%	$5	$6	$8	$10	$25	$35	$60	$90	$315	$1,150
Auctions: $294, MS-64RB, July 2014; $247, MS-64RB, October 2014; $3,525, EF-40, April 2013; $66, AU-55BN, October 2014														
1882, Misplaced Date (q)	(r)	5	60.6	80%					$450	$875	$1,700	$6,000		
Auctions: $220, EF-45, February 2007														
1882, Proof	3,100	403	64.6									$150	$325	$1,000
Auctions: $823, PF-66RB, September 2014; $734, PF-66BN, November 2014; $2,703, PF-65RD, January 2014; $323, PF-65BN, July 2014														
1883	45,591,500	829	62.5	90%	$5	$6	$8	$10	$25	$35	$60	$90	$315	$1,150
Auctions: $2,585, MS-66RD, February 2014; $499, MS-65RB, July 2014; $241, MS-65BN, July 2014; $217, MS-64RB, October 2014														
1883, Proof	6,609	595	64.6									$150	$325	$1,200
Auctions: $5,581, PF-67RB, August 2014; $2,938, PF-66RD, March 2013; $646, PF-66BN, November 2014; $441, PF-65RB, November 2014														
1884	23,257,800	756	62.3	89%	$5	$7	$10	$14	$27	$40	$75	$120	$450	$1,350
Auctions: $4,994, MS-66RD, June 2014; $1,645, MS-65RD, September 2014; $257, MS-64RB, August 2014														
1884, Proof	3,942	489	64.8									$150	$325	$1,200
Auctions: $7,050, PF-67Cam, June 2013; $4,113, PF-67RD, September 2014; $1,880, PF-66RD, July 2014; $306, PF-64RD, October 2014														
1885	11,761,594	730	61.3	83%	$8	$9	$15	$30	$65	$80	$110	$200	$650	$1,750
Auctions: $12,925, MS-66RD, April 2013; $1,528, MS-66RB, November 2014; $1,645, MS-65RD, October 2014														
1885, Proof	3,790	470	64.9									$150	$325	$1,200
Auctions: $4,994, PF-68BN, September 2013; $1,528, PF-66RB, July 2014; $2,115, PF-65RD, October 2014; $529, PF-65RB, October 2014														
1886, All kinds	17,650,000													
1886, Variety 1		469	56.2	56%	$6	$8	$20	$50	$140	$175	$200	$250	$975	$3,500
Auctions: $8,813, MS-66RB, June 2013; $1,410, MS-64RD, July 2014; $764, MS-64RB, November 2014; $235, MS-63BN, September 2014														
1886, Variety 2		532	57.1	65%	$7	$12	$25	$75	$175	$220	$325	$500	$2,900	$10,000
Auctions: $9,400, MS-65RD, January 2013; $2,115, MS-65RB, August 2014; $482, MS-60RB, July 2014; $247, AU-58BN, October 2014														
1886, All kinds, Proof	4,290													
1886, Variety 1, Proof		134	64.6									$150	$325	$1,800
Auctions: $3,819, PF-66RD, June 2014; $1,880, PF-66RB, October 2014; $1,763, PF-65RD, October 2014; $558, PF-64RB, August 2014														
1886, Variety 2, Proof		77	64.5									$350	$750	$10,000
Auctions: $1,116, PF-66BN, April 2013; $1,763, PF-64RB+, November 2014; $306, PF-64BN, November 2014														
1887	45,223,523	679	61.4	89%	$3	$4	$5	$8	$18	$28	$55	$80	$575	$1,250
Auctions: $4,700, MS-66RD, November 2014; $8,813, MS-66RD, February 2013; $382, MS-65RB, November 2014														
1887, DblDie Obverse	(s)	33	39.1	15%					$250	$490	$1,000	$2,500	$8,000	
Auctions: $881, MS-62BN, October 2013; $176, VF-25BN, October 2014														
1887, Proof	2,960	329	64.4									$150	$300	$3,500
Auctions: $16,450, PF-66RD, June 2014; $823, PF-66BN, November 2014; $382, PF-64RB, October 2014; $3,120, PF-65RD, January 2018														

q. The bases of at least four 1s are evident within the beads of the necklace. **r.** Included in circulation-strike 1882 mintage figure.
s. Included in circulation-strike 1887 mintage figure.

1888, Last 8 Over 7
FS-01-1888-301.

1891, Doubled Die Obverse
FS-01-1891-101.

1894, Doubled Date
FS-01-1894-301.

	Mintage	Cert	Avg	%MS	G-4	VG-8	F-12	VF-20	EF-40	AU-50	MS-60BN	MS-63BN	MS-65RB	MS-65RD
												PF-63BN	PF-64RB	PF-65RD
1888	37,489,832	810	59.1	83%	$3	$4	$5	$8	$22	$27	$65	$130	$725	$1,500
Auctions: $11,750, MS-66RD, June 2014; $1,704, MS-65RD, July 2014; $1,880, MS-65RD, September 2014; $529, MS-64RD, October 2014														
1888, Last 8 Over 7	(t)	13	39.2	15%	$1,250	$1,500	$2,000	$3,500	$7,500	$17,500	$30,000	$50,000		
Auctions: $99,142, MS-66, January 2016; $23,500, AU-58, April 2013														
1888, Proof	4,582	289	64.2									$150	$315	$3,500
Auctions: $15,275, PF-66RD, October 2014; $382, PF-64RB, August 2014; $2,585, PF, February 2013; $294, PF-64BN, December 2014														
1889	48,866,025	836	62.0	91%	$3	$4	$5	$7	$18	$27	$60	$80	$400	$2,000
Auctions: $13,513, MS-66RD, October 2014; $10,575, MS-66RD, October 2014; $4,113, MS-65RD, April 2014; $1,880, MS-65RD, October 2014														
1889, Proof	3,336	280	64.3									$150	$315	$1,750
Auctions: $4,113, PF-66RD, February 2013; $499, PF-65RB, July 2014; $341, PF-64RB, July 2014; $282, PF-64BN, November 2014														
1890	57,180,114	785	62.4	92%	$3	$4	$5	$7	$16	$27	$60	$80	$410	$1,200
Auctions: $4,113, MS-66RB, March 2014; $470, MS-64RD, July 2014; $170, MS-64RB, August 2014; $170, MS-63BN, July 2014														
1890, Proof	2,740	274	64.1									$150	$315	$1,650
Auctions: $1,058, PF-65RD, October 2014; $1,293, PF-65RD, August 2013; $1,293, PF-64Cam, September 2014; $470, PF-64RD, November 2014														
1891	47,070,000	903	62.6	92%	$3	$4	$5	$7	$15	$27	$60	$80	$400	$1,200
Auctions: $9,106, MS-66RD, November 2014; $1,528, MS-65RD, July 2014; $1,293, MS-65RD, August 2014; $135, MS-64RB, August 2014														
1891, Doubled Die Obverse	(u)	12	45.9	25%					$250	$450	$775	$1,150		
Auctions: $138, VF-35, December 2011; $1,320, MS-64BN, February 2018														
1891, Proof	2,350	299	64.1									$150	$315	$1,375
Auctions: $18,213, PF-65DCam, July 2014; $911, PF-64Cam, September 2014; $558, PF-64RB, November 2014; $176, PF-62RB, November 2014														
1892	37,647,087	810	62.7	93%	$3	$4	$5	$8	$20	$27	$60	$80	$375	$1,000
Auctions: $8,813, MS-66RD, August 2013; $3,055, MS-65RD, October 2014; $1,293, MS-65RD, October 2014; $306, MS-64RD, October 2014														
1892, Proof	2,745	301	64.4									$150	$315	$1,200
Auctions: $3,525, PF-67RD, November 2013; $2,585, PF-66Cam, November 2014; $2,233, PF-65RD, October 2014; $1,175, PF-64Cam, July 2014														
1893	46,640,000	972	62.8	94%	$3	$4	$5	$8	$20	$27	$60	$80	$320	$1,000
Auctions: $6,463, MS-67RD, April 2013; $282, MS-64RD, October 2014; $176, MS-64RB, November 2014; $135, MS-63RB, November 2014														
1893, Proof	2,195	270	64.1									$150	$315	$1,300
Auctions: $823, PF-65RB, November 2014; $499, PF-64RD, April 2013; $284, PF-64RB, October 2014; $247, PF-63RB, November 2014														
1894	16,749,500	906	60.5	83%	$5	$6	$15	$20	$50	$70	$85	$115	$385	$1,000
Auctions: $3,290, MS-66RD, January 2014; $2,585, MS-66RD, October 2014; $2,174, MS-66RD, November 2014; $414, MS-64RB, July 2014														
1894, Doubled Date	(v)	109	46.5	51%	$30	$40	$65	$130	$225	$385	$675	$1,200	$4,000	$11,000
Auctions: $5,875, MS-64RD, January 2013; $4,113, MS-64RB, September 2014; $1,116, MS-62, January 2015														
1894, Proof	2,632	310	64.1									$150	$315	$1,200
Auctions: $5,581, PF-66RD, September 2013; $1,351, PF-65Cam, November 2014; $558, PF-65RB, November 2014														

t. Included in circulation-strike 1888 mintage figure. **u.** Included in circulation-strike 1891 mintage figure. **v.** Included in circulation-strike 1894 mintage figure.

	Mintage	Cert	Avg	%MS	G-4	VG-8	F-12	VF-20	EF-40	AU-50	MS-60BN	MS-63BN	MS-65RB	MS-65RD
												PF-63BN	PF-64RB	PF-65RD
1895	38,341,574	968	62.6	94%	$3	$4	$5	$8	$15	$25	$45	$65	$200	$700
	Auctions: $23,500, MS-67RD, November 2014; $7,050, MS-66RD, January 2014; $1,880, MS-66RD, October 2014; $206, MS-64RB, October 2014													
1895, Proof	2,062	281	64.4									$160	$315	$1,200
	Auctions: $9,988, PF-66Cam, June 2014; $1,880, PF-66RB, November 2014; $823, PF-64RB, November 2014; $260, PF-62RB, November 2014													
1896	39,055,431	735	62.5	92%	$3	$4	$5	$8	$15	$25	$45	$65	$220	$800
	Auctions: $1,528, MS-65RD, July 2014; $259, MS-64RD, July 2014; $182, MS-64RB, August 2014; $59, MS-63BN, October 2014													
1896, Proof	1,862	232	64.3									$150	$300	$1,350
	Auctions: $5,875, PF-65Cam, June 2014; $646, PF-65BN, November 2014; $295, PF-64RB, September 2014; $194, PF-64BN, November 2014													
1897	50,464,392	927	62.4	92%	$3	$4	$5	$8	$15	$25	$45	$65	$200	$800
	Auctions: $31,725, MS-67RD, August 2014; $7,050, MS-66RD, January 2014; $529, MS-64RD, September 2014; $118, MS-64RD, October 2014													
1897, Proof	1,938	265	64.5									$150	$300	$1,200
	Auctions: $6,169, PF-67RD, October 2014; $588, PF-65RB, July 2014; $411, PF-63RB, November 2014; $10,575, PF, January 2013													
1898	49,821,284	999	62.5	92%	$3	$4	$5	$8	$15	$25	$45	$65	$195	$500
	Auctions: $2,820, MS-66RD, April 2013; $368, MS-65RB+, November 2014; $458, MS-64RD+, October 2014; $212, MS-64RD, October 2014													
1898, Proof	1,795	272	64.7									$150	$300	$1,200
	Auctions: $7,931, PF-66Cam, June 2014; $27,025, PF-66RB, August 2014; $2,233, PF-66RD, August 2014; $353, PF-64RB, November 2014													
1899	53,598,000	1,625	63.1	94%	$3	$4	$5	$8	$15	$25	$45	$65	$195	$475
	Auctions: $3,525, MS-66RD, January 2014; $2,233, MS-66RD, September 2014; $1,351, MS-66RD, October 2014; $558, MS-65RD, October 2014													
1899, Proof	2,031	269	64.7									$150	$300	$1,200
	Auctions: $5,875, PF-67RD, June 2014; $764, PF-64Cam, November 2014; $823, PF-66RB, November 2014; $478, PF-65RB, October 2014													
1900	66,831,502	1,098	62.5	93%	$2	$3	$5	$6	$10	$20	$40	$60	$165	$475
	Auctions: $9,988, MS-67RD, December 2013; $2,115, MS-66RD+, July 2014; $1,998, MS-66RD, October 2014; $529, MS-65RD, December 2014													
1900, Proof	2,262	266	64.6									$150	$300	$1,200
	Auctions: $2,350, PF-66RB+, August 2014; $2,115, PF-66RD, October 2014; $5,581, PF-66RD, April 2013; $411, PF-64RD, October 2014													
1901	79,609,158	1,924	63.0	95%	$2	$3	$5	$6	$10	$20	$40	$60	$165	$450
	Auctions: $2,115, MS-67RB, November 2013; $1,293, MS-66RD, August 2014; $588, MS-65RD, August 2014; $194, MS-64RD, July 2014													
1901, Proof	1,985	283	64.7									$150	$300	$1,200
	Auctions: $2,500, PF-67RB, July 2014; $1,528, PF-66RD, October 2014; $999, PF-66RB, August 2014; $4,700, PF, March 2014													
1902	87,374,704	1,888	62.5	93%	$2	$3	$5	$6	$10	$20	$40	$60	$165	$525
	Auctions: $1,998, MS-66RD, July 2014; $2,585, MS-66RD, December 2013; $705, MS-65RD, November 2014; $165, MS-64RD, July 2014													
1902, Proof	2,018	292	64.5									$150	$300	$1,200
	Auctions: $7,344, PF-67RD, June 2014; $823, PF-66RB, November 2014; $1,146, PF-65RD, October 2014; $341, PF-64RB, July 2014													
1903	85,092,703	1,720	62.3	92%	$2	$3	$5	$6	$10	$20	$40	$60	$165	$450
	Auctions: $4,406, MS-67RD, July 2014; $1,998, MS-66RD, October 2014; $1,528, MS-66RD, November 2014; $411, MS-65RD, August 2014													
1903, Proof	1,790	260	64.6									$150	$300	$1,200
	Auctions: $2,820, PF-66RD, October 2014; $1,763, PF-66RD, November 2014; $499, PF-64RD, July 201412/29/2014 $10,575, PF, January 2013													
1904	61,326,198	1,497	62.6	93%	$2	$3	$5	$6	$10	$20	$40	$60	$165	$475
	Auctions: $2,585, MS-66RD, June 2014; $441, MS-65RD, November 2014; $183, MS-65RB, July 2014; $59, MS-63RB, November 2014													
1904, Proof	1,817	249	64.2									$150	$300	$1,200
	Auctions: $6,463, PF-67RB, October 2014; $4,994, PF-66Cam, June 2014; $2,585, PF-65Cam, October 2014; $7,931, PF-65RB, July 2014													
1905	80,717,011	1,742	62.7	93%	$2	$3	$5	$6	$10	$20	$40	$60	$165	$500
	Auctions: $19,975, MS-67RD, April 2013; $6,169, MS-66RD+, September 2014; $2,115, MS-66RD, September 2014; $456, MS-65RD, August 2014													
1905, Proof	2,152	261	64.4									$150	$300	$1,200
	Auctions: $411, PF-64RD, October 2014; $529, PF-64RB, November 2014; $8,225, PF, March 2014; $223, PF-63RB, October 2014													
1906	96,020,530	2,004	62.1	90%	$2	$3	$5	$6	$10	$20	$40	$60	$165	$450
	Auctions: $23,500, MS-67RD, June 2014; $2,585, MS-66RD, August 2014; $617, MS-65RD, September 2014; $247, MS-62BN, July 2014													
1906, Proof	1,725	238	64.4									$150	$300	$1,200
	Auctions: $21,150, PF-67Cam, June 2014; $2,820, PF-66RB+, November 2014; $1,704, PF-66RB, November 2014; $2,939, PF-64RB, July 2014													
1907	108,137,143	2,172	62.1	91%	$2	$3	$5	$6	$10	$20	$40	$60	$165	$450
	Auctions: $23,500, MS-67RD, December 2013; $364, MS-65RD, October 2014; $329, MS-65RB, October 2014; $247, MS-64RD, October 2014													
1907, Proof	1,475	214	64.5									$150	$300	$1,250
	Auctions: $4,113, PF-66RD, April 2014; $764, PF-65RD, October 2014; $306, PF-64RB, October 2014; $382, PF-62BN, November 2014													

	Mintage	Cert	Avg	%MS	G-4	VG-8	F-12	VF-20	EF-40	AU-50	MS-60BN	MS-63BN	MS-65RB	MS-65RD
												PF-63BN	PF-64RB	PF-65RD
1908	32,326,367	1,803	62.8	94%	$2	$3	$5	$6	$10	$20	$40	$60	$165	$450
Auctions: $19,975, MS-67RD, February 2013; $3,525, MS-66RD, August 2014; $4,113, MS-66RD+, October 2014; $1,293, MS-65RD, August 2014														
1908, Proof	1,620	285	64.6									$150	$300	$1,200
Auctions: $1,293, PF-66RB, November 2014; $1,175, PF-65RD, January 2014; $382, PF-64RD, October 2014; $2,585, PF-62RB, July 2014														
1908-S	1,115,000	3,663	43.3	30%	$90	$100	$125	$145	$175	$250	$290	$400	$850	$2,000
Auctions: $4,882, MS-66RD, August 2014; $1,763, MS-65RD, October 2014; $3,290, MS-65, March 2015														
1909	14,368,470	2,440	61.9	92%	$12	$15	$17	$20	$25	$30	$45	$65	$175	$475
Auctions: $3,819, MS-67RD, January 2014; $11,163, MS-67RD, August 2014; $4,113, MS-66RD+, September 2014														
1909, Proof	2,175	265	64.6									$150	$300	$1,300
Auctions: $12,925, PF-67RD, June 2014; $1,645, PF-66RD, August 2014; $1,645, PF-64Cam, November 2014; $206, PF-63RB, July 2014														
1909-S	309,000	3,697	38.8	26%	$300	$325	$400	$475	$600	$700	$1,000	$1,200	$2,500	$5,000
Auctions: $9,989, MS-66RD, June 2014; $9,988, MS-66, September 2015; $5,875, MS-65RD, August 2014														

LINCOLN, WHEAT EARS REVERSE (1909–1958)

Variety 1 (Bronze, 1909–1942): **Designer:** *Victor D. Brenner.* **Weight:** *3.11 grams.* **Composition:** *.950 copper, .050 tin and zinc.* **Diameter:** *19 mm.* **Edge:** *Plain.* **Mints:** *Philadelphia, Denver, and San Francisco.*

Variety 1, Bronze (1909–1942)

Mintmark location, all varieties 1909 to date, is on the obverse below the date.

Variety 1, Bronze, Matte Proof

Variety 2 (Steel, 1943): **Weight:** *2.70 grams.* **Composition:** *Steel, coated with zinc.* **Diameter:** *19 mm.* **Edge:** *Plain.* **Mints:** *Philadelphia, Denver, and San Francisco.*

Variety 2, Steel (1943)

Variety 1 Resumed (1944–1958): **Weight:** *3.11 grams.* **Composition:** *1944–1946—.950 copper and .050 zinc; 1947–1958—.950 copper and .050 tin and zinc.* **Diameter:** *19 mm.* **Edge:** *Plain.* **Mints:** *Philadelphia, Denver, and San Francisco.*

Variety 1 Resumed, Bronze (1944–1958)

Variety 1 Resumed, Bronze, Mirror Proof

History. The Lincoln cent debuted in 1909 in honor of the hundredth anniversary of the birth of Abraham Lincoln. Sculptor and engraver Victor David had been chosen to design the new cent because the artistry of Chief Engraver Charles Barber was under heavy criticism at the time. The new cent was released on August 2, 1909, and the earliest coins of the year's issue had Brenner's initials (V.D.B.) on the reverse; this was soon discontinued. (His initials would be restored in 1918, on the obverse, on Lincoln's shoulder.) This was the first U.S. cent to feature the motto IN GOD WE TRUST.

From 1909 to 1942 the coins were struck in bronze. In 1943, during World War II, zinc-coated steel was used for their planchets, as a way to reserve copper for the war effort. The bronze alloy would be resumed in 1944. (Although no bronze cents were officially issued in 1943, a few pieces struck on bronze or silver planchets are known to exist for that year; bronze examples have recently sold for more than $200,000. Such errors presumably occur when an older planchet is mixed in with the normal supply of planchets and goes through the minting process. Through a similar production error, a few 1944 cents were struck on steel planchets. Beware the many regular steel cents of 1943 that were later plated with copper, either as novelties or to deceive collectors; a magnet will reveal their true nature.) In 1944, 1945, and 1946, the Mint used salvaged gun-cartridge cases as its source metal for coining cents. In Mint State, the color of cents of these years can appear slightly different from other bronze Wheat Ears cents.

The Philadelphia, Denver, and San Francisco mints all produced Lincoln Wheat Ears cents, but not in all years. The Wheat Ears reverse design was used from 1909 until the coin's 50th anniversary in 1959, at which time it was replaced with a view of the Lincoln Memorial.

Striking and Sharpness. As a rule, Lincoln cents of 1909 through 1914 are fairly well struck. From 1915 through the end of the 1920s, many are weak, with Denver Mint coins particularly so. Issues of the 1930s onward are mostly well struck. With many different die pairs used over a long period of time, striking quality varies. On the obverse, check for details in Lincoln's hair and beard. Also check the lettering and the inner edge of the rim. Tiny marks on the shoulder of Lincoln indicate a weak strike there; this area cannot be used to determine wear on high-grade coins. (During striking, there was not enough die pressure to fill this, the deepest point of the obverse die; therefore, stray marks on the raw planchet remain evident in this spot.) On the reverse check the wheat stalks, letters, and inner rim. A weak strike will usually manifest itself on the O of ONE (the area directly opposite Lincoln's shoulder). Coins struck from overused or "tired" dies can have grainy or even slightly wavy fields on either side.

Availability. Of the earlier Lincoln Wheat Ears cents, those of 1909 are easily found in MS; later early dates are scarcer, although Philadelphia varieties were made in higher quantities and are more often seen. Beginning in the early 1930s, collectors saved bank-wrapped rolls of Mint State cents in large quantities (starting mainly in 1934, though the low-mintage 1931-S was also hoarded). Dates after this time all are plentiful, although some more so than others, and there are a number of scarce and rare varieties. The collector demand for scarcer Lincoln cents and higher-grade issues is intense, resulting in a strong market. Many Mint State coins before the 1930s have been dipped and recolored, this being particularly true of pieces listed as RD. Others are stained and blotchy.

Proofs. Matte Proof Lincoln cents of a new style were made from 1909 to 1916. These have minutely matte or pebbled surfaces caused by special treatment of the dies. The rims are square and sharp. Such pieces cannot easily be told from certain circulation strikes with similar borders. Certified holders usually list these simply as "Proof," not "Matte Proof." Buy only coins that have been verified by an expert. Most are brown, or brown with tinges of red. Nearly all full "red" coins have been dipped or recolored.

Exceptional specimens dated 1917 are reported to exist, although no records exist to indicate they are true Proofs.

Mirror-finish Proofs were made from 1936 to 1942 and again from 1950 to 1958. Proofs of this era are mostly from dies polished overall (including the portrait), although some later issues have frosted ("cameo") portraits. Quality can be a problem for the 1936 to 1942 issues. Check for carbon spots and recoloring. Proofs of later dates are easy to find.

Generally, Proofs below 63 are unattractive and are not desired by most collectors.

GRADING STANDARDS

Caveat: These grading standards do not take sharpness of strike into account.

MS-60 to 70 (Mint State). *Obverse and Reverse:* At MS-65 and higher, the luster is rich on all areas, except perhaps the shoulder (which may be grainy and show original planchet surface). There is no rubbing, and no contact marks are visible except under magnification. Coins with full or nearly full mint orange-red color can be designated RD; those with full or nearly full brown-toned surfaces can be designated BN; and those with a sub-

1909-S, V.D.B. Graded MS-64RB.

stantial percentage of red-orange and of brown can be called RB. Ideally, MS-65 or finer coins should have good eye appeal, which in the RB category means nicely blended colors, not stained or blotched. Below MS-65, full RD coins become scarce, and at MS–60 to 62 they are virtually non-existent, unless they have been dipped. Copper is a very active metal, and influences that define the grade—such as slight abrasions, contact marks, and so on—also affect the color. The ANA grading standards allow for "dull" and/or "spotted" coins at MS–60 and 61, as well as incomplete luster. In the marketplace, interpretations often vary widely. BN and RB coins at MS–60 and 61 are apt to be more attractive than (dipped) RD coins.

Illustrated coin: The rose-orange color of this cent is better than is usually expected for a coin graded Red Brown. Note some toning streaks on the obverse, lighter than the surrounding surfaces, across Lincoln's forehead and nose.

AU-50, 53, 55, 58 (About Uncirculated). *Obverse:* Slight wear shows on Lincoln's cheekbone to the left of his nose, and also on his beard. At AU–55 or 58 there may be some hints of mint red-orange. Most coins in About Uncirculated are BN, but they are seldom designated by color. *Reverse:* Slight wear is evident on the stalks of wheat to the left and right. Otherwise, the same standards apply as for the obverse.

1920-S. Graded AU-58.

EF-40, 45 (Extremely Fine). *Obverse:* Light wear is seen on Lincoln's portrait, and hair detail is gone on the higher areas, especially above the ear. *Reverse:* Light wear is seen overall, but the parallel lines in the wheat stalks are clearly separated.

1914-D. Graded EF-45.

VF-20, 30 (Very Fine). *Obverse:* Lincoln's portrait is worn all over, with most hair detail gone at the center. Hair separation is seen at the back and the top of the head, but hairs are blended together. The jaw outline is clear. The center of the ear is defined and the bowtie is clear. The date and lettering is sharp. *Reverse:* More wear is seen, but still the lines in the wheat stalks are separated. Lettering shows wear but is very clear.

Illustrated coin: This coin features even wear and few marks.

1922-D, No D. Graded VF-20.

F-12, 15 (Fine). *Obverse:* More wear is seen overall. Hair definition is less. The center of the ear is partially visible. The jaw outline and bowtie are clear. *Reverse:* Most lines in the wheat stalks are either weak or blended with others, but more than half of the separating lines are clear.

Illustrated coin: Other than one deep contact mark in the cheek, the surfaces are smooth.

1922-D, No D. Graded F-15.

VG-8, 10 (Very Good). *Obverse:* The portrait is more worn, with only slight hair strands visible (thick strands blended). The ear opening is visible. The bowtie and jacket show fewer details. *Reverse:* The lines in the wheat stalks are blended together in flat areas. Perhaps 40% to 50% of the separating lines can be seen. The rim may be weak in areas.

1909-S. Graded VG-10.

G-4, 6 (Good). *Obverse:* The portrait is well worn. Some slight details are seen at the top of the head and the bottom of the coat. LIBERTY is weak. The rim may touch or blend with the tops of the letters forming IN GOD WE TRUST. The date and mintmark (if any) are very clear. *Reverse:* The wheat stalks are flat, with just a few scattered details visible.

1914-D. Graded G-6.

AG-3 (About Good). *Obverse:* Wear is extensive. The portrait is mostly in outline form, with only scattered details visible. LIBERTY is weak and perhaps with some letters missing. IN GOD WE TRUST blends in with the rim, and several letters are very weak or missing. *Reverse:* The rim is worn down to blend with the outside of the wheat stalks in some areas, although some hints of the edge of the stalks can be seen. Lettering is weak, with up to several letters missing.

1913-D. Graded AG-3.

PF-60 to 70 (Matte Proof). *Obverse and Reverse:* At the Matte PF-65 level or higher there are no traces of abrasion or contact marks. Color will range from brown (BN)—the most common—to brown with significant tinges of mint red-orange (RB), or with much mint color (RD). Most RD coins have been dipped. Some tiny flecks are normal on coins certified as PF-65 but should be microscopic or absent above that. Coins in the PF-60 to 63 range are BN or sometimes RB—almost impossible to be RD unless dipped. Lower-grade Proofs usually have poor eye appeal.

1909, V.D.B. Matte Proof. Graded PF-68RD.

Illustrated coin: Most of the red tint is medium orange, but there is a faint pink tint to the upper-left obverse.

PF-60 to 70 (Mirror Proof). *Obverse and Reverse:* PF-65 and higher coins are usually RB (colors should be nicely blended) or RD, the latter with bright red-orange fading slightly to hints of brown. Some tiny flecks are normal on coins certified as PF-65 but should be microscopic or absent above that. PF-60 and 61 coins can be dull, stained, or spotted but still have some original mint color. Coins with fingerprints must be given a low numerical grade. Lower-grade Proofs usually have poor eye appeal.

1936. Mirror Proof. Graded PF-66RD.

Illustrated coin: The mirrored surfaces are free of blemish.

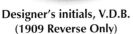

Designer's initials, V.D.B.
(1909 Reverse Only)

No V.D.B. on Reverse
(1909–1958)

V.D.B. on Shoulder
(Starting 1918)

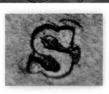

1909-S, S Over
Horizontal S
FS-01-1909S-1502.

	Mintage	Cert	Avg	%MS	G-4	VG-8	F-12	VF-20	EF-40	AU-50	MS-60BN	MS-63BN	MS-65RD
											PF-63RB	PF-64RB	PF-65RD
1909, V.D.B.	27,995,000	13,960	63.4	96%	$15	$16	$17	$18	$19	$20	$25	$30	$165
Auctions: $881, MS-67RD, July 2014; $823, MS-67RD, September 2014; $1,763, MS-67RD, June 2013; $499, MS-66RD+, August 2014													
1909, V.D.B., Proof (a)	1,194	53	65.0								$11,500	$22,500	
Auctions: $258,500, PF-67RB+, August 2014; $55,813, PF-66RB, June 2014; $22,800, P-64RD, April 2018													
1909-S, V.D.B. † †† (b)	484,000	9,428	43.3	38%	$600	$650	$675	$725	$850	$1,000	$1,200	$1,350	$4,500
Auctions: $117,500, MS-67RD, February 2014; $70,500, MS-67, August 2016; $17,625, MS-66RD, August 2014													
1909	72,702,618	1,910	63.4	97%	$4	$5	$6	$7	$8	$12	$17	$20	$160
Auctions: $1,880, MS-67RD, August 2014; $1,763, MS-67RD, November 2014; $4,406, MS-67RD, April 2013; $670, MS-66RD+, October 2014													
1909, Proof	2,618	240	64.5								$750	$1,150	$2,700
Auctions: $6,463, PF-66RB+, August 2014; $5,875, PF-66RD, April 2013; $1,782, PF-65RD, August 2014; $1,657, PF-64RD, August 2014													
1909-S	1,825,000	3,785	38.9	35%	$80	$90	$100	$130	$150	$225	$300	$350	$1,000
Auctions: $10,281, MS-67RD, February 2013; $4,700, MS-66RD, November 2014; $3,760, MS-66, March 2016													
1909-S, S Over Horizontal S	(c)	614	48.5	60%	$95	$100	$120	$150	$200	$275	$325	$370	$1,250
Auctions: $1,880, MS-66RD, September 2014; $1,880, MS-66, August 2015; $969, MS-65RD, July 2014													
1910	146,801,218	1,348	63.3	95%	$0.35	$0.50	$1	$1.50	$4	$10	$18	$25	$230
Auctions: $4,406, MS-67RD, June 2014; $3,055, MS-67RD, September 2014; $2,938, MS-67RD, November 2014													
1910, Proof	4,118	241	64.2								$675	$1,100	$2,500
Auctions: $7,638, PF-67RB, August 2014; $1,764, PF-65RB, July 2014; $470, PF-63RB, August 2014; $3,290, PF, January 2013													
1910-S	6,045,000	1,492	55.1	71%	$17	$20	$22	$25	$45	$80	$100	$120	$650
Auctions: $15,275, MS-66RD, June 2014; $1,880, MS-66RD, August 2014; $1,998, MS-66RD, October 2014; $206, MS-64RB, November 2014													
1911	101,177,787	749	63.3	96%	$0.45	$0.65	$1.50	$2.50	$6	$11	$21	$50	$400
Auctions: $7,050, MS-67RD, April 2014; $1,645, MS-66RD, October 2014; $441, MS-65RD, August 2014; $165, MS-64RD, August 2014													
1911, Proof	1,725	202	64.3								$675	$1,050	$3,500
Auctions: $9,400, PF-66RD, June 2014; $14,688, PF-66RB, August 2014; $853, PF-65BN, October 2014; $705, PF-64RB, August 2014													
1911-D	12,672,000	873	58.0	74%	$6	$7	$10	$20	$50	$75	$95	$125	$950
Auctions: $8,225, MS-66RD, April 2014; $7,050, MS-66RD, October 2014; $6,169, MS-66RD, October 2014; $3,819, MS-65RD, September 2014													
1911-S	4,026,000	1,222	45.2	42%	$35	$45	$55	$60	$75	$110	$185	$235	$2,250
Auctions: $14,100, MS-66RD, October 2014; $881, MS-65RB, November 2014; $2,820, MS-65RD, August 2013; $505, MS-64RD, October 2014													
1912	68,153,060	708	62.9	94%	$1.25	$1.65	$2.25	$5.50	$13	$25	$35	$50	$500
Auctions: $18,800, MS-67RD, April 2013; $499, MS-65RD, December 2014; $441, MS-65RD, October 2014; $118, MS-64RD, July 2014													
1912, Proof	2,172	218	64.3								$675	$1,050	$4,500
Auctions: $3,966, PF-66RB, February 2014; $14,100, PF-66RB+, August 2014; $999, PF-65RB, October 2014; $940, PF-64RB, July 2014													
1912-D	10,411,000	664	55.8	66%	$7	$8	$10	$25	$65	$100	$170	$250	$1,250
Auctions: $8,238, MS-66RD, September 2014; $1,998, MS-65RD+, November 2014; $7,050, MS-65RD, February 2013													
1912-S	4,431,000	976	47.5	50%	$20	$25	$30	$40	$75	$110	$180	$255	$1,500
Auctions: $2,820, MS-65RD, October 2014; $4,406, MS-65RD, November 2013; $1,410, MS-64RD, August 2014													

Note: No early references (pre-1960s), Mint records, or reliable market listings have been found to confirm the existence of true 1917 Proofs. "Examples seen have had nice matte-like surfaces, sometimes on just one side, but have lacked the vital combination of broad, flat rims on both sides and a mirror Proof edge (when viewed edge-on from the side)" (*A Guide Book of Lincoln Cents*). The leading certification services do not recognize Proofs of this year. The editors of this book also do not believe that true Proofs of 1917 exist.
† Ranked in the *100 Greatest U.S. Coins* (fourth edition). †† Ranked in the *100 Greatest U.S. Modern Coins* (fourth edition). **a.** Of the 1,194 coins reported struck, an estimated 400 to 600 were issued. **b.** Many counterfeits exist—some die struck, some made by adding an "S" to a Philadelphia coin. **c.** Included in 1909-S mintage figure.

**1917, Doubled Die
Obverse
FS-01-1917-101.**

	Mintage	Cert	Avg	%MS	G-4	VG-8	F-12	VF-20	EF-40	AU-50	MS-60BN PF-63RB	MS-63BN PF-64RB	MS-65RD PF-65RD
1913	76,532,352	748	62.2	93%	$0.85	$1	$2	$4	$18	$27	$35	$55	$425
Auctions: $19,975, MS-67RD, January 2013; $1,410, MS-66RD, July 2014; $529, MS-65RD, July 2014; $470, MS-65RD, August 2014													
1913, Proof	2,983	315	64.5								$675	$1,050	$2,500
Auctions: $25,850, PF-67RD, January 2014; $8,225, PF-67RB, August 2014; $1,410, PF-65RB, November 2014; $1,058, PF-64RD, October 2014													
1913-D	15,804,000	642	57.3	73%	$3	$3.50	$4.50	$10	$50	$70	$110	$175	$1,350
Auctions: $10,575, MS-66RD, January 2014; $8,225, MS-66RD, October 2014; $881, MS-64RD, August 2014; $705, MS-64RD, September 2014													
1913-S	6,101,000	854	48.1	52%	$10	$15	$20	$30	$60	$100	$175	$225	$3,000
Auctions: $4,406, MS-65RD, June 2014; $676, MS-64RD, July 2014; $388, MS-63RD, September 2014; $823, MS-61BN, October 2014													
1914	75,238,432	781	60.3	86%	$0.75	$1	$2	$6	$20	$40	$55	$70	$500
Auctions: $28,200, MS-67RD, August 2013; $2,585, MS-66RD, November 2014; $499, MS-65RD, July 2014; $270, MS-64RD, September 2014													
1914, Proof	1,365	155	64.7								$675	$1,100	$2,500
Auctions: $3,525, PF-66BN, June 2014; $8,226, PF-66RB+, August 2014; $4,406, PF-66RB, October 2014; $1,410, PF-65RB, July 2014													
1914-D (d)	1,193,000	5,441	23.9	8%	$150	$175	$225	$250	$700	$1,450	$2,000	$3,000	$15,000
Auctions: $28,200, MS-65RD+, October 2014; $18,800, MS-65RD, January 2014; $17,625, MS-65, March 2016													
1914-S	4,137,000	913	41.9	31%	$20	$25	$30	$40	$85	$175	$325	$460	$5,500
Auctions: $5,875, MS-65RD, September 2014; $6,463, MS-65RD, September 2013; $1,528, MS-64RD, July 2014; $793, MS-64BN, October 2014													
1915	29,092,120	668	60.0	84%	$1.75	$2.50	$5	$18	$60	$70	$90	$105	$750
Auctions: $10,575, MS-67RD, September 2014; $3,525, MS-66RD, January 2014; $1,293, MS-66RD, November 2014; $1,116, MS-65RD, August 2014													
1915, Proof	1,150	130	64.7								$600	$1,200	$3,500
Auctions: $4,406, PF-66RB, July 2014; $22,325, PF-66RB+, August 2014; $17,625, PF-65RD, January 2014; $801, PF-64BN, October 2014													
1915-D	22,050,000	1,003	57.1	76%	$2	$3	$4	$7	$22	$45	$85	$120	$1,100
Auctions: $4,465, MS-66RD, October 2014; $7,638, MS-66RD, June 2013; $1,063, MS-65RD, September 2014; $940, MS-65RD, November 2014													
1915-S	4,833,000	763	44.7	41%	$20	$25	$30	$35	$70	$135	$200	$235	$5,000
Auctions: $23,500, MS-66RD, September 2013; $7,638, MS-65RD, November 2014; $3,055, MS-64RD, October 2014; $852, MS-63RB, July 2014													
1916	131,833,677	939	62.9	95%	$0.30	$0.50	$0.75	$2	$8	$13	$18	$35	$300
Auctions: $2,350, MS-67RD, March 2014; $1,880, MS-67RD, August 2014; $2,820, MS-67RD, October 2014; $505, MS-66RD, July 2014													
1916, Proof	1,050	94	64.8								$1,250	$2,500	$12,000
Auctions: $30,550, PF-66RB+, August 2014; $1,880, PF-64RB, October 2014; $7,931, PF-64RB, June 2014; $4,700, PF-63RB, July 2014													
1916-D	35,956,000	850	60.6	84%	$1	$1.75	$3	$6	$15	$35	$75	$150	$1,250
Auctions: $17,625, MS-66RD, June 2014; $282, MS-65RB, August 2014; $823, MS-64RD+, July 2014; $441, MS-64RD, October 2014													
1916-S	22,510,000	838	57.8	71%	$1.75	$2.25	$3.50	$8	$25	$50	$105	$175	$7,000
Auctions: $911, MS-65RB, July 2014; $7,638, MS-65RD, August 2013; $1,183, MS-64RD, October 2014; $1,410, MS-64RD, November 2014													
1917	196,429,785	850	60.5	90%	$0.30	$0.40	$0.50	$2	$4	$10	$16	$32	$375
Auctions: $823, MS-66RD, September 2014; $1,586, MS-66RD+, November 2014; $2,585, MS-66RD, January 2013; $145, MS-64RD, September 2014													
1917, Doubled Die Obverse	(e)	80	32.1	15%	$85	$145	$225	$450	$1,000	$1,600	$2,750	$5,750	$19,500
Auctions: $499, MS-65RB, October 2014; $329, MS-64RB, July 2014; $705, VF-35, January 2015; $6,600, MSF-64RD, January 2018													
1917-D	55,120,000	711	59.5	79%	$0.80	$1	$1.75	$4.50	$35	$50	$80	$125	$1,500
Auctions: $9,400, MS-65RD, August 2014; $2,350, MS-65RD, August 2013; $1,116, MS-64RD, August 2014; $2,703, MS-64RD, November 2014													
1917-S	32,620,000	495	59.2	79%	$0.50	$0.65	$1	$2.50	$10	$25	$75	$160	$6,750
Auctions: $11,750, MS-67RD, August 2014; $17,625, MS-67RD, November 2014; $881, MS-66RD, November 2014; $4,113, MS-65RD, December 2013													

d. Many counterfeits exist, including crude fakes, sophisticated die-struck forgeries, and altered 1944-D cents (the latter, unlike an authentic 1914-D cent, will have the designer's initials, V.D.B., on the shoulder). **e.** Included in 1917 mintage figure.

1922, No D
FS-01-1922-401.

1922, Weak D

	Mintage	Cert	Avg	%MS	G-4	VG-8	F-12	VF-20	EF-40	AU-50	MS-60BN	MS-63BN	MS-65RD
											PF-63RB	PF-64RB	PF-65RD
1918	288,104,634	661	63.0	95%	$0.20	$0.30	$0.50	$1.50	$3	$8	$16	$27	$350
	Auctions: $423, MS-64BN, September 2014; $200, MS-63RB, August 2014; $74, MS-62BN, November 2014; $14,100, MS, March 2014												
1918-D	47,830,000	530	58.8	74%	$0.75	$1.25	$2.50	$4	$12	$35	$80	$140	$3,500
	Auctions: $25,850, MS-66RD, August 2013; $11,163, MS-65RD, October 2014; $1,528, MS-64RD, November 2014; $764, MS-64RB, August 2014												
1918-S	34,680,000	597	59.3	74%	$0.50	$1	$2	$3	$11	$32	$80	$185	$7,000
	Auctions: $823, MS-67RD, August 2014; $1,058, MS-67RD, October 2014; $499, MS-66RD, August 2014; $3,525, MS-64RD, February 2014												
1919	392,021,000	852	63.1	95%	$0.20	$0.30	$0.40	$1	$3.25	$5	$14	$28	$150
	Auctions: $8,225, MS-68RD, April 2014; $1,058, MS-67RD, October 2014; $499, MS-66RD, August 2014; $182, MS-65RD, September 2014												
1919-D	57,154,000	625	61.3	87%	$0.50	$0.75	$1	$4	$10	$32	$65	$110	$1,150
	Auctions: $1,763, MS-65RD, January 2014; $1,410, MS-65RD, October 2014; $353, MS-64RB, July 2014; $311, MS-64RB, August 2014												
1919-S	139,760,000	705	60.2	81%	$0.20	$0.40	$1	$2	$6	$18	$50	$115	$4,000
	Auctions: $7,638, MS-65RD, April 2014; $482, MS-64RB, July 2014; $259, MS-64RB, November 2014; $123, MS-63BN, December 2014												
1920	310,165,000	797	62.9	95%	$0.20	$0.30	$0.35	$0.50	$2.25	$4	$15	$28	$250
	Auctions: $940, MS-66RD, January 2013; $881, MS-66RD+, September 2014; $705, MS-66RD, September 2014; $200, MS-65RD, November 2014												
1920-D	49,280,000	544	60.3	82%	$1	$2	$3	$6.50	$19	$40	$80	$110	$2,500
	Auctions: $22,325, MS-66RD, June 2014; $283, MS-64RB, November 2014; $182, MS-63RB, October 2014; $45, MS-60BN, November 2014												
1920-S	46,220,000	554	59.0	72%	$0.50	$0.65	$1.50	$2.25	$10	$35	$110	$185	$12,500
	Auctions: $3,173, MS-64RD, October 2014; $2,115, MS-64RD, February 2013; $259, MS-63RB, November 2014; $79, MS-62BN, November 2014												
1921	39,157,000	620	62.5	93%	$0.50	$0.60	$1.30	$2.10	$9	$22	$50	$80	$350
	Auctions: $3,290, MS-66RD, January 2014; $411, MS-65RD, September 2014; $112, MS-64RD, October 2014; $16, MS-60RD, November 2014												
1921-S	15,274,000	799	55.5	58%	$1.50	$2.25	$3.50	$7	$35	$75	$135	$190	$11,500
	Auctions: $1,293, MS-65RB, September 2014; $499, MS-64RB, July 2014; $1,880, MS-64RD, August 2013; $282, MS-63RB, November 2014												
1922-D	7,160,000	1,839	41.1	40%	$20	$21	$25	$27	$40	$75	$110	$165	$1,350
	Auctions: $2,585, MS-65RD, August 2013; $499, MS-64RD, November 2014; $229, MS-63RD, July 2014; $106, MS-62RB, November 2014												
1922, No D (f)	(g)	3,551	20.8	2%	$450	$550	$650	$750	$1,500	$3,750	$10,000	$20,000	
	Auctions: $82,250, MS-65BN, April 2013; $20,563, MS-63, February 2015; $3,819, AU-55BN, August 2014; $1,080, EF-40, January 2018												
1922, Weak D (f)	(g)	633	16.3	3%	$25	$35	$50	$70	$160	$200	$350	$1,000	
	Auctions: $2,174, MS, April 2014; $376, AU-58BN, October 2014; $329, AU-58BN, October 2014; $153, AU-55BN, October 2014												
1923	74,723,000	615	62.9	96%	$0.35	$0.45	$0.65	$1	$5	$9.50	$15	$30	$350
	Auctions: $4,700, MS-67RD, June 2013; $1,645, MS-66RD+, September 2014; $247, MS-64RD+, July 2014; $84, MS-64RD, November 2014												
1923-S	8,700,000	496	54.6	55%	$5	$7	$8	$12	$40	$90	$220	$390	$16,500
	Auctions: $2,350, MS-65RB, June 2014; $3,055, MS-64RB, October 2014; $823, MS-64RB, November 2014; $353, MS-62RB, August 2014												
1924	75,178,000	474	63.0	95%	$0.20	$0.30	$0.40	$0.85	$5	$10	$24	$50	$400
	Auctions: $16,450, MS-67RD, April 2013; $12,925, MS-67RD, July 2014; $470, MS-65RD, November 2014; $259, MS-64RD, November 2014												
1924-D	2,520,000	1,381	41.3	33%	$40	$45	$50	$60	$125	$175	$300	$350	$12,500
	Auctions: $9,400, MS-65RD, January 2014; $2,820, MS-64RD, November 2014; $1,410, MS-64, March 2016												
1924-S	11,696,000	539	55.0	62%	$2	$2.50	$3.50	$5.50	$20	$75	$125	$225	$17,500
	Auctions: $9,400, MS-64RD, January 2014; $764, MS-64RB, November 2014; $529, MS-63RB, October 2014; $88, MS-60BN, November 2014												

f. 1922 cents with a weak or completely missing mintmark were made from extremely worn dies that originally struck normal 1922-D cents. Three different die pairs were involved; two of them produced "Weak D" coins. One die pair (no. 2, identified by a "strong reverse") is acknowledged as having struck "No D" coins. Weak D cents are worth considerably less. Beware of fraudulently removed mintmark.
g. Included in 1922-D mintage figure.

	Mintage	Cert	Avg	%MS	G-4	VG-8	F-12	VF-20	EF-40	AU-50	MS-60BN	MS-63BN	MS-65RD
											PF-63RB	PF-64RB	PF-65RD
1925	139,949,000	868	64.1	98%	$0.20	$0.25	$0.35	$0.60	$3	$6.50	$10	$20	$115
	Auctions: $1,410, MS-67RD, August 2014; $2,115, MS-67RD, September 2013; $110, MS-65RD, December 2014; $44, MS-64RD, September 2014												
1925-D	22,580,000	677	60.8	86%	$1	$1.30	$2.50	$5	$13	$30	$75	$90	$3,000
	Auctions: $4,113, MS-65RD, January 2014; $764, MS-64RD+, July 2014; $382, MS-64RD, September 2014; $129, MS-63RB, October 2014												
1925-S	26,380,000	533	59.1	74%	$1	$1.50	$2	$4	$12	$30	$90	$200	$18,000
	Auctions: $4,700, MS-65RB, February 2014; $852, MS-64RB, July 2014; $259, MS-63RB, October 2014; $200, MS-62BN, November 2014												
1926	157,088,000	1,096	64.3	98%	$0.20	$0.25	$0.30	$0.50	$2	$4	$8	$18	$65
	Auctions: $1,116, MS-67RD, January 2014; $353, MS-66RD, July 2014; $259, MS-65RD, October 2014; $84, MS-65RD, November 2014												
1926-D	28,020,000	515	59.6	80%	$1.35	$1.75	$3.50	$5.25	$14	$32	$85	$125	$1,750
	Auctions: $4,700, MS-65RD, February 2013; $353, MS-64RB, November 2014; $353, MS-64RB, December 2014; $364, MS-63RB, July 2014												
1926-S	4,550,000	1,017	52.4	45%	$9	$10	$13	$17	$35	$75	$155	$325	$90,000
	Auctions: $9,988, MS-65RB, October 2013; $1,058, MS-64RB, November 2014; $1,058, MS-63RB, August 2014; $259, MS-62BN, November 2014												
1927	144,440,000	806	63.4	96%	$0.20	$0.25	$0.30	$0.60	$2	$3.50	$10	$20	$125
	Auctions: $7,638, MS-67RD, February 2014; $1,880, MS-67RD, October 2014; $368, MS-66RD, September 2014; $115, MS-65RD, August 2014												
1927-D	27,170,000	611	61.0	84%	$1.25	$1.75	$2.75	$3.75	$7.50	$25	$62	$85	$1,750
	Auctions: $2,233, MS-65RD, January 2014; $617, MS-65RB, July 2014; $159, MS-64RB, September 2014; $212, MS-64RB, December 2014												
1927-S	14,276,000	477	59.7	77%	$1.50	$2	$3	$5	$15	$40	$85	$140	$8,500
	Auctions: $529, MS-64RB, July 2014; $1,763, MS-64RD, June 2013; $535, MS-63RD, November 2014; $86, MS-62BN, November 2014												
1928	134,116,000	883	63.7	97%	$0.20	$0.25	$0.30	$0.60	$2	$3	$9	$13	$120
	Auctions: $1,058, MS-67RD, September 2014; $3,408, MS-67RD, April 2013; $499, MS-66RD, July 2014; $120, MS-65RD, October 2014												
1928-D	31,170,000	571	61.4	85%	$0.75	$1	$1.75	$3	$5.50	$17	$37	$80	$1,000
	Auctions: $7,050, MS-66RD, November 2014; $1,410, MS-65RD, June 2014; $141, MS-64RD, September 2014; $51, MS-63RB, November 2014												
1928-S	17,266,000	370	61.0	84%	$1	$1.60	$2.75	$3.75	$9.50	$30	$75	$100	$4,500
	Auctions: $4,406, MS-65RD, September 2013; $764, MS-64RB, October 2014; $470, MS-64RB, November 2014; $382, MS-63RB, November 2014												
1929	185,262,000	1,058	64.2	98%	$0.20	$0.25	$0.30	$0.75	$2	$4	$8	$14	$100
	Auctions: $5,581, MS-67RD, April 2014; $1,528, MS-67RD, August 2014; $705, MS-67RD, September 2014; $382, MS-66RD+, August 2014												
1929-D	41,730,000				$0.40	$0.85	$1.25	$2.25	$5.50	$13	$25	$37	$550
	Auctions: $4,113, MS-66RD, January 2014; $2,585, MS-66RD, August 2014; $1,645, MS-66RD, October 2014; $458, MS-65RD, July 2014												
1929-S	50,148,000	1,254	62.9	94%	$0.50	$0.90	$1.65	$2.35	$5.80	$14	$21	$29	$375
	Auctions: $4,700, MS-66RD, October 2014; $4,113, MS-66RD, March 2013; $411, MS-65RD, October 2014; $65, MS-64RD, October 2014												
1930	157,415,000	3,836	65.3	100%	$0.15	$0.20	$0.25	$0.50	$1.25	$2	$6	$10	$40
	Auctions: $3,525, MS-67RD, February 2014; $823, MS-67RD, August 2014; $108, MS-66RD, October 2014; $40, MS-65RD, October 2014												
1930-D	40,100,000	763	64.0	97%	$0.20	$0.25	$0.30	$0.55	$2.50	$4	$12	$28	$145
	Auctions: $1,645, MS-66RD, June 2014; $441, MS-66RD, October 2014; $142, MS-65RD, August 2014; $141, MS-65RD, September 2014												
1930-S	24,286,000	1,791	64.8	99%	$0.20	$0.25	$0.30	$0.60	$1.75	$6	$10	$12	$80
	Auctions: $6,463, MS-66RD, April 2014; $2,377, MS-66RD, August 2014; $499, MS-66RD, October 2014; $84, MS-65RD, November 2014												
1931	19,396,000	737	64.0	97%	$0.50	$0.75	$1	$1.50	$4	$9	$20	$35	$125
	Auctions: $5,288, MS-67RD, August 2013; $999, MS-66RD, August 2014; $153, MS-65RD, July 2014; $42, MS-64RB, October 2014												
1931-D	4,480,000	846	59.2	69%	$5	$6	$7	$8.50	$13.50	$37	$60	$70	$1,000
	Auctions: $4,113, MS-66RD, April 2013; $1,528, MS-65RD, August 2014; $270, MS-65RB, October 2014; $165, MS-64RB, July 2014												
1931-S	866,000	5,179	54.4	58%	$60	$75	$85	$100	$125	$150	$175	$195	$550
	Auctions: $2,350, MS-66RD, January 2014; $646, MS-65RD, October 2014; $646, MS-65, August 2015												
1932	9,062,000	785	64.4	97%	$1.50	$1.75	$2	$2.50	$4.50	$12	$20	$28	$100
	Auctions: $259, MS-66RD, November 2014; $940, MS-66RD, September 2013; $95, MS-65RD, October 2014; $34, MS-64RB, October 2014												
1932-D	10,500,000	527	63.6	92%	$1.50	$1.75	$2.50	$2.75	$4.50	$11	$19	$28	$175
	Auctions: $8,519, MS-67RD, November 2013; $206, MS-65RD, August 2014; $56, MS-64RD, September 2014; $49, MS-64RD, October 2014												
1933	14,360,000	732	64.6	98%	$1.50	$1.75	$2.50	$3	$6.25	$13	$20	$30	$105
	Auctions: $2,115, MS-67RD, October 2014; $3,557, MS-67RD, August 2013; $112, MS-65RD, July 2014; $32, MS-64RB, July 2014												
1933-D	6,200,000	1,147	64.2	97%	$3.50	$3.75	$5.50	$7.25	$12	$19	$23	$25	$135
	Auctions: $5,581, MS-67RD, February 2014; $764, MS-67RD, October 2014; $558, MS-66RD+, November 2014; $141, MS-65RD, August 2014												

1934, Doubled Die Obverse
FS-01-1934-101.

1936, Doubled Die Obverse
FS-01-1936-101.

	Mintage	Cert	Avg	%MS	G-4	VG-8	F-12	VF-20	EF-40	AU-50	MS-60BN / PF-63RB	MS-63BN / PF-64RB	MS-65RD / PF-65RD
1934	219,080,000	2,350	65.6	99%	$0.15	$0.18	$0.20	$0.30	$1	$4	$7	$8	$35
Auctions: $1,058, MS-67RD, September 2014; $1,058, MS-67RD+, November 2014; $764, MS-67RD, December 2013												
1934, Doubled Die Obverse (h)	(i)	5	60.6	80%								$300	
Auctions: $1,600, MS-64RB, October 2011												
1934-D	28,446,000	1,035	64.7	98%	$0.20	$0.25	$0.50	$0.75	$2.25	$7.50	$20	$22	$65
Auctions: $11,163, MS-67RD, April 2014; $229, MS-66RD, July 2014; $123, MS-66RD, October 2014; $223, MS-66RD, December 2014												
1935	245,388,000	2,409	65.7	99%	$0.15	$0.18	$0.20	$0.25	$0.50	$1	$3	$5	$35
Auctions: $1,293, MS-67RD, March 2014; $106, MS-67RD, October 2014; $92, MS-67RD, November 2014; $106, MS-64RB, November 2014												
1935-D	47,000,000	1,647	65.6	100%	$0.15	$0.18	$0.20	$0.25	$0.50	$2	$5	$6	$40
Auctions: $823, MS-67RD, February 2014; $153, MS-67RD, August 2014; $141, MS-67RD, October 2014; $588, MS-67RD, November 2014												
1935-S	38,702,000	1,005	64.7	99%	$0.15	$0.18	$0.25	$0.50	$2	$5	$12	$17	$60
Auctions: $1,469, MS-67RD, October 2014; $3,055, MS-66RD+, July 2014; $1,175, MS-66RD, October 2014; $106, MS-65RD, December 2014												
1936	309,632,000	2,985	65.3	98%	$0.15	$0.18	$0.25	$0.50	$1.50	$2.60	$3	$4	$30
Auctions: $705, MS-67RD, February 2014; $353, MS-67RD, July 2014; $2,820, MS-67RD+, September 2014; $306, MS-67RD, October 2014												
1936, Doubled Die Obverse (j)	(k)	180	48.0	41%	—		$75	$125	$200	$350	$500	$1,500	
Auctions: $646, MS-62BN, August 2014; $259, AU-50, April 2014; $80, VF-30BN, November 2014; $76, VF-30BN, November 2014												
1936, Satin, PF	5,569	202	64.0								$185	$425	$1,800
Auctions: $2,585, PF-67RB, July 2017; $1,800, PF-65RD, November 2017; $336, PF-63RB, May 2018												
1936, Brilliant, PF	(l)	395	64.0								$200	$485	$2,500
Auctions: $18,600, PF-67RD, January 2018; $5,280, PF-66RD, January 2018; $1,527, PF-63RDCam, February 2017												
1936-D	40,620,000	1,833	65.9	100%	$0.15	$0.20	$0.30	$0.50	$1	$2	$3	$4	$20
Auctions: $646, MS-67RD, August 2013; $411, MS-67RD, October 2014; $145, MS-67RD, October 2014; $79, MS-67RD, December 2014												
1936-S	29,130,000	1,531	65.5	100%	$0.15	$0.25	$0.40	$0.55	$1	$3	$5	$6	$25
Auctions: $4,259, MS-67RD, February 2014; $2,703, MS-67RD, September 2014; $2,585, MS-67RD, November 2014												
1937	309,170,000	4,536	66.0	100%	$0.15	$0.20	$0.30	$0.50	$1	$2	$3	$4	$15
Auctions: $90, MS-67RD, August 2014; $94, MS-67RD, October 2014; $2,233, MS-67RD+, November 2013; $35, MS-66RD, November 2014												
1937, Proof	9,320	923	64.3								$65	$90	$350
Auctions: $21,150, PF-67Cam, September 2013; $5,288, PF-66Cam, August 2014; $1,763, PF-65Cam, October 2014; $3,643, PF-64RD, July 2014												
1937-D	50,430,000	3,026	66.1	100%	$0.15	$0.20	$0.25	$0.40	$1	$3	$5	$6	$17
Auctions: $135, MS-67RD, January 2014; $123, MS-67RD, August 2014; $106, MS-67RD, August 2014; $40, MS-66RD, August 2014												
1937-S	34,500,000	1,929	65.8	100%	$0.15	$0.20	$0.30	$0.40	$1	$3	$5	$8	$25
Auctions: $1,998, MS-67RD, January 2014; $881, MS-67RD+, July 2014; $764, MS-67RD+, July 2014; $55, MS-66RD, July 2014												
1938	156,682,000	2,932	66.0	100%	$0.15	$0.20	$0.30	$0.40	$1	$2	$4	$7	$15
Auctions: $2,585, MS-67RD+, September 2014; $106, MS-67RD, October 2014; $2,820, MS-67RD, November 2013; $27, MS-66RD, November 2014												
1938, Proof	14,734	1,079	64.5								$60	$80	$200
Auctions: $2,585, PF-66Cam, January 2014; $1,058, PF-66Cam, September 2014; $1,469, PF-66Cam, November 2014												
1938-D	20,010,000	2,307	66.1	100%	$0.20	$0.30	$0.50	$0.80	$1.25	$3	$4	$7	$15
Auctions: $3,055, MS-67RD, January 2014; $3,290, MS-67RD, August 2014; $100, MS-67RD, November 2014; $89, MS-67RD, December 2014												
1938-S	15,180,000	2,996	66.0	100%	$0.40	$0.50	$0.60	$0.75	$1.10	$3	$4	$6	$15
Auctions: $2,115, MS-67RD+, July 2014; $118, MS-67RD, July 2014; $92, MS-67RD, August 2014; $40, MS-66RD, August 2014												

h. The remains of a secondary 3 and 4 are evident below the primary digits. **i.** Included in 1934 mintage figure. **j.** FS-01-1936-101. **k.** Included in circulation-strike 1936 mintage figure. **l.** Included in 1936, Satin, Proof mintage figure.

	Mintage	Cert	Avg	%MS	G-4	VG-8	F-12	VF-20	EF-40	AU-50	MS-60BN	MS-63BN	MS-65RD
											PF-63RB	PF-64RB	PF-65RD
1939	316,466,000	3,356	65.9	100%	$0.15	$0.18	$0.20	$0.25	$0.50	$1	$2	$3	$10
	Auctions: $108, MS-67RD, August 2014; $106, MS-67RD, October 2014; $705, MS-67RD, June 2013; $38, MS-66RD, December 2014												
1939, Proof	13,520	1,060	64.6								$55	$70	$180
	Auctions: $2,820, PF-67RD, January 2014; $1,410, PF-67RD, October 2014; $270, PF-66RD, November 2014; $212, PF-65RD, September 2014												
1939-D	15,160,000	2,244	66.0	100%	$0.50	$0.60	$0.65	$0.85	$1.25	$3	$4	$5	$11
	Auctions: $529, MS-67RD, April 2014; $86, MS-67RD, October 2014; $100, MS-67RD, November 2014; $69, MS-67RD, December 2014												
1939-S	52,070,000	3,809	66.0	100%	$0.15	$0.20	$0.30	$0.75	$1	$2.50	$3	$4	$15
	Auctions: $1,175, MS-67RD+, July 2014; $1,116, MS-67RD+, August 2014; $3,966, MS-67RD, August 2013; $24, MS-66RD, November 2014												
1940	586,810,000	2,938	66.0	100%	$0.15	$0.18	$0.20	$0.40	$0.60	$1	$2	$3	$14
	Auctions: $3,819, MS-67RD, January 2014; $212, MS-67RD, July 2014; $147, MS-67RD, September 2014; $74, MS-65RD, November 2014												
1940, Proof	15,872	1,051	64.5								$45	$60	$150
	Auctions: $7,931, PF-67RD, June 2013; $4,700, PF-67RD, August 2014; $6,463, PF-67RD, October 2014; $764, PF-66RD, July 2014												
1940-D	81,390,000	1,561	66.1	100%	$0.15	$0.18	$0.25	$0.60	$0.75	$2	$3	$4	$15
	Auctions: $94, MS-67RD, August 2014; $68, MS-67RD, November 2014; $119, MS-67RD, December 2014; $159, MS-67RD, January 2013												
1940-S	112,940,000	3,085	66.0	100%	$0.15	$0.18	$0.20	$0.50	$1	$1.75	$3	$4	$15
	Auctions: $999, MS-67RD+, November 2014; $100, MS-67RD, November 2014; $79, MS-67RD, December 2014; $306, MS-67RD, June 2013												
1941	887,018,000	3,456	65.8	99%	$0.15	$0.18	$0.20	$0.30	$0.60	$1.50	$2	$3	$14
	Auctions: $147, MS-67RD, July 2014; $212, MS-67RD, August 2014; $259, MS-67RD, October 2014; $4,994, MS-65RD, November 2013												
1941, Proof	21,100	1,172	64.4								$40	$55	$150
	Auctions: $28,200, PF-67RD, November 2013; $705, PF-66RD, August 2014; $382, PF-66RD, October 2014; $705, PF-64RD, July 2014												
1941-D	128,700,000	1,943	66.3	100%	$0.15	$0.18	$0.20	$0.50	$1	$3	$4	$5	$15
	Auctions: $2,115, MS-67RD+, August 2014; $165, MS-67RD, August 2014; $63, MS-67RD, August 2014; $441, MS-67RD, August 2013												
1941-S	92,360,000	2,687	66.2	100%	$0.15	$0.18	$0.30	$0.50	$1	$3	$4	$5	$15
	Auctions: $646, MS-67RD, August 2014; $306, MS-67RD, October 2014; $119, MS-67RD, December 2014; $1,880, MS-67RD, November 2013												
1942	657,796,000	3,294	65.8	100%	$0.15	$0.18	$0.20	$0.25	$0.50	$0.75	$1	$2	$14
	Auctions: $3,290, MS-67RD+, July 2014; $112, MS-63RB, November 2014; $14,100, AU-58, November 2013; $282, Fair-2BN, November 2014												
1942, Proof	32,600	1,780	64.1								$40	$55	$150
	Auctions: $1,880, PF-66Cam, November 2014; $2,115, PF-66Cam, June 2013; $999, PF-65Cam, July 2014; $212, PF-64Cam, November 2014												
1942-D	206,698,000	3,767	66.0	100%	$0.15	$0.18	$0.20	$0.25	$0.50	$0.85	$1	$2	$14
	Auctions: $170, MS-67RD, August 2014; $141, MS-67RD, December 2014; $3,055, MS-67RD, November 2013; $20, MS-65RD, November 2014												
1942-S	85,590,000	2,251	65.9	99%	$0.20	$0.25	$0.30	$0.85	$1.25	$5.50	$7	$8	$20
	Auctions: $3,290, MS-67RD, February 2014; $2,350, MS-67RD+, September 2014												

	Mintage	Cert	Avg	%MS	F-12	VF-20	EF-40	AU-50	MS-63BN	MS-65	MS-66	MS-67	MS-68
1943, Steel (a)	684,628,670	15,036	65.9	100%	$0.30	$0.35	$0.40	$0.50	$2.50	$8	$35	$175	$2,500
	Auctions: $382, MS-67, July 2014; $182, MS-67, November 2014; $1,058, EF-45, September 2014; $1,763, VF-25, October 2014												
1943, Bronze † ‡‡ (a)	(b)	11	57.2	36%			$150,000	$200,000					
	Auctions: $218,500, AU-58, January 2010												
1943, Silver (a)	(b)	0	n/a				$3,500	$5,500					
	Auctions: $4,313, AU-58, March 2010												
1943-D	217,660,000	9,439	66.1	100%	$0.35	$0.40	$0.45	$0.75	$3	$10	$35	$225	$1,250
	Auctions: $1,175, MS-68, July 2014; $705, MS-68, July 2014; $2,820, MS-68, April 2013; $209, MS-67, October 2014												

† Ranked in the *100 Greatest U.S. Coins* (fourth edition). ‡‡ Ranked in the *100 Greatest U.S. Error Coins*. **a.** Due to a copper shortage in the critical war year 1943, the Treasury used zinc-coated steel for regular-issue cents. A handful were accidentally struck on old bronze and silver planchets, instead of the intended steel planchets. Today about a dozen are known to exist. Numerous regular steel cents have been plated with copper as novelties or with intent to deceive; their true nature is easily revealed with a magnet. **b.** Included in 1943 mintage figure.

1943-D, Boldly Doubled Mintmark
FS-01-1943D-501.

	Mintage	Cert	Avg	%MS	F-12	VF-20	EF-40	AU-50	MS-63BN	MS-65	MS-66	MS-67	MS-68
1943-D, Boldly Doubled Mintmark (c)	(d)	44	63.8	100%	$40	$50	$60	$70	$100	$1,000	$2,000	$10,000	
Auctions: $1,116, MS-65, December 2013; $411, MS-64, March 2015; $353, MS-63, November 2014													
1943-S	191,550,000	9,861	65.9	100%	$0.40	$0.65	$0.75	$1	$6	$20	$50	$225	$3,000
Auctions: $306, MS-67, August 2014; $153, MS-67, November 2014; $135, MS-67, December 2014; $165, MS-66, October 2014													

c. FS-01-1943D-501. **d.** Included in 1943-D mintage figure.

1944-D, D Over S
FS-01-1944D-511.

1946-S, S Over D
FS-01-1946S-511.

	Mintage	Cert	Avg	%MS	VF-20	EF-40	AU-50	MS-63RB	MS-65RB	MS-65RD	MS-67RD
									PF-65RD	PF-66RD	PF-67RD
1944	1,435,400,000	4,695	65.8	100%	$0.10	$0.20	$0.35	$1	$5	$12	$125
Auctions: $2,233, MS-67RD+, September 2014; $79, MS-67RD, November 2014; $30,550, AU-58, November 2013											
1944, Steel ‡‡		4	57.8	25%			$30,000	$45,000			
1944-D	430,578,000	4,293	65.5	98%	$0.10	$0.20	$0.35	$0.85	$4	$14	$100
Auctions: $141, MS-67RD, July 2014; $119, MS-67RD, September 2014; $58, MS-67RD, August 2014; $30,550, AU-53, November 2013											
1944-D, D Over S	(a)	346	54.5	53%	$100	$175	$235	$450	$700	$2,000	
Auctions: $1,116, MS-64RD, January 2014; $470, MS-64RB, September 2014; $517, MS-64, August 2016											
1944-S	282,760,000	6,606	66.0	100%	$0.15	$0.20	$0.35	$0.85	$4	$13	$75
Auctions: $141, MS-67RD, May 2014; $101, MS-67RD, July 2014; $96, MS-67RD, July 2014											
1945	1,040,515,000	3,470	65.7	100%	$0.10	$0.20	$0.35	$0.85	$2	$8	$185
Auctions: $764, MS-67RD, November 2014; $41, MS-66RD, August 2014; $36, MS-66RD, August 2014; $3,819, MS-68RD, November 2013											
1945-D	266,268,000	4,764	65.9	100%	$0.10	$0.20	$0.35	$0.85	$2	$9	$125
Auctions: $2,115, MS-67RD, June 2014; $165, MS-67RD, July 2014; $2,585, MS-67RD, September 2014; $99, MS-67RD, October 2014											
1945-S	181,770,000	5,021	66.2	100%	$0.15	$0.20	$0.35	$0.85	$2	$9	$75
Auctions: $106, MS-67RD, September 2014; $89, MS-67RD, December 2014; $84, MS-67RD, October 2014; $7,050, AU-58, November 2013											
1946	991,655,000	2,118	65.4	100%	$0.10	$0.20	$0.35	$0.60	$2	$14	$900
Auctions: $7,168, MS-67RD, January 2014; $2,585, MS-67RD, October 2014; $2,585, MS-67RD, November 2014; $470, MS-66RD+, August 2014											
1946-D	315,690,000	2,888	65.9	100%	$0.10	$0.20	$0.35	$0.60	$2	$10	$200
Auctions: $2,115, MS-67RD, March 2014; $176, MS-67RD, August 2014; $129, MS-67RD, November 2014; $182, MS-67RD, December 2014											
1946-S	198,100,000	5,648	65.9	100%	$0.15	$0.20	$0.35	$0.60	$2	$10	$185
Auctions: $470, MS-67RD, July 2014; $470, MS-67RD, December 2014; $940, MS-67RD, September 2013; $20, MS-66RD, November 2014											
1946-S, S Over D	(b)	20	62.1	85%	$35	$75	$125	$225	$400	$850	
Auctions: $541, MS-67, August 2016; $1,998, MS-66RD, June 2014											
1947	190,555,000	1,716	65.5	100%	$0.10	$0.20	$0.40	$1	$3	$12	$1,750
Auctions: $3,525, MS-67RD, July 2014; $4,113, MS-67RD, April 2013; $294, MS-66RD+, August 2014; $106, MS-66RD, November 2014											
1947-D	194,750,000	2,512	65.8	100%	$0.10	$0.20	$0.40	$0.60	$2	$10	$250
Auctions: $176, MS-67RD, October 2014; $764, MS-67RD, February 2013											
1947-S	99,000,000	3,806	65.9	100%	$0.20	$0.25	$0.50	$0.85	$2	$12	$200
Auctions: $1,704, MS-67RD, February 2014; $1,998, MS-67RD+, August 2014; $1,293, MS-67RD+, August 2014; $153, MS-67RD, November 2014											

‡‡ Ranked (along with the 1944-D and 1944-S steel cents) in the *100 Greatest U.S. Error Coins*. **a.** Included in 1944-D mintage figure. **b.** Included in 1946-S mintage figure.

1951-D, D Over S
FS-01-1951D-512.

	Mintage	Cert	Avg	%MS	VF-20	EF-40	AU-50	MS-63RB	MS-65RB	MS-65RD	MS-67RD
									PF-65RD	PF-66RD	PF-67RD
1948	317,570,000	1,565	65.5	100%	$0.10	$0.20	$0.35	$0.85	$2	$15	$3,000
	Auctions: $7,168, MS-67RD, January 2014; $441, MS-66RD+, September 2014; $135, MS-66RD, October 2014; $153, MS-66RD, November 2014										
1948-D	172,637,500	2,180	65.7	100%	$0.10	$0.20	$0.35	$0.60	$2	$11	$650
	Auctions: $353, MS-67RD, October 2014; $259, MS-67RD, November 2014; $188, MS-67RD, November 2014; $999, MS-67RD, August 2013										
1948-S	81,735,000	3,515	66.0	100%	$0.20	$0.30	$0.35	$1	$3	$9	$100
	Auctions: $1,998, MS-67RD+, August 2014; $212, MS-67RD, August 2014; $101, MS-67RD, August 2014; $306, MS-67RD, June 2013										
1949	217,775,000	1,397	65.6	100%	$0.10	$0.20	$0.35	$1	$3	$15	$1,250
	Auctions: $3,055, MS-67RD, July 2014; $247, MS-66RD, October 2014; $159, MS-66RD, October 2014; $4,406, MS, March 2014										
1949-D	153,132,500	1,999	65.6	100%	$0.10	$0.20	$0.35	$1	$3	$14	$550
	Auctions: $1,058, MS-67RD, October 2014; $1,164, MS-67RD, November 2014; $353, MS-67RD, December 2014; $1,763, MS-67RD, June 2013										
1949-S	64,290,000	3,640	66.0	100%	$0.25	$0.30	$0.35	$2	$4	$16	$185
	Auctions: $3,173, MS-67RD, March 2014; $247, MS-67RD, August 2014; $153, MS-67RD, September 2014; $41, MS-66RD, August 2014										
1950	272,635,000	1,519	65.5	100%	$0.10	$0.20	$0.35	$0.85	$2	$18	$850
	Auctions: $1,410, MS-67RD, August 2014; $1,293, MS-67RD, September 2014; $3,055, MS-67RD, August 2013; $96, MS-66RD, August 2014										
1950, Proof	51,386	1,705	65.2						$70	$100	$375
	Auctions: $5,141, PF-67DCam, January 2014; $12,925, PF-66DCam+, September 2014; $482, PF-66Cam, July 2014; $306, PF-65Cam, November 2014										
1950-D	334,950,000	2,265	65.6	100%	$0.10	$0.20	$0.35	$0.60	$2	$17	$600
	Auctions: $353, MS-67RD, November 2014; $282, MS-67RD, December 2014; $212, MS-67RD, December 2014; $15,275, MS-67RD, November 2013										
1950-S	118,505,000	2,334	65.9	100%	$0.15	$0.25	$0.35	$0.85	$2	$13	$275
	Auctions: $9,400, MS-67RD+, September 2014; $588, MS-67RD, October 2014; $529, MS-67RD, December 2014; $1,293, MS-67RD, June 2013										
1951	284,576,000	1,218	65.4	99%	$0.10	$0.25	$0.35	$0.70	$2	$18	$750
	Auctions: $2,291, MS-67RD, July 2014; $5,288, MS-67RD, August 2013; $353, MS-66RD+, August 2014; $411, MS-66RD+, October 2014										
1951, Proof	57,500	1,622	65.6						$65	$100	$225
	Auctions: $1,763, PF-67Cam, April 2013; $376, PF-67RB, September 2014; $206, PF-67RB, November 2014; $90, PF-66RB, September 2014										
1951-D	625,355,000	3,455	65.6	100%	$0.10	$0.12	$0.35	$0.60	$2	$9	$225
	Auctions: $282, MS-67RD, September 2014; $94, MS-67RD, November 2014; $1,410, MS-67RD, June 2013										
1951-D, D Over S	(c)	35	63.7	94%				$100			
	Auctions: $2,350, MS-67RD, April 2014; $82, MS-65RD, August 2014										
1951-S	136,010,000	2,111	65.8	100%	$0.25	$0.30	$0.50	$1	$3	$11	$350
	Auctions: $823, MS-67RD, January 2014; $170, MS-67RD, August 2014; $529, MS-67RD, September 2014; $617, MS-67RD, November 2014										
1952	186,775,000	1,513	65.7	100%	$0.10	$0.15	$0.35	$1	$3	$16	$1,650
	Auctions: $4,994, MS-67RD, April 2014; $2,350, MS-67RD, July 2014; $270, MS-66RD, August 2014; $135, MS-66RD, December 2014										
1952, Proof	81,980	1,728	66.0						$50	$75	$125
	Auctions: $1,528, PF-67Cam, April 2013; $306, PF-66Cam, July 2014; $646, PF-66Cam, October 2014; $646, PF-66RB, September 2014										
1952-D	746,130,000	3,901	65.7	100%	$0.10	$0.15	$0.25	$0.75	$2	$9	$350
	Auctions: $823, MS-67RD, September 2014; $646, MS-67RD, September 2014; $411, MS-67RD, November 2014; $1,058, MS-67RD, December 2013										
1952-S	137,800,004	2,508	66.0	100%	$0.15	$0.20	$0.35	$2	$4	$13	$150
	Auctions: $4,113, MS-67RD+, November 2014; $123, MS-67RD, November 2014; $999, MS-67RD, June 2013										

c. Included in 1951-D mintage figure.

1955, Doubled Die Obverse
FS-01-1955-101.

1955, Doubled Die Obverse, Closeup of Date

1956-D, D Above Shadow D
FS-01-1956D-508.

	Mintage	Cert	Avg	%MS	VF-20	EF-40	AU-50	MS-63RB	MS-65RB / PF-65RD	MS-65RD / PF-66RD	MS-67RD / PF-67RD
1953	256,755,000	1,605	65.4	99%	$0.10	$0.15	$0.20	$0.50	$1	$18	$2,000
	Auctions: $14,100, MS-67RD, January 2014; $8,813, MS-67RD, August 2014; $5,889, MS-67RD, August 2014; $4,700, MS-67RD, October 2014										
1953, Proof	128,800	2,462	66.3						$30	$40	$100
	Auctions: $2,585, PF-67Cam, February 2014; $499, PF-67Cam, July 2014; $1,293, PF-66DCam, October 2014; $223, PF-66Cam, November 2014										
1953-D	700,515,000	3,068	65.6	100%	$0.10	$0.15	$0.20	$0.50	$1	$11	$750
	Auctions: $2,115, MS-67RD, July 2014; $1,998, MS-67RD, November 2014; $3,525, MS-67RD, August 2013; $100, MS-66RD+, October 2014										
1953-S	181,835,000	3,618	65.9	100%	$0.10	$0.15	$0.20	$0.60	$2	$12	$185
	Auctions: $3,055, MS-67RD, March 2014; $306, MS-67RD, July 2014; $153, MS-67RD, November 2014; $69, MS-67RD, December 2014										
1954	71,640,050	2,081	65.4	100%	$0.25	$0.35	$0.45	$0.60	$2	$27	$5,000
	Auctions: $23,500, MS-67RD, March 2014; $1,175, MS-66RD+, July 2014; $1,645, MS-66RD+, August 2014; $881, MS-66RD+, October 2014										
1954, Proof	233,300	2,730	66.5						$20	$30	$60
	Auctions: $2,820, PF-68Cam, April 2013; $115, PF-66Cam, September 2014; $129, PF-66Cam, November 2014; $112, PF-66Cam, November 2014										
1954-D	251,552,500	4,036	65.8	100%	$0.10	$0.12	$0.20	$0.50	$1	$10	$450
	Auctions: $141, MS-67RD, October 2014; $123, MS-67RD, December 2014; $1,293, MS-67RD, June 2013; $36, MS-66RD+, October 2014										
1954-S	96,190,000	9,138	65.9	100%	$0.10	$0.12	$0.20	$0.50	$1	$8	$115
	Auctions: $70, MS-67RD, August 2014; $119, MS-67RD, December 2014; $1,880, MS-67RD, August 2013										
1955	330,958,200	2,761	65.0	97%	$0.10	$0.12	$0.15	$0.35	$1	$19	$800
	Auctions: $1,998, MS-67RD, September 2014; $3,819, MS-67RD, December 2013; $49, MS-66RD, July 2014; $60, MS-66RD, October 2014										
1955, Doubled Die Obverse †	(d)	3,607	58.5	46%	$1,400	$1,600	$1,750	$4,000	$10,000	$30,000	
	Auctions: $25,850, MS-64RD, January 2014; $4,994, MS-64RB, August 2014; $22,325, MS-64, March 2016										
1955, Proof	378,200	5,338	67.2						$18	$30	$50
	Auctions: $7,638, PF-68DCam, April 2013; $940, PF-67DCam, July 2014; $74, PF-67Cam, September 2014; $135, PF-67Cam, November 2014										
1955-D	563,257,500	5,186	65.6	99%	$0.10	$0.12	$0.15	$0.35	$1	$9	$750
	Auctions: $7,050, MS-67RD, April 2013; $165, MS-66RD+, September 2014; $130, MS-66RD+, October 2014										
1955-S	44,610,000	18,246	65.9	100%	$0.20	$0.30	$0.40	$0.85	$3	$8	$115
	Auctions: $2,115, MS-67RD, February 2014; $470, MS-67RD, July 2014; $270, MS-67RD, August 2014; $170, MS-67RD, October 2014										
1956	420,745,000	2,944	65.6	100%	$0.10	$0.12	$0.15	$0.35	$1	$13	$500
	Auctions: $3,819, MS-67RD, August 2013; $823, MS-67RD, September 2014; $823, MS-67RD, September 2014; $588, MS-67RD, November 2014										
1956, Proof	669,384	5,436	67.3						$10	$25	$30
	Auctions: $7,638, PF-68DCam, June 2013; $705, PF-67DCam, July 2014; $247, PF-66DCam, October 2014; $341, PF-68RD, July 2014										
1956-D	1,098,201,100	5,178	65.5	99%	$0.10	$0.12	$0.15	$0.30	$1	$9	$300
	Auctions: $589, MS-67RD, July 2014; $705, MS-67RD, August 2014; $3,525, MS-67RD+, November 2014; $1,175, MS-67RD, November 2013										
1956-D, D Above Shadow D (f)	(g)	102	63.0	89%	$10	$25	$30	$35		$170	
	Auctions: $1,293, MS-67RD, February 2014										

† Ranked in the *100 Greatest U.S. Coins* (fourth edition). **d.** Included in circulation-strike 1955 mintage figure. **e.** Value in MS-60BN, $2,350; in MS-63BN, $3,500; in MS-65BN, $12,000. Varieties exist with doubling that, while still strong, is weaker than that pictured; these command premiums, but are not nearly as valuable. Note that many counterfeit 1955 Doubled Die cents exist. On authentic pieces, there is a faint die scratch under the left horizontal bar of the T in CENT. **f.** The remains of a totally separated D mintmark are evident in the field below the primary D. **g.** Included in 1956-D mintage figure.

1958, Doubled Die Obverse
FS-01-1958-101.

	Mintage	Cert	Avg	%MS	VF-20	EF-40	AU-50	MS-63RB	MS-65RB	MS-65RD	MS-67RD
									PF-65RD	PF-66RD	PF-67RD
1957	282,540,000	2,722	65.7	100%	$0.10	$0.12	$0.15	$0.30	$1	$15	$1,500
	Auctions: $515, MS-67RD, September 2014; $470, MS, December 2013; $3,360, MS-67RD, April 2018										
1957, Proof	1,247,952	8,068	67.3						$10	$25	$30
	Auctions: $1,028, PF-68Cam, July 2014; $1,058, PF-68Cam, April 2013; $282, PF-67Cam, November 2014; $84, PF-67Cam, November 2014										
1957-D	1,051,342,000	5,806	65.6	99%	$0.10	$0.12	$0.15	$0.30	$1	$9	$250
	Auctions: $705, MS-67RD, August 2014; $558, MS-67RD, October 2014; $2,115, MS-67RD, June 2013										
1958	252,525,000	4,649	65.6	100%	$0.10	$0.12	$0.15	$0.30	$1	$9	$450
	Auctions: $194, MS-67RD, August 2014; $881, MS-67RD, October 2014; $1,528, MS-67RD, June 2013										
1958, Doubled Die Obverse (h,i)	(j)	0	n/a					—			
	Auctions: No auction records available.										
1958, Proof	875,652	6,186	67.4	100%					$8	$20	$30
	Auctions: $1,293, PF-67DCam, June 2013; $1,293, PF-68Cam, July 2014; $74, PF-67Cam, November 2014; $62, PF-67Cam, November 2014										
1958-D	800,953,300	7,541	65.7	99%	$0.10	$0.12	$0.15	$0.30	$1	$8	$150
	Auctions: $1,939, MS-67RD, January 2014; $106, MS-67RD, August 2014; $2,585, MS-67RD+, September 2014; $212, MS-67RD, September 2014										

h. 3 examples are known. **i.** No specimens have been reported being found in circulation, Wheat cent bags, Uncirculated rolls, "or other means that would lead to credibility of a true accidental release from the mint" (*Cherrypickers' Guide to Rare Die Varieties*, sixth edition, volume I). **j.** Included in circulation-strike 1958 mintage figure.

LINCOLN, MEMORIAL REVERSE (1959–2008)

Copper Alloy (1959–1982): **Designer:** *Victor D. Brenner (obverse), Frank Gasparro (reverse).*
Weight: *3.11 grams.* **Composition:** *1959–1962—.950 copper, .050 tin and zinc; 1962–1982—.950 copper, .050 zinc.* **Diameter:** *19 mm.* **Edge:** *Plain.* **Mints:** *Philadelphia, Denver, and San Francisco.*

Copper Alloy (1959–1982)   **Copper Alloy, Proof**

Copper-Plated Zinc (1982–2008): **Designer:** *Victor D. Brenner (obverse), Frank Gasparro (reverse).* **Weight:** *2.5 grams.* **Composition:** *copper-plated zinc (core: .992 zinc, .008 copper, with a plating of pure copper; total content .975 zinc, .025 copper).* **Diameter:** *19 mm.* **Edge:** *Plain.* **Mints:** *Philadelphia, Denver, and San Francisco.*

Copper-Plated Zinc (1982–2008)   **Copper-Plated Zinc, Proof**

History. In 1959 a new cent design, by Frank Gasparro, was introduced to mark the 150th anniversary of Abraham Lincoln's birth. Victor Brenner's portrait of Lincoln was maintained on the obverse. The new reverse featured a view of the Lincoln Memorial in Washington, D.C., with Daniel Chester French's massive statue of the president faintly visible within. In 1969 the dies were modified to strengthen the design, and Lincoln's head on the obverse was made slightly smaller. In 1973 the dies were further modified, and the engraver's initials (FG) were enlarged. In 1974 the initials were reduced slightly. During 1982 the dies were modified again and the bust, lettering, and date were made slightly smaller. The Lincoln Memorial reverse was used until 2009, when a switch was made to four new reverse designs honoring the bicentennial of Lincoln's birth. Lincoln Memorial cents were struck for circulation at the Philadelphia, Denver, and San Francisco mints, with the latter in smaller numbers. Partway through 1982 the bronze alloy was discontinued in favor of copper-coated zinc.

Striking and Sharpness. Striking varies and can range from "sloppy" to needle sharp. On the obverse, check Lincoln's hair and beard (although the sharpness of this feature varied in the dies; for more information see *A Guide Book of Lincoln Cents* [Bowers]). Tiny marks on the shoulder of Lincoln indicate a weak strike there. On the reverse the sharpness can vary, including on the tiny statue of Lincoln and the shrubbery. On the reverse there can be light striking on the steps of the Memorial, and at IBU and M of E PLURIBUS UNUM. The quality of the fields can vary, as well. Some early copper-coated zinc cents, particularly of 1982 and 1983, can have planchet blisters or other problems. All Proof Lincoln Memorial cents are of the mirror type, usually with cameo or frosted contrast between the devices and the fields. High quality is common. Special Mint Set (SMS) coins were struck in lieu of Proofs from 1965 to 1967, and in some instances these closely resemble Proofs.

Availability. Coins in this series are plentiful for standard dates and mintmarks. Collectible varieties exist, and are eagerly sought by specialists, who use the *Cherrypickers' Guide to Rare Die Varieties* as their standard reference. Some of the more popular varieties are illustrated and listed herein.

GRADING STANDARDS

Caveat: These grading standards do not take sharpness of strike into account.

MS-60 to 70 (Mint State). *Obverse and Reverse:* At MS-65 and higher, the luster is rich on all areas, except perhaps the shoulder (which may be grainy and show original planchet surface). There is no rubbing, and no contact marks are visible except under magnification. Coins with full or nearly full mint orange-red color can be designated RD; those with full or nearly full brown-toned surfaces can be designated BN; and those with a sub-

1998-D. Graded MS-68.

stantial percentage of red-orange and of brown can be called RB. Ideally, MS-65 or finer coins should have good eye appeal, which in the RB category means nicely blended colors, not stained or blotched. Below MS-65, full RD coins become scarce, and at MS–60 to 62 they are virtually non-existent, unless they have been dipped. Copper is a very active metal, and influences such as slight abrasions, contact marks, and so on that define the grade also affect the color. The ANA grading standards allow for "dull" and/or "spotted" coins at MS–60 and 61, as well as incomplete luster. In the marketplace, interpretations often vary widely. BN and RB coins at MS–60 and 61 are apt to be more attractive than (dipped) RD coins.

AU-50, 53, 55, 58 (About Uncirculated).

Obverse: Same guidelines as for the preceding type except that tinges of original mint-red are sometimes seen on coins that have not been cleaned. *Reverse:* Slight wear is seen on the Lincoln Memorial, particularly on the steps, the columns, and the horizontal architectural elements above.

Illustrated coin: The doubling of the obverse die of this popular variety is easily visible to the naked eye.

1969-S, Double Die Obverse. Graded AU-58.

EF-40, 45 (Extremely Fine). *Obverse:* Light wear is seen on Lincoln's portrait, and hair detail is gone on the higher areas, especially above the ear. *Reverse:* Most detail is gone from the steps of the Lincoln Memorial, and the columns and other higher-relief architectural elements show wear.

The Lincoln cent with Memorial reverse is seldom collected in grades lower than EF-40.

1962-D. Graded EF-40.

PF-60 to 70 (Proof). *Obverse and Reverse:* PF-65 and higher coins are usually RB (colors should be nicely blended) or RD, the latter with bright red-orange fading slightly to hints of brown. Some tiny flecks are normal on coins certified as PF-65 but should be microscopic or absent above that. PF–60 and 61 coins can be dull, stained, or spotted and still have some original mint color. Coins with fingerprints must be given a low numerical grade. Lower-grade Proofs usually have poor eye appeal. Generally, Proofs below PF-64 are not desired by most collectors.

1959. Graded PF-69RD Cameo.

1960, Large Date

1960, Small Date

1960-D, D Over D, Small Over Large Date
FS-01-1960D-101/501.

	Mintage	Cert	Avg	%MS	MS-63RB / PF-65RD	MS-65RD / PF-67RD	MS-66RD / PF-67Cam	MS-67RD / PF-68DCam
1959	609,715,000	1,759	65.6	100%	$0.20	$0.30	$37	$550
1959, Proof	1,149,291	6,968	67.4		$3	$22	$55	$750
1959-D	1,279,760,000	1,642	65.8	100%	$0.50	$0.55	$25	$475

1969-S, Doubled Die Obverse
FS-01-1969S-101.

	Mintage	Cert	Avg	%MS	MS-63RB / PF-65RD	MS-65RD / PF-67RD	MS-66RD / PF-67Cam	MS-67RD / PF-68DCam
1960, Large Date (a)	586,405,000	2,360	65.6	100%	$0.20	$0.30	$30	
1960, Small Date (a)	(b)	1,573	65.5	100%	$3	$7	$38	
1960, Large Date, Proof	1,691,602	5,655	67.4		$2	$26	$45	$300
1960, Small Date, Proof	(c)	4,115	67.3		$22	$37	$75	$1,500
1960, Lg Dt Over Sm Dt, Proof (d)	(c)	0	n/a		—			
1960, Sm Dt Over Lg Dt, Proof (e)	(c)	0	n/a		—			
1960-D, Large Date (a,f)	1,580,884,000	1,507	65.4	99%	$0.20	$0.30	$30	
1960-D, Small Date (a)	(g)	1,732	65.5	99%	$0.20	$0.30	$30	$1,250
1960, D Over D, Small Over Large Date	(g)	298	64.2	97%	$150	$300	$800	
1961	753,345,000	1,058	65.1	99%	$0.15	$0.30	$50	
1961, Proof	3,028,244	6,119	67.3		$1.50	$23	$40	$300
1961-D	1,753,266,700	1,347	65.4	99%	$0.15	$0.30	$70	$100
1962	606,045,000	1,173	65.6	100%	$0.15	$0.30	$50	
1962, Proof	3,218,019	6,776	67.4		$1.50	$10	$15	$100
1962-D	1,793,148,140	1,048	65.4	99%	$0.15	$0.30	$75	$250
1963	754,110,000	1,564	65.3	100%	$0.15	$0.30	$60	
1963, Proof	3,075,645	7,149	67.5		$1.50	$10	$14	$55
1963-D	1,774,020,400	765	65.2	99%	$0.15	$0.30	$100	$350
1964	2,648,575,000	1,033	65.2	100%	$0.15	$0.30	$65	
1964, Proof	3,950,762	10,953	67.8		$1.50	$10	$11	$23
1964-D	3,799,071,500	610	65.2	98%	$0.15	$0.30	$42	
1965	1,497,224,900	552	65.7	100%	$0.20	$0.50	$27	
1965, Special Mint Set	2,360,000	2,165	66.4	100%	$11	$55		
1966	2,188,147,783	396	65.2	98%	$0.20	$0.50	$60	
1966, Special Mint Set	2,261,583	2,995	66.8	100%	$10	$25		
1967	3,048,667,100	429	65.4	99%	$0.20	$0.50	$90	
1967, Special Mint Set	1,863,344	3,040	66.8	100%	$11	$42		
1968	1,707,880,970	513	65.4	100%	$0.25	$0.60	$33	
1968-D	2,886,269,600	996	65.4	99%	$0.15	$0.40	$27	
1968-S	258,270,001	49	62.2	84%	$0.15	$0.40	$29	
1968-S, Proof	3,041,506	1,218	67.2		$1	$12	$16	$50
1969	1,136,910,000	1,717	65.6	100%	$0.35	$0.70	$55	
1969-D	4,002,832,200	884	65.2	99%	$0.15	$0.30	$28	
1969-S	544,375,000	1,099	64.3	93%	$0.15	$0.50	$65	
1969-S, Doubled Die Obverse †† (h)	(i)	15	58.6	47%	$65,000			
1969-S, Proof	2,934,631	1,348	67.1		$1	$11	$13	$33

†† Ranked in the *100 Greatest U.S. Modern Coins* (fourth edition). **a.** The alignment of the 1 and 9 in the date can be used for a quick determination of Large versus Small Date. Large Date: the top of the 1 is significantly lower than the top of the 9. Small Date: the tops of the 1 and 9 are at the same level. **b.** Included in circulation-strike 1960, Large Date, mintage figure. **c.** Included in 1960, Large Date, Proof, mintage figure. **d.** FS-01-1960-101. **e.** FS-01-1960-102. A PF-68RD example sold in a 2009 auction for $2,300. **f.** A variety once called 1960-D, Large Date, D Over Horizontal D, has been disproved as such, and is now considered simply a triple-punched D. **g.** Included in 1960-D, Large Date, mintage figure. **h.** Beware of specimens that exhibit only strike doubling, as opposed to a true doubled die; these are worth only face value. See Appendix A of the *Cherrypickers' Guide to Rare Die Varieties*, sixth edition, volume I. **i.** Included in circulation-strike 1969-S mintage figure.

1970-S, Small Date (High 7)

1970-S, Large Date (Low 7)

1970-S, Proof, Doubled Die Obverse
FS-01-1970S-101.

1972, Doubled Die Obverse
FS-01-1972-101.

	Mintage	Cert	Avg	%MS	MS-63RB / PF-65RD	MS-65RD / PF-67RD	MS-66RD / PF-67Cam	MS-67RD / PF-68DCam
1970	1,898,315,000	505	65.6	100%	$0.30	$0.65	$25	$250
1970-D	2,891,438,900	741	65.1	100%	$0.15	$0.30	$70	$850
1970-S, All kinds	690,560,004							
1970-S, Small Date (High 7) ††		950	64.5	100%	$25	$55	$200	
1970-S, Large Date (Low 7)		1,678	64.7	97%	$0.20	$0.50	$30	$950
1970-S, Doubled Die Obverse ††		31	63.6	90%	—			
1970-S, All kinds, Proof	2,632,810							
1970-S, Small Date (High 7), Proof		603	66.5		$40	$65	$150	
1970-S, Large Date (Low 7), Proof		1,253	66.9		$1	$15	$25	$65
1971	1,919,490,000	753	65.3	98%	$0.25	$0.60	$25	
1971, Doubled Die Obverse	(h)	32	63.2	91%	$50			
1971-D	2,911,045,600	342	65.4	100%	$0.20	$0.50	$24	$500
1971-S	525,133,459	480	65.3	98%	$0.20	$0.50	$50	
1971-S, Proof	3,220,733	1,382	67.2		$1	$18	$30	$120
1971-S, Doubled Die Obverse, Proof ††	(i)	248	66.3		$500	$1,000	$1,500	
1972	2,933,255,000	857	65.0	96%	$0.15	$0.30	$32	
1972, Doubled Die Obverse †† (j)	(k)	2,496	64.2	98%	$400	$600	$950	$2,750
1972-D	2,665,071,400	285	65.2	98%	$0.15	$0.30	$28	
1972-S	376,939,108	360	64.8	98%	$0.25	$0.75	$78	$1,000
1972-S, Proof	3,260,996	853	67.2		$1	$15	$20	$35
1973	3,728,245,000	572	65.7	100%	$0.15	$0.30	$30	$600
1973-D	3,549,576,588	547	65.6	100%	$0.15	$0.30	$30	
1973-S	317,177,295	363	65.3	99%	$0.25	$0.85	$50	
1973-S, Proof	2,760,339	292	67.3		$1	$13	$16	$30
1974	4,232,140,523	492	65.8	100%	$0.15	$0.30	$27	$175
1974-D	4,235,098,000	500	65.6	99%	$0.15	$0.30	$20	$100
1974-S	409,426,660	251	64.6	99%	$0.25	$0.75	$100	$750
1974-S, Proof	2,612,568	350	67.3		$1	$13	$16	$30
1975	5,451,476,142	809	65.9	100%	$0.15	$0.30	$25	$150
1975-D	4,505,275,300	250	65.7	100%	$0.15	$0.30	$25	$350
1975-S, Proof	2,845,450	547	67.2		$3.50	$13	$16	$30
1976	4,674,292,426	300	65.8	100%	$0.15	$0.30	$25	$55
1976-D	4,221,592,455	151	65.3	100%	$0.15	$0.30	$35	$750
1976-S, Proof	4,149,730	829	67.1		$3.20	$13	$16	$30
1977	4,469,930,000	331	65.9	100%	$0.15	$0.30	$55	$130
1977-D	4,194,062,300	451	65.2	100%	$0.15	$0.30	$90	$650
1977-S, Proof	3,251,152	451	68.1		$2.50	$13	$16	$30

†† Ranked in the *100 Greatest U.S. Modern Coins* (fourth edition). **h.** Included in 1971 mintage figure. **i.** Included in 1971-S, Proof, mintage figure. **j.** Several less dramatically doubled varieties exist; these command premiums over the normal coin but are worth considerably less than the variety pictured. Counterfeits of the 1972 doubled die are frequently encountered. **k.** Included in 1972 mintage figure.

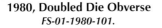

1980, Doubled Die Obverse
FS-01-1980-101.

1982, Large Date   **1982, Small Date**

1983, Doubled Die Reverse
FS-01-1983-801.

1984, Doubled Ear
FS-01-1984-101.

	Mintage	Cert	Avg	%MS	MS-63RB / PF-65RD	MS-65RD / PF-67RD	MS-66RD / PF-67Cam	MS-67RD / PF-68DCam
1978	5,558,605,000	304	65.4	99%	$0.15	$0.30	$80	$625
1978-D	4,280,233,400	256	65.4	99%	$0.15	$0.30	$75	$425
1978-S, Proof	3,127,781	487	67.5		$2.50	$13	$16	$30
1979	6,018,515,000	689	66.4	100%	$0.15	$0.30	$20	$70
1979-D	4,139,357,254	373	65.3	99%	$0.15	$0.30	$60	
1979-S, Type 1, Proof	3,677,175	619	68.2		$5	$11	$13	$17
1979-S, Type 2, Proof	(l)	927	68.2		$6	$17	$20	$30
1980	7,414,705,000	265	65.2	100%	$0.15	$0.30	$25	$125
1980, Doubled Die Obverse	(m)	233	61.7	79%	$225	$350		
1980-D (n)	5,140,098,660	335	65.2	99%	$0.15	$0.30	$40	$400
1980-S, Proof	3,554,806	905	68.4		$2.50	$10	$11	$15
1981	7,491,750,000	291	65.6	99%	$0.15	$0.30	$35	$125
1981-D	5,373,235,677	237	65.5	99%	$0.15	$0.30	$40	$225
1981-S, Type 1, Proof	4,063,083	1,188	68.3		$3	$10	$11	$15
1981-S, Type 2, Proof	(o)	869	67.9		$15	$28	$38	$55
1982, Large Date	10,712,525,000	932	65.5	99%	$0.20	$0.35	$25	$55
1982, Small Date	(p)	325	64.8	96%	$0.30	$0.50	$45	$125
1982-D, Large Date	6,012,979,368	291	64.7	94%	$0.15	$0.30	$20	$35
1982, Zinc, Large Date	(p)	588	66.3	99%	$0.35	$0.50	$35	$60
1982, Zinc, Small Date ✝✝	(p)	531	66.3	100%	$0.50	$0.85	$35	
1982-D, Zinc, Large Date	(q)	382	66.4	100%	$0.20	$0.40	$25	$45
1982-D, Zinc, Small Date	(q)	371	65.9	100%	$0.15	$0.30	$15	$275
1982-S, Small Date, Proof	3,857,479	493	68.1		$2.50	$10	$11	$15
1983	7,752,355,000	417	65.4	98%	$0.15	$0.30	$15	$45
1983, Doubled Die Reverse ✝✝ (r)	(s)	1,022	64.8	98%	$250	$375	$500	$1,000
1983-D	6,467,199,428	340	66.0	99%	$0.15	$0.30	$15	$31
1983-S, Proof	3,279,126	591	68.4		$3	$10	$11	$15
1984	8,151,079,000	311	66.0	99%	$0.15	$0.30	$15	$35
1984, Doubled Ear ✝✝ (t)	(u)	584	65.5	99%	$175	$225	$325	$500
1984-D	5,569,238,906	284	66.2	99%	$0.15	$0.30	$15	$35
1984-S, Proof	3,065,110	533	68.9		$4	$10	$11	$15

✝✝ Ranked in the *100 Greatest U.S. Modern Coins* (fourth edition). **l.** Included in 1979-S, Type 1, Proof, mintage figure. **m.** Included in 1980 mintage figure. **n.** A variety previously listed in the *Cherrypickers' Guide* as a 1980-D, D Over S, has since been delisted from that catalog. It should command no premium. **o.** Included in 1981-S, Type 1, Proof, mintage figure. **p.** Included in 1982, Large Date, mintage figure. **q.** Included in 1982-D mintage figure. **r.** All reverse lettering is strongly doubled, as are the designer's initials and portions of the Lincoln Memorial. **s.** Included in 1983 mintage figure. **t.** Values are for coins certified as the Doubled Ear variety (FS-101). More than 1,500 certifications exist for all 1984 doubled-die varieties; this number certainly includes FS-101, but it is unknown how many. **u.** Included in 1984 mintage figure.

1992, Normal AM	1992, Close AM

1995, Doubled Die Obverse
FS-01-1995-101.

	Mintage	Cert	Avg	%MS	MS-63RB	MS-65RD	MS-66RD	MS-67RD
					PF-65RD	PF-67RD	PF-67Cam	PF-68DCam
1985	5,648,489,887	630	66.3	100%	$0.15	$0.30	$15	$35
1985-D	5,287,339,926	475	66.8	100%	$0.15	$0.30	$15	$29
1985-S, Proof	3,362,821	586	68.9		$5	$11	$12	$15
1986	4,491,395,493	371	66.4	100%	$0.15	$0.30	$15	$35
1986-D	4,442,866,698	380	66.8	100%	$0.15	$0.30	$15	$35
1986-S, Proof	3,010,497	538	68.9		$7	$11	$12	$15
1987	4,682,466,931	443	66.7	100%	$0.15	$0.30	$15	$29
1987-D	4,879,389,514	560	66.6	100%	$0.15	$0.30	$15	$32
1987-S, Proof	4,227,728	785	68.9		$5	$10	$11	$13
1988	6,092,810,000	256	66.3	99%	$0.15	$0.30	$20	$40
1988-D	5,253,740,443	321	66.6	99%	$0.15	$0.30	$15	$25
1988-S, Proof	3,262,948	526	69.0		$9	$11	$12	$13
1989	7,261,535,000	389	66.1	99%	$0.15	$0.30	$15	$25
1989-D	5,345,467,111	372	66.4	100%	$0.15	$0.30	$15	$30
1989-S, Proof	3,220,194	611	68.9		$9	$11	$12	$13
1990	6,851,765,000	256	1.0	66	$0.15	$0.30	$19	$36
1990-D	4,922,894,533	328	66.8	99%	$0.15	$0.30	$15	$25
1990-S, Proof	3,299,559	884	69.0		$5	$10	$11	$13
1990-S, No S, Proof ††	(v)	79	67.9		$2,250	$2,500	$2,750	$4,500
1991	5,165,940,000	237	66.7	100%	$0.15	$0.30	$14	$25
1991-D	4,158,446,076	375	66.8	100%	$0.15	$0.30	$14	$25
1991-S, Proof	2,867,787	850	69.1		$12	$13	$14	$16
1992	4,648,905,000	581	67.0	100%	$0.15	$0.30	$14	$25
1992, Close AM †† (w)	(x)	10	60.2	60%		—		
1992-D	4,448,673,300	365	66.6	99%	$0.15	$0.30	$14	$25
1992-D, Close AM †† (w)	(y)	32	60.8	75%		—		
1992-S, Proof	4,176,560	2,394	69.0		$5	$10	$11	$12
1993	5,684,705,000	299	66.4	99%	$0.15	$0.30	$14	$25
1993-D	6,426,650,571	457	66.7	99%	$0.15	$0.30	$14	$25
1993-S, Proof	3,394,792	2,090	68.9		$9	$10	$11	$12
1994	6,500,850,000	238	66.6	99%	$0.15	$0.30	$14	$25
1994-D	7,131,765,000	299	66.8	99%	$0.15	$0.30	$15	$27
1994-S, Proof	3,269,923	1,808	69.0		$9	$11	$12	$13
1995	6,411,440,000	362	66.5	99%	$0.15	$0.30	$15	$30
1995, Doubled Die Obverse ††	(z)	18,639	67.2	100%	$35	$50	$90	$125
1995-D	7,128,560,000	308	66.9	99%	$0.15	$0.30	$15	$35
1995-S, Proof	2,797,481	2,353	69.1		$9	$11	$12	$13

†† Ranked in the *100 Greatest U.S. Modern Coins* (fourth edition). **v.** An estimated 100 to 250 Proofs of 1990 were struck without the S mintmark (apparently from a circulation-strike die, without a mintmark, which had been given a mirror finish). This error escaped the notice of at least 14 people during die preparation and coining. **w.** The reverse hub used for cents from 1974 to 1992 had the AM of AMERICA separated. A new reverse hub with the AM close together was used for all cents in 1993. At least one new reverse die of each type was used for 1992-P and -D cents made for circulation but it is not known if this usage was deliberate or accidental. Proof coinage reverted to the wide-AM design in 1994. In subsequent years a few dies from the circulation-strike hub were used for making Proof coins. **x.** Included in 1992 mintage figure. **y.** Included in 1992-D mintage figure. **z.** Included in 1995 mintage figure.

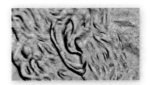

1997, Doubled Ear
FS-01-1997-101.

1999, Normal AM   **1999, Wide AM**   **1999-S, Proof, Normal AM**   **1999-S, Proof, Close AM**

	Mintage	Cert	Avg	%MS	MS-63RB / PF-65RD	MS-65RD / PF-67RD	MS-66RD / PF-67Cam	MS-67RD / PF-68DCam
1996	6,612,465,000	252	66.8	100%	$0.15	$0.30	$12	$18
1996 , Wide AM (w)	(aa)	(bb)			—	—		
1996-D	6,510,795,000	437	66.9	100%	$0.15	$0.30	$12	$18
1996-S, Proof	2,525,265	1,865	69.1		$4.50	$9	$10	$12
1997	4,622,800,000	208	66.4	100%	$0.15	$0.30	$15	$42
1997, Doubled Ear	(cc)	49	65.2	100%	$275	$500		
1997-D	4,576,555,000	256	66.7	100%	$0.15	$0.30	$14	$30
1997-S, Proof	2,796,678	1,646	69.1		$10	$12	$13	$14
1998	5,032,155,000	198	66.2	98%	$0.15	$0.30	$12	$18
1998, Wide AM (w)	(dd)	327	64.9	98%	$12	$25	$40	$600
1998-D	5,225,353,500	238	66.7	100%	$0.15	$0.30	$17	$57
1998-S, Proof	2,086,507	1,741	69.0		$9	$10	$11	$12
1998-S, Close AM, Proof †† (cc)	(ff)	144	68.4	99%	$150	$175	$185	$200
1999	5,237,600,000	272	65.5	99%	$0.15	$0.30	$13	$30
1999, Wide AM ‡ (w)	(gg)	187	64.3	94%		$500		$1,500
1999-D	6,360,065,000	288	66.8	100%	$0.15	$0.30	$12	$25
1999-S, Proof	3,347,966	6,627	69.1		$6	$9	$10	$12
1999-S, Close AM, Proof (cc)	(hh)	340	68.4		$80	$100	$125	$150
2000	5,503,200,000	1,349	64.6	95%	$0.15	$0.30	$12	$25
2000, Wide AM (w)	(ii)	1,022	65.5	100%	$10	$20	$35	$55
2000-D	8,774,220,000	215	66.6	100%	$0.15	$0.30	$12	$25
2000-S, Proof	4,047,993	5,667	69.1		$4	$7	$8	$10
2001	4,959,600,000	116	66.8	100%	$0.15	$0.30	$11	$18
2001-D	5,374,990,000	200	66.8	100%	$0.15	$0.30	$11	$18
2001-S, Proof	3,184,606	4,529	69.1		$4	$7	$8	$10
2002	3,260,800,000	131	67.3	100%	$0.15	$0.30	$11	$15
2002-D	4,028,055,000	156	67.2	100%	$0.15	$0.30	$12	$19
2002-S, Proof	3,211,995	4,814	69.1		$4	$7	$8	$10
2003	3,300,000,000	291	67.1	100%	$0.15	$0.30	$11	$15
2003-D	3,548,000,000	177	66.5	100%	$0.15	$0.30	$10	$15
2003-S, Proof	3,298,439	7,853	69.1		$4	$7	$8	$10

†† Ranked in the *100 Greatest U.S. Modern Coins* (fourth edition). **w.** The reverse hub used for cents from 1974 to 1992 had the AM of AMERICA separated. A new reverse hub with the AM close together was used for all cents in 1993. At least one new reverse die of each type was used for 1992-P and -D cents made for circulation but it is not known if this usage was deliberate or accidental. Proof coinage reverted to the wide-AM design in 1994. In subsequent years a few dies from the circulation-strike hub were used for making Proof coins. **aa.** Included in 1996 mintage figure. **bb.** Included in certified-population figure for 1996. **cc.** Varieties were made in the circulation-strike style, with the A and the M in AMERICA nearly touching each other. On normal Proofs the two letters have a wide space between them. **dd.** Included 1998-S, Proof, mintage figure. **ee.** Included in 1999 mintage figure. **ff.** Included in 1999-S, Proof, mintage figure. **gg.** Included in 2000 mintage figure. **hh.** Included in 1999-S, Proof, mintage figure. **ii.** Included in 2000 mintage figure.

	Mintage	Cert	Avg	%MS	MS-63RB / PF-65RD	MS-65RD / PF-67RD	MS-66RD / PF-67Cam	MS-67RD / PF-68DCam
2004	3,379,600,000	178	66.8	100%	$0.15	$0.30	$10	$20
2004-D	3,456,400,000	149	66.5	100%	$0.15	$0.30	$10	$18
2004-S, Proof	2,965,422	5,329	69.1		$4	$7	$8	$10
2005	3,935,600,000	194	68.0	100%	$0.15	$0.30	$10	$25
2005, Satin Finish	1,160,000	2,402	67.2	100%	$5	$10	$15	$20
2005-D	3,764,450,500	231	67.6	100%	$0.15	$0.30	$20	$40
2005-D, Satin Finish	1,160,000	2,278	66.9	100%	$5	$10	$15	$20
2005-S, Proof	3,344,679	10,825	69.1		$4	$7	$8	$10
2006	4,290,000,000	91	65.3	99%	$0.15	$0.30	$10	$18
2006, Satin Finish	847,361	1,394	67.1	100%	$5	$10	$15	$20
2006-D	3,944,000,000	138	66.0	100%	$0.15	$0.30	$13	$25
2006-D, Satin Finish	847,361	1,089	66.8	100%	$5	$10	$15	$20
2006-S, Proof	3,054,436	5,220	69.2		$4	$7	$8	$10
2007	3,762,400,000	178	65.9	100%	$0.15	$0.30	$16	$30
2007, Satin Finish	895,628	279	66.9	100%	$5	$10	$15	$20
2007-D	3,638,800,000	126	65.8	100%	$0.15	$0.30	$16	$33
2007-D, Satin Finish	895,628	224	66.3	100%	$5	$10	$15	$20
2007-S, Proof	2,577,166	4,660	69.1		$4	$7	$8	$10
2008	2,558,800,000	85	66.2	100%	$0.15	$0.30	$10	$15
2008, Satin Finish	745,464	169	67.8	100%	$5	$10	$15	$20
2008-D	2,849,600,000	96	66.0	100%	$0.15	$0.30	$15	$30
2008-D, Satin Finish	745,464	143	67.3	100%	$5	$10	$15	$20
2008-S, Proof	2,169,561	3,680	69.1		$4	$7	$8	$10

LINCOLN, BICENTENNIAL REVERSES (2009)

Designer: *Victor D. Brenner (obverse); see image captions for reverse designers.*
Weight: *Regular-issue coins—2.5 grams; special coins included in collector sets—3.1 grams.*
Composition: *Regular-issue coins—copper-plated zinc (core: .992 zinc, .008 copper, with a plating of pure copper; total content .975 zinc, .025 copper); special coins included in collector sets—.950 copper, .050 tin and zinc.* **Diameter:** *19 mm.* **Edge:** *Plain.* **Mints:** *Philadelphia, Denver, and San Francisco.*

Circulation Strike

Birth and Early Childhood
Reverse designer: Richard Masters.

Formative Years
Reverse designer: Charles Vickers.

Professional Life
Reverse designer: Joel Iskowitz.

Presidency
Reverse designer: Susan Gamble.

Proof

Birth and Early Childhood, Proof

Formative Years, Proof

Professional Life, Proof

Presidency, Proof

History. The one-cent coins issued during 2009 pay unique tribute to President Abraham Lincoln, commemorating the bicentennial of his birth and the 100th anniversary of the first issuance of the Lincoln cent. Four different reverse designs were issued by the U.S. Mint, each representing a major aspect of Lincoln's life. The obverse retained the traditional profile portrait of previous years.

The reverse designs, released quarterly throughout 2009, are:

- Birth and Early Childhood (designer, Richard Masters; sculptor, Jim Licaretz), depicting a small log cabin like the one in which Lincoln was born in Kentucky.

- Formative Years (designer and sculptor, Charles Vickers), showing a youthful Abe Lincoln taking a break from rail-splitting to read a book, in Indiana.

- Professional Life (designer, Joel Iskowitz; sculptor, Don Everhart), with Lincoln standing in front of the Illinois state capitol in Springfield, symbolic of his pre-presidential career in law and politics.

- Presidency (designer, Susan Gamble; sculptor, Joseph Menna), depicting the partially completed U.S. Capitol dome in Washington, D.C., as it appeared when Lincoln held office.

The coins issued for general circulation were made of the exact same copper-plated composition used in the cent since 1982. Special versions struck for inclusion in collector sets were made of the same alloy as the first Lincoln cents of 1909—95 parts copper and 5 parts tin and zinc—and with a Satin finish.

Several die varieties (both circulation-strike and Proof) exist with minor doubling in the Formative Years reverse. Their values, which vary generally according to the severity of the doubling, are not yet firmly established with an active buy-and-sell market. These and other Lincoln cent die varieties are studied in greater depth in the *Cherrypickers' Guide to Rare Die Varieties*.

Striking and Sharpness. Striking is generally sharp. The quality of the fields can vary. Some 2009 cents, even from original rolls and bags, have surface marks that look like water spots. All Proof Lincoln Bicentennial cents are mirror Proofs, usually with cameo or frosted contrast between the devices and the fields.

Availability. Cents of this year were minted in quantities that, while large, were much smaller than for previous years (in the hundreds of millions, rather than multiple billions), if each of the four designs is considered individually. They are readily available in the numismatic marketplace, and are starting to be seen more frequently in circulation. High-quality Proofs (PF-69 and 70) are common in the secondary market.

GRADING STANDARDS

Caveat: These grading standards do not take sharpness of strike into account.

MS-60 to 70 (Mint State). *Obverse and Reverse:* At MS-65 and higher, luster is rich on all areas; there is no rubbing, and no contact marks are visible except under magnification. Coins with full or nearly full mint orange-red color can be designated RD; those with a substantial percentage of red-orange and of brown can be called RB; and those with full (or nearly full) brown-toned surfaces can be designated BN. Some 2009 cents, even from original rolls and bags, have surface marks that look like water spots.

2009-D, Formative Years. Graded MS-67RD.

The Lincoln Bicentennial cent is seldom collected in grades lower than MS-60.

PF-60 to 70 (Proof). *Obverse and Reverse:*
PF-65 and higher coins are RB (with colors
nicely blended) or RD, the latter with bright
red-orange color sometimes fading to hints of
brown. Some tiny flecks are normal on coins
certified as PF-65 but should be microscopic or
absent above that level. PF–60 and 61 coins can
be dull, stained, or spotted and still have some
original mint luster. Proof coins with fingerprints are impaired and must be given a lower
numerical grade. Lower-grade Proofs usually
have poor eye appeal. Generally, Proofs of these types below PF-65 are not desired by most collectors.

**2009-S, Birthplace and Early Childhood.
Graded PF-70RD Deep Cameo.**

| 2009, Formative Years, Seven Fingers *FS-01-2009-801.* *Other varieties exist.* | 2009, Formative Years, Seven Fingers *FS-01-2009-802.* *Other varieties exist.* | 2009, Formative Years, Doubled Pinky *FS-01-2009-805.* *Other varieties exist.* | 2009, Formative Years, Skeleton Finger *FS-01-2009-808.* *Other varieties exist.* |

	Mintage	Cert	Avg	%MS	MS-63RB	MS-65RD	MS-66RD / PF-65RD	MS-67RD / PF-67RD	MS-68RD / PF-67Cam	MS-69RD / PF-68DCam
2009, Birth and Early Childhood	284,400,000	13,959	65.8	100%	$0.15	$0.30	$12	$20		
2009, Birth and Early Childhood, copper, Satin Finish	784,614	1,660	67.7	100%		$10			$15	$35
2009-D, Birth and Early Childhood	350,400,000	4,969	65.9	100%	$0.15	$0.30	$12	$20		
2009-D, Birth and Early Childhood, copper, Satin Finish	784,614	1,743	67.7	100%		$10			$17	$100
2009-S, Birth and Early Childhood, Proof	2,995,615	14,440	69.1				$4	$7	$8	$10
2009, Formative Years (a)	376,000,000	27,059	65.9	100%	$0.15	$0.30	$12	$20		
2009, Formative Years, copper, Satin Finish	784,614	1,557	67.6	100%		$10			$15	$35
2009-D, Formative Years (a)	363,600,000	2,663	65.9	100%	$0.15	$0.30	$12	$20		
2009-D, Formative Years, copper, Satin Finish	784,614	1,602	67.6	100%		$10			$15	$100
2009-S, Formative Years, Proof	2,995,615	14,330	69.1				$4	$7	$8	$10
2009, Professional Life	316,000,000	17,489	66.0	100%	$0.15	$0.30	$12	$20		
2009, Professional Life, copper, Satin Finish	784,614	1,927	67.8	100%		$10			$15	$35
2009-D, Professional Life	336,000,000	1,966	66.0	100%	$0.15	$0.30	$12	$20		
2009-D, Professional Life, copper, Satin Finish	784,614	1,561	67.6	100%		$10			$15	$100
2009-S, Professional Life, Proof	2,995,615	14,385	69.1				$4	$7	$8	$10
2009, Presidency	129,600,000	4,472	65.9	100%	$0.15	$0.30	$12	$20		
2009, Presidency, copper, Satin Finish	784,614	1,565	67.6	100%		$10			$15	$35

a. Several varieties exist with minor die doubling. Their values vary and their market is not yet firmly established.

| | Mintage | Cert | Avg | %MS | MS-63RB | MS-65RD | MS-66RD | MS-67RD | MS-68RD | MS-69RD |
							PF-65RD	PF-67RD	PF-67Cam	PF-68DCam
2009-D, Presidency	198,000,000	1,420	65.9	100%	$0.15	$0.30	$12	$20		
2009-D, Presidency, copper, Satin Finish	784,614	1,699	67.6	100%		$10			$15	$100
2009-S, Presidency, Proof	2,995,615	14,596	69.1				$4	$7	$8	$10

LINCOLN, SHIELD REVERSE (2010 TO DATE)

Designer: *Victor D. Brenner (obverse) and Lyndall Bass (reverse).* **Weight:** *2.5 grams.* **Composition:** *Copper-plated zinc (core: .992 zinc, .008 copper, with a plating of pure copper; total content .975 zinc, .025 copper).* **Diameter:** *19 mm.* **Edge:** *Plain.* **Mints:** *Philadelphia, Denver, and San Francisco.*

Circulation Strike

Proof

History. Symbolically capping the life story told by the Lincoln Bicentennial cents of 2009, today's cents feature a reverse design "emblematic of President Lincoln's preservation of the United States as a single and united country." This is the seventh reverse used on the Lincoln type since 1909.

The shield motif was designed by U.S. Mint Artistic Infusion Program Associate Designer Lyndall Bass, and engraved by Mint Sculptor-Engraver Joseph Menna. It was unveiled during the launch ceremony for the fourth and final 2009 Bicentennial cent, held at the Ulysses S. Grant Memorial at the Capitol Building in Washington, D.C., November 12, 2009.

In addition to a new reverse design, the Shield Reverse cents feature a modern update of Victor David Brenner's original portrait for the 1909 Lincoln cent.

Striking and Sharpness. Striking is generally sharp. All Proof Lincoln, Shield Reverse, cents are mirror Proofs, usually with cameo or frosted contrast between the devices and the fields.

Availability. Cents of this design are minted in large quantities. They are readily available in the numismatic marketplace, and have successfully entered circulation through normal distribution channels. High-quality Proofs (PF-69 and 70) are common in the secondary market.

GRADING STANDARDS

Caveat: These grading standards do not take sharpness of strike into account.

MS-60 to 70 (Mint State). *Obverse and Reverse:* At MS-65 and higher, luster is rich on all areas; there is no rubbing, and no contact marks are visible except under magnification. Coins with full or nearly full mint orange-red color can be designated RD; those with a substantial percentage of red-orange and of brown can be called RB; and those with full (or nearly full) brown-toned surfaces can be designated BN. Some 2009 cents, even from original rolls and bags, have surface marks that look like water spots.

2011-D. Graded MS-67RD.

The Lincoln, Shield Reverse, cent is seldom collected in grades lower than MS-60.

PF-60 to 70 (Proof). *Obverse and Reverse:* PF-65 and higher coins are RB (with colors nicely blended) or RD, the latter with bright red-orange color sometimes fading to hints of brown. Some tiny flecks are normal on coins certified as PF-65 but should be microscopic or absent above that level. PF–60 and 61 coins can be dull, stained, or spotted and still have some original mint luster. Proof coins with fingerprints are impaired and must

2012-S. Graded PF-70RD Deep Cameo.

be given a lower numerical grade. Lower-grade Proofs usually have poor eye appeal. Generally, Proofs of this type below PF-65 are not desired by most collectors.

	Mintage	Cert	Avg	%MS	MS-63RB	MS-65RD	MS-66RD	MS-67RD
					PF-65RD	PF-67RD	PF-67Cam	PF-68DCam
2010	1,963,630,000	6,618	65.5	100%	$0.15	$0.30	$10	$15
2010, Satin Finish	583,897	280	67.0	100%	$5	$10	$15	$20
2010-D	2,047,200,000	1,972	65.6	100%	$0.15	$0.30	$10	$15
2010-D, Satin Finish	583,897	375	67.6	100%	$5	$10	$15	$20
2010-S, Proof	1,689,364	5,803	69.1		$4	$7	$8	$10
2011	2,402,400,000	497	66.3	100%	$0.15	$0.30	$10	$15
2011-D	2,536,140,000	281	66.8	100%	$0.15	$0.30	$10	$15
2011-S, Proof	1,673,010	7,467	69.1		$5	$7	$8	$10
2012	3,132,000,000	285	66.9	100%	$0.15	$0.30	$10	$15
2012-D	2,883,200,000	176	66.9	100%	$0.15	$0.30	$10	$15
2012-S, Proof	1,239,148	1,392	69.1		$5	$7	$8	$10
2013	3,750,400,000	562	66.3	100%	$0.15	$0.30	$10	$15
2013-D	3,319,600,000	388	66.9	100%	$0.15	$0.30	$10	$15
2013-S, Proof	1,274,505	2,622	69.1		$5	$7	$8	$10
2014	3,990,800,000	745	66.6	100%	$0.15	$0.30	$10	$15
2014-D	4,155,600,000	725	66.6	100%	$0.15	$0.30	$10	$15
2014-S, Proof	1,190,369	4,148	69.3		$5.00	$7.50	$8	$10
2015	4,691,614,029	583	66.2	100%	$0.15	$0.30	$10	$15
2015-D	4,674,314,029	359	66.6	100%	$0.15	$0.30	$10	$15
2015-S, Proof	1,050,164	4,011	69.3		$5.00	$7.50	$8	$10
2016	4,698,000,000	251	66.5	100%	$0.15	$0.30	$10	$15
2016-D	4,420,400,000	394	66.6	100%	$0.15	$0.30	$10	$15
2016-S, Proof	1,011,624	1,900	69.5		$5.00	$7.50	$8	$10
2017-P (a)	4,361,220,000	2,552	66.6	100%	$0.15	$0.30	$10	$15
2017-D	4,272,800,000	483	66.4	100%	$0.15	$0.30	$10	$15
2017-S, Enhanced Unc.	979,477	0	n/a			$7.50	$8	$10
2017-S, Proof	4,066,800,000	13,835	69.9		$5	$7.50	$8	$10
2018	3,736,400,000	380	66.0	99%	$0.15	$0.30	$10	$15
2018-D	844,220	387	66.7	100%	$0.15	$0.30	$10	$15
2018-S, Proof		17,141	69.8		$5	$7.50	$8	$10
2019					$0.15	$0.30	$10	$15
2019-D					$0.15	$0.30	$10	$15
2019-S, Proof					$5	$7.50	$8	$10
2019-W (b)					$5	$8		
2019-W, Proof (b)							$12	$15
2019-W, Reverse Proof (b)							$18	$25

a. All 2017-dated cents struck at the Philadelphia Mint bear a P mintmark in honor of the 225th anniversary of U.S. coinage. **b.** In 2019, the Mint included special cents from the West Point Mint as premiums in each of three separate products: In the 2019 Silver Proof Set, a 2019-W Reverse Proof cent; and in the 2019 Uncirculated Mint Set, a 2019-W Uncirculated cent.

Two-Cent Pieces
1864–1873

AN OVERVIEW OF TWO-CENT PIECES

The two-cent piece was introduced in 1864. Made of bronze, it was designed by U.S. Mint chief engraver James B. Longacre, and was the first circulating U.S. coin to bear the motto IN GOD WE TRUST. At the time, coins were scarce in circulation because of the ongoing Civil War and the public's tendency to hoard hard currency, and silver and gold issues were entirely absent. Treasury officials felt that the two-cent piece would prove to be very popular as a companion to the Indian Head cent. However, the introduction of the nickel three-cent piece in 1865 negated much of this advantage, the production of two-cent pieces declined, and by 1873, when the denomination was discontinued, its only coinage consisted of Proofs for collectors.

A full "type set" of the two-cent piece consists of but a single coin. Most available in Mint State are the issues of 1864 and 1865, often seen with original mint orange color fading to natural brown. Proofs are available for all years.

The Coinage Act of 1873 eliminated not only the two-cent piece but also the three-cent silver and half dime.

FOR THE COLLECTOR AND INVESTOR: TWO-CENT PIECES AS A SPECIALTY

Two-cent pieces can be collected by date and variety. A basic display consists of an 1864, Large Motto; 1864, Small Motto (rare); 1873, Close 3; and 1873, Open 3, the latter two being available only in Proof format. Some specialists opt to include just one of the 1873 varieties.

Collectors should select both circulation strikes and Proofs with care, for the number of truly choice *original* (unprocessed, undipped, not retoned) coins is but a small percentage of the whole. As a type, though, the two-cent piece is readily available for collecting.

Several specialized studies of two-cent pieces have been published over a long span of years, the first of significance being "Two-Cent Pieces of the United States," by S.W. Freeman, published in the *Numismatist*, June 1954.

TWO-CENT PIECES (1864–1873)

Designer: *James B. Longacre.* **Weight:** *6.22 grams.*
Composition: *.950 copper, .050 tin and zinc.* **Diameter:** *23 mm.*
Edge: *Plain.* **Mint:** *Philadelphia.*

Circulation Strike

Proof

History. The two-cent piece, struck in bronze like the new Indian Head cents, made its debut under the Mint Act of April 22, 1864. Coins of all kinds were scarce in circulation at the time, due to hoarding. The outcome of the Civil War was uncertain, and Americans desired "hard money." Many millions of two-cent pieces were struck in 1864, after which the mintage declined, due to once-hoarded Indian Head cents becoming available again and to the new nickel three-cent coins being introduced in 1865. Continually decreasing quantities were made through 1872, and only Proofs were struck in the coin's final year, 1873.

Striking and Sharpness. Points to check for sharpness on the obverse include WE in the motto, the leaves, and the horizontal shield lines. On the reverse check the wreath details and the border letters. Check the denticles on both sides. Most coins are quite well struck.

Availability. Most MS coins are dated 1864 or 1865, after which the availability declines sharply, especially for the issue of 1872. Among 1864 coins most seen are of the Large Motto variety. Small Motto coins are elusive. Coins with much or nearly all *original* mint red-orange color are rare for the later years, with most in the marketplace being recolored. The 1864, Small Motto, Proof, is a great rarity, with fewer than two dozen estimated to exist. Coins of 1873 were made only in Proof format, of the Close 3 and Open 3 styles. Proofs of most dates are easily enough acquired. Very few have original color. Do not overlook the many nice brown and red-and-brown pieces on the market (some investors acquire only "red" copper coins, leaving many great values among others). Refer to the comments under Proof Indian Head cents.

GRADING STANDARDS

MS-60 to 70 (Mint State). *Obverse and Reverse:* At MS-65 and higher, the luster is rich on all areas. There is no rubbing, and no contact marks are visible except under magnification. Coins with full or nearly full mint orange-red color can be designated RD (the color on this is often more orange than red), those with full or nearly full brown-toned surfaces can be designated BN, and those with a substantial percentage of red-orange

1864, Large Motto, RPD; Leone-9. Graded MS-66RD.

and of brown can be called RB. Ideally, MS-65 or finer coins should have good eye appeal, which in the RB category means nicely blended colors, not stained or blotched, the latter problem mostly with dipped and irregularly retoned coins. Below MS-65, full RD coins become scarce, although MS-64RD coins can be attractive. These usually have more flecks and tiny spots, while the color remains bright. At MS–60 to 62, RD coins are virtually nonexistent, unless they have been dipped. The ANA standards allow for "dull" and/or "spotted" coins at MS–60 and 61 as well as incomplete luster. As a rule, MS–60 to 63BN coins can be fairly attractive if not spotted or blotched, but those with hints of color usually lack eye appeal.

AU-50, 53, 55, 58 (About Uncirculated).
Obverse: WE shows light wear, this being the prime place to check. The arrowheads and leaves also show light wear. At AU-50, level wear is more noticeable. At AU–53 and 55, wear is less. At AU-58, friction is evident, rather than actual wear. Luster, toned brown, is nearly complete at AU-58, but may be incomplete in the field. *Reverse:* At AU-50, light wear is seen on the ribbon and the higher-relief areas of the leaves and grains, while the lower areas retain their detail. Some luster may be present in protected areas. At AU–53 and 55, wear is lesser and luster is more extensive. An AU-58 coin will have nearly full luster and show only light friction.

1871. Graded AU-58.

EF-40, 45 (Extremely Fine). *Obverse:* Wear is more extensive. WE shows wear extensively, but still is clear. The leaves lack detail on their highest points. Some scattered marks are normal at this and lower grades. *Reverse:* The higher-relief parts of the leaves and ribbon bow show further wear, as do other areas.

1864, Small Motto. Graded EF-45.

VF-20, 30 (Very Fine). *Obverse:* WE is clear, but not strong. Leaves show more wear, as do all other areas. *Reverse:* Still more wear is seen, but the leaves still are separately defined. The wheat grains are very clear.

1864, Small Motto. Graded VF-20.

F-12, 15 (Fine). *Obverse:* WE is the defining factor and is very weak, but readable, if only barely. Other areas show more wear. The edges of some leaves are gone, blending them into adjacent leaves. *Reverse:* Wear is more extensive. Near the apex of the wreath the edges of some leaves are gone, blending them into adjacent leaves. The grains of wheat are clear, but some are slightly weak.

    Illustrated coin: WE is very weak.

1872. Graded F-15.

VG-8, 10 (Very Good). *Obverse:* WE is gone, although the ANA grading standards and *Photograde* suggest "very weak." IN GOD and TRUST are readable, but some areas may be weak. The inner edges of most leaves are gone. *Reverse:* The wear appears to be less extensive than on the obverse. All lettering is bold. A few grains of wheat may be well worn or even missing.

1872. Graded VG-8.

G-4, 6 (Good). *Obverse:* Wear is more extensive, and the leaf bunches are in flat clumps. IN GOD and TRUST are very worn, with a letter or two not visible. *Reverse:* All letters are clear. The wreath is mostly in outline on G-4. On G-6, perhaps half the grains are visible.

1864, Small Motto. Graded G-4.

AG-3 (About Good). *Obverse:* The motto shows only a few letters. The leaves are flat. Only a few horizontal shield stripes can be seen. *Reverse:* The wreath is in outline form. The letters are weak, with 20% to 40% worn away entirely.

1872. Graded AG-3.

PF-60 to 70 (Proof). *Obverse and Reverse:* Gem PF-65 two-cent pieces will have very few hairlines, and these visible only under a strong magnifying glass. At any level and color, a Proof with hairlines has likely been cleaned, a fact usually overlooked. At PF-67 or higher there should be no evidence of hairlines or friction at all. Such a coin is fully original. PF-60 coins can be dull from repeated dipping and cleaning and are often toned iridescent colors or have mottled surfaces. At PF-63, the mirrorlike fields should be attractive, and hairlines should be minimal, most easily seen when the coin is held at an angle to the light. No rubbing is seen. PF-64 coins are even nicer. As a general rule, Proofs of 1873 are of very high quality but, unless dipped or cleaned, are nearly always toned light brown.

1872. Graded PF-64RD.

1864, Small Motto   1864, Large Motto

1865, Plain 5   1865, Fancy 5

	Mintage	Cert	Avg	%MS	G-4	F-12	VF-20	EF-40	AU-50	MS-60BN	MS-63BN / PF-63BN	MS-64BN / PF-64BN	MS-65RD / PF-65RB
1864, Small Motto (a)	(b)	648	50.4	60%	$235	$400	$575	$800	$1,000	$1,500	$1,750	$2,000	$13,500
Auctions: $2,232, MS-65BN, January 2015; $29,375, MS-65, February 2015; $763, EF-45, October 2015; $540, EF-40, February 2018													
1864, Large Motto (c)	19,822,500	3,931	60.6	84%	$15	$25	$30	$50	$80	$110	$175	$200	$1,150
Auctions: $1,116, MS-66BN, June 2015; $305, MS-65BN, May 2015; $129, MS-63BN, January 2015; $111, AU-58, October 2015													
1864, Small Motto, Proof † (d)	(e)	8	64.8								$25,000	$30,000	$85,000
Auctions: $105,750, PF-66RD, June 2014													
1864, Large Motto, Proof	100+	129	64.6								$750	$1,150	$4,500
Auctions: $3,760, PF-66BN, October 2015; $3,642, PF-66BN, January 2015; $3,535, PF-65RB, August 2015; $646, PF-62BN, February 2015													
1865 (f)	13,640,000	2,541	60.2	81%	$15	$25	$30	$50	$80	$110	$175	$200	$1,150
Auctions: $540, MS-65RB, May 2015; $399, MS-65BN, February 2015; $646, MS-64RD, August 2015; $199, MS-64BN, January 2015													
1865, Proof	500+	157	64.7								$450	$550	$1,500
Auctions: $2,820, PF-66RB, October 2015; $3,290, PF-65RB, June 2015; $1,997, PF-65RB, January 2015; $1,178, PF-65BN, January 2015													
1866	3,177,000	539	58.4	74%						$120	$175	$220	$2,000
Auctions: $1,692, MS-65RD, July 2015; $587, MS-64RD, January 2015; $517, MS-64RB, October 2015; $212, MS-64BN, April 2015													
1866, Proof	725+	171	64.7								$450	$550	$1,250
Auctions: $4,700, PF-66RB, July 2015; $1,527, PF-65RB, January 2015; $1,175, PF-65RB, September 2015; $470, PF-64BN, January 2015													

† Ranked in the *100 Greatest U.S. Coins* (fourth edition). **a.** The circulated Small Motto is distinguished by a wider D in GOD, and the first T in TRUST nearly touching the ribbon crease at left. **b.** Included in circulation-strike 1864, Large Motto, mintage figure. **c.** The circulated Large Motto is distinguished by a narrow D in GOD, and a 1 mm gap between the first T in TRUST and the ribbon crease. **d.** 20 to 30 examples are known. **e.** Included in 1864, Large Motto, Proof, mintage figure. **f.** Circulated varieties show the tip of the 5 either plain or fancy (curved).

1867, Doubled Die Obverse
FS-02-1867-101.

1869, Doubled Die Obverse
FS-02-1869-101.

	Mintage	Cert	Avg	%MS	G-4	F-12	VF-20	EF-40	AU-50	MS-60BN	MS-63BN	MS-64BN	MS-65RD
											PF-63BN	PF-64BN	PF-65RB
1867	2,938,750	634	58.6	76%	$20	$30	$35	$50	$80	$130	$190	$235	$3,250
	Auctions: $646, MS-64RB, August 2015; $423, MS-64RB, October 2015; $282, MS-64BN, February 2015; $141, MS-61BN, May 2015												
1867, Doubled Die Obverse (g)	**(h)**	65	44.8	37%	$125	$185	$350	$700	$1,150	$2,000	$3,000	$3,750	
	Auctions: $22,325, MS-65RD, January 2014; $1,175, AU-55, March 2016												
1867, Proof	*625+*	203	64.7								$450	$550	$1,250
	Auctions: $940, PF-65RB, August 2015; $763, PF-65BN, September 2015; $646, PF-64BN, January 2015												
1868	2,803,750	614	58.9	74%	$20	$36	$50	$75	$110	$150	$250	$375	$5,000
	Auctions: $1,292, MS-65RB, January 2015; $1,057, MS-65RB, October 2015; $834, MS-64RB, June 2015; $211, MS-63BN, February 2015												
1868, Proof	*600+*	191	64.8								$450	$550	$1,250
	Auctions: $470, PF-64BN, January 2015												
1869	1,546,500	531	58.2	74%	$25	$40	$55	$80	$125	$160	$250	$375	$2,850
	Auctions: $2,820, MS-65RD, September 2015; $1,540, MS-65RB, January 2015; $763, MS-65BN, July 2015; $329, MS-64BN, June 2015												
1869, Doubled Die Obverse	**(i)**	0	n/a							$600	$900	$1,250	
	Auctions: No auction records available.												
1869, Proof	*600+*	237	64.6								$450	$550	$1,300
	Auctions: $2,820, PF-66RB, July 2015; $1,527, PF-66RB, October 2015; $1,881, PF-65RD, September 2015; $822, PF-65BN, January 2015												
1870	861,250	413	56.2	69%	$35	$55	$85	$150	$200	$275	$300	$575	$6,000
	Auctions: $1,762, MS-65RB, August 2015; $329, MS-63RB, October 2015; $258, MS-62BN, May 2015; $62, EF-40, January 2015												
1870, Proof	*1,000+*	275	64.5								$450	$600	$1,350
	Auctions: $3,290, PF-67BN, July 2015; $1,821, PF-65RD, February 2015; $1,116, PF-65RB, January 2015; $705, PF-65BN, September 2015												
1871	721,250	605	56.0	67%	$40	$85	$110	$165	$225	$300	$375	$800	$7,500
	Auctions: $1,292, MS-64RD, January 2015; $1,008, MS-64RB, August 2015; $411, MS-64BN, June 2015; $282, MS-61BN, July 2015												
1871, Proof	*960+*	277	64.6								$450	$600	$1,375
	Auctions: $8,233, PF-66RD, July 2015; $2,115, PF-65RB, August 2015; $1,057, PF-64RB, February 2015; $881, PF-64RB, January 2015												
1872	65,000	372	32.3	23%	$400	$550	$775	$1,100	$1,650	$2,800	$3,750	$4,000	$22,500
	Auctions: $3,760, MS-65, March 2016; $2,350, MS-62, October 2016; $999, AU-50, December 2015												
1872, Proof	*950+*	345	64.5								$900	$1,000	$1,750
	Auctions: $1,762, PF-66RB, June 2015; $1,410, PF-65BN, August 2015; $1,292, PF-65BN, February 2015; $2,820, PF-64BN, June 2015												
1873, Close 3, Proof	*400*	280	63.9								$3,200	$3,500	$4,750
	Auctions: $4,700, PF-66BN, June 2015; $5,141, PF-66, March 2015; $3,535, PF-65RB, October 2015												
1873, Open 3, Proof (Alleged Restrike)	*200*	130	63.6								$3,000	$3,150	$5,000
	Auctions: $11,162, PF-66RB, October 2015; $5,640, PF-66BN, January 2015; $3,966, PF-65, February 2015												

g. This variety is somewhat common in low-end circulated grades, but is considered rare in EF and AU, and very rare in MS.
h. Included in circulation-strike 1867 mintage figure. **i.** Included in circulation-strike 1869 mintage figure.

Three-Cent Pieces
1851–1889

AN OVERVIEW OF THREE-CENT PIECES

SILVER THREE-CENT PIECES

The silver three-cent piece or *trime* is one of the more curious coins in American numismatics. The rising price of silver in 1850 created a situation in which silver coins cost more to produce than their face value. Mintages dropped sharply and older pieces disappeared from circulation. In 1851 a solution was provided by the three-cent piece. Instead of being made with 90% silver content, the fineness was set at 75%. Accordingly, the coins were worth less intrinsically, and there was no advantage in melting them. Large quantities were made through 1853. In that year, the standards for regular silver coins were changed, and other denominations reappeared on the marketplace, making the trime unnecessary. Mintages dropped beginning in 1854, until 1873, when production amounted to just 600 Proofs for collectors.

Of the three varieties of trimes, Variety 2 (1854–1858) is at once the scarcest and, by far, the most difficult to find with a sharp strike. In fact, not one in fifty Variety 2 coins is needle sharp. Curiously, when such pieces are found they are likely to be dated 1855, the lowest-mintage issue of the type. Trimes of the Variety 1 design (1851–1853) vary widely in striking, but can be found sharp. Variety 3 coins (1859–1873) often are sharp.

Mint State coins are readily found for Variety 1 and are usually in grades from MS–60 to 63 or so, although quite a few gems are around with attractive luster. Sharply struck gems are another matter and require some searching to find. Mint State Variety 2 trimes are all rare, and when seen are apt to be miserably struck and in lower grades. Variety 3 coins are readily found in Mint State, including in MS-65 and higher grades.

The term *trime* was first used by the director of the United States Mint, James Ross Snowden, at the time of the coins' production.

Proofs were made of all years, but not in quantity until 1858, when an estimated 210 were struck. For all dates after 1862, high-grade Proofs are much more readily available today than are Mint State coins. Circulated examples are available of all three varieties. While extensively worn coins of Variety 1 are available, most Variety 2 coins are Fine or better and most Variety 3 pieces are VF or better.

FOR THE COLLECTOR AND INVESTOR:
SILVER THREE-CENT PIECES AS A SPECIALTY

Trimes cover a fairly long span of years and embrace several design types, but comprise no "impossible" rarities. Accordingly, it is realistic to collect one of each Philadelphia Mint coin from 1851 to 1873 plus the 1851-O. There are two overdates in the series, 1862, 2 Over 1 (which is distinct and occurs only in circulation-strike format) and 1863, 3 Over 2 (only Proofs, and not boldly defined), which some specialists collect and others ignore. A curious variety of 1852 has the first digit of the date over an inverted 2.

Typically, a high-grade set includes Mint State examples of all issues 1851 through 1857 and Proofs after that date. As noted, Variety 2 trimes usually are very poorly struck, save the occasionally encountered sharp 1855. As an example, a specialist in the series who found an 1856 with needle-sharp details, at three times the regular market price, might be well advised to buy it. After 1862, Mint State coins are rare for most dates. The formation of a choice Mint State set 1851 through 1872 plus a Proof 1873 would be a formidable challenge.

A set of circulated coins can be gathered through and including 1862, after which such pieces become very rare. Most later dates will have to be acquired on a catch-as-catch-can basis, perhaps by acquiring impaired Proofs for certain of the years.

NICKEL THREE-CENT PIECES

Nickel three-cent pieces were introduced in 1865 to help fill the need for coins in circulation. At the time, silver and gold issues were hoarded, and were available only at a premium. The nickel three-cent piece joined the Indian Head cent and the new (as of 1864) two-cent piece. The coin proved to be very popular in its time, and millions were struck. In 1866 the nickel five-cent piece was introduced, after which time the demand for the nickel three-cent piece diminished somewhat. However, pieces were made in quantity until 1876. In that year silver coins again returned to circulation, and mintages for the nickel three-cent piece dropped sharply. Only Proofs were made in 1877 and 1878. In later years, mintages ranged from small to modest, except for 1881.

Mint State coins are readily available for the early years, although many if not most have weak striking in areas or are from clashed dies. Pristine, sharp Mint State coins on the market are mostly of later years, in the 1880s, where such pieces are the rule, not the exception.

FOR THE COLLECTOR AND INVESTOR:
NICKEL THREE-CENT PIECES AS A SPECIALTY

Nickel three-cent coins are interesting to collect by date sequence from 1865 to 1889. Varieties are provided by the 1873, Close 3, and 1873, Open 3, and the 1887, 7 Over 6, overdate. A set of Mint State coins is considerably more difficult to form than a run of Proofs. A hand-selected set of well-struck coins MS-65 or finer could take several years to complete.

Among Proofs, the rarest year is 1865, probably followed by the "perfect date" (not overdate) 1887. Proofs of the 1860s and early 1870s are scarce in PF-65 with excellent strike and eye appeal. Proofs of the latter decade of coinage are much more readily available and usually are choice.

SILVER THREE-CENT PIECES (TRIMES) (1851–1873)

Variety 1 (1851–1853): **Designer:** *James B. Longacre.* **Weight:** *0.80 gram.*
Composition: *.750 silver, .250 copper.* **Diameter:** *14 mm.*
Edge: *Plain.* **Mints:** *Philadelphia and New Orleans.*

Variety 1 (1851–1853)   Variety 1, Proof

Variety 2 (1854–1858): **Designer:** *James B. Longacre.* **Weight:** *0.75 gram.*
Composition: *.900 silver, .100 copper.* **Diameter:** *14 mm.* **Edge:** *Plain.* **Mint:** *Philadelphia.*

Variety 2 (1854–1858)   Variety 2, Proof

Variety 3 (1859–1873): **Designer:** *James B. Longacre.* **Weight:** *0.75 gram.*
Composition: *.900 silver, .100 copper.* **Diameter:** *14 mm.* **Edge:** *Plain.* **Mint:** *Philadelphia.*

Variety 3 (1859–1873)   Variety 3, Proof

History. In 1850 Americans began hoarding their silver coins, as the flood of gold from California made silver disproportionately valuable. To provide a small coin for commerce, the Mint introduced the silver three-cent piece, or *trime*. These were .750 fine (as opposed to the standard .900 fineness), and contained less than 3¢ of metal, so there was no incentive to hoard or melt them. Three different designs were made, Variety 1 of which was struck from 1851 to 1853. These coins were popular in their time and circulated widely. These are distinguished from the other two designs by having no outline or frame around the obverse star. The Act of February 21, 1853, reduced the amount of silver in other denominations (from the half dime to the half dollar, but not the dollar), which discouraged people from hoarding them. The tiny trime lost the public's favor, and mintages decreased.

In 1854 the design was changed considerably, creating Variety 2, which was made through 1858. The alloy was modified to the standard for other issues and the weight was lightened. A raised border was added to the obverse star plus two line frames around it. On the reverse an olive branch was placed above the III and a bundle of arrows below it. This new motif proved to be very difficult to strike up properly.

In 1859 the design was modified again, creating Variety 3. Demand for the denomination continued to be small, and after 1862 very few were made for circulation, as silver coins were hoarded by the war-weary public and began to trade at a premium. Under the Coinage Act of 1873 the trime was discontinued, and that year only Proofs were struck. Also in that year, nearly the entire production of non-Proof coins of 1863 to 1872 was melted.

Striking and Sharpness. On the Variety 1 obverse the tiny shield at the center of the star often lacks certain details. On the reverse check the details and strength of the III. On both sides check the rims. Needle-sharp coins are in the minority. Sharpness of strike has been nearly completely overlooked in the marketplace.

Trimes of Variety 2 are usually poorly struck, with some or all of these characteristics: obverse lettering weak in places; frames around the star of inconsistent strength or missing in certain areas; shield weak in places; reverse stars irregular and poorly formed; olive branch and arrows weak in areas; weak or irregular rims. Now and then a sharp 1855 is found.

Most Variety 3 trimes are sharply struck. Points to look for include full outlines around the star, full shield on the star, and full leaf details and sharp stars.

Most Proofs are needle sharp and have mirrored surfaces, although some of the late 1860s and early 1870s can have slightly grainy or satiny lustrous surfaces. Striking quality varies. Lint marks and surface problems are not unusual. Careful examination is recommended.

Availability. Circulated examples of the Variety 1 trimes are plentiful. MS coins are often seen, although the 1851-O is scarce in MS and high circulated grades. Most MS coins are lustrous and attractive, especially at 63 and above. Circulated Variety 2 coins are scarce in all grades, particularly so at MS-64 and higher. With a needle-sharp strike, MS-65 and higher are *rarities*. Among Variety 3 trimes, circulated coins of the years 1859 to 1862 are easy to find. All later dates range from scarce to rare in circulation-strike format. MS-63 and better coins 1865 and later are very rare. A few Proofs were made in the early 1850s and are great rarities today. After 1857, production increased to an estimated 210 or so in 1858, through 500 to 700 or so as a yearly average in the 1860s to 1873.

GRADING STANDARDS

MS-60 to 70 (Mint State). *Obverse and Reverse:* At MS-60, some abrasion and very minor contact marks are evident, most noticeably on the obverse star and the C ornament on the reverse. At MS-63, abrasion is hard to detect except under magnification. An MS-65 coin will have no abrasion. Luster should be full and rich (not grainy). Grades above MS-65 are defined by having fewer marks as perfection is approached. Most high-grade Mint State coins are of the Variety 3 design.

1853, Variety 1. Graded MS-66.

AU-50, 53, 55, 58 (About Uncirculated). *Obverse:* Light wear is most obvious on the star arms and shield on Variety 1, and on the points of the frames on Variety 2 and Variety 3. At AU-50, luster is evident, but only on part of the field. At AU-58 luster is nearly complete. *Reverse:* Light wear is seen on the C ornament and III. On Variety 2 and 3, light wear is seen on the leaves and arrows.

Illustrated coin: This is sharply struck, as are most Variety 3 trimes.

1863, Variety 3. Graded AU-50.

EF-40, 45 (Extremely Fine). *Obverse:* More wear is seen, most noticeable on the ridges of the star arms, this in addition to more wear on the frames (Variety 2 and Variety 3). Luster is absent, or seen only in traces. *Reverse:* More wear is seen on the C ornament and III. On Variety 2 and Variety 3 more wear is seen on the leaves and arrows.

1869, Variety 3. Graded EF-45.

VF-20, 30 (Very Fine). *Obverse:* Further wear reduced the relief of the star. On Variety 2 and Variety 3 the frames show further wear and begin to blend together. The center shield shows wear, and its border is indistinct in areas, but its horizontal and vertical stripes are fully delineated (unless the coin was weakly struck). *Reverse:* Still more wear is seen on the C ornament and III. On Variety 2 and Variety 3 the high-relief areas of the

1862, Variety 3. Graded VF-30.

leaves and the feathers of the arrow are partially worn away. Stars are flat at their centers (on sharply struck coins in addition to, as expected, on weak strikes).

F-12, 15 (Fine). *Obverse:* The star is worn so as to have lost most of its relief. On Variety 2 and Variety 3 the frames are mostly blended together. The center shield shows wear, and its border is flat (or else showing only slight separation of its two outlines), but its horizontal and vertical stripes still are delineated (unless the coin was weakly struck). *Reverse:* Still more wear is seen on the C ornament and III. On Variety 2 and Variety 3 the

1851, Variety 1. Graded F-12.

high-relief areas of the leaves, and the feathers of the arrow, have slight if any detail. Stars are flat. The designs within the C ornament are missing much detail.

VG-8, 10 (Very Good). *Obverse:* The border is incomplete in places, but all lettering is bold. The horizontal and vertical stripes within the shield begin to blend together, but most remain well delineated. *Reverse:* Still more wear is seen on all areas. The designs within the C ornament have more detail gone.

    Illustrated coin: The obverse of this coin shows VG wear, but if the dent in the star was considered it would grade lower.

1852, Variety 1. Graded VG-10.

G-4, 6 (Good). *Obverse:* The border is worn into the tops of the letters and the bottom of the date. The shield is blended into the star, and only traces of the shield outline remain. In this grade most coins seen are Variety 1. *Reverse:* The border is worn into the outer parts of the stars. Additional wear is seen in all other areas.

1851, Variety 1. Graded G-6.

AG-3 (About Good). *Obverse:* The star is flat. Strong elements of the shield are seen, but the tiny lines are mostly or completely blended together. Lettering and date are weak and partially missing, but the date must be identifiable. In this grade most coins seen are Variety 1. *Reverse:* The border is worn into the stars, with outer elements of the stars now gone. Additional wear is seen in all other areas. The designs within the C ornament are only in outline form.

1853, Variety 1. Graded AG-3.

PF-60 to 70 (Proof). *Obverse and Reverse:* Proofs that are extensively cleaned and have many hairlines, or that are dull and grainy, are lower level, such as PF–60 to 62. These are difficult to verify as Proofs. For a trime with medium hairlines and good reflectivity, an assigned grade of PF-64 is indicated, and with relatively few hairlines, gem PF-65. PF-66 should have hairlines so delicate that magnification is needed to see them. Above that, a Proof should be free of such lines.

1857, Variety 2. Graded PF-66.

Illustrated coin: Note the remarkable sharpness of strike, particularly evident on the obverse.

	Mintage	Cert	Avg	%MS	G-4	VG-8	F-12	VF-20	EF-40	AU-50	MS-60	MS-63	MS-65
											PF-63	PF-64	PF-65
1851	5,447,400	1,270	60.9	87%	$30	$45	$50	$65	$80	$165	$200	$275	$675
	Auctions: $3,055, MS-67, July 2015; $2,115, MS-66, June 2015; $1,292, MS-66, September 2015; $446, MS-64, January 2015												
1851, Proof (a)		0	n/a								—		
	Auctions: No auction records available.												
1851-O	720,000	470	58.5	73%	$45	$65	$75	$100	$175	$275	$550	$1,000	$3,000
	Auctions: $11,163, MS-67, July 2014; $12,925, MS-66, December 2013; $793, MS-62, October 2014; $317, AU-55, October 2014												

a. 1 or 2 examples are known.

1852, 1 Over Inverted 2	**1853, Repunched Date**	**1854, Repunched Date**
FS-3S-1852-301.	*FS-3S-1853-301.*	*FS-3S-1854-301.*

	Mintage	Cert	Avg	%MS	G-4	VG-8	F-12	VF-20	EF-40	AU-50	MS-60 / PF-63	MS-63 / PF-64	MS-65 / PF-65
1852, 1 Over Inverted 2 (b)	**(c)**	1	61.0	100%				—		$775	$950	$1,150	$1,425	$1,950
Auctions: No auction records available.													
1852	18,663,500	1,656	57.1	77%	$30	$45	$50	$65	$80	$165	$200	$275	$675
Auctions: $2,643, MS-67, June 2015; $1,057, MS-66, July 2015; $1,028, MS-66, August 2015; $705, MS-65, January 2015													
1852, Proof (d)		0	n/a								—		
Auctions: No auction records available.													
1853	11,400,000	897	53.7	66%	$30	$45	$50	$65	$80	$165	$200	$275	$675
Auctions: $1,233, MS-66, June 2015; $587, MS-65, October 2015; $423, MS-64, January 2015; $152, AU-58, September 2015													
1853, Repunched Date (e)	**(f)**	0	n/a						$100	$200	$260	$300	$1,000
Auctions: No auction records available.													
1854	671,000	375	59.1	73%	$40	$55	$60	$75	$120	$225	$350	$700	$2,650
Auctions: $3,290, MS-66, June 2015; $2,820, MS-65, January 2015; $646, MS-62, September 2015; $199, AU-53, April 2015													
1854, Repunched Date (g)	**(h)**	0	n/a						$185	$325	$500	$800	$3,500
Auctions: No auction records available.													
1854, Proof	25–35	8	64.1								$12,000	$18,500	$35,000
Auctions: $32,900, PF-65, January 2015; $41,125, PF-65, June 2014; $14,688, PF-64, October 2014; $6,463, PF-63, August 2015													
1855	139,000	154	53.5	53%	$40	$65	$75	$125	$200	$350	$600	$1,450	$8,000
Auctions: $9,400, MS-66, August 2015; $1,645, MS-64, January 2015; $399, AU-55, April 2015; $305, EF-45, July 2015													
1855, Proof	30–40	24	64.8								$5,000	$8,500	$15,000
Auctions: $21,150, PF-66Cam, October 2014; $8,225, PF-64, October 2014; $14,400, PF-65, January 2018													
1856	1,458,000	352	58.0	69%	$40	$45	$50	$70	$120	$235	$360	$700	$2,500
Auctions: $1,292, MS-64, July 2015; $1,086, MS-64, October 2015; $329, MS-62, May 2015; $352, AU-58, April 2015													
1856, Proof	40–50	32	64.5								$5,000	$7,500	$12,500
Auctions: $22,325, PF-66, August 2016; $19,388, PF-66, February 2015; $9,988, PF-64, October 2015													
1857	1,042,000	356	58.1	76%	$40	$45	$50	$70	$120	$235	$360	$800	$3,000
Auctions: $5,405, MS-66, January 2015; $2,820, MS-65, September 2015; $940, MS-64, October 2015; $646, AU-58, April 2015													
1857, Proof	60–80	36	64.6								$3,750	$5,000	$10,000
Auctions: $15,863, PF-66, June 2014													
1858	1,603,700	643	57.4	67%	$40	$45	$50	$70	$120	$235	$360	$700	$2,250
Auctions: $5,875, MS-67, July 2015; $1,821, MS-65, February 2015; $1,116, MS-64, September 2015; $353, AU-58, April 2015													
1858, Proof	210	106	64.5								$2,500	$4,500	$6,500
Auctions: $12,925, PF-67, August 2015; $6,462, PF-65, October 2015													
1859	364,200	345	60.2	77%	$40	$45	$50	$60	$90	$175	$215	$300	$1,000
Auctions: $1,762, MS-66, January 2015; $1,645, MS-66, September 2015; $881, MS-65, October 2015; $763, MS-65, August 2015													
1859, Proof	800	111	64.1								$800	$1,100	$2,000
Auctions: $4,700, PF-66Cam, August 2015; $2,643, PF-66, June 2015; $1,880, PF-65, January 2015; $1,586, PF-64Cam, February 2015													
1860	286,000	341	58.1	64%	$40	$45	$50	$60	$90	$175	$215	$300	$1,000
Auctions: $434, MS-64, October 2015; $317, MS-63, April 2015; $211, MS-61, May 2015; $166, AU-55, January 2015													
1860, Proof	1,000	79	63.8								$1,000	$1,500	$4,000
Auctions: $4,935, PF-65, August 2015; $960, PF-64, January 2018													

b. An inverted 2 is visible beneath the primary 1. "A secondary date punch was obviously punched into the die in an inverted orientation and then corrected after some effacing of the die" (*Cherrypickers' Guide to Rare Die Varieties,* sixth edition, volume I). **c.** Included in circulation-strike 1852 mintage figure. **d.** 1 example is known. **e.** Secondary digits are visible to the north of the primary 1 and 8. This repunched date can be detected on lower-grade coins. **f.** Included in 1853 mintage figure. **g.** Secondary digits are visible to the west of the primary digits on the 8 and 5. **h.** Included in circulation-strike 1854 mintage figure.

1862, 2 Over 1
FS-3S-1862-301.

	Mintage	Cert	Avg	%MS	G-4	VG-8	F-12	VF-20	EF-40	AU-50	MS-60 / PF-63	MS-63 / PF-64	MS-65 / PF-65
1861	497,000	863	60.8	77%	$40	$45	$50	$60	$90	$175	$215	$300	$875
Auctions: $2,938, MS-67, June 2015; $1,410, MS-66, January 2015; $519, MS-64, August 2015; $164, AU-53, May 2015													
1861, Proof	1,000	91	64.1								$750	$1,100	$1,750
Auctions: $3,055, PF-66, June 2015; $2,351, PF-66, September 2015; $1,175, PF-65, January 2015													
1862, 2 Over 1 (i)	(j)	339	63.4	90%	$40	$45	$50	$60	$95	$190	$240	$350	$1,050
Auctions: $1,762, MS-66, June 2015; $881, MS-65, August 2015; $540, MS-64, February 2015; $329, AU-58, April 2015													
1862	343,000	1,150	62.5	87%	$40	$45	$50	$60	$90	$175	$215	$285	$875
Auctions: $2,585, MS-67, September 2015; $1,116, MS-66, June 2015; $734, MS-65, January 2015; $223, AU-58, April 2015													
1862, Proof	550	138	64.0								$750	$1,100	$1,750
Auctions: $2,127, PF-66, October 2015; $2,115, PF-65, January 2015; $1,527, PF-65, August 2015; $646, PF-63, June 2015													
1863	21,000	81	64.2	96%	$475	$550	$600	$650	$750	$1,000	$1,250	$2,000	$3,500
Auctions: $7,050, MS-67, January 2015; $5,875, MS-67, October 2015													
1863, So-Called 3 Over 2, Proof	(k)	0	n/a								$2,500	$4,500	$7,500
Auctions: $8,812, PF-67, January 2015; $12,925, PF-65, July 2015; $5,405, PF-64, October 2015; $2,640, PF-63, January 2018													
1863, Proof	460	139	64.3								$750	$1,100	$1,500
Auctions: $3,995, PF-66Cam, January 2015; $1,703, PF-65Cam, January 2015													
1864	12,000	92	63.4	92%	$475	$525	$625	$650	$750	$850	$1,200	$1,400	$3,000
Auctions: $3,760, MS-66, October 2015; $1,116, MS-63, June 2015; $1,880, AU-58, January 2015													
1864, Proof	470	174	64.6								$750	$1,000	$1,500
Auctions: $2,585, PF-66, August 2015; $3,055, PF-65Cam, January 2015; $1,116, PF-65, July 2015; $1,088, PF-64Cam, August 2015													
1865	8,000	106	62.5	87%	$475	$525	$575	$600	$700	$850	$1,750	$2,350	$4,500
Auctions: $5,170, MS-67, August 2015; $4,230, MS-66, October 2015; $1,527, MS-64, January 2015; $2,232, MS-63, January 2015													
1865, Proof	500	159	64.4								$750	$1,000	$1,500
Auctions: $3,642, PF-67, October 2015; $3,995, PF-66, June 2015; $1,645, PF-65, August 2015; $3,290, PF-64, January 2015													
1866	22,000	87	62.9	89%	$450	$525	$575	$625	$800	$950	$1,400	$1,800	$3,750
Auctions: $11,750, MS-67, October 2015; $8,812, MS-66, October 2015; $998, EF-40, January 2015; $940, EF-40, July 2015													
1866, Proof	725	206	64.2								$750	$1,000	$1,500
Auctions: $6,462, PF-67, January 2015; $1,762, PF-66, August 2015; $1,292, PF-64, September 2015; $705, PF-63, July 2015													
1867	4,000	46	60.7	83%	$450	$525	$575	$650	$850	$1,200	$1,700	$3,000	$12,500
Auctions: $14,100, MS-65, October 2015; $4,465, MS-64, August 2015; $3,643, MS-64, September 2015; $1,292, AU-50, July 2015													
1867, Proof	625	263	64.4								$750	$1,000	$1,500
Auctions: $1,762, PF-66, September 2015; $1,527, PF-65, August 2015; $998, PF-64, January 2015; $822, PF-64, July 2015													

i. A secondary 1 is evident beneath the 2 of the date. "This overdate is believed to be due more to economy (the Mint having used a good die another year) than to error. Circulated examples are about as common as the regular-dated coin" (*Cherrypickers' Guide to Rare Die Varieties*, sixth edition, volume I). **j.** Included in circulation-strike 1862 mintage figure. **k.** Included in 1863, Proof, mintage figure.

	Mintage	Cert	Avg	%MS	F-12	VF-20	EF-40	AU-50	MS-60	MS-63	MS-64 / PF-63	MS-65 / PF-64	MS-66 / PF-65
1868	3,500	36	60.4	83%	$850	$1,150	$1,750	$2,500	$4,000	$5,500	$15,000	$22,500	$27,500
Auctions: $21,150, MS-66, October 2015; $28,200, MS-66, May 2015; $5,405, AU-58, July 2015; $648, MS-66, February 2018
1868, Proof	600	269	64.1								$750	$1,000	$1,500
Auctions: $3,525, PF-66, October 2015; $1,410, PF-66, January 2015; $1,997, PF-65, August 2015; $940, PF-63, September 2015
1869	4,500	50	62.4	86%	$550	$700	$1,100	$1,200	$1,400	$2,200	$4,000	$6,750	$8,000
Auctions: $9,987, MS-65, October 2015; $4,230, MS-64, October 2015; $1,645, MS-62, August 2015; $940, EF-40, July 2015
1869, Proof	600	181	64.4								$750	$1,000	$1,500
Auctions: $7,050, PF-67, August 2015; $1,880, PF-66, January 2015; $1,645, PF-65, October 2015; $423, PF-62, June 2015
1869, So-Called 9 Over 8, Proof (a)	(b)	0	n/a								$3,750	$6,000	$8,500
Auctions: $9,987, PF-66, August 2015
1870	3,000	91	61.7	80%	$550	$650	$750	$950	$1,200	$1,800	$3,000	$4,500	$7,500
Auctions: $7,116, MS-66, October 2015; $470, EF-40, May 2015
1870, Proof	1,000	245	64.0								$750	$1,000	$1,500
Auctions: $1,880, PF-66, January 2015; $1,762, PF-65, September 2015; $1,762, PF-64, October 2015; $3,055, PF-63, October 2015
1871	3,400	149	63.7	91%	$550	$650	$950	$1,050	$1,100	$1,200	$1,500	$2,000	$3,000
Auctions: $3,290, MS-67, June 2015; $1,880, MS-66, February 2015; $1,645, MS-64, January 2015; $1,086, MS-63, November 2015
1871, Proof	960	221	64.0								$750	$1,000	$1,500
Auctions: $2,291, PF-66, January 2015; $1,527, PF-65, September 2015; $881, PF-63, July 2015; $646, PF-61, June 2015
1872	1,000	48	61.5	85%	$1,000	$1,250	$1,800	$2,250	$2,750	$4,000	$7,000	$10,000	$15,000
Auctions: $14,100, MS-67, August 2015; $54,050, MS-67, February 2015; $4,935, MS-65, October 2015; $13,200, MS-66, January 2018
1872, Proof	950	233	64.1								$750	$1,000	$1,500
Auctions: $11,750, PF-67Cam, January 2015; $2,585, PF-66, August 2015; $3,290, PF-65, October 2015; $1,645, PF-65, August 2015
1873, Close 3, Proof (a)	600	373	64.1								$2,000	$2,500	$3,000
Auctions: $12,220, PF-67, February 2015; $3,055, PF-66Cam, June 2015

a. Proof only. b. Included in 1869, Proof, mintage figure.

NICKEL THREE-CENT PIECES (1865–1889)

Designer: *James B. Longacre.* **Weight:** *1.94 grams.* **Composition:** *.750 copper, .250 nickel.*
Diameter: *17.9 mm.* **Edge:** *Plain.* **Mint:** *Philadelphia.*

Circulation Strike   **Proof**

History. The copper-nickel three-cent coin debuted in the final year of the Civil War, 1865. The American public was still hoarding silver coins (a situation that would continue until 1876), including the silver three-cent piece. The highest-denomination coin remaining in circulation at the time was the recently introduced two-cent piece. After 1875, when silver coins circulated once again, the three-cent denomination became redundant and mintages dropped. The last pieces were coined in 1889.

Striking and Sharpness. On the obverse check the hair and other portrait details. On the reverse the tiny vertical lines in the Roman numeral III can be weak. Check the denticles on both sides of the coin. Among circulation strikes, clashed dies are common, particularly for the earlier high-mintage years. Generally, coins of the 1860s and 1870s have weakness in one area or another. Many if not most of the 1880s are well struck. Proofs from 1878 onward often have satiny or frosty fields, rather than mirrored surfaces, and resemble circulation strikes.

Availability. Circulated examples of dates from 1865 to the mid-1870s are readily available. MS coins, particularly from the 1860s, are easily found, but often have areas of weakness or lack aesthetic appeal. MS coins of the 1880s are readily found for most dates (except for 1883, 1884, 1885, and 1887), some of them probably sold as Proofs. Many Proofs of the era had slight to extensive mint luster. Proofs were struck of all dates and can be found easily enough in the marketplace. The rarest is the first year of issue, 1865, of which only an estimated 500 or so were made. The vast majority of 1865s have a repunched date. Second rarest (not counting PF-only date of 1877) is the 1887 (perfect date, not the overdate) with a production of about 1,000 coins. Proofs of the years 1865 to 1876 can be difficult to find as true gems, while later Proofs are nearly all gems.

GRADING STANDARDS

MS-60 to 70 (Mint State). *Obverse and Reverse:* Mint luster is complete in the obverse and reverse fields. Lower grades such as MS–60, 61, and 62 can show some evidence of abrasion. This is usually on the area of the hair to the right of the face (on the obverse), and on the highest parts of the wreath (on the reverse). Abrasion can appear as scattered contact marks elsewhere. At MS-63, these marks are few, and on MS-65 they are fewer yet. In grades above MS-65, marks can only be seen under magnification.

1865. Graded MS-61.

AU-50, 53, 55, 58 (About Uncirculated). *Obverse:* Light wear is seen on the portrait, most notably on the upper cheek and on the hair to the right of the face. Mint luster is present in the fields, ranging from partial at AU-50 to nearly complete at AU-58. All details are sharp, unless lightly struck. *Reverse:* Light wear is seen on the top and bottom horizontal edges of the III and the wreath. Luster is partial at AU-50, increasing to nearly full at AU-58. All details are sharp, unless lightly struck.

1881. Graded AU-55.

EF-40, 45 (Extremely Fine). *Obverse:* More wear is seen on the cheek and the hair to the right of the face and neck. The hair to the right of the coronet beads shows light wear. *Reverse:* The wreath still shows most detail on the leaves. Some wear is seen on the vertical lines within III (but striking can also cause weakness). Overall the reverse appears to be very bold.

1889. Graded EF-40.

VF-20, 30 (Very Fine). *Obverse:* Most hair detail is gone, with a continuous flat area to the right of the face and neck, where the higher hair strands have blended together. The hair to the right of the coronet beads shows about half of the strands. *Reverse:* Higher details of the leaves are worn away; the central ridges are seen on some. Wear on the vertical lines in III has caused some to merge, but most are separate.

1880. Graded VF-25.

F-12, 15 (Fine). *Obverse:* Wear is more extensive. The forehead blends into the hair above it. About 10% to 29% of the hair detail to the right of the coronet remains, and much detail is seen lower, at the right edge opposite the ear and neck. Denticles are distinct. *Reverse:* The top (highest-relief) part of most leaves is flat. Many vertical lines in III are fused. Denticles are distinct.

1882. Graded F-15.

VG-8, 10 (Very Good). *Obverse:* Less hair detail shows. Denticles all are clear. *Reverse:* The leaves show more wear. The inner edges of some leaves are worn away, causing leaves to merge. Only about half, or slightly fewer, of the lines in III are discernible.

1865. Graded VG-10.

G-4, 6 (Good). *Obverse:* Most hair details are gone, but some remain at the lower right. The rim is worn smooth in areas, and many denticles are missing. The lettering is weak, but readable. *Reverse:* The leaves mostly are worn flat. Very few lines remain in III. The rim is worn smooth in areas, and many denticles are missing.

1867. Graded G-4.

AG-3 (About Good). *Obverse:* The rim is worn away and into the tops of most of the letters. The date remains bold. *Reverse:* The rim is worn away and into some of the leaves.

1867. Graded AG-3.

PF-60 to 70 (Proof). *Obverse and Reverse:* PF–60, 61, and 62 coins show varying amounts of hairlines in the field, decreasing as the grade increases. Fields may be dull or cloudy on lower-level pieces. At PF-65, hairlines are visible only under magnification and are very light; the cheek of Miss Liberty does not show any friction or "album slide marks." Above PF-65, hairlines become fewer, and in ultra-high grades are nonexistent, this mean-

1878. Graded PF-65.

ing that the coins have never been subject to wiping or abrasive cleaning. At PF-65 or better, expect excellent aesthetic appeal. Blotched, deeply toned, or recolored coins are sometimes seen at Proof levels from PF–60 through 65 or even 66 and should be avoided, but these are less often seen than on contemporary Proof nickel five-cent pieces.

1866, Doubled Die Obverse
FS-3N-1866-101.

	Mintage	Cert	Avg	%MS	G-4	VG-8	VF-20	EF-40	AU-50	MS-60	MS-63 PF-63	MS-65 PF-65	MS-66 PF-66
1865	11,382,000	2,075	59.6	77%	$18	$20	$30	$40	$65	$100	$160	$550	$1,100
	Auctions: $1,880, MS-66, January 2015; $399, MS-64, May 2015; $199, MS-61, November 2015; $111, AU-58, June 2015												
1865, Proof	500+	196	64.7								$1,500	$4,250	$6,500
	Auctions: $4,583, PF-66, November 2016; $5,288, PF-65, July 2015; $4,113, PF-64, August 2016												
1866	4,801,000	837	60	80%	$18	$20	$28	$40	$65	$100	$160	$550	$1,500
	Auctions: $7,637, MS-67, August 2015; $1,527, MS-66, June 2015; $111, MS-63, February 2015; $89, MS-62, April 2015												
1866, Doubled Die Obverse (a)	(b)	5	48.4	20%				$150	$250	$350	$450	$1,000	
	Auctions: No auction records available.												
1866, Proof	725+	306	64.5								$350	$1,100	$2,000
	Auctions: $2,820, PF-66, January 2015; $1,880, PF-66, September 2015; $1,527, PF-65, August 2015; $1,292, PF-65, June 2015												

a. Moderate doubling is visible on AMERICA and on portions of the hair. "The dies clashed midway through the obverse's life. Mid– and late–die-state coins exhibit the clash marks and die cracks as progression occurs. This variety has proven extremely scarce" (*Cherrypickers' Guide to Rare Die Varieties*, sixth edition, volume I). **b.** Included in circulation-strike 1866 mintage figure.

	Mintage	Cert	Avg	%MS	G-4	VG-8	VF-20	EF-40	AU-50	MS-60	MS-63 PF-63	MS-65 PF-65	MS-66 PF-66
1867	3,915,000	634	59.0	74%	$15	$20	$30	$40	$65	$100	$160	$650	$1,650
Auctions: $238, MS-64, January 2015; $141, MS-63, February 2015; $111, MS-62, May 2015; $79, AU-58, August 2015													
1867, Proof	625+	313	64.7								$350	$850	$1,500
Auctions: $9,400, PF-68, July 2015; $1,880, PF-66, January 2015; $1,527, PF-66, September 2015; $763, PF-65, August 2015													
1868	3,252,000	597	59.5	77%	$15	$20	$30	$40	$65	$100	$160	$625	$1,100
Auctions: $881, MS-66, August 2015; $822, MS-65, January 2015; $111, MS-63, February 2015; $117, MS-62, April 2015													
1868, Proof	600+	286	64.8								$350	$1,050	$1,450
Auctions: $1,065, PF-66, January 2015; $1,116, PF-65, September 2015; $705, PF-65, August 2015; $446, PF-64, January 2015													
1869	1,604,000	402	60.7	81%	$15	$20	$30	$40	$65	$125	$185	$750	$1,500
Auctions: $1,292, MS-66, August 2015; $141, MS-63, February 2015; $105, MS-62, February 2015; $129, MS-61, November 2015													
1869, Proof	600+	376	64.7								$350	$750	$1,150
Auctions: $5,170, PF-67, July 2015; $881, PF-66, January 2015; $1,028, PF-65, October 2015; $705, PF-65, January 2015													
1870	1,335,000	429	60.3	79%	$20	$25	$30	$40	$65	$140	$195	$725	$1,450
Auctions: $223, MS-64, March 2015; $164, MS-63, November 2015; $129, MS-62, May 2015; $84, AU-58, April 2015													
1870, Proof	1,000+	354	64.4								$350	$750	$1,150
Auctions: $1,175, PF-66, January 2015; $763, PF-65, September 2015; $329, PF-64, April 2015; $235, MS-61, November 2015													
1871	604,000	238	59.5	80%	$20	$25	$30	$40	$65	$140	$195	$750	$1,500
Auctions: $3,525, MS-67, January 2015; $2,723, MS-66, September 2015; $2,350, MS-66, February 2015; $282, MS-64, May 2015													
1871, Proof	960+	366	64.5								$350	$750	$1,150
Auctions: $5,875, PF-67Cam, October 2015; $940, PF-66, February 2015; $763, PF-65, January 2015; $258, PF-63, November 2015													
1872	862,000	198	59.2	75%	$20	$25	$30	$40	$65	$150	$210	$1,200	$2,200
Auctions: $881, MS-66, January 2015; $940, MS-65, October 2015; $211, MS-63, May 2015; $117, MS-62, July 2015													
1872, Proof	950+	435	64.5								$350	$750	$1,150
Auctions: $4,700, PF-66, February 2015; $1,600, PF-66, July 2015; $505, PF-65, June 2015; $293, PF-63, November 2015													
1873, Close 3	390,000	109	55.6	65%	$20	$25	$30	$40	$65	$150	$210	$1,350	$2,750
Auctions: $2,232, MS-66, August 2015; $423, MS-64, June 2015; $399, MS-64, October 2015; $237, MS-63, February 2015													
1873, Open 3	783,000	96	53.8	64%	$20	$25	$30	$40	$70	$160	$350	$1,500	$4,000
Auctions: $3,055, MS-65, January 2015; $587, MS-64, June 2015; $223, MS-63, October 2015; $199, MS-63, May 2015; $780, MS-65, March 2018													
1873, Close 3, Proof	1,100+	449	64.4								$350	$750	$1,250
Auctions: $969, PF-66, August 2015; $734, PF-65, June 2015; $540, PF-65, January 2015; $290, PF-64, November 2015													
1874	790,000	194	57.2	70%	$20	$25	$30	$40	$65	$150	$210	$975	$2,000
Auctions: $2,115, MS-66, October 2015; $188, MS-63, August 2015; $176, MS-62, January 2015; $79, AU-58, February 2015													
1874, Proof	700+	340	64.6								$350	$750	$1,100
Auctions: $601, PF-66, January 2015; $564, PF-66, October 2015; $587, PF-65, June 2015; $329, PF-64, April 2015													
1875	228,000	230	62.0	89%	$20	$25	$35	$45	$80	$175	$225	$800	$1,500
Auctions: $646, MS-65, August 2015; $329, MS-64, November 2015; $446, AU-58, April 2015; $129, AU-55, May 2015													
1875, Proof	700+	252	64.3								$350	$1,000	$1,500
Auctions: $998, PF-65, January 2015; $646, PF-65, June 2015; $470, PF-64, January 2015; $305, PF-64, October 2015													
1876	162,000	131	57.8	72%	$20	$25	$35	$65	$110	$200	$260	$1,600	$2,250
Auctions: $1,880, MS-66, June 2015; $1,292, MS-65, February 2015; $940, MS-64, July 2015; $616, AU-58, May 2015													
1876, Proof	1,150+	400	64.5								$350	$700	$1,050
Auctions: $1,057, PF-66, September 2015; $881, PF-66, July 2015; $517, PF-65, January 2015; $540, PF-64, May 2015													
1877, Proof (c)	900	458	64.8								$2,250	$4,000	$4,750
Auctions: $7,344, PF-66, November 2016; $5,875, PF-66, August 2016; $3,525, PF-65, May 2016; $2,820, PF-64, August 2016													
1878, Proof (c)	2,350	693	64.8								$875	$1,000	$1,100
Auctions: $1,527, PF-67, August 2015; $1,410, PF-66, March 2016; $646, PF-63, January 2015; $374, PF-60, May 2015													

c. Proof only.

1887, 7 Over 6, Proof
FS-3N-1887-302.

	Mintage	Cert	Avg	%MS	G-4	VG-8	VF-20	EF-40	AU-50	MS-60	MS-63 / PF-63	MS-65 / PF-65	MS-66 / PF-66
1879	38,000	177	57.1	69%	$60	$70	$100	$125	$175	$300	$400	$950	$1,200
Auctions: $998, MS-66, July 2015; $1,057, MS-65, August 2015; $575, MS-65, January 2015; $258, AU-53, May 2015													
1879, Proof	3,200	953	65.1								$400	$625	$750
Auctions: $2,820, PF-68, January 2015; $998, PF-67, July 2015; $675, PF-66Cam, August 2015; $411, PF-65, May 2015													
1880	21,000	204	58.5	77%	$100	$120	$150	$200	$220	$350	$450	$850	$1,250
Auctions: $705, MS-65, August 2015; $564, MS-64, January 2015; $296, MS-63, October 2015; $211, MS-60, May 2015													
1880, Proof	3,955	981	65.0								$400	$550	$750
Auctions: $540, PF-66, June 2015; $470, PF-66, January 2015; $376, PF-65, November 2015; $298, PF-64, April 2015													
1881	1,077,000	639	58.7	70%	$20	$25	$30	$40	$65	$125	$185	$650	$1,000
Auctions: $493, MS-65, July 2015; $152, MS-63, July 2015; $94, MS-62, August 2015; $89, AU-58, October 2015													
1881, Proof	3,575	1,014	65.2								$375	$550	$750
Auctions: $3,760, PF-68, February 2015; $1,057, PF-67, February 2015; $587, PF-66, January 2015; $282, PF-63, April 2015													
1882	22,200	130	49.1	39%	$125	$135	$200	$225	$275	$450	$600	$1,850	$2,750
Auctions: $587, MS-64, January 2015; $199, VF-30, February 2015; $164, VF-25, October 2015; $164, F-15, July 2015													
1882, Proof	3,100	1,041	65.1								$400	$550	$750
Auctions: $4,230, PF-68, January 2015; $446, PF-65, March 2015; $258, PF-62, August 2015; $199, PF-60, May 2015													
1883	4,000	51	52.7	49%	$275	$350	$500	$550	$850	$1,500	$2,750	$10,000	$15,000
Auctions: $7,638, MS-65, August 2016; $940, AU-50, May 2016; $588, EF-45, September 2016; $16,800, MS-66, April 2018													
1883, Proof	6,609	1,542	64.7								$400	$550	$750
Auctions: $5,287, PF-68, January 2015; $705, PF-66, February 2015; $376, PF-65, November 2015; $235, PF-64, January 2015													
1884	1,700	33	51.3	39%	$550	$875	$1,450	$2,000	$2,750	$3,500	$6,500	$17,500	$25,000
Auctions: $2,115, MS-61, December 2015; $1,998, EF-45, February 2015; $1,880, VF-30, July 2016													
1884, Proof	3,942	1,197	64.8								$400	$550	$750
Auctions: $998, PF-67, October 2015; $734, PF-66, August 2015; $376, PF-65, January 2015; $305, PF-64, February 2015													
1885	1,000	36	57.2	67%	$875	$1,100	$1,750	$2,500	$3,000	$4,500	$6,500	$12,500	$17,500
Auctions: $16,450, MS-66, June 2015; $8,225, MS-65, November 2016; $7,050, MS-64, August 2016; $3,408, AU-55, October 2016													
1885, Proof	3,790	1,005	64.6								$400	$550	$750
Auctions: $646, PF-66, June 2015; $340, PF-64, February 2015; $329, PF-64, January 2015; $258, PF-60, August 2015													
1886, Proof (c)	4,290	1,068	64.7								$400	$625	$800
Auctions: $900, PF-67, January 2015; $505, PF-66, January 2015; $517, PF-65, August 2015; $329, PF-64, February 2015													
1887	5,001	112	55.0	59%	$275	$325	$450	$525	$625	$700	$850	$1,500	$2,250
Auctions: $1,703, MS-66, August 2015; $1,763, MS-66, February 2015; $763, MS-63, July 2015; $705, EF-45, January 2015													
1887, Proof	2,960	353	64.2								$400	$825	$950
Auctions: $1,880, PF-67, June 2015; $540, PF-65, July 2015; $517, PF-65, January 2015; $423, PF-64, May 2015													
1887, 7 Over 6, Proof (d)	(e)	484	64.8								$450	$700	$900
Auctions: $2,585, PF-66, August 2015; $998, PF-66, October 2015; $517, PF-64Cam, January 2015; $376, PF-62, August 2015													
1888	36,501	311	59.1	67%	$50	$65	$75	$90	$150	$300	$400	$750	$1,250
Auctions: $1,527, MS-67, January 2015; $564, MS-65, September 2015; $305, MS-63, May 2015; $446, AU-58, February 2015													
1888, Proof	4,582	1,072	64.8								$400	$550	$750
Auctions: $3,055, PF-68, October 2015; $1,762, PF-67, February 2015; $600, PF-66, January 2015; $446, PF-65, February 2015													
1889	18,125	251	59.1	66%	$80	$120	$165	$235	$265	$350	$450	$800	$1,350
Auctions: $1,645, MS-66, January 2015; $795, MS-66, June 2015; $188, AU-55, May 2015; $176, AU-50, July 2015													
1889, Proof	3,436	1,063	65.0								$400	$550	$750
Auctions: $734, PF-67, January 2015; $646, PF-66, August 2015; $399, PF-65, September 2015; $282, PF-64, January 2015													

c. Proof only. **d.** Strong remnants of the underlying 6 are evident on either side of the lower portion of the 7, with the 1 and both 8's clearly repunched. This Proof overdate is relatively common; note that the regular date can be valued higher than the variety. **e.** Included in 1887, Proof, mintage figure.

Nickel Five-Cent Pieces
1866 to Date

AN OVERVIEW OF NICKEL FIVE-CENT PIECES

Five-cent pieces made of nickel were introduced in 1866, in an era in which the silver half dime as well as other silver denominations were not seen in circulation. More than a dozen designs and their variations have graced the "nickel" in the past 140-plus years.

While Shield nickels of both varieties are slightly scarce in upper Mint State levels, they are within the financial reach of most collectors. Proofs are available of each variety, but the 1866–1867, With Rays, and the 1913 Buffalo, Variety 1, issues are rare.

The quality of strike presents a challenge across the various types of nickel five-cent pieces, most particularly with the 1866–1867, With Rays, for there are fewer possibilities from which to choose. Although 1913–1938 Buffalo, Variety 2, nickels are often poorly struck, there are enough sharp ones that finding a choice example should present no great challenge for the collector.

FOR THE COLLECTOR AND INVESTOR: FIVE-CENT PIECES AS A SPECIALTY

Shield nickels of the 1866–1883 era are often collected by date sequence. A full set includes 1866 and 1867, With Rays, plus 1867 to 1883, Without Rays. In addition, there is the 1879, 9 Over 8, overdate, which is found only in Proof format but is readily available (constituting perhaps a third or so of the Proof mintage of 3,200 for the 1879 year) and the 1883, 3 Over 2 (scarce, and available only as a circulation strike).

Circulation strikes are available of all Shield nickel dates, 1866 to 1883, except 1877 and 1878, which were made only in Proof format. A set of Proofs can be completed except for the 1867, With Rays, which is exceedingly rare in Proof, with an estimated population of fewer than two dozen coins. Most 1878 Proofs are frosty and appear not much different from Mint State, but only Proofs were made this year.

In circulated grades, Shield nickels are available in proportion to their mintage figures. The dates 1879 to 1881 had high Proof mintages (in the context of Proof figures), but low circulation-strike mintages, and thus they are key dates in the latter format. In other words, a gem MS-65 1880 Shield nickel (16,000 coined, but few were saved, as collectors acquired Proofs instead) is exceedingly rare today. In the same year 3,955 Proofs were struck, all were preserved by collectors and dealers, and today the Proof 1880 is one of the most plentiful dates.

Liberty Head nickels of the 1883, Without CENTS (or "No CENTS"), variety are plentiful in Mint State and also in Proof. Later dates With CENTS, through 1912, are generally available in proportion to their mintages. The 1885 and 1886 are considered to be key dates. Proofs are readily collectible, although pristine high-quality examples can be hard to find. The 1912-D and 1912-S are scarce. In 1913 an estimated five Liberty Head nickels were privately made, and today stand as famous rarities.

Among Buffalo nickels, 1913 to 1938, the different dates and mints can be collected easily enough in circulated grades, although certain issues such as 1913-S, Variety 2; 1921-S; and 1926-S are on the scarce side. An overdate, 1918-D, 8 Over 7, is a rarity at all grade levels. Curious varieties are provided by the very rare 1916, Doubled Date; the scarce 1937-D, 3-Legged (the die was heavily polished, resulting in some loss of detail); and the fascinating and readily available 1938-D, D Over S, overmintmark.

In choice or gem Mint State most branch-mint Buffalo nickels, 1914–1927, are fairly scarce, and some are

Popularized in the 1890s and throughout the beginning of the 1900s, coin-operated machines took cents and other denominations, but the coin of choice was the nickel. Pictured is a postcard for Horn & Hardart restaurants, 1930s, where patrons would serve themselves with such coin-operated devices.

quite rare. Most branch-mint coins of the 1920s are lightly struck in one area or another, with the 1926-D being particularly infamous in this regard. Sharply struck examples of such varieties are worth much more than lightly struck ones, although the grading services take no particular note of such differences. Matte Proofs of dates 1913 to 1916 were struck, and mirror-finish Proofs were made in 1936 and 1937. These exist today in proportion to their mintages.

Jefferson nickels from 1938 to date are readily collectible in Mint State and Proof format. Many otherwise common varieties can be very rare if sharply struck.

SHIELD (1866–1883)

Designer: *James B. Longacre.* **Weight:** *5 grams.* **Composition:** *.750 copper, .250 nickel.*
Diameter: *20.5 mm.* **Edge:** *Plain.* **Mint:** *Philadelphia.*

Variety 1, Rays Between Stars
(1866–1867)

Variety 1, Rays Between Stars,
Proof

Variety 2, Without Rays
(1867–1883)

Variety 2, Without Rays, Proof

History. The nickel five-cent piece was introduced in 1866. At the time, silver coins (except the trime) did not circulate in the East or Midwest. The new denomination proved popular, and "nickels" of the Shield variety were made continuously from 1866 to 1883. All 1866 nickels have rays between the stars on the reverse, as do a minority of 1867 issues, after which this feature was dropped. In 1877 and 1878 only Proofs were made, with no circulation strikes. The design, by Chief Engraver James B. Longacre, is somewhat similar to the obverse of the two-cent piece. Some Shield nickels were still seen in circulation in the 1930s, by which time most had been worn nearly smooth.

Striking and Sharpness. Sharpness can be a problem for Shield nickels in the 1860s through 1876, much less so for later years. On the obverse the horizontal shield stripes, vertical stripes, and leaves should be checked. The horizontal stripes in particular can be blended together. On the reverse the star centers can be weak. Check all other areas as well. Die cracks are seen on *most* circulation-strike Shield nickels, and do not affect value. Proof Shield nickels were struck of all dates 1866 to 1883, including two varieties of 1867 (With Rays, a great rarity, and the usually seen Without Rays). Fields range from deeply mirrorlike to somewhat grainy in character to mirror-surface, depending on a given year. Many of 1878, a date struck only in Proof format, have *lustrous* surfaces or prooflike surfaces combined with some luster, resembling a circulation strike. While most Proofs are sharp, some have weakness on the shield on the obverse and/or the star centers on the reverse. Lint marks or tiny recessed marks from scattered debris on the die faces are sometimes encountered, especially on issues of the 1870s, but not factored into the grade in commercial certification unless excessive.

Availability. Circulated coins generally are available in proportion to their mintage quantities (exceptions being the 1873, Open 3, and 1873, Close 3, varieties, which tend to be elusive in all grades despite their relatively high mintage). MS coins are similarly available, except that 1880 is a rarity. Those dated 1882 and 1883 are plentiful.

GRADING STANDARDS

MS-60 to 70 (Mint State). *Obverse and Reverse:* At MS-60 some abrasion and very minor contact marks are evident, most noticeably on high points of the shield on the obverse and the field on the reverse. Sometimes light striking on the shield and stars can be mistaken for light wear, and marks on the numeral 5 on the reverse can be from the original planchet surface not struck up fully. At MS-63 abrasions are hard to detect except

1873, Open 3. Graded MS-66.

under magnification. An MS-65 coin will have no abrasion. Luster should be full and rich (not grainy). Grades above MS-65 are defined by having no marks that can be seen by the naked eye. Higher-grade coins display deeper luster or virtually perfect prooflike surfaces, depending on the dies used.

Illustrated coin: Note the faint golden toning along the obverse border.

AU-50, 53, 55, 58 (About Uncirculated). *Obverse:* Light wear is on the outside edges of the leaves, the frame of the shield, and the horizontal stripes (although the stripes can also be weakly struck). Mint luster is present in the fields, ranging from partial at AU-50 to nearly complete at AU-58. All details are sharp, unless lightly struck. *Reverse:* Light wear is seen on the numeral 5, and friction is seen in the field, identifiable as a change of color (loss of luster).

1867, Rays. Graded AU-58.

Luster is partial at AU-50, increasing to nearly full at AU-58. All details are sharp, unless lightly struck.

EF-40, 45 (Extremely Fine). *Obverse:* Nearly all shield border and leaf detail is visible. Light wear is seen on the shield stripes (but the horizontal stripes can be weakly struck). *Reverse:* More wear is seen on the numeral 5. The radial lines in the stars (if sharply struck to begin with) show slight wear. The field shows more wear.

1867, Rays. Graded EF-40.

VF-20, 30 (Very Fine). *Obverse:* The frame details and leaves show more wear, with much leaf detail gone. The shield stripes show more wear, and some of the vertical lines will begin to blend together. *Reverse:* More wear is seen overall, but some radial detail can still be seen on the stars.

1868. Graded VF-20.

F-12, 15 (Fine). *Obverse:* Most leaves are flat and have little detail, but will remain outlined. The shield frame is mostly flat. Most horizontal lines are blended together, regardless of original strike. Many vertical lines in the stripes are blended together. IN GOD WE TRUST is slightly weak. *Reverse:* All areas are in outline form except for slight traces of the star radials. Lettering is bold.

1867, Without Rays. Graded F-12.

VG-8, 10 (Very Good). *Obverse:* Many leaves are flat and blended with adjacent leaves. The frame is blended and has no details. Only a few horizontal lines may show. Vertical lines in the stripes are mostly blended. IN GOD WE TRUST is weak. *Reverse:* All elements are visible only in outline form. The rim is complete.

1879. Graded VG-10.

G-4, 6 (Good). *Obverse:* The shield and elements are seen in outline form except the vertical stripe separations. IN GOD WE TRUST is weak, and a few letters may be missing. *Reverse:* The rim is mostly if not completely worn away and into the tops of the letters.

    Illustrated coin: Overall this coin is slightly better than G-4, but the 5 in the date is weak, making G-4 an appropriate attribution.

1881. Graded G-4.

AG-3 (About Good). *Obverse:* The rim is worn down and blended with the wreath. Only traces of IN GOD WE TRUST can be seen. The date is fully readable. *Reverse:* The rim is worn down and blended with the letters, some of which may be missing.

1880. Graded AG-3.

PF-60 to 70 (Proof). *Obverse and Reverse:* PF–60, 61, and 62 coins show varying amounts of hairlines in the reverse field in particular, decreasing as the grade increases. Fields may be dull or cloudy on lower-level pieces. At PF-65, hairlines are visible only under magnification and are very light and usually only on the reverse. Above PF-65, hairlines become fewer, and in ultra-high grades are nonexistent, this meaning that the coins have never been subject to wiping or abrasive cleaning. At PF-65 or better, expect excellent aesthetic appeal.

1882. Graded PF-66.

1866, Repunched Date
Several varieties exist.

	Mintage	Cert	Avg	%MS	G-4	VG-8	F-12	VF-20	EF-40	AU-50	MS-60	MS-63	MS-65
											PF-63	PF-65	PF-66
1866, Rays	14,742,500	1,676	59.9	77%	$30	$45	$50	$100	$155	$240	$300	$425	$1,600
	Auctions: $2,056, MS-65, January 2015; $616, MS-64, February 2015; $176, MS-60, August 2015; $211, AU-58, May 2015												
1866, Repunched Date (a)	**(b)**	29	49.5	41%	$60	$100	$175	$250	$450	$1,000	$1,500	$3,250	
	Auctions: $12,925, MS-64, August 2014; $8,813, MS-64, October 2014; $1,293, AU-50, March 2013; $1,175, AU-50, August 2014												
1866, Rays, Proof	*600+*	273	64.7								$1,750	$3,000	$3,500
	Auctions: $2,585, PF-66, September 2015; $3,055, PF-65, January 2015; $1,997, PF-64, January 2015; $1,057, PF-61, October 2015												

a. There are at least five similar, very strong repunched dates for 1866; the values shown are typical for each. **b.** Included in circulation-strike 1866, Rays, mintage figure.

1873, Close 3	1873, Open 3	1873, Close 3, Doubled-Die Obverse

Several varieties exist. Pictured are
FS-05-1873-101 (left) and FS-05-1873-102 (right).

	Mintage	Cert	Avg	%MS	G-4	VG-8	F-12	VF-20	EF-40	AU-50	MS-60	MS-63	MS-65
											PF-63	PF-65	PF-66
1867, Rays	2,019,000	631	58.1	68%	$35	$50	$65	$130	$190	$285	$375	$500	$3,000
Auctions: $998, MS-64, January 2015; $705, MS-64, October 2015; $517, MS-63, June 2015; $117, EF-40, January 2015													
1867, Rays, Proof †	25+	31	64.5								$30,000	$40,000	$55,000
Auctions: $64,625, PF-66, January 2015; $25,850, PF-65, August 2015; $34,075, PF-64, August 2015													
1867, No Rays	28,890,500	1,013	59.6	73%	$25	$30	$35	$40	$65	$110	$140	$225	$800
Auctions: $1,116, MS-66, October 2015; $705, MS-65, January 2015; $305, MS-64, May 2015; $111, MS-60, February 2015													
1867, No Rays, Proof	600+	256	64.3								$475	$1,250	$2,500
Auctions: $3,760, PF-66, September 2015; $2,115, PF-66, October 2015; $1,410, PF-65, February 2015; $376, PF-63, January 2015													
1867, No Rays, Pattern Reverse, Proof (c)	(d)	3	65.0								$6,500	$10,000	
Auctions: $3,760, PF-66, June 2015													
1868	28,817,000	876	60.2	77%	$25	$30	$35	$40	$65	$110	$140	$225	$700
Auctions: $1,763, MS-66, October 2015; $940, MS-66, August 2016; $764, MS-65, October 2016; $164, MS-63, January 2015.													
1868, Proof	600+	216	64.7								$350	$900	$1,750
Auctions: $1,762, PF-66, September 2015; $1,116, PF-65, June 2015; $822, PF-65, January 2015; $270, PF-63, April 2015													
1869	16,395,000	520	60.2	82%	$25	$30	$35	$40	$65	$110	$140	$225	$750
Auctions: $587, MS-65, September 2015; $246, MS-64, May 2015; $176, AU-58, January 2015; $56, AU-50, February 2015													
1869, Proof	600+	348	64.6								$350	$700	$1,250
Auctions: $3,055, PF-67, June 2015; $1,116, PF-66, July 2015; $881, PF-65, January 2015; $646, PF-65, August 2015													
1870	4,806,000	232	58.7	78%	$30	$35	$60	$80	$90	$140	$210	$300	$1,350
Auctions: $7,638, MS-66, December 2015; $4,465, MS-66, February 2015; $1,292, MS-64, January 2015; $423, MS-64, August 2015													
1870, Proof	1,000+	317	64.3								$350	$700	$1,250
Auctions: $1,292, PF-66, October 2015; $763, PF-65, January 2015; $646, PF-65, October 2015; $258, PF-63, June 2015													
1871	561,000	102	55.5	68%	$80	$100	$150	$215	$280	$375	$450	$675	$1,950
Auctions: $4,230, MS-66, August 2016; $3,290, MS-66, August 2016; $3,055, MS-65, January 2015; $2,820, MS-66, October 2016													
1871, Proof	960+	330	64.5								$350	$800	$1,250
Auctions: $1,527, PF-66, September 2015; $1,410, PF-66, August 2015; $881, PF-65, October 2015; $646, PF-65, January 2015													
1872	6,036,000	272	58.8	72%	$35	$45	$85	$105	$125	$175	$235	$300	$1,350
Auctions: $3,525, MS-66, August 2016; $3,055, MS-66, May 2015; $1,997, MS-66, January 2015; $1,293, MS-65, October 2016													
1872, Proof	950+	358	64.8								$350	$675	$1,000
Auctions: $3,055, PF-67, July 2015; $2,585, PF-67, September 2015; $998, PF-66, January 2015; $493, PF-65, January 2015													
1873, Close 3	436,050	63	59.8	75%	$30	$40	$80	$100	$140	$200	$350	$750	$2,000
Auctions: $1,997, MS-65, August 2015; $822, MS-64, January 2015													
1873, Close 3, Doubled Die Obverse (e)	(f)	18	53.9	56%				$600	$1,000	$2,000	$3,000	$4,000	$10,000
Auctions: $1,880, MS-64, February 2015													
1873, Open 3	4,113,950	89	59.6	80%	$30	$35	$60	$80	$100	$140	$210	$300	$1,850
Auctions: $2,115, MS-66, July 2015; $1,880, MS-66, August 2015; $763, MS-64, October 2015; $600, MS-64, May 2015													
1873, Close 3, Proof	1,100+	365	64.5								$350	$675	$1,000
Auctions: $2,820, PF-67, January 2015; $1,292, PF-66, October 2015; $376, PF-64, February 2015; $258, PF-63, May 2015													

† Ranked in the *100 Greatest U.S. Coins* (fourth edition). **c.** These were made from a pattern (Judd-573) reverse die that is slightly different than the regular Without Rays design. **d.** 21 to 30 examples are known. **e.** There are several varieties of 1873, Close 3, Doubled Die Obverse. The values shown are representative of the more avidly sought varieties; others command smaller premiums. **f.** Included in circulation-strike 1873, Close 3, mintage figure.

1883, 3 Over 2
Several varieties exist, as well as pieces with a recut 3. Pictured are FS-05-1883-301 (left) and FS-05-1883-305 (right).

	Mintage	Cert	Avg	%MS	G-4	VG-8	F-12	VF-20	EF-40	AU-50	MS-60 / PF-63	MS-63 / PF-65	MS-65 / PF-66
1874	3,538,000	167	60.7	79%	$30	$40	$70	$95	$120	$170	$250	$325	$1,200
Auctions: $5,170, MS-66, October 2015; $2,820, MS-66, August 2015													
1874, Proof	700+	304	64.6								$350	$725	$1,100
Auctions: $3,290, PF-67, September 2015; $2,115, PF-66, January 2015; $340, PF-64, May 2015; $258, PF-63, January 2015													
1875	2,097,000	161	59.2	79%	$45	$60	$100	$130	$160	$220	$275	$360	$1,250
Auctions: $5,640, MS-66, January 2015; $3,290, MS-66, October 2015; $229, AU-55, May 2015; $188, AU-50, January 2015													
1875, Proof	700+	293	64.4								$350	$1,100	$1,650
Auctions: $3,290, PF-67, August 2015; $1,527, PF-66, January 2015; $881, PF-65, July 2015; $517, PF-64, March 2015													
1876	2,530,000	259	61.3	86%	$40	$55	$85	$130	$145	$200	$260	$325	$1,000
Auctions: $940, MS-65, June 2015; $376, MS-64, August 2015; $105, AU-55, January 2015; $164, AU-50, January 2015													
1876, Proof	1,150+	403	64.6								$350	$750	$1,000
Auctions: $2,350, PF-67, February 2015; $998, PF-66, July 2015; $763, PF-65, August 2015; $376, PF-64, January 2015													
1877, Proof (g)	900	428	64.5								$3,250	$4,500	$5,000
Auctions: $9,987, PF-67, September 2015; $6,462, PF-66, July 2015; $4,230, PF-65, June 2015; $3,525, PF-64, January 2015													
1878, Proof (g)	2,350	616	64.4								$1,250	$1,650	$2,000
Auctions: $1,880, PF-67, January 2015; $2,232, PF-66, July 2015; $1,233, PF-65, January 2015; $1,265, PF-64, June 2015													
1879	25,900	86	56.5	71%	$400	$500	$600	$660	$850	$1,050	$1,750	$2,000	$3,000
Auctions: $10,575, MS-67, July 2015; $5,405, MS-66, August 2016; $4,935, MS-66, March 2016; $2,820, MS-65, July 2015													
1879, Proof	3,200	572	64.8								$350	$650	$800
Auctions: $6,462, PF-68, January 2015; $564, PF-65, August 2015; $352, PF-64, May 2015; $282, PF-62, October 2015													
1879, 9 Over 8, Proof (h)	(i)	0	n/a								$500	$850	$1,100
Auctions: $2,361, PF-67, June 2015; $646, PF-65, August 2015; $470, PF-64, January 2015; $305, AU-58, November 2015													
1880	16,000	41	44.8	24%	$1,500	$2,000	$2,500	$3,000	$6,000	$7,500	$12,000	$20,000	$70,000
Auctions: $117,000, MS-66, January 2015; $8,233, AU-53, August 2016; $5,405, EF-45, March 2016; $3,995, AU-53, October 2015													
1880, Proof	3,955	901	64								$350	$675	$850
Auctions: $6,462, PF-68, January 2015; $3,995, PF-67, October 2015; $505, PF-65, January 2015; $423, PF-64, May 2015													
1881	68,800	176	46.1	48%	$250	$350	$425	$510	$600	$775	$1,150	$1,350	$2,750
Auctions: $3,173, MS-66, August 2016; $3,055, MS-66, December 2015; $2,350, MS66, October 2015; $822, AU58, January 2015													
1881, Proof	3,575	827	64.9								$350	$675	$850
Auctions: $1,292, PF-67, July 2015; $616, PF-66, October 2015; $493, PF-65, January 2015; $250, PF-62, April 2015													
1882	11,472,900	1,065	59.1	81%	$25	$30	$35	$45	$65	$110	$150	$225	$650
Auctions: $3,055, MS-67, July 2016; $734, MS-66, February 2015; $493, MS-65, January 2015; $235, MS-64, October 2015													
1882, Proof	3,100	936	65.1								$350	$600	$850
Auctions: $15,275, PF-67, August 2015; $1,116, PF-66, August 2015; $705, PF-65, January 2015; $352, PF-64, May 2015													
1883	1,451,500	1,758	61.9	83%	$25	$30	$35	$45	$65	$110	$150	$225	$650
Auctions: $2,938, MS-67, August 2015; $2,820, MS-67, January 2015; $1,057, MS-66, January 2015; $705, MS-66, August 2016													
1883, 3 Over 2 (j)	(k)	44	57.0	61%	$250	$325	$650	$950	$1,250	$1,500	$2,100	$2,500	$5,500
Auctions: $7,050, MS-65, January 2015; $1,527, MS-63, January 2015; $1,292, MS-60, June 2015; $1,175, AU-58, January 2015													
1883, Proof	5,419	1,139	64.8								$350	$600	$850
Auctions: $6,462, PF-68, January 2015; $470, PF-65, March 2015; $329, PF-64, August 2015; $282, PF-63, October 2015													

g. Proof only. **h.** This variety is confirmed only with Proof finish, although Breen mentions two circulation strikes and further mentions that there are "at least two varieties" (*Walter Breen's Complete Encyclopedia of U.S. and Colonial Coins*). In the *Guide Book of Shield and Liberty Head Nickels*, Bowers discusses research and theories from Breen, DeLorey, Spindel, and Julian, noting that the variety's overdate status is "not determined." **i.** Included in 1879, Proof, mintage figure. **j.** Several varieties exist. For more information, see the *Cherrypickers' Guide to Rare Die Varieties*, sixth edition, volume I. "Beware of 1882 Shield nickels with a filled-in, blobby 2, as these are very frequently offered as 1883, 3 Over 2. This is possibly the single most misunderstood coin in all U.S. coinage." (Howard Spindel, communication to Q. David Bowers, quoted in *A Guide Book of Shield and Liberty Head Nickels*.) **k.** Included in circulation-strike 1883 mintage figure.

LIBERTY HEAD (1883–1913)

Designer: *Charles E. Barber.* **Weight:** *5 grams.* **Composition:** *.750 copper, .250 nickel.*
Diameter: *21.2 mm.* **Edge:** *Plain.* **Mints:** *Philadelphia, Denver, and San Francisco.*

Variety 1, Without CENTS   **Variety 1, Without CENTS, Proof**
(1883)

Variety 2, With CENTS   *Mintmark locations is on the*   **Variety 2, With CENTS, Proof**
(1883–1912)   *reverse, to the left of CENTS.*

History. Liberty Head nickels were popular in their time, minted in large quantities most years, and remained in circulation through the 1940s, by which time most were worn down to grades such as AG-3 and G-4. Stray coins could still be found in the early 1950s. Serious numismatic interest in circulated examples began in the 1930s with the popularity of Whitman and other coin boards, folders, and albums. Many of the scarcer dates were picked from circulation at that time. The five known 1913 Liberty Head nickels were not an authorized Mint issue, and were never placed into circulation.

Striking and Sharpness. Many Liberty Head nickels have areas of light striking. On the obverse, this is often seen at the star centers, particularly near the top border. The hair above the forehead can be light as well, and always is thus on 1912-S (the obverse die on this San Francisco issue is slightly bulged). On the reverse, E PLURIBUS UNUM can vary in sharpness of strike. Weakness is often seen at the wreath bow and on the ear of corn to the left (the kernels in the ear can range from indistinct to bold). Even Proofs can be weakly struck in areas. Mint luster can range from minutely pebbly or grainy (but still attractive) to a deep, rich frost. Some later Philadelphia coins show stress marks in the field, particularly the obverse, from the use of "tired" dies. This can be determined only by observation, as "slabbed" grades for MS coins do not indicate the quality of the luster or surfaces. Proof Liberty Head nickels were struck of all dates 1883 to 1912, plus both varieties of 1883 (with and without CENTS). The fields range from deeply mirrorlike to somewhat grainy character to mirror-surface, depending on a given year. While most Proofs are sharp, some have weakness at the star centers and/or the kernels on the ear of corn to the left of the ribbon bow. These weaknesses are overlooked by the certification services. Generally, later issues are more deeply mirrored than are earlier ones. Some years in the 1880s and 1890s can show graininess, a combination of mint luster and mirror quality. Lint marks or tiny recessed marks from scattered debris on the die faces are sometimes encountered, but not factored into third-party–certified grades unless excessive.

Availability. All issues from 1883 to 1912 are readily collectible, although the 1885 (in particular), 1886, and 1912-S are considered to be key dates. Most readily available are well-worn coins in AG-3 and G-4. As a class, VF, EF, and AU pieces are very scarce in relation to demand. MS coins are generally scarce in the 1880s, except for the 1883, Without CENTS, which is plentiful in all grades. MS pieces are less scarce in the 1890s and are easily found for most 20th-century years, save for 1909, 1912-D, and 1912-S, all of which are elusive.

GRADING STANDARDS

MS-60 to 70 (Mint State). *Obverse and Reverse:* Mint luster is complete in the obverse and reverse fields. Lower grades such as MS–60, 61, and 62 can show some evidence of abrasion, usually on the portrait on the obverse and highest parts of the wreath on the reverse, and scattered contact marks elsewhere. At MS-63 these marks are few, and at MS-65 they are fewer yet. In grades above MS-65, marks can only be seen under magnification.

1894. Graded MS-65.

AU-50, 53, 55, 58 (About Uncirculated). *Obverse:* Light wear is seen on the portrait and on the hair under LIB. Mint luster is present in the fields, ranging from partial at AU-50 to nearly complete at AU-58. All details are sharp, unless lightly struck. *Reverse:* Light wear is seen on the V, the other letters, and the wreath. Luster is partial at AU-50, increasing to nearly full at AU-58. All details are sharp, unless lightly struck.

1885. Graded AU-58.

EF-40, 45 (Extremely Fine). *Obverse:* Nearly all hair detail is visible, save for some lightness above the forehead. Stars show radial lines (except for those that may have been lightly struck). Overall bold appearance. *Reverse:* The wreath still shows most detail on the leaves. Denticles are bold inside the rim.

1885. Graded EF-40.

VF-20, 30 (Very Fine). *Obverse:* Letters in LIBERTY are all well defined. Hair detail is seen on the back of the head and some between the ear and the coronet. Denticles are bold. Some stars show radial lines. *Reverse:* Detail is seen in the wreath leaves. Lettering and denticles are bold, although E PLURIBUS UNUM may range from medium-light to bold (depending on the strike).

1888. Graded VF-20.

F-12, 15 (Fine). *Obverse:* All of the letters in LIBERTY are readable, although the I may be quite weak. The detail beginning at the front of hair is visible. Denticles are well defined. *Reverse:* Detail of the leaves begins to fade in the wreath. Denticles are well defined all around the border. E PLURIBUS UNUM has medium definition, and is complete.

1885. Graded F-15.

VG-8, 10 (Very Good). *Obverse:* Three or more letters in LIBERTY can be discerned. This can be a combination of two full letters and two or more partial letters. Some hair detail shows at the back of the head. The rim is well outlined and shows traces of most or even all denticles. *Reverse:* The wreath and lettering are bold, but in outline form. E PLURIBUS UNUM is readable, but may be weak. The rim is complete all around, with traces of most denticles present.

1885. Graded VG-8.

G-4, 6 (Good). *Obverse:* The rim is complete all around. Some denticles show on the inside of the rim. The date, Liberty head, and stars are in outline form. No letters of LIBERTY are visible in the coronet. *Reverse:* V and the wreath are visible in outline form. Most letters are complete, but may be faint. E PLURIBUS UNUM is very weak (this feature can vary, and on some G-4 coins it is better defined). The rim is complete in most areas, but may blend with the field in some parts.

1885. Graded G-6.

AG-3 (About Good). *Obverse:* The head is outlined, with only the ear hole as a detail. The date is well worn; the bottom of the digits can be weak or incomplete. The stars are solid, without detail; some may be incomplete. The rim is indistinct or incomplete in some areas. *Reverse:* Details are nearly all worn away, showing greater effects of wear than does the obverse. V is in outline form. The wreath is in outline form, and may be

1885. Graded AG-3.

indistinct in areas. Lettering ranges from faint to missing, but with some letters readable. The rim is usually worn down into the letters.

PF-60 to 70 (Proof). *Obverse and Reverse:*
PF–60, 61, and 62 coins show varying amounts of hairlines in the field, decreasing as the grade increases. Fields may be dull or cloudy on lower-level pieces. At PF-65, hairlines are visible only under magnification and are very light; the cheek of Miss Liberty does not show any abrasion or "album slide marks." Above PF-65, hairlines become fewer, and in ultra-high grades are nonexistent, this meaning that

1883, With CENTS. Graded PF-66 Deep Cameo.

the coins have never been subject to wiping or abrasive cleaning. At PF-65 or better, expect excellent aesthetic appeal. Blotched, deeply toned, or recolored coins can be found at most Proof levels from PF–60 through 65 or even 66, and should be avoided. Watch for artificially toned lower-grade Proofs colored to mask the true nature of the fields.

Illustrated coin: This Proof shows spotting in the fields.

	Mintage	Cert	Avg	%MS	G-4	VG-8	F-12	VF-20	EF-40	AU-50	MS-60	MS-63	MS-65
											PF-63	PF-64	PF-65
1883, Without CENTS	5,474,300	7,662	63.1	92%	$7	$8	$9	$11	$15	$20	$35	$50	$225
Auctions: $3,525, MS-67, January 2015; $282, MS-66, June 2015; $164, MS-65, April 2015; $329, MS-64, October 2015													
1883, Without CENTS, Proof	5,219	1,009	64.6								$300	$450	$800
Auctions: $4,935, PF-67, August 2015; $3,055, PF-67, January 2015; $1,057, PF-66, January 2015; $379, PF-64, August 2015													
1883, With CENTS	16,026,200	1,155	60.3	81%	$20	$30	$35	$55	$85	$120	$150	$200	$600
Auctions: $5,875, MS-66, October 2015; $2,115, MS-66, January 2015; $1,292, MS-66, June 2015; $258, MS-64, February 2015													
1883, With CENTS, Proof	6,783	719	64.6								$275	$400	$700
Auctions: $881, PF-64, January 2015; $851, PF-66, September 2015; $822, PF-65, July 2015; $188, PF-63, May 2015													
1884	11,270,000	466	59.2	79%	$20	$30	$35	$55	$85	$130	$190	$300	$1,350
Auctions: $5,875, MS-67, August 2016; $8,225, MS-66, August 2015; $1,997, MS-66, February 2015; $1,351, MS-65, September 2015													
1884, Proof	3,942	785	64.5								$250	$375	$650
Auctions: $3,055, PF-67, June 2015; $763, PF-66, January 2015; $399, PF-65, April 2015; $376, PF-64, May 2015													
1885	1,472,700	839	26.9	26%	$375	$550	$750	$1,000	$1,200	$1,600	$2,000	$3,250	$6,500
Auctions: $14,100, MS-66, January 2015; $11,163, MS-66, August 2016; $5,875, MS-65, March 2016; $7,050, MS-65, August 2015													
1885, Proof	3,790	812	64.7								$1,150	$1,250	$1,350
Auctions: $2,232, PF-67, January 2015; $1,762, PF-66, June 2015; $1,292, PF-65, October 2015; $1,086, PF-64Cam, August 2015													
1886	3,326,000	767	29.1	28%	$225	$265	$425	$500	$700	$825	$1,200	$2,100	$4,250
Auctions: $13,513, MS-66, August 2016; $3,760, MS-65, September 2016; $3,525, MS-65, October 2016; $763, AU-55, August 2015													
1886, Proof	4,290	801	64.6								$650	$675	$950
Auctions: $2,115, PF-67, January 2015; $969, PF-65, February 2015; $793, PF-65, October 2015; $558, PF-64, May 2015													
1887	15,260,692	474	62.0	88%	$15	$20	$35	$50	$75	$110	$140	$195	$800
Auctions: $8,225, MS-67, December 2015; $7,638, MS-66, May 2015; $5,405, MS-66, January 2015; $1,293, MS-65, September 2016													
1887, Proof	2,960	574	64.3								$250	$345	$550
Auctions: $2,500, PF-67, January 2015; $705, PF-66, June 2015; $211, PF-63, October 2015; $141, PF-62, March 2015													
1888	10,167,901	399	58.2	81%	$30	$40	$60	$120	$175	$220	$275	$350	$1,000
Auctions: $7,050, MS-66, July 2016; $3,055, MS-66, September 2015; $1,763, MS-65, July 2016; $1,293, MS-65, December 2015													
1888, Proof	4,582	786	64.5								$250	$345	$550
Auctions: $3,642, PF-67, February 2015; $525, PF-66, January 2015; $423, PF-65, October 2015; $247, PF-64, May 2015													
1889	15,878,025	573	63.2	95%	$15	$20	$30	$50	$75	$120	$140	$175	$650
Auctions: $1,600, MS-66, January 2015; $705, MS-65, July 2015; $350, MS-64, October 2015; $141, MS-62, April 2015													
1889, Proof	3,336	629	64.6								$250	$345	$550
Auctions: $446, PF-66, January 2015; $493, PF-65, January 2015; $399, PF-65, October 2015; $182, PF-63, July 2015													

1899, Repunched Date, Early Die State

1899, Repunched Date, Late Die State

FS-05-1899-301.

	Mintage	Cert	Avg	%MS	G-4	VG-8	F-12	VF-20	EF-40	AU-50	MS-60 / PF-63	MS-63 / PF-64	MS-65 / PF-65
1890	16,256,532	337	62	90%	$10	$20	$25	$40	$65	$110	$160	$200	$950
	Auctions: $16,450, MS-67, October 2015; $9,400, MS-66, May 2015; $3,055, MS-66, October 2016; $705, MS-65, July 2015												
1890, Proof	2,740	474	64.1								$250	$345	$550
	Auctions: $2,467, PF-67, February 2015; $376, PF-65, January 2015; $376, PF-65, October 2015; $282, PF-64, May 2015												
1891	16,832,000	430	62.7	92%	$7	$12	$25	$45	$70	$125	$160	$200	$700
	Auctions: $4,406, MS-66, July 2016; $1,998, MS-66, October 2016; $1,058, MS-65, January 2015; $211, MS-64, October 2015												
1891, Proof	2,350	475	64.4								$250	$345	$550
	Auctions: $2,820, PF-67, February 2015; $705, PF-66, January 2015; $282, PF-64, November 2015; $141, PF-62, May 2015												
1892	11,696,897	483	61.9	90%	$6	$10	$20	$40	$65	$110	$140	$160	$1,000
	Auctions: $3,055, MS-66, January 2015; $1,645, MS-66, August 2015; $1,880, MS-66, July 2015; $822, MS-65, February 2015												
1892, Proof	2,745	514	64.4								$250	$345	$550
	Auctions: $625, PF-66, January 2015; $517, PF-65, October 2015; $282, PF-64, August 2015; $184, PF-63, May 2015												
1893	13,368,000	468	62.9	94%	$6	$10	$20	$40	$65	$110	$140	$160	$750
	Auctions: $1,880, MS-66, January 2015; $1,527, MS-65, February 2015; $1,058, MS-66, July 2016; $176, MS-62, May 2015												
1893, Proof	2,195	465	64.5								$250	$345	$550
	Auctions: $1,292, PF-66, July 2015; $517, PF-65, September 2015; $458, PF-65, January 2015; $434, PF-65, October 2015												
1894	5,410,500	350	58.8	79%	$20	$35	$100	$165	$225	$300	$350	$425	$1,250
	Auctions: $2,526, MS-66, July 2016; $1,410, MS-66, October 2016; $1,527, MS-65, August 2015; $493, MS-64, October 2015												
1894, Proof	2,632	456	64.3								$250	$345	$550
	Auctions: $1,292, PF-67, October 2015; $564, PF-66, January 2015; $540, PF-65, July 2015; $117, PF-60, May 2015												
1895	9,977,822	356	62.2	92%	$6	$8	$22	$45	$70	$115	$140	$200	$1,100
	Auctions: $21,150, MS-67, July 2015; $4,994, MS-65, March 2015; 2,585, MS-65, January 2015; $2,233, MS-65, September 2016												
1895, Proof	2,062	432	64.2								$250	$345	$550
	Auctions: $3,995, PF-67, January 2015; $646, PF-66, August 2015; $399, PF-65, May 2015; $258, PF-64, February 2015												
1896	8,841,058	346	60.3	85%	$9	$18	$35	$65	$90	$150	$190	$265	$1,500
	Auctions: $8,813, MS-66, May 2015; $4,582, MS-66, June 2015; $2,350, MS-66, March 2016; $1,234, MS-65, October 2016												
1896, Proof	1,862	420	64.4								$250	$345	$550
	Auctions: $646, PF-66, October 2015; $587, PF-65, January 2015; $282, PF-64, February 2015; $139, PF-62, May 2015												
1897	20,426,797	465	62.5	93%	$4	$5	$12	$27	$45	$70	$100	$160	$800
	Auctions: $3,525, MS-66, October 2016; $3,055, MS-66, January 2015; $1,057, MS-65, July 2015; $616, MS-64, August 2015												
1897, Proof	1,938	463	64.7								$250	$345	$550
	Auctions: $4,022, PF-68, January 2015; $352, PF-65, November 2015; $176, PF-63, May 2015; $111, PF-60, February 2015												
1898	12,530,292	421	62.7	94%	$4	$5	$12	$27	$45	$75	$150	$185	$600
	Auctions: $2,350, MS-66, March 2015; $1,410, MS-66, August 2016; $763, MS-65, January 2015; $646, MS-65, August 2015												
1898, Proof	1,795	431	64.5								$250	$345	$550
	Auctions: $505, PF-66, January 2015; $364, PF-65, October 2015; $258, PF-64, September 2015; $164, PF-63, May 2015												
1899	26,027,000	749	62.8	94%	$2	$3	$8	$20	$30	$60	$90	$140	$550
	Auctions: $8,813, MS-67, August 2015; $4,230, MS-67, August 2016; $4,230, MS-66, January 2015; $705, MS-66, May 2016												
1899, Repunched Date (a)	(b)	0	n/a						$85	$150	$190	$240	$800
	Auctions: No auction records available.												
1899, Proof	2,031	460	64.7								$250	$345	$550
	Auctions: $1,410, PF-67, July 2015; $423, PF-65, January 2015; $258, PF-64, September 2015; $176, PF-63, May 2015												

a. "The loop of a 9, or possibly (but unlikely) an 8, is evident within the lower loop of the second 9. Some specialists believe this to be an 1899/8 overdate. However, we feel it is simply a repunched date, with the secondary 9 far to the south of the primary 9 at the last digit" (*Cherrypickers' Guide to Rare Die Varieties*, sixth edition, volume I). **b.** Included in circulation-strike 1899 mintage figure.

1900, Doubled-Die Reverse
FS-05-1900-801.

	Mintage	Cert	Avg	%MS	G-4	VG-8	F-12	VF-20	EF-40	AU-50	MS-60 PF-63	MS-63 PF-64	MS-65 PF-65
1900	27,253,733	846	63.1	95%	$2	$3	$8	$15	$30	$65	$90	$140	$500
Auctions: $7,050, MS-67, January 2015; $4,700, MS-67, August 2016; $1,998, MS-66, July 2016; $117, MS-63, November 2015													
1900, Doubled-Die Reverse (c)	(d)	4	61.5	75%					$110	$160	$235	$310	$875
Auctions: No auction records available.													
1900, Proof	2,262	478	64.8								$250	$345	$550
Auctions: $5,640, PF-68, January 2015; $675, PF-66, August 2015; $387, PF-65, May 2015; $340, PF-64, March 2015													
1901	26,478,228	767	62.9	96%	$2	$3	$5	$15	$30	$60	$85	$125	$450
Auctions: $8,812, MS-67, January 2015; $4,700, MS-67, August 2016; $1,399, MS-66, October 2015; $317, MS-65, May 2015													
1901, Proof	1,985	518	64.9								$250	$345	$550
Auctions: $940, PF-67, January 2015; $587, PF-66, September 2015; $446, PF-65, October 2015; $305, PF-64, January 2015													
1902	31,480,579	765	62.5	93%	$2	$3	$4	$15	$30	$60	$85	$125	$450
Auctions: $5,405, MS-67, January 2015; $1,645, MS-66, June 2015; $1,058, MS-66, August 2016; $881, MS-66, August 2016													
1902, Proof	2,018	473	64.7								$250	$345	$550
Auctions: $1,028, PF-67, January 2015; $646, PF-66, June 2015; $399, PF-65, March 2015; $317, PF-64, October 2015													
1903	28,004,935	850	62.9	95%	$2	$3	$4	$15	$30	$60	$85	$125	$450
Auctions: $4,230, MS-67, October 2016; $3,525, MS-67, November 2016; $1,645, MS-66, January 2015; $423, MS-65, August 2015													
1903, Proof	1,790	543	64.9								$250	$345	$550
Auctions: $540, PF-66, October 2015; $376, PF-65, September 2015; $293, PF-64, January 2015; $129, PF-61, May 2015													
1904	21,403,167	716	63.1	95%	$2	$3	$4	$15	$30	$60	$85	$125	$450
Auctions: $1,645, MS-66, June 2015; $999, MS-66, October 2016; $352, MS-65, August 2015; $176, MS-64, February 2015													
1904, Proof	1,817	485	64.3								$250	$345	$550
Auctions: $998, PF-66, January 2015; $365, PF-65, October 2015; $258, PF-64, April 2015; $179, PF-63, May 2015													
1905	29,825,124	867	62.6	93%	$2	$3	$4	$15	$30	$60	$85	$125	$450
Auctions: $4,935, MS-67, October 2016; $2,585, MS-66, January 2015; $852, MS-65, March 2015; $517, MS-64, September 2016													
1905, Proof	2,152	461	64.6								$250	$345	$550
Auctions: $3,525, PF-67, June 2015; $2,585, PF-66, February 2015; $1,410, PF-66, October 2015; $285, PF-64, January 2015													
1906	38,612,000	632	61.6	88%	$2	$3	$4	$15	$30	$60	$85	$125	$550
Auctions: $5,875, MS-66, January 2015; $423, MS-65, August 2015; $152, MS-64, May 2015; $211, MS-63, February 2015													
1906, Proof	1,725	453	64.6								$250	$345	$550
Auctions: $3,290, PF-68, August 2015; $1,527, PF-67, October 2015; $1,292, PF-67, January 2015; $587, PF-66, June 2015													
1907	39,213,325	619	61.7	89%	$2	$3	$4	$15	$30	$60	$85	$125	$650
Auctions: $7,931, MS-66, January 2015; $3,055, MS-66, August 2016; $1,645, MS-66, July 2015; $494, MS-65, October 2016													
1907, Proof	1,475	370	64.7								$250	$345	$550
Auctions: $2,350, PF-67, February 2015; $616, PF-66, June 2015; $540, PF-66, January 2015; $253, PF-64, September 2015													
1908	22,684,557	568	61.4	90%	$2	$3	$4	$15	$30	$60	$85	$125	$650
Auctions: $5,288, MS-66, August 2015; $1,293, MS-66, October 2016; $705, MS-65, August 2015; $176, MS-64, October 2015													
1908, Proof	1,620	447	64.6								$250	$345	$550
Auctions: $8,225, PF-68, October 2015; $2,115, PF-67, January 2015; $763, PF-66, February 2015; $517, PF-65, June 2015													

c. Doubling on this very popular variety is evident on all reverse design elements, including the V, with a stronger spread on the lower quadrant of the reverse. **d.** Included in circulation-strike 1900 mintage figure.

1913, Liberty Head

	Mintage	Cert	Avg	%MS	G-4	VG-8	F-12	VF-20	EF-40	AU-50	MS-60 / PF-63	MS-63 / PF-64	MS-65 / PF-65
1909	11,585,763	417	60.6	85%	$3	$4	$5	$18	$35	$75	$100	$140	$750
Auctions: $4,465, MS-66, October 2015; $2,585, MS-66, August 2016; $793, MS-65, August 2015; $705, MS-65, February 2015													
1909, Proof	4,763	1,342	65								$250	$345	$550
Auctions: $1,086, PF-67, October 2015; $493, PF-66, January 2015; $258, PF-64, February 2015; $117, PF-60, April 2015													
1910	30,166,948	657	61.4	87%	$2	$3	$4	$15	$30	$60	$85	$125	$450
Auctions: $3,760, MS-66, January 2015; $211, MS-64, September 2015; $130, MS-63, May 2015; $60, AU-58, June 2015													
1910, Proof	2,405	702	64.9								$250	$345	$550
Auctions: $6,462, PF-68, January 2015; $587, PF-66, June 2015; $399, PF-65, November 2015; $282, PF-64, April 2015													
1911	39,557,639	1,262	62.3	92%	$2	$3	$4	$15	$30	$60	$85	$125	$450
Auctions: $4,230, MS-66, May 2015; $646, MS-66, July 2016; $1,249, MS-65, January 2015; $141, MS-64, October 2015; $99, MS-63, May 2015													
1911, Proof	1,733	585	64.7								$250	$345	$550
Auctions: $600, PF-66, January 2015; $365, PF-65, October 2015; $258, PF-64, June 2015; $170, PF-63, February 2015													
1912	26,234,569	1,107	61.8	91%	$2	$3	$4	$15	$30	$60	$85	$125	$450
Auctions: $5,875, MS-66, January 2015; $446, MS-65, January 2015; $141, MS-64, April 2015; $94, MS-63, September 2015; $74, AU-58, June 2015													
1912, Proof	2,145	583	64.5								$250	$345	$550
Auctions: $2,232, PF-67, January 2015; $910, PF-66, July 2015; $489, PF-65, April 2015; $199, PF-63, October 2015													
1912-D	8,474,000	820	59.1	85%	$3	$4	$10	$40	$90	$175	$300	$400	$1,750
Auctions: $4,230, MS-66, January 2015; $1,703, MS-65, July 2015; $646, MS-64, September 2015; $305, MS-63, May 2015													
1912-S	238,000	1,526	29.3	34%	$145	$155	$175	$450	$850	$1,250	$1,500	$1,850	$2,850
Auctions: $5,170, MS-66, July 2015; $3,525, MS-65, January 2015; $2,585, MS-65, October 2015; $1,997, MS-64, February 2015													
1913 † (e)		0	n/a									$3,500,000	
Auctions: No auction records available.													
1913, Proof † (e)		2	47.5								$3,500,000	$3,750,000	
Auctions: $3,290,000, PF-64, January 2014; $3,172,500, PF-63, April 2013													

† Both 1913 Liberty Head Nickel varieties are ranked in the *100 Greatest U.S. Coins* (fourth edition), as a single entry. **e.** An estimated five 1913 Liberty Head nickels (four circulation-strike and one Proof) were struck under irregular circumstances at the Mint. Some researchers consider them all to be Proofs. They were dispersed and are now held in various public and private collections.

INDIAN HEAD OR BUFFALO (1913–1938)

Designer: *James Earle Fraser.* **Weight:** *5 grams.* **Composition:** *.750 copper, .250 nickel.*
Diameter: *21.2 mm.* **Edge:** *Plain.* **Mints:** *Philadelphia, Denver, and San Francisco.*

  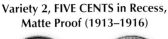

**Variety 1, FIVE CENTS
on Raised Ground (1913)**

*Mintmark location for all
varieties is on the reverse,
below FIVE CENTS.*

**Variety 1, FIVE CENTS
on Raised Ground, Proof**

**Variety 2, FIVE CENTS
in Recess (1913–1938)**

**Variety 2, FIVE CENTS in Recess,
Matte Proof (1913–1916)**

**Variety 2, FIVE CENTS in
Recess, Satin Proof (1936)**

**Variety 2, FIVE CENTS in Recess,
Mirror Proof (1936–1937)**

History. The Indian Head nickel five-cent piece today is almost universally known as the "Buffalo" nickel, after the American bison on the reverse. The design made its debut in 1913. James Earle Fraser, a sculptor well known in the private sector, was its creator. The obverse features an authentic portrait of a Native American, modeled as a composite from life, with three subjects posing. Unlike any preceding coin made for circulation, the Buffalo nickel had little in the way of open, smooth field surfaces. Instead, most areas on the obverse and reverse were filled with design elements or, especially on the reverse, an irregular background, as on a bas-relief plaque. Soon after the first coins were released, it was thought that the inscription FIVE CENTS, on a high area of the motif, would wear too quickly. The Mint modified the design to lower the ground under the bison, which had been arranged in the form of a mound (on what became known as Variety 1). The flat-ground design is called Variety 2.

Striking and Sharpness. Most circulation-strike Buffalo nickels are poorly struck in one or more areas, and for many Denver and San Francisco issues of the 1920s the striking is very poor. However, enough sharp strikes exist among common dates of the 1930s that one can be found with some patience. Certification services do not reflect the quality of strike on their labels, so examine carefully. The matter of striking sharpness on Buffalo nickels is an exceedingly important aspect for the connoisseur (who might prefer, for example, a sharply struck coin in AU-58 over a fully lustrous MS example with much shallower detail). Points to check on the obverse include the center of the coin, especially the area immediately above the tie on the braid. On the reverse check the fur on the head of the bison, and the fur "line" above the bison's shoulder on its back. On both sides, examine the overall striking of letters and other details.

Availability. Among circulated varieties of standard dates and mintmarks, availability is in proportion to their mintages. Among early issues the 1913-S, Variety 2, is the scarcest. The date wore away more quickly on the Variety 1 coins than on the modified design used from later 1913 through the end of the series. In the 1920s the 1926-S is the hardest to find. Collectors sought Buffalo nickels from circulation until the 1960s, after which most were gone. By that time the dates in the teens were apt to have their dates completely worn away, or be AG-3 or G-4. Among MS nickels, the issues of 1913 were saved in quantity as novelties, although 1913-S, Variety 2, is slightly scarce. Philadelphia Mint issues are readily available through the 1920s, while MS-63 and finer mintmarked issues from 1914 to 1927 can range from scarce to rare. From 1931 to 1938, all dates and mintmarks were saved in roll quantities, and all are plentiful today. Many Buffalo nickels in MS are very rare if with Full Details, this being especially true for mintmarked issues after 1913, into the early 1930s. Sharpness of strike is not noted on certification holders, but a connoisseur would probably rather own a Full Details coin in MS-65 than an MS-66 or higher with a flat strike.

Proofs. Proof Buffalo nickels are of two main styles. Matte Proofs were made from 1913 to 1916 and are rare. These have minutely granular or matte surfaces, are sharply struck with Full Details of the design on both sides, and have edges (as viewed edge-on) that are mirrored, a distinctive figure. These are easily confused with circulation strikes except for the features noted. Certified holders usually list these simply as "Proof," not "Matte Proof." Some early Proofs of 1936 have satiny rather than mirror-like fields. Later Proofs of 1936 and all of 1937 have a mirror surface in the fields. The motifs of the 1936 and 1937 mirror Proofs are lightly polished in the die (not frosty or matte).

GRADING STANDARDS

MS-60 to 70 (Mint State). *Obverse and Reverse:* Mint luster is complete in the obverse and reverse fields, except in areas not fully struck up, in which graininess or marks from the *original planchet surface* can be seen. Lower grades such as MS–60, 61, and 62 can show some evidence of abrasion, usually on the center of the obverse above the braid, and on the reverse at the highest parts of the bison. These two checkpoints are often areas of light

1937-D. Graded MS-67.

striking, so abrasion must be differentiated from original planchet marks. At MS-63 evidences of abrasion are few, and at MS-65 they are fewer yet. In grades above MS-65, a Buffalo nickel should be mark-free.

AU-50, 53, 55, 58 (About Uncirculated). *Obverse:* Light wear is seen on the highest area of the cheek, to the left of the nose, this being the most obvious checkpoint. Light wear is also seen on the highest-relief areas of the hair. Luster is less extensive, and wear more extensive, at AU-50 than at higher grades. An AU-58 coin will have only slight wear and will retain the majority of luster. *Reverse:* Light wear is seen on the shoulder

1925-S. Graded AU-53.

and hip, these being the key checkpoints. Light wear is also seen on the flank of the bison and on the horn and top of the head. Luster is less extensive, and wear more extensive, at AU-50 than at higher grades. An AU-58 coin will have only slight wear and will retain the majority of luster.

EF-40, 45 (Extremely Fine). *Obverse:* More wear is seen on the cheek (in particular) and the rest of the face. The center of the coin above the braid is mostly smooth. Other details are sharp. *Reverse:* More wear is evident. The tip of the horn is well defined on better strikes. The shoulder, flank, and hip show more wear. The tip of the tail may be discernible, but is mostly worn away.

1937-D. Graded EF-40.

VF-20, 30 (Very Fine). *Obverse:* The hair above the braid is mostly flat, but with some details visible. The braid is discernible. The feathers lack most details. On Variety 1 coins the date is light. *Reverse:* Wear is more extensive, with most fur detail on the high area of the shoulder gone, the tip of the tail gone, and the horn flat. Ideally the tip of the horn should show, but in the marketplace many certified coins do not show this. On some coins this is due to a shallow strike.

1937-D, 3-Legged. Graded VF-20.

 Illustrated coin: On this highly desirable variety one of the buffalo's forelegs has been polished off of the die, probably as the result of an attempt to remove clash marks.

F-12, 15 (Fine). *Obverse:* Only slight detail remains in the hair above the braid. Some of the braid twists are blended together. LIBERTY is weak, and on some coins the upper part of the letters is faint. The rim still is separate. On all coins, the date shows extensive wear. On Variety 1 coins it is weak. *Reverse:* The horn is half to two-thirds visible. Fur details are gone except on the neck at the highest part of the back.

1918-D. Graded F-12.

VG-8, 10 (Very Good). *Obverse:* Hair details above the braid are further worn, as is the hair at the top of the head. Most braid twists are blended together. The rim is worn down to the tops of the letters in LIBERTY. The date is light on all coins and very weak on those of Variety 1. *Reverse:* The base of the horn is slightly visible. Fur details are worn more, but details can still be seen on the neck and top of the back. The hip and flank beneath are worn flat.

1913-D. Graded VG-8.

G-4, 6 (Good). *Obverse:* Scarcely any hair details are seen at the center, and the braid is flat. The rim and tops of the letters in LIBERTY are blended. The date is weak but readable, with at least the last two numerals showing on earlier issues. *Reverse:* The rim is worn to blend into the tops of some or all letters in UNITED STATES OF AMERICA (except for Variety 1). E PLURIBUS UNUM and FIVE CENTS are full, and the mint-mark, if any, is clear. The front part of the bison's head blends into the rim.

1918-D, 8 Over 7. Graded G-4.

AG-3 (About Good). *Obverse:* The head is mostly flat, but the facial features remain clear. LIBERTY is weak and partly missing. The date may be incomplete but must be identifiable. *Reverse:* Further wear is seen. On Variety 1 coins, UNITED STATES OF AMERICA is full and readable. On the Variety 2 the rim is worn further into the letters. The reverse of the Variety 1 nickels is bolder as the overall grade is defined by the date, which wore away more quickly than on the Variety 2.

1913-D, Variety 2. Graded AG-3.

PF-60 to 70 (Matte Proof). *Obverse and Reverse:* Most Matte Proofs are in higher grades. Those with abrasion or contact marks can be graded PF–60 to 62; these are not widely desired. PF-64 can have some abrasion. Tiny flecks are not common, but are sometimes seen. At the Matte PF-65 level or higher there will no traces of abrasion or flecks. Differences between higher-grade Proofs are highly subjective, and one certified at PF-65 can be similar to another at PF-67, and vice-versa.

1915. Graded Matte PF-67.

PF-60 to 70 (Mirror Proof). *Obverse and Reverse:* Most mirror Proofs are in higher grades. PF–60 to 62 coins can have abrasion or minor handling marks, but are usually assigned such grades because of staining or blotches resulting from poor cleaning. PF–63 and 64 can have minor abrasion and staining. Tiny flecks are not common, but are sometimes seen, as are dark stripe lines from the glued seams in the cellophane envelopes used by the Mint. PF-65

1937. Graded Mirror PF-66.

and higher coins should be free of stains, flecks, and abrasion of any kind. Differences between higher-grade Proofs are highly subjective, and one certified PF-65 can be similar to another at PF-67, and vice-versa.

**1913, Variety 1,
3-1/2 Legged**
FS-05-1913-901.

1914, 4 Over 3
FS-05-1914-101.

	Mintage	Cert	Avg	%MS	G-4	VG-8	F-12	VF-20	EF-40	AU-50	MS-60	MS-63	MS-65
											PF-63	PF-64	PF-65
1913, Variety 1	30,992,000	7,987	64.1	96%	$12	$15	$16	$20	$25	$35	$45	$60	$170
Auctions: $822, MS-67, February 2015; $211, MS-66, March 2015; $129, MS-65, January 2015; $84, MS-64, August 2015													
1913, Variety 1, 3-1/2 Legged (a)	(b)	1	64.0	100%					$400	$500	$750	$1,500	$10,000
Auctions: $10,350, MS-64, April 2009													
1913, Variety 1, Proof	1,520	310	65.4								$1,350	$2,000	$3,750
Auctions: $7,637, PF-67, July 2015; $4,230, PF-66, June 2015; $3,760, PF-66, January 2015; $2,115, PF-64, January 2015													
1913-D, Variety 1	5,337,000	2,213	62.6	89%	$15	$20	$25	$35	$40	$60	$75	$80	$300
Auctions: $1,997, MS-67, June 2015; $329, MS-66, February 2015; $199, MS-65, August 2015; $84, MS-64, January 2015													
1913-S, Variety 1	2,105,000	1,701	59.2	77%	$45	$50	$60	$70	$85	$110	$130	$165	$700
Auctions: $2,585, MS-66, January 2015; $998, MS-64, August 2015; $164, MS-63, October 2015; $152, MS-62, February 2015													
1913, Variety 2	29,857,186	1,980	62.8	91%	$10	$12	$15	$20	$25	$30	$40	$65	$300
Auctions: $2,820, MS-67, January 2015; $564, MS-66, October 2015; $493, MS-66, July 2015; $223, MS-65, March 2015													
1913, Variety 2, Proof	1,514	241	65.4								$1,000	$1,500	$2,000
Auctions: $3,525, PF-67, January 2015; $3,231, PF-66, October 2015; $1,762, PF-66, February 2015; $1,645, PF-65, January 2015													
1913-D, Variety 2	4,156,000	1,262	52.0	55%	$120	$150	$175	$200	$235	$250	$300	$400	$1,100
Auctions: $1,997, MS-66, January 2015; $310, MS-63, June 2015; $211, AU-58, May 2015; $170, EF-45, February 2015													
1913-S, Variety 2	1,209,000	1,952	45.0	41%	$250	$325	$375	$475	$550	$750	$900	$1,100	$3,250
Auctions: $3,055, MS-65, January 2015; $1,645, MS-62, February 2015; $727, MS-60, August 2015; $446, AU-58, May 2015													
1914	20,664,463	1,541	58.2	78%	$20	$22	$25	$30	$35	$45	$60	$85	$425
Auctions: $8,225, MS-67, January 2015; $1,116, MS-66, October 2015; $705, MS-66, September 2016; $246, MS-64, February 2015													
1914, 4 Over 3 (c)	(d)	32	50.2	41%	$200	$250	$325	$525	$700	$1,000	$2,250	$5,000	$30,000
Auctions: $8,338, MS-64, April 2012													
1914, Proof	1,275	419	65.4								$900	$1,300	$2,000
Auctions: $6,462, PF-67, February 2015; $2,820, PF-66, August 2015; $1,762, PF-66, January 2015; $1,527, PF-65, August 2015													
1914-D	3,912,000	1,234	51.1	54%	$90	$125	$160	$220	$325	$350	$450	$550	$1,300
Auctions: $587, MS-64, January 2015; $376, MS-63, May 2015; $340, AU-58, February 2015; $211, EF-45, October 2015													
1914-S	3,470,000	1,493	57.2	69%	$26	$38	$45	$65	$90	$160	$200	$425	$2,000
Auctions: $1,468, MS-65, July 2015; $305, MS-63, March 2015; $235, MS-62, November 2015; $123, AU-58, January 2015													
1915	20,986,220	1,452	62.3	89%	$6	$8	$9	$15	$25	$45	$60	$100	$300
Auctions: $5,640, MS-67, January 2015; $540, MS-66, February 2015; $940, MS-65, August 2015; $823, MS-66, July 2016													
1915, Proof	1,050	346	65.2								$1,000	$1,500	$2,000
Auctions: $8,812, PF-67, August 2015; $4,817, PF-67, June 2015; $3,760, PF-67, October 2015; $1,645, PF-66, January 2015													
1915-D	7,569,000	985	57.7	62%	$20	$35	$40	$70	$130	$160	$270	$350	$1,400
Auctions: $376, MS-64, September 2015; $258, MS-63, January 2015; $236, MS-62, May 2015; $124, AU-58, February 2015													
1915-S	1,505,000	804	48.0	51%	$45	$75	$100	$200	$400	$500	$650	$1,100	$3,000
Auctions: $3,525, MS-66, October 2015; $3,704, MS-65, August 2015; $1,527, MS-64, June 2015; $1,057, MS-63, January 2015													

a. The reverse die was heavily polished, possibly to remove clash marks, resulting in a die with most of the bison's front leg missing. **b.** Included in circulation-strike 1913, Variety 1, mintage figure. **c.** The straight top bar of the underlying 3 is visible at the top of the 4. The start of the 3's diagonal is seen on the upper right, outside of the 4. On some coins, a hint of the curve of the lower portion of the 3 shows just above the crossbar of the 4. **d.** Included in circulation-strike 1914 mintage figure.

**1916, Doubled
Die Obverse**
FS-05-1916-101.

**1916, Missing
Designer's Initial**
FS-05-1916-401.

**1918, Doubled
Die Reverse**
FS-05-1918-801.

1918-D, 8 Over 7
FS-05-1918D-101.

	Mintage	Cert	Avg	%MS	G-4	VG-8	F-12	VF-20	EF-40	AU-50	MS-60	MS-63	MS-65
											PF-63	PF-64	PF-65
1916	63,497,466	2,046	61.8	88%	$6	$7	$8	$10	$15	$25	$50	$85	$300
Auctions: $7,050, MS-67, February 2015; $646, MS-66, August 2016; $235, MS-65, February 2015; $94, MS-64, November 2015													
1916, Doubled Die Obverse (e)	(f)	107	37.2	12%	$3,750	$5,500	$7,750	$11,000	$17,500	$32,000	$60,000	$150,000	
Auctions: $30,550, AU-55, January 2014; $28,200, AU-55, August 2014													
1916, Missing Initial (g)	(f)	0	n/a					$135	$200	$280	$375	$600	
Auctions: $341, AU-55, February 2014													
1916, Proof	600	173	65.4								$1,500	$2,700	$3,750
Auctions: $4,230, PF-66, January 2015; $4,113, PF-66, October 2015; $2,820, PF-64, August 2015; $2,232, PF-64, January 2015													
1916-D	13,333,000	1,216	59.4	73%	$16	$28	$30	$45	$90	$120	$175	$260	$1,350
Auctions: $1,086, MS-65, January 2015; $493, MS-64, February 2015; $235, MS-63, April 2015; $158, MS-62, November 2015													
1916-S	11,860,000	940	58.9	71%	$10	$15	$20	$40	$90	$125	$190	$275	$2,000
Auctions: $3,290, MS-66, January 2015; $2,592, MS-65, February 2015; $1,880, MS-65, October 2015; $188, MS-62, July 2015													
1917	51,424,019	972	61.7	88%	$8	$9	$10	$12	$15	$35	$60	$150	$475
Auctions: $1,763, MS-66, November 2016; $705, MS-66, January 2015; $376, MS-65, August 2015; $176, MS-64, April 2015													
1917-D	9,910,000	906	54.1	59%	$18	$30	$50	$85	$150	$275	$375	$750	$2,000
Auctions: $1,880, MS-65, October 2015; $1,233, MS-64, October 2015; $793, MS-63, January 2015; $329, AU-58, February 2015													
1917-S	4,193,000	829	47.2	43%	$22	$40	$75	$115	$200	$325	$650	$1,450	$3,750
Auctions: $4,230, MS-66, January 2015; $1,527, MS-64, June 2015; $1,028, MS-63, August 2015; $616, MS-62, October 2015													
1918	32,086,314	620	60.5	83%	$6	$7	$8	$15	$35	$50	$125	$325	$1,150
Auctions: $3,055, MS-66, August 2015; $3,055, MS-65, December 2015; $1,645, MS-65, March 2016; $1,292, MS-65, January 2015													
1918, Doubled Die Reverse (h)	(i)	4	43.0	25%	$190	$260	$375	$525	$1,450	$2,300	$3,500	$7,000	
Auctions: $170, VF-20, August 2013													
1918-D, 8 Over 7 † (j)	(k)	867	18.5	5%	$900	$1,250	$2,500	$5,500	$8,500	$12,000	$35,000	$57,500	$265,000
Auctions: $1,292, VG-10, March 2015; $940, G-6, January 2015; $822, G-6, July 2015; $763, G-4, January 2015													
1918-D	8,362,000	720	46.8	45%	$22	$35	$65	$135	$225	$350	$550	$1,050	$3,250
Auctions: $5,875, MS-66, January 2015; $2,937, MS-65, July 2015; $575, AU-58, February 2015; $423, AU-58, October 2015													
1918-S	4,882,000	701	51.0	55%	$14	$27	$55	$110	$200	$325	$585	$2,500	$13,500
Auctions: $2,820, MS-63, February 2015; $998, MS-62, January 2015; $399, AU-55, June 2015; $235, EF-45, August 2015													
1919	60,868,000	1,146	62.2	89%	$2.25	$3	$3.50	$8	$15	$35	$55	$125	$500
Auctions: $6,463, MS-67, August 2015; $5,875, MS-67, January 2015; $1,645, MS-66, August 2015; $1,410, MS-65, June 2015													
1919-D	8,006,000	788	45.4	36%	$15	$30	$75	$135	$250	$450	$700	$1,500	$6,000
Auctions: $1,762, MS-64, January 2015; $1,410, MS-63, June 2015; $519, AU-58, October 2015; $305, AU-53, November 2015													
1919-S	7,521,000	863	48.5	41%	$9	$20	$50	$125	$250	$375	$675	$1,800	$10,000
Auctions: $2,585, MS-64, August 2015; $1,292, MS-63, February 2015; $493, AU-58, October 2015; $282, AU-55, January 2015													

† Ranked in the *100 Greatest U.S. Coins* (fourth edition). **e.** The date, chin, throat, feathers, and the tie on the braid are all doubled. "Beware of 1916 nickels with strike doubling on the date offered as this variety. . . . The true doubled die must look like the coin shown here" (*Cherrypickers' Guide to Rare Die Varieties*, sixth edition, volume I). **f.** Included in circulation-strike 1916 mintage figure. **g.** The initial F, for Fraser—normally below the date—is clearly absent. Some dies exist with a partially missing or weak initial; these do not command the premium of the variety with a completely missing initial. **h.** Doubling is most obvious to the north on E PLURIBUS UNUM. Some coins show a die crack from the rim to the bison's rump, just below the tail. **i.** Included in 1918 mintage figure. **j.** "Look for the small die crack immediately above the tie on the braid, leading slightly downward to the Indian's jaw. The beginning of this die break can usually be seen even on lower-grade coins" (*Cherrypickers' Guide to Rare Die Varieties*, sixth edition, volume I). **k.** Included in 1918-D mintage figure.

	Mintage	Cert	Avg	%MS	G-4	VG-8	F-12	VF-20	EF-40	AU-50	MS-60	MS-63	MS-65
											PF-63	PF-64	PF-65
1920	63,093,000	883	62.2	90%	$1.50	$2.50	$3	$7	$15	$30	$65	$145	$600
	Auctions: $8,225, MS-67, February 2015; $881, MS-66, November 2016; $764, MS-65, November 2016; $176, MS-64, January 2015												
1920-D	9,418,000	729	51.9	57%	$8	$15	$32	$115	$275	$350	$600	$1,400	$4,750
	Auctions: $3,525, MS-65, January 2015; $1,645, MS-64, June 2015; $881, MS-63, October 2015; $705, MS-62, February 2015												
1920-S	9,689,000	774	51.6	51%	$4.50	$12	$28	$100	$200	$300	$650	$1,750	$15,000
	Auctions: $8,812, MS-65, September 2015; $2,585, MS-64, January 2015; $1,410, MS-63, August 2015; $881, AU-58, February 2015												
1921	10,663,000	763	60.2	81%	$4	$6	$8	$24	$50	$75	$150	$320	$800
	Auctions: $7,050, MS-67, August 2015; $3,995, MS-67, November 2016; $3,055, MS-66, September 2015; $400, MS-64, March 2016;												
1921-S	1,557,000	1,142	32.0	21%	$60	$115	$155	$375	$950	$1,100	$1,750	$2,500	$7,500
	Auctions: $2,585, MS-64, October 2015; $646, AU-50, January 2015; $399, VF-30, August 2015; $199, VF-20, February 2015												
1923	35,715,000	954	62.5	89%	$2	$3	$4	$6	$15	$35	$65	$160	$575
	Auctions: $9,400, MS-67, August 2015; $1,880, MS-66, January 2015; $470, MS-65, April 2015; $176, MS-64, May 2015												
1923-S	6,142,000	1,197	51.1	58%	$8	$10	$30	$135	$250	$400	$600	$900	$6,000
	Auctions: $4,347, MS-65, January 2015; $1,086, MS-64, August 2015; $387, AU-58, May 2015; $282, AU-53, November 2015												
1924	21,620,000	659	62.2	89%	$1.50	$2	$5	$10	$25	$45	$75	$160	$750
	Auctions: $7,050, MS-67, March 2015; $1,645, MS-66, October 2016; $724, MS-65, September 2015; $352, MS-64, March 2015												
1924-D	5,258,000	814	47.8	52%	$8.50	$12	$30	$85	$235	$325	$450	$800	$4,500
	Auctions: $4,465, MS-65, January 2015; $1,880, MS-64, September 2015; $763, AU-58, April 2015; $223, EF-45, July 2015												
1924-S	1,437,000	1,068	28.8	16%	$15	$35	$110	$475	$1,000	$1,700	$2,500	$4,500	$13,500
	Auctions: $5,287, MS-64, July 2015; $1,292, AU-50, June 2015; $470, EF-40, January 2015; $105, F-15, September 2015												
1925	35,565,100	1,004	63.6	95%	$3	$3.50	$4	$8	$15	$35	$45	$100	$400
	Auctions: $7,344, MS-67, August 2015; $4,230, MS-67, June 2015; $2,468, MS-66, August 2016; $352, MS-65, March 2015												
1925-D	4,450,000	789	53.0	65%	$10	$20	$40	$95	$165	$300	$450	$800	$4,000
	Auctions: $940, MS-64, February 2015; $472, MS-62, January 2015; $470, MS-61, July 2015; $352, AU-58, July 2015												
1925-S	6,256,000	927	48.2	46%	$5	$9	$18	$90	$180	$275	$600	$1,850	$20,000
	Auctions: $1,762, MS-64, January 2015; $1,292, MS-63, July 2015; $188, AU-50, May 2015; $135, EF-40, February 2015												
1926	44,693,000	1,455	63.6	96%	$1.25	$1.75	$2.50	$5	$10	$20	$35	$75	$200
	Auctions: $6,463, MS-67, December 2015; $4,465, MS-67, November 2016; $646, MS-66, November 2016; $176, MS-65, October 2016												
1926-D	5,638,000	869	53.7	67%	$10	$18	$28	$110	$185	$300	$350	$600	$4,000
	Auctions: $3,995, MS-65, July 2015; $1,410, MS-64, January 2015; $376, MS-63, April 2015; $258, MS-62, November 2015												
1926-S	970,000	2,066	28.4	10%	$25	$45	$100	$275	$900	$2,500	$4,500	$8,500	$95,000
	Auctions: $11,750, MS-64, January 2015; $2,350, AU-58, February 2015; $1,997, AU-53, June 2015; $705, EF-45, September 2015												
1927	37,981,000	1,069	63.5	95%	$1.25	$1.75	$2.50	$5	$15	$20	$35	$80	$250
	Auctions: $4,935, MS-67, September 2016; $999, MS-66, January 2015; $881, MS-66, December 2015; $164, MS-65, September 2015												
1927, Presentation Strike, Proof (l)	(m)	5	65.0								$30,000	$45,000	
	Auctions: $43,125, SP-65, January 2012												
1927-D	5,730,000	778	59.7	83%	$2.50	$6	$10	$35	$80	$135	$165	$350	$5,000
	Auctions: $4,935, MS-65, January 2015; $646, MS-64, October 2015; $376, MS-63, May 2015; $188, AU-58, September 2015												
1927-S	3,430,000	711	53.7	52%	$1.50	$3	$5	$35	$95	$185	$850	$2,250	$12,000
	Auctions: $3,525, MS-64, January 2015; $1,116, MS-62, October 2015; $329, AU-58, August 2015; $282, AU-55, February 2015												
1928	23,411,000	903	63.3	92%	$1.25	$1.75	$2.50	$5	$15	$25	$35	$80	$280
	Auctions: $5,875, MS-67, June 2015; $1,528, MS-66, November 2016; $258, MS-65, October 2015; $258, MS-65, November 2015												
1928-D	6,436,000	1,551	63.1	97%	$1.50	$2.50	$5	$15	$45	$50	$60	$110	$600
	Auctions: $517, MS-65, September 2015; $481, MS-65, August 2015; $129, MS-64, January 2015; $99, MS-63, February 2015												
1928-S	6,936,000	726	60.3	79%	$1.75	$2	$2.50	$11	$26	$110	$260	$550	$2,850
	Auctions: $7,343, MS-65, October 2015; $2,115, MS-65, January 2015; $822, MS-64, August 2015; $458, MS-63, February 2015												

l. Some experts believe that certain 1927 nickels were carefully made circulation strikes; such pieces are sometimes certified as "Examples" or "Presentation Strikes." Professional numismatic opinions vary. See Bowers, *A Guide Book of Buffalo and Jefferson Nickels*. **m.** The mintage figure is unknown.

1935, Doubled Die Reverse
FS-05-1935-801.

1936-D, 3-1/2 Legged
FS-05-1936D-901.

	Mintage	Cert	Avg	%MS	G-4	VG-8	F-12	VF-20	EF-40	AU-50	MS-60	MS-63	MS-65
											PF-63	PF-64	PF-65
1929	36,446,000	1,221	63.0	94%	$1.25	$1.50	$2.50	$5	$15	$20	$40	$75	$275
Auctions: $8,225, MS-67, September 2016; $5,402, MS-66, January 2015; $212, MS-65, October; $258, MS-64, August 2015
1929-D	8,370,000	791	62.3	92%	$1.25	$2	$2.50	$7	$32	$45	$60	$130	$950
Auctions: $763, MS-65, October 2015; $376, MS-64, February 2015; $282, MS-64, January 2015; $129, MS-63, May 2015
1929-S	7,754,000	911	62.8	91%	$1.25	$1.50	$2	$4	$12	$25	$55	$80	$375
Auctions: $340, MS-65, January 2015; $329, MS-65, October 2015; $129, MS-64, April 2015; $79, MS-63, May 2015
1930	22,849,000	1,464	63.2	93%	$1.25	$1.50	$2.50	$4	$11	$20	$35	$75	$220
Auctions: $3,525, MS-67, June 2015; $2,585, MS-67, October 2016; $1,763, MS-66, September 2016; $353, MS-65, October 2016
1930-S	5,435,000	755	62.5	91%	$1.25	$1.50	$2.50	$4	$15	$35	$65	$120	$385
Auctions: $1,880, MS-66, January 2015; $364, MS-65, February 2015; $188, MS-64, August 2015; $111, MS-63, May 2015
1931-S	1,200,000	2,079	61.8	89%	$15	$16	$20	$25	$35	$55	$65	$100	$300
Auctions: $616, MS-66, August 2015; $1,057, MS-65, January 2015; $517, MS-65, October 2015; $111, MS-64, May 2015
1934	20,213,003	1,139	63.4	91%	$1.25	$1.50	$2.50	$4	$10	$18	$50	$65	$300
Auctions: $9,988, MS-67, January 2015; $3,525, MS-67, August 2016; $1,880, MS-66, September 2016; $188, MS-65, August 2016
1934-D	7,480,000	1,207	63.0	95%	$1.50	$2.50	$4	$9	$20	$45	$80	$125	$550
Auctions: $1,880, MS-66, October 2015; $188, MS-64, August 2015; $152, MS-64, January 2015; $117, MS-63, April 2015
1935	58,264,000	1,622	63.4	92%	$1	$1.50	$1.75	$2	$5	$10	$22	$45	$120
Auctions: $3,995, MS-67, July 2016; $1,763, MS-67, October 2016; $229, MS-66, March 2015; $164, MS-66, September 2015
1935, Doubled Die Reverse (n)	(o)	196	30.3	6%	$45	$65	$100	$160	$500	$1,300	$4,000	$6,000	$25,000
Auctions: $329, EF-40, January 2015; $282, VF-35, January 2015; $95, VF-20, July 2015
1935-D	12,092,000	1,297	63.4	96%	$1	$1.50	$2.50	$6	$18	$42	$75	$85	$400
Auctions: $2,232, MS-67, January 2015; $1,410, MS-66, September 2015; $352, MS-65, March 2015; $89, MS-64, May 2015
1935-S	10,300,000	1,387	63.6	96%	$1	$1.50	$2	$2.50	$4	$18	$55	$70	$210
Auctions: $2,585, MS-67, January 2015; $305, MS-66, October 2015; $164, MS-65, March 2015; $74, MS-64, May 2015
1936	118,997,000	3,275	64.1	92%	$1	$1.50	$1.75	$2	$3	$9	$25	$40	$80
Auctions: $646, MS-67, December 2015; $352, MS-67, May 2015; $153, MS-66, August 2016; $339, MS-64, August 2015
1936, Proof, Both kinds	4,420												
1936, Satin Finish, Proof		641	65.8								$1,050	$1,250	$1,400
Auctions: $6,462, PF-68, July 2015; $2,585, PF-67, June 2015; $1,527, PF-67, October 2015; $1,527, PF-66, January 2015
1936, Brilliant Finish, Proof		578	65.5								$1,150	$1,500	$1,850
Auctions: $5,875, PF-68, August 2015; $3,290, PF-67, July 2015; $1,762, PF-66, February 2015; $1,762, PF-65, January 2015
1936-D	24,814,000	2,316	64.0	97%	$1	$1.50	$1.75	$2	$4	$12	$40	$45	$100
Auctions: $1,527, MS-67, January 2015; $123, MS-66, November 2015; $117, MS-66, February 2015; $69, MS-65, April 2015
1936-D, 3-1/2 Legged (p)	(q)	41	26.0	0%	$400	$600	$1,000	$1,500	$3,000	$4,250	$12,500		
Auctions: $3,290, AU-50, January 2014
1936-S	14,930,000	1,636	64.4	97%	$1	$1.50	$1.75	$2	$4	$12	$38	$45	$95
Auctions: $822, MS-67, January 2015; $270, MS-66, February 2015; $188, MS-66, November 2015; $94, MS-65, May 2015

n. Strong doubling is evident on FIVE CENTS, E PLURIBUS UNUM, and the eye, horn, and mane of the bison. This variety (FS-05-1935-801) is extremely rare above VF, and fewer than a dozen are known in MS. Do not mistake it for the more moderately doubled FS-05-1935-803, which commands much lower premiums. **o.** Included in 1935 mintage figure. **p.** The right front leg has been partially polished off the die—similar to the 1937-D, 3-Legged, variety, but not as severe. (This variety is not from the same die as the 1937-D.) Fewer than 40 are known in all grades. Incorrectly listed by Breen as 1936-P. **q.** Included in 1936-D mintage figure.

1937-D, 3-Legged
FS-05-1937D-901.

1938-D, D Over S
FS-05-1938D-511.

	Mintage	Cert	Avg	%MS	G-4	VG-8	F-12	VF-20	EF-40	AU-50	MS-60	MS-63	MS-65
											PF-63	PF-64	PF-65
1937	79,480,000	7,790	65.2	98%	$1	$1.50	$1.75	$2	$3	$9	$25	$40	$60
	Auctions: $8,225, MS-68, August 2016; $2,820, MS-67, September 2015; $1,059, MS-67, October 2015; $999, MS-67, August 2016												
1937, Proof	5,769	1,601	65.6								$1,000	$1,100	$1,200
	Auctions: $3,525, PF-68, August 2015; $3,055, PF-67, January 2015; $1,351, PF-66, July 2015; $1,292, PF-65, June 2015												
1937-D	17,826,000	4,256	64.9	97%	$1	$1.50	$1.75	$3	$4	$10	$35	$45	$60
	Auctions: $540, MS-67, January 2015; $423, MS-67, February 2015; $69, MS-66, June 2015; $48, MS-65, March 2015												
1937-D, 3-Legged (r)	(s)	6,816	49.0	25%	$450	$475	$550	$600	$675	$850	$1,850	$4,250	$30,000
	Auctions: $822, AU-55, February 2015; $822, AU-53, August 2015; $646, EF-45, July 2015; $493, F-12, January 2015												
1937-S	5,635,000	3,600	65.0	99%	$1	$1.50	$1.75	$3	$6	$9	$32	$42	$65
	Auctions: $881, MS-67, October 2015; $446, MS-67, January 2015; $62, MS-66, March 2015; $52, MS-64, June 2015												
1938-D	7,020,000	32,054	65.7	100%	$3.50	$4	$4.50	$4.75	$5	$8	$22	$36	$60
	Auctions: $188, MS-67, October 2015; $129, MS-67, January 2015; $50, MS-66, February 2015; $28, MS-65, August 2015												
1938-D, D Over D	(t)	2,620	65.6	100%	$4.50	$6.50	$9	$11	$20	$25	$45	$50	$75
	Auctions: $822, MS-67, October 2015; $564, MS-67, January 2015; $129, MS-66, February 2015; $60, MS-65, June 2015												
1938-D, D Over S (u)	(t)	2,120	65.2	99%	$5.50	$8	$10	$14	$20	$32	$55	$80	$160
	Auctions: $646, MS-67, August 2015; $517, MS-66, November 2015; $188, MS-66, March 2015; $94, MS-65, January 2015												

r. The reverse die was polished heavily, perhaps to remove clash marks, resulting in the shaft of the bison's right front leg missing. Beware altered examples fraudulently passed as genuine. "Look for a line of raised dots from the middle of the bison's belly to the ground as one of the diagnostics on the genuine specimen" (*Cherrypickers' Guide to Rare Die Varieties*, sixth edition, volume I). **s.** Included in 1937-D mintage figure. **t.** Included in 1938-D mintage figure. **u.** There are five different D Over S dies for this date. Varieties other than the one listed here (FS-05-1938D-511) command smaller premiums.

JEFFERSON (1938–2003)

Designer: *Felix Schlag.* **Weight:** *5 grams.* **Composition:** *1938–1942, 1946–2003—.750 copper, .250 nickel; 1942–1945—.560 copper, .350 silver, .090 manganese, with net weight .05626 oz. pure silver.* **Diameter:** *21.2 mm.* **Edge:** *Plain.* **Mints:** *Philadelphia, Denver, and San Francisco.*

Circulation Strike

Mintmark location, 1938–1941 and 1946–1964, is on the reverse, to the right of Monticello.

Mintmark location, 1942–1945, is on the reverse, above Monticello.

Proof

Wartime Silver Alloy (1942–1945)

Mintmark location, 1968–2004, is on the obverse, near the date.

Wartime Silver Alloy, Proof

History. The Jefferson nickel, designed by Felix Schlag in a public competition, made its debut in 1938, and has been a numismatic favorite since. The obverse features a portrait of Thomas Jefferson after the famous bust by Jean Antoine Houdon, and the reverse a front view of Jefferson's home, Monticello.

From partway through 1942 to the end of 1945 a copper-silver-manganese alloy replaced the traditional 75% copper and 25% nickel composition. This was to help save nickel for the war effort. These silver-content coins bear a distinctive P, D, or S mintmark above the dome of Monticello. Starting in 1966, Felix Schlag's initials, FS, were added below the presidential bust. The coinage dies were remodeled to strengthen the design in 1971, 1972, 1977, and 1982. The mintmark position, originally on the reverse to the right of Monticello, was moved to the obverse starting in 1968.

Striking and Sharpness. On the obverse, check for weakness on the portrait, especially in the lower jaw area. On the reverse, most circulation strikes have weak details on the six steps of Monticello, especially under the third pillar from the left, as this section on the reverse was opposite in the dies (in the press) from the high parts of the Jefferson portrait, and metal could not effectively flow in both directions at once. Planchet weight allowance was another cause, the dies being spaced slightly too far apart. Jefferson nickels can be classified as "Full Steps" (FS) if either five or six of Monticello's porch steps (with the top step counting as one) are clear. Notations of 5FS or 6FS can indicate the number of visible steps. It is easier to count the incuse lines than the raised steps. If there are four complete, unbroken lines, the coin qualifies as Full Steps (with five steps); five complete, unbroken lines indicate six full steps. There must be no nicks, cuts, or scratches interrupting the incuse lines. It is difficult to determine a full five-step count on the 1938 and some 1939 issues, as the steps are wavy and ill-defined; a great deal of subjectivity is common for these dates. Even if the steps are mostly or fully defined, check other areas to determine if a coin has Full Details overall. Interestingly, nickels of the 1950s and 1960s are among the most weakly struck. The silver-content coins of the 1940s usually are well struck. Some nickels of the 1950s to 1970s discolored easily, perhaps due to some impurities in the alloy. Proofs were struck from 1938 to 1942, 1950 to 1964, and 1968 to 2003. All have mirror fields. Striking is usually with Full Details, although there are scattered exceptions. Most survivors are in high grade, PF-64 and upward. Most since the 1970s have frosted or cameo contrast on the higher features. Special Mint Set (SMS) coins were struck in lieu of Proofs from 1965 to 1967; these in some instances closely resemble Proofs.

Availability. All basic dates and mintmarks were saved in roll quantities. Scarce issues in MS include 1939-D and 1942-D. The low-mintage 1950-D was a popular speculation in its time, and most of the mintage went into numismatic hands, making MS coins common today. Many different dates and mints are rare if with 5FS or 6FS; consult *A Guide Book of Buffalo and Jefferson Nickels* for details.

GRADING STANDARDS

MS-60 to 70 (Mint State). *Obverse and Reverse:* Mint luster is complete in the obverse and reverse fields, except in areas not fully struck up, in which graininess or marks from the *original planchet surface* can be seen. This may include the jaw, the back of Jefferson's head, and the higher-relief central features of Monticello. The highest parts of the design may have evidence of abrasion and/or contact marks in lower MS grades. Lower grades such

1939. Graded MS-66.

as MS–60, 61, and 62 can show some evidence of abrasion, usually on the same areas that display weak striking. At MS-63, evidences of abrasion are few, and at MS-65 they are fewer yet. In grades above MS-65, a Jefferson nickel should be mark-free.

AU-50, 53, 55, 58 (About Uncirculated). *Obverse:* The cheekbone and the higher points of the hair show light wear, more at AU-50 than at AU-58. Some mint luster will remain on some AU-55 and most AU-58 coins. *Reverse:* The central part of Monticello shows light wear, but is difficult to evaluate as this area often shows weakness of strike. Some mint luster will remain on some AU-55 and most AU-58 coins.

1943-P, 3 Over 2. Graded AU-58.

EF-40, 45 (Extremely Fine). *Obverse:* More wear is evident on the cheekbone. The higher parts of the hair are without detail. *Reverse:* Monticello shows wear overall. The bottom edge of the triangular area above the columns at the center are worn away.

1942-D, D Over Horizontal D. Graded EF-40.

VF-20, 30 (Very Fine). *Obverse:* Most hair detail is lost, except for the back of the head and lower area. The cheekbone is flat and mostly blended into the hair at the right. *Reverse:* Many shallow-relief architectural features are worn away. The windows remain clear and the four columns are distinct.

The Jefferson nickel is seldom collected in grades lower than VF-20.

1945-P, Doubled-Die Reverse. Graded VF-20.

PF-60 to 70 (Proof). *Obverse and Reverse:* Most Proof Jefferson nickels are in higher grades. Those with abrasion or contact marks can be graded PF–60 to 62 or even 63; these are not widely desired by collectors. PF-64 can have some abrasion. Tiny flecks are sometimes seen on coins of 1938 to 1942, as are discolorations (even to the extent of black streaks); these flaws are from cellophane holders. You should avoid such coins. Undipped Proofs of

1975-S. Graded PF-70 Deep Cameo.

the early era often have a slight bluish or yellowish tint. At PF-65 or higher there are no traces of abrasion or flecks. Evaluation of differences between higher-grade Jefferson Proofs is highly subjective; one certified at PF-65 might be similar to another at PF-67, and vice-versa. Striking is typically with full details, although there are scattered exceptions. At PF–69 and 70 there are no traces of abrasion, contact marks, or other flaws.

Five Steps

Six Steps

**1939, Doubled
Die Reverse**
FS-05-1939-801.

	Mintage	Cert	Avg	%MS	VF-20	EF-40	AU-50	MS-60	MS-63	MS-65	MS-65FS	MS-67
										PF-65	PF-66	PF-67
1938	19,496,000	1,214	65.4	98%	$0.50	$1	$1.50	$3	$5	$16	$135	$200
	Auctions: $188, MS-66, August 2015; $164, MS-66, May 2015; $141, MS-66, September 2015; $141, MS-66, October 2015											
1938, Proof	19,365	1,254	65.5							$100	$120	$350
	Auctions: $1,997, PF-68, October 2015; $1,057, PF-68, January 2015; $399, PF-67, July 2015; $94, PF-66, August 2015											
1938-D	5,376,000	2,740	66.0	99%	$1.50	$2	$3	$7	$10	$15	$125	$135
	Auctions: $881, MS-67, August 2015; $423, MS-67, January 2015; $141, MS-66, February 2015; $111, MS-66, September 2015											
1938-S	4,105,000	1,449	65.8	99%	$2.50	$3	$3.50	$4.50	$8	$16	$200	$375
	Auctions: $282, MS-67, January 2015; $305, MS-66, February 2015; $258, MS-66, October 2015; $129, MS-65, May 2015											
1939	120,615,000	1,270	65.0	93%	$0.25	$0.50	$1	$2	$2.50	$12	$47	$200
	Auctions: $1,116, MS-67FS, January 2015; $223, MS-66FS, February 2015; $36, MS-66, April 2015; $223, MS-65FS, February 2015											
1939, Doubled Die Reverse (a)	(b)	266	55.0	55%	$100	$135	$165	$200	$375	$900	$2,100	$3,500
	Auctions: $89, EF-40, November 2014; $86, EF-40, November 2014; $70, EF-40, November 2014; $7,050, EF-40, August 2013											
1939, Proof	12,535	898	65.4							$120	$170	$400
	Auctions: $2,115, PF-67, January 2015; $447, PF-67, February 2015; $129, PF-66, August 2015; $84, PF-65, October 2015											
1939-D	3,514,000	1,321	65.4	97%	$10	$13	$30	$60	$70	$80	$425	$325
	Auctions: $282, MS-67, January 2015; $129, MS-67, May 2015; $188, MS-66, November 2015; $135, MS-66, January 2015											
1939-S	6,630,000	714	65.0	96%	$2	$5	$10	$18	$35	$70	$350	$275
	Auctions: $1,528, MS-67, November 2013; $764, MS-66FS, June 2015; $247, MS-65FS, November 2014; $229, MS-65FS, September 2014											
1940	176,485,000	669	65.8	98%	$0.25	$0.40	$0.75	$1	$1.50	$15	$40	$145
	Auctions: $1,645, MS-67FS, June 2015; $1,320, MS-67FS, July 2015; $969, MS-67FS, August 2016; $153, MS-67, July 2015											
1940, Proof	14,158	902	65.4							$100	$120	$350
	Auctions: $6,463, PF-68, October 2015; $259, PF-67, January 2015; $94, PF-66, May 2015; $79, PF-65, June 2015											
1940-D	43,540,000	1,391	65.9	99%	$0.35	$0.50	$1	$2	$2.50	$15	$35	$65
	Auctions: $229, MS-67FS, November 2013											
1940-S	39,690,000	425	65.5	99%	$0.35	$0.50	$1	$2.25	$3	$12	$60	$235
	Auctions: $5,170, MS-67FS, June 2015; $282, MS-67FS, May 2015; $125, MS-66FS, February 2015; $69, MS-66FS, January 2015											
1941	203,265,000	656	65.8	99%	$0.20	$0.30	$0.50	$0.75	$1.50	$12	$55	$220
	Auctions: $2,010, MS-67FS, December 2015; $1,410, MS-67FS, October 2016; $940, VF-20, October 2014											
1941, Proof	18,720	1,073	65.4							$75	$110	$400
	Auctions: $200, PF-67, April 2015; $112, PF-66, May 2015; $106, PF-66, May 2015; $60, PF-65, August 2015											
1941-D	53,432,000	1,375	66.1	99%	$0.25	$0.40	$1.50	$2.50	$3.50	$12	$37	$70
	Auctions: $1,058, MS-67FS, June 2015; $166, MS-67FS, February 2015; $69, MS-67, February 2015; $54, MS-67, February 2015											
1941-S (c)	43,445,000	296	65.5	98%	$0.30	$0.50	$1.50	$3	$4	$12	$70	$165
	Auctions: $2,585, MS-66FS, April 2014; $282, MS-66FS, November 2014; $259, MS-66FS, January 2015; $106, MS-66FS, August 2015											

a. Very strong doubling is evident to the east of the primary letters, most noticeably on MONTICELLO and FIVE CENTS. Lesser doubling is also visible on UNITED STATES OF AMERICA and the right side of the building. **b.** Included in circulation-strike 1939 mintage figure. **c.** Large and small mintmark varieties exist.

1942-D, D Over Horizontal D
FS-05-1942D-501.

1943-P, 3 Over 2
FS-05-1943P-101.

1943-P, Doubled Die Obverse
The "Doubled Eye" variety. FS-05-1943P-106.

	Mintage	Cert	Avg	%MS	VF-20	EF-40	AU-50	MS-60	MS-63	MS-65 / PF-65	MS-65FS / PF-66	MS-67 / PF-67
1942	49,789,000	682	65.2	99%	$0.30	$0.45	$1.25	$4	$6	$15	$72	$150
	Auctions: $4,700, MS-66FS, July 2015; $2,115, MS-67FS, September 2016; $1,763, MS-66FS, July 2015; $188, MS-66FS, August 2015											
1942, Proof	29,600	1,817	65.7							$90	$100	$175
	Auctions: $1,410, PF-68, January 2015; $423, PF-67, June 2015; $118, PF-66, May 2015; $79, PF-66, January 2015											
1942-D	13,938,000	1,240	65.7	99%	$1	$2	$5	$28	$38	$60	$65	$170
	Auctions: $541, MS-67FS, January 2015; $494, MS-67FS, July 2015; $100, MS-66FS, January 2015; $89, MS-66FS, February 2015											
1942-D, D Over Horizontal D (d)	(e)	90	46.6	23%	$75	$200	$500	$1,500	$3,000	*$8,000*		
	Auctions: $15,275, MS-66, April 2013; $764, AU-58, October 2014; $329, AU-50, August 2014; $44, F-12, September 2014											
1942-P, Silver	57,873,000	5,498	66.2	99%	$2	$2.50	$3.25	$7	$12	$20	$60	$72
	Auctions: $764, MS-67FS, September 2015; $153, MS-67, September 2015; $129, MS-66FS, January 2015											
1942-P, Proof, Silver	27,600	2,900	65.5							$110	$160	$275
	Auctions: $230, PF-67, January 2015; $223, PF-67, January 2015; $100, PF-66, January 2015; $74, PF-64, March 2015											
1942-S	32,900,000	4,267	66.2	100%	$2	$2.50	$3.25	$7	$12	$25	$175	$215
	Auctions: $2,820, MS-67FS, August 2015; $176, MS-66FS, January 2015; $153, MS-66FS, January 2015; $54, MS-65FS, September 2015											
1943-P, 3 Over 2 (f)	(g)	338	53.5	61%	$50	$100	$165	$225	$260	$700	$1,000	$2,350
	Auctions: $588, MS-66, October 2015; $539, MS-65, January 2015; $376, MS-64, January 2015; $333, MS-63, June 2015											
1943-P	271,165,000	5,222	65.8	98%	$2	$2.50	$3	$5	$8	$20	$35	$55
	Auctions: $881, MS-67FS, June 2015; $646, MS-67FS, January 2015; $118, MS-67, August 2015; $62, MS-66FS, June 2015											
1943-P, Doubled Die Obverse (h)	(g)	145	62.6	83%	$25	$40	$60	$90	$160	$650	$850	$1,100
	Auctions: $1,293, MS-66FS, September 2015; $940, MS-66FS, July 2015; $823, MS-66, June 2015; $411, MS-65, October 2015											
1943-D	15,294,000	8,430	66.2	100%	$2	$3.50	$4	$6	$12	$20	$37	$50
	Auctions: $3,760, MS-67FS, August 2015; $1,645, MS-67FS, July 2015; $62, MS-66FS, September 2015; $30, MS-66, September 2015											
1943-S	104,060,000	5,273	66.2	100%	$2	$2.50	$3	$5	$8	$20	$40	$85
	Auctions: $1,645, MS-67FS, February 2015; $517, MS-67FS, January 2015; $94, MS-66FS, January 2015; $69, MS-66FS, June 2015											
1944-P (i)	119,150,000	3,425	66.0	100%	$2	$2.50	$3.25	$7	$12	$30	$70	$130
	Auctions: $259, MS-67, February 2015; $223, MS-67, February 2015; $212, MS-67, February 2015; $106, MS-67, May 2015											
1944-D	32,309,000	5,742	66.3	100%	$2	$2.50	$3	$6	$12	$25	$30	$65
	Auctions: $1,528, MS-67FS, July 2015; $1,410, MS-67FS, January 2015; $100, MS-66FS, January 2015; $79, MS-66FS, April 2015											
1944-S	21,640,000	5,253	66.2	100%	$2	$2.50	$3	$5	$10	$22	$135	$90
	Auctions: $5,170, MS-67FS, July 2015; $2,350, MS-67FS, January 2015; $329, MS-66FS, January 2015; $188, MS-65FS, January 2015											

Note: Genuine examples of some wartime dates were struck in nickel, in error. **d.** The initial D mintmark was punched into the die horizontally, then corrected. "This is the rarest of the major Jefferson nickel varieties in Mint State" (*Cherrypickers' Guide to Rare Die Varieties*, sixth edition, volume I). **e.** Included in 1942-D mintage figure. **f.** "This popular variety was created when the die was first hubbed with a 1942-dated hub, then subsequently hubbed with a 1943-dated hub. The diagonal of the 2 is visible within the lower opening of the 3. Doubling is also visible on LIBERTY and IN GOD WE TRUST. . . . There is at least one 1943-P five-cent piece that has a faint, short die gouge extending upward from the lower ball of the 3; this is often mistaken for the overdate" (*Cherrypickers' Guide to Rare Die Varieties*, sixth edition, volume I). **g.** Included in 1943-P mintage figure. **h.** This variety is nicknamed the "Doubled Eye." Doubling is visible on the date, LIBERTY, the motto, and, most noticeably, Jefferson's eye. **i.** 1944 nickels without mintmarks are counterfeits.

**1945-P, Doubled
Die Reverse**
FS-05-1945P-803.

	Mintage	Cert	Avg	%MS	VF-20	EF-40	AU-50	MS-60	MS-63	MS-65	MS-65FS	MS-67
										PF-65	PF-66	PF-67
1945-P	119,408,100	3,565	65.8	100%	$2	$2.50	$3	$5	$8	$20	$110	$435
Auctions: $9,988, MS-67FS, July 2015; $329, MS-67, October 2015; $223, MS-66FS, January 2015; $58, MS-66, January 2015												
1945-P, DblDie Reverse (j)	**(k)**	212	64.2	95%	$20	$30	$50	$75	$130	$800	$6,000	
Auctions: $400, MS-65, January 2015; $353, MS-65, February 2015; $212, MS-65, January 2015; $176, MS-64, January 2015												
1945-D	37,158,000	5,922	66.3	100%	$2	$2.50	$3	$5	$8	$20	$35	$80
Auctions: $705, MS-67FS, January 2015; $54, MS-66FS, May 2015; $50, MS-66FS, January 2015; $48, MS-66FS, May 2015												
1945-S	58,939,000	6,087	66.2	100%	$2	$2.50	$3	$5	$8	$20	$175	$175
Auctions: $3,055, MS-67FS, August 2015; $1,116, MS-67FS, January 2015; $1,058, MS-66FS, January 2015												
1946	161,116,000	287	65.0	98%	$0.25	$0.30	$0.35	$0.75	$2.50	$15	$175	
Auctions: $1,763, MS-67, December 2013; $1,528, MS-66FS, August 2016; $1,175, MS-66FS, November 2016; $259, MS-65FS, May 2015												
1946-D	45,292,200	878	65.5	99%	$0.35	$0.40	$0.45	$1	$2.50	$12	$30	$335
Auctions: $2,350, MS-67FS, September 2015; $1,528, MS-67FS, January 2015; $1,175, MS-67FS, October 2015;												
1946-S	13,560,000	761	65.6	99%	$0.40	$0.45	$0.50	$1	$2.00	$11	$110	$120
Auctions: $353, MS-66FS, December 2014; $306, MS-66FS, July 2015; $223, MS-66FS, October 2014; $529, MS-66FS, April 2014												
1947	95,000,000	414	65.4	99%	$0.25	$0.30	$0.35	$0.75	$1.75	$12	$57	$120
Auctions: $3,760, MS-67FS, January 2015; $564, MS-66FS, July 2015; $153, MS-66FS, February 2015; $150, MS-66FS, January 2015												
1947-D	37,822,000	720	65.7	100%	$0.30	$0.35	$0.40	$0.90	$1.75	$11	$25	$115
Auctions: $940, MS-67FS, October 2015; $79, MS-66FS, January 2015; $74, MS-66FS, May 2015; $69, MS-66FS, November 2015												
1947-S	24,720,000	371	65.2	99%	$0.40	$0.45	$0.50	$1	$1.75	$12	$43	$525
Auctions: $2,056, MS-66FS, June 2014												

Note: Genuine examples of some wartime dates were struck in nickel, in error. **j.** There are several collectible doubled-die reverses for this date. Values are for the variety pictured (FS-05-1945P-801), with a strongly doubled reverse. The doubling spread increases from left to right. **k.** Included in 1945-P mintage figure.

1949-D, D Over S
FS-05-1949D-501.

	Mintage	Cert	Avg	%MS	MS-60	MS-63	MS-65	MS-65FS	MS-66	MS-66FS	MS-67	MS-67FS
										PF-65	PF-66	PF-67
1948	89,348,000	226	65.2	99%	$1	$1.50	$10	$175	$55	$1,000		
Auctions: $1,646, MS-66FS, August 2016; $1,058, MS-66FS, October 2016; $112, MS-65FS, January 2015; $106, MS-65FS, July 2015												
1948-D	44,734,000	602	65.7	100%	$1.60	$4	$10	$25	$37	$70	$125	
Auctions: $588, MS-67FS, January 2015; $112, MS-66FS, November 2015												
1948-S	11,300,000	740	66.0	100%	$1.50	$2.50	$9	$37	$35	$265	$170	
Auctions: $7,050, MS-67FS, January 2015; $4,935, MS-67FS, July 2015; $517, MS-67, January 2015												
1949	60,652,000	273	65.2	99%	$2.50	$9	$12	$1,500	$30			
Auctions: $1,880, MS-65FS, December 2015; $1,553, MS-65FS, February 2010												
1949-D	36,498,000	689	65.4	99%	$1.50	$6	$10	$42	$28	$125	$265	
Auctions: $734, MS-67, January 2015; $411, MS-67, July 2014; $84, MS-67, December 2014												
1949-D, D Over S (a)	**(b)**	70	62.4	94%	$150	$200	$500	$1,450	$850			
Auctions: $564, MS-66, January 2015; $541, MS-66, January 2015; $541, MS-66, July 2015; $494, MS-66, October 2015												
1949-S	9,716,000	334	65.4	99%	$1.75	$5	$10	$175	$55	$850		
Auctions: $15,275, MS-67FS, January 2014; $235, MS-65FS, November 2014; $188, MS-65FS, November 2014												

a. The top serif of the S is visible to the north of the D, with the upper left loop of the S visible to the west of the D. "This variety is quite rare in Mint State and highly sought after. Some may still be found in circulated grades. Some examples have been located in original Mint sets" (*Cherrypickers' Guide to Rare Die Varieties*, sixth edition, volume I). **b.** Included in 1949-D mintage figure.

1954-S, S Over D
FS-05-1954S-501.

	Mintage	Cert	Avg	%MS	MS-60	MS-63	MS-65	MS-65FS	MS-66	MS-66FS PF-65	MS-67 PF-66	MS-67FS PF-67
1950	9,796,000	486	65.7	100%	$2	$3.25	$8	$170	$42	$335		
Auctions: $2,820, MS-67, September 2016; $106, MS-65FS, January 2015; $94, MS-65FS, July 2015												
1950, Proof	51,386	1,736	65.9							$75	$85	$125
Auctions: $329, PF-68, October 2015; $188, PF-68, August 2015; $141, PF-66Cam, November 2015; $50, PF-65, July 2015												
1950-D	2,630,030	4,033	65.5	100%	$14	$16	$25	$50	$53	$110	$190	$750
Auctions: $1,293, MS-67FS, August 2015; $250, MS-67, January 2015; $306, MS-66FS, February 2015; $118, MS-66FS, February 2015												
1951	28,552,000	291	65.4	100%	$3	$6.50	$15	$300	$70	$850		
Auctions: $1,410, MS-66FS, October 2016; $282, MS-66FS, August 2015; $259, MS-65FS, January 2015; $235, MS-65, August 2015												
1951, Proof	57,500	1,733	66.7							$65	$75	$120
Auctions: $823, PF-68Cam, January 2015; $705, PF-68Cam, October 2015; $129, PF-67Cam, June 2015; $58, PF-67, February 2015												
1951-D	20,460,000	620	65.7	100%	$4	$7	$11	$70	$30	$250	$235	
Auctions: $2,820, MS-66FS, June 2013												
1951-S	7,776,000	475	65.7	100%	$1.50	$2	$12	$175	$37	$850		
Auctions: $646, MS-67, August 2015; $194, MS-67, September 2015; $1,293, MS-66FS, January 2015; $881, MS-66FS, January 2015												
1952	63,988,000	257	65.5	100%	$1	$4	$9	$875	$135	$2,100	$375	
Auctions: $1,175, MS-67, August 2016; $1,058, MS-67, October 2016; $259, MS-66FS, July 2014; $259, MS-64FS, November 2014												
1952, Proof	81,980	1,768	66.9							$45	$60	$75
Auctions: $176, PF-67Cam, January 2015; $153, PF-67Cam, December 2015; $64, PF-66Cam, December 2015; $26, PF-66, March 2015												
1952-D	30,638,000	413	65.7	100%	$3.50	$6.25	$15	$150	$35	$290	$500	
Auctions: $16,450, MS-67FS, July 2015; $12,338, MS-67FS, January 2015; $329, MS-66FS, August 2015; $112, MS-65FS, January 2015												
1952-S	20,572,000	696	65.6	100%	$1	$1.50	$12	$265	$38	$1,600		
Auctions: $235, MS-65FS, August 2015; $212, MS-65FS, January 2015												
1953	46,644,000	268	65.4	100%	$0.25	$0.75	$8	$1,700	$38	$3,750		
Auctions: $129, PF-67Cam, December 2015; $26, PF-66Cam, August 2015; $54, PF-66, June 2015												
1953, Proof	128,800	2,406	67.1							$45	$50	$65
Auctions: $15,275, PF-68DCam, April 2013; $65, PF-68, September 2014; $135, PF-67Cam, November 2014; $35, PF-67, July 2014												
1953-D	59,878,600	608	65.6	100%	$0.25	$1	$9	$190	$38	$750	$385	
Auctions: $129, MS-67, January 2015; $1,880, MS-66FS, July 2015; $135, MS-65FS, August 2015; $141, MS-65, October 2015												
1953-S	19,210,900	488	65.2	100%	$0.75	$1	$10	$4,500	$75			
Auctions: $1,293, MS-64FS, June 2013												
1954	47,684,050	320	65.0	100%	$1	$1.50	$15	$215	$28	$1,050	$190	
Auctions: $999, MS-66FS, November 2014; $259, MS-65FS, January 2015; $207, MS-65FS, February 2010												
1954, Proof	233,300	2,678	67.3							$22	$40	$55
Auctions: $5,875, PF-68DCam, March 2013												
1954-D	117,183,060	272	64.2	98%	$0.60	$1	$30	$600	$100	$1,400	$265	
Auctions: $646, MS-65FS, January 2015; $282, MS-65FS, August 2015; $200, MS-65FS, August 2015; $176, MS-65FS, August 2015												
1954-S	29,384,000	703	64.7	99%	$1.75	$2	$15	$5,250	$100			
Auctions: $1,410, MS-64FS, January 2015; $764, MS-64FS, October 2015												
1954-S, S Over D (c)	**(d)**	186	62.7	94%	$26	$40	$145	$435	$425			
Auctions: $329, MS-66, January 2015; $159, MS-65, April 2015; $147, MS-65, February 2015; $84, MS-64, April 2015												

c. The overall strength of the strike is the important factor in this overmintmark's value. **d.** Included in 1954-S mintage figure.

1955-D, D Over S
FS-05-1955D-501.

	Mintage	Cert	Avg	%MS	MS-60	MS-63	MS-65	MS-65FS	MS-66	MS-66FS / PF-65	MS-67 / PF-66	MS-67FS / PF-67
1955	7,888,000	416	65.0	100%	$0.75	$1	$15	$675	$100			
Auctions: $3,643, MS-66FS, September 2016; $382, MS-65FS, April 2014												
1955, Proof	378,200	4,346	67.6							$18	$30	$45
Auctions: $1,175, PF-68DCam, October 2015; $646, PF-68DCam, August 2015; $69, PF-66, July 2015; $54, PF-63, May 2015												
1955-D	74,464,100	414	64.5	98%	$0.50	$0.75	$20	$4,000	$140			
Auctions: $165, MS-66, August 2014; $69, MS-66, November 2015; $999, MS-64FS, February 2013												
1955-D, D Over S (e)	(f)	186	64.2	96%	$36	$57.50	$175	$390	$750			
Auctions: $823, MS-66, August 2015; $165, MS-65, January 2015; $50, MS-63, November 2015												
1956	35,216,000	688	65.4	100%	$0.50	$0.75	$20	$67	$38	$165		$1,650
Auctions: $9,400, MS-67FS, June 2015; $1,293, MS-66FS, December 2015; $588, MS-66FS, June 2014												
1956, Proof	669,384	3,748	67.5							$5	$25	$40
Auctions: $47, PF-69, October 2014; $5,581, PF-68DCam, June 2013												
1956-D	67,222,940	456	65.5	100%	$0.50	$0.75	$20	$575	$34	$1,700	$285	
Auctions: $911, MS-65FS, February 2013												
1957	38,408,000	419	65.0	100%	$0.50	$0.75	$15	$80	$55	$1,500		
Auctions: $441, MS-66FS, April 2014; $400, MS-67, August 2016												
1957, Proof	1,247,952	3,615	67.4							$4	$12	$20
Auctions: $881, PF-68Cam, June 2013												
1957-D	136,828,900	609	65.4	100%	$0.50	$0.70	$15	$150	$30	$1,300		
Auctions: $1,087, MS-66FS, August 2015; $376, MS-66FS, August 2015; $259, MS-66FS, August 2015; $188, MS-66FS, January 2015												
1958	17,088,000	275	64.3	100%	$0.60	$0.80	$12	$900	$85			
Auctions: $1,116, MS-66FS, November 2014; $764, MS-65, January 2014; $42, MS-64FS, June 2015												
1958, Proof	875,652	3,402	67.4							$8	$12	$20
Auctions: $7,050, PF-68DCam, April 2013												
1958-D	168,249,120	711	65.4	99%	$0.40	$0.50	$12	$33	$45	$38	$200	$2,100
Auctions: $1,763, MS-67FS, December 2013												
1959	27,248,000	552	65.3	99%	$0.25	$0.50	$10	$55	$65	$475		
Auctions: $764, MS-66FS, August 2016; $617, MS-66FS, September 2016; $165, MS-66FS, August 2015; $165, MS-66FS, August 2015												
1959, Proof	1,149,291	3,403	67.4							$3	$10	$20
Auctions: $7,050, PF-69DCam, April 2013; $1,293, PF-68DCam, September 2014; $494, PF-67DCam, August 2015												
1959-D	160,738,240	460	65.4	99%	$0.25	$0.50	$8	$190	$65	$1,100		
Auctions: $306, MS-66FS, July 2015; $223, MS-66FS, January 2015; $118, MS-65FS, January 2015; $107, MS-65FS, September 2015												
1960	55,416,000	372	65.2	99%	$0.25	$0.50	$8	$2,000	$65			
Auctions: $1,495, MS-65FS, February 2010												
1960, Proof	1,691,602	3,787	67.4							$3	$10	$18
Auctions: $6,463, PF-69DCam, March 2013; $229, PF-69Cam, September 2014												
1960-D	192,582,180	371	65.4	99%	$0.25	$0.50	$10	$2,500	$130		$425	
Auctions: $223, MS-66, February 2013												

e. There are 10 or more different D Over S varieties for 1955. Values shown are for the strongest (FS-05-1955D-501); others command smaller premiums. f. Included in 1955-D mintage figure.

	Mintage	Cert	Avg	%MS	MS-60	MS-63	MS-65	MS-65FS	MS-66	MS-66FS	MS-67	MS-67FS
										PF-65	PF-66	PF-67
1961	73,640,100	365	65.5	100%	$0.25	$0.50	$20	$1,500	$47	$2,650		
	Auctions: $2,530, MS-65FS, February 2010											
1961, Proof	3,028,144	3,944	67.3							$3	$10	$18
	Auctions: $1,763, PF-69DCam, April 2013											
1961-D	229,342,760	309	65.0	100%	$0.25	$0.50	$20	$6,500	$200		$1,750	
	Auctions: $11,163, MS-64FS, February 2013											
1962	97,384,000	364	65.2	99%	$0.25	$0.50	$10	$43	$40	$350	$285	
	Auctions: $21,150, MS-67FS, August 2013											
1962, Proof	3,218,019	4,289	67.3							$3	$10	$18
	Auctions: $823, PF-69DCam, September 2013											
1962-D	280,195,720	202	64.5	98%	$0.25	$0.50	$30		$300			
	Auctions: $89, MS-63FS, November 2014; $118, MS-63FS, June 2013											
1963	175,776,000	619	65.4	100%	$0.25	$0.50	$10	$150	$43	$675	$650	
	Auctions: $1,058, MS-66FS, July 2016; $705, MS-66FS, October 2016; $541, MS-66FS, July 2015; $79, MS-65FS, January 2015											
1963, Proof	3,075,645	4,853	67.4							$3	$10	$18
	Auctions: $329, PF-69UCam, July 2015; $317, PF-69DCam, December 2014; $823, PF-69DCam, September 2013											
1963-D	276,829,460	185	64.0	97%	$0.25	$0.50	$25	$4,750				
	Auctions: $7,475, MS-65FS, February 2010											
1964	1,024,672,000	333	65.2	99%	$0.25	$0.50	$8	$260	$33	$1,200		
	Auctions: $881, MS-66FS, July 2015; $147, MS-65, January 2015; $129, MS-64, August 2015; $62, MS-64, August 2015											
1964, Proof	3,950,762	8,499	68.1							$3	$10	$18
	Auctions: $176, PF-69DCam, January 2015; $112, PF-69DCam, January 2015; $94, PF-69UCam, July 2015											
1964-D	1,787,297,160	411	65.1	99%	$0.25	$0.50	$5	$575	$38	$1,450		
	Auctions: $2,350, MS-66FS, January 2015; $969, MS-66FS, January 2015; $282, MS-65FS, January 2015											
1965	136,131,380	659	65.9	100%	$0.25	$0.50	$5	$60	$50	$250	$5,500	
	Auctions: $165, MS-67, December 2014; $646, MS-66, August 2013											
1965, Special Mint Set	2,360,000	2,439	66.6							$5 (g)	$20	$45
	Auctions: $5,288, PF-67DCam, July 2014; $123, PF-67Cam, September 2014; $79, PF-67Cam, January 2015											
1966	156,208,283	110	65.1	97%		$0.25	$5	$50	$25	$225	$175	
	Auctions: $56, MS-66, July 2014; $322, MS-65DCam, February 2010											
1966, Special Mint Set	2,261,583	2,242	66.8							$5 (h)	$20	$35
	Auctions: $329, PF-67Cam, July 2015; $94, PF-67Cam, January 2015											
1967	107,325,800	289	65.5	99%		$0.25	$5	$50	$25	$235	$185	
	Auctions: $132, MS-66, February 2013											
1967, Special Mint Set	1,863,344	2,651	66.8							$5 (i)	$20	$30
	Auctions: $188, PF-68Cam, August 2015; $823, PF-67DCam, July 2015; $40, PF-67Cam, February 2015											

g. Value in PF-64FS is $10; in PF-65FS, $55. **h.** Value in PF-64FS is $10; in PF-65FS, $65. **i.** Value in PF-64FS is $10; in PF-65FS, $60.

	Mintage	Cert	Avg	%MS	MS-63	MS-64FS	MS-65	MS-65FS	MS-66	MS-66FS	MS-67	MS-67FS
										PF-66	PF-67Cam	PF-69DC
1968-D	91,227,880	629	65.5	100%	$0.25		$4		$35			
	Auctions: No auction records available.											
1968-S	100,396,004	307	65.6	100%	$0.25	$475	$5	$1,250	$35	$3,000	$275	
	Auctions: No auction records available.											
1968-S, Proof	3,041,506	1,413	67.8							$4	$16	$115
	Auctions: $4,406, PF-65, August 2013											
1969-D	202,807,500	442	65.5	100%	$0.25	$10	$4		$115			
	Auctions: $94, MS-66, February 2013											
1969-S	120,165,000	201	65.0	100%	$0.25		$2		$275			
	Auctions: $188, PF-69DCam, January 2015											
1969-S, Proof	2,934,631	1,346	67.8							$4	$10	$400
	Auctions: $282, PF-69DCam, November 2014; $1,116, PF-69DCam, June 2013											

	Mintage	Cert	Avg	%MS	MS-63	MS-64FS	MS-65	MS-65FS	MS-66	MS-66FS	MS-67 PF-66	MS-67FS PF-67Cam	MS-67FS PF-69DC
1970-D	515,485,380	505	64.9	100%	$0.25		$10		$180				
Auctions: $200, MS-63, August 2013; $200, MS-62, July 2014; $176, MS-62, August 2015													
1970-S	238,832,004	225	64.9	100%	$0.25	$225	$8	$400	$225	$1,500			
Auctions: $999, MS-66FS, December 2013; $89, MS-64FS, November 2014													
1970-S, Proof	2,632,810	1,317	67.7								$4	$15	$300
Auctions: $499, PF-69DCam, September 2013; $411, PF-69DCam, September 2014; $376, PF-69DCam, January 2015													

	Mintage	Cert	Avg	%MS	MS-63	MS-64FS	MS-65	MS-65FS	MS-66	MS-66FS	MS-67 PF-66	MS-67FS PF-67Cam	MS-69FS PF-69DC
1971	106,884,000	348	64.9	99%	$0.75	$10	$3	$30	$50	$100			
Auctions: $127, MS-66FS, February 2010													
1971-D	316,144,800	674	66.0	100%	$0.30	$10	$3	$20	$30	$60		$750	
Auctions: $646, MS-67FS, August 2013													
1971-S, Proof	1,655	101	67.6								$1,100	$1,200	$3,000
Auctions: $1,704, PF-69Cam, August 2015; $881, PF-68Cam, October 2015; $1,175, PF-67Cam, January 2015; $940, PF-67, January 2015													
1971-S, No S, Proof †† (a)	3,220,733	1,300	67.7								$8	$20	$600
Auctions: $1,528, PF-69DCam, June 2013													
1972	202,036,000	123	65.2	99%	$0.25	$10	$3	$40	$60	$300			
Auctions: $141, MS-66FS, November 2014; $276, MS-66FS, March 2012													
1972-D	351,694,600	165	64.9	99%	$0.25	$10	$3	$40	$75	$350			
Auctions: $212, MS-63, November 2014; $823, MS-63, August 2013													
1972-S, Proof	3,260,996	1,006	67.6								$8	$20	$120
Auctions: $58, PF-69DCam, November 2015; $52, PF-69DCam, November 2015; $42, PF-69DCam, October 2015													
1973	384,396,000	221	65.1	100%	$0.25	$10	$3	$30	$45	$150	$110		
Auctions: $103, MS-66FS, February 2013													
1973-D	261,405,000	252	65.4	100%	$0.25	$10	$3	$25	$30	$60	$90		
Auctions: $353, MS-65, February 2014													
1973-S, Proof	2,760,339	301	67.8								$7	$15	$30
Auctions: $44, PF-69DCam, September 2009													
1974	601,752,000	230	64.9	100%	$0.25	$40	$3	$175	$35	$675			
Auctions: $1,116, MS-66FS, July 2016; $110, MS-65FS, March 2014; $54, MS-65FS, January 2015; $46, MS-65FS, November 2014													
1974-D	277,373,000	155	65.2	99%	$0.25	$15	$3	$40	$45	$110		$1,550	
Auctions: $34, MS-66FS, November 2014; $200, MS-62, April 2013													
1974-S, Proof	2,612,568	382	67.1								$8	$12	$20
Auctions: $25, PF-69DCam, March 2008													
1975	181,772,000	221	65.5	100%	$0.50	$20	$3	$50	$55	$250			
Auctions: $2,820, MS-67FS, January 2015; $129, MS-66FS, August 2015													
1975-D	401,875,300	152	65.3	100%	$0.25	$15	$3	$60	$55	$225			
Auctions: $176, MS-66FS, August 2015; $153, MS-64FS, August 2015													
1975-S, Proof	2,845,450	533	67.9								$8	$12	$20
Auctions: $42, PF-68Cam, August 2013													
1976	367,124,000	89	64.7	100%	$0.45	$30	$3	$175	$37	$675		$3,250	
Auctions: $1,265, MS-66FS, February 2012													
1976-D	563,964,147	215	65.0	100%	$0.45	$10	$3	$30	$40	$250			
Auctions: $235, MS-65, February 2014; $94, MS-64, July 2014													
1976-S, Proof	4,149,730	808	67.8								$8	$12	$20
Auctions: $36, PF-70DCam, January 2010													

†† Ranked in the *100 Greatest U.S. Modern Coins* (fourth edition). **a.** 1971-S, Proof, nickels without the S mintmark were made in error after an assistant engraver forgot to punch a mintmark into a die. The U.S. Mint estimates that 1,655 such error coins were struck.

1979-S, Filled S (Type 1), Proof	1979-S, Clear S (Type 2), Proof	1981-S, Rounded S (Type 1), Proof	1981-S, Flat S (Type 2), Proof

	Mintage	Cert	Avg	%MS	MS-63	MS-64FS	MS-65	MS-65FS	MS-66	MS-66FS	MS-67 / PF-66	MS-67FS / PF-67Cam	MS-69FS / PF-69DC
1977	585,376,000	146	65.3	100%	$0.25	$70	$3	$150	$48	$775			
Auctions: $705, MS-66FS, July 2016; $306, MS-65, September 2015; $881, MS-64, October 2014; $329, MS-63, September 2013													
1977-D	297,313,422	220	64.8	100%	$0.50	$10	$3	$35	$40	$250			
Auctions: $940, MS-68, August 2013													
1977-S, Proof	3,251,152	730	68.3								$7	$12	$20
Auctions: $1,116, PF-70DCam, April 2013													
1978	391,308,000	149	65.2	100%	$0.25	$35	$3	$175	$55	$750			
Auctions: $43, MS-64, July 2014; $259, MS-64, September 2013; $282, MS-63, October 2014													
1978-D	313,092,780	227	64.8	100%	$0.25	$15	$3	$40	$55	$75			
Auctions: $104, MS-66FS, February 2010													
1978-S, Proof	3,127,781	723	68.6								$7	$12	$20
Auctions: $165, PF-70DCam, February 2015; $153, PF-70DCam, February 2015; $129, PF-70DCam, July 2015													
1979	463,188,000	119	65.1	99%	$0.25	$40	$3	$300	$50	$650			
Auctions: $200, MS-63, January 2015; $129, MS-60, September 2015													
1979-D	325,867,672	286	64.8	99%	$0.25	$10	$4	$30	$37	$125			
Auctions: $182, MS-66FS, February 2013													
1979-S, Proof, Both kinds	3,677,175												
1979-S, Type 1, Proof		788	68.6								$7	$12	$22
Auctions: $1,763, PF-70DCam, June 2013													
1979-S, Type 2, Proof		860	68.8								$8	$13	$30
Auctions: $646, PF-70DCam, June 2013													
1980-P	593,004,000	171	65.5	100%	$0.25	$10	$4	$45	$30	$225			
Auctions: $329, MS-64, January 2015; $259, MS-65, January 2015; $240, MS-64, January 2015; $188, MS-60, January 2015													
1980-D	502,323,448	150	65.0	99%	$0.25	$10	$3	$20	$60	$250			
Auctions: $217, MS-66FS, February 2013													
1980-S, Proof	3,554,806	1,009	68.7								$7	$12	$20
Auctions: No auction records available.													
1981-P	657,504,000	195	65.6	99%	$0.25	$100	$3	$500	$50	$1,750			
Auctions: $282, MS-66, January 2015; $223, MS-62, January 2015													
1981-D	364,801,843	177	65.0	100%	$0.25	$10	$3	$30	$35	$150			
Auctions: $206, MS-66FS, June 2014													
1981-S, Proof, Both kinds	4,063,083												
1981-S, Type 1, Proof		1,173	68.6								$7	$12	$20
Auctions: $1,528, PF-70DCam, June 2013													
1981-S, Type 2, Proof		1,015	68.9								$10	$13	$30
Auctions: $3,525, PF-70DCam, April 2013													
1982-P	292,355,000	92	65.1	98%	$5	$12	$10	$50	$35	$275			
Auctions: $881, MS-67, February 2014; $2,350, MS-62, September 2014; $306, MS-62, February 2015													
1982-D	373,726,544	165	65.2	99%	$2	$25	$6	$55	$30	$325			
Auctions: $374, MS-66FS, February 2010													
1982-S, Proof	3,857,479	854	68.8								$8	$12	$20
Auctions: No auction records available.													

	Mintage	Cert	Avg	%MS	MS-63	MS-64FS	MS-65	MS-65FS	MS-66	MS-66FS	MS-67	MS-67FS	MS-69FS
											PF-66	PF-67Cam	PF-69DC
1983-P	561,615,000	84	64.5	94%	$2	$60	$9	$400	$60	$875			
Auctions: $141, MS-64, January 2015; $64, MS-64, January 2015; $36, MS-64, August 2015													
1983-D	536,726,276	121	65.2	98%	$1.50	$15	$4	$175	$35	$675			
Auctions: $863, MS-66FS, June 2010; $112, MS-65FS, November 2014													
1983-S, Proof	3,279,126	793	68.8								$8	$12	$20
Auctions: $1,528, PF-70DCam, June 2013													
1984-P	746,769,000	144	65.4	100%	$1	$10	$3	$25	$40	$75			
Auctions: $66, MS-66FS, February 2013													
1984-D	517,675,146	136	65.1	99%	$0.25	$10	$3	$30	$65	$135			
Auctions: $36, MS-65FS, February 2013													
1984-S, Proof	3,065,110	602	68.6								$10	$12	$20
Auctions: $705, PF-70DCam, June 2013													
1985-P	647,114,962	129	65.5	100%	$0.50	$25	$3	$50	$60	$135			
Auctions: $89, MS-66FS, November 2014; $70, MS-66FS, November 2014; $259, MS-62, November 2013													
1985-D	459,747,446	114	65.3	100%	$0.50	$10	$3	$40	$45	$125		$1,500	
Auctions: $196, MS-66FS, June 2010													
1985-S, Proof	3,362,821	635	68.9								$8	$12	$20
Auctions: $1,528, PF-70DCam, June 2013													
1986-P	536,883,483	139	65.7	100%	$0.50	$10	$3	$50	$35	$175			
Auctions: $705, MS-66FS, August 2015; $99, MS-66FS, February 2013; $47, MS-66FS, November 2014													
1986-D	361,819,140	114	65.4	100%	$1	$10	$3	$35	$50	$300			
Auctions: $253, MS-66FS, February 2010													
1986-S, Proof	3,010,497	490	68.9								$9	$13	$20
Auctions: $3,525, PF-70DCam, April 2013													
1987-P	371,499,481	382	66.0	100%	$0.25	$10	$2.75	$15	$60	$65		$225	
Auctions: $329, MS-67FS, June 2014													
1987-D	410,590,604	345	65.6	100%	$0.25	$10	$3.50	$20	$30	$125			
Auctions: $173, MS-67FS, April 2008													
1987-S, Proof	4,227,728	633	68.9								$8	$12	$20
Auctions: $558, PF-70DCam, June 2013													
1988-P	771,360,000	124	65.8	100%	$0.25	$12	$3	$30	$35	$100			
Auctions: $329, MS-67, August 2013; $79, MS-64, August 2015; $69, MS-64, July 2014													
1988-D	663,771,652	192	65.3	99%	$0.25	$10	$3	$35	$32	$125			
Auctions: $165, MS-67, June 2014													
1988-S, Proof	3,262,948	572	68.7								$9	$13	$25
Auctions: $823, PF-70DCam, June 2013													
1989-P	898,812,000	217	65.9	100%	$0.25	$10	$2.75	$20	$25	$35		$650	
Auctions: $18, AU-50, August 2013													
1989-D	570,842,474	142	65.1	100%	$0.25	$12	$2.75	$40	$35	$180			
Auctions: $188, MS-66FS, February 2013													
1989-S, Proof	3,220,194	607	69.0								$8	$12	$20
Auctions: $82, PF-70DCam, May 2013													
1990-P	661,636,000	157	66.0	99%	$0.25	$10	$2.75	$20	$25	$40			
Auctions: $24, MS-66FS, October 2009													
1990-D	663,938,503	127	65.0	99%	$0.25	$9	$2.75	$30	$45	$200			
Auctions: $129, MS-67FS, June 2014													
1990-S, Proof	3,299,559	864	69.1								$8	$12	$20
Auctions: $441, PF-69DCam, June 2014													
1990-S, Proof, Dbl Die Obverse ††	(b)	35	68.9									$250	
Auctions: $129, MS-67FS, June 2014													

†† Ranked in the *100 Greatest U.S. Modern Coins* (fourth edition). **b.** Included in 1990-S, Proof mintage figure.

	Mintage	Cert	Avg	%MS	MS-63	MS-64FS	MS-65	MS-65FS	MS-66	MS-66FS	MS-67 / PF-66	MS-67FS / PF-67Cam	MS-69FS / PF-69DC
1991-P	614,104,000	96	65.6	100%	$0.30	$10	$2.75	$45	$35	$190			
Auctions: $90, MS-66FS, February 2013													
1991-D	436,496,678	103	65.3	100%	$0.30	$10	$2.75	$25	$35	$160			
Auctions: $76, MS-66FS, February 2013													
1991-S, Proof	2,867,787	773	69.1								$10	$12	$20
Auctions: $64, PF-70DCam, August 2013													
1992-P	399,552,000	203	65.8	100%	$1.50	$10	$3	$20	$28	$50		$1,250	
Auctions: $88, MS-67FS, August 2013													
1992-D	450,565,113	121	65.2	100%	$0.25	$10	$2.75	$30	$40	$160			
Auctions: $72, MS-66FS, February 2013													
1992-S, Proof	4,176,560	1,508	69.1								$8	$12	$20
Auctions: $45, PF-70DCam, May 2013													
1993-P	412,076,000	130	65.8	100%	$0.25	$10	$1	$30	$35	$75			
Auctions: $68, MS-66FS, February 2013													
1993-D	406,084,135	174	65.4	100%	$0.25	$10	$1	$20	$30	$40	$450	$425	
Auctions: $374, MS-67FS, February 2010													
1993-S, Proof	3,394,792	1,549	69.0								$8	$12	$20
Auctions: $47, PF-70DCam, October 2009													
1994-P	722,160,000	162	66.0	100%	$0.25	$10	$2.50	$25	$30	$100	$35		
Auctions: $235, MS-70, January 2015; $881, MS-63, April 2013													
1994-P, Special Uncirculated ✝✝ (c)	167,703	2,210	7.3	100%	$50	$75	$100	$125	$130	$150	$250	$450	
Auctions: $123, MS-70, November 2014; $66, MS-69FS, March 2013; $40, MS-69, September 2014; $38, MS-69, November 2014													
1994-D	715,762,110	102	64.8	99%	$0.25	$10	$1	$30	$35	$100	$50		
Auctions: $92, MS-66FS, February 2013													
1994-S, Proof	3,269,923	1,394	69.1								$8	$12	$20
Auctions: $33, PF-70DCam, April 2013													
1995-P	774,156,000	187	66.2	100%	$0.25	$20	$1	$40	$20	$90	$25	$250	
Auctions: $499, MS-65, August 2013; $141, MS-63, July 2014													
1995-D	888,112,000	59	65.0	98%	$0.50	$10	$1	$25	$30	$175	$35	$850	
Auctions: $940, MS-67FS, April 2014													
1995-S, Proof	2,797,481	1,355	69.1								$10	$13	$20
Auctions: $79, PF-70DCam, February 2010													
1996-P	829,332,000	195	65.7	100%	$0.25	$18	$1	$20	$25	$30	$35	$350	
Auctions: $129, MS-64, January 2015; $69, MS-64, January 2015													
1996-D	817,736,000	224	65.3	100%	$0.25	$20	$1	$22	$25	$35	$40	$200	
Auctions: $161, MS-67FS, February 2010													
1996-S, Proof	2,525,265	1,391	69.1								$8	$12	$25
Auctions: $56, PF-70DCam, February 2010													
1997-P	470,972,000	79	65.9	100%	$0.50	$10	$2	$45	$25	$175	$50	$350	
Auctions: $306, MS-70FS, July 2015; $118, MS-69FS, February 2015													
1997-P, Special Uncirculated ✝✝ (b)	25,000	1,068	3.2	100%	$55	$75	$75	$85	$100	$95	$110	$150	
Auctions: $200, MS-70FS, October 2014; $499, MS-70FS, June 2014; $223, MS-69FS, November 2014; $118, MS-69, November 2014													
1997-D	466,640,000	95	65.2	99%	$1	$15	$2	$50	$20	$100	$25	$500	
Auctions: $33, MS-66FS, June 2014													
1997-S, Proof	2,796,678	1,365	69.3								$8	$12	$25
Auctions: $36, PF-70DCam, December 2009													

✝✝ Ranked in the *100 Greatest U.S. Modern Coins* (fourth edition). **c.** Special "frosted" Uncirculated nickels were included in the 1993, Thomas Jefferson, commemorative dollar packaging (sold in 1994) and in the 1997, Botanic Garden, sets (see related listing in the "Government Commemorative Sets" section). They resemble Matte Proof coins.

	Mintage	Cert	Avg	%MS	MS-63	MS-64FS	MS-65	MS-65FS	MS-66	MS-66FS	MS-67	MS-67FS	MS-69FS
												PF-66	PF-67Cam	PF-69DC
1998-P	688,272,000	90	65.1	100%	$0.35	$8	$1	$35	$45	$125	$110	$400	
	Auctions: $176, MS-65, July 2014; $940, MS-64, August 2014; $42, MS-62, November 2014												
1998-D	635,360,000	96	64.1	97%	$0.35	$10	$1	$100	$60	$450	$150		
	Auctions: $66, MS-65FS, November 2014; $90, MS-65FS, June 2014												
1998-S, Proof	2,086,507	1,561	69.3								$8	$12	$25
	Auctions: $47, PF-70DCam, November 2009												
1999-P	1,212,000,000	197	65.4	97%	$0.25	$10	$1	$15	$25	$75	$35	$250	
	Auctions: $56, MS-65FS, August 2015; $46, MS-64FS, August 2015; $40, MS-65FS, August 2015; $23, MS-63, August 2015												
1999-D	1,066,720,000	172	65.5	99%	$0.25	$8	$1	$15	$30	$300	$50		
	Auctions: $106, MS-64, September 2015; $89, MS-64, August 2015												
1999-S, Proof	3,347,966	6,107	69.1								$9	$12	$25
	Auctions: $42, PF-70DCam, September 2009												
2000-P	846,240,000	114	65.6	100%	$0.25	$10	$1	$12	$18	$35	$25	$500	
	Auctions: $470, MS-67FS, August 2013												
2000-D	1,509,520,000	171	65.9	99%	$0.25	$10	$1	$12	$18	$50	$25	$500	
	Auctions: $613, MS-67FS, July 2015; $36, MS-65, August 2015; $56, MS-64FS, August 2015; $56, MS-63, August 2015												
2000-S, Proof	4,047,993	6,463	69.1								$7	$12	$25
	Auctions: $17, PF-69DCam, March 2014												
2001-P	675,704,000	87	65.8	99%	$0.25	$8	$1	$10	$12	$20	$25	$40	
	Auctions: $50, MS-67FS, June 2013												
2001-D	627,680,000	66	65.6	98%	$0.25	$8	$1	$10	$12	$20	$25	$130	
	Auctions: $138, MS-67FS, February 2010												
2001-S, Proof	3,184,606	4,969	69.2								$7	$12	$25
	Auctions: $17, PF-69DCam, March 2014												
2002-P	539,280,000	72	65.5	100%	$0.25	$8	$1	$10	$12	$20	$30	$75	
	Auctions: $72, MS-67FS, June 2014												
2002-D	691,200,000	57	65.3	95%	$0.25	$8	$1	$10	$12	$90			
	Auctions: $74, MS-66FS, February 2013												
2002-S, Proof	3,211,995	5,397	69.1								$7	$12	$25
	Auctions: $15, PF-69DCam, February 2013												
2003-P	441,840,000	181	65.7	99%	$0.25	$8	$1	$10	$12	$20	$22	$50	
	Auctions: $1,058, MS-68FS, November 2013												
2003-D	383,040,000	129	65.1	100%	$0.25	$8	$1	$15	$12	$80			
	Auctions: $86, MS-66FS, February 2013												
2003-S, Proof	3,298,439	9,139	69.2								$7	$12	$25
	Auctions: $15, PF-69DCam, March 2014												

WESTWARD JOURNEY (2004–2005)

Designers: *See image captions for designers.* **Weight:** *5 grams.* **Composition:** *.750 copper, .250 nickel.* **Diameter:** *21.2 mm.* **Edge:** *Plain.* **Mints:** *Philadelphia, Denver, and San Francisco.*

| Westward Journey, Obverse (2004) *Designer: Felix Schlag.* | Peace Medal Reverse (2004) *Designer: Norman E. Nemeth.* | Keelboat Reverse (2004) *Designer: Al Maletsky.* | Westward Journey, Obverse (2005) *Designer: Joe Fitzgerald.* | American Bison Reverse (2005) *Designer: Jamie Franki.* | Ocean in View Reverse (2005) *Designer: Joe Fitzgerald.* |

| Westward Journey, Obverse, Proof | Peace Medal Reverse, Proof | Keelboat Reverse, Proof | Westward Journey, Obverse, Proof | American Bison Reverse, Proof | Ocean in View Reverse, Proof |

Mintmark location, 2005, is on the obverse, near the date (2004 location is the same as previous years).

History. In 2004 special designs commemorating the Westward Journey (Lewis and Clark expedition) were introduced. They utilized the previous obverse design paired with two different reverse designs, one representing the Peace Medals given out by Lewis and Clark, the other showing the keelboat that provided much of their transportation. Two new reverse designs were introduced for 2005, showing the American Bison and a representation of Clark's journal entry upon spotting what he thought was the Pacific Ocean (in actuality, they were still approximately 20 miles from the coast). They were paired with a new obverse, a tightly cropped profile of Jefferson facing right.

Striking and Sharpness. On the obverse, check for weakness on the portrait. Proofs were struck for each design. All have mirror fields. Most have frosted or cameo contrast on the higher features.

Availability. All basic dates and mintmarks were saved in roll quantities.

GRADING STANDARDS

MS-60 to 70 (Mint State). *Obverse and Reverse:* Mint luster is complete in the obverse and reverse fields. Check the higher parts of the obverse and reverse for abrasion and contact marks.

The Westward Journey nickels are seldom collected in grades lower than MS-60.

2004-D, Peace Medal. Graded MS-66.

PF-60 to 70 (Proof). *Obverse and Reverse:* Evaluation of differences between higher-grade Jefferson Proofs is highly subjective; one certified at PF-65 might be similar to another at PF-67, and vice-versa. All Proof Westward Journey nickels have mirror fields. Striking is typically with full details, although there are scattered exceptions. Nearly all Westward Journey nickel Proofs are as issued, in PF–69 or 70.

2005-S, Ocean in View. Graded PF-70 Ultra Cameo.

	Mintage	Cert	Avg	%MS	MS-63	MS-65	MS-66	MS-67
						PF-65	PF-67	PF-69DC
2004-P, Peace Medal	361,440,000	2,112	63.7	97%	$0.25	$0.75	$8	$50
Auctions: $200, MS-67, February 2013								
2004-D, Peace Medal	372,000,000	513	65.6	100%	$0.25	$0.75	$5	$30
Auctions: $374, MS-68, February 2010								
2004-S, Peace Medal, Proof	2,992,069	11,895	69.2			$8	$12	$25
Auctions: $15, PF-69DCam, March 2014								
2004-P, Keelboat	366,720,000	269	65.6	100%	$0.25	$0.75	$5	$20
Auctions: $299, MS-68, February 2010								
2004-D, Keelboat	344,880,000	324	65.9	100%	$0.25	$0.75	$5	$20
Auctions: No auction records available.								
2004-S, Keelboat, Proof	2,965,422	11,908	69.2			$8	$12	$25
Auctions: $31, PF-70DCam, November 2013								
2005-P, American Bison	448,320,000	4,275	66.7	100%	$0.35	$1.25	$8	$30
Auctions: $28, MS-69, January 2010								
2005-P, American Bison, Satin Finish	1,160,000	3,709	67.0	100%	$0.50	$1	$3	$10
Auctions: No auction records available.								
2005-D, American Bison	487,680,000	4,584	66.1	100%	$0.35	$1.25	$8	$25
Auctions: $388, MS-66, June 2014; $170, MS-64, November 2014; $26, MS-64, November 2014; $84, MS-64, November 2014								
2005-D, American Bison, Satin Finish	1,160,000	3,219	66.6	100%	$0.50	$1	$3	$10
Auctions: No auction records available.								
2005-S, American Bison, Proof	3,344,679	19,259	69.2			$10	$14	$30
Auctions: $34, PF-70DCam, July 2013								
2005-P, Ocean in View	394,080,000	3,286	66.5	100%	$0.25	$0.75	$6	$25
Auctions: $19, MS-66, February 2010								
2005-P, Ocean in View, Satin Finish	1,160,000	3,040	66.7	100%	$0.50	$1	$3	$10
Auctions: No auction records available.								
2005-D, Ocean in View	411,120,000	3,481	66.5	100%	$0.25	$0.75	$5	$22
Auctions: $15, MS-65, August 2009								
2005-D, Ocean in View, Satin Finish	1,160,000	3,248	66.6	100%	$0.50	$1	$3	$10
Auctions: No auction records available.								
2005-S, Ocean in View, Proof	3,344,679	18,964	69.2			$8	$12	$25
Auctions: $21, PF-70DCam, November 2013								

JEFFERSON MODIFIED (2006 TO DATE)

Designers: *Jamie Franki (obverse) and Felix Schlag (reverse).* **Weight:** *5 grams.* **Composition:** *.750 copper, .250 nickel.* **Diameter:** *21.2 mm.* **Edge:** *Plain.* **Mints:** *Philadelphia, Denver, and San Francisco.*

Circulation Strike

Mintmark location, 2006 to date, is on the obverse, below the date.

Proof

History. 2006 saw the return of Felix Schlag's reverse design showing a front view of Jefferson's home, Monticello. It also featured the debut of another new Jefferson portrait on the obverse, this time in three-quarters profile.

Striking and Sharpness. On the obverse, check for weakness on the portrait. Jefferson nickels can be classified as "Full Steps" (FS) if either five or six of Monticello's porch steps (with the top step counting as one) are clear. Notations of 5FS or 6FS can indicate the number of visible steps. It is easier to count the incuse lines than the raised steps. If there are four complete, unbroken lines, the coin qualifies as Full Steps (with five steps); five complete, unbroken lines indicate six full steps. There must be no nicks, cuts, or scratches interrupting the incuse lines. Even if the steps are mostly or fully defined, check other areas to determine if a coin has Full Details overall. Proofs were struck; all have mirror fields. Striking is usually with Full Details, although there are scattered exceptions. Most survivors are in high grade, PF-64 and upward. Most have frosted or cameo contrast on the higher features.

Availability. All basic dates and mintmarks were saved in roll quantities.

GRADING STANDARDS

MS-60 to 70 (Mint State). *Obverse and Reverse:* Mint luster is complete in the obverse and reverse fields. Check the higher parts of the obverse and reverse for abrasion and contact marks.

The Jefferson Modified nickel is seldom collected in grades lower than MS-60.

2011-P. Graded MS-67FS.

PF-60 to 70 (Proof). *Obverse and Reverse:* Evaluation of differences between higher-grade Jefferson Proofs is highly subjective; one certified at PF-65 might be similar to another at PF-67, and vice-versa. All Proof Jefferson Modified nickels have mirror fields. Striking is typically with full details, although there are scattered exceptions. Nearly all Jefferson Modified nickel Proofs are as issued, in PF–69 or 70.

2006-S. Graded PF-70 Deep Cameo.

	Mintage	Cert	Avg	%MS	MS-63	MS-65	MS-65FS	MS-66	MS-66FS	MS-67	MS-67FS / PF-65	MS-68FS / PF-67	MS-69FS / PF-69DC
2006-P, Monticello	693,120,000	281	65.3	100%	$0.25	$0.75	$4	$3	$5	$8	$10	$20	$30
Auctions: $705, MS-67FS, July 2014; $19, MS-64FS, January 2013													
2006-P, Monticello, Satin Finish	847,361	1,233	66.8	100%	$0.50	$1	$2	$3	$5	$10	—	—	—
Auctions: No auction records available.													
2006-D, Monticello	809,280,000	319	65.7	100%	$0.25	$0.75	$5	$4	$6	$9	$22	$30	$50
Auctions: $11, MS-67, July 2008													
2006-D, Monticello, Satin Finish	847,361	1,341	66.9	100%	$0.50	$1	$2	$3	$5	$10	—	—	—
Auctions: No auction records available.													
2006-S, Monticello, Proof	3,054,436	7,347	69.3								$5	$12	$25
Auctions: $32, PF-70DCam, April 2013													
2007-P	571,680,000	46	65.1	100%	$0.25	$0.50	$4	$3	$5	$8	$10	$20	$30
Auctions: $11, MS-68FS, July 2008													
2007-P, Satin Finish	895,628	252	66.3	100%	$0.50	$1	$2	$3	$5	$10	—	—	—
Auctions: No auction records available.													
2007-D	626,160,000	28	64.8	100%	$0.25	$0.50	$5	$4	$6	$9	$22	$30	$50
Auctions: $14, MS-68FS, July 2008													
2007-D, Satin Finish	895,628	217	66.2	100%	$0.50	$1	$2	$3	$5	$10	—	—	—
Auctions: No auction records available.													
2007-S, Proof	2,577,166	5,528	69.3								$4	$12	$30
Auctions: $15, PF-69DCam, May 2013													
2008-P	279,840,000	94	65.5	100%	$0.25	$0.50	$4	$3	$5	$8	$10	$20	$30
Auctions: No auction records available.													
2008-P, Satin Finish	745,464	84	66.9	100%	$0.50	$1	$2	$3	$5	$10	—	—	—
Auctions: No auction records available.													
2008-D	345,600,000	60	64.9	100%	$0.25	$0.50	$5	$4	$6	$9	$22	$30	$50
Auctions: No auction records available.													
2008-D, Satin Finish	745,464	104	67.0	100%	$0.50	$1	$2	$3	$5	$10	—	—	—
Auctions: No auction records available.													
2008-S, Proof	2,169,561	4,113	69.5								$4	$12	$30
Auctions: $56, PF-70DCam, June 2009													
2009-P	39,840,000	209	65.3	100%	$0.30	$0.70	$4	$3	$5	$8	$10	$20	$30
Auctions: No auction records available.													
2009-P, Satin Finish	784,614	191	67.0	100%	$0.50	$1	$2	$3	$5	$10	—	—	—
Auctions: No auction records available.													
2009-D	46,800,000	161	65.1	100%	$0.30	$0.70	$5	$4	$6	$9	$22	$30	$50
Auctions: No auction records available.													
2009-D, Satin Finish	784,614	196	67.0	100%	$0.50	$1	$2	$3	$5	$10	—	—	—
Auctions: No auction records available.													
2009-S, Proof	2,179,867	6,201	69.3								$4	$12	$30
Auctions: $79, PF-70UCam, November 2009													
2010-P	260,640,000	73	65.8	100%	$0.25	$0.50	$4	$3	$5	$8	$10	$20	$30
Auctions: $15, MS-67FS, June 2013													
2010-P, Satin Finish	583,897	82	66.9	100%	$0.50	$1	$2	$3	$5	$10	—	—	—
Auctions: No auction records available.													
2010-D	229,920,000	109	65.9	100%	$0.25	$0.50	$5	$4	$6	$9	$22	$30	$50
Auctions: No auction records available.													
2010-D, Satin Finish	583,897	96	67.4	100%	$0.50	$1	$2	$3	$5	$10	—	—	—
Auctions: No auction records available.													

	Mintage	Cert	Avg	%MS	MS-63	MS-65	MS-65FS	MS-66	MS-66FS	MS-67	MS-67FS	MS-68FS	MS-69FS
											PF-65	PF-67	PF-69DC
2010-S, Proof	1,689,216	4,229	69.3								$4	$12	$30
2011-P	450,000,000	180	66.5	100%	$0.25	$0.50	$4	$3	$5	$8	$10	$20	$30
2011-D	540,240,000	233	66.6	100%	$0.25	$0.50	$5	$4	$6	$9	$22	$30	$50
2011-S, Proof	1,453,276	5,735	69.3								$4	$12	$30
2012-P	464,640,000	113	66.7	100%	$0.25	$0.50	$4	$3	$5	$8	$10	$20	$30
2012-D	558,960,000	114	66.7	100%	$0.25	$0.50	$5	$4	$6	$9	$20	$27	$40
2012-S, Proof	1,237,415	2,205	69.5								$4	$12	$30
2013-P	607,440,000	98	66.4	100%	$0.25	$0.50	$4	$3	$5	$8	$10	$20	$30
2013-D	615,600,000	92	66.6	100%	$0.25	$0.50	$5	$4	$6	$9	$20	$27	$40
2013-S, Proof	802,460	2,287	69.4								$4	$12	$30
2014-P	635,520,000	137	67.0	100%	$0.25	$0.50	$4	$3	$5	$8	$10	$20	$30
2014-D	570,720,000	148	67.1	100%	$0.25	$0.50	$5	$4	$6	$9	$20	$27	$40
2014-S, Proof	665,100	2,760	69.3								$4	$12	$30
2015-P	752,880,000	0	n/a		$0.25	$0.50	$4	$3	$5	$8	$10	$20	$30
2015-D	846,720,000	0	n/a		$0.25	$0.50	$5	$4	$6	$9	$20	$27	$40
2015-S, Proof	*1,050,164*	0	n/a								$4	$12	$30
2016-P	786,960,000	0	n/a		$0.25	$0.50	$5	$4	$6	$9	$20	$27	$40
2016-D	759,600,000	0	n/a		$0.25	$0.50	$5	$4	$6	$9	$20	$27	$40
2016-S, Proof	*1,011,624*	0	n/a								$4	$12	$30
2017-P	*710,160,000*	0	n/a		$0.25	$0.50	$5	$4	$6	$9	$20	$27	$40
2017-D	*663,120,000*	0	n/a		$0.25	$0.50	$5	$4	$6	$9	$20	$27	$40
2017-S, Enhanced Unc.											$4	$12	$30
2017-S, Proof	*(979,477)*	0	n/a								$4	$12	$30
2018-P	*629,520,000*	0	n/a		$0.25	$0.50	$5	$4	$6	$9	$20	$27	$40
2018-D	*626,880,000*	0	n/a		$0.25	$0.50	$5	$4	$6	$9	$20	$27	$40
2018-S, Proof	*(844,220)*	0	n/a								$4	$12	$30
2018-P					$0.25	$0.50	$5	$4	$6	$9	$20	$27	$40
2018-D					$0.25	$0.50	$5	$4	$6	$9	$20	$27	$40
2018-S, Proof											$4	$12	$30

Half Dismes
1792

AN OVERVIEW OF HALF DISMES

Half dimes or five-cent silver coins were provided for in the Mint Act of April 2, 1792. The spelling was stated as *half disme*. The latter word (likely pronounced "dime," as in modern usage, but perhaps in some places as "deem," in the French mode) was used intermittently in government correspondence for years afterward, but on coins dated 1794 and beyond it appeared only as *dime*.

President George Washington, in his fourth annual message to the House of Representatives, November 6, 1792, referred to the half disme:

> In execution of the authority given by the Legislature, measures have been taken for engaging some artists from abroad to aid in the establishment of our Mint; others have been employed at home. Provision has been made of the requisite buildings, and these are now putting into proper condition for the purposes of the establishment.
>
> There has also been a small beginning in the coinage of half-dismes; the want of small coins in circulation calling the first attention to them. The regulation of foreign coins, in correspondence with the principles of our national Coinage, as being essential to their due operation, and to order in our money-concerns, will, I doubt not, be resumed and completed.

The 1792 half dismes are studied in *United States Pattern Coins* (the hobby's standard reference on pattern coins and experimental and trial pieces), and some numismatists have traditionally referred to them as patterns. It is true that they were struck at a private shop in Philadelphia while the official Mint buildings were still in planning. However, several factors point to their status as regular circulating coins. The half disme was authorized as a federal issue by congressional legislation. Its mintage was considerable—some 1,500 or so pieces—and, as noted by President Washington, the coins were meant to alleviate the national need for small change. Furthermore, nearly all surviving examples show signs of extensive wear.

The 1792 half dismes are not commonly collected, simply because they are not common coins; only 200 to 300 are estimated to still exist. However, their rarity, the romance of their connection to the nation's founding, and the mysteries and legends surrounding their creation make them a perennial favorite among numismatists.

The 1792 half disme has often been considered to be a pattern by some numismatists. Nevertheless, the coins entered circulation as currency over the next decade.

HALF DISME (1792)

Designer: *Unknown (possibly Robert Birch).* **Weight:** *1.35 grams.*
Composition: *.8924 silver, .1076 copper.* **Diameter:** *16.5 mm.*
Edge: *Reeded.* **Mint:** *John Harper's shop, Philadelphia.*

Judd-7, Pollock-7,
Logan-McCloskey–1.

History. Rumors and legends are par for the course with the 1792 half disme. Martha Washington is sometimes said to have posed for the portrait of Miss Liberty, despite the profile's dissimilarity to life images of the first lady. Longstanding numismatic tradition says that President George Washington had his own silver tableware taken to the mint factory to be melted down, with these little coins being the result. Whether these Washingtonian connections are true or not, other facts are certain: while the Philadelphia Mint was in the planning stage (its cornerstone would be laid on July 31, 1792), dies were being cut for the first federal coinage of that year. The designer may have been Robert Birch, a Mint engraver who created (or helped create) the dies for the half disme, the disme, and other coins. The half dismes were struck in a private facility owned by saw-maker John Harper, in mid-July. It is believed, from Thomas Jefferson's records, that 1,500 were made. Most were placed into circulation. The coin's designs, with a unique head of Miss Liberty and an outstretched eagle, would not be revived when normal production of the half dime denomination started at the Mint's official facilities in 1795.

Striking and Sharpness. These coins usually are fairly well struck, but with some lightness on Miss Liberty's hair above her ear, and on the eagle's breast. Some examples have adjustment marks from the planchet being filed to adjust the weight prior to striking.

Availability. Most of the estimated 200 to 300 surviving coins show extensive wear. Some AU and MS coins exist, several in choice and gem state, perhaps from among the four examples that Mint Director David Rittenhouse is said to have reserved for himself.

GRADING STANDARDS

MS-60 to 70 (Mint State). *Obverse:* No wear is visible. Luster ranges from nearly full at MS-60 to frosty at MS-65 or higher. Toning often masks the surface, so careful inspection is required. *Reverse:* No wear is visible. The field around the eagle is lustrous, ranging from not completely full at MS-60 to deep and frosty at MS-65 and higher.

1792. Graded MS-64.

AU-50, 53, 55, 58 (About Uncirculated). *Obverse:* Light wear is seen on the cheek and on the hair (not as easily observable, as certain areas of the hair may be lightly struck). Luster ranges from light and mostly in protected areas at AU-50, to extensive at AU-58. Friction is evident in the field, less so in the higher ranges. *Reverse:* Light wear is seen on the eagle, but is less noticeable on the letters. Luster ranges from light and mostly in protected areas at AU-50, to extensive at AU-58. Friction is evident in the field, less in the higher ranges.

1792. Graded AU-55.

EF-40, 45 (Extremely Fine). *Obverse:* The hair shows medium wear to the right of the face and on the bust end. The fields have no luster. Some luster may be seen among the hair strands and letters. *Reverse:* The eagle shows medium wear on its breast and the right wing, less so on the left wing. HALF DISME shows wear. The fields have no luster. Some luster may be seen among the design elements and letters.

1792. Graded EF-40.

VF-20, 30 (Very Fine). *Obverse:* More wear is seen on the hair, including to the right of the forehead and face, where only a few strands may be seen. The hair tips at the right are well detailed. The bust end is flat on its high area. Letters all show light wear. *Reverse:* The eagle displays significant wear, with its central part flat and most of the detail missing from the right wing. Letters all show light wear.

1792. Graded VF-30.

F-12, 15 (Fine). *Obverse:* The portrait, above the neck, is essentially flat, but details of the eye, the nose, and, to a lesser extent, the lips can be seen. The bust end and neck truncation are flat. Some hair detail can be seen to the right of the neck and behind the head, with individual strands blended into heavy groups. Both obverse and reverse at this grade and lower are apt to show marks, minor digs, and other evidence of handling.

1792. Graded F-12.

Reverse: Wear is more advanced than on a Very Fine coin, with significant reduction of the height of the lettering, and with some letters weak in areas, especially if the rim nearby is flat.

VG-8, 10 (Very Good). *Obverse:* The head has less detail than a Fine coin and is essentially flat except at the neck. Some hair, in thick strands, can be seen. The letters show extensive wear, but are readable. *Reverse:* The eagle is mostly flat, and the letters are well worn, some of them incomplete at the borders. Detail overall is weaker than on the obverse.

1792. Graded VG-10.

G-4, 6 (Good). *Obverse:* There is hardly any detail on the portrait, except that the eye can be seen, as well as some thick hair tips. The date is clear. Around the border the edges of the letters are worn away, and some are weak overall. *Reverse:* The eagle is only in outline form. The letters are very worn, with some missing.

1792. Graded G-6.

AG-3 (About Good). *Obverse:* Extreme wear has reduced the portrait to an even shallower state. Around the border some letters are worn away completely, some partially. The 1792 date can be seen but is weak and may be partly missing. *Reverse:* Traces of the eagle will remain and there are scattered letters and fragments of letters. Most of the coin is worn flat.

    Illustrated coin: The scratches on the obverse should be noted.

1792. Graded AG-3.

	Mintage	Cert	Avg	%MS	AG-3	G-4	VG-8	F-12	VF-20	EF-40	AU-50	MS-60	MS-62
1792 †	1,500	41	47.3	39%	$12,500	$27,500	$40,000	$50,000	$80,000	$110,500	$135,000	$150,000	$185,000
	Auctions: $212,750, AU-58, March 2012												

† Ranked in the *100 Greatest U.S. Coins* (fourth edition).

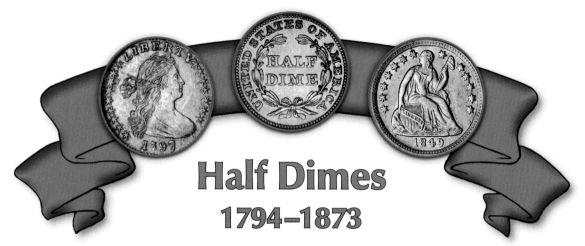

Half Dimes
1794–1873

AN OVERVIEW OF HALF DIMES

The first half dimes, dated 1794 and of the Flowing Hair type, were not actually struck until 1795. In that year additional half dimes with the 1795 date were made. In 1796 and 1797 the short-lived Draped Bust obverse combined with the Small Eagle reverse was used, after which no half dimes were struck until 1801. From that year through 1805, excepting 1804, the Draped Bust obverse was used in combination with the Heraldic Eagle reverse. Then followed a long span of years without any coinage of the denomination. In 1829 the laying of the cornerstone for the second Philadelphia Mint precipitated a new issue, the Capped Bust design, some examples of which were made for the ceremony. Production was resumed for circulation, and half dimes of this motif were made through 1837. In that year the Liberty Seated motif, by Christian Gobrecht, was introduced, to be continued without interruption through 1873, although there were a number of design modifications and changes during that span.

Assembling a set of the different half-dime types is a challenge for the collector. The 1794 and 1795, Flowing Hair, half dimes are fairly scarce at all levels and are quite rare in choice Mint State. Then come the Draped Bust obverse, Small Eagle reverse half dimes of 1796 and 1797. In the late 1960s, researcher Jim Ruddy found that of the various silver types (including the more famous 1796–1797 half dollars), half dimes of this type were the hardest to complete a photographic set of, from the lowest grades to the highest.

Draped Bust obverse, Heraldic Eagle reverse half dimes of the 1800–1805 years are scarce in all grades, more so than generally realized. In Mint State they are very rare, although on occasion some dated 1800 turn up (not often for the others). Finding a *sharply struck* example is next to impossible, and a collector may have to give up on this aspect and settle for one that has some weakness in areas.

Capped Bust half dimes and the several variations of Liberty Seated half dimes will pose no problem at all, and with some small amount of patience a collector will be able to find a sharply struck example in nearly any grade desired.

FOR THE COLLECTOR AND INVESTOR: HALF DIMES AS A SPECIALTY

Collecting half dimes by early die varieties of 1794–1837, and/or by dates and mintmarks (beginning with the 1838-O), has captured the fancy of many numismatists over the years. As these coins are so small it is necessary to have a magnifying glass when studying the series—something the collector of silver dollars and double eagles does not need.

One of the earlier enthusiasts in the field was Philadelphia attorney and numismatist Harold P. Newlin, who in 1883 issued *A Classification of the Early Half Dimes of the United States*. Newlin's two

favorite varieties were the 1792 half disme and the rare 1802, and after reading his enticing prose about the desirability of each, no doubt some collectors in 1883 put both coins on their "must have" lists.

Among early half dimes the rarest and most expensive is the 1802. In 1883 Newlin listed just 16 examples known to him. Although no one has compiled an up-to-date registry, it is likely that fewer than 30 exist. Most are well worn. Other early half dimes range from rare to very rare.

Capped Bust half dimes of the 1829–1837 years are all easily available as dates, but some of the die varieties are very rare. Today, most half dimes on the market are not attributed by varieties, making the search for such things rewarding when a rarity is found for the price of a regular coin.

The new design upon the resumption of the denomination in 1829 was created by Chief Engraver William Kneass. It is thought to have been based upon an earlier design by John Reich.

In 1978 the numismatic world was startled to learn that Chicago dealer Edward Milas had located an 1870-S half dime, a variety not earlier known to exist and not listed in the annual Mint reports. Other than this coin, still unique today, the dates and mints in the Liberty Seated series 1837 to 1873-S are readily collectible by date and mint, with no great rarities. There are several very curious varieties within that span, the most interesting of which may be the 1858, Over Inverted Date. The date was first punched into the die upside down, the error was noted, and then it was corrected.

FLOWING HAIR (1794–1795)

Designer: *Unknown.* **Engraver:** *Robert Scot.*
Weight: *1.35 grams.* **Composition:** *.8924 silver, .1076 copper.*
Diameter: *Approximately 16.5 mm.* **Edge:** *Reeded.* **Mint:** *Philadelphia.*

Logan-McCloskey–8.

History. Half dimes dated 1794 and 1795, of the Flowing Hair type, were all struck in the calendar year 1795, although dies were ready by the end of 1794. The Flowing Hair motif was also used on half dollars and silver dollars of the same years, but not on other denominations.

Striking and Sharpness. Many Flowing Hair half dimes have problems of one sort or another, including adjustment marks (from the planchet being filed down to proper weight) and/or light striking in some areas. On the obverse, check the hair and stars, and on the reverse the breast of the eagle. It may not be possible to find a *needle-sharp* example, but with some extensive searching a fairly decent strike can be obtained. Sharp striking and excellent eye appeal add dramatically to the value.

Availability. Examples appear on the market with frequency, typically in lower circulated grades. Probably 250 to 500 could be classified as MS, most of these dated 1795. Some searching is needed to locate choice examples in any grade. As a rule, half dimes are more readily available than are half dollars and dollars of the same design, and when found are usually more attractive and have fewer problems.

GRADING STANDARDS

MS-60 to 70 (Mint State). *Obverse:* At MS-60 some abrasion and contact marks are evident, most noticeably on the cheek and in the fields. Luster is present, but may be dull or lifeless, and interrupted in patches. At MS-63, contact marks are very few, and abrasion is hard to detect except under magnification. An MS-65 coin has no abrasion, and contact marks are so minute as to require magnification. Luster should be full and rich. Coins

1795; LM-10. Graded MS-63.

graded above MS-65 are more theoretical than actual for this type—but they do exist, and are defined by having fewer marks as perfection is approached. *Reverse:* Comments apply as for the obverse, except that abrasion and contact marks are most noticeable on the eagle at the center. The field area is small and is protected by lettering and the wreath, and in any given grade shows fewer marks than on the obverse.

Illustrated coin: This coin reveals increased olive and blue iridescence under bright light. The central weakness is typical for the striking of this die marriage.

AU-50, 53, 55, 58 (About Uncirculated). *Obverse:* Light wear is seen on the hair area immediately to the left of the face and neck, on the cheek, and on the top of the neck truncation, more so at AU-50 than at AU–53 or 55. An AU-58 coin will have minimal traces of wear. An AU-50 will have luster in protected areas among the stars and letters, with little in the open fields or on the portrait. At AU-58, most luster is present in the fields, but is worn

1794; LM-3. Graded AU-55.

away on the highest parts of the motifs. *Reverse:* Light wear is seen on the eagle's body and right wing. At AU-50, detail is lost in most feathers in this area. However, striking can play a part, and some coins are weak to begin with. Light wear is seen on the wreath and lettering. Luster is the best key to actual wear. This will range from perhaps 20% remaining in protected areas at AU-50 to nearly full mint bloom at AU-58.

Illustrated coin: Liberty's hair displays impressive detail for this grade.

EF-40, 45 (Extremely Fine). *Obverse:* More wear is evident on the portrait, especially on the hair to the left of the face and neck; the cheek; and the tip of the neck truncation. Excellent detail remains in low-relief areas of the hair. The stars show wear, as do the date and letters. Luster, if present at all, is minimal and in protected areas. *Reverse:* The eagle, this being the focal point to check, shows more wear. Observe in combination with a knowl-

1794; LM-2. Graded EF-40.

edge of the die variety, to determine the sharpness of the coin when it was first struck. Some were flat at the center at the time they were made. Additional wear is on the wreath and letters, but many details are present. Some luster may be seen in protected areas, and if present is slightly more abundant than on the obverse.

VF-20, 30 (Very Fine). *Obverse:* The hair is well worn at the VF-20 level, less so at VF-30. The strands are blended so as to be heavy. The cheek shows only slight relief, and the tip of the neck truncation is flat. The stars have more wear, making them appear larger (an optical illusion). *Reverse:* The body of the eagle shows few if any feathers, while the wings have about half of the feathers visible, depending on the strike. The leaves lack

1795; LM-8. Graded VF-30.

detail and are in outline form. Scattered, non-disfiguring marks are normal for this and lower grades. Any major defects should be noted separately.

F-12, 15 (Fine). *Obverse:* Wear is more extensive than on a Very Fine coin, reducing the definition of the thick strands of hair. The cheek has less detail, and the stars appear larger. The rim is distinct and many denticles remain visible. *Reverse:* Wear is more extensive. Now, feather details are reduced, mostly remaining on the right wing. The wreath and lettering are more worn, and the rim is usually weak in areas, although some denticles can be seen.

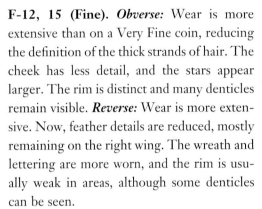

1794; LM-1. Graded F-12.

Illustrated coin: Two light adjustment marks on the lower left of the portrait date from the time of striking.

VG-8, 10 (Very Good). *Obverse:* The portrait is mostly seen in outline form, with most hair strands gone, although the tips at the lower left are clear. The ear is discernible, as is the eye. The stars appear larger still, again an illusion. The rim is weak in areas. LIBERTY and the date are readable and usually full, although some letters may be weak at their tops. *Reverse:* The eagle is mostly an outline, although some traces of feathers may be seen

1795; LM-9. Graded VG-8.

in the tail and the lower part of the inside of the right wing. The rim is worn, as are the letters, with some weak, but the motto is readable.

G-4, 6 (Good). *Obverse:* Wear is more extensive, and some stars may be missing or only partially visible. The head is an outline, although a few elements of thick hair strands may be seen. The eye is visible only in outline form. The rim is well worn or even missing. LIBERTY is worn, and parts of some letters may be missing, but elements of all are readable. The date is readable, but worn. *Reverse:* The eagle is flat and discernible in outline

1795; LM-8. Graded G-6.

form. The wreath is well worn. Some of the letters may be partly missing. At this level some "averaging" can be done. If the letters are stronger than usual in one area, but some are missing in another area, the coin can still qualify as G-4.

Illustrated coin: There are several adjustment marks on the obverse, but this coin lacks the bisecting obverse die crack typical of later issues struck from this die pair. The reverse die on this coin was rotated 20 degrees out of the normal alignment.

AG-3 (About Good). *Obverse:* Wear is so extensive that the coin is barely identifiable. The head is in outline form, LIBERTY is mostly gone, and the date, while readable, may be partially missing. *Reverse:* The reverse is well worn with parts of the wreath and lettering missing.

1794; LM-4. Graded AG-3.

	Mintage	Cert	Avg	%MS	AG-3	G-4	VG-8	F-12	VF-20	EF-40	AU-50	MS-60
1794	(a)	147	49.4	37%	$850	$1,500	$1,800	$2,850	$4,000	$7,500	$11,000	$17,500
	Auctions: $129,250, MS-65, August 2014; $5,875, EF-45, March 2015; $6,463, EF-40, August 2014; $7,638, F-12, August 2016											
1795	86,416	396	49.1	33%	$550	$1,350	$1,600	$2,000	$3,250	$6,000	$8,000	$11,500
	Auctions: $73,438, MS-66, September 2015; $58,750, MS-65, March 2015; $734, F-12, September 2015; $494, F-12, September 2016											

a. Included in 1795 mintage figure.

DRAPED BUST,
SMALL EAGLE REVERSE (1796–1797)

Designer: *Probably Gilbert Stuart.* **Engraver:** *Robert Scot.*
Weight: *1.35 grams.* **Composition:** *.8924 silver, .1076 copper.*
Diameter: *Approximately 16.5 mm.* **Edge:** *Reeded.* **Mint:** *Philadelphia.*

LM-2.

History. Although the Draped Bust obverse design was used on various copper and silver coins circa 1795 to 1808, it was employed in combination with the *Small Eagle* reverse only on silver coins of 1795 to 1798—for the half dime series, only in 1796 and 1797.

Striking and Sharpness. Most 1796–1797 half dimes are weak in at least one area. Points to check for sharpness include the hair of Miss Liberty, the centers of the stars, the bust line, and, on the reverse, the center of the eagle. Check for planchet adjustment marks (these are infrequent). Denticles around the border are usually decent, but may vary in strength from one part of the border to another. Sharp striking and excellent eye appeal add to the value dramatically.

Availability. This type is fairly scarce in *any* grade; in MS-63 and finer, no more than a few dozen examples have been traced. As is advisable for other early silver types, beware of deeply toned or vividly iridescent-toned pieces whose flawed surface characters are obscured by the toning, but which are offered as MS; in truth some of these are barely better than EF.

GRADING STANDARDS

MS-60 to 70 (Mint State). *Obverse:* At MS-60 some abrasion and contact marks are evident, most noticeably on the cheek, on the drapery, and in the right field. Luster is present, but may be dull or lifeless, and interrupted in patches. At MS-63, contact marks are very few, and abrasion is hard to detect except under magnification, although this type is sometimes graded liberally due to its rarity. An MS-65 coin has no abrasion, and contact

1797, 16 Stars; LM-2, Valentine-4. Graded MS-62.

marks are so minute as to require magnification. Luster should be full and rich. Coins graded above MS-65 are more theoretical than actual for this type—but they do exist, and are defined by having fewer marks as perfection is approached. *Reverse:* Comments apply as for the obverse, except that abrasion and marks are most noticeable on the eagle at the center, a situation complicated by the fact that this area was often flatly struck. Grading is best done by the obverse, then verified by the reverse. The field area is small and is protected by lettering and the wreath, and in any given grade shows fewer marks than on the obverse.

Illustrated coin: Note the clash marks in the right obverse field, which are typical for this die variety.

AU-50, 53, 55, 58 (About Uncirculated). *Obverse:* Light wear is seen on the hair area above the ear and extending to left of the forehead, on the ribbon, and on the bosom—more so at AU-50 than at AU–53 or 55. An AU-58 coin has minimal traces of wear. An AU-50 coin has luster in protected areas among the stars and letters, with little in the open fields or on the portrait. At AU-58, most luster is present in the fields, but is worn away on the high-

1796, LIKERTY; LM-1. Graded AU-50.

est parts of the motifs. *Reverse:* Light wear is seen on the eagle's body (keep in mind this area might be lightly struck) and edges of the wings. Light wear is seen on the wreath and lettering. Luster is the best key to actual wear. This ranges from perhaps 20% remaining in protected areas at AU-50 to nearly full mint bloom at AU-58.

Illustrated coin: This is the LIKERTY variety, its fanciful name derived from the top and bottom lines of the B being defective.

EF-40, 45 (Extremely Fine). *Obverse:* More wear is evident on the upper hair area and the ribbon and on the drapery and bosom. Excellent detail will remain in low relief areas of the hair. The stars show wear as will the date and letters. Luster, if present at all, is minimal and in protected areas. *Reverse:* The eagle shows more wear, this being the focal point to check. On most examples, many feathers remain on the interior areas of the wings.

1796, LIKERTY; LM-1. Graded EF-40.

Check the eagle in combination with a knowledge of the die variety to determine the sharpness of the coin when it was first struck. Additional wear is evident on the wreath and letters, but many details are present. Some luster may be seen in protected areas and, if present, is slightly more abundant than on the obverse.

VF-20, 30 (Very Fine). *Obverse:* The higher-relief areas of hair are well worn at VF-20, less so at VF-30. The drapery and bosom show extensive wear. The stars have more wear, making them appear larger (an optical illusion seen on most worn silver coins of this era). *Reverse:* The body of the eagle shows few if any feathers, while the wings have about half of the feathers visible, depending on the strike. The leaves lack most detail and are in outline form. Scattered, non-disfiguring marks are normal for this and lower grades; any major distractions should be noted separately.

1796, LIKERTY; LM-1. Graded VF-30.

F-12, 15 (Fine). *Obverse:* Wear is more extensive than on a Very Fine coin. Wear is particularly noticeable on the hair, face, and bosom, and the stars appear larger. About half the hair detail remains, most noticeably behind the neck and shoulder. The rim may be partially worn away and may blend into the field. *Reverse:* Wear is more extensive. Feather details are diminished, with fewer than half remaining on the wings. The wreath and lettering are worn further, and the rim is usually weak in areas, although some denticles can be seen.

1797, 13 Stars; LM-4. Graded F-15.

VG-8, 10 (Very Good). *Obverse:* The portrait is mostly seen in outline form, with most hair strands gone, although there is some definition at the back of the hair and behind the shoulder. The ear is discernible, as is the eye. The stars appear larger still, again an illusion. The rim is weak in areas. LIBERTY and the date are readable and usually full, although some letters may be weak at their tops. *Reverse:* The eagle is mostly an outline,

1796, LIKERTY; LM-1. Graded VG-8.

with parts blending into the field (on lighter strikes). The rim is worn, as are the letters, with some weak, but the motto is readable.

G-4, 6 (Good). *Obverse:* Wear is more extensive, and some stars may be partly missing. The head is an outline. The eye is visible only in outline form. The rim is well worn or even missing in areas. LIBERTY is worn, and parts of some letters may be missing, but elements of all should be readable. The date is readable, but worn. *Reverse:* The eagle is flat and discernible in outline form, and may be blending into the field. The wreath is well

1797, 16 Stars. Graded G-4.

worn. Some of the letters may be partly missing. At this level some "averaging" can be done. If the letters are stronger than usual in one area, but some are missing in another area, the coin can still qualify as G-4.

AG-3 (About Good). *Obverse:* Wear is so extensive that the coin is barely identifiable. The head is in outline form. LIBERTY is mostly gone, as are some of the stars. The date, while readable, may be partially worn away. *Reverse:* The reverse is well worn, with parts of the wreath and lettering missing.

1796, LIKERTY; LM-1. Graded AG-3.

| 1796, 6 Over 5 | 1796, LIKERTY |

| 1797, 15 Stars | 1797, 16 Stars | 1797, 13 Stars |

	Mintage	Cert	Avg	%MS	AG-3	G-4	VG-8	F-12	VF-20	EF-40	AU-50	MS-60	MS-63
1796, 6 Over 5	10,230	15	52.2	67%	$875	$2,250	$2,750	$4,000	$5,250	$9,500	$15,000	$25,000	$40,000
Auctions: $31,725, MS-63, August 2013													
1796	(a)	18	50.7	33%	$700	$1,800	$2,000	$3,500	$5,000	$8,750	$13,500	$16,500	$35,000
Auctions: No auction records available.; $4,440, VF-30, March 2018													
1796, LIKERTY (b)	(a)	55	47.1	27%	$700	$1,500	$2,000	$3,450	$4,750	$8,750	$12,500	$16,000	$35,000
Auctions: $17,625, MS-61, September 2013; $1,586, Fair-2, October 2014; $676, Fair-2, October 2014													
1797, 15 Stars	44,527	34	45.1	18%	$700	$1,500	$1,800	$3,450	$4,750	$8,750	$12,500	$16,000	$25,000
Auctions: $70,500, MS-64, June 2014; $7,638, AU-55, October 2014; $7,638, AU-53, March 2015; $494, G-4, September 2015													
1797, 16 Stars	(c)	23	45.3	35%	$750	$1,750	$2,400	$3,600	$4,750	$8,750	$12,500	$16,000	$25,000
Auctions: $54,344, MS-65, June 2014; $734, Fair-2, October 2014; $1,763, Fair-2, August 2014													
1797, 13 Stars	(c)	7	40.0	0%	$950	$2,250	$3,500	$5,000	$6,500	$13,500	$25,000	$42,500	$65,000
Auctions: $25,850, AU-55, February 2013													

a. Included in 1796, 6 Over 5, mintage figure. **b.** A die imperfection makes the B in LIBERTY somewhat resemble a K. **c.** Included in 1797, 15 Stars, mintage figure.

DRAPED BUST,
HERALDIC EAGLE REVERSE (1800–1805)

Designer: *Robert Scot.* **Weight:** *1.35 grams.* **Composition:** *.8924 silver, .1076 copper.*
Diameter: *Approximately 16.5 mm.* **Edge:** *Reeded.* **Mint:** *Philadelphia.*

LM-1.

History. The combination of Draped Bust obverse / Heraldic Eagle reverse was used in the silver half dime series from 1800 to 1805. The obverse style, standardized with 13 stars, is the same as used in 1796 and 1797. During this span the rare 1802 was produced, and none were minted with the date 1804.

Striking and Sharpness. Most 1800–1805 half dimes are lightly struck in one area or another. The obverse stars usually show some weakness. On many coins the central details of Miss Liberty are not sharp. On the reverse the upper right of the shield and the adjacent part of the eagle's wing are often soft, and several or even most stars may be lightly defined (sharp stars show sharply peaked centers); high parts of the clouds are often weak. The area on the reverse opposite the bosom of Miss Liberty may be flat or weak, due to the metal having to flow in both directions when the coins were struck. (The area curving obliquely up and to the right of the eagle's head—exactly mirroring the curvature of the bust on the obverse—is especially prone to weakness of strike.) Denticles are likely to be weak or missing in areas. Many have Mint-caused adjustment marks, from overweight planchets being filed down to proper specifications. In summary, *a sharply struck coin is a goal, not necessarily a reality*. In this series, sharp striking and excellent eye appeal will add to a coin's value dramatically, this being particularly true for all issues from 1801 to 1805.

Availability. This is a challenging type to find with nice eye appeal. Many toned pieces have been recolored to hide flaws or to improve eye appeal. Some are porous or have other problems. The majority of pieces surviving today are dated 1800, and nearly all of the AU or finer coins are of this date.

GRADING STANDARDS

MS-60 to 70 (Mint State). *Obverse:* At MS-60 some abrasion and contact marks are evident, most noticeably on the cheek, on the drapery, and in the right field. Luster is present, but may be dull or lifeless, and interrupted in patches. At MS-63, contact marks are very few, and abrasion is hard to detect except under magnification, although this type is sometimes graded liberally due to its rarity. An MS-65 coin will have no abrasion,

1800; LM-1, V-1. Graded MS-63.

and contact marks are so minute as to require magnification. Luster should be full and rich. Coins graded above MS-65 are more theoretical than actual for this type—but they do exist, and are defined by having fewer marks as perfection is approached. *Reverse:* Comments apply as for the obverse, except that abrasion and contact marks are most noticeable on the eagle's neck, the tips of the wing, and the tail. The field area is complex—with stars above the eagle, the arrows and olive branch, and other features, there is not much open space. Accordingly, marks will not be as noticeable as on the obverse.

AU-50, 53, 55, 58 (About Uncirculated). *Obverse:* Light wear is seen on the hair area above the ear and extending to left of the forehead, on the ribbon, and on the bosom, more so at AU-50 than at AU–53 or 55. An AU-58 coin will have minimal traces of wear. An AU-50 coin will have luster in protected areas among the stars and letters, with little in the open fields or on the portrait. At AU-58, most luster is present in the fields,

1803, Large 8; LM-2. Graded AU-58.

but is worn away on the highest parts of the motifs. *Reverse:* Comments as for Mint State coins, except that the eagle's neck, the tips and top of the wings, the clouds, and the tail show noticeable wear, as do other features. Luster ranges from perhaps 20% remaining in protected areas at AU-50 to nearly full mint bloom at AU-58. Often the reverse of this type retains much more luster than the obverse.

    Illustrated coin: Note the areas of rich, blue toning.

EF-40, 45 (Extremely Fine). *Obverse:* More wear is evident on the upper hair area and the ribbon, and on the drapery and bosom. Excellent detail remains in low-relief areas of the hair. The stars show wear, as do the date and letters. Luster, if present at all, is minimal and only in protected areas. *Reverse:* Wear is greater than on an About Uncirculated coin, overall. The neck lacks feather detail on its highest points. Feathers lose some detail near

1800; LM-1. Graded EF-45.

the edges of the wings, and some areas of the horizontal lines in the shield may be blended together. Some traces of luster may be seen, more so at EF-45 than at EF-40.

　Illustrated coin: The obverse cud break is as struck.

VF-20, 30 (Very Fine). *Obverse:* The higher-relief areas of hair are well worn at VF-20, less so at VF-30. The drapery and bosom show extensive wear. The stars have more wear, making them appear larger (an optical illusion seen on most worn silver coins of this era). *Reverse:* Wear is greater, including on the shield and wing feathers. Star centers are flat. Other areas have lost detail as well.

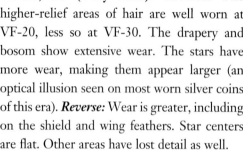

1800; LM-1. Graded VF-20.

F-12, 15 (Fine). *Obverse:* Wear is more extensive than on a Very Fine coin, particularly noticeable on the hair, face, and bosom, and the stars appear larger. About half the hair detail remains, most noticeably behind the neck and shoulder. The rim may be partially worn away and may blend into the field. *Reverse:* Wear is even more extensive, with the shield and wing feathers being points to observe. The incuse E PLURIBUS UNUM

1801; LM-2. Graded F-15.

may have a few letters worn away. The clouds all seem to be connected. The stars are weak. Parts of the border and lettering may be weak.

VG-8, 10 (Very Good). *Obverse:* The portrait is mostly seen in outline form, with most hair strands gone, although there is some definition at the back of the hair and behind the shoulder. The ear is discernible, as is the eye. The stars appear larger still, again an illusion. The rim is weak in areas. LIBERTY and the date are readable and usually full, although some letters may be weak at their tops. *Reverse:* Half or so of the letters in the

1800; LM-1. Graded VG-8.

motto are worn away. Most feather details are worn away, although separation of some of the lower feathers may be seen. Some stars are faint. The border blends into the field in areas, and some letters are weak.

G-4, 6 (Good). *Obverse:* Some stars may be partly missing. The head is an outline. The eye is visible only in outline form. The rim is well worn or even missing in areas. LIBERTY is worn, and parts of some letters may be missing, but elements of all should be readable. The date is readable, but worn. *Reverse:* The upper part of the eagle is flat, and feathers are noticeable only at the lower edge of the wings and do not have detail. The upper part of the

1801; LM-2. Graded G-6.

shield is flat. Only a few letters of the motto can be seen. The rim is worn extensively, and a few letters may be missing.

AG-3 (About Good). *Obverse:* Wear is so extensive that the coin is barely identifiable. The head is in outline form. LIBERTY is mostly gone; same for the stars. The date, while readable, may be partially worn away. *Reverse:* Extensive wear is seen overall, with the rim worn away and some areas worn smooth. The eagle can be discerned in outline form, but not necessarily completely. A few stray motto letters may remain.

1800. Graded AG-3.

1800, LIBEKTY

	Mintage	Cert	Avg	%MS	AG-3	G-4	VG-8	F-12	VF-20	EF-40	AU-50	MS-60	MS-63
1800	24,000	167	44.5	22%	$450	$1,100	$1,500	$2,000	$3,000	$6,000	$8,500	$12,500	$20,000
	Auctions: $25,850, MS-64, August 2014; $4,994, AU-50, October 2014; $2,350, EF-40, November 2014; $676, EF-40, October 2015												
1800, LIBEKTY (a)	16,000	44	45.3	30%	$450	$1,200	$1,750	$2,500	$3,250	$6,200	$8,500	$13,000	$22,000
	Auctions: $31,725, MS-64, April 2014; $3,086, VF-25, October 2014; $617, Fair-2, October 2014												

a. A defective die punch gives the R in LIBERTY the appearance of a K.

1803, Large 8   **1803, Small 8**

	Mintage	Cert	Avg	%MS	AG-3	G-4	VG-8	F-12	VF-20	EF-40	AU-50	MS-60	MS-63
1801	27,760	28	35.8	18%	$450	$1,450	$1,750	$2,500	$4,000	$6,500	$10,000	$17,500	$27,500
	Auctions: $5,581, EF-40, February 2014												
1802 †	3,060	3	50.0	0%	$25,000	$55,000	$70,000	$95,000	$125,000	$225,000	$350,000		
	Auctions: $61,688, AU-58, August 2015; $3,290, VF-25, August 2016; $823, VG-8, August 2016; $541, AG-3, September 2015												
1803, Large 8	37,850	10	34.1	20%	$700	$1,250	$1,500	$2,000	$3,000	$6,500	$9,000	$14,000	$25,000
	Auctions: $7,050, AU-50, February 2014												
1803, Small 8	(b)	3	39.0	0%	$900	$1,750	$2,500	$3,500	$5,000	$9,000	$17,500	$55,000	$85,000
	Auctions: $5,922, EF-35, April 2013; $646, VF-20, November 2016; $999, Fair-2, October 2014												
1805	15,600	30	27.9	3%	$750	$1,450	$1,500	$2,750	$3,750	$10,000	$25,000		
	Auctions: $1,998, VF-35, August 2015; $823, VF-20, November 2016; $1,058, F-15, February 2015; $646, VG-10, July 2016												

† Ranked in the *100 Greatest U.S. Coins* (fourth edition). **b.** Included in 1803, Large 8, mintage figure.

CAPPED BUST (1829–1837)

Engraver: *William Kneass, after a design by John Reich.* **Weight:** *1.35 grams (changed to 1.34 grams in 1837).* **Composition:** *.8924 silver, .1076 copper (changed to .900 silver, .100 copper in 1837).* **Diameter:** *Approximately 15.5 mm.* **Edge:** *Reeded.* **Mint:** *Philadelphia.*

Circulation Strike   **Proof**
LM-7.   *LM-4.*

History. Half dimes of the Capped Bust design were first struck the morning of July 4, 1829, to be included in the cornerstone time capsule of the new (second) Philadelphia Mint building and, presumably, to have some inexpensive coins on hand for distribution as souvenirs. Engraver John Reich's design was not new; it had been used on half dollars as early as 1807. It was logical to employ it on the new half dime, a coin that had not been made since 1805. The new half dimes proved popular and remained in circulation for many years.

Striking and Sharpness. Striking varies among Capped Bust half dimes, and most show lightness in one area or another. On the obverse, check the hair details to the left of the eye, as well as the star centers. On the reverse, check the eagle's feathers and neck. The motto, which can be a problem on certain other coins of this design (notably half dollars), is usually bold on the half dimes. Denticles range from well defined to somewhat indistinct, and, in general, are sharper on the obverse than on the reverse.

Proofs. Proofs were struck in small quantities, generally as part of silver Proof sets, although perhaps some were made to mark the Mint cornerstone event mentioned above; facts are scarce. True Proofs have fully mirrored fields. Scrutinize deeply toned pieces (deep toning often masks the true nature of a coin, e.g., if it is not a true Proof, or if it has been cleaned or repaired). Some pieces attributed as "Proofs" are not Proofs. This advice applies across the entire Capped Bust silver series.

Availability. Finding an example in any desired grade should not be a challenge. Finding one with Full Details will take more time. Connoisseurship is required at the MS level, given the high value of these coins.

GRADING STANDARDS

MS-60 to 70 (Mint State). *Obverse:* At MS-60 some abrasion and contact marks are evident, most noticeably on the cheek, on the hair below the left part of LIBERTY, and on the area near the drapery clasp. Luster is present, but may be dull or lifeless, and interrupted in patches. At MS-63, contact marks are very few, and abrasion is hard to detect except under magnification. An MS-65 coin has no abrasion, and has contact marks so minute as to require magnification. Luster should be full and rich, usually more so on half dimes than larger coins of the Capped Bust type. Grades above MS-65 are seen now and again, and are defined by having fewer marks as perfection is approached. *Reverse:* Comments apply as for the obverse, except that abrasion and contact marks are most noticeable on the eagle's neck, the top of the wings, the claws, and the flat band that surrounds the incuse motto. The field is mainly protected by design elements and does not show abrasion as much as does the obverse.

1830; LM-3. Graded MS-65.

AU-50, 53, 55, 58 (About Uncirculated). *Obverse:* Light wear is seen on the cap, the hair below LIBERTY, the hair near the clasp, and the drapery at the bosom. At AU-58, the luster is extensive except in the open area of the field, especially to the right. At AU–50 and 53, luster remains only in protected areas. *Reverse:* Wear is visible on the eagle's neck, the top of the wings, the claws, and the flat band above the eagle. An AU-58 coin will have nearly full luster. At AU–50 and 53, there will still be significant luster, more than on the obverse.

Illustrated coin: Note the rings of toning on the obverse, displaying russet, cobalt, and rosy iridescence.

1829; LM-4. Graded AU-58.

EF-40, 45 (Extremely Fine). *Obverse:* Wear is most noticeable on the higher areas of the hair. The cap shows more wear, as does the cheek. Stars, usually protected by the rim, still show their centers (unless lightly struck). Luster, if present, is in protected areas among the star points and close to the portrait. *Reverse:* The wings show wear on the higher areas of the feathers, and some details are lost. Feathers in the neck are light. The eagle's claws and the leaves show wear. Luster may be present in protected areas, even if there is little or none on the obverse.

1837, Small 5 C.; LM-4. Graded EF-40.

VF-20, 30 (Very Fine). *Obverse:* Wear has caused most of the hair to be combined into thick tresses without delicate features. The curl on the neck is flat. Most stars, unless they were weakly struck, retain their interior lines. *Reverse:* Wear is most evident on the eagle's neck, to the left of the shield, and on the leaves and claws. Most feathers in the wing remain distinct.

1834; LM-2. Graded VF-30.

F-12, 15 (Fine). *Obverse:* Wear is more extensive, with much of the hair blended together. The drapery is indistinct at its upper edge. Stars have lost some detail at the centers, but still have relief (are not flat). *Reverse:* Wear is more extensive, now with only about half of the feathers remaining on the wings. Some of the horizontal lines in the shield may be worn away.

1830; LM-6. Graded F-12.

VG-8, 10 (Very Good). *Obverse:* The hair is less distinct, with the area surrounding the face blended into the facial features. LIBERTY is complete, but weak in areas. The stars are nearly flat, although some interior detail can be seen on certain strikings. *Reverse:* Feathers are fewer and mostly appear on the right wing. Other details are weaker. All lettering remains easily visible.

1829. Graded VG-8.

G-4, 6 (Good). *Obverse:* The portrait is mostly in outline, with few interior details discernible. LIBERTY may still be readable or may be partially worn away, depending on the variety. Stars are flat at their centers. *Reverse:* The eagle mostly is in outline form, although some feathers can be seen in the right wing. All letters around the border are clear. E PLURIBUS UNUM may be weak, sometimes with a few letters worn away.

1829; LM-8. Graded G-6.

AG-3 (About Good). *Obverse:* The portrait is an outline, although traces of LIBERTY can still be seen. The rim is worn down, and some stars are weak. The date remains clear. *Reverse:* The reverse shows more wear overall than the obverse, with the rim indistinct in areas and many letters worn away.

1835, Small Date, Large 5 C. Graded AG-3.

PF-60 to 70 (Proof). *Obverse and Reverse:* Proofs that are extensively cleaned and have many hairlines, or that are dull and grainy, are lower level, such as PF–60 to 62. These are not of great interest to specialists unless they are of rare die varieties (such as 1829, LM–1 to 3, described in the image caption). With medium hairlines, an assigned grade of PF–64 may be in order, and with relatively few hairlines, gem PF–65. PF–66 should have

1829; LM-2, V-3. Graded PF-67+.

hairlines so delicate that magnification is needed to see them. Above that, a Proof should be free of such lines. Grading is highly subjective with early Proofs, and eye appeal also is a factor.

Illustrated coin: Stunning in sharpness of strike and attractiveness of toning, this coin is the finest-known Proof of this type.

	Mintage	Cert	Avg	%MS	G-4	VG-8	F-12	VF-20	EF-40	AU-50	MS-60 / PF-60	MS-63 / PF-63	MS-65 / PF-65
1829	1,230,000	749	57.2	62%	$60	$75	$100	$125	$200	$300	$425	$925	$3,000
Auctions: $881, MS-63, October 2015; $705, MS-63, January 2015; $353, MS-60, June 2015; $329, AU-58, September 2015													
1829, Proof	20–30	8	64.4								$4,500	$10,000	$35,000
Auctions: $36,719, PF-65Cam, January 2014													
1830	1,240,000	639	57.3	66%	$50	$65	$80	$115	$175	$275	$400	$850	$2,500
Auctions: $852, MS-63, October 2015; $646, MS-62, February 2015; $400, MS-60, May 2015; $353, AU-58, August 2015													
1830, Proof	10–15	4	64.5								$6,500	$15,000	$37,000
Auctions: $49,938, PF-66, September 2013; $30,550, PF-64, August 2014													
1831	1,242,700	802	59.6	70%	$50	$65	$80	$115	$175	$250	$400	$850	$2,500
Auctions: $564, MS-62, June 2015; $376, MS-61, October 2015; $259, MS-60, March 2015; $212, AU-58, January 2015													
1831, Proof	20–30	1	67.0								$4,500	$12,500	$35,000
Auctions: $73,438, PF-67, January 2014													
1832	965,000	979	58.5	68%	$50	$65	$80	$115	$175	$250	$400	$850	$2,500
Auctions: $823, MS-63, June 2015; $541, MS-62, January 2015; $376, MS-61, March 2015; $247, AU-55, March 2015													
1832, Proof	5–10	2	64.0								$6,000	$12,500	$40,000
Auctions: $19,550, PF-64, March 2004													
1833	1,370,000	655	58.3	66%	$50	$65	$80	$115	$175	$250	$400	$850	$2,500
Auctions: $8,813, MS-67, January 2015; $764, MS-63, January 2015; $470, MS-62, January 2015; $282, MS-60, August 2015													

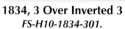

1834, 3 Over Inverted 3
FS-H10-1834-301.

1835, Large Date

1835, Small Date

Large 5 C.

Small 5 C.

	Mintage	Cert	Avg	%MS	G-4	VG-8	F-12	VF-20	EF-40	AU-50	MS-60	MS-63	MS-65
											PF-60	PF-63	PF-65
1834	1,480,000	637	58.4	65%	$50	$65	$80	$115	$175	$250	$400	$850	$2,500
	Auctions: $6,463, MS-67, September 2015; $646, MS-63, October 2015; $517, MS-62, August 2015; $282, AU-55, June 2015												
1834, 3 Over Inverted 3	(a)	25	55.5	52%	$50	$65	$80	$135	$200	$350	$550	$1,200	$4,000
	Auctions: $25,850, MS-67, May 2015; $5,640, MS-66, August 2016; $1,774, MS-65, February 2015; $376, AU-55, November 2015												
1834, Proof	25–35	14	65.0								$4,500	$10,000	$27,500
	Auctions: $32,900, PF-66, November 2013; $12,925, PF-64, October 2014; $14,100, PF-64, August 2014												
1835, All kinds	2,760,000												
1835, Large Date and 5 C.		52	56.0	60%	$50	$65	$80	$115	$175	$250	$400	$850	$2,500
	Auctions: $376, AU-58, March 2015; $188, AU-50, February 2015; $129, AU-50, July 2015; $89, EF-45, May 2015												
1835, Large Date, Small 5 C.		22	57.9	50%	$50	$65	$80	$115	$175	$250	$400	$850	$2,500
	Auctions: $376, MS-62, September 2015												
1835, Small Date, Large 5 C.		31	55.4	58%	$50	$65	$80	$115	$175	$250	$400	$850	$2,500
	Auctions: $165, MS-60, May 2015												
1835, Small Date and 5 C.		43	55.9	60%	$50	$65	$80	$115	$175	$250	$400	$850	$2,500
	Auctions: $494, MS-62, June 2015; $400, MS-62, June 2015; $400, MS-61, July 2015												
1836, Small 5 C.	1,900,000	40	53.8	48%	$50	$65	$80	$115	$175	$250	$400	$850	$2,500
	Auctions: $153, EF-45, May 2015												
1836, Large 5 C.	(b)	26	56.4	65%	$50	$65	$80	$115	$175	$250	$400	$850	$2,500
	Auctions: $423, AU-58, October 2015; $201, AU-55, February 2015; $74, AU-50, February 2015; $129, EF-45, January 2015												
1836, 3 Over Inverted 3	(b)	35	52.9	51%	$55	$75	$100	$135	$200	$350	$675	$1,200	$3,750
	Auctions: $329, AU-58, January 2015												
1836, Proof	5–10	2	65.5								$4,500	$10,000	$35,000
	Auctions: $47,000, PF-66, February 2014												
1837, Small 5 C.	871,000	32	58.4	66%	$85	$100	$150	$185	$300	$500	$975	$2,100	$10,000
	Auctions: $1,880, MS-63, June 2013; $660, AU-50, March 2018												
1837, Large 5 C.	(c)	29	51.7	48%	$55	$75	$80	$125	$185	$250	$450	$850	$3,500
	Auctions: $5,288, MS-65, March 2015; $159, AU-50, March 2015; $118, AU-50, June 2015; $129, VF-35, February 2015												
1837, Proof (d)	5–10	0	n/a										
	Auctions: No auction records available.												

a. Included in circulation-strike 1834 mintage figure. **b.** Included in 1836, Small 5 C., mintage figure. **c.** Included in 1837, Small 5 C., mintage figure. **d.** The 1837, Proof, coin is untraced.

LIBERTY SEATED (1837–1873)

Variety 1, No Stars on Obverse (1837–1838): **Designer:** *Christian Gobrecht.*
Weight: *1.34 grams.* **Composition:** *.900 silver, .100 copper.*
Diameter: *15.5 mm.* **Edge:** *Reeded.* **Mints:** *Philadelphia and New Orleans.*

**Variety 1, No Stars
on Obverse (1837–1838)**

**Variety 1, No Stars
on Obverse, Proof**

Variety 2, Stars on Obverse (1838–1853): **Designer:** *Christian Gobrecht.*
Weight: *1.34 grams.* **Composition:** *.900 silver, .100 copper.* **Diameter:** *15.5 mm.*
Edge: *Reeded.* **Mints:** *Philadelphia and New Orleans.*

**Variety 2, Stars on
Obverse (1838–1853)**

**Variety 2, Stars
on Obverse, Proof**

Variety 3, Arrows at Date, Reduced Weight (1853–1855):
Designer: *Christian Gobrecht.* **Weight:** *1.24 grams.* **Composition:** *.900 silver, .100 copper.*
Diameter: *15.5 mm.* **Edge:** *Reeded.* **Mints:** *Philadelphia and New Orleans.*

**Variety 3, Arrows at Date,
Reduced Weight (1853–1855)**

**Variety 3, Arrows at Date,
Reduced Weight, Proof**

Variety 2 Resumed, With Weight Standard of Variety 3 (1856–1859):
Designer: *Christian Gobrecht.* **Weight:** *1.24 grams.* **Composition:** *.900 silver, .100 copper.*
Diameter: *15.5 mm.* **Edge:** *Reeded.* **Mints:** *Philadelphia and New Orleans.*

**Variety 2 Resumed, Weight
Standard of Variety 3 (1856–1859)**

**Variety 2 Resumed, Weight
Standard of Variety 3, Proof**

Variety 4, Legend on Obverse (1860–1873): **Designer:** *Christian Gobrecht.*
Weight: *1.24 grams.* **Composition:** *.900 silver, .100 copper.* **Diameter:** *15.5 mm.*
Edge: *Reeded.* **Mints:** *Philadelphia, New Orleans, and San Francisco.*

**Variety 4, Legend on
Obverse (1860–1873)**

*Mintmark location,
1860–1869 and
1872–1873, is on the
reverse, below the bow.*

*Mintmark location,
1870–1872, is on the
reverse, above the bow.*

**Variety 4, Legend
on Obverse, Proof**

History. The Liberty Seated design without obverse stars, known as Variety 1, was used in the half dime and dime series only at the Philadelphia Mint in 1837 and the New Orleans Mint in 1838 (1838-O). The motif, by Christian Gobrecht, follows the obverse inaugurated on the 1836 silver dollar. Miss Liberty has no drapery at her elbow. In 1838 13 obverse stars were added, and in 1840 a restyling (drapery added to the elbow) by Robert Ball Hughes appeared. Arrows were added to the sides of the date starting in 1853, through 1855; these denoted the reduction of weight under the terms of the Act of February 21, 1853. The earlier design resumed in 1856. The reverse design stayed the same during these changes. In 1860 on the half dime the legend UNITED STATES OF AMERICA was moved to the obverse, in place of the stars. The reverse displayed a "cereal wreath" (as it was called in Mint records) enclosing the words HALF DIME.

Striking and Sharpness. For half dimes dated 1837 to 1838, check the highest parts of the Liberty Seated figure (especially the head and horizontal shield stripes) and, on the reverse, the leaves. Check the denticles on both sides. These coins are very attractive, and the starless obverse gives them a cameo-like appearance. For half dimes dated 1838 to 1859, strike quality varies widely. Most from 1838 to 1852 are sharper than later ones, but there are exceptions. (Coins with "mushy" details are especially common among the high-mintage dates of the mid- to late 1850s.) On the obverse, check the star centers, the head and center of Miss Liberty, and the denticles. On the reverse, check the wreath leaves and denticles. Excellent strike and deeply mirrored fields characterized nearly all Proofs. Points to check on coins dated 1860 to 1873 include the head of Miss Liberty on the obverse, the wreath details on the reverse (particularly at the inside upper left, above the H of HALF) and the denticles on both sides. Generally, MS coins have excellent luster, although some struck from relapped dies tend to be prooflike and with many striae. The word LIBERTY is not an infallible guide to grading at lower levels, as on some dies the shield was in lower relief, and the letters wore away less quickly. This guideline should be used in combination with other features. Generally, Proofs are well made, with deeply mirrored fields, although some of the late 1860s and early 1870s can have weak areas. Average quality in the marketplace is higher than for larger Liberty Seated denominations.

Availability. Liberty Seated half dimes are easily available as a type, but with many scarce varieties. The Philadelphia coins are easily available in all grades. The 1838-O is a rarity in true Mint State, often is over-graded, and typically has low eye appeal. Such issues as 1849-O and 1846 are extreme rarities at the true MS level. San Francisco coins, first made in 1863, are rare in MS for the first several years. Grades above MS-65 are seen with regularity, more often than the related No Stars dimes. Quality varies widely, and many MS coins are artificially toned.

Proofs. It is likely that at least several dozen Proofs were made of the 1837 half dime, although perhaps more were made of the related dime. Today, attractive examples exist and are rare. Nearly all designated as Proofs are, indeed, Proofs. If you aspire to acquire one, select an example with deep mirror surfaces. 1858 was the first year Proofs were widely sold to collectors, and an estimated 210 silver sets were distributed. (Proofs were made of earlier dates, but in much smaller numbers.) It is believed that 800 Proofs were struck of 1859, of which slightly more than 400 found buyers. From 1860 to 1873, Proof coins were made in fair quantities each year and are readily available today. The quality of Proofs on the market varies widely, mainly due to cleaning and dipping. Patience and care are needed to find a choice example.

GRADING STANDARDS

MS-60 to 70 (Mint State). *Obverse:* At MS-60 some abrasion and contact marks are evident, most noticeably on the bosom, thighs, and knees. Luster is present, but may be dull or lifeless, and interrupted in patches in the large open field. At MS-63, contact marks are very few, and abrasion is hard to detect except under magnification. An MS-65 coin has no abrasion, and contact marks are so minute as to require magnification. Luster

1844-O, Small O; V-2. Graded MS-64.

should be full and rich, except for Philadelphia (but not San Francisco) half dimes of the early and mid-1860s. Most Mint State coins of 1861 to 1865, Philadelphia issues, will have extensive die striae (from the dies being incompletely finished). Some low-mintage Philadelphia issues may be prooflike (and some may even be mislabeled as Proofs). Clashmarks are common in this era. Half dimes of this type can be very beautiful at this level. *Reverse:* Comments apply as for the obverse except that in lower Mint State grades abrasion and contact marks are most noticeable on the highest parts of the leaves and the ribbon, less so on HALF DIME. The field is mainly protected by design elements and does not show abrasion as much as does the open-field obverse on a given coin.

Illustrated coin: This coin was struck in medallic alignment, as is seen with multiple examples of 1844-O, V-2.

AU-50, 53, 55, 58 (About Uncirculated). *Obverse:* Light wear is seen on the thighs and knees, bosom, and head. At AU-58, the luster is extensive, but incomplete. Friction is seen in the large open field. At AU–50 and 53, luster is less. *Reverse:* Wear is noticeable on the leaves and ribbon. An AU-58 coin has nearly full luster—more so than on the obverse, as the design elements protect the small field areas. At AU–50 and 53, there still is significant luster, more than on the obverse.

1853, Arrows. Graded AU-50.

EF-40, 45 (Extremely Fine). *Obverse:* Further wear is seen on all areas, especially the thighs and knees, bosom, and head. Little or no luster is seen. *Reverse:* Further wear is seen on all areas, most noticeably at the leaves to each side of the wreath apex, and on the ribbon bow knot. Leaves retain details except on the higher areas.

1852-O. Graded EF-40.

VF-20, 30 (Very Fine). *Obverse:* Further wear is seen. Most details of the gown are worn away, except in the lower-relief areas above and to the right of the shield. Hair detail is gone on the higher points. *Reverse:* Wear is more extensive. The highest leaves are flat, particularly the larger leaves at the top of the wreath.

1846. Graded VF-35.

F-12, 15 (Fine). *Obverse:* The seated figure is well worn, but with some detail above and to the right of the shield. LIBERTY on the shield is fully readable, but weak in areas. *Reverse:* Most detail of the leaves is gone. The rim is worn but remains bold, and most if not all denticles are visible.

1844-O; V-6. Graded F-15.

VG-8, 10 (Very Good). *Obverse:* The seated figure is more worn, but some detail can be seen above and to the right of the shield. The shield is discernible. In LIBERTY at least three letters are readable but very weak at VG-8; a few more appear at VG-10. *Reverse:* Further wear has combined the details of most leaves. The rim is complete, but weak in areas. On most coins the reverse appears to be in a slightly higher grade than the obverse.

1846. Graded VG-10.

G-4, 6 (Good). *Obverse:* The seated figure is worn smooth. At G-4 there are no letters in LIBERTY remaining. At G-6, traces of one or two can be seen. *Reverse:* Wear is more extensive. The leaves are all combined and in outline form. The rim is clear but well worn and missing in some areas, causing the outer parts of the peripheral letters to be worn away in some instances. On most coins the reverse appears to be in a slightly higher grade than the obverse.

Illustrated coin: This is a No Stars variety.

1837, Small Date. Graded G-4.

AG-3 (About Good). *Obverse:* The seated figure is mostly visible in outline form, with no detail. The rim is worn away. The date remains clear. *Reverse:* Many if not most letters are worn away, as are parts of the wreath, though this and the interior letters are discernible. The rim can usually be seen, but is weak.

Illustrated coin: This is a No Stars variety.

1837, Small Date. Graded AG-3.

PF-60 to 70 (Proof). *Obverse and Reverse:* Proofs that are extensively cleaned and have many hairlines, or that are dull and grainy, are lower level, such as PF–60 to 62. These are not widely desired, save for the rare (in any grade) date of 1846. Both the half dime and dime Proofs of 1837 were often cleaned, resulting in coins which have lost much of their mirror surface. With medium hairlines and good reflectivity, a grade of PF-64 is

1873. Graded PF-66 Ultra Cameo.

assigned, and with relatively few hairlines, gem PF-65. In various grades hairlines are most easily seen in the obverse field. PF-66 should have hairlines so delicate that magnification is needed to see them. Above that, a Proof should be free of such lines.

1837, Small Date
Note the flat-topped 1.

1837, Large Date
Note the pointed-top 1.

No Drapery From Elbow
(1837–1840)

Drapery From Elbow
(Starting 1840)

	Mintage	Cert	Avg	%MS	G-4	VG-8	F-12	VF-20	EF-40	AU-50	MS-60	MS-63	MS-65
											PF-60	PF-63	PF-65
1837, Small Date	1,405,000	50	58.5	66%	$40	$55	$90	$145	$250	$450	$600	$950	$3,000
	Auctions: $7,050, MS-67, January 2015; $1,175, MS-64, July 2015; $705, MS-63, January 2015; $793, MS-62, June 2015												
1837, Large Date	(a)	25	61.7	84%	$40	$55	$80	$145	$250	$450	$600	$850	$2,500
	Auctions: $8,225, MS-67, January 2015; $3,290, MS-66, September 2015; $2,115, MS-65, September 2015; $541, MS-62, January 2015												
1837, Proof	15–20	10	64.3								$7,000	$12,500	$32,500
	Auctions: $105,750, PF-67, June 2014												
1838-O, No Stars	70,000	43	46.0	30%	$150	$215	$400	$750	$2,000	$3,000	$5,250	$10,750	$25,550
	Auctions: $21,150, MS-65, October 2015; $17,625, MS-64, October 2015; $7,050, MS-62, October 2015; $4,700, MS-62, July 2015												

a. Included in 1837, Small Date, mintage figure.

1838, Large Stars

1838, Small Stars

1840-O, No Drapery, Normal Reverse
Note four-leaf cluster next to DIME.

1840-O, No Drapery, Transitional Reverse
Note three-leaf cluster next to DIME.

	Mintage	Cert	Avg	%MS	G-4	VG-8	F-12	VF-20	EF-40	AU-50	MS-60	MS-63	MS-65
											PF-60	PF-63	PF-65
1838, No Drapery, Large Stars	2,225,000	726	60.4	75%	$18	$21	$28	$45	$125	$200	$280	$475	$1,350
Auctions: $5,523, MS-67, October 2015; $2,585, MS-66, January 2015; $999, MS-65, January 2015; $705, MS-64, January 2015													
1838, No Drapery, Small Stars	(a)	62	57.0	63%	$22	$40	$70	$175	$250	$375	$625	$1,000	$3,500
Auctions: $3,290, MS-66, October 2015; $2,820, MS-65, October 2015; $423, AU-58, October 2015; $306, AU-55, February 2015													
1838, Proof	4–5	2	64.5								$8,500	$10,500	$45,000
Auctions: $129,250, PF-67, October 2014; $182,125, PF-66, January 2014													
1839, No Drapery	1,069,150	310	60.4	74%	$20	$25	$35	$50	$100	$185	$275	$450	$1,700
Auctions: $5,405, MS-66, October 2015; $1,175, MS-65, February 2015; $400, MS-63, January 2015; $329, MS-60, October 2015													
1839, Proof	5–10	3	64.7								$12,000	$15,000	$37,500
Auctions: $27,600, PF-65Cam, April 2008; $24,000, PF-65, January 2018													
1839-O, No Drapery	1,291,600	81	51.9	42%	$20	$25	$40	$85	$200	$325	$850	$2,100	$8,000
Auctions: $16,450, MS-67, May 2015; $7,050, MS-65, October 2015; $1,998, MS-63, January 2015; $1,175, MS-62, August 2015													
1840, No Drapery	1,034,000	301	59.9	73%	$20	$25	$30	$45	$100	$185	$275	$450	$1,450
Auctions: $6,000, MS-67, August 2015; $2,585, MS-66, October 2015; $1,293, MS-65, October 2015; $470, MS-64, January 2015													
1840, No Drapery, Proof	5–10	3	65.7								$8,500	$10,500	$35,000
Auctions: $30,550, PF-64, April 2014													
1840-O, No Drapery	695,000	57	51.5	25%	$40	$55	$85	$125	$220	$475	$1,200	$3,750	$15,000
Auctions: $18,213, MS-66, June 2014; $11,163, MS-65, October 2015; $141, EF-45, July 2014; $80, VF-25, September 2014													
1840-O, No Drapery, Transitional Reverse (b)	100	4	40.8	0%	$300	$500	$675	$800	$1,200	$2,000	$3,500	$12,000	
Auctions: $431, F-15, November 2011													
1840, Drapery	310,085	63	59.3	76%	$35	$50	$70	$140	$210	$360	$500	$900	$3,250
Auctions: $3,995, MS-65, October 2015; $1,763, MS-65, August 2015; $329, AU-55, April 2015													
1840, Drapery, Proof	(c)	0	n/a										
Auctions: No auction records available.													
1840-O, Drapery	240,000	45	45.9	13%	$45	$75	$150	$300	$750	$1,550	$10,000	$22,000	
Auctions: $9,988, AU-58, October 2015; $282, VF-30, September 2015													
1841	1,150,000	184	60.6	80%	$16	$20	$30	$35	$70	$150	$190	$325	$975
Auctions: $1,528, MS-66, January 2015; $1,175, MS-65, October 2015; $940, MS-65, October 2015; $141, AU-55, January 2015													
1841, Proof	10–20	4	64.3								$8,500	$12,500	$30,000
Auctions: $28,200, PF-65, October 2014; $46,000, PF-65, January 2008													
1841-O	815,000	57	51.1	28%	$60	$90	$140	$200	$325	$500	$1,000	$3,250	$8,000
Auctions: $8,225, MS-66, October 2015; $3,173, MS-64, October 2015; $470, AU-55, April 2015													

a. Included in 1838, No Drapery, Large Stars, mintage figure. b. "This rare transitional variety exhibits large letters and open or split buds on the reverse die, along with a small O mintmark. The key diagnostic of the variety is three-leaf clusters on either side of the word DIME, while the common reverse has four-leaf clusters" (*Cherrypickers' Guide to Rare Die Varieties*, sixth edition, volume II). c. The mintage figure is unknown.

1848, Medium Date

1848, Large Date

1849, So-Called 9 Over 6
FS-H10-1849-302.

1849, 9 Over 8
FS-H10-1849-301.

	Mintage	Cert	Avg	%MS	G-4	VG-8	F-12	VF-20	EF-40	AU-50	MS-60	MS-63	MS-65
											PF-60	PF-63	PF-65
1842	815,000	180	59.5	68%	$16	$20	$27	$35	$75	$150	$225	$400	$1,250
Auctions: $3,055, MS-66, May 2015; $1,058, MS-66, October 2015; $652, MS-64, August 2015; $400, MS-63, July 2015													
1842, Proof	*10–20*	5	64.8								$8,000	$10,000	$20,000
Auctions: $12,075, PF-64, January 2010													
1842-O	350,000	37	45.4	22%	$55	$75	$125	$215	$550	$900	$1,275	$2,250	$13,000
Auctions: $18,800, MS-66, May 2015; $13,513, MS-66, October 2015; $1,998, MS-63, October 2015; $1,763, MS-63, October 2015													
1843	815,000	245	58.9	67%	$25	$35	$40	$60	$90	$160	$225	$400	$1,350
Auctions: $1,645, MS-66, October 2015; $676, MS-63, October 2015; $259, MS-62, August 2015; $165, AU-58, April 2015													
1843, 1843 Over 1843, Proof	*10–20*	1	67								$8,000	$10,000	$20,000
Auctions: $55,813, PF-67, January 2014													
1844	430,000	168	61.1	84%	$20	$25	$35	$55	$115	$200	$275	$500	$1,250
Auctions: $1,058, MS-66, January 2015; $1,293, MS-65, October 2015; $823, MS-64, October 2015; $423, MS-63, October 2015													
1844, Proof	*15–25*	6	64.5								$8,000	$10,000	$22,500
Auctions: $35,250, PF-67, February 2014; $12,925, PF-64, October 2014													
1844-O	220,000	44	34.5	11%	$80	$160	$300	$750	$1,250	$2,750	$5,000	$10,000	$23,000
Auctions: $7,050, MS-64, October 2015; $1,293, EF-45, January 2015; $317, EF-40, January 2015; $494, VF-30, September 2015													
1845	1,564,000	225	58.6	67%	$16	$20	$27	$35	$60	$145	$225	$365	$1,150
Auctions: $3,995, MS-67, May 2015; $1,175, MS-66, June 2015; $793, MS-64, October 2015; $306, MS-63, March 2015													
1845, Proof	*10–15*	6	65.3								$10,000	$15,000	$30,000
Auctions: $64,625, PF-68, January 2014													
1846	27,000	62	28.4	2%	$850	$1,275	$1,650	$2,350	$4,000	$6,750	$11,000	$28,000	
Auctions: $564, MS-61, September 2016; $1,175, AU-55, March 2016; $999, AU-53, August 2016; $517, EF-45, September 2016													
1846, Proof	*10–20*	8	65.5								$8,000	$12,500	$22,000
Auctions: $35,250, PF-66, June 2014													
1847	1,274,000	221	57.8	67%	$20	$25	$35	$70	$95	$150	$225	$400	$1,000
Auctions: $1,763, MS-66, January 2015; $940, MS-65, January 2015; $447, MS-64, April 2015; $259, MS-63, January 2015													
1847, Proof	*8–12*	3	64.7								$8,000	$10,000	$22,000
Auctions: $38,188, PF-67, October 2014; $36,719, PF-66Cam, April 2014													
1848, Medium Date	668,000	97	57.7	57%	$16	$25	$40	$60	$95	$180	$285	$600	$3,500
Auctions: $3,525, MS-65, May 2015; $1,293, MS-64, June 2015; $447, MS-63, February 2015; $329, AU-58, April 2015													
1848, Large Date	**(d)**	35	54.7	51%	$35	$50	$80	$150	$190	$350	$750	$2,500	$4,500
Auctions: $14,100, MS-66, May 2015; $1,645, MS-62, September 2015; $470, AU-58, February 2015; $306, AU-53, February 2015													
1848, Proof	*6–8*	2	65								$9,000	$12,000	$22,500
Auctions: $63,250, PF-66, July 2008													
1848-O	600,000	78	61	82%	$22	$25	$45	$85	$210	$325	$650	$1,400	$2,750
Auctions: $12,338, MS-67, January 2014													
1849, All kinds	1,309,000												
1849, 9 Over 6 (e)		39	56.7	67%	$35	$50	$75	$120	$200	$350	$700	$1,200	$2,100
Auctions: $2,585, MS-65, June 2014; $200, MS-60, September 2014													
1849, 9 Over Widely Placed 6 (f)		23	53.6	43%	$50	$70	$100	$150	$275	$380	$620	$1,400	$2,750
Auctions: $5,405, MS-67, October 2015; $541, MS-62, March 2015; $306, MS-62, April 2015; $270, AU-58, April 2015													

d. Included in 1848, Medium Date, mintage figure. **e.** Fivaz and Stanton contend that this is actually a 9 Over 8 overdate (*Cherrypickers' Guide to Rare Die Varieties*, sixth edition, volume II). **f.** The 4 of the date is at least triple punched, with one secondary 4 south and one east of the primary 4. There is also a secondary numeral east of the lower portion of the 9.

	Mintage	Cert	Avg	%MS	G-4	VG-8	F-12	VF-20	EF-40	AU-50	MS-60	MS-63	MS-65
											PF-60	PF-63	PF-65
1849, Normal Date		157	57.3	56%	$25	$30	$40	$58	$100	$175	$265	$750	$1,600
	Auctions: $4,406, MS-67, June 2014; $270, MS-61, November 2014; $188, AU-58, November 2014												
1849, Proof	8–12	4	65								$8,000	$10,000	$22,500
	Auctions: $22,325, PF-65, June 2014												
1849-O	140,000	54	49.6	37%	$45	$75	$145	$285	$625	$1,200	$2,175	$4,000	$8,500
	Auctions: $4,465, MS-64, October 2015; $1,528, MS-61, September 2015; $1,293, AU-53, January 2015; $223, VF-30, February 2015												
1850	955,000	233	61.4	82%	$22	$30	$40	$60	$90	$180	$220	$375	$925
	Auctions: $7,050, MS-67, October 2015; $1,116, MS-66, March 2015; $705, MS-65, July 2015; $494, MS-64, June 2015												
1850, Proof	8–12	4	64								$12,000	$20,000	$40,000
	Auctions: $44,650, PF-67, May 2015; $61,688, PF-65, October 2015; $19,975, PF-64, May 2015; $17,626, PF-62, August 2016												
1850-O	690,000	67	55	51%	$30	$40	$60	$100	$200	$275	$675	$1,400	$4,000
	Auctions: $11,456, MS-67, January 2015; $7,638, MS-66, October 2015; $1,293, MS-63, October 2015; $212, AU-50, September 2015												
1851	781,000	160	58.8	73%	$18	$22	$28	$40	$75	$140	$190	$325	$1,000
	Auctions: $8,813, MS-67, May 2015; $4,171, MS-67, January 2015; $646, MS-64, October 2015; $235, MS-62, April 2015												
1851-O	860,000	115	56.2	56%	$25	$30	$35	$50	$110	$235	$450	$925	$4,200
	Auctions: $5,170, MS-66, May 2015; $4,465, MS-65, October 2015; $588, MS-62, March 2015; $376, MS-61, February 2015												
1852	1,000,500	181	61.9	83%	$18	$22	$28	$40	$75	$140	$190	$325	$1,050
	Auctions: $1,410, MS-66, October 2015; $705, MS-65, January 2015; $317, MS-63, March 2015; $141, AU-58, September 2015												
1852, Proof	10–15	9	64.2								$8,000	$10,000	$22,500
	Auctions: $30,550, PF-65, January 2014; $19,975, PF-65, June 2015; $14,100, PF-64, October 2014												
1852-O	260,000	55	51.5	40%	$30	$40	$75	$150	$275	$500	$950	$2,250	$7,000
	Auctions: $646, AU-58, August 2015; $353, AU-50, January 2015; $206, AU-50, June 2015; $84, VF-20, June 2015												
1853, No Arrows	135,000	143	59.1	77%	$60	$85	$140	$225	$325	$500	$750	$1,200	$2,300
	Auctions: $2,510, MS-66, July 2015; $1,880, MS-65, September 2015; $1,175, MS-64, January 2015; $940, MS-63, January 2015												
1853-O, No Arrows	160,000	34	33.8	6%	$350	$600	$775	$1,200	$2,400	$3,850	$6,200	$12,500	$29,000
	Auctions: $32,900, MS-65, October 2014; $25,850, MS-65, October 2014; $3,819, AU-55, April 2013; $1,175, VF-25, January 2015												
1853, With Arrows	13,210,020	1,309	56.9	59%	$20	$25	$30	$35	$70	$140	$190	$310	$850
	Auctions: $7,638, MS-67, August 2015; $1,880, MS-66, August 2015; $470, MS-64, January 2015; $259, MS-63, January 2015												
1853, With Arrows, Proof (g)	3–5	2	62.5								$30,000		
	Auctions: No auction records available.												
1853-O, With Arrows	2,200,000	109	51.6	43%	$25	$30	$40	$65	$100	$240	$350	$1,250	$3,500
	Auctions: $15,275, MS-67, October 2015; $5,405, MS-66, October 2015; $376, MS-61, October 2015; $259, AU-58, September 2015												
1854	5,740,000	645	57.8	67%	$20	$25	$30	$35	$65	$140	$200	$300	$1,100
	Auctions: $7,050, MS-67, October 2015; $1,645, MS-66, June 2015; $1,116, MS-65, January 2015; $494, MS-64, February 2015												
1854, Proof	15–25	10	64.6								$4,000	$7,500	$10,000
	Auctions: $9,694, PF-65, August 2013												
1854-O	1,560,000	103	58.1	64%	$20	$24	$35	$45	$90	$200	$300	$900	$3,350
	Auctions: $15,275, MS-67, October 2015; $4,465, MS-66, October 2015; $1,058, MS-64, October 2015; $999, MS-63, October 2015												
1855	1,750,000	255	60.2	75%	$20	$25	$30	$35	$75	$150	$210	$375	$1,650
	Auctions: $8,813, MS-67, February 2015; $2,585, MS-66, July 2015; $1,293, MS-65, July 2015; $353, MS-63, August 2015												
1855, Proof	15–25	20	65.1								$4,000	$7,500	$11,500
	Auctions: $21,150, PF-66, June 2014; $11,750, PF-65, October 2014; $8,519, PF-65, June 2015												
1855-O	600,000	81	58.6	65%	$30	$40	$55	$85	$200	$380	$850	$1,500	$4,500
	Auctions: $4,230, MS-65, October 2015; $84, VF-35, April 2015												
1856	4,880,000	488	59.3	72%	$18	$22	$25	$35	$60	$115	$175	$285	$800
	Auctions: $1,410, MS-66, October 2015; $846, MS-65, January 2015; $447, MS-63, May 2015; $212, MS-63, January 2015												
1856, Proof	40–60	22	64.7								$2,500	$4,000	$7,500
	Auctions: $8,813, PF-65, October 2015; $4,230, PF-64, October 2015; $4,113, PF-64, July 2015; $3,800, PF-64, January 2018												
1856-O	1,100,000	100	55.8	36%	$18	$22	$25	$55	$135	$285	$550	$1,100	$2,500
	Auctions: $3,408, MS-66, October 2015; $1,645, MS-65, October 2015; $470, AU-58, April 2015; $235, AU-55, January 2015												

g. This coin is extremely rare.

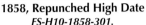

1858, Repunched High Date
FS-H10-1858-301.

1858, Over Inverted Date
FS-H10-1858-302.

1860, Obverse of 1859, Reverse of 1860
Transitional pattern, with stars (Judd-267).

	Mintage	Cert	Avg	%MS	G-4	VG-8	F-12	VF-20	EF-40	AU-50	MS-60	MS-63	MS-65
											PF-60	PF-63	PF-65
1857	7,280,000	864	59.3	75%	$18	$22	$25	$35	$60	$115	$175	$285	$700
Auctions: $6,463, MS-68, September 2015; $2,585, MS-67, September 2015; $1,058, MS-66, June 2015; $646, MS-65, January 2015													
1857, Proof	*40–60*	28	65								$2,200	$3,000	$5,000
Auctions: $21,738, PF-67Cam, January 2014; $7,050, PF-66, August 2014; $4,935, PF-66, May 2015													
1857-O	1,380,000	237	57.4	62%	$18	$22	$25	$45	$80	$175	$300	$500	$1,250
Auctions: $3,525, MS-67, June 2015; $1,293, MS-66, October 2015; $1,058, MS-65, October 2015; $329, MS-62, October 2015													
1858	3,500,000	752	60.3	78%	$18	$22	$25	$35	$60	$125	$170	$320	$700
Auctions: $2,800, MS-67, January 2015; $999, MS-66, September 2015; $881, MS-65, January 2015; $388, MS-64, March 2015													
1858, Repunched High Date (h)	(i)	7	44.9	14%	$35	$50	$80	$125	$200	$325	$650	$1,300	$3,200
Auctions: $135, AU-50, November 2014; $65, VF-30, July 2011													
1858, Over Inverted Date (j)	(i)	28	53.8	46%	$40	$60	$100	$150	$250	$350	$800	$1,600	$4,500
Auctions: $7,638, MS-65, February 2014													
1858, Proof	*300*	82	64.1								$750	$1,200	$3,000
Auctions: $3,055, PF-65Cam, October 2015; $823, PF-62, September 2015													
1858-O	1,660,000	237	59.7	76%	$18	$22	$30	$50	$80	$155	$240	$480	$1,150
Auctions: $517, MS-64, August 2015; $470, MS-64, October 2015; $435, MS-63, May 2015; $212, MS-61, April 2015													
1859	340,000	246	61.8	83%	$18	$22	$30	$45	$80	$135	$200	$425	$925
Auctions: $5,640, MS-68, January 2015; $3,290, MS-67, October 2015; $2,585, MS-67, August 2015; $329, MS-63, October 2015													
1859, Proof	*800*	231	64								$550	$1,100	$2,500
Auctions: $5,640, PF-66Cam, September 2015; $3,525, PF-66, October 2015; $2,585, PF-65, October 2015; $1,293, PF-64, March 2015													
1859, Obverse of 1859 (With Stars), Reverse of 1860, Proof (k)	*20*	6	63.5								$20,000	$35,000	$55,000
Auctions: $34,500, PF-63, August 2010													
1859-O	560,000	127	60.1	73%	$25	$35	$65	$90	$165	$225	$285	$500	$1,750
Auctions: $4,935, MS-66, October 2015; $881, MS-64, October 2015; $423, MS-63, August 2015; $282, MS-62, October 2015													
1860, Obverse of 1859 (With Stars), Reverse of 1860 (l)	*100*	55	64.4	100%					$2,500	$3,000	$3,750	$6,000	
Auctions: $5,750, MS-66, February 2012													
1860, Legend on Obverse	798,000	533	62.1	85%	$16	$20	$25	$30	$50	$85	$175	$300	$600
Auctions: $2,115, MS-67, January 2015; $881, MS-66, January 2015; $705, MS-65, January 2015; $447, MS-64, January 2015													
1860, Proof	1,000	112	64.4								$350	$550	$1,100
Auctions: $2,115, PF-66Cam, July 2014; $$3,290, PF-66Cam, April 2014; 1,528, PF-65Cam, July 2014													
1860-O	1,060,000	253	59.7	72%	$20	$25	$30	$45	$80	$120	$170	$320	$1,000
Auctions: $7,050, MS-67, August 2015; $1,116, MS-65, October 2015; $447, MS-64, June 2015; $259, MS-63, October 2015													

h. The date was first punched into the die very high, then corrected and punched into its normal location. The original high-date punch is clearly visible within the upper portions of the primary date. **i.** Included in circulation-strike 1858 mintage figure. **j.** The date was first punched into the die in an inverted orientation, and then corrected. The bases of the secondary digits are evident above the primary digits. **k.** This transitional issue, made surreptitiously at the Mint for a private collector, has the new Liberty Seated die made in the old style of 1859, but with the date of 1860. The reverse is the regular die of 1860, with a cereal wreath. Classified as Judd-267 (*United States Pattern Coins*, tenth edition). **l.** Classified as Judd-232 (*United States Pattern Coins*, tenth edition), this features the obverse design of 1859 and the reverse of 1860.

1861, So-Called 1 Over 0
FS-H10-1861-301.

	Mintage	Cert	Avg	%MS	G-4	VG-8	F-12	VF-20	EF-40	AU-50	MS-60	MS-63	MS-65
											PF-60	PF-63	PF-65
1861	3,360,000	663	58.9	69%	$20	$25	$30	$40	$70	$120	$160	$275	$650
	Auctions: $2,820, MS-67, October 2015; $1,763, MS-66, August 2015; $617, MS-65, August 2015; $329, MS-64, January 2015												
1861, So-Called 1 Over 0	(m)	0	n/a		$35	$45	$50	$90	$200	$325	$525	$800	$1,750
	Auctions: $3,290, MS-66, October 2015; $1,645, MS-65, June 2015; $1,293, MS-64, January 2015; $588, MS-62, February 2015												
1861, Proof	1,000	93	64.4								$350	$550	$1,100
	Auctions: $6,169, PF-67, June 2014												
1862	1,492,000	700	61.9	85%	$25	$30	$45	$55	$70	$100	$160	$300	$650
	Auctions: $2,115, MS-67, January 2015; $494, MS-65, January 2015; $329, MS-64, January 2015; $259, MS-63, August 2015												
1862, Proof	550	184	64.4								$350	$550	$1,100
	Auctions: $3,760, PF-67Cam, June 2015; $1,293, PF-66Cam, October 2015; $960, PF-65, August 2015; $541, PF-63, September 2015												
1863	18,000	120	62	88%	$200	$280	$330	$425	$600	$750	$825	$975	$1,650
	Auctions: $9,988, MS-68, October 2015; $3,995, MS-67, January 2015; $1,645, MS-66, October 2015; $1,410, MS-66, July 2015												
1863, Proof	460	178	64.1								$350	$550	$1,100
	Auctions: $3,760, PF-67, October 2015; $4,700, PF-66Cam, October 2015; $1,293, PF-66, March 2015; $1,175, PF-65, January 2015												
1863-S	100,000	96	59.6	75%	$45	$60	$100	$200	$300	$400	$750	$1,175	$3,850
	Auctions: $4,935, MS-66, October 2015; $4,230, MS-65, October 2015; $1,645, MS-64, October 2015; $764, MS-60, June 2015												
1864	48,000	50	56.5	76%	$325	$440	$675	$850	$1,100	$1,200	$1,300	$1,475	$2,800
	Auctions: $2,585, MS-65, January 2015; $1,410, MS-64, July 2015; $646, MS-64, January 2015; $541, MS-63, June 2015												
1864, Proof	470	149	64.2								$350	$550	$1,100
	Auctions: $4,700, PF-67, August 2014; $4,259, PF-67, June 2014; $1,175, PF-66, September 2015												
1864-S	90,000	59	54.7	53%	$65	$100	$175	$250	$400	$750	$1,100	$1,850	$3,750
	Auctions: $4,935, MS-66, October 2015; $2,115, MS-64, October 2015; $224, VF-35, August 2015												
1865	13,000	54	57.5	74%	$400	$475	$550	$750	$900	$1,200	$1,300	$1,650	$2,200
	Auctions: $7,638, MS-67, October 2015; $376, G-6, February 2015												
1865, Proof	500	164	64.1								$350	$550	$1,100
	Auctions: $1,763, PF-66Cam, July 2015; $1,116, PF-65Cam, August 2015; $764, PF-64Cam, September 2015; $435, PF-63, March 2015												
1865-S	120,000	52	52.6	38%	$50	$80	$125	$200	$350	$550	$1,100	$2,450	$6,500
	Auctions: $881, AU-55, January 2015; $212, EF-40, June 2015												
1866	10,000	63	58.0	78%	$325	$400	$500	$650	$850	$1,000	$1,100	$1,225	$2,500
	Auctions: $5,640, MS-67, January 2015; $3,055, MS-66, October 2015; $940, MS-61, October 2015; $999, EF-45, January 2015												
1866, Proof	725	176	64.1								$350	$550	$1,100
	Auctions: $19,975, PF-67DCam, January 2015; $2,820, PF-65DCam, January 2015; $580, PF-64, June 2015; $541, PF-63, July 2015												
1866-S	120,000	77	58.1	58%	$45	$60	$90	$150	$225	$325	$500	$900	$4,000
	Auctions: $7,638, MS-66, May 2015; $3,760, MS-65, October 2015; $564, MS-61, April 2015; $482, AU-58, April 2015												
1867	8,000	86	59.5	83%	$450	$525	$625	$750	$850	$1,000	$1,200	$1,500	$2,250
	Auctions: $2,585, MS-66, October 2015; $8,813, MS-65, October 2015; $1,410, MS-63, September 2015												
1867, Proof	625	226	64.5								$350	$550	$1,100
	Auctions: $1,528, PF-66Cam, August 2015; $999, PF-65, January 2015; $823, PF-64Cam, July 2015; $705, PF-64, October 2015												
1867-S	120,000	68	57.2	57%	$30	$40	$60	$90	$250	$345	$575	$1,150	$3,250
	Auctions: $3,055, MS-66, February 2015; $2,585, MS-65, August 2015; $881, MS-63, January 2015; $458, AU-58, April 2015												

m. Included in circulation-strike 1861 mintage figure.

1872, Doubled Die Obverse
FS-H10-1872-101.

	Mintage	Cert	Avg	%MS	G-4	VG-8	F-12	VF-20	EF-40	AU-50	MS-60 PF-60	MS-63 PF-63	MS-65 PF-65
1868	88,600	76	60.1	83%	$55	$65	$120	$185	$325	$475	$675	$800	$1,600
Auctions: $4,230, MS-67, October 2015; $517, AU-58, April 2015													
1868, Proof	600	180	64.1								$350	$550	$1,100
Auctions: $2,585, PF-66Cam, February 2015; $1,058, PF-65Cam, October 2015; $588, PF-64, September 2015; $376, PF-62, May 2015													
1868-S	280,000	150	61	69%	$16	$25	$40	$50	$85	$145	$320	$700	$1,800
Auctions: $5,170, MS-66, October 2015; $1,410, MS-65, October 2015; $282, MS-62, April 2015; $212, MS-60, January 2015													
1869	208,000	106	62.8	86%	$30	$40	$50	$70	$110	$175	$275	$450	$1,100
Auctions: $3,760, MS-67, May 2015; $1,880, MS-66, October 2015; $1,058, MS-65, July 2015; $999, MS-65, October 2015													
1869, Proof	600	215	64.3								$350	$550	$1,100
Auctions: $2,585, PF-67Cam, June 2015; $2,115, PF-67, January 2015; $1,410, PF-66, January 2015; $588, PF-64, January 2015													
1869-S	230,000	81	60.2	78%	$30	$40	$50	$90	$150	$250	$335	$500	$3,500
Auctions: $4,465, MS-67, May 2015; $3,290, MS-65, October 2015; $306, AU-58, April 2015; $282, AU-55, April 2015													
1870	535,000	301	60.4	78%	$16	$20	$25	$30	$45	$80	$175	$400	$950
Auctions: $2,820, MS-67, September 2015; $949, MS-66, October 2015; $235, MS-62, February 2015; $129, MS-62, May 2015													
1870, Proof	1,000	182	64.2								$350	$550	$1,100
Auctions: $1,293, PF-66Cam, October 2015; $764, PF-64Cam, July 2015; $541, PF-63, September 2015; $259, PF-62, May 2015													
1870-S † (n)		1	63	100%								*$2,000,000*	
Auctions: $661,250, MS-63, July 2004													
1871	1,873,000	494	60.2	73%	$16	$20	$25	$30	$60	$80	$150	$250	$600
Auctions: $1,410, MS-66, August 2015; $400, MS-64, May 2015; $361, MS-64, July 2015; $62, AU-55, January 2015													
1871, Proof	960	203	64.2								$350	$550	$1,100
Auctions: $2,468, PF-67Cam, August 2015; $1,175, PF-65Cam, August 2015; $1,293, PF-66, January 2015; $823, PF-64, January 2015													
1871-S	161,000	123	60.7	68%	$18	$22	$32	$65	$80	$180	$250	$450	$1,350
Auctions: $423, MS-64, January 2015; $235, MS-62, May 2015; $259, MS-61, April 2015; $208, AU-58, April 2015													
1872	2,947,000	427	59.2	72%	$16	$20	$25	$30	$45	$80	$150	$300	$675
Auctions: $3,760, MS-67, May 2015; $1,469, MS-66, August 2015; $376, MS-64, May 2015; $106, AU-58, April 2015													
1872, DblDie Obv (o)	(p)	9	48.2	0%					$250	$350	$650	$1,500	
Auctions: $89, EF-45, August 2011													
1872, Proof	950	180	64.2								$350	$550	$1,100
Auctions: $3,525, PF-67Cam, March 2015; $1,058, PF-65Cam, October 2015; $999, PF-64Cam, October 2015													
1872-S, All kinds	837,000												
1872-S, Mintmark above bow		167	61.6	78%	$20	$25	$30	$45	$55	$100	$180	$300	$750
Auctions: $2,468, MS-67, May 2015; $764, MS-66, July 2015; $529, MS-65, January 2015; $282, MS-63, April 2015													
1872-S, Mintmark below bow		162	62	80%	$20	$25	$30	$45	$55	$120	$160	$285	$675
Auctions: $2,585, MS-67, January 2015; $1,058, MS-66, September 2015; $353, MS-64, January 2015; $282, MS-63, March 2015													
1873, Close 3 (q)	712,000	151	59.6	73%	$16	$20	$25	$30	$45	$80	$150	$350	$1,100
Auctions: $2,820, MS-67, October 2015; $1,528, MS-66, January 2015; $165, MS-62, January 2015; $100, MS-60, May 2015													
1873, Proof	600	245	64.3								$350	$550	$1,100
Auctions: $1,528, PF-66, March 2015; $1,469, PF-66, June 2015; $1,293, PF-65, January 2015; $580, PF-64, June 2015													
1873-S Close 3 (q)	324,000	263	62	84%	$16	$20	$25	$30	$65	$125	$150	$300	$675
Auctions: $1,175, MS-66, October 2015; $646, MS-65, June 2015; $423, MS-64, August 2015; $376, MS-64, November 2015													

† Ranked in the *100 Greatest U.S. Coins* (fourth edition). **n.** The 1870-S coin is unique. **o.** "Doubling is evident on UNITED STATES OF AMERICA and on most elements of Miss Liberty. AMERICA is the strongest point" (*Cherrypickers' Guide to Rare Die Varieties*, sixth edition, volume II). **p.** Included in circulation-strike 1872 mintage figure. **q.** Close 3 only.

Dimes
1796 to Date

AN OVERVIEW OF DIMES

A collection of dimes ranging from 1796 to date includes many interesting issues. As a type, none are super-rare, but earlier types, combining low mintages with commonly weak striking, can be a challenge for the collector.

The 1796–1797 dime with Draped Bust obverse, Small Eagle reverse, is the rarest of the dime types by far, with fewer than 50,000 pieces minted. These hail from an era in which there was no numismatic interest in saving such coins. Finding a choice example in whatever grade desired will require time and effort.

Then comes the Draped Bust obverse, Heraldic Eagle reverse type, made from 1798 through 1807 (except for 1799). Today these are available easily enough in circulated grades, but are elusive in Mint State. Nearly all are lightly struck—another challenge. Capped Bust dimes of the 1809–1828 years also require connoisseurship to locate a sharply struck specimen. For all of these early types some compromise with perfection is required.

Later Capped Bust dimes of 1828 to 1837 can be found well struck, as can be the later variations within the Liberty Seated type. Barber, Mercury, and Roosevelt dimes are easy to find in just about any grade desired.

Proofs are most readily available from the Liberty Seated era to the present and are sometimes included in type sets, usually answering the call for sharply struck pieces, as most (but not all) were made with care.

FOR THE COLLECTOR AND INVESTOR: DIMES AS A SPECIALTY

Dimes have been a very popular denomination to collect on a systematic basis. Generally, interest is separated into different eras. Those of the early years, the Draped Bust and Capped Bust issues, 1796 to 1837, are enthusiastically sought not only for dates and major varieties (as, for example, those listed in the charts to follow), but also by more rarefied die varieties. Aficionados use the book *Early United States Dimes, 1796–1837*, whose listings are by JR numbers, for John Reich, the designer of the Capped Bust silver issues. The

Controversy over Chief Engraver John R. Sinnock's design arose after claims that Sinnock had borrowed his design from Selma Burke's bas relief, as seen at the Recorder of Deeds building in Washington, D.C.

John Reich Collectors Society (www.jrcs.org), publisher of the *John Reich Journal*, serves as a forum for the exchange of ideas and new information.

Among early varieties, the 1796; 1797, 16 Stars; and 1797, 13 Stars, are each rare in all grades. Dimes with the Heraldic Eagle reverse, 1798–1807, are generally scarce, but not prohibitively rare, although Mint State coins are elusive. Among the reverse dies some were shared with contemporary quarter eagles of like design and diameter—feasible as there is no indication of denomination on them. Indeed, there was no mark of value on any dime until 1809.

Among Classic Head dimes of the 1809–1828 years, the 1822 is the key date and is especially rare in high grades. Among the modified Classic Head dimes of 1829–1837, all varieties listed in this book are available without difficulty. An example of how a newly discovered variety can be considered unique or exceedingly rare, and later be recognized as plentiful, is provided by the 1830, 30 Over 29, overdate, first publicized by Don Taxay in 1970 in *Scott's Comprehensive Catalogue of United States Coinage* (cover-dated 1971). The overdate was then considered one of a kind, but since then dozens more have been identified.

Liberty Seated dimes of the various varieties have been a popular specialty over a long period of time. There are no impossible rarities except for the unique 1873-CC, Without Arrows, but certain other varieties are very hard to find, including the Carson City issues of the early 1870s.

Barber dimes can be collected by date and mint from 1892 to 1916, except for the 1894-S, of which only 24 are believed to have been struck, with only about 10 accounted for today. The other Barber varieties range from common to scarce. Mercury dimes, 1916–1945, have an enthusiastic following. The key issues are 1916-D (in particular); 1921; 1921-D; 1942, 2 Over 1; and 1942-D, 2 Over 1. Roosevelt dimes from 1946 to date can easily be collected by date and mint and are very popular.

DRAPED BUST, SMALL EAGLE REVERSE (1796–1797)

Designer: *Probably Gilbert Stuart.* **Engraver:** *Robert Scot.*
Weight: *2.70 grams.* **Composition:** *.8924 silver, .1076 copper.*
Diameter: *Approximately 19 mm.* **Edge:** *Reeded.* **Mint:** *Philadelphia.*

John Reich-2.

History. Dimes were first minted for circulation in 1796. There are no records of publicity surrounding their debut. The coins featured the Draped Bust obverse, as used on cents and other silver coins, combined with the Small Eagle reverse. Some 1796 dimes exhibit prooflike surfaces, suggesting that they may have been "presentation pieces," but no records exist to confirm this possibility.

Striking and Sharpness. Most dimes of this type have weakness or problems in one area or another, usually more so on those dated 1797. Points to check for sharpness include the hair of Miss Liberty, the drapery lines on the bust, the centers of the stars, and, on the reverse, the breast and wing feathers of the eagle. Also check for adjustment marks. A sharply struck coin is a goal, not necessarily a reality. Sharp striking and excellent eye appeal add dramatically to the value.

Availability. This is the rarest and most expensive type in the dime series. Within any desired grade, examples should be selected with great care, as many have problems of one sort or another. MS coins are especially rare; when seen they are usually dated 1796. Dimes of 1797 are much rarer in all grades, and nearly impossible to find in MS-63 or finer.

GRADING STANDARDS

MS-60 to 70 (Mint State). *Obverse:* At MS-60, some abrasion and contact marks are evident, most noticeably on the cheek, the drapery, and the right field. Luster is present, but may be dull or lifeless, and interrupted in patches. At MS-63, contact marks are very few, and abrasion is hard to detect except under magnification, although this type is sometimes graded liberally due to its rarity. An MS-65 coin has no abrasion, and contact

1796; JR-3. Graded MS-63.

marks are so minute as to require magnification. Luster should be full and rich. Coins graded above MS-65 are more theoretical than actual for this type—but they do exist, and are defined by having fewer marks as perfection is approached. *Reverse:* Comments apply as for the obverse, except that abrasion and marks are most noticeable on the eagle at the center, a situation complicated by the fact that this area was sometimes lightly struck. The field area is small and is protected by lettering and the wreath, and in any given grade shows fewer marks than on the obverse.

Illustrated coin: This coin is one of only two known with this triangular rim break on the reverse. The dies were likely discarded shortly after the break occurred. Also note the die break from the rim break to the eagle's left wing.

AU-50, 53, 55, 58 (About Uncirculated). *Obverse:* Light wear is seen on the hair area above the ear and extending to left of the forehead, on the ribbon, and on the bosom, more so at AU-50 than at AU-53 or 55. An AU-58 coin has minimal traces of wear. An AU-50 coin has luster in protected areas among the stars and letters, with little in the open fields or on the portrait. At AU-58, most luster is present in the fields, but is worn

1796; JR-3. Graded AU-50.

away on the highest parts of the motifs. Generally, grading guidelines for this dime type follow those of the related half dimes. *Reverse:* Light wear is seen on the eagle's body (keep in mind that the higher parts of this area might be lightly struck) and the edges of the wings. Light wear is seen on the wreath and lettering. Luster is the best key to actual wear. This ranges from perhaps 20% remaining in protected areas (at AU-50) to nearly full mint bloom (at AU-58).

EF-40, 45 (Extremely Fine). *Obverse:* More wear is evident on the upper hair area and the ribbon, and on the drapery and bosom. Excellent detail remains in low-relief areas of the hair. The stars show wear as do the date and letters. Luster, if present at all, is minimal and in protected areas. *Reverse:* The eagle shows more wear, this being the focal point to check. Many feathers remain in the interior areas of the wings. Additional wear is

1796; JR-5. Graded EF-45.

on the wreath and letters, but many details are present. Some luster may be seen in protected areas, and if present is slightly more abundant than on the obverse.

Illustrated coin: Note the single adjustment mark running across the eagle's chest. Most examples of this die variety bear similar adjustment marks at varying angles.

VF-20, 30 (Very Fine). *Obverse:* The higher-relief areas of hair are well worn at VF-20, less so at VF-30. The drapery and bosom show extensive wear. The stars have more wear, making them appear larger (an optical illusion seen on most worn silver coins of this era). *Reverse:* The body of the eagle shows few if any feathers, while the wings have about half of the feathers visible, depending on the strike. At VF-30 more than half of the

1796; JR-6. Graded VF-30.

feathers may show. The leaves lack most detail and are in outline form. Scattered, non-disfiguring marks are normal for this and lower grades. Any major defects should be noted separately.

F-12, 15 (Fine). *Obverse:* Wear is more extensive than on a Very Fine coin, particularly noticeable on the hair, face, and bosom, and the stars appear larger. About half the hair detail remains, most noticeably behind the neck and shoulder. The rim may be partially worn away and blend into the field. *Reverse:* Wear is more extensive. Now, feather details are diminished, with fewer than half remaining on the wings. The wreath and lettering

1796; JR-4. Graded F-12.

are worn further, and the rim is usually weak in areas, although some denticles can be seen.

Illustrated coin: This coin falls at the low end of the Fine range.

VG-8, 10 (Very Good). *Obverse:* The portrait is mostly seen in outline form, with most hair strands gone, although there is some definition at the back of the hair and behind the shoulder. The ear is discernible, as is the eye. The stars appear larger still, again an illusion. The rim is weak in areas. LIBERTY and the date are readable and usually full, although some letters may be weak at their tops. *Reverse:* The eagle is mostly an outline

1796; JR-4. Graded VG-8.

with parts blending into the field (on lighter strikes). The rim is worn, as are the letters, with some weak, but the motto is readable.

G-4, 6 (Good). *Obverse:* Wear is more extensive, and some stars may be partly missing. The head is an outline. The eye is visible only in outline form. The rim is well worn or even missing in areas. LIBERTY is worn, and parts of some letters may be missing, but elements of all should be readable. The date is readable, but worn. *Reverse:* The eagle is flat and discernible in outline form, and may be blending into the field. The wreath is well worn. Some of the letters may be partly missing. At this level some "averaging" can be done. If the letters are stronger than usual in one area, but some are missing in another area, the coin can still qualify as G-4.

1796; JR-6. Graded G-4.

AG-3 (About Good). *Obverse:* Wear is so extensive that the coin is barely identifiable. The head is in outline form. LIBERTY is mostly gone, same for the stars. The date, while readable, may be partially worn away. *Reverse:* The reverse is well worn with parts of the wreath and lettering missing.

1796; JR-2. Graded AG-3.

1797, 16 Stars   1797, 13 Stars

	Mintage	Cert	Avg	%MS	AG-3	G-4	VG-8	F-12	VF-20	EF-40	AU-50	MS-60	MS-63
1796	22,135	254	48.7	39%	$1,100	$2,750	$3,500	$5,000	$6,500	$10,000	$15,000	$23,000	$35,000 **(a)**
	Auctions: $793,125, MS-68, August 2014; $881,250, MS-67, June 2014; $32,900, MS-63, March 2015; $17,625, MS-62, September 2015												
1797, All kinds	25,261												
1797, 16 Stars		21	39.7	33%	$1,100	$2,750	$4,000	$5,000	$7,000	$12,000	$18,500	$35,000	$65,000
	Auctions: $35,250, MS-62, April 2014; $1,020, F-2, April 2018												
1797, 13 Stars		23	27.1	4%	$1,200	$2,800	$4,000	$6,250	$8,250	$16,500	$21,000	$55,000	$80,000
	Auctions: $38,188, AU-58, April 2014												

a. Value in MS-65 is $105,000.

DRAPED BUST, HERALDIC EAGLE REVERSE (1798–1807)

Designer: *Robert Scot.* **Weight:** *2.70 grams.* **Composition:** *.8924 silver, .1076 copper.*
Diameter: *Approximately 19 mm.* **Edge:** *Reeded.* **Mint:** *Philadelphia.*

JR-1.

History. Dimes of this style were minted each year from 1798 to 1807 (with the exception of 1799 and 1805). The designs follow those of other silver coins of the era.

Striking and Sharpness. Nearly all have one area or another of light striking. On the obverse, check the hair details and drapery lines, and the star centers. On the reverse, the upper right of the shield and the adjacent part of the eagle's wing often are soft, and several or even most stars may be lightly defined (sharp stars show sharply peaked centers); high parts of the clouds are often weak. Denticles are likely to be weak or missing in areas on either side. Expect to compromise on the strike; a sharply struck coin is a goal, not necessarily a reality. Certain reverse dies of this type were also used to coin quarter eagles. Sharp striking and excellent eye appeal dramatically add to a Draped Bust dime's value, this being particularly true for the dates most often seen in MS: 1805 and 1807 (which are usually weakly struck, especially 1807).

Availability. Although certain die varieties are rare, the basic years are available, with 1805 and 1807 being the most often seen. As a class, MS coins are rare. Again, when seen they are usually dated 1805 or 1807, and have areas of striking weakness. Coins of 1801 through 1804 are scarce in VF and higher grades, very scarce in AU and better.

GRADING STANDARDS

MS-60 to 70 (Mint State). *Obverse:* At MS-60 some abrasion and contact marks are evident, most noticeably on the cheek, the drapery at the shoulder, and the right field. Luster is present, but may be dull or lifeless, and interrupted in patches. At MS-63, contact marks are very few, and abrasion is hard to detect except under magnification. An MS-65 coin has no abrasion, and contact marks are so minute as to require magnifica-

1802; JR-4. Graded MS-62.

tion. Luster should be full and rich. Coins graded above MS-65 are more theoretical than actual for this type—but they do exist, and are defined by having fewer marks as perfection is approached. *Reverse:* Comments apply as for the obverse, except that abrasion and marks are most noticeable on the eagle's neck, the tips of the wing, and the tail. The field area is complex, without much open space, given the stars above the eagle, the arrows and olive branch, and other features. Accordingly, marks are not as noticeable as on the obverse.

Illustrated coin: Attractive luster and toning increase the eye appeal and desirability of this coin, despite softer-than-average striking. More than one important 20th-century collector has called this the finest dime of its kind.

AU-50, 53, 55, 58 (About Uncirculated).
Obverse: Light wear is seen on the hair area above the ear and extending to left of the forehead, on the ribbon, and on the drapery at the shoulder, more so at AU-50 than at AU–53 or 55. An AU-58 coin has minimal traces of wear. An AU-50 coin has luster in protected areas among the stars and letters, with little in the open fields or on the portrait. At AU-58, most luster is present in the fields, but is worn

1800; JR-2. Graded AU-50.

away on the highest parts of the motifs. *Reverse:* Comments as preceding, except that the eagle's neck, the tips and top of the wings, the clouds, and the tail now show noticeable wear, as do other features. As always, a familiarity with a given die variety will help differentiate striking weakness from actual wear. Luster ranges from perhaps 20% remaining in protected areas (at AU-50) to nearly full mint bloom (at AU-58). Often the reverse of this type will retain much more luster than the obverse.

EF-40, 45 (Extremely Fine). *Obverse:* More wear is evident on the upper hair area and the ribbon and on the drapery and bosom. Excellent detail remains in low-relief areas of the hair. The stars show wear, as do the date and letters. Luster, if present at all, is minimal and in protected areas. *Reverse:* The neck lacks feather detail on its highest points. Feathers have lost some detail near the edges of the wings, and some areas of the horizontal lines

1802; JR-2. Graded EF-45.

in the shield may be blended together, particularly at the right (an area that is also susceptible to weak striking). Some traces of luster may be seen, more so at EF-45 than at EF-40.

Illustrated coin: Note the die crack on the reverse from above OF to below the eagle's left foot. There is also some die clashing evident in the field behind the eagle. This reverse was used to coin dimes long after it was damaged.

VF-20, 30 (Very Fine). *Obverse:* The higher-relief areas of hair are well worn at VF-20, less so at VF-30. The drapery and bosom show extensive wear. The stars have more wear, making them appear larger (an optical illusion seen on most worn silver coins of this era). *Reverse:* Wear is greater, including on the shield and wing feathers. Star centers are flat. Other areas have lost detail, as well. E PLURIBUS UNUM is complete (this incuse feature tended to wear away slowly).

1801; JR-1. Graded VF-20.

Illustrated coin: Here is a problem-free example with normal wear for this grade.

F-12, 15 (Fine). *Obverse:* Wear is more extensive than on a Very Fine coin, particularly noticeable on the hair, face, and bosom, and the stars appear larger. About half the hair detail remains, most noticeably behind the neck and shoulder. The rim may be partially worn away and blend into the field. *Reverse:* Wear is even more extensive, with the shield and wing feathers being points to observe. About half of the feathers are visible

1805; JR-2. Graded F-15.

(depending on striking). E PLURIBUS UNUM may have a few letters worn away. The clouds all seem to be connected. The stars are weak. Parts of the border and lettering may be weak.

    Illustrated coin: There are some digs in the fields of both the obverse and reverse.

VG-8, 10 (Very Good). *Obverse:* The portrait is mostly seen in outline form, with most hair strands gone, although there is some definition at the back of the hair and behind the shoulder. The ear may be discernible. The eye is evident. The stars appear larger still, again an illusion. The rim is weak in areas. LIBERTY and the date are readable and usually full, although some letters may be weak at their tops. *Reverse:* Half or so of the

1798, 8 Over 7; JR-2. Graded VG-8.

letters in the motto are worn away. Most feathers are worn away, although separation of some may be seen. Some stars are faint. The border blends into the field in areas, and some letters are weak. Sharpness can vary widely depending on the die variety. At this level, grading by the obverse first, then checking the reverse, is recommended.

G-4, 6 (Good). *Obverse:* Some stars may be partly missing. The head is an outline. The eye is visible only in outline form. The rim is well worn or even missing in areas. LIBERTY is worn, and parts of some letters may be missing, but elements of all should be readable. The date is readable, but worn. *Reverse:* The upper part of the eagle is flat, and feathers are noticeable at the lower edge of the wing. Some scattered feather detail may or may not be seen. The

1807; JR-1. Graded G-4.

upper part of the shield is flat or nearly so, depending on the variety. Only a few letters of the motto can be seen, although this depends on the variety. The rim is worn extensively, and a few letters may be missing.

AG-3 (About Good). *Obverse:* Wear is very extensive, and some stars and letters are extremely weak or missing entirely. The date is readable. *Reverse:* Extensive wear is seen overall, with the rim worn away and some areas worn smooth. The eagle can be discerned in outline form, but not necessarily completely. A few stray motto letters may remain. Sometimes the obverse can be exceedingly worn (but the date must be readable) and the reverse with more detail, or vice-versa.

1803; JR-3. Graded AG-3.

1798, 8 Over 7

1798, 8 Over 7, 16 Stars on Reverse

1798, 8 Over 7, 13 Stars on Reverse

1798, Large 8

1798, Small 8

	Mintage	Cert	Avg	%MS	AG-3	G-4	VG-8	F-12	VF-20	EF-40	AU-50	MS-60	MS-63
1798, All kinds	27,550												
1798, 8 Over 7, 16 Stars on Reverse		6	41.5	17%	$350	$850	$1,200	$1,500	$2,500	$3,500	$5,000	$10,000	$18,000
Auctions: $88,125, MS-65, November 2013; $960, G-6, January 2018													
1798, 8 Over 7, 13 Stars on Reverse		55	50.5	56%	$750	$2,000	$4,500	$6,000	$6,750	$11,000	$25,000	$55,000	
Auctions: $58,750, MS-62, January 2014													
1798, Large 8		23	47.8	30%	$325	$850	$1,200	$1,650	$2,500	$3,750	$4,500	$8,500	$20,000 (a)
Auctions: $70,500, MS-63, June 2014; $499, AG-3, August 2014													
1798, Small 8		4	33.3	25%	$350	$1,250	$2,250	$3,000	$5,500	$9,500	$15,000	$35,000	$65,000
Auctions: $103,500, MS-64, January 2012													
1800	21,760	54	40.6	11%	$325	$1,000	$1,050	$1,650	$2,750	$4,000	$8,500	$22,500	$42,500
Auctions: $352,500, MS-66, June 2014; $259, Fair-2, October 2014; $900, G-6, February 2018													
1801	34,640	37	31.9	16%	$325	$1,150	$1,250	$2,000	$3,750	$6,000	$11,000	$40,000	$55,000
Auctions: $4,406, VF-25, February 2014; $411, Fair-2, August 2014													
1802	10,975	40	31.0	13%	$650	$1,500	$2,250	$3,000	$4,500	$8,750	$17,500	$35,000	
Auctions: $67,563, MS-62, September 2013; $541, AG-3, September 2015													
1803	33,040	38	27.2	11%	$350	$1,100	$1,500	$1,800	$3,000	$6,000	$10,000	$45,000	
Auctions: $35,250, AU-53, August 2013; $823, Fair-2, November 2014; $1,200, VG-10, January 2018													

a. Value in MS-65 is $85,000.

| 1804, 13 Stars on Reverse | 1804, 14 Stars on Reverse | 1805, 4 Berries | 1805, 5 Berries |

	Mintage	Cert	Avg	%MS	AG-3	G-4	VG-8	F-12	VF-20	EF-40	AU-50	MS-60	MS-63
1804, All kinds	8,265												
1804, 13 Stars on Reverse		4	34.3	0%	$1,250	$3,250	$5,500	$9,500	$15,000	$30,000	$70,000		
Auctions: $48,175, EF-45, April 2013													
1804, 14 Stars on Reverse		9	30.2	11%	$2,000	$6,500	$13,500	$22,500	$27,500	$55,000	$85,000		
Auctions: $367,188, MS-63, April 2013													
1805, All kinds	120,780												
1805, 4 Berries		288	39.9	35%	$250	$600	$1,000	$1,400	$1,850	$3,000	$3,500	$7,500	$9,000 **(b)**
Auctions: $49,938, MS-66, April 2014; $800, VG-10, February 2018													
1805, 5 Berries		45	31.0	20%	$250	$600	$1,000	$1,400	$1,900	$3,000	$3,750	$8,000	$17,500
Auctions: $1,998, VF-20, June 2013; $528, G-6, January 2018													
1807	165,000	279	43.4	36%	$250	$550	$850	$1,300	$1,750	$2,750	$3,250	$5,500	$9,500 **(b)**
Auctions: $55,813, MS-65, June 2014; $2,587, AU-53, August 2014; $317, G-4, October 2014; $643, VG-8, March 2018													

b. Value in MS-65 is $37,500.

CAPPED BUST (1809–1837)

Variety 1, Wide Border (1809–1828): **Designer:** *John Reich.*
Weight: *2.70 grams.* **Composition:** *.8924 silver, .1076 copper.*
Diameter: *Approximately 18.8 mm.* **Edge:** *Reeded.* **Mint:** *Philadelphia.*

| Variety 1, Wide Border (1809–1828) JR-2. | Variety 1, Wide Border, Proof JR-12. |

Variety 2, Modified Design (1828–1837): **Designer:** *John Reich.*
Weight: *2.70 grams (changed to 2.67 grams, .900 fine in 1837).*
Composition: *.8924 silver, .1076 copper.*
Diameter: *Approximately 18.5 mm.* **Edge:** *Reeded.* **Mint:** *Philadelphia.*

| Variety 2, Modified Design (1828–1837) JR-6. | Variety 2, Modified Design, Proof JR-1. |

History. The wide-border dimes were struck intermittently from 1809 to 1828. The design, by John Reich, closely follows that inaugurated with the Capped Bust half dollars of 1807. New equipment at the U.S. Mint was used to make the 1828, Small Date, dimes, and those subsequent. The slightly modified design includes smaller denticles or beads in the border and other minor differences, and they are of uniform diameter. The 2 in the 1828, Small Date, dime has a square (not curled) base.

Striking and Sharpness. Many if not most Wide Border dimes have areas of light striking. On the obverse, check the star centers, the hair details, and the drapery at the bosom. On the reverse, check the eagle, especially the area in and around the upper right of the shield. Denticles are sometimes weak, but are usually better defined on the reverse than on the obverse. The height of the rims on both sides can vary, and coins with a low rim or rims tend to show wear more quickly. Most dimes of the modified design (Variety 2) are fairly well struck, with fewer irregularities of strike than those of 1809 to 1828. On the obverse, check the hair and the brooch. The stars usually are sharp, but don't overlook them. On the reverse, check the details of the eagle. The denticles usually are sharp.

Availability. There are no extremely rare dates in this series, so all are available to collectors, but certain die varieties range from rare to extremely rare. In MS, most are scarce and some rare. The dates of the early 1830s to 1835 are the most readily available. Those exhibiting a strong strike, with Full Details, command a premium, especially the earlier dates. Most have nice eye appeal.

Proofs. Proof Capped Bust dimes of 1809 to 1828 were struck in small numbers, likely mostly as part of presentation sets. As is the case with any and all early Proofs, you should insist on a coin with deeply and fully (not partially) mirrored surfaces, well struck, and with good contrast. Carefully examine deeply toned pieces (deep toning can mask the true nature of a coin, e.g., if it is not a true Proof, or if it has been cleaned or repaired). More than just a few pieces attributed as "Proofs" are not Proofs at all. Proofs were made of each year from 1828 to 1837 and are rare. Beware of "Proofs" that have deeply toned surfaces or fields that show patches of mint frost. Buy slowly and carefully.

GRADING STANDARDS

MS-60 to 70 (Mint State). *Obverse:* The rims are more uniform for the 1828–1837 variety than for the 1809–1828 variety, striking is usually very sharp, and any abrasion occurs evenly on both sides. At MS-60 some abrasion and contact marks are evident, most noticeably on the cheek and on the area near the drapery clasp. Luster is present, but may be dull or lifeless, and interrupted in patches. At MS-63, contact marks are very few, and

1831; JR-5. Graded MS-64.

abrasion is hard to detect except under magnification. An MS-65 coin has no abrasion, and contact marks are so minute as to require magnification. Luster should be full and rich. Grades above MS-65 are seen now and again, and are defined by having fewer marks as perfection is approached. *Reverse:* Comments apply as for the obverse, except that abrasion and contact marks are most noticeable on the eagle's neck, the top of the wings, the claws, and the flat band that surrounds the incuse motto. The field is mainly protected by design elements and does not show abrasion as much as does the obverse.

AU-50, 53, 55, 58 (About Uncirculated). *Obverse:* The rims are more uniform for the 1828–1837 variety than for the 1809–1828 variety, striking is usually very sharp, and any abrasion occurs evenly on both sides. Light wear is seen on the cap, the hair below LIBERTY, the hair near the clasp, and the drapery at the bosom. At AU-58, the luster is extensive except in the open area of the field, especially to the right. At AU–50 and 53, lus-

1814; JR-5. Graded AU-55.

ter remains only in protected areas. As is true of all high grades, sharpness of strike can affect the perception of wear. *Reverse:* Wear is evident on the eagle's neck, the top of the wings, and the claws. An AU-58 has nearly full luster. At AU–50 and 53, there still is significant luster, more than on the obverse.

Illustrated coin: The stars on this coin are weakly struck.

EF-40, 45 (Extremely Fine). *Obverse:* The rims are more uniform for the 1828–1837 variety than for the 1809–1828 variety, striking is usually very sharp, and the wear occurs evenly on both sides. Wear is more extensive, most noticeable on the higher areas of the hair. The cap shows more wear, as does the cheek. Stars still show their centers (unless lightly struck, and *many* are). Luster, if present, is in protected areas among the star

1834, Large 4; JR-1. Graded EF-40.

points and close to the portrait. *Reverse:* The wings show wear on the higher areas of the feathers (particularly on the right wing), and some details are lost. Feathers in the neck are light. The eagle's claws show wear. Luster may be present in protected areas, even if there is little or none on the obverse.

VF-20, 30 (Very Fine). *Obverse:* The rims are more uniform for the 1828–1837 variety than for the 1809–1828 variety, striking is usually very sharp, and wear occurs evenly on both sides. Wear is more extensive, and most of the hair is combined into thick tresses without delicate features. The curl on the neck is flat. Unless they were weakly struck to begin with, most stars retain their interior lines. *Reverse:* Wear is most evident on the eagle's

1825. Graded VF-30.

neck, to the left of the shield, and on the leaves and claws. Most feathers in the wing remain distinct.

F-12, 15 (Fine). *Obverse:* The rims are more uniform for the 1828–1837 variety than for the 1809–1828 variety, striking is usually very sharp, and wear occurs evenly on both sides. (For both varieties the striking is not as important at this and lower grades.) Wear is more extensive, with much of the hair blended together. The drapery is indistinct along part of its upper edge. Stars have lost detail at the center and some may be flat. The height of

1821; JR-7. Graded F-15.

obverse rim is important in the amount of wear the coin has received. *Reverse:* Wear is more extensive, now with only about a third to half of the feathers remaining on the wings, more on the wing to the left. Some of the horizontal lines in the shield may be worn away.

VG-8, 10 (Very Good). *Obverse:* The hair is less distinct, with the area surrounding the face blended into the facial features. LIBERTY is complete, but weak in areas. Stars are nearly flat. *Reverse:* Feathers are fewer and mostly visible on the eagle's left wing. Other details are weaker. All lettering remains easily readable, although some letters may be faint.

1822; JR-1. Graded VG-8.

G-4, 6 (Good). *Obverse:* The portrait is mostly in outline, with few interior details discernible. LIBERTY may still be readable or may be partially worn away, depending on the variety (this varies due to the strike characteristics of some die marriages). Stars are flat at their centers. *Reverse:* The eagle is mostly in outline form, although some feathers can be seen in the right wing. All letters around the border are clear on a sharp strike;

1820, Large 0. Graded G-4.

some letters are light or missing on a coin with low rims. E PLURIBUS UNUM may be weak, often with some letters worn away.

   Illustrated coin: This is an attractive, problem-free coin at this grade.

AG-3 (About Good). *Obverse:* The portrait is an outline, although traces of LIBERTY can still be seen. The rim is worn down, and some stars are weak. The date remains clear although weak toward the rim. *Reverse:* The reverse shows more wear overall than the obverse, with the rim indistinct in areas and many if not most letters worn away.

1811, 11 Over 09; JR-1. Graded AG-3.

PF-60 to 70 (Proof). *Obverse and Reverse:* Generally, Proof dimes of the 1828–1837 variety are of better quality than the 1809–1828 variety and have Full Details in almost all areas. Proofs of this type can have areas of light striking, such as at the star centers. Proofs that are extensively cleaned and have many hairlines, or that are dull and grainy, are lower level, such as PF–60 to 62. These are not of great interest to specialists unless they

1835; JR-4. Graded PF-65 Cameo.

are of rare die varieties. A PF-64 has fewer hairlines, but they are obvious, perhaps slightly distracting. A Gem PF-65 should have fewer still and full mirrored surfaces (no trace of cloudiness or dullness). PF-66 should have hairlines so delicate that magnification is needed to see them. Above that, a Proof should be free of such lines. Grading is highly subjective with early Proofs, and eye appeal also is a major factor.

Illustrated coin: Note the awkward mix of numerals in the date. Punches of different sizes were used, and the 3 in particular looks clumsy and large in comparison to the 8 and the 5.

| **1811, 11 Over 09** | **1814, Small Date** | **1814, Large Date** | **1814, STATESOFAMERICA** |

	Mintage	Cert	Avg	%MS	G-4	VG-8	F-12	VF-20	EF-40	AU-50	MS-60	MS-63	MS-65
											PF-60	PF-63	PF-65
1809	51,065	52	36.5	35%	$750	$950	$1,400	$2,250	$3,500	$4,500	$5,500	$8,000	$25,000
Auctions: $940, VG-8, December 2015; $646, G-4, July 2015; $1,080, F-12, January 2018
1811, 11 Over 09	65,180	62	41.8	29%	$200	$350	$1,000	$1,150	$1,700	$2,200	$4,000	$6,750	$27,500
Auctions: $8,225, MS-64, February 2014; $1,058, VF-25, September 2016; $764, VF-20, November 2015; $960, F-15, January 2018
1814, All kinds	421,500												
1814, Small Date		34	56.2	59%	$70	$115	$145	$275	$725	$1,200	$2,200	$4,500	$16,000
Auctions: $5,875, MS-64, January 2014; $259, EF-40, October 2014; $176, F-12, August 2016
1814, Large Date		30	50.8	53%	$65	$125	$135	$250	$650	$1,000	$2,000	$4,000	$12,500
Auctions: $999, AU-50, June 2015; $588, EF-40, August 2015; $234, VF-25, May 2018
1814, STATESOFAMERICA		14	45.5	43%	$225	$500	$750	$1,000	$1,650	$2,250	$3,000	$6,250	$25,000
Auctions: $11,456, AU-58, March 2015; $1,234, VF-30, January 2015; $374, VG-10, February 2012

1820, Large 0   1820, Small 0   1820, STATESOFAMERICA

1821, Large Date   1821, Small Date

1823, 3 Over 2   1823, 3 Over 2, Small E's   1823, 3 Over 2, Large E's

1824, 4 Over 2   1824 and 1827, Flat Top 1   1824 and 1827, Pointed Top 1

	Mintage	Cert	Avg	%MS	G-4	VG-8	F-12	VF-20	EF-40	AU-50	MS-60 / PF-60	MS-63 / PF-63	MS-65 / PF-65
1820, All kinds	942,587												
1820, Large 0		10	39.5	30%	$65	$115	$150	$225	$550	$675	$1,400	$2,750	$12,500
	Auctions: $1,939, AU-58, January 2015; $911, AU-53, July 2015; $764, AU-53, August 2015; $223, AU-50, May 2015												
1820, Small 0		48	40.4	25%	$65	$115	$150	$225	$650	$1,200	$1,500	$3,500	$15,000
	Auctions: $1,293, MS-60, February 2014; $564, EF-40, January 2018												
1820, STATESOFAMERICA		15	42.4	40%	$150	$300	$450	$700	$1,200	$1,750	$3,000	$5,250	$17,500
	Auctions: $1,176, EF-40, January 2015; $1,176, EF-40, February 2015; $306, F-15, August 2016; $441, F-12, August 2014												
1820, Proof	2–5	1	66.0								$12,000	$20,000	$75,000
	Auctions: $80,500, PF-66, February 2008												
1821, All kinds	1,186,512												
1821, Small Date		73	45.4	44%	$75	$115	$150	$225	$525	$1,000	$1,750	$4,000	$15,000
	Auctions: $5,581, MS-64, March 2013; $1,175, MS-60, August 2014; $764, EF-45, June 2015; $432, EF-45, March 2018												
1821, Large Date		115	35.7	19%	$75	$115	$150	$225	$525	$800	$1,700	$3,250	$12,500
	Auctions: $1,058, AU-55, July 2015; $823, AU-53, February 2015; $564, EF-45, January 2015; $153, EF-40, May 2015												
1821, Proof	5–8	4	64.5								$10,000	$20,000	$60,000
	Auctions: $55,200, PF-65, April 2005												
1822	100,000	52	28.2	27%	$2,250	$2,750	$3,750	$6,750	$8,750	$12,500	$20,000	$26,500	$70,000
	Auctions: $70,500, MS-66, February 2013												
1822, Proof (a)	2–5	0	n/a								$25,000	$45,000	$150,000
	Auctions: $440,625, PF-66Cam, June 2014												
1823, 3 Over 2, All kinds	440,000												
1823, 3 Over 2, Small E's		7	41.9	29%	$100	$150	$225	$400	$700	$1,100	$1,650	$3,250	$14,000
	Auctions: $7,050, MS-65, April 2013; $288, VF-20, March 2018												
1823, 3 Over 2, Large E's		17	42.8	53%	$100	$150	$225	$400	$700	$1,100	$1,650	$3,250	$15,000
	Auctions: $7,050, MS-65, April 2013												

a. This coin is extremely rare.

1828, Large Date,
Curl Base 2 (Variety 1)

1828, Small Date,
Square Base 2 (Variety 2)

1829, Curl Base 2

1829, Small 10 C.

1829, Medium 10 C.

1829, Large 10 C.

	Mintage	Cert	Avg	%MS	G-4	VG-8	F-12	VF-20	EF-40	AU-50	MS-60 PF-60	MS-63 PF-63	MS-65 PF-65
1824, 4 Over 2, Flat Top 1 in 10 C.	510,000	13	20.9	0%	$100	$150	$225	$400	$1,000	$1,500	$2,250	$4,000	$17,500
Auctions: No auction records available.; $168, VG-10, March 2018													
1824, 4 Over 2, Pointed Top 1 in 10 C.	(b)	2	14.5	0%	$325	$750	$1,500	$5,500	$7,500				
Auctions: No auction records available.													
1824, 4 Over 2, Proof	4–6	4	66.0								$10,000	$18,000	$50,000
Auctions: $42,550, PF-65, July 2005													
1825	(b)	132	46.9	43%	$65	$115	$150	$225	$525	$950	$1,800	$3,250	$15,000
Auctions: $823, AU-53, July 2015; $564, AU-50, June 2015; $341, VF-30, August 2015; $282, VF-20, February 2015													
1825, Proof	4–6	3	65.0								$8,000	$18,000	$40,000
Auctions: $18,400, PF-63, June 2011													
1827, Flat Top 1 in 10 C.	1,215,000	2	10.0	0%	$225	$375	$900	$1,800	$3,000	$4,500			
Auctions: No auction records available.													
1827, Pointed Top 1 in 10 C.	(c)	0	n/a		$65	$115	$165	$250	$525	$700	$1,400	$3,000	$13,500
Auctions: $517, AU-53, June 2015; $881, AU-50, October 2015; $541, AU-50, June 2015; $400, EF-45, October 2015													
1827, Proof	10–15	7	65.4								$8,000	$18,000	$40,000
Auctions: $120,750, PF-67, February 2008													
1828, Variety 1, Large Date, Curl Base 2	(d)	29	44.0	24%	$115	$175	$275	$650	$1,000	$1,200	$3,750	$5,250	$20,000
Auctions: $4,113, AU-58, November 2013													
1828, Variety 2, Small Date, Square Base 2	(e)	56	47.9	41%	$65	$100	$175	$250	$475	$750	$1,300	$2,500	$12,000
Auctions: $2,820, MS-63, April 2013													
1828, Proof	4–6	2	64.0								$8,500	$18,000	$35,000
Auctions: $29,900, PF-65, February 2008													
1829, All kinds	770,000												
1829, Curl Base 2 (f)		9	6.7	0%	$5,000	$7,500	$15,000	$20,000					
Auctions: $7,638, VG-8, June 2014													
1829, Small 10 C.		58	40.4	31%	$45	$50	$55	$120	$375	$475	$1,200	$2,000	$9,000
Auctions: $764, AU-58, June 2015; $588, AU-53, July 2015; $329, AU-53, May 2015; $282, EF-45, April 2015													
1829, Medium 10 C.		8	37.5	38%	$45	$50	$55	$120	$350	$450	$1,000	$2,000	$8,500
Auctions: $717, AU-55, August 2013													
1829, Large 10 C.		18	44.7	33%	$45	$50	$55	$125	$400	$750	$2,000	$4,000	$9,000
Auctions: $259, F-12, November 2013													
1829, Proof	6–10	4	63.5								$7,500	$15,000	$35,000
Auctions: $37,375, PF-66, June 2002													

b. Included in 1824, 4 Over 2, Flat Top 1 in 10 C., mintage figure. **c.** Included in 1827, Flat Top 1 in 10 C., mintage figure. **d.** 1828, Variety 1 and Variety 2, have a combined mintage of 125,000. **e.** 1828, Variety 1 and Variety 2, have a combined mintage of 125,000. **f.** Only one working die for the 1829 dime coinage featured a curled 2, rather than the normal square-based 2. Nearly all known examples are in low grades.

1830, 30 Over 29

1830, Large 10 C.

1830, Small 10 C.

1833, Last 3 Normal

1833, Last 3 High

1834, Small 4

1834, Large 4

	Mintage	Cert	Avg	%MS	G-4	VG-8	F-12	VF-20	EF-40	AU-50	MS-60 PF-60	MS-63 PF-63	MS-65 PF-65
1830, All kinds	510,000												
1830, 30 Over 29 (g)		41	53.4	44%	$55	$65	$100	$140	$400	$650	$1,300	$4,000	$19,000
Auctions: $23,500, MS-66, June 2014; $270, VF-35, December 2014; $212, VF-35, July 2015													
1830, Large 10 C.		0	n/a		$45	$55	$65	$100	$275	$500	$1,200	$2,500	$12,500
Auctions: $823, MS-61, June 2015; $200, AU-50, February 2015; $306, EF-45, July 2015; $123, EF-40, January 2015													
1830, Small 10 C.		6	40.2	50%	$45	$55	$85	$125	$375	$650	$1,200	$2,500	$9,000
Auctions: $1,221, MS-63, January 2012													
1830, Proof (h)	5–8	3	64.0								$7,500	$15,000	$50,000
Auctions: $18,800, PF-63, April 2014													
1831	771,350	377	51.5	49%	$35	$45	$50	$100	$275	$450	$1,000	$2,000	$7,500
Auctions: $999, MS-62, January 2015; $1,880, AU-58, January 2015; $646, AU-55, October 2015; $541, AU-55, June 2015													
1831, Proof	15–25	13	65.0								$7,500	$15,000	$40,000
Auctions: $58,750, PF-66Cam, January 2014; $1,560, PF-66, January 2018													
1832	522,500	355	50.5	47%	$35	$45	$50	$100	$275	$450	$1,000	$2,000	$7,500
Auctions: $646, AU-55, October 2015; $575, AU-55, October 2015; $223, EF-40, January 2015; $141, VF-30, May 2015													
1832, Proof (i)	2–5	0	n/a								—		
Auctions: No auction records available.													
1833, All kinds	485,000												
1833		396	47.6	41%	$35	$45	$50	$100	$275	$450	$1,000	$2,000	$7,500
Auctions: $1,543, AU-58, August 2015; $646, AU-55, February 2015; $353, AU-55, May 2015; $400, AU-53, February 2015													
1833, Last 3 High		33	46.1	36%	$35	$45	$50	$100	$275	$450	$1,000	$2,000	$7,500
Auctions: $17,625, MS-66, April 2013													
1833, Proof	5–10	5	65.6								$8,000	$15,000	$40,000
Auctions: $13,800, PF-64, January 2009													
1834, All kinds	635,000												
1834, Small 4		14	34.1	21%	$30	$45	$50	$100	$275	$450	$1,500	$2,250	$9,000
Auctions: $1,116, MS-62, June 2015; $940, AU-58, October 2015; $676, AU-55, July 2015; $447, AU-53, August 2015													
1834, Large 4		67	42.1	28%	$30	$45	$50	$100	$275	$450	$1,000	$2,000	$7,500
Auctions: $270, MS-60, February 2015; $447, AU-55, August 2015; $423, AU-53, May 2015													
1834, Proof	5–10	3	65.7								$7,500	$15,000	$30,000
Auctions: $35,250, PF-65, October 2014													

g. The tail of the 2 is evident to the right of the lower curve of the 3. The very top of the 9 is evident below the 0. Surface doubling from the initial 1829 punch is also evident on the 8. There are three of four known dies of this overdate; all are similar and command similar values. Today the variety is known to be more common than thought in the early 1970s, when it was first publicized. **h.** Values are for JR-6. A very few Proof versions of the 1830, 30 Over 29, dime are known. A PF-60, JR-4, sold at auction in January 2012 for $5,750. **i.** This coin is extremely rare.

	Mintage	Cert	Avg	%MS	G-4	VG-8	F-12	VF-20	EF-40	AU-50	MS-60	MS-63	MS-65
											PF-60	PF-63	PF-65
1835	1,410,000	639	48.0	41%	$30	$45	$50	$100	$275	$450	$1,000	$2,000	$7,500
	Auctions: $1,058, AU-58, February 2015; $764, AU-58, January 2015; $282, EF-45, January 2015; $188, EF-40, May 2015												
1835, Proof	5–10	7	64.6								$10,000	$15,000	$35,000
	Auctions: $41,125, PF-65Cam, April 2014												
1836	1,190,000	290	48.7	40%	$30	$45	$50	$100	$275	$450	$1,000	$2,000	$7,500
	Auctions: $646, AU-58, July 2015; $376, EF-45, September 2015; $240, EF-45, August 2015; $200, EF-40, May 2015												
1836, Proof	2–5	2	63.5								$10,000	$15,000	$40,000
	Auctions: $6,900, PF-66, September 1998												
1837	359,500	197	49.2	49%	$30	$45	$50	$100	$275	$450	$1,000	$2,000	$7,500
	Auctions: $400, AU-50, May 2015; $125, VF-35, February 2015; $129, VF-25, January 2015; $123, VF-25, February 2015												
1837, Proof	2–5	1	64.0								$8,750	$15,000	$40,000
	Auctions: $23,000, MS-64 Specimen, April 2010												

LIBERTY SEATED (1837–1891)

Variety 1, No Stars on Obverse (1837–1838): **Designer:** *Christian Gobrecht.*
Weight: *2.67 grams.* **Composition:** *.900 silver, .100 copper.* **Diameter:** *17.9 mm.*
Edge: *Reeded.* **Mints:** *Philadelphia and New Orleans.*

Variety 1, No Stars on Obverse
(1837–1838)

Variety 1, No Stars on Obverse,
Proof

Variety 2, Stars on Obverse (1838–1853): **Designer:** *Christian Gobrecht.*
Weight: *2.67 grams.* **Composition:** *.900 silver, .100 copper.* **Diameter:** *17.9 mm.*
Edge: *Reeded.* **Mints:** *Philadelphia, New Orleans, and San Francisco.*

 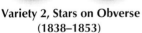

Variety 2, Stars on Obverse
(1838–1853)

Mintmark location,
1837–1860 (Variety 2),
is on the reverse,
above the bow.

Variety 2, Stars on Obverse,
Proof

Variety 3, Stars on Obverse, Arrows at Date, Reduced Weight (1853–1855):
Designer: *Christian Gobrecht.* **Weight:** *2.49 grams.* **Composition:** *.900 silver, .100 copper.*
Diameter: *17.9 mm.* **Edge:** *Reeded.* **Mints:** *Philadelphia, New Orleans, and San Francisco.*

Variety 3, Stars on Obverse,
Arrows at Date, Reduced
Weight (1853–1855)

Variety 3, Stars on Obverse,
Arrows at Date, Reduced
Weight, Proof

Variety 2 Resumed, With Weight Standard of Variety 3 (1856–1860):
Designer: *Christian Gobrecht.* **Weight:** *2.49 grams.* **Composition:** *.900 silver, .100 copper.*
Diameter: *17.9 mm.* **Edge:** *Reeded.* **Mints:** *Philadelphia, New Orleans, and San Francisco.*

Variety 2 Resumed, Weight Standard of Variety 3 (1856–1860)	Variety 2 Resumed, Weight Standard of Variety 3, Proof

Variety 4, Legend on Obverse (1860–1873): **Designer:** *Christian Gobrecht.*
Weight: *2.49 grams.* **Composition:** *.900 silver, .100 copper.* **Diameter:** *17.9 mm.*
Edge: *Reeded.* **Mints:** *Philadelphia, New Orleans, San Francisco, and Carson City.*

Variety 4, Legend on Obverse (1860–1873)

Mintmark location, 1860 (Variety 4)–1891, is on the reverse, below the bow.

Variety 4, Legend on Obverse, Proof

Variety 5, Legend on Obverse, Arrows at Date, Increased Weight (1873–1874):
Designer: *Christian Gobrecht.* **Weight:** *2.50 grams.* **Composition:** *.900 silver, .100 copper.*
Diameter: *17.9 mm.* **Edge:** *Reeded.* **Mints:** *Philadelphia, New Orleans, San Francisco, and Carson City.*

Variety 5, Legend on Obverse, Arrows at Date, Increased Weight (1873–1874)	Variety 5, Legend on Obverse, Increased Weight, Proof

Variety 4 Resumed, With Weight Standard Variety of 5 (1875–1891):
Designer: *Christian Gobrecht.* **Weight:** *2.50 grams.* **Composition:** *.900 silver, .100 copper.*
Diameter: *17.9 mm.* **Edge:** *Reeded.* **Mints:** *Philadelphia, New Orleans, San Francisco, and Carson City.*

Variety 4 Resumed, Weight Standard Variety of 5 (1875–1891)	Variety 4 Resumed, Weight Standard Variety of 5, Proof

History. The first of the Liberty Seated designs, with no stars on the obverse, was inspired by Christian Gobrecht's silver dollar of 1836. The reverse features a different motif, with a wreath and inscription. This variety was made only at the Philadelphia Mint in 1837 and at the New Orleans Mint in 1838. Liberty Seated dimes of the Stars on Obverse varieties were first made without drapery at Miss Liberty's elbow. These early issues have the shield tilted sharply to the left. Drapery was added in 1840, and the shield reoriented, this being the style of the 1840s onward. Variety 3 coins (minted in part of 1853, and all of

1854 and 1855) have arrows at the date, signifying the reduction in weight brought on by the Coinage Act of February 21, 1853. The earlier design resumed in 1856 at the new weight standard. Liberty Seated dimes were made in large quantities, and circulated widely. In 1860 the Liberty Seated design continued with UNITED STATES OF AMERICA replacing the stars on the obverse. A new reverse featured what the Mint called a "cereal wreath," encircling ONE DIME in two lines. In 1873 the dime was increased in weight to 2.50 grams (from 2.49); arrows at the date in 1873 and 1874 indicate this change, making Variety 5. Variety 4 (without the arrows) resumed from 1875 and continued to the end of the series in 1891.

Striking and Sharpness. Coins of these varieties usually are fairly well struck for the earlier years, somewhat erratic in the 1870s, and better from the 1880s to 1891. Many Civil War dimes of Philadelphia, 1861 to 1865, have parallel die striae from the dies not being finished (this being so for virtually all silver and gold issues of that period). Some dimes, especially dates from 1879 to 1881, are found prooflike. Check the highest parts of the Liberty Seated figure (especially the head and horizontal shield stripes), the star centers, and, on the reverse, the leaves. Check the denticles on both sides. Avoid coins struck from "tired" or overused dies, as evidenced by grainy rather than lustrous fields (on higher-grade coins). Issues of the Carson City Mint in the early 1870s, particularly 1873-CC, With Arrows, are often seen with porous surfaces (a post-striking effect).

Note that the word LIBERTY on the shield is not an infallible key to attributing lower grades. On some dies such as those of the early 1870s the shield was in low relief on the coins and wore away slowly, with the result that part or all of the word can be readable in grades below F-12.

Availability. The 1837 is readily available in all grades, including MS-65 and higher. The 1838-O is usually seen with wear and is a rarity if truly MS-63 or above. Beware coins with deep or vivid iridescent toning, which often masks friction or evidence of wear. Coins with uniformly grainy etching on both sides have been processed and should be avoided. The 1838 to 1860 dimes are plentiful as a rule, although certain dates and varieties are rare. Most MS coins on the market are dated in the 1850s and are often found MS–63 to 65. While certain issues of the 1860s through 1881 range from scarce to very rare, those from 1882 to 1891 are for the most part very common, even in MS-63 and finer.

Proofs. Examples of Proofs have deep-mirror surfaces and are mostly quite attractive. Proofs of 1837 (but not 1838-O) were struck in an unknown small quantity, but seemingly more than the related 1837 half dime. Proofs were made of most years and are mostly available from 1854 onward, with 1858 and especially 1859 being those often seen. Some Proofs of the 1860s and early 1870s can be carelessly struck, with areas of lightness and sometimes with lint marks. Those of the mid-1870s onward are usually sharply struck and without problems. Proof Liberty Seated dimes of this variety were made continuously from 1860 to 1891. They exist today in proportion to their mintages. Carefully examine deeply toned pieces to ensure the toning does not hide flaws.

GRADING STANDARDS

MS-60 to 70 (Mint State). *Obverse:* At MS-60, some abrasion and contact marks are evident, most noticeably on the bosom and thighs and knees. Luster is present, but may be dull or lifeless, and interrupted in patches in the large open field. At MS-63, contact marks are very few, and abrasion is hard to detect except under magnification. An MS-65 coin has no abrasion, and contact marks are so minute as to require magnification. Luster

1876-CC, Variety 1. Graded MS-64.

should be full and rich, except for Philadelphia (but not San Francisco) dimes of the early and mid-1860s. Most Mint State coins of the 1861 to 1865 years, Philadelphia issues, have extensive die striae (from not completely finishing the die). Some low-mintage Philadelphia issues may be prooflike. Clashmarks are common in this era. This is true of contemporary half dimes as well. Half dimes of this type can be very beautiful at this level. Grades above MS-65 are seen with regularity, more so than for the related No Stars dimes. *Reverse:* Comments apply as for the obverse, except that in lower Mint State grades abrasion and contact marks are most noticeable on the highest parts of the leaves and the ribbon, less so on ONE DIME. At MS-65 or higher there are no marks visible to the unaided eye. The field is mainly protected by design elements and does not show abrasion as much as does the open-field obverse on a given coin.

Illustrated coin: Note the blend of pink, lilac, and gold tones.

AU-50, 53, 55, 58 (About Uncirculated).
Obverse: Light wear is seen on the thighs and knees, bosom, and head. At AU-58, the luster is extensive, but incomplete. Friction is seen in the large open field. At AU–50 and 53, luster is less. *Reverse:* Wear is evident on the leaves (especially at the top of the wreath) and ribbon. An AU-58 coin has nearly full luster, more so than on the obverse, as the design elements protect the small field areas. At AU–50 and 53, there still is significant luster, more than on the obverse.

1838-O, No Stars; F-101. Graded AU-58.

EF-40, 45 (Extremely Fine). *Obverse:* Further wear is seen on all areas, especially the thighs and knees, bosom, and head. Little or no luster is seen. *Reverse:* Further wear is seen on all areas, most noticeably at the leaves to each side of the wreath apex and on the ribbon bow knot. Leaves retain details except on the higher areas.

1838-O, No Stars; F-102. Graded EF-45.

VF-20, 30 (Very Fine). *Obverse:* Further wear is seen. Most details of the gown are worn away, except in the lower-relief areas above and to the right of the shield. Hair detail is mostly or completely gone. *Reverse:* Wear is more extensive. The highest leaves are flat.

1872-CC; F-101. Graded VF-30.

F-12, 15 (Fine). *Obverse:* The seated figure is well worn, with little detail remaining. LIBERTY on the shield is fully readable but weak in areas. On the 1838–1840 subtype Without Drapery, LIBERTY is in higher relief and will wear more quickly; ER may be missing, but other details are at the Fine level. *Reverse:* Most detail of the leaves is gone. The rim is worn but bold, and most if not all denticles are visible.

1874-CC. Graded F-15.

VG-8, 10 (Very Good). *Obverse:* The seated figure is more worn, but some detail can be seen above and to the right of the shield. The shield is discernible. In LIBERTY at least three letters are readable but very weak at VG-8; a few more visible at VG-10. On the 1838–1840 subtype Without Drapery, LIBERTY is in higher relief, and at Very Good only one or two letters may be readable. However, LIBERTY is not an infallible

1843-O; F-101. Graded VG-8.

way to grade this type, as some varieties have the word in low relief on the die, so it wore away slowly. *Reverse:* Further wear has combined the details of most leaves. The rim is complete, but weak in areas. The reverse appears to be in a slightly higher grade than the obverse.

G-4, 6 (Good). *Obverse:* The seated figure is worn smooth. At G-4 there are no letters in LIBERTY remaining on most (but not all) coins. At G-6, traces of one or two can be seen (except on the early No Drapery coins). *Reverse:* Wear is more extensive. The leaves are all combined and in outline form. The rim is well worn and missing in some areas, causing the outer parts of the peripheral letters to be worn away in some instances. On

1873-CC. Graded G-4.

most coins the reverse appears to be in a slightly higher grade than the obverse.

 Illustrated coin: The scratch on the obverse lessens the desirability of this coin.

AG-3 (About Good). *Obverse:* The seated figure is mostly visible in outline form, with no detail. The rim is worn away. The date remains clear. *Reverse:* Many if not most letters are worn away, at least in part. The wreath and interior letters are discernible. The rim is weak.

1874-CC. Graded AG-3.

PF-60 to 70 (Proof). *Obverse and Reverse:* Proofs that are extensively cleaned and have many hairlines, or that are dull and grainy, are lower level, such as PF–60 to 62. These command less attention than more visually appealing pieces, save for the scarce (in any grade) dates of 1844 and 1846, and 1863 through 1867. Both the half dime and dime Proofs of 1837 were often cleaned, resulting in coins that have lost much of their mirror surface. With

1886. Graded PF-67.

medium hairlines and good reflectivity, an assigned grade of PF-64 is indicated, and with relatively few hairlines, Gem PF-65. In various grades hairlines are most easily seen in the obverse field. PF-66 should have hairlines so delicate that magnification is needed to see them. Above that, a Proof should be free of such lines.

1837, Large Date

1837, Small Date

No Drapery From Elbow, Tilted Shield (1838–1840)

Drapery From Elbow, Upright Shield (1840–1891)

1838, Small Stars

1838, Large Stars

1838, So-Called Partial Drapery

	Mintage	Cert	Avg	%MS	G-4	F-12	VF-20	EF-40	AU-50	MS-60	MS-63 / PF-60	MS-64 / PF-63	MS-65 / PF-65
1837, All kinds	682,500												
1837, Large Date		39	48.8	41%	$45	$100	$275	$500	$750	$1,100	$1,800	$4,000	$7,750
Auctions: $8,813, MS-66, March 2016; $1,586, MS-64, October 2016; $881, AU-58, July 2016													
1837, Small Date		35	54.6	49%	$50	$120	$325	$500	$750	$1,200	$2,000	$4,500	$8,500
Auctions: $1,645, MS-64, March 2016; $764, MS-63, November 2016; $447, AU-58, August 2016													
1837, Proof	25–35	26	63.9								$6,000	$12,000	$35,000
Auctions: $8,813, PF-62, January 2015													
1838-O, Variety 1	489,034	186	39.9	16%	$100	$180	$400	$800	$1,200	$3,600	$5,500	$8,500	$22,500
Auctions: $6,463, MS-64, January 2015; $999, AU-55, January 2015; $646, VF-35, January 2015; $376, VF-25, February 2015													
1838, Variety 2, All kinds	1,992,500												
1838, Small Stars		76	57.6	66%	$25	$55	$85	$175	$400	$700	$1,350	$2,000	$4,000
Auctions: $2,820, MS-65, June 2015													
1838, Large Stars		386	58.8	66%	$30	$40	$48	$150	$300	$500	$850	$1,200	$3,000
Auctions: $646, MS-62, December 2015; $282, AU-50, November 2015; $235, EF-45, March 2016													
1838, Partial Drapery (a)		22	60.5	68%	$30	$60	$100	$200	$500	$850	$2,000		
Auctions: $1,293, MS-62, January 2015; $89, VF-20, February 2015													
1838, Proof (b)	2–3	0	n/a										
Auctions: $161,000, PF-67Cam, January 2008													

a. The so-called "partial drapery" is not a design variation; rather, it is evidence of die clashing from the E in DIME on the reverse.
b. The 1838, Proof, dime may be unique.

1839-O, Repunched Mintmark	1841-O, Transitional Reverse, Small O	1841-O, Transitional Reverse, Large O	Regular Reverse Style of 1841-O

	Mintage	Cert	Avg	%MS	G-4	F-12	VF-20	EF-40	AU-50	MS-60	MS-63	MS-64	MS-65
											PF-60	PF-63	PF-65
1839	1,053,115	241	60.0	70%	$20	$30	$48	$145	$300	$475	$850	$1,100	$3,000
Auctions: $9,988, MS-67, May 2015; $1,410, MS-64, September 2015; $764, MS-63, February 2015; $388, AU-55, June 2015													
1839, Proof	4–5	3	64.3								$10,000	$20,000	$45,000
Auctions: $39,950, PF-65, May 2015; $28,200, PF-64, May 2015; $12,925, PF-62, August 2016													
1839-O	1,291,600	84	53.4	44%	$25	$75	$145	$240	$425	$800	$1,950	$3,000	$7,000
Auctions: $15,863, MS-67, May 2015; $823, AU-55, October 2015; $764, AU-50, June 2015; $470, AU-50, June 2015													
1839-O, Repunched Mintmark	(c)	1	30.0	0%	$40	$100	$225	$325	$700	$750	$3,500		
Auctions: $13,800, MS-66+, February 2012													
1839-O, Proof	2–3	1	65.0									$25,000	$70,000
Auctions: $74,750, PF-65, October 2008													
1840, No Drapery	981,500	150	55.2	55%	$20	$30	$48	$150	$300	$425	$850	$1,200	$3,200
Auctions: $3,290, MS-65, August 2016; $1,998, MS-65, June 2015; $270, AU-55, February 2015													
1840, No Drapery, Proof	4–5	6	64.8								$10,000	$15,000	$30,000
Auctions: $27,600, PF-65Cam, August 2007													
1840-O, No Drapery	1,175,000	45	38.3	16%	$60	$120	$180	$480	$1,025	$7,000	$14,500	$22,500	$40,000
Auctions: $376, AU-50, June 2015; $206, AU-50, June 2015; $423, EF-45, September 2015; $188, VF-30, November 2015													
1840, Drapery	377,500	25	43.8	28%	$90	$180	$300	$800	$1,300	$3,000	$12,000	$19,500	$30,000
Auctions: $27,025, MS-64, May 2015; $2,585, MS-62, January 2015; $84, VF-20, January 2015; $216, VF-20, March 2018													
1841 (d)	1,622,500	79	59.0	68%	$20	$30	$35	$60	$140	$425	$775	$1,200	$3,600
Auctions: $223, AU-55, March 2015; $212, AU-55, January 2015; $141, AU-53, August 2015; $79, AU-53, January 2015													
1841, Proof (d)	2–3	1	63.0									$55,000	
Auctions: $41,125, PF-63Cam, October 2014													
1841, No Drapery, Proof	2–3	2	60.0									$65,000	
Auctions: $305,500, PF-67, November 2013													
1841-O	2,007,500	84	48.7	25%	$25	$45	$100	$150	$325	$850	$1,400	$5,400	$9,000
Auctions: $353, AU-55, June 2015; $329, AU-53, January 2015; $259, AU-53, July 2015; $106, EF-45, June 2015													
1841-O, Transitional Reverse, Small O (e)	(f)	4	9.3	0%									
Auctions: $940, G-6, June 2013													
1841-O, Transitional Reverse, Large O (e)	(f)	3	8.3	0%									
Auctions: $2,611, F-12, January 2014													
1842	1,887,500	184	49.8	45%	$20	$30	$35	$50	$125	$400	$650	$1,200	$3,000
Auctions: $4,700, MS-66, May 2015; $3,760, MS-66, January 2015; $3,290, MS-65, June 2015; $881, MS-64, August 2015													
1842, Proof	6–10	4	63.8								$10,000	$15,000	$40,000
Auctions: $37,375, PF-65Cam, April 2008													
1842-O	2,020,000	37	46.4	24%	$35	$90	$175	$475	$1,300	$3,500	$6,500	$8,500	$20,000
Auctions: $14,100, MS-65, May 2015; $306, AU-50, August 2015; $447, EF-45, February 2015; $141, VF-35, January 2015													

c. Included in circulation-strike 1839-O mintage figure. **d.** Two examples are known of 1841, No Drapery, Small Stars, Upright Shield. One is a Proof and the other is a circulation strike in VF. **e.** The 1841-O, Transitional Reverse, varieties were struck with a reverse die that was supposed to have been discontinued in 1840, but saw limited use into 1841. Note the closed buds (not open, as in the regular reverse die of 1841); also note that the second leaf from the left (in the group of four leaves to the left of the bow knot) reaches only halfway across the bottom of the U in UNITED. **f.** Included in 1841-O mintage figure.

	Mintage	Cert	Avg	%MS	G-4	F-12	VF-20	EF-40	AU-50	MS-60	MS-63	MS-64	MS-65
											PF-60	PF-63	PF-65
1843	1,370,000	75	56.2	53%	$20	$30	$35	$50	$125	$475	$800	$2,100	$4,200
	Auctions: $881, MS-64, June 2015; $705, MS-63, August 2016; $141, AU-53, July 2015												
1843, Proof	*10–15*	10	64.3								$5,000	$10,000	$25,000
	Auctions: $25,850, PF-66, June 2014												
1843-O	150,000	52	23.3	0%	$175	$600	$1,350	$3,500	$11,000	$70,000			
	Auctions: $423, F-12, February 2015; $206, VG-10, January 2015; $84, G-3, June 2015												
1844	72,500	105	24.3	9%	$175	$375	$600	$3,250	$3,750	$4,000	$9,500	$15,000	$26,500
	Auctions: $881, EF-45, August 2016; $705, VF-30, July 2015; $447, $235, VG-10, August 2016; $1,080, EF-45, January 2018												
1844, Proof	*4–8*	2	64.0								$12,500	$22,500	$45,000
	Auctions: $44,063, PF-65, October 2014; $31,725, PF-64, May 2015												
1845	1,755,000	151	59.0	68%	$20	$30	$35	$50	$150	$400	$800	$1,250	$3,500
	Auctions: $4,935, MS-66, May 2015; $3,290, MS-65, January 2015; $646, MS-63, June 2015; $141, AU-53, November 2015												
1845, Proof	*6–10*	5	64.8								$5,000	$8,500	$25,000
	Auctions: $30,550, PF-66, May 2015; $19,975, PF-65, April 2013												
1845-O	230,000	46	31.2	4%	$90	$240	$550	$1,000	$3,000	$12,000	$24,000		
	Auctions: $123,376, MS-69, May 2015; $541, AU-50, June 2015; $865, EF-40, January 2015; $364, VF-25, January 2015												
1846	31,300	61	23.8	2%	$200	$600	$1,150	$2,500	$8,500	$20,000	$45,000		
	Auctions: $2,115, EF-40, March 2016; $1,058, VF-25, August 2016; $646, F-12, September 2016; $999, VF-30, January 2018												
1846, Proof	*8–12*	7	63.9								$7,500	$12,000	$35,000
	Auctions: $31,725, PF-65, March 2013												
1847	245,000	39	50.5	33%	$20	$40	$70	$180	$425	$1,550	$4,000	$6,500	$10,000
	Auctions: $4,700, MS-63, October 2014; $229, EF-45, November 2014												
1847, Proof	*3–5*	1	66.0								$8,000	$13,000	$35,000
	Auctions: $35,250, PF-66Cam, March 2013; $44,063, PF-66, October 2014												
1848	451,500	67	55.8	57%	$20	$32	$50	$85	$180	$725	$975	$2,200	$6,500
	Auctions: $6,463, MS-65, May 2015; $400, AU-58, April 2015; $306, AU-58, July 2015												
1848, Proof	*10–15*	9	64.6								$5,000	$10,000	$17,500
	Auctions: $18,800, PF-65, May 2015; $14,100, PF-65, August 2016; $15,275, PF-64, January 2015												
1849	839,000	79	55.5	58%	$20	$30	$40	$75	$180	$375	$900	$1,500	$3,500
	Auctions: $14,100, MS-66, March 2015; $1,763, MS-65, August 2016; $46, VF-30, April 2015												
1849, Proof	*4–6*	3	65.3								$10,000	$12,500	$35,000
	Auctions: $35,250, PF-65, August 2013; $21,150, PF-64, January 2015												
1849-O	300,000	83	45.9	23%	$25	$75	$150	$375	$950	$2,500	$5,500	$11,000	
	Auctions: $5,288, MS-64, January 2015; $3,525, MS-63, June 2015; $617, AU-55, January 2015; $165, AU-50, July 2015												
1850	1,931,500	145	54.4	57%	$20	$30	$40	$60	$150	$300	$700	$1,500	$4,500
	Auctions: $940, MS-64, June 2015; $881, MS-64, August 2016; $646, MS-63, January 2015												
1850, Proof	*4–6*	4	64.5								$10,000	$15,000	$35,000
	Auctions: $44,650, PF-67, May 2015; $19,975, PF-64, May 2015												
1850-O	510,000	28	40.9	21%	$25	$100	$120	$300	$900	$2,000	$3,600	$5,400	$8,500
	Auctions: $823, AU-58, January 2015; $1,058, AU-55, July 2015; $74, VF-20, August 2015												
1851	1,026,500	75	54.8	55%	$20	$30	$40	$70	$200	$425	$850	$1,800	$5,000
	Auctions: $20,563, MS-67, June 2013; $8,225, MS-67, May 2015; $170, AU-53, October 2014												
1851-O	400,000	38	49.4	16%	$25	$40	$120	$300	$1,000	$2,500	$3,750	$6,500	$15,000
	Auctions: $15,275, MS-65, May 2015; $165, EF-40, January 2015; $106, EF-40, June 2015												
1852	1,535,500	97	57.3	64%	$20	$30	$40	$60	$125	$300	$650	$1,100	$3,000
	Auctions: $9,400, MS-67, July 2015; $1,058, MS-64, November 2016; $646, MS-64, September 2016												
1852, Proof	*5–10*	8	64.4								$5,000	$10,000	$25,000
	Auctions: $20,563, PF-65, May 2015; $9,400, PF-65, September 2015; $8,225, PF-62, January 2014												
1852-O	430,000	55	54.2	53%	$30	$90	$180	$325	$550	$1,800	$3,600	$4,800	$12,500
	Auctions: $259, EF-40, January 2015; $129, VF-20, January 2015												

	Mintage	Cert	Avg	%MS	G-4	F-12	VF-20	EF-40	AU-50	MS-60	MS-63 / PF-60	MS-64 / PF-63	MS-65 / PF-65
1853, No Arrows	95,000	119	52.6	68%	$110	$300	$500	$650	$800	$950	$1,550	$2,200	$2,500
	Auctions: $1,998, MS-64, February 2015; $1,880, MS-64, July 2015; $376, VF-20, August 2016												
1853, With Arrows	12,173,000	967	57.4	63%	$20	$25	$30	$50	$150	$325	$675	$1,000	$1,750
	Auctions: $764, MS-64, October 2016; $494, MS-62, August 2016; $141, AU-55, March 2016												
1853, Proof	5–10	5	64.6								$12,500	$25,000	$65,000
	Auctions: $37,600, PF-66, December 2015; $34,075, PF-65, October 2014												
1853-O	1,100,000	49	43.5	14%	$25	$85	$125	$300	$650	$2,650	$3,600	$6,500	$12,000
	Auctions: $1,880, AU-55, June 2015; $200, EF-40, July 2015; $89, VF-25, August 2015; $54, VF-25, January 2015												
1854	4,470,000	259	58.0	61%	$20	$25	$30	$50	$175	$325	$675	$950	$1,700
	Auctions: $3,055, MS-66, October 2016; $1,175, MS-65, September 2016; $764, MS-64, December 2015												
1854, Proof	8–12	9	65.0								$6,000	$10,000	$25,000
	Auctions: $19,975, PF-65, October 2014; $17,625, PF-65, January 2015; $11,163, PF-64, August 2016												
1854-O	1,770,000	91	57.8	73%	$20	$25	$45	$85	$225	$425	$1,000	$1,500	$5,500
	Auctions: $8,225, MS-66, May 2015; $646, MS-62, August 2015												
1855	2,075,000	106	59.8	71%	$20	$25	$30	$60	$185	$325	$850	$1,100	$3,000
	Auctions: $881, MS-64, March 2016; $705, MS-64, September 2016; $646, MS-63, June 2015												
1855, Proof	8–12	15	64.9								$6,000	$10,000	$25,000
	Auctions: $29,375, PF-67, October 2015; $14,100, PF-64, May 2015; $9,400, PF-64, September 2015												
1856, All kinds	5,780,000												
1856, Large Date		27	46.9	19%	$40	$90	$120	$180	$300	$600	$2,100	$3,600	$9,500
	Auctions: $6,463, MS-64, October 2015; $2,233, MS-63, October 2015; $114, EF-45, March 2018												
1856, Small Date		103	50.3	46%	$16	$20	$30	$60	$145	$300	$550	$950	$2,250
	Auctions: $1,880, MS-65, March 2016; $1,763, MS-65, January 2015; $494, MS-63, October 2015												
1856, Proof	40–50	24	64.6								$2,500	$4,000	$12,000
	Auctions: $14,100, PF-66, August 2016; $6,463, PF-65, October 2015; $5,405, PF-65, August 2015												
1856-O	1,180,000	63	52.7	46%	$20	$60	$90	$150	$360	$800	$1,350	$2,650	$6,000
	Auctions: $3,672, MS-65, October 2014; $1,469, MS-63, November 2013; $74, AU-50, February 2015; $147, EF-45, November 2014												
1856-S	70,000	30	39.3	13%	$240	$650	$1,200	$1,700	$2,500	$7,200	$15,000	$25,000	$45,000
	Auctions: $1,410, VF-30, January 2015; $341, G-6, January 2015												
1857	5,580,000	520	59.0	69%	$16	$20	$30	$50	$130	$300	$550	$850	$1,950
	Auctions: $2,080, MS-66, October 2015; $700, MS-64, July 2016; $705, MS-64, October 2016												
1857, Proof	45–60	39	64.6								$2,000	$3,750	$5,500
	Auctions: $7,638, PF-66, October 2015; $4,700, PF-65, August 2015; $2,233, PF-64, March 2016												
1857-O	1,540,000	231	57.8	63%	$18	$25	$35	$70	$200	$425	$750	$1,000	$2,150
	Auctions: $2,468, MS-66, May 2015; $1,998, MS-66, June 2015; $423, MS-62, February 2015; $212, AU-55, August 2015												
1858	1,540,000	141	58.8	70%	$16	$20	$30	$50	$130	$300	$550	$850	$1,850
	Auctions: $4,935, MS-67, June 2015; $2,585, MS-66, June 2015												
1858, Proof	(g)	78	64.4								$1,000	$2,000	$4,250
	Auctions: $7,051, PF-66, August 2016; $1,175, PF-64, March 2016; $1,293, PF-63, September 2016												
1858-O	290,000	49	55.6	41%	$25	$40	$85	$150	$360	$900	$2,000	$4,000	$7,500
	Auctions: $517, AU-58, January 2015; $188, EF-45, April 2015												
1858-S	60,000	36	33.5	8%	$150	$325	$825	$1,250	$1,950	$7,200	$17,000	$24,000	
	Auctions: $1,116, EF-40, January 2015; $999, VF-35, March 2015; $646, VF-20, January 2015; $306, F-12, February 2015												
1859	429,200	152	61.9	84%	$20	$22	$32	$60	$140	$300	$650	$850	$2,000
	Auctions: $2,174, MS-65, November 2015; $341, MS-62, March 2015; $40, AU-53, January 2015; $112, AU-50, September 2015												
1859, Proof	(g)	210	64.5								$900	$1,250	$2,250
	Auctions: $5,875, PF-67, March 2016; $2,115, PF-65, September 2016; $1,998, PF-65, March 2016												

g. The mintage figure is unknown.

**1859 Pattern Dime: Obverse of 1859,
Reverse of 1860, Proof**
Judd-233

**1861, Six Vertical
Shield Lines**

	Mintage	Cert	Avg	%MS	G-4	F-12	VF-20	EF-40	AU-50	MS-60	MS-63	MS-64	MS-65
											PF-60	PF-63	PF-65
1859, Obverse of 1859, Reverse of 1860, Proof (h)	(i)	12	64.7								$10,000	$18,500	$25,000
Auctions: $5,875, PF-67Cam, October 2014; $4,113, PF-66Cam, July 2014; $3,672, PF-66Cam, October 2014; $2,585, PF-65, July 2014													
1859-O	480,000	118	58.5	68%	$20	$25	$60	$95	$275	$400	$850	$1,150	$2,250
Auctions: $5,405, MS-67, June 2015; $494, MS-63, February 2015; $329, MS-61, January 2015; $106, AU-50, February 2015													
1859-S	60,000	25	28.5	8%	$180	$475	$1,050	$2,750	$5,500	$18,000	$30,000	$48,000	$90,000
Auctions: $376, EF-40, February 2015; $200, F-12, January 2015; $447, G-6, February 2015													
1860-S, Variety 2	140,000	42	45.1	17%	$60	$150	$300	$480	$950	$2,500	$8,100	$12,500	$42,500
Auctions: $37,600, MS-65, May 2015; $1,998, MS-62, May 2015; $999, AU-58, March 2015; $823, AU-50, January 2015													
1860, Variety 4	606,000	122	62.5	87%	$16	$20	$32	$40	$100	$200	$325	$500	$1,150
Auctions: $11,163, MS-67, May 2015; $1,410, MS-66, June 2015; $1,880, MS-65, January 2015; $423, MS-64, June 2015													
1860, Variety 4, Proof	1,000	157	64.5								$350	$600	$1,300
Auctions: $5,405, PF-68, August 2015; $6,463, PF-67, October 2014; $1,646, PF-65+, September 2014; $734, PF-64, July 2014													
1860-O, Variety 4	40,000	49	27.7	6%	$525	$1,500	$2,500	$5,000	$8,500	$18,000	$35,000	$75,000	
Auctions: $64,625, MS-64, May 2015; $2,350, VF-35, February 2015; $999, VF-20, September 2015													
1861 (j)	1,883,000	146	58.7	75%	$16	$22	$30	$40	$100	$200	$325	$450	$1,150
Auctions: $3,290, MS-66, January 2015; $764, MS-65, January 2015; $376, MS-64, January 2015; $259, MS-63, January 2015													
1861, Proof	1,000	101	63.9								$350	$650	$1,300
Auctions: $4,935, PF-66, December 2015; $3,055, PF-65, August 2016; $705, PF-64, August 2015													
1861-S	172,500	28	43.0	29%	$150	$425	$650	$900	$1,200	$6,000	$18,000	$30,000	$42,000
Auctions: $51,700, MS-66, January 2015; $823, EF-40, February 2015; $764, VF-25, February 2015; $235, VF-20, January 2015													
1862	847,000	182	62.2	89%	$16	$25	$30	$40	$100	$185	$350	$500	$1,150
Auctions: $1,763, MS-66, July 2015; $1,175, MS-66, December 2015; $1,998, MS-65, August 2016													
1862, Proof	550	98	63.7								$350	$650	$1,300
Auctions: $1,293, PF-65, June 2015; $1,175, PF-65, August 2016													
1862-S	180,750	19	39.8	26%	$150	$300	$550	$1,000	$2,400	$4,200	$9,000	$12,000	
Auctions: $35,250, MS-65, October 2014; $646, AU-50, October 2014; $646, VF-30, April 2014; $388, VF-25, July 2014													
1863	14,000	42	56.0	81%	$600	$1,000	$1,100	$1,150	$1,300	$1,500	$2,400	$3,000	$4,000
Auctions: $5,170, MS-66, May 2015; $2,820, MS-63, January 2015; $881, G-6, August 2015													
1863, Proof	460	158	64.5								$325	$600	$1,300
Auctions: $1,821, PF-66, August 2016; $1,528, PF-65, December 2015; $1,175, PF-65, March 2016													
1863-S	157,500	31	50.9	32%	$120	$300	$480	$900	$1,200	$3,600	$9,500	$12,500	$30,000
Auctions: $30,550, MS-66, May 2015; $881, EF-45, January 2015; $153, F-15, January 2015													

h. In 1859 the Mint made a dime pattern, of which some 13 to 20 examples are known. These "coins without a country" do not bear the nation's identity (UNITED STATES OF AMERICA). They are transitional pieces, not made for circulation, but struck at the time that the dime's legend was being transferred from the reverse to the obverse (see Variety 4). For more information, consult *United States Pattern Coins*, 10th edition (Judd). **i.** The mintage figure is unknown. **j.** The dime's dies were modified slightly in 1861. The first (scarcer) variety has only five vertical lines in the top part of the shield.

	Mintage	Cert	Avg	%MS	G-4	F-12	VF-20	EF-40	AU-50	MS-60	MS-63 / PF-60	MS-64 / PF-63	MS-65 / PF-65
1864	11,000	44	57.1	75%	$300	$650	$925	$1,000	$1,150	$1,200	$2,150	$2,750	$5,500
Auctions: $23,500, MS-67, August 2016; $999, VF-25, February 2015; $1,293, F-15, September 2016													
1864, Proof	470	155	64.3								$325	$600	$1,300
Auctions: $1,293, PF-65, August 2016; $1,058, PF-65, October 2016; $887, PF-64, September 2016													
1864-S	230,000	41	45.5	39%	$120	$240	$360	$800	$1,000	$1,300	$2,000	$7,000	$10,000
Auctions: $1,528, MS-62, January 2015; $1,293, MS-61, March 2015; $1,058, AU-55, February 2015; $153, VF-30, January 2015													
1865	10,000	52	57.1	73%	$425	$750	$900	$1,000	$1,150	$1,300	$2,100	$2,500	$3,500
Auctions: $3,916, MS-66, June 2015; $1,528, EF-40, October 2014													
1865, Proof	500	113	64.1								$350	$650	$1,300
Auctions: $2,703, PF-66, October 2015; $646, PF-64, August 2016; $1,058, PF-63, November 2015													
1865-S	175,000	31	35.3	13%	$120	$360	$725	$1,200	$3,000	$7,000	$19,500	$30,000	$40,000
Auctions: $5,875, MS-62, January 2015; $517, AU-50, January 2015; $823, VF-35, January 2015; $212, VF-30, January 2015													
1866	8,000	43	55.8	77%	$750	$1,100	$1,250	$1,400	$1,750	$1,850	$2,500	$2,750	$3,250
Auctions: $4,465, MS-66, May 2015; $3,760, MS-66, June 2015													
1866, Proof	725	166	64.4								$325	$600	$1,300
Auctions: $2,585, PF-66, August 2016; $2,585, PF-65, December 2015; $1,175, PF-65, August 2016													
1866-S	135,000	34	39.4	32%	$120	$240	$425	$625	$1,500	$3,600	$7,200	$9,500	$15,000
Auctions: $14,100, MS-66, May 2015; $588, EF-40, August 2015; $541, EF-40, January 2015; $165, VF-20, June 2015													
1867	6,000	45	60.7	84%	$600	$925	$1,200	$1,300	$1,400	$1,500	$2,100	$3,200	$4,500
Auctions: $2,468, MS-64, July 2014; $1,998, MS-63, August 2016; $1,763, MS-63, February 2015													
1867, Proof	625	134	64.2								$325	$600	$1,300
Auctions: $6,169, PF-66, November 2016; $1,058, PF-65, March 2016; $881, PF-65, August 2016													
1867-S	140,000	31	48.3	45%	$120	$240	$400	$725	$1,550	$2,000	$5,100	$7,500	$10,000
Auctions: $2,585, MS-62, January 2015; $2,233, MS-62, June 2015; $447, AU-50, April 2015; $376, VF-30, January 2015													
1868	464,000	41	56.8	76%	$18	$30	$40	$65	$150	$300	$850	$1,500	$4,000
Auctions: $3,819, MS-65, March 2015; $118, EF-45, April 2015; $62, EF-40, January 2015													
1868, Proof	600	156	63.9								$325	$600	$1,300
Auctions: $12,925, PF-67, September 2016; $3,055, PF-65, October 2015; $541, PF-64, August 2016													
1868-S	260,000	25	50.1	56%	$60	$150	$250	$550	$650	$1,000	$1,500	$2,500	$5,000
Auctions: $541, AU-53, March 2015; $89, EF-40, March 2015													
1869	256,000	28	51.6	54%	$22	$40	$85	$150	$200	$400	$900	$1,750	$3,250
Auctions: $7,638, MS-67, May 2015; $79, AU-50, January 2015; $125, VF-25, September 2015													
1869, Proof	600	179	64.1								$325	$600	$1,300
Auctions: $823, PF-65, August 2016; $823, PF-64, June 2015; $475, PF-63, July 2015													
1869-S	450,000	58	60.3	78%	$18	$25	$50	$225	$250	$450	$800	$1,300	$3,000
Auctions: $3,995, MS-66, May 2015; $2,585, MS-65, January 2015; $764, MS-62, March 2015; $306, AU-53, March 2015													
1870	470,500	73	60.4	79%	$16	$25	$30	$50	$100	$225	$450	$800	$1,650
Auctions: $588, MS-64, January 2015; $176, MS-61, July 2015; $188, AU-58, July 2015													
1870, Proof	1,000	158	64.1								$325	$600	$1,300
Auctions: $2,585, PF-66, October 2016; $1,528, PF-65, October 2015; $823, PF-64, August 2016													
1870-S	50,000	36	39.6	33%	$250	$575	$725	$900	$1,200	$1,800	$2,750	$3,750	$7,500
Auctions: $1,116, AU-53, March 2015; $646, VF-30, July 2015; $223, VF-20, January 2015; $306, VG-8, February 2015													
1871	906,750	71	59.7	68%	$16	$25	$30	$50	$150	$250	$425	$850	$1,600
Auctions: $3,995, MS-66, December 2015; $235, AU-58, January 2015; $141, AU-55, July 2015													
1871, Proof	960	149	64.0								$325	$600	$1,300
Auctions: $1,645, PF-66, January 2015; $517, PF-64, August 2016; $423, PF-62, October 2016													
1871-CC	20,100	22	32.0	18%	$3,000	$6,000	$8,500	$15,000	$25,000	$50,000	$115,000	$175,000	$300,000
Auctions: $270,250, MS-65, October 2014; $27,025, AU-55, May 2013; $6,463, AU-50, July 2014; $3,525, EF-40, January 2015													
1871-S	320,000	29	54.8	45%	$25	$120	$180	$325	$750	$1,600	$3,600	$5,000	$10,000
Auctions: $4,230, MS-64, October 2015; $364, EF-45, March 2015; $69, VF-20, January 2015; $40, VF-20, February 2015													

1872, Doubled Die Reverse
FS-10-1872-801.

1873, With Arrows,
Doubled Die Obverse
FS-10-1873-101.

1873, Close 3   **1873, Open 3**

	Mintage	Cert	Avg	%MS	G-4	F-12	VF-20	EF-40	AU-50	MS-60	MS-63	MS-64	MS-65
											PF-60	PF-63	PF-65
1872	2,395,500	81	58.5	72%	$18	$25	$30	$40	$90	$175	$300	$650	$1,100
	Auctions: $17,625, MS-68, May 2015; $494, MS-64, February 2015; $69, MS-60, January 2015												
1872, Doubled Die Reverse (k,l)	(m)	2	37.5	0%	$100	$350	$550	$850	$1,500	$1,750			
	Auctions: $425, VF-20, May 2008												
1872, Proof	950	146	63.8								$325	$600	$1,300
	Auctions: $5,170, PF-67, September 2016; $823, PF-65, August 2016; $588, PF-64, July 2016												
1872-CC	35,480	41	26.9	0%	$1,250	$3,250	$5,000	$11,500	$20,000	$75,000	$200,000		
	Auctions: $182,125, MS-63, May 2015; $2,233, EF-40, January 2015; $1,410, EF-40, February 2015; $1,293, VF-20, June 2015												
1872-S	190,000	24	52.6	46%	$25	$120	$180	$325	$500	$1,800	$3,500	$7,500	$25,000
	Auctions: $28,200, MS-65, May 2015; $1,647, MS-60, March 2015; $376, EF-40, January 2015; $69, VF-30, January 2015												
1873, No Arrows, Close 3	*1,506,800*	45	57.9	62%	$16	$30	$48	$70	$120	$240	$480	$950	$1,500
	Auctions: $6,463, MS-67, June 2014; $259, AU-58, October 2014												
1873, No Arrows, Open 3	*60,000*	35	51.0	40%	$20	$50	$75	$130	$200	$600	$1,500	$4,500	$15,000
	Auctions: $9,400, MS-64, August 2013; $353, AU-55, October 2014; $259, AU-55, October 2014; $259, AU-55, February 2015												
1873, No Arrows, Close 3, Proof	600	174	64.3								$325	$600	$1,300
	Auctions: $14,100, PF-68Cam, May 2015; $8,813, PF-67Cam, January 2015; $1,116, PF-65Cam, June 2015												
1873-CC, No Arrows † (n,o)	12,400	0	n/a								$3,000,000		
	Auctions: $7,475, VF-20, January 2012												
1873, With Arrows	2,377,700	192	56.3	59%	$18	$25	$55	$150	$300	$550	$900	$1,650	$4,000
	Auctions: $11,750, MS-66, June 2015; $2,233, MS-65, January 2015; $400, MS-62, May 2015; $329, MS-61, March 2015												
1873, With Arrows, Doubled Die Obverse (p)	(q)	4	27.8	25%	$500	$1,200	$1,700	$3,300	$7,500	$20,000			
	Auctions: $3,220, VF-25, October 2011												
1873, With Arrows, Proof	500	105	64.1								$700	$1,000	$3,750
	Auctions: $9,988, PF-67Cam, September 2014; $9,988, PF-66Cam, September 2014; $16,450, PF-67, November 2013												
1873-CC, With Arrows	*18,791*	40	16.0	3%	$3,250	$5,000	$7,500	$14,000	$42,500	$70,000	$125,000	$200,000	$275,000
	Auctions: $3,290, AU-50, January 2015; $3,290, EF-40, January 2015; $2,820, EF-40, February 2015; $7,638, VF-35, January 2015												
1873-S	455,000	60	61.8	88%	$22	$35	$60	$175	$450	$1,000	$2,000	$3,500	$7,500
	Auctions: $3,890, MS-64, January 2015; $2,233, MS-64, January 2015; $1,058, MS-62, March 2015; $46, AU-50, January 2015												

† Ranked in the *100 Greatest U.S. Coins* (fourth edition). **k.** The first die hubbing was almost completely obliterated by the second, which was rotated about 170 degrees from the first. The key indicators of this variety are inside the opening of the D, and near the center arm of the E in ONE. **l.** This coin is considered rare. **m.** Included in circulation-strike 1872 mintage figure. **n.** Most of the mintage of 1873-CC (Without Arrows) was melted after the law of 1873, affecting the statuses and physical properties of U.S. coinage, was passed. **o.** This coin is considered unique. **p.** Doubling is evident on the shield and on the banner across the shield. Although well known for decades, very few examples of this variety have been reported. **q.** Included in circulation-strike 1873, With Arrows, mintage figure.

1875-CC, Mintmark Above Bow **1875-CC, Mintmark Below Bow** **1876-CC, Variety 1 Reverse** **1876-CC, Variety 2 Reverse**
FS-10-1876CC-901.

	Mintage	Cert	Avg	%MS	G-4	F-12	VF-20	EF-40	AU-50	MS-60	MS-63 / PF-60	MS-64 / PF-63	MS-65 / PF-65
1874	2,940,000	272	57.3	64%	$18	$25	$55	$150	$310	$600	$1,000	$1,400	$4,500
Auctions: $8,225, MS-67, December 2015; $2,820, MS-66, March 2016; $652, MS-63, October 2016													
1874, Proof	700	184	63.8								$700	$1,000	$3,750
Auctions: $3,772, PF-65, October 2015; $764, PF-63, July 2015; $282, PF-58, August 2016													
1874-CC	10,817	13	32.8	8%	$7,500	$14,000	$20,000	$32,500	$55,000	$85,000	$150,000		
Auctions: $6,463, EF-40, January 2015; $2,585, G-3, February 2015; $4,230, Fair-2, January 2015													
1874-S	240,000	48	56.8	67%	$25	$65	$110	$225	$500	$900	$2,000	$3,000	$6,500
Auctions: $505, AU-58, March 2015; $306, AU-50, February 2015													
1875	10,350,000	426	60.9	85%	$15	$20	$25	$35	$80	$150	$250	$400	$700
Auctions: $617, MS-66, July 2016; $588, MS-65, August 2016; $329, MS-64, May 2016													
1875, Proof	700	159	64.4								$300	$600	$1,000
Auctions: $5,405, PF-67, October 2015; $764, PF-65, August 2016; $588, PF-64, August 2015													
1875-CC, All kinds	4,645,000												
1875-CC, Above Bow		154	52.9	56%	$45	$50	$100	$130	$200	$400	$1,100	$1,600	$3,500
Auctions: $5,170, MS-67, September 2015; $3,760, MS-66, January 2015; $3,525, MS-65, October 2015; $823, MS-64, January 2015													
1875-CC, Below Bow		68	55.8	68%	$45	$50	$200	$275	$300	$450	$1,500	$1,950	$4,500
Auctions: $4,230, MS-65, May 2015; $1,880, MS-65, August 2015													
1875-S, All kinds	9,070,000												
1875-S, Below Bow		70	56.9	69%	$15	$20	$25	$40	$95	$175	$285	$475	$1,200
Auctions: $2,233, MS-66, May 2015; $999, MS-66, October 2015; $940, MS-65, August 2015; $600, MS-65, October 2015													
1875-S, Above Bow		33	62.4	79%	$15	$20	$25	$35	$85	$160	$275	$500	$1,400
Auctions: $3,055, MS-66, May 2015; $1,880, MS-66, July 2015; $705, MS-63, August 2015; $400, MS-63, March 2015													
1876	11,460,000	338	60.9	85%	$15	$20	$25	$35	$80	$150	$250	$400	$800
Auctions: $1,293, MS-67, October 2015; $764, MS-66, December 2015; $823, MS-65, September 2016													
1876, Proof	1,250	161	63.7								$300	$600	$1,000
Auctions: $1,410, PF-66, October 2015; $764, PF-65, September 2016; $541, PF-64, August 2016													
1876-CC	8,270,000	395	53.8	63%	$30	$50	$65	$85	$150	$350	$675	$1,250	$1,750
Auctions: $9,988, MS-67, January 2015; $2,056, MS-66, September 2015; $1,146, MS-65, January 2015; $353, MS-60, October 2015													
1876-CC, Variety 2 Reverse (r)	(s)	3	56.3	33%				$300	$475	$1,200	$2,500	$5,000	
Auctions: $3,738, MS-64, February 2012													
1876-CC, Proof	3–4	5	65.2										$65,000
Auctions: $38,188, PF-65, October 2014													
1876-S	10,420,000	100	58.9	75%	$15	$20	$25	$35	$80	$150	$250	$450	$1,750
Auctions: $2,401, MS-66, June 2015; $2,056, MS-66, August 2015; $388, MS-64, March 2015; $100, MS-60, January 2015													
1877	7,310,000	159	61.7	86%	$15	$20	$25	$35	$80	$150	$250	$450	$850
Auctions: $1,645, MS-66, October 2015; $764, MS-65, June 2015; $235, MS-62, February 2015													
1877, Proof	510	123	63.9								$300	$600	$1,000
Auctions: $1,410, PF-66, September 2016; $1,880, PF-65, October 2015; $823, PF-65, August 2016													
1877-CC	7,700,000	456	57.1	73%	$30	$50	$60	$80	$120	$300	$550	$1,100	$2,100
Auctions: $4,935, MS-67, January 2015; $2,115, MS-66, July 2015; $1,116, MS-65, January 2015; $881, MS-64, August 2015													
1877-S	2,340,000	91	61.8	87%	$15	$20	$25	$35	$80	$150	$300	$650	$1,750
Auctions: $494, MS-64, May 2015; $353, MS-64, March 2015; $129, AU-58, January 2015													

r. The scarce Variety 2 reverse exhibits a single point to the end of the left ribbon; the common Variety 1 reverse has a split at the ribbon's end. **s.** Included in circulation-strike 1876-CC mintage figure.

	Mintage	Cert	Avg	%MS	G-4	F-12	VF-20	EF-40	AU-50	MS-60	MS-63	MS-64	MS-65
											PF-60	PF-63	PF-65
1878	1,677,200	92	61.8	87%	$15	$20	$25	$35	$80	$150	$250	$425	$1,000
Auctions: $5,170, MS-67, May 2015; $1,645, MS-66, October 2015; $376, MS-63, May 2015; $188, MS-62, October 2015													
1878, Proof	800	166	63.9								$300	$600	$1,000
Auctions: $2,233, PF-66Cam, August 2015; $1,058, PF-65Cam, August 2015; $881, PF-64, January 2015; $676, PF-64, March 2015													
1878-CC	200,000	75	50.1	61%	$175	$275	$400	$500	$875	$1,250	$2,500	$3,500	$5,000
Auctions: $7,638, MS-67, May 2015; $541, EF-45, January 2015; $235, EF-40, January 2015; $353, VF-25, February 2015													
1879	14,000	206	63.0	92%	$200	$325	$400	$500	$550	$575	$650	$800	$1,100
Auctions: $2,174, MS-67, January 2015; $3,525, MS-66, June 2015; $494, MS-63, January 2015													
1879, Proof	1,100	304	64.2								$300	$600	$1,000
Auctions: $4,935, PF-68, May 2015; $2,115, PF-67Cam, January 2015; $1,116, PF-65Cam, July 2015; $999, PF-65, October 2015													
1880	36,000	148	60.8	84%	$150	$250	$350	$400	$500	$650	$700	$800	$1,250
Auctions: $1,763, MS-67, January 2015; $646, MS-63, June 2015; $376, EF-45, June 2015; $223, F-12, January 2015													
1880, Proof	1,355	317	64.5								$300	$600	$1,000
Auctions: $1,058, PF-65Cam, January 2015; $664, PF-64, March 2015; $646, PF-64, February 2015; $376, PF-60, May 2015													
1881	24,000	87	55.4	70%	$160	$260	$375	$425	$525	$675	$775	$950	$1,300
Auctions: $8,225, MS-67, May 2015; $2,820, MS-67, August 2015; $823, MS-64, January 2015; $646, MS-62, July 2015													
1881, Proof	975	253	64.6								$300	$600	$1,000
Auctions: $4,583, PF-67Cam, January 2015; $1,116, PF-66Cam, July 2015; $1,234, PF-66, February 2015; $1,012, PF-65, January 2015													
1882	3,910,000	381	63.0	92%	$15	$20	$25	$35	$80	$150	$250	$425	$650
Auctions: $1,645, MS-67, January 2015; $600, MS-65, June 2015; $400, MS-64, November 2015; $176, MS-63, March 2015													
1882, Proof	1,100	350	64.6								$300	$600	$1,000
Auctions: $2,586, PF-67, August 2015; $1,763, PF-66Cam, January 2015; $1,175, PF-66, January 2015; $705, PF-64, January 2015													
1883	7,674,673	487	61.5	87%	$15	$20	$25	$35	$80	$150	$250	$425	$650
Auctions: $1,586, MS-67, September 2015; $1,234, MS-66, September 2015; $712, MS-65, August 2015; $329, MS-64, January 2015													
1883, Proof	1,039	304	64.4								$300	$600	$1,000
Auctions: $2,350, PF-67, January 2015; $1,188, PF-66, August 2015; $3,760, PF-65, August 2015; $705, PF-64Cam, January 2015													
1884	3,365,505	390	63.0	91%	$15	$20	$25	$35	$80	$150	$250	$425	$650
Auctions: $2,585, MS-67, May 2015; $1,528, MS-66, January 2015; $329, MS-64, June 2015; $212, MS-63, January 2015													
1884, Proof	875	314	64.9								$300	$600	$1,000
Auctions: $3,290, PF-67Cam, August 2015; $1,763, PF-66Cam, September 2015; $1,116, PF-65Cam, October 2015; $1,002, PF-65, March 2015													
1884-S	564,969	60	59.5	72%	$20	$32	$60	$100	$300	$750	$1,100	$1,500	$5,000
Auctions: $14,100, MS-66, October 2015; $1,175, MS-64, July 2015; $999, MS-63, March 2015; $705, MS-61, June 2015													
1885	2,532,497	356	62.8	91%	$15	$20	$25	$35	$80	$150	$250	$425	$650
Auctions: $8,813, MS-67, August 2015; $764, MS-66, January 2015; $194, MS-63, January 2015; $129, MS-61, November 2015													
1885, Proof	930	286	64.8								$300	$600	$1,000
Auctions: $5,640, PF-68Cam, August 2015; $4,465, PF-67Cam, May 2015; $1,351, PF-66Cam, October 2015; $1,293, PF-65Cam, August 2015													
1885-S	43,690	59	33.9	24%	$550	$1,000	$1,400	$2,250	$4,000	$5,500	$8,500	$15,000	$27,500
Auctions: $1,645, VF-35, January 2015; $1,175, VF-25, January 2015; $505, F-12, October 2015; $499, VG-8, October 2015													
1886	6,376,684	596	62.2	88%	$15	$20	$25	$35	$80	$150	$250	$425	$650
Auctions: $1,293, MS-67, July 2015; $1,116, MS-66, June 2015; $1,293, MS-65, January 2015; $353, MS-64, November 2015													
1886, Proof	886	293	64.6								$300	$600	$1,000
Auctions: $1,998, PF-67, July 2015; $1,528, PF-66, June 2015; $999, PF-65, January 2015; $999, PF-65, January 2015													
1886-S	206,524	54	58.7	76%	$30	$50	$75	$135	$200	$550	$1,000	$2,000	$3,250
Auctions: $8,813, MS-67, October 2014; $4,700, MS-66, September 2014; $6,463, MS-66, June 2013; $2,585, MS-65, October 2014													
1887	11,283,229	571	60.9	84%	$15	$20	$25	$35	$80	$150	$250	$425	$650
Auctions: $2,820, MS-67, May 2015; $1,528, MS-66, January 2015; $588, MS-65, January 2015; $423, MS-64, February 2015													
1887, Proof	710	211	64.5								$300	$600	$1,000
Auctions: $3,173, PF-67Cam, September 2015; $3,525, PF-66, October 2015; $1,058, PF-65Cam, May 2015; $999, PF-65, June 2015													
1887-S	4,454,450	267	59.9	79%	$15	$20	$25	$35	$80	$150	$300	$450	$1,000
Auctions: $6,463, MS-67, June 2015; $1,586, MS-66, May 2015; $999, MS-65, October 2015; $423, MS-64, August 2015													

**1891-O, O Over
Horizontal O**
FS-10-1891o-501.

**1891-S, Repunched
Mintmark**
FS-10-1891S-501.

	Mintage	Cert	Avg	%MS	G-4	F-12	VF-20	EF-40	AU-50	MS-60	MS-63	MS-64	MS-65
											PF-60	PF-63	PF-65
1888	5,495,655	326	61.1	85%	$15	$20	$25	$35	$80	$150	$250	$425	$650
	Auctions: $1,293, MS-66, August 2015; $423, MS-64, October 2015; $217, MS-63, October 2015; $89, AU-58, January 2015												
1888, Proof	832	214	64.5								$300	$600	$1,000
	Auctions: $3,995, PF-67Cam, May 2015; $1,410, PF-66Cam, July 2015; $1,351, PF-65Cam, August 2015; $1,200, PF-65Cam, September 2015												
1888-S	1,720,000	70	57.6	64%	$15	$20	$25	$35	$100	$250	$850	$1,150	$3,250
	Auctions: $501, MS-63, March 2015; $390, MS-62, October 2015; $56, AU-50, October 2015												
1889	7,380,000	348	61.5	85%	$15	$20	$25	$35	$80	$150	$250	$425	$650
	Auctions: $3,819, MS-67, January 2015; $2,350, MS-66, January 2015; $517, MS-64, October 2015; $176, MS-63, July 2015												
1889, Proof	711	177	64.6								$300	$600	$1,000
	Auctions: $4,700, PF-68, October 2015; $1,939, PF-67, July 2015; $1,175, PF-66, January 2015; $1,058, PF-65, October 2015												
1889-S	972,678	83	60.1	64%	$20	$30	$50	$80	$150	$450	$1,000	$1,650	$4,750
	Auctions: $2,115, MS-65, January 2015; $329, MS-62, March 2015; $74, AU-55, January 2015; $129, AU-50, September 2015												
1890	9,910,951	570	61.3	85%	$15	$20	$25	$35	$80	$150	$250	$425	$750
	Auctions: $4,700, MS-67, September 2015; $1,058, MS-66, October 2015; $588, MS-65, June 2015; $282, MS-64, February 2015												
1890, Proof	590	209	64.4								$300	$600	$1,000
	Auctions: $1,939, PF-66Cam, August 2015; $1,410, PF-66, February 2015; $1,116, PF-66, July 2015												
1890-S, Large S	1,423,076	106	60.3	78%	$18	$25	$55	$85	$150	$350	$700	$1,000	$1,500
	Auctions: $6,169, MS-66, May 2015; $676, MS-64, March 2015; $1,293, MS-63, September 2015; $270, MS-62, January 2015												
1890-S, Small S (t)	(u)	(v)						—	—	—			
	Auctions: $1,208, MS-65, February 2006												
1891	15,310,000	990	61.8	85%	$15	$20	$25	$35	$80	$150	$250	$400	$650
	Auctions: $1,645, MS-67, July 2015; $1,116, MS-66, March 2015; $588, MS-65, January 2015; $282, MS-64, October 2015												
1891, Proof	600	225	64.8								$300	$600	$1,000
	Auctions: $6,463, PF-67Cam, November 2013												
1891-O	4,540,000	214	59.5	82%	$15	$20	$30	$50	$100	$175	$350	$550	$1,500
	Auctions: $2,000, MS-66, September 2015; $1,528, MS-65, January 2015; $306, MS-63, August 2015; $60, AU-50, June 2015												
1891-O, O Over Horizontal O (w)	(x)	2	51.5	0%	$60	$120	$150	$225	$1,000	$3,000			
	Auctions: $253, AU-58, May 2010												
1891-O, Proof (y)	2–3	2	66.0										
	Auctions: No auction records available.												
1891-S	3,196,116	170	62.0	86%	$15	$20	$25	$35	$80	$175	$300	$450	$1,000
	Auctions: $881, MS-66, August 2015; $764, MS-65, January 2015; $235, MS-63, March 2015; $141, MS-61, January 2015												
1891-S, Repunched Mintmark (z)	(aa)	0	n/a		$20	$45	$55	$85	$115	$300			
	Auctions: $5,750, MS-66, September 2010												

t. This coin is considered rare. **u.** Included in 1890-S, Large S, mintage figure. **v.** Included in certified population for 1890-S, Large S. **w.** The primary O mintmark was punched over a previously punched horizontal O. **x.** Included in circulation-strike 1891-O mintage figure. **y.** This coin is considered extremely rare. **z.** The larger primary S mintmark (known as the medium S) was punched squarely over the smaller S, which is evident within both loops. **aa.** Included in 1891-S mintage figure.

BARBER OR LIBERTY HEAD (1892–1916)

Designer: *Charles E. Barber.* **Weight:** *2.50 grams.* **Composition:** *.900 silver, .100 copper (net weight: .07234 oz. pure silver).* **Diameter:** *17.9 mm.* **Edge:** *Reeded.*
Mints: *Philadelphia, Denver, New Orleans, and San Francisco.*

Circulation Strike

Mintmark location
is on the reverse,
below the bow.

Proof

History. This dime belongs to a suite of silver coins (including the quarter and half dollar) designed by U.S. Mint chief engraver Charles E. Barber. It features a large Liberty Head styled similarly to contemporary French coinage. The reverse of the dime continues the "cereal wreath" motif of the late Liberty Seated era.

Striking and Sharpness. Check the details of the hair on the obverse. The reverse usually is sharp. If weakness is seen, it is typically in the wreath details. The denticles usually are sharp on the obverse and reverse. The Proofs of 1892 to 1901 usually have cameo contrast between the designs and the mirror fields. Later Proofs vary in contrast.

Availability. With the exception of the rare 1894-S, of which fewer than a dozen are known, all dates and mintmarks are collectible. Probably 90% or more of the survivors are in lower grades such as AG-3 and G-4. The word LIBERTY in the headband, a key to grading, tended to wear away quickly. Relatively few are in grades from Fine upward. MS coins are somewhat scarce, this being especially true of the branch-mint issues. MS-63 and finer Barber dimes usually are from the Philadelphia Mint or, if from a branch mint, are dated after 1905. Proof Barber dimes survive in proportion to their mintages. Choice and Gem examples are more easily found among dimes than among quarters and half dollars of this type. All were originally sold in silver-coin sets.

GRADING STANDARDS

MS-60 to 70 (Mint State). *Obverse:* At MS-60, some abrasion and contact marks are evident, most noticeably on the cheek and the obverse field to the right. Luster is present, but may be dull or lifeless. Many Barber coins have been cleaned, especially of the earlier dates. At MS-63, contact marks are very few; abrasion still is evident, but less than at lower levels. An MS-65 coin may have minor abrasion on the cheek, but contact marks are so minute as to require magnification.

1910. Graded MS-65.

Luster should be full and rich. *Reverse:* Comments apply as for the obverse, except that in lower Mint State grades abrasion and contact marks are most noticeable on the highest parts of the leaves and the ribbon, less so on ONE DIME. At MS-65 or higher, there are no marks visible to the unaided eye. The field is mainly protected by design elements and does not show abrasion as much as does the obverse on a given coin.

Illustrated coin: The striking on this example is razor sharp.

AU-50, 53, 55, 58 (About Uncirculated). *Obverse:* Light wear is seen on the head, especially on the forward hair under LIBERTY. At AU-58, the luster is extensive, but incomplete, especially on the higher parts and in the right field. At AU–50 and 53, luster is less. *Reverse:* Wear is seen on the leaves and ribbon. An AU-58 coin will have nearly full luster, more so than on the obverse, as the design elements protect the small field areas. At AU–50 and 53, there still is significant luster.

1910. Graded AU-53.

EF-40, 45 (Extremely Fine). *Obverse:* Further wear is seen on the head. The hair above the forehead lacks most detail. LIBERTY shows wear but still is strong. *Reverse:* Further wear is seen on all areas, most noticeably at the wreath and ribbon. Leaves retain excellent details except on the higher areas.

1895-O. Graded EF-40.

VF-20, 30 (Very Fine). *Obverse:* The head shows more wear, now with nearly all detail gone in the hair above the forehead. LIBERTY shows wear, but is complete. The leaves on the head all show wear, as does the upper part of the cap. *Reverse:* Wear is more extensive. The details in the highest leaves are weak or missing, but in lower levels the leaf details remain strong.

1914-S. Graded VF-30.

F-12, 15 (Fine). *Obverse:* The head shows extensive wear. LIBERTY, the key place to check, is weak, especially at ER, but is fully readable. The ANA grading standards and *Photograde* adhere to this. PCGS suggests that lightly struck coins "may have letters partially missing." Traditionally, collectors insist on full LIBERTY. *Reverse:* Much detail of the leaves in the higher areas is gone. The rim remains bold.

1901-S. Graded F-12.

   Illustrated coin: LIBERTY is readable, but letters ER are light.

VG-8, 10 (Very Good). *Obverse:* A net of three letters in LIBERTY must be readable. Traditionally LI is clear, and after that there is a partial letter or two. *Reverse:* Further wear has made the wreath flat; now only in outline form with only a few traces of details. The rim is complete.

1903-S. Graded VG-10.

G-4, 6 (Good). *Obverse:* The head is in outline form, with the center flat. Most of the rim is there. All letters and the date are full. *Reverse:* The leaves are all combined and in outline form. The rim is weak in areas.

1895-O. Graded G-6.

AG-3 (About Good). *Obverse:* The lettering is readable, but the parts near the border may be worn away. The date is clear. *Reverse:* The wreath and interior letters are partially worn away. The rim is weak.

1895-O. Graded AG-3.

PF-60 to 70 (Proof). *Obverse and Reverse:* Proofs that are extensively cleaned and have many hairlines, or that are dull and grainy, are lower level, such as PF–60 to 62. These are not widely desired, save for the rare (in any grade) year of 1895, and even so most collectors would rather have a lustrous MS-60 than a dull PF-60. With medium hairlines and good reflectivity, an assigned grade of PF-64 is indicated. Tiny horizontal lines on Miss Liberty's cheek, known

1911. Graded PF-67 Deep Cameo.

as *slide marks*, from National and other album slides scuffing the relief of the cheek, are endemic among Barber silver coins. With noticeable marks of this type, the highest grade assignable is PF-64. With relatively few hairlines, a rating of PF-65 can be given. PF-66 should have hairlines so delicate that magnification is needed to see them. Above that, a Proof should be free of any hairlines or other problems.

Illustrated coin: Proof dimes of 1911 are rare (only 543 minted), but one with a Deep Cameo finish, as displayed by this coin, is *extremely* rare. The coin is fully struck on both sides, and has neither a blemish nor a trace of toning.

1893, 3 Over 2 | **1897, Repunched Date**
FS-10-1897-301.

	Mintage	Cert	Avg	%MS	G-4	VG-8	F-12	VF-20	EF-40	AU-50	MS-60 / PF-60	MS-63 / PF-63	MS-65 / PF-65
1892	12,120,000	1,354	61.5	85%	$7	$7.50	$18	$25	$30	$75	$125	$185	$475
	Auctions: $8,813, MS-66, September 2016; $881, MS-64, November 2016; $447, AU-58, June 2016; $153, AU-58, March 2016											
1892, Proof	1,245	299	64.6								$285	$500	$1,000
	Auctions: $8,225, PF-68, October 2016; $3,760, PF-67, March 2016; $1,821, PF-67, August 2016; $1,469, PF-66, September 2016											
1892-O	3,841,700	243	57.8	72%	$12	$15	$35	$50	$75	$95	$175	$350	$1,250
	Auctions: $1,645, MS-65, August 2016; $676, AU-55, July 2016; $494, VF-20, March 2016											
1892-S	990,710	162	47.0	52%	$65	$115	$200	$240	$280	$330	$425	$775	$2,800
	Auctions: $2,350, MS-65, August 2016; $940, AU-58, June 2016; $705, EF-40, August 2016; $306, VG-10, March 2016											
1893, 3 Over 2 (a)	**(b)**	0	n/a		$140	$155	$200	$250	$350	$650	$1,350	$1,800	$5,000
	Auctions: $2,233, MS-63, January 2015; $1,763, MS-63, June 2015; $1,528, MS-62, February 2015; $1,351, AU-58, August 2016											
1893	3,339,940	294	58.9	79%	$8	$12	$20	$30	$45	$80	$150	$250	$750
	Auctions: $999, MS-65, September 2016; $1,410, MS-64, August 2016; $823, MS-63, May 2016; $329, AU-55, October 2016											
1893, Proof	792	270	65.0								$285	$500	$1,000
	Auctions: $3,995, PF-67, August 2016; $1,528, PF-66, March 2016; $1,293, PF-66, October 2016; $999, PF-65, September 2016											
1893-O	1,760,000	176	50.6	61%	$30	$45	$120	$150	$190	$230	$325	$500	$1,800
	Auctions: $1,763, MS-65, October 2016; $223, AU-58, August 2016; $306, EF-40, July 2015; $141, VF-35, July 2015											
1893-S (c)	2,491,401	140	52.6	62%	$15	$25	$40	$60	$90	$150	$325	$550	$2,500
	Auctions: $15,275, MS-65, August 2016; $1,528, AU-55, July 2016; $1,293, EF-45, October 2016; $100, G-6, November 2015											
1894	1,330,000	227	49.8	58%	$30	$45	$120	$160	$180	$220	$300	$400	$850
	Auctions: $3,290, MS-66, March 2016; $999, MS-64, October 2016; $541, AU-58, July 2016; $165, EF-45, August 2016											
1894, Proof	972	321	64.9								$285	$500	$1,000
	Auctions: $2,820, PF-67, March 2016; $793, PF-65, July 2016; $764, PF-65, October 2016											
1894-O	720,000	140	27.7	16%	$70	$95	$200	$300	$425	$700	$1,750	$2,300	$11,000
	Auctions: $6,169, MS-66, November 2016; $10,869, MS-65, October 2016; $734, AU-53, August 2016; $447, EF-40, March 2016											
1894-S, Proof † (d)	24	5	64.2									$1,500,000	$2,000,000
	Auctions: $1,552,500, PF-64, October 2007											
1895	690,000	175	42.6	46%	$80	$160	$350	$500	$550	$650	$725	$800	$2,000
	Auctions: $5,640, MS-66, October 2015; $1,116, MS-64, June 2015; $764, MS-63, October 2015; $423, AU-50, September 2015											
1895, Proof	880	316	64.9								$285	$500	$1,000
	Auctions: $4,465, PF-68Cam, September 2015; $1,058, PF-66Cam, September 2015; $1,175, PF-66, October 2015; $764, PF-63, October 2015											
1895-O	440,000	369	16.7	7%	$475	$600	$900	$1,350	$2,500	$3,500	$6,000	$10,000	$32,500
	Auctions: $1,293, EF-40, January 2015; $793, EF-40, July 2015; $588, VF-20, October 2015; $617, VG-10, February 2015											
1895-S	1,120,000	214	46.0	52%	$42	$60	$135	$190	$240	$325	$500	$850	$3,500
	Auctions: $3,760, MS-65, June 2015; $2,468, MS-65, October 2015; $1,175, MS-64, January 2015; $881, MS-62, February 2015											
1896	2,000,000	135	56.0	74%	$10	$22	$50	$75	$100	$125	$175	$350	$1,000
	Auctions: $1,293, MS-66, October 2015; $1,528, MS-65, June 2015; $400, MS-64, January 2015; $353, MS-63, August 2015											
1896, Proof	762	253	64.9								$285	$500	$1,000
	Auctions: $15,275, PF-68Cam, June 2014; $1,763, PF-67, March 2015; $676, PF-64, July 2014; $588, PF-64, July 2014											
1896-O	610,000	131	27.9	21%	$80	$160	$290	$375	$475	$800	$1,150	$2,000	$7,500
	Auctions: $11,750, MS-65, October 2015; $4,935, MS-65, June 2015; $3,290, AU-58, July 2015; $676, EF-45, June 2015											
1896-S	575,056	149	36.1	40%	$80	$175	$280	$350	$400	$550	$750	$1,100	$3,000
	Auctions: $5,875, MS-66, August 2015; $3,055, MS-65, October 2015; $2,820, MS-65, January 2015; $447, AU-53, April 2015											

† Ranked in the *100 Greatest U.S. Coins* (fourth edition). **a.** Overlaid photographs indicate this is not a true overdate. **b.** Included in circulation-strike 1893 mintage figure. **c.** Boldly doubled mintmark. **d.** The reason for the low mintage of the Proof 1894-S dime is unknown. Popular theories, among others, include a rounding out of the Mint's record books, or a special presentation to bankers visiting the San Francisco Mint. Fewer than a dozen examples are known to exist. Five of these coins were reserved for assay.

	Mintage	Cert	Avg	%MS	G-4	VG-8	F-12	VF-20	EF-40	AU-50	MS-60	MS-63	MS-65
											PF-60	PF-63	PF-65
1897	10,868,533	456	60.9	84%	$4	$5	$8	$15	$32	$75	$135	$200	$475
	Auctions: $2,585, MS-67, January 2015; $2,200, MS-67, August 2015; $541, MS-65, January 2015; $270, MS-64, January 2015												
1897, Repunched Date (e)	(f)	1	63.0	100%						$80	$120	$200	
	Auctions: No auction records available.												
1897, Proof	731	245	64.8								$285	$500	$1,000
	Auctions: $5,889, PF-68Cam, January 2015; $3,819, PF-68, March 2015; $2,938, PF-67, January 2015; $999, PF-66, January 2015												
1897-O	666,000	140	34.1	35%	$65	$115	$300	$375	$475	$600	$1,000	$1,500	$3,000
	Auctions: $5,640, MS-66, May 2015; $4,230, MS-66, June 2015; $1,998, MS-64, July 2015; $353, EF-40, August 2015												
1897-S	1,342,844	108	48.2	46%	$18	$35	$100	$120	$175	$300	$500	$800	$3,000
	Auctions: $5,170, MS-66, May 2015; $2,585, MS-65, October 2015; $1,410, MS-64, August 2015; $259, MS-60, March 2015												
1898	16,320,000	504	60.0	80%	$4	$5	$8	$12	$26	$75	$130	$200	$475
	Auctions: $1,028, MS-66, September 2015; $646, MS-65, January 2015; $306, MS-64, January 2015; $153, MS-63, February 2015												
1898, Proof	735	291	65.1								$285	$500	$1,000
	Auctions: $1,998, PF-67, June 2015; $1,087, PF-66, July 2015; $1,058, PF-65, March 2015; $646, PF-64, January 2015												
1898-O	2,130,000	94	50.8	56%	$12	$25	$85	$150	$200	$300	$475	$900	$3,000
	Auctions: $3,760, MS-65, January 2015; $2,115, MS-65, January 2015; $153, AU-50, July 2015; $107, VF-25, January 2015												
1898-S	1,702,507	69	52.1	55%	$8	$15	$32	$45	$80	$150	$500	$1,100	$2,500
	Auctions: $2,115, MS-64, September 2015; $141, AU-53, July 2015; $89, AU-50, February 2015; $84, AU-50, January 2015												
1899	19,580,000	361	59.3	78%	$4	$5	$8	$12	$25	$75	$130	$200	$475
	Auctions: $6,169, MS-68, September 2015; $1,645, MS-66, August 2015; $1,058, MS-66, October 2015; $230, MS-64, April 2015												
1899, Proof	846	239	64.8								$285	$500	$1,000
	Auctions: $1,410, PF-66, October 2015; $999, PF-66, January 2015; $999, PF-65, January 2015; $646, PF-64, July 2015												
1899-O	2,650,000	117	46.7	47%	$10	$18	$65	$100	$150	$225	$400	$900	$3,750
	Auctions: $1,998, MS-64, September 2015; $940, MS-63, June 2015; $764, MS-63, June 2015; $84, EF-40, January 2015												
1899-S	1,867,493	104	57.4	69%	$8.50	$16	$32	$35	$45	$110	$300	$650	$2,000
	Auctions: $6,463, MS-67, January 2015; $100, AU-53, April 2015												
1900	17,600,000	261	60.1	79%	$4	$5	$8	$12	$25	$75	$125	$225	$575
	Auctions: $5,405, MS-67, September 2015; $2,585, MS-66, June 2015; $482, MS-65, April 2015; $306, MS-64, October 2015												
1900, Proof	912	236	64.7								$285	$500	$1,000
	Auctions: $2,350, PF-67Cam, January 2015; $1,146, PF-66Cam, July 2015; $999, PF-65, January 2015; $646, PF-64, January 2015												
1900-O	2,010,000	116	42.7	38%	$18	$38	$115	$160	$220	$350	$650	$1,000	$4,000
	Auctions: $3,995, MS-66, May 2015; $2,115, MS-64, February 2015; $764, MS-61, February 2015; $141, AU-50, May 2015												
1900-S	5,168,270	166	56.1	51%	$5	$6	$12	$20	$30	$75	$175	$325	$1,350
	Auctions: $4,230, MS-66, May 2015; $3,525, MS-66, June 2015; $764, MS-64, January 2015; $42, AU-50, January 2015												
1901	18,859,665	318	60.0	79%	$4	$5	$7	$10	$26	$75	$125	$225	$500
	Auctions: $999, MS-66, February 2015; $423, MS-65, January 2015; $259, MS-64, January 2015; $176, MS-63, July 2015												
1901, Proof	813	249	64.7								$285	$500	$1,000
	Auctions: $14,100, PF-68, May 2015; $1,645, PF-67, January 2015; $999, PF-66, January 2015; $940, PF-65, July 2015												
1901-O	5,620,000	117	52.0	47%	$4	$5.50	$16	$28	$75	$180	$450	$800	$2,200
	Auctions: $1,763, MS-64, September 2015; $1,175, MS-64, October 2015; $423, MS-62, April 2015; $135, AU-55, January 2015												
1901-S	593,022	164	31.6	23%	$80	$135	$375	$500	$550	$750	$1,250	$2,000	$4,500
	Auctions: $2,350, MS-64, September 2015; $377, AU-50, May 2015; $376, EF-40, November 2015; $259, VF-30, January 2015												
1902	21,380,000	248	55.7	65%	$4	$5	$6	$8	$25	$75	$125	$225	$525
	Auctions: $259, MS-64, January 2015; $212, MS-64, August 2015; $200, MS-64, September 2015; $100, AU-58, March 2015												
1902, Proof	777	211	64.2								$285	$500	$1,000
	Auctions: $1,116, PF-66, October 2015; $999, PF-65, January 2015; $646, PF-64, January 2015; $423, PF-63, November 2015												
1902-O	4,500,000	119	54.1	54%	$4	$6	$15	$32	$65	$175	$400	$700	$4,000
	Auctions: $1,410, MS-64, September 2015; $1,399, MS-64, September 2015; $356, AU-58, January 2015; $123, AU-53, April 2015												
1902-S	2,070,000	92	49.7	51%	$9	$20	$55	$80	$140	$200	$400	$650	$2,750
	Auctions: $235, AU-58, August 2015; $153, AU-55, January 2015; $106, AU-50, May 2015; $94, VF-35, February 2015												

e. More than one repunched date exists for 1897. This listing is for FS-10-1897-301 (see the *Cherrypickers' Guide to Rare Die Varieties*, sixth edition, volume II), one of the most dramatic RPDs of the series. The secondary digits of the date are evident west of the primary digits. f. Included in circulation-strike 1897 mintage figure.

1905-O, Normal O   **1905-O, Micro O**

	Mintage	Cert	Avg	%MS	G-4	VG-8	F-12	VF-20	EF-40	AU-50	MS-60 PF-60	MS-63 PF-63	MS-65 PF-65
1903	19,500,000	175	57.3	70%	$4	$5	$6	$8	$25	$75	$125	$225	$800
	Auctions: $1,998, MS-66, May 2015; $1,528, MS-66, October 2015; $259, MS-64, January 2015; $165, MS-63, January 2015												
1903, Proof	755	217	64.4								$285	$500	$1,000
	Auctions: $2,233, PF-67, October 2015; $1,058, PF-66, January 2015; $1,058, PF-66, July 2015; $329, PF-62, January 2015												
1903-O	8,180,000	188	54.0	43%	$5	$6	$14	$25	$55	$110	$275	$550	$3,000
	Auctions: $8,813, MS-67, May 2015; $2,350, MS-65, July 2015; $881, MS-64, February 2015; $306, AU-58, July 2015												
1903-S	613,300	145	29.5	19%	$85	$130	$375	$500	$675	$825	$1,100	$1,350	$2,500
	Auctions: $3,055, MS-66, May 2015; $2,820, MS-66, June 2015; $1,058, AU-58, January 2015; $282, AU-50, October 2015												
1904	14,600,357	205	59.1	77%	$4	$5	$6	$9	$25	$75	$125	$250	$900
	Auctions: $2,585, MS-66, May 2015; $1,763, MS-66, January 2015; $306, MS-64, January 2015; $50, AU-58, January 2015												
1904, Proof	670	227	64.3								$285	$500	$1,000
	Auctions: $2,233, PF-67Cam, March 2015; $1,821, PF-67, January 2015; $1,080, PF-66, October 2015; $1,146, PF-65Cam, January 2015												
1904-S	800,000	141	39.6	35%	$45	$75	$160	$250	$325	$500	$850	$1,200	$4,500
	Auctions: $10,117, MS-66, January 2015; $400, AU-55, August 2015; $376, AU-55, May 2015; $153, EF-40, January 2015												
1905	14,551,623	211	57.2	68%	$4	$5	$6	$10	$25	$75	$125	$240	$600
	Auctions: $1,528, MS-66, January 2015; $1,293, MS-66, September 2015; $517, MS-65, September 2015; $235, MS-64, September 2015												
1905, Proof	727	212	64.7								$285	$500	$1,000
	Auctions: $4,465, PF-68, January 2015; $2,800, PF-67, July 2015; $1,000, PF-65Cam, June 2015; $940, PF-65, July 2015												
1905-O	3,400,000	169	54.6	69%	$5	$10	$35	$60	$100	$150	$300	$425	$1,100
	Auctions: $1,998, MS-66, October 2015; $1,645, MS-65, October 2015; $564, MS-64, January 2015; $153, AU-58, August 2015												
1905-O, Micro O	(g)	48	30.7	13%	$60	$90	$150	$300	$725	$1,150	$2,700	$5,500	$12,500
	Auctions: $4,113, MS-62, June 2014; $282, VF-25, August 2014; $223, VF-25, October 2014												
1905-S	6,855,199	194	56.3	59%	$4	$6	$9	$20	$40	$95	$250	$325	$1,000
	Auctions: $1,528, MS-66, October 2015; $141, MS-61, January 2015; $69, MS-60, October 2015												
1906	19,957,731	400	58.6	75%	$4	$5	$6	$10	$25	$75	$125	$200	$475
	Auctions: $3,525, MS-67, July 2015; $259, MS-64, May 2015; $212, MS-64, July 2015; $165, MS-63, April 2015												
1906, Proof	675	188	64.6								$285	$500	$1,000
	Auctions: $1,645, PF-67, January 2015; $1,050, PF-65, January 2015; $646, PF-64, January 2015; $447, PF-63, October 2015												
1906-D	4,060,000	120	54.8	70%	$4	$5	$8	$15	$35	$80	$175	$350	$1,100
	Auctions: $3,055, MS-66, May 2015; $646, MS-64, July 2015; $182, MS-62, August 2015; $118, AU-58, October 2015												
1906-O	2,610,000	149	57.8	79%	$6	$14	$45	$75	$110	$130	$200	$300	$1,000
	Auctions: $4,935, MS-67, August 2015; $1,116, MS-66, January 2015; $764, MS-65, June 2015; $153, MS-60, February 2015												
1906-S	3,136,640	127	57.6	72%	$4	$6	$13	$25	$45	$110	$275	$450	$825
	Auctions: $4,465, MS-66, May 2015; $1,763, MS-66, August 2015; $999, MS-64, August 2015; $212, AU-58, August 2015												
1907	22,220,000	476	57.5	75%	$4	$5	$6	$10	$25	$75	$125	$225	$475
	Auctions: $705, MS-66, August 2015; $329, MS-65, May 2015; $259, MS-64, January 2015; $165, MS-63, May 2015												
1907, Proof	575	183	64.7								$285	$500	$1,000
	Auctions: $6,463, PF-68, May 2015; $2,115, PF-67, January 2015; $1,351, PF-66, January 2015; $600, PF-64, January 2015												
1907-D	4,080,000	87	57.3	71%	$4	$5	$10	$20	$45	$110	$300	$600	$1,500
	Auctions: $1,293, MS-65, June 2015; $1,175, MS-64, July 2015; $1,058, MS-64, July 2015; $494, MS-63, June 2015												
1907-O	5,058,000	168	57.1	74%	$4	$7	$30	$45	$70	$110	$200	$325	$900
	Auctions: $1,645, MS-66, January 2015; $400, MS-64, February 2015; $153, MS-63, May 2015; $212, MS-62, June 2015												
1907-S	3,178,470	111	54.8	50%	$4	$6	$15	$27	$75	$150	$400	$700	$1,850
	Auctions: $1,070, MS-64, July 2015; $482, MS-62, February 2015; $79, AU-55, January 2015; $106, AU-50, July 2015												

g. Included in 1905-O mintage figure.

	Mintage	Cert	Avg	%MS	G-4	VG-8	F-12	VF-20	EF-40	AU-50	MS-60	MS-63	MS-65
											PF-60	PF-63	PF-65
1908	10,600,000	337	59.5	82%	$4	$5	$6	$10	$25	$75	$125	$225	$475
	Auctions: $1,293, MS-66, June 2015; $499, MS-65, January 2015; $259, MS-64, February 2015; $240, MS-64, July 2015												
1908, Proof	545	191	64.7								$285	$500	$1,000
	Auctions: $1,528, PF-67, September 2015; $1,410, PF-66, June 2015; $940, PF-65, January 2015; $622, PF-64, June 2015												
1908-D	7,490,000	207	54.8	61%	$4	$5	$6	$10	$30	$75	$130	$300	$750
	Auctions: $646, MS-65, July 2015; $588, MS-65, February 2015; $200, MS-63, July 2015; $60, AU-53, February 2015												
1908-O	1,789,000	125	54.3	66%	$6	$12	$45	$65	$95	$150	$300	$500	$1,000
	Auctions: $1,528, MS-66, August 2015; $764, MS-64, June 2015; $447, MS-63, June 2015; $182, AU-58, April 2015												
1908-S	3,220,000	97	55.4	55%	$4	$6	$15	$25	$45	$170	$350	$500	$1,350
	Auctions: $4,700, MS-67, August 2015; $153, AU-53, July 2015; $42, EF-45, January 2015												
1909	10,240,000	316	58.8	80%	$4	$5	$6	$10	$25	$75	$125	$225	$475
	Auctions: $881, MS-66, May 2015; $212, MS-64, April 2015; $170, MS-63, July 2015; $118, MS-62, July 2015												
1909, Proof	650	257	64.6								$285	$500	$1,000
	Auctions: $1,528, PF-67, October 2015; $1,058, PF-65Cam, February 2015; $881, PF-65, January 2015; $646, PF-64, January 2015												
1909-D	954,000	115	54.5	65%	$8	$20	$60	$90	$140	$225	$500	$800	$1,850
	Auctions: $3,055, MS-66, May 2015; $212, AU-53, May 2015; $100, EF-40, July 2015												
1909-O	2,287,000	117	55.0	66%	$5	$8	$13	$25	$70	$150	$250	$575	$1,400
	Auctions: $4,935, MS-66, May 2015; $2,820, MS-66, July 2015; $999, MS-64, February 2015; $235, AU-53, April 2015												
1909-S	1,000,000	104	49.2	60%	$9	$20	$80	$130	$180	$310	$450	$750	$2,200
	Auctions: $9,400, MS-67, September 2015; $9,988, MS-66, May 2015; $517, MS-62, July 2015; $235, MS-60, October 2015												
1910	11,520,000	494	59.8	83%	$4	$5	$6	$10	$24	$75	$125	$225	$475
	Auctions: $1,410, MS-66, October 2015; $646, MS-65, February 2015; $259, MS-64, February 2015; $188, MS-63, February 2015												
1910, Proof	551	219	64.7								$285	$500	$1,000
	Auctions: $8,813, PF-68, May 2015; $1,880, PF-67, August 2015; $1,058, PF-66, October 2015; $646, PF-64, January 2015												
1910-D	3,490,000	97	56.5	68%	$4	$5	$10	$20	$48	$95	$220	$300	$1,200
	Auctions: $3,643, MS-66, January 2015; $1,293, MS-64, June 2015; $588, MS-63, August 2015; $353, AU-58, October 2015												
1910-S	1,240,000	79	50.9	52%	$6	$9	$50	$70	$110	$180	$425	$550	$1,900
	Auctions: $7,344, MS-67, June 2014; $2,820, MS-66, July 2014; $411, MS-62, July 2014												
1911	18,870,000	998	59.6	82%	$4	$5	$6	$10	$24	$75	$125	$225	$475
	Auctions: $1,116, MS-66, September 2015; $401, MS-65, August 2015; $243, MS-64, February 2015; $165, MS-63, May 2015												
1911, Proof	543	224	64.9								$285	$500	$1,000
	Auctions: $3,760, PF-67Cam, January 2015; $1,528, PF-66Cam, July 2015; $860, PF-65, September 2015; $646, PF-64, January 2015												
1911-D	11,209,000	276	57.2	71%	$4	$5	$6	$10	$24	$75	$125	$225	$425
	Auctions: $3,525, MS-67, June 2015; $370, MS-65, September 2015; $306, MS-64, September 2015; $118, MS-62, May 2015												
1911-S	3,520,000	196	60.4	82%	$4	$5	$10	$20	$40	$100	$200	$375	$750
	Auctions: $4,818, MS-67, September 2015; $1,410, MS-66, August 2015; $734, MS-65, July 2015; $529, MS-64, February 2015												
1912	19,349,300	1,030	59.3	80%	$4	$5	$6	$10	$24	$75	$125	$225	$475
	Auctions: $2,056, MS-67, May 2015; $911, MS-66, January 2015; $400, MS-65, August 2015; $240, MS-64, January 2015												
1912, Proof	700	181	64.4								$285	$500	$1,000
	Auctions: $2,350, PF-67, August 2015; $1,020, PF-65, September 2015; $999, PF-65, January 2015; $588, PF-64, January 2015												
1912-D	11,760,000	371	54.1	64%	$4	$5	$6	$10	$24	$75	$125	$225	$600
	Auctions: $6,169, MS-67, August 2015; $6,169, MS-66, May 2015; $517, MS-65, September 2015; $306, MS-64, November 2015												
1912-S	3,420,000	181	59.5	72%	$4	$5	$6	$12	$32	$90	$170	$300	$625
	Auctions: $1,293, MS-66, June 2013; $999, MS-65, May 2015; $206, MS-62, July 2014; $206, MS-62, August 2014												

	Mintage	Cert	Avg	%MS	G-4	VG-8	F-12	VF-20	EF-40	AU-50	MS-60 / PF-60	MS-63 / PF-63	MS-65 / PF-65
1913	19,760,000	902	57.3	75%	$4	$5	$6	$10	$24	$75	$125	$225	$425
Auctions: $564, MS-66, October 2015; $999, MS-65, October 2015; $200, MS-64, April 2015; $118, MS-62, April 2015													
1913, Proof	622	199	64.1								$285	$500	$1,000
Auctions: $4,935, PF-67Cam, May 2015; $3,290, PF-66Cam, July 2015; $2,056, PF-66, October 2015; $1,036, PF-65, September 2015													
1913-S	510,000	261	33.0	34%	$35	$55	$125	$190	$250	$320	$500	$1,100	$2,700
Auctions: $2,967, MS-66, October 2015; $1,058, MS-63, June 2015; $881, MS-63, October 2015; $617, MS-61, June 2015													
1914	17,360,230	920	58.4	80%	$4	$5	$6	$10	$24	$75	$125	$200	$475
Auctions: $2,703, MS-67, January 2015; $1,763, MS-66, June 2015; $564, MS-65, January 2015; $259, MS-64, October 2015													
1914, Proof	425	163	64.5								$285	$500	$1,000
Auctions: $3,055, PF-67, January 2015; $650, PF-64, January 2015; $470, PF-63, October 2015													
1914-D	11,908,000	573	55.2	67%	$4	$5	$6	$10	$24	$75	$125	$200	$475
Auctions: $823, MS-66, October 2015; $470, MS-65, January 2015; $165, MS-63, February 2015; $118, AU-58, May 2015													
1914-S	2,100,000	171	58.3	77%	$4	$5	$10	$18	$40	$80	$175	$250	$900
Auctions: $1,645, MS-66, October 2015; $881, MS-65, August 2015; $646, MS-64, March 2015; $400, MS-64, February 2015													
1915	5,620,000	380	58.4	80%	$4	$5	$6	$10	$24	$75	$125	$225	$425
Auctions: $1,880, MS-67, June 2015; $1,175, MS-66, May 2015; $235, MS-64, February 2015; $141, MS-62, January 2015													
1915, Proof	450	142	64.3								$285	$500	$1,000
Auctions: $1,763, PF-67, January 2015; $999, PF-65, August 2015; $940, PF-64, October 2015; $153, PF-60, August 2015													
1915-S	960,000	150	55.4	62%	$7	$12	$35	$50	$70	$140	$275	$400	$1,150
Auctions: $1,998, MS-66, January 2015; $1,200, MS-65, June 2015; $823, MS-64, August 2015; $517, MS-64, October 2015													
1916	18,490,000	1,346	58.8	79%	$4	$5	$6	$10	$24	$75	$125	$225	$425
Auctions: $646, MS-66, January 2015; $588, MS-65, January 2015; $242, MS-64, January 2015; $120, MS-62, January 2015													
1916-S	5,820,000	352	59.4	76%	$4	$5	$6	$10	$24	$75	$125	$240	$600
Auctions: $2,233, MS-66, January 2015; $1,058, MS-66, June 2015; $282, MS-64, May 2015; $188, MS-63, October 2015													

WINGED LIBERTY HEAD OR "MERCURY" (1916–1945)

Designer: *Adolph A. Weinman.* **Weight:** *2.50 grams.* **Composition:** *.900 silver, .100 copper (net weight .07234 oz. pure silver).* **Diameter:** *17.9 mm.* **Edge:** *Reeded.* **Mints:** *Philadelphia, Denver, and San Francisco.*

Circulation Strike

Mintmark location is on the reverse, at the base of the branch.

Proof

History. In 1916 a new dime, designed by sculptor Adolph A. Weinman (who also created the half dollar that debuted that year), replaced Charles Barber's Liberty Head type. Officially Weinman's design was known as the Winged Liberty Head, but numismatists commonly call the coin the *Mercury* dime, from Miss Liberty's wing-capped resemblance to the Roman god. The reverse depicts a fasces (symbolic of strength in unity) and an olive branch (symbolic of peaceful intentions). Production was continuous from 1916 to 1945, except for 1922, 1932, and 1933. The Mint also created a 2016 gold Mercury dime at a smaller dimension. See page 449.

Striking and Sharpness. Many Mercury dimes exhibit areas of light striking, most notably in the center horizontal band across the fasces, less so in the lower horizontal band. The bands are composed of two parallel lines with a separation or "split" between. The term Full Bands, abbreviated FB, describes coins with both parallel lines in the center band distinctly separated. *In addition*, some dimes may display weak striking in other areas (not noted by certification services or others), including at areas of Liberty's hair, the rim, and the date. Dimes of 1921 in particular can have FB but poorly struck dates. Proof dies were completely polished, including the portrait.

Availability. Certain coins, such as 1916-D; 1921-P; 1921-D; 1942, 2 Over 1; and 1942-D, 2 Over 1, are elusive in any grade. Others are generally available in lower circulated grades, although some are scarce. In MS many of the issues before 1931 range from scarce to rare. If with FB and also sharply struck in other areas, some are rare. MS coins usually are very lustrous. In the marketplace certain scarce early issues such as 1916-D, 1921, and 1921-D are often graded slightly more liberally than are later varieties. Proofs were minted from 1936 to 1942 and are available in proportion to their mintages.

GRADING STANDARDS

MS-60 to 70 (Mint State). *Obverse:* At MS-60, some abrasion and contact marks are evident on the highest part of the portrait, including the hair immediately to the right of the face and the upper left part of the wing. At MS-63, abrasion is slight at best, less so for MS-64. Album slide marks on the cheek, if present, should not be at any grade above MS-64. An MS-65 coin should display no abrasion or contact marks except under mag-

1928. Graded MS-66FB.

nification, and MS-66 and higher coins should have none at all. Luster should be full and rich. *Reverse:* Comments apply as for the obverse, except that the highest parts of the fasces, these being the horizontal bands, are the places to check. The field is mainly protected by design elements and does not show contact marks readily.

AU-50, 53, 55, 58 (About Uncirculated). *Obverse:* Light wear is seen on the cheek, the hair immediately to the right of the face, the left edge of the wing, and the upper right of the wing. At AU-58, the luster is extensive, but incomplete, especially on the higher parts and in the field. At AU–50 and 53, luster is less. *Reverse:* Light wear is seen on the higher parts of the fasces. An AU-58 coin has nearly full luster, more so than on the obverse, as the

1942, 2 Over 1. Graded AU-50.

design elements protect the field areas. At AU–50 and 53, there still is significant luster. Generally, the reverse appears to be in a slightly higher grade than the obverse.

EF-40, 45 (Extremely Fine). *Obverse:* Further wear is seen on the head. Many of the hair details are blended together, as are some feather details at the left side of the wing. *Reverse:* The horizontal bands on the fasces may be fused together. The diagonal bands remain in slight relief against the vertical lines (sticks).

1942-D, 2 Over 1; FS-101. Graded EF-45.

VF-20, 30 (Very Fine). *Obverse:* The head shows more wear, now with the forehead and cheek mostly blending into the hair. More feather details are gone. *Reverse:* Wear is more extensive, but the diagonal and horizontal bands on the fasces still are separated from the thin vertical sticks.

1942-D, 2 Over 1; FS-101. Graded VF-20.

F-12, 15 (Fine). *Obverse:* The head shows more wear, the hair has only slight detail, and most of the feathers are gone. In the marketplace a coin in F-12 grade usually has slightly less detail than stated by the ANA grading standards or *Photograde*, from modern interpretations. *Reverse:* Many of the tiny vertical sticks in the fasces are blended together. The bands can be barely discerned and may be worn away at the highest-relief parts.

1916-D. Graded F-12.

VG-8, 10 (Very Good). *Obverse:* Wear is more extensive on the portrait, and only a few feathers are seen on the wing. The outlines between the hair and cap and of the wing are distinct. Lettering is clear, but light in areas. *Reverse:* The rim is complete, or it may be slightly worn away in areas. Only a few traces of the vertical sticks remain in the fasces. Current interpretations in the marketplace are given here and are less strict than those

1921. Graded VG-8.

listed by the ANA grading standards and *Photograde*. Often, earlier issues are graded more liberally than are later dates.

G-4, 6 (Good). *Obverse:* Wear is more extensive, with not all of the outline between the hair and the wing visible. The rim is worn into the edges of the letters and often into the bottom of the last numeral in the date. *Reverse:* The rim is worn away, as are the outer parts of the letters. The fasces is flat or may show a hint of a vertical stick or two. The leaves are thick from wear. The mintmark, if any, is easily seen.

1916-D. Graded G-4.

AG-3 (About Good). *Obverse:* The rim is worn further into the letters. The head is mostly outline all over, except for a few indicates of edges. Folds remain at the top of the cap. The date is clearly visible. *Reverse:* The rim is worn further into the letters. The mintmark, if any, is clear but may be worn away slightly at the bottom. The apparent wear is slightly greater on the reverse than on the obverse.

1916-D. Graded AG-3.

PF-60 to 70 (Proof). *Obverse and Reverse:* Proofs that are extensively cleaned and have many hairlines, or that are dull and grainy, are lower level, such as PF–60 to 62. These are not widely desired, and represent coins that have been mistreated. With medium hairlines and good reflectivity, assigned grades of PF–63 or 64 are appropriate. Tiny horizontal lines on Miss Liberty's cheek, known as *slide marks*, from National and other album slides

1942. Graded PF-67.

scuffing the relief of the cheek, are common; coins with such marks should not be graded higher than PF-64, but sometimes are. With relatively few hairlines and no noticeable slide marks, a rating of PF-65 can be given. PF-66 should have hairlines so delicate that magnification is needed to see them. Above that, a Proof should be free of any hairlines or other problems.

Full Bands

	Mintage	Cert	Avg	%MS	G-4	VG-8	F-12	VF-20	EF-40	AU-50	MS-60	MS-63	MS-65
1916	22,180,080	2,848	62.4	94%	$4	$5	$7	$8	$15	$25	$35	$48	$150
	Auctions: $1,116, MS-67, October 2015; $106, MS-65, November 2015; $153, MS-64, July 2016; $541, AU-58, August 2016												
1916-D † (a)	264,000	4,785	9.9	5%	$800	$1,500	$2,500	$4,000	$6,000	$8,250	$12,500	$16,000	$25,000
	Auctions: $6,463, AU-53, July 2016; $3,995, VF-25, August 2016; $646, G-4, September 2016; $1,116, VG-8, October 2016												

† Ranked in the *100 Greatest U.S. Coins* (fourth edition). **a.** Beware of altered or otherwise spurious mintmarks.

	Mintage	Cert	Avg	%MS	G-4	VG-8	F-12	VF-20	EF-40	AU-50	MS-60	MS-63	MS-65
1916-S	10,450,000	1,027	58.4	86%	$4	$6	$9	$12	$20	$25	$42	$65	$215
	Auctions: $646, MS-65, July 2016; $165, MS-64, August 2016; $1,116, MS-66, October 2016; $400, MS-66, November 2016												
1917	55,230,000	863	62.3	88%	$3	$3.25	$3.50	$6	$8	$12	$30	$60	$170
	Auctions: $235, MS-65, March 2016; $564, MS-66, August 2016; $611, MS-66, September 2016; $1,998, MS-67, October 2016												
1917-D	9,402,000	592	60.7	79%	$4.50	$6	$11	$22	$45	$95	$145	$350	$1,050
	Auctions: -$1, MS-65, July 2015; $5,875, MS-65, October 2015; $118, AU-58, July 2016; $2,938, MS-65, October 2016												
1917-S	27,330,000	610	61.3	82%	$3	$3.25	$4	$7	$12	$30	$60	$180	$500
	Auctions: $1,293, MS-66, December 2015; $823, MS-65, March 2016; $1,410, MS-66, August 2016; $881, MS-66, September 2016												
1918	26,680,000	455	62.0	86%	$3	$4	$6	$12	$25	$40	$70	$125	$425
	Auctions: $1,175, MS-65, October 2015; $940, MS-65, December 2015; $1,058, MS-66, July 2016; $3,290, MS-66, October 2016												
1918-D	22,674,800	534	60.7	83%	$3	$4	$6	$12	$24	$50	$125	$250	$800
	Auctions: $1,880, MS-66, September 2015; $1,763, MS-62, December 2015; $165, AU-58, July 2016; $1,116, MS-62, September 2016												
1918-S	19,300,000	416	61.4	85%	$3	$3.25	$5	$10	$18	$40	$120	$275	$725
	Auctions: $1,528, MS-66, December 2015; $2,820, MS-64, September 2016; $881, MS-66, October 2016; $646, MS-65, November 2016												
1919	35,740,000	518	61.8	86%	$3	$3.25	$4	$6	$10	$30	$45	$150	$375
	Auctions: $1,058, MS-66, October 2015; $1,763, MS-66, December 2015; $141, MS-61, July 2016; $517, MS-65, August 2016												
1919-D	9,939,000	391	60.3	83%	$4	$7	$12	$24	$35	$75	$200	$450	$1,600
	Auctions: $646, MS-64, December 2015; $329, MS-62, May 2016; $3,290, MS-64, August 2016; $1,763, MS-65, October 2016												
1919-S	8,850,000	289	59.0	65%	$3.50	$4	$8	$16	$35	$75	$200	$450	$1,500
	Auctions: $1,645, MS-65, August 2015; $1,645, MS-66, October 2015; $764, MS-64, November 2015; $881, MS-64, August 2016												
1920	59,030,000	799	63.2	95%	$3	$3.25	$3.50	$5	$8	$15	$35	$75	$260
	Auctions: $646, MS-66, March 2016; $494, MS-66, July 2016; $881, MS-66, August 2016; $423, MS-66, September 2016												
1920-D	19,171,000	431	61.0	82%	$3	$3.50	$4.50	$8	$20	$45	$145	$350	$775
	Auctions: $2,115, MS-65, October 2015; $1,175, MS-64, September 2016; $2,585, MS-65, October 2016; $4,230, MS-66, November 2016												
1920-S	13,820,000	302	61.1	79%	$3.25	$4	$5	$8	$18	$45	$145	$325	$1,450
	Auctions: $5,170, MS-65, July 2015; $4,935, MS-65, August 2015; $4,700, MS-65, December 2015; $259, AU-58, July 2016												
1921	1,230,000	1,605	22.3	15%	$45	$75	$125	$250	$550	$850	$1,250	$2,250	$3,500
	Auctions: $538,286, VF-25, January 2016; $8,905, EF-45, April 2016; $1,763, AU-58, August 2016; $6,463, MS-66, November 2016												
1921-D	1,080,000	1,698	22.1	15%	$60	$130	$200	$350	$675	$1,200	$1,450	$2,500	$3,750
	Auctions: $423, EF-45, June 2016; $259, VF-20, July 2016; $564, AU-50, August 2016; $3,290, MS-64, October 2016												
1923 (b)	50,130,000	935	63.0	93%	$3	$3.25	$3.50	$5	$7	$16	$30	$45	$130
	Auctions: $1,116, MS-67, August 2015; $588, MS-66, November 2015; $259, MS-65, July 2016; $1,175, MS-67, November 2016												
1923-S	6,440,000	330	59.4	74%	$3	$4	$8	$18	$65	$105	$160	$400	$1,250
	Auctions: $1,704, MS-66, July 2015; $1,293, MS-65, August 2015; $2,115, MS-64, October 2015; $65, 0, September 2016												
1924	24,010,000	540	63.8	95%	$3	$3.25	$4	$6	$15	$30	$45	$100	$210
	Auctions: $2,115, MS-67, October 2015; $823, MS-66, November 2015; $2,115, MS-67, August 2016; $3,760, MS-67, September 2016												
1924-D	6,810,000	453	60.5	82%	$3.50	$4.50	$8	$24	$70	$110	$175	$500	$950
	Auctions: $1,175, MS-65, October 2015; $1,058, MS-65, March 2016; $764, MS-63, July 2016; $3,995, MS-65, October 2016												
1924-S	7,120,000	362	60.0	77%	$3.50	$4	$6	$10	$60	$110	$200	$525	$1,250
	Auctions: $7,638, MS-65, July 2016; $400, MS-61, August 2016; $14,100, MS-65, September 2016; $3,055, MS-65, October 2016												
1925	25,610,000	346	62.7	89%	$3	$3.25	$4	$5	$10	$20	$30	$85	$225
	Auctions: $588, MS-65, July 2016; $494, MS-65, September 2016; $447, MS-65, October 2016; $517, MS-65, November 2016												
1925-D	5,117,000	301	58.7	67%	$4	$5	$12	$45	$120	$200	$375	$750	$1,700
	Auctions: $664, MS-62, November 2015; $2,585, MS-65, December 2015; $165, AU-55, May 2016; $6,463, MS-66, July 2016												
1925-S	5,850,000	261	60.2	75%	$3.25	$4	$8	$18	$70	$110	$180	$500	$1,400
	Auctions: $341, MS-63, February 2015; $1,998, MS-64, September 2015; $2,585, MS-65, October 2015; $1,116, MS-64, December 2015												
1926	32,160,000	718	63.2	93%	$3	$3.25	$3.50	$5	$7	$16	$25	$65	$250
	Auctions: $1,645, MS-66, March 2016; $3,760, MS-67, August 2016; $823, MS-66, September 2016; $529, MS-66, November 2016												
1926-D	6,828,000	466	61.3	85%	$3.25	$4.50	$6	$10	$28	$50	$125	$275	$600
	Auctions: $1,763, MS-65, December 2015; $306, MS-64, May 2016; $3,290, MS-66, August 2016; $3,525, MS-66, September 2016												

b. Dimes dated 1923-D or 1930-D are counterfeit.

1928-S, Small S   **1928-S, Large S**   **1929-S, Doubled Die Obverse**
           FS-10-1928S-501.   *FS-10-1929S-101.*

	Mintage	Cert	Avg	%MS	G-4	VG-8	F-12	VF-20	EF-40	AU-50	MS-60	MS-63	MS-65
1926-S	1,520,000	405	45.4	32%	$13	$15	$26	$60	$250	$450	$1,100	$1,750	$3,500
Auctions: $676, AU-58, July 2015; $705, AU-58, November 2015; $5,888, MS-65, September 2016; $5,170, MS-65, November 2016
1927	28,080,000	541	62.3	91%	$3	$3.25	$3.50	$5	$7	$15	$30	$60	$150
Auctions: $1,116, MS-66, August 2016; $2,585, MS-67, September 2016; $2,115, MS-67, October 2016; $494, MS-66, November 2016
1927-D	4,812,000	281	58.9	69%	$3.50	$5.50	$8	$25	$80	$100	$200	$400	$1,200
Auctions: $881, MS-65, August 2015; $1,410, MS-64, October 2015; $7,931, MS-64, August 2016; $8,813, MS-66, November 2016
1927-S	4,770,000	241	60.0	76%	$3.25	$4	$6	$12	$28	$50	$275	$550	$1,400
Auctions: $1,410, 63, August 2015; $6,463, MS-65, October 2015; $5,405, MS-65, August 2016; $5,640, MS-65, October 2016
1928	19,480,000	465	63.7	95%	$3	$3.25	$3.50	$5	$7	$18	$30	$55	$130
Auctions: $1,528, MS-67, October 2015; $999, MS-66, November 2015; $423, MS-66, August 2016; $494, MS-66, September 2016
1928-D	4,161,000	281	59.5	78%	$4	$5	$8	$20	$50	$95	$175	$360	$850
Auctions: $1,058, MS-64, September 2015; $1,645, MS-65, October 2015; $353, MS-62, August 2016; $1,293, MS-64, September 2016
1928-S (c)	7,400,000	5	56.4	40%	$3	$3.25	$4	$6	$16	$45	$150	$320	$400
Auctions: $2,820, MS-65, March 2016; $329, MS-62, July 2016; $3,878, MS-66, August 2016; $3,290, MS-66, October 2016
1929	25,970,000	891	64.1	96%	$3	$3.25	$3.50	$5	$6	$12	$22	$35	$75
Auctions: $212, MS-65, November 2015; $1,528, MS-67, July 2016; $1,293, MS-67, August 2016; $1,293, MS-67, October 2016
1929-D	5,034,000	1,219	64.3	98%	$3	$3.50	$5	$8	$15	$24	$30	$36	$75
Auctions: $470, MS-66, July 2016; $1,998, MS-67, August 2016; $1,293, MS-67, September 2016; $1,998, MS-67, October 2016
1929-S	4,730,000	401	63.2	91%	$3	$3.25	$3.75	$5	$10	$20	$35	$45	$125
Auctions: $2,585, MS-67, October 2015; $764, MS-66, December 2015; $2,056, MS-67, August 2016; $3,290, MS-67, September 2016
1929-S, Doubled Die Obverse (d)	(e)	4	58.5	50%								$150	$200
Auctions: $170, AU-58, December 2009
1930 (b)	6,770,000	444	63.3	92%	$3	$3.25	$3.50	$5	$8	$16	$30	$50	$125
Auctions: $2,115, MS-66, February 2015; $7,050, MS-67, June 2015; $3,055, MS-66, October 2015; $999, MS-66, November 2016
1930-S	1,843,000	307	62.7	90%	$3	$4	$5	$7	$15	$45	$80	$150	$210
Auctions: $5,170, MS-67, July 2016; $1,763, MS-66, August 2016; $1,645, MS-66, October 2016; $600, MS-67, November 2016
1931	3,150,000	458	63.3	92%	$3	$3.10	$4	$6	$10	$22	$35	$70	$150
Auctions: $823, MS-66, November 2015; $823, MS-66, July 2016; $494, MS-65, August 2016; $1,175, MS-66, October 2016
1931-D	1,260,000	560	62.2	90%	$8	$9	$12	$20	$35	$60	$90	$140	$280
Auctions: $1,175, MS-67, December 2015; $329, MS-66, June 2016; $881, MS-66, September 2016; $1,528, MS-67, October 2016
1931-S	1,800,000	419	60.4	84%	$4	$5	$6	$10	$16	$45	$90	$150	$300
Auctions: $2,233, MS-66, September 2015; $1,998, MS-65, October 2015; $15,275, MS-67, August 2016; $646, MS-64, November 2016

b. Dimes dated 1923-D or 1930-D are counterfeit. **c.** Two mintmark styles exist: Large S (scarce) and Small S (common). About 80% of 1928-S dimes are of the Small S style. The scarcer Large S is worth about two to three times the values listed (which are for the Small S). **d.** Moderate doubling is evident on the date and IN GOD WE TRUST. **e.** Included in 1929-S mintage figure.

	Mintage	Cert	Avg	%MS	F-12	VF-20	EF-40	AU-50	MS-60	MS-63	MS-65	MS-65FB	MS-66
											PF-65	PF-66	PF-67
1934	24,080,000	1,005	64.5	96%	$2.75	$3	$3.25	$16	$25	$35	$50	$140	$65
Auctions: $588, MS-67, March 2016; $129, MS-66, July 2016; $470, MS-67, August 2016; $470, MS-67, November 2016
1934-D	6,772,000	688	64.3	96%	$2.75	$3	$8	$33	$50	$60	$85	$325	$230
Auctions: $881, MS-67, October 2015; $1,175, MS-67, December 2015; $705, MS-67, August 2016; $646, MS-66, September 2016

1936-S, Possible Overdate
FS-10-1936S-110.

	Mintage	Cert	Avg	%MS	F-12	VF-20	EF-40	AU-50	MS-60	MS-63	MS-65 PF-65	MS-65FB PF-66	MS-66 PF-67
1935	58,830,000	1,488	65.1	97%	$2.75	$3	$3.25	$7	$10	$15	$35	$75	$60
Auctions: $705, MS-67, November 2015; $153, MS-66, March 2016; $223, MS-66, July 2016; $881, MS-67, September 2016													
1935-D	10,477,000	506	63.8	94%	$2.75	$3	$8	$26	$35	$50	$90	$525	$325
Auctions: $28,200, 0, March 2016; $2,174, MS-67, August 2016; $353, MS-65, October 2016; $940, MS-66, November 2016													
1935-S	15,840,000	628	64.9	98%	$2.75	$3	$5	$16	$22	$30	$40	$350	$80
Auctions: $65, MS-66, February 2015; $1,058, MS-67, November 2015; $1,998, MS-67, December 2015; $881, MS-66, August 2016													
1936	87,500,000	2,040	65.1	97%	$2.75	$3	$3.25	$7	$10	$18	$30	$90	$48
Auctions: $646, MS-67, November 2015; $940, MS-67, July 2016; $2,938, MS-68, August 2016; $646, MS-67, November 2016													
1936, Proof	4,130	1,078	64.9								$1,050	$1,150	$2,600
Auctions: $2,350, PF-67, March 2016; $1,469, MS-66, August 2016; $1,880, MS-67, October 2016; $705, MS-64, November 2016													
1936-D	16,132,000	612	64.2	93%	$2.75	$3	$6	$16	$25	$40	$55	$275	$80
Auctions: $1,351, MS-67, August 2015; $826, MS-67, November 2015; $1,645, MS-67, December 2015; $588, MS-67, September 2016													
1936-S	9,210,000	1,105	65.4	99%	$2.75	$3	$3.25	$13	$23	$30	$38	$95	$55
Auctions: $423, MS-67, September 2015; $705, MS-67, November 2015; $564, MS-67, December 2015; $505, MS-67, July 2016													
1936-S, Possible Overdate (a)	**(b)**	0	n/a								$600		
Auctions: $1,500, MS-65FB, November 2011													
1937	56,860,000	4,136	65.7	99%	$2.75	$3	$3.25	$7	$10	$15	$30	$60	$40
Auctions: $764, MS-68, January 2015; $541, MS-68, June 2015; $129, MS-67, August 2016													
1937, Proof	5,756	1,253	65.4								$525	$550	$750
Auctions: $1,528, PF-68, March 2016; $3,525, MS-68, August 2016; $646, MS-67, September 2016; $447, MS-67, October 2016													
1937-D	14,146,000	1,004	65.3	97%	$2.75	$3	$4	$12	$21	$30	$45	$100	$85
Auctions: $541, MS-67, January 2015; $353, MS-66, February 2015; $353, MS-67, July 2016; $2,820, MS-68, August 2016													
1937-S	9,740,000	1,100	65.4	98%	$2.75	$3	$3.25	$12	$20	$30	$40	$185	$80
Auctions: $2,233, MS-67, August 2015; $541, MS-67, November 2015; $552, MS-67, July 2016; $588, MS-67, August 2016													
1938	22,190,000	1,654	65.5	99%	$2.75	$3	$3.25	$7	$10	$15	$30	$85	$55
Auctions: $740, MS-67, June 2015; $940, MS-67, August 2015; $646, MS-67, November 2015; $482, MS-67, July 2016													
1938, Proof	8,728	1,799	65.4								$300	$325	$600
Auctions: $646, MS-67, November 2015; $4,113, MS-68, December 2015; $423, MS-67, August 2016; $1,293, MS-67, November 2016													
1938-D	5,537,000	1,792	65.5	99%	$2.75	$3	$4	$11	$18	$25	$35	$65	$75
Auctions: $4,230, MS-68, December 2015; $212, MS-67, June 2016; $1,058, MS-67, August 2016; $1,116, MS-67, November 2016													
1938-S	8,090,000	1,011	65.2	97%	$2.75	$3	$3.50	$12	$20	$28	$42	$160	$80
Auctions: $823, MS-67, August 2015; $588, MS-67, November 2015; $564, MS-67, July 2016; $1,763, MS-67, August 2016													
1939	67,740,000	3,379	65.8	98%	$2.75	$3	$3.25	$6	$8	$12	$26	$180	$40
Auctions: $764, MS-67, November 2015; $4,935, MS-68, August 2016; $5,170, MS-68, September 2016; $999, MS-67, November 2016													
1939, Proof	9,321	2,003	65.9								$225	$235	$425
Auctions: $470, PF-67, November 2015; $1,116, PF-68, March 2016; $1,058, PF-68, August 2016; $423, MS-67, September 2016													
1939-D	24,394,000	3,503	65.7	99%	$2.75	$3	$3.25	$6	$8	$12	$32	$55	$60
Auctions: $7,638, MS-69, December 2015; $259, MS-66, March 2016; $1,528, MS-68, August 2016; $376, MS-68, September 2016													
1939-S	10,540,000	824	65.1	98%	$2.75	$3	$4	$13	$23	$30	$42	$625	$110
Auctions: $1,293, MS-66, August 2015; $2,585, MS-67, September 2015; $999, MS-66, November 2015; $3,995, MS-67, August 2016													

a. "The secondary image of a 2 is evident beneath the 3 of the date. Most evident is the flat portion of the base of the underlying 2. Remains of what is likely a secondary 9 are evident to the left of the primary 9. Many die polish marks are also evident throughout the surface of the obverse. No doubling is evident on other elements. . . . The length of time between the striking of the last 1929-dated coins and this 1936 coin would seem to eliminate the possibility of a 2 underlying the 3. However, examination has matched the shapes on the image under the 3 to that of the 2 on 1929-dated dimes. Stranger things have happened. Keep in mind that 1936 was during the Great Depression, when Mint personnel wanted to save money whenever possible." (*Cherrypickers' Guide to Rare Die Varieties*, sixth edition, volume II) **b.** Included in 1936-S mintage figure.

1941-S, Small S

1941-S, Large S
FS-10-1941S-511.

1942, 42 Over 41
FS-10-1942-101.

1942-D, 42 Over 41, Repunched Mintmark
FS-10-1942D-101.

	Mintage	Cert	Avg	%MS	F-12	VF-20	EF-40	AU-50	MS-60	MS-63	MS-65 / PF-65	MS-65FB / PF-66	MS-66 / PF-67
1940	65,350,000	3,515	65.7	98%	$2.75	$3	$3.25	$5	$7	$12	$30	$50	$45
Auctions: $400, MS-67FB, September 2015; $200, MS-67FB, August 2015; $165, MS-67FB, May 2015; $112, MS-67FB, February 2015													
1940, Proof	11,827	2,194	65.6								$180	$200	$325
Auctions: $1,293, MS-68, June 2015; $940, MS-68, December 2015; $141, PF-65, March 2016; $2,350, MS-68, October 2016													
1940-D	21,198,000	2,475	65.5	99%	$2.75	$3	$3.25	$5	$7	$14	$35	$50	$60
Auctions: $1,763, MS-68, February 2015; $999, MS-68, October 2015													
1940-S	21,560,000	2,594	65.6	99%	$2.75	$3	$3.25	$6	$8	$15	$35	$100	$40
Auctions: $617, MS-67, February 2015; $1,293, MS-67, November 2015; $470, MS-67, July 2016; $541, MS-67, August 2016													
1941	175,090,000	4,766	65.2	97%	$2.75	$3	$3.25	$5	$7	$12	$30	$50	$45
Auctions: $7,050, MS-68, July 2015; $646, MS-67, August 2015; $165, MS-67, March 2016; $999, MS-67, August 2016													
1941, Proof	16,557	2,809	65.5								$175	$200	$325
Auctions: $7,050, MS-68, October 2015; $141, PF-66, March 2016; $400, PF-67, August 2016; $2,468, MS-68, September 2016													
1941-D	45,634,000	3,518	65.3	98%	$2.75	$3	$3.25	$6	$8	$14	$25	$50	$32
Auctions: $24, MS-66, July 2015; $353, MS-67, November 2015; $212, MS-67, March 2016; $423, MS-68, August 2016													
1941-S	43,090,000	4,743	65.6	99%	$2.75	$3	$3.25	$5	$7	$12	$30	$50	$38
Auctions: $165, MS-67FB, May 2015; $259, MS-67FB, September 2015; $306, MS-67, March 2016; $400, MS-67, September 2016													
1941-S, Large S (c)	(d)	30	54.8	63%							$325		
Auctions: $217, MS-66, September 2015													
1942, 42 Over 41 (e)	(f)	1,878	39.5	6%	$450.00	$550	$650	$1,000	$2,500	**$4,750 (g)**	$15,000	$45,000	$20,000
Auctions: $1,116, AU-58, January 2015; $646, AU-53, January 2015; $470, EF-40, January 2015; $400, VF-30, February 2015													
1942	205,410,000	5,565	65.1	97%	$2.75	$3	$3.25	$4.50	$6	$12	$30	$50	$45
Auctions: $188, MS-67, March 2016; $646, MS-67, July 2016; $3,290, MS-68, August 2016; $3,525, MS-68, October 2016													
1942, Proof	22,329	4,111	65.7								$175	$200	$300
Auctions: $999, PF-68, March 2016; $940, MS-68, September 2016; $881, MS-68, October 2016; $4,113, MS-68, November 2016													
1942-D, 42 Over 41 (h)	(i)	1,070	36.4	9%	$425	$525	$600	$1,000	$2,500	**$4,750 (j)**	$10,000	$32,000	$12,000
Auctions: $940, AU-55, February 2015; $853, AU-50, January 2015; $588, EF-40, June 2015; $400, VF-25, February 2015													
1942-D	60,740,000	4,511	64.7	95%	$2.75	$3	$3.25	$4.50	$6	$12	$28	$48	$45
Auctions: $881, MS-68, October 2015; $141, MS-67, March 2016; $1,058, MS-68, August 2016													
1942-S	49,300,000	1,889	65.1	97%	$2.75	$3	$3.25	$6	$8	$20	$30	$150	$50
Auctions: $400, MS-67, January 2015; $2,820, MS-67, July 2015; $306, MS-67, March 2016; $3,525, MS-67, September 2016													
1943	191,710,000	5,762	65.4	98%	$2.75	$3	$3.25	$4.50	$6	$12	$27	$55	$35
Auctions: $129, MS-67, March 2016; $1,645, MS-67, August 2016; $1,293, MS-67, October 2016; $1,528, MS-67, November 2016													

c. This is the "Trumpet Tail" S mintmark, which is rare for this date. The upper serif points downward and the lower serif is rounded, like the bell of a trumpet. There are several dies known for the Large S dime, including one that is repunched. For more information, see the *Cherrypickers' Guide*. **d.** Included in 1941-S mintage figure. **e.** Doubling is evident in the 42 over 41 overdate, and slightly evident on IN GOD WE TRUST. Values for this variety fluctuate. **f.** Included in circulation-strike 1942 mintage figure. **g.** Value in MS-64 is $7,200. **h.** Doubling is evident in the 42 over 41 overdate, slightly evident on IN GOD WE TRUST, and as a D over D repunched mintmark (slanted west). Values for this variety fluctuate. **i.** Included in 1942-D mintage figure. **j.** Value in MS-64 is $7,200.

1943-S, Trumpet Tail Mintmark
FS-10-1943S-511.

1945-D, D Over Horizontal D
FS-10-1945D-506.

1945-S, S Over Horizontal S
FS-10-1945S-503.

1945-S, Normal S

1945-S, Micro S
FS-10-1945S-512.

	Mintage	Cert	Avg	%MS	F-12	VF-20	EF-40	AU-50	MS-60	MS-63	MS-65 / PF-65	MS-65FB / PF-66	MS-66 / PF-67
1943-D	71,949,000	5,994	65.5	99%	$2.75	$3	$3.25	$4.50	$6	$15	$30	$50	$45
Auctions: $1,116, MS-68, December 2015; $153, MS-67, March 2016; $447, MS-67, July 2016; $1,410, MS-68, September 2016													
1943-S	60,400,000	3,480	65.8	99%	$2.75	$3	$3.25	$5	$7	$16	$30	$70	$40
Auctions: $1,351, MS-67, June 2015; $3,525, MS-68, October 2015; $646, MS-67, December 2015; $1,028, MS-67, July 2016													
1943-S, Trumpet Tail Mintmark (k)	(l)	7	62.6	71%							$450	$750	$500
Auctions: $130, MS-62, December 2011													
1944	231,410,000	6,937	65.4	98%	$2.75	$3	$3.25	$4.50	$6	$12	$25	$80	$45
Auctions: $12,925, MS-68, August 2015; $1,586, MS-67, October 2015; $1,293, MS-67, July 2016; $1,293, MS-67, September 2016													
1944-D	62,224,000	7,769	65.8	99%	$2.75	$3	$3.25	$5	$7	$15	$30	$50	$48
Auctions: $94, MS-67, August 2016; $705, MS-68, September 2016; $881, MS-68, October 2016; $764, MS-68, November 2016													
1944-S	49,490,000	5,653	65.8	99%	$2.75	$3	$3.25	$5	$7	$15	$30	$55	$50
Auctions: $1,763, MS-67, December 2015; $176, MS-67, March 2016; $188, MS-67, June 2016; $881, MS-67, November 2016													
1945	159,130,000	7,601	65.5	99%	$2.75	$3	$3.25	$4.50	$6	$12	$30	$9,000	$45
Auctions: $100, MS-0, November 2015; $13,513, MS-65, December 2015; $494, MS-67, March 2016; $14,688, MS-66, November 2016													
1945-D	40,245,000	7,518	65.7	99%	$2.75	$3	$3.25	$4.50	$6	$12	$26	$45	$50
Auctions: $200, MS-67FB, September 2015; $112, MS-67FB, November 2015; $353, MS-68, August 2016; $2,820, MS-67, August 2016													
1945-D, D Over Horizontal D (m)	(n)	6	44.3	0%							$950		
Auctions: No auction records available.													
1945-S	41,920,000	6,330	65.9	99%	$2.75	$3	$3.25	$4.50	$6	$12	$30	$125	$40
Auctions: $423, MS-67, March 2016; $588, MS-67, July 2016; $881, MS-67, August 2016; $541, MS-68, September 2016													
1945-S, S Over Horizontal S (o)	(p)	0	n/a								$950		
Auctions: No auction records available.													
1945-S, Micro S (q)	(p)	1,275	64.9	98%	$3.25	$3.50	$6	$18	$30	$40	$100	$650	$120
Auctions: $441, MS-67, November 2015; $705, MS-65, December 2015; $1,116, MS-67, August 2016; $823, MS-66, October 2016													

k. This variety is considerably rarer than the 1941-S, Large S, which also features a Trumpet S mintmark. It is extremely rare in MS, and examples with FB command a significant premium. The top serif of the S points downward, with the lower serif rounded, much like the bell of a trumpet. **l.** Included in 1943-S mintage figure. **m.** The first D mintmark was punched into the die horizontally and then corrected. **n.** Included in 1945-D mintage figure. **o.** The first S mintmark was punched into the die horizontally and then corrected. **p.** Included in 1945-S mintage figure. **q.** The S mintmark is significantly smaller than that of the normal S punch. This variety has the only mintmark punch of this type and size known to have been used during the 1940s. It was originally used for Philippine coins of 1907 through 1920.

ROOSEVELT (1946 TO DATE)

Silver (1946–1964, and some modern Proofs): **Designer:** *John R. Sinnock.*
Weight: *2.50 grams.* **Composition:** *.900 silver, .100 copper (net weight: .07234 oz. pure silver).*
Diameter: *17.9 mm.* **Edge:** *Reeded.* **Mints:** *Philadelphia, Denver, San Francisco, and West Point.*

Silver, Circulation Strike

Mintmark location
is on the reverse, to
the left of the fasces.

Silver, Proof

Clad (1965 to date): **Designer:** *John R. Sinnock.* **Weight:** *2.27 grams.*
Composition: *Outer layers of copper-nickel (.750 copper, .250 nickel) bonded to inner core of pure copper.*
Diameter: *17.9 mm.* **Edge:** *Reeded.* **Mints:** *Philadelphia, Denver, and San Francisco.*

Clad, Circulation Strike

Mintmark location
is on the obverse,
above the date.

Clad, Proof

History. After President Franklin D. Roosevelt died in 1945, the Treasury rushed to create a coin in his honor. The ten-cent denomination was particularly appropriate, given the president's active support of the March of Dimes' fundraising efforts to cure polio. The obverse of the coin bears Roosevelt's profile portrait, while the reverse features a torch flanked by branches of olive and oak.

Striking and Sharpness. Compared to earlier coinage series, collectors and dealers have paid relatively little attention to the sharpness of Roosevelt dimes. The obverse portrait is such that lightness of strike on the higher points is difficult to detect. On the reverse, check the leaves and the details of the torch. Some with complete separation on the lower two bands have been called Full Torch (FT) or Full Bands (FB), but interest in this distinction seems to be minimal in today's marketplace.

Availability. All are common, although some are more common than others. MS coins in higher grades are usually very lustrous.

Note: Values of common-date silver coins have been based on a silver current bullion price of $15.50 per ounce, and may vary with the prevailing spot price.

GRADING STANDARDS

MS-60 to 70 (Mint State). *Obverse:* At MS-60, some abrasion and contact marks are evident on the cheek, the hair above the ear, and the neck. At MS-63, abrasion is slight at best, less so for MS-64. An MS-65 coin should display no abrasion or contact marks except under magnification, and MS-66 and higher coins should have none at all. Luster should be full and rich. *Reverse:* Comments apply as for

1955-D. Graded MS-68FB.

the obverse, except that the highest parts of the torch, flame, and leaves are the places to check. On both sides the fields are protected by design elements and do not show contact marks readily.

AU-50, 53, 55, 58 (About Uncirculated).
Obverse: Light wear is seen on the cheek and higher-relief part of the hair. At AU-58, the luster is extensive, but incomplete, especially on the higher parts and in the field. At AU–50 and 53, luster is less. *Reverse:* Light wear is seen on the higher parts of the torch and leaves. An AU-58 coin has nearly full luster. At AU–50 and 53, there still is significant luster.

1962-D. Graded AU-58.

EF-40, 45 (Extremely Fine). *Obverse:* Further wear is seen on the head. Some details are gone in the hair to the right of the forehead. *Reverse:* Further wear is seen on the torch, but the vertical lines are visible, some just barely. The higher-relief details in the leaves, never strong to begin with, are worn away.

The Roosevelt dime is seldom collected in grades lower than EF-40.

1950-S. Graded EF-40.

PF-60 to 70 (Proof). *Obverse and Reverse:* Proofs that are extensively cleaned and have many hairlines, or that are dull and grainy, are lower level, such as PF–60 to 62. These are not widely desired, and represent coins that have been mistreated. Fortunately, only a few Proof Roosevelt dimes are in this category. With medium hairlines and good reflectivity, assigned grades of PF–63 or 64 are appropriate. PF-65 may have hairlines so delicate that magnification is needed to see them. Above that, a Proof should be free of any hairlines or other problems.

1983-S, No S. Graded PF-69 Deep Cameo.

Illustrated coin: The S mintmark is missing from this popular variety.

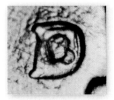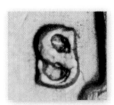

1950-D, D Over S	1950-S, S Over D
FS-10-1950D-501.	*FS-10-1950S-501.*

	Mintage	Cert	Avg	%MS	EF-40	MS-63	MS-65	MS-66	MS-67	MS-67FT
								PF-65	PF-66	PF-67
1946	255,250,000	1,929	65.9	99%	$2	$4.25	$12	$28	$55	$250
1946-D	61,043,500	2,217	66.1	100%	$2	$4.25	$14	$30	$50	$150
1946-S	27,900,000	2,676	66.3	100%	$2	$4.50	$20	$32	$75	$150
1947	121,520,000	1,384	65.6	97%	$2	$6	$12	$24	$75	$225

	Mintage	Cert	Avg	%MS	EF-40	MS-63	MS-65	MS-66	MS-67	MS-67FT
								PF-65	PF-66	PF-67
1947-D	46,835,000	1,204	66.2	100%	$2	$6.50	$12	$24	$45	$250
1947-S	34,840,000	2,133	66.3	100%	$2	$6	$12	$30	$45	$150
1948	74,950,000	1,162	66.0	100%	$2	$4.25	$12	$30	$85	$175
1948-D	52,841,000	1,364	66.2	100%	$2	$6	$12	$30	$55	$125
1948-S	35,520,000	1,625	66.3	100%	$2	$5.50	$12	$32	$55	$125
1949	30,940,000	1,242	65.9	99%	$3	$27	$38	$45	$100	$650
1949-D	26,034,000	1,863	66.1	100%	$3	$12	$20	$35	$55	$115
1949-S	13,510,000	2,390	66.2	99%	$5	$45	$55	$75	$85	$1,250
1950	50,130,114	1,414	65.9	99%	$3	$13	$16	$35	$125	$225
1950, Proof	51,386	1,514	66.3					$50	$65	$120
1950-D	46,803,000	1,877	66.3	100%	$2	$6	$12	$28	$55	$115
1950-D, D Over S (a)	**(b)**	0	n/a			$400	$650	$775	$1,050	
1950-S	20,440,000	1,562	66.2	99%	$5	$38	$55	$75	$85	$300
1950-S, S Over D (c)	**(d)**	0	n/a			$250	$400	$750	$900	$1,675
1951	103,880,102	1,643	66.1	100%	$2	$4.25	$10	$30	$65	$150
1951, Proof	57,500	1,881	66.7					$50	$65	$100
1951-D	56,529,000	978	66.1	100%	$2	$4	$10	$28	$100	$125
1951-S	31,630,000	1,648	66.3	100%	$3	$14	$25	$45	$55	$115
1952	99,040,093	1,067	65.9	100%	$2	$4.25	$10	$30	$75	$125
1952, Proof	81,980	1,636	66.7					$35	$50	$85
1952-D	122,100,000	1,185	66.1	100%	$2	$4.25	$9	$25	$65	$135
1952-S	44,419,500	1,747	66.3	100%	$3	$8	$12	$35	$50	$225
1953	53,490,120	857	65.9	100%	$2	$4	$8	$15	$75	$850
1953, Proof	128,800	2,254	66.8					$38	$55	$80
1953-D	136,433,000	1,171	66.0	100%	$2	$4	$9	$20	$55	$175
1953-S	39,180,000	2,788	66.2	100%	$3	$4	$9	$25	$55	$400
1954	114,010,203	1,395	65.9	100%	$2	$4	$8	$20	$55	$375
1954, Proof	233,300	2,752	67.0					$18	$25	$30
1954-D	106,397,000	1,015	66.0	100%	$2	$4	$9	$14	$100	$150
1954-S	22,860,000	2,402	66.1	100%	$2	$4	$9	$16	$55	$350
1955	12,450,181	2,527	65.9	100%	$2	$4	$8	$16	$75	$1,000
1955, Proof	378,200	4,750	67.5					$15	$20	$25
1955-D	13,959,000	1,661	65.6	100%	$2	$4	$8	$15	$95	$200
1955-S	18,510,000	3,709	65.9	100%	$2	$4	$8	$15	$55	$1,250
1956	108,640,000	2,274	66.2	100%	$2	$3	$6	$14	$45	$450
1956, Proof	669,384	4,131	67.6					$8	$10	$18
1956-D	108,015,100	1,043	66.0	100%	$2	$3	$6	$15	$35	$275
1957	160,160,000	2,292	66.2	100%	$2	$3	$6	$14	$35	$2,000
1957, Proof	1,247,952	4,849	67.5					$5	$8	$25
1957-D	113,354,330	1,598	66.0	100%	$2	$3	$6	$14	$35	$165
1958	31,910,000	2,286	66.2	100%	$2	$3	$7	$15	$25	$2,000
1958, Proof	875,652	3,996	67.4					$5	$8	$10
1958-D	136,564,600	1,773	66.1	100%	$2	$3	$7	$14	$25	$125
1959	85,780,000	1,574	65.9	99%	$2	$3	$6	$15	$100	$325
1959, Proof	1,149,291	4,439	67.6					$5	$8	$10
1959-D	164,919,790	1,139	66.1	100%	$2	$3	$6	$14	$40	$120

a. The diagonal stroke of the initially punched S mintmark is visible within the opening of the primary D mintmark. The lower curve of the S is evident on the lower right curve of the D. **b.** Included in 1950-D mintage figure. **c.** The S mintmark is punched squarely over a previously punched D. CONECA lists this coin as an S Over Inverted S, indicating that the line enclosing the lower loop is that of the long upper serif on an inverted S. However, Fivaz and Stanton, in the *Cherrypickers' Guide to Rare Die Varieties*, sixth edition, volume II, "believe this to be an [overmintmark] (actually S/S/D) because the long upper serif of an S would not enclose the lower opening. In addition, the curve of the face of a D is clearly evident in the upper opening." **d.** Included in 1950-S mintage figure.

1960, Doubled Die Obverse, Proof
FS-10-1960-102. Various die states exist.

1963, Doubled Die Reverse
FS-10-1963-805.

1963, Doubled Die Reverse, Proof
FS-10-1963-802. Other varieties exist

1963-D, Doubled Die Reverse
FS-10-1963D-801.

	Mintage	Cert	Avg	%MS	EF-40	MS-63	MS-65	MS-66	MS-67	MS-67FT
								PF-65	PF-66	PF-67
1960	70,390,000	1,290	65.9	100%	$2	$3	$6	$14	$65	$325
1960, Proof	1,691,602	5,188	67.5					$5	$10	$18
1960, Doubled Die Obverse, Proof	(e)	82	64.1					$150	$250	
1960-D	200,160,400	957	65.9	100%	$2	$3	$5	$15	$75	$375
1961	93,730,000	1,229	65.9	100%	$2	$3	$5	$12	$75	$750
1961, Proof	3,028,244	5,306	67.4					$5	$8	$12
1961-D	209,146,550	936	65.9	100%	$2	$3	$5	$12	$25	$225
1962	72,450,000	1,466	65.8	100%	$2	$3	$5	$12	$35	$350
1962, Proof	3,218,019	5,111	67.3					$5	$8	$10
1962-D	334,948,380	1,106	65.9	99%	$2	$3	$5	$12	$30	$200
1963	123,650,000	1,250	65.8	99%	$2	$3	$5	$12	$30	$2,000
1963, Doubled Die Reverse (f)	(g)	11	63.3	91%		$25	$38	$100		
1963, Proof	3,075,645	6,889	67.5					$5	$8	$10
1963, Doubled Die Reverse, Proof (h)	(i)	524	66.9					$150	$250	
1963-D	421,476,530	1,161	65.7	99%	$2	$3	$5	$12	$30	$750
1963-D, Doubled Die Reverse (j)	(k)	14	63.6	93%		$125	$175	$250		
1964 (l)	929,360,000	1,764	65.5	99%	$2	$3	$5	$12	$30	$500
1964, Proof	3,950,762	13,510	67.8					$5	$8	$10

e. Included in 1960, Proof, mintage figure. **f.** Doubling is evident on UNITED, E PLURIBUS, the olive branch, and the stem. Lesser doubling is also visible on ONE DIME. **g.** Included in circulation-strike 1963 mintage figure. **h.** Several less-valuable 1963, Proof, DDRs exist. Values shown are for FS-10-1963-802. **i.** Included in 1963, Proof, mintage figure. **j.** Doubling is evident on all reverse lettering, with the most obvious doubling on AMERICA and on the top of the flame. Most MS examples are MS-63 and lower. **k.** Included in 1963-D mintage figure. **l.** The 9 in the date has either a pointed tail or a straight tail.

1964-D, Doubled Die Reverse
FS-10-1964D-801. Other varieties exist.

1967, Doubled Die Obverse
FS-10-1967-101.

1968-S, Doubled Die Obverse, Proof
FS-10-1968S-102.

1968-S, No S, Proof
FS-10-1968S-501.

1970, Doubled Die Reverse
FS-10-1970-801.

	Mintage	Cert	Avg	%MS	EF-40	MS-63	MS-65	MS-66	MS-67	MS-67FT
								PF-65	PF-66	PF-67
1964-D (l)	1,357,517,180	1,776	65.6	98%	$2	$3	$5	$12	$50	$350
1964-D, Doubled Die Reverse (m)	(n)	3	58.7	33%	$35	$100	$160	$235	$400	$750
1965	1,652,140,570	125	65.4	97%			$2	$15	$75	$1,000
1965, Special Mint Set	2,360,000	2,532	67.1					$11	$13	$17
1966	1,382,734,540	185	66.2	97%			$2.25	$6	$30	$800
1966, Special Mint Set	2,261,583	2,526	67.3					$11	$13	$20
1967	2,244,007,320	171	64.6	84%			$2	$5	$25	$650
1967, Doubled Die Obverse (o)	(p)	0	n/a				$400	$600	$850	
1967, Special Mint Set	1,863,344	2,957	67.2					$12	$14	$18
1968	424,470,400	206	65.8	99%			$2	$5	$25	$600
1968-D	480,748,280	715	66.2	100%			$2	$5	$20	$75
1968-S, Proof	3,041,506	1,208	67.9					$2	$4	$6
1968-S, Doubled Die Obverse, Proof (q)	(r)	12	67.0					$350	$500	$750
1968-S, No S, Proof †† (s)	(r)	10	67.9					$12,500	$15,000	$17,500
1969	145,790,000	95	65.1	99%			$3	$6	$30	
1969-D	563,323,870	774	66.0	100%			$2	$6	$25	$750
1969-S, Proof	2,394,631	1,012	68.1					$2	$4	$6
1970	345,570,000	164	64.4	96%			$2	$6	$35	
1970, Doubled Die Reverse (t)	(u)	4	62.3	75%			$300	$650	$1,000	
1970-D	754,942,100	515	65.1	99%			$2	$5	$35	
1970-S, Proof	2,632,810	1,098	67.7					$2	$4	$6

†† Ranked in the *100 Greatest U.S. Modern Coins* (fourth edition). **l.** The 9 in the date has either a pointed tail or a straight tail. **m.** There are several varieties of 1964-D with a doubled-die reverse. The variety pictured and valued here is FS-10-1964D-801. For more information, see the *Cherrypickers' Guide to Rare Die Varieties*, sixth edition, volume II. **n.** Included in 1964-D mintage figure. **o.** This is a very rare doubled die. Its doubling is evident on IN GOD WE TRUST, the date, and the designer's initials. **p.** Included in circulation-strike 1967 mintage figure. **q.** There are several 1968-S, Proof, doubled-die obverse varieties. The one listed here is FS-10-1968S-102 (see the *Cherrypickers' Guide to Rare Die Varieties*, sixth edition, volume II). **r.** Included in 1968-S, Proof, mintage figure. **s.** The S mintmark was inadvertently left off the coinage die; this defect was probably discovered before the end of the die's life. **t.** Doubling on this extremely rare variety is evident on all reverse lettering, especially on UNITED STATES OF AMERICA, with slightly weaker doubling on ONE DIME. **u.** Included in circulation-strike 1970 mintage figure.

1979-S, Filled S (Type 1), Proof	1979-S, Clear S (Type 2), Proof	1981-S, Rounded S (Type 1), Proof	1981-S, Flat S (Type 2), Proof

	Mintage	Cert	Avg	%MS	EF-40	MS-63	MS-65	MS-66 / PF-65	MS-67 / PF-66	MS-67FT / PF-67
1970-S, No S, Proof †† (s)	(v)	188	67.6					$800	$950	$1,100
1971	162,690,000	77	64.9	100%			$2.50	$6	$40	
1971-D	377,914,240	147	65.7	100%			$2.25	$6	$50	$700
1971-S, Proof	3,220,733	1,385	68.1					$2	$4	$6
1972	431,540,000	95	65.0	99%			$2	$6	$60	
1972-D	330,290,000	189	65.7	100%			$2	$6	$40	$800
1972-S, Proof	3,260,996	1,154	68.0					$2	$4	$6
1973	315,670,000	94	65.2	100%			$2	$5	$70	$1,200
1973-D	455,032,426	155	65.4	100%			$2	$6	$50	$500
1973-S, Proof	2,760,339	441	67.7					$2	$4	$6
1974	470,248,000	55	64.9	100%			$2	$5	$25	
1974-D	571,083,000	109	65.4	100%			$2	$5	$25	$1,000
1974-S, Proof	2,612,568	391	67.9					$2	$4	$6
1975	585,673,900	117	65.2	99%			$2	$5	$25	$1,000
1975-D	313,705,300	191	66.2	99%			$2	$5	$30	$600
1975-S, Proof	2,845,450	547	68.0					$2.50	$4	$6
1975-S, No S, Proof †† (s)	(w)	0	n/a						$175,000	
1976	568,760,000	135	66.1	100%			$2	$5	$25	$1,200
1976-D	695,222,774	136	65.8	97%			$2	$5	$40	$1,200
1976-S, Proof	4,149,730	879	68.1					$2.75	$4	$6
1977	796,930,000	181	65.8	100%			$2	$5	$25	$1,200
1977-D	376,607,228	111	65.5	100%			$2	$5	$35	$550
1977-S, Proof	3,251,152	836	68.5					$2.50	$4	$6
1978	663,980,000	90	65.6	99%			$2	$5	$27	$300
1978-D	282,847,540	84	65.6	100%			$2	$5	$25	
1978-S, Proof	3,127,781	739	68.9					$2.50	$4	$6
1979	315,440,000	160	65.7	100%			$2	$5	$30	
1979-D	390,921,184	135	65.6	100%			$2	$5	$30	
1979-S, Type 1, Proof	3,677,175	871	69.0					$2.50	$4	$6
1979-S, Type 2, Proof	(x)	1,085	69.2					$5	$6	$8
1980-P	735,170,000	143	65.8	99%			$2	$5	$25	
1980-D	719,354,321	95	65.7	100%			$2	$5	$30	
1980-S, Proof	3,554,806	1,083	68.5					$2.50	$4	$6
1981-P	676,650,000	223	65.9	100%			$2	$5	$40	$70
1981-D	712,284,143	330	66.4	100%			$2	$5	$20	$80
1981-S, Type 1, Proof	4,063,083	1,288	68.9					$2.50	$4	$6
1981-S, Type 2, Proof	(y)	666	69.1					$5.50	$6	$8

†† Ranked in the *100 Greatest U.S. Modern Coins* (fourth edition). **s.** The S mintmark was inadvertently left off the coinage die; this defect was probably discovered before the end of the die's life. **v.** Included in 1970-S, Proof, mintage figure. **w.** Included in 1975-S, Proof, mintage figure. **x.** Included in the 1979-S, Type 1, Proof, mintage figure. **y.** Included in the 1981-S, Type 1, Proof, mintage figure.

1982, No S,
Strong Strike
FS-10-1982-501.

1982, No S,
Weak Strike
FS-10-1982-502.

| | Mintage | Cert | Avg | %MS | EF-40 | MS-63 | MS-65 | MS-66 | MS-67 | MS-67FT |
								PF-65	PF-66	PF-67
1982, No Mintmark, Strong Strike ‡ (z)	(aa)	60	65.3	100%			$200	$350	$550	$1,250
1982, No Mintmark, Weak Strike ‡ (z)	(aa)	412	64.2	92%			$65	$100	$250	
1982-P	519,475,000	189	66.2	98%			$7.50	$18	$50	$900
1982-D	542,713,584	125	65.8	98%			$2.50	$6	$25	$600
1982-S, Proof	3,857,479	758	69.0					$2.50	$4	$6
1983-P	647,025,000	115	65.7	97%			$6.50	$15	$30	$250
1983-D	730,129,224	53	65.8	96%			$3.25	$8.50	$25	$200
1983-S, Proof	3,279,126	838	69.2					$3	$4	$6
1983-S, No S, Proof †† (s)	(bb)	151	68.8					$750	$800	$950
1984-P	856,669,000	157	66.4	99%			$2	$5	$20	$100
1984-D	704,803,976	118	65.4	100%			$2.25	$5	$20	$150
1984-S, Proof	3,065,110	573	69.1					$2.50	$4	$6
1985-P	705,200,962	121	66.5	100%			$2.25	$5	$25	$150
1985-D	587,979,970	187	66.8	100%			$2.25	$5	$30	$100
1985-S, Proof	3,362,821	627	69.1					$3	$4	$6
1986-P	682,649,693	172	65.9	99%			$2.50	$5	$20	$800
1986-D	473,326,970	175	66.3	99%			$2.50	$5	$20	$700
1986-S, Proof	3,010,497	483	69.1					$4	$5	$7
1987-P	762,709,481	141	66.2	99%			$2	$5	$25	$800
1987-D	653,203,402	170	66.1	99%			$2	$5	$20	$200
1987-S, Proof	4,227,728	630	69.1					$3	$4	$6
1988-P	1,030,550,000	134	65.8	96%			$2	$5	$35	$225
1988-D	962,385,489	149	66.3	99%			$2	$5	$40	$100
1988-S, Proof	3,262,948	442	69.1					$4	$5	$7
1989-P	1,298,400,000	134	66.1	99%			$2	$5	$20	$100
1989-D	896,535,597	189	66.3	99%			$2	$6	$20	$75
1989-S, Proof	3,220,194	456	69.0					$3	$4	$6
1990-P	1,034,340,000	77	66.0	97%			$2	$6	$20	$1,000
1990-D	839,995,824	102	66.2	98%			$2	$4	$25	$2,000
1990-S, Proof	3,299,559	658	69.3					$2.50	$4	$6
1991-P	927,220,000	68	66.4	99%			$2	$4	$20	$100
1991-D	601,241,114	72	65.8	100%			$2	$4	$20	$200
1991-S, Proof	2,867,787	662	69.4					$4	$5	$7
1992-P	593,500,000	90	67.0	100%			$2	$5	$35	$150
1992-D	616,273,932	70	66.2	100%			$2	$4	$30	$175
1992-S, Proof	2,858,981	491	69.5					$3	$4	$6
1992-S, Proof, Silver	1,317,579	1,596	69.2					$6	$7	$8
1993-P	766,180,000	121	66.4	98%			$2	$4	$30	$200
1993-D	750,110,166	101	65.7	99%			$2	$4	$25	$500

†† Ranked in the *100 Greatest U.S. Modern Coins* (fourth edition). **s.** The S mintmark was inadvertently left off the coinage die; this defect was probably discovered before the end of the die's life. **z.** The P mintmark was omitted from this working die. There are two versions of this variety: one with a strong strike, and one with a weak strike. The strong strike is far more valuable and in demand than the weak. **aa.** Included in 1982-P mintage figure. **bb.** Included in 1983-S, Proof, mintage figure.

	Mintage	Cert	Avg	%MS	EF-40	MS-63	MS-65	MS-66	MS-67	MS-67FT
								PF-65	PF-66	PF-67
1993-S, Proof	2,633,439	513	69.4					$5	$6	$7
1993-S, Proof, Silver	761,353	1,232	69.2					$7	$8	$9
1994-P	1,189,000,000	120	66.4	98%			$2	$4	$25	$200
1994-D	1,303,268,110	64	65.4	98%			$2	$4	$25	$150
1994-S, Proof	2,484,594	636	69.5					$5	$6	$8
1994-S, Proof, Silver	785,329	1,153	69.2					$8	$9	$10
1995-P	1,125,500,000	72	66.8	100%			$2	$4	$30	$300
1995-D	1,274,890,000	89	66.0	98%			$2	$5	$35	$425
1995-S, Proof	2,117,496	418	69.5					$10	$16	$20
1995-S, Proof, Silver	679,985	1,313	69.1					$14	$23	$30
1996-P	1,421,163,000	159	66.7	98%			$2	$4	$25	$45
1996-D	1,400,300,000	194	66.2	99%			$2	$4	$20	$75
1996-W †† (cc)	1,457,000	5,286	66.5	100%			$20	$30	$45	$70
1996-S, Proof	1,750,244	439	69.4					$3	$6	$8
1996-S, Proof, Silver	775,021	1,212	69.1					$8	$10	$15
1997-P	991,640,000	74	66.6	99%			$2	$6	$60	$100
1997-D	979,810,000	77	66.1	99%			$2	$6	$50	$100
1997-S, Proof	2,055,000	350	69.6					$8	$10	$15
1997-S, Proof, Silver	741,678	1,284	69.2					$12	$16	$24
1998-P	1,163,000,000	109	66.5	99%			$2	$3	$18	$100
1998-D	1,172,250,000	97	65.8	99%			$2	$3	$15	$125
1998-S, Proof	2,086,507	327	69.5					$4	$6	$8
1998-S, Proof, Silver	878,792	1,371	69.3					$6	$8	$10
1999-P	2,164,000,000	126	66.7	98%			$2	$3	$15	$30
1999-D	1,397,750,000	115	66.4	99%			$2	$3	$15	$40
1999-S, Proof	2,543,401	2,374	69.2					$4	$6	$8
1999-S, Proof, Silver	804,565	3,961	69.2					$7	$8	$12
2000-P	1,842,500,000	64	65.4	89%			$2	$3	$15	$30
2000-D	1,818,700,000	84	66.4	96%			$2	$3	$15	$30
2000-S, Proof	3,082,572	1,400	69.2					$2.50	$4	$7
2000-S, Proof, Silver	965,421	4,326	69.3					$5	$6	$8
2001-P	1,369,590,000	62	66.5	100%			$2	$3	$12	$30
2001-D	1,412,800,000	81	66.2	95%			$2	$3	$12	$30
2001-S, Proof	2,294,909	1,134	69.4					$2.50	$4	$7
2001-S, Proof, Silver	889,697	3,845	69.4					$5	$6	$8
2002-P	1,187,500,000	39	66.4	97%			$2	$3	$12	$30
2002-D	1,379,500,000	49	66.5	98%			$2	$3	$12	$30
2002-S, Proof	2,319,766	1,576	69.3					$2.50	$4	$7
2002-S, Proof, Silver	892,229	3,578	69.4					$5	$6	$8
2003-P	1,085,500,000	144	66.0	100%			$2	$3	$10	$30
2003-D	986,500,000	104	65.8	100%			$2	$3	$10	$30
2003-S, Proof	2,172,684	3,516	69.3					$2.50	$4	$7
2003-S, Proof, Silver	1,125,755	4,555	69.3					$4.50	$5	$8
2004-P	1,328,000,000	117	66.6	100%			$2	$3	$8	$30
2004-D	1,159,500,000	77	66.8	100%			$2	$3	$8	$35
2004-S, Proof	1,789,488	1,425	69.3					$3	$5	$7
2004-S, Proof, Silver	1,175,934	4,472	69.5					$5	$6	$8
2005-P	1,412,000,000	44	67.0	100%			$2	$3	$8	$65
2005-P, Satin Finish	1,160,000	2,088	66.9	100%	$1	$2	$3	$5	$7	$10

†† Ranked in the *100 Greatest U.S. Modern Coins* (fourth edition). **cc.** Issued in Mint sets only, to mark the 50th anniversary of the design.

	Mintage	Cert	Avg	%MS	EF-40	MS-63	MS-65	MS-66 / PF-65	MS-67 / PF-66	MS-67FT / PF-67
2005-D	1,423,500,000	96	66.1	99%			$2	$3	$8	$70
2005-D, Satin Finish	1,160,000	2,226	66.9	100%	$1	$2	$3	$5	$7	$10
2005-S, Proof	2,275,000	6,091	69.3					$2.50	$4	$7
2005-S, Proof, Silver	1,069,679	5,495	69.5					$5	$6	$8
2006-P	1,381,000,000	113	65.8	99%			$2	$3	$6	$22
2006-P, Satin Finish	847,361	1,139	66.9	100%	$1	$2	$3	$5	$7	$10
2006-D	1,447,000,000	98	66.1	100%			$2	$3	$6	$22
2006-D, Satin Finish	847,361	1,119	66.8	100%	$1	$2	$3	$5	$7	$10
2006-S, Proof	2,000,428	1,981	69.4					$2.50	$4	$7
2006-S, Proof, Silver	1,054,008	3,006	69.5					$5	$6	$8
2007-P	1,047,500,000	26	66.2	100%			$2	$3	$6	$22
2007-P, Satin Finish	895,628	159	66.2	100%	$1	$2	$3	$5	$7	$10
2007-D	1,042,000,000	194	66.2	100%			$2	$3	$6	$22
2007-D, Satin Finish	895,628	188	66.4	100%	$1	$2	$3	$5	$7	$10
2007-S, Proof	1,702,116	1,672	69.6					$2.50	$4	$7
2007-S, Proof, Silver	875,050	3,504	69.6					$5	$6	$8
2008-P	391,000,000	24	66.0	100%			$2	$3	$5	$22
2008-P, Satin Finish	745,464	53	67.7	100%	$1	$2	$3	$5	$7	$10
2008-D	624,500,000	96	66.2	100%			$2	$3	$5	$22
2008-D, Satin Finish	745,464	37	67.9	100%	$1	$2	$3	$5	$7	$10
2008-S, Proof	1,405,674	1,307	69.7					$2.50	$4	$7
2008-S, Proof, Silver	763,887	3,766	69.8					$5	$6	$8
2009-P	96,500,000	347	65.8	100%			$2	$3	$5	$22
2009-P, Satin Finish	784,614	1	66.0	100%	$1	$2	$3	$5	$7	$10
2009-D	49,500,000	214	66.0	100%			$2	$3	$5	$22
2009-D, Satin Finish	784,614	2	69.0	100%	$1	$2	$3	$5	$7	$10
2009-S, Proof	1,482,502	3,358	69.6					$2.50	$4	$7
2009-S, Proof, Silver	697,365	3,891	69.7					$5	$6	$8
2010-P	557,000,000	128	66.6	100%			$2	$3	$4	$20
2010-P, Satin Finish	583,897	3	68.7	100%	$1	$2	$3	$5	$7	$10
2010-D	562,000,000	110	66.2	100%			$2	$3	$4	$20
2010-D, Satin Finish	583,897	2	66.5	100%	$1	$2	$3	$5	$7	$10
2010-S, Proof	1,103,815	1,358	69.5					$2.50	$4	$7
2010-S, Proof, Silver	585,401	3,785	69.7					$5	$6	$8
2011-P	748,000,000	197	67.3	100%			$2	$3	$4	$20
2011-D	754,000,000	201	67.1	100%			$2	$3	$4	$20
2011-S, Proof	1,098,835	2,329	69.5					$2.50	$4	$7
2011-S, Proof, Silver	574,175	4,729	69.7					$5	$6	$8
2012-P	808,000,000	95	67.0	100%			$2	$3	$4	$20
2012-D	868,000,000	102	66.8	100%			$2	$3	$4	$20
2012-S, Proof	841,972	1,445	69.5					$2.50	$4	$7
2012-S, Proof, Silver	395,443	1,610	69.8					$5	$6	$8
2013-P	1,086,500,000	86	66.8	100%			$2	$3	$4	$20
2013-D	1,025,500,000	115	67.1	100%			$2	$3	$4	$20
2013-S, Proof	802,460	1,739	69.6					$2.50	$4	$7
2013-S, Proof, Silver	419,719	831	69.8	100%				$5	$6	$8
2014-P	1,125,500,000	134	67.3	100%			$2	$3	$4	$20
2014-D	1,177,000,000	0	n/a				$2	$3	$4	$20
2014-S, Proof	665,100	1,375	69.5					$2.50	$4	$7
2014-S, Proof, Silver	393,037	2,878	69.8					$5	$6	$8

	Mintage	Cert	Avg	%MS	EF-40	MS-63	MS-65	MS-66	MS-67	MS-67FT
								PF-65	PF-66	PF-67
2015-P	1,497,510,000	0	n/a				$2	$3	$4	$20
2015-P, Reverse Proof, Silver	74,430	0	n/a					$20	$30	$50
2015-D	1,543,500,000	0	n/a				$2	$3	$4	$20
2015-S, Proof	(662,854)	0	n/a					$2.50	$4	$7
2015-S, Proof, Silver	(387,310)	0	n/a					$5	$6	$8
2015-W, Proof, Silver	74,430	0	n/a					$15	$25	$40

In 2016 a special .9999 fine gold striking of Adolph A. Weinman's Winged Liberty Head or "Mercury" dime was created to celebrate the 100th anniversary of its introduction. It is smaller than the silver strikings, with a diameter of 16.5 mm and weighing 3.11035 grams. Struck at West Point, it has a reeded edge. Similar strikings were made for the 1916 quarter and half dollar designs.

	Mintage	Cert	Avg	%MS	SP-67	SP-70
2016-W, Mercury Dime Centennial Gold Coin ††	124,885				$250	$300

†† 2016 Centennial Gold Coins in all denominations are ranked in the *100 Greatest U.S. Modern Coins* (fourth edition), as a single entry.

Normally scheduled production of clad and silver Roosevelt dimes, in the same standards and specifications as previously, continued in 2016 and beyond, and was not disrupted by the gold Mercury dime.

	Mintage	Cert	Avg	%MS	EF-40	MS-63	MS-65	MS-66	MS-67	MS-67FT
								PF-65	PF-66	PF-67
2016-P	1,517,000,000	0	n/a				$2	$3	$4	$20
2016-D	1,437,000,000	0	n/a				$2	$3	$4	$20
2016-S, Proof	(641,775)	0	n/a					$2.50	$4	$7
2016-S, Proof, Silver	(419,496)	0	n/a					$5	$6	$8
2017-P	1,437,500,000						$2	$3	$4	$20
2017-D	1,290,500,000						$2	$3	$4	$20
2017-S, Proof	(621,384)							$2.50	$4	$7
2017-S, Proof, Silver	(406,994)							$5	$6	$8
2018-P	1,193,000,000						$2	$3	$4	$20
2018-D	1,006,000,000						$2	$3	$4	$20
2018-S, Proof	(535,221)							$2.50	$4	$7
2018-S, Proof, Silver	(350,820)							$5	$6	$8
2019-P							$2	$3	$4	$20
2019-D							$2	$3	$4	$20
2019-S, Proof (a)								$2.50	$4	$7
2019-S, Proof, Silver (b)								$5	$6	$8

a. For its 225th anniversary, the Mint issued a special set of Enhanced Uncirculated coins from the San Francisco Mint; they are not included in the listings here. **b.** Beginning in 2019, the Mint changed its composition for silver Proofs to .999 fine.

Twenty-Cent Pieces
1875–1878

AN OVERVIEW OF TWENTY-CENT PIECES

The twenty-cent piece, made in silver, proved to be the shortest-lived denomination in American coinage history. The coins were struck in quantity in their first year of issue, 1875, after which it was learned that the public confused them with quarter dollars. Mintages dropped sharply, and in 1877 and 1878 coinage was limited to just Proofs for collectors.

Both sides of the twenty-cent piece were designed by U.S. Mint chief engraver William Barber. The obverse is simply an adaptation of the Liberty Seated motif earlier used on other denominations. The reverse is new and depicts a perched eagle (of the same general appearance as introduced by Barber on the 1873 silver trade dollar).

Only one twenty-cent piece is needed for inclusion in a type set. By far the most readily available in Mint State is the 1875-S, followed by the 1875-CC. These are often somewhat lightly struck on the reverse, particularly near the top of the eagle's wings. The 1875 and 1876 Philadelphia coins are occasionally encountered in Mint State and are usually well struck.

Senator John P. Jones was involved with the minting of the twenty-cent piece silver coin.

Proofs are readily available for all years, 1875 through 1878.

FOR THE COLLECTOR AND INVESTOR: TWENTY-CENT PIECES AS A SPECIALTY

A full date-and-mintmark set of twenty-cent pieces consists of the 1875, 1875-CC, 1875-S, 1876, 1876-CC, 1877, and 1878, the latter two years being available only in Proof format. The great challenge in forming a set is the 1876-CC, of which 10,000 were minted, but, seemingly, all but about two dozen were melted. Those that do survive are typically encountered in Mint State and are widely heralded when they are offered at auction.

LIBERTY SEATED (1875–1878)

Designer: *William Barber.* **Weight:** *5 grams.* **Composition:** *.900 silver, .100 copper.*
Diameter: *22 mm.* **Edge:** *Plain.* **Mints:** *Philadelphia, Carson City, and San Francisco.*

Mintmark location
is on the reverse,
below the eagle.

Circulation Strike   **Proof**

History. The twenty-cent coin debuted in 1875 as a convenient denomination to make change in the West (at the time silver coins did not circulate in the East or Midwest). The coins sometimes were confused with quarter dollars, given their similar Liberty Seated design on the obverse, and their similar size. The quantity minted dropped considerably in 1876, and in 1877 and 1878 only Proofs were struck. Despite the brief time of their production, these coins were still seen in circulation through the early 1900s, by which time they were often casually used as quarters. Proof coins were made of all years 1875 to 1878.

Striking and Sharpness. Areas of weakness are common. On the obverse, check the head of Miss Liberty and the stars. The word LIBERTY is *raised* on this coin, a curious departure from other Liberty Seated coins of the era, on which it is recessed or incuse (the Gobrecht silver dollars of 1836 and 1839 being exceptions). On the reverse, check the eagle's feathers, especially the top of the wing on the left, but other areas can be weak as well. Some 1875-S coins are highly prooflike. The 1877 and 1878 are Proof-only issues with no related circulation strikes. Most have been cleaned or even lightly polished. Many Proofs in the marketplace have been convincingly retoned to mask problems. Proofs are usually well struck, but more than just a few are somewhat flat on the hair details of Miss Liberty.

Availability. Most often seen is the high-mintage 1875-S, although the 1875 and 1875-CC are encountered with frequency. The 1876 is quite scarce and when seen is usually in high grades and well struck. The 1876-CC is a rarity, and only about two dozen are known, nearly all of which are MS. The eye appeal of MS coins can vary widely. The number of letters in LIBERTY on certain coins graded from VG through VF can vary widely in the marketplace. Proofs most often seen are those of 1875 and 1876. For some unexplained reason, high-quality Proofs of the series' final two years are very hard to find.

GRADING STANDARDS

MS-60 to 70 (Mint State). *Obverse:* At MS-60, some abrasion and contact marks are evident, most noticeably on the bosom and thighs and knees. Luster is present, but may be dull or lifeless. At MS-63, contact marks are very few, and abrasion is hard to detect except under magnification. An MS-65 coin has no abrasion, and contact marks are sufficiently minute as to require magnification. Check the knees of Liberty and the right field.

1875; BF-1. Graded MS-64.

Luster should be full and rich. *Reverse:* Comments apply as for the obverse, except that in lower–Mint State grades abrasion and contact marks are most noticeable on the eagle's breast and the top of the wing to the left. At MS-65 or higher, there are no marks visible to the unaided eye. The field is mainly protected by design elements and does not show abrasion as much as does the obverse on a given coin.

Illustrated coin: Semi-Proof surfaces contrast nicely against the frosted devices of this well-struck piece.

AU-50, 53, 55, 58 (About Uncirculated).
Obverse: Light wear is seen on the thighs and knees, bosom, and head. At AU-58, the luster is extensive but incomplete, especially in the right field. At AU–50 and 53, luster is less. *Reverse:* Very light wear is evident on the eagle's breast (the prime focal point) and at the top of the wings. An AU-58 coin will have nearly full luster, more so than on the obverse, as the design elements protect the small field areas. At AU–50 and 53, there still are traces of luster.

1875-CC. Graded AU-55.

EF-40, 45 (Extremely Fine). *Obverse:* Further wear is seen on all areas, especially the thighs and knees, bosom, and head. Little or no luster is seen on most coins. From this grade downward, sharpness of strike of the stars and the head does not matter to connoisseurs. *Reverse:* More wear is evident on the eagle's breast and the top of the wings. Some feathers may be blended together, but most details are defined.

1875-S. Graded EF-45.

VF-20, 30 (Very Fine). *Obverse:* Further wear is seen. Most details of the gown are worn away, except in the lower-relief areas above and to the right of the shield. Hair detail is mostly or completely gone. As to whether LIBERTY should be completely readable, this seems to be a matter of debate. On many coins in the marketplace the word is weak or missing one to several letters. ANA grading standards and PCGS require full LIBERTY. *Reverse:* Wear is more extensive, but at least three-quarters of the feathers in the breast and wings are distinct. At VF-30 the head is flat with distinct details; head details are less distinct at VF-20.

1875-S. Graded VF-30.

F-12, 15 (Fine). *Obverse:* The seated figure is well worn, but with some detail above and to the right of the shield. LIBERTY has at least three letters visible (per ANA grading standards). In the marketplace, some have more letters missing. *Reverse:* Wear is extensive, with about half of the feathers flat or blended with others and head details are indistinct except for the eye.

1875-CC. Graded F-15.

VG-8, 10 (Very Good). *Obverse:* The seated figure is more worn, but some detail can be seen above and to the right of the shield. The shield is discernible. In LIBERTY a letter or two may be visible per ANA grading standards. In the marketplace, many have no letters. *Reverse:* Further wear has flattened about half of the feathers. Those remaining are on the inside of the wings. The rim is full and shows many if not most denticles.

1875-S. Graded VG-10.

G-4, 6 (Good). *Obverse:* The seated figure is worn nearly smooth, but with some slight detail above and to the right of the shield. At G-4, there are no letters in LIBERTY remaining. On some at the G-6 level, there may be a trace of letters. *Reverse:* Most feathers in the eagle are gone. The border lettering is weak. The rim is visible partially or completely (depending on the strike).

1875-CC. Graded G-6.

AG-3 (About Good). *Obverse:* The seated figure is mostly visible in outline form, with only a hint of detail. Much of the rim is worn away. The date remains clear. *Reverse:* The border letters are partially worn away. The eagle is mostly in outline form, but with a few details discernible. The rim is weak or missing.

1875-CC. Graded AG-3.

PF-60 to 70 (Proof). *Obverse and Reverse:* Proofs that are extensively cleaned and have many hairlines, or that are dull and grainy, are lower level, such as PF–60 to 62. These are not widely desired. With medium hairlines and good reflectivity, an assigned grade of PF-64 is indicated, and with relatively few hairlines, Gem PF-65. In various grades hairlines are most easily seen in the obverse field. PF-66 should have hairlines so delicate that

1877. Graded PF-61.

magnification is needed to see them. Above that, a Proof should be free of such lines.

Illustrated coin: Lovely frosted devices are complemented by indigo toning in the peripheries of the fields.

	Mintage	Cert	Avg	%MS	G-4	VG-8	F-12	VF-20	EF-40	AU-50	MS-60	MS-63	MS-65
											PF-60	PF-63	PF-65
1875	38,500	500	53.1	48%	$235	$275	$350	$400	$500	$600	$825	$1,450	$5,000
	Auctions: $1,292, MS-64, August 2015; $940, MS-62, July 2015; $881, MS-61, January 2015; $352, AU-50, February 2015												
1875, Proof	1,200	253	63.6								$1,300	$2,500	$7,500
	Auctions: $7,050, PF-65, August 2015; $4,465, PF-64Cam, July 2015; $3,995, PF-64, January 2015; $2,585, PF-63Cam, October 2015												
1875-CC	133,290	1,091	37.6	28%	$250	$325	$425	$575	$850	$1,200	$1,950	$3,500	$10,000
	Auctions: $7,050, MS-65, August 2015; $2,820, MS-62, January 2015; $2,056, MS-62, September 2015; $1,116, AU-55, June 2015												
1875-S (a)	1,155,000	3,326	48.6	45%	$85	$100	$130	$150	$250	$400	$650	$1,100	$2,350
	Auctions: $52,875, MS-68, August 2015; $6,462, MS-66, June 2015; $2,467, MS-65, March 2015; $540, MS-61, January 2015; $352, AU-53, April 2015												
1875-S, Proof	*10–20*	2	63								$15,000	$35,000	$75,000
	Auctions: No auction records available.												
1876	14,750	453	58.1	64%	$235	$275	$350	$400	$425	$600	$900	$1,800	$5,500
	Auctions: $15,275, MS-66, June 2015; $4,700, MS-65, July 2015; $4,465, MS-65, January 2015; $940, AU-58, October 2015												
1876, Proof	1,150	302	63.6								$1,300	$2,500	$7,500
	Auctions: $25,850, PF-68, August 2015; $4,230, PF-64, February 2015; $3,995, PF-64, January 2015; $3,760, PF-63Cam, October 2015												
1876-CC †	10,000	7	64.6	100%						$175,000	$250,000	$350,000	$550,000
	Auctions: $564,000, MS-65, January 2013												
1877, Proof	510	262	63.7								$10,000	$13,500	$22,500
	Auctions: $7,637, PF-65, July 2015; $15,275, PF-64, August 2016; $3,995, PF-62, June 2015; $3,995, PF-62, October 2015												
1878, Proof	600	317	63.5								$4,250	$5,500	$10,000
	Auctions: $28,200, PF-66, August 2016; $4,700, PF-64, March 2015; $3,290, PF-62, September 2016; $1,827, AU-50, September 2015												

† Ranked in the *100 Greatest U.S. Coins* (fourth edition). **a.** There are at least two misplaced-date die varieties of the 1875-S twenty-cent piece. These do not command a premium in the marketplace. A repunched mintmark is likewise common.

Quarter Dollars
1796 to Date

This survey of U.S. dimes is based on the work of Q. David Bowers,
a numismatic professional and author in the field for more than 60 years.

AN OVERVIEW OF QUARTER DOLLARS

In *Mega Red*, fifth edition, we present the most comprehensive study of early U.S. quarter dollars ever made in a general-interest book. We have drawn upon many sources, including specialized references, auction results, historical documents, news accounts, numismatic researchers, and more.

We hope you will find this information to be valuable and perhaps numismatically inspirational. Collecting early quarters, especially those of the Capped Bust type, can be very affordable (although the 1823 and 1827 are very notable exceptions).

The first federal quarters were made at the Philadelphia Mint in 1796 and featured the Draped Bust obverse combined with the Small Eagle reverse. This was the only year of the type. It was not until 1804 that the next coinage took place: the Draped Bust obverse was retained in combination with the Heraldic Eagle reverse that had been used on other silver denominations in the late 18th century. The Draped Bust / Heraldic Eagle type proved to be ephemeral and was discontinued after 1807, after which the denomination was not struck again until the Capped Bust type was introduced in 1815. It continued to 1838, when it was replaced by the Liberty Seated design. With some changes this style was continued to 1891, after which the Barber, Standing Liberty, and Washington coinages took place.

From the beginning days of wide numismatic interest in America in the 1850s, to today, quarters of the Draped Bust and Capped Bust types have always been popular to collect. In the early times this was usually done by date, without reference to the size of numerals or letters.

In 1881 John W. Haseltine, the leading Philadelphia coin dealer at the time, published his *Type Table*, which listed die varieties of quarters, half dollars, and dollars.[1] The Haseltine study was never a best-seller, and uses of it were sporadic. The scenario changed in 1925 with the publication of Ard W. Browning's excellent study, *The Early Quarter Dollars of the United States, 1796–1838, With a Few Remarks Concerning Their Types, Varieties and Rarity, Illustrated on Eight Photographic Plates.* Published by Wayte Raymond in New York City, it illustrated coins attributed to the collection of the author. However, no Browning collection of quarter dollars is otherwise recorded in numismatic literature. Perhaps it was sold *en bloc* to one of the major collectors of the day, such as Colonel E.H.R. Green.

Browning was virtually unknown on the numismatic scene. He worked in a mental hospital and seems to have been a very private individual. In the same year, 1925, his application for membership in the American Numismatic Association was published, listing Central Islip, Long Island, New York, as his address; his sponsors were Rud. Kohler and Julius Guttag.

In 1929 Raymond had a new publicity campaign for Browning's book, offering it in regular format for $6 and in a special edition limited to 10 numbered copies, with interleaved pages and full leather binding, for $15. In 1991 Walter Breen updated the book.

Later books include *Early Quarter Dollars of the U.S. Mint 1796–1838* by Rory Rea, Glenn Peterson, Bradley Karoleff, and John Kovach, 2000, and the great tour de force, Steve M. Tompkins's *Early United States Quarters, 1796–1838*, 2008. The latter is the standard resource today, along with occasional censuses and updated information in the *John Reich Journal*, the publication of the John Reich Collectors Society (online at www.JRCS.org). With a nod to Ard Browning, collectors and researchers still use "B" numbers.

The *John Reich Journal* is a gold mine of information. Today, a basic library containing the mentioned books and back issues of the *Journal* can make everyone an expert! In addition, the annual *Guide Book of United States Coins* gives a quick overview of the more popular varieties and mintages published for each year. The present fifth edition of *Mega Red* includes information supplied by Barry Sunshine, a dedicated specialist who was the main contributor to the section on early U.S. dimes in *Mega Red*, fourth edition.

As a general comment, most quarters of the 1796 to 1838 years in the marketplace are in circulated grades, About Good to Very Fine. Most collectors who are John Reich Collectors Society members collect these quarters in either Good to Fine or Extremely Fine to Almost Uncirculated range. Acquiring the vast majority of die varieties is both affordable and an exciting challenge, the 1796, 1823, and 1827 being expensive exceptions. The 1796 is in double demand, both from quarter-dollar specialists and from type collectors who need it to illustrate the only year of the design type. There are two varieties of the 1796, B-1 and B-2, the first being much rarer.

Several rarity scales are available to numismatists; this chapter references the standard Sheldon scale (by Dr. William H. Sheldon). The meanings of the rarity abbreviations are as follows:

Rarity	Number Known		Rarity	Number Known
R-1	1,250+		High R-6	13–20
R-2	501–1,250		Low R-7	7–12
R-3	201–500		High R-7	4–6
R-4	76–200		R-8	2 or 3
R-5	31–75		R-9	Unique
Low R-6	21–30			

Many educated early quarter collectors are able to "cherrypick" rare varieties for the cost of a common-priced example. Aspiring to and collecting Mint State and Proof strikes is beyond the patience and budget of most numismatists. Working with a generous budget over a span of 40 years D. Brent Pogue formed a cabinet of early quarters beyond comparison, with Gem being the usual grade. These were later auctioned by Stack's Bowers Galleries. Many of the images used in the following pages are from the Pogue Collection.

Among later quarters in the small-diameter series from 1831 to 1838, Almost Uncirculated coins can be a collectible and affordable grade, and Mint State coins appear on the market with some frequency. Proofs are extremely rare, and years can pass between offerings of a given date or variety. There are many differences of opinion and debates between numismatists over the characteristics of a Proof. We are not aware of anyone assembling an early Proof quarter collection beyond the Pogue cabinet.

Now, to our presentation of the different types, dates, and Browning varieties.

DRAPED BUST QUARTER DOLLARS (1796, 1804–1807)

Small Eagle Reverse (1796): Designer: *Probably Gilbert Stuart.* **Engraver:** *Robert Scot.*
Heraldic Eagle Reverse: Designer: *Robert Scot.* **Both varieties: Weight:** *104 grains.*
Composition: *.8924 silver, .1076 copper.* **Diameter:** *27.5 mm.* **Edge:** *Reeded.* **Mint:** *Philadelphia.*

1796, Small Eagle Reverse
(Browning–2)

1805, Heraldic Eagle Reverse
(Browning–3)

HISTORY AND BACKGROUND

The first coinage of the denomination under the provisions of the Mint Act of April 2, 1792, did not take place until 1796.

In 1792 President George Washington appointed David Rittenhouse, local maker of clocks and scientific apparatus, to be director of the Mint. Premises were rented in the machine shop of John Harper on Cherry Street, where incoming equipment was stored. Silver half dismes to the extent of 1,500 pieces were minted there on June 15, under the direction of Secretary of State Thomas Jefferson.

In the meantime, two adjoining old buildings were refurbished and new ones built for the Mint, with construction beginning in late summer. In the autumn much equipment was in place, additional half dismes were struck, and a number of pattern coins were made.

The Mint Act provided for the production copper, silver, and gold coins in the new Mint facility. While copper half cents and cents were struck there in

**Mint Director
David Rittenhouse.**

1793, silver coins, excepting half dismes, were not produced at the outset, as chief coiner Henry Voigt and assayer Albion Cox were required to post $10,000 personal surety bonds, something neither was capable of doing. By 1794, this requirement was satisfied and production of half dollars and silver dollars commenced. (Although half dimes dated 1794 exist, pieces with this date were not struck until 1795.) The first gold coins were struck in late summer 1795.

In the 1790s the Mint did not coin silver denominations for its own account but, instead, struck them to specific requests of depositors of bullion (usually in the form of foreign coins). After spring 1795, when a large-capacity press was obtained, the vast majority of silver was converted into dollars. There was little call for the smaller denominations, with the result that half dimes, dimes, quarter dollars, and half dollars of 1796 and 1797 were made only in small numbers, and in 1798 and 1799 certain of these were not made at all.

The two joined-front buildings of the Philadelphia Mint in the 1790s.

Robert Scot, Engraver

The Philadelphia Mint was authorized under the Coinage Act of April 2, 1792. Machinery was acquired, and a temporary facility was set up in the shop of John Harper, where they awaited the finishing of Mint buildings. This was accomplished in the late summer, after which operations were conducted there. Pattern coins as well as silver half dismes for circulation were made. The engravers included Bob Birch and Henry Voigt. Pattern dismes were also made, these from dies by Voigt. In 1792 Joseph Wright, an engraver of exceptional skill, made patterns. In the summer of 1793 he was hired to be the official engraver at the Mint. Unfortunately, he succumbed to the yellow-fever epidemic of that year and died in September.

Robert Scot, born in the British Isles in 1740, learned the skills of engraving printing plates and metal parts for clocks and other devices in Edinburgh, Scotland. He was also a maker of pocket watches. Scot came to America in 1775. He engraved metal plates for bills of exchange and other items for superintendent of finance Robert Morris during the Revolutionary War. In 1780 he was appointed engraver for the State of Virginia. He moved to Philadelphia in 1781 and set up a business engraving plates for maps and illustrations. In 1783 he engraved a frontispiece for a Masonic sermon preached by Wm. Smith, D.D., and published by Hall & Sellers. Circa 1788 he engraved plates for Thomas Dobson's edition of *Rees' Encyclopedia*. His name appears in the *Philadelphia Directory* for 1791 as an engraver at 36 Chestnut St., later moving to 2 Carters Alley.

On November 23, 1793, he was appointed engraver at the Mint by director David Rittenhouse. In the ensuing years he engraved coin dies, and was assisted for a time in the mid-1890s by John Gardner (who was not involved with dimes). He kept up his private business, which now included engraving bank notes. This trade passed in 1810 to Murray, Draper, Fairman & Co. in the same city.

Scot engraved the dies for the Draped Bust obverse and Small Eagle and Heraldic Eagle reverses. On occasion, work on medals, punches, and other items was done by outside contractors, including John Reich at the turn of the 19th century. He was later hired as a full-time assistant to Scot in 1807, as Mint director Robert Patterson felt that Scot was not able to do all the work required (see the later Reich biography). It has been popular numismatically to criticize Scot's work, but his coins prove otherwise. He was less active in later years and is said to have been in poor health and with failing eyesight. He remained as Mint engraver as a sinecure until his passing on November 3, 1823.

Early Quarter Dollars

The first quarter dollars were struck in 1796, with the first delivery being 1,800 coins on April 9. The last delivery was 252 coins on February 28, 1797, thought to be all dated 1796 (what a surprise it would be otherwise!). This brought the total to 6,146 coins.

After that there was no quarter mintage at all until 1804, by which time the reverse design was changed to the Heraldic Eagle type, thus isolating the 1796 as not only the first year of issue but also the only year of this design combination.

The motif of the 1796 quarter is characterized by the head of Miss Liberty facing to the right, her hair behind, some tied with a ribbon at the back and with other tresses falling to her shoulder. Her bosom at the lower right is draped in cloth. LIBERTY is above her head and the date 1796 is below. Eight stars are at the left border and seven to the right, representing the 15 states in the Union at the time (the most recent additions being Vermont and Kentucky). Prominent dentils are around the border, in effect framing the design.

The Draped Bust obverse is from a design first used on the silver dollar of autumn 1795, claimed generations later by his descendants to have been the work of noted artist Gilbert Stuart (who is probably best remembered today for his painting of George Washington, reproductions of which became a familiar sight in schools across the land). It is thought that Philadelphia socialite Anna Willess Williams was the model.

The reverse design for the Small Eagle type features an eagle perching on a cloud (probably difficult to do in real life!), surrounded by a wreath, open at the top and tied with a ribbon bow at the bottom. Around the border is the inscription UNITED STATES OF AMERICA. As on the early half dimes and dimes, the coin has no mark of value. Dentils are around the border but are not as prominent as on the obverse. The Heraldic Eagle reverse was adopted from the Great Seal of the United States, the motif used on other silver coins of the era. UNITED STATES OF AMERICA encircles the design at the border. The denomination is rendered as 25 C., with the 25 and C being separated by the eagle's tail. Dentils are placed around the inner border.

Once the drawings had been approved for the dollar, probably toward the middle of August, they were sent to John Eckstein, who was called by fellow artist Thomas Sully a "thorough-going drudge" in his field. Eckstein, who was paid $30 on September 9 for his work, executed a pair of plaster models, not of the whole coin, but just the Liberty head and reverse eagle/wreath combination. This design was subsequently used on the half dimes, dimes, quarters, and half dollars of 1796.

The 1795 Draped Bust obverse, Small Eagle reverse dollar set the design later used on other silver coins including the 1796 quarter dollar.

The reverse illustrates a "small" eagle perched on a cloud, enclosed within a wreath, encircled by the inscription UNITED STATES OF AMERICA. The edge is reeded. Interestingly, no mark of denomination appears on early dime issues. It was not until 1804 and the new design that a mark of value, 25 C., was used for the first time.

DRAPED BUST QUARTER DOLLARS (1796, 1804–1807): GUIDE TO COLLECTING

In terms of collecting, the 1796, which exists in two die varieties, is dynamically affected by the combination of its low mintage and being the only Draped Bust quarter with the Small Eagle reverse. This has resulted in a strong demand from type-set collectors, far exceeding what would be normal demand from quarter dollar specialists for a given date and varieties.

Many if not most of the Mint State quarters of the Browning-2 variety are highly mirrorlike and are sometimes designated as Proofs. On B-2 the head of the eagle is characteristically weakly struck. In contrast, those of B-1, about 10 times rarer overall, have a much smaller percentage available in Mint State and usually are well struck on the reverse. The Proof tradition is exemplified by this narrative created by John Kraljevich for the Stack's Bowers Galleries sale of the D. Brent Pogue Collection coin graded MS-66 by PCGS:

> When B. Max Mehl described this very coin in 1922 he said: "Broad milled borders. Beautiful Proof. Well struck up. Rare." In our sale of the Milton Holmes Collection, cataloger Norman Stack expanded with this: "Perfect brilliant Proof! A flawless gem that could possibly be matched by one or two others offered in the last 30 years—certainly no finer can exist. Sharp, well struck with perfect milled borders and just about equal to any modern Brilliant Proof in appearance. An unusually bold impression with sharp eagle on reverse. Delightful blue tinge of iridescence."

After 1796, no quarters were again made until 1804, when the Draped Bust obverse was combined with the Heraldic Eagle reverse. For the first time a denomination was given on the reverse: 25 C. The entire mintage of 6,738 quarters of this year was delivered on June 12. Quarters were minted in 1805,

1806, and 1807 (the final delivery was on April 14, 1807), after which the denomination was not resumed until 1815, with the new Capped Bust motif.

Collecting one of each date of the 1804 to 1807 series plus the 1806, 6 Over 5, overdate is easy enough to do. The 1804 stands out as being far rarer than the others and thus much more expensive. The striking is better on the 1804 than on the other dates, with the sharpness declining to the point that some of 1807 are quite flat on the rims and obverse stars. Mint State coins are rare in all instances, and Gems of any of the 1804 to 1807 dates are far, far rarer than are those of 1796.

DRAPED BUST, SMALL EAGLE REVERSE (1796)

GRADING STANDARDS

MS-60 to 70 (Mint State). *Obverse:* At MS-60, some abrasion and contact marks are evident, most noticeably on the cheek, the drapery, and the right field. Luster is present, but may be dull or lifeless, and interrupted in patches. On prooflike coins the contact marks are more prominent. At MS-63, contact marks are very few, and abrasion is hard to detect except under magnification, although this type is sometimes graded liberally due to its

1796; Browning-2. Graded MS-62.

rarity. An MS-65 coin has no abrasion, and contact marks are so minute as to require magnification. Luster should be full and rich. Grades above MS-65 are defined by having fewer marks as perfection is approached. *Reverse:* Comments apply as for the obverse, except that abrasion and contact marks are most noticeable on the eagle at the center, a situation complicated by the fact that this area is typically flatly struck (except on the Browning-2 variety). Grading is best done by the obverse, then verified by the reverse. The field area is small and is protected by lettering and the wreath and in any given grade shows fewer marks than on the obverse.

Illustrated coin: This coin is well struck on the obverse, and the weak striking on the eagle's breast and head is typical of this issue.

AU-50, 53, 55, 58 (About Uncirculated).
Obverse: Light wear is seen on the hair area above the ear and extending to left of the forehead, on the ribbon, on the drapery at the shoulder, and on the high points of the bust line, more so at AU-50 than at AU–53 or 55. An AU-58 coin has minimal traces of wear. An AU-50 coin has luster in protected areas among the stars and letters, with little in the open fields or on the portrait. At AU-58, most

1796; Browning-2. Graded AU-58.

luster remains in the fields, but is worn away on the highest parts of the motifs. *Reverse:* Light wear is seen on the eagle's body (keep in mind this area is nearly always lightly struck) and the edges of the wings. Light wear is seen on the wreath and lettering. Luster is the best key to actual wear. This ranges from perhaps 20% remaining in protected areas (at AU-50) to nearly full mint bloom (at AU-58).

EF-40, 45 (Extremely Fine). *Obverse:* More wear is evident on the upper hair area and the ribbon, and on the drapery and bosom. Excellent detail remains in low-relief areas of the hair. The stars show wear as do the date and letters. Luster, if present at all, is minimal and in protected areas. *Reverse:* The eagle shows more wear, this being the focal point to check. Most feathers remain on the interior areas of the wings. Additional wear is on the wreath and letters, but many details are present. Some luster may be seen in protected areas and if present is slightly more abundant than on the obverse.

1796; Browning-1. Graded EF-40.

VF-20, 30 (Very Fine). *Obverse:* The higher-relief areas of hair are well worn at VF-20, less so at VF-30, although much detail remains on the areas below the ear. The drapery and bosom show extensive wear. The stars have more wear, making them appear larger (an optical illusion seen on most worn silver coins of this era). *Reverse:* The body of the eagle shows few if any feathers, while the wings have about half of the feathers visible, mostly on the right wing, depending on the strike. The leaves lack most detail and are in outline form. Scattered, non-disfiguring marks are normal for this and lower grades. Any major defects should be noted separately.

1796; Browning-2. Graded VF-30.

F-12, 15 (Fine). *Obverse:* Wear is more extensive than on a Very Fine coin, particularly noticeable on the hair, face, and bosom. The stars appear larger. About half the hair detail remains, most noticeably behind the neck and shoulder. The denticles remain strong (while on most other silver denominations of this design they become weak at this grade level). *Reverse:* Wear is more extensive. Now feather details are diminished, with fewer than half remaining on the wings. The wreath and lettering are worn further, and the rim is slightly weak in areas, although most denticles can be seen.

1796; Browning-2. Graded F-12.

VG-8, 10 (Very Good). *Obverse:* The portrait is mostly seen in outline form, with most hair strands gone, although there is some definition at the back of the hair and behind the shoulder. The ear is discernible, as is the eye. The stars appear larger still, again an illusion. The rim is weak in areas. Most denticles are seen, some of them even bold. LIBERTY and the date are readable and usually full, although

1796; Browning-2. Graded VG-10.

some letters may be weak at their tops (the high rim and denticles protect the design more on the quarter dollar than on other silver coins of this type). *Reverse:* The eagle is mostly an outline, with parts blending into the field (on lighter strikes), although some slight feather detail can be seen on the right wing. The rim is worn, as are the letters, with some weak, but the motto is readable. Most denticles remain clear.

G-4, 6 (Good). *Obverse:* Wear is more extensive. The head is an outline. The rim still is present, as are most of the denticles, most well defined. LIBERTY is worn, but complete. The date is bold. *Reverse:* The eagle is flat and discernible in outline form, blending into the field in areas. The wreath is well worn. Some of the letters may be partly missing. Some rim areas and denticles are discernible. At this level some "averaging" can be done. If the letters are stronger than usual in one area, but some are missing in another area, the coin can still qualify as G-4.

1796; Browning-1. Graded G-4.

AG-3 (About Good). *Obverse:* Wear is so extensive that the coin is barely identifiable. The head is in outline form, LIBERTY is mostly gone, same for the stars, and the date, while readable, may be partially worn away. *Reverse:* The reverse is well worn, with parts of the wreath and lettering missing.

1796; Browning-2. Graded AG-3.

1796 Draped Bust, Small Eagle Reverse, Quarter Dollar

1796 • **Circulation-Strike Mintage:** 6,146.

B-1. R-4. *Availability in circulated grades:* 125 to 150 estimated. *Availability in Mint State:* 9 to 12 known.

Commentary: This variety is about twice or more scarcer than B-2, and when found is apt to be in lesser average grades. A few have the eagle's head well struck. The easiest way to distinguish this scarce variety from the B-2 variety

Browning-1.

is the location of the 6 in the date. The B-1 variety has the top of the 6 even with the other digits in the date, while the B-2 variety has the top of the 6 practically touching the bust on the device. The strike on this variety is generally average. The finest known of this variety is the Eliasberg example graded Mint State-66. Any collector trying to locate any example of a 1796 quarter should take their time and locate one that they would enjoy owning for many years, as it requires an investment. Select a coin of quality that you will enjoy showing to other collectors.

B-2. R-3. *Availability in circulated grades:* 450 to 500 estimated. *Availability in Mint State:* 35 to 45.

Commentary: This is the variety usually seen. Many if not most Mint State coins are prooflike (see introductory remarks above). This variety is the more available, and most come well struck except for the eagle's head.

B-2.

There are several examples that are truly spectacular including the Mint State-67 Knoxville-Pogue example, the Mint State-66+ Newman coin, and the Mint State-66 Foxfire example. Each of those is legendary and wonderful to view.

In *Coin World*, October 30, 1968, veteran dealer Abe Kosoff told of an interesting group of 1796 quarter dollars from the Col. E.H.R. Green estate handled by Burdette G. Johnson, who seemed to make estates a specialty and also was involved with the dispersal of the Virgil Brand holdings. Kosoff related that James G. Macallister, the Philadelphia dealer, went to St. Louis to acquire a number of the Green pieces. From that point he went to New York City to visit Kosoff, who with Abner Kreisberg operated the Numismatic Gallery. In Abe Kosoff's words:

> When he [Macallister] reached New York City on his return trip he stopped in to see me at the Numismatic Gallery. Mac used to wear a homburg hat and a heavy overcoat. From one inside pocket he took out a long package about 15 to 18 inches, narrow, in brown wrapping paper.
>
> On the show counter he unwrapped it and displayed row after row of 1796 quarters, every one Mint State. "Ninety bucks, take your pick," he said. Before the "wow" got out of my mouth, out of another inside pocket Mac took out another package, very much like the first. "These will cost you $125 each," he advised. This group contained the so-called "Proof" 1796 quarters, brilliant gems, each and every one. The first parcel contained the frosty coins. I don't really recall how many I bought, perhaps five or six of each. All in all I would say there were about 100 pieces, possibly a few more or less.

The present writer recalls that at the American Numismatic Association convention held in Omaha, Nebraska in August 1955, dealer Aubrey Bebee showed him a prooflike 1796 quarter, apologizing, in a way, that it was too much, but the coin was so nice. Prooflike coins were seen on occasion in that decade, but in later years they were absorbed into many collections, with the result that today the offering of such a coin is a very special occasion.

	Cert	Avg	%MS	AG-3	G-4	VG-8	F-12	VF-20	EF-40	AU-50	MS-60	MS-63
1796, most common variety	192	34.3	21%	$7,500	$11,000	$18,000	$25,000	$32,500	$46,000	$60,000	$80,000	$135,000

DRAPED BUST, HERALDIC EAGLE REVERSE (1804–1807)
GRADING STANDARDS

MS-60 to 70 (Mint State). *Obverse:* At MS-60, some abrasion and contact marks are evident, most noticeably on the cheek, the drapery, and the right field. Luster is present, but may be dull or lifeless, and interrupted in patches. At MS-63, contact marks are very few, and abrasion is hard to detect except under magnification. An MS-65 coin will have no abrasion, and contact marks are so minute

1806; Browning-9. Graded MS-66.

as to require magnification. Luster should be full and rich. Coins graded above MS-65 are more theoretical than actual for this type—but they do exist, and are defined by having fewer marks as perfection is approached. As noted in the introduction, expect weakness in some areas. *Reverse:* Comments apply as for the obverse, except that abrasion and contact marks are most noticeable on the eagle's neck, the tips of the wing, and the tail. The field area is complex, without much open space, given the stars above the eagle, the arrows and olive branch, and other features. Accordingly, marks are not as noticeable as on the obverse.

Illustrated coin: This coin is lightly struck on the right obverse stars and at the center of the reverse. Some planchet adjustment marks are mostly hidden. Some tiny carbon streaks are on the obverse (seemingly typical for Browning-9).

AU-50, 53, 55, 58 (About Uncirculated).
Obverse: Light wear is seen on the hair area above the ear and extending to left of the forehead, on the ribbon, and on the drapery at the shoulder, more so at AU-50 than at AU–53 or 55. An AU-58 coin has minimal traces of wear. An AU-50 coin has luster in protected areas among the stars and letters, with little in the open fields or on the portrait. At AU-58, most luster is present in the

1804; Browning-1. Graded AU-58.

fields, but is worn away on the highest parts of the motifs. *Reverse:* Comments as preceding, except that the eagle's neck, the tips and top of the wings, the clouds, and the tail now show noticeable wear, as do other features. Luster ranges from perhaps 20% remaining in protected areas (at AU-50) to nearly full mint bloom (at AU-58). Often the reverse retains much more luster than the obverse, more so on quarter dollars than on other denominations of this design.

Illustrated coin: Lightly struck on the obverse stars. The reverse has some light areas but is sharp overall. A few planchet adjustment marks are visible. Abundant luster and good eye appeal rank this as an exceptional example of this date, the most difficult of the type to find in high grades.

EF-40, 45 (Extremely Fine). *Obverse:* More wear is evident on the upper hair area and the ribbon, and on the drapery at the shoulder and the bosom. Excellent detail remains in low-relief areas of the hair. The stars show wear, as do the date and letters (note: on most coins of this type the stars are softly struck). Luster, if present at all, is minimal and in protected areas. *Reverse:* Wear is greater than on an About Uncirculated coin, overall. The

1804; Browning-1. Graded EF-45.

neck lacks feather detail on its highest points. Feathers have lost some detail near the edges of the wings, and some areas of the horizontal lines in the shield may be blended together. Some traces of luster may be seen, more so at EF-45 than at EF-40.

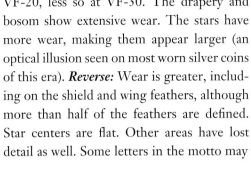

VF-20, 30 (Very Fine). *Obverse:* The higher-relief areas of hair are well worn at VF-20, less so at VF-30. The drapery and bosom show extensive wear. The stars have more wear, making them appear larger (an optical illusion seen on most worn silver coins of this era). *Reverse:* Wear is greater, including on the shield and wing feathers, although more than half of the feathers are defined. Star centers are flat. Other areas have lost

1804; Browning-1. Graded VF-30.

detail as well. Some letters in the motto may be missing, depending on the strike.

F-12, 15 (Fine). *Obverse:* Wear is more extensive than on a Very Fine coin, particularly noticeable on the hair, face, and bosom. The stars appear larger. About half the hair detail remains with the tresses fused so as to appear thick, most noticeably behind the neck and shoulder. The rim may be partially worn away and blend into the field. *Reverse:* Wear is even more extensive, with the shield and wing feathers being points to observe.

1804; Browning-1. Graded F-12.

About half of the feathers can be seen. The incuse E PLURIBUS UNUM may have a few letters worn away. The clouds all seem to be connected. The stars are weak. Parts of the border and lettering may be weak. As with most quarters of this type, peculiarities of striking can account for some weakness.

VG-8, 10 (Very Good). *Obverse:* The portrait is mostly seen in outline form, with most hair strands gone, although there is slight definition at the back of the hair and behind the shoulder. The ear is discernible, as is the eye. The stars appear larger still, again an illusion. The rim is weak in areas. LIBERTY and the date are readable and usually full, although some letters may be weak at their tops. *Reverse:* Wear is more extensive. Half

1804; Browning-1. Graded VG-8.

or so of the letters in the motto are worn away. Most feathers are worn away, although separation of some of the lower feathers may be seen. Some stars are faint. The border blends into the field in areas (depending on striking), and some letters are weak.

G-4, 6 (Good). *Obverse:* Wear is more extensive, and some stars may be partly missing. The head is an outline. The eye is visible only in outline form. The rim is well worn or even missing in areas. LIBERTY is worn, and parts of some letters may be missing, but elements of all should be readable. The date is readable, but worn. *Reverse:* Wear is more extensive. The upper part of the eagle is flat, and feathers are noticeable only at some (but

1804; Browning-1. Graded G-4.

not necessarily all) of the lower edge of the wings, and do not have detail. The shield lacks most of its detail. Only a few letters of the motto can be seen (depending on striking). The rim is worn extensively, and a few letters may be missing.

AG-3 (About Good). *Obverse:* Wear is so extensive that the coin is barely identifiable. The head is in outline form, LIBERTY is mostly gone. Same for the stars. The date, while readable, may be partially worn away. *Reverse:* Extensive wear is seen overall, with the rim worn away and some areas worn smooth. The eagle can be discerned in outline form, but not necessarily completely. A few stray motto letters may remain. Some-

1804; Browning-1. Graded AG-3.

times the obverse appears to be more worn than the reverse, or vice-versa.

1804 Draped Bust, Heraldic Eagle Reverse, Quarter Dollar

1804 • **Circulation-Strike Mintage:** 6,738.

B-1. R-3. *Availability in circulated grades:* 400 to 425 estimated. *Availability in Mint State:* 8 to 12.

Commentary: After a seven-year hiatus, the Mint resumed producing quarters. The 1804 quarter is the first year with the Heraldic Eagle reverse. Generally, 1804 quarters are very scarce. The B-1 variety is more available than the

B-1.

B-2. Collectors looking for this date should cherrypick a well-struck example, as they exist. The finest known example is a Gem example that sold for $345,000 in January 2011. It is interesting to note that this same coin sold in 1975 for only $10,500.

B-2. R-5. *Availability in circulated grades:* 35 to 45 estimated. *Availability in Mint State:* One (MS-65).

Commentary: This variety is very scarce and will require patience to find. Examples in higher grades are especially difficult to locate. The distinguishing difference between the B-1 and the very scarce B-2 is that on the B-2,

B-2.

the 4 in the date is very high and is almost touching the device of Liberty. When Walter Breen revised the Browning reference in 1992, he listed nine examples, with only five better than VG.

	Cert	Avg	%MS	AG-3	G-4	VG-8	F-12	VF-20	EF-40	AU-50	MS-60	MS-63
1804, most common variety	132	17.0	4%	$2,500	$3,500	$6,500	$8,500	$13,000	$25,000	$44,000	$80,000	$175,000

1805 Draped Bust, Heraldic Eagle Reverse, Quarter Dollar

1805 • **Circulation-Strike Mintage:** 121,394.

B-1. R-4+. *Availability in circulated grades:* 90 to 100 estimated. *Availability in Mint State:* Fewer than four known.

Commentary: This is a scarce variety and can be noted as the 5 in the date is touching Liberty on the device and on the reverse C in 25 C. is not touching Liberty's tail. Many 1805 quarters that exist are heavily clashed.

B-1.

B-2. R-2. *Availability in circulated grades:* 750 to 850 estimated. *Availability in Mint State:* Fewer than 10 known.

Commentary: The possibly finest known B-2 sold in a January 2008 auction at the amazing price of $402,500. One interesting characteristic of B-2 that is later die states show obverse die cracks running through the rightmost stars.

B-2.

B-3. R-2. *Availability in circulated grades:* 800 to 850 estimated. *Availability in Mint State:* Fewer than seven known.

Commentary: Most of these varieties are weakly struck on the reverse, so patience is required to find a well-struck example. The finest known example is the Pogue example that sold in auction for $82,250 in January 2016.

B-3.

B-4. R-4. *Availability in circulated grades:* 175 to 200 estimated. *Availability in Mint State:* Fewer than eight known.

Commentary: The obverse die was later overdated to produce 1806, 6 Over 5, B-1 (see listing below). One characteristic of this variety is the C. on the reverse is embedded in the eagle's tail.

B-4.

B-5. R-5. *Availability in circulated grades:* 60 to 75 estimated. *Availability in Mint State:* None known.

Commentary: This variety was discovered by Walter Breen circa 1956. One characteristic is the C on the reverse is touching the eagle's tail. This is the rarest variety of the 1805 series and it very difficult to find an example with nice eye appeal.

B-5.

	Cert	Avg	%MS	AG-3	G-4	VG-8	F-12	VF-20	EF-40	AU-50	MS-60	MS-63
1805, most common variety	366	22.7	5%	$250	$450	$650	$950	$1,800	$3,750	$5,500	$11,000	$19,500

1806 Draped Bust, Heraldic Eagle Reverse, Quarter Dollar

1806, 6 Over 5 • **Circulation-Strike Mintage:** Included in 1806 mintage.

B-1. R-2. *Availability in circulated grades:* 800 to 900 estimated. *Availability in Mint State:* 15 to 20.

Commentary: The 1806, 6 Over 5, is the earliest overdate in the quarter dollar series and is the only overdate within the 1804–1807 design type. This overdated die is very unusual, indeed, and it is clearly visible without the need of a loupe. Both the obverse and reverse dies were originally used to strike 1805 Browning-4 quarters, thus this is technically the same die marriage, only with the obverse die altered to read 1806. Most overdates involve coinage dies which were not previously in use and had not been hardened. This obverse had been hardened. Probably, it was heated again and softened to accommodate the 6 punch, and then hardened again.

B-1.

A similar occurrence took place among quarter eagles of the same year, with 1806, 6 Over 5, quarter eagles being the same die marriage as those dated 1805. Among other overdates, the vast majority are dies that were not used for coinage but were in a vault at the Mint until overdated and used for the first time to strike coins. This variety is, as noted, a curious exception.[2]

There are a fair number of original eye appealing examples of this overdate, but buyers should be selective. The two finest examples known are graded MS-65+ and MS-66, and have recently been sold in auction for $176,250 and $188,000 respectively. Both coins are gorgeous examples.

	Cert	Avg	%MS	AG-3	G-4	VG-8	F-12	VF-20	EF-40	AU-50	MS-60	MS-63
1806, 6 Over 5	147	24.2	7%	$300	$500	$700	$1,100	$2,000	$4,250	$6,000	$13,000	$25,000

1806 • Circulation-Strike Mintage: 206,124.

B-2. R-2. *Availability in circulated grades:* 750 to 1,000 estimated. *Availability in Mint State:* 12 to 15 known.

Commentary: This is a fairly common variety. Star 13 is not close to the bust, and on the reverse the C is very close to the eagle's tail and touches A3. With patience a very nice eye appealing example can be found. Very late die states have significant die breaks and cracks on the reverse.

B-3. R-1. *Availability in circulated grades:* 1,500 to 1,800 estimated. *Availability in Mint State:* 10 to 15 known.

Commentary: This common variety uses the same obverse die as B-2, but on the reverse the 5 in 25 doesn't touch any devices. Middle and late die states show crumbling either on the obverse, reverse, or both.

B-4. R-5. *Availability in circulated grades:* 55 to 65 estimated. *Availability in Mint State:* None known.

Commentary: On this variety, Star 1 on the obverse is low in relationship to Liberty. Typically, with patience advanced early quarters collectors can cherrypick this variety.

B-5. R-4. *Availability in circulated grades:* 85 to 100 estimated. *Availability in Mint State:* Fewer than five known.

Commentary: This variety has Star 1 on the obverse far from the bust; the lower star on the reverse touches the eagle's beak.

B-6. R-5. *Availability in circulated grades:* 50 to 60 estimated. *Availability in Mint State:* Two known.

Commentary: On the obverse, the TY in LIBERTY is lower at the base than the R. The reverse is the same as B-5.

B-2.

B-3.

B-4.

B-5.

B-6.

B-7. R-5. *Availability in circulated grades:* 50 to 60 estimated. *Availability in Mint State:* None known.

Commentary: This variety shares the same obverse as B-6. On the reverse the stem of the olive branch touches the C in C. at the top.

B-7.

B-8. R-6. *Availability in circulated grades:* 20 to 25 estimated. *Availability in Mint State:* None known.

Commentary: This is the scarcest variety of all the 1806 strikes. The highest-known grade is About Uncirculated. This variety shares the same obverse as the B-6. On the reverse the olive branch touches the C in C. at the bottom left. There are several examples that have a reverse cud; those are very rare.

B-8.

B-9. R-1. *Availability in circulated grades:* 1,100 to 1,300 estimated. *Availability in Mint State:* About 10 known.

Commentary: On this variety the distance between the 25 and the U in UNITED on the reverse is greater than the other varieties.

B-9.

B-10. R-5. *Availability in circulated grades:* 50 to 60 estimated. *Availability in Mint State:* Fewer than five known.

Commentary: This obverse shares the same obverse as the B-5, but the reverse has the C in C. with more distance from the last A in AMERICA.

B-10.

	Cert	Avg	%MS	AG-3	G-4	VG-8	F-12	VF-20	EF-40	AU-50	MS-60	MS-63
1806, most common variety	542	23.0	8%	$225	$450	$650	$950	$1,800	$3,750	$5,500	$11,000	$20,000

1807 Draped Bust, Heraldic Eagle Reverse, Quarter Dollar

1807 • **Circulation-Strike Mintage:** 220,643.

B-1. R-2. *Availability in circulated grades:* 750 to 900 estimated. *Availability in Mint State:* About 15 known.

Commentary: The distinction between this variety and the slightly scarcer B-2 below is the distance between Stars 1 and 2 on the obverse. On B-1 the two stars are farther apart, whereas the two stars on B-2 are very close

B-1.

together. Generally, there are sufficient examples to satisfy demand. Collectors looking for a Draped Bust quarter typically choose the 1807 or 1806 date for the type set. However, at the Gem level, only two or three exist. One of those Gems sold in November 2017 Pogue Collection auction for $162,000.

B-2. R-3. *Availability in circulated grades:* 300 to 350 estimated. *Availability in Mint State:* 10 to 13 known.

Commentary: This variety is scarcer than B-1. One of the finest known examples is the Eric P. Newman example, graded MS-66, that sold for $411,250 in a November 2013 auction. The Newman example is nicely struck and extremely colorfully toned. Generally, all 1807 quarters are weakly struck.

B-2.

	Cert	Avg	%MS	AG-3	G-4	VG-8	F-12	VF-20	EF-40	AU-50	MS-60	MS-63
1807, most common variety	290	22.8	12%	$225	$450	$700	$950	$1,750	$3,750	$5,500	$11,000	$19,500

CAPPED BUST QUARTER DOLLARS (1815–1838)

Variety 1, Large Diameter (1815–1828): **Designer:** *John Reich.* **Weight:** *104 grains.* **Composition:** *.8924 silver, .1076 copper.* **Diameter:** *Approximately 27 mm.* **Variety 2, Small Diameter (1831–1838):** **Designer:** *William Kneass.* **Weight:** *1815–1837, 104 grains; 1837–1838, 103 grains.* **Composition:** *1815–1837, .8924 silver, .1076 copper; 1837–1838, .900 silver, .100 copper.* **Diameter:** *24.3 mm.* **Both varieties:** **Edge:** *Reeded.* **Mint:** *Philadelphia.*

Variety 1, Large Diameter (1815–1828)
Browning-1.

Variety 2, Reduced Diameter, Motto Removed (1831–1838) *Browning-1.*

HISTORY AND BACKGROUND

In 1807, John Reich, appointed assistant engraver at the Mint that same year, redesigned the silver half dollar and the gold half eagle to depict Miss Liberty in a cloth cap fit loosely over her head, a style numismatically known as the Capped Bust design. Eventually, this was accepted on other silver and gold denominations the next year they were coined.

At the time, production of certain values was intermittent. True to form, after 1807 the next quarter coinage wasn't until 1815. This came about when Bailly Blanchard, cashier of the Planters Bank on Bryan Street in New Orleans, sent a letter on June 6 to the Philadelphia Mint advising that he had shipped $14,577.62½ in silver aboard the *South Carolina*, a coastwise packet ship under the command of Captain Joseph Robinson.[3] According to contemporary accounts this was an elegantly outfitted vessel that carried passengers and cargo. The silver probably was in the form of Spanish-American coins. After they were assayed and the value of silver for coinage had been determined, the net amount was to be returned in quarter dollars. Blanchard explained that the only other coins circulating in New Orleans were 6-1/4 and 12-1/2 reals, and that he urgently wanted federal quarters.

The *South Carolina* arrived in Philadelphia on July 6, having spent about five weeks at sea. New dies had to be prepared for the coinage, and there were other delays, The order came under Warrant No. 732, December 16, 1815, for 69,232 coins, of which 56,934 were shipped to the Planters Bank, with the remainder going to the Bank of Pennsylvania on December 30, and some to Jones, Firth & Co. on January 10 (including additional 1815-dated quarters struck in early 1816.[4] A quantity of quarters of this date was kept intact for many years (see information below under the 1815 quarter listing).

As for other denominations sharing this design, the first Capped Bust half dime was made in 1829, the first dime in 1809, and the first quarter eagle in 1808. After 1804, no silver dollars or $10 gold eagles were made until 1836 and 1838 respectively, by which time new designs by engraver Christian Gobrecht were used.

For the quarter series, the years struck were intermittent during the run of the large-diameter type, 1815 to 1828, then continuous with the modified small-diameter quarters from 1831 to 1838. During the same era, Spanish-American silver one-reals, valued at 25 cents, were circulating as legal tender and were widely used. In fact, they were much more common in circulation than federal quarters. A quarter had substantial value in its era. In the 1830s a typical day's wage for a laborer was 50 cents.

In 1832 the second United States Mint was completed in Philadelphia, a facility that would remain in use until 1901. In 1838 branch mints were opened in Charlotte, Dahlonega, and New Orleans, but no Capped Bust quarters were ever struck at those locations.

The second Philadelphia Mint opened in 1833.

THE PANIC OF 1837

In the early 1830s there was wild speculation in the purchase of federal lands in the states west of Pennsylvania. Many purchases were made with bank bills of uncertain value and promissory notes, ignoring the law that payment had to be made in gold and silver coins (specie) or in paper money issued by banks that had reserves of such coins. To reinforce the law President Andrew Jackson on July 11, 1836, directed Secretary of the Treasury Levi Woodbury to issue the Specie Circular. Allowing time for news to travel in the days before the telegraph, the deadline of August 15 was set to have the directive take effect. Exceptions were made for people buying land who pledged to settle on it and engage in agriculture. The speculation ended.

At the same time there were other troubles. With its 20-year charter of 1816 not renewed, the Bank of the United States closed all of its branches. Although the real effect of this has been a subject of debate by economists ever since, the news was disturbing. In New York City in early 1837 there was a riot when flour in storage was not released in quantity. Matters worsened, and on May 11, 1837, banks in New

York City suspended exchanging their own bank bills at par for gold or silver. This spread, and soon there were no gold and silver coins in circulation. They were available at brokers and banks, but only by paying a premium in paper money for them.

Newly-minted quarters and other coins did not reach the public for face value. Spanish-American silver, mostly well worn, continued to circulate on a limited basis.

Newspapers ran advertisements from many brokers and exchange houses in the business of buying and selling gold. Meanwhile a flood of small private notes took the place of coins.

As an example, the *Evening Chronicle*, New York, ran this on June 20:

Small Notes

Small notes for change, engraved expressly for storekeepers, hotels, tradesmen, manufacturers, &c., to supply the present scarcity of specie. The great demand for these notes have made it necessary to engrave an entire new set on Steel Plates, with beautiful vignettes, the high finish of which renders them secure from counterfeit. Notes for $1, 75, 50, 25 and 12½ cents, printed on bank note paper, equal to bank bills in appearance and beauty, payable to bearer at sight in trade or bankable bills. The above notes are now ready for delivery. Orders from any part of the United States promptly attended to, on application to J. NEALE, Engraver and Printer, 6 John St., 5 doors from Broadway, N.B. Tradesmen and country merchants are invited to call and see specimens previous to making their purchases.

The monetary confusion lasted into 1838 and in addition to scrip notes spawned millions of copper cent-sized private issues known today has Hard Times tokens. It was not until early 1843 that the economy was again strong.

JOHN REICH, ENGRAVER

John Reich (Johann Matthaus Reich) was born in Fürth, Germany, in 1768, where his father was a prolific medalist said to have been of indifferent talent. Father and son worked together on a number of memorial medals released between the years 1789 and 1800. After working in his father's shop, Reich emigrated from Hamburg to America aboard the *Anna*, arriving in Philadelphia in August 1800. After a year's indenture to a Philadelphia coppersmith, Reich was "freed" by Henry Voigt, then chief coiner at the Mint.

In his early years Reich did contract work on medals for the Mint and acquitted himself in fine style. Working privately for Joseph Sansom, he engraved the dies for several fine medals, including Washington, after Gilbert Stuart; Benjamin Franklin, from the Jean-Antoine Houdon bust; the American Beaver medal; a peace medal; and a Tripoli medal presented to Commander Edward Preble in 1806.

In January 1806 this was advertised in Philadelphia:

A medal in honor of the memory of Washington has been struck at Philadelphia, under the direction of J. Reich, a German artist. The face, a head of General Washington, in his uniform. Inscription, GENERAL WASHINGTON, C.C.A.U.S. (Commander in Chief of the Armies of the United States). Reverse, under the date of the acquisition of Independence, the American eagle, with the thunder-bolt in its claws and the olive branch in its beak, descending upon the section of the globe, on which the United States are delineated by their boundaries.[5]

Another Washington medal, after Stuart's head, is advertised as issued in Philadelphia, October 9, 1806, "In commemoration of the retirement of Washington." The medal is described in *Poulson's Advertiser* as being struck in silver and bearing the following inscriptions:

Face, A Head of Washington as President. Inscription—G. Washington. Pre. Unit. Sts. Reverse. The ensigns of authority (civil and military) deposited, in laurels, upon the tablet of the United States. Inscription. Commis. Resigned: Presidency Relinquished. 17 97 [*sic*].

The announcement is further made that the dies were executed by "the celebrated Artist John Reich; the likeness from a drawing of Stuart sketched on purpose."

On March 25, 1807, Mint director Robert Patterson wrote to President Thomas Jefferson:

> Our present Engraver, Scot, though indeed a meritorious and faithful officer, is yet so far advanced in life, that he cannot very long be expected to continue his labors. In the event of his sickness or death, the business of the Institution would probably be stopped for some time, since few, if any one could be found qualified to supply his place except Mr. Reich, an artist with whose talents, I presume, you are not unacquainted; and this gentleman not finding business here sufficient for his support, is, I understand, about to remove to Europe. A small salary would, however, retain him in the country, and secure his services to the Mint. And, in truth, the beauty of our coins would be greatly improved by the assistance of his masterly hand.
>
> An assistant engraver [John Gardner] was formerly employed by Mr. Rittenhouse, and by Mr. DeSaussure—and with your approbation, Sir, I would immediately employ Mr. Reich in that capacity. He is willing for the present to accept of the moderate compensation of six hundred dollars per annum; and should this gentleman be employed, perhaps more than his salary would be saved to the public, in which is usually expended on the engraving of dies for medals, but which might then be executed by an artist in their own service, with little or no additional experience.

On April 2, 1807, Patterson wrote to Jefferson again:

> With your approbation I have employed Mr. John Reich as an assistant engraver in the mint at the annual salary of six hundred dollars. He has covenanted to execute any work in the line of his profession, that may be required of him either by the director or chief engraver, whether for the immediate use of the Mint, or for that of the United States, when ordered by any special resolution or act of Congress for that purpose, or by the President, provided that in the execution of any such work, no extraordinary hours of labor or attendance be required without an adequate compensation therefor, so that if any seals should be wanted for the public offices, or dies for the purpose of striking Indian or other medals, they can now be executed in the best stile at the Mint, without any extra expense to the government.
>
> Mr. Reich is now preparing a set of new dies in which some improvements in the devices will be introduced, (adhering, however, strictly to the letter of the law) which it is hoped will meet with public approbation.

The first order of business was to develop new motifs for the coinage. Reich's "Capped Bust" design, as we call it today, was used on the half dollar and half eagle, as noted earlier, followed by its use on the half dime, quarter, and quarter eagle, as also noted. On the Capped Bust, Large Diameter, quarter dollar, the bust has seven stars to the left and six to the right, with the date below and denticles around the inside border. The Small Diameter obverse features the same essential design, but with a different edge treatment. The Large and Small Diameter reverses are also essentially the same: at the center is the perched eagle as used on other silver coins of the era, with UNITED STATES OF AMERICA around the border; the denomination is expressed as 25 C. The Large Diameter quarter bears a banner with the motto E PLURIBUS UNUM in the field above the eagle's head—a feature omitted from the Small Diameter reverse. As with the obverse denticles, those around the border on the Small Diameter reverse are more regular in appearance and more compactly arranged than on the Large Diameter.

Reich also created what we call the "Classic Head" design today, featuring Miss Liberty facing to the left, wearing a band inscribed LIBERTY across her head, with hair tresses visible above. This motif was first used on cents of 1808 and continued thereon through 1814. On half cents the Classic Head first appeared in 1809, and was used on them for a long time afterward, on the intermittent coinage through 1836. In 1834, when chief engraver William A. Kneass made dies for the new Classic Head quarter eagles and half eagles, he swiped Reich's motif of 1808.[6] Kneass was not very original in the things he did, and seemed to be in low gear while at the Mint.

Reich worked at the Mint for the next 10 years, resigning on March 31, 1817, due to failing eyesight or, as some have it, dissatisfaction with his unchanged salary of $600 per year. He traveled westward to Pittsburgh to restore his health and to pursue other interests. He is said by some to have died in Albany, New York, in 1833, although this has been questioned. His name, so important in numismatic circles today, had never been mentioned in an *Annual Report of the Director of the Mint.* (Actually, this was not unusual, and for decades later few other Mint artists were mentioned, either.) In time his coinage became a numismatic specialty, and today the John Reich Collectors Society (JRCS) honors his name. Many of Reich's obverse dies have a small notch in the 13th star, leading to the conclusion that this was his secret sign, called a *privy mark* in numismatic nomenclature, to identify his work.

On the personal side, Reich had a deep interest in music and was well acquainted with the classics. He was one of the founders of the Society of Artists, organized in Philadelphia in 1810, and is entered on the list of Fellows of the Society as "die-sinker at the United States Mint." In 1812 he was one of the first group of Pennsylvania Academicians. The intellectual and social-participation side of Reich has not been well studied.

WILLIAM KNEASS, ENGRAVER

In the chronicles of the Capped Bust design, William Kneass, successor to Scot as engraver, performed a minor role, making or supervising some adjustments to the design, denticles, and coinage.

Kneass was born in Lancaster, Pennsylvania, on September 25, 1780, the son of Christopher and Anna (Feltman) Kneass. In Lancaster on June 23, 1804, he married Mary Turner Honeyman. Later, after her passing, he married Jane Kramer.

It is not known how he learned the art of engraving, but from 1804 and 1805 onward he worked at that trade in Philadelphia, including as a partner in Kneass & Dellaker, and from 1817 to 1820 with James H. Young in Young, Kneass & Co., general engravers. During the War of 1812 he served as a volunteer association in the Field Engineers, a group that built fortifications on the western side of Philadelphia. Later, in 1815, he engraved a plan of this construction based on a drawing by his close friend William Strickland. Kneass named one of his six children after Strickland.

On January 29, 1824, he was appointed as engraver at the Mint, an arrangement facilitated by his friend Adam Eckfeldt, the chief coiner. Biographical notes years later by Patterson DuBois at the Mint included this:

> Mr. Kneass is well remembered as an affable, genial "gentleman of the old-school," who had the rare quality of engaging and winning the esteem and affection of children and youth, in whose companionship he found rich delight. Prior to his appointment he had an engraving office on Fourth above Chestnut Street, Philadelphia, which was a well-known rendezvous for the leading wits and men of culture, for which Philadelphia was then eminent.[7]

At the Mint, Kneass did not leave behind a distinguished record of numismatic accomplishments. He is best remembered today for his Classic Head quarter eagle and half eagle of 1834, essentially copies of John Reich's Classic Head design used earlier on the 1808 copper cent. No pattern coins can be definitely attributed to him.

On August 27, 1835, Kneass suffered an incapacitating stroke, after which he did virtually no creative work. Fortunately, Christian Gobrecht was hired at the Mint at this time, under the title of "second" (not assistant) engraver, as the talented and long-admired Gobrecht did not want to be considered lower in position than Kneass. Kneass died on August 27, 1840, after which Gobrecht was given the office. The title of "chief" engraver was not used at this early time.

CAPPED BUST QUARTER DOLLARS (1815–1828): GUIDE TO COLLECTING

Today, Capped Bust quarters from 1815 to 1838 are very popular with specialists in early American silver coins. The 1823, 3 Over 2, is sufficiently rare that only a few collectors are able to own one. The 1827, 7 Over 4 Over 3, usually just called 1827, seems to have been made only in Proof format, although a circulation production of 4,000 is listed; that listing probably referred to coinage from earlier-dated dies. A restrike of the 1827 was also made.

The reduced-diameter quarters of 1831 to 1838 were produced each year. Although some die combinations are rare, collecting one of each date is easily enough done. News and information printed in the *John Reich Collectors Society Journal* adds to the enjoyment of building a collection.

CAPPED BUST QUARTER DOLLARS (1815–1828)

GRADING STANDARDS

MS-60 to 70 (Mint State). *Obverse:* At MS-60, some abrasion and contact marks are evident, most noticeably on the cheek, the hair below LIBERTY, and the area near the drapery clasp. Luster is present, but may be dull or lifeless, and interrupted in patches. At MS-63, contact marks are very few, and abrasion is hard to detect except under magnification. An MS-65 coin has no abrasion, and contact marks are so minute as to require magnifica-

1831, Large Letters; Browning-5. Graded MS-62.

tion. Luster should be full and rich. Grades above MS-65 are seen now and again and are defined by having fewer marks as perfection is approached. Grading for Reduced Diameter, Motto Removed, examples is similar, except the rims are more uniform, striking is usually very sharp, and the wear occurs evenly on both sides. *Reverse:* Comments apply as for the obverse, except that abrasion and contact marks are most noticeable on the eagle's neck, the top of the wings, the claws, and the flat band that surrounds the incuse motto. The field is mainly protected by design elements and does not show abrasion as much as does the obverse on a given coin.

AU-50, 53, 55, 58 (About Uncirculated). *Obverse:* Light wear is seen on the cap, the hair below LIBERTY, the curl on the neck, the hair near the clasp, and the drapery. At AU-58, the luster is extensive except in the open area of the field, especially to the right. At AU–50 and 53, luster remains only in protected areas. Grading for Reduced Diameter, Motto Removed, examples is similar, except the rims are more uniform, striking is usually

1834; Browning-2. Graded AU-55.

very sharp, and the wear occurs evenly on both sides. *Reverse:* Wear is evident on the eagle's neck, the top of the wings, the claws, and the flat band above the eagle. An AU-58 coin has nearly full luster. At AU–50 and 53, there still is significant luster, more than on the obverse. Generally, light wear is most obvious on the obverse.

EF-40, 45 (Extremely Fine). *Obverse:* Wear is more extensive, most noticeably on the higher areas of the hair. The cap shows more wear, as does the cheek. Most or all stars have some radial lines visible (unless lightly struck, as many are). Luster, if present, is in protected areas among the star points and close to the portrait. Grading for Reduced Diameter, Motto Removed, examples is similar, except the rims are more uniform, striking is

1831, Small Letters; Browning-4. Graded EF-40.

usually very sharp, and the wear occurs evenly on both sides. *Reverse:* The wings show wear on the higher areas of the feathers, and some details are lost. Feathers in the neck are light on some (but not on especially sharp strikes). The eagle's claws and the leaves show wear. Luster may be present in protected areas, even if there is little or none on the obverse.

VF-20, 30 (Very Fine). *Obverse:* Wear is more extensive, and most of the hair is combined into thick tresses without delicate features. The curl on the neck is flat. Details of the drapery are well defined at the lower edge. Unless they were weakly struck, the stars are mostly flat although a few may retain radial lines. Grading for Reduced Diameter, Motto Removed, examples is similar, except the rims are more uniform, striking is usually

1828. Graded VF-20.

very sharp, and the wear occurs evenly on both sides. *Reverse:* Wear is most evident on the eagle's neck, to the left of the shield, and on the leaves and claws. Most feathers in the wing remain distinct, but some show light wear. Overall, the reverse on most quarters at this level shows less wear than the obverse.

F-12, 15 (Fine). *Obverse:* Wear is more extensive, with much of the hair blended together. The drapery is indistinct at its upper edge. The stars are flat. Grading for Reduced Diameter, Motto Removed, examples is similar, except the rims are more uniform, striking is usually very sharp, and the wear occurs evenly on both sides. *Reverse:* Wear is more extensive, now with only about half of the feathers remaining on the wings. The claws on the right are fused at their upper parts.

1815. Graded F-15.

VG-8, 10 (Very Good). *Obverse:* The hair is less distinct, with the area above the face blended into the facial features. LIBERTY is complete, but can be weak in areas. At the left the drapery and bosom are blended together in a flat area. The rim is worn away in areas, and blends into the field. *Reverse:* Feathers are fewer and mostly on the eagle's wing to the left. Other details are weaker. E PLURIBUS UNUM is weak, perhaps with some letters missing. All border lettering remains easily readable.

1828, 25 Over 50 C.; Browning-3. Graded VG-10.

Illustrated coin: Gunmetal toning in the fields contrasts nicely with the lighter devices. The overpunched denomination shows signs of the 50 punched first into the die to the left of both 2 and 5.

G-4, 6 (Good). *Obverse:* The portrait is mostly in outline, with few interior details discernible. LIBERTY may still be readable or may be partially worn away, depending on the variety. Most or all of the border is worn away, and the outer parts of the stars are weak. *Reverse:* The eagle mostly is in outline form, although some feathers can be seen in the wing to the left. All letters around the border are clear. E PLURIBUS UNUM is mostly or completely worn away.

1815; Browning-1. Graded G-4.

AG-3 (About Good). *Obverse:* The portrait is an outline. Most of LIBERTY can still be seen. Stars are weak or missing toward what used to be the rim. The date remains clear, but may be weak at the bottom. *Reverse:* The reverse shows more wear than at G-4, but parts of the rim may remain clear.

1825, 5 Over 4; Browning-3. Graded AG-3.

PF-60 to 70 (Proof). *Obverse and Reverse:* Proofs that are extensively cleaned and have many hairlines, or that are dull and grainy, are lower level, such as PF–60 to 62. While any early Proof coin will attract attention, lower-level examples are not of great interest to specialists unless they are of rare die varieties. With medium hairlines, an assigned grade of PF-64 may be in order and with relatively few, Gem PF-65. PF-66 should have

1833; Browning-1. Graded PF-64 Cameo.

hairlines so delicate that magnification is needed to see them. Above that, a Proof should be free of such lines. Grading is highly subjective with early Proofs, and eye appeal also is a factor.

Illustrated coin: This coin features frosted devices and reflective fields, though the fields are marred by some light scratches.

1815 Capped Bust Quarter Dollar

1815 • **Circulation-Strike Mintage:** 89,235.

B-1. R-1. *Availability in circulated grades:* 1,000 to 1,500 estimated. *Availability in Mint State:* 75 to 100 known.

Commentary: 1815 marks the debut of the Capped Bust quarter. While there are sufficient quantities available to choose from, finding an eye-appealing example will take some patience. As

B-1.

it is a first-year type, many Mint State examples exist. Some lack eye appeal and cherrypicking is recommended. The finest known is the Eric Newman example that grades MS-66+ and sold at auction in November 2013 for $282,000.

Some 1815 quarters have a E or L stamped on the top of the obverse. Many stories and theories exist for its reason for the counterstamp, but none have been confirmed. The earliest citation seen is in Dr. George W. Massamore's *Catalogue of Several Small Collections of United States and Foreign Coins* sold in Baltimore on August 31, 1881. Many of these counterstamps are in higher grade when found. "1815 Quarter Dollar, sharp, bold, Uncirculated impression, the finest I have ever seen, has a very small L faintly stamped above the head, extremely rare." The coin brought $1.75. These counterstamps seem to have been recently released from a hoard, for in 1882 over 20 examples were listed in auction catalogs. *Mason's Coin Collectors' Herald*, March 1882, included this: "We recently purchased an 1815 U.S. quarter-dollar in bright, uncirculated condition, having a small L on field near top of obverse, apparently from the die, though incused." Curiously, these letters are also found on 1825 B-2, but nowhere else in the series. This would seem to indicate that a large number of 1815 quarters in Mint State were on hand somewhere by 1825 or later when the same entity had a quantity of 1825 quarters from a particular run from a single die pair.

	Cert	Avg	%MS	AG-3	G-4	VG-8	F-12	VF-20	EF-40	AU-50	MS-60	MS-63
1815	172	43.1	35%	$150	$200	$400	$700	$950	$2,250	$3,000	$5,000	$8,000

1818 Capped Bust Quarter Dollar

1818, 8 Over 5 • **Circulation-Strike Mintage:** Included in 1818 mintage.

B-1. R-2. *Availability in circulated grades:* 750 to 1,250 estimated. *Availability in Mint State:* 50 to 75 known.

Commentary: The overdate feature is barely visible due to relapping of the die.

Detail of the overdate.

B-3. R-2. *Availability in circulated grades:* 200 to 350 estimated. *Availability in Mint State:* 60 to 90 known.

Commentary: No trace of the undertype 7 is seen except on a few high-grade examples.

B-3.

	Cert	Avg	%MS	AG-3	G-4	VG-8	F-12	VF-20	EF-40	AU-50	MS-60	MS-63
1818, 8 Over 5, most common variety	108	51.9	57%	$100	$125	$200	$350	$650	$1,700	$2,350	$4,000	$7,500

1818 • Circulation-Strike Mintage: 361,174.

B-2. R-1. *Availability in circulated grades:* 1,000 to 1,500 estimated. *Availability in Mint State:* 50 to 75 known.

B-4. R-2. *Availability in circulated grades:* 700 to 900 estimated. *Availability in Mint State:* 55 to 80 known.

B-5. High R-4. *Availability in circulated grades:* 75 to 90 estimated. *Availability in Mint State:* 5 to 8 known.

B-6. R-4. *Availability in circulated grades:* 100 to 150 estimated. *Availability in Mint State:* 7 to 10 known.

B-2.

B-4.

B-5.

B-6.

B-7. High R-4. *Availability in circulated grades:* 75 to 90 estimated. *Availability in Mint State:* None known.

B-7.

B-8. R-3. *Availability in circulated grades:* 200 to 350 estimated. *Availability in Mint State:* 8 to 12 known.

Commentary: A few Proofs were also struck from this die pair.

B-8.

B-9. R-5. *Availability in circulated grades:* 30 to 40 estimated. *Availability in Mint State:* 1 (Bowers and Merena Galleries sale of March 1998).

Commentary: This is the rarest of the 10 die combinations, including overdates, of this year.

B-9.

B-10. R-3. *Availability in circulated grades:* 200 to 350 estimated. *Availability in Mint State:* 6 to 8.

B-10.

	Cert	Avg	%MS	AG-3	G-4	VG-8	F-12	VF-20	EF-40	AU-50	MS-60	MS-63
1818, Normal Date, most common variety	522	39.1	27%	$70	$125	$200	$300	$600	$1,500	$2,250	$4,000	$7,250

1819 Capped Bust Quarter Dollar

1819 • **Circulation-Strike Mintage:** 144,000.

B-1, Large 9. R-5. *Availability in circulated grades:* 40 to 60 estimated. *Availability in Mint State:* 1 (Bowers and Merena Galleries sale of March 1997).

Commentary: This is a scarce variety in any grade. As is the case with all die varieties, there is a good opportunity for cherrypicking, as most certified coins lack attribution numbers.

B-1.

Detail of the Large 9.

B-2, Large 9. R-2. *Availability in circulated grades:* 700 to 900 estimated. *Availability in Mint State:* 8 to 12 known.

Commentary: Readily available in circulated grades; rare in Mint State.

B-2.

	Cert	Avg	%MS	AG-3	G-4	VG-8	F-12	VF-20	EF-40	AU-50	MS-60	MS-63
1819, Large 9, most common variety	27	35.6	11%	$70	$125	$200	$300	$600	$1,600	$2,450	$5,000	$10,000

B-3, Small 9. R-1. *Availability in circulated grades:* 1,000 to 1,500 estimated. *Availability in Mint State:* 20 to 35 known.

B-3.

Detail of the Small 9.

B-4, Small 9. R-4. *Availability in circulated grades:* 75 to 100 estimated. *Availability in Mint State:* 2 to 4 known.

Commentary: This, the rarest variety of the year, was the first die combination struck.

B-4.

	Cert	Avg	%MS	AG-3	G-4	VG-8	F-12	VF-20	EF-40	AU-50	MS-60	MS-63
1819, Small 9, most common variety	41	21	10%	$70	$125	$200	$300	$600	$1,600	$2,250	$4,250	$8,500

1820 Capped Bust Quarter Dollar

1820 • **Circulation-Strike Mintage:** 127,444.

B-1, Large 0. R-4. *Availability in circulated grades:* 85 to 115 estimated. *Availability in Mint State:* 3 to 5 known.

Commentary: Scarce in all grades. Proofs were struck, this being the earliest date recorded for such. At least two are known.

B-1.

B-2, Large 0. R-2. *Availability in circulated grades:* 650 to 800 estimated. *Availability in Mint State:* 12 to 16 known.

Commentary: Common in circulated grades. Available in Mint State, but some patience is required. The Norweb Collection included a one-sided Proof.

B-2.

Detail of the Large 0.

B-3, Large 0. R-3. *Availability in circulated grades:* 200 to 300 estimated. *Availability in Mint State:* 9 to 12 known.

B-3.

	Cert	Avg	%MS	AG-3	G-4	VG-8	F-12	VF-20	EF-40	AU-50	MS-60	MS-63
1820, Large 0, most common variety	27	39.1	19%	$70	$125	$200	$300	$600	$1,600	$3,000	$5,000	$10,000

B-4, Small 0. R-2. *Availability in circulated grades:* 700 to 850 estimated. *Availability in Mint State:* 4 to 6 known.

Commentary: One of many varieties that is readily collectible in circulated grades, B-4 stands tall as a rarity in Mint State. The Norweb Collection included a one-sided Proof.

B-4.

Detail of the Small 0.

B-5, Small 0. R-5. *Availability in circulated grades:* 50 to 60 estimated. *Availability in Mint State:* 4 to 6 known.

Commentary: This variety was struck in 1821 after the first mintage of 1821 B-4. Rare in all grades.

B-5.

	Cert	Avg	%MS	AG-3	G-4	VG-8	F-12	VF-20	EF-40	AU-50	MS-60	MS-63
1820, Small 0, most common variety	18	35.8	17%	$70	$125	$200	$300	$600	$2,000	$2,450	$5,000	$8,000

1821 Capped Bust Quarter Dollar

1821 • Circulation-Strike Mintage: 216,851.

B-1. R-2. *Availability in circulated grades:* 700 to 850 estimated. *Availability in Mint State:* 6 to 10 known.

Commentary: Easily enough found in circulated grades, including Extremely Fine and About Uncirculated, the 1821, B-1 is a rarity in Mint State.

B-1.

Proofs were struck of this variety. The Eliasberg coin, later certified by PCGS and PF-67, was described as follows in 1997:

> Every minute die detail is boldly defined. Well-centered with sharp border dentils on both obverse and reverse. With regard to strike and presentation, this is perhaps the ultimate Capped Bust quarter dollar. The obverse and reverse devices are frosty and lightly toned with a predominance of salmon and ivory. The pristine fields display complete fully-mirrored brilliance, lightly toned toward the central devices with pale blue and violet iridescence toward the rims. The mirrored surface of the fields is complete including between border dentils. A few very insignificant imperfections are noted with the aid of magnification. Otherwise, the surfaces are virtually flawless.

The combination of frosted, lustrous devices with sharp mirrored fields provides an aesthetically stunning cameo appearance. Several Proof examples of this variety are listed in the literature. However, we cannot imagine that any specimen could be nicer than this.

B-2. R-4. *Availability in circulated grades:* 80 to 120 estimated. *Availability in Mint State:* 5 to 8 known.

Commentary: Elusive at all grade levels. Proofs were struck of this variety.

B-2.

B-3. R-2. *Availability in circulated grades:* 750 to 900 estimated. *Availability in Mint State:* 25 to 35 known.

Commentary: Proofs were struck of this variety.

B-3.

B-4. R-3. *Availability in circulated grades:* 200 to 300 estimated. *Availability in Mint State:* 50 to 75 known.

B-4.

B-5. R-5. *Availability in circulated grades:* 60 to 80 estimated. *Availability in Mint State:* 30 to 45 known.

Commentary: Although this is one of the rarest die combinations of the era, for some unknown reason it is one of the most available in Mint State. Some Proofs were struck from this combination. The National Coin Collection in the Smithsonian Institution has a full 1821 Proof set from the Mint Cabinet, the earliest-dated set known.

B-5.

B-6. R-7. *Availability in circulated grades:* 4 to 5 estimated. *Availability in Mint State:* 1 (John J. Pittman Gem, sold by David Akers in May 1998).

Commentary: This variety was discovered in 1991 and reported in *Coin World* February 9 that year. Several others have been found, but this remains the rarest circulation-strike variety of the 1815–1828 large-diameter Capped Bust series.

B-6.

	Cert	Avg	%MS	AG-3	G-4	VG-8	F-12	VF-20	EF-40	AU-50	MS-60	MS-63
1821, most common variety	265	38.6	23%	$70	$125	$200	$300	$600	$1,600	$2,250	$4,000	$7,000

1822 Capped Bust Quarter Dollar

1822 • Circulation-Strike Mintage: 64,080.

B-1. R-2. *Availability in circulated grades:* 800 to 1,000 estimated. *Availability in Mint State:* 20 to 30 known.

Commentary: Some Proofs were struck from this combination. There are a good number of 1822s on the market in all grades to satisfy collectors, and it is possible to locate an example that has very nice eye appeal. The finest known is a Mint State example that graded

B-1.

MS-67 and sold in auction in June 2015 for $164,500. Specialists can differentiate this variety from the B-2 as the obverse die is referred to as a Flat Base 2 in the date, whereas the B-2 has the Curl Base 2 in the date.

In the Bowers and Merena Galleries sale of the Garrett Collection, Part II, March 1980, the coin now graded PF-67 by PCGS was described as follows (excerpted):

> The bust of Liberty is rather deeply toned while the eagle and scroll are much lighter ivory. Light silver with pale lilac giving way to faint blue iridescence towards the edges. The high points of the hair curls along with some of the stars are rather lightly defined, probably the result of die spacing. The reverse is generally bold with shallow definition only at the tops of the wings and on the lower olive leaves. Most legend letters on the reverse show evidence of doubling, probably an indication of the piece having received two blows from the press. Frosted devices with deeply mirrored fields. There are probably just five or six Proof examples known today with the present example being one of the finest. Another prize for the connoisseur.

B-3. R-8. *Availability in circulated grades:* One known. *Availability in Mint State:* None known.

Commentary: In 2017, a newly discovered example was identified that marries the 1822 obverse with the reverse that was used for the 1823, 3 Over 2, quarter. This reverse shows broken upper arrows shaft and lower arrow head. Currently, there is only one known, in About Good condition.

	Cert	Avg	%MS	AG-3	G-4	VG-8	F-12	VF-20	EF-40	AU-50	MS-60	MS-63
1822, most common variety	127	36.3	17%	$200	$300	$375	$750	$1,100	$1,800	$3,000	$7,250	$10,500

1822, 25 Over 50 C. • **Circulation-Strike Mintage:** Included in 1822 mintage.

B-2. R-5. *Availability in circulated grades:* 40 to 60 estimated. *Availability in Mint State:* 5 to 7 known.

B-2.

Commentary: Proofs were struck from this combination. This very scarce variety is known for its engraving blunder as the Mint engraver punched a 50 on the reverse. Upon discovery of the error he reengraved the 25 over the 50. This can be identified by viewing the 5 in the 25, which shows a tail. This error reverse die was used again in 1828. Collectors looking for an attractive example of this variety will require a fair amount of patience. Any example in Fine condition or

Detail of the 25 Over 50 C.

better is quite a find. The finest known example for this variety is the Louis Eliasberg coin graded MS-66. It last sold at auction in April 2009 for $184,000.

In the Bowers and Merena Galleries sale of the Garrett Collection, Part II, March 1980, the coin now graded PF-65 by PCGS was described thusly (excerpted):

> A magnificent Proof example. Full Proof surfaces on both obverse and reverse, including within the shield stripes, with the exception of a small frosty area below Miss Liberty's chin . . . the obverse and reverse have light lilac toning with blue iridescent overtones. The strike is outstanding.

The Garrett Collection was a turning point in American numismatics. Up to that time, 99% of the active dealers and collectors went by the "brilliant is best" credo, dipping toned coins no matter how attractive they were. If you find this improbable, dig out some advertisements from the era. The only major exception among dealers was the New Netherlands Coin Company. The four Garrett sales were so dynamic, Abe Kosoff wrote that while evaluating current market prices, the Garrett results should be ignored as they were not representative!

	Cert	Avg	%MS	AG-3	G-4	VG-8	F-12	VF-20	EF-40	AU-50	MS-60	MS-63
1822, 25 Over 50 C.	15	35.3	20%	$4,250	$6,000	$10,000	$16,000	$25,000	$37,500	$42,500	$57,500	$75,000

1823 Capped Bust Quarter Dollar

1823, 3 Over 2 • **Circulation-Strike Mintage:** 17,800.

B-1. R-6. *Availability in circulated grades:* 25 to 30 estimated. *Availability in Mint State:* One known.

Commentary: The 1823, 3 Over 2, is one of the rarest American silver coins. More than half of the known examples are in very low grades or have problems. The finest known is the Gardner example that was graded by NGC at MS-61 and is now currently graded by PCGS as AU-58. *Early United States Quarters 1796–1838* has a large section on this variety, including historical auction listings. Most of the surviving examples are in Fine condition and below.

B-1.

Detail of the overdate.

	Cert	Avg	%MS	AG-3	G-4	VG-8	F-12	VF-20	EF-40	AU-50	MS-60
1823, 3 Over 2	7	42.7	14%	$27,500	$42,500	$55,000	$75,000	$100,000	$150,000	$190,000	$275,000

1824 Capped Bust Quarter Dollar

1824, 4 Over 2 • Circulation-Strike
Mintage: 168,000.

B-1.

B-1. R-3. *Availability in circulated grades:* 350 to 450 estimated. *Availability in Mint State:* 4 to 6 known.

Commentary: The 1824, 4 Over 2, is a scarce variety and is considered a semi-key in the series. Even though the mintage is stated as 168,000, many professional numismatics and researchers believe the mintage is around 16,000. The date is an overdate that used an 1822-dated obverse die that the Mint did not use at the time. The engraver later punched a 4 over the second 2 and created the overdate. The overdate is very faint, so it is not very easy to see unless you look carefully for it.

Detail of the overdate.

Any 1824, 4 Over 2, quarter that has high eye appeal attracts a premium. The finest known is believed to be the Eliasberg example that sold in April 1997 for $24,200. Any example graded 55 or higher is quite a find. Proofs were struck of this variety.

	Cert	Avg	%MS	AG-3	G-4	VG-8	F-12	VF-20	EF-40	AU-50	MS-60	MS-63
1824, 4 Over 2	89	24.0	3%	$500	$800	$1,100	$2,000	$2,750	$5,250	$17,500	$25,000	$55,000

1825 Capped Bust Quarter Dollar

1825, 5 Over 4 Over 2 • Circulation-Strike **Mintage:** Included in 1824 mintage.

B-1. R-5. *Availability in circulated grades:* 40 to 45 estimated. *Availability in Mint State:* One (the Louis E. Eliasberg coin sold by Bowers and Merena Galleries in 1997).

Commentary: Earlier called 1825, 5 Over 2, the variety was redefined as 1825, 5 Over 4 Over 2, by Steve Tompkins in *Early United States Quarters 1796–1838.*

B-1.

Detail of the overdate.

B-2. R-2. *Availability in circulated grades:* 800 to 1,000 estimated. *Availability in Mint State:* 40 to 70.

Commentary: Earlier called 1825, 5 Over 2, the variety was redefined as 1825, 5 Over 4 Over 2, by Steve Tompkins. This is one of the most readily available Mint State coins of the 1815–1828 Large Diameter type. Proofs were struck of this variety. For a discussion of E and L counterstamps, see the commentary under 1815, B-1.

B-2.

	Cert	Avg	%MS	AG-3	G-4	VG-8	F-12	VF-20	EF-40	AU-50	MS-60	MS-63
1825, 5 Over 4 Over 2 , most common variety	17	34.9	0%	$350	$500	$750	$1,100	$1,350	$4,500	$8,250	$16,000	$27,500

B-3. *Availability in circulated grades:* 200 to 300 estimated. *Availability in Mint State:* 10 to 15 known.

Commentary: Earlier called 1825, 5 Over 4, the variety was redefined as 1825, 5 Over 4 Over 2, by Steve Tompkins.

B-1.

Detail of the overdate.

	Cert	Avg	%MS	AG-3	G-4	VG-8	F-12	VF-20	EF-40	AU-50	MS-60	MS-63
1825, 5 Over 4 Over 5	158	43	22%	$75	$125	$200	$325	$600	$1,500	$2,200	$3,500	$6,500

1827 Capped Bust Quarter Dollar

1827, 7 Over 4 Over 3, Original, Curl Base 2 in 25 C. • Circulation-Strike Mintage: 4,000.

B-1. R-7. *Availability in circulated grades:* 1 known.

Commentary: The circulated example is thought to be a worn Proof, not a circulation strike. Steve Tompkins believes these to be prooflike and not Proof; see the Proof commentary for this coin.[8] *Early United States Quarters 1796–1838* has a large section on this variety, including historical auction listings. Likely the 4,000 circulation strikes were from an earlier-dated obverse die.

B-1.

Detail of the Curl Base 2.   Detail of the overdate

1827, 7 Over 4 Over 3, Original, Curl Base 2 in 25 C. • Proof Mintage: 12 to 14 estimated.

B-1. R-7. *Availability in Proof format:* 9 recorded by Steve Tompkins and Karl Moulton (one PF-20, circulated; the others PF-60 to 64).

Commentary: The D. Brent Pogue coin described by John Kraljevich and sold by Stack's Bowers Galleries is certified as PF-66. An excerpt from the catalog:

> The present coin is yet another familiar face to us. It was in our Garrett Collection Part II sale in March 1980. We had the honor of presenting it for sale after it had been hidden away since the 19th century. We described it as choice in every respect. "It is fully brilliant with just the slightest hint of golden toning. No finer specimen could possibly exist."
>
> Fewer than 10 original specimens are known to exist today. Numismatic tradition has it that in 1827 Joseph J. Mickley, who lived locally, visited the Philadelphia Mint and obtained four Proof 1827 quarters for face value. Again, facts are scarce. It seems that if he did acquire them this way, no record was kept of it.

	Cert	Avg	%MS	PF-60	PF-63	PF-65
1827, 7 Over 3, Original, Proof	4	52.5		$125,000	$225,000	$550,000

1827, 7 Over 4 Over 3, Restrike, Square Base 2 in 25 C. • Proof Mintage: 15–25.

B-2. High R-6. *Availability in Mint State:* 11 recorded by Steve Tompkins.

Commentary: *Early United States Quarters 1796–1838* has a large section on this variety, including historical auction listings.

In addition, Steve Tompkins records five restrikes in copper.

B-2.

Detail of the Square Base 2.   Detail of the overdate

	Cert	Avg	%MS	PF-63	PF-65
1827, 7 Over 3, Restrike, Proof	10	64.2		$65,000	$115,000

1828 Capped Bust Quarter Dollar

1828 • Circulation-Strike Mintage: 102,000.

B-1, Curl Base 2. R-1. *Availability in circulated grades:* 1,100 to 1,400 known. *Availability in Mint State:* 30 to 45 known.

Commentary: This variety is the most readily available of all the 1828 quarters and can be identified by the Curl Base 2 in the date and, on

B-1.

the reverse, by the location of the scroll, which starts beneath the center of the D in UNITED. Proofs were struck of this variety.

B-2, Square Base 2. R-4+. *Availability in circulated grades:* 55 to 65 estimated. *Availability in Mint State:* Steve Tompkins cites just one auction record.

Commentary: This variety can be identified by the Square Base 2 in the date on the obverse and the location of the scroll on the reverse. The scroll begins in the center of the D in UNITED.

B-2.

Detail of the Square Base 2.

B-4, Curl Base 2. R-3. *Availability in circulated grades:* 250 to 325 estimated. *Availability in Mint State:* 20 to 25 known.

Commentary: This variety can be identified by the Curl Base 2 in the date and the lower position of the F in OF on the reverse. Proofs were struck of this variety.

B-4.

Detail of the Curl Base 2.

	Cert	Avg	%MS	AG-3	G-4	VG-8	F-12	VF-20	EF-40	AU-50	MS-60	MS-63
1828, most common variety	180	41.5	26%	$75	$115	$180	$300	$550	$1,500	$2,500	$3,500	$7,500

1828, 25 Over 50 C. • **Circulation-Strike Mintage:** Included in 1828 mintage.

B-3. R-5. *Availability in circulated grades:* 40 to 50 estimated. *Availability in Mint State:* Fewer than 10 known.

Commentary: The 1828, 25 Over 50 C., is a semi-key issue. The reverse die was also used in 1822 (see above). The finest known example is the Newman/Gardner specimen, graded MS-67, which sold in May 2015 for $282,000.

B-3.

Detail of the 25 Over 50 C.

	Cert	Avg	%MS	AG-3	G-4	VG-8	F-12	VF-20	EF-40	AU-50	MS-60	MS-63
1828, 25 Over 50 C.	24	34.0	17%	$750	$1,250	$1,750	$2,250	$3,500	$7,000	$10,000	$15,000	$90,000

1831 Capped Bust Quarter Dollar

1831 • Circulation-Strike Mintage: 398,000.

B-1, Small Letters. R-3. *Availability in circulated grades:* 300 to 450 estimated. *Availability in Mint State:* 50 to 75 known.

Commentavry: This is the first year the quarter was struck in the smaller, 24.3-millimeter size. Proofs were struck of this variety according to Walter Breen, but no example has been verified by Steve Tompkins.

B-2, Small Letters. R-2. *Availability in circulated grades:* 750 to 1,000 estimated. *Availability in Mint State:* 50 to 75 known.

Commentary: Proofs were struck of this variety to the extent of a half-dozen or so, according to Walter Breen. No unequivocal Proof has been seen by Steve Tompkins, who has examined several highly prooflike coins.

B-3, Small Letters. R-5. *Availability in circulated grades:* 30 to 40 estimated. *Availability in Mint State:* None known.

Commentary: This is one of the rarest varieties of the 1831–1838 type. No unimpaired Mint State examples are known; Steve Tompkins cited a damaged MS-60 sold by Heritage Auctions and an unconfirmed MS-62.

B-4, Small Letters. R-1. *Availability in circulated grades:* 1,250 to 1,750 estimated. *Availability in Mint State:* 75 to 100+ known.

Commentary: Proofs were struck of this variety.

B-1.

B-2.

B-3.

B-4.

Detail of the Small Letters.

	Cert	Avg	%MS	G-4	VG-8	F-12	VF-20	EF-40	AU-50	MS-60	MS-63	MS-65
1831, Small Letters, most common variety	69	49.5	23%	$70	$100	$125	$150	$350	$700	$2,000	$3,750	$25,000

B-5, Large Letters. R-3. *Availability in circulated grades:* 300 to 450 estimated. *Availability in Mint State:* 55 to 80 known.

Commentary: This is a popular variety, with large 1's over smaller 1's. Proofs were struck of this variety, and 10 or so are known—the highest population for any Proof variety up to this date.

B-5.

Detail of the Large Letters.

B-6, Large Letters. R-3. *Availability in circulated grades:* 300 to 450 estimated. *Availability in Mint State:* 15 to 20 known.

B-6.

B-7, Large Letters. High R-5. *Availability in circulated grades:* 30 to 40 estimated. *Availability in Mint State:* None known.

Commentary: This is one of the rarer varieties of the decade.

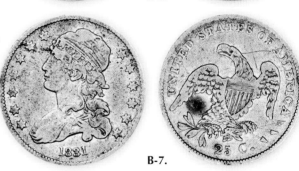

B-7.

	Cert	Avg	%MS	G-4	VG-8	F-12	VF-20	EF-40	AU-50	MS-60	MS-63	MS-65
1831, Large Letters, most common variety	47	48.5	28%	$70	$100	$125	$150	$350	$700	$2,100	$3,750	$26,000

1832 Capped Bust Quarter Dollar

1832 • Circulation-Strike Mintage: 320,000.

B-1. R-1. *Availability in circulated grades:* 1,250 to 1,750 estimated. *Availability in Mint State:* 20 to 30 known.

Commentary: Proofs were struck of this variety.

B-1.

B-2. R-2. *Availability in circulated grades:* 800 to 1,000 estimated. *Availability in Mint State:* 75 to 100 known.

Commentary: The 1832, B-2 is easy to find in any grade desired. Proofs were struck of this variety.

B-2.

	Cert	Avg	%MS	G-4	VG-8	F-12	VF-20	EF-40	AU-50	MS-60	MS-63	MS-65
1832, most common variety	192	45.3	27%	$70	$100	$125	$150	$350	$700	$2,000	$3,750	$25,000

1833 Capped Bust Quarter Dollar

1833 • Circulation-Strike Mintage: 156,000.

B-1. R-2. *Availability in circulated grades:* 800 to 1,000 estimated. *Availability in Mint State:* 75 to 100 known.

Commentary: Proofs were struck of this variety.

B-1.

B-2. R-2. *Availability in circulated grades:* 800 to 1,000 estimated. *Availability in Mint State:* 30 to 45 known.

Commentary: Proofs were struck of this variety.

B-2.

	Cert	Avg	%MS	G-4	VG-8	F-12	VF-20	EF-40	AU-50	MS-60	MS-63	MS-65
1833, most common variety	197	47	27%	$80	$110	$135	$200	$450	$800	$2,200	$4,500	$25,000

1834 Capped Bust Quarter Dollar

1834 • Circulation-Strike Mintage: 286,000.

Commentary: In the summer of 1834 gold coins again appeared in circulation, having been absent since 1820, after which time their melt-down value was greater than their face value, and coinage was done only for export. The Coinage Act of June 28, 1834, reduced the weight of gold coins, after which they circulated freely. *Niles' Weekly Register* included these accounts:

September 27, 1834: In Cincinnati, J. Washington Mason, as a joke had a jeweler gild six current silver quarter dollars, which he was able to convince others were the new designs of gold coins.

October 4, 1834: It was stated that multiple reports had been received of quarter dollars being gilded and passed as counterfeit half eagles. "The cap I of Liberty, and the motto e pluribus unum must be restored, else the new 25 cent pieces will be rapidly manufactured into half eagles, and the new coins will not be allowed to obtain that freedom of circulation which we have long desired might be given to those of gold."[9]

B-1, O Over F in OF. R-1. *Availability in circulated grades:* 1,250 to 1,750 estimated. *Availability in Mint State:* 50 to 75 known.

Commentary: Proofs were struck from this die pair.

B-5.

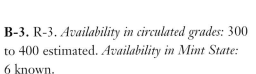

Detail of the O Over F.

	Cert	Avg	%MS	G-4	VG-8	F-12	VF-20	EF-40	AU-50	MS-60	MS-63	MS-65
1834, O Over F in OF	60	46.3	17%	$80	$110	$150	$200	$350	$750	$2,000	$5,000	$25,000

B-2. R-4. *Availability in circulated grades:* 80 to 110 estimated. *Availability in Mint State:* 45 to 70 known.

Commentary: Proofs were made from this combination.

B-2.

B-3. R-3. *Availability in circulated grades:* 300 to 400 estimated. *Availability in Mint State:* 6 known.

Commentary: Specialists can easily find a circulated example, but Mint State coins are inexplicably rare.

B-3.

B-4. R-1. *Availability in circulated grades:* 1,250 to 1,750 estimated. *Availability in Mint State:* 75 to 100+ known.

Commentary: Proofs were struck of this variety.

B-4.

B-5. R-5. *Availability in circulated grades:* 40 to 60 estimated. *Availability in Mint State:* 3 or 4.

Commentary: This is another rare die combination from the 1830s.

B-5.

	Cert	Avg	%MS	G-4	VG-8	F-12	VF-20	EF-40	AU-50	MS-60	MS-63	MS-65
1834, most common variety	590	45.1	25%	$70	$100	$125	$150	$350	$700	$2,000	$4,000	$27,500

1835 Capped Bust Quarter Dollar

1835 • Circulation-Strike Mintage: 1,952,000.

B-1. R-1. *Availability in circulated grades:* 1,250 to 1,750 estimated. *Availability in Mint State:* 35 to 50 known.

Commentary: Proofs were struck of this variety.

B-1.

B-2. Low R-1 or High R-2. *Availability in circulated grades:* 900 to 1,200 estimated. *Availability in Mint State:* 20 to 30 known.

Commentary: In all grades this is the most-often seen die variety of 1835.

B-2.

B-3. High R-4. *Availability in circulated grades:* 75 to 100 estimated. *Availability in Mint State:* One cited by Steve Tompkins (Stack's, July 1985).

Commentary: This variety is scarce in any grade and almost impossible to find in Mint State.

B-3.

B-4. R-3. *Availability in circulated grades:* 300 to 450 estimated. *Availability in Mint State:* 7 to 10 known.

B-4.

B-5. R-2. *Availability in circulated grades:* 800 to 1,000 estimated. *Availability in Mint State:* 20 to 30 known.

Commentary: The 1835, B-5 is common in circulated grades but very rare in Mint State.

B-5.

B-6. R-2. *Availability in circulated grades:* 800 to 1,000 estimated. *Availability in Mint State:* 6 to 9 known.

Commentary: Like the preceding variety, this is surprisingly elusive in Mint State.

B-6.

B-7. R-2. *Availability in circulated grades:* 800 to 1,000 estimated. *Availability in Mint State:* 50 to 75 known.

Commentary: Proofs were struck of this variety.

B-7.

B-8. High R-4. *Availability in circulated grades:* 75 to 90 estimated. *Availability in Mint State:* 4 to 6 known.

Commentary: This variety is scarce in circulated grades and hardly ever seen in Mint State.

B-8.

	Cert	Avg	%MS	G-4	VG-8	F-12	VF-20	EF-40	AU-50	MS-60	MS-63	MS-65
1835, most common variety	626	42.5	15%	$70	$100	$125	$150	$350	$700	$2,000	$4,250	$22,500

1836 Capped Bust Quarter Dollar

1836 • **Circulation-Strike Mintage:** 472,000.

B-1. R-2. *Availability in circulated grades:* 800 to 1,000 estimated. *Availability in Mint State:* 5 to 8 known.

Commentary: Another variety that is easy to find in circulated grades but is a rarity in Mint State.

B-1.

B-2. R-2. *Availability in circulated grades:* 800 to 1,000 estimated. *Availability in Mint State:* 20 to 30 known.

Commentary: Proofs were struck of this variety.

B-2.

B-3. R-1. *Availability in circulated grades:* 1,250 to 1,750 estimated. *Availability in Mint State:* 25 to 35 known.

Commentary: In late states both obverse and reverse dies are extensively cracked (see detail of obverse cracks above).

B-1.

Detail of the Obverse
Die Crack.

Detail of the Reverse
Die Crack.

B-4. R-4. *Availability in circulated grades:* 75 to 100 estimated. *Availability in Mint State:* 4 to 6 known.

Commentary: This is another variety that is readily available in circulated grades—but Mint State coins are another question entirely.

B-4.

B-5. R-6. *Availability in circulated grades:* 15 to 20 estimated. *Availability in Mint State:* None known.

Commentary: This is one of the rarer varieties of the type. Specialists have the opportunity to cherrypick as almost no 1836 quarters in certified holders are identified by die variety. This particular variety was unknown to Ard Browning when he wrote his 1925 study. The first example was cherrypicked at the 1988 ANA convention by Bob Spangler.

B-5.

	Cert	Avg	%MS	G-4	VG-8	F-12	VF-20	EF-40	AU-50	MS-60	MS-63	MS-65
1836, most common variety	233	38.5	16%	$70	$100	$125	$150	$350	$700	$2,000	$4,250	$37,000

1837 Capped Bust Quarter Dollar

1837 • Circulation-Strike Mintage: 252,400.

B-1. R-3. *Availability in circulated grades:* 300 to 450 estimated. *Availability in Mint State:* 8 to 12 known.

Commentary: Steve Tompkins notes that this variety was struck after 1835 B-8, 1836 B-1, and 1837 B-3 and B-4, making it a poster example of Mint employees' storing dies in a vault and using them in later years. This practice, widely discussed in the literature, involved all denominations, and explains why early Mint Reports do not precisely match the number of coins struck with a particular date.

B-1.

B-2. R-1. *Availability in circulated grades:* 1,250 to 1,750 estimated. *Availability in Mint State:* 45 to 55 known.

Commentary: Proofs were struck of this variety.

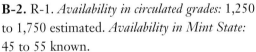

B-2.

B-3. R-4. *Availability in circulated grades:* 90 to 120 estimated. *Availability in Mint State:* 15 to 20 known.

Commentary: This one is scarce all around.

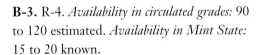

B-3.

B-4. R-3. *Availability in circulated grades:* 300 to 450 estimated. *Availability in Mint State:* 20 to 30 known.

B-4.

B-5. R-5. *Availability in circulated grades:* 30 to 50 estimated. *Availability in Mint State:* 12 to 18 known.

Commentary: Elusive in all grades. Proofs were struck of this variety per some observers, including the present author for the Eliasberg coin. However, some have suggested that these are proof*like* circulation strikes. The subject of what

B-5.

is and what is not a Proof has been controversial for a long time. Many branch-mint coins described as prooflike years ago have been certified as Proof in modern times. Most examples of the 1878 Shield nickel, stated by the Mint to have been struck only as Proofs and included in sets of minor (cent, three-cent, and five-cent) Proof coins have frosty surfaces with no mirror quality. Such debates make numismatic study fascinating for those involved.

B-6. R-8. *Availability in circulated grades:* Two reported.

Commentary: Two examples of B-6 have been reported, an F-12 and an F-15.

B-6.

	Cert	Avg	%MS	G-4	VG-8	F-12	VF-20	EF-40	AU-50	MS-60	MS-63	MS-65
1837, most common variety	298	47.5	31%	$70	$100	$125	$150	$350	$700	$2,000	$4,250	$26,000

1838 Capped Bust Quarter Dollar

1838 • Circulation-Strike Mintage: 366,000.

B-1. R-1. *Availability in circulated grades:* 1,200 to 1,700 estimated. *Availability in Mint State:* 75 to 100 known.

Commentary: The 1838 is the final year of the Capped Bust quarters. There are several Gem Mint State coins. The highest price realized for such is one sold in September 2015 for $82,250. There are three known Proofs.

B-1.

	Cert	Avg	%MS	G-4	VG-8	F-12	VF-20	EF-40	AU-50	MS-60	MS-63	MS-65
1838	283	45.3	25%	$70	$100	$125	$150	$350	$700	$2,000	$4,250	$26,000

LIBERTY SEATED QUARTERS (1838–1891)

All Varieties: **Designer:** *Christian Gobrecht.* **Composition:** *.900 silver, .100 copper.* **Diameter:** *24.3 mm.* **Edge:** *Reeded.* ***Variety 1, No Motto Above Eagle (1838–1853):*** **Weight:** *6.68 grams.* **Mints:** *Philadelphia and New Orleans.* ***Variety 2, Arrows at Date, Rays Around Eagle (1853):*** **Weight:** *6.22 grams.* **Mints:** *Philadelphia and New Orleans.* ***Variety 3, Arrows at Date, No Rays (1854–1855) and Variety 1 Resumed, With Weight Standard of Variety 2 (1856–1865):*** **Weight:** *6.22 grams.* **Mints:** *Philadelphia, New Orleans, and San Francisco.* ***Variety 4, Motto Above Eagle (1866–1873):*** **Weight:** *6.22 grams.* **Mints:** *Philadelphia, San Francisco, and Carson City.* ***Variety 5, Arrows at Date (1873–1874):*** **Weight:** *6.25 grams.* **Mints:** *Philadelphia, San Francisco, and Carson City.* ***Variety 4 Resumed, With Weight Standard of Variety 5 (1875–1891):*** **Weight:** *6.25 grams.* **Mints:** *Philadelphia, New Orleans, and San Francisco.*

Variety 1 (1838–1853)

Mintmark location is on the reverse, below the eagle, for all varieties.

Variety 1, Proof

Variety 2 (1853)

Variety 2, Proof

Variety 3 (1854–1855)

Variety 3, Proof

Variety 1 Resumed, Weight Standard of Variety 2 (1856–1865)

Variety 1 Resumed, Weight Standard of Variety 2, Proof

Variety 4 (1866–1873)

Variety 4, Proof

Variety 5 (1873–1874)   **Variety 5, Proof**

**Variety 4 Resumed, Weight   Variety 4 Resumed, Weight
Standard of Variety 5 (1875–1891)   Standard of Variety 5, Proof**

HISTORY AND BACKGROUND

The Liberty Seated motif by Mint engraver Christian Gobrecht was introduced on quarters in 1838 following the coinage of Capped Bust quarters earlier in the year. By that time the obverse design had already appeared on the silver dollar of 1836 and the half dimes and dimes of 1837. Its use on the half dollar would await the following year, 1839.

CHRISTIAN GOBRECHT, ENGRAVER

In numismatics today Christian Gobrecht is considered to be one of the most talented, most accomplished engravers in the history of the Mint. *The Gobrecht Journal*, the magazine of the Liberty Seated Collectors Club, bears his name.

Gobrecht was born in Hanover, York County, Pennsylvania on December 23, 1785, the sixth son of John Christopher Gobrecht and Elizabeth (Sands) Gobrecht. Christian demonstrated an early talent for art and mechanics. In his youth he was apprenticed to a clockmaker in Manheim, Pennsylvania, after which he moved to Baltimore, where he engraved dials and other ornaments for timepieces. While there he also did other engraving work, much of it in association with William H. Freeman, a leading maker of bank-note plates. Still later he became an engraver of type punches for newspapers and documents, while continuing to engrave plates for banknotes.

Christian Gobrecht.

Sometime around 1811 Gobrecht moved to Philadelphia, where by 1816 he was at work as a banknote engraver with Murray, Draper, Fairman & Co. In 1817 he devised a medal-ruling machine which, by means of a pantograph, depicted the contours of a coin or medal as lines on a flat surface, such as a copper engraving plate. The copper or other plate to be ruled was movable, and the item copied remained stationary. At least two versions of this machine were made, the first being able to copy only straight lines and the second with the capability of copying curved as well as straight lines. Not long afterward, others copied certain aspects of his mechanisms, without credit. History has not treated Gobrecht kindly in this regard, as his contributions to this device have been largely ignored.

On May 31, 1818, the artist took as his wife Mary Hamilton Hewes, the daughter of Thomas Hamilton and the widow of Daniel Hewes. The couple had two sons and two daughters. Around 1820–1821,

Christian Gobrecht invented and manufactured a parlor reed organ operated by keys and bellows, the first example of which was sold to a resident of Lancaster, Pennsylvania. Another example made in 1832 was kept by Gobrecht himself (and at the turn of the 20th century was still owned by his descendants). Intrigued by the automata of Maelzel (whose supposedly mechanical chess player delighted the courts of Europe and was the sensation of its time), Gobrecht created a talking doll and an improvement on the ancient camera lucida device. By 1826 Gobrecht had furnished designs and die models as a private contractor to the Philadelphia Mint.

During the 1820s and early 1830s he executed many commissions for the Mint and private clients, including the seal of St. Peter's Church, the Massachusetts Mechanics Charitable Association award medal (which is encountered with some frequency today), the award medal for the New England Society for the Promotion of Manufactures and the Arts, the Franklin Institute award medal, and a widely admired medal depicting Charles Carroll of Carrollton.

After Robert Scot, engraver at the Mint since 1793, died in 1823, Gobrecht wrote to President James Monroe requesting to be interviewed for the position. Nothing came of this, and William Kneass, an engraver considered to be far less talented by modern historians, was named to the post, a political appointment by presidential prerogative. Mint Director Samuel Moore probably would have chosen Gobrecht, based on his knowledge of the engraver's excellent work.

On February 14, 1825, Moore wrote to Monroe's successor, President John Quincy Adams, and solicited his permission to introduce, "in the character of assistant engraver, Christian Gobrecht of this city, an artist of great merit." Again, to no avail. Time passed. In 1835 Congress passed an act establishing branch mints at Charlotte, North Carolina; Dahlonega, Georgia; and New Orleans, Louisiana. Many more dies would be needed for this expansion.

In the summer, Mint Director Samuel Moore retired and was succeeded by Robert Maskell Patterson, who sought to employ Gobrecht. While full-time employment of Gobrecht was being considered, Kneass suffered a debilitating stroke on August 27, which in effect made it impossible for him to perform the full work of chief or lead engraver, although the title at that time was simply "engraver." Director Patterson reiterated his predecessor's request for help in the engraving department, and Christian Gvobrecht began work at the Mint in September. As noted above, his title was second engraver (not assistant engraver). Gobrecht's salary was $1,500 per year.

The 1795 Draped Bust obverse, Small Eagle reverse dollar set the design later used on other silver coins including the 1796 quarter dollar.

THE LIBERTY SEATED DESIGN

After production of silver dollars in 1804, coinage of that denomination was suspended. Nearly all had been exported, and the Treasury Department felt that their usefulness for domestic commerce was lost. After the dollar was discontinued, the half dollar became the largest silver coin of the realm. They became a familiar sight in commerce and in bank reserves. In 1835 as Director Patterson settled into his office he advanced the idea of having a new silver dollar made.

On August 1 he wrote to Thomas Sully, one of the most highly regarded artists in Philadelphia:

> In entering upon the execution of my office here I have felt it to be one of the first objects requiring my attention, to endeavor to introduce a change in our coin that may make it a more creditable specimen of taste and art. To accomplish this purpose I look naturally to your valuable aid and accordingly beg that you will execute for the Mint a drawing of what you shall judge a suitable design for the face of the coin.

The only law which governs us in this matter is the following: "Upon the said coins there shall be the following devices and legends, namely: upon one side of said coins there shall be an impression emblematic of liberty, with an inscription of the word Liberty, and the year of the coinage; and upon the reverse of each of the gold and silver coins there shall be the figure or representation of an eagle with this inscription, United States of America, and upon the reverse of each of the copper coins there shall be an inscription which shall impress the denomination of the piece, namely cent or half cent, as the case may require."

For the impression emblematic of liberty you know that our coins have heretofore used a bust. It appears to me that it would be better to introduce an entire figure. When a likeness is to be given as on the European coins the head along is very properly used in order that the features may be distinctly represented. But, when an emblem only is called for it would seem rather desirable to avoid this individuality in the features. Besides, there is certainly more room for a display of taste and beauty of form when a full figure issued.

The round form of the coin, its small size, and the practical necessity of covering as much of the face as possible seem to require that the figure be in a sitting posture, sitting for example on a rock.

To be distinctly emblematic of liberty I would propose that the figure hold in her right hand the liberty pole surmounted by the pileus, an emblem which is universally understood. I would also suggest that the left hand be made to rest upon the United States shield on which the word Liberty required by law may be inscribed.

For the reverse of the coin I propose an eagle, flying, and rising in its flight amidst a constellation, irregularly disposed, of 24 stars and carrying in its claws a scroll with the words E Pluribus Unum, of many stars our constellation, of many states one union.

As I am desirous that the real American bald eagle should be represented and not, like the heraldic eagle, a mere creature of imagination I have requested Mr. Titian R. Peale to make a design in conformity with the above suggestions and therefore will not trouble you with the reverse of the coin, at least not for the moment.

By 1835 the liberty cap or pileus motif was very familiar, indeed "universally understood," dating back to at least the era of ancient coinage, when it was featured on many coins. Such a cap was presented to slaves when they were given their freedom. In colonial America the liberty cap was widely used to represent freedom from the shackles of British rule. Many towns and cities had liberty poles set up in prominent places—tall and with a cap at the top. Such were common sights into the early 19th century.

On August 1, 1835, engraver Kneass made a rough sketch of a seated figure with pole and cap, based on his conversation with Director Patterson.

On October 5 Patterson wrote to Treasury Secretary Levi Woodbury seeking his and presidential approval for creating silver dollars with the Liberty Seated obverse combined with a flying eagle reverse. Once this was received, information relating to the new design was made available to the press.

In November the *Philadelphia Gazette* told of work in progress:

Sketch of Liberty seated made on August 1, 1835, by engraver William Kneass. (Library Company of Philadelphia)

We learn that a new die for the coins of the United States, is now in a state of preparation, and will be ready for use in the ensuing year. The design was prepared by Sully, and is said to be exceedingly beautiful. It is a full length image of the Goddess of liberty, in a sitting posture, with one hand resting on a shield containing the coat of arms of the United States. On the reverse, will be the American eagle, as at present, without however the shield and coat of arms with which his breast is disfigured, and which somewhat resembles a gridiron, exhibiting the bad taste of broiling a bird with his feathers on. The first coin struck with the new device, will be the dollar, of which there have none been coined for thirty years.[10]

On January 8, 1836, impressions of the obverse design in fusible metal were sent to Treasury Secretary Levi Woodbury in Washington for him to show to President Andrew Jackson. On the 12th Woodbury advised Patterson that the president had approved of the design but suggested some modifications. In the same month Gobrecht started work on the reverse. On the 12th Woodbury advised Patterson that President Andrew Jackson had approved of the design but had suggested some modifications. In the same month Gobrecht started work on the reverse eagle (not related to Liberty Seated quarters and thus not discussed in detail here).

Drawing of Liberty by Thomas Sully. (Library Company of Philadelphia)

Silver dollars, later called Gobrecht dollars by numismatists, were first delivered in December 1836. In 1837 Liberty Seated half dimes and dimes were made with a wreath motif reverse. These were followed in 1838 by the quarter dollar and in 1839 by the half dollar, with the Liberty Seated obverse and a perched eagle on the reverse.

In the meantime Gobrecht worked on other new designs, including a Liberty Head in several forms, culminating with the Braided Hair or Coronet depiction of Miss Liberty used on gold coins beginning 1838–1840 and half cents and large cents starting in 1839 and 1840. He attended to the other duties of the position as well. Christian Gobrecht remained at the Mint until his death in Philadelphia on July 23, 1844.

Drawing of Liberty by Thomas Sully. (Library Company of Philadelphia)

The Liberty Seated design continued in use for many years, finally ending with the dime, quarter, and half dollar in 1891. Modifications were made by later engravers, including James B. Longacre, who was the engraver from 1844 to 1869, William Barber from 1869 to 1879, and Charles E. Barber beginning in 1880.

OVERVIEW OF LIBERTY SEATED QUARTERS

Christian Gobrecht's design on the new 1838 quarter depicts Liberty seated on a rock, her left hand holding a liberty cap on a pole and her right hand holding a shield inscribed LIBERTY. There is no drapery at her elbow. Thirteen stars are around the border. The result is a cameo-like appearance of rare beauty. The reverse consists a perched eagle clutching arrows and an olive branch, with UNITED STATES OF AMERICA above and to the sides, and QUAR. DOL. below.

In 1840 drapery was added to Liberty's elbow and an adjustment was made in the alignment of the shield. Through the 1840s and 1850s many different varieties were produced. In 1853 the Liberty Seated design was modified by the addition of tiny arrowheads to the left and right of the date, to signify a decrease in the authorized weight from 103.125 grains to 96 grains. Rays were added to the reverse. The rays were removed in 1854, but the arrows remained until 1855. From 1856 onward the reduced weight remained in effect, until modified in February 1873.

In 1866 the motto IN GOD WE TRUST was added to the reverse of the quarter, half dollar, and silver dollar, and to the gold $5, $10, and $20. In February 1873 the weight of the quarter was increased slightly, and arrowheads signifying this were added to the date, and continued in 1874. Later Liberty Seated quarters through the end of the series if 1891 were of increased weight but did not have arrows.

Each of the above is discussed in detail below. In 1892 the designs were replaced by those of Charles E. Barber.

LIBERTY SEATED QUARTER TYPES

1838–1840 • LIBERTY SEATED, VARIETY 1, NO MOTTO ABOVE EAGLE, NO DRAPERY

On the obverse of the coin, Liberty is seated on a rock in three-quarter profile to the right, her head turned back toward the left. Her left arm is raised and bent at the elbow; in her left hand she holds a liberty pole with cap. There is no extra drapery at the elbow. Her right arm reaches downward, her right hand resting on the corner of a shield inscribed with the word LIBERTY. The shield, placed at the base of the rock, is tilted sharply to the left. There are thirteen stars around the border, arranged seven to the left of the seated figure, one between her head and the liberty cap, and five at the right border. The date is between the base of the seated figure and the border. Dentils are around the border. On the reverse is a perched eagle with UNITED STATES OF AMERICA across the top border and QUAR. DOL. below, all in small letters. *Designer:* Christian Gobrecht • *Composition:* .900 silver, .100 copper • *Diameter:* 24.3 mm • *Weight:* 103.125 grains (6.68 grams) • *Edge:* Reeded.

1840–1853 • LIBERTY SEATED, VARIETY 1, NO MOTTO ABOVE EAGLE, WITH DRAPERY

The obverse bears the Liberty Seated motif described previously but now slightly modified by Robert Ball Hughes, most notably with the addition of extra drapery at Liberty's elbow. The reverse is of the same design, but now with larger letters around the border. *Designer:* Christian Gobrecht • *Composition:* .900 silver, .100 copper • *Diameter:* 24.3 mm • *Weight:* 103.125 grains (6.68 grams) • *Edge:* Reeded.

1853 • LIBERTY SEATED, VARIETY 2, ARROWS AT DATE, RAYS AROUND EAGLE

The obverse is essentially as preceding. However, thanks to the Coinage Act of February 21, 1853, a new, reduced weight was adopted for the quarter; arrows have been added at either side of the date to indicate the new standard. Likewise, the reverse is largely as before, but now with resplendent rays around the eagle. *Designer:* Christian Gobrecht, as modified by Robert Ball Hughes; arrows added by someone on the Mint staff • *Composition:* .900 silver, .100 copper • *Diameter:* 24.3 mm • *Weight:* 96 grains (6.22 grams) • *Edge:* Reeded.

1854–1855 • LIBERTY SEATED, VARIETY 3, ARROWS AT DATE, NO RAYS

The obverse is as preceding. Likewise, the reverse is as before, but with the rays removed. *Designer:* Christian Gobrecht, as modified by Robert Ball Hughes; arrows added by someone on the Mint staff • *Composition:* .900 silver, .100 copper • *Diameter:* 24.3 mm • *Weight:* 96 grains (6.22 grams) • *Edge:* Reeded.

1856–1865 • Liberty Seated, Variety 1 Resumed (Weight Standard of Variety 2)

The obverse and reverse designs are as preceding (with new weight standard) but with the arrows removed—the design is the same as that used before 1853. Accordingly, many collectors building type sets ignore this subtype. *Designer:* Christian Gobrecht, as modified by Robert Ball Hughes • *Composition:* .900 silver, .100 copper • *Diameter:* 24.3 mm • *Weight:* 96 grains (6.22 grams) • *Edge:* Reeded.

1866–1873 • Liberty Seated, Variety 4, Motto Above Eagle

The obverse is as preceding. Likewise, the reverse is as before, but with the motto IN GOD WE TRUST added on a scroll above the perched eagle. *Designer:* Christian Gobrecht, as modified by Robert Ball Hughes • *Composition:* .900 silver, .100 copper • *Diameter:* 24.3 mm • *Weight:* 96 grains (6.22 grams) • *Edge:* Reeded.

1873–1874 • Liberty Seated, Variety 5, Arrows at Date

The Liberty Seated obverse motif remains the same as preceding. The reverse changes only slightly. Following the Mint Act of February 12, 1873, the weight of the quarter was increased by a very small amount, and arrowheads were added to each side of the date to denote the change. *Designer:* Christian Gobrecht, as modified by Robert Ball Hughes; arrows added by someone on the Mint staff • *Composition:* .900 silver, .100 copper • *Diameter:* 24.3 mm • *Weight:* 96.45 grains (6.25 grams) • *Edge:* Reeded.

1875–1891 • Liberty Seated, Variety 4 Resumed (Weight Standard of Variety 5)

The obverse and reverse designs are as preceding, except that the arrows by the date on the reverse have been removed. The weight is unchanged, conforming to the Coinage Act of February 12, 1873. As the design is identical to that used from 1866–1874, many collectors building type sets ignore this subtype. *Designer:* Christian Gobrecht, as modified by Robert Ball Hughes • *Composition:* .900 silver, .100 copper • *Diameter:* 24.3 mm • *Weight:* 96.45 grains (6.25 grams) • *Edge:* Reeded.

ASPECTS OF CIRCULATION

From their inception in 1838, Liberty Seated dimes circulated widely in the East and Mideast. The Philadelphia Mint struck coinage in this denomination continuously over the years, although quantities varied widely. The New Orleans Mint produced Liberty Seated quarters from 1840 to 1860, and again in 1891. Coinage at the San Francisco Mint began in 1855 and continued to 1878, and again in 1891. The Carson City Mint struck quarters from 1870 to 1878.

1798 two-real silver coin struck at the Lima Mint in Peru. Spanish-American silver 2-real coins were more plentiful in circulation than were federal quarters.

During this era two-real Spanish-American silver coins, worth about 25 cents, were legal tender in America, a provision that extended into 1860. In general circulation during that time, they were much more plentiful than federal quarters.

The Civil War was declared on April 15, 1861. In the North it was envisioned as an easy win, and President Abraham Lincoln called for men to enlist for 90 days, after which time it surely would be over. That did not happen. The first major clash, the Battle of Bull Run in late July, resulted in a Confederate victory. Union troops scattered and fled. By late 1861 the outcome remained uncertain. In late December, gold coins began to be hoarded. "Hard money" offered security. In March 1862 the Treasury Department began issuing Legal Tender Notes. These could be exchanged only for other paper notes and were not redeemable at par in federal silver or gold coins. Fear increased, and by late spring all silver coins were gone from circulation in the East and in the Midwest. In the meantime, on the West Coast there were no Legal Tender bills in circulation. The Constitution of the State of California, adopted in 1850, forbid the use of paper money there. Silver coins continued to circulate at par, and any paper money brought into the state was accepted by merchants only at a deep discount. Because of this most Liberty Seated quarters struck in San Francisco saw more continuous use than did Philadelphia and New Orleans quarters of the same era, with the result that today S-Mint quarters are generally found in lower grades.

After the war ended in April 1865 it was thought that silver coins would soon return to commerce. However, the federal Treasury had its difficulties, and paper money was distrusted. It was not until April 1876 that quarters and other silver coins were again seen in quantity in circulation in the East and Midwest. This reappearance caused a glut of coins in commerce, with the result that the mintages of quarters were low from 1879 through the end of the series in 1891.

Liberty Seated quarters remained in circulation for many years, still found in pocket change into the 1920s and to a lesser extent the 1930s, by which time the growing interest in coin collecting prompted any surviving pieces to be saved. By then, coins in circulation were worn down to such grades as Good and Very Good.

PROOF LIBERTY SEATED QUARTERS

Proofs were struck at the Philadelphia Mint for all years from 1838 through 1891, although no sets with all copper and silver denominations are known for 1851 and 1853. Some quarters of these years are highly mirrorlike and have been called Proofs, but whether they were intentionally struck as such is a matter of debate. In modern times some third-party grading services have called prooflike branch mint coins Proofs, but there is no documentation that any were ever intended as such.

Proof quarters were first widely sold in 1858 when 210 silver Proof sets were struck.

From 1838 to 1858 Proofs were available as single coins and as part of silver sets for face value upon request to the Mint. In 1958 it seems that 210 sets were made plus single coins. In 1859 the Mint anticipated a great demand for Proofs and made 800 silver sets, followed by 1,000 each in 1860 and 1861, Proofs of the 1860 and 1861 quarters are far and away the rarest of the decade of the 1860s, as many collectors ignored them at the new retail price of $3 per set. It is likely that more than half of the coins were placed into circulation.

Among later sets the figures reached lows of 460 and 470 in 1863 and 1864, although most survive today. Ordering Proofs from the Mint involved either paying in silver or gold coins (only available at a premium in the marketplace) or by paying a strong premium in paper money. The Mint would not accept federal paper money at par.

Today, a complete run of Proof dates from 1858 to 1891 can be formed without difficulty. Typical grades are PF-63 and 64. Gems or PF-65 and finer coins are in the minority and are usually found among coins of the last dozen or so years of production. Gradeflation has been endemic in recent times, and many Proofs graded 64 in, say, the 1980s are certified as 65 or 66 today. This situation is well known and has been discussed widely in the numismatic press.

LIBERTY SEATED QUARTERS (1838–1891): GUIDE TO COLLECTING

Apart from Proof coins, called Master Coins in the early days, there was not much interest in Liberty Seated quarters during the years they were issued. Circulation strikes were ignored, including New Orleans and San Francisco branch mint issues and the later coins of Carson City. The curators of the Mint Cabinet, which was organized in June 1838, had no interest in them. As a result many branch mint quarters made in large quantities range from scarce to very rare in Mint State today. Most of the early New Orleans issues range from very rare to nearly impossible to find in Mint State For certain Philadelphia quarters, high-level Mint State coins are few and far between.

Branch-mint Liberty Seated quarters were mentioned only occasionally in the two leading periodicals of the late 19th and early 20th centuries—the *American Journal of Numismatics* and *The Numismatist*. It may come as a surprise to learn that so far is known, not a single numismatist collected Carson City quarters in the years they were issued from 1870 to 1878.

An awakening happened in 1893 with the publication of *Mint Marks, A Treatise on the Coinage of United States Branch Mints.* The author was Augustus G. Heaton, a talented writer, poet, and artist. This study was quickly followed by Ed. Frossard's sale of the William M. Friesner Collection on June 7 and 8, 1894, the first auction to ever feature mintmarked coins in depth. Selected coins, descriptions, and sale prices for Liberty Seated quarters (including all of Carson City) include these:

> 1840-O Without drapery at elbow. O mintmark over of R. Uncirculated; rare. 95 cents
>
> 1840-O Without drapery at elbow. O mintmark over A [in QUAR]. From circulation. 25 cents (face value!)
>
> 1840-O Without drapery at elbow. O mintmark to right of R. Uncirculated; rare. 75 cents
>
> 1842-O Large Date. Very fine. 80 cents
>
> 1842-O Small Date. Very good. $2
>
> 1852-O Extremely Fine, pin puncture. $2.10 (highest priced O-Mint quarter)
>
> 1858-S Fair. 30 cents (earliest S-Mint quarter in sale)
>
> 1864-S Very Good. 40 cents
>
> 1867-S VG. $3 (highest priced S-Mint quarter)
>
> 1869-S Rather poor. Scarce. 35 cents
>
> 1870-CC Very Fair. Scarce. $4
>
> 1871-S Very Fine. Rare. $3
>
> 1872-CC Poor. Very scarce. 75 cents
>
> 1873-CC Arrows. Good. Scarce. $5 (highest priced branch mint quarter in the sale)
>
> 1875-CC Fine. 25 cents.
>
> 1876-CC Uncirculated. 35 cents
>
> 1877-CC Extremely Fine. 45 cents
>
> 1878-CC Uncirculated. 30 cents
>
> 1878-S Uncirculated. 40 cents
>
> 1891-S Uncirculated. 40 cents; another, 65 cents.

The above is very significant in light of the neglect given mintmarks in the early years, and that Friesner, the leading collector of branch mint coins, could not find some of the varieties.[11] The sale also vividly demonstrated that a branch mint coin could be worth much more than a Philadelphia coin. Of course, today the Friesner prices in retrospect were unbelievable bargains.

Although the Heaton study and the Friesner auction engendered an interest in mintmarked coins, there was no widespread interest in this specialty until the 1909-S V.D.B. Lincoln cent caused a sensation in August of that year. Even so, collecting Liberty Seated quarters other than Proofs gained very little traction.

At that time and continuing for years afterward there was no book or guide listing basic varieties of coins by date and mintmark and giving market value. This did not happen until 1934 with *The Standard Catalogue of United States Coins*, followed years later by *A Guide Book of United States Coins* from 1946 (cover date 1947) onward by Western Publishing Co. (today known as Whitman Publishing).

As collections were formed, it was nearly always the case that Liberty Seated quarters, especially the branch mint issues, were harder to assemble than half dimes, dimes, half dollars, and dollars.

The Liberty Seated Collectors Club was formed in the early 1970s as a forum for enthusiasts in that field. *The Gobrecht Journal* has been published from 1974 onward. Today the non-profit group has over 600 members and welcomes anyone interested to join.

Every so often inventories of members' holdings are published. Most collections are comprised mainly of circulated issues—affordable and allowing for the majority of dates and mintmarks to be acquired.

BEING A SMART BUYER

First and foremost—and this is true of all Liberty Seated denominations—do not be a slave to grading numbers. There are two more factors that can be equally or even more important. Sharpness of strike is very important, and there are many quarters that within a certain certified grade can have a needle-sharp strike or can be weak in areas. Eye appeal is equally important. Coins can be beautiful to view or they can be dark, stained, or otherwise ugly. I would rather have an MS-63 coin that is sharply struck and has good eye appeal than an MS-66 with lightly struck areas and that is not very attractive. Even better, the MS-63 is apt to cost but a fraction of the MS-66!

Cherrypicking Liberty Seated quarters for quality can pay dividends. The grading services pay little or no attention to strike or eye appeal. This provides the opportunity to acquire sharp coins, for varieties for which such exist, without paying any more for them.

In addition there are many interesting varieties of which the public is not aware—such as repunched and misplaced dates—that often cost no more. The *Cherrypickers' Guide to Rare Die Varieties of United States Coins* describes many such pieces. The standard specialized work on the series is *The Comprehensive Encyclopedia of United States Liberty Seated Quarters* by Larry Briggs, 1991, available from sellers of out-of-print numismatic books.

For circulated coins, avoid those with nicks or scratches. Proofs are usually quite good, but some have light striking on Liberty's head and quite a few have scattered lint marks from residue on the dies. Eye appeal can vary.

AVAILABILITY IN CERTAIN GRADES

Comments regarding the numbers existing in various grades are based on conservative grating interpretation. In recent years gradeflation and resubmissions to certification services have increased the numbers of coins listed in PCGS and NGC population reports. In any event, these reports give the number of submissions, not the number of *different* specimens. If the same coin is sent in six times, it appears that six coins have been certified, not just one. A lot of modern rarity "research" based on studies of population reports can be disregarded.

Gradeflation is difficult to analyze. When I wrote *A Guide Book of Liberty Seated Coins* in 2015, I spent many hours studying the availability of coins in various grades. For many varieties the auctions of leading collections such as T. Harrison and John Work Garrett, Louis E. Eliasberg, Eugene Gardner, and others contained many exceptional coins and were duly noted. Beyond that, important quarters were offered in many other sales. The population reports were studied but, as noted, taken with a large grain of salt.

Today as I write these words for the 5th edition of *Mega Red* the true population of quarters has not changed. There have been no important hoards discovered, nor have there been any surprises from long-hidden collections appearing on the market. Stated another way, the availability figures I used in 2015 should be able to be used today. I have re-reviewed and changed a few. I am conservative. In the marketplace many MS-64 coins of years ago have been graded MS-65 or MS-66, and MS-65 coins have been graded MS-66 and MS-67. We also now have plus marks, stars, and other notations in addition to numbers. Perhaps a decade from now, many of today's MS-65 coins will be certified as MS-68+. Who knows?

The reason for gradeflation is that it seems to be win-win. The owner of an MS-64 coin is delighted to pay a fee to have it graded MS-65 or MS-66 if the coin increases dramatically in value. It is a win for the grading services as well; it is more profitable to grade the same coin multiple times than to grade it just once.

This brings me back to connoisseurship: Use the grade on a holder as the *starting point*. Remember that some MS-64 coins in old holders are of higher quality than MS-65 or 66 coins in new holders. Study the sharpness of strike and evaluate eye appeal. There are many MS-63 quarters that under this test are much more desirable than MS-65 quarters with weak striking or ugly surfaces. You are on your own when doing this. It will take time and patience, but your reward will be to build a truly great collection.

Also, while Mint State coins are more desirable than are, say, EF-40 coins, an element of practicality intervenes. As mentioned, very few members of the Liberty Seated Collectors Club aspire to forming a complete set of Mint State and Proof coins, as this would cost hundreds of thousands of dollars, even in low number ranges. Coins in Very Fine, Extremely Fine, and About Uncirculated grades are often inexpensive, and the best part of a full set of dates and mintmarks can be acquired. Unless you have a very strong bank account, this is the way to go.

MARKET NOTES

Today at the end of the second decade of the 21st century the market for many federal coins is not as strong as it was several years ago. This is mostly true of coins minted in the past 50 years and certified in high Mint State categories that were sold to speculators, not to established long-term collectors. Liberty Seated quarters in circulated and low Mint State grades have not been affected as much. Some higher-grade Mint State and Proof coins have dropped in price, probably due in part to gradeflation. Today there are many more certified 66-grade coins available than there were in the late 1980s when PCGS and NGC started business. Back then such coins were great rarities. Of course, the coins are the same, but gradeflation has affected the prices vis-à-vis currently listed grades.

You have a lot to think about and evaluate. Read and study as much as you can. Go slowly and carefully, and good luck.

LIBERTY SEATED (1838–1891)

GRADING STANDARDS

MS-60 to 70 (Mint State). *Obverse:* At MS-60, some abrasion and contact marks are evident, most noticeably on the bosom and thighs and knees. Luster is present, but may be dull or lifeless. At MS-63, contact marks are very few, and abrasion is hard to detect except under magnification. An MS-65 coin has no abrasion, and contact marks are sufficiently minute as to require magnification. Check the knees of Liberty and the right

1853, Repunched Date, No Arrows or Rays; FS-301. Graded MS-67.

field. Luster should be full and rich. Most Mint State coins of the 1861 to 1865 years, Philadelphia issues, have extensive die striae (from not completely finishing the die). *Reverse:* Comments apply as for the obverse, except that in lower Mint State grades abrasion and contact marks are most noticeable on the eagle's neck, the claws, and the top of the wings (harder to see there, however). At MS-65 or higher there are no marks visible to the unaided eye. The field is mainly protected by design elements and does not show abrasion as much as does the obverse on a given coin.

Illustrated coin: Note the delicate toning in the fields. In addition to hints of green, rose, and teal there is a good deal of luster as well.

AU-50, 53, 55, 58 (About Uncirculated). *Obverse:* Light wear is seen on the thighs and knees, bosom, and head. At AU-58, the luster is extensive, but incomplete, especially in the right field. At AU–50 and 53, luster is less. *Reverse:* Wear is evident on the eagle's neck, claws, and top of the wings. An AU-58 coin has nearly full luster, more so than on the obverse, as the design elements protect the small field areas. At AU–50 and 53, there still are traces of luster.

1891. Graded AU-53.

EF-40, 45 (Extremely Fine). *Obverse:* Further wear is seen on all areas, especially the thighs and knees, bosom, and head. Little or no luster is seen on most coins. From this grade downward, sharpness of strike of the stars and the head does not matter to connoisseurs. *Reverse:* Further wear is evident on the eagle's neck, claws, and wings. Some feathers in the right wing may be blended together.

1843. Graded EF-40.

VF-20, 30 (Very Fine). *Obverse:* Further wear is seen. Most details of the gown are worn away, except in the lower-relief areas above and to the right of the shield. Hair detail is mostly or completely gone. *Reverse:* Wear is more extensive, with more feathers blended together, especially in the right wing. The area below the shield shows more wear.

Illustrated coin: The surfaces of this coin are unusually smooth and problem free for the issue.

1860-S. Graded VF-20.

F-12, 15 (Fine). *Obverse:* The seated figure is well worn, but with some detail above and to the right of the shield. LIBERTY is readable but weak in areas. *Reverse:* Wear is extensive, with about half of the feathers flat or blended with others.

1854-O. Graded F-12.

VG-8, 10 (Very Good). *Obverse:* The seated figure is more worn, but some detail can be seen above and to the right of the shield. The shield is discernible. In LIBERTY at least the equivalent of two or three letters (can be a combination of partial letters) must be readable but can be very weak at VG-8, with a few more visible at VG-10. However, LIBERTY is not an infallible guide to grade this type, as some varieties had the word in low relief on the die, so it wore away slowly. *Reverse:* Further wear has flattened all but a few feathers, and the horizontal lines of the shield are indistinct. The leaves are only in outline form. The rim is visible all around, as are the ends of most denticles.

1872-CC. Graded VG-10.

Illustrated coin: Note the faint red toning evident in areas of this otherwise pleasingly gray coin.

G-4, 6 (Good). *Obverse:* The seated figure is worn smooth. At G-4 there are no letters in LIBERTY remaining on most (but not all) coins; some coins, especially of the early 1870s, are exceptions. At G-6, traces of one or two can barely be seen. *Reverse:* The designs are only in outline form, although some vertical shield stripes can be seen on some. The rim is worn down, and tops of the border letters are weak or worn away, although the inscription can still be read.

1872-CC. Graded G-6.

AG-3 (About Good). *Obverse:* The seated figure is mostly visible in outline form, with only a hint of detail. Much of the rim is worn away. The date remains clear. *Reverse:* The border letters are partially worn away. The eagle is mostly in outline form, but with a few details discernible. The rim is weak or missing.

1862-S. Graded AG-3.

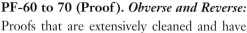

PF-60 to 70 (Proof). *Obverse and Reverse:* Proofs that are extensively cleaned and have many hairlines, or that are dull and grainy, are lower level, such as PF–60 to 62. These are not widely desired by connoisseurs. With medium hairlines and good reflectivity, an assigned grade of PF-64 is appropriate and with relatively few hairlines, Gem PF-65. In various grades hairlines are most easily seen in the obverse field. PF-66 should have hairlines so delicate that magnification is needed to see them. Above that, a Proof should be free of such lines.

1860. Graded PF-65.

1838 Liberty Seated Quarter

1838, No Drapery • Circulation-Strike
Mintage: 466,000.

Commentary: This issue is very popular and in everlasting demand, being the first year of the type. It is nearly always weak in areas, especially the head and stars, but there are occasional exceptions. Varieties exist: Open Claws, the more common version, and Closed Claws, perhaps 8 to 10 times rarer. These varieties were first reported by Larry Briggs. These are not widely collected, so finding one by cherrypicking is a possibility.

Availability in Mint State: In his 1991 book, Larry Briggs ranked this as the most readily available Mint State Liberty Seated quarter prior to 1853. Probably somewhat more than 200 Mint State coins exist based on the grading standards of 20 years ago, likely more than 300 by gradeflation standards. MS-65 and finer coins (using new interpretations for this and following comments) are rare, with fewer than a dozen in existence.

Availability in circulated grades: Readily available. Most are in lower grade ranges, but enough Extremely Fine and About Uncirculated coins exist to satisfy the demand of specialists.

	Cert	Avg	%MS	G-4	VG-8	F-12	VF-20	EF-40	AU-50	MS-60	MS-63	MS-65
1838, No Drapery	192	52.9	43%	$35	$50	$75	$175	$450	$950	$1,700	$4,000	$35,000

1838, No Drapery, Proof • Proof

Mintage: One verified.

Availability in Proof format: This coin is apparently unique. It graded PF-63, and was sold at the Anderson-Dupont and Gardner sales.

	Cert	Avg	%MS	PF-63
1838, No Drapery, Proof	0	n/a		$250,000

1839 Liberty Seated Quarter

1839, No Drapery • Circulation-Strike
Mintage: 491,146.

Commentary: Coins of this year are often weakly struck. There are three varieties, based on the styling of the eagle's claw: Closed Claws, Open Claws, and Very Long Claws, the latter consisting of about 10% of the surviving copies. The Long Claws reverse is mated with two obverses, one with the border dentils somewhat resembling beads or pellets.[12]

Availability in Mint State: Around 100 are available. MS-65 coins are very rare, with probably only a half dozen or so extant.

Availability in circulated grades: While readily available in lower grades, this issue is scarce at the About Uncirculated level.

	Cert	Avg	%MS	G-4	VG-8	F-12	VF-20	EF-40	AU-50	MS-60	MS-63	MS-65
1839, No Drapery	146	50.8	26%	$35	$50	$75	$175	$450	$1,050	$1,750	$4,250	$45,000

1839, No Drapery, Proof • Proof
Mintage: One verified.

Availability in Proof format: Only one Proof has been confirmed to exist, the coin that was part of the F.C.C. Boyd Collection (1945), later in the Pittman and Gardner collections, which graded PF-65.

	Cert	Avg	%MS	PF-65
1839, No Drapery, Proof	1	65.0		$300,000

1840-O Liberty Seated Quarter, No Drapery
1840-O, No Drapery • Circulation-Strike Mintage: 382,200.

Commentary: New Orleans strikes from 1840 without drapery usually have areas of weakness. Jack Marston, in "The Transitional 1840-O No Drapery Quarter" (*The Gobrecht Journal*, March 1992), noted: "On the obverse you will notice that the dentils are very small and in some

places almost non-existent. This feature creates considerably more space around the figure of Liberty and around the stars and the dates. This feature is like no other Liberty Seated quarter before or after it."

The New Orleans Hoard of Liberty Seated silver coins of various denominations and types, mostly quarter dollars of 1840-O (a few) and 1841-O (many), came to light around noon, October 29, 1982, when excavations for the new Meridien Hotel in the French Quarter of that city revealed three long-buried wooden boxes filled with coins![13]

Availability in Mint State: Most Mint State pieces seen are from the famous New Orleans Hoard, described above. They typically show what Larry W. Briggs called "dull and/or corroded surfaces," from burial in the ground. Coins not from the hoard are rare, probably fewer than two dozen, with only two or three graded MS-65 or higher.

Availability in circulated grades: 1840-O, No Drapery, quarters are one of the most plentiful early quarters in worn grades from AG-3 up. Some etched pieces from the New Orleans Hoard are About Uncirculated.

	Cert	Avg	%MS	G-4	VG-8	F-12	VF-20	EF-40	AU-50	MS-60	MS-63	MS-65
1840-O, No Drapery	144	46.5	23%	$40	$60	$85	$195	$450	$950	$2,200	$5,500	$35,000

1840 Liberty Seated Quarter, With Drapery

1840, With Drapery • Circulation-Strike
Mintage: 188,127.

Commentary: The strike varies, but on average most are more strongly struck than those of the preceding two years.

Availability in Mint State: About 50 exist, with fewer than a half dozen graded MS-65. A small hoard of seven pieces turned up in Baltimore circa 1984.[14]

Availability in circulated grades: These are readily available in circulated grades through Very Fine. Extremely Fine and About Uncirculated coins are slightly scarce.

	Cert	Avg	%MS	G-4	VG-8	F-12	VF-20	EF-40	AU-50	MS-60	MS-63	MS-65
1840, Drapery	43	51.1	30%	$35	$45	$70	$175	$425	$750	$1,650	$4,800	$18,000

1840, With Drapery, Proof • Proof
Mintage: Six or seven estimated.

Availability in Proof format: Four or five are estimated to be known. Hub Type I and II reverses, the last being four or five times scarcer (see Briggs book).[15]

	Cert	Avg	%MS	PF-65
1840, Drapery, Proof	2	64.5		$75,000

1840-O Liberty Seated Quarter, With Drapery

1840-O, With Drapery • Circulation-Strike **Mintage:** 43,000.

Commentary: Quality varies, but well-struck coins can be found. There are Large O and Small O varieties, with about 50 to 75 of the Large O variety known[16]. The reverse, Briggs 1-B, Large O, has denticles hand-entered in New Orleans to prolong the life of the dies.

Availability in Mint State: 75 to 100 exist, including a half dozen or so graded MS-65 or finer.

Availability in circulated grades: This coin is easily available most lower grades. About Uncirculated coins are scarce.

	Cert	Avg	%MS	G-4	VG-8	F-12	VF-20	EF-40	AU-50	MS-60	MS-63	MS-65
1840-O, Drapery	76	50.8	36%	$40	$60	$115	$215	$450	$800	$1,400	$3,800	$20,000

1841 Liberty Seated Quarter

1841 • **Circulation-Strike Mintage:** 120,000.

Availability in Mint State: There are about 50 Mint State coins, including four or five graded MS-65 or finer.

Availability in circulated grades: Many of these exist, mostly in lower grades.

	Cert	Avg	%MS	G-4	VG-8	F-12	VF-20	EF-40	AU-50	MS-60	MS-63	MS-65
1841	59	56.5	59%	$65	$100	$125	$225	$400	$750	$1,200	$2,250	$8,500

1841, Proof • **Proof Mintage:** Seven to nine estimated.

Availability in Proof format: Five or six are known.

	Cert	Avg	%MS	PF-60	PF-63
1841, Proof	1	66.0		$50,000	$75,000

1841-O Liberty Seated Quarter

1841-O • **Circulation-Strike Mintage:** 452,000.

Commentary: Most of these are fairly well struck, but there are many exceptions.

Availability in Mint State: 100 to 125 are available, but only one or two are graded MS-65 or better.

Availability in circulated grades: This issue is readily available in any grade desired.

	Cert	Avg	%MS	G-4	VG-8	F-12	VF-20	EF-40	AU-50	MS-60	MS-63	MS-65
1841-O	64	55.3	53%	$35	$50	$75	$165	$315	$425	$850	$1,900	$10,000

VARIETY: *1841-O, Doubled Die Obverse (FS-25-1841o-101 [001]).* Doubling is evident on the shield and ribbon and on the first three stars. Prior to a number of them being found in the New Orleans Hoard, this variety was very rare.[17]

1842 Liberty Seated Quarter

1842, Large (Medium) Date •
Circulation-Strike Mintage: 88,000.

Commentary: The Large (Medium) Date version of this year's quarter usually has lightness on the head and a few stars, sometimes with slight weakness on the eagle.

Availability in Mint State: 25 or so exist in Mint State, including one or two graded MS-65 or higher.

Availability in circulated grades: This coin is scarce in any grade, and rare at About Uncirculated. Most examples are well worn.

	Cert	Avg	%MS	G-4	VG-8	F-12	VF-20	EF-40	AU-50	MS-60	MS-63	MS-65
1842, Large Date	44	51.6	32%	$75	$100	$150	$250	Large (Medium) Date			$4,500	$12,500

1842, Small Date, Proof • Proof
Mintage: 9 to 11 estimated.

Commentary: Apparently, the few quarter dollar Proofs made in 1842 were of the Small Date type; none were Large Date. Presumably, the 1842, Small Date, obverse dies in this and the half dollar series were made early in the year 1842, at which time it was thought that the logotype was too small, and the later circulation-strike pieces, constituting the majority, were of the Large Date format. This would also explain the rarity of the 1842-O, Small Date, quarter, and half dollar.

Availability in Proof format: Seven specimens have been identified.[18]

Detail of the Small Date.

Availability in circulated grades: No circulated Proofs have been seen in the marketplace.

	Cert	Avg	%MS	PF-63	PF-65
1842, Small Date, Proof	2	65.0		$60,000	$125,000

1842-O Liberty Seated Quarter

1842-O, Small Date • Circulation-Strike

Mintage: Small part of 769,000.

Commentary: This is generally conceded to be the rarest New Orleans Liberty Seated quarter, with the 1849-O a close competitor.

Availability in Mint State: Two or three are known at this grade level, with MS-63 being the finest.

Availability in circulated grades: Larry Briggs suggests that about 200 to 250 exist, including all grades. Most range from About Good to Fine.[19]

Detail of the Small Date.

	Cert	Avg	%MS	G-4	VG-8	F-12	VF-20	EF-40	AU-50	MS-60	MS-63
1842-O, Small Date	19	21.2	5%	$600	$1,150	$1,600	$3,000	$7,500	$11,000	$27,500	$70,000

1842-O, Large (Medium) Date •

Circulation-Strike Mintage: Large part of 769,000.

Availability in Mint State: 40 or fewer Mint State copies exist, mostly in lower grades. No MS-65 coins have been seen by the author.

Availability in circulated grades: This coin is readily available in lower grades, but quite scarce at the About Uncirculated level.

Detail of the Large (Medium) Date.

	Cert	Avg	%MS	G-4	VG-8	F-12	VF-20	EF-40	AU-50	MS-60	MS-63
1842-O, Large Date	57	37.2	26%	$35	$45	$55	$125	$275	$600	$1,750	$4,500

1843 Liberty Seated Quarter

1843 • Circulation-Strike Mintage: 645,600

Commentary: One interesting die variety is the "Lightning Bolt reverse," Briggs Reverse C. This die has a zigzag die crack which runs from the border between the I and C in AMERICA through to the eagle's wing.

Availability in Mint State: 125 or so are known, including two or three graded MS-65 or better.

Availability in circulated grades: The 1843 Liberty Seated quarter struck in Philadelphia is common in all grades.

	Cert	Avg	%MS	G-4	VG-8	F-12	VF-20	EF-40	AU-50	MS-60	MS-63	MS-65
1843	101	57.5	52%	$30	$35	$45	$75	$200	$350	$675	$1,300	$4,500

1843, Proof • **Proof Mintage:** 12 to 14 estimated.

Availability in Proof format: 9 to 11 are known.

	Cert	Avg	%MS	PF-60	PF-63	PF-65
1843, Proof	4	61.0		$12,500	$20,000	$45,000

1843-O Liberty Seated Quarter

1843-O • **Circulation-Strike Mintage:** 968,000.

Commentary: These coins are usually fairly well struck except for some denticles.

Availability in Mint State: Around 25 Mint State coins exist, with one graded MS-65 or better.

Availability in circulated grades: Most New Orleans quarters from 1843 are well worn and have problems. Extremely Fine and About Uncirculated coins are rare.

	Cert	Avg	%MS	G-4	VG-8	F-12	VF-20	EF-40	AU-50	MS-60	MS-63
1843-O	57	42.7	12%	$35	$75	$150	$250	$550	$900	$2,450	$6,500

VARIETY: *1843-O, Large O Mintmark (FS-25-1843o-501 [001.5])*. The mintmark used to create this variety was likely intended for use on a half dollar die.

1844 Liberty Seated Quarter

1844 • **Circulation-Strike Mintage:** 421,200.

Commentary: These coins are usually sharp.

Availability in Mint State: About 45 are available in Mint State, including one or two graded MS-65 or finer.

Availability in circulated grades: The 1844 Philadelphia quarter is common in all circulated grades.

	Cert	Avg	%MS	G-4	VG-8	F-12	VF-20	EF-40	AU-50	MS-60	MS-63	MS-65
1844	84	55.4	44%	$30	$40	$50	$80	$165	$325	$650	$1,650	$14,500

1844, Proof • **Proof Mintage:** Five estimated.

Availability in Proof format: Two or three are confirmed.

	Cert	Avg	%MS	PF-60	PF-63	PF-65
1844, Proof	1	66.0				$175,000

1844-O Liberty Seated Quarter

1844-O • **Circulation-Strike Mintage:** 740,000.

Commentary: Some strikes used the same reverse die as the 1843-O, Large O, quarter. Of these, about two-thirds to three-quarters have the normal coin turn, while the remainder have medal turn. This makes 1844-O, Reverse of 1843-O, Large O, Medal Turn, a very scarce variety.[20]

Availability in Mint State: Approximately 35 exist, including two or three graded MS-65 or higher.

Availability in circulated grades: Nearly all of these coins are well worn, and are very common as such. About Uncirculated coins are elusive.

	Cert	Avg	%MS	G-4	VG-8	F-12	VF-20	EF-40	AU-50	MS-60	MS-63	MS-65
1844-O	56	49.0	29%	$35	$45	$65	$115	$250	$475	$1,250	$2,500	$10,000

1845 Liberty Seated Quarter

1845 • **Circulation-Strike Mintage:** 922,000.

Commentary: Strike quality varies for this issue. Thus, cherrypicking is recommended.

Availability in Mint State: 60 to 70 are known, including about a half dozen graded MS-65 or finer.

Availability in circulated grades: This coin is relatively common in the context of the series.

	Cert	Avg	%MS	G-4	VG-8	F-12	VF-20	EF-40	AU-50	MS-60	MS-63	MS-65
1845	123	55.6	46%	$30	$35	$45	$80	$165	$235	$500	$1,250	$6,000

1845, Proof • **Proof Mintage:** 11 to 13 estimated.

Availability in Proof format: Seven to nine are known.

	Cert	Avg	%MS	PF-63	PF-65
1845, Proof	8	64.6		$20,000	$35,000

1846 Liberty Seated Quarter

1846 • **Circulation-Strike Mintage:** 510,000.

Commentary: A repunched date variety, 46 Over 46, unlisted by Fivaz-Stanton, is readily available.

Availability in Mint State: 80 to 90 Mint State coins are available, including three to five graded MS-65 or finer.

Availability in circulated grades: Although readily available in lower grades, this coin is elusive at the About Uncirculated level.

	Cert	Avg	%MS	G-4	VG-8	F-12	VF-20	EF-40	AU-50	MS-60	MS-63	MS-65
1846	79	53.9	38%	$45	$75	$100	$125	$225	$425	$800	$1,850	$12,500

1846, Proof • **Proof Mintage:** 16 to 19 estimated.

Availability in Proof format: 12 to 14 are known.

	Cert	Avg	%MS	PF-60	PF-63	PF-65
1846, Proof	11	64.5		$5,000	$10,000	$20,000

1847 Liberty Seated Quarter

1847 • **Circulation-Strike Mintage:** 734,000.

Commentary: This coin is usually sharply struck.

Availability in Mint State: There are about 50 Mint State coins, including three graded MS-65 or finer.

Availability in circulated grades: The 1847 Liberty Seated quarter is readily available in circulated grades.

	Cert	Avg	%MS	G-4	VG-8	F-12	VF-20	EF-40	AU-50	MS-60	MS-63	MS-65
1847	70	53.4	46%	$35	$50	$70	$95	$160	$275	$600	$1,650	$6,500

VARIETY: *1847, Doubled Die Reverse, Repunched Date (FS-25-1847-801 [002]).* The Repunched Date is considered of secondary importance to the doubled die. Doubling can be seen on UNITED STATES OF AMERICA, QUAR. DOL., the olive leaves, the eagle's left talon and eye, and the horizontal shield lines. the Repunched Date can be seen as a secondary 7 to the left of the primary 7.

1847, Proof • **Proof Mintage:** 13 to 16 estimated.

Availability in Proof format: 9 to 11 exist, most of which grade PF-64 to 66—a remarkable situation.

	Cert	Avg	%MS	PF-60	PF-63	PF-65
1847, Proof	4	65.3		$5,000	$10,000	$25,000

1847-O Liberty Seated Quarter

1847-O • **Circulation-Strike Mintage:** 368,000.

Commentary: These coins are usually found with lightness on the obverse. The vast majority of coins in all grades have die cracks on the reverse.[22] There are three mintmark placements for the 1847-O: Left, Centered, and Right. All are available, but Centered is the most challenging.[23]

Availability in Mint State: No more than a half dozen are confirmed in Mint State. One graded MS-65 or better may exist.

Availability in circulated grades: The New Orleans Liberty Seated quarter of 1847 is scarce in all lower grades, very scarce at Extremely Fine, and rare at About Uncirculated.[21]

	Cert	Avg	%MS	G-4	VG-8	F-12	VF-20	EF-40	AU-50	MS-60	MS-63
1847-O	43	39.1	12%	$100	$175	$300	$600	$1,000	$2,000	$6,000	$12,500

1848 Liberty Seated Quarter

1848 • **Circulation-Strike Mintage:** 146,000.

Availability in Mint State: Fewer than 10 exist, an amazing rarity. One or two are graded MS-65 or finer.

Availability in circulated grades: Reflecting the much lower mintage than prior years, this Philadelphia issue is quite scarce.

	Cert	Avg	%MS	G-4	VG-8	F-12	VF-20	EF-40	AU-50	MS-60	MS-63	MS-65
1848	38	47.8	29%	$45	$95	$150	$275	$450	$650	$1,250	$4,750	$12,000

VARIETY: *1848, Doubled Date (FS-Unlisted). Briggs 1-A.* The first impact of the four-digit logotype was light and slightly above and to the left of the finished product. Larry Briggs has reported two of these with the reverse rotated 90 degrees.[24]

1848, Proof • **Proof Mintage:** 13 to 15 estimated.

Availability in Proof format: 9 to 11 are estimated to exist.

	Cert	Avg	%MS	PF-60	PF-63	PF-65
1848, Proof	2	65.0		$5,000	$10,000	$30,000

1849 Liberty Seated Quarter

1849 • **Circulation-Strike Mintage:** 340,000.

Availability in Mint State: About 40 are known, including one or two graded MS-65 or finer.

Availability in circulated grades: This coin is commonly found well worn, but slightly scarce in About Uncirculated condition.

	Cert	Avg	%MS	G-4	VG-8	F-12	VF-20	EF-40	AU-50	MS-60	MS-63	MS-65
1849	94	52.7	31%	$35	$75	$95	$115	$250	$400	$1,000	$1,850	$9,500

1849, Proof • **Proof Mintage:** 10 to 12 estimated.

Availability in Proof format: Six to eight are estimated to exist.

	Cert	Avg	%MS	PF-60	PF-63	PF-65
1849, Proof	3	64.3		$5,000	$10,000	$27,500

1849-O Liberty Seated Quarter

1849-O • **Circulation-Strike Mintage:** 16,000 estimated.

Commentary: While the mintage is not in *The Annual Report of the Director of the Mint*, both Walter Breen and Larry Briggs have estimated the figure at 16,000.[25]. That amount should probably be deducted from the 1850-O mintage.

Availability in Mint State: 10 or so are known, with none grading at MS-65. Many are overgraded.

Availability in circulated grades: Most of these New Orleans strikes show extensive wear and have problems.

	Cert	Avg	%MS	G-4	VG-8	F-12	VF-20	EF-40	AU-50	MS-60	MS-63
1849-O	39	32.8	13%	$1,100	$1,500	$2,000	$3,000	$7,000	$8,500	$17,500	$20,000

1850 Liberty Seated Quarter

1850 • **Circulation-Strike Mintage:** 1,908,000.

Commentary: Issues of this year are usually well struck. Many were likely melted for their bullion content.

Availability in Mint State: About 25 exist, including two or three graded MS-65 or finer.

Availability in circulated grades: 1850 Philadelphia quarter coins are slightly scarce. Most are well worn.

	Cert	Avg	%MS	G-4	VG-8	F-12	VF-20	EF-40	AU-50	MS-60	MS-63	MS-65
1850	35	56.1	51%	$50	$95	$185	$275	$400	$650	$1,350	$2,500	$11,000

VARIETY: *1850, Misplaced Date (FS-25-1850-301).* The base of an extra 1 is spectacularly punched on the raised rim, a very deep detail in the die.

1850, Proof • **Proof Mintage:** Six to eight estimated.

Availability in Proof format: Four or five are known.

	Cert	Avg	%MS	PF-60	PF-63	PF-65
1850, Proof	3	64.0				$75,000

1850-O Liberty Seated Quarter

1850-O • **Circulation-Strike Mintage:** 396,000.

Commentary: While this coin is usually poorly struck, especially at the rims, there are exceptions.

Availability in Mint State: About 25 Mint State coins are available, including one or two graded MS-65 or finer. Larry Briggs has reported on the discovery of five or six Uncirculated pieces around 1986.[26]

Availability in circulated grades: This coin is available in any grade desired through Extremely Fine. About Uncirculated coins are scarce.

	Cert	Avg	%MS	G-4	VG-8	F-12	VF-20	EF-40	AU-50	MS-60	MS-63	MS-65
1850-O	66	51.7	38%	$75	$115	$150	$225	$500	$750	$1,600	$4,000	$13,500

1851 Liberty Seated Quarter

1851 • **Circulation-Strike Mintage:** 160,000. **Proof Mintage:** See below.

Commentary: Some coins of 1851 and 1853 have been called Proofs over a long period of years, but it uncertain if they were actually struck as such or they were from dies polished after relapping or for other reasons. No Proof sets of this year are known.

Availability in Mint State: 45 to 50 are available, including six to nine graded MS-65 or higher.

Availability in circulated grades: Overall, this issue is very scarce, but enough are available that any desired grade through Very Fine can be found. Studies have shown that the 1851 is slightly scarcer than the 1851-O, despite the latter's much lower mintage. Probably, many of the Philadelphia strikes were melted in the East, while most of the New Orleans coins remained in circulation.[27]

	Cert	Avg	%MS	G-4	VG-8	F-12	VF-20	EF-40	AU-50	MS-60	MS-63	MS-65
1851	41	48.3	29%	$100	$175	$275	$400	$700	$1,000	$1,450	$2,350	$6,500

1851-O Liberty Seated Quarter

1851-O • **Circulation-Strike Mintage:** 88,000.

Commentary: The 1851-O New Orleans quarter is considered one of the key issues of the decade. It usually has very weak head detail and an overall lightness on the obverse.

Availability in Mint State: There are about 10 Mint State coins, up to and including MS-63.

Availability in circulated grades: Most show extensive wear and/or damage.

	Cert	Avg	%MS	G-4	VG-8	F-12	VF-20	EF-40	AU-50	MS-60	MS-63
1851-O	40	26.2	8%	$375	$550	$900	$1,000	$2,500	$3,350	$6,700	$32,500

1852 Liberty Seated Quarter

1852 • **Circulation-Strike Mintage:** 177,060.

Commentary: The Mint outdid itself this year with the date logotype, with the 2 more ornate than seen on any coin of this design up to this point in time. Briggs 2-A is a normal date that slopes slightly down to the right (Briggs 1-A, with a repunched date, has a horizontal date; see below). Two are known with the reverse rotated 90 degrees.[28]

Availability in Mint State: About 60 exist, including four to six graded MS-65 or higher.

Availability in circulated grades: This coin is available in any grade desired.

	Cert	Avg	%MS	G-4	VG-8	F-12	VF-20	EF-40	AU-50	MS-60	MS-63	MS-65
1852	56	55.6	55%	$125	$225	$325	$450	$600	$750	$1,100	$2,100	$5,500

VARIETY: *1852, Repunched Date (FS-Unlisted). Briggs 1-A.* The repunched date runs horizontally. This die was used to strike Proof coins as well.

1852, Proof • **Proof Mintage:** Five or six estimated.

Availability in Proof format: Four or five are known. This die, with the double-punched 52 in the date, was also used to make circulation strikes.[29]

	Cert	Avg	%MS	PF-65
1852, Proof	1	65.0		$75,000

1852-O Liberty Seated Quarter

1852-O • Circulation-Strike Mintage: 96,000.

Commentary: This is one of the key issues among early Liberty Seated quarters, especially in the better grades. It is usually struck with weak areas. It also has a rather curious beveled rim that seems to have accelerated the effects of wear in circulation.

Availability in Mint State: Only two or three, graded MS-60 to 62, exist. Additionally, a group of seven sea-salvage Mint State pieces with environmental etching came to light in 1988.[30]

Availability in circulated grades: Most examples of this coin are well circulated. Extremely Fine and About Uncirculated coins are rarities.

	Cert	Avg	%MS	G-4	VG-8	F-12	VF-20	EF-40	AU-50	MS-60	MS-63
1852-O	30	29.1	7%	$350	$500	$850	$1,500	$2,250	$5,500	$9,500	$40,000

1853 Liberty Seated Quarter, No Arrows or Rays

1853, No Arrows or Rays • Circulation-Strike Mintage: 44,200.

Commentary: The last two date numerals are repunched on genuine coins. Years ago this was sometimes called 1853, 3 Over 2. The net mintage representing the quantity actually released is not known; it has been estimated at various levels from several thousand coins on up.

Availability in Mint State: About 50 are available, including 12 to 15 graded MS-65 or finer, a remarkable amount for this early date.

Availability in circulated grades: Circulated coins of this issue are rare. About 100 to 150 are known graded AG-3 through AU-58. Most are in higher grades such as Extremely Fine and About Uncirculated.

	Cert	Avg	%MS	G-4	VG-8	F-12	VF-20	EF-40	AU-50	MS-60	MS-63	MS-65
1853, No Arrows or Rays	45	45.9	42%	$1,250	$2,000	$2,500	$3,250	$4,000	$4,500	$6,250	$7,500	$12,000

1853 Liberty Seated Quarter, With Arrows and Rays

1853, With Arrows and Rays •
Circulation-Strike Mintage: 15,254,200.
Proof Strike Mintage: See below.

Commentary: See comments under 1851, above. It is unknown if Proofs were ever struck. Some have held that coins offered as Proofs are actually prooflike Mint State coins.

Availability in Mint State: 1,300 to 1,600 are available, including 50 or more graded MS-65 or finer. Larry Briggs considers this and the 1876 tied for being the most common Mint State Liberty Seated quarters.

Availability in circulated grades: This coin is extremely common and available in any grade desired. It is the most common issue in the Liberty Seated series up to this point in time.

	Cert	Avg	%MS	G-4	VG-8	F-12	VF-20	EF-40	AU-50	MS-60	MS-63	MS-65
1853, With Arrows and Rays	1,317	49.3	33%	$25	$30	$35	$50	$175	$350	$1,000	$2,000	$10,000

VARIETY: *1853, 853 Over 854 (FS-25-1853-301 [003]).* This curious variety shows clear traces of 854 under the final 1853 date. Part of the earlier right-side arrow shaft is also visible. It is likely that in late 1853, dies were being made in advance for use in 1854. There was a call for an 1853-dated die to be used toward the end of the 1853 year, and an 1854 die was overdated.[31] Several dozen are known, mostly in circulated grades. As this variety is not widely known, finding one listed as a regular variety is a strong possibility.

	Cert	Avg	%MS	G-4	VG-8	F-12	VF-20	EF-40	AU-50	MS-60	MS-63	MS-65
1853, With Arrows and Rays, 3 Over 4	55	40.9	20%	$55	$100	$175	$250	$350	$675	$1,850	$4,000	$30,000

1853-O Liberty Seated Quarter, With Arrows and Rays

1853-O, With Arrows and Rays •
Circulation-Strike Mintage: 1,332,000.

Commentary: Usually with some flatness at the obverse center. One variety has concentric circular marks in the obverse shield, an unusual feature caused from an incompletely machined die face.[32] This obverse was combined with two different reverses.[33]

Availability in Mint State: About 20, including one graded MS-65 or finer. Surprisingly rare!

Availability in circulated grades: Easily obtainable, but seen far less often than its Philadelphia Mint counterpart.

	Cert	Avg	%MS	G-4	VG-8	F-12	VF-20	EF-40	AU-50	MS-60	MS-63	MS-65
1853-O, With Arrows and Rays	107	44.4	16%	$35	$70	$100	$150	$400	$1,100	$4,250	$10,000	$27,500

VARIETY: *1853-O, O Over Horizontal O (FS-25-1853o-501).* The mintmark was first punched horizontally, and then corrected. Traces of the first O are visible, primarily at the top of the central opening. Perhaps 40 to 60 are known, all reported examples of which are in circulated grades. The finest seen by Larry Briggs is AU-55.34

1854 Liberty Seated Quarter, With Arrows, No Rays

1854, With Arrows, No Rays •

Circulation-Strike Mintage: 12,380,000.

Commentary: Strike quality for this issue varies, as is true of nearly all large-mintage issues.

Availability in Mint State: 900 to 1,200, including 30 to 40 graded MS-65 or better. This the most readily available Liberty Seated quarter in Mint State, per Larry Briggs. *MS-65 or better: 30 to 40.*

Availability in circulated grades: These are easily available in any grade desired.

	Cert	Avg	%MS	G-4	VG-8	F-12	VF-20	EF-40	AU-50	MS-60	MS-63	MS-65
1854, With Arrows, No Rays	689	51.6	35%	$25	$30	$35	$45	$85	$250	$625	$1,200	$6,500

1854, With Arrows, No Rays, Proof •

Proof Mintage: 45 to 55 estimated.

Availability in Proof format: 30 to 40 are known.

	Cert	Avg	%MS	PF-60	PF-63	PF-65
1854, With Arrows, No Rays, Proof	10	64.2		$8,500	$15,000	$30,000

1854-O Liberty Seated Quarter, With Arrows, No Rays

1854-O, With Arrows, No Rays •

Circulation-Strike Mintage: 1,484,000.

Availability in Mint State: Approximately 75 are available, including two or three graded MS-65 or finer.

Availability in circulated grades: One of the more available New Orleans quarters, this strike is common.

	Cert	Avg	%MS	G-4	VG-8	F-12	VF-20	EF-40	AU-50	MS-60	MS-63	MS-65
1854-O, With Arrows, No Rays	100	45.2	33%	$35	$40	$50	$55	$125	$300	$1,100	$1,750	$15,000

VARIETY: *1854-O, Huge O Mintmark (FS-25-1854o-501 [004]).* The mintmark is large and somewhat misshapen, for reasons unknown. It might be die damage according to one theory, or overly aggressive polishing according to another. Or perhaps the die was shipped into New Orleans from Philadelphia (where all dies were made) without the mintmark, the error was realized, and an improvised mintmark was added at New Orleans by some inexpert tooling. The bottom of the laurel branch and the tops of R and D in QUAR. DOL. show damage. Dozens are known, all in circulated grades except a single example sold as a regular coin in 1976 at an Indiana coin show.[35]

	Cert	Avg	%MS	G-4	VG-8	F-12	VF-20	EF-40	AU-50
1854-O, With Arrows, No Rays, Huge O	68	20.3	0%	$600	$1,150	$1,450	$1,850	$3,850	$6,500

1855 Liberty Seated Quarter, With Arrows, No Rays

1855, With Arrows, No Rays •
Circulation-Strike Mintage: 2,857,000.

Availability in Mint State: About 200 exist in Mint State, including 9 to 12 graded MS-65 or higher. Larry Briggs considers this among the most commonly available Liberty Seated quarters in Mint State, along with 1856; 1858; 1861; 1862; and 1873, With Arrows.

Availability in circulated grades: All circulated grades are commonly found.

	Cert	Avg	%MS	G-4	VG-8	F-12	VF-20	EF-40	AU-50	MS-60	MS-63	MS-65
1855, With Arrows, No Rays	186	53.3	38%	$25	$30	$40	$50	$125	$250	$625	$1,300	$10,000

1855, With Arrows, No Rays, Proof •
Proof Mintage: 30 to 40 estimated.

Availability in Proof format: 20 to 25 are known.

	Cert	Avg	%MS	PF-60	PF-63	PF-65
1855, With Arrows, No Rays, Proof	10	64.6		$8,500	$15,000	$30,000

1855-O Liberty Seated Quarter, With Arrows, No Rays

1855-O, With Arrows, No Rays •
Circulation-Strike Mintage: 176,000.

Commentary: Weak striking for this issue is the norm.

Availability in Mint State: Approximately 15 Mint State examples are believed to exist, including two or three graded MS-65 or finer.

Availability in circulated grades: Coins in circulated grades are mostly well-worn, with problems. About Uncirculated coins are very rare.

	Cert	Avg	%MS	G-4	VG-8	F-12	VF-20	EF-40	AU-50	MS-60	MS-63
1855-O, With Arrows, No Rays	33	40.7	30%	$125	$185	$300	$550	$850	$2,000	$3,000	$12,500

1855-S Liberty Seated Quarter, With Arrows, No Rays

1855-S, With Arrows, No Rays •
Circulation-Strike Mintage: 396,400.

Commentary: Strikes of this coin can be weak in areas.

Availability in Mint State: About 20 Mint State copies are known, including one confirmed MS-65 or higher.

Availability in circulated grades: This coin is very elusive in all grades, with most showing extensive circulation. Many show traces of solder or tooling from having been used as buttons.[36]

	Cert	Avg	%MS	G-4	VG-8	F-12	VF-20	EF-40	AU-50	MS-60	MS-63	MS-65
1855-S, With Arrows, No Rays	33	40.6	15%	$100	$225	$350	$600	$1,000	$1,450	$2,850	$7,500	$25,000

1855-S, With Arrows, No Rays, Proofs • **Proof Mintage:** 1+.

Availability in Proof format: Only one has been reported. It was in the Richmond Collection auctioned by David Lawrence Rare Coins in 2005, graded as PF-63 by NGC. The grade was increased to PF-64 when it was offered again by Heritage Auctions in August 2011 and August 2013. It may have been created to the order of San Francisco Mint Superintendent Robert Aiken Birdsall.[37]

	Cert	Avg	%MS	PF-63
1855-S, With Arrows, No Rays, Proof	1	64.0		—

1856 Liberty Seated Quarter

1856 • **Circulation-Strike Mintage:** 7,264,000.

Commentary: Strike quality for 1856 Philadelphia quarters varies from slightly weak to needle sharp.

Availability in Mint State: 550 to 650 exist in Mint State, including 25 to 35 graded MS-65 or finer. Larry Briggs considers this among the most commonly available Liberty Seated quarters in Mint State, along with 1855, With Arrows, No Rays; 1858; 1861; 1862; and 1873, With Arrows.

Availability in circulated grades: All circulated grades are common.

	Cert	Avg	%MS	G-4	VG-8	F-12	VF-20	EF-40	AU-50	MS-60	MS-63	MS-65
1856	273	52.8	44%	$25	$30	$35	$45	$75	$185	$350	$650	$3,000

1856, Proof • **Proof Mintage:** 55 to 65 estimated.

Availability in Proof format: 40 to 50 are known. The reverse die is bulged at the right. The same die was used in 1857 for all Proofs and for some Proofs in 1858.

	Cert	Avg	%MS	PF-60	PF-63	PF-65
1856, Proof	27	64.0		$3,500	$5,000	$12,500

1856-O Liberty Seated Quarter

1856-O • Circulation-Strike Mintage: 968,000.

Commentary: New Orleans strikes of this year usually show weakness in the head and obverse stars.

Availability in Mint State: Around 15 Mint State examples are known, including two or three graded MS-65 or finer. This coin in Mint State is surprisingly rare.

Availability in circulated grades: Most copies from this date and Mint are well circulated, making About Uncirculated coins scarce.

	Cert	Avg	%MS	G-4	VG-8	F-12	VF-20	EF-40	AU-50	MS-60	MS-63	MS-65
1856-O	78	46.4	19%	$30	$40	$75	$125	$250	$475	$1,000	$2,500	$12,000

1856-S Liberty Seated Quarter

1856-S • Circulation-Strike Mintage: 286,000.

Availability in Mint State: About 10 are known, including one graded MS-65 or finer.

Availability in circulated grades: Circulated grades are rare. Most are well-worn.

	Cert	Avg	%MS	G-4	VG-8	F-12	VF-20	EF-40	AU-50	MS-60	MS-63	MS-65
1856-S	24	38.3	13%	$250	$325	$500	$800	$2,250	$3,500	$7,500	$13,500	$40,000

VARIETY: *1856-S, S Over Small S (FS-25-1856S-501 [005]).* A larger S is punched over an earlier S mintmark possibly intended for a half dime. This is a rare variety, especially in Very Fine grade or higher.

	Cert	Avg	%MS	G-4	VG-8	F-12	VF-20	EF-40
1856-S, S Over Small S	5	19.0	0%	$500	$850	$1,500	$3,000	$6,000

1857 Liberty Seated Quarter

1857 • Circulation-Strike Mintage: 9,644,000.

Commentary: One very scarce and popular variety with Liberty Seated Collectors Club members, the "Smoking Liberty," has a die line or die crack at Liberty's lower hand, giving the illusion that she is holding a cigarette.

Availability in Mint State: 600 to 700 are known, including 50 to 75 graded MS-65 or higher.

Availability in circulated grades: These are very common.

	Cert	Avg	%MS	G-4	VG-8	F-12	VF-20	EF-40	AU-50	MS-60	MS-63	MS-65
1857	564	54.7	54%	$25	$30	$35	$45	$75	$185	$350	$600	$2,750

VARIETY: *1857, Clash Marks from 1857 Cent (FS-25-1857-901 [006]).* During the production of 1857 Flying Eagle cents, a coining press was inadvertently fitted with an 1857 cent reverse die and an 1857 quarter reverse die. The two dies came together without an intervening planchet, and each die left clash marks on the other. Quarters with clash marks from the cent die are known and are slightly scarce. This feature is most prom-

inent above the eagle's wing to the left. Nearly all are in circulated grades. Likewise, a number of cents are known today with the outline in mirror image of the quarter dollar die, most prominently above ONE. A detail of such a cent, the eagle's head, is shown above. The clashed cent is listed as Snow-8, Fivaz-Stanton-01-1857-901 (005).

	Cert	Avg	%MS	G-4	VG-8	F-12	VF-20	EF-40	AU-50
1857, Clash Marks	5	50.2	40%	$100	$150	$250	$450	$800	$1,500

1857, Proof • Proof Mintage: 35 to 45 estimated.

Availability in Proof format: 25 to 30 are known. The reverse die, bulged at the right, was also used to strike all 1856 Proof quarters and some Proofs of 1858.

	Cert	Avg	%MS	PF-60	PF-63	PF-65
1857, Proof	34	64.0		$3,000	$4,000	$11,000

1857-O Liberty Seated Quarter

1857-O • Circulation-Strike Mintage: 1,180,000.

Availability in Mint State: 40 or so exist, with potentially one graded MS-65 or finer. A few are highly prooflike.

Availability in circulated grades: Most of the circulated coins are well worn, making About Uncirculated coins rare.

	Cert	Avg	%MS	G-4	VG-8	F-12	VF-20	EF-40	AU-50	MS-60	MS-63
1857-O	82	49.6	22%	$35	$50	$90	$150	$300	$500	$1,200	$3,000

1857-S Liberty Seated Quarter

1857-S • **Circulation-Strike Mintage:** 82,000.

Availability in Mint State: There are about 30 graded at Mint State, including one graded MS-65 or higher.

Availability in circulated grades: This coin is very scarce in circulated grades, more so than 1855-S, 1856-S, or 1858-S. That is somewhat anomalous, as the 1857-S in About Uncirculated grade is the most often seen San Francisco quarter of the 1850s.[38] Most examples show extensive wear and have corrosion or other problems.

	Cert	Avg	%MS	G-4	VG-8	F-12	VF-20	EF-40	AU-50	MS-60	MS-63
1857-S	46	47.5	20%	$175	$300	$425	$800	$1,150	$1,850	$3,500	$6,000

1858 Liberty Seated Quarter

1858 • **Circulation-Strike Mintage:** 7,368,000.

Commentary: Although usually well struck, some copies have areas of weakness.

Availability in Mint State: 1,100 to 1,300 Mint State coins are available, including 50 to 70 graded MS-65 or finer. Larry Briggs considers this among the most readily available Liberty Seated quarters in Mint State, along with 1855, With Arrows, No Rays; 1856; 1861; 1862; and 1873, With Arrows.

Availability in circulated grades: Copies are readily available in any grade desired.

	Cert	Avg	%MS	G-4	VG-8	F-12	VF-20	EF-40	AU-50	MS-60	MS-63	MS-65
1858	434	54.2	49%	$25	$30	$35	$45	$75	$185	$350	$600	$2,750

1858, Proof • **Proof Mintage:** 210+.

Availability in Proof format: Approximately 210 were made for inclusion in silver Proof sets, with most surviving today in lower Proof grades. It is possible that additional pieces were made. Some, but not all, are from the die used to strike Proof quarters in 1856 and 1857, with its distinctive bulge at the right.

	Cert	Avg	%MS	PF-60	PF-63	PF-65
1858, Proof	76	63.6		$1,500	$2,000	$6,000

1858-O Liberty Seated Quarter

1858-O • **Circulation-Strike Mintage:** 520,000.

Commentary: The head of Liberty is usually weak.

Availability in Mint State: About 40 are known at this grade level, including two or three graded MS-65 or finer.

Availability in circulated grades: Most examples are well worn. About Uncirculated coins are hard to find.

	Cert	Avg	%MS	G-4	VG-8	F-12	VF-20	EF-40	AU-50	MS-60	MS-63	MS-65
1858-O	44	48.9	14%	$30	$40	$75	$125	$350	$650	$3,250	$10,000	$25,000

1858-S Liberty Seated Quarter

1858-S • **Circulation-Strike Mintage:** 121,000.

Commentary: The mintmark can be found in its normal centered placement, slightly to the left, and tilted to the right.

Availability in Mint State: Only five or so are in Mint State, making this a great rarity. One example is confirmed graded MS-65 or better.

Availability in circulated grades: This coin is scarce at all levels and rare at the About Uncirculated level.

	Cert	Avg	%MS	G-4	VG-8	F-12	VF-20	EF-40	AU-50	MS-60
1858-S	41	35.6	2%	$250	$400	$600	$1,000	$3,500	$5,000	$22,500

1859 Liberty Seated Quarter

1859 • **Circulation-Strike Mintage:** 1,344,000.

Commentary: Briggs describes minor differences in the reverse dies used.

Availability in Mint State: 140 to 160 Mint State examples are known, including 7 to 10 graded MS-65 or higher.

Availability in circulated grades: Circulated-grade examples are common, mostly in the lower grades.

	Cert	Avg	%MS	G-4	VG-8	F-12	VF-20	EF-40	AU-50	MS-60	MS-63	MS-65
1859	146	54.3	44%	$25	$30	$45	$65	$90	$200	$425	$900	$4,500

1859, Proof • **Proof Mintage:** 800.

Availability in Proof format: 500 or so of this issue survive, mostly in lower Proof grades.

	Cert	Avg	%MS	PF-60	PF-63	PF-65
1859, Proof	154	64.1		$1,000	$1,500	$4,500

1859-O Liberty Seated Quarter

1859-O • **Circulation-Strike Mintage:** 260,000.

Commentary: This New Orleans strike usually exhibits some weakness on the head.

Availability in Mint State: 25 to 30 exist in Mint State, including two or three graded MS-65 or finer.[39]

Availability in circulated grades: These are available easily enough, mostly in well-worn grades.

	Cert	Avg	%MS	G-4	VG-8	F-12	VF-20	EF-40	AU-50	MS-60	MS-63	MS-65
1859-O	45	51.6	27%	$50	$75	$100	$150	$300	$550	$2,500	$6,500	$22,500

1859-S Liberty Seated Quarter

1859-S • **Circulation-Strike Mintage:** 80,000.

Availability in Mint State: None have been reported.

Availability in circulated grades: San Francisco strikes from 1859 are rare in all grades. Most are in low grades and have problems. Some have etching or corrosion suggesting they may have been unearthed.[40]

	Cert	Avg	%MS	G-4	VG-8	F-12	VF-20	EF-40	AU-50
1859-S	24	29.0	0%	$375	$625	$950	$1,450	$4,500	$12,000

1860 Liberty Seated Quarter

1860 • **Circulation-Strike Mintage:** 804,400.

Availability in Mint State: 90 to 110 Mint State examples are known, including 8 to 10 graded MS-65 or finer.

Availability in circulated grades: This is a slightly scarce issue. Most are well worn.

	Cert	Avg	%MS	G-4	VG-8	F-12	VF-20	EF-40	AU-50	MS-60	MS-63	MS-65
1860	130	55.6	41%	$25	$30	$35	$65	$100	$195	$500	$850	$5,000

1860, Proof • Proof Mintage: 1,000.

Availability in Proof format: Although 1,000 Proofs were struck, likely no more than 600 or so were actually sold. Many copies have lightness at the star centers. Most of them have survived, but in lower Proof grades.

	Cert	Avg	%MS	PF-60	PF-63	PF-65
1860, Proof	111	63.9		$700	$1,200	$4,000

1860-O Liberty Seated Quarter

1860-O • Circulation-Strike Mintage: 388,000.

Commentary: These coins usually have some lightness on the obverse. This is the last New Orleans Mint quarter until 1891.

Availability in Mint State: This is the most plentiful New Orleans quarter in Mint State. *MS-60 to 62: 60 to 75 • MS-63: 25 to 32 • MS-64: 7 to 10 • MS-65 or better: 3 to 5.*

Availability in circulated grades: This issue is slightly scarce.

	Cert	Avg	%MS	G-4	VG-8	F-12	VF-20	EF-40	AU-50	MS-60	MS-63	MS-65
1860-O	79	53.2	35%	$30	$45	$55	$85	$250	$475	$1,000	$1,750	$12,500

1860-S Liberty Seated Quarter

1860-S • Circulation-Strike Mintage: 56,000.

Availability in Mint State: No Mint State examples were originally reported, but the Eugene Gardner coin, with friction on the higher points, is now graded MS-61.

Availability in circulated grades: This is a very rare coin, the most elusive of all San Francisco Mint quarters of this type.[41] Examples are normally in low grades, and usually have problems.[42]

	Cert	Avg	%MS	G-4	VG-8	F-12	VF-20	EF-40	AU-50
1860-S	22	27.4	0%	$1,000	$1,500	$3,000	$5,000	$9,000	$18,500

1861 Liberty Seated Quarter

1861 • **Circulation-Strike Mintage:** 4,853,600.

Availability in Mint State: 600 to 700 are known, including 80 to 100 graded MS-65 or higher. Larry Briggs considers this among the most readily available Liberty Seated quarters in Mint State, along with 1855, With Arrows, No Rays; 1856; 1858; 1862; and 1873, With Arrows.

Availability in circulated grades: Common. Mostly in lower grades.

	Cert	Avg	%MS	G-4	VG-8	F-12	VF-20	EF-40	AU-50	MS-60	MS-63	MS-65
1861	641	57.1	54%	$25	$30	$35	$65	$100	$200	$350	$725	$2,750

1861, Proof • **Proof Mintage:** 1,000.

Availability in Proof format: Although 1,000 Proofs were struck, likely no more than 500 or so were actually sold, perhaps even fewer. Several hundred examples survive today, mostly in lower grades caused by multiple cleanings over the years.

	Cert	Avg	%MS	PF-60	PF-63	PF-65
1861, Proof	104	63.6		$700	$1,200	$4,000

1861-S Liberty Seated Quarter

1861-S • **Circulation-Strike Mintage:** 96,000.

Commentary: These coins usually exhibit some lightness on the obverse and at 5 to 9 o'clock on the reverse.

Availability in Mint State: None have been reported in Mint State—one of very few Liberty Seated coins for which this can be said.

Availability in circulated grades: This coin is rare at any level. Most examples show extensive wear and have problems. An evenly worn coin without problems is especially rare.

	Cert	Avg	%MS	G-4	VG-8	F-12	VF-20	EF-40	AU-50
1861-S	35	27.7	0%	$600	$900	$1,250	$2,000	$4,500	$8,500

1862 Liberty Seated Quarter

1862 • **Circulation-Strike Mintage:** 932,000.

Commentary: Philadelphia strikes of this year are usually sharp.

Availability in Mint State: 500 to 600 exist in Mint State, including 40 to 50 graded MS-65 or higher. Larry Briggs considers this among the most readily available Liberty Seated quarters in Mint State, along with 1855, With Arrows, No Rays; 1856; 1858; 1861; and 1873, With Arrows.

Availability in circulated grades: This coin is more elusive that the high mintage might suggest.

	Cert	Avg	%MS	G-4	VG-8	F-12	VF-20	EF-40	AU-50	MS-60	MS-63	MS-65
1862	172	57	61%	$25	$35	$50	$75	$115	$210	$400	$750	$2,750

1862, Proof • **Proof Mintage:** 550 (430+ per Breen).

Availability in Proof format: Most Proof strikes from this year survive, but in lower grades.

	Cert	Avg	%MS	PF-60	PF-63	PF-65
1862, Proof	134	63.7		$700	$1,200	$4,000

1862-S Liberty Seated Quarter

1862-S • **Circulation-Strike Mintage:** 67,000.

Commentary: Examples usually come with some lightness on the obverse and at 5 to 9 o'clock on the reverse.

Availability in Mint State: 25 or so are available in Mint State, with none confirmed graded MS-65 or higher.

Availability in circulated grades: This San Francisco strike is rare in all circulated grades, especially so in higher levels.

	Cert	Avg	%MS	G-4	VG-8	F-12	VF-20	EF-40	AU-50	MS-60	MS-63
1862-S	46	42.3	24%	$175	$300	$450	$600	$1,250	$2,500	$4,250	$7,500

1863 Liberty Seated Quarter

1863 • **Circulation-Strike Mintage:** 191,600.

Commentary: This year's Philadelphia issue is usually sharp.

Availability in Mint State: 200 to 250 Mint State examples are known, including 25 to 35 graded MS-65 or higher.

Availability in circulated grades: This is a scarce issue. From this year through the end of the decade, many Philadelphia coins are available in higher grades such as Extremely Fine and About Uncirculated.

	Cert	Avg	%MS	G-4	VG-8	F-12	VF-20	EF-40	AU-50	MS-60	MS-63	MS-65
1863	65	56.1	62%	$75	$110	$175	$275	$450	$550	$800	$1,350	$5,000

1863, Proof • **Proof Mintage:** 460.

Availability in Proof format: Most of the mintage survives, but in lower Proof grades.

	Cert	Avg	%MS	PF-60	PF-63	PF-65
1863, Proof	156	63.6		$700	$1,200	$4,000

1864 Liberty Seated Quarter

1864 • **Circulation-Strike Mintage:** 93,600.

Commentary: These coins are usually sharp.

Availability in Mint State: 110 to 130 Mint State coins exist, including 10 to 11 graded MS-65 or finer.

Availability in circulated grades: This coin is rare in any grade.

	Cert	Avg	%MS	G-4	VG-8	F-12	VF-20	EF-40	AU-50	MS-60	MS-63	MS-65
1864	62	52.5	56%	$125	$215	$300	$425	$575	$700	$1,250	$2,500	$5,500

1864, Proof • **Proof Mintage:** 470.

Availability in Proof format: Most of the mintage survives, but in lower Proof grades. 35 to 50 exist in PF-65 or higher grades. This ratio can be applied to all Proofs of this era.

	Cert	Avg	%MS	PF-60	PF-63	PF-65
1864, Proof	187	63.9		$700	$1,200	$4,000

1864-S Liberty Seated Quarter

1864-S • Circulation-Strike Mintage: 20,000.

Availability in Mint State: No more than 5 copies are graded Mint State, including one confirmed graded MS-65. This is an exceptionally rare coin. The finest may be the Louis E. Eliasberg specimen, which graded MS-66 in 1997 and might well earn a gradeflated 67 or higher today. (This example, ex Friesner Collection as discussed in the introductory information, was regarded "Very Good" in 1894.)

Availability in circulated grades: Circulated-grade copies are very rare. Most show extensive wear.

	Cert	Avg	%MS	G-4	VG-8	F-12	VF-20	EF-40	AU-50	MS-60	MS-63
1864-S	42	29.3	12%	$875	$1,000	$1,500	$2,000	$4,000	$5,500	$12,000	$22,500

1865 Liberty Seated Quarter

1865 • Circulation-Strike Mintage: 58,800.

Availability in Mint State: About 60 Mint State copies are known, including 9 to 12 graded MS-65 or higher.

Availability in circulated grades: This coin is rare in circulated grades, with most in the higher ranges.

	Cert	Avg	%MS	G-4	VG-8	F-12	VF-20	EF-40	AU-50	MS-60	MS-63	MS-65
1865	50	47.5	32%	$100	$165	$250	$350	$450	$750	$1,250	$1,850	$10,000

1865, Proof • Proof Mintage: 500.

Availability in Proof format: Most of the mintage survived, with about 30 to 40 graded PF-65 or higher.

	Cert	Avg	%MS	PF-60	PF-63	PF-65
1865, Proof	181	63.9		$700	$1,200	$4,000

1865-S Liberty Seated Quarter

1865-S • Circulation-Strike Mintage: 41,000.

Commentary: San Francisco strikes of this year typically show some very slight weakness at the star centers, at the tops of the date digits, and from 5 to 9 o'clock on the reverse.

Availability in Mint State: About 35 of these exist in Mint State, including one or two graded MS-65 or higher.

Availability in circulated grades: This is a rare coin in all circulated grades, with most examples being well worn.

	Cert	Avg	%MS	G-4	VG-8	F-12	VF-20	EF-40	AU-50	MS-60	MS-63	MS-65
1865-S	43	49.9	42%	$225	$350	$475	$650	$1,100	$1,600	$3,500	$4,500	$17,500

1866 Liberty Seated Quarter, No Motto

1866, No Motto • Proof Mintage: 1.

Availability in Proof format: One example of this strike has been reported. The 1866, No Motto, quarter (one known), half dollar (one known), and dollar (two known) were secretly made at the Mint at a later date, possibly under the aegis of A. Loudon Snowden in the late 1870s or early 1880s, and sold through John W. Haseltine.

	Cert	Avg	%MS	PF-63
1866, No Motto, Proof	0	n/a		—

1866 Liberty Seated Quarter, With Motto

1866, With Motto • Circulation-Strike Mintage: 16,800.

Commentary: There is nearly always lightness on at the star centers and at the obverse shield area. "I've only seen two or three sharp circulation strikes in my life," Larry Briggs commented.[43]

Availability in Mint State: Around 75 Mint State copies are known, including 7 to 10 graded MS-65 or higher.

Availability in circulated grades: This issue is rare in circulated grades, with most having relatively little wear.

	Cert	Avg	%MS	G-4	VG-8	F-12	VF-20	EF-40	AU-50	MS-60	MS-63	MS-65
1866, With Motto	46	50.9	61%	$750	$1,000	$1,250	$1,500	$2,000	$2,450	$2,800	$3,150	$8,500

1866, With Motto, Proof • Proof
Mintage: 725.

Availability in Proof format: Of the
survivors, which is most of the mintage,
about 35 to 45 graded PF-65 or higher.

	Cert	Avg	%MS	PF-60	PF-63	PF-65
1866, With Motto, Proof	158	64.0		$500	$850	$2,500

1866-S Liberty Seated Quarter, With Motto

1866-S, With Motto • Circulation-
Strike Mintage: 28,000.

Commentary: In his *Mint Marks* monograph
in 1893, Augustus G. Heaton commented:
"The 1866-S is the first of the series with the
motto IN GOD WE TRUST. It is also the
first to dismiss the large S mint mark and show
a very small s that continues with little change
through the rest of the San Francisco Mint quarters." The reverse die was also used to strike 1868-S and
1869-S quarters (Larry Briggs).

For further reading see "The 1866-S Quarter" (*The Gobrecht Journal*, March 1983), by Bill Cregan.
He illustrates a worn piece and comments that it is very underrated, even in relation to its sparse 28,000
mintage. He notes that the 1864-S has appeared at public sale five times more often than the 1866-S.
"Stretching rarity even further, the 1866-S might rank in rarity with the Carson City quarters minted
1870–1873, which were all scarce," the same writer concluded. Moreover, he was not aware that a coin
existed even in as high as the About Uncirculated level.

Availability in Mint State: 10 or fewer Mint State copies are known, including one or two graded
MS-65 or higher.

Availability in circulated grades: These are rare in circulated grades. Most examples are well worn.

	Cert	Avg	%MS	G-4	VG-8	F-12	VF-20	EF-40	AU-50	MS-60	MS-63	MS-65
1866-S, With Motto	26	29.6	19%	$450	$750	$1,200	$1,650	$2,300	$3,500	$5,000	$10,000	$35,000

1867 Liberty Seated Quarter

1867 • Circulation-Strike Mintage:
20,000.

Availability in Mint State: 20 or so are
known, including one or two graded MS-65
or finer.

Availability in circulated grades: 1867 Philadelphia strikes are rare in circulated grades. Most are in higher grades.

	Cert	Avg	%MS	G-4	VG-8	F-12	VF-20	EF-40	AU-50	MS-60	MS-63
1867	34	43.6	35%	$350	$550	$700	$1,000	$1,500	$1,850	$2,250	$4,500

1867, Proof • **Proof Mintage:** 625.

Availability in Proof format: With most of the mintage surviving, about 30 to 40 are graded PF-65 or finer.

	Cert	Avg	%MS	PF-60	PF-63	PF-65
1867, Proof	169	64.0		$500	$850	$2,250

1867-S Liberty Seated Quarter

1867-S • **Circulation-Strike Mintage:** 48,000.

Commentary: These San Francisco issues usually exhibit weakness on the stars and head on the obverse and some weakness on the reverse.

Availability in Mint State: No more than 5 Mint State copies are known, including one graded MS-65 or higher.

Availability in circulated grades: This is another rare San Francisco year. Most copies are well worn.

	Cert	Avg	%MS	G-4	VG-8	F-12	VF-20	EF-40	AU-50	MS-60	MS-63	MS-65
1867-S	19	26.2	11%	$600	$750	$1,150	$1,750	$3,500	$7,000	$10,500	$15,000	$35,000

1868 Liberty Seated Quarter

1868 • **Circulation-Strike Mintage:** 29,400.

Commentary: Philadelphia strikes of this year are usually sharp—see the introductory information. Philadelphia Mint quarters did not circulate at face value during this era and were available only by paying a premium.

Availability in Mint State: State: 175 or so Mint State examples exist, including seven to nine graded MS-65 or higher.

Availability in circulated grades: This coin is seldom seen. Most examples are in higher grades.

	Cert	Avg	%MS	G-4	VG-8	F-12	VF-20	EF-40	AU-50	MS-60	MS-63	MS-65
1868	32	51.4	53%	$185	$275	$400	$500	$700	$850	$1,750	$3,500	$9,000

1868, Proof • Proof Mintage: 600.

Availability in Proof format: Most of the mintage survives, with about 20 to 30 graded PF-65 or higher.

	Cert	Avg	%MS	PF-60	PF-63	PF-65
1868, Proof	155	63.5		$500	$850	$2,250

1868-S Liberty Seated Quarter

1868-S • **Circulation-Strike Mintage:** 96,000.

Commentary: Weakness on the obverse can usually be seen on this issue.

Availability in Mint State: Five or so are considered Mint State, including two graded MS-65 or finer.

Availability in circulated grades: This coin is rare in circulated grades. Most copies have extensive wear and problems.

	Cert	Avg	%MS	G-4	VG-8	F-12	VF-20	EF-40	AU-50	MS-60	MS-63	MS-65
1868-S	42	39.2	24%	$125	$175	$350	$750	$1,000	$1,750	$5,500	$9,500	$20,000

1869 Liberty Seated Quarter

1869 • **Circulation-Strike Mintage:** 16,000.

Availability in Mint State: Around 25 Mint State examples exist, including two or three graded MS-65 or higher.

Availability in circulated grades: This is another rare year for Philadelphia quarters in circulated grades. Survivors are mainly in grades from AG-3 to Fine-12 or Extremely Fine and About Uncirculated, an interesting distribution.[44]

	Cert	Avg	%MS	G-4	VG-8	F-12	VF-20	EF-40	AU-50	MS-60	MS-63	MS-65
1869	27	41.6	41%	$500	$650	$850	$1,000	$1,250	$1,500	$2,250	$4,500	$10,000

1869, Proof • Proof Mintage: 600.

Availability in Proof format: Only 25 to 35 of the survivors, which is most of the mintage, graded PF-65 and higher.

	Cert	Avg	%MS	PF-60	PF-63	PF-65
1869, Proof	175	63.5		$500	$850	$2,250

1869-S Liberty Seated Quarter

1869-S • **Circulation-Strike Mintage:** 76,000.

Commentary: San Francisco coins of this year usually show lightness in areas. A die crack connects many of the stars.

Availability in Mint State: Five or six are known, including one MS-65 or finer.

Availability in circulated grades: Despite being scarce in circulated grades, this coin is seen on the market with some frequency. Most examples are well worn.

	Cert	Avg	%MS	G-4	VG-8	F-12	VF-20	EF-40	AU-50	MS-60	MS-63	MS-65
1869-S	33	36.4	15%	$175	$250	$425	$650	$1,250	$1,650	$4,000	$7,000	$17,500

1870 Liberty Seated Quarter

1870 • **Circulation-Strike Mintage:** 86,400.

Commentary: Striking is usually sharp for this coin.

Availability in Mint State: 110 to 120 are known, including 9 to 12 graded MS-65 or above.

Availability in circulated grades: This is a very scarce coin, yet still more readily available than other Philadelphia quarters of a similar time period and mintage.

	Cert	Avg	%MS	G-4	VG-8	F-12	VF-20	EF-40	AU-50	MS-60	MS-63	MS-65
1870	33	50.8	36%	$65	$100	$150	$250	$450	$600	$1,000	$1,750	$5,000

1870, Proof • **Proof Mintage:** 1,000.

Availability in Proof format: The mintage increased sharply from the 600 for the year preceding, which might be explained by production problems for Proofs. Quite a few of the silver Proofs of this year are sloppily made, and one can imagine that certain others were produced, discarded, and replaced by better pieces. In any event, today the higher-mintage 1870 is no more plentiful than the lower mintage 1869. About 25 to 35 exist in PF-65 or finer grades.

	Cert	Avg	%MS	PF-60	PF-63	PF-65
1870, Proof	163	63.5		$500	$850	$2,250

1870-CC Liberty Seated Quarter

1870-CC • Circulation-Strike Mintage: 8,340.

Commentary: Lightness is seen at most star centers for this issue. There is often weakness on the lower part of the reverse. The first delivery of 1870-CC quarters occurred on April 20, 1870, when 3,540 were struck. The second delivery of 1,400 pieces occurred on May 24, followed by the third and final delivery of 3,400 on August 15. This is the rarest of the Carson City quarters excepting the 1873-CC No Arrows. All were circulated regionally. There was no numismatic interest in them at the time, nor was there until the early 1890s. In 1893 Augustus G. Heaton reflected that "It has the smallest coinage of the CC series and is exceedingly rare." The 1870-CC, 1871-CC, 1872-CC, and the 1873-CC With Arrows quarters were all struck from the same reverse die. No Carson City coins were minted in 1874. The next piece, 1875-CC, is from a different reverse die and has the mintmark in an entirely different position with relation to the bottom arrow feather.[46]

Availability in Mint State: A single Mint State example is known. Graded MS-64 prooflike, this spectacular piece was sold at a Louis E. Eliasberg auction in 1997.[45]

Availability in circulated grades: This is a very rare Carson City strike, considered a key issue of the series. Many coins have problems, which can be said of all the Carson City quarters through 1873.

	Cert	Avg	%MS	G-4	VG-8	F-12	VF-20	EF-40	AU-50
1870-CC	26	26.2	4%	$11,000	$13,500	$20,000	$27,500	$45,000	$85,000

1870-S Liberty Seated Quarter

1870-S • Mintage: One or more.

Commentary: Six pairs of quarter dies were sent from Philadelphia to San Francisco on January 15, 1870, but there is no record of any quarters having been struck for circulation. At least one was made to be placed in the cornerstone of the second San Francisco Mint, but it has not been traced today.

1871 Liberty Seated Quarter

1871 • Circulation-Strike Mintage: 118,200.

Commentary: At first glance, most coins usually sharp. Two obverse dies had LIBERTY overpolished, creating a lightness that can be seen under magnification.[47]

Availability in Mint State: 50 or so are available in Mint State, including two or three graded MS-65 or higher.

Availability in circulated grades: This coin is very scarce in circulated grades. It is usually seen Very Fine or finer.

	Cert	Avg	%MS	G-4	VG-8	F-12	VF-20	EF-40	AU-50	MS-60	MS-63	MS-65
1871	47	51.9	53%	$50	$75	$125	$175	$325	$450	$750	$1,500	$7,000

1871, Proof • **Proof Mintage:** 960.

Availability in Proof format: Most of the mintage survives, but only 25 to 35 in grades of PF-65 and higher.

	Cert	Avg	%MS	PF-60	PF-63	PF-65
1871, Proof	148	63.6		$500	$850	$2,500

1871-CC Liberty Seated Quarter

1871-CC • **Circulation-Strike Mintage:** 10,890.

Availability in Mint State: This is an exceedingly rare Carson City issue, with only three Mint State 1871-CC Liberty Seated quarters known.

Availability in circulated grades: This is a very rare coin in all circulated grades.

	Cert	Avg	%MS	G-4	VG-8	F-12	VF-20	EF-40	AU-50	MS-60	MS-63	MS-65
1871-CC	15	22.0	7%	$8,000	$12,500	$17,500	$25,000	$40,000	$55,000			$350,000

1871-S Liberty Seated Quarter

1871-S • **Circulation-Strike Mintage:** 30,900.

Commentary: Most San Francisco strikes of this year are sharp, but some have obverse lightness. Lower-grade coins show weakness from 5 to 9 o'clock. In 1893 Augustus G. Heaton observed, "The piece is very rare."[48]

Availability in Mint State: 35 to 40 examples are Mint State, including three or four graded MS-65 or higher.

Availability in circulated grades: This coin is rare, with most examples showing extensive wear.

	Cert	Avg	%MS	G-4	VG-8	F-12	VF-20	EF-40	AU-50	MS-60	MS-63	MS-65
1871-S	26	51.7	54%	$900	$1,400	$2,350	$3,200	$4,000	$5,500	$7,250	$10,000	$20,000

1872 Liberty Seated Quarter

1872 • Circulation-Strike Mintage: 182,000.

Commentary: Numismatists of this era who collected by date sequence usually bought Proofs. Mint State coins were not desired. And, if they had been, they would have been very difficult to find, as no Philadelphia silver coins were released into circulation for face value after the spring of 1862. This continued until after April 20, 1876, although there were a few occasional releases several years earlier.

Availability in Mint State: About 25 Mint State pieces are known, including four or five graded MS-65 or higher.

Availability in circulated grades: This coin is scarce in circulated grades.

	Cert	Avg	%MS	G-4	VG-8	F-12	VF-20	EF-40	AU-50	MS-60	MS-63	MS-65
1872	60	51.2	42%	$50	$85	$115	$185	$300	$500	$900	$2,250	$7,500

1872, Proof • Proof Mintage: 950.

Availability in Proof format: Most of this coin's mintage survives, including 50 to 65 graded PF-65 or higher.

	Cert	Avg	%MS	PF-60	PF-63	PF-65
1872, Proof	180	64.0		$500	$850	$2,000

1872-CC Liberty Seated Quarter

1872-CC • Circulation-Strike Mintage: 22,850.

Commentary: There are some areas of slight weakness on both sides of Carson City strikes from this year.

Availability in Mint State: There are two confirmed Mint State examples of this coin. One example, graded MS-65 at the time, sold at a Louis E. Eliasberg auction in 1997; with gradeflation, it may earn a higher grade today..

Availability in circulated grades: Coins of this year and mint are rare in any grade, and very rare at the Extremely Fine and About Uncirculated levels. Many coins have problems. Counterfeits are seen now and again. Buying NGC or PCGS coins is recommended.

	Cert	Avg	%MS	G-4	VG-8	F-12	VF-20	EF-40	AU-50	MS-60
1872-CC	32	18.8	3%	$2,000	$3,000	$4,500	$8,500	$12,000	$16,000	$55,000

1872-S Liberty Seated Quarter

1872-S • **Circulation-Strike Mintage:** 83,000.

Commentary: This issue is usually found with lightly struck star centers, sometimes with slight weakness at LIBERTY, and with reverse weakness from 5 to 9 o'clock. This common reverse weakness is most noticeable on well-worn coins. In his article "Liberty Seated Quarter Dollars Survey," published in *The Gobrecht Journal*, March 1987, Roy D. Ash noted that among San Francisco Mint issues, far fewer had been seen of the 1872-S than of any other studied, with only 12 examples reported in a survey he conducted. Runner-up in rarity was the 1871-S with 21 examples, closely followed by the 1866-S with 22, 1864-S with 23, and 1860-S and 1867-S tied at 25. Most plentiful was the 1888-S. This sentiment was echoed a few years later by Bill Cregan in "The Rare 1872-S Quarter" (*The Gobrecht Journal*, July 1990): "Some specialists even believe the 1872-S quarter is as difficult to obtain as some of the rarest date Carson City quarters."

Availability in Mint State: There are two confirmed copies in Mint State. One, MS-62, was sold by Louis E. Eliasberg in 1997. The other, an MS-66 example, was sold in a Eugene H. Gardner auction in 2104

Availability in circulated grades: This coin is very rare in all grades.

	Cert	Avg	%MS	G-4	VG-8	F-12	VF-20	EF-40	AU-50	MS-60	MS-63	MS-65
1872-S	20	40.4	40%	$2,000	$2,600	$3,200	$4,750	$6,000	$7,000	$10,000	$13,000	$36,000

1873 Liberty Seated Quarter, No Arrows

1873, No Arrows, Close 3 • **Circulation-Strike Mintage:** 40,000.

Availability in Mint State: Five or fewer Mint State copies are known, all MS-60 to 62.

Availability in circulated grades: Probably 100 or so exist copies exist across all grades. A Liberty Seated Collectors Club survey found 28 in members' hands.

B-1.

Detail of the Close 3.

	Cert	Avg	%MS	G-4	VG-8	F-12	VF-20	EF-40	AU-50	MS-60	MS-63
1873, No Arrows, Close 3	16	28.6	13%	$450	$700	$900	$1,300	$3,500	$4,500	$18,000	$35,000

1873, No Arrows, Close 3, Proof •

Proof Mintage: 1,100.

Availability in Proof format: Most of the mintage survives, including 30 to 40 graded PF-65 or higher.

	Cert	Avg	%MS	PF-60	PF-63	PF-65
1873, No Arrows, Proof	169	63.6		$500	$850	$2,000

1873, No Arrows, Open 3 •

Circulation-Strike Mintage: 172,000.

Availability in Mint State: 75 or so Mint State copies exist, including 8 to 11 graded MS-65 or higher.

Availability in circulated grades: This is a readily available coin.

B-1.

Detail of the Open 3.

	Cert	Avg	%MS	G-4	VG-8	F-12	VF-20	EF-40	AU-50	MS-60	MS-63	MS-65
1873, No Arrows, Open 3	38	54.7	58%	$30	$45	$85	$150	$300	$425	$675	$1,850	$5,500

1873-CC Liberty Seated Quarter, No Arrows

1873-CC, No Arrows • Circulation-Strike Mintage: 4,000.

Commentary: This Carson City issue is well struck except for star centers at the right side of the obverse. The mintage of the 1873-CC No Arrows quarter dollar is believed to have been only 4,000 coins. Apparently, most were melted between April 1, 1873, and July 10, 1873) as being obsolete; the Coinage Act of 1873 had specified a slightly increased authorized weight, and later 1873-CC, With Arrows, quarters were made under this new standard. This is one of the most famous, most heralded rarities in the Liberty Seated series. A detailed history and registry is given in the Louis E. Eliasberg Collection catalog, 1997. The reverse die used for these quarters was also used for a short run of 1876-CC quarters.[50]

Availability in Mint State: Three Mint State examples are known: an MS-64 specimen sold as part of the Battle Born Collection in 2014; an MS-63 specimen, ex Eliasberg Collection, sold by Eugene H. Gardner in 2015; and the James A. Stack coin, the finest example.

Availability in circulated grades: Two examples are known. One has VG details and the other is Very Fine.[49]

	Cert	Avg	%MS	EF-40	AU-50	MS-60	MS-63
1873-CC, No Arrows	21	22.0	5%	$125,000	$150,000	$200,000	$400,000

1873 Liberty Seated Quarter, With Arrows

1873, With Arrows • Circulation-Strike
Mintage: 1,271,200.

Commentary: Quality varies, but most have some slight weakness.

Availability in Mint State: 300 to 400 Mint State examples are known, including 22 to 24 graded MS-65 or higher. Larry Briggs considers this among the most readily available Liberty

Seated quarters in Mint State, along with 1855, With Arrows, No Rays; 1856; 1858; 1861; and 1862.

Availability in circulated grades: Coins in circulated grades are fairly plentiful in relation to the demand.

	Cert	Avg	%MS	G-4	VG-8	F-12	VF-20	EF-40	AU-50	MS-60	MS-63	MS-65
1873, With Arrows	260	54.6	45%	$25	$30	$45	$60	$225	$425	$850	$1,650	$4,000

1873, With Arrows, Proof • Proof
Mintage: 800 (540 Breen).

Availability in Proof format: Most of the mintage survived, but only about 30 to 40 in PF-65 and higher grades.

	Cert	Avg	%MS	PF-60	PF-63	PF-65
1873, With Arrows, Proof	149	63.8		$900	$1,350	$5,500

1873-CC Liberty Seated Quarter, With Arrows

1873-CC, With Arrows • Circulation-Strike Mintage: 12,462.

Commentary: Examples may show some lightness, but this varies from coin to coin. Cherrypicking is advised, but you can't be too picky as there are not many in the marketplace.

Availability in Mint State: One or two are available.
The author called the Eliasberg coin MS-63/65 in 1997; as of a few years ago it was certified as MS-66.

Availability in circulated grades: Rare. Most show extensive wear.

	Cert	Avg	%MS	G-4	VG-8	F-12	VF-20	EF-40	AU-50	MS-60	MS-63
1873-CC, With Arrows	23	22.7	4%	$5,000	$9,000	$12,500	$17,000	$25,000	$45,000	$85,000	$125,000

1873-S Liberty Seated Quarter, With Arrows

1873-S, With Arrows • Circulation-Strike Mintage: 156,000.

Availability in Mint State: There are four to six examples at Mint State, including or three graded MS-65 or finer.

Availability in circulated grades: This is a rare issue. Mostly copies are well worn.

	Cert	Avg	%MS	G-4	VG-8	F-12	VF-20	EF-40	AU-50	MS-60	MS-63	MS-65
1873-S, With Arrows	66	49.8	35%	$100	$125	$175	$250	$450	$650	$1,750	$4,500	$17,500

1874 Liberty Seated Quarter, With Arrows

1874, With Arrows • Circulation-Strike Mintage: 471,200.

Commentary: Philadelphia coins of this year often exhibit some lightness on Liberty's head.

Availability in Mint State: 160 to 180 exist, including 14 to 18 graded MS-65 or finer.

Availability in circulated grades: This is a readily available coin, including in higher grades.

	Cert	Avg	%MS	G-4	VG-8	F-12	VF-20	EF-40	AU-50	MS-60	MS-63	MS-65
1874, With Arrows	104	55.8	51%	$25	$30	$40	$65	$200	$450	$850	$1,350	$3,500

1874, With Arrows, Proof • Proof Mintage: 700.

Availability in Proof format: Most strikes from this year survive, of which 30 to 40 are graded PF-65 or finer.

	Cert	Avg	%MS	PF-60	PF-63	PF-65
1874, With Arrows, Proof	252	64.0		$900	$1,350	$5,500

1874-S Liberty Seated Quarter, With Arrows

1874-S, With Arrows • Circulation-Strike Mintage: 392,000.

Availability in Mint State: Mint State copies run from 225 to 200, including 90 to 120 from a hoard. For details see Q. David Bowers, *Lost and Found Coin Hoards and Treasures*.

Availability in circulated grades: This year's San Francisco quarters are scarce in circulated grades, and most show extensive circulation wear.

	Cert	Avg	%MS	G-4	VG-8	F-12	VF-20	EF-40	AU-50	MS-60	MS-63	MS-65
1874-S, With Arrows	156	60.2	77%	$25	$35	$65	$100	$265	$485	$850	$1,350	$3,500

1875 Liberty Seated Quarter

1875 • Circulation-Strike Mintage: 4,292,800.

Availability in Mint State: 700 to 900 copies exist, including 70 to 90 graded MS-65 or finer.

Availability in circulated grades: This coin is common in all circulated grades.

	Cert	Avg	%MS	G-4	VG-8	F-12	VF-20	EF-40	AU-50	MS-60	MS-63	MS-65
1875	343	58.2	66%	$25	$30	$35	$45	$65	$160	$275	$550	$1,750

1875, Proof • Proof Mintage: 700.

Availability in Proof format: Most of this year's Proof strikes survive, including 25 to 35 graded PF-65 or finer.

	Cert	Avg	%MS	PF-60	PF-63	PF-65
1875, Proof	166	63.8		$475	$750	$1,400

1875-CC Liberty Seated Quarter

1875-CC • Circulation-Strike Mintage: 140,000.

Commentary: The obverse of some pieces is highly prooflike. Some weakness is usual. Many exanokes have four or five letters of LIBERTY visible but a Fair to About Good reverse.[51] In the July 1977 number of *The Gobrecht Journal*, Eddie Randell's article, "An

Auction Comparison Between the 1875-CC and 1878-S Quarters," pointed out that the 1875-CC was much rarer than realized. Interestingly, Randell said that he first noticed the variety when he ordered the Empire Investors Report in 1963. Surprisingly, a survey of auction catalogues of the 1960s and 1970s yielded 21 auction appearances for the famous and rare 1878-S but just nine for the somewhat overlooked 1875-CC. The March 1981 issue of *The Gobrecht Journal* contained an article by John W. McCloskey, "The 1875-CC Quarter," which paid tribute to its rarity, noting that "the listed mintage of 140,000 pieces doesn't stand out as anything unusual in a series that has 45 other dates with lower figures given. Yet in terms of availability is one of the most difficult dates in the series to find. Please note that I do not mean to imply that the 1875-CC quarter is prohibitively rare, but only wish to indicate that it is just not available in today's market." Additional comments on the 1875-CC by the same author appeared in the subsequent July and November issues.

Availability in Mint State: 35 to 45 Mint State examples exist, including five to seven graded MS-65 or finer. Many are prooflike.

Availability in circulated grades: This coin is fairly scarce in circulated grades.

	Cert	Avg	%MS	G-4	VG-8	F-12	VF-20	EF-40	AU-50	MS-60	MS-63	MS-65
1875-CC	53	46.4	30%	$175	$300	$600	$750	$1,250	$2,000	$3,750	$7,500	$25,000

1875-S Liberty Seated Quarter

1875-S • Circulation-Strike Mintage: 680,000.

Commentary: Coins of this year are usually weak in areas.

Availability in Mint State: 175 to 200 are available, including 15 to 20 graded MS-65 or finer.

Availability in circulated grades: This is a quite scarce San Francisco issue.

	Cert	Avg	%MS	G-4	VG-8	F-12	VF-20	EF-40	AU-50	MS-60	MS-63	MS-65
1875-S	103	55.6	58%	$45	$60	$95	$130	$250	$325	$600	$1,000	$3,500

1876 Liberty Seated Quarter

1876 • Circulation-Strike Mintage: 17,816,000.

Commentary: Strike quality varies widely, but sharp coins can be found.

Availability in Mint State: 1.400 to 1,600 Mint State coins are available, including 130 to 160 graded MS-65 or higher.

Availability in circulated grades: This is an extremely common coin.

	Cert	Avg	%MS	G-4	VG-8	F-12	VF-20	EF-40	AU-50	MS-60	MS-63	MS-65
1876	604	56.7	62%	$25	$30	$35	$45	$65	$160	$275	$550	$1,600

1876, Proof • **Proof Mintage:** 1,150.

Availability in Proof format: An estimated 60% of Proof strikes survive, of which 60 to 90 are graded PF-65 or higher. It is thought that many Proofs were spent by Centennial Exhibition visitors who were not numismatists and later tired of their novelty. There are two general reverse types: Type I, with TAT closely spaced; and Type II, with the same letters spaced slightly farther apart.

	Cert	Avg	%MS	PF-60	PF-63	PF-65
1876, Proof	224	63.8		$475	$750	$1,400

1876-CC Liberty Seated Quarter

1876-CC • **Circulation-Strike Mintage:** 4,944,000.

Commentary: A definitive study of this issue can be found in John McCloskey's article "Varieties of the 1876-CC Quarter," from the November 1978 issue of *The Gobrecht Journal.*

Availability in Mint State: 300 to 350 Mint State copies are known, including 16 to 22 graded MS-65 or finer.

Availability in circulated grades: 1876 is one of the most commonly available years of all Carson City coins of the era.

	Cert	Avg	%MS	G-4	VG-8	F-12	VF-20	EF-40	AU-50	MS-60	MS-63	MS-65
1876-CC	394	47.4	41%	$50	$85	$125	$150	$200	$300	$600	$1,100	$4,500

1876-S Liberty Seated Quarter

1876-S • **Circulation-Strike Mintage:** 8,596,000.

Availability in Mint State: 500 to 600 examples in Mint State exist, including 22 to 26 graded MS-65 or finer.

Availability in circulated grades: This is a common coin.

	Cert	Avg	%MS	G-4	VG-8	F-12	VF-20	EF-40	AU-50	MS-60	MS-63	MS-65
1876-S	308	59.4	71%	$25	$30	$35	$45	$65	$160	$275	$550	$1,800

1877 Liberty Seated Quarter

1877 • Circulation-Strike Mintage: 10,911,200.

Availability in Mint State: 1,250 to 1,500 Mint State copies are available, including 100 to 150 graded MS-65 or finer.

Availability in circulated grades: This Philadelphia-strike coin is common. Many are at very low grades and must have remained in circulation well into the 20th century.

	Cert	Avg	%MS	G-4	VG-8	F-12	VF-20	EF-40	AU-50	MS-60	MS-63	MS-65
1877	429	59.8	75%	$25	$30	$35	$45	$65	$160	$275	$550	$1,300

1877, Proof • Proof Mintage: 510.

Availability in Proof format: Most of this mintage survives, of which 50 to 60 are graded PF-65 or finer.

	Cert	Avg	%MS	PF-60	PF-63	PF-65
1877, Proof	147	63.9		$475	$750	$1,400

1877-CC Liberty Seated Quarter

1877-CC • Circulation-Strike Mintage: 4,192,000.

Availability in Mint State: There are 600 to 750 examples in Mint State, including 60 to 80 graded MS-65 or finer. This is the most commonly available Carson City quarter in Mint State by far. In the 1950s a small hoard of these came on the market.

Availability in circulated grades: This is a common issue in circulated grades, with most copies well worn.

	Cert	Avg	%MS	G-4	VG-8	F-12	VF-20	EF-40	AU-50	MS-60	MS-63	MS-65
1877-CC	531	54.7	63%	$50	$85	$125	$150	$200	$300	$600	$1,100	$2,250

1877-S Liberty Seated Quarter

1877-S • **Circulation-Strike Mintage:** 8,996,000.

Commentary: 1877 San Francisco strikes usually exhibit some weakness, but there are many exceptions to be found.

Availability in Mint State: 750 to 850 Mint State copies exist, including 60 to 80 graded MS-65 or higher.

Availability in circulated grades: This is a common coin.

	Cert	Avg	%MS	G-4	VG-8	F-12	VF-20	EF-40	AU-50	MS-60	MS-63	MS-65
1877-S	383	58.6	71%	$25	$30	$35	$45	$65	$160	$275	$550	$1,300

VARIETY: *1877-S, S Over Horizontal S (FS-25-1877S-501).* The die sinker in the Engraving Department at the Philadelphia Mint first punched the S mintmark in a "lazy" or horizontal position, recognized his blunder, and corrected it by overpunching the S in the correct position. Most are in circulated grades. Approximately 30 to 40 Mint State coins are known, most in ranges up to MS-64. Some of these are from a group of 13 that appeared at an Indiana coin show in 1986.[52]

	Cert	Avg	%MS	G-4	VG-8	F-12	VF-20	EF-40	AU-50	MS-60	MS-63	MS-65
1877-S, S Over Horizontal S	47	58.9	60%	$30	$45	$85	$150	$285	$500	$850	$2,000	$4,000

1878 Liberty Seated Quarter

1878 • **Circulation-Strike Mintage:** 2,260,000.

Availability in Mint State: 225 to 275 are known, including 15 to 50 graded MS-65 or finer.

Availability in circulated grades: This coin is common in circulated grades, many in higher grades.

	Cert	Avg	%MS	G-4	VG-8	F-12	VF-20	EF-40	AU-50	MS-60	MS-63	MS-65
1878	118	56.2	64%	$25	$30	$35	$45	$65	$160	$275	$550	$2,250

1878, Proof • Proof Mintage: 800.

Availability in Proof format: Most of the Proofs survive, including 40 to 50 graded PF-65 or finer.

	Cert	Avg	%MS	PF-60	PF-63	PF-65
1878, Proof	204	63.6		$475	$750	$1,400

1878-CC Liberty Seated Quarter

1878-CC • Circulation-Strike Mintage: 996,000.

Commentary: Briggs Obverse 1 accounts for approximately one-third of extant 1878-CC quarters, and it is the most interesting variety of the issue. A long, thin die gouge diagonally bisects Liberty's midsection, and is crossed by a second, much shorter die gouge that originates at Liberty's left (facing) forearm. Examples are mostly in circulated grades.

Availability in Mint State: 275 to 325 copies exist in Mint State, including 28 to 35 graded MS-65 or higher.

Availability in circulated grades: This is a readily available coin, although not common. Many are in very low grades.

	Cert	Avg	%MS	G-4	VG-8	F-12	VF-20	EF-40	AU-50	MS-60	MS-63	MS-65
1878-CC	274	54.7	61%	$55	$75	$85	$125	$200	$375	$1,000	$1,500	$4,000

1878-S Liberty Seated Quarter

1878-S • Circulation-Strike Mintage: 140,000.

Availability in Mint State: 40 to 50 Mint State copies are known, including just two or three graded MS-65 or finer. [53]

Availability in circulated grades: This is a rare issue.

	Cert	Avg	%MS	G-4	VG-8	F-12	VF-20	EF-40	AU-50	MS-60	MS-63	MS-65
1878-S	33	52.2	55%	$250	$400	$600	$900	$1,250	$1,700	$3,500	$6,500	$15,000

1879 Liberty Seated Quarter

1879 • Circulation-Strike Mintage: 13,600.

Commentary: Theses coins usually have weak areas.

Availability in Mint State: 600 to 700 examples in Mint State exist, including 120 to 160 graded MS-65 or higher. These and other low-mintage quarters from the later years of the Liberty Seated series were recognized at the time of issue and many were saved by dealers and collectors.

Availability in circulated grades: 1879 Philadelphia coins are rare in circulated grades. Most are in higher grades.

	Cert	Avg	%MS	G-4	VG-8	F-12	VF-20	EF-40	AU-50	MS-60	MS-63	MS-65
1879	216	63.3	92%	$200	$275	$350	$425	$475	$550	$675	$850	$2,100

1879, Proof • **Proof Mintage:** 1,100.

Availability in Proof format: Most Proof strikes survive. Beginning with this year and continuing to the end of the series, a fairly high proportion of surviving Proofs are in grades of 64 and higher.

	Cert	Avg	%MS	PF-60	PF-63	PF-65
1879, Proof	305	63.9		$475	$750	$1,400

1880 Liberty Seated Quarter

1880 • **Circulation-Strike Mintage:** 13,600.

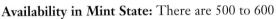

Commentary: For a detailed account of variations in reverse dies of this era, see the Briggs study.

Availability in Mint State: There are 500 to 600 Mint State copies, including 120 to 160 graded MS-65 or higher.

Availability in circulated grades: These are rare in circulated grades. Most are in higher grades.

	Cert	Avg	%MS	G-4	VG-8	F-12	VF-20	EF-40	AU-50	MS-60	MS-63	MS-65
1880	134	62.8	88%	$200	$275	$350	$425	$475	$550	$675	$850	$2,250

1880, Proof • **Proof Mintage:** 1,355.

Availability in Proof format: Most of the mintage survives, including 80 to 100 graded PF-65 or finer.

	Cert	Avg	%MS	PF-60	PF-63	PF-65
1880, Proof	381	64.3		$475	$750	$1,400

1881 Liberty Seated Quarter

1881 • **Circulation-Strike Mintage:** 12,000.

Commentary: These strikes are usually found with weak areas.

Availability in Mint State: In Mint State, 175 to 200 are available, including 25 to 32 graded MS-65 or finer. The attention given at the time to the low-mintage 1879 and 1880 releases had faded by 1881. The interest continued to fade into later years with a slump occurring toward the end of the decade.

Availability in circulated grades: This is a rare coin in circulated grades. Most are in higher grades.

	Cert	Avg	%MS	G-4	VG-8	F-12	VF-20	EF-40	AU-50	MS-60	MS-63	MS-65
1881	104	59.5	82%	$200	$275	$350	$425	$475	$550	$675	$850	$2,100

1881, Proof • Proof Mintage: 975.

Availability in Proof format: Most of this year's Proof strikes survive, including 120 to 160 graded PF-65 or finer.

	Cert	Avg	%MS	PF-60	PF-63	PF-65
1881, Proof	294	64.3		$475	$750	$1,400

1882 Liberty Seated Quarter

1882 • Circulation-Strike Mintage: 15,200.

Availability in Mint State: 200 to 223 Mint State examples exist, including 45 to 50 graded MS-65 or higher.

Availability in circulated grades: This is another rare Philadelphia issue. Most are found in higher grades.

	Cert	Avg	%MS	G-4	VG-8	F-12	VF-20	EF-40	AU-50	MS-60	MS-63	MS-65
1882	78	60.0	82%	$200	$275	$350	$425	$475	$550	$675	$850	$2,100

1882, Proof • Proof Mintage: 1,100.

Availability in Proof format: Most of the mintage survives, including 100 to 140 graded PF-65 or finer.

	Cert	Avg	%MS	PF-60	PF-63	PF-65
1882, Proof	301	64.2		$475	$750	$1,400

1883 Liberty Seated Quarter

1883 • Circulation-Strike Mintage: 14,400.

Availability in Mint State: 120 to 140 are available, including 25 to 32 graded MS-65 or higher.

Availability in circulated grades: This is a rare issue. Most are in higher grades.

	Cert	Avg	%MS	G-4	VG-8	F-12	VF-20	EF-40	AU-50	MS-60	MS-63	MS-65
1883	84	58.7	85%	$200	$275	$350	$425	$475	$550	$675	$850	$2,400

1883, Proof • **Proof Mintage:** 1.039.

Availability in Proof format: Most Proof strikes survive, including 120 to 160 graded PF-65 or finer.

	Cert	Avg	%MS	PF-60	PF-63	PF-65
1883, Proof	355	64.2		$475	$750	$1,400

1884 Liberty Seated Quarter

1884 • **Circulation-Strike Mintage:** 8,000.

Availability in Mint State: 110 to 130 copies exist, including 25 to 32 graded MS-65 or higher.

Availability in circulated grades: This strike is rare. Most are in higher grades. Well-worn coins are very rare, not that it makes a difference.

	Cert	Avg	%MS	G-4	VG-8	F-12	VF-20	EF-40	AU-50	MS-60	MS-63	MS-65
1884	100	57.4	78%	$300	$400	$500	$625	$725	$800	$900	$1,150	$2,100

1884, Proof • **Proof Mintage:** 875.

Availability in Proof format: Most Proofs survive, including 120 to 160 graded PF-65 or finer.

	Cert	Avg	%MS	PF-60	PF-63	PF-65
1884, Proof	282	64.5		$475	$750	$1,400

1885 Liberty Seated Quarter

1885 • **Circulation-Strike Mintage:** 13,600.

Commentary: This is a usually well struck issue.

Availability in Mint State: 200 to 230 copies are known in Mint State, including 30 to 40 graded MS-65 or higher.

Availability in circulated grades: This coin is rare. Most are in higher grades.

	Cert	Avg	%MS	G-4	VG-8	F-12	VF-20	EF-40	AU-50	MS-60	MS-63	MS-65
1885	83	60.0	77%	$200	$250	$350	$500	$575	$700	$850	$1,100	$2,400

1885, Proof • Proof Mintage: 940.

Availability in Proof format: Most Proof strikes survive, including 110 to 140 graded PF-65 or finer.

	Cert	Avg	%MS	PF-60	PF-63	PF-65
1885, Proof	267	64.3		$475	$750	$1,400

1886 Liberty Seated Quarter

1886 • Circulation-Strike Mintage: 5,000.

Commentary: All circulation strikes are weak at the tops of both 8's and at LIBERTY on the shield.

Availability in Mint State: 100 to 125 Mint State copies are available, including 18 to 24 graded MS-65 or higher. All Mint State coins are prooflike, without exception.[54]

Availability in circulated grades: This year is the rarest Philadelphia Mint Liberty Seated quarter. Nearly all are in higher grades.

	Cert	Avg	%MS	G-4	VG-8	F-12	VF-20	EF-40	AU-50	MS-60	MS-63	MS-65
1886	42	57.4	76%	$400	$550	$750	$950	$1,100	$1,250	$1,500	$1,900	$2,600

1886, Proof • Proof Mintage: 886.

Availability in Proof format: Most Proofs survive, including 110 to 130 graded PF-65 or finer. Some have flat star centers. In the 1940s and early 1950s Charles E. Green and his wife, Ruth Green, of Skokie, Illinois, took a fancy to Proof quarter dollars of this date and endeavored to hoard as many as possible. Eventually they succeeded in obtaining several hundred coins.

	Cert	Avg	%MS	PF-60	PF-63	PF-65
1886, Proof	293	64.5		$475	$750	$1,400

1887 Liberty Seated Quarter

1887 • **Circulation-Strike Mintage:** 10,000.

Commentary: These coins are usually weak in areas. Circulation strikes have a raised line from a scratch in the die below LIBERTY on the shield.

Availability in Mint State: 220 to 250 are available in Mint State, including 50 to 65 graded MS-65 or higher.

Availability in circulated grades: This Philadelphia issue is very scarce. Most are in higher grades.

	Cert	Avg	%MS	G-4	VG-8	F-12	VF-20	EF-40	AU-50	MS-60	MS-63	MS-65
1887	101	61.7	85%	$250	$350	$425	$500	$575	$625	$850	$1,150	$2,500

1887, Proof • Proof Mintage: 710.

Availability in Proof format: Most of this year's Proof strikes survive, including 80 to 100 graded PF-65 or finer.

	Cert	Avg	%MS	PF-60	PF-63	PF-65
1887, Proof	232	64.4		$475	$750	$1,400

1888 Liberty Seated Quarter

1888 • **Circulation-Strike Mintage:** 10,000.

Commentary: Philadelphia strikes of this year are often found with lightly struck star centers.

Availability in Mint State: 230 to 260 copies exist, including 60 to 75 graded MS-65 or higher.

Availability in circulated grades: This is a rare coin in circulated grades. Most are in higher grades.

	Cert	Avg	%MS	G-4	VG-8	F-12	VF-20	EF-40	AU-50	MS-60	MS-63	MS-65
1888	130	63.2	94%	$250	$350	$425	$500	$550	$600	$700	$900	$1,600

1888, Proof • **Proof Mintage:** 832.

Availability in Proof format: Most Proofs from this year survive, including 60 to 75 graded PF-65 or finer. Interest in these low-mintage coins was fading during this time.

	Cert	Avg	%MS	PF-60	PF-63	PF-65
1888, Proof	224	64.1		$475	$750	$1,400

1888-S Liberty Seated Quarter

1888-S • **Circulation-Strike Mintage:** 1,216,000.

Commentary: San Francisco strikes from 188 are usually very sharp, except for examples from two obverse dies where LIBERTY was polished to create weakness.

Availability in Mint State: 150 to 180 copies are known, including 10 to 14 graded MS-65 or higher. Mint State copies are elusive despite the very large mintage.

Availability in circulated grades: This coin is very scarce.

	Cert	Avg	%MS	G-4	VG-8	F-12	VF-20	EF-40	AU-50	MS-60	MS-63	MS-65
1888-S	148	56.4	67%	$25	$30	$35	$45	$70	$200	$360	$750	$3,000

1889 Liberty Seated Quarter

1889 • **Circulation-Strike Mintage:** 12,000.

Availability in Mint State: 400 to 500 coins are known in Mint State, including 120 to 150 graded MS-65 or higher.

Availability in circulated grades: This coin is rare. Most are in higher grades.

	Cert	Avg	%MS	G-4	VG-8	F-12	VF-20	EF-40	AU-50	MS-60	MS-63	MS-65
1889	177	62.7	89%	$200	$275	$425	$500	$550	$600	$700	$900	$1,950

1889, Proof • **Proof Mintage:** 711.

Availability in Proof format: Most Proof strikes survive, including 60 to 90 graded PF-65 or finer.

	Cert	Avg	%MS	PF-60	PF-63	PF-65
1889, Proof	193	64.5		$475	$750	$1,400

1890 Liberty Seated Quarter

1890 • Circulation-Strike Mintage: 80,000.

Commentary: Strikes from Philadelphia in 1890 usually have flat star centers. A few are highly prooflike on the obverse and have been called one-sided Proofs.[55]

Availability in Mint State: 300 to 340 Mint State copies exist, including 60 to 80 graded MS-65 or higher.

Availability in circulated grades: This is a scarce coin in circulated grades. Most are in higher grades.

	Cert	Avg	%MS	G-4	VG-8	F-12	VF-20	EF-40	AU-50	MS-60	MS-63	MS-65
1890	189	62.4	86%	$95	$135	$180	$275	$325	$375	$485	$900	$1,400

1890, Proof • Proof Mintage: 590.

Availability in Proof format: Most Proof strikes survive, including 90 to 120 graded PF-65 or finer. A few are highly prooflike on the obverse and have been called one-sided Proofs.[55]

	Cert	Avg	%MS	PF-60	PF-63	PF-65
1890, Proof	231	64.8		$475	$750	$1,400

1891 Liberty Seated Quarter

1891 • Circulation-Strike Mintage: 3,920,000.

Commentary: These coins are usually weak in areas.

Availability in Mint State: 950 to 1,100 copies are available, including 100 to 130 graded MS-65 or higher.

Availability in circulated grades: This is a common coin, with most in higher grades.

	Cert	Avg	%MS	G-4	VG-8	F-12	VF-20	EF-40	AU-50	MS-60	MS-63	MS-65
1891	671	60.4	76%	$25	$30	$35	$45	$65	$160	$260	$550	$1,800

1891, Proof • **Proof Mintage:** 600.

Availability in Proof format: Most Proof strikes survive, including 70 to 90 graded PF-65 or finer.

	Cert	Avg	%MS	PF-60	PF-63	PF-65
1891, Proof	236	64.6		$1,100	$23,000	$35,000

1891-O Liberty Seated Quarter

1891-O • **Circulation-Strike Mintage:** 68,000.

Commentary: Strike quality for this issue varies. Some are highly prooflike and have been certified as branch mint Proofs; at the very least they are special strikings.[58] This is the first and only New Orleans Mint quarter dollar struck after 1860, and the only New Orleans Mint Liberty Seated quarter dollar with the motto IN GOD WE TRUST on the reverse.

Availability in Mint State: 18 to 22 Mint state copies exist, including three or four graded MS-65 or higher.

Availability in circulated grades: This is a scarce coin in lower grades. Some Fair to About Good coins have nearly all details worn smooth, but four or five letters in LIBERTY remain readable.[56] It is rare at Very Fine and Extremely Fine levels, and even more so in About Uncirculated grade.[57]

	Cert	Avg	%MS	G-4	VG-8	F-12	VF-20	EF-40	AU-50	MS-60	MS-63	MS-65
1891-O	40	35.8	33%	$350	$550	$1,000	$1,650	$2,500	$3,350	$5,000	$12,500	$30,000

1891-S Liberty Seated Quarter

1891-S • **Circulation-Strike Mintage:** 2,216,000.

Commentary: Quality varies for this final San Francisco Liberty Seated quarter, but they are usually fairly sharp.

Availability in Mint State: 250 to 300 Mint State copies are known, including 20 to 25 graded MS-65 or higher. They are often prooflike. *MS-60 to 62: 90 to 120.*

Availability in circulated grades: This is a common issue, with most in higher grades.

	Cert	Avg	%MS	G-4	VG-8	F-12	VF-20	EF-40	AU-50	MS-60	MS-63	MS-65
1891-S	198	58.8	71%	$25	$30	$35	$45	$70	$160	$260	$550	$2,000

BARBER OR LIBERTY HEAD QUARTER DOLLARS (1892–1916)

Designer: *Charles E. Barber.* **Weight:** *6.25 grams.*
Composition: *.900 silver, .100 copper (net weight .18084 oz. pure silver).*
Diameter: *24.3 mm.* **Edge:** *Reeded.* **Mints:** *Philadelphia, Denver, New Orleans, and San Francisco.*

Circulation Strike

Mintmark location
is on the reverse,
below the eagle.

Proof

THE NEW DESIGN

By the late 1890s the Liberty Seated dime, quarter, and half dollar had been a familiar sight for multiple generations. It was time for a change. In *The Annual Report of the Director of the Mint* for 1887 James P. Kimball endorsed the making of new designs. In October 1889 Edward O. Leech became Mint director, succeeding Kimball. Leech invited 10 leading artists to redesign the silver dime, quarter, and half dollar.[59]

Traditionally, new coinage motifs had originated with the artists and engravers in Philadelphia, not from artists in the private sector. The artists who received the invitation discussed the matter among themselves and then wrote to Leech to state that they would only do this if $100 would be paid for each sketch submitted and $500 for each accepted design. Otherwise a lot of time and effort would be wasted, as only a few designs were to be chosen from the many desired to be submitted.

Response was not enthusiastic. Responses were mainly from amateurs, with no mention of any from a skilled coin or medal engraver. The designs were reviewed by Henry Mitchell and Augustus Saint-Gaudens, artists in the private sector with the last being especially prominent, and by Charles E. Barber, chief engraver at the Mint. Their report to Leech on June 3:

> Dear Sir:
>
> We would respectfully report that in conformity with your written request we have opened in the presence of the director of the Mint the new designs or models submitted for the silver coins of the United States, under Department circular of April 4, 1891, and have carefully examined the same.
>
> We are of the opinion that none of the designs or models submitted are such a decided improvement upon the present designs of the silver coins of the United States as to be worthy of adoption by the government.
>
> We would respectfully recommend that the services of one or more artists distinguished for work in designing for relief be engaged at a suitable compensation to prepare for the consideration of the Department new designs for the coins of the United States.

In July 1891 Director Leech, having accomplished nothing with artists in the private sector, tapped Chief Engraver Charles E. Barber to prepare coinage designs. The engraver then set about the task, sometimes getting off topic, such as creating a reverse inspired by the Una and the Lion reverse on the 1839 British £5 gold coin, it was said. Barber had a mind of his own and had a higher opinion of his talent than did others in the community of artists. The New York City contingent in particular thought his work on medals was sub-par, and it is said that Saint-Gaudens called his art "wretched." However, Barber was indeed in charge of finalizing coin designs that had been accepted by the Treasury, and he resented the input of sculptors in the private sector.

Barber went to work and created an obverse design of Miss Liberty, copied from a French coin. For the reverse of the quarter and half dollar he created a heraldic eagle holding an olive branch and arrows with stars above and an inscription around the border.

After due discussions and some changes, Leech showed the designs to President Benjamin Harrison, who passed them around among Cabinet members. Harrison suggested some minor changes. Not long afterward the Treasury Department issued this description of the common obverse used on the three denominations:

Charles E. Barber.

> On the obverse, Head of Liberty looking to the right; olive wreath around the head and Phrygian cap on the back; on the band or fillet on the front is inscribed "Liberty"; and surrounding the medallion are 13 stars to represent the 13 original states. Directly over the head at the top of the coin is the legend "In God We Trust," and beneath the bust the date.

The commentary concluded with the opinion that the new designs "are a great improvement over those now in use." Thus the "ugly" Liberty Seated motif was scheduled to be replaced. Would there be a dawning of public enthusiasm for the new motifs? It was hoped so. However, this was not to be.

Harper's Weekly, November 21, 1891, included this scathing article by Jno. Gilmore Speed illustrated by a *rather crude* image of an 1891 pattern supplied by the Treasury Department:

The Design for the New Silver Coins

The mountain has labored and brought forth a mouse.[60] There was much ado last spring about selecting a design for the new silver coins to be made by the mints of the United States. The director of the Mint, Mr. Leech, took a great deal of advice from artists and invited suggestions as to the design to be adopted, and then chose to have the new coins modeled in the department by the engraver of the Mint . . .

He invited a number of sculptors and artists to submit designs, but last spring many of the best men joined in a communication declining to participate in a competition in which even those who were successful would be but poorly paid for the work done. However, this was not the only reason which influenced them in declining. If an American artist had felt that he was doing something to prevent his government from making an artistic blunder he would have been willing to waive the question of compensation; but the other conditions were too hard. The time given in which to make the designs was only six weeks, and this was considered too short a period during which first-class work could be done. In addition, again, these artists were not asked to make designs for the whole coin, but for only one side.

Knowing that the department would probably employ some incompetent artisan to make the other side, artists of standing were indisposed to have their work thus spoiled by part of the coin being good, and the rest atrociously bad. The design adopted shows that this is precisely what would have happened, and the artists who foresaw such a probability were wise in their judgment . . .

Indeed, the difficulties in the way of making a good modern coin are so great that Mr. Augustus Saint-Gaudens did not hesitate to say that in his opinion there were only three or four men in America capable of designing a really admirable coin.

"But," said he, looking at a photograph of the new design made by Mr. Barber, "there are a hundred men who could have done very much better than this. This is inept; this looks like it had been designed by a young lady of sixteen, a miss who had taken only a few lessons in modelling. It is beneath criticism, beneath contempt . . .

Mr. Kenyon Cox, when shown the photographs of the new design, sniffed the air as though it were foul, and said, impatiently, "Every time the government has anything to do in art matters it shows its utter incapacity to deal with such things." When he was asked to express an opinion of the design, he looked at it a moment and said, "It is beneath criticism," and then added, "I think it disgraceful that this great country should have such a coin as this." Mr. Cox was disinclined to say more, for he evidently felt very strongly on the subject, and was too full of disgust at the artistic inferiority of the new design to express himself freely and still preserve his amiable politeness…

Mr. J.S. Hartley, the sculptor, who, when I called at his studio, had just put the finishing touches on his model for the heroic statue of Ericsson to be placed in the Central Park, examined the photographs carefully… Of the obverse side, however, with a head of Liberty wearing a Phrygian cap and a laurel wreath, he said that it was evidently the work of an amateur who had mastered very few of the rudiments of modelling. The head he thought unintellectual, and the face even worse, as it suggested that of a disreputable woman just recovering from a prolonged debauch…

Several designers were also visited, and to them were the photographs shown. Without exception they pronounced the work to be devoid of merit, and no improvement whatever on the old coins. Such seems to be the universal opinion of the new design of those qualified to judge in such matters. But it has been adopted, and on the 1st of next January the mints will begin stamping the coins with dies made from Mr. Barber's design. And so it will continue until Congress does a good act by repealing a bad law, and enable the government officials to secure the services of men competent to make designs more worthy of the country.

PATTERN COIN

Only one pattern is known for the Barber quarter. Dated 1891 the obverse very closely follows the adopted design of 1892, but with slight differences. These include adjustments of the border letters, the details of the ribbon and its relationship to the stars, and the position of the stars in relation to the portrait and lettering.

The only existing example is in the National Numismatic Collection in the Smithsonian Institution. The reason for not more quarter varieties being made is that the half dollar was used to try out various ideas, with the thought that whatever was adopted for the half dollar could be used on the quarter as well.

The *American Journal of Numismatics* reviewed the designs in its issue of January 1892 with a mixture of approval with condemnation, in part stating, "There is yet a long distance between them and the ideal National coin. Perhaps that will never be reached."

Pattern 1891 quarter, Judd-1761. The obverse is described above. The reverse mainly differs in having clouds and a different arrangement of the stars.

A MODERN REVIEW

In contrast to comments of years earlier, Cornelius Vermeule, numismatist and a curator at the Museum of Fine Art, Boston, writing in 1971 praised the Barber design to the skies:

The designs of Barber's coins were more attuned to the times than even he perhaps realized. The plumpish, matronly *gravitas* of Liberty had come to America seven years earlier in the person of Frédéric Bartholdi's giant statue on Bedloe's Island in New York Harbor.[61]

Such sculptures, whether called Liberty or Columbia or The Republic or a personification of intellect, were dominant themes of the Chicago World's Fair, the Columbian Exposition of 1892, termed by Saint-Gaudens "the greatest meeting of artists since the fifteenth century." Chief among these statues was Daniel Chester French's colossal *Republic*, a Pheidian matron holding aloft an eagle on an orb in one hand and a Liberty cap on an emblem in the other. The heavy profile, solemn eyes, thick jaw, and massive neck of the statue in harmony with what Charles Barber had created for the coinage in the year of the Fair's opening.[62]

Of all American coins long in circulation, no series has stood the wearing demands of modern coinage as well as the half dollar, quarter, dime developed by the chief engraver at Philadelphia. Liberty's cap, incised diadem, and wreath of laurel were designed to echo all the depth and volume of her Olympian countenance. These classical substances are offset, almost literally, by sharply rectangular denticles of the raised rims and by the strength of thirteen six-pointed stars.

On the reverse of two large coins, an equal constellation of stars has five points and is clustered above the eagle's shaggy, craggy profile. On both sides the simple dignity of motto, legend, and denomination binds the pictorialism into a cohesive tondo. The wealth of irregular surfaces and sharp angles is an almost electrifying aesthetic experience. The wreath of the dime's reverse carries the plasticity of the eagle's feathers into miniature dimensions and entwines the less complicated inscription in forthright fashion. This wreath also exhibits its own freshness and sculptural activity; leaves, berries, and stems are alive with a carefully controlled sense of nature. Even when these coins have been nearly smooth, their outlines suggest the harmony of interior detail in careful planes of relief that make Uncirculated specimens a pleasure to contemplate. The sculptor was unsurpassed in the mechanics of creating a durable design of monumental validity.[63]

It is appropriate at this point to state that criticizing new coin designs had been a tradition for many years. In fact, the first copper cents issued for circulation in 1793 were condemned as being unfit. The Morgan silver dollar design of 1878 received unending criticism. Numismatists feel differently, of course. Today, early copper cents, Morgan silver dollars, and Barber silver coins are collected with a passion.

Can the 1892 be viewed as occult? In *The Numismatist*, MY 1899, George W. Rice discussed the Barber quarters of 1892, including the two reverse varieties, ending his article with this:

> The attention of those inclined to superstition is invited to this coin; it is a veritable "hoo-doo."
>
> There are thirteen stars on the obverse and thirteen on the reverse; there are thirteen letters in E PLURIBUS UNUM; also thirteen arrows in the cluster. Yet with all this, did you ever know one of these quarters to be refused because of the ill fortune supposed to attend this number thirteen?

COINAGE AND CIRCULATION OF BARBER QUARTERS

Minting of the Barber coins commenced on January 2, 1892. The first delivery to the cashier consisted of $2,000 in dimes, $1,000 worth of quarters and $5,000 in half dollars. A shipment of $50 face value was sent that day to Mint Director Edward O. Leech in Washington. These were received on the 4th, at which time a set of three was given to President Grover Cleveland and other sets were given to friends.[64]

Production of the dimes, quarters, and half dollars for circulation took place at the three mints then currently in operation—Philadelphia, New Orleans, and San Francisco. The new Denver Mint coined pieces starting in 1906. After 1909 the New Orleans Mint shut down forever. Coinage of all three denominations usually but not always took place at each of the mints in each year. Dimes and quarters of the Barber design were made through 1916, when they were replaced by the Mercury and Standing Liberty designs respectively. Barber half dollars were made through 1915, followed in 1916 by the Liberty Walking motif.

BARBER OR LIBERTY HEAD QUARTER DOLLARS (1892–1916): GUIDE TO COLLECTING

BARBER QUARTERS MINTAGES AS A GUIDE TO RARITY

In descending order, from most common to rarest:

20 million or fewer	**5 million or fewer**	**2.5 million or fewer**	**1 million or fewer**
1899 12,624,000	1905 4,967,523	1907-D. . . . 2,484,000	1911-S 988,000
1902 12,196,967	1902-O. . . . 4,748,000	1892-O. . . . 2,460,000	1892-S 964,079
1898 11,100,000	1907-O. . . . 4,560,000	1904-O. . . . 2,456,000	1911-D. 933,600
1900 10,016,000	1895 4,440,000	1910 2,244,000	1908-S 784,000
10 million or fewer	1912 4,400,000	1906-O. . . . 2,056,000	1909-O. 712,000
1903 9,759,309	1908 4,232,000	1905-S 1,884,000	1912-S 708,000
1904 9,588,143	1896 3,874,000	1898-O. . . . 1,868,000	1899-S 708,000
1909 9,268,000	1911 3,720,000	1900-S 1,858,585	1915-S 704,000
1901 8,892,000	1915-D. . . . 3,694,000	1916 1,788,000	1897-S 542,229
1892, Types	1906 3,655,760	1895-S 1,764,681	**500,000 or fewer**
I & II . . . 8,236,000	1903-O. . . . 3,500,000	1901-O. . . . 1,612,000	1913 484,000
1897 8,140,000	1915 3,480,000	1902-S 1,524,612	1914-S 264,000
1907 7,132,000	1894 3,432,000	1910-D. . . . 1,500,000	1896-S 188,039
1916-D. . . . 6,540,800	1900-O. . . . 3,416,000	1896-O. . . . 1,484,000	**100,000 or fewer**
1914 6,244,250	1893-O. . . . 3,396,000	1893-S 1,454,535	1901-S 72,664
1908-O. . . . 6,244,000	1906-D. . . . 3,280,000	1913-D. . . . 1,450,800	1913-S 40,000
1908-D. . . . 5,788,000	1914-D. . . . 3,046,000	1897-O. . . . 1,414,800	
1893 5,444,023	1894-O. . . . 2,852,000	1907-S 1,360,000	
1909-D. . . . 5,114,000	1895-O. . . . 2,816,000	1909-S 1,348,000	
	1894-S 2,648,821	1905-O. . . . 1,230,000	
	1899-O. . . . 2,644,000	1903-S 1,036,000	
		1898-S 1,020,592	

COLLECTING BARBER QUARTERS

Barber quarters and the two other Barber silver denominations began to be widely collected starting in the 1930s when Raymond "National" and other albums were widely sold and made it convenient to store and display coins at the same time. Whitman folders entered the scene, were inexpensive, and did much to boost interest. Even though the Depression pervaded the country, the face value of a dime was not a deterrent and more of these were saved than of quarters or half dollars, but thousands of the higher denominations were set aside as well.

All Barber coins were available in circulation, dating back to 1892, but most were of 20th century dates. The design of all three denominations is such that even with a modest amount of wear, most of LIBERTY on the obverse disappeared. Amazingly, by 1935 many Barber coins made just 20 years earlier had been worn down to G-4 or even lower. It is probably correct to estimate that of surviving circulated Barber quarters over 90% are in grades from AG-3 to G-4. This average low grade has no counterpart among other major types of quarter dollars.

By the 1930s typical grades for quarters were About Good (AG-3) to Good (G-4) for those dated in the 1890s and Good for those in the early 20th century. Today, to qualify as VG-8 grade some letters in LIBERTY must be visible. To merit the F-12 designation all letters need to be readable per traditional standards, although those in highest relief can be weak. Modern gradeflation has seen some coins certified as F-12 or even slightly higher, with a letter or two missing. Exceptions to the rule of well-worn coins were the occasional pieces that had been set aside by choice or chance in the early years. Today we have the situation that perhaps 90% of the coins in collectors' hands are well worn. This is unique to the Barber coin series and does not apply, for example, to Liberty Seated and earlier quarters, or to later Standing Liberty and Washington issues.

In the grades of AG-3 and G-4, the most elusive issues are those with a combination of low mintage and early dates, these being most of the mintmarked issues of the 1890s as well as the 1901-S. For Mint State coins the same can be said in general, except that for coins having the same mintage range, San Francisco and New Orleans pieces are generally hard to find. Quarters from the various mints often show weak striking on the reverse. Remarkably, there is no record of any caches or hoards yielding a significant number of Mint State quarters.

ASPECTS OF STRIKING

Grading numbers do not consider the quality or sharpness of the strike, which for some coins can be weak in areas. A third-party certified MS-65 quarter, for example, can be sharply struck or in can be weak in areas. Probably 90% of coin buyers are not aware of this. Accordingly, as a reader of this book you can go treasure hunting, for sharp coins cost no more!

A rare 1901-S quarter in AG-3 grade. The vast majority of Barber quarters of the earlier years that survive today are in grades of AG-3 and G-4.

Key points to look for: On the obverse check the hair directly above Liberty's forehead. On the right side of the reverse check where the wing meets the shield and also check the eagle's talons.

David Lawrence commented that New Orleans Barber quarters are notoriously weakly struck, but coins from Philadelphia and San Francisco can be very weak as well, especially on Miss Liberty's hair and the eagle's talons on the right. These weaknesses are especially evident on issues after the hub change in 1900. "Basically, the later the date after 1900, the poorer the strike," he concluded. Further, while some early circulation-strike issues are encountered with prooflike surfaces, in general this mirrorlike finish is unusual among Barber quarters. Attractive pieces are especially prized by collectors.

Many circulation strikes are weakly struck at the upper right of the shield and on the eagle's talon at the right and on the arrow feathers, the illustrated 1907-O being an extreme example. As certified coin grades take no notice of striking, cherry picking for quality costs no more.

PROOF BARBER QUARTERS

Proof Barber quarters were minted at Philadelphia for every year from 1892 to 1915, but not for the 1916 Barber quarter These were available a part of silver Proof sets. From 1892 to 1904, such sets included the Barber dime, quarter, and half dollar and the Morgan silver dollar. From 1905 to 1915 just the lower three denominations were in the set.

Today, all Proofs are readily collectible. As a general rule the earlier dates are more elusive in grades of PF-65 and better. Availability is also proportional to the mintage figures. Some Proofs are weakly struck on the reverse at the eagle's claw holding arrows.

Proof 1892 Barber quarter, first year of the type.

QUARTERS FROM A 1945 HOARD

Tim Glaue contributed "Barbers From a Fruit Cellar Find" to the *Journal of the Barber Coin Collectors Society*, April 2012. He told of 1,193 coins found in a Kerr glass fruit jar in the cellar of an Ann Arbor, Michigan house, the latest of which was dated 1945, indicating the year the coins were hidden away. The inventory of Barber quarters reflects the grades of coins in circulation at that time:

1892: 1 AG-3; 1893-O: 1 AG-3; 1897: 1AG-3; 1898 1 AG-3, 3 G-4; 1899 1 AG-3 and 4 G-4; 1901 2 AG-3, 1 G-4; 1902 2 AG-3, 2 G-4; 1904 1 AG-3, 1 G-4; 1905 1 AG-3; 1906 1 AG-3; 1908 1 AG-3, 1 F-12; 1909 1 AG-3; 1909-D 2 G-4; 1909-O 1 AG-3; 1911 1 AG-3, 1 G-4; 1914 1 G-4; 1915 1 G-4; 1916 1 G-4; and 1916-D 1 AG-3, 1 G-4.

As to the present author's experience, in 1952 and 1953 when I began collecting coins from circulation, Barber dimes were fairly scarce, quarters less so, and there were quite a few half dollars. The typical grade was AG-3.

FURTHER COMMENTS

For each Barber quarter, estimates of availability are given Mint State, circulated grades, and Proof. These are for *conservatively graded* examples. Due to resubmissions, gradeflation, etc., PCGS and NGC population reports sometimes have higher numbers. Many MS-64 coins of a few years ago are now certified as MS-65, this being true of other quarter dollar types as well.

In the 1980s there was a great flurry of speculator interest in many coin series. The result is that prices of coins in higher Mint State and Proof grades increased dramatically. The investors later departed. Now, at the end of the second decade of the 21st century, many high-grade dimes are less expensive than they were years earlier! Today the market is mainly composed of true collectors.

The Barber Coin Collectors Society, founded in 1989. forms a meeting place for specialists and enthusiasts in coins designed by Charles E. Barber and issues a fine journal. Details can be found on the Internet.

As to being a smart buyer, the guidelines given for Liberty Seated quarters are equally applicable here.

For further reference, *The Complete Guide to Barber Quarters* by David Lawrence, 1994, is an essential reference for the specialist and is recommended as a comprehensive source.

BARBER QUARTER HUB CHANGES

In early 1892 it was found that the quarters did not stack properly. To correct this Charles E. Barber made slight adjustments to both sides. The engraver wrote to Mint Director Edward O. Leech to say that on the obverse he had increased the width of the border and had decreased the radius circle that contained the words IN GOD WE TRUST.[65] These obverse differences are subtle and can best be seen by studying the distance of the stars and letters to the denticles. On the earlier dies the spacing is ever so slightly farther away. The changes to the reverse were obvious.

Less well known are obverse changes.[66] Obverse Hub I was used from 1892 through 1900, and Obverse Hub II from 1900 to the end of the series in 1916. The differences are slight. On Obverse Hub II the relief is imperceptibly lower, the denticles are longer and slightly more widely spaced, Liberty's inner ear has more detail. The alterations worked. A stack of 21 of the new coins introduced in 1900 was equal in height to a stack of 20 of the earlier type.

These differences were ignored by collectors for many years. In recent decades they have become popular, and nearly all specialists such as member of the Barber Coin Collectors Club endeavor to obtain one of each reverse for the three date and mintmark varieties of 1892.

In 1900 Reverse Hub III was introduced with slight changes. In that year coins from all three mints were made with the II as well as the III reverses.

The earliest Barber quarters from all three mints have the so-called Type I reverse from Reverse Hub I. This can be distinguished at a glance by looking at the E in UNITED at the upper left. On Type I part of the crossbar of the letter can be seen above the eagle's wing while on Type II, so called, from Reverse Hub II the wing covers this feature completely. The Type II hub was used from partway through 1892 into 1900 in which year the Type III hub was introduced.

Detail of Reverse Hub I showing part of the crossbar of E in UNITED visible above the wing.

Detail of Reverse Hub II with the crossbar not visible and with the wing of the eagle not protruding through the top of the E. This hub was used through part of the year 1900.

Upon close inspection there are many differences between the Reverse Hub I and II. Overall, the Reverse Hub II eagle and other features are slightly smaller, permitting a wider space between the letters and the denticles. The stars above the eagle are slightly different on each. For quick reference see below ST in STATES.[67]

Barber or Liberty Head Quarter Dollars (1892–1916)

Grading Standards

MS-60 to 70 (Mint State). *Obverse:* At MS-60, some abrasion and contact marks are evident, most noticeably on the cheek and the obverse field to the right. Luster is present, but may be dull or lifeless. Many Barber coins have been cleaned, especially of the earlier dates. At MS-63, contact marks are very few. Abrasion still is evident, but less than at lower levels. Indeed, the cheek of Miss Liberty virtually showcases abrasion. An MS-65 coin

1896-S. Graded MS-65.

may have minor abrasion, but contact marks are so minute as to require magnification. Luster should be full and rich. *Reverse:* Comments apply as for the obverse, except that in lower Mint State grades abrasion and contact marks are most noticeable on the head and tail of the eagle and on the tips of the wings. At MS-65 or higher, there are no marks visible to the unaided eye. The field is mainly protected by design elements, and often appears to grade a point or two higher than the obverse.

Illustrated coin: This brilliant coin shows full satin luster.

AU-50, 53, 55, 58 (About Uncirculated). *Obverse:* Light wear is seen on the head, especially on the forward hair under LIBERTY. At AU-58, the luster is extensive but incomplete, especially on the higher parts and in the right field. At AU–50 and 53, luster is less. *Reverse:* Wear is evident on the head and tail of the eagle and on the tips of the wings. At AU–50 and 53, there still is significant luster. An AU-58 coin (as determined by the obverse) can have the reverse appear to be full Mint State.

1911-D. Graded AU-50.

EF-40, 45 (Extremely Fine). *Obverse:* Further wear is seen on the head. The hair above the forehead lacks most detail. LIBERTY shows wear, but still is strong. *Reverse:* Further wear is seen on the head and tail of the eagle and on the tips of the wings, most evident at the left and right extremes of the wings. At this level and below, sharpness of strike on the reverse is not important.

Illustrated coin: Note the subtle lilac and gold toning.

1913-S. Graded EF-40.

VF-20, 30 (Very Fine). *Obverse:* The head shows more wear, now with nearly all detail gone in the hair above the forehead. LIBERTY shows wear, but is complete. The leaves on the head all show wear, as does the upper part of the cap. *Reverse:* Wear is more extensive, particularly noticeable on the outer parts of the wings, the head, the shield, and the tail.

Illustrated coin: The dig and discoloration in Liberty's cheek decrease the appeal of this example.

1896-S. Graded VF-20.

F-12, 15 (Fine). *Obverse:* The head shows extensive wear. LIBERTY, the key place to check, is weak, especially at ER, but is fully readable. The ANA grading standards and *Photograde* adhere to this. PCGS suggests that lightly struck coins "may have letters partially missing." Traditionally, collectors insist on full LIBERTY. *Reverse:* More wear is seen on the reverse in the places as above. E PLURIBUS UNUM is light, with one to several letters worn away.

1913-S. Graded F-15.

VG-8, 10 (Very Good). *Obverse:* A net of three letters in LIBERTY must be readable. Traditionally, LI is clear, and after that there is a partial letter or two. *Reverse:* Further wear has smoothed more than half of the feathers in the wing. The shield is indistinct except for a few traces of interior lines. The motto is partially worn away. The rim is full, and many if not most denticles can be seen.

1914-S. Graded VG-10.

G-4, 6 (Good). *Obverse:* The head is in outline form, with the center flat. Most of the rim is there. All letters and the date are full. *Reverse:* The eagle shows only a few feathers, and only a few scattered letters remain in the motto. The rim may be worn flat in some or all of the area, but the peripheral lettering is clear.

1913-S. Graded G-4.

AG-3 (About Good). *Obverse:* The stars and motto are worn, and the border may be indistinct. Distinctness varies at this level. The date is clear. Grading is usually determined by the reverse. *Reverse:* The rim is gone and the letters are partially worn away. The eagle is mostly flat, perhaps with a few hints of feathers.

1901-S. Graded AG-3.

PF-60 to 70 (Proof). *Obverse and Reverse:* Proofs that are extensively cleaned and have many hairlines, or that are dull and grainy, are lower level, such as PF–60 to 62. These are not widely desired by collectors. With medium hairlines and good reflectivity, an assigned grade of PF-64 is appropriate. Tiny horizontal lines on Miss Liberty's cheek, known as slide marks, from National and other album slides scuffing the relief of the

1913. Graded PF-68 Cameo.

cheek, are endemic on all Barber silver coins. With noticeable marks of this type, the highest grade assignable is PF-64. With relatively few hairlines, a rating of PF-65 can be given. PF-66 should have hairlines so delicate that magnification is needed to see them. Above that, a Proof should be free of any hairlines or other problems.

Illustrated coin: Exceptional fields offset the bright devices to high advantage.

1892 Barber Quarter, Type I Reverse

1892, Type I Reverse • **Circulation-Strike Mintage:** Smaller part of 8,236,000.

Commentary: Usually found well struck.

Availability in Mint State: Several thousand or more. Of these 300 to 350 are graded MS-65 or higher.

Availability in circulated grades: 15,000 to 18,000. Most are AG-3 or G-4. There are many in higher circulated grades from having been saved as the first year of issue.

Detail of the Type I Reverse.

	Cert	Avg	%MS	G-4	VG-8	F-12	VF-20	EF-40	AU-50	MS-60	MS-63	MS-65
1892, Type I	1,742	60.3	72%	$10	$12	$26	$45	$75	$130	$250	$375	$800

1892, Type I Reverse • **Proof Mintage:** 100 estimated.

Availability: Of the 1,245 Proofs struck this year the vast majority have the Type II reverse. The Type I is very rare, but as it is not widely noticed, the cost may be no more. Most Proofs survive, including 5 to 10 graded PF-65 or finer.

Detail of the Type I Reverse.

	Cert	Avg	%MS	PF-60	PF-63	PF-65
1892, Type I, Proof	396	64.7		$350	$650	$1,250

1892 Barber Quarter, Type II Reverse

1892, Type II Reverse • **Circulation-Strike Mintage:** Larger part of 8,236,000.

Commentary: Usually found well struck.

Availability in Mint State: Several thousand or more, slightly more than the preceding. Of these 500 to 600 are graded MS-65 or higher.

Availability in circulated grades: 35,000 to 40,000. Most are AG-3 or G-4, a comment that applies to all Barber quarters of this decade. Similar to the situation for Type I, this issue is readily available in high circulated grades as many were saved as the first year of issue.

Detail of the Type II Reverse.

	Cert	Avg	%MS	G-4	VG-8	F-12	VF-20	EF-40	AU-50	MS-60	MS-63	MS-65
1892, Type II	1,742	60.3	72%	$10	$12	$26	$45	$75	$130	$250	$375	$800

1892, Type II Reverse • **Proof Mintage:** Part of 1,245.

Availability: Quite rare in relation to the record mintage. Likely many sets were sold as souvenirs and the coins spent or mishandled. *PF-60 to 64: 550 to 750; PF-65 or better: 70 to 85.*

Detail of the Type II Reverse.

	Cert	Avg	%MS	PF-60	PF-63	PF-65
1892, Type II, Proof	396	64.7		$350	$650	$1,250

1892-O Barber Quarter, Type I Reverse

1892-O, Type I Reverse • **Circulation-Strike Mintage:** Part of 2,640,000.

Commentary: The 1892-O Type I quarter is significantly rarer than the Type II, just the opposite of the situation with 1892-S. Mintmark O centered over the opening at the letter R, and below the center tail feather constituting the "normal" position (for 1892 only). In subsequent years the mintmark was moved to between the R and the D or over the D.

Availability in Mint State: Readily found in lower Mint State grades plus 50 to 60 graded MS-65 or higher.

Availability in circulated grades: 4,000 to 5,000.

Detail of the Type I Reverse.

	Cert	Avg	%MS	G-4	VG-8	F-12	VF-20	EF-40	AU-50	MS-60	MS-63	MS-65
1892-O, Type I	441	59.2	67%	$15	$20	$45	$60	$95	$160	$275	$400	$1,200

1892-O Barber Quarter, Type II Reverse

1892-O, Type II Reverse • **Circulation-Strike Mintage:** Part of 2,460,000.

Availability in Mint State: Lower-level Mint State examples are easily found. An estimated 100 to 120 are graded MS-65 or higher.

Availability in circulated grades: 6,000 to 8,000.

Detail of the Type II Reverse.

	Cert	Avg	%MS	G-4	VG-8	F-12	VF-20	EF-40	AU-50	MS-60	MS-63	MS-65
1892-O, Type II	441	59.2	67%	$15	$20	$45	$60	$95	$160	$275	$400	$1,200

1892-S Barber Quarter, Type I Reverse

1892-S, Type I Reverse • Circulation-Strike Mintage: Part of 964,079.

Commentary: Mintmark S centered over the opening at the letter R, and below the center tail feather constituting the "normal" position (for 1892 only). In subsequent years the mintmark was moved to between the R and the D or over the D.

Availability in Mint State: Scarce but not particularly hard to find in lower Mint State grades. 12 to 15 are graded MS-65 or higher.

Availability in circulated grades: 1,200 to 1,400 One of the scarcer issues, a key in the early series. In high circulated grades these are rare.

Detail of the Type I Reverse.

	Cert	Avg	%MS	G-4	VG-8	F-12	VF-20	EF-40	AU-50	MS-60	MS-63	MS-65
1892-S, Type I	134	48.0	49%	$30	$50	$80	$130	$200	$300	$475	$1,150	$4,000

VARIETY: *1892-S, Strongly Doubled Mintmark (FS-25-1892S-501).* The mintmark on this variety is doubled strongly to the north. 60 to 80 are known, mostly in lower grades.

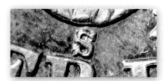

1892-S Barber Quarter, Type II Reverse

1892-S, Type II Reverse • Circulation-Strike Mintage: Part of 964,079.

Commentary: Quality varies. Be on the lookout for a sharp example.

Availability in Mint State: Grades such as MS-63 and 64 are more readily available than are gems but in an absolute basis are scarce; 15 to 20 are graded MS-65 or higher.

Availability in circulated grades: 1,600 to 2,000. One of the scarcer issues. In high circulated grades such coins are rare in proportion to the demand for them.

Notes: A few of these were rolled out as souvenirs at the World's Columbian Exposition.

Detail of the Type II Reverse.

	Cert	Avg	%MS	G-4	VG-8	F-12	VF-20	EF-40	AU-50	MS-60	MS-63	MS-65
1892-S, Type II	134	48.0	49%	$30	$50	$80	$130	$200	$300	$475	$1,150	$4,000

1893 Barber Quarter

1893 • **Circulation-Strike Mintage:** 5,444,023.

Commentary: Usually well struck.

Availability in Mint State: Readily available in lower Mint State grades. An estimated 100 to 120 are graded MS-65 or finer.

Availability in circulated grades: 10,000 to 12,000.

	Cert	Avg	%MS	G-4	VG-8	F-12	VF-20	EF-40	AU-50	MS-60	MS-63	MS-65
1893	330	57.7	68%	$10	$12	$26	$45	$75	$130	$235	$340	$1,000

1893, Proof • **Proof Mintage:** 792.

Availability: *PF-60 to 64: 425 to 525; PF-65 or better: 100 to 120.*

	Cert	Avg	%MS	PF-60	PF-63	PF-65
1893, Proof	299	65.0		$350	$650	$1,250

1893-O Barber Quarter

1893-O • **Circulation-Strike Mintage:** 3,396,000.

Commentary: Average quality is the rule, not the exception, for New Orleans quarters.

Availability in Mint State: Many exist in grades MS-60 to 64. An estimated 75 to 90 are graded MS-65 or higher.

Availability in circulated grades: 12,000 to 14,000.

	Cert	Avg	%MS	G-4	VG-8	F-12	VF-20	EF-40	AU-50	MS-60	MS-63	MS-65
1893-O	215	56.6	61%	$10	$14	$30	$60	$110	$170	$275	$400	$1,500

1893-S Barber Quarter

1893-S • Circulation-Strike Mintage: 1,454,535.

Commentary: In Ed. Frossard's June 1894 sale of the William M. Friesner Collection two 1893-S quarters were offered, one with the S mintmark over D and the other with the S between R and D—a very early listing of mintmark positions.

Availability in Mint State: For some reason not known today, the 1893-S in any Mint State grade is elusive. An estimated 45 to 55 are graded MS-65 or higher.

Availability in circulated grades: 4,000 to 5,000.

	Cert	Avg	%MS	G-4	VG-8	F-12	VF-20	EF-40	AU-50	MS-60	MS-63	MS-65
1893-S	103	49.2	57%	$20	$35	$60	$110	$175	$300	$425	$900	$5,000

1894 Barber Quarter

1894 • Circulation-Strike Mintage: 3,432,000.

Commentary: Quality varies.

Availability in Mint State: Easier to find in lower grades. An estimated 80 to 95 are graded MS-65 or higher.

Availability in circulated grades: 12,000 to 15,000.

	Cert	Avg	%MS	G-4	VG-8	F-12	VF-20	EF-40	AU-50	MS-60	MS-63	MS-65
1894	188	57.4	71%	$10	$12	$35	$50	$95	$150	$240	$350	$1,050

1894, Proof • Proof Mintage: 972.

Availability: *PF-60 to 64: 600 to 700; PF-65 or better: 80 to 95.*

	Cert	Avg	%MS	PF-60	PF-63	PF-65
1894, Proof	338	64.7		$350	$650	$1,250

1894-O Barber Quarter

1894-O • **Circulation-Strike Mintage:** 2,852,000.

Availability in Mint State: Not common, in lower Mint State grades, but readily available in proportion to the number of specialists seeking them. An estimated 60 to 70 are graded MS-65 or higher.

Availability in circulated grades: 6,000 to 8,000.

	Cert	Avg	%MS	G-4	VG-8	F-12	VF-20	EF-40	AU-50	MS-60	MS-63	MS-65
1894-O	156	54.8	65%	$10	$20	$45	$70	$130	$230	$325	$525	$1,800

1894-S Barber Quarter

1894-S • **Circulation-Strike Mintage:** 2,648,821.

Availability in Mint State: Same comment as preceding. An estimated 50 to 60 are graded MS-65 or higher.

Availability in circulated grades: 2,000 to 2,500.

	Cert	Avg	%MS	G-4	VG-8	F-12	VF-20	EF-40	AU-50	MS-60	MS-63	MS-65
1894-S	209	58.0	72%	$10	$15	$40	$60	$120	$210	$325	$525	$1,800

1895 Barber Quarter

1895 • **Circulation-Strike Mintage:** 4,440,000.

Commentary: Average strikes are the rule, but sharp examples can be found.

Availability in Mint State: Easy to find in lesser Mint State grades. The number of people building a set of Barber quarters in MS-63 or higher grades is not large at any given time, so prices rarity-for-rarity across the board are much less than in the successor Standing Liberty quarter series of 1916–1930. An estimated 100 to 120 are graded MS-65 or higher.

Availability in circulated grades: 15,000 to 20,000.

	Cert	Avg	%MS	G-4	VG-8	F-12	VF-20	EF-40	AU-50	MS-60	MS-63	MS-65
1895	237	55.4	68%	$10	$14	$30	$45	$80	$140	$250	$450	$1,250

1895, Proof • **Proof Mintage:** 880.

Availability: *PF-60 to 64: 500 to 600; PF-65 or better: 65 to 80.*

	Cert	Avg	%MS	PF-60	PF-63	PF-65
1895, Proof	274	65.0		$350	$650	$1,250

1895-O Barber Quarter

1895-O • **Circulation-Strike Mintage:** 2,816,000.

Commentary: Often weak in areas.

Availability in Mint State: David Lawrence considered this to be one of 17 issues considered to be "very scarce" in any Mint State category. MS-63 and 64 coins are more readily available but are not easy to find. An estimated 30 to 35 are graded MS-65 or higher. At the gem level the 1895-O is among the rarer Barber quarters despite its generous mintage.

Availability in circulated grades: 6,000 to 8,000.

	Cert	Avg	%MS	G-4	VG-8	F-12	VF-20	EF-40	AU-50	MS-60	MS-63	MS-65
1895-O	125	52.1	55%	$12	$20	$50	$70	$140	$230	$400	$900	$2,000

1895-S Barber Quarter

1895-S • **Circulation-Strike Mintage:** 1,764,681.

Commentary: Some from relapped dies are highly prooflike.

Availability in Mint State: MS-63 and 64 coins are available as an alternative to the hard-to-find and expensive gem pieces. As noted earlier, with cherrypicking it is possible to find certified MS-64 coins that are more attractive and more desirable (in my opinion) than graded MS-65 quarters with a so-so appearance. Only an estimated 27 to 32 are graded MS-65 or higher. One of the rarer Barber quarters at the gem level, surprisingly so in view of the generous mintage.

Availability in circulated grades: 5,000 to 7,000.

	Cert	Avg	%MS	G-4	VG-8	F-12	VF-20	EF-40	AU-50	MS-60	MS-63	MS-65
1895-S	121	46.9	46%	$20	$32	$70	$120	$170	$275	$420	$900	$2,500

VARIETY: *1895-S, Large S Over Small S (FS-Unlisted).* The Eliasberg coin description: "On the reverse the S is sharply doubled, with a 'ghost S,' slightly smaller in size, appearing to the left of the larger S, the latter being centered over the upright of the D in DOLLAR. Quite possibly a mintmark punch one size too small was at first used, then corrected." This variety can be found with some looking, and is often cherrypicked without paying a premium price.

1896 Barber Quarter

1896 • Circulation-Strike Mintage: 3,874,000.

Availability in Mint State: Lower-level Mint State coins are easy to find. An estimated 100 to 120 are graded MS-65 or higher.

Availability in circulated grades: 15,000 to 20,000.

	Cert	Avg	%MS	G-4	VG-8	F-12	VF-20	EF-40	AU-50	MS-60	MS-63	MS-65
1896	209	56.2	74%	$10	$14	$30	$45	$80	$135	$250	$325	$875

1896, Proof • Proof Mintage: 762.

Availability: *PF-60 to 64: 400 to 500; PF-65 or better: 70 to 80.*

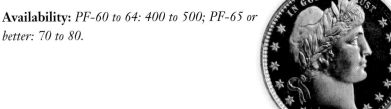

	Cert	Avg	%MS	PF-60	PF-63	PF-65
1896, Proof	325	65.4		$350	$650	$1,250

1896-O Barber Quarter

1896-O • Circulation-Strike Mintage: 1,484,000.

Commentary: This coin often comes very softly struck, and many have mushy denticles. Well-struck coins are scarce. David Lawrence commented that the 1896-O is the first of the New Orleans Mint Barber quarters that is truly scarce in all grades.

Availability in Mint State: After the 1901-S David Lawrence considered this to be one of the six next rarest Barber quarters in various Mint State levels. Choice MS-63 and 64 coins are special. An estimated 25 to 30 are graded MS-65 or higher. Such coins are few and far between in the marketplace.

Availability in circulated grades: 3,000 to 4,000.

	Cert	Avg	%MS	G-4	VG-8	F-12	VF-20	EF-40	AU-50	MS-60	MS-63	MS-65
1896-O	182	33.2	29%	$55	$85	$200	$320	$550	$800	$1,000	$1,500	$6,000

1896-S Barber Quarter

1896-S • **Circulation-Strike Mintage:** 188,039.

Availability in Mint State: Any Mint State coin from 60 up is rare and important. After the 1901-S David Lawrence considered this to be one of the six next rarest Barber quarters in various Mint State levels. An estimated 10 to 15 are graded MS-65 or higher, reflecting that only a few specialized collections have ever included one. At the gem level the 1896-S has always been a rarity. David Lawrence commented to the writer in 1997 after viewing the Eliasberg coin: "I have sold three gem 1901-S quarters, but not a single 1896-S higher than MS-64! I have only seen one MS-65 offered, and it had a large spot on the reverse. The 1896-S is highly underrated in MS-65 or higher grades. Recall that your Norweb Collection coin graded MS-64."

Availability in circulated grades: 1,600 to 1,800. These are rarer than the lower-mintage 1901-S in terms of certified coins, but among "raw" coins the 1896-S is more often found.[68] David Lawrence considered this to be one the five hardest to find quarters in Extremely Fine and About Uncirculated grades. While the 1896-S is rarer than 1901-S and 1913-S at the gem level, in all circulated grades, it is the number-3 coin of the Big 3 (i.e., it is the most widely available of the three).

	Cert	Avg	%MS	G-4	VG-8	F-12	VF-20	EF-40	AU-50	MS-60	MS-63	MS-65
1896-S	514	11.3	6%	$700	$1,500	$2,400	$4,000	$5,250	$7,000	$10,000	$15,000	$45,000

1897 Barber Quarter

1897 • **Circulation-Strike Mintage:** 8,140,000.

Commentary: Usually well struck. Typically, Mint State coins have good eye appeal.

Availability in Mint State: Many exist from MS-60 to 64. An estimated 100 to 120 are graded MS-65 or higher, fewer than might be estimated from the mintage. Collectors of the era nearly all collected by date, and a Proof 1897 was the usual choice.

Availability in circulated grades: 30,000 to 35,000.

	Cert	Avg	%MS	G-4	VG-8	F-12	VF-20	EF-40	AU-50	MS-60	MS-63	MS-65
1897	298	55.7	67%	$9	$14	$26	$40	$70	$120	$240	$350	$800

1897, Proof • **Proof Mintage:** 731.

Availability: *PF-60 to 64: 400 to 500; PF-65 or better: 70 to 85.*

	Cert	Avg	%MS	PF-60	PF-63	PF-65
1897, Proof	272	64.8		$350	$650	$1,250

1897-O Barber Quarter

1897-O • **Circulation-Strike Mintage:** 1,414,800.

Commentary: Usually with moderate lightness of strike on the right side of the reverse at the upper right of the shield and adjacent wing and, more pronounced, on the eagle's talons.

Availability in Mint State: An estimated 50 to 60 are graded MS-65 or higher. A key issue at this level.

Availability in circulated grades: 4,000 to 5,000. In circulated grades from Very Fine and up, it is almost as hard to find as the better-known 1897-S.

	Cert	Avg	%MS	G-4	VG-8	F-12	VF-20	EF-40	AU-50	MS-60	MS-63	MS-65
1897-O	144	33.1	29%	$40	$65	$180	$340	$385	$600	$850	$1,750	$3,000

1897-S Barber Quarter

1897-S • **Circulation-Strike Mintage:** 542,229.

Commentary: Usually well struck. Mint State coins usually have good eye appeal. This is the last year in the Barber quarter series in which some branch-mint coins have the mintmark over the D in DOLLAR. All but one reverse die had the mintmark far to the right,

over the D in DOLLAR. The variety from the one reverse with the mintmark between the R and D (known as the "center mintmark") is very scarce and highly collected by knowledgeable collectors, and generally is offered with a substantial premium by those who recognize it.[69]

Availability in Mint State: After the 1901-S David Lawrence considered this to be one of the six next rarest Barber quarters in various Mint State levels. An estimated 60 to 70 are graded MS-65 or higher.

Availability in circulated grades: 2,000 to 2,500. David Lawrence considered this to be one of the five hardest-to-find quarters in About Uncirculated grades.

	Cert	Avg	%MS	G-4	VG-8	F-12	VF-20	EF-40	AU-50	MS-60	MS-63	MS-65
1897-S	247	22.5	19%	$125	$150	$300	$550	$825	$1,000	$1,600	$2,200	$6,500

1898 Barber Quarter

1898 • Circulation-Strike Mintage: 11,100,000.

Commentary: Usually well struck.

Availability in Mint State: Lower-level Mint State coins are common in relation to the demand for them. An estimated 150 to 180 are graded MS-65 or higher.

Availability in circulated grades: 30,000 to 35,000. Most are AG-3 or G-4, although higher circulated grades are easy to find.

	Cert	Avg	%MS	G-4	VG-8	F-12	VF-20	EF-40	AU-50	MS-60	MS-63	MS-65
1898	388	52.4	60%	$9	$10	$26	$45	$70	$125	$225	$350	$800

1898, Proof • Proof Mintage: 735.

Availability: *PF-60 to 64: 400 to 500; PF-65 or better: 60 to 70.*

	Cert	Avg	%MS	PF-60	PF-63	PF-65
1898, Proof	319	65.6		$350	$650	$1,250

1898-O Barber Quarter

1898-O • Circulation-Strike Mintage: 1,868,000.

Commentary: Usually with some lightness on the right side of the reverse.

Availability in Mint State: As is true of so many Barber silver coins, advanced collectors with well-fortified bank accounts usually settle for an MS-63 or 64. David Lawrence suggested that in Mint State the 1898-O is rarer than the 1896-O, and, who knows, it may be. Estimating rarity is hard to do, and ideas change. An estimated 30 to 35 are graded MS-65 or higher.

Availability in circulated grades: 4,000 to 5,000. Very hard to find in Extremely Fine and About Uncirculated grades.

	Cert	Avg	%MS	G-4	VG-8	F-12	VF-20	EF-40	AU-50	MS-60	MS-63	MS-65
1898-O	89	45.8	46%	$15	$28	$70	$140	$300	$390	$625	$1,500	$6,000

1898-S Barber Quarter

1898-S • **Circulation-Strike Mintage:** 1,020,592.

Commentary: Usually well struck, some with exceptional eye appeal. Rarely prooflike. As noted above, some or most of this mintage was shipped to the Philippine Islands after the Spanish-American War ended in the summer of the year. As a result such quarters were scarce in domestic circulation.

Availability in Mint State: Surprise! In connection with reviewing the Eliasberg coins David Lawrence commented that the 1898-S is "truly scarce in Mint State as most, if not all, of the mintage went to the Philippines, and coins were not saved in high grades." He considered this to be one of the six next rarest Barber quarters in various Mint State levels from MS-60 upward, not including the 1901-S which is rarer. John Frost commented:

> From my personal experience 1898-S in Mint State comes nice, with most examples offered being MS-64 and higher, and thus resulting in a higher percentage of gems than normally expected. There are very few low Mint State grade examples. An additional problem is that many, even most of the certified examples in MS-60 to 62 are not Mint State at all but would be considered by experienced specialists to be AU-58s at best. I've seen several cleaned AU coins in major service holders calling them MS-61 and 62. Like the 1904-S Barber half, this issue is considerably rarer in true Mint State than the population reports would have you believe. In his book David Lawrence called the 1898-S in any Mint State grade the "best kept secret in the Barber quarter series" and I agree. After passing on three obviously not-new "Mint State" slabbed examples, I paid quadruple bid for a raw MS-62 in an old R.M. Smythe auction and thought I stole it. Knowledgeable collectors know this coin's true rarity, and if they cannot afford one of the occasionally-offered gems, they will pay through the nose to get a lower grade, but still actually a Mint State example.[70]

Only an estimated 10 to 15 are graded MS-65 or higher.

Availability in circulated grades: 2,000 to 2,500. Many Very Fine and Extremely Fine coins are often cleaned. Many such pieces were repatriated from the Philippines.

	Cert	Avg	%MS	G-4	VG-8	F-12	VF-20	EF-40	AU-50	MS-60	MS-63	MS-65
1898-S	78	51.3	49%	$11	$25	$40	$55	$100	$200	$400	$1,400	$6,500

1899 Barber Quarter

1899 • **Circulation-Strike Mintage:** 12,624,000.

Commentary: Usually well struck. This is the largest circulation-strike mintage in the Barber quarter series, edging 1902 by a small margin. The same situation occurred for half dollars.

Availability in Mint State: Common in lower Mint State levels in relation to the number of collectors seeking such pieces. An estimated 125 to 140 are graded MS-65 or higher.

Availability in circulated grades: 50,000 to 60,000. Most are AG-3 or G-4, sometimes Very Good.

	Cert	Avg	%MS	G-4	VG-8	F-12	VF-20	EF-40	AU-50	MS-60	MS-63	MS-65
1899	408	50.5	56%	$9	$10	$26	$45	$75	$125	$240	$375	$800

1899, Proof • Proof Mintage: 846.

Availability: *PF-60 to 64: 500 to 600; PF-65 or better: 60 to 70.*

	Cert	Avg	%MS	PF-60	PF-63	PF-65
1899, Proof	195	64.9		$350	$650	$1,250

VARIETY: *1899, Doubled Die Reverse (FS-25-1899-901).* Strong doubling is seen at QUARTER DOLLAR and the arrows; elsewhere, the strength of the doubling varies. This very rare variety is thought to be the most prominent doubled die in the entire Barber series.[71]

1899-O Barber Quarter

1899-O • Circulation-Strike Mintage: 2,644,000.

Commentary: Usually well struck, rare for a New Orleans quarter of the decade. There are exceptions, however.

Availability in Mint State: Lower-level Mint State coins are easy enough to find. An estimated 40 to 50 are graded MS-65 or higher.

Availability in circulated grades: 10,000 to 12,000.

	Cert	Avg	%MS	G-4	VG-8	F-12	VF-20	EF-40	AU-50	MS-60	MS-63	MS-65
1899-O	108	55.2	58%	$11	$18	$35	$70	$120	$260	$400	$900	$2,750

1899-S Barber Quarter

1899-S • Circulation-Strike Mintage: 708,000.

Commentary: Usually well struck. Some high-grade pieces are prooflike. Much of this coinage was shipped to the Philippine Islands for circulation there.

Availability in Mint State: David Lawrence considered this to be one of 17 issues considered to be "very scarce" in any Mint State category. An estimated 60 to 70 are graded MS-65 or higher.

Availability in circulated grades: 1,500 to 1,800. Occasionally repatriated coins from the Philippines are found in Very Fine or so grade, cleaned, but not as often as for 1898-S. Nice Extremely Fine and About Uncirculated coins are seldom seen.

	Cert	Avg	%MS	G-4	VG-8	F-12	VF-20	EF-40	AU-50	MS-60	MS-63	MS-65
1899-S	59	53.3	47%	$27	$40	$95	$110	$140	$270	$425	$1,500	$4,500

1900 Barber Quarter

1900 • **Circulation-Strike Mintage:** 10,016,000.

Commentary: Usually well struck. All Proofs and a small percentage of circulation strikes are from hubs I/II. Most circulation strikes are II/III.[72]

Availability in Mint State: Lower-level Mint State coins are common. An estimated 150 to 180 are graded MS-65 or higher.

Availability in circulated grades: 50,000 to 60,000. Most are G-4.

	Cert	Avg	%MS	G-4	VG-8	F-12	VF-20	EF-40	AU-50	MS-60	MS-63	MS-65
1900	308	56.8	71%	$9	$10	$26	$45	$75	$125	$240	$375	$1,200

1900, Proof • **Proof Mintage:** 912.

Availability: Type I Obverse Hub, Type II Reverse Hub. *PF-60 to 64: 450 to 600; PF-65 or better: 65 to 80.*

	Cert	Avg	%MS	PF-60	PF-63	PF-65
1900, Proof	267	64.8		$350	$650	$1,250

1900-O Barber Quarter

1900-O • **Circulation-Strike Mintage:** 3,416,000.

Commentary: Usually lightly struck on the right side of the reverse. Exceptions can be found and are elusive. I/II and II/II hub combinations are standard.

Availability in Mint State: Easy enough to find in lower Mint State grades. An estimated 60 to 70 are graded MS-65 or higher.

Availability in circulated grades: 20,000 to 25,000. Most are G-4.

	Cert	Avg	%MS	G-4	VG-8	F-12	VF-20	EF-40	AU-50	MS-60	MS-63	MS-65
1900-O	115	51.1	55%	$12	$26	$65	$110	$150	$310	$525	$750	$3,250

1900-S Barber Quarter

1900-S • **Circulation-Strike Mintage:** 1,858,585.

Commentary: Usually sharply struck. Rarely somewhat prooflike. I/II and II/II hub combinations are standard.

Availability in Mint State: David Lawrence considered this to be one of 17 issues considered to be "very scarce" in any Mint State category. An estimated 45 to 55 are graded MS-65 or higher.

Availability in circulated grades: 9,000 to 14,000. Most are G-4. Nice Very Fine and Extremely Fine coins can be found with looking, but original-surface About Uncirculated coins are very difficult to locate.

	Cert	Avg	%MS	G-4	VG-8	F-12	VF-20	EF-40	AU-50	MS-60	MS-63	MS-65
1900-S	132	52.5	31%	$10	$15	$35	$55	$80	$130	$350	$1,000	$3,000

1901 Barber Quarter

1901 • **Circulation-Strike Mintage:** 8,892,000.

Commentary: Obverse Hub II from this year forward.

Availability in Mint State: Lower-level Mint State coins are plentiful. An estimated 100 to 120 are graded MS-65 or higher.

Availability in circulated grades: 50,000 to 60,000. Most are G-4. A slightly better Philadelphia coin in Very Good and higher grades.

	Cert	Avg	%MS	G-4	VG-8	F-12	VF-20	EF-40	AU-50	MS-60	MS-63	MS-65
1901	342	46.7	54%	$9	$10	$26	$45	$80	$135	$240	$375	$900

1901, Proof • **Proof Mintage:** 813.

Availability: *PF-60 to 64: 290 to 340; PF-65 or better: 60 to 70.*

	Cert	Avg	%MS	PF-60	PF-63	PF-65
1901, Proof	255	64.9		$350	$650	$1,250

1901-O Barber Quarter

1901-O • **Circulation-Strike Mintage:** 1,612,000.

Availability in Mint State: David Lawrence considered this to be one of 17 issues that are "very scarce" in any Mint State category. The 1901-O is another Barber quarter rarity in gem preservation. Only 30 to 35 are estimated to exist graded MS-65 or higher.

Availability in circulated grades: 6,000 to 7,500. Most are G-4. This issue is underrated in higher circulated grades, and Very Fine to About Uncirculated coins are very scarce. This coin is often one of the last issues a collector needs to complete a set, excluding the 1896-S, 1901-S, and 1913-S.[73]

	Cert	Avg	%MS	G-4	VG-8	F-12	VF-20	EF-40	AU-50	MS-60	MS-63	MS-65
1901-O	87	31.0	21%	$40	$60	$140	$275	$550	$750	$950	$2,250	$6,750

1901-S Barber Quarter

1901-S • **Circulation-Strike Mintage:** 72,664.

Commentary: Mint State 1901-S quarters are, indeed, notable rarities. So far as is known, none were saved in roll or other quantities. The contention that A.C. Gies of Pittsburgh, Pennsylvania, had a roll of this date and also of other Barber quarters has been dismissed for reasons examined in detail (including notes from John J. Ford Jr.) in the book by the writer, *Lost and Found Hoards and Treasures*. In essence, rumors of rolls held by Gies, Pukall, Raymond, and others, and dating before 1909, are simply fantasy. Rolls that were put away by these gentlemen were primarily of lower denominations such as cents and nickels.

The 1901-S is also the most frequently faked Barber coin. Many Good and Very Good coins exist with added mintmarks, so care must be taken. Either try to acquire a certified example or learn the diagnostics of both pairs of dies used to strike this coin.[74]

Availability in Mint State: The 1901-S is the runaway key to the Barber quarter series in terms of demand at all levels. Any Mint State coin from 60 onward is rare. An estimated 8 to 12 are graded MS-65 or higher.

Availability in circulated grades: 1,800 to 2,200. Most are AG-3 and G-4. Well over 1,000 have been certified by PCGS and NGC—many more than for any other quarter in the Barber series. This is because even in G-4 the 1901-S sells for multiple thousands of dollars. While this coin is available in grades up to Very Good, examples in Fine to About Uncirculated are rarely seen. The rarity of 1901-S became widely recognized in the 1930s when for the first time the *Standard Catalogue of United States Coins* listed mintage figures in addition to values. Accordingly, in relation to the mintage a higher percentage of 1901-S quarters survive than do other issues of the era. In terms of actual survivors this is far and away the rarest Barber quarter.

	Cert	Avg	%MS	G-4	VG-8	F-12	VF-20	EF-40	AU-50	MS-60	MS-63	MS-65
1901-S	369	8.0	3%	$4,250	$8,500	$13,500	$20,000	$27,500	$32,500	$40,000	$50,000	$75,000

1902 Barber Quarter

1902 • **Circulation-Strike Mintage:** 12,196,967.

Availability in Mint State: Easy to find in all lower Mint State levels. An estimated 150 to 180 are graded MS-65 or higher.

Availability in circulated grades: 80,000 to 100,000. Most are G-4.

	Cert	Avg	%MS	G-4	VG-8	F-12	VF-20	EF-40	AU-50	MS-60	MS-63	MS-65
1902	330	53.0	56%	$9	$10	$26	$45	$65	$120	$240	$375	$800

1902, Proof • Proof Mintage: 777.

Availability: *PF-60 to 64: 400 to 500; PF-65 or better: 60 to 70.*

	Cert	Avg	%MS	PF-60	PF-63	PF-65
1902, Proof	230	64.3		$350	$650	$1,250

1902-O Barber Quarter

1902-O • **Circulation-Strike Mintage:** 4,748,000.

Commentary: Usually with lightness on the right side of the reverse. Some are sharper than others and thus being patient when looking for one is worthwhile.

Availability in Mint State: David Lawrence considered this to be one of 17 issues that are "very scarce" in any Mint State category. Easily available at lower levels. An estimated 60 to 70 are graded MS-65 or higher.

Availability in circulated grades: 25,000 to 30,000. Most are G-4.

	Cert	Avg	%MS	G-4	VG-8	F-12	VF-20	EF-40	AU-50	MS-60	MS-63	MS-65
1902-O	110	49.7	43%	$10	$16	$50	$85	$140	$225	$475	$1,000	$3,000

1902-S Barber Quarter

1902-S • **Circulation-Strike Mintage:** 1,524,612.

Availability in Mint State: MS-63 and 64 coins form an alternative to MS-65 for a high-level collection. An estimated 55 to 65 are graded MS-65 or higher.

Availability in circulated grades: 6,000 to 7,500. Most are G-4. Coins grading Very Fine to About Uncirculated are more difficult to find than the mintage figure might suggest.

	Cert	Avg	%MS	G-4	VG-8	F-12	VF-20	EF-40	AU-50	MS-60	MS-63	MS-65
1902-S	111	53.1	53%	$14	$22	$55	$90	$160	$240	$500	$700	$3,000

1903 Barber Quarter

1903 • **Circulation-Strike Mintage:** 9,759,309.

Availability in Mint State: Lower-range Mint State coins are easily enough found. An estimated 50 to 60 are graded MS-65 or higher. Amazingly rare considering the very high mintage.

Availability in circulated grades: 60,000 to 80,000. Most are G-4. Among circulated Philadelphia Mint quarters of this era the 1903 is one the scarcer issues Fine or better.

	Cert	Avg	%MS	G-4	VG-8	F-12	VF-20	EF-40	AU-50	MS-60	MS-63	MS-65
1903	142	53.6	54%	$9	$10	$26	$45	$65	$120	$240	$400	$1,650

1903, Proof • **Proof Mintage:** 755.

Availability: *PF-60 to 64: 400 to 500; PF-65 or better: 85 to 100.*

	Cert	Avg	%MS	PF-60	PF-63	PF-65
1903, Proof	286	65.1		$350	$650	$1,250

1903-O Barber Quarter

1903-O • **Circulation-Strike Mintage:** 3,500,000.

Commentary: Usually fairly well struck—an exception among New Orleans quarters.

Availability in Mint State: In MS-63 and 64 grades it is elusive. An estimated 30 to 35 are graded MS-65 or higher.

Availability in circulated grades: 20,000 to 25,000. Most are G-4.

	Cert	Avg	%MS	G-4	VG-8	F-12	VF-20	EF-40	AU-50	MS-60	MS-63	MS-65
1903-O	101	48.6	40%	$10	$12	$40	$60	$120	$275	$425	$900	$3,500

1903-S Barber Quarter

1903-S • Circulation-Strike Mintage: 1,036,000.

Commentary: Usually well struck. Most Mint State coins have excellent eye appeal.

Availability in Mint State: Scarce but quite available in lower Mint State categories. An estimated 70 to 90 are graded MS-65 or higher.

Availability in circulated grades: 5,000 to 6,000. Most are G-4.

	Cert	Avg	%MS	G-4	VG-8	F-12	VF-20	EF-40	AU-50	MS-60	MS-63	MS-65
1903-S	85	56.6	71%	$15	$25	$45	$85	$150	$275	$425	$900	$2,000

1904 Barber Quarter

1904 • Circulation-Strike Mintage: 9,588,143.

Availability in Mint State: Readily available in grades below the gem level. An estimated 70 to 90 are graded MS-65 or higher.

Availability in circulated grades: 60,000 to 80,000. Most are G-4.

	Cert	Avg	%MS	G-4	VG-8	F-12	VF-20	EF-40	AU-50	MS-60	MS-63	MS-65
1904	175	54.2	57%	$9	$10	$26	$45	$70	$120	$240	$375	$1,250

1904, Proof • Proof Mintage: 670.

Availability: *PF-60 to 64: 350 to 450; PF-65 or better: 80 to 95.*

	Cert	Avg	%MS	PF-60	PF-63	PF-65
1904, Proof	264	64.7		$350	$650	$1,250

1904-O Barber Quarter

1904-O • Circulation-Strike Mintage: 2,456,000.

Commentary: In his book, David Lawrence reported that this issue is usually poorly struck and "often with some depression on the face."

Availability in Mint State: Readily available in lower Mint State grades. An estimated 70 to 85 are graded MS-65 or higher.

Availability in circulated grades: 12,000 to 15,000. Most are G-4.

	Cert	Avg	%MS	G-4	VG-8	F-12	VF-20	EF-40	AU-50	MS-60	MS-63	MS-65
1904-O	143	45.5	39%	$30	$40	$85	$150	$240	$450	$700	$1,000	$4,000

1905 Barber Quarter

1905 • Circulation-Strike Mintage: 4,967,523.

Commentary: Usually well struck, but there are scattered exceptions.

Availability in Mint State: Easy to find in any lower Mint State grade desired. An estimated 100 to 120 are graded MS-65 or higher.

Availability in circulated grades: 30,000 to 35,000.

	Cert	Avg	%MS	G-4	VG-8	F-12	VF-20	EF-40	AU-50	MS-60	MS-63	MS-65
1905	223	46.4	52%	$30	$35	$50	$65	$70	$120	$240	$385	$950

1905, Proof • Proof Mintage: 727.

Availability: *PF-60 to 64: 350 to 450; PF-65 or better: 95 to 115.*

	Cert	Avg	%MS	PF-60	PF-63	PF-65
1905, Proof	248	64.6		$350	$650	$1,250

1905-O Barber Quarter

1905-O • Circulation-Strike Mintage: 1,230,000.

Commentary: Striking quality varies, but sharp examples can be found.

Availability in Mint State: David Lawrence considered this to be one of 17 issues that are "very scarce" in any Mint State category. An estimated 60 to 70 are graded MS-65 or higher.

Availability in circulated grades: 6,000 to 7,500. Most are G-4. Coins in all grades above Very Good are in great demand, and Extremely Fine and About Uncirculated coins are very scarce.

	Cert	Avg	%MS	G-4	VG-8	F-12	VF-20	EF-40	AU-50	MS-60	MS-63	MS-65
1905-O	101	42.2	44%	$40	$60	$120	$220	$260	$350	$475	$1,200	$4,500

1905-S Barber Quarter

1905-S • Circulation-Strike Mintage: 1,884,000.

Commentary: Usually well struck, but some have lightness in the usual places on the reverse.

Availability in Mint State: David Lawrence considered this to be one of 17 issues that are "very scarce" in any Mint State category. An estimated 45 to 55 are graded MS-65 or higher. A 20th-century rarity despite its high mintage.

Availability in circulated grades: 9,000 to 14,000. Most are G-4.

	Cert	Avg	%MS	G-4	VG-8	F-12	VF-20	EF-40	AU-50	MS-60	MS-63	MS-65
1905-S	121	44.0	40%	$30	$40	$75	$100	$105	$225	$350	$900	$3,500

1906 Barber Quarter

1906 • Circulation-Strike Mintage: 3,655,760.

Availability in Mint State: Readily available in any Mint State grade desired. An estimated 220 to 265 are graded MS-65 or higher.

Availability in circulated grades: 25,000 to 30,000. Most are G-4. Easy to find in any grade desired.

Commentary: Usually well struck, but there are exceptions.

	Cert	Avg	%MS	G-4	VG-8	F-12	VF-20	EF-40	AU-50	MS-60	MS-63	MS-65
1906	205	58.8	79%	$9	$10	$26	$45	$70	$120	$240	$375	$800

1906, Proof • Proof Mintage: 675.

Availability: *PF-60 to 64: 350 to 450; PF-65 or better: 90 to 110.*

	Cert	Avg	%MS	PF-60	PF-63	PF-65
1906, Proof	209	64.9		$350	$650	$1,250

1906-D Barber Quarter

1906-D • **Circulation-Strike Mintage:** 3,280,000.

Commentary: Often weakly struck in areas.

Availability in Mint State: Not hard to find in any desired grade from MS-60 upward. An estimated 75 to 90 are graded MS-65 or higher.

Availability in circulated grades: 20,000 to 25,000. Most are G-4.

Notes: This is the first year of Denver Mint quarters.

	Cert	Avg	%MS	G-4	VG-8	F-12	VF-20	EF-40	AU-50	MS-60	MS-63	MS-65
1906-D	130	59.0	75%	$9	$10	$30	$50	$70	$145	$250	$425	$1,650

1906-O Barber Quarter

1906-O • **Circulation-Strike Mintage:** 2,056,000.

Commentary: On average, the 1906-O is the most weakly struck coin in the series. On the obverse, even About Uncirculated coins may not have a full band under LIBERTY. Usually lightly struck where the upper right of the shield joins the wing and on the eagle's talons—the usual places—but some are sharper than others.

Availability in Mint State: Easy enough to find in any desired Mint State category. An estimated 175 to 200 are graded MS-65 or higher.

Availability in circulated grades: 9,000 to 14,000. Most are G-4. Due to poor striking, finding Very Fine and Extremely Fine coins is a challenge; they often look more worn than they actually are.

	Cert	Avg	%MS	G-4	VG-8	F-12	VF-20	EF-40	AU-50	MS-60	MS-63	MS-65
1906-O	139	60.0	77%	$9	$10	$40	$60	$100	$200	$300	$500	$1,350

1907 Barber Quarter

1907 • **Circulation-Strike Mintage:** 7,132,000.

Commentary: Usually well struck.

Availability in Mint State: Easy to find at all Mint State levels. An estimated 150 to 180 are graded MS-65 or higher.

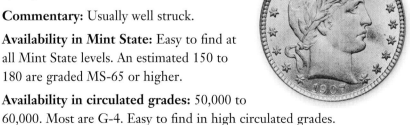

Availability in circulated grades: 50,000 to 60,000. Most are G-4. Easy to find in high circulated grades.

	Cert	Avg	%MS	G-4	VG-8	F-12	VF-20	EF-40	AU-50	MS-60	MS-63	MS-65
1907	392	56.4	65%	$9	$10	$26	$40	$65	$120	$240	$375	$800

1907, Proof • **Proof Mintage:** 575.

Availability: *PF-60 to 64: 250 to 300; PF-65 or better: 40 to 50.* The 1907 and 1915 are the rarest Barber quarters at the gem level.

	Cert	Avg	%MS	PF-60	PF-63	PF-65
1907, Proof	289	65.0		$350	$650	$1,250

1907-D Barber Quarter

1907-D • **Circulation-Strike Mintage:** 2,484,000.

Commentary: Often weak, but sharp coins can be found with some searching. A minor doubled-die obverse exists, with doubling seen in the ribbons to the left of Liberty's neck.

Availability in Mint State: Lower Mint State coins are easy to find. Only an estimated 45 to 55 are graded MS-65 or higher. By all logic the 1907-D with its high mintage should be readily available in gem Mint State, but reality is otherwise.

Availability in circulated grades: 15,000 to 18,000. Most are G-4. Surprisingly elusive in high circulated grades.

	Cert	Avg	%MS	G-4	VG-8	F-12	VF-20	EF-40	AU-50	MS-60	MS-63	MS-65
1907-D	112	54.5	66%	$9	$10	$26	$48	$70	$175	$250	$550	$2,500

1907-O Barber Quarter

1907-O • **Circulation-Strike Mintage:** 4,560,000.

Commentary: David Lawrence noted that the 1907-O was "the poorest struck coin in the series," with some pieces having distortions, scars, and other problems. Moreover, he suggested that the 1907-O is "undervalued in all Mint State grades

and in AU as well." I second this. Does even one sharp coin exist? John Frost commented: "The 1907-O is considered the poorest and most unusually struck coin in the series, versus the 1906-O which is the weakest strike, but without the oddities found on the 1907-O coins, such as 'mumps' (distortions on neck and jaw), scars, etc."[75]

Availability in Mint State: Slightly scarce at lower Mint State levels. An estimated 70 to 85 are graded MS-65 or higher, a low population considering the high mintage.

Availability in circulated grades: 25,000 to 30,000. Most are G-4.

	Cert	Avg	%MS	G-4	VG-8	F-12	VF-20	EF-40	AU-50	MS-60	MS-63	MS-65
1907-O	200	55.2	67%	$9	$10	$26	$45	$70	$135	$275	$400	$1,700

1907-S Barber Quarter

1907-S • Circulation-Strike Mintage: 1,360,000.

Commentary: Usually well struck with a nice appearance.

Availability in Mint State: David Lawrence considered this to be one of 17 issues that are "very scarce" in any Mint State category. An estimated 95 to 115 are graded MS-65 or higher.

Availability in circulated grades: 6,000 to 8,000. Most are G-4. Very difficult to locate in grades above Very Fine.

	Cert	Avg	%MS	G-4	VG-8	F-12	VF-20	EF-40	AU-50	MS-60	MS-63	MS-65
1907-S	74	54.8	72%	$10	$18	$45	$70	$140	$280	$475	$900	$3,250

1908 Barber Quarter

1908 • Circulation-Strike Mintage: 4,232,000.

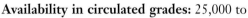

Commentary: Usually sharp.

Availability in Mint State: Easily found in Mint State. An estimated 150 to 180 are graded MS-65 or higher.

Availability in circulated grades: 25,000 to 30,000. Most are G-4. Strangely enough, while Good to Very Fine and also About Uncirculated coins are all extremely common, Extremely Fine coins are surprisingly hard to find. There seems to be no explanation for this oddity.[76]

	Cert	Avg	%MS	G-4	VG-8	F-12	VF-20	EF-40	AU-50	MS-60	MS-63	MS-65
1908	243	58.4	72%	$9	$10	$26	$45	$70	$120	$240	$375	$800

1908, Proof • Proof Mintage: 545.

Availability: *PF-60 to 64: 290 to 340; PF-65 or better: 50 to 60.*

	Cert	Avg	%MS	PF-60	PF-63	PF-65
1908, Proof	189	64.8		$350	$650	$1,250

1908-D Barber Quarter

1908-D • Circulation-Strike Mintage: 5,788,000.

Commentary: Usually fairly well struck.

Availability in Mint State: Readily available at lower Mint State levels. An estimated 100 to 120 are graded MS-65 or higher. Rare in relation to the generous mintage.

Availability in circulated grades: 35,000 to 42,500. Most are G-4. Easy to find in higher circulated grades as well.

	Cert	Avg	%MS	G-4	VG-8	F-12	VF-20	EF-40	AU-50	MS-60	MS-63	MS-65
1908-D	266	51.7	56%	$9	$10	$26	$45	$70	$120	$240	$375	$800

1908-O Barber Quarter

1908-O • Circulation-Strike Mintage: 6,244,000.

Commentary: Usually weak in areas and sometimes with lumps on the neck.

Availability in Mint State: Easily available in grades from MS-60 to 64. An estimated 140 to 170 are graded MS-65 or higher.

Availability in circulated grades: 25,000 to 30,000. Most are G-4.

	Cert	Avg	%MS	G-4	VG-8	F-12	VF-20	EF-40	AU-50	MS-60	MS-63	MS-65
1908-O	254	53.5	68%	$9	$10	$26	$45	$65	$120	$240	$375	$800

1908-S Barber Quarter

1908-S • Circulation-Strike Mintage: 784,000.

Commentary: Usually well struck and quite attractive.

Availability in Mint State: David Lawrence counted this among 17 issues considered to be "very scarce" in any Mint State category. An estimated 50 to 60 are graded MS-65 or higher.

Availability in circulated grades: 4,000 to 5,000. Most are G-4. Very hard to find in Very Fine and higher grades.

	Cert	Avg	%MS	G-4	VG-8	F-12	VF-20	EF-40	AU-50	MS-60	MS-63	MS-65
1908-S	131	46.6	56%	$18	$38	$85	$165	$325	$465	$750	$1,200	$3,500

1909 Barber Quarter

1909 • Circulation-Strike Mintage: 9,268,000.

Commentary: Usually sharp.

Availability in Mint State: Another readily available date. An estimated 175 to 200 are graded MS-65 or higher. Although there are more than enough to supply specialists, it is remarkable that so few exist in relation to the very high mintage.

Availability in circulated grades: 60,000 to 80,000. Most are G-4. Easy to find in higher grades.

	Cert	Avg	%MS	G-4	VG-8	F-12	VF-20	EF-40	AU-50	MS-60	MS-63	MS-65
1909	526	55.7	66%	$9	$10	$26	$45	$65	$120	$240	$375	$800

1909, Proof • **Proof Mintage:** 650.

Availability: *PF-60 to 64: 350 to 450; PF-65 or better: 75 to 90.*

	Cert	Avg	%MS	PF-60	PF-63	PF-65
1909, Proof	271	64.8		$350	$650	$1,250

1909-D Barber Quarter

1909-D • Circulation-Strike Mintage: 5,114,000.

Commentary: Usually well struck.

Availability in Mint State: Easy to find in any desired grade. An estimated 50 to 180 are graded MS-65 or higher.

Availability in circulated grades: 30,000 to 35,000. Most are G-4. Higher-grade circulated coins are common in relation to the demand for them.

	Cert	Avg	%MS	G-4	VG-8	F-12	VF-20	EF-40	AU-50	MS-60	MS-63	MS-65
1909-D	321	49.5	51%	$9	$10	$26	$45	$85	$150	$240	$375	$800

1909-O Barber Quarter

1909-O • Circulation-Strike Mintage: 712,000.

Commentary: The swan song New Orleans quarter is normally found with weakness in the usual places, but there are scattered exceptions that have fairly decent details.

Availability in Mint State: MS-63 and 64 coins can be a compromise for a high-level set if an MS-65 coin cannot be found or is considered to be too expensive. Only an estimated 20 to 24 exist graded MS-65 or higher.

Availability in circulated grades: 4,000 to 5,000. Most are G-4. Coins grading Very Fine to About Uncirculated are seldom seen.

	Cert	Avg	%MS	G-4	VG-8	F-12	VF-20	EF-40	AU-50	MS-60	MS-63	MS-65
1909-O	94	35.9	41%	$50	$175	$500	$1,000	$2,250	$3,500	$4,000	$5,000	$7,500

1909-S Barber Quarter

1909-S • Circulation-Strike Mintage: 1,348,000.

Commentary: Usually sharp.

Availability in Mint State: Readily available. An estimated 100 to 120 are graded MS-65 or higher.

Availability in circulated grades: 25,000 to 30,000. Most are G-4. Scarce in higher circulated grades.

	Cert	Avg	%MS	G-4	VG-8	F-12	VF-20	EF-40	AU-50	MS-60	MS-63	MS-65
1909-S	115	50.0	63%	$9	$10	$35	$55	$90	$185	$285	$725	$1,650

1910 Barber Quarter

1910 • Circulation-Strike Mintage: 2,244,000.

Commentary: Striking varies, but sharp coins can be found.

Availability in Mint State: Another quarter that is easy to find and usually has nice eye appeal. An estimated 150 to 180 are graded MS-65 or higher.

Availability in circulated grades: 12,000 to 15,000. Most are G-4. Higher-grade circulated coins are common.

	Cert	Avg	%MS	G-4	VG-8	F-12	VF-20	EF-40	AU-50	MS-60	MS-63	MS-65
1910	201	55.1	73%	$9	$10	$26	$45	$80	$140	$240	$375	$800

1910, Proof • **Proof Mintage:** 551.

Availability: *PF-60 to 64: 275 to 325; PF-65 or better: 55 to 65.*

	Cert	Avg	%MS	PF-60	PF-63	PF-65
1910, Proof	267	65.1		$350	$650	$1,250

1910-D Barber Quarter

1910-D • **Circulation-Strike Mintage:** 1,500,000.

Commentary: Quality varies. Take time to find a sharp one.

Availability in Mint State: Lower-grade Mint State coins are widely available. An estimated 55 to 65 are graded MS-65 or higher.

Availability in circulated grades: 6,000 to 7,500. Most are G-4.

	Cert	Avg	%MS	G-4	VG-8	F-12	VF-20	EF-40	AU-50	MS-60	MS-63	MS-65
1910-D	130	53.3	61%	$10	$11	$45	$70	$125	$240	$350	$800	$1,650

1911 Barber Quarter

1911 • **Circulation-Strike Mintage:** 3,720,000.

Availability in Mint State: Easy to find. An estimated 180 to 220 are graded MS-65 or higher.

Availability in circulated grades: 20,000 to 25,000. Most are G-4. Common in all grades.

	Cert	Avg	%MS	G-4	VG-8	F-12	VF-20	EF-40	AU-50	MS-60	MS-63	MS-65
1911	296	58.5	73%	$9	$10	$26	$45	$70	$125	$240	$375	$800

1911, Proof • **Proof Mintage:** 543.

Availability: *PF-60 to 64: 280 to 330; PF-65 or better: 70 to 85.*

	Cert	Avg	%MS	PF-60	PF-63	PF-65
1911, Proof	236	65.3		$350	$650	$1,250

1911-D Barber Quarter

1911-D • Circulation-Strike Mintage: 933,600.

Availability in Mint State: David Lawrence regarded this as one of 17 issues considered to be "very scarce" in any Mint State category. An estimated 20 to 24 are graded MS-65 or higher. At the gem level this is a major rarity.

Availability in circulated grades: 4,000 to 5,000. Most are G-4. Common in low grades. In Fine or better preservation 1911-D quarters are surprisingly hard to find.

	Cert	Avg	%MS	G-4	VG-8	F-12	VF-20	EF-40	AU-50	MS-60	MS-63	MS-65
1911-D	119	41.7	41%	$30	$40	$150	$300	$400	$600	$850	$1,200	$4,250

1911-S Barber Quarter

1911-S • Circulation-Strike Mintage: 988,000.

Commentary: Usually sharp.

Availability in Mint State: Plentiful in relation to the demand for them. An estimated 200 to 260 are graded MS-65 or higher. It is an interesting pursuit to study the availability of gem coins in relation to their mintages. There are absolutely no rules!

Availability in circulated grades: 4,000 to 5,000. Most are G-4. High-grade coins are elusive, but not as much so as for the 1911-D.

	Cert	Avg	%MS	G-4	VG-8	F-12	VF-20	EF-40	AU-50	MS-60	MS-63	MS-65
1911-S	170	58.7	76%	$9	$10	$55	$85	$165	$280	$375	$775	$1,500

1912 Barber Quarter

1912 • Circulation-Strike Mintage: 4,400,000.

Commentary: Quality varies, but sharp coins can be found.

Availability in Mint State: One of the more readily available issues in any Mint State level. An estimated 300 to 400 are graded MS-65 or higher.

Availability in circulated grades: 25,000 to 35,000. Most are G-4. Common in higher grades.

	Cert	Avg	%MS	G-4	VG-8	F-12	VF-20	EF-40	AU-50	MS-60	MS-63	MS-65
1912	447	57.7	76%	$9	$10	$26	$45	$70	$120	$240	$375	$800

1912, Proof • **Proof Mintage:** 700.

Availability: *PF-60 to 64: 500 to 550; PF-65 or better: 65 to 80.*

	Cert	Avg	%MS	PF-60	PF-63	PF-65
1912, Proof	213	64.6		$350	$650	$1,250

1912-S Barber Quarter

1912-S • **Circulation-Strike Mintage:** 708,000.

Commentary: Quality varies, as is so often the case with late-date Barber quarters. Careful searching will yield a sharp one.

Availability in Mint State: David Lawrence counted this among 17 issues considered to be "very scarce" in any Mint State category. An estimated 55 to 65 are graded MS-65 or higher.

Availability in circulated grades: 4,000 to 5,000. Most are G-4. Hard to find Very Fine or better.

	Cert	Avg	%MS	G-4	VG-8	F-12	VF-20	EF-40	AU-50	MS-60	MS-63	MS-65
1912-S	107	52.0	64%	$20	$30	$65	$90	$125	$220	$400	$825	$1,750

1913 Barber Quarter

1913 • **Circulation-Strike Mintage:** 484,000.

Commentary: Repeating a theme, this is another Barber quarter for which careful hunting will pay dividends.

Availability in Mint State: Readily available despite its relatively low mintage. An estimated 120 to 140 are graded MS-65 or higher.

Availability in circulated grades: 2,500 to 3,000. Most are G-4. With a circulation-strike mintage the same as that of the famous 1909-S V.D.B. cent, the quarter is much rarer in high circulated grades.[77]

	Cert	Avg	%MS	G-4	VG-8	F-12	VF-20	EF-40	AU-50	MS-60	MS-63	MS-65
1913	137	45.8	47%	$22	$35	$100	$180	$400	$525	$600	$800	$2,250

1913, Proof • **Proof Mintage:** 613.

Availability: *PF-60 to 64: 290 to 340; PF-65 or better: 75 to 90.*

	Cert	Avg	%MS	PF-60	PF-63	PF-65
1913, Proof	246	64.5		$350	$650	$1,250

1913-D Barber Quarter

1913-D • **Circulation-Strike Mintage:** 1,450,800.

Commentary: Often soft on the usual reverse places. Some nice strikes exist, however.

Availability in Mint State: Many nice coins exist. In lower Mint State levels they are plentiful in relation to the demand for them. An estimated 120 to 140 are graded MS-65 or higher.

Availability in circulated grades: 6,000 to 7,500. Most are G-4. Coins grading Very Fine or higher are elusive.

	Cert	Avg	%MS	G-4	VG-8	F-12	VF-20	EF-40	AU-50	MS-60	MS-63	MS-65
1913-D	183	54.0	62%	$12	$15	$35	$60	$85	$175	$275	$400	$1,150

1913-S Barber Quarter

1913-S • **Circulation-Strike Mintage:** 40,000.

Commentary: The 1913-S has a striking peculiarity most people don't know about that can aid in authentication. Every example seems to be unevenly struck, with weakness most easily seen on the left side of the obverse. This is true on coins struck from either of the two pairs of dies used for this issue. On AG-3 and G-4 coins, the left obverse rim will be barely present or absent, while the right rim is strong. This uneven strike is also seen on high-grade coins, although it is less obvious to the unaided eye. If a low-grade purported 1913-S quarter looks evenly struck, approach with caution, as it may be an altered coin with an added mintmark.[78] The 1913-S quarter mintage of 40,000 coins is the lowest for any regular 20th-century circulation-strike silver coin.

Availability in Mint State: Of the three key issues in the Barber quarter series, the 1896-S, 1901-S, and 1913-S, the last is much more readily available in Mint State than are the other two. The reasons for this is not clear. Long-time Pittsburgh collector A.C. Gies is known to have saved bank-wrapped rolls of coins beginning with the year 1901, and from time to time has been cited as the source for most 1913-S Barber quarters surviving today in Mint State. It is believed that most of his rolls were of minor denominations, and there is no record that he or anyone else dispersed a roll quantity of the 1913-S. An estimated 60 to 70 are graded MS-65 or higher.

Availability in circulated grades: 1,000 to 1,200. Most are AG-3 to G-4. Many of these were plucked from circulation in the 1930s, mostly AG-3 and G-4, when collectors took note of the low mintage figure. Nice VG coins are usually available, and occasionally in Fine, but in Very Fine and above, it is a vastly different story. High circulated grades are almost never seen, as apparently very few people saved them once they entered circulation. In fact, there are more Mint state examples known of the 1913-S than Very Fine, Extremely Fine, and About Uncirculated combined. There are likely only a dozen or so known in Extremely Fine, and probably 15-20 known in About Uncirculated.

	Cert	Avg	%MS	G-4	VG-8	F-12	VF-20	EF-40	AU-50	MS-60	MS-63	MS-65
1913-S	549	9.9	8%	$1,650	$2,200	$5,000	$7,000	$9,000	$12,500	$15,000	$18,500	$32,500

1914 Barber Quarter

1914 • **Circulation-Strike Mintage:** 6,244,250.

Commentary: Quality varies. Look for an exception.

Availability in Mint State: One of the more readily available issues. An estimated 300 to 360 are graded MS-65 or higher.

Availability in circulated grades: 45,000 to 55,000. Most are G-4. Easy to find in any grade desired.

	Cert	Avg	%MS	G-4	VG-8	F-12	VF-20	EF-40	AU-50	MS-60	MS-63	MS-65
1914	678	55.2	66%	$9	$10	$22	$40	$65	$120	$240	$375	$800

1914, Proof • **Proof Mintage:** 380.

Availability: *PF-60 to 64: 275 to 325; PF-65 or better: 50 to 60.*

	Cert	Avg	%MS	PF-60	PF-63	PF-65
1914, Proof	203	64.8		$350	$650	$1,250

1914-D Barber Quarter

1914-D • **Circulation-Strike Mintage:** 3,046,000.

Commentary: Quality varies. Take time to find a sharp one.

Availability in Mint State: Easy to find. An estimated 190 to 230 are graded MS-65 or higher.

Availability in circulated grades: 20,000 to 25,000. Most are G-4. Common in higher grades.

	Cert	Avg	%MS	G-4	VG-8	F-12	VF-20	EF-40	AU-50	MS-60	MS-63	MS-65
1914-D	350	55.6	69%	$9	$10	$22	$40	$65	$120	$240	$375	$800

1914-S Barber Quarter

1914-S • **Circulation-Strike Mintage:** 264,000.

Commentary: The mintmark is often filled in and is a hallmark of certain authentic specimens, according to David Lawrence's book. The same writer notes the existence of a slightly repunched date. This must mean a hub shift, as by this time date logotypes were not used.

Availability in Mint State: MS-63 and 64 coins are somewhat scarce. An estimated 50 to 60 are graded MS-65 or higher.

Availability in circulated grades: 1,500 to 2,000. Most are G-4. Fine and Very Fine coins are occasionally found, but higher-grade examples are elusive.

	Cert	Avg	%MS	G-4	VG-8	F-12	VF-20	EF-40	AU-50	MS-60	MS-63	MS-65
1914-S	425	15.8	12%	$125	$180	$375	$550	$825	$975	$1,400	$1,650	$6,500

1915 Barber Quarter

1915 • **Circulation-Strike Mintage:** 3,480,000.

Commentary: Quality varies, but there are quite a few sharp strikes.

Availability in Mint State: One of the more plentiful issues. An estimated 300 to 360 are graded MS-65 or higher.

Availability in circulated grades: 20,000 to 25,000. Most are G-4. Easy to find in any grade desired.

	Cert	Avg	%MS	G-4	VG-8	F-12	VF-20	EF-40	AU-50	MS-60	MS-63	MS-65
1915	497	55.9	72%	$9	$10	$22	$40	$65	$120	$240	$375	$800

1915, Proof • **Proof Mintage:** 450.

Availability: *PF-60 to 64: 275 to 325; PF-65 or better: 40 to 50.* The 1907 and 1915 are the rarest Barber quarters at the gem level.

	Cert	Avg	%MS	PF-60	PF-63	PF-65
1915, Proof	175	64.3		$425	$750	$1,500

1915-D Barber Quarter

1915-D • **Circulation-Strike Mintage:** 3,694,000.

Commentary: Another variety that is often weakly struck, but for which sharp coins can be found.

Availability in Mint State: Plentiful. An estimated 500 to 600 are graded MS-65 or higher. At the gem level this is the second-most-common Barber quarter, but it trails the 1916-D by a long distance.

Availability in circulated grades: 25,000 to 30,000. Most are G-4. Easy to find in any grade desired.

	Cert	Avg	%MS	G-4	VG-8	F-12	VF-20	EF-40	AU-50	MS-60	MS-63	MS-65
1915-D	641	57.8	73%	$9	$10	$22	$40	$70	$120	$240	$375	$800

1915-S Barber Quarter

1915-S • **Circulation-Strike Mintage:** 704,000.

Commentary: David Lawrence commented to the author in 1997: "Most of the Mint State 1915-S quarters I have seen are rather 'ticky-tacky' in appearance and do not have smooth surfaces."

Availability in Mint State: Slightly scarce at the gem level, but easily available otherwise. An estimated 100 to 120 are graded MS-65 or higher.

Availability in circulated grades: 4,000 to 5,000. Most are G-4. Somewhat scarce in higher circulated grades.

	Cert	Avg	%MS	G-4	VG-8	F-12	VF-20	EF-40	AU-50	MS-60	MS-63	MS-65
1915-S	212	50.9	58%	$25	$40	$60	$85	$115	$200	$285	$425	$1,150

1916 Barber Quarter

1916 • **Circulation-Strike Mintage:** 1,788,000.

Commentary: Quality varies, and usually with some lightness on the reverse. Sharp coins can be found, however.

Availability in Mint State: Easy to find. An estimated 250 to 300 are graded MS-65 or higher.

Availability in circulated grades: 9,000 to 14,000. Most are G-4. Higher-grade circulated coins, while a tiny percentage of the overall population, are easily found.

	Cert	Avg	%MS	G-4	VG-8	F-12	VF-20	EF-40	AU-50	MS-60	MS-63	MS-65
1916	454	56.8	70%	$9	$10	$22	$40	$70	$120	$240	$375	$800

1916-D Barber Quarter

1916-D • **Circulation-Strike Mintage:** 6,540,800.

Commentary: Quality varies. Most have areas of lightness on the right side of the reverse.

Availability in Mint State: The most common Barber quarter. An estimated 1,500 to 2,000 are graded MS-65 or higher. At the gem level the 1916-D quarter is the only Barber silver coin with the estimated number of surviving gems crossing the 1,000 line, and by far.[79]

Availability in circulated grades: 50,000 to 60,000. Most are G-4. The most common coin in the entire Barber quarter series.

	Cert	Avg	%MS	G-4	VG-8	F-12	VF-20	EF-40	AU-50	MS-60	MS-63	MS-65
1916-D	1,539	58.8	75%	$9	$10	$22	$40	$70	$120	$240	$375	$800

STANDING LIBERTY QUARTER DOLLARS (1916–1930)

Designer: *Hermon A. MacNeil.* **Weight:** *6.25 grams.* **Composition:** *.900 silver, .100 copper (net weight .18084 oz. pure silver).* **Diameter:** *24.3 mm.* **Edge:** *Reeded.* **Mints:** *Philadelphia, Denver, and San Francisco.*

Variety 1, No Stars Below Eagle (1916–1917)

Mintmark location is on the obverse, at the top left of the date, for both varieties.

Variety 2, Stars Below Eagle (1917–1930)

HISTORY AND BACKGROUND

The relatively short series of Standing Liberty quarters bears little resemblance to the predecessor Barber quarters. When coin collecting became widely popular in America in the mid-1930s, all varieties could be found in circulation. Those of 1916 to 1924, with the date on a pedestal (of which more will be said) were in high grades *except for the date*, which on some coins was worn away! In contrast, those of 1925 and later with the date recessed were all in high grades with the date bold. Certain dates and mints were available in Mint State in roll quantities. Some issues were scarcer than others, but all could be picked from circulation. This was a much different scenario than that for Barber quarters in circulation that averaged AG-3 and G-4, with all elements of the design worn nearly smooth, with hardly any in higher grades.

Although many complaints had been registered about the design of Barber coins, no such adverse commentary attended the introduction of the Standing Liberty quarters. They were admired from the outset.

Today in the early 21st century quarters of this design remain very high on the popularity list.

THE NEW DESIGN

Initiated by President Theodore Roosevelt, American circulating coinage was completely redesigned, starting in 1907 with the $10 gold eagle and $20 double eagle by famous sculptor Augustus Saint-Gaudens. Next followed the $2.50 quarter eagle and $5 half eagle Bela Lyon Pratt in 1908 and the Lincoln cent by Victor D. Brenner in 1909.

Remaining to be redesigned were the dime, quarter, and half dollar. Silver dollars had not been minted since 1904 and replacing the Morgan design was not a matter to be considered. Hundreds of millions of silver dollars remained in Treasury and other vaults, and there was no expectation that additional pieces would ever be minted.

The challenge was to replace Charles E. Barber's disliked Liberty Head design in use on the dime, quarter, and half dollar since 1892.

At the time the New York Numismatic Club was one of the most active of such organizations in America. Beginning in 1909, monthly meetings were held in a private room at Keen's Old English Chop House at 36th Street and Sixth Avenue, New York City, where a fine dinner was followed by discussions, programs, and exchanges of information. On the evening of December 11, 1914, action was taken to encourage the Mint to create new designs. Thomas L. Elder, a member of the executive committee, had severely criticized the existing issues. Members agreed, and William H. Woodin, a long-time collector who controlled the American Car and Foundry Company, was named as chairman. Elder reinforced his stance in "Some Phases and Needs of American Numismatics," a paper delivered in January to the American Numismatic Society, noting in part:

> I would strongly recommend also that all the numismatic societies interest themselves in a movement to improve the present United States silver coinage of the regular issues. These include the half dollar, quarter, and dime, a type adopted in 1892. The designs may be changed without act of Congress in 1917, when the 25 years of issue shall have elapsed. These coins are almost unparalleled in modern issues for ugliness, and they are in no way indicative of the power and progress of the United States, in fact they should be considered unacceptable to the smallest islands of the seas. In this movement art alliances and sculptor societies should lend their aid and influence…

Dissatisfaction with the current Barber coins was fully realized by the Treasury Department. Mint Director Robert W. Woolley met with the Commission of Fine Arts, the body that reviewed designs and made non-binding recommendations, in New York City on December 5 and 6, 1915. By that time artists at the Philadelphia Mint had been working on motifs for about a half year. New designs prepared by Charles E. Barber were rejected early in the meeting. It was decided that Adolph A. Weinman and Hermon A. MacNeil be invited to submit motifs. A third sculptor was desired, and Albin Polasek was chosen. On December 27 Woolley met with the three sculptors at the New York Assay Office to discuss the project and determine their interest. The answers were affirmative. Models were to be submitted by April 15, 1916.[80]

Success attended these efforts. In July 1916 *The Numismatist* included this:

> On May 30 Secretary [William G.] McAdoo announced the adoption of the new designs for the subsidiary silver coins. They will probably be issued soon after July 1, the beginning of the new fiscal year. The half dollar and dime were designed by Adolph A. Weinman, and the quarter dollar by Hermon A. MacNeil. Several sculptors were commissioned to submit sets of sketch models. From more than 50 models Secretary McAdoo and Mr. Woolley, director of the Mint, selected three sets. Not only will there be a change of design, but each of the three denominations will have a different obverse and reverse. This idea was suggested by Mr. Woolley . . .

The design of the 25-cent piece is intended to typify the awakening of the country to its own protection. Liberty, a full figure, is shown stepping toward the country's gateway, bearing upraised a shield from which the covering is being drawn. The right hand bears an olive branch of peace. Above the head is the word "Liberty" and below the feet "1916." The reverse bears a figure of an eagle in full flight, wings extended, and the inscriptions "United States of America" and "E Pluribus Unum." Both the half dollar and quarter bear the phrase "In God We Trust" . . .

Collectors will await with deep interest the appearance of the new coins.

Hermon A. MacNeil in his studio.
(*Mehl's Numismatic Monthly*, March 1917)

Mercury dimes were released into circulation in October 1916. In December the Treasury Department sent samples of the three new coins to the American Numismatic Society, where they were placed on exhibit. The new quarters and half dollars were released in January 1917. While the popular press paid much attention to the new dimes, the later-released quarter and half dollar were not as newsworthy as novelties, and fewer articles appeared.

Of the three new silver coin designs of 1916, arrangements concerning Hermon A. MacNeil's Standing Liberty quarter were the most complex. Most numismatists agree that the sculptor's original design (shown below) was more beautiful than its modification done by the Engraving Department at the Mint without MacNeil's knowledge or consent.

The end result, nonetheless, was a quarter dollar that numismatists have admired since it was first made. An excellent study of these coins can be found in J.H. Cline's *Standing Liberty Quarters*, which has appeared in multiple editions over the years. Of the three new designs for 1916, Standing Liberty quarters were made for the shortest time—only until 1930, and with no coinage in 1922. Today a collection of such pieces is beautiful to behold.

Thus begins the story of the series.

Hermon Atkins MacNeil

Hermon Atkins MacNeil, born in Everett, Massachusetts on February 27, 1866, became an accomplished sculptor. He is best remembered today as the creator of the Standing Liberty quarter dollar. After his elementary and high school education he pursued his career as a designer and sculptor at the Normal Art School in Boston. MacNeil taught industrial art at Cornell University from 1886 to 1889. He then went to Europe worked with Henri Chapu at the Académie Julian and with Alexandre Fulguière at the École des Beaux-Arts in Paris. After returning to America in 1891 he settled in Chicago to assist Philip Martiny for a year by making sketches for architectural and other art for the World's Columbian Exposition. MacNeil also opened a studio and taught at the Chicago Art Institute. Afterward he traveled to the Southwest to study Indian culture. This catalyzed an interest that inspired him to feature Native Americans in a number of works, including a medal for the Society of Medalists based on a dance he had witnessed in northern Arizona.

MacNeil's *Hopi Prayer for Rain* medal, 1931, the third in the Society of Medalists series.

His wife, Carol (née Brooks), was a talented artist and sculptor in her own right, having studied under her artist father and also in Paris and in America, under sculptor Lorado Taft. They married on Christmas Day, 1895. The union produced two children. Carol was well known for her work and received many commissions and awards. She died in 1944.

Hermon A. MacNeil worked in Rome from 1896 to 1900 as one of the first two winners of the Rinehart Scholarship in Sculpture. He then went to New York, where he opened a studio. Beginning with the *McKinley Memorial* in 1907 (depicted on the reverse of the 1916 and 1917 commemorative gold dollars) he received many commissions for memorials and statuary groups. In 1916 he had studios at 160 Fifth Avenue (on the roof with natural lighting, where he designed the quarter) in New York City and at his home in College Point, Long Island. For a time was an instructor at the Pratt Institute in Brooklyn. In 1923 the American Numismatic Society awarded him the J. Sanford Saltus medal. For the society he designed the medal to commemorate the 300th anniversary of the purchase of Manhattan by the Dutch.

He was a member of the American Academy of Arts and Letters, the National Academy of Design, National Institute of Arts and Letters, the Architectural League of New York, and the Municipal Arts Society, and he served as president of the National Sculpture Society. the World's Columbian Exposition in Chicago in 1893 he was awarded a medal for design, at the Paris Exhibition in 1900 he was given a silver medal for his *The Sun Vow* and *Last Act of the Moqui Snake Dance* groups, at the Pan-American Exposition in Buffalo in 1901 he was award a gold medal, and many other honors could be mentioned.

For the Louisiana Purchase Exposition in St. Louis in 1904 he designed the *Fountain of Liberty*, one of the prime attractions there. Among a long list of civic sculptures are *Coming of the White Man* for City Park, Portland, Oregon; the *McKinley Memorial*, Columbus, Ohio (depicted on the reverse of the 1916 and 1916 commemorative gold dollars); *Justice, the Guardian of Liberty* on the United States Supreme Court building (considered by some to be his best work); General George Washington for the Washington Arch in Washington Square in New York City; *Soldiers' and Sailors' Memorial* groups for Whitinsville, Massachusetts and Albany, New York.

MacNeil died on October 2, 1947. After his passing, the contents of his home-studio were about to be discarded when a neighbor, commercial illustrator John A. Coughlin, rescued many items including letters and scrapbooks, now mostly preserved in the Smithsonian Institution. Certain of his casts and models were scattered. His ideal design for the 1916 quarter, with dolphins and other touches, turned up in a yard sale in 2001.

MacNeil and His Ideal Design

Roger W. Burdette, as guest cataloger for Stack's Bowers Galleries offering in the Minot Sale, 1988, of a plaster model by Hermon MacNeil of his ideal obverse for the 1916 quarter, gave this commentary:

> On seeing this spectacular piece for the first time the reaction is, "Wow! So that's what a Standing Liberty quarter is supposed to look like!" But after a moment, the eye is drawn to two playful dolphins aside Liberty's feet, then to the motto IN GOD WE TRUST draped across Miss Liberty, to sprigs of laurel and last, the missing olive branch. What kind of Standing Liberty quarter is this? The truth is *this* is what Hermon MacNeil had intended his new quarter to look like.

Plaster model by Hermon A. MacNeil showing his ideal design with for the Standing Liberty quarter. Much to his dismay the dolphins, wreath, IN GOD WE TRUST on the ribbon, and certain other features were changed at the Mint without his being consulted.

In May 1916 MacNeil submitted his first design models for the new quarter. This first obverse looked much like the regular quarters dated 1916 and familiar to collectors. But over the next weeks MacNeil became increasingly dissatisfied with his work. With changes in mind, MacNeil requested permission from Mint Director Robert Woolley to revise the obverse. The sculptor said he wanted:

1. To bring the head of the figure a trifle lower so as not to appear to be holding up the rim of the coin.

2. To prevent the figure appearing "bowlegged."

3. To minimize the sagging of the covering of the shield by having it pulled up a little tighter.

I should also like to see the letters of the word Liberty slightly smaller.

Since Adolph Weinman, who was designing the new dime and half dollar, had already been given permission to change his original compositions, Woolley agreed.

During July and August 1916 Hermon MacNeil radically rearranged and modified the elements of his obverse design. Except for the names given to parts of the design, nearly everything was changed. The overall relief was made more pronounced, and drapery softened. Starting with the border, the original dot-dot-dash pattern was replaced with a cable or chain surrounding the central elements. The portal walls through which Liberty steps were plain—unadorned with either motto or detail. On the upper step at the base of the wall are two dolphins, one on each side of Liberty's feet. The dolphins represent the Atlantic and Pacific oceans, much as they did on the 1915 Panama-Pacific International Exposition gold dollar designed by Charles Keck or Robert Aitken's $50 gold piece. Above each dolphin's tail is a laurel branch symbolic of civil triumph; at the upper rim is the word LIBERTY in letters somewhat smaller and much sharper than on the first obverse.

The figure of Liberty differs completely from that on the first design, although she is still semi-nude. She now wears cross-laced sandals in the ancient Roman style and carries a shield embossed with an eagle. The shield covering is also more closely fit and less baggy. A long sash or ribbon engraved IN GOD WE TRUST connects the shield and her outstretched right hand ending near the laurel branch. There is no olive branch of peace, the whole new design being more militant and actively protective.

Treasury Secretary McAdoo approved the design on August 19, and asked MacNeil to provide a photograph showing the proposed location of the artist's monogram or initial. (This photo still exists.) This was done and the new Mint Director, F.J.H. von Engelken, replied on September 1, "Placing of signature under head of dolphin on right of Quarter Dollar approved. You are at liberty to use either the letter 'M' alone, or that monogram of two letters."

MacNeil was asked to expedite delivery of bronze casts and these were scheduled for delivery on September 9. From this point forward the mint should have made reductions and struck a few pattern pieces for von Engelken and others to examine. But from here to the end of the year official records are silent. No pattern coins are known.

In October 1916 MacNeil offered to help finalize the quarter designs, but the Mint decided that "it was deemed inexpedient to authorize Mr. MacNeil to come to Philadelphia."

The Mint engravers had scrapped the sculptor's original reverse design, replacing the two olive branches in front and behind the eagle, with a total of 13 small stars. The flying eagle remained low on the coin as if it were just rising skyward. This Mint concoction was used on both 1916 and 1917 Type I quarters.

As the year 1917 opened Mint Director von Engelken was eager to release the newly designed quarters. A small quantity of coins dated 1916 had been struck to mark the official release year, but a revised, more detailed obverse created by the Mint's engraving department graced the 1917 coins.

Despite radical changes, Mr. MacNeil's Liberty on the new quarter is indeed a beautiful piece of work. The idea conceived by the artist is highly expressive of national sentiment.

PATTERN QUARTERS

During 1916 various patterns were made for the new quarter. Most of these were done without consulting MacNeil, a unique situation among the various relationships with outside artists and the Engraving Department at the Mint. No official records have been found about the production quantities or details.

Pattern 1916 quarter, a Mint modification of MacNeil's design, Judd-1988 as attributed in *United States Pattern Coins* by Dr. J. Hewitt Judd.

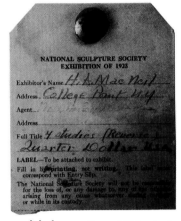

Plaster model by Hermon A. MacNeil of a design not known to have been made in pattern form. The date is in Roman numerals. (Roger W. Burdette, *Renaissance of American Coinage* 1916–1921)

Pattern 1916 quarter, Judd-1989.

Plaster models for a pattern 1916 quarter made by Hermon A. MacNeil and exhibited at the National Sculpture Society. On the reverse the S in PLURIBUS is backward. The exhibit tag is on the back of the model for the reverse.

The Numismatist, April 1917, included this:

The Girl on the Quarter

From a recent newspaper article by Marguerite Norse we extract the following facts regarding Miss Dora Doscher, who posed for Mr. Hermon A. MacNeil while designing the female figure that appears on our new quarter dollar, and who is now referred to by her friends as "the Girl on the Quarter:

Miss Doscher is 22 years of age, and is 5 feet 4-1/2 inches in height. Through her own efforts she has developed from a half invalid child to a most perfect type of American womanhood. Her days are spent in artistic and intellectual pursuits. She is a lecturer, scenario writer, and trained nurse. At the first intimation of war she enrolled in the Red Cross service and stood from that day ready for a moment's call. She presents an attractive appearance in the Red Cross uniform.

The measurements from which the late Karl Bitter modeled the figure surmounting the Pulitzer Memorial Fountain that stands in the Plaza in New York City were taken from Miss Doscher. Mr. Bitter's *Diana* that stands in the Metropolitan Museum of Art was modeled from the "coin girl."

The figure comes down a flight of steps in an attitude of welcome to the world. In one extended hand she holds a laurel branch of peace, on the left arm she carries a shield. Though she offers peace first she is prepared to defend her honor and her rights. The design suggests a step forward in civilization, protection, and defense with peace as the ultimate goal.

Doris Doscher was born on January 24, 1882, making her more than the 22 years of age quoted above. It was common for models, actresses, and others to state that they were younger than they really were.

She modeled for Karl Bitter's *Fountain of Abundance*, completed by Isidore Konti and Karl Gruppe, placed in the Pulitzer Fountain in front of the Plaza Hotel in New York City in 1915. Doris also modeled for *The Angel of Peace*, placed in front of the Flushing Memorial in New York. Beginning in 1917 she acted in several silent films, most notably, *Birth of a Race* (produced in Tampa by the Photoplay Corporation in cooperation with the Selig Polyscope Company and said to have cost a million dollars to produce), in which she took the part of Eve in the Garden of Eden.[81] On the screen her name was Doris Doree.

In interviews she stated she modeled as *Columbia* on the quarter. Later, she wrote many articles on various subjects including beauty, sports, health, dieting, and food and gained national recognition. She gave advice to newspaper readers, such as in "Win Back Your Husband's Love." She became "beauty specialist" at the New York *Evening World*. In July 1930 she married Dr. William H. Baum. Doris died on March 9, 1970, at the age of 88.

Dora Doscher, the model for Liberty.

In later years, numismatic writer Walter Breen and some others claimed that a lady named Irene McDowell was the model, but this information is false.[82]

DESIGN MODIFICATIONS

MacNeil was not satisfied with the Engraving Department's alteration of his ideal design, and in 1917 met with them to make some changes. The next *Report of the Commission of Fine Arts* included this:

Designs for Silver Coinage

The Commission had the privilege of advising the director of the Mint in regard to the subsidiary silver coinage, which is subject to change of design every 25 years. The Commission suggested that no form of art is so universal and therefore of such wide influence as is the silver coinage, and therefore no pains should be spared to make it as artistic as the talents of American artists and the capabilities of our mint permit.

After submission of designs, the half-dollar and the dime were entrusted to Adolph A. Weinman and the quarter-dollar to Hermon A. MacNeil. Through misunderstandings the artist's final design for the quarter-dollar was not used, and a bill has been introduced in Congress to permit certain modifications in the coin in order to make it conform entirely to the artist's ideas. The way is thus opened to secure as designers of our coinage artists of proved merit and to have their ideas carried out. The relations between the Mint and the Commission throughout a protracted discussion have been altogether satisfactory.

This resulted in an act, "Modifications of the Designs of the Current Quarter," H.R. 3548, submitted to Congress on June 17, 1917, by Representative William Ashbrook:

The Committee on Coinage, Weights, and Measures, to whom was referred H. R. 3548, providing for the modification of the designs of the current quarter dollar, having had the same under consideration unanimously instructed the chairman to report the bill to the House with the recommendation that the bill be passed.

The object of the bill is set forth in the following letter from the secretary of the Treasury to the chairman of the Committee on Coinage, Weights, and Measures, April 16, 1917:

I have the honor to submit for your consideration a draft of an act to authorize the modification of the designs of the current quarter dollar in accordance with a specimen submitted by Mr. Hermon A. Mac-Neil, the sculptor whose designs were accepted May 23, 1916, for the quarter dollar now being issued.

The modifications proposed are slight, the principal one being that the eagle has been raised and three of the stars placed beneath the eagle. On the reverse the lettering has been rearranged and the collision with the pinions of the wings obviated. These changes, together with a slight concavity, will produce a coin materially improved in artistic merit, and not interfere in any way with its practical use.

I am sorry to have to ask for this change, but since the original dies were made the artist has found that the were not true to the original design and that a great improvement can be made in the artistic value and appearance of the coin by making the slight changes the act contemplates.

Liberty was encased in a suit of mail, symbolizing military preparedness in view of the World War, a change not mentioned above. The olive branch in her right hand was modified in shape, and a leaf that crossed the L on the Type I coins was removed. On the reverse the stars were rearranged to place three below the eagle. The shield was modified with fewer rivets. Congress approved the modifications on July 9, 1917, "for the purpose of increasing its artistic merit."

In revisionist history years later Walter H. Breen and quite a few others stated that the reason for the change was public outcry concerning the semi-nudity of Liberty. No contemporary articles or documents have been located to reinforce this assertion.

On the Standing Liberty quarter of 1916 and later years the date was raised on a pedestal or plaque at the bottom. This caused the numbers to wear quickly, often to the extent of their complete removal. In 1925 a modification was made and the date position was recessed, solving the problem.

The 1917 Type 2 quarter of modified design.

Release and Distribution

In contrast to the release of the first Mercury dimes in October 1916, the new quarters and half dollars, including those dated 1916, were not placed into circulation until after the Treasury authorization of January 17, 1917.

On December 2, 1916, the Treasury announced:

> Issuance of the new [coins] was deferred today by the Treasury Department until the beginning of 1917. The extraordinary demand for small coins is overtaxing the facilities of the mints, and officials believed calls for the new quarter and half dollar coins would swamp the mints if they are issued at this time.

In early 1917 the low-mintage quarters dated 1916 were mixed in with quarters of 1917, resulting in those of 1916 not being showcased in newspapers, although a few articles pro and con were published.

Standing Liberty Quarters in Circulation

As noted, the new quarters of 1916 and 1917 both entered circulation in January 1917. The public claimed many as souvenirs, after which the novelty passed.

Mintages continued from 1917 onward at the Philadelphia, Denver, and San Francisco mints, but not all mints in all years. In 1922 no quarters were minted, and in 1921 and 1925 only the Philadelphia Mint struck them. These coins entered circulation and were widely used. Numismatists did not pay much attention to them as the specialty of collecting by dates and mintmarks was not widespread and would not be until the next decade.

Quarters in Circulation in the 1930s

By the mid-1930s, when collecting coins by date and mint became widely popular with the distribution of Wayte Raymond's "National" albums and somewhat later, Whitman holders, most Standing Liberty quarters of the 1916 to 1924 years had the dates worn away completely or only faintly discernible.

This situation, completely amazing, was dramatically revealed by a survey published in *The Numismatic Scrapbook*, January 1939. A study of 5,000 quarters taken from circulation in Rock Island, Illinois over a period of 10 months included Barber, Standing Liberty, and Washington issues. The Standing Liberty quarters:

Type I, 1916: *1916: 0; 1917, Type I: X; 1917-D, Type I: 4; 1917-S, Type I: 1.* **Type I quarters with dates worn away:** Philadelphia: 61, Denver: 11, San Francisco: 7; no date or mint: 6. The dateless coins were identifiable as Type I by having no stars below the eagle on the reverse.

Type II, 1917–1924, Pedestal Date: *1917, Type II: 2; 1917-D, Type II: 0; 1917-S, Type II: 0; 1918: 2; 1918-D: 1; 1918-S: 3; 1919: 1; 1919-D: 2; 1919-S: 0; 1920: 6; 1920-D: 1; 1920-S: 2; 1921: 0; 1923: 16; 1923-S: 0; 1924: 7; 1924-D: 2; 1924-S: 0.* **Type II quarters with dates worn away:** Philadelphia 790, Denver 226, San Francisco 271; no date or mint: 90.

Type II, 1925–1930, Recessed Date: *1925: 129; 1926: 129; 1926-D: 19; 1926-S: 31; 1927: 102; 1927-D: 14; 1927-S: 6; 1928: 62; 1928-D: 27; 1928-S: 28; 1929: 86; 1929-D: 29; 1929-S: 9; 1930: 32; 1930-S: 15.*

It is seen that among Type I quarters and early 1917–1924 Type II quarters with the date on a raised pedestal the vast majority of coins in circulation by 1939 had no dates visible! Accordingly, unlike for the dimes and half dollars of this era it was virtually impossible to build a collection of the 1916 to 1924 dates from circulation. Those that were identifiable were mostly only barely so.

STANDING LIBERTY QUARTER DOLLARS (1916–1930): GUIDE TO COLLECTING

ASPECTS OF STRIKING

Facts concerning striking sharpness or lack thereof in the Standing Liberty quarter series are not widely known, leading to the "Full Head" illusion which holds that if the head of Miss Liberty is fairly sharp (not completely full), it is certified as Full Head and worth a lot more money, even if other parts of the coin, notably including the rivets in the shield, are weak! To me this makes no sense at all.

As is the case with Mercury dimes and Liberty Walking half dollars, sharpness of details on Standing Liberty quarters is determined by the spacing of the dies in a coining press. If the dies are positioned closely apart, all details will be struck sharply, but the dies will wear more quickly. If they are spaced farther apart, the features deepest in the dies will not be struck up and will be flat or weak.

To reiterate, on Standing Liberty quarters flatness can occur mainly on the obverse on the head of Liberty, the details in the shield (especially the rivets), the sash above Liberty's waist, and, much less often, the lower part of Liberty and the date. Type I quarters of 1916 usually are indistinct in some areas. Those of 1917 are often very well struck. In contrast, very few Type II quarters have full head and shield details. Scarcely any numismatic attention has been paid to anything except the head! I find this to be amazing.

A much finer collection can be formed, in my opinion, by selecting coins that have full shield rivets and with head details partially full. The cost will be much less! The preceding differs from conventional wisdom, of course.

On the reverse flatness mostly occurs on the eagle but is not particularly noticeable.

If you are a connoisseur you will want to examine both sides carefully and pick a coin that has full details. This can be a reality for Type I, especially 1917 (1916 can be a challenge). If, instead, FD (Full Details) were the standard instead of FH, some varieties do not exist. (Don't tell anyone!)

This 1917-S Type II quarter exemplifies a Full Details quarter, with not only the head full, but the rivets as well.

A 1916 Standing Liberty quarter certified as MS-65FH that, on close inspection, shows some indistinctness on the head and weakness on rivets on the shield. The label on the coin will sell it to 99% of buyers, but connoisseurs would probably keep looking.

A 1924-S quarter certified as MS-66FH, with the head details not sharp and with missing shield rivets at the lower left—a poster example of the Full Head delusion.

A Mint State 1927-S quarter with a typical strike—details missing on the head and shield. Most Type II quarters have such weakness. The compensation is that they are much less expensive than coins certified as Full Head.

Repeating the above, the majority of coin buyers are content to have coins labeled Full Head on the holders. A study of such FH coins can be found in J.H. Cline's *Standing Liberty Quarters*. This view does not take into consideration weakness in other areas, although sometimes such is mentioned. The 1926-S is a good example. He estimates in the fourth edition (2007) that about 50 FH examples exist and adds: "On even the finest 1926-S out there the third and fourth rivets are missing from the outer shield."

Dramatic examples are provided by market values of the 1926-D in the present book. A regular MS-65 is priced at $425 while one with Full Head is priced at $23,000! A 1927-S is priced at $11,500 and $170,000 respectively. Anyone contemplating buying a Full Head 1927-S for $170,000 might well ask himself or herself: *Do I really want to pay the price of a high-performance sports car for a coin that may not have full facial details and may be weak in other areas?*

For a really deluxe specimen of any Standing Liberty quarter, find one that has sharp rivets in the shield, a fairly full head, and sharp details elsewhere. If it is certified as FH be sure your bank account is well fortified. For really excellent *numismatic value for the price paid*, find one that has sharp rivets in the shield, some facial details but not a Full Head, and sharp details elsewhere. By cherrypicking these can be obtained at no more cost than that of a poorly struck coin!

THE RON POPE SURVEY

In 2004 Ron Pope did a study of the sharpness or lack thereof in the Standing Liberty quarter series.[83] While many had so-called Full Heads, his survey revealed that coins with Full Details—including the head, all shield details, the date, and the eagle on the reverse—were a different story completely. This and the narrative following tie in nicely with the preceding paragraphs.

The following can be a very valuable guide for connoisseurs and anyone else wishing to avoid overpaying for "Full Head" coins that are weak in other features. After each date, the number of coins examined is shown in parentheses, followed by the percentage of those coins that had Full Details:

1916 (144) 13%	1918 (221) 5%	1920 (532) 3%
1917, Type I (1,042) 76%	1918-D (214) 2%	1920-D (107) 4%
1917-D, Type I (284) 67%	1918-S, 8 Over 7 (108) 0%	1920-S (266) 0.4%
1917-S Type I (198) 62%	1918-S (269) 0.4%	1921 (141) 6%
1917, Type II (259) 15%	1919 (238) 8%	1923 (413) 3%
1917-D, Type II (161) 2%	1919-D (121) 2%	1923-S (107) 2%
1917-S, Type II (162) 4%	1919-S (174) 2%	1924 (226) 3%

1924-D (337) 2%   1927 (343) 1%   1929 (476) 2%
1924-S (189) 0.5%   1927-D (170) 0%   1929-D (214) 0.4%
1925 (281) 3%   1927-S (145) 0%   1929-S (332) 0%
1926 (300) 1%   1928 (228) 6%   1930 (1,008) 4%
1926-D (351) 0%   1928-D (379) 1%   1930-S (275) 0.4%
1926-S (134) 0%   1928-S (318) 0.6%

To summarize, the following varieties had no Full Details coins at all: 1918-S, 8 Over 7; 1926-D; 1926-S; 1927-D; 1927-S; and 1929-S; never mind that all of these can be found in certified holders marked Full Head, some being *common* with such labels.

These varieties had fewer than 1% with Full Details: 1918-S: 0.4%; 1920-S: 0.4%, 1924-S: 0.5%, 1928-S: 0.6%, 1929-D: 0.4%, and 1930-S: 0.4%.

These had just 1% with Full Details: 1926; and 1928-D.

BEING A SMART BUYER

There are enough Standing Liberty quarters in the marketplace that with very little effort the typical or casual collector can easily acquire a full set of dates and mintmarks in MS-64 or MS-65 in a short time. Quality, however, will be a mixed bag.

My advice is to be a connoisseur. Buy only certified coins, such as from PCGS, NGC, or ANACS. If you feel that having a so-called Full Head coin is desirable in view of the great premium often required, then be certain that the coin has full details everywhere else. Keep in mind that on such coins the head details still may be weak for some features. A top-of-the-line Full Head quarter should have *nearly* full facial sharpness and should have all of the rivets visible. The center of the shield should be distinct as well. Otherwise you are wasting your money, in my opinion.

In conclusion, and to re-emphasize the author's desire for numismatists to get the best value for their money, it is a good buying strategy (and will save a lot of money) to acquire coins not marked Full Head but with reasonably good details elsewhere, such as on the shield, as mentioned earlier. This goes against the conventional wisdom that *all that counts is the label on a holder*.

Eye appeal is another consideration. A certified MS-65 quarter can be dark, stained, spotted, and ugly, in which case I suggest you avoid it. Among Mint State coins look for pieces that have rich frosty mint luster and are brilliant or with light iridescent toning. Most "rainbow" toning is artificial except for that on certain coins with concentric toning from long-term storage in Raymond albums. A curious aspect of thinking for the vast majority of buyers is that they consider *any* MS-65 coin, even one with no eye appeal, to be better than, say, a gorgeous MS-63 or 64.

Further, over the years there has been "gradeflation" with certified coins. Many that were MS-64 twenty years ago are graded MS-65 or even higher today. In the late 1980s MS-66 and MS-67 grades were few and far between in the population reports published by PCGS and NGC. Today, such grades are very common.

Not everyone can afford a Mint State 1916, 1918/7-S overdate, 1926-S, or 1927-S quarter. If this includes you, cherrypick nice Very Fine, Extremely Fine, or About Uncirculated coins with care, selecting only coins with nice eye appeal.

Take your time. All the coins that meet your particular requirements are in the marketplace, but to find them may take a few weeks or months. Study each coin carefully before making a purchase decision. The thrill of the chase is part of what numismatics is all about.

Caveat: The availability of certified Mint State "Full Head" coins in the following pages is from population reports that, for expensive varieties, include many resubmissions of the same coins. These figures are given in view of the popularity of such information and are not necessarily guidelines for a careful connoisseur who desires other parts of a coin to be sharply struck.

STANDING LIBERTY QUARTER DOLLARS (1916–1930)

GRADING STANDARDS

MS-60 to 70 (Mint State). *Obverse:* At MS-60 some abrasion and contact marks are evident on the higher areas, which are also the areas most likely to be weakly struck. This includes the rivets on the shield to the left and the central escutcheon on the shield, the head, and the right leg of Miss Liberty. The luster may not be complete in those areas on weakly struck coins, even those certified above MS-65—the *original planchet surface*

1919. Graded MS-65FH.

may be revealed as it was not smoothed out by striking. Accordingly, grading is best done by evaluating abrasion and mint luster as it is observed. Luster may be dull or lifeless at MS–60 to 62 but should have deep frost at MS-63 or better, particularly in the lower-relief areas. At MS-65 or better, it should be full and rich. *Reverse:* Striking is usually quite good, permitting observation of luster in all areas. Check the eagle's breast and the surface of the right wing. Luster may be dull or lifeless at MS–60 to 62 but should have deep frost at MS-63 or better, particularly in the lower-relief areas. At MS-65 or better, it should be full and rich.

Illustrated coin: See the subtle notes of gold, blue, and pink on this lustrous example.

AU-50, 53, 55, 58 (About Uncirculated). *Obverse:* Light wear is seen on the figure of Miss Liberty, especially noticeable around her midriff and right knee. The shield shows wear, as does the highest part of the sash where it crosses Miss Liberty's waist. At AU-58 the luster is extensive, but incomplete on the higher areas, although it should be nearly full in the panels of the parapet to the left and right, and in the upper field. At AU–50 and 53, luster is

1917-S, Variety 1. Graded AU-53.

less. *Reverse:* Wear is most evident on the eagle's breast, the edges of both wings, and the interior area of the right wing. Luster is nearly complete at AU-58, but at AU-50, half or more is gone.

EF-40, 45 (Extremely Fine). *Obverse:* Wear is more extensive, with the higher parts of Miss Liberty now without detail and the front of the right leg flat. The shield is worn. On coins dated from 1917 to 1924 the date shows wear at the top (on those of 1925 to 1930, with the date recessed, the numbers are bold). Little or no luster is seen, except perhaps among the letters. *Reverse:* The eagle shows more wear, with the surface of the right wing being mostly flat. Little or no luster is evident.

1927-S. Graded EF-45.

VF-20, 30 (Very Fine). *Obverse:* Wear is more extensive. The higher-relief areas of Miss Liberty are flat, and the sash crossing her waist is mostly blended into it (some sharply struck pieces being exceptions). The left side of the shield is mostly flat, although its outline can be seen. On quarters dated 1917 to 1924 the top of the date shows more wear. *Reverse:* The eagle shows further wear, with the body blending into the wing above

1919-S. Graded VF-20.

it. Much feather detail is gone from the wing to the left (on quarters dated 1925 to 1930; less so for those dated 1917 to 1924). Most detail is gone from the right wing.

F-12, 15 (Fine). *Obverse:* Miss Liberty is worn nearly flat. Most detail in her gown is gone, except to the left of her leg and below her knee to the right. The stars on the parapet are well worn, with some indistinct. The top of the date is weak. Quarters of the rare 1916 date are slightly weaker than those of 1917 in this and lower grades. On quarters of 1917 to 1924 the top of the date is weak. On those dated 1925 to 1930 the date remains strong.

1917-D. Graded F-12.

Reverse: The eagle shows further wear, this being greater on 1925 to 1930 issues than on the earlier dates.

VG-8, 10 (Very Good). *Obverse:* The obverse is worn further, with fewer details in the skirt, and part of the shield border to the left blended into the standing figure. The date is partially worn away at the top, and quarters from 1917 to 1924 have less detail. Those from 1925 to 1930 retain more detail, and the date is full. *Reverse:* The eagle is worn further, with only about a third of the feathers now discernible, these mostly on the wing to the left.

1921. Graded VG-10.

G-4, 6 (Good). *Obverse:* The wear is more extensive. Most coins have the stars missing, the standing figure flat, and much of the date worn away, although still clearly identifiable. Quarters of 1925 to 1930 show more detail and the date is clear. *Reverse:* The eagle is mostly in outline form, with only a few feather details visible. The rim is worn into the letters, and on quarters of 1916 to 1924, E PLURIBUS UNUM is very faint; it is clear on quarters of later dates.

1927-S. Graded G-6.

AG-3 (About Good). *Obverse:* The obverse is worn nearly smooth, and the date is mostly gone. On some coins just one or two digits are seen. Fortunately, those digits are usually on the right, such as a trace of just a 6, which will identify the coin as a 1916. On quarters of 1925 to 1930 the wear is more extensive than for G-4, but most features are discernible and the date is clear. *Reverse:* The eagle is flat, and the border is worn down further.

1921. Graded AG-3.

On quarters of 1916 to 1924, E PLURIBUS UNUM is extremely faint or even missing in areas; it remains readable on quarters of later dates.

1916 Standing Liberty Quarter

1916 • Circulation-Strike Mintage: 52,000.

Availability in Mint State: 1,500 to 2,500, mostly saved by numismatists in 1917 when the new design was widely appreciated. This number may be on the low side.

Over the years I have handled numerous 1916 quarters, probably numbering in the range of several hundred. I have never owned a roll of these, but I did see one roll owned by a Pennsylvania numismatist in the 1950s.

Populations of certified MS-65 and higher labeled "Full Head": NGC, 74; PCGS, 110[84]

Availability in circulated grades: 1,500 to 2,500, graded by the wear on the date. For this and other Type I quarters, higher-level circulated coins can have a lot of original mint luster. As the design of the obverse of the 1916 quarter is slightly different, a coin with the date completely missing can be identified as a 1916, although few have done this. Many dateless quarters of 1916–1924 were melted during the great boom in bullion silver prices in the late 1970s.

Aspects of sharpness: In the Ron Pope survey for 1916 quarters 144 were examined were examined and 13% had Full Details. In general the 1916 coins of a slightly different design than the later ones are weak overall. The most obvious spots to check are the head, upper left of the shield, and the eagle's breast. This precipitated a slight modification in 1917. This change is generally overlooked, and both 1916 and early 1917 quarters are called Type I. Well-worn coins often have the left side of the date more worn than the right, that with the result that on a few just the 6 is visible.

Commentary: For several numismatic generations the 1916 Standing Liberty quarter has been a celebrated rarity combining a low mintage of just 52,000 coins with first-year-of-issue honors. Today, examples are very rare in relation to the demand for them. This is, of course, a wonderful combination of appeals for any rarity! Among regular-issue 20th-century United States coins from cents through silver dollars (excluding commemoratives and unusual varieties such as overdates), only the 1913-S quarter has a lower mintage with just 40,000 struck.

From *Mehl's Numismatic Monthly*, March 1917: "New Halves and Quarters of 1916 Not Rare" Washington, January 26—Reports reached the Treasury Department today from numerous sources that sharpers have been selling at a premium the newly designed quarters and half dollars coined in 1916, representing that the new coins are rare. To correct any impression that the coins are rare, officials today authorized the statement that 2,330,000 halves and 52,000 quarters of the new design were struck off in 1916." [Author's modern comment: Sharpers my foot!]

In May 1917 Henry Chapman, one of the few dealers at the time who accommodated his clients by providing new issues, advertised: "1916 quarter dollar. New design. Brilliant Uncirculated $1.00." In November 1918 he offered: "25c 1916 new type, Fine 55c, Unc. $1.25." Chapman maintained a store stock of current issues as did John Zug in Maryland and William K. Pukall in New Jersey. Most other dealers ignored new releases and concentrated on rare coins from the past. In October 1925 John B. Boss, a Philadelphia dealer, advertised: "We have a small stock of 1916 new-type quarters, Unc., which have an auction record of $2.10 each. Price $1 postpaid while they last."

Reports of 40-coin rolls have appeared in print from time to time. In *The Coin Dealer Newsletter Monthly Supplement*, August 8, 1997, J.H. Cline commented concerning the 1916 recently sold in the Eliasberg Collection sale: "This one was probably purchased by Eliasberg before the breakup of several rolls of 1916s in an estate in the Northeast. I saw one of these rolls in 1953/1954. All were blast white and I believe many were sold by New York dealer Lester Merkin."[85] I was numismatically aware in 1953 and 1954 and do not recall of ever hearing of such a hoard.

	Cert	Avg	%MS	G-4	VG-8	F-12	VF-20	EF-40	AU-50	MS-60	MS-63	MS-65FH
1916	908	44.2	48%	$3,000	$4,750	$6,000	$7,000	$9,000	$11,000	$12,500	$15,000	$35,000

1917 Standing Liberty Quarter, No Stars Below Eagle

1917, No Stars Below Eagle •
Circulation-Strike Mintage: 8,740,000.

Availability in Mint State: Many thousands; far and away the most plentiful Type I quarter.

Populations of certified MS-65 and higher labeled "Full Head": NGC, 1,159; PCGS, 1,934.

Availability in circulated grades: Common. Worn dates, often with higher quality on the rest of the coin.

Aspects of sharpness: In the Ron Pope survey of 1917 Type I quarters 1,042 were examined and 76% had Full Details. No other variety in the series scored so high. With relatively few exceptions, 1917 Type I quarters from the Philadelphia Mint are extremely well struck, with head

Detail of the Type I Obverse.

details—the cheek and facial features of Miss Liberty and, especially the wreath she wears around her head—excellently defined. The shield details are excellent as well.

Commentary: This is the one variety in the Type I series that has always been easy to find in high Mint State levels and, as noted, sharply struck. Most have excellent eye appeal as well. As such a 1917 Type I is an ideal coin to add to a type set.

In November 1918 Henry Chapman offered: "25c 1917 without stars below eagle, Unc. $1, with stars, 75c." Chapman's retail stock was considered the finest in the country at the time, with John Zug, the mail-order dealer based in Bowie, Maryland being the runner-up.

	Cert	Avg	%MS	G-4	VG-8	F-12	VF-20	EF-40	AU-50	MS-60	MS-63	MS-65FH
1917, No Stars Below Eagle	6,791	59.4	78%	$18	$30	$50	$70	$90	$140	$225	$325	$900

1917-D Standing Liberty Quarter, No Stars Below Eagle

1917-D, No Stars Below Eagle •
Circulation-Strike Mintage: 1,509,200.

Availability in Mint State: Thousands, but far fewer than the Philadelphia issue. Many were saved due to the novelty and appreciation of the design when first issued.

Populations of certified MS-65 and higher labeled "Full Head": NGC, 279; PCGS, 517.

Availability in circulated grades: Scarce. Grading is by wear on the date as is true of other Type I quarters.

Aspects of sharpness: In the Ron Pope survey of 1917-D, Type I quarters 284 were examined and 67% had Full Details, the second highest such in the study. Due to the differences in mintage quantities, the Denver and San **Detail of the Type I Obverse.**
Francisco quarters of this type are scarce in comparison to Philadelphia Mint coins.

Commentary: After the coins were placed in circulation the date wore away quickly and on most was completely gone by the late 1930s, this comment being true of all of the 1916 to 1924 issues, before the date placement area was modified. If the D mintmark is visible and there are no stars below the eagle, these can still be attributed as 1917-D, Type I as no other Denver coins of the type were made.

	Cert	Avg	%MS	G-4	VG-8	F-12	VF-20	EF-40	AU-50	MS-60	MS-63	MS-65FH
1917-D, No Stars Below Eagle	1,931	59.0	73%	$25	$65	$95	$125	$175	$225	$300	$375	$1,350

1917-S Standing Liberty Quarter, No Stars Below Eagle

1917-S, No Stars Below Eagle •
Circulation-Strike Mintage: 1,952,000.

Availability in Mint State: Thousands, but fewer than the lower-mintage 1917-D, Type I. As a general rule across the board, mintage for mintage, the survival rate (expressed as a percentage) of San Francisco coins is less than those of Denver and Philadelphia.

Populations of certified MS-65 and higher labeled "Full Head": NGC, 179; PCGS, 314.

Availability in circulated grades: Same comment as for 1917-D, Type I.

Aspects of sharpness: In the Ron Pope survey of 1917-S, **Detail of the Type I Obverse.**
Type I, quarters 198 were examined and 62% had Full Details. This was a creditable showing even though less than for the quarters of the other two mints. Even though more were coined of the 1917-S, Mint State coins are scarcer than are 1917-D quarters.

Commentary: Those with the date gone can still be attributed if the mintmark is visible and there are no stars below the eagle, as also noted under 1917-D above.

	Cert	Avg	%MS	G-4	VG-8	F-12	VF-20	EF-40	AU-50	MS-60	MS-63	MS-65FH
1917-S, No Stars Below Eagle	1,289	52.9	61%	$30	$75	$115	$150	$200	$275	$350	$425	$2,500

1917 Standing Liberty Quarter, Stars Below Eagle

1917, Stars Below Eagle • Circulation-Strike Mintage: 13,880,000.

Availability in Mint State: Many thousands but fewer than for 1917 Type I.

Populations of certified MS-65 and higher labeled "Full Head": NGC, 198; PCGS, 369.

Availability in circulated grades: Common.

Aspects of sharpness: In the Ron Pope survey of 1917, Type II, quarters 259 were examined and 15% had Full Details. This initiated an era of generally unsatisfactory strikes for Type II quarters; among them quarters, the 1917 Philadelphia issue is the only one for which more than 10% of existing Mint State coins have Full Details. As such it is a good candidate for a type set.

Detail of the Type II Obverse.

Commentary: As is true of all varieties issued before 1925, the date wore away quickly, with the result that by the 1930s only a fraction of the mintage survived with the date visible.

	Cert	Avg	%MS	G-4	VG-8	F-12	VF-20	EF-40	AU-50	MS-60	MS-63	MS-65FH
1917, Stars Below Eagle	1,571	60.2	77%	$20	$32	$45	$55	$75	$110	$150	$275	$900

1917-D Standing Liberty Quarter, Stars Below Eagle

1917-D, Stars Below Eagle • Circulation-Strike Mintage: 6,224,400.

Availability in Mint State: Thousands, but across the board Type I quarters are in smaller quantities than Type II quarters with similar mintages.

Populations of certified MS-65 and higher labeled "Full Head": NGC, 34; PCGS, 101.

Availability in circulated grades: Common. Nearly all Standing Liberty quarters, a few rare issues excepted, are available in quantities sufficient to meet numismatic demand.

Aspects of sharpness: In the Ron Pope survey of 1917-D, Type II, quarters 161 were examined and 2% had Full Details. As such they are far rarer than coins certified with Full Head, the last being easy to find in the marketplace. Most are somewhat weak on the shield and sash. In circulated grades this issue is far rarer than the mintage indicates as on most coins the date was worn away.

Detail of the Type II Obverse.

Commentary: Nearly all are weakly struck at the shield.

	Cert	Avg	%MS	G-4	VG-8	F-12	VF-20	EF-40	AU-50	MS-60	MS-63	MS-65FH
1917-D, Stars Below Eagle	842	58.4	67%	$30	$45	$65	$90	$110	$150	$225	$300	$1,500

1917-S Standing Liberty Quarter, Stars Below Eagle

1917-S, Stars Below Eagle •
Circulation-Strike Mintage: 5,552,000.

Availability in Mint State: Thousands, but somewhat fewer than 1917-D.

Populations of certified MS-65 and higher labeled "Full Head": NGC, 41; PCGS, 99.

Availability in circulated grades: Common in relation to the demand.

Aspects of sharpness: In the Ron Pope survey of 1917-S Type II quarters 162 were examined and 4% had Full Details. Despite this relatively high (!) score for sharpness, most coins are weak overall and have minimal eye appeal. Circulated coins are far less common than expected as the dates wore away on most.

Detail of the Type II Obverse.

Commentary: Nearly all are weakly struck at the shield.

	Cert	Avg	%MS	G-4	VG-8	F-12	VF-20	EF-40	AU-50	MS-60	MS-63	MS-65FH
1917-S, Stars Below Eagle	808	58.8	69%	$35	$50	$75	$105	$125	$165	$235	$325	$2,500

1918 Standing Liberty Quarter

1918 • Circulation-Strike Mintage: 14,240,000.

Availability in Mint State: Plentiful in relation to the demand.

Populations of certified MS-65 and higher labeled "Full Head": NGC, 83; PCGS, 161.

Availability in circulated grades: Common.

Aspects of sharpness: In the Ron Pope survey of 1918 quarters 221 were examined and 5% had Full Details.

Commentary: One of the more plentiful early quarters across the board.

	Cert	Avg	%MS	G-4	VG-8	F-12	VF-20	EF-40	AU-50	MS-60	MS-63	MS-65FH
1918	904	60.3	73%	$20	$25	$30	$35	$55	$95	$150	$250	$2,000

1918-D Standing Liberty Quarter

1918-D • Circulation-Strike Mintage: 7,380,000.

Availability in Mint State: Same comment as preceding. The number of collectors forming a Mint State set of these quarters is not known, but it is probably no more than several thousand at most and may be no more than one or two thousand.

Populations of certified MS-65 and higher labeled "Full Head": NGC, 46; PCGS, 98.

Availability in circulated grades: Common.

Aspects of sharpness: In the Ron Pope survey of 1918-D quarters 214 were examined and 2% had Full Details. Many are weakly struck at the center in addition to the shield and head. Circulated coins are far less common than expected as the dates wore away on most.

Commentary: This is one of many issues for which cherrypicking for quality will yield a finer coin for no more cost.

	Cert	Avg	%MS	G-4	VG-8	F-12	VF-20	EF-40	AU-50	MS-60	MS-63	MS-65FH
1918-D	741	57.7	61%	$22	$30	$60	$75	$120	$150	$200	$360	$3,500

1918-S, 8 Over 7, Standing Liberty Quarter

1918-S, 8 Over 7 • **Circulation-Strike**
Mintage: Small part of the of 1918-S.

Availability in Mint State: Probably fewer than 100, certainly fewer than 200. Mostly at lower Mint State levels.

Populations of certified MS-65 and higher labeled "Full Head": NGC, 0; PCGS, 0.

Availability in circulated grades: The rarest in the series. Fewer than 1,000 probably exist, and it would be hard to confirm even that many.

Aspects of sharpness: In the Ron Pope survey of 1918-S, 8 Over 7 quarters 108 were examined and 0%—not a single coin—had Full Details. The few that have been

Detail of the overdate.

certified as Full Head do not stand up to close scrutiny if other features, such as the lower left of the shield and Liberty's sash and clothing near the center, are studied. About a dozen have been certified as Full Head by PCGS and NGC.

Commentary: This variety was not recognized until the 1930s, and even then not much attention was paid to it, as it was omitted from popular holders and folders. Even dedicated numismatists were apt to be unaware of its existence. On February 26, 1938, Thomas L. Elder offered this at auction as lot 262: "1918 over '17. Three stars under eagle. Uncirculated. Very rare. First in the sales." When the overdate finally became widely noticed in the 1940s it was omitted from many "want lists." It came into its own at a later time. Today, examples are widely desired. Such pieces are the key to the series, in Mint State far rarer than any other variety. Nearly all are in circulated grades.

	Cert	Avg	%MS	G-4	VG-8	F-12	VF-20	EF-40	AU-50	MS-60	MS-63	MS-65FH
1918-S, 8 Over 7	331	40.2	18%	$1,600	$2,200	$3,500	$4,250	$7,000	$10,000	$14,000	$25,000	$250,000

1918-S Standing Liberty Quarter

1918-S • **Circulation-Strike Mintage:** 11,072,000.

Availability in Mint State: Thousands, mostly at lower levels.

Populations of certified MS-65 and higher labeled "Full Head": NGC, 22; PCGS, 53.

Availability in circulated grades: Common, but, to repeat, pre-1925 quarters with raised date on the pedestal are far fewer in number than are later issues.

Aspects of sharpness: In the Ron Pope survey of 1918-S quarters 269 were examined and only 0.4% had Full Details. The lower left of the shield and the sash are points of weakness. Several dozen Full Head coins have been certified by PCGS and NGC. Circulated coins are far less common than expected as the dates wore away on most.

Commentary: The ready availability of this and the vast majority of other Standing Liberty quarters in lower Mint State levels has made them very popular over the years.

	Cert	Avg	%MS	G-4	VG-8	F-12	VF-20	EF-40	AU-50	MS-60	MS-63	MS-65FH
1918-S	982	55.5	61%	$20	$25	$35	$45	$60	$120	$180	$300	$10,000

1919 Standing Liberty Quarter

1919 • **Circulation-Strike Mintage:** 11,324,000.

Availability in Mint State: Thousands exist.

Populations of certified MS-65 and higher labeled "Full Head": NGC, 120; PCGS, 260.

Availability in circulated grades: Common.

Aspects of sharpness: In the Ron Pope survey of 1919 quarters 238 were examined and 8% had Full Details, a remarkably high showing with just a few varieties scoring higher. Circulated coins are far less common than expected as the dates wore away on most.

Commentary: In all grades this is one of the more plentiful Type II quarters dated before 1925.

	Cert	Avg	%MS	G-4	VG-8	F-12	VF-20	EF-40	AU-50	MS-60	MS-63	MS-65FH
1919	1,124	60.3	75%	$25	$35	$50	$65	$80	$105	$150	$210	$1,650

1919-D Standing Liberty Quarter

1919-D • **Circulation-Strike Mintage:** 1,944,000.

Availability in Mint State: Scarce in relation to other issues of the era, but there are enough to go around.

Populations of certified MS-65 and higher labeled "Full Head": NGC, 10; PCGS, 25.

Availability in circulated grades: Readily available.

Aspects of sharpness: In the Ron Pope survey of 1919-D quarters 121 were examined and 2% had Full Details. The lower left of the sash and central clothing details are points to check.

Commentary: For coins certified as Full Head, even though other aspects may not be sharp, a huge premium must be paid. Circulated coins are far less common than expected as the dates wore away on most.

	Cert	Avg	%MS	G-4	VG-8	F-12	VF-20	EF-40	AU-50	MS-60	MS-63	MS-65FH
1919-D	484	46.2	36%	$65	$90	$180	$350	$500	$600	$1,200	$1,800	$45,000

1919-S Standing Liberty Quarter

1919-S • Circulation-Strike Mintage: 1,836,000.

Availability in Mint State: Enough are available to supply the demand, but the 1919-S is elusive in relation to other issues of the era and always commands a sharp premium.

Populations of certified MS-65 and higher labeled "Full Head": NGC, 12; PCGS, 21.

Availability in circulated grades: Circulated coins are far less common than expected as the dates wore away on most.

Aspects of sharpness: In the Ron Pope survey of 1919-S quarters 174 were examined and 2% had Full Details.

Commentary: Similar to the 1919-D, for coins certified as Full Head, even though other aspects may not be sharp, a huge premium must be paid. Avoid certified Full Head coins and seek pieces that are fairly well struck overall—and save a lot of money.

	Cert	Avg	%MS	G-4	VG-8	F-12	VF-20	EF-40	AU-50	MS-60	MS-63	MS-65FH
1919-S	501	46.8	33%	$65	$90	$150	$300	$500	$600	$1,000	$2,000	$36,000

1920 Standing Liberty Quarter

1920 • Circulation-Strike Mintage: 27,860,000.

Availability in Mint State: Thousands survive of this high-mintage issue.

Populations of certified MS-65 and higher labeled "Full Head": NGC, 74; PCGS, 174.

Availability in circulated grades: Common.

Aspects of sharpness: In the Ron Pope survey of 1920 quarters 532 were examined and 3% had Full Details.

Commentary: Coins that are fairly well struck overall are easy to find, even if without Full Head. Check the shield first.

	Cert	Avg	%MS	G-4	VG-8	F-12	VF-20	EF-40	AU-50	MS-60	MS-63	MS-65FH
1920	1,782	60.6	76%	$12	$16	$25	$30	$45	$75	$125	$210	$1,450

1920-D Standing Liberty Quarter

1920-D • **Circulation-Strike Mintage:** 3,586,400.

Availability in Mint State: Not easily located.

Populations of certified MS-65 and higher labeled "Full Head": NGC, 21; PCGS, 53.

Availability in circulated grades: Common.

Aspects of sharpness: In the Ron Pope survey of 1920-D quarters 107 were examined and 4% had Full Details.

Commentary: This is a good coin to cherrypick for a fairly well-struck shield and other features, even though the facial features may be indistinct. Circulated coins are far less common than expected as the dates wore away on most.

	Cert	Avg	%MS	G-4	VG-8	F-12	VF-20	EF-40	AU-50	MS-60	MS-63	MS-65FH
1920-D	408	52.9	52%	$50	$60	$80	$120	$165	$235	$400	$1,000	$8,500

1920-S Standing Liberty Quarter

1920-S • **Circulation-Strike Mintage:** 6,380,000.

Availability in Mint State: Thousands exist, but far fewer than most issues later in the decade.

Populations of certified MS-65 and higher labeled "Full Head": NGC, 11; PCGS, 26.

Availability in circulated grades: Common.

Aspects of sharpness: In the Ron Pope survey of 1920-S quarters 266 were examined and 0.4% had Full Details. As is true of most other varieties in the series, those that have been certified as Full Head do not stand up to close scrutiny if other features such as the lower left of the shield and the clothing details at the center are studied. For coins certified as Full Head, even though other aspects may not be sharp, an extreme premium must be paid. This is another variety to cherrypick for sharpness other than the head. Circulated coins are far less common than expected as the dates wore away on most.

	Cert	Avg	%MS	G-4	VG-8	F-12	VF-20	EF-40	AU-50	MS-60	MS-63	MS-65FH
1920-S	592	57.5	63%	$20	$25	$35	$50	$70	$150	$275	$700	$22,500

1921 Standing Liberty Quarter

1921 • **Circulation-Strike Mintage:** 1,916,000.

Availability in Mint State: Thousands, but fewer than most other quarters of the era. There are enough MS coins to fill the needs of specialists.

Populations of certified MS-65 and higher labeled "Full Head": NGC, 28; PCGS, 86.

Availability in circulated grades: For many years the 1921 has been considered one of the key issues in circulated grades.

Aspects of sharpness: In the Ron Pope survey of 1921 quarters 141 were examined and 6% had Full Details. The 1921 and 1928 with 6% having Full Details are tied for second in this quality among Type II quarters, with only 1917 higher (with 15%). Some 1921 Standing Liberty quarters are certified as having a Full Head, but the coins are weak in other areas, at the first digit of the date and to a lesser extent the fourth digit (this being the only variety in the series often seen with this weakness arrangement). Circulated coins are far less common than expected as the dates wore away on most.

Commentary: During the previous year, 1920, production of Standing Liberty quarters occurred at all three mints, and to the extent of over 35 million pieces. In 1921 the nation was in an economic recession, and the quantity of quarters produced took a precipitous fall to just 1,916,000—about 1/20th of what it had been earlier! In the year after that, 1922, no quarter dollars were struck at all. Circulated coins are far less common than expected as the dates wore away on most.

	Cert	Avg	%MS	G-4	VG-8	F-12	VF-20	EF-40	AU-50	MS-60	MS-63	MS-65FH
1921	1,112	43.4	41%	$125	$175	$350	$550	$700	$900	$1,200	$1,900	$8,000

1923 Standing Liberty Quarter

1923 • Circulation-Strike Mintage: 9,716,000.

Availability in Mint State: Thousands exist, but fewer than for the typical Philadelphia quarter of later in the decade.

Populations of certified MS-65 and higher labeled "Full Head": NGC, 43; PCGS, 100.

Availability in circulated grades: Common.

Aspects of sharpness: In the Ron Pope survey of 1923 quarters 413 were examined and 3% had Full Details. Circulated coins are far less common than expected as the dates wore away on most.

	Cert	Avg	%MS	G-4	VG-8	F-12	VF-20	EF-40	AU-50	MS-60	MS-63	MS-65FH
1923	1,579	61.2	82%	$12	$18	$25	$35	$45	$80	$150	$200	$2,750

1923-S Standing Liberty Quarter

1923-S • Circulation-Strike Mintage: 1,360,000.

Availability in Mint State: Several thousand or so and rare in its context. However, enough are available to satisfy specialists.

Populations of certified MS-65 and higher labeled "Full Head": NGC, 79; PCGS, 105.

Availability in circulated grades: In circulated

grades this is considered to be the rarest of the regular dates and mintmarks in the Standing Liberty series.

Aspects of sharpness: In the Ron Pope survey of 1923-S quarters 107 were examined and 2% had Full Details. Most but not all that have been certified as Full Head do not stand up to close scrutiny if other features are studied, although some come close. There are enough such Full Head coins around that the price differential for such is not huge. Circulated coins are far less common than expected as the dates wore away on most.

Commentary: This has always been a key variety. When reviewing certified coin populations remember that scarce dates and mintmarks are often resubmitted, inflating the numbers. Accordingly, a 1923-S is much more likely to be submitted than a Philadelphia coin of this year.

	Cert	Avg	%MS	G-4	VG-8	F-12	VF-20	EF-40	AU-50	MS-60	MS-63	MS-65FH
1923-S	872	45.8	38%	$250	$350	$600	$850	$1,200	$1,700	$2,100	$3,000	$6,500

1924 Standing Liberty Quarter

1924 • **Circulation-Strike Mintage:** 10,920,000.

Availability in Mint State: Easily found in Mint State.

Populations of certified MS-65 and higher labeled "Full Head": NGC, 90; PCGS, 189.

Availability in circulated grades: Plentiful.

Aspects of sharpness: In the Ron Pope survey of 924 quarters 226 were examined and 3% had Full Details. Circulated coins are far less common than expected as the dates wore away on most.

Commentary: Common.

	Cert	Avg	%MS	G-4	VG-8	F-12	VF-20	EF-40	AU-50	MS-60	MS-63	MS-65FH
1924	1,148	60.5	79%	$12	$16	$22	$32	$45	$80	$150	$225	$1,200

1924-D Standing Liberty Quarter

1924-D • **Circulation-Strike Mintage:** 3,112,000.

Availability in Mint State: Thousands exist, but far fewer than Denver quarters of later in the decade.

Populations of certified MS-65 and higher labeled "Full Head": NGC, 41; PCGS, 85.

Availability in circulated grades: Common.

Aspects of sharpness: In the Ron Pope survey of 1924-D quarters 337 were examined and 2% had Full Details. Those that have been certified as Full Head do not stand up to close scrutiny if other features such as the lower left of the shield and central clothing details are studied. Circulated coins are far less common than expected as the dates wore away on most.

	Cert	Avg	%MS	G-4	VG-8	F-12	VF-20	EF-40	AU-50	MS-60	MS-63	MS-65FH
1924-D	1,577	62.1	88%	$40	$45	$70	$100	$150	$180	$225	$350	$3,500

1924-S Standing Liberty Quarter

1924-S • Circulation-Strike Mintage: 2,860,000.

Availability in Mint State: Thousands, but far rather than many issues of the decade.

Populations of certified MS-65 and higher labeled "Full Head": NGC, 38; PCGS, 49.

Availability in circulated grades: Common.

Aspects of sharpness: In the Ron Pope survey of 1924-S quarters 189 were examined and 0.5% had Full Details. This is another variety to cherrypick for sharpness other than the head. Circulated coins are far less common than expected as the dates wore away on most.

	Cert	Avg	%MS	G-4	VG-8	F-12	VF-20	EF-40	AU-50	MS-60	MS-63	MS-65FH
1924-S	606	58.0	67%	$18	$28	$35	$55	$110	$225	$300	$800	$5,500

1925 Standing Liberty Quarter

1925 • Circulation-Strike Mintage: 12,280,000.

Availability in Mint State: Thousands exist.

Populations of certified MS-65 and higher labeled "Full Head": NGC, 142; PCGS, 270.

Availability in circulated grades: Common.

Aspects of sharpness: In the Ron Pope survey of 1925 quarters 281 were examined and 3% had Full Details.

Commentary: In 1925 Philadelphia was the only mint to strike quarters. Beginning with this year the date is in a recessed position. Accordingly, Standing Liberty quarters of this and later years were readily identifiable in circulation when collecting by date and mintmark became popular in the 1930s.

	Cert	Avg	%MS	G-4	VG-8	F-12	VF-20	EF-40	AU-50	MS-60	MS-63	MS-65FH
1925	1,225	61.0	81%	$7.50	$8	$10	$20	$40	$70	$130	$200	$750

1926 Standing Liberty Quarter

1926 • Circulation-Strike Mintage: 11,316,000.

Availability in Mint State: Thousands exist.

Populations of certified MS-65 and higher labeled "Full Head": NGC, 65; PCGS, 163.

Availability in circulated grades: Common.

Aspects of sharpness: In the Ron Pope survey of 1926 quarters 300 were examined and only 1% had Full Details. This is another variety to cherrypick for sharpness other than the head. There are many attractive coins in the marketplace. Only a few buyers will take the time to do this.

Commentary: Across the board the 1926 is common in all grades. Full Details coins are very rare, and hardly anyone takes notice of them.

	Cert	Avg	%MS	G-4	VG-8	F-12	VF-20	EF-40	AU-50	MS-60	MS-63	MS-65FH
1926	1,292	61.4	81%	$7.50	$8	$9	$20	$40	$70	$130	$150	$1,200

1926-D Standing Liberty Quarter

1926-D • **Circulation-Strike Mintage:** 1,716,000.

Availability in Mint State: Among all Standing Liberty quarter dates the most plentiful in Mint State today is the 1926-D. This is the only issue the author has handled in fairly large quantities in rolls, having had several dozen mint rolls over the years, including a group purchased in the 1950s from the Miners National Bank of Wilkes-Barre, Pennsylvania—coins kept in a vault for decades. There must have been other hoards as well, the details of which the author is unaware.

Populations of certified MS-65 and higher labeled "Full Head": NGC, 9; PCGS, 35.

Availability in circulated grades: Common.

Aspects of sharpness: In the Ron Pope survey of 1926-D quarters 351 were examined and 0%—not a single coin—had Full Details. On careful study some came quite close. This is poster example of an issue to cherrypick for sharpness other than the head.

Commentary: Taken as a whole the 1926-D quarter is the least satisfactory of all Standing Liberty issues from the standpoint of striking quality. Dozens of Full Head quarters have been certified by PCGS and NGC and cost a tremendous premium to buy. In another series the same can be said for 1926-D Buffalo nickels, most of which are weakly struck.

In October 1937 B. Max Mehl must have had a small hoard, for in *The Numismatic Scrapbook Magazine* he devoted an entire page to this: "I offer a brilliant Mint Uncirculated quarter dollar of 1926, Denver Mint, which is listed for $1.25 to $1.50, for only seventy-five cents!" Bank-wrapped rolls were common in numismatic circles until the coin boom that started in 1960 resulted in the breaking up of quantities of many early coins. The 1926-D was viewed as the most common variety in the series at the Mint State level.

Walter Breen's Complete Encyclopedia of U.S. and Colonial Coins, 1988, included this: "Plentiful in Mint State from bags recovered from banks in the early 1930s. Usually weak at head and drapery; full heads are prohibitively rare." No other record of *bags* has been found. These were seen in *rolls* with some frequency into the late 1950s, the only Standing Liberty quarter for which this could be said, except for the occasional rolls of other dates and mintmarks of the era (although the author has never seen a roll of 1927-S).

	Cert	Avg	%MS	G-4	VG-8	F-12	VF-20	EF-40	AU-50	MS-60	MS-63	MS-65FH
1926-D	2,258	63.0	96%	$7.50	$10	$22	$35	$70	$110	$150	$225	$23,000

1926-S Standing Liberty Quarter

1926-S • Circulation-Strike Mintage: 2,700,000.

Availability in Mint State: Hard to find at Mint State levels. Compare the availability of the 1926-S with that of the lower mintage 1927-D. How interesting!

Populations of certified MS-65 and higher labeled "Full Head": NGC, 20; PCGS, 100.

Availability in circulated grades: Slightly scarce in the context of later dates and mintmarks.

Aspects of sharpness: In the Ron Pope survey of 1926-S quarters 134 were examined and 0%—not even one coin—had Full Details. Most fail at the center and lower left of the shield. This is a poster example of an issue to cherrypick for sharpness other than the head. Several dozen Full Head coins have been certified by PCGS and NGC and sell at many multiples of coins that are not so labeled.

Commentary: Finding a Full Details coin would be an accomplishment, but the audience aware of this nicety is very small. Few buyers have any knowledge beyond what is imprinted on a holder and the current market price.

	Cert	Avg	%MS	G-4	VG-8	F-12	VF-20	EF-40	AU-50	MS-60	MS-63	MS-65FH
1926-S	443	54.5	57%	$7.50	$10	$15	$28	$90	$150	$375	$800	$25,000

1927 Standing Liberty Quarter

1927 • Circulation-Strike Mintage: 11,912,000.

Availability in Mint State: Thousands exist.

Populations of certified MS-65 and higher labeled "Full Head": NGC, 112; PCGS, 232.

Availability in circulated grades: Common.

Aspects of sharpness: In the Ron Pope survey of 1927 quarters 343 were examined and only 1% had Full Details. Striking quality was poor at all three mints this year. This is another variety to cherrypick for sharpness other than the head and also for eye appeal. There quite a few around that are nearly Full Details and are attractive.

Commentary: Across the board this is one of the most plentiful Standing Liberty quarters.

	Cert	Avg	%MS	G-4	VG-8	F-12	VF-20	EF-40	AU-50	MS-60	MS-63	MS-65FH
1927	1,518	60.2	76%	$7.50	$8	$9	$17	$35	$70	$130	$200	$750

1927-D Standing Liberty Quarter

1927-D • Circulation-Strike Mintage: 976,000.

Availability in Mint State: Thousands exist, but the coin is slightly scarce due to its low mintage.

Populations of certified MS-65 and higher labeled "Full Head": NGC, 59; PCGS, 104.

Availability in circulated grades: Common.

Aspects of sharpness: In the Ron Pope survey of 1927-D quarters 170 were examined and 0%—none—had Full Details. This is still another variety to cherrypick for sharpness other than the head. Over 100 Full Head coins have been certified by PCGS and NGC without regard shield sharpness and certain other details.

Commentary: Bank-wrapped rolls of 1927-D quarters, which had the second-lowest mintage (after 1927-S) of the later-date 1925–1930 issues, were available in the 1950s, but far fewer than for 1926-D. These were always saleable due to their general scarcity among coins found in circulation. In the 1960s most original rolls of Standing Liberty quarters were broken up and the coins sold individually.

	Cert	Avg	%MS	G-4	VG-8	F-12	VF-20	EF-40	AU-50	MS-60	MS-63	MS-65FH
1927-D	989	59.6	86%	$15	$20	$30	$75	$140	$190	$225	$330	$2,100

1927-S Standing Liberty Quarter

1927-S • Circulation-Strike Mintage: 396,000.

Availability in Mint State: This is far and away the key issue among later issues. Probably the number surviving is in the hundreds, not the thousands.

Populations of certified MS-65 and higher labeled "Full Head": NGC, 5; PCGS, 7.

Availability in circulated grades: Scarcest issue of the era.

Aspects of sharpness: In the Ron Pope survey of 1927-S quarters 145 were examined and 0%—no coins whatsoever—had Full Details. The usual suspects are shield and central clothing details. Again, here is a variety to cherrypick for sharpness other than the head. Over two dozen Full Head coins have been certified by PCGS and NGC and sell for huge premiums.

Commentary: The 1927-S has always been a key issue in the series. Even before 1960 Mint State coins were found one at a time, and not often, in the marketplace. No rolls or other groups have been reported.

	Cert	Avg	%MS	G-4	VG-8	F-12	VF-20	EF-40	AU-50	MS-60	MS-63	MS-65FH
1927-S	1,339	24.8	11%	$35	$45	$110	$325	$950	$2,250	$4,750	$7,000	$170,000

1928 Standing Liberty Quarter

1928 • Circulation-Strike Mintage: 6,336,000.

Availability in Mint State: Thousands exist.

Populations of certified MS-65 and higher labeled "Full Head": NGC, 79; PCGS, 164.

Availability in circulated grades: Common.

Aspects of sharpness: In the Ron Pope survey of 1928 quarters 228 were examined and 6% had Full Details. The 1921 and 1928, each with 6% Full Details, are tied for second in this quality among Type II quarters, with only 1917 higher (with 15%).

Commentary: The Pope survey does not necessarily square with population reports as the last are often expanded by multiple resubmissions, yielding little net data.

	Cert	Avg	%MS	G-4	VG-8	F-12	VF-20	EF-40	AU-50	MS-60	MS-63	MS-65FH
1928	990	61.0	80%	$7.50	$8	$9	$17	$35	$65	$120	$175	$1,400

1928-D Standing Liberty Quarter

1928-D • Circulation-Strike Mintage: 1,627,600.

Availability in Mint State: Thousands exist, but this issue is scarcer than some others of the era.

Populations of certified MS-65 and higher labeled "Full Head": NGC, 34; PCGS, 59.

Availability in circulated grades: Common.

Aspects of sharpness: In the Ron Pope survey of 1928-D quarters 379 were examined and only 1% had Full Details. This is another variety to cherrypick for sharpness other than the head as coins labeled Full Head are very expensive.

Commentary: 1928-D quarters were available in quantity at face value plus postage from the Treasury Department at a later time, per a notice received by the American Numismatic Association on April 23, 1932.

	Cert	Avg	%MS	G-4	VG-8	F-12	VF-20	EF-40	AU-50	MS-60	MS-63	MS-65FH
1928-D	1,466	63.0	92%	$7.50	$8	$9	$17	$35	$65	$120	$175	$3,000

1928-S Standing Liberty Quarter

1928-S • Circulation-Strike Mintage: 2,644,000.

Availability in Mint State: Thousands exist.

Populations of certified MS-65 and higher labeled "Full Head": NGC, 275; PCGS, 281.[86]

Availability in circulated grades: Common.

Aspects of sharpness: In the Ron Pope survey of 1928-S quarters 318 were examined and 0.6% had Full Details—far, far from what might be assumed from population reports. This is another variety to cherrypick for sharpness other than the head.

Commentary: 1928-S quarters were available in quantity at face value plus postage from the Treasury Department at a later time, per a notice received by the American Numismatic Association on April 23, 1932.

	Cert	Avg	%MS	G-4	VG-8	F-12	VF-20	EF-40	AU-50	MS-60	MS-63	MS-65FH
1928-S	1,460	62.6	89%	$7.50	$8	$9	$22	$40	$70	$120	$190	$1,000

VARIETY: *1928-S, Inverted Mintmark (FS-25-1828S-501).* On some examples, the mintmark was punched upside down in the die, making it wider and heavier on top. As these have not been widely noticed they can often be found by cherrypicking.

1929 Standing Liberty Quarter

1929 • Circulation-Strike Mintage: 11,140,000.

Availability in Mint State: Thousands exist, but years ago hardly ever seen in roll quantities (in contrast with, say, 1926-D).

Populations of certified MS-65 and higher labeled "Full Head": NGC, 228; PCGS, 377.

Availability in circulated grades: Common.

Aspects of sharpness: In the Ron Pope survey of 1929 quarters 476 were examined and 2% had Full Details.

Commentary: 1929 quarters were available in quantity at face value plus postage from the Treasury Department at a later time, per a notice received by the American Numismatic Association on April 23, 1932.

Although population reports are fun to read, take this information to heart: For the 1929 quarter PCGS has certified 377 in MS-65 or higher with Full Head. In contrast, only 185 regular (without Full Head) 1929 quarters have been certified at this level. In the real world, non–Full Head coins are very, very common and *true* Full Head coins are rare. The vast majority of coin buyers are not aware of such as few take the time to truly study what they hope to buy. This gives informed buyers such as *you* a great advantage with relation to value obtained for the prices paid.

	Cert	Avg	%MS	G-4	VG-8	F-12	VF-20	EF-40	AU-50	MS-60	MS-63	MS-65FH
1929	1,896	61.3	80%	$7.50	$8	$9	$17	$35	$65	$120	$175	$700

1929-D Standing Liberty Quarter

1929-D • Circulation-Strike Mintage: 1,358,000.

Availability in Mint State: Thousands exist, but this is not among the most common issues of the era.

Populations of certified MS-65 and higher labeled "Full Head": NGC, 30; PCGS, 68.

Availability in circulated grades: Common.

Aspects of sharpness: In the Ron Pope survey of 1929-D quarters 214 were examined and 0.4% had Full Details. This is another variety to cherrypick for sharpness other than the head. Certified Full Head coins are easy enough to find and cost a great premium over those that are nearly as nice, but are not so labeled. Striking quality dropped even lower toward the end of the series.

Commentary: These seem to have been fully paid out by the Treasury Department in this and the next one or two years, as there is no record of the government having any undistributed quantities later.

	Cert	Avg	%MS	G-4	VG-8	F-12	VF-20	EF-40	AU-50	MS-60	MS-63	MS-65FH
1929-D	992	60.6	75%	$7.50	$8	$9	$17	$35	$65	$120	$175	$5,000

1929-S Standing Liberty Quarter

1929-S • Circulation-Strike Mintage: 1,764,000.

Availability in Mint State: Thousands exist, but they are scarcer than contemporary Philadelphia Mint issues.

Populations of certified MS-65 and higher labeled "Full Head": NGC, 259; PCGS, 387.

Availability in circulated grades: Common.

Aspects of sharpness: In the Ron Pope survey of 1929-S quarters 332 were examined and 0%—again, not a single coin—had Full Details. This is another variety to cherrypick for sharpness other than the head. Points to check include details of the shield, central clothing, and eagle's breast. In sharp contrast, hundreds of Full Head coins have been certified by PCGS and NGC.

Commentary: 1929-S quarters were available in quantity at face value plus postage from the Treasury Department at a later time, per a notice received by the American Numismatic Association on April 23, 1932.

	Cert	Avg	%MS	G-4	VG-8	F-12	VF-20	EF-40	AU-50	MS-60	MS-63	MS-65FH
1929-S	1,418	61.4	83%	$7.50	$8	$9	$17	$35	$65	$120	$175	$700

1930 Standing Liberty Quarter

1930 • **Circulation-Strike Mintage:** 5,632,000.

Availability in Mint State: Thousands exist.

Populations of certified MS-65 and higher labeled "Full Head": NGC, 664; PCGS, 1,202.

Availability in circulated grades: Common.

Aspects of sharpness: In the Ron Pope survey of 1930 quarters 1,008 were examined and 4% had Full Details.

Commentary: 1930 quarters were available in quantity at face value plus postage from the Treasury Department at a later time, per a notice received by the American Numismatic Association on April 23, 1932. Due to its high mintage the 1930 quarter is very common in Mint State today, with nearly all being typical strikes with lightness.

	Cert	Avg	%MS	G-4	VG-8	F-12	VF-20	EF-40	AU-50	MS-60	MS-63	MS-65FH
1930	3,589	61.7	79%	$7.50	$8	$9	$17	$35	$65	$120	$175	$675

1930-S Standing Liberty Quarter

1930-S • **Circulation-Strike Mintage:** 1,556,000.

Availability in Mint State: Thousands exist, but many fewer than for its Philadelphia counterpart.

Populations of certified MS-65 and higher labeled "Full Head": NGC, 247; PCGS, 324.

Availability in circulated grades: Common.

Aspects of sharpness: In the Ron Pope survey of 1930-S quarters 275 were examined and 0.4% had Full Details. Scott's *Catalogue and Encyclopedia of United States Coins*, written by Don Taxay and published in 1971, stated that there was no such thing as a 1930-S quarter dollar with a Full Head. When the book came out, collectors and dealers were surprised to read this. This book was largely based on input from Walter Breen, backed by John J. Ford Jr., and in many areas it was lightly researched.

The present author and a number of other numismatists soon identified a number of *truly* Full Head coins. Today, coins certified as Full Head are common as the standards for sharpness have dropped sharply. However, nearly all are lacking in sharpness of some of the other details. Quite a few "almost" coins have lightness at the lower left of the shield and on the eagle's breast.

Commentary: 1930-S quarters were available in quantity at face value plus postage from the Treasury Department at a later time, per a notice received by the American Numismatic Association on April 23, 1932.

	Cert	Avg	%MS	G-4	VG-8	F-12	VF-20	EF-40	AU-50	MS-60	MS-63	MS-65FH
1930-S	1,089	61.7	84%	$7.50	$8	$9	$17	$35	$65	$120	$175	$700

WASHINGTON, EAGLE REVERSE, QUARTER DOLLARS (1932–1998)

Designer: *John Flanagan.* **Weight:** *Silver issue—6.25 grams; clad issue—5.67 grams; silver Proofs—6.25 grams.* **Composition:** *Silver issue—.900 silver, .100 copper (net weight .18084 oz. pure silver); clad issue—outer layers of copper nickel (.750 copper, .250 nickel) bonded to inner core of pure copper; silver Proofs—.900 silver, .100 copper (net weight .18084 oz. pure silver).* **Diameter:** *24.3 mm.* **Edge:** *Reeded.* **Mints:** *Philadelphia, Denver, and San Francisco.*

Circulation Strike   **Proof**

Mintmark location, 1932–1964, is on the reverse, below the eagle.   **Mintmark location, 1965 to date, is on the obverse, to right of the hair ribbon.**

Bicentennial Variety: Designers: *John Flanagan and Jack L. Ahr.* **Weight:** *Silver issue—5.75 grams; copper-nickel issue—5.67 grams.* **Composition:** *Silver issue—outer layers of .800 silver, .200 copper bonded to inner core of .209 silver, .791 copper (net weight .0739 oz. pure silver); copper-nickel issue—outer layers of .750 copper, .250 nickel bonded to inner core of pure copper.* **Diameter:** *24.3 mm.* **Edge:** *Reeded.* **Mints:** *Philadelphia, Denver, and San Francisco.*

Bicentennial variety   **Bicentennial variety, Proof**

HISTORY AND BACKGROUND

In the midst of the Roaring Twenties, as the American economy thundered along, plans were being made for an important national event that was still several years distant. Public- and private-sector officials alike were tasked with planning for the bicentennial of the birth of George Washington, which would take place in 1932. How best to honor this important anniversary of the Father of Our Country? Numerous plans were considered, proposed, and scrapped. The United States George Washington Bicentennial Commission was formed; its members discussed a commemorative medal, a related half dollar, stamps, perhaps even a world's fair like the Panama-Pacific International Exposition of 1915. (The 1926 Sesquicentennial Exposition in Philadelphia turned out to be a financial dud, however, ending thoughts of a similar event in 1932.)

In 1930 Congress passed a bill authorizing a Washington bicentennial commemorative coin, but President Herbert Hoover vetoed it. Given the number of commemorative coins minted in the previous 10 years, as well as the number of pending bills for coinage and additional requests in earlier stages, Hoover was concerned about the integrity of the U.S. monetary system. He worried that a proliferation of commemoratives would be a boon to counterfeiters—lacking standard coinage, the public would be unable to determine which coins were real and which were not. He noted that Congress had already addressed this issue when it provided that "no change in the design or die of any coin shall be made

President Hoover addresses a joint session of Congress at a bicentennial ceremony commemorating the 200th anniversary of the birth of George Washington, February 22, 1932. Had Hoover not vetoed a commemorative coin in honor of the occasion, the classic circulating Washington quarter might never have existed.

oftener than once in twenty-five years from and including the year of the first adoption of the design, model, die, or hub from the same coin."[87] Instead, Hoover offered, "The government would be glad to assist such celebrations in the creation of appropriate medals which do not have coinage functions."

On February 21, 1930, a new group—the George Washington Bicentennial Committee—was established by an act of Congress. They soon were at work on an appropriate *regular-issue* half dollar to honor the occasion. The half dollar was their logical coin of choice, as the largest regularly circulating silver denomination. It was decided to open a competition for designs that would serve for both a circulating commemorative coin and a medal, with the artists being subject to the following guidelines under the direction of Secretary of the Treasury Andrew W. Mellon:

> That, subject to the approval of Congress, the coinage of the United States silver half dollars during the calendar year 1932 shall have a commemorative character.

> That the obverse shall bear a head of Washington based on the Houdon bust at Mount Vernon.

> That the design of the reverse is left to the sculptor, with the proviso that it shall be national in conception.

> That one sculptor be selected to design both the coin (if Congress shall provide) and the medal (already provided for).

> That each competitor shall submit in plaster for one design for each the obverse and reverse of the medal. The designs for the coin will be considered when and if Congress shall so provide.

The Houdon bust was already the most familiar coin and medal representation of Washington, having been used on the 1900 Lafayette dollar, 1926 Sesquicentennial half dollar, and hundreds of tokens and medals. All entries were to be submitted by October 27, 1930, at which time they would be reviewed by the Commission of Fine Arts—an advisory group whose members would make recommendations to the Treasury Department.

Houdon's bust of Washington at Mount Vernon inspired hundreds of designs on coins and medals, like the 1900 Lafayette dollar, the 1926 Sesquicentennial half dollar, and the 1790 Washington Before Boston medal (ranked second in the *100 Greatest American Medals and Tokens*).

As the competition was underway, an obstacle to using the half dollar for the new motif became more apparent. Although its large format made an attractive canvas on which to honor the birth of the first U.S. president, the half dollar was not the best choice in a struggling economy. There had been no need in the United States for half dollars, and none had been coined since 1929.

Thus, on February 9, 1931, Representative Perkins introduced HR 16973 to change the chosen format to the quarter dollar, instead of the half dollar. The House of Representatives Coinage Committee issued a memorandum on February 13, 1931, addressing several issues, including the ban on changing design more often than once every 25 years. The proposed legislation was required in order to overcome that prohibition. The memorandum concluded:

> As the new design would replace the present type of quarter dollar, it would be in no sense a "special coin," and the issue thereof would not be contrary to the Department's policy of opposing the issue of "special coins."
>
> The plan would serve several purposes:
>
> 1. It would replace an unsatisfactory design now being issued. *[Modern fans of the Standing Liberty quarter design then in use might disagree!]*
> 2. It would be in a popular denomination; and
> 3. It would permit the Treasury Department to contribute a notable feature to the coming celebration.

The Commission of Fine Arts had concluded its design competition and the entry by the accomplished sculptor Laura Gardin Fraser, who was also the choice of the Bicentennial Medal Committee. She had a contract to do the commemorative medal, and it seemed natural that she should create a coin to match. Both groups wanted Fraser's designs, and both wanted the half dollar for coin on which they would be placed—but they were destined to lose on both points.

On March 4, 1931, Congress authorized the quarter dollar for the Washington bicentennial. The Treasury Department was in a position to cooperate (or not) with the Medal Committee and the Commission of Fine Arts, but the it alone was in charge of the final decision. Over the protests of the commission's chairman, Secretary Mellon initiated a new competition to seek a design for the quarter dollar. This second competition attracted more than 100 entries by 98 artists, a few of whom submitted more than one design, as they were allowed to do.

The commission again selected a model by Laura Gardin Fraser, but Secretary Mellon strongly preferred a submission by artist John Flanagan.

Mellon left office on February 12, 1932, to take up an appointment as ambassador to Great Britain. Although a final decision in the matter had not been made, his successor, Ogden L. Mills, chose to adhere to Mellon's choice. "The duty of making the selection falls upon the secretary of the Treasury," Mills said, "and not upon the Commission of Fine Arts, the function of that body being purely advisory."

The official choice was made, and on April 16, the name of competition winner John Flanagan was publicly disclosed. John Sinnock, chief engraver at the Mint, prepared the final models needed for the process of creating working dies.

JOHN F. FLANAGAN, MEDALIST

John F. Flanagan, designer of the Washington quarter.

John F. Flanagan (1865–1952), a sculptor and medalist born in Newark, New Jersey, was a studio assistant to sculptor Augustus Saint-Gaudens from 1885 to 1890. Flanagan learned from the master the techniques of creating human figures in plaster, metal, and stone. In particular, he worked on the Saint-Gaudens statue of Lincoln that now stands in Lincoln Park, Chicago.

For the World's Columbian Exposition, opened to the public in Chicago in 1893, Flanagan assisted Frederick MacMonnies in the creation of the Columbia Fountain. MacMonnies, although his name is not familiar in popular numismatics today, is well remembered by medal specialists. Importantly, he considered John F. Flanagan to be "the leading medalist of America." In the 1890s, Flanagan lived in Europe and spent most of his time there. In Paris, he became internationally known for his relief work. In 1902 he settled in New York City, where he remained for the rest of his career.

In 1904, at the Louisiana Purchase Exposition, several of Flanagan's works were on display. Working in his New York City studio, Flanagan created many highly acclaimed medals and plaques, including the official award medal for the Panama-Pacific International Exposition. In 1905, Flanagan went to Cornish, New Hampshire, and modeled a portrait of Saint-Gaudens from life. The art remained unfinished at Saint-Gaudens's death in 1907. In 1920, he resumed work, now with a commission from New York University's Hall of Remembrance for American Artists.

Flanagan joined the American Numismatic Society on November 17, 1909, this being the year after it moved into its well-appointed building on Audubon Terrace on Broadway between West 155th and West 156th streets. This building was a meeting place for sculptors and artists interested in medals. Victor D. Brenner, creator of the Lincoln cent of 1909, had been a member of the society since 1894.

In 1909, Flanagan created a medal for the Massachusetts Horticultural Society, depicting a kneeling gardener with a greenhouse in the background—evocative of a fine estate. After the sinking of the *Titanic* on April 15, 1912, Congress voted that a gold medal be made to honor Captain Arthur Henry Rostron, whose crew helped rescue many survivors; Flanagan won the design competition. In 1915, Flanagan was named an associate member of the Academy of Design. In the same year, several of his sculptures were on view, by invitation, at the Tower of Jewels at the Panama-Pacific International Exposition in San Francisco. In 1920 he created a medal titled *From the People of the United States to the City of Verdun.*[88]

In the 1920s and 1930s Flanagan's address was 1931 Broadway, New York City. By that time his list of accomplishments was lengthy. For the Library of Congress, he created a monumental clock. For the Knickerbocker Hotel, famous in its time, he sculpted a highly acclaimed marble relief of Aphrodite. A bronze portrait of aviation pioneer Samuel Pierpont Langley was made on commission for the Smithsonian Institution.[89] It seems that he was kept continually busy with a stream of public and private projects, at least through the heady economic times extending to the late 1920s. Included were dozens of portrait plaques of artists, notable Americans, and commissioned subjects. After that time, new work became scarce, although many buildings and civic projects authorized before 1930 were carried to completion.

THE FINAL DESIGN

Although the Flanagan portrait is usually described as a close copy of the Houdon bust, in fact it is not. Both the Flanagan and the Fraser portraits show a peruke of long hair tied by a ribbon, similar to that on the Houdon bust. But Flanagan outlined the head differently, and modified the bust's simple hair by adding a heavy roll of curled hair around the base of the head and a ribbon flourish at the end of the peruke—artistic license that does not seem to have been widely commented upon at the time (except, perhaps, behind closed doors at the Commission of Fine Arts). Laura Gardin Fraser's version was much closer to the original. The heavy roll of curled hair was distinctive to Flanagan's interpretation, although some early adaptations of Houdon's bust do have a light roll of hair.

The head is well positioned on the new quarter. On the 1932 issue, the letters in the lower left obverse field are not bold (per numismatic terminology, they are in the Light Motto style). Early in 1934 (no quarters were made in 1933), after more Light Motto coins were made, the letters were strengthened to create the Heavy Motto, in effect from that time onward.

Mintmarks, D or S, were placed below the wreath on silver issues struck at Denver and San Francisco, respectively, from 1932 to 1964. No mintmarks were used from 1965 to 1967, when the Treasury Department, under Mint Director Eva Adams, sought to "punish" numismatists for supposedly creating a nationwide coin shortage. Later issues, made of clad metal, have a D or S mintmark, later joined by P

Laura Gardin Fraser's design, selected for the bicentennial medal but rejected for the circulating coin, unquestionably hewed more closely to the Houdon model. It was revived, with slight modifications, for the 1999 Washington Death Bicentennial gold $5 commemorative coin shown here.

John Flanagan's rendering depicted a more formal, "powdered-wig" look that deviated from the style of the Houdon bust. Perhaps he meant to depict Washington more as he appeared in the public imagination: as the first president of the United States of America.

The famed terra-cotta Houdon bust at Mount Vernon was produced from a life mask of George Washington. As these photographs show, Washington's hair is depicted quite simply, as if Houdon wished to capture the dignity of the man apart from the trappings of the great office he held.

when the Philadelphia Mint used this letter. The location is on the obverse to the right of the ribbon at the lower part of Washington's hair.

At long last, the Mint had a new coin design that had no problems in striking! The heads of Washington and the eagle are both arranged with the relief spread over a large area, with no high-relief points. Accordingly, the vast majority of Washington quarters of the 1932-to-1998 era are well struck. This aspect, although not widely mentioned in numismatic texts, is a blessing for collectors.

THREE REVERSE VARIETIES

On the reverse the national bird is depicted as especially bold, with heavy wings opened and extending downward. The eagle is firmly perched on a bundle of arrows. Similar bold eagles in the art deco style were popular as architectural ornaments at the time. A wreath below completes the arc of the eagle's wings and adds a nice effect. Above the eagle's head is the motto E PLURIBUS / UNUM in small letters on two lines. UNITED STATES OF AMERICA is around the top border, and QUARTER DOLLAR is at the lower border.

Over the years, both the obverse and the reverse of the coin underwent gradual changes. On the reverse, three distinct varieties of the Washington quarter emerged. These are hardly ever mentioned in print, but are easily noticeable on close examination. They are as follows:

Reverse Variety A (starting 1932): The Variety A (Breen nomenclature is *Type A*; Hicks nomenclature is *Variety I*) reverse is from an original design by John Flanagan. The relief is low, and the E and S in STATES nearly touch. The border between the field and the edges of the letters and motif is often indistinct. There is only one bold leaf to the left of the arrowheads, and the leaf above the A in DOLLAR is very weak and hardly visible. This reverse was used on circulation strikes from 1932 to 1958 and on Proofs of 1936.

Reverse Variety B (starting 1937): Variety B (Breen Type B, Hicks Variety II) was introduced this year. The relief was strengthened by a lowering of the field. In this variety, the E and S in STATES appear distinctly separated. There are two bold leaves to the left of the arrowheads; the stronger leaf touches or nearly touches top of the A in DOLLAR. The leaf touches on some Proofs, and nearly touches on dies that were more extensively relapped. Stronger than on Variety A. Certain letters and the edges of feathers were retouched. This reverse was used on Proofs of 1937 to 1964 and on circulation strikes from 1959 to 1964. Details on the Proofs are sharper than on circulation strikes.

Reverse Variety C (starting 1964): Variety C (Breen Type C, Hicks Variety III) was introduced this year. It is similar to Variety A in general relief. Leaf details include the centers for the first time. The leaf above the A in DOLLAR is short and does not touch the letter. This variety was probably made in anticipation of the clad coinage that commenced in 1965, but it is known on some of the silver 1964-D coins.

Reverse Variety B (middle) was introduced on the 1937 Proof quarter and was continued on Proofs through 1964. Reverse B was employed on circulation strikes from 1959 to 1964. Compare to Reverse A (left). Reverse C (right) was first used for circulation on certain 1964-D quarters.

Although it doesn't constitute a separate variety, in 1993 the relief of the reverse was lowered and the feathers and lettering were sharpened. This was in keeping with a general trend with the obverse of lowering the relief and sharpening the details.

THREE EARLY MOTTO STYLES

In 1934, there were two obverse hub changes: the "Medium Motto" and the "Heavy Motto." The Medium Motto was used for just a short time in 1934, then for all coinage of 1935. The Heavy Motto was ntroduced in June 1934 and was used on 1934 and 1934-D coins, and in 1936. Later it became the standard. Light, Medium, and Heavy Motto varieties exist for 1934. Medium and Heavy Motto varieties exist for 1934-D.

Light Motto: The central peak of the W in WE is lower than the sides. The letters and field blend without strong differentiation of the letter edges. Used for 1932, 1932-D, 1932-S, and some 1934 coins.

Medium Motto: The central peak of the W in WE is lower than the sides. It has the same style as the Light Motto, but the letters are stronger and are not faded into the field. This was used for some 1934 and 1934-D coins and all 1935 coinage.

Heavy Motto: The central peak of the W in WE is higher than the sides, and the letters are heavier (thicker) than the those on the other 1934 varieties. This was used for some 1934 and 1934-D coins; then it became standard beginning in 1936.

A DEVELOPING OBVERSE PORTRAIT

Over its 88 years of service so far, Flanagan's portrait of Washington was gradually modified, in some cases to improve its appearance, in others to adapt the design to changing mechanical demands. Through the 1940s the changes involved mostly improvements to the profile of Washington. Starting in 1965, the relief was lowered repeatedly; and starting in the 1980s, the details in the hair were frequently sharpened. The following list and associated images capture most of these changes. From one coin to the next the difference is often scarcely noticeable without close study—but alongside the original 1932 version, a modern America the Beautiful obverse is strikingly different, even to the untrained eye.

1932—Original design.

1934—See Light, Heavy, and Medium Motto styles in the previous section.

1938—The profile details were slightly strengthened.

1944—The profile details were slightly strengthened; minor changes were made to the peruke and ribbon; the designer's initials became slightly distorted.

1945—The designer's initials were corrected.

1965—A new obverse hub with slightly lower relief was introduced for the clad coinage.

1974—A new obverse hub was introduced, with the relief lowered slightly and certain details sharpened.

1976—Another new obverse hub was introduced, with the dual date "1776 • 1976," a slightly lower relief, and sharpening of certain details.

1977—Certain details were reworked and the relief was lowered even further.

1982–1983—The diameter of the design area was slightly reduced to move them farther from the rim.

1987—The hairline and curls were sharpened.

1988—The hairline and curls were sharpened further.

1992—The hairline and curls were sharpened still further; the border was widened slightly; and the relief was slightly lowered.

1994–1998—The relief was slightly and repeatedly lowered, and the hairline and curls repeatedly sharpened.

1999—The obverse was redesigned for the 50 State Quarters Program, and the date was moved to the reverse.

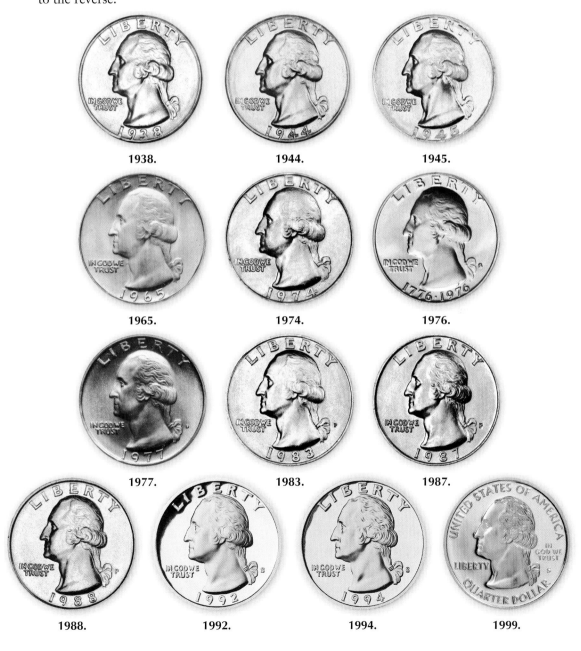

| 1938. | 1944. | 1945. |

| 1965. | 1974. | 1976. |

| 1977. | 1983. | 1987. |

| 1988. | 1992. | 1994. | 1999. |

Minting the Coins

Production commenced in the summer of 1932, but there was no need for more quarter dollars in commerce at that time. None had been made since 1930, when 5,632,000 of the Standing Liberty design were struck at the Philadelphia Mint and 1,556,000 at the San Francisco Mint.

Money was scarce in people's pockets in 1932, and the Mint had no plans for a generous production. By year's end, the Philadelphia Mint had struck 5,404,000 coins, Denver had made 436,800, and San Francisco had produced 408,000. On August 1, 1932, the quarters were released into circulation.

In September, *The Numismatist* printed a report on the new coin. The article reminded readers that it carried a new design to commemorate the 200th anniversary of Washington's birth, and was not a "commemorative" coin in numismatic terms. It pointed out that the Washington quarter corrects the problem of wear that had plagued the design it replaced, and that had earned the Standing Liberty motif "almost universal objection." In conclusion:

> All in all, it is an attractive coin. The bust of Washington stands out in strong relief in contrast to the reverse, which appears somewhat crowded, particularly the part above the eagle's head. But sculptors are better judges of such things than laymen.

The supply of 1932 quarters was sufficient that no more were made in 1933. This was the very depth of the Depression. In 1934, coinage of the quarter resumed, with the Philadelphia, Denver, and San Francisco mints producing coins each year for the rest of the decade (except for San Francisco in 1938).

The coinage from each of the three mints continued through 1954, with the exception of San Francisco in 1949. The year 1954 marked the end of making quarter dollars for the San Francisco Mint; and, after coining cents and dimes in 1955, it was announced that the facility would discontinue operations as a mint and would serve only as an assay office and storage facility. From 1955 through 1964, quarters were made each year at the Philadelphia and Denver mints.

In 1936 the Philadelphia Mint offered Proof sets for sale; it was the first such coinage since 1916. Each contained a Lincoln cent, Buffalo nickel, Mercury dime, Washington quarter, and Liberty Walking half dollar. Sets were sold at $1.81 each, and single coins could also be ordered. In the first year, 3,837 Proof quarters were made, in comparison to 5,569 cents. Proof sets continued to be produced through 1942, then were discontinued due to the exigencies of World War II. In 1942 the mintage of Proof quarters was 21,123, compared to 32,600 Proof cents.

During this period, quarters were also less popular than the other denominations with regard to collecting circulation strikes. The cent, nickel, and dime were regarded as inexpensive, and the higher-denomination Liberty Walking half dollar was admired for its artistry. Washington quarters fell betwixt and between.

The Great Confusion of 1965–1967

In 1964, the price of silver was rising on international markets, and was seemingly headed to the point that it would cost more than face value to mint silver dimes, quarters, and half dollars (the higher denominations then being made). The Treasury Department made a sweeping change: beginning in 1965, silver coins would no longer be made, except for half dollars, which would have a sharply reduced silver content. Thus a tradition of minted silver coins that had started in 1794 came to an end. Later, some silver coins would be made for collectors and sold at a premium. In 1971 silver was dropped from the half dollars. The substitute metal was a clad composition—a metal sandwich with an outer layer of copper-nickel (75% copper and 25% nickel, the same alloy used for five-cent pieces) bonded to a core of 100% copper.

In 1965 the public was still agog about coins. Lincoln cents, Jefferson nickels, and all other denominations were being hoarded, especially the lower values. Cents were scarce at supermarkets and stores, and some advertised to pay a few cents' premium for every 100 coins brought to them. In the meantime,

Kennedy half dollars continued to be minted, but all were hoarded by the public. For years afterward, despite mintages of hundreds of millions of coins, the Kennedy half dollars did not circulate. The quarter dollar became the highest-value circulating coin of the United States.

This was a dynamic change. In time, as new vending machines were developed, and when arcade machines (first pinball, then digital games like Pac Man, Donkey Kong, and the like) became a passion for the younger set, their slots took quarters. Half dollars remained out of circulation. To this day they are rarely seen in commerce.

In 1965, Mint Director Eva Adams continued to blame coin collectors for the coin shortage—an erroneous view that was loudly protested by the numismatic press. Numismatists did not cause the problem, the general public did, in combination with sluggishness in the Federal Reserve System's distribution process.

To punish coin collectors, Director Adams, backed by Congress, carried out the decree that Proof sets would no longer be made and that mintmarks (D for Denver) would be removed from coins. Moreover, the Silver Bullion Depository at West Point, on the grounds of the Military Academy (and later called the West Point Bullion Depository), was equipped with coining presses to turn out cents, but without mintmarks. The San Francisco Mint, now known as the San Francisco Assay Office, once again began to produce coins for circulation, its first since 1955 (when it had last made cents and dimes). Adams declared that no mintmark would be used. Included were silver quarters dated 1964 and without mintmark. The San Francisco Assay Office / Mint began in 1966 to produce Special Mint Sets (SMSs)—quasi-Proofs—that were dated 1965. Special Mint Sets were also made in 1966 and 1967 with dates of those two years. In time the San Francisco Mint designation was restored, and it remains in use today.

Despite numerous pronouncements by Treasury officials to the contrary, the numismatic community felt that it was receiving the lion's share of the blame, while virtually nothing was being done to discourage everyday citizens from hoarding coins. The topsy-turvy mintmarkless and date-mix situation lasted until 1968, when Denver coins got their mintmarks back. In the same year, the mintmark position on the quarter changed to be on the obverse, at the lower right, opposite the end of Washington's wig. From 1968 onward, the figures in Mint Reports reflected where the coins were struck, and, generally, with the date on the coin matching the calendar date.[90]

THE QUARTER REMAINS DOMINANT

In the late 1960s the price of silver rose, and silver coins in circulation became worth more than face value. The public rushed to sell them to coin dealers, bullion brokers, and others, who sent them to refineries. By the early 1970s, no more were to be seen in commerce. In the meantime, half dollars old and new disappeared from circulation, and the quarter dollar remained established as the largest denomination in wide use.

In 1968, the Mint resumed its production of Proof sets. This time they were produced by the San Francisco Assay Office, as it was then called (the term Mint was later restored), instead of by the Philadelphia Mint. The Proofs were struck on slow, knuckle-style presses, some of them dating back to the 19th century. Though old, they were very effective for the job. Each coin was struck twice in rapid eye-blink succession, to bring up the details fully. Each coin bore an S mintmark. From that time to the present day, Proof sets with quarters have been issued—a continuous run (except for the year 1975) of nearly 90 years.

THE BICENTENNIAL

To observe the Bicentennial of American Independence in 1976 the Treasury Department announced that three coin denominations—the quarter dollar, half dollar, and dollar—would have obverses of regular style, but dated "1776 • 1976" (commonly described in numismatic literature as 1776–1976), combined with reverses of a commemorative nature.

The National Bicentennial Coin Design Competition was launched, and many professional artists entered. The winner for the quarter dollar was Jack L. Ahr, of Arlington Heights, Illinois, whose motif of a colonial drummer boy was considered by numismatists to be very attractive.

On Wednesday, April 24, 1974, the three winners were hosted at the White House, where they were signed up as ANA members and each was presented with a $5,000 check. Two days later, the artists visited the Philadelphia Mint to meet with the staff of the Engraving Department and view the process of transforming a design to models, then through the Janvier transfer lathe, to smaller size to make hubs. Mint Director Mary Brooks stated that she expected that 1.4 billion quarters, 400 million half dollars, and 225 million dollars would be minted with the new motifs. Clad metal was to be used for coins struck at all three mints, plus silver for special pieces to be made only at San Francisco. During the following year, 1975, the mints struck regular-design quarters from 1974 as well as many coins with the 1776–1976 date. Thus the mints in 1975 were re-striking and pre-striking, but were making no quarters dated 1975!

The Bicentennial coins were released in 1976. It was a slump time in the coin market, and sales of Proof coins and silver versions were so sluggish that the Mint had supplies on hand for sale for several years afterward.

The Bicentennial Reverse.

LATER ISSUES

The regular Washington quarter dollar design was resumed in 1977. From then until 1998, circulation-strike coinage took place at the Philadelphia and Denver Mints, and Proofs were made at San Francisco. From 1992 through 1998, special silver Proofs were made at San Francisco, these in addition to regular clad Proofs of the same years. In 1999 the 50 State Quarters® Program was inaugurated. For the next 10 years, five states per year would be honored with a special reverse design on the quarter dollar. The order was the same as the sequence in which each acquired statehood, beginning with Delaware. The program was extended for one year to include six United States territories. Following this program, the America the Beautiful Program was created to honor a site of "national or historic significance" from each state, the District of Columbia, and five United States territories.

WASHINGTON, EAGLE REVERSE, QUARTER DOLLARS (1932–1998)

GRADING STANDARDS

MS-60 to 70 (Mint State). *Obverse:* At MS-60, some abrasion and contact marks are evident on the hair above the ear and at the top of the head below the E of LIBERTY. At MS-63, abrasion is slight at best, less so for MS-64. An MS-65 coin should display no abrasion or contact marks except under magnification, and MS-66 and higher coins should have none at all. Luster should be full and rich. *Reverse:* Comments apply as for the

1939-D. Graded MS-64.

obverse, except that the eagle's breast and legs are the places to check. On both sides the fields are protected by design elements and do not show contact marks readily.

AU-50, 53, 55, 58 (About Uncirculated). *Obverse:* Light wear is seen on the cheek, the high areas of the hair, and the neck. At AU-58, the luster is extensive but incomplete, especially on the higher parts and in the field. At AU–50 and 53, luster is less. *Reverse:* Light wear is seen on the breast, legs, and upper edges of the wings of the eagle. An AU-58 coin has nearly full luster. At AU-50 and 53, there still is significant luster.

1932-S. Graded AU-55.

EF-40, 45 (Extremely Fine). *Obverse:* Further wear is seen on the head. Higher-relief details are gone in the hair. The higher-relief parts of the neck show wear, most noticeably just above the date. *Reverse:* Further wear is seen on the eagle. Most breast feathers, not strong to begin with, are worn away.

1932-D. Graded EF-40.

VF-20, 30 (Very Fine). *Obverse:* Most hair detail is worn away, except above the curls. The delineation between the temple and the edge of the hair is faint. The curl by the ear is worn flat. Tips of the letters in LIBERTY and the date digits touch the rim in some instances. *Reverse:* More details of the eagle are worn away, and the outlines of the feathers in the wing, while nearly all present, are faint. Tips of the letters touch the rim in some instances on this and lower grades, but this can vary from coin to coin depending on the strength of the rim.

1942-D, Doubled Die Obverse; FS-101. Graded VF-30.

F-12, 15 (Fine). *Obverse:* Most of the hair is worn flat, with no distinction between the face and the beginning of the hair. There is some detail remaining just above and below the curls. *Reverse:* More feathers are worn away. The end of the branch at the left is worn so as to blend into the wing. The edge of the rim is barely visible and in some areas is worn away. (In this and the Very Good grade, opinions concerning the rim vary in the ANA grading standards and in *Photograde*; PCGS is silent on the matter.)

1932-D. Graded F-12.

VG-8, 10 (Very Good). *Obverse:* Further wear is seen on the head, with most of the upper part of the curls now blending into the hair above. *Reverse:* The rim is worn into the tops of the letters. There is no detail on the leaves. About half of the feathers are outlined, but only faintly.

1932-S. Graded VG-10.

G-4, 6 (Good). *Obverse:* Further wear is seen in all areas. On 1932 and some 1934 coins the IN GOD WE TRUST motto is so worn that some letters are missing. *Reverse:* The rim is worn further into the letters. Fewer details are seen on the eagle's wing. On both sides the coin appears to be "worn flat," with little in relief.

1932-D. Graded G-4.

AG-3 (About Good). *Obverse:* Wear is more extensive, with about half of the letters gone. *Reverse:* Wear is more extensive, with about half of the letters gone. Slight detail remains in the eagle's wings. The mintmark, if any, is very clear.

1942. Graded AG-3.

PF-60 to 70 (Proof). *Obverse and Reverse:* Proofs that are extensively cleaned and have many hairlines, or that are dull and grainy, are lower level, such as PF–60 to 62. These are not widely desired, and represent coins that have been mistreated. Most low-level Proofs are of the 1936 to 1942 dates. With medium hairlines and good reflectivity, assigned grades of PF–63 or 64 are appropriate. PF–66 should have hairlines so delicate that magnification is needed to see them. Above that, a Proof should be free of any hairlines or other problems.

1974-S. Graded PF-70 Deep Cameo.

1932 Washington, Eagle Reverse, Quarter

1932 • **Circulation-Strike Mintage:** 5,404,000.

Availability: The 1932 Philadelphia Mint Washington quarter has always been popular as the first year of issue. Mint State coins are readily available but are certainly scarce in comparison to dates after 1934. The typical coin graded at MS-63 or higher is apt to be lustrous and have good eye appeal. As many were saved by the public, then spent once the novelty passed, there are quite a few around in About Uncirculated and lower Mint State grades. When marks are present they are usually most noticeable on the portrait and the left obverse field.

Commentary: All 1932 quarters are of the Light Motto variety with the edges of the IN GOD WE TRUST letters blending into the field.

Quarters of the new design were released into circulation on August 1, 1932. There was considerable interest at first, and many were saved as souvenirs. However, in this deep Depression year few bank-wrapped rolls or other quantities were saved by anyone. Later, Mint State examples would prove to be plentiful on the numismatic market, but usually offered one or a few at a time, never in quantity.

Allen Harriman, in the *Coin Dealer Newsletter Monthly Supplement*, July 1980 wrote, "Of all the P-mints, this is the one most often encountered in AU-55 "slider" and MS-60 condition." Such pieces represent coins the public saved at the time of release but spent afterward when the novelty had passed.

All quarters of this date have a higher rim on the reverse than do later silver quarters issued 1934 to 1964.

	Cert	Avg	% MS	VG-8	F-12	VF-20	EF-40	AU-50	MS-60	MS-62	MS-63	MS-64	MS-65	MS-66	MS-67
1932	2,020	62.4	86%	$8	$9	$10	$11	$15	$25	$40	$60	$95	$275	$675	$22,500

1932-D Washington, Eagle Reverse, Quarter

1932-D • **Circulation-Strike Mintage:** 436,800.

Availability: Although the mintage figure of the 1932-D is slightly higher than for 1932-S (408,000) in grades of MS-63 or better the 1932-D is at least five to 10 times rarer than the 1932-S. As such, it is far and away the key issue of the series. When the 1932-D was minted and distributed, no effort was made to handle the coins gently. As a result, most pieces saved in Mint State in 1932, and surviving to the present day, are apt to be in MS-60 to MS-62 grades. Similar to other coins in the series, nicks and marks are most obvious on the portrait and in the left obverse field. Such marks generally get lost on the reverse and are not distracting there.

In worn grades the 1932-D is available in proportion to its mintage and is seen about as often as is the 1932-S. Examples in such grades as Good and Very Good were occasionally found in circulation in the early 1950s, after which they disappeared almost entirely. Due to the high price of Mint State coins, circulated examples enjoy a wide market. Many fakes exist in the form of D mintmarks added to Philadelphia Mint coins.

Commentary: All 1932-D quarters are of the Light Motto variety with the edges of the IN GOD WE TRUST letters blending into the field. The D mintmark on genuine coins is often small and in high relief, sometimes filled at the center. The small D had been the standard for the entire Standing Liberty quarter production at the Denver Mint from 1917 to 1929. A ghost outline of a larger D, an artifact of machine damage doubling, is seen north and east of the final D.

All quarters of this date have a higher rim on the reverse than do later silver quarters issued 1934 to 1964.

	Cert	Avg	% MS	VG-8	F-12	VF-20	EF-40	AU-50	MS-60	MS-62	MS-63	MS-64	MS-65	MS-66
1932-D	4,325	38.2	25%	$110	$125	$150	$175	$350	$1,100	$1,200	$1,500	$1,650	$8,500	$75,000

1932-S Washington, Eagle Reverse, Quarter

1932-S • Circulation-Strike Mintage: 408,000.

Availability: In *worn grades* the 1932-S is slightly scarcer than the 1932-D, as evidenced by finds in circulation decades ago. However, the 1932-D is priced higher (makes no sense!). There are many About Uncirculated 1932-S quarters around—pieces that were plucked from circulation in 1932 and 1933, then spent in the days just before collecting dates and mintmarks became wildly popular, starting in 1934.

Among Mint State coins, most are in lower grades, again representing pieces saved by the public. Quite a few of the About Uncirculated and lower Mint State level 1932 quarters from each of the mints have yellowish toning and/or black specks and freckles, why I don't know. This coloration is not often seen among later dates. Perhaps it is because most of the later ones were taken from bank-wrapped rolls, whereas the 1932 coins were saved one at a time. Mint State 1932-S quarters are more available than are those of 1932-D.

With the 1932-D, the 1932-S is a key to the series—far outranking any other later dates and mintmarks.

Commentary: All 1932-S quarters are of the Light Motto variety with the edges of the IN GOD WE TRUST letters blending into the field.

All quarters of this date have a higher rim on the reverse than do later silver quarters issued 1934 to 1964.

	Cert	Avg	% MS	VG-8	F-12	VF-20	EF-40	AU-50	MS-60	MS-62	MS-63	MS-64	MS-65	MS-66
1932-S	4,928	46.0	38%	$100	$115	$130	$150	$200	$450	$750	$850	$900	$2,500	$28,500

1934 Washington, Eagle Reverse, Quarter

1934 • Circulation-Strike Mintage: 31,912,052.

Availability: The 1934 quarter is readily available in Mint State, although hardly common. Most coins have a distinctive satiny finish and are very attractive (the same satin is seen on Peace dollars of this date and mint, but not on other issues of this year). There are several varieties of this date listed below. While most collectors are satisfied with a single example to illustrate the date, the Light Motto, Heavy Motto (easy to find), and Doubled Obverse Die are sought by many. The Medium Motto is not as popular.

Commentary: Notice of the motto differences was published by Edward S. Horowitz, as part of an article, "The Washington Quarter," in *The Numismatist*, October 1944:

"All collectors have noted that the words 'In God We Trust' appear in lower relief on all 1932 quarters. In other words, they are not much higher than the surface of the coin, and are not clear-cut as is the balance of the wording. What most collectors and dealers do not seem to know is that the 1934 quarter was struck from two separate and distinct dies, one having the words 'In God We Trust' in low relief, the same as the 1932 coins, and the other having these words in high relief, the same as on the quarters of all succeeding years.

"From my conversation and correspondence with dealers and collectors I have come in contact with very few who seem to know about these two distinct dies, and the catalogue says nothing on the subject. All 1934 quarters taken from circulation appear to be of the high relief type, indicating that the one with the low relief motto is really a scarce coin.

"The records of the Philadelphia Mint, which is the only one using the low relief die in 1934, show that on June 30, 1934, working dies were delivered to the Coining Department with the motto 'In God We Trust' in higher relief, prepared on order of the director of the Mint. The records there further show that up to June 30, 6,432,000 pieces had been coined that year, all in May and June; and that 25,480,052 were coined from July to December inclusive.

"No accurate data is available as to when the new dies were placed in operation, but it is reasonable to assume that this was probably done immediately. This assumption is based first upon the fact that the new die was undoubtedly prepared because of some objection to the old one, and would therefore naturally be placed in use as soon as ready; and second, upon the fact that all 1934 quarters the writer has found over a period of years in circulation, are of the second type. It would therefore appear that the ratio of scarcity of the first type to the second is at least 4 to 1, based on quantity minted. Actually the ratio is probably much greater, at least so far as Uncirculated coins are concerned. We know from experience that collectors and dealers in previous years, from 1942 back, usually did not begin to accumulate rolls of Uncirculated coins until at least several months after they began to appear, and often not even then."

Today, certain of the certification services are attributing 1934 quarters by the three motto differences, but the vast majority on population reports are simply listed as 1934.

VARIETY: *1934, Light Motto (FS-25-1934-401).* This variety was made through the first part of 1932, but not widely saved. It is the same Light Motto style as used for all the coinage of 1932. The center of the W in WE is lower than the sides. As this variety is not widely noticed, there is ample opportunity for cherrypicking. URS-13.

	Cert	Avg	% MS	VG-8	F-12	VF-20	EF-40	AU-50	MS-60	MS-62	MS-63	MS-64	MS-65	MS-66	MS-67
1934, Light Motto	308	63.4	89%	$7.50	$7.75	$8	$10	$24	$60	$80	$135	$190	$200	$375	$2,000

VARIETY: *1934, Medium Motto (FS-25-1934-402).* This variety has the center of the W in WE lower than sides, like the Light Motto variety, but with the letters thinner, more blunt, and in higher relief. Market prices are usually (but not always) the same as for the Light Motto, as the Medium Motto is not widely recognized. URS-22.

VARIETY: *1934, Heavy Motto (FS-25-1934-402).* On this reworked obverse, the motto has thick, heavy letters, and the center of the W in WE is higher than the sides. URS-21.

	Cert	Avg	% MS	VG-8	F-12	VF-20	EF-40	AU-50	MS-60	MS-62	MS-63	MS-64	MS-65	MS-66	MS-67
1934, Heavy Motto	65	62.3	80%	$7.50	$7.75	$8	$10	$15	$30	$40	$50	$65	$165	$475	$3,000

VARIETY: *1934, Doubled Die Obverse (FS-25-1934-101).* Occuring on the Medium Motto variety, prominent doubling can be seen, especially at the motto. The reverse is also slightly doubled. It is one of just a few doubled die Washington quarter varieties listed in the *Guide Book of United States Coin*, making it a very popular Washington quarter variety. • Quite a few have been run through the certification services, with the current population totaling over 500 pieces, mostly in circulated grades. URS-12. *MS-60 to 62: 37; MS-63: 44; MS-65: 47; MS-65: 22; and MS-66: 16.*

	Cert	Avg	% MS	VG-8	F-12	VF-20	EF-40	AU-50	MS-60	MS-62	MS-63	MS-64	MS-65	MS-66
1934, Doubled-Die Obverse				$75	$85	$200	$300	$600	$1,000	$1,350	$1,700	$1,900	$3,250	$5,250

1934-D Washington, Eagle Reverse, Quarter

1934-D • **Circulation-Strike Mintage:** 3,527,200.

Availability: Mint State coins are scarce in relation to most later issues, but enough are around that you will find one without difficulty. The luster is of a pleasing but unusual matte-satiny finish, as also used on Peace silver dollars of this year and mint. Dies were prepared at the Philadelphia Mint and shipped unhardened to Denver, where they were hardened and finished for use. Some special process must have been used for quarters and dollars of this date (but not cents, dimes, or nickels).

Medium and Heavy Motto varieties exist, but are not widely known or collected. Most numismatists are content to have just one example of this date and mint. See illustrations under 1932.

Although the 1934-D was minted to the extent of several million coins, this was a year deep in the Depression, and few were saved. This and the 1932-D are the only quarter dollars that the editor has never handled in roll quantities.

	Cert	Avg	% MS	VG-8	F-12	VF-20	EF-40	AU-50	MS-60	MS-62	MS-63	MS-64	MS-65	MS-66	MS-67
1934-D	1,359	61.1	77%	$7.50	$8	$12	$25	$85	$250	$280	$340	$400	$475	$1,150	$4,250

VARIETY: *1934-D, Medium Motto (FS-Unlisted).* This is the same Medium Motto as on the Philadelphia strike. Opinion is divided as to whether the Medium Motto is scarcer than the Heavy Motto, or vice versa. In his 1988 *Encyclopedia*, Walter Breen estimated that 1,000,000 Medium Motto coins were struck, with 2,500,000 having the Heavy Motto. However, in the marketplace the Medium Motto is seen more often. David W. Lange of NGC suggests that Breen's estimates should be reversed.[91] • Estimated mintage: 2,000,000. Certification service data are not of much use, for most 1934-D quarters have not been identified by motto style.

VARIETY: *1934-D, Mintmark of 1932 (FS-25-1934D-501).* The D mint mark is smaller and heavier than that used on other 1934-D quarters. About 1,500,000 are believed to have been minted. The mintmark matches the size of the 1932 D mintmark; the presumption is that these were struck from a leftover die. URS-3.

1935 Washington, Eagle Reverse, Quarter

1935 • **Circulation-Strike Mintage:** 32,484,000.

Availability: Beginning this year, bank-wrapped rolls were saved in quantity of all Washington quarters except 1936-D. The 1935 is plentiful today, but in view of the demand for such coins they are no longer seen in quantity. The typical coin is well struck and richly lustrous. An MS-65 coin, selected for eye appeal, will be just right for the advanced collector.

Commentary: All 1935 quarters from each of the mints are of the Medium Motto variety, even though the Heavy Motto had been created in 1934 and would become the standard from 1936 onward.

	Cert	Avg	% MS	VG-8	F-12	VF-20	EF-40	AU-50	MS-60	MS-62	MS-63	MS-64	MS-65	MS-66	MS-67
1935	1,980	64.4	94%	$7.50	$7.75	$8	$9	$10	$22	$30	$35	$50	$70	$120	$385

1935-D Washington, Eagle Reverse, Quarter

1935-D • **Circulation-Strike Mintage:** 5,780,000.

Availability: The 1935-D is easily enough available in an absolute sense, but is at least five times more elusive than the 1935 Philadelphia issue in choice and gem Mint State, MS-63 and above. Examples usually have rich frost and good eye appeal.

Commentary: All 1935 quarters from each of the mints are of the Medium Motto variety.

	Cert	Avg	% MS	VG-8	F-12	VF-20	EF-40	AU-50	MS-60	MS-62	MS-63	MS-64	MS-65	MS-66	MS-67
1935-D	1,291	61.5	79%	$7.50	$8	$10	$20	$125	$240	$265	$275	$325	$425	$500	$1,400

1935-S Washington, Eagle Reverse, Quarter

1935-S • **Circulation-Strike Mintage:** 5,660,000.

Availability: The 1935-S is similar to the 1935-D, but seen more often. Years ago, rolls of the 1935-S were easily found, while those of 1935-D required some searching. High grade examples usually have excellent frost and good eye appeal.

Commentary: All 1935 quarters from each of the mints are of the Medium Motto variety.

	Cert	Avg	% MS	VG-8	F-12	VF-20	EF-40	AU-50	MS-60	MS-62	MS-63	MS-64	MS-65	MS-66	MS-67
1935-S	1,419	62.6	83%	$7.50	$8	$9	$15	$38	$100	$120	$135	$160	$215	$385	$1,200

1936 Washington, Eagle Reverse, Quarter

1936 • **Circulation-Strike Mintage:** 41,300,000.

Availability: This is the first really common date in Mint State, with at least two or three times more known than of the 1935, which itself is plentiful. Most are brilliant, lustrous, and attractive.

Commentary: Beginning in this year the Heavy Motto variety (used for some 1934 and 1934-D coinage) became the standard.

	Cert	Avg	% MS	EF-40	AU-50	MS-60	MS-63	MS-64	MS-65	MS-66	MS-67
1936	1,758	64.7	96%	$8	$10	$25	$35	$40	$90	$130	$485

VARIETY: *1936, Doubled Die Obverse (FS-25-1936-101).* This variety shows very noticeable doubling in the motto, especially at the uprights of I in IN and T in TRUST. This is a good variety to cherrypick, as most 1936 quarters have not been checked for this feature. While rare, demand is high if you can find one. 76 examples have been certified. Breen-4281. URS-7. *MS-60 to 62: 11; MS-63: 12; MS-64: 8; MS-65: 1; MS-66: 2; MS-67: 1.*

1936, Proof • **Proof Mintage:** 3,837.

Availability: Proofs are often seen on the market, but are the scarcest of any issue from this year to the present.

Commentary: Proofs were offered as part of five coin sets (cent, nickel, dime, quarter, half dollar) for $1.81 or could be purchased singly. This method of ordering prevailed through 1942.

	Cert	Avg	% MS	PF-64	PF-65	PF-67
1936, Proof	971	64.4		$800	$1,100	$5,750

1936-D Washington, Eagle Reverse, Quarter

1936-D • **Circulation-Strike Mintage:** 5,374,000.

Availability: The 1936-D quarter has always been scarce in Mint State, but common in worn grades. Rolls of 1936-S were saved in quantity, but not 1936-D. Finding a lustrous, attractive 1936-D will take some doing, but will hardly be a problem, as at any given time there are examples on the market. Circulated coins are common, but in my opinion overpriced (see notes below).

Commentary: In 1936 at the Denver Mint, 5,374,000 Washington quarters were produced, certainly a common coin by any consideration. Thus, numismatists did not bother to save them. Moreover, many were busy with the great commemorative coin craze. A number of years later, according to Lee F. Hewitt, founder and editor of the *Numismatic Scrapbook Magazine*, when Wayte Raymond's "National" holders had been popular for a few years and when Whitman and other holders became available in quantity, it was discovered that Uncirculated examples of this "common" variety were relatively scarce. Today, the 1936-D remains a key issue in Mint State. However, worn pieces are not at all difficult to find. They exist in proportion to their original mintage. There is no logical reason why a worn 1936-D in a grade such as Very Fine, Extremely Fine, or About Uncirculated should be priced more than a worn 1936-S. The only reason this has happened is that those who know that *Mint State* are scarce, assume *all* are scarce.

Walter Breen in his 1988 *Encyclopedia* listed 1936-D over horizontal D, Breen-4285. Bill Fivaz comment: "I do not believe this exists. It is not listed in the James Wiles book, nor have J.T. Stanton and I included it in the *Cherrypicker's Guide to Rare Die Varieties*."[92]

	Cert	Avg	% MS	EF-40	AU-50	MS-60	MS-63	MS-64	MS-65	MS-66	MS-67
1936-D	1,212	60.3	74%	$55	$250	$525	$850	$900	$1,000	$1,250	$4,700

1936-S *Washington, Eagle Reverse, Quarter*

1936-S • **Circulation-Strike Mintage:** 3,828,000.

Availability: Many rolls of 1936-S were saved in and around the year of issue, making quantities plentiful on the market until the 1960s, when the expansion of the hobby caused most rolls to be broken apart and distributed. The typical 1936-S is lustrous and attractive.

	Cert	Avg	% MS	EF-40	AU-50	MS-60	MS-63	MS-64	MS-65	MS-66	MS-67
1936-S	1,446	63.7	95%	$15	$50	$120	$140	$150	$235	$350	$950

VARIETY: *1936-S, Repunched Mintmark (FS-Unlisted).* An S is dramatically punched over a previous S to the south-southeast. This variety was discovered by Jose Cortez. A few pieces have been noticed by the certification services. Although this variety is not in great demand, if you want one, simply look through regular 1936-S quarters until you locate an example. URS-2.

1937 *Washington, Eagle Reverse, Quarter*

1937 • **Circulation-Strike Mintage:** 19,696,000.

Availability: The 1937 is plentiful in all Mint State categories up through 66, but somewhat scarcer above that. Most quarters of this date have not been run through a certification service, so be careful when contemplating paying a high price for a condition rarity. In the future, more will be certified.

Notes: Circulation strikes have the Variety A reverse.

	Cert	Avg	% MS	EF-40	AU-50	MS-60	MS-63	MS-64	MS-65	MS-66	MS-67
1937	1,143	64.4	96%	$8	$12	$25	$35	$50	$95	$135	$525

VARIETY: *1937, Doubled Die Obverse (FS-25-1937-101 [012]).* Examples show very noticeable doubling at the bases of the letters in the motto and at the date. This variety is listed in the *Guide Book of United States Coins.* Most known pieces are in circulated grades. Gem Mint State coins are rare. Fivaz-Stanton identifies this as "one of the most important varieties in the series." Breen-4287. URS-7.

	Cert	Avg	% MS	EF-40	AU-50	MS-60	MS-63	MS-64	MS-65	MS-66
1937, Doubled-Die Obverse	48	26.4	10%	$700	$1,500	$2,450	$3,200	$4,500	$9,000	$16,000

1937, Proof • Proof Mintage: 5,542.

Availability: Proofs of this year are the second scarcest date from 1936 to the present. The mintage of 5,542 coins was the lowest for any Proof denomination of the 1937 year.

Notes: Introduced on Proofs of this year. Relief was strengthened by lowering the field. ES in STATES distinctly separated. *Two bold leaves to left of arrowheads. Stronger leaf touches or nearly touches top of A in DOLLAR.* Leaf touches on some Proofs; nearly touches on dies which were more extensively relapped. Stronger than on Variety A. Certain letters and the edges of feathers were retouched. • Used on Proofs of 1937 to 1964 and circulation strikes from 1959 to 1964. Details on the Proofs are sharper than on circulation strikes.

	Cert	Avg	% MS	PF-64	PF-65	PF-67
1937, Proof	972	65.1		$325	$425	$900

1937-D Washington, Eagle Reverse, Quarter

1937-D • **Circulation-Strike Mintage:** 7,189,600.

Availability: The 1937-D is another issue from the 1930s that was saved in roll quantities. The typical specimen is very lustrous and with good eye appeal.

	Cert	Avg	% MS	EF-40	AU-50	MS-60	MS-63	MS-64	MS-65	MS-66	MS-67
1937-D	1,205	64.0	95%	$15	$30	$70	$90	$100	$135	$225	$825

1937-S Washington, Eagle Reverse, Quarter

1937-S • Circulation-Strike Mintage: 1,652,000.

Availability: With its enticingly low mintage the 1937-S has always been high on the list of collectors' favorites. Mint State coins, while somewhat scarce, are available in the marketplace. Most are lustrous and very attractive. In the context of quarters of the 1930s, circulated coins are elusive.

Commentary: This is the third-lowest mintage issue in the series (after 1932-S and 1932-D). However, many were saved in roll quantities. The writer and James F. Ruddy sought to buy all the rolls we could find of these, circa the late 1950s, and were able to find only a few dozen. In an article, "Investing in Washington Quarters," in *The Numismatist*, October 1944, Edward S. Horowitz included this: "Two later dates of Washington quarters are probably underrated, and may stage a surprise some day. They are the 1937-S quarter, with a total coinage of only 1,652,000, and the 1939-S quarter with a coinage of 2,628,000. In comparison with other recent coins of greater coinage, they are behind the market."

David W. Lange Commentary: Aside from its scarcity, there is something else that sets the 1937-S quarter dollar apart from every other issue in this long running series. For reasons now forgotten, the obverse rim of the 1937-S quarter was raised above the normal level . . . It isn't really noticeable on Uncirculated coins. Since most collectors of the Washington series don't bother with worn examples, it's easy to overlook this phenomenon. Still, the obverse rim of 1937-S quarters is clearly higher than on other dates, a fact that becomes quite apparent when examining heavily worn coins . . ."[93]

	Cert	Avg	% MS	EF-40	AU-50	MS-60	MS-63	MS-64	MS-65	MS-66	MS-67
1937-S	1,176	63.2	92%	$35	$95	$150	$250	$275	$335	$535	$1,575

1938 Washington, Eagle Reverse, Quarter

1938 • Circulation-Strike Mintage: 9,472,000.

Availability: The 1938 in Mint State has always been scarce, the key issue among Philadelphia Mint quarters in the series. The reason may be that as Proofs were available, not many rolls were saved. In the early 1950s, when roll and bag quantities of Uncirculated Washington quarters often traded among dealers, single rolls of the 1938 were hard to find. The typical coin is lustrous and attractive.

Commentary: Circulation strikes have the Variety A reverse; Proofs have the Variety B reverse used on Proofs 1937 to 1964. • Allen Harriman, writing in the *Coin Dealer Newsletter, Monthly Supplement*, July 1980, commented: "This low mintage issue is by far the scarcest of all the P-mint Washington quarters."

	Cert	Avg	% MS	EF-40	AU-50	MS-60	MS-63	MS-64	MS-65	MS-66	MS-67
1938	1,127	63.5	90%	$15	$45	$95	$110	$150	$190	$250	$675

1938, Proof • Proof Mintage: 8,045.

Availability: Proofs exist in proportion to their mintage, with probably 7,000 or so surviving from the original distribution of 8,045.

	Cert	Avg	% MS	PF-64	PF-65	PF-67
1938, Proof	1,241	65.0		$160	$200	$1,050

1938-S Washington, Eagle Reverse, Quarter

1938-S • **Circulation-Strike Mintage:** 2,832,000.

Availability: The 1938-S is on the scarce side by virtue of its low mintage. Because of this it is a long-time favorite. As is true of most other quarters of the era, Mint State coins are apt to be lustrous and with good eye appeal.

	Cert	Avg	% MS	EF-40	AU-50	MS-60	MS-63	MS-64	MS-65	MS-66	MS-67
1938-S	1,419	64.0	96%	$20	$55	$105	$140	$150	$155	$275	$650

1939 Washington, Eagle Reverse, Quarter

1939 • **Circulation-Strike Mintage:** 33,540,000.

Availability: Plentiful by virtue of its large mintage. Choice and gem Mint State examples abound.

Commentary: Circulation strikes have the Variety A reverse.

	Cert	Avg	% MS	EF-40	AU-50	MS-60	MS-63	MS-64	MS-65	MS-66	MS-67
1939	1,928	65.2	97%	$8	$12	$15	$25	$30	$60	$100	$225

1939, Proof • Proof Mintage: 8,795.

Availability: Proofs are scarce, but when found are usually of choice or gem quality.

Commentary: Proofs have the Variety B reverse used on Proofs 1937 to 1964.

	Cert	Avg	% MS	PF-64	PF-65	PF-67
1939, Proof	1,241	65.4		$140	$200	$525

1939-D Washington, Eagle Reverse, Quarter

1939-D • **Circulation-Strike Mintage:** 7,092,000.

Availability: Easily available in any grade desired.

Commentary: Some have a heavily punched mintmark with the center opening small, others have a lighter mintmark with opening larger. Several varieties of repunched mintmarks are described by James Wiles.

	Cert	Avg	% MS	EF-40	AU-50	MS-60	MS-63	MS-64	MS-65	MS-66	MS-67
1939-D	1,413	64.6	96%	$11	$20	$40	$50	$50	$85	$135	$350

1939-D, D Over S, Washington, Eagle Reverse, Quarter

1939-D, D Over S • **Circulation-Strike Mintage:** Small part of preceding.

Availability: This is a very rare variety. If you opt to include overmintmarks as part of your date and mintmark collection, this will be a great challenge. The open center of the D mintmark shows the center curve of a previous S, and part of the left upper curve of the S can be seen to the left of the upright of D. Listed by Fivaz and Stanton as URS-2, indicating great rarity. However, as this overmintmark is not widely known, here is an opportunity for cherrypicking. Check all of the regular 1939-D quarters you can find!

Detail of the D Over S.

Commentary: FS-25-1939D-501 • URS-2 • As the Fivaz-Stanton text points out, this is the *real* 1939-D, D Over S. Some repunched D 1939-D coins have been illustrated as "1939-D, D Over S," with the comment that they are not overmintmarks—which, of course, they are not.

1939-S Washington, Eagle Reverse, Quarter

1939-S • **Circulation-Strike Mintage:** 2,628,000.

Availability: Although the 1939-S has the fourth lowest mintage figure in the series (after 1932-S, 1932-D, and 1937-S), many were saved in roll quantities, and on an absolute basis they are not *rare*. However, in the context of the several hundred varieties of Washington quarters made from 1932 to date, it is one of the scarcer issues.

Commentary: In an article, "Investing in Washington Quarters," in *The Numismatist,* October 1944, Edward S. Horowitz included this: "Two later dates of Washington quarters are probably underrated, and may stage a surprise some day. They are the 1937-S quarter, with a total coinage of only 1,652,000, and the 1939-S quarter with a coinage of 2,628,000. In comparison with other recent coins of greater coinage, they are behind the market."

	Cert	Avg	% MS	EF-40	AU-50	MS-60	MS-63	MS-64	MS-65	MS-66	MS-67
1939-S	1,167	63.7	92%	$20	$60	$95	$135	$185	$250	$300	$725

1940 Washington, Eagle Reverse, Quarter

1940 • **Circulation-Strike Mintage:** 35,704,000. **Proof Mintage:** 11,246.

Availability: Easily available, a comment that pertains to all other standard date and mintmark issues from this point forward.

Commentary: Circulation strikes have the Variety A reverse.

	Cert	Avg	% MS	EF-40	AU-50	MS-60	MS-63	MS-64	MS-65	MS-66	MS-67
1940	1,442	65.1	97%	$8	$9	$17	$35	$40	$50	$80	$235

1940, Proof • **Proof Mintage:** 11,246.

Availability: Proofs are slightly scarce, per the mintage.

Commentary: Proofs have the Variety B reverse used on Proofs 1937 to 1964.

	Cert	Avg	% MS	PF-64	PF-65	PF-67
1940, Proof	1,505	65.4		$95	$120	$500

1940-D Washington, Eagle Reverse, Quarter

1940-D • **Circulation-Strike Mintage:** 2,797,600.

Availability: In the context of quarters of the decade the 1940-D is slightly scarce. See notes below.

Commentary: In "Grading Insights," *Coin World,* Randy Campbell commented: The 1940-D Washington quarter dollar, with a mintage

of about 2.8 million, has always been popular with collectors and dealers. The typical 1940-D Washington quarter dollar displays a wide range of luster quality. Full gems will have blazing, original, mint frost. However, many examples of this date exhibit substandard luster that is impaired by cleaning, overdipping or improper storage. A significant percentage of 1940-D Washington quarter dollars will have worse than average surface abrasions. Those that are moderately contact marked tend to grade in the MS-63 to MS-64 range. Those with heavy contact marks usually grade MS-60 to MS-62 (if they are still Uncirculated).[94]

	Cert	Avg	% MS	EF-40	AU-50	MS-60	MS-63	MS-64	MS-65	MS-66	MS-67
1940-D	1,268	64.1	94%	$24	$65	$120	$165	$190	$250	$365	$900

VARIETY: *1940-D, Doubled Die Obverse (FS-25-1940D-101).* Strong, attractive doubling can be seen on the motto, with lighter doubling visible at LIBERTY and the date. URS-6.

VARIETY: *1940-D, Dramatically Repunched Mintmark (FS-25-1940D-501 [012.4]).* The main D mintmark os separated from and punched to the east of an earlier, lighter D. Such a dramatic separation is rare, with only about 10 similar examples across the entirety of United States coinage. Discovered by Lee Hiemke in the late 20th century, this dramatic variety was overlooked by a generation of earlier collectors. The same die was used to create the 1941-D Doubled Die Reverse variety (see separate entry).URS-3.

1940-S Washington, Eagle Reverse, Quarter

1940-S • **Circulation-Strike Mintage:** 8,244,000.

Availability: A popular and easily available variety.

	Cert	Avg	% MS	EF-40	AU-50	MS-60	MS-63	MS-64	MS-65	MS-66	MS-67
1940-S	1,234	65.1	97%	$9	$16	$21	$32	$40	$45	$80	$400

1941 Washington, Eagle Reverse, Quarter

1941 • **Circulation-Strike Mintage:** 79,032,000.

Availability: Availability: Plentiful in Mint State.

Commentary: Circulation strikes have the Variety A reverse.

	Cert	Avg	% MS	EF-40	AU-50	MS-60	MS-63	MS-64	MS-65	MS-66	MS-67
1941	1,912	65.3	98%	$7.50	$8	$10	$14	$20	$33	$50	$250

VARIETY: *1941, Doubled Die Obverse (FS-25-1941-101 [012.7]).* Light but obvious doubling can be seen on this variety, most notable at GOD WE and UST in the motto. Several other doubled die obverses exist for 1941, including FS-25-1941-102. URS-7.

1941, Proof • **Proof Mintage:** 15,287.

Commentary: Proofs of this era usually show light gray or hazy toning unless they have been dipped. Proofs have the Variety B reverse used on Proofs 1937 to 1964.

	Cert	Avg	% MS	PF-64	PF-65	PF-67
1941, Proof	1,840	65.4		$75	$115	$250

1941-D Washington, Eagle Reverse, Quarter

1941-D • **Circulation-Strike Mintage:** 16,714,800.

Availability: A popular and readily available issue.

	Cert	Avg	% MS	EF-40	AU-50	MS-60	MS-63	MS-64	MS-65	MS-66	MS-67
1941-D	1,405	65.0	98%	$8	$13	$32	$55	$50	$65	$110	$150

VARIETY: *1941-D, Doubled Die Reverse (FS-25-1941D-801).* Doubling can be best seen on STATES OF AMERICA; with lighter evidence by the D of UNITED and the AR of DOLLAR. This was made with the same die used for FS-25-1940D-501, with the D mintmark separated from and punched to the east of an earlier, lighter D. URS-7.

1941-S Washington, Eagle Reverse, Quarter

1941-S • **Circulation-Strike Mintage:** 16,080,000.

Availability: Readily available in choice and gem preservation.

Commentary: Large and small mintmark varieties per the *Guide Book* and the Breen *Encyclopedia*. The elusive Large S was used on at least four dies. The lower left serif is called the

"trumpet tail" due to its shape. Some have the upper loop of the S filled. The *Cherrypickers' Guide to Rare Die Varieties* gives illustrations and details.

	Cert	Avg	% MS	EF-40	AU-50	MS-60	MS-63	MS-64	MS-65	MS-66	MS-67
1941-S	1,236	64.6	95%	$8	$11	$28	$50	$50	$57	$105	$425

1942 Washington, Eagle Reverse, Quarter

1942 • **Circulation-Strike Mintage:** 102,096,000.

Availability: Circulation strikes are plentiful. Proofs, while scarce in comparison to those of the 1950s and later, have the highest mintage of the early years, 1936 to 1942. No further Proofs were made until 1950.

Commentary: Circulation strikes have the Variety A reverse.

	Cert	Avg	% MS	EF-40	AU-50	MS-60	MS-63	MS-64	MS-65	MS-66	MS-67
1942	1,294	64.8	96%	$7.50	$8	$9	$10	$15	$27	$105	$675

1942, Proof • **Proof Mintage:** 21,123.

Commentary: Proofs have the Variety B reverse used on Proofs 1937 to 1964.

	Cert	Avg	% MS	PF-64	PF-65	PF-67
1942, Proof	2,274	65.2		$75	$100	$225

VARIETY: *1942, Doubled Die Obverse (FS-25-1942-101).* Doubling is seen on the motto, especially on GOD and TRUST. This variety is listed in the *Guide Book of United States Coins.* URS-5.

1942-D Washington, Eagle Reverse, Quarter

1942-D • **Circulation-Strike Mintage:** 17,487,200.

Availability: Popular and readily available wartime issue.

	Cert	Avg	% MS	EF-40	AU-50	MS-60	MS-63	MS-64	MS-65	MS-66	MS-67
1942-D	1,413	65.2	99%	$8	$10	$17	$20	$20	$27	$115	$425

VARIETY: *1942-D, Doubled Die Obverse (FS-25-1942D-101 [015]).* Doubling can be found on LIBERTY, the date, and the motto. It is listed in the *Guide Book of United States Coins* and considered a Top 10 Washington variety by Fivaz-Stanton. URS-9.

	Cert	Avg	% MS	EF-40	AU-50	MS-60	MS-63	MS-64	MS-65	MS-66
1942-D, Doubled-Die Obverse	60	30.6	7%	$350	$750	$1,800	$3,500	$5,000	$7,000	$10,500

VARIETY: *1942-D, Doubled Die Reverse (FS-25-1942D-801 [016]).* The doubling is seen on the eagle's beak, the arrows, and the branch above the mintmark.. URS-5.

	Cert	Avg	% MS	AU-50	MS-60	MS-63	MS-64	MS-65	MS-66
1942-D, Doubled Die Reverse	22	43.8	36%	$385	$500	$700	$850	$1,150	$4,000

1942-S Washington, Eagle Reverse, Quarter

1942-S • **Circulation-Strike Mintage:** 19,384,000.

Availability: Popular and readily available wartime issue.

Commentary: Breen distinguishes between sharp-serif and knob-tailed S mintmarks.

	Cert	Avg	% MS	EF-40	AU-50	MS-60	MS-63	MS-64	MS-65	MS-66	MS-67
1942-S	1,355	64.0	93%	$10	$20	$70	$115	$135	$150	$200	$750

1943 Washington, Eagle Reverse, Quarter

1943 • **Circulation-Strike Mintage:** 99,700,000.

Availability: Easily available high-mintage issue. Beginning in this year, collectors, dealers, and investors set aside bank-wrapped rolls in much larger quantities than for earlier times.

	Cert	Avg	% MS	EF-40	AU-50	MS-60	MS-63	MS-64	MS-65	MS-66	MS-67
1943	2,171	65.0	97%	$7.50	$8	$9	$10	$15	$37	$75	$250

VARIETY: *1943, Doubled Die Obverse (FS-25-1943-102).* Doubling is seen on the motto, LIBERTY, and date. This is one of the few doubled-die varieties listed in the *Guide Book of United States Coins.* URS-2.

	Cert	Avg	% MS	EF-40	AU-50	MS-60	MS-63	MS-64	MS-65	MS-66
1943, Doubled Die Obverse	110	56.3	65%	$2,500	$3,500	$5,000	$7,500	$9,500	$12,000	$14,500

1943-D Washington, Eagle Reverse, Quarter

1943-D • **Circulation-Strike Mintage:** 16,095,600.

Availability: Easily available in choice and gem Mint State. As a general rule for this era, the branch mint coins were saved in smaller quantities than were Philadelphia quarters. However, enough were set aside that all are plentiful today.

	Cert	Avg	% MS	EF-40	AU-50	MS-60	MS-63	MS-64	MS-65	MS-66	MS-67
1943-D	1,190	65.2	98%	$8	$15	$28	$39	$50	$55	$70	$550

VARIETY: *1943-D, Doubled Die Obverse (FS-25-1943D-101).* The chin, ear, hair curls, and queue are the locations of doubling on this varitey. URS-3. [ED: Dave called out FS number and description of 1943-S DDO. There IS a 1943-D DDO issue, and I put its data in here instead of the incorrect 1943-S data, but I'm not sure if Dave even want this variety in here (we do NOT list EVERY CPG variety in MR5 Expanded Section.)]

1943-S Washington, Eagle Reverse, Quarter

1943-S • **Circulation-Strike Mintage:** 21,700,000.

Availability: Plentiful and popular. Although quality is usually not a problem with quarters of the 1950s through 1964, cherrypicking for nice luster and eye appeal is worthwhile.

	Cert	Avg	% MS	EF-40	AU-50	MS-60	MS-63	MS-64	MS-65	MS-66	MS-67
1943-S	1,313	65.0	97%	$9	$13	$26	$42	$50	$55	$105	$600

VARIETY: *1943-S, Doubled Die Obverse (FS-25-1943S-101 [017]).* Look to the motto, LIBERTY, the designer's initial, and the date for very strong doubling. This variety is listed in the *Guide Book of United States Coins.* URS-9.

	Cert	Avg	% MS	EF-40	AU-50	MS-60	MS-63	MS-64	MS-65	MS-66	MS-67
1943-S, Doubled Die Obverse	128	43.6	45%	$200	$350	$500	$1,000	$1,350	$1,650	$3,800	$7,500

1944 Washington, Eagle Reverse, Quarter

1944 • Circulation-Strike Mintage:
104,956,000.

Availability: One of the most common issues of the era.

Commentary: All 1944 quarters show doubling on the earlobe and nostril from doubling of the master hub or master die.

	Cert	Avg	% MS	EF-40	AU-50	MS-60	MS-63	MS-64	MS-65	MS-66	MS-67
1944	2,316	65.4	98%	$7.50	$8	$9	$10	$15	$26	$48	$300

1944-D Washington, Eagle Reverse, Quarter

1944-D • Circulation-Strike Mintage:
14,600,800.

Availability: Choice and gem Mint State coins are readily available. As is true of most other quarters of this era, the typical Uncirculated coin taken from a bank-wrapped roll is apt to be MS-63 or MS-64.

Commentary: All 1944 quarters show doubling on the earlobe and nostril from doubling of the master hub or master die.

	Cert	Avg	% MS	EF-40	AU-50	MS-60	MS-63	MS-64	MS-65	MS-66	MS-67
1944-D	1,997	65.7	99%	$8	$10	$17	$20	$20	$37	$70	$275

1944-S Washington, Eagle Reverse, Quarter

1944-S • Circulation-Strike Mintage:
12,560,000.

Availability: Choice and gem Mint State coins are readily available.

Commentary: All 1944 quarters show doubling on the earlobe and nostril from doubling of the master hub or master die.

	Cert	Avg	% MS	EF-40	AU-50	MS-60	MS-63	MS-64	MS-65	MS-66	MS-67
1944-S	1,949	65.7	99%	$8	$10	$14	$20	$20	$30	$57	$225

VARIETY: *1944-S, Doubled Die Obverse (FS-25-1944S-101 [017.5]).* Beyond the master hub/die doubling, additional doubling is strongest at the motto, while lighter doubling can be seen at LIBERTY, the date, and the designer's initials. URS-9.

1945 Washington, Eagle Reverse, Quarter

1945 • **Circulation-Strike Mintage:** 74,372,000.

Availability: Choice and gem Mint State coins are readily available.

	Cert	Avg	% MS	EF-40	AU-50	MS-60	MS-63	MS-64	MS-65	MS-66	MS-67
1945	1,732	65.1	99%	$7.50	$8	$9	$10	$15	$33	$80	$525

VARIETY: *1945, Doubled Die Obverse (FS-25-1945-101 [018]).* Doubling shows at the motto, LIBERTY, and the date. URS-7.

1945-D Washington, Eagle Reverse, Quarter

1945-D • **Circulation-Strike Mintage:** 12,341,600.

Availability: Choice and gem Mint State coins are readily available.

	Cert	Avg	% MS	EF-40	AU-50	MS-60	MS-63	MS-64	MS-65	MS-66	MS-67
1945-D	1,246	65.3	99%	$8	$12	$18	$25	$25	$33	$50	$575

1945-S Washington, Eagle Reverse, Quarter

1945-S • **Circulation-Strike Mintage:** 17,004,001.

Availability: Choice and gem Mint State coins are readily available.

Commentary: Trumpet-tailed and knob-tailed S varieties.

	Cert	Avg	% MS	EF-40	AU-50	MS-60	MS-63	MS-64	MS-65	MS-66	MS-67
1945-S	1,656	65.4	99%	$7.50	$8	$9	$13	$17	$33	$75	$435

1946 *Washington, Eagle Reverse, Quarter*

1946 • Circulation-Strike Mintage: 53,436,000.

Availability: Choice 1946 quarters are easily found.

	Cert	Avg	% MS	EF-40	AU-50	MS-60	MS-63	MS-64	MS-65	MS-66	MS-67
1946	1,023	65.2	98%	$7	$8	$9	$10	$15	$35	$80	$850

1946-D *Washington, Eagle Reverse, Quarter*

1946-D • Circulation-Strike Mintage: 9,072,800.

Availability: Readily available, although the mintage is low for the era.

	Cert	Avg	% MS	EF-40	AU-50	MS-60	MS-63	MS-64	MS-65	MS-66	MS-67
1946-D	2,649	65.6	100%	$7.50	$8	$9	$10	$20	$33	$42	$275

VARIETY: *1946-D, D Over D (FS-25-1946D-501).* North of the main strike of the D can be seen a faint impression of an earlier strike, just touching the branch above. Discovered by Bill Fivaz. URS-2.

1946-S *Washington, Eagle Reverse, Quarter*

1946-S • Circulation-Strike Mintage: 4,204,000.

Availability: The 1946-S was very popular in its time due to the restricted mintage of just 4,204,000 coins. A higher percentage of pieces than usual went to investors who anticipated they would become scarce. Today, the 1946-S is readily available.

Commentary: Trumpet-tailed and knob-tailed S varieties.

	Cert	Avg	% MS	EF-40	AU-50	MS-60	MS-63	MS-64	MS-65	MS-66	MS-67
1947	6,082	65.5	100%	$7.50	$8	$11	$19	$25	$32	$65	$265

1947 Washington, Eagle Reverse, Quarter

1947 • **Circulation-Strike Mintage:** 22,556,000.

Availability: Easily available at different levels of Mint State. From this year through the very early 1950s, the interest in hoarding bank-wrapped rolls diminished. Accordingly, although there are enough 1947 quarters to go around, they and others of the next several years are not as common as are those of the earlier part of the decade.

	Cert	Avg	% MS	EF-40	AU-50	MS-60	MS-63	MS-64	MS-65	MS-66	MS-67
1947	1,713	65.4	99%	$7.50	$8	$11	$19	$25	$32	$65	$265

1947-D Washington, Eagle Reverse, Quarter

1947-D • **Circulation-Strike Mintage:** 15,338,400.

Availability: Choice and gem pieces are readily available.

	Cert	Avg	% MS	EF-40	AU-50	MS-60	MS-63	MS-64	MS-65	MS-66	MS-67
1947-D	2,666	65.7	100%	$7.50	$8	$11	$17	$20	$32	$42	$140

1947-S Washington, Eagle Reverse, Quarter

1947-S • **Circulation-Strike Mintage:** 5,532,000.

Availability: The rather low mintage for the 1947-S did not attract much attention at the time (unlike 1946-S) as the coin market was in a slump. However, enough were saved that Mint State pieces are readily available.

Commentary: Trumpet-tailed and knob-tailed S varieties.

	Cert	Avg	% MS	EF-40	AU-50	MS-60	MS-63	MS-64	MS-65	MS-66	MS-67
1947-S	4,885	65.7	100%	$7	$8	$9	$15	$20	$25	$38	$175

1948 Washington, Eagle Reverse, Quarter

1948 • **Circulation-Strike Mintage:** 35,196,000.

Availability: Choice and gem Mint State coins are readily available. Mintage figures trended upward this year.

	Cert	Avg	% MS	EF-40	AU-50	MS-60	MS-63	MS-64	MS-65	MS-66	MS-67
1948	2,311	65.4	99%	$7	$8	$9	$10	$20	$24	$42	$170

1948-D Washington, Eagle Reverse, Quarter

1948-D • **Circulation-Strike Mintage:** 16,766,800.

Availability: Choice and gem Mint State coins are readily available.

	Cert	Avg	% MS	EF-40	AU-50	MS-60	MS-63	MS-64	MS-65	MS-66	MS-67
1948-D	1,595	65.3	99%	$7.50	$8	$13	$18	$25	$45	$65	$600

1948-S Washington, Eagle Reverse, Quarter

1948-S • **Circulation-Strike Mintage:** 15,960,000.

Availability: Choice and gem Mint State coins are readily available.

	Cert	Avg	% MS	EF-40	AU-50	MS-60	MS-63	MS-64	MS-65	MS-66	MS-67
1948-S	2,709	65.5	99%	$7	$8	$9	$13	$20	$37	$70	$285

1949 Washington, Eagle Reverse, Quarter

1949 • **Circulation-Strike Mintage:** 9,312,000.

Availability: Choice and gem Mint State coins are readily available.

	Cert	Avg	% MS	EF-40	AU-50	MS-60	MS-63	MS-64	MS-65	MS-66	MS-67
1949	1,453	65.1	98%	$10	$14	$35	$47	$55	$65	$95	$325

1949-D Washington, Eagle Reverse, Quarter

1949-D • **Circulation-Strike Mintage:** 10,068,400.

Availability: Choice and gem Mint State coins are readily available.

	Cert	Avg	% MS	EF-40	AU-50	MS-60	MS-63	MS-64	MS-65	MS-66	MS-67
1949-D	1,526	65.2	99%	$8	$10	$16	$38	$45	$55	$85	$235

1949-D, D Over D, Washington, Eagle Reverse, Quarter

1949-D, D Over D • **Circulation-Strike Mintage:** Small part of the preceding.

Availability: An ever popular variety. There is room for one in every specialized collection. As most albums do not include spaces for overmintmarks, they are priced for less than their elusive nature might suggest.

Commentary: This overmintmark was first identified by Mike Ellis, president of the Combined Organization of Numismatic Error Collectors of America (CONECA). Confirmed by J.T. Stanton, it was published in *Numismatic News*, July 8, 1997, and in *Cherrypickers' News*, No. 10, July 1997. Now listed as FS-25-1950D-501.

Detail of the D Over D.

1950 Washington, Eagle Reverse, Quarter

1950 • Circulation-Strike Mintage: 24,920,126.

Availability: Choice and gem Mint State coins are readily available. Proofs were made this year for the first time since 1942. The earlier Proof strikings of 1950 are not as mirrorlike as the later ones made this year.

Commentary: Circulation strikes have the Variety A reverse.

	Cert	Avg	% MS	EF-40	AU-50	MS-60	MS-63	MS-64	MS-65	MS-66	MS-67
1950	1,390	65.5	99%	$7	$8	$9	$10	$15	$32	$55	$315

1950, Proof • Proof Mintage: 51,386.

Commentary: Proofs have the Variety B reverse used on Proofs 1937 to 1964.

	Cert	Avg	% MS	PF-64	PF-65	PF-67
1950, Proof	1,984	65.9		$60	$65	$145

1950-D Washington, Eagle Reverse, Quarter

1950-D • Circulation-Strike Mintage: 21,075,600.

Availability: Choice and gem Mint State coins are readily available.

	Cert	Avg	% MS	EF-40	AU-50	MS-60	MS-63	MS-64	MS-65	MS-66	MS-67
1950-D	1,547	64.8	97%	$7	$8	$9	$10	$15	$34	$65	$225

**VARIETY: *1950-D, D Over S (FS-25-1950D-601 [021]).* A very interes-ting and desirable variety for the specialist. Scarcer than market prices indicate, as the demand is not great (but is increasing). URS-9.

	Cert	Avg	% MS	EF-40	AU-50	MS-60	MS-63	MS-64	MS-65	MS-66
1950-D, D Over S	141	47.4	26%	$150	$225	$325	$550	$1,250	$2,900	$6,750

1950-S Washington, Eagle Reverse, Quarter

1950-S • **Circulation-Strike Mintage:** 10,284,004.

Availability: Choice and gem Mint State coins are readily available.

Commentary: A variety with double-punched S is known.

	Cert	Avg	% MS	EF-40	AU-50	MS-60	MS-63	MS-64	MS-65	MS-66	MS-67
1950-S	1,554	64.6	95%	$7.50	$8	$12	$16	$20	$35	$58	$265

1950-S, S Over D, Washington, Eagle Reverse, Quarter

1950-S, S Over D • **Circulation-Strike Mintage:** Small part of preceding.

Availability: Another overmintmark that is somewhat scarce, is highly interesting, and is well worth owning.

Commentary: Listed widely, including as FS-25-1950-S 501.

Detail of the S Over D.

	Cert	Avg	% MS	EF-40	AU-50	MS-60	MS-63	MS-64	MS-65	MS-66	MS-67
1950-S, S Over D	115	51.1	52%	$150	$250	$350	$500	$650	$1,150	$1,650	$6,000

1951 Washington, Eagle Reverse, Quarter

1951 • **Circulation-Strike Mintage:** 43,448,102.

Availability: Choice and gem Mint State coins are readily available. The Proof mintage is higher than that of 1950. The market remained in a slump in 1951, but would awake soon.

Commentary: Circulation strikes have the Variety A reverse.

	Cert	Avg	% MS	EF-40	AU-50	MS-60	MS-63	MS-64	MS-65	MS-66	MS-67
1951	1,566	65.4	99%	$7	$8	$9	$10	$15	$26	$50	$235

1951, Proof • **Proof Mintage:** 57,500.

Commentary: Proofs have the Variety B reverse used on Proofs 1937 to 1964.

	Cert	Avg	% MS	PF-64	PF-65	PF-67
1951, Proof	1,925	66.0		$55	$65	$110

1951-D Washington, Eagle Reverse, Quarter

1951-D • **Circulation-Strike Mintage:** 35,354,800.

Availability: Choice and gem Mint State coins are readily available.

	Cert	Avg	% MS	EF-40	AU-50	MS-60	MS-63	MS-64	MS-65	MS-66	MS-67
1951-D	1,678	65.4	100%	$7	$8	$9	$10	$15	$32	$55	$285

VARIETY: *1951-D, D Over D (FS-25-1951D-501).* Discovered by Jeffrey Cole. Published and illustrated as D Over S in *Coin World*, September 10, 1986. Breen-4358. The status of this has changed. Now it is listed as FS-25-1951D-501, D Over D, with the comment "This variety is thought by some to be D/S; it is D/D."

1951-S Washington, Eagle Reverse, Quarter

1951-S • **Circulation-Strike Mintage:** 9,048,000.

Availability: Choice and gem Mint State coins are readily available.

	Cert	Avg	% MS	EF-40	AU-50	MS-60	MS-63	MS-64	MS-65	MS-66	MS-67
1951-S	1,645	65.8	100%	$7.50	$8	$10	$15	$20	$35	$70	$145

1952 Washington, Eagle Reverse, Quarter

1952 • **Circulation-Strike Mintage:** 38,780,093.

Availability: Choice and gem Mint State coins are readily available. Proofs were rapidly catching on with the public, and it was not unusual for dealers and investor to order five or 10 sets instead of just one. The coin market began to strengthen.

Commentary: Circulation strikes have the Variety A reverse.

	Cert	Avg	% MS	EF-40	AU-50	MS-60	MS-63	MS-64	MS-65	MS-66	MS-67
1952	1,225	65.5	99%	$7.50	$8	$9	$10	$15	$24	$50	$135

1952, Proof • **Proof Mintage:** 81,980

Commentary: Proofs have the Variety B reverse used on Proofs 1937 to 1964.

	Cert	Avg	% MS	PF-64	PF-65	PF-67
1952, Proof	1,895	66.3		$40	$45	$100

1952-D Washington, Eagle Reverse, Quarter

1952-D • **Circulation-Strike Mintage:** 49,795,200.

Availability: Choice and gem Mint State coins are readily available.

	Cert	Avg	% MS	EF-40	AU-50	MS-60	MS-63	MS-64	MS-65	MS-66	MS-67
1952-D	1,001	65.2	99%	$7	$8	$9	$10	$15	$28	$65	$1,350

1952-S Washington, Eagle Reverse, Quarter

1952-S • **Circulation-Strike Mintage:** 13,707,800.

Availability: Choice and gem Mint State coins are readily available.

	Cert	Avg	% MS	EF-40	AU-50	MS-60	MS-63	MS-64	MS-65	MS-66	MS-67
1952-S	1,929	65.7	100%	$7.50	$8	$12	$20	$25	$36	$52	$115

1953 Washington, Eagle Reverse, Quarter

1953 • Circulation-Strike Mintage: 18,536,120.

Availability: Choice and gem Mint State coins are readily available. Proofs were ordered in record numbers. The Mint became alarmed at the prospect. Soon, limits on orders were put in place, which in the next few years only served to fuel demand further. Beginning about this time, interest in saving bank-wrapped rolls of new coins went into high gear. Although most emphasis was on the lower denominations, particularly Lincoln cents, countless thousands of rolls and even bags of new quarters were set aside.

Commentary: Circulation strikes have the Variety A reverse.

	Cert	Avg	% MS	EF-40	AU-50	MS-60	MS-63	MS-64	MS-65	MS-66	MS-67
1953	1,031	65.3	99%	$7	$8	$9	$10	$15	$25	$60	$215

1953, Proof • **Proof Mintage:** 128,800.

Commentary: Proofs have the Variety B reverse used on Proofs 1937 to 1964.

	Cert	Avg	% MS	PF-64	PF-65	PF-67
1953, Proof	3,453	66.7		$40	$45	$80

1953-D Washington, Eagle Reverse, Quarter

1953-D • Circulation-Strike Mintage: 56,112,400.

Availability: Can be difficult to locate in higher grades.

	Cert	Avg	% MS	EF-40	AU-50	MS-60	MS-63	MS-64	MS-65	MS-66	MS-67
1953-D	1,065	65.0	99%	$7	$8	$9	$10	$15	$32	$48	$700

VARIETY: *1953-D, Repunched Mintmark (FS-25-1953D-501).* A strike of the D mintmark can be seen over an earlier strike of the mintmark. There is not a consensus as to whether the earlier strike was inverted or horizontal. This variety is not widely known and is an excellent cherrypicking opportunity. URS-3.

1953-D, D Over S, Washington, Eagle Reverse, Quarter

1953-D, D Over S • Circulation-Strike
Mintage: Small part of preceding.

Availability: This curious overmintmark is actually 1953-D, with three impressions of the D punch, over two earlier S mintmarks! This variety is not well known, and thus can be a cherrypicker's delight.

Commentary: FS-25-1953D-601 (022.3).

Detail of the D Over S.

1953-S Washington, Eagle Reverse, Quarter

1953-S • Circulation-Strike Mintage:
14,016,000.

Availability: Easily available in choice and gem Mint State.

	Cert	Avg	% MS	EF-40	AU-50	MS-60	MS-63	MS-64	MS-65	MS-66	MS-67
1953-S	2,498	65.6	100%	$7	$8	$9	$10	$15	$23	$47	$185

1954 Washington, Eagle Reverse, Quarter

1954 • Circulation-Strike Mintage:
54,412,203.

Availability: Easily available in choice and gem Mint State. Proofs were made in record high quantities, but nothing like the mintage figures of years to come.

Commentary: Circulation strikes have the Variety A reverse.

	Cert	Avg	% MS	EF-40	AU-50	MS-60	MS-63	MS-64	MS-65	MS-66	MS-67
1954	2,182	65.4	99%	$7	$8	$9	$10	$15	$24	$30	$180

1954, Proof • **Proof Mintage:** 233,300.

Commentary: Proofs have the Variety B reverse used on Proofs 1937 to 1964.

	Cert	Avg	% MS	PF-64	PF-65	PF-67
1954, Proof	4,065	67.0		$15	$25	$60

1954-D Washington, Eagle Reverse, Quarter

1954-D • **Circulation-Strike Mintage:** 42,305,500.

Availability: Easily available in choice and gem Mint State.

	Cert	Avg	% MS	EF-40	AU-50	MS-60	MS-63	MS-64	MS-65	MS-66	MS-67
1954-D	1,322	65.2	100%	$7	$8	$9	$10	$15	$25	$58	$900

1954-S Washington, Eagle Reverse, Quarter

1954-S • **Circulation-Strike Mintage:** 11,834,722.

Availability: Easily available in choice and gem Mint State. This is the last of the San Francisco Mint silver quarters of the standard Washington design.

	Cert	Avg	% MS	EF-40	AU-50	MS-60	MS-63	MS-64	MS-65	MS-66	MS-67
1954-S	4,696	65.6	100%	$7	$8	$9	$10	$15	$23	$50	$235

1955 Washington, Eagle Reverse, Quarter

1955 • **Circulation-Strike Mintage:** 18,180,181.

Availability: Easily available in choice and gem Mint State. Proofs attained a record mintage.

Commentary: Circulation strikes have the Variety A reverse.

	Cert	Avg	% MS	EF-40	AU-50	MS-60	MS-63	MS-64	MS-65	MS-66	MS-67
1955	2,634	65.3	99%	$7	$8	$9	$10	$15	$25	$55	$400

1955, Proof • **Proof Mintage:** 378,200.

Commentary: Proofs have the Variety B reverse used on Proofs 1937 to 1964.

	Cert	Avg	% MS	PF-64	PF-65	PF-67
1955, Proof	5,972	67.4		$15	$25	$50

1955-D Washington, Eagle Reverse, Quarter

1955-D • **Circulation-Strike Mintage:** 3,182,400.

Availability: Easily available in choice and gem Mint State, despite a low mintage. The investment potential was widely recognized at the time, and many were saved. Hoarding rolls of all denominations was a passion by this time, driven by the ever-escalating price of the low-mintage 1950-D nickel. The entire market was robust.

	Cert	Avg	% MS	EF-40	AU-50	MS-60	MS-63	MS-64	MS-65	MS-66	MS-67
1955-D	2,902	64.5	100%	$7.50	$8	$9	$10	$15	$40	$90	$1,100

1956 Washington, Eagle Reverse, Quarter

1956 • **Circulation-Strike Mintage:** 44,144,000.

Availability: Easily available in choice and gem Mint State. Proofs were an especially hot spot in the market, with much excitement. Those who were lucky enough to have ordered sets under the restrictions in place could sell "futures" at a profit before the coins were

delivered. Sol Kaplan, Cincinnati dealer, was in the forefront of the market and posted bid and ask prices, including on a chalkboard at conventions. Some prices for older sets changed *hourly.*

Commentary: Circulation strikes have the Variety A reverse.

	Cert	Avg	% MS	EF-40	AU-50	MS-60	MS-63	MS-64	MS-65	MS-66	MS-67
1956	3,403	65.7	100%	$7	$8	$9	$10	$15	$18	$31	$90

1956, Proof • Proof Mintage: 669,384.

Commentary: Proofs have the Variety B reverse used on Proofs 1937 to 1964.

	Cert	Avg	% MS	PF-64	PF-65	PF-67
1956, Proof	7,075	67.5		$11	$15	$50

1956-D Washington, Eagle Reverse, Quarter

1956-D • Circulation-Strike Mintage: 32,334,500.

Availability: Easily available in choice and gem Mint State.

Commentary: Variety A and B reverses, see 1937.

	Cert	Avg	% MS	EF-40	AU-50	MS-60	MS-63	MS-64	MS-65	MS-66	MS-67
1956-D	1,062	65.4	100%	$7	$8	$9	$10	$15	$25	$42	$700

VARIETY: *1956-D, D Over Inverted D (FS-25-1956D-501 [022.4]).* After initially being struck inverted, the mintmark's orientation was corrected and restruck on this popular variety. URS-7.

1957 Washington, Eagle Reverse, Quarter

1957 • Circulation-Strike Mintage: 46,532,000.

Availability: Easily available in choice and gem Mint State. The Proof mintage crossed the million mark for the first time. However, the market for Proofs crashed by the time most people received their sets from the Mint, placing a damper on all investment in modern coins—

Proof sets as well as rolls. Quantities of rolls saved were less from this point, continuing through 1959.

Commentary: Circulation strikes have the Variety A reverse.

	Cert	Avg	% MS	EF-40	AU-50	MS-60	MS-63	MS-64	MS-65	MS-66	MS-67
1957	2,239	65.7	99%	$7	$8	$9	$10	$15	$20	$27	$70

1957, Proof • Proof Mintage: 1,247,952.

Commentary: Proofs have the Variety B reverse used on Proofs 1937 to 1964.

	Cert	Avg	% MS	PF-64	PF-65	PF-67
1957, Proof	6,030	67.3		$11	$15	$45

1957-D Washington, Eagle Reverse, Quarter

1957-D • Circulation-Strike Mintage: 77,924,160.

Availability: Easily available in choice and gem Mint State.

Commentary: Variety A and B reverses, see 1937.

	Cert	Avg	% MS	EF-40	AU-50	MS-60	MS-63	MS-64	MS-65	MS-66	MS-67
1957-D	1,841	65.5	99%	$7	$8	$9	$10	$15	$23	$38	$165

1958 Washington, Eagle Reverse, Quarter

1958 • Circulation-Strike Mintage: 6,360,000.

Availability: Easily available in choice and gem Mint State. The mintage of Proofs took a nosedive due to the weak market.

Commentary: Circulation strikes have the Variety A reverse.

	Cert	Avg	% MS	EF-40	AU-50	MS-60	MS-63	MS-64	MS-65	MS-66	MS-67
1958	4,097	65.8	100%	$7	$8	$9	$10	$15	$18	$33	$85

1958, Proof • Proof Mintage: 875,652.

Commentary: Proofs have the Variety B reverse used on Proofs 1937 to 1964.

	Cert	Avg	% MS	PF-64	PF-65	PF-67
1958, Proof	4,992	67.2		$11	$15	$40

1958-D Washington, Eagle Reverse, Quarter

1958-D • Circulation-Strike Mintage: 78,124,900.

Availability: Easily available in choice and gem Mint State.

Commentary: Variety A and B reverses, see 1937.

	Cert	Avg	% MS	EF-40	AU-50	MS-60	MS-63	MS-64	MS-65	MS-66	MS-67
1958-D	2,336	65.6	99%	$7	$8	$9	$10	$15	$23	$33	$165

1959 Washington, Eagle Reverse, Quarter

1959 • Circulation-Strike Mintage: 24,384,000.

Availability: Easily available in choice and gem Mint State. Interest in Proofs revived to an extent, and the mintage was more than a million.

Commentary: Circulation strikes have the Variety B reverse.

	Cert	Avg	% MS	EF-40	AU-50	MS-60	MS-63	MS-64	MS-65	MS-66	MS-67
1959	1,773	65.5	100%	$7	$8	$9	$10	$15	$20	$40	$850

1959, Proof • Proof Mintage: 1,149,291.

Commentary: Proofs have the Variety B reverse.

	Cert	Avg	% MS	PF-64	PF-65	PF-67
1959, Proof	5,512	67.4		$11	$12	$35

1959-D Washington, Eagle Reverse, Quarter

1959-D • **Circulation-Strike Mintage:** 62,054,232.

Availability: Easily available in choice and gem Mint State.

Commentary: Variety A and B reverses, see 1937.

	Cert	Avg	% MS	EF-40	AU-50	MS-60	MS-63	MS-64	MS-65	MS-66	MS-67
1959-D	1,463	65.1	99%	$7	$8	$9	$10	$15	$20	$45	$900

1960 Washington, Eagle Reverse, Quarter

1960 • **Circulation-Strike Mintage:** 29,164,000.

Availability: Easily available in choice and gem Mint State. The coin market was on fire, driven by the advent of *Coin World*, the first weekly publication in the field, and by the excitement of the 1960 Small Date Lincoln cent. All series benefited. The Library of Coins album series, marketed widely by the Coin and Currency Institute, proved to be a popular and attractive way to store and display sets of coins.

Commentary: Circulation strikes have the Variety B reverse.

	Cert	Avg	% MS	EF-40	AU-50	MS-60	MS-63	MS-64	MS-65	MS-66	MS-67
1960	1,286	65.4	100%	$7	$8	$9	$10	$15	$17	$40	$850

1960, Proof • **Proof Mintage:** 1,691,602.

Commentary: Proofs have the Variety B reverse.

	Cert	Avg	% MS	PF-64	PF-65	PF-67
1960, Proof	5,741	67.1		$10	$11	$30

1960-D Washington, Eagle Reverse, Quarter

1960-D • **Circulation-Strike Mintage:** 63,000,324.

Availability: Easily available in choice and gem Mint State.

Commentary: Variety A and B reverses, see 1937.

	Cert	Avg	% MS	EF-40	AU-50	MS-60	MS-63	MS-64	MS-65	MS-66	MS-67
1960-D	969	65.1	99%	$7	$8	$9	$10	$15	$18	$40	$1,750

1961 Washington, Eagle Reverse, Quarter

1961 • **Circulation-Strike Mintage:** 37,036,000.

Availability: Easily available in choice and gem Mint State. Proof mintages continued to climb, and another record was set. The market was dynamic in all series. Interest spread to mint errors, die varieties, tokens, paper money, and other series outside of the mainstream (*i.e.*, not listed in the *Guide Book of United States Coins*).

Commentary: Circulation strikes have the Variety B reverse.

	Cert	Avg	% MS	EF-40	AU-50	MS-60	MS-63	MS-64	MS-65	MS-66	MS-67
1961	1,144	65.2	99%	$7	$8	$9	$10	$12	$15	$42	$1,850

1961, Proof • **Proof Mintage:** 3,028,244.

Commentary: Proofs have the Variety B reverse.

	Cert	Avg	% MS	PF-64	PF-65	PF-67
1961, Proof	7,617	67.3		$10	$11	$30

1961-D Washington, Eagle Reverse, Quarter

1961-D • **Circulation-Strike Mintage:** 83,656,928.

Availability: Easily available in choice and gem Mint State. Rolls were hoarded in unprecedented quantities from 1960 through 1964.

Commentary: Variety A and B reverses, see 1937.

	Cert	Avg	% MS	EF-40	AU-50	MS-60	MS-63	MS-64	MS-65	MS-66	MS-67
1961-D	801	64.9	99%	$7	$8	$9	$10	$12	$17	$85	$3,300

1962 Washington, Eagle Reverse, Quarter

1962 • **Circulation-Strike Mintage:** 36,156,000.

Availability: Easily available in choice and gem Mint State. Market prices kept rising across the board. Proof production stabilized as slightly over three million, about the level that the Mint found comfortable to produce without having to place other facilities in use.

Commentary: Circulation strikes have the Variety B reverse.

	Cert	Avg	% MS	EF-40	AU-50	MS-60	MS-63	MS-64	MS-65	MS-66	MS-67
1962	1,420	65.4	99%	$7	$8	$9	$10	$12	$15	$45	$1,950

1962, Proof • **Proof Mintage:** 3,218,019.

Commentary: Proofs have the Variety B reverse.

	Cert	Avg	% MS	PF-64	PF-65	PF-67
1962, Proof	6,923	67.2		$10	$11	$30

1962-D Washington, Eagle Reverse, Quarter

1962-D • **Circulation-Strike Mintage:** 127,554,756.

Availability: Easily available in choice and gem Mint State.

Commentary: Variety A and B reverses, see 1937.

	Cert	Avg	% MS	EF-40	AU-50	MS-60	MS-63	MS-64	MS-65	MS-66	MS-67
1962-D	780	64.8	98%	$7	$8	$9	$10	$12	$17	$110	$3,500

1963 Washington, Eagle Reverse, Quarter

1963 • **Circulation-Strike Mintage:** 74,316,000.

Availability: Mint State coins are available in just about any level desired. The market continued its upward movement. *The Coin Dealer Newsletter* was launched, and included bid and ask prices for rolls and Proof sets.

Commentary: Circulation strikes have the Variety B reverse.

	Cert	Avg	% MS	EF-40	AU-50	MS-60	MS-63	MS-64	MS-65	MS-66	MS-67
1963	2,038	65.3	99%	$7	$8	$9	$10	$12	$15	$40	$750

1963, Proof • **Proof Mintage:** 3,075,645.

Commentary: Proofs have the Variety B reverse.

	Cert	Avg	% MS	PF-64	PF-65	PF-67
1963, Proof	8,587	67.4		$10	$11	$30

1963-D Washington, Eagle Reverse, Quarter

1963-D • **Circulation-Strike Mintage:** 135,288,184.

Availability: Common in all grades.

Commentary: Variety A and B reverses, see 1937. Doubled obverse die variety listed in Breen.

	Cert	Avg	% MS	EF-40	AU-50	MS-60	MS-63	MS-64	MS-65	MS-66	MS-67
1963-D	850	64.9	98%	$7	$8	$9	$10	$12	$17	$65	$850

1964 Washington, Eagle Reverse, Quarter

1964 • **Circulation-Strike Mintage:** 560,390,585.

Availability: Choice and gem Mint State coins are readily available. This was the last year of regular silver coinage. Exceptional quantities of rolls were hoarded, and Proof sets reached a record mintage. Storm clouds were rising on the coin market, and this was the last year of good times until the early 1970s.

Commentary: Circulation strikes and Proofs have the Variety B reverse. Breen's listing of a variety with Reverse C (see 1964-D) not confirmed by Fivaz and Stanton.

The Philadelphia Mint continued striking silver 1964-dated quarters in early 1965. The date was not changed, per the "date freeze" mandate of Mint Director Eva Adams. She blamed coin collectors for the current coin shortage and sought to stymie the collecting of new coins. In 1965 the *San Francisco Mint* (then called the San Francisco Assay Office) struck more than 15,000,000 mintmarkless 1964-dated silver quarters in 1965 and a further 4,640,865 in early 1966.[95]

	Cert	Avg	% MS	EF-40	AU-50	MS-60	MS-63	MS-64	MS-65	MS-66	MS-67
1964	1,969	64.9	98%	$7	$8	$9	$10	$12	$15	$45	$700

1964, Proof • **Proof Mintage:** 3,950,762.

Commentary: Proofs have the Variety B reverse.

	Cert	Avg	% MS	PF-64	PF-65	PF-67
1964, Proof	11,519	67.8		$10	$11	$30

1964-D Washington, Eagle Reverse, Quarter

1964-D • **Circulation-Strike Mintage:** 704,135,528.

Availability: Choice and gem Mint State coins are readily available.

Commentary: Variety A and B reverses, see 1937. Also rare Variety C reverse, see above.

The Denver Mint continued striking silver 1964-D quarters through 1965. The date was not changed, per the "date freeze" mandate of Mint Director Eva Adams.[96]

	Cert	Avg	% MS	EF-40	AU-50	MS-60	MS-63	MS-64	MS-65	MS-66	MS-67
1964-D	2,302	64.7	96%	$7	$8	$9	$10	$12	$15	$42	$450

VARIETY: *1964-D, Misplaced Mintmark (FS-25-1964D-502).* This is another example of a completely separated misplaced mintmark. In this instance the secondary D can be found in the space below the branch above the mintmark area. URS-2.

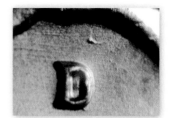

VARIETY: *1964-D, Type C Reverse (FS-25-1964D-901).* A new reverse die had been created, intended for use beginning in 1965. A few examples from Denver were struck with that die. See the earlier discussion of Reverse Types on page 651. URS-4.

1965 Washington, Eagle Reverse, Quarter

1965 • **Circulation-Strike Mintage:** 1,819,717,540.

Availability: Although clad quarters dated 1965 were made in unprecedented quantities, crossing the billion mark for the first time, there was scarcely any interest anymore in saving rolls, for clad metal, unlike silver, faced an uncertain future. For this year through the rest of the decade, very small quantities of quarter rolls were saved in proportion to the mintage figures.

Commentary: Example(s?) known on 90% silver planchet.

The mintage of this year set an all-time high record, not equaled since that time. This high figure is explained by the production of 1965-dated quarters into the year 1966, due to the "date freeze" set in place by Mint Director Eva Adams, and by the fact that Denver quarters bore no mintmark in 1965 and thus appeared identical to Philadelphia coins. The Denver Mint did not resume using the D mintmark until 1968.

Clad quarters were first released into circulation in November 1965.

	Cert	Avg	% MS	MS-63	MS-65	MS-66	MS-67
1965	307	64.8	96%	$1	$9	$30	$185

1965, Special Mint Set, Washington, Eagle Reverse, Quarter

1965, Special Mint Set • Circulation-Strike Mintage: 2,360,000.

Availability: 2,360,000 Special Mint Sets of coins dated 1965 were struck *in 1966* at the San Francisco Mint (but with no mintmark) for sale to collectors. These were carefully made and have a satiny partially mirrored surface.

As noted, Special Mint Sets (SMS) with this date were produced, but were struck in 1966. Production of SMS continued through 1967 in lieu of Proofs.

	Cert	Avg	% MS	MS-65	MS-66	MS-67	PF-65	PF-67Cam	PF-68CAM
1965, Special Mint Set	3,331	66.9		$12	$35	$350	$12	$375	$600

VARIETY: *1965, Special Mint Set, Doubled Die Obverse (FS-25-1965-101 [026]).* All the lettering shows strong doubling, as does the eye and date. It is an extremely rare, avidly sought variety. URS-3.

1966 Washington, Eagle Reverse, Quarter

1966 • Circulation-Strike Mintage: 821,101,500.

Availability: Mint State coins are readily available. Quality of 1966 and other early clad quarters is a different matter, and most coins have extensive marks (including from the original planchets), or striking, or eye appeal, or all of these considerations.

	Cert	Avg	% MS	MS-63	MS-65	MS-66	MS-67
1966	105	65.0	95%	$1	$7	$25	$125

1966, Special Mint Set, Washington, Eagle Reverse, Quarter

1966, Special Mint Set • Circulation-Strike Mintage: 2,261,583.

Availability: 2,261,583 Special Mint Sets of coins were struck at the San Francisco Mint (but with no mintmark) for sale to collectors. These were carefully made and have a partially mirrored surface.

	Cert	Avg	% MS	MS-65	MS-66	MS-67	PF-65	PF-67Cam	PF-68CAM
1966, Special Mint Set	3,171	66.9		$12	$50	$350	$12	$115	$1,450

1967 Washington, Eagle Reverse, Quarter

1967 • **Circulation-Strike Mintage:** 1,524,031,848.

Availability: Mint State coins are readily available, but cherrypicking is recommended to obtain quality.

Commentary: The mintage for this year is the second highest all-time record (1965 is highest).

	Cert	Avg	% MS	MS-63	MS-65	MS-66	MS-67
1967	130	65.7	97%	$1	$6	$35	$150

1967, Special Mint Set, Washington, Eagle Reverse, Quarter

1967, Special Mint Set • **Circulation-Strike Mintage:** 1,863,344.

Availability: 1,183,344 Special Mint Sets of coins were struck at the San Francisco Mint (but with no mintmark) for sale to collectors. These were carefully made and have a partially mirrored surface.

	Cert	Avg	% MS	MS-65	MS-66	MS-67	PF-65	PF-67Cam	PF-68CAM
1967, Special Mint Set	3,860	67.0		$12	$35	$175	$12	$50	$200

1968 Washington, Eagle Reverse, Quarter

1968 • **Circulation-Strike Mintage:** 220,731,500.

Availability: Mint State coins are readily available on an absolute basis, although quality can be a problem. Clad coins continued to be ignored by investors.

	Cert	Avg	% MS	MS-63	MS-65	MS-66	MS-67
1968	249	65.8	98%	$1.25	$8	$25	$100

1968-D Washington, Eagle Reverse, Quarter

1968-D • **Circulation-Strike Mintage:** 101,534,000.

Availability: The same comment as for the 1968 Philadelphia quarters. Around this time Ken Bressett, editor of the *Guide Book*, was one of the first to comment that clad coins, ignored by investors, might prove to be scarce someday.

	Cert	Avg	% MS	MS-63	MS-65	MS-66	MS-67
1968-D	747	66.0	100%	$1.10	$6	$15	$55

1968-S Washington, Eagle Reverse, Quarter

1968-S • **Proof Mintage:** 3,041,506.

Availability: Beginning this year, Proofs were packaged attractive hard plastic holders. The quality was better than ever before, and from this point onward, cameo contrast became a feature of many (but not all) Proof coins.

	Cert	Avg	% MS	PF-65	PF-67Cam	PF-68DC
1968S, Proof	1,134	67.4		$5	$15	$150

VARIETY: *1968-S, Doubled Die Obverse (FS-25-1968S-101) and 1968-S, Doubled Die Reverse (FS-25-1968S-801 [027]).* Doubled die obverse and doubled die reverse varieties are known and command a strong premium. Listed as FS-25-1968-S-101 (URS-3) and 801 (URS-6) respectively.

1969 Washington, Eagle Reverse, Quarter

1969 • **Circulation-Strike Mintage:** 176,212,000.

Availability: Mint State coins are readily available although attractive gems are elusive in comparison to the typical lower level Mint State issues. Cherrypicking for quality is advised. In this era plastic holders, such as those marketed by Capital Plastics, were a popular way to display sets of coins, including Washington quarters.

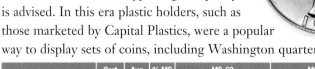

	Cert	Avg	% MS	MS-63	MS-65	MS-66	MS-67
1969	117	64.9	97%	$3	$10	$35	$350

1969-D Washington, Eagle Reverse, Quarter

1969-D • Circulation-Strike Mintage: 114,372,000.

Availability: Mint State coins are readily available. Cherrypicking for quality is advised. Clad coins continued to be ignored in their own time.

	Cert	Avg	% MS	MS-63	MS-65	MS-66	MS-67
1969-D	601	65.8	99%	$2.50	$10	$25	$75

1969-S Washington, Eagle Reverse, Quarter

1969-S • Proof Mintage: 2,934,631.

Availability: Readily available and with good eye appeal.

	Cert	Avg	% MS	PF-65	PF-67Cam	PF-68DC
1969S, Proof	1,508	67.9		$5	$15	$100

VARIETY: *1969-S, Doubled Die Obverse (FS-25-1968S-101 [027.08]).* Strong doubling can be found on the lettring and the date. URS-4.

1970 Washington, Eagle Reverse, Quarter

1970 • Circulation-Strike Mintage: 136,420,000.

Availability: Mint State coins are readily available. Cherrypicking for quality is advised.

	Cert	Avg	% MS	MS-63	MS-65	MS-66	MS-67
1970	302	65.3	100%	$1	$10	$40	$100

1970-D Washington, Eagle Reverse, Quarter

1970-D • **Circulation-Strike Mintage:** 417,341,364.

Availability: Mint State coins are readily available. Cherrypicking for quality is advised.

	Cert	Avg	% MS	MS-63	MS-65	MS-66	MS-67
1970-D	1,214	65.7	99%	$1	$6	$10	$35

1970-S Washington, Eagle Reverse, Quarter

1970-S • **Proof Mintage:** 2,632,810.

Availability: Attractive and of high quality—this is the general rule for coins in the marketplace today.

Commentary: The writer purchased a 1970-S Proof quarter plainly struck over a 1900 Barber quarter. The coin was publicly offered, and was seized by the Treasury Department. Apparently the concoction of a creative Mint employee, the piece somehow escaped into a 1970-S Proof set, no doubt initially baffling its discoverer.

	Cert	Avg	% MS	PF-65	PF-67Cam	PF-68DC
1970-S, Proof	1,218	67.9		$5	$15	$125

1971 Washington, Eagle Reverse, Quarter

1971 • **Circulation-Strike Mintage:** 109,284,000.

Availability: Mint State coins are readily available. Cherrypicking for quality is advised.

	Cert	Avg	% MS	MS-63	MS-65	MS-66	MS-67
1971	142	64.8	99%	$1	$6	$50	$150

1971-D Washington, Eagle Reverse, Quarter

1971-D • **Circulation-Strike Mintage:** 258,634,428.

Availability: Mint State coins are readily available. Cherrypicking for quality is advised.

	Cert	Avg	% MS	MS-63	MS-65	MS-66	MS-67
1971-D	302	65.9	100%	$1	$6	$20	$100

1971-S Washington, Eagle Reverse, Quarter

1971-S • **Proof Mintage:** 3,220,733.

Availability: Attractive and of high quality, as usual. The San Francisco Mint set new high standards in production.

	Cert	Avg	% MS	PF-65	PF-67Cam	PF-68DC
1971-S, Proof	1,374	67.8		$5	$15	$300

1972 Washington, Eagle Reverse, Quarter

1972 • **Circulation-Strike Mintage:** 215,048,000.

Availability: Mint State coins are readily available. Cherrypicking for quality is advised.

	Cert	Avg	% MS	MS-63	MS-65	MS-66	MS-67
1972	246	65.6	100%	$1	$6	$25	$175

1972-D Washington, Eagle Reverse, Quarter

1972-D • **Circulation-Strike Mintage:** 311,067,732.

Availability: Mint State coins are readily available. Cherrypicking for quality is advised. As improbable as it may seem in retrospect, there was no emphasis on high quality. Bank-wrapped rolls were Uncirculated,

and that was that—no sorting through to find gems. This situation remained in effect for much of the decade.

	Cert	Avg	% MS	MS-63	MS-65	MS-66	MS-67
1972-D	654	66.1	100%	$1	$6	$18	$30

1972-S Washington, Eagle Reverse, Quarter

1972-S • **Proof Mintage:** 3,260,996.

Availability: High quality and beautiful appearance as usual.

	Cert	Avg	% MS	PF-65	PF-67Cam	PF-68DC
1972-S, Proof	997	68.0		$5	$10	$30

1973 Washington, Eagle Reverse, Quarter

1973 • **Circulation-Strike Mintage:** 346,924,000.

Availability: Mint State coins are readily available. Cherrypicking for quality is advised.

	Cert	Avg	% MS	MS-63	MS-65	MS-66	MS-67
1973	152	65.3	99%	$1	$6	$25	$175

1973-D Washington, Eagle Reverse, Quarter

1973-D • **Circulation-Strike Mintage:** 232,977,400.

Availability: Mint State coins are readily available. Cherrypicking for quality is advised.

	Cert	Avg	% MS	MS-63	MS-65	MS-66	MS-67
1973-D	167	65.1	99%	$1	$6	$25	$175

1973-S Washington, Eagle Reverse, Quarter

1973-S • **Proof Mintage:** 2,760,339.

Availability: Nice!

	Cert	Avg	% MS	PF-65	PF-67Cam	PF-68DC
1973-S, Proof	438	68.1		$5	$10	$20

1974 Washington, Eagle Reverse, Quarter

1974 • **Circulation-Strike Mintage:** 801,456,000.

Availability: Mint State coins are readily available. Cherrypicking for quality is advised. The investment end of the coin market entered a slow period that would reach its nadir in 1976, after which it would become warm, then hot.

Commentary: Many of the 1974-dated Washington quarters were struck in 1975, pursuant to Public Law 93-531 (December 26, 1974). In 1975 most activities at the mints were in striking the 1776–1976 Bicentennial quarters. Accordingly, while no 1975-dated quarters were made, 1974 quarters were *restruck*, and 1776–1976 quarters were *prestruck*.

	Cert	Avg	% MS	MS-63	MS-65	MS-66	MS-67
1974	128	65.1	98%	$1	$6	$25	$175

1974-D Washington, Eagle Reverse, Quarter

1974-D • **Circulation-Strike Mintage:** 353,160,300.

Availability: Mint State coins are readily available. Cherrypicking for quality is advised.

	Cert	Avg	% MS	MS-63	MS-65	MS-66	MS-67
1974-D	181	65.4	99%	$1	$7	$25	$75

1974-S Washington, Eagle Reverse, Quarter

1974-S • **Proof Mintage:** 2,612,568.

Availability: Beautiful and of high quality.

Commentary: One variety has a doubled S-mintmark.

	Cert	Avg	% MS	PF-65	PF-67Cam	PF-68DC
1974-S, Proof	456	68.1		$5	$10	$20

1776–1976 Washington, Bicentennial Reverse, Quarter, Copper-Nickel Clad

1776–1976, Bicentennial Reverse, Copper-Nickel Clad • **Circulation-Strike Mintage:** 809,784,016.

Availability: Mint State coins are readily available. Cherrypicking for quality is advised. Especially large quantities were saved.

	Cert	Avg	% MS	MS-63	MS-65	MS-66	MS-67
1776–1976, Copper-Nickel Clad	485	65.5	99%	$1.25	$6	$15	$50

1776–1976-D Washington, Bicentennial Reverse, Quarter, Copper-Nickel Clad

1776–1976-D, Bicentennial Reverse, Copper-Nickel Clad • **Circulation-Strike Mintage:** 860,118,839.

Availability: Common in Mint State, although gems are in the minority. Many were saved.

Commentary: A doubled-die obverse variety is listed in Breen.

	Cert	Avg	% MS	MS-63	MS-65	MS-66	MS-67
1776–1976-D, Copper-Nickel Clad	824	65.5	98%	$1.25	$6	$15	$60

1776–1976-S Washington, Bicentennial Reverse, Quarter, Copper-Nickel Clad

1776–1976-S, Bicentennial Reverse, Copper-Nickel Clad • Proof Mintage: 7,059,099.

Availability: Easily available due to the extraordinary high mintage. Sales fell short of expectation, and sets were still available from the Mint for several years afterward.

Commentary: In August 1974 at the American Numismatic Association convention held that year in Bal Harbour, Florida, visitors were given a preview of the Proof coinage. On view were examples of each of the three Bicentennial denominations, but *without* S mintmark. The whereabouts of these coins is not known today.

	Cert	Avg	% MS	PF-65	PF-67Cam	PF-68DC
1776–1976-S, Copper-Nickel Clad, Proof	1,195	66.1	100%	$5	$10	$20

1776–1976-S Washington, Bicentennial Variety, Quarter, Silver Clad

1776–1976-S, Bicentennial Reverse, Silver Clad • Circulation-Strike Mintage: 11,000,000 (est.).

Availability: Choice and gem Mint State coins are easily obtained, but at a premium due to their silver content.

	Cert	Avg	% MS	MS-63	MS-65	MS-66	MS-67
1776–1976-S, Silver Clad	1,776	68.0		$4	$7	$15	$40

1776–1976-S, Bicentennial Reverse, Silver Clad, Proof • Proof Mintage: 4,000,000 (est.).

Availability: Choice and gem Proof coins are easily obtained, but at a premium due to their silver content.

	Cert	Avg	% MS	PF-65	PF-67Cam	PF-68DC
1776–1976-S, Silver Clad, Proof	3,373	68.1		$8	$12	$25

A GALLERY OF MODERN WASHINGTON, EAGLE REVERSE, QUARTER DOLLARS (1977 TO 1998)

Following the Bicentennial issues, the quarter reverted to the Eagle Reverse design that had already run for over 50 years, destined to run for over 20 more. On the following pages are shown images for all the main listings of Washington quarters from 1977 to 1998.

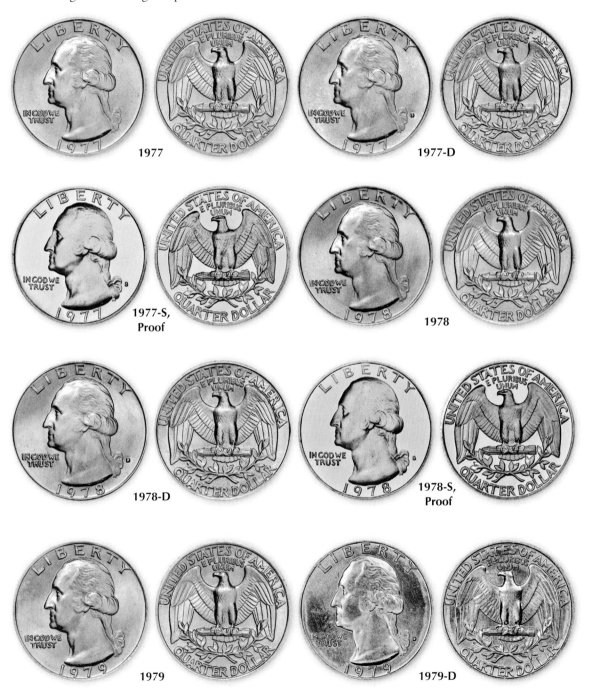

1977

1977-D

1977-S, Proof

1978

1978-D

1978-S, Proof

1979

1979-D

1979-S,
Type 1, Proof

1979-S,
Type 2, Proof

1980-P

1980-D

1980-S,
Proof

1981-P

1981-D

1981-S,
Type 1, Proof

1981-S,
Type 2, Proof

1982-P

1982-D

1982-S,
Proof

1983-P

1983-D

1983-S,
Proof

1984-P

1984-D

1984-S,
Proof

1985-P

1985-D

1985-S, Proof

1986-P

1986-D

1986-S, Proof

1987-P

1987-D

1987-S, Proof

1988-P

1988-D

1988-S, Proof

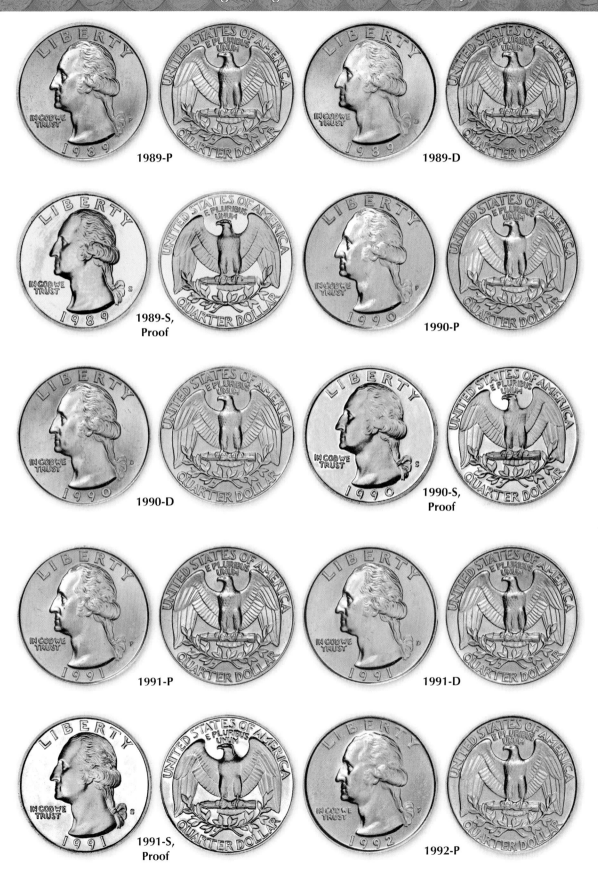

1989-P

1989-D

1989-S, Proof

1990-P

1990-D

1990-S, Proof

1991-P

1991-D

1991-S, Proof

1992-P

1992-D

1992-S,
Proof

1993-P

1993-D

1993-S,
Proof

1994-P

1994-D

1994-S,
Proof

1995-P

1995-D

1995-S, Proof

1996-P

1996-D

1996-S, Proof

1997-P

1997-D

1997-S, Proof

1998-P

1998-D

1998-S, Proof

1979-S, Filled S (Type 1), Proof	1979-S, Clear S (Type 2), Proof	1981-S, Rounded S (Type 1), Proof	1979-S, Clear S (Type 2), Proof

	Mintage	Cert	Avg	%MS	MS-63 PF-65	MS-65 PF-67Cam	MS-66 PF-68DC	MS-67
1977	468,556,000	142	65.5	99%	$1	$6	$20	$100
	Auctions: $123, MS-67, September 2014; $52, MS-66, August 2015; $100, MS-60, September 2015							
1977-D	256,524,978	110	65.0	98%	$1	$6	$25	$125
	Auctions: $229, MS-67, September 2014							
1977-S, Proof	3,251,152	872	68.8			$5	$10	$20
	Auctions: $70, PF-70DCam, August 2014; $103, PF-70DCam, November 2014; $90, PF-70DCam, May 2013							
1978	521,452,000	175	65.4	99%	$1	$6	$20	$100
	Auctions: $165, MS-67, January 2015; $470, MS-65, February 2015; $247, MS-65, August 2015; $259, MS-60, July 2015							
1978-D	287,373,152	164	65.4	99%	$1	$6	$25	$175
	Auctions: $26, MS-66, August 2014							
1978-S, Proof	3,127,781	752	68.8			$5	$10	$18
	Auctions: $61, PF-70DCam, August 2014; $80, PF-70DCam, May 2013; $12, PF-70DCam, March 2015							
1979	515,708,000	195	65.7	99%	$1	$6	$25	$125
	Auctions: $411, MS-66, June 2014; $200, MS-64, February 2015; $176, MS-64, November 2014							
1979-D	489,789,780	159	65.4	99%	$1	$6	$25	$125
	Auctions: $441, MS-67, September 2013							
1979-S, Proof, All kinds (a)	3,677,175							
1979-S, Type 1 ("Filled" S), Proof		971	68.8			$5	$10	$18
	Auctions: $68, PF-70DCam, August 2014							
1979-S, Type 2 ("Clear" S), Proof		1,048	69.0			$5	$10	$18
	Auctions: $529, PF-70DCam, September 2014; $76, PF-70DCam, August 2014; $72, PF-70DCam, September 2014							
1980-P	635,832,000	390	65.8	99%	$1	$6	$18	$85
	Auctions: $74, MS-65, November 2015; $56, MS-62, August 2015; $141, AU-58, January 2015							
1980-D	518,327,487	168	65.5	99%	$1	$6	$20	$175
	Auctions: $1,380, MS-67, February 2007							
1980-S, Proof	3,554,806	1,140	68.7			$5	$10	$18
	Auctions: $79, PF-70DCam, May 2013							
1981-P	601,716,000	310	66.0	100%	$1	$6	$17	$100
	Auctions: $176, MS-65, August 2013							
1981-D	575,722,833	327	65.6	99%	$1	$6	$22	$150
	Auctions: $259, MS-67, September 2013							
1981-S, Proof, All kinds (b)	4,063,083							
1981-S, Type 1 ("Rounded" S), Proof		1,393	68.8			$4	$8	$16
	Auctions: $70, PF-70DCam, May 2013							
1981-S, Type 2 ("Flat" S), Proof		917	69.0			$4	$8	$16
	Auctions: $705, PF-70DCam, April 2013							
1982-P	500,931,000	150	65.5	99%	$7	$30	$85	$375
	Auctions: $646, MS-67, January 2015; $282, MS-63, September 2015; $353, AU-50, January 2015							
1982-D	480,042,788	267	65.6	99%	$5	$18	$65	$325
	Auctions: $30, MS-66, March 2013							

a. The mintmark style was changed during 1979 Proof production, creating two distinctly different types. "The Type 2 is the rare variety, and is easily distinguished from the common Type 1. The Type 1 has a very indistinct blob, whereas the Type 2 shows a well-defined S" (*Cherrypickers' Guide to Rare Die Varieties*, sixth edition, volume II). b. The mintmark style was changed during the 1981 Proof production, creating two distinct types. "The Type 2 is the rare variety, and is not easily distinguished from the common Type 1. For most collectors, the easiest difference to discern on the Type 2 is the flatness on the top curve of the S, which is rounded on the Type 1. Additionally, the surface of the Type 2 mintmark is frosted, and the openings in the loops slightly larger" (*Cherrypickers' Guide to Rare Die Varieties*, sixth edition, volume II).

**1989-D,
Repunched
Mintmark**
FS-25-1989D-501.

	Mintage	Cert	Avg	%MS	MS-63	MS-65 PF-65	MS-66 PF-67Cam	MS-67 PF-68DC
1982-S, Proof	3,857,479	935	69.0			$4	$8	$16
Auctions: $103, PF-70DCam, May 2014; $56, PF-70DCam, September 2014; $47, PF-70DCam, November 2014								
1983-P ‡	673,535,000	859	65.0	98%	$30	$65	$200	$400
Auctions: $74, MS-66, July 2014; $74, MS-66, September 2014; $423, AU-58, January 2015								
1983-D	617,806,446	106	65.3	100%	$10	$45	$150	$500
Auctions: $1,058, MS-67, June 2014; $108, MS-66, August 2014; $92, MS-66, September 2014; $84, MS-66, January 2015								
1983-S, Proof	3,279,126	871	68.8			$4	$8	$16
Auctions: $72, PF-70DCam, September 2014; $90, PF-70DCam, August 2013								
1984-P	676,545,000	173	65.3	97%	$2	$10	$20	$125
Auctions: $1,058, MS-67, September 2013								
1984-D	546,483,064	91	64.6	98%	$2	$12	$65	$300
Auctions: $764, MS-67, September 2013								
1984-S, Proof	3,065,110	637	69.0			$4	$8	$16
Auctions: $80, PF-70DCam, May 2013; $55, PF-70DCam, August 2014; $50, PF-70DCam, August 2015								
1985-P	775,818,962	205	65.5	98%	$2	$15	$25	$100
Auctions: $764, MS-65, June 2014								
1985-D	519,962,888	212	65.7	99%	$1	$9	$25	$100
Auctions: $66, MS-66, March 2013								
1985-S, Proof	3,362,821	691	69.0			$4	$8	$16
Auctions: $86, PF-70DCam, May 2013								
1986-P	551,199,333	204	64.8	98%	$2.50	$12	$30	$125
Auctions: $129, MS-64, October 2014; $103, MS-66, September 2014; $100, MS-66, August 2015; $30, MS-66, November 2014								
1986-D	504,298,660	231	65.6	99%	$6	$18	$25	$100
Auctions: $104, MS-66, November 2007								
1986-S, Proof	3,010,497	622	69.1			$4	$8	$16
Auctions: $39, PF-70DCam, August 2013								
1987-P	582,499,481	160	65.2	99%	$1	$9	$40	$200
Auctions: $59, MS-66, December 2007								
1987-D	655,594,696	179	65.6	99%	$1	$6	$20	$150
Auctions: $676, MS-67, January 2015; $66, MS-66, September 2014								
1987-S, Proof	4,227,728	835	69.0			$4	$8	$16
Auctions: No auction records available.								
1988-P	562,052,000	175	65.1	99%	$1.25	$15	$30	$175
Auctions: $66, MS-66, March 2013								
1988-D	596,810,688	154	65.5	100%	$1	$10	$20	$125
Auctions: $66, MS-66, November 2007								
1988-S, Proof	3,262,948	547	69.1			$4	$8	$16
Auctions: $55, PF-70DCam, August 2013								
1989-P	512,868,000	146	65.1	98%	$1	$12	$30	$150
Auctions: $216, MS-66, August 2009								
1989-D	896,535,597	138	65.3	98%	$1	$7	$25	$125
Auctions: $70, MS-66, March 2013								
1989-D, Repunched Mintmark (c)	(j)	0	n/a		$20	$25	$50	
Auctions: No auction records available.								
1989-S, Proof	3,220,194	617	68.9			$4	$8	$16
Auctions: $79, PF-70DCam, January 2010								

‡ Ranked in the *100 Greatest U.S. Modern Coins*. **c.** The secondary D mintmark is visible west of the primary D. **d.** Included in 1989-D mintage figure.

1990-S, Doubled Die Obverse, Proof
FS-25-1990S-101.

	Mintage	Cert	Avg	%MS	MS-63 / PF-65	MS-65 / PF-67Cam	MS-66 / PF-68DC	MS-67
1990-P	613,792,000	172	65.9	99%	$1	$10	$20	$100
Auctions: $282, MS-64, June 2014								
1990-D	927,638,181	185	65.8	100%	$1	$10	$20	$125
Auctions: $646, MS-68, April 2014; $52, MS-67, August 2014								
1990-S, Proof	3,299,559	822	69.2			$4	$8	$16
Auctions: $53, PF-68DCam, April 2013								
1990-S, Doubled Die Obverse, Proof ‡ (e)	(I)	5	68.2			$225	$700	
Auctions: $4,888, PF-70DCam, April 2012								
1991-P	570,968,000	136	65.9	99%	$1	$12	$30	$100
Auctions: $90, MS-66, November 2007								
1991-D	630,966,693	94	65.4	100%	$1	$12	$30	$225
Auctions: $66, MS-66, March 2013								
1991-S, Proof	2,867,787	782	69.3			$4	$8	$16
Auctions: $69, PF-70DCam, January 2010								
1992-P	384,764,000	155	65.9	100%	$1.50	$16	$35	$250
Auctions: $242, MS-66, February 2008								
1992-D	389,777,107	132	65.3	98%	$1	$16	$35	$350
Auctions: $1,763, MS-67, November 2013; $47, MS-66, July 2014								
1992-S, Proof	2,858,981	588	69.2			$4	$8	$16
Auctions: $50, PF-70DCam, January 2010								
1992-S, Proof, Silver	1,317,579	1,637	69.2			$9	$12	$22
Auctions: $109, PF-70DCam, January 2010								
1993-P	639,276,000	200	66.1	98%	$1	$7	$20	$85
Auctions: $86, MS-67, August 2014; $306, MS-64, June 2014; $282, MS-64, February 2015								
1993-D	645,476,128	166	65.9	99%	$1	$7	$25	$100
Auctions: $1,298, MS-67, January 2015; $59, MS-67, August 2014; $101, MS-66, September 2014; $36, AU-58, July 2014								
1993-S, Proof	2,633,439	585	69.3			$4	$8	$16
Auctions: $58, PF-70DCam, May 2013								
1993-S, Proof, Silver	761,353	1,256	69.1			$9	$12	$22
Auctions: $70, PF-70DCam, August 2013								
1994-P	825,600,000	136	65.9	100%	$1	$10	$25	$100
Auctions: $70, MS-66, March 2013								
1994-D	880,034,110	118	65.0	96%	$1	$10	$30	$150
Auctions: $123, MS-66, September 2014; $212, MS-64, July 2014								
1994-S, Proof	2,484,594	551	69.3			$4	$8	$16
Auctions: $69, PF-70DCam, January 2010								
1994-S, Proof, Silver	785,329	1,165	69.1			$9	$14	$25
Auctions: $76, PF-70DCam, September 2014; $96, PF-70DCam, May 2013								
1995-P	1,004,336,000	139	66.5	100%	$1.25	$14	$20	$65
Auctions: $129, MS-67, March 2013								

‡ Ranked in the *100 Greatest U.S. Modern Coins*. **e.** Very strong doubling is visible on the date and the mintmark, with slightly less dramatic doubling on IN GOD WE TRUST. **f.** Included in 1990-S, Proof, mintage figure.

	Mintage	Cert	Avg	%MS	MS-63 PF-65	MS-65 PF-67Cam	MS-66 PF-68DC	MS-67
1995-D	1,103,216,000	147	66.1	100%	$1	$13	$20	$75
Auctions: $165, MS-67, September 2014; $38, MS-64, July 2015								
1995-S, Proof	2,117,496	439	69.4			$8	$10	$20
Auctions: $69, PF-70DCam, January 2010								
1995-S, Proof, Silver	679,985	1,318	69.1			$9	$14	$25
Auctions: $68, PF-70DCam, September 2014; $69, PF-70DCam, November 2014; $135, PF-70DCam, May 2013								
1996-P	925,040,000	211	66.5	100%	$1	$10	$18	$30
Auctions: $441, MS-68, March 2013								
1996-D	906,868,000	238	66.2	100%	$1	$10	$18	$30
Auctions: $447, MS-68, March 2013; $165, MS-64, November 2014; $79, MS-63, January 2015								
1996-S, Proof	1,750,244	522	69.3			$5	$8	$18
Auctions: $84, PF-70DCam, January 2010								
1996-S, Proof, Silver	775,021	1,278	69.1			$9	$14	$25
Auctions: $76, PF-70DCam, May 2013								
1997-P	595,740,000	134	66.3	100%	$1	$11	$18	$40
Auctions: $15, MS-60, January 2013								
1997-D	599,680,000	131	66.1	99%	$1	$12	$18	$40
Auctions: $66, MS-67, March 2013								
1997-S, Proof	2,055,000	443	69.5			$5	$8	$18
Auctions: $69, PF-70DCam, January 2010								
1997-S, Proof, Silver	741,678	1,307	69.2			$9	$14	$25
Auctions: $89, PF-70DCam, January 2010								
1998-P	896,268,000	164	66.6	99%	$1	$7	$18	$40
Auctions: $364, MS-68, September 2014; $329, MS-68, June 2014; $306, MS-66, January 2015; $159, MS-64, November 2014								
1998-D	821,000,000	149	65.4	97%	$1	$7	$20	$100
Auctions: $1,528, MS-67+, January 2015;$364, MS-67, September 2014; $32, MS-66, June 2014; $69, MS-63, August 2015								
1998-S, Proof	2,086,507	488	69.5			$6	$8	$18
Auctions: $9,988, PF-65, August 2014								
1998-S, Proof, Silver	878,792	1,465	69.2			$9	$12	$22
Auctions: $70, PF-70DCam, May 2013								

WASHINGTON, STATE, D.C., AND TERRITORIAL (1999–2009)

Designers: *John Flanagan (obverse); see image captions for reverse designers.* **Weight:** *Clad issue—5.67 grams; silver Proofs—6.25 grams.* **Composition:** *Clad issue—Outer layers of copper-nickel (.750 copper, .250 nickel) bonded to inner core of pure copper; silver Proofs— .900 silver, .100 copper (net weight .18084 oz. pure silver).* **Diameter:** *24.3 mm.* **Edge:** *Reeded.* **Mints:** *Clad issue—Philadelphia, Denver, and San Francisco; silver Proofs—San Francisco.*

Circulation Strike

Proof

THE 50 STATE QUARTERS PROGRAM

The 50 State Quarters Program®, first suggested by Harvey Stack and shepherded into law and reality by Rep. Michael Castle, was launched in the order that the states ratified the Constitution and became part of the Union.

Every year five states of the Union were each to suggest designs for the reverse of the quarter dollar, the motifs to depict some aspect of history, tradition, nature, or fame. Prohibitions included busts, state seals, state flags, logotypes, and depictions of living people. The first issue in 1999 featured Delaware and the latest was for Hawaii in 2008.

Many designs were taken from sketches provided by the public in addition to professional artists. The governor of each state made the final choice with the consent of the secretary of the Treasury. Selected motifs varied from the famous, such as the Old Man in the Mountain for New Hampshire and the first flight of the Wright brothers for North Carolina to the seeming obscure, as the scissortail flycatcher for Nebraska.

Early in the program Kermit the Mint Spokesfrog, a Muppet, published the coins on television and in print. Kermit hopped to the 1999 Connecticut quarter launch program, but wasn't seen much after that. Perhaps he simply croaked, or perhaps he was eaten by Peter, the Mint Eagle, who appeared at a number of releases.

The Mint continued to be creative with its marketing and along the way new ideas were implemented, among the later ones being the offering of small 100-coin bags of individual issues, 1,000-coin bags, and rolls. The program took place during the Mint directorships of Philip Diehl, Jeh Johnson, Henrietta Holsman Fore, and Edmund Moy.

Interest was intense at the beginning, but in time faded. Quantities of later quarters were much smaller than those for the first years. Distribution was curiously erratic from a numismatic viewpoint. The Federal Reserve System distributed coins to fill requests from member banks, which usually had little to do with the states being honored. Despite such situations, the quarters were a spectacular success.

Rep. Castle's 2006 estimate that the program might earn the United States Treasury department $3.4 billion was based on the difference between the cost of manufacture and the face value that the Federal Reserve System paid. When all was said and done, the profit was about $6.1 billion!

The program also encouraged collecting coins at face value from circulation, and many folders and albums were sold for that purpose.

D.C. AND TERRITORIAL QUARTERS OF 2009:
SEQUEL TO THE STATE QUARTERS PROGRAM

When the 50 State Quarters Program was first envisioned in 2006 it was anticipated that in time all 50 states would be individually showcased, at the rate of five designs per year starting in 1999. The program was a great success and concluded in 2008, as described previously. The earlier issues were more popular than the later ones, but overall the public as well as members of the numismatic community were satisfied.

As the program neared its end there was a movement to extend it by including the District of Columbia and the American territories. The former in particular had long hoped to gain some of the privileges of the states, such as having representatives in Congress. To be honored in the program were the District of Columbia; the commonwealths of Puerto Rico (another long-time state-hopeful area) and the Northern Mariana Islands; and the territories of Guam, the U.S. Virgin Islands, and American Samoa.

One incorporated territory was omitted—Palmyra Atoll. One reason may be that as it has no permanent residents it has no citizens to propose designs. The program ran its course but received only mild interest from the numismatic community. This was due to two factors: (1) Interest in the State quarters had faded sharply by 2009, and (2) except for the District of Columbia, few citizens knew much about the places being honored.

WASHINGTON, STATE, D.C., AND TERRITORIAL QUARTER DOLLARS (1999–2009)

GRADING STANDARDS

MS-60 to 70 (Mint State). *Obverse:* At MS-60, some abrasion and contact marks are evident on the highest-relief parts of the hair and the cheek. At MS-63, abrasion is slight at best, less so at MS-64. An MS-65 coin should display no abrasion or contact marks except under magnification, and MS-66 and higher coins should have none at all. Luster should be full. *Reverse:* Check the highest-relief areas of the design (these differ from coin to coin). Otherwise, comments are as for the obverse.

2004-D, Wisconsin, Extra Leaf Low. Graded MS-66.

AU-50, 53, 55, 58 (About Uncirculated). *Obverse:* Light wear is seen on the cheek, the high areas of the hair, and the neck. At AU-58, the luster is extensive, but incomplete, especially on the higher parts and in the field. At AU–50 and 53, luster is less. About Uncirculated coins usually lack eye appeal. *Reverse:* Light wear is seen on the higher-relief areas. Otherwise, comments are as for the obverse.

2004-D, Wisconsin, Extra Leaf High. Graded AU-58.

State, D.C., and Territorial quarter dollars are seldom collected in grades lower than AU-50.

PF-60 to 70 (Proof). *Obverse and Reverse:* These coins are so recent, and as only a few have been cleaned, most approach perfection and can be designated PF–68 to 70, the latter only if no contact marks or other problems can be seen under magnification. A cleaned coin with extensive hairlines would not be collectible for most numismatists and would be classified at a lower level such as PF–60 to 63. Those with lighter hairlines qualify for PF–64 or 65.

2008-S, Alaska. Graded PF-70 Ultra Cameo.

A GALLERY OF STATE, D.C., AND TERRITORIAL QUARTER DOLLARS (1999–2008)

On the following pages are the reverse designs for all the main listings of State quarters from 1999 to 2008.

Modified Obverse, Philadelphia, 1999 to Date
Original designer: John Flanagan.

Modified Obverse, Denver, 1999 to Date
Original designer: John Flanagan.

Modified Obverse, San Francisco, Circulation Strike, 1999 to Date
Original designer: John Flanagan.

Modified Obverse, San Francisco, Proof, 1999 to Date
Original designer: John Flanagan.

1999, Delaware
Reverse designer: William Cousins.

(shown above left)

1999, New Jersey
Reverse designer: Alfred Maletsky.

1999, Pennsylvania
Reverse designer: John Mercanti.

1999, Georgia
Reverse designer: T. James Ferrell.

1999, Connecticut
Reverse designer: T. James Ferrell.

2000, Massachusetts
Reverse designer:
Thomas D. Rogers Sr.

2000, Maryland
Reverse designer:
Thomas D. Rogers Sr.

2000, South Carolina
Reverse designer:
Thomas D. Rogers Sr.

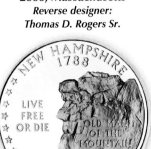

2000, New Hampshire
Reverse designer:
William Cousins.

2000, Virginia
Reverse designer:
Edgar Z. Steever.

2001, New York
Reverse designer:
Alfred Maletsky.

2001, North Carolina
Reverse designer:
John Mercanti.

2001, Rhode Island
Reverse designer:
Thomas D. Rogers Sr.

2001, Vermont
Reverse designer:
T. James Ferrell.

2001, Kentucky
Reverse designer:
T. James Ferrell.

2002, Tennessee
Reverse designer:
Donna Weaver.

2002, Ohio
Reverse designer:
Donna Weaver.

2002, Louisiana
*Reverse designer:
John Mercanti.*

2002, Indiana
*Reverse designer:
Donna Weaver.*

2002, Mississippi
*Reverse designer:
Donna Weaver.*

2003, Illinois
*Reverse designer:
Donna Weaver.*

2003, Alabama
*Reverse designer:
Norman E. Nemeth.*

2003, Maine
*Reverse designer:
Donna Weaver.*

2003, Missouri
*Reverse designer:
Alfred Maletsky.*

2003, Arkansas
*Reverse designer:
John Mercanti.*

2004, Michigan
*Reverse designer:
Donna Weaver.*

2004, Florida
*Reverse designer:
T. James Ferrell.*

2004, Texas
*Reverse designer:
Norman E. Nemeth.*

2004, Iowa
*Reverse designer:
John Mercanti.*

2004, Wisconsin
Reverse designer:
Alfred Maletsky.

**2004-D, Wisconsin,
Normal Reverse**

**2004-D, Wisconsin,
Extra Leaf High**
FS-25-2004D-WI-5901.

**2004-D, Wisconsin,
Extra Leaf Low**
FS-25-2004D-WI-5902.

2005, California
Reverse designer:
Don Everhart.

2005, Minnesota
Reverse designer:
Charles Vickers.

2005, Oregon
Reverse designer:
Donna Weaver.

2005, Kansas
Reverse designer:
Norman E. Nemeth.

2005, West Virginia
Reverse designer:
John Mercanti.

2006, Nevada
Reverse designer:
Don Everhart.

2006, Nebraska
Reverse designer:
Charles Vickers.

2006, Colorado
Reverse designer:
Norman E. Nemeth.

2006, North Dakota
Reverse designer:
Donna Weaver.

2006, South Dakota
Reverse designer:
John Mercanti.

2007, Montana
Reverse designer:
Don Everhart.

2007, Washington
Reverse designer:
Charles Vickers.

2007, Idaho
Reverse designer:
Don Everhart.

2007, Wyoming
Reverse designer:
Norman E. Nemeth.

2007, Utah
Reverse designer:
Joseph Menna.

2008, Oklahoma
Reverse designer:
Phebe Hemphill.

2008, New Mexico
Reverse designer:
Don Everhart.

2008, Arizona
Reverse designer:
Joseph Menna.

2008, Alaska
Reverse designer:
Charles Vickers.

2008, Hawaii
Reverse designer:
Don Everhart.

2009, District of Columbia
Reverse designer:
Don Everhart.

2009, Puerto Rico
Reverse designer:
Joseph Menna.

2009, Guam
Reverse designer:
Jim Licaretz.

2009, American Samoa
Reverse designer:
Charles Vickers.

2009, U.S. Virgin Islands
Reverse designer:
Joseph Menna.

2009, Northern Mariana Islands
Reverse designer:
Phebe Hemphill.

| | Mintage | Cert | Avg | %MS | AU-50 | MS-63 | MS-65 | MS-66 | MS-67 |
					PF-65	PF-66DC	PF-69DC
1999-P, Delaware	373,400,000	1,224	66.0	100%	$0.50	$2	$5	$25	$55
1999-D, Delaware	401,424,000	1,358	66.0	100%	$0.50	$2	$5	$25	$55
1999-S, Delaware, Proof	3,713,359	6,723	69.2				$7	$8	$20
1999-S, Delaware, Proof, Silver	804,565	12,897	69.0				$30	$35	$50
1999-P, Pennsylvania	349,000,000	1,112	66.1	100%	$0.50	$2	$5	$25	$55
1999-D, Pennsylvania	358,332,000	993	65.9	100%	$0.50	$2	$5	$25	$55
1999-S, Pennsylvania, Proof	3,713,359	6,492	69.2				$7	$8	$20
1999-S, Pennsylvania, Proof, Silver	804,565	12,326	69.1				$30	$35	$50
1999-P, New Jersey	363,200,000	1,063	66.1	100%	$0.50	$2	$5	$25	$55
1999-D, New Jersey	299,028,000	1,196	66.0	100%	$0.50	$2	$5	$25	$55
1999-S, New Jersey, Proof	3,713,359	6,489	69.2				$7	$8	$20
1999-S, New Jersey, Proof, Silver	804,565	12,418	69.1				$30	$35	$50
1999-P, Georgia	451,188,000	1,173	65.7	99%	$0.50	$2	$5	$25	$55
1999-D, Georgia	488,744,000	1,172	65.8	99%	$0.50	$2	$5	$25	$55
1999-S, Georgia, Proof	3,713,359	6,525	69.2				$7	$8	$20
1999-S, Georgia, Proof, Silver	804,565	12,523	69.1				$30	$35	$50
1999-P, Connecticut	688,744,000	1,348	65.6	99%	$0.50	$1.50	$5	$25	$55
1999-D, Connecticut	657,880,000	2,280	65.4	100%	$0.50	$1.50	$5	$25	$55
1999-S, Connecticut, Proof	3,713,359	6,561	69.3				$7	$8	$20
1999-S, Connecticut, Proof, Silver	804,565	12,338	69.1				$30	$35	$50
2000-P, Massachusetts	628,600,000	914	66.2	100%	$0.35	$1	$4	$15	$40
2000-D, Massachusetts	535,184,000	661	66.1	100%	$0.35	$1	$4	$15	$40
2000-S, Massachusetts, Proof	4,020,172	4,628	69.2				$3	$4	$15
2000-S, Massachusetts, Proof, Silver	965,421	9,695	69.2				$8	$10	$20

	Mintage	Cert	Avg	%MS	AU-50	MS-63	MS-65	MS-66	MS-67
							PF-65	PF-66DC	PF-69DC
2000-P, Maryland	678,200,000	631	65.9	99%	$0.35	$1	$4	$15	$40
2000-D, Maryland	556,532,000	641	66.0	100%	$0.35	$1	$4	$15	$40
2000-S, Maryland, Proof	4,020,172	4,530	69.2				$3	$4	$15
2000-S, Maryland, Proof, Silver	965,421	9,825	69.2				$8	$10	$20
2000-P, South Carolina	742,576,000	605	66.1	100%	$0.35	$1	$4	$15	$40
2000-D, South Carolina	566,208,000	748	66.3	100%	$0.35	$1	$4	$15	$40
2000-S, South Carolina, Proof	4,020,172	4,583	69.2				$3	$4	$15
2000-S, South Carolina, Proof, Silver	965,421	9,489	69.2				$8	$10	$20
2000-P, New Hampshire	673,040,000	560	65.6	99%	$0.35	$1	$4	$15	$40
2000-D, New Hampshire	495,976,000	582	66.0	100%	$0.35	$1	$4	$15	$40
2000-S, New Hampshire, Proof	4,020,172	4,589	69.2				$3	$4	$15
2000-S, New Hampshire, Proof, Silver	965,421	9,479	69.1				$8	$10	$20
2000-P, Virginia	943,000,000	675	66.1	100%	$0.35	$1	$4	$15	$40
2000-D, Virginia	651,616,000	593	66.1	99%	$0.35	$1	$4	$15	$40
2000-S, Virginia, Proof	4,020,172	4,573	69.2				$3	$4	$15
2000-S, Virginia, Proof, Silver	965,421	9,622	69.2				$8	$10	$20
2001-P, New York	655,400,000	397	66.1	100%	$0.35	$1	$4	$15	$40
2001-D, New York	619,640,000	467	66.2	100%	$0.35	$1	$4	$15	$40
2001-S, New York, Proof	3,094,140	3,670	69.2				$3	$8	$15
2001-S, New York, Proof, Silver	889,697	7,862	69.2				$10	$15	$20
2001-P, North Carolina	627,600,000	386	66.3	100%	$0.35	$1	$4	$15	$40
2001-D, North Carolina	427,876,000	415	66.3	100%	$0.35	$1	$4	$15	$40
2001-S, North Carolina, Proof	3,094,140	3,760	69.2				$3	$8	$15
2001-S, North Carolina, Proof, Silver	889,697	7,794	69.2				$10	$15	$20
2001-P, Rhode Island	423,000,000	316	66.0	100%	$0.35	$1	$4	$15	$40
2001-D, Rhode Island	447,100,000	370	66.0	100%	$0.35	$1	$4	$15	$40
2001-S, Rhode Island, Proof	3,094,140	3,360	69.2				$3	$8	$15
2001-S, Rhode Island, Proof, Silver	889,697	7,870	69.2				$10	$15	$20
2001-P, Vermont	423,400,000	1,882	65.7	100%	$0.35	$1	$4	$15	$40
2001-D, Vermont	459,404,000	383	66.3	100%	$0.35	$1	$4	$15	$40
2001-S, Vermont, Proof	3,094,140	3,533	69.3				$3	$8	$15
2001-S, Vermont, Proof, Silver	889,697	7,922	69.3				$10	$15	$20
2001-P, Kentucky	353,000,000	392	66.3	100%	$0.35	$1.25	$5	$16	$40
2001-D, Kentucky	370,564,000	305	66.1	100%	$0.35	$1.25	$5	$16	$40
2001-S, Kentucky, Proof	3,094,140	3,395	69.3				$3	$8	$15
2001-S, Kentucky, Proof, Silver	889,697	7,818	69.2				$10	$15	$20
2002-P, Tennessee	361,600,000	312	66.5	100%	$0.75	$1.75	$3	$18	$40
2002-D, Tennessee	286,468,000	313	66.4	100%	$0.75	$1.75	$3	$18	$40
2002-S, Tennessee, Proof	3,084,245	2,946	69.2				$3	$5	$15
2002-S, Tennessee, Proof, Silver	892,229	7,583	69.2				$8	$10	$20
2002-P, Ohio	217,200,000	349	66.7	100%	$0.35	$1	$1.50	$10	$30
2002-D, Ohio	414,832,000	292	66.2	100%	$0.35	$1	$1.50	$10	$30
2002-S, Ohio, Proof	3,084,245	2,933	69.3				$3	$5	$15
2002-S, Ohio, Proof, Silver	892,229	7,677	69.2				$8	$10	$20
2002-P, Louisiana	362,000,000	267	66.7	100%	$0.35	$1	$1.50	$10	$30
2002-D, Louisiana	402,204,000	223	66.3	100%	$0.35	$1	$1.50	$10	$30
2002-S, Louisiana, Proof	3,084,245	2,941	69.2				$3	$5	$15
2002-S, Louisiana, Proof, Silver	892,229	7,394	69.2				$8	$10	$20
2002-P, Indiana	362,600,000	313	66.5	99%	$0.35	$1	$1.50	$10	$30
2002-D, Indiana	327,200,000	249	66.3	100%	$0.35	$1	$1.50	$10	$30
2002-S, Indiana, Proof	3,084,245	2,965	69.2				$3	$5	$15
2002-S, Indiana, Proof, Silver	892,229	7,511	69.2				$8	$10	$20

	Mintage	Cert	Avg	%MS	AU-50	MS-63	MS-65 PF-65	MS-66 PF-66DC	MS-67 PF-69DC
2002-P, Mississippi	290,000,000	284	66.3	100%	$0.35	$1	$1.50	$10	$30
2002-D, Mississippi	289,600,000	232	66.4	100%	$0.35	$1	$1.50	$10	$30
2002-S, Mississippi, Proof	3,084,245	3,001	69.3				$3	$5	$15
2002-S, Mississippi, Proof, Silver	892,229	7,775	69.2				$8	$10	$20
2003-P, Illinois	225,800,000	258	65.9	100%	$0.50	$1.50	$2	$12	$32
2003-D, Illinois	237,400,000	2,074	65.2	100%	$0.50	$1.50	$2	$12	$32
2003-S, Illinois, Proof	3,408,516	5,613	69.3				$3	$5	$15
2003-S, Illinois, Proof, Silver	1,125,755	8,403	69.2				$8	$9	$20
2003-P, Alabama	225,000,000	281	65.7	100%	$0.35	$1	$1.50	$10	$30
2003-D, Alabama	232,400,000	2,076	65.1	100%	$0.35	$1	$1.50	$10	$30
2003-S, Alabama, Proof	3,408,516	5,699	69.3				$3	$5	$15
2003-S, Alabama, Proof, Silver	1,125,755	8,396	69.2				$8	$9	$20
2003-P, Maine	217,400,000	250	65.8	100%	$0.35	$1	$1.50	$10	$30
2003-D, Maine	231,400,000	2,076	65.2	100%	$0.35	$1	$1.50	$10	$30
2003-S, Maine, Proof	3,408,516	5,565	69.2				$3	$5	$15
2003-S, Maine, Proof, Silver	1,125,755	8,285	69.2				$8	$9	$20
2003-P, Missouri	225,000,000	266	65.9	99%	$0.35	$1	$1.50	$10	$30
2003-D, Missouri	228,200,000	2,087	65.2	100%	$0.35	$1	$1.50	$10	$30
2003-S, Missouri, Proof	3,408,516	5,756	69.3				$3	$5	$15
2003-S, Missouri, Proof, Silver	1,125,755	8,387	69.2				$8	$9	$20
2003-P, Arkansas	228,000,000	240	65.8	100%	$0.35	$1	$1.50	$10	$30
2003-D, Arkansas	229,800,000	2,113	65.2	100%	$0.40	$1	$1.50	$10	$30
2003-S, Arkansas, Proof	3,408,516	5,704	69.3				$3	$5	$15
2003-S, Arkansas, Proof, Silver	1,125,755	8,425	69.2				$8	$9	$20
2004-P, Michigan	233,800,000	2,359	65.2	100%	$0.35	$0.75	$3	$10	$30
2004-D, Michigan	225,800,000	403	67.3	100%	$0.35	$0.75	$3	$10	$30
2004-S, Michigan, Proof	2,740,684	3,860	69.3				$3	$5	$15
2004-S, Michigan, Proof, Silver	1,769,786	9,815	69.3				$8	$10	$20
2004-P, Florida	240,200,000	2,351	65.2	100%	$0.35	$0.75	$3	$10	$30
2004-D, Florida	241,600,000	306	66.9	100%	$0.35	$0.75	$3	$10	$30
2004-S, Florida, Proof	2,740,684	3,786	69.3				$3	$5	$15
2004-S, Florida, Proof, Silver	1,769,786	9,635	69.2				$8	$10	$20
2004-P, Texas	278,800,000	2,387	65.2	100%	$0.35	$0.75	$3	$10	$30
2004-D, Texas	263,000,000	327	66.9	100%	$0.35	$0.75	$3	$10	$30
2004-S, Texas, Proof	2,740,684	3,902	69.3				$3	$5	$15
2004-S, Texas, Proof, Silver	1,769,786	10,043	69.3				$8	$10	$20
2004-P, Iowa	213,800,000	2,320	65.1	100%	$0.35	$0.75	$3	$10	$30
2004-D, Iowa	251,400,000	288	66.9	100%	$0.35	$0.75	$3	$10	$30
2004-S, Iowa, Proof	2,740,684	3,941	69.4				$3	$5	$15
2004-S, Iowa, Proof, Silver	1,769,786	9,919	69.3				$8	$10	$20
2004-P, Wisconsin	226,400,000	2,553	65.2	100%	$0.35	$0.75	$3	$10	$30
2004-D, Wisconsin	226,800,000	2,795	65.7	100%	$0.35	$0.75	$10	$15	$30
2004-D, Wisconsin, Extra Leaf High ‡ (a)	(b)	4,776	64.8	96%	$75	$150	$200	$300	$500
2004-D, Wisconsin, Extra Leaf Low ‡ (a)	(b)	6,436	64.9	97%	$50	$130	$165	$275	$450
2004-S, Wisconsin, Proof	2,740,684	3,930	69.3				$3	$5	$15
2004-S, Wisconsin, Proof, Silver	1,769,786	10,049	69.3				$8	$10	$20
2005-P, California	257,200,000	460	65.9	100%	$0.30	$0.75	$5	$10	$30
2005-P, California, Satin Finish	1,160,000	2,839	67.0	100%			$3	$5	$12
2005-D, California	263,200,000	289	66.2	99%	$0.30	$0.75	$5	$10	$30

‡ Ranked in the *100 Greatest U.S. Modern Coins*. **a.** Some 2004-D, Wisconsin, quarters show one of two different die flaws on the reverse, in the shape of an extra leaf on the corn. **b.** Included in 2004-D, Wisconsin, mintage figure.

	Mintage	Cert	Avg	%MS	AU-50	MS-63	MS-65	MS-66	MS-67
							PF-65	PF-66DC	PF-69DC
2005-D, California, Satin Finish	1,160,000	2,519	66.9	100%			$3	$5	$12
2005-S, California, Proof	3,262,960	8,595	69.3				$3	$4.50	$15
2005-S, California, Proof, Silver	1,678,649	10,884	69.4				$8	$10	$20
2005-P, Minnesota	239,600,000	364	65.1	98%	$0.30	$0.75	$5	$10	$30
2005-P, Minnesota, Satin Finish	1,160,000	2,959	67.2	100%			$3	$5	$12
2005-D, Minnesota	248,400,000	184	66.1	99%	$0.30	$0.75	$5	$10	$30
2005-D, Minnesota, Satin Finish	1,160,000	2,737	67.1	100%			$3	$5	$12
2005-S, Minnesota, Proof	3,262,960	8,560	69.3				$3	$4.50	$15
2005-S, Minnesota, Proof, Silver	1,678,649	10,634	69.4				$8	$10	$20
2005-P, Oregon	316,200,000	256	65.2	100%	$0.30	$0.75	$5	$10	$30
2005-P, Oregon, Satin Finish	1,160,000	3,007	67.2	100%			$3	$5	$12
2005-D, Oregon	404,000,000	142	66.2	100%	$0.30	$0.75	$5	$10	$30
2005-D, Oregon, Satin Finish	1,160,000	2,736	67.1	100%			$3	$5	$12
2005-S, Oregon, Proof	3,262,960	8,522	69.3				$3	$4.50	$15
2005-S, Oregon, Proof, Silver	1,678,649	10,627	69.4				$8	$10	$20
2005-P, Kansas	263,400,000	333	65.0	98%	$0.30	$0.75	$5	$10	$30
2005-P, Kansas, Satin Finish	1,160,000	2,556	66.8	100%			$3	$5	$12
2005-D, Kansas	300,000,000	229	66.3	100%	$0.30	$0.75	$5	$10	$30
2005-D, Kansas, Satin Finish	1,160,000	2,645	67.0	100%			$3	$5	$12
2005-S, Kansas, Proof	3,262,960	8,577	69.3				$3	$4.50	$15
2005-S, Kansas, Proof, Silver	1,678,649	10,748	69.3				$8	$10	$20
2005-P, West Virginia	365,400,000	300	65.3	100%	$0.30	$0.75	$5	$10	$30
2005-P, West Virginia, Satin Finish	1,160,000	2,831	67.0	100%			$3	$5	$12
2005-D, West Virginia	356,200,000	185	66.2	99%	$0.30	$0.75	$5	$10	$30
2005-D, West Virginia, Satin Finish	1,160,000	2,431	66.9	100%			$3	$5	$12
2005-S, West Virginia, Proof	3,262,960	8,588	69.3				$3	$4.50	$15
2005-S, West Virginia, Proof, Silver	1,678,649	10,755	69.4				$8	$10	$20
2006-P, Nevada	277,000,000	275	66.1	100%	$0.30	$0.75	$1	$10	$30
2006-P, Nevada, Satin Finish	847,361	1,055	66.6	100%			$3	$5	$12
2006-D, Nevada	312,800,000	358	66.5	100%	$0.30	$0.75	$1	$10	$30
2006-D, Nevada, Satin Finish	847,361	1,279	66.9	100%			$3	$5	$12
2006-S, Nevada, Proof	2,882,428	5,953	69.4				$3	$4.50	$15
2006-S, Nevada, Proof, Silver	1,585,008	9,576	69.5				$8	$9	$20
2006-P, Nebraska	318,000,000	142	66.0	100%	$0.30	$0.75	$2	$10	$30
2006-P, Nebraska, Satin Finish	847,361	1,340	67.0	100%			$3	$5	$12
2006-D, Nebraska	273,000,000	264	66.5	100%	$0.30	$0.75	$2	$10	$30
2006-D, Nebraska, Satin Finish	847,361	1,593	67.2	100%			$3	$5	$12
2006-S, Nebraska, Proof	2,882,428	5,954	69.4				$3	$4.50	$15
2006-S, Nebraska, Proof, Silver	1,585,008	9,466	69.5				$8	$9	$20
2006-P, Colorado	274,800,000	256	66.2	100%	$0.30	$0.75	$2	$10	$30
2006-P, Colorado, Satin Finish	847,361	1,188	66.8	100%			$3	$5	$12
2006-D, Colorado	294,200,000	424	66.4	100%	$0.30	$0.75	$2	$10	$30
2006-D, Colorado, Satin Finish	847,361	1,509	67.2	100%			$3	$5	$12
2006-S, Colorado, Proof	2,882,428	5,941	69.4				$3	$4.50	$15
2006-S, Colorado, Proof, Silver	1,585,008	9,562	69.5				$8	$9	$20
2006-P, North Dakota	305,800,000	182	65.8	99%	$0.30	$0.75	$2	$10	$30
2006-P, North Dakota, Satin Finish	847,361	1,141	66.8	100%			$3	$5	$12
2006-D, North Dakota	359,000,000	271	66.2	100%	$0.30	$0.75	$2	$10	$30
2006-D, North Dakota, Satin Finish	847,361	1,542	67.1	100%			$3	$5	$12
2006-S, North Dakota, Proof	2,882,428	5,952	69.4				$3	$4.50	$15
2006-S, North Dakota, Proof, Silver	1,585,008	9,559	69.5				$8	$9	$20

	Mintage	Cert	Avg	%MS	AU-50	MS-63	MS-65	MS-66	MS-67
							PF-65	PF-66DC	PF-69DC
2006-P, South Dakota	245,000,000	166	66.0	100%	$0.30	$0.75	$2	$10	$30
2006-P, South Dakota, Satin Finish	847,361	1,319	66.9	100%			$3	$5	$12
2006-D, South Dakota	265,800,000	188	66.2	99%	$0.30	$0.75	$2	$10	$30
2006-D, South Dakota, Satin Finish	847,361	1,550	67.1	100%			$3	$5	$12
2006-S, South Dakota, Proof	2,882,428	5,960	69.5				$3	$4.50	$15
2006-S, South Dakota, Proof, Silver	1,585,008	9,555	69.5				$8	$9	$20
2007-P, Montana	257,000,000	114	66.1	100%	$0.30	$0.75	$4	$10	$30
2007-P, Montana, Satin Finish	895,628	325	66.5	100%			$3	$5	$12
2007-D, Montana	256,240,000	159	65.9	99%	$0.30	$0.75	$4	$10	$30
2007-D, Montana, Satin Finish	895,628	322	66.5	100%			$3	$5	$12
2007-S, Montana, Proof	2,374,778	3,429	69.5				$3	$4.50	$15
2007-S, Montana, Proof, Silver	1,313,481	7,972	69.4				$8	$9	$20
2007-P, Washington	265,200,000	143	66.1	100%	$0.30	$0.75	$4	$10	$30
2007-P, Washington, Satin Finish	895,628	309	66.4	100%			$3	$5	$12
2007-D, Washington	280,000,000	150	66.0	99%	$0.30	$0.75	$4	$10	$30
2007-D, Washington, Satin Finish	895,628	340	66.7	100%			$3	$5	$12
2007-S, Washington, Proof	2,374,778	3,217	69.5				$3	$4.50	$15
2007-S, Washington, Proof, Silver	1,313,481	7,928	69.4				$8	$9	$20
2007-P, Idaho	294,600,000	76	65.8	100%	$0.30	$0.75	$4	$10	$30
2007-P, Idaho, Satin Finish	895,628	348	66.6	100%			$3	$5	$12
2007-D, Idaho	286,800,000	118	66.2	100%	$0.30	$0.75	$4	$10	$30
2007-D, Idaho, Satin Finish	895,628	328	66.5	100%			$3	$5	$12
2007-S, Idaho, Proof	2,374,778	3,234	69.5				$3	$4.50	$15
2007-S, Idaho, Proof, Silver	1,313,481	7,980	69.4				$8	$9	$20
2007-P, Wyoming	243,600,000	73	65.2	100%	$0.30	$0.75	$4	$10	$30
2007-P, Wyoming, Satin Finish	895,628	288	66.1	100%			$3	$5	$12
2007-D, Wyoming	320,800,000	134	65.9	99%	$0.30	$0.75	$4	$10	$30
2007-D, Wyoming, Satin Finish	895,628	331	66.4	100%			$3	$5	$12
2007-S, Wyoming, Proof	2,374,778	3,158	69.4				$3	$4.50	$15
2007-S, Wyoming, Proof, Silver	1,313,481	7,841	69.3				$8	$9	$20
2007-P, Utah	255,000,000	128	65.6	100%	$0.30	$0.75	$4	$10	$30
2007-P, Utah, Satin Finish	895,628	304	66.3	100%			$3	$5	$12
2007-D, Utah	253,200,000	192	66.2	100%	$0.30	$0.75	$4	$10	$30
2007-D, Utah, Satin Finish	895,628	329	66.6	100%			$3	$5	$12
2007-S, Utah, Proof	2,374,778	3,178	69.5				$3	$4.50	$15
2007-S, Utah, Proof, Silver	1,313,481	7,985	69.4				$8	$9	$20
2008-P, Oklahoma	222,000,000	68	65.7	99%	$0.30	$0.75	$2	$10	$30
2008-P, Oklahoma, Satin Finish	745,464	129	67.3	100%			$3	$5	$12
2008-D, Oklahoma	194,600,000	102	66.2	100%	$0.30	$0.75	$2	$10	$30
2008-D, Oklahoma, Satin Finish	745,464	107	67.2	100%			$3	$5	$12
2008-S, Oklahoma, Proof	2,078,112	3,511	69.5				$3	$5	$18
2008-S, Oklahoma, Proof, Silver	1,192,908	8,375	69.5				$8	$10	$22
2008-P, New Mexico	244,200,000	85	65.4	100%	$0.30	$0.75	$2	$10	$30
2008-P, New Mexico, Satin Finish	745,464	107	67.1	100%			$3	$5	$12
2008-D, New Mexico	244,400,000	123	66.3	100%	$0.30	$0.75	$2	$10	$30
2008-D, New Mexico, Satin Finish	745,464	81	67.0	100%			$3	$5	$12
2008-S, New Mexico, Proof	2,078,112	3,574	69.4				$3	$5	$18
2008-S, New Mexico, Proof, Silver	1,192,908	8,236	69.5				$8	$10	$22
2008-P, Arizona	244,600,000	126	65.8	100%	$0.30	$0.75	$2	$10	$30
2008-P, Arizona, Satin Finish	745,464	126	67.3	100%			$3	$5	$12

	Mintage	Cert	Avg	%MS	AU-50	MS-63	MS-65	MS-66	MS-67
							PF-65	PF-66DC	PF-69DC
2008-D, Arizona	265,000,000	48	65.9	98%	$0.75	$2	$10	$30	$30
2008-D, Arizona, Satin Finish	745,464	92	67.4	100%		$3	$5	$12	$12
2008-S, Arizona, Proof	2,078,112	3,659	69.6			$3	$5	$18	$18
2008-S, Arizona, Proof, Silver	1,192,908	8,607	69.5			$8	$10	$22	$22
2008-P, Alaska	251,800,000	66	65.6	100%	$0.75	$2	$10	$30	$30
2008-P, Alaska, Satin Finish	745,464	122	67.2	100%		$3	$5	$12	$12
2008-D, Alaska	254,000,000	67	65.9	100%	$0.75	$2	$10	$30	$30
2008-D, Alaska, Satin Finish	745,464	90	66.9	100%		$3	$5	$12	$12
2008-S, Alaska, Proof	2,078,112	3,493	69.5			$3	$5	$18	$18
2008-S, Alaska, Proof, Silver	1,192,908	8,534	69.5			$8	$10	$22	$22
2008-P, Hawaii	254,000,000	138	65.4	100%	$0.75	$2	$10	$30	$30
2008-P, Hawaii, Satin Finish	745,464	127	67.2	100%		$3	$5	$12	$12
2008-D, Hawaii	263,600,000	66	65.7	100%	$0.75	$2	$10	$30	$30
2008-D, Hawaii, Satin Finish	745,464	101	67.0	100%		$3	$5	$12	$12
2008-S, Hawaii, Proof	2,078,112	3,516	69.4			$3	$10	$25	$25
2008-S, Hawaii, Proof, Silver	1,192,908	8,547	69.4			$8	$10	$22	$22
2009-P, District of Columbia	83,600,000	89	66.1	100%	$1	$2	$10	$30	$30
2009-P, District of Columbia, Satin Finish	784,614	247	67.6	100%		$3	$5	$12	$12
2009-D, District of Columbia	88,800,000	121	66.3	100%	$1	$2	$10	$30	$30
2009-D, District of Columbia, Satin Finish	784,614	254	67.9	100%		$3	$5	$12	$12
2009-S, District of Columbia, Proof	2,113,478	4,150	69.6			$3	$4.50	$15	$15
2009-S, District of Columbia, Proof, Silver	996,548	6,508	69.7			$8	$9	$20	$20
2009-P, Puerto Rico	53,200,000	95	65.9	100%	$1	$2	$10	$30	$30
2009-P, Puerto Rico, Satin Finish	784,614	180	67.5	100%		$3	$5	$12	$12
2009-D, Puerto Rico	86,000,000	82	66.6	100%	$1	$2	$10	$30	$30
2009-D, Puerto Rico, Satin Finish	784,614	234	67.8	100%		$3	$5	$12	$12
2009-S, Puerto Rico, Proof	2,113,478	4,134	69.6			$3	$4.50	$15	$15
2009-S, Puerto Rico, Proof, Silver	996,548	6,685	69.7			$8	$9	$20	$20
2009-P, Guam	45,000,000	48	66.1	100%	$1	$2	$10	$30	$30
2009-P, Guam, Satin Finish	784,614	227	67.3	100%		$3	$5	$12	$12
2009-D, Guam	42,600,000	67	66.6	100%	$1	$2	$10	$30	$30
2009-D, Guam, Satin Finish	784,614	215	67.5	100%		$3	$5	$12	$12
2009-S, Guam, Proof	2,113,478	4,036	69.6			$3	$4.50	$15	$15
2009-S, Guam, Proof, Silver	996,548	6,448	69.7			$8	$9	$20	$20
2009-P, American Samoa	42,600,000	106	66.5	100%	$1	$2	$10	$30	$30
2009-P, American Samoa, Satin Finish	784,614	293	67.8	100%		$3	$5	$12	$12
2009-D, American Samoa	39,600,000	135	67.0	100%	$1	$2	$10	$30	$30
2009-D, American Samoa, Satin Finish	784,614	338	68.2	100%		$3	$5	$12	$12
2009-S, American Samoa, Proof	2,113,478	4,202	69.6			$3	$4.50	$15	$15
2009-S, American Samoa, Proof, Silver	996,548	6,590	69.7			$8	$9	$20	$20
2009-P, U.S. Virgin Islands	41,000,000	125	66.6	100%	$1	$2	$12	$32	$32
2009-P, U.S. Virgin Islands, Satin Finish	784,614	286	67.2	100%		$3	$5	$12	$12
2009-D, U.S. Virgin Islands	41,000,000	118	66.6	100%	$1	$2	$12	$32	$32
2009-D, U.S. Virgin Islands, Satin Finish	784,614	315	67.8	100%		$3	$5	$12	$12
2009-S, U.S. Virgin Islands, Proof	2,113,478	4,176	69.6			$3	$4.50	$15	$15
2009-S, U.S. Virgin Islands, Proof, Silver	996,548	6,562	69.7			$8	$9	$20	$20
2009-P, Northern Mariana Islands	35,200,000	120	66.7	100%	$1	$2	$10	$30	$30
2009-P, Northern Mariana Islands, Satin Finish	784,614	296	67.8	100%		$3	$5	$12	$12
2009-D, Northern Mariana Islands	37,600,000	123	66.7	100%	$1	$2	$10	$30	$30
2009-D, Northern Mariana Islands, Satin Finish	784,614	286	67.7	100%		$3	$5	$12	$12

	Mintage	Cert	Avg	%MS	AU-50	MS-63	MS-65	MS-66	MS-67
							PF-65	PF-66DC	PF-69DC
2009-S, Northern Mariana Islands, Proof	2,113,478	4,177	69.6		4,177	69.6	$3	$4.50	$15
2009-S, Northern Mariana Islands, Proof, Silver	996,548	6,550	69.7		6,550	69.7	$8	$9	$20

WASHINGTON, AMERICA THE BEAUTIFUL™ (2010 TO DATE)

Designers: *John Flanagan (obverse); see image captions for reverse designers.* **Weight:** *Clad issue—5.67 grams; silver Proofs, 2010–2018—6.25 grams; silver Proofs, 2019 to date—6.34 grams.* **Composition:** *Clad issue—Outer layers of copper-nickel (.750 copper, .250 nickel) bonded to inner core of pure copper; silver Proofs, 2010–2018—.900 silver, .100 copper (net weight, .1808 oz. pure silver); silver Proofs, 2019 to date—.999 silver, .001 copper (net weight, .2065 oz. pure silver).* **Diameter:** *24.3 mm.* **Edge:** *Reeded.* **Mints:** *Clad issue—Philadelphia, Denver, San Francisco, and West Point; silver Proofs—San Francisco.*

Circulation Strike   **2019 West Point mintmark**   **Proof**

HISTORY AND BACKGROUND

Seeing the success of the 50 State Quarters Program, Rep. Michael Castle initiated and promoted a new coinage series. The America's Beautiful National Parks Quarter Dollar Coin Act of 2008 was signed by President George W. Bush on December 23, 2008.

Oops! After the fact it was realized that some states did not have a national park!

Behind-the-scenes regrouping took place, and the coins became known as America the Beautiful quarters. States that did not have national parks were searched for other historic or natural sites. This resulted in the showcasing of many remarkable places that relatively few people other than residents in the regions had ever heard of—for example, El Yunque National Forest (2011) and Bombay Hook National Wildlife Refuge (2015). This invited research and inquiry to learn about these, aided with much information provided by the United States Mint.

Beginning with Hot Springs National Park in 2010 the America the Beautiful subjects have been issued in the chronological order in which they came under national protection.

Quarters with places few had ever heard of did not engender much public interest. Mintages of the various issues fell far below those of the State quarters. Not simplifying matters was the Federal Reserve System's program—which in a way makes sense—of supplying new quarters to member banks that request them. If a bank needs coins it is sent the supply currently on hand, which like as not has nothing to do with the location of the bank in relation to the showcased subject. When the New Hampshire quarters were released in 2013 the author did not learn of a single bank in the state that received a supply—as no new coins were needed.

Today the State, Territorial, and America the Beautiful quarters are needed to complete a set of the denomination as well as for a type set of U.S. coins in general from 1792 to date—more than doubling the number of basic types in 1998 before the new series began. The United States Mint used the America the Beautiful program to further promote coin collecting in 2019, when it issued 10 million special quarters into circulation. Struck at West Point and bearing a W mintmark, the coins helped launch a nationwide "treasure hunt" starting that April during National Coin Week.

NATIONAL PARKS AND SITES IN THE AMERICA THE BEAUTIFUL PROGRAM

Hot Springs National Park—Hot Springs National Park was established April 20, 1832. The water that rises from the earth in this Arkansas park is steaming hot—and more than 4,000 years old. Hot Springs was the United States' first federally protected reservation, a precursor to the national park system.

Yellowstone National Park—This landscape, situated mostly in the state of Wyoming, is best known for its geysers. It was the first U.S. national park, established March 1, 1872. Yellowstone is managed and preserved by the federal government for everyone to enjoy.

Yosemite National Park—The giant sequoia trees in Yosemite National Park are the largest of all living things on earth. The park, in California's Sierra Nevada Mountains, was established October 1, 1890. Other famous features include Tunnel View, the vista of Bridalveil Fall, and the granite cliffs of El Capitan and Half Dome.

Grand Canyon National Park—In the Grand Canyon the mighty Colorado River carved through layers of rock that took more than a billion years to form. Grand Canyon National Park, in Arizona, was first established as a forest reserve on February 20, 1893.

Mount Hood National Forest—Northern Oregon's Mount Hood is the second-most-climbed mountain in the world. A potentially active volcano, it last erupted more than a hundred years ago and today is informally considered to be dormant. Mount Hood National Forest was protected as part of the Cascade Range on September 28, 1893.

Gettysburg National Military Park—Thousands of history buffs come to Pennsylvania every July from around the world, to reenact the American Civil War's important Battle of Gettysburg. The region of the battle and nearby historic sites was established as a national military park February 11, 1895.

Glacier National Park—Glacier National Park was first protected on February 22, 1897. The Native Americans called this area of Montana "the backbone of the world." Also known as the "Crown of the Continent," Glacier is the headwaters for streams flowing to the Pacific Ocean, the Gulf of Mexico, and Hudson's Bay.

Olympic National Park—First designated as a protected area on February 22, 1897, Olympic National Park illustrates that rain forests exist outside the tropics. Olympic is in Washington State, near the northern border of the continental United States.

Vicksburg National Military Park—The USS *Cairo*, displayed in Vicksburg National Military Park, was the first U.S. ship to be sunk by a mine, on December 12, 1862. The Mississippi park was established on February 21, 1899, to commemorate the siege and defense of Vicksburg during the Civil War.

Chickasaw National Recreation Area—Situated in the foothills of the Arbuckle Mountains in south-central Oklahoma, Chickasaw National Recreation Area was first set aside on July 1, 1902. Between 1917 and 1925 a small zoo was kept here, including deer, elk, bison, ostriches, and a bald eagle. Today, water attractions are its main feature.

El Yunque National Forest—Puerto Rico's El Yunque, first protected in January 1903, is the only tropical rain forest in the national forest system. Despite being among the smaller national forests, it is one of the most biologically diverse, with hundreds of animal and plant species.

Chaco Culture National Historical Park—This New Mexico park, established in March 1907, is home to the massive buildings of the ancient Pueblo peoples—testament to their organizational and engineering abilities. They were the largest buildings in North America until the 1800s.

Acadia National Park—Acadia, on Maine's rocky coast, is one of the first places in the United States to see the sun rise each morning. It was officially protected in July 1916, making it the oldest designated national-park area east of the Mississippi River.

Hawai'i Volcanoes National Park—This park, established in August 1916, includes two active volcanoes. Kilauea is one of the world's most active, and Mauna Loa is the world's largest, starting on the ocean floor and rising 56,000 feet (including 13,600 above sea level).

Denali National Park and Preserve—Denali, in Alaska, has been called "six million acres of wild land bisected by one ribbon of road." The wilderness slowly rises up to high alpine tundra and snowy mountains—including North America's tallest peak, Denali, more than 20,000 feet tall. The region has been protected since 1917.

White Mountain National Forest—New Hampshire's White Mountain National Forest, part of America's protected forest land since May 1918, ranges from eastern New Hampshire to western Maine. Its scenery includes mountainous hardwood forests, clear lakes and streams, and alpine peaks.

Perry's Victory and International Peace Memorial—This memorial complex in Ohio, maintained by the nation since 1919, honors those who fought in the Battle of Lake Erie during the War of 1812. It also celebrates the long-lasting peace shared by Great Britain, Canada, and the United States.

Great Basin National Park—The marble and limestone caves of Nevada's Great Basin region were officially recognized as a national treasure in 1922. Today the greater wilderness area is a national park, including the towering Wheeler Peak Glacier, one of the southernmost glaciers in the country.

Fort McHenry National Monument and Historic Shrine—America's valiant defense of Fort McHenry during the Battle of Baltimore, partway through the War of 1812, inspired Francis Scott Key to write our national anthem, "The Star-Spangled Banner." In 1925 the historic fort was established as a national park under the U.S. Department of War.

Mount Rushmore National Memorial—Mount Rushmore's famous memorial was established in 1925. Construction of its majestic figures of George Washington, Thomas Jefferson, Theodore Roosevelt, and Abraham Lincoln began in 1927 and ended in 1941. The granite presidential portraits are surrounded by the beauty of South Dakota's Black Hills.

Great Smoky Mountains National Park—Established in May 1926, Great Smoky Mountains National Park features rugged scenery, diverse wildlife, more than 800 hiking trails, and 384 miles of roadway in the forested mountains straddling Tennessee and North Carolina. This is the most heavily visited of America's national parks.

Shenandoah National Park—Less than a hundred miles from Washington, D.C., Virginia's Shenandoah National Park offers a haven of hiking, picnicking, natural scenery, and outdoor adventure. Forty percent of its nearly 200,000 acres are protected as wilderness, making it a refuge for local plants and animals.

Arches National Park—This "red rock wonderland" in eastern Utah, federally protected since 1929, has more than 2,000 natural stone arches and hundreds of colorful soaring pinnacles, fins, and giant balanced rocks. Situated in the Colorado Plateau, its lowest elevation is nearly a mile above sea level.

Great Sand Dunes National Park—The tallest dunes in North America are in Colorado's Great Sand Dunes National Park—along with grasslands, wetlands, pine forests, tundra, and alpine lakes. This wilderness includes some 30 square miles of sloping sands in mounds up to 750 feet high. The area has been protected since March 1932.

Everglades National Park—Florida's Everglades, the largest subtropical wilderness in the United States, protects a fragile ecosystem including many rare and endangered animal species. The wildlife refuge, first protected as a national forest in May 1934, covers some 1.5 million acres.

Homestead National Monument of America—This educational site commemorates the Homestead Act of 1862, which gave adventurous settlers up to 160 acres of federal land in exchange for five years of residence and cultivation. While the act was in effect, 45 percent of Nebraska's territory was parceled out to hearty sodbusters.

Kisatchie National Forest—Louisiana's Kisatchie National Forest, protected since June 1936, includes 604,000 acres of natural beauty, learning, recreation, and wildlife, tucked away in the state's central bayous. The wilderness is accessible only on horseback or by foot.

Blue Ridge Parkway—Running from North Carolina to Virginia, the Blue Ridge Parkway is 469 miles of roadway that offers a cross-section of Appalachian mountain history tying together diverse landscapes and early settlements. A leisurely four-day trip covers Indian reservations, forests, folk art, villages, mountain views, and more.

Bombay Hook National Wildlife Refuge—On the southern shore of Delaware Bay sits 16,000 acres of freshwater pools, swamps, upland forests, and tidal salt marshes. Bombay Hook National Wildlife Refuge is home to hundreds of thousands of birds, some nesting, some migrating between Canada and Latin America.

Saratoga National Historical Park—American soldiers defeated a major British army here in autumn 1777. It was a turning point in the Revolutionary War. The battlefield preserved by Saratoga National Historical Park covers about 3,000 acres, with nine miles of self-guided driving tours through its key locations.

Shawnee National Forest—The Little Grand Canyon, rock outcroppings in the Garden of the Gods and the Devil's Backbone, numerous scenic waterfalls, wildlife, and other natural attractions await visitors to Shawnee National Forest in southern Illinois. Its 160-mile trail connects the Mississippi and Ohio rivers.

Cumberland Gap National Historical Park—American bison, Native Americans, longhunters, explorers, and pioneers all traveled this gateway route from civilization through the mountains into the wilderness frontier of Kentucky. Today, 20,000 acres are set aside for enjoying the Cumberland Gap's scenery and connecting with the United States' early history.

Harpers Ferry National Historical Park—Harpers Ferry in West Virginia was a lightning rod for political and military activity in the mid-1800s. Abolitionist John Brown led a raid on a federal arsenal there in 1859, seeking an armed uprising of slaves. During the Civil War the village flipped between Union and Confederate control eight times.

Theodore Roosevelt National Park—Young Teddy Roosevelt came to Dakota Territory in 1883 to hunt bison. The rugged landscape inspired his later conservation efforts. As president he started the U.S. Forest Service, formalized the creation of national monuments, and protected some 230 million acres of land.

Fort Moultrie (Fort Sumter National Monument)—In April 1861 Fort Sumter in South Carolina's Charleston harbor was bombarded by the Confederacy, starting the American Civil War. Sumter and the nearby Revolutionary War–era Fort Moultrie were part of the military action around the city of Charleston.

Effigy Mounds National Monument—This national site in Iowa preserves more than 200 prehistoric earthworks and effigy mounds built by American Indians. The park has no paved public automobile access roads; however, visitors enjoy the natural surroundings of 14 miles of hiking trails, along with historical displays and demonstrations.

Frederick Douglass National Historic Site—Born into slavery in 1818, Frederick Douglass escaped to freedom and became a leader fighting for justice and equality in America's abolitionist movement. His inspiring legacy is preserved at his Washington, D.C., home, called Cedar Hill, where he lived his last 17 years.

Ozark National Scenic Riverways—Southern Missouri is home to a national park created to protect the Current and Jacks Fork rivers. With 80,000 acres, Ozark National Scenic Riverways offers water recreation including canoeing, kayaking, and rafting—not to mention horseback riding, fishing, hunting, hiking, cave exploration, and other outdoor adventures.

Ellis Island (Statue of Liberty National Monument)—Ellis Island houses the former immigration station that opened in 1892 and welcomed more than 12 million newcomers to America. It is situated in Upper New York Bay; in 1998 the U.S. Supreme Court ruled that most of the island is in New Jersey.

George Rogers Clark National Historical Park—In Indiana's Vincennes Historic District, on the banks of the Wabash River, is George Rogers Clark National Historical Park. The region was the site of Fort Sackville, a British encampment heroically captured by American soldiers during the Revolutionary War.

Pictured Rocks National Lakeshore—Forty-two miles of Lake Superior shoreline are preserved in Michigan's Pictured Rocks National Lakeshore. Famous for its dramatic colorful rock cliffs, unusual sandstone formations, and birch-forested trails, the park also features shipwrecks and an 1800s lighthouse.

Apostle Islands National Lakeshore—Wisconsin's Apostle Islands National Lakeshore encompasses a stretch of Lake Superior shoreline and 21 islands. Dramatic cliffs and sandstone sea caves, hiking trails, beaches, and marinas await the park's visitors. Wildlife (including North America's largest concentration of black bears), lighthouses, and a famous shipwreck also beckon.

Voyageurs National Park—"Leave your car and set out on the water highways of the North Woods," says the National Park Service about Voyageurs National Park in Minnesota. The region offers an immersion into the beautiful wilderness French-Canadian voyageurs, or traveling fur traders, experienced in the 1700s and 1800s.

Cumberland Island National Seashore—Cumberland is Georgia's largest barrier island—home to pristine maritime forests, a wilderness of beaches and dunes, wide marshes, and freshwater lakes. The park is accessible only by boat. It preserves many historic sites of native Americans, missionaries, and wealthy industrialists, including the ruins of a Carnegie mansion.

Block Island National Wildlife Refuge—Twelve miles off the coast of Rhode Island, the wildlife refuge at Block Island protects more than 70 diverse species of migratory songbirds that visit the area every autumn. Small birds pushed off their southern migration routes by strong winds land here to rest before continuing on their way.

Lowell National Historical Park—This Massachusetts park includes sites in and around the city of Lowell relating to the Industrial Revolution and the importance of the American textile industry. The "factory town" saw developments in technology as well as in social progress, including planned communities and the education and protection of workers.

American Memorial Park—On the island of Saipan in the Northern Mariana Islands, American Memorial Park was created as a living memorial recognizing the sacrifices made in the Marianas Campaign of World War II. Its court of honor, flag circle, carillon bell tower, and Visitor Center provide education amidst the beautiful environment.

War in the Pacific National Historical Park—This park on the Pacific island of Guam was set aside to remember the battles that raged in the Pacific Theater of World War II. Its memorials honor the bravery and sacrifices of all who participated in these battles, Japanese as well as Allied.

San Antonio Missions National Historical Park—This Texas park preserves four of the five Spanish frontier missions (except for the Alamo) in San Antonio. The Catholic outposts were communities set up to spread Christianity among the region's native populations from the 1600s to the 1800s.

Frank Church River of No Return Wilderness—Central Idaho boasts the largest federally managed wilderness in the continental United States. Its nearly 2.4 million acres include mountain ranges, canyons, thousands of miles of hiking trails, and six national forests. Frank Church was a senator who fought to preserve the region's wild lands.

National Park of American Samoa—This 13,500-acre park in the U.S. territory of American Samoa stretches across three islands: Tutuila, Ofu, and Ta'ū. Roughly one-third of the park is coral reefs and ocean, with tropical rainforests, local wildlife, scenic hiking, and Samoan culture among its other highlights.

Weir Farm National Historic Site—This property in Connecticut honors the life and work of American Impressionist painter J. Alden Weir—one of the Ten American Painters—and other artists who visited or lived at the site beginning in the late 1800s. The farm preserves Weir's studio as well as his most important subject: the land.

Salt River Bay National Historical Park and Ecological Preserve—This preserve in the U.S. Virgin Islands protects upland watersheds, river and ocean environments, and mangrove forests—home to threatened and endangered species. It also includes historic places including Columbus's landing site, a French colonial fort, and archaeological sites.

Marsh-Billings Rockefeller National Historical Park—In Woodstock, Vermont, is the site of a managed forest and progressive dairy farm started by Frederick Billings and preserved by others starting in the 1800s. Sugar maples, 400-year-old hemlocks, covered bridges, and rambling stone walls tell the region's stories of land stewardship.

Tallgrass Prairie National Preserve—Kansas's Flint Hills region is home to 11,000 acres of tallgrass prairie managed jointly by the National Park Service and the Nature Conservancy. Bison graze here, and visitors learn about the area's ranching legacy, American Indians, and the prairie ecosystem in the "sea of grass."

Tuskegee Airmen National Historic Site—This site at Moton Field in Tuskegee, Alabama, honors the contributions of African American airmen in World War II. This was the primary flight-training base for the pioneers known as the Tuskegee Airmen—instructors, pilots, navigators, bombardiers, maintenance and support staff, and other personnel.

WASHINGTON, AMERICA THE BEAUTIFUL™ QUARTER DOLLARS (2010 TO DATE)

GRADING STANDARDS

MS-60 to 70 (Mint State). *Obverse:* At MS-60, some abrasion and contact marks are evident on the highest-relief parts of the hair and the cheek. At MS-63, abrasion is slight at best, less so at MS-64. An MS-65 coin should display no abrasion or contact marks except under magnification, and MS-66 and higher coins should have none at all. Luster should be full. *Reverse:* Check the highest-relief areas of the design (these differ from coin to coin). Otherwise, comments are as for the obverse.

2010-D, Hot Springs (AR). Graded MS-68.

PF-60 to 70 (Proof). *Obverse and Reverse:* These coins are so recent, and as only a few have been cleaned, most approach perfection and can be designated PF–68 to 70, the latter only if no contact marks or other problems can be seen under magnification. A cleaned coin with extensive hairlines would not be collectible for most numismatists and would be classified at a lower level such as PF–60 to 63. Those with lighter hairlines qualify for PF–64 or 65.

**2010-S, Grand Canyon (AZ).
Graded PF-69 Ultra Cameo.**

A GALLERY OF WASHINGTON, AMERICA THE BEAUTIFUL, QUARTER DOLLARS (2010 TO DATE)

On the following pages are the reverse designs for all America the Beautiful quarters that have been released to date.

**2010, Hot Springs
National Park (AR)**
Reverse designer: Don Everhart.

**2010, Yellowstone
National Park (WY)**
Reverse designer: Don Everhart.

**2010, Yosemite
National Park (CA)**
Reverse designer: Joseph Menna.

**2010, Grand Canyon
National Park (AZ)**
Reverse designer: Phebe Hemphill.

**2010, Mt. Hood
National Forest (OR)**
Reverse designer: Phebe Hemphill.

**2011, Gettysburg
National Military Park (PA)**
Reverse designer: Joel Iskowitz.

**2011, Glacier
National Park (MT)**
Reverse designer: Barbara Fox.

**2011, Olympic
National Park (WA)**
Reverse designer: Susan Gamble.

**2011, Vicksburg
National Military Park (MS)**
Reverse designer: Thomas Cleveland.

**2011, Chickasaw
National Recreation Area (OK)**
Reverse designer: Donna Weaver.

**2012, El Yunque
National Forest (PR)**
Reverse designer: Gary Whitley.

**2012, Chaco Culture
National Historical Park (NM)**
Reverse designer: Donna Weaver.

**2012, Acadia
National Park (ME)**
Reverse designer: Barbara Fox.

**2012, Hawai'i Volcanoes
National Park (HI)**
Reverse designer: Charles L. Vickers.

**2012, Denali National
Park and Preserve (AK)**
Reverse designer: Susan Gamble.

2013, White Mountain National Forest (NH)
Reverse designer: Phebe Hemphill.

2013, Perry's Victory and International Peace Memorial (OH)
Reverse designer: Don Everhart.

2013, Great Basin National Park (NV)
Reverse designer: Ronald D. Sanders.

2013, Fort McHenry National Monument and Historic Shrine (MD)
Reverse designer: Joseph Menna.

2013, Mount Rushmore National Memorial (SD)
Reverse designer: Joseph Menna.

2014, Great Smoky Mountains National Park (TN)
Reverse designer: Chris Costello.

2014, Shenandoah National Park (VA)
Reverse designer: Phebe Hemphill.

2014, Arches National Park (UT)
Reverse designer: Donna Weaver.

2014, Great Sand Dunes National Park (CO)
Reverse designer: Don Everhart.

2014, Everglades National Park (FL)
Reverse designer: Joel Iskowitz.

2015, Homestead National Monument of America (NE)
Reverse designer: Ronald D. Sanders.

2015, Kisatchie National Forest (LA)
Reverse designer: Susan Gamble.

2015, Blue Ridge Parkway (NC)
Reverse designer: Frank Morris.

**2015, Bombay Hook
National Wildlife Refuge (DE)**
Reverse designer: Joel Iskowitz.

**2015, Saratoga National
Historical Park (NY)**
Reverse designer: Barbara Fox.

**2016, Shawnee
National Forest (IL)**
Reverse designer: Justin Kunz.

**2016, Cumberland Gap
National Historic Park (KY)**
Reverse designer: Barbara Fox.

**2016, Harpers Ferry
National Historical Park (WV)**
Reverse designer: Thomas Hipschen.

**2016, Theodore Roosevelt
National Park (ND)**
Reverse designer: Joel Iskowitz.

**2016, Fort Moultrie at Fort Sumter
National Monument (SC)**
Reverse designer: Richard Scott.

**2017, Effigy Mounds
National Monument (IA)**
Reverse designer: Richard Masters.

**2017, Frederick Douglass
National Historic Site (DC)**
Reverse designer: Thomas Hipschen.

**2017, Ozark
National Scenic Riverways (MO)**
Reverse designer: Ronald D. Sanders.

**2017, Ellis Island (Statue of Liberty
National Monument) (NJ)**
Reverse designer: Barbara Fox.

2017, George Rogers Clark National Historical Park (IN)
Reverse designer: Frank Morris.

2018, Pictured Rocks National Lakeshore (MI)
Reverse designer: Paul C. Balan.

2018, Apostle Islands National Lakeshore (WI)
Reverse designer: Richard Masters.

2018, Voyageurs National Park (MN)
Reverse designer: Patricia Lucas-Morris.

2018, Cumberland Island National Seashore (GA)
Reverse designer: Donna Weaver.

2018, Block Island National Wildlife Refuge (RI)
Reverse designer: Chris Costello.

2019, Lowell National Historical Park (MA)
Reverse designer: Joel Iskowitz.

2019, American Memorial Park (NMI)
Reverse designer: Donna Weaver.

2019, San Antonio Missions National Historial Park (TX)
Reverse designer: Joel Iskowitz.

2019, War in the Pacific National Historical Park (Guam)
Reverse designer: Chris Costello.

2019, Frank Church River of No Return Wilderness (ID)
Reverse designer: Emily Damstra.

	Mintage	Cert	Avg	%MS	AU-50	MS-63	MS-65 PF-65	MS-66 PF-66DC	MS-67 PF-69DC
2010-P, Hot Springs National Park (AR)	35,600,000	711	66.1	100%	$0.45	$0.50	$1	$10	$30
2010-P, Hot Springs National Park (AR), Satin Finish	583,897	366	67.5	100%			$3	$5	$12
2010-D, Hot Springs National Park (AR)	34,000,000	1,547	65.6	100%	$0.45	$0.50	$1	$10	$30
2010-D, Hot Springs National Park (AR), Satin Finish	583,897	417	67.5	100%			$3	$5	$12
2010-S, Hot Springs National Park (AR), Proof	1,402,889	4,044	69.5				$3	$4.50	$15
2010-S, Hot Springs, National Park (AR), Proof, Silver	859,417	11,246	69.6				$8	$9	$20
2010-P, Yellowstone National Park (WY)	33,600,000	446	66.1	100%	$0.45	$0.50	$2	$10	$30
2010-P, Yellowstone National Park (WY), Satin Finish	583,897	345	67.4	100%			$3	$5	$12
2010-D, Yellowstone National Park (WY)	34,800,000	764	65.8	100%	$0.45	$0.50	$2	$10	$30
2010-D, Yellowstone National Park (WY), Satin Finish	583,897	360	67.4	100%			$3	$5	$12
2010-S, Yellowstone National Park (WY), Proof	1,404,259	4,083	69.5				$3	$4.50	$15
2010-S, Yellowstone National Park (WY), Proof, Silver	859,417	11,256	69.7				$8	$9	$20
2010-P, Yosemite National Park (CA)	35,200,000	288	66.1	100%	$0.50	$0.75	$2	$12	$30
2010-P, Yosemite National Park (CA), Satin Finish	583,897	372	67.3	100%			$3	$5	$12
2010-D, Yosemite National Park (CA)	34,800,000	617	66.0	100%	$0.50	$0.75	$2	$12	$30
2010-D, Yosemite National Park (CA), Satin Finish	583,897	397	67.4	100%			$3	$5	$12
2010-S, Yosemite National Park (CA), Proof	1,401,522	4,009	69.5				$3	$4.50	$15
2010-S, Yosemite National Park (CA), Proof, Silver	859,417	11,155	69.6				$8	$9	$20
2010-P, Grand Canyon National Park (AZ)	34,800,000	374	66.3	100%	$0.45	$0.50	$1	$10	$30
2010-P, Grand Canyon National Park (AZ), Satin Finish	583,897	386	67.5	100%			$3	$5	$12
2010-D, Grand Canyon National Park (AZ)	35,400,000	630	66.1	100%	$0.45	$0.50	$1	$10	$30
2010-D, Grand Canyon National Park (AZ), Satin Finish	583,897	433	67.7	100%			$3	$5	$12
2010-S, Grand Canyon National Park (AZ), Proof	1,401,462	3,995	69.5				$3	$4.50	$15
2010-S, Grand Canyon National Park (AZ), Proof, Silver	859,417	11,173	69.6				$8	$9	$20
2010-P, Mt. Hood National Forest (OR)	34,400,000	215	66.1	100%	$0.45	$0.50	$2	$10	$30
2010-P, Mt. Hood National Forest (OR), Satin Finish	583,897	338	67.3	100%			$3	$5	$12
2010-D, Mt. Hood National Forest (OR)	34,400,000	415	65.6	100%	$0.45	$0.50	$2	$10	$30
2010-D, Mt. Hood National Forest (OR), Satin Finish	583,897	433	67.5	100%			$3	$5	$12
2010-S, Mt. Hood National Forest (OR), Proof	1,398,106	4,010	69.4				$3	$4.50	$15
2010-S, Mt. Hood National Forest (OR), Proof, Silver	859,417	11,350	69.6				$8	$9	$20
2011-P, Gettysburg National Military Park (PA)	30,800,000	756	66.3	100%	$0.50	$0.75	$1.25	$12	$30
2011-D, Gettysburg National Military Park (PA)	30,400,000	303	66.5	100%	$0.50	$0.75	$1.25	$12	$30
2011-S, Gettysburg National Military Park (PA), Proof	1,273,068	2,756	69.5				$3	$4.50	$15
2011-S, Gettysburg National Military Park (PA), Proof, Silver	722,076	5,993	69.7				$8	$9	$20
2011-P, Glacier National Park (MT)	30,400,000	292	67.1	100%	$0.45	$0.50	$1	$10	$30
2011-D, Glacier National Park (MT)	31,200,000	457	65.9	100%	$0.45	$0.50	$1	$10	$30
2011-S, Glacier National Park (MT), Proof	1,269,422	2,754	69.6				$3	$4.50	$15
2011-S, Glacier National Park (MT), Proof, Silver	722,076	6,150	69.7				$8	$9	$20
2011-P, Olympic National Park (WA)	30,400,000	308	67.1	100%	$0.45	$0.50	$2	$10	$30
2011-D, Olympic National Park (WA)	30,600,000	556	66.2	100%	$0.45	$0.50	$2	$10	$30
2011-S, Olympic National Park (WA), Proof	1,268,231	2,768	69.6				$3	$4.50	$15
2011-S, Olympic National Park (WA), Proof, Silver	722,076	5,973	69.7				$8	$9	$20
2011-P, Vicksburg National Military Park (MS)	30,800,000	280	66.8	100%	$0.45	$0.50	$1	$10	$30
2011-D, Vicksburg National Military Park (MS)	33,400,000	475	66.3	100%	$0.45	$0.50	$1	$10	$30
2011-S, Vicksburg National Military Park (MS), Proof	1,268,623	2,761	69.5				$3	$4.50	$15
2011-S, Vicksburg National Military Park (MS), Proof, Silver	722,076	6,015	69.7				$8	$9	$20
2011-P, Chickasaw National Recreation Area (OK)	73,800,000	324	67.2	100%	$0.45	$0.50	$1	$10	$30
2011-D, Chickasaw National Recreation Area (OK)	69,400,000	430	66.2	100%	$0.45	$0.50	$1	$10	$30
2011-S, Chickasaw National Recreation Area (OK), Proof	1,266,825	2,749	69.5				$3	$4.50	$15
2011-S, Chickasaw National Recreation Area (OK), Proof, Silver	722,076	5,931	69.6				$8	$9	$20
2012-P, El Yunque National Forest (PR)	25,800,000	562	66.1	100%	$0.45	$0.50	$2	$10	$30
2012-D, El Yunque National Forest (PR)	25,000,000	252	66.8	100%	$0.45	$0.50	$2	$10	$30

	Mintage	Cert	Avg	%MS	AU-50	MS-63	MS-65	MS-66	MS-67
							PF-65	PF-66DC	PF-69DC
2012-S, El Yunque National Forest (PR) (a)	1,680,140	610	66.4	100%		$1	$8	$12	$35
2012-S, El Yunque National Forest (PR), Proof	1,012,094	2,022	69.3				$3	$4.50	$15
2012-S, El Yunque National Forest (PR), Proof, Silver	608,060	4,954	69.7				$8	$9	$20
2012-P, Chaco Culture National Historical Park (NM)	22,000,000	146	67.2	100%	$0.45	$0.50	$2	$10	$30
2012-D, Chaco Culture National Historical Park (NM)	22,000,000	355	66.2	100%	$0.45	$0.50	$2	$10	$30
2012-S, Chaco Culture National Historical Park (NM) (a)	1,389,020	375	66.5	100%		$1	$8	$12	$35
2012-S, Chaco Culture National Historical Park (NM), Proof	961,464	2,011	69.3				$3	$4.50	$15
2012-S, Chaco Culture National Historical Park (NM), Proof, Silver	608,060	4,703	69.7				$8	$9	$20
2012-P, Acadia National Park (ME)	24,800,000	343	65.6	100%	$0.45	$0.50	$1	$10	$30
2012-D, Acadia National Park (ME)	21,606,000	114	66.7	100%	$0.45	$0.50	$1	$10	$30
2012-S, Acadia National Park (ME) (a)	1,409,120	453	66.3	100%		$1	$8	$12	$35
2012-S, Acadia National Park (ME), Proof	962,038	2,015	69.3				$3	$4.50	$15
2012-S, Acadia National Park (ME), Proof, Silver	608,060	4,873	69.7				$8	$9	$20
2012-P, Hawai'i Volcanoes National Park (HI)	46,200,000	133	67.1	100%	$0.45	$0.50	$1	$10	$30
2012-D, Hawai'i Volcanoes National Park (HI)	78,600,000	406	66.1	100%	$0.45	$0.50	$1	$10	$30
2012-S, Hawai'i Volcanoes National Park (HI) (a)	1,409,120	406	66.4	100%		$1	$8	$12	$35
2012-S, Hawai'i Volcanoes National Park (HI), Proof	962,447	2,017	69.3				$3	$4.50	$15
2012-S, Hawai'i Volcanoes National Park (HI), Proof, Silver	608,060	5,014	69.7				$8	$9	$20
2012-P, Denali National Park and Preserve (AK)	135,400,000	152	67.0	100%	$0.40	$0.50	$1	$10	$30
2012-D, Denali National Park and Preserve (AK)	166,600,000	439	66.2	100%	$0.40	$0.50	$1	$10	$30
2012-S, Denali National Park and Preserve (AK) (a)	1,409,220	532	66.2	100%		$1	$8	$12	$35
2012-S, Denali National Park and Preserve (AK), Proof	959,602	2,019	69.3				$3	$4.50	$15
2012-S, Denali National Park and Preserve (AK), Proof, Silver	608,060	4,900	69.7				$8	$9	$20
2013-P, White Mountain National Forest (NH)	68,800,000	538	66.5	100%	$0.45	$0.50	$1	$10	$30
2013-D, White Mountain National Forest (NH)	107,600,000	295	67.1	100%	$0.45	$0.50	$1	$10	$30
2013-S, White Mountain National Forest (NH) (a)	1,606,900	350	66.4	100%		$1	$8	$12	$35
2013-S, White Mountain National Forest (NH), Proof	989,803	1,868	69.5				$3	$4.50	$15
2013-S, White Mountain National Forest (NH), Proof, Silver	467,691	4,976	69.7				$8	$9	$20
2013-P, Perry's Victory and Int'l Peace Memorial (OH)	107,800,000	464	66.5	100%	$0.45	$0.50	$2	$10	$30
2013-D, Perry's Victory and Int'l Peace Memorial (OH)	131,600,000	264	67.2	100%	$0.45	$0.50	$2	$10	$30
2013-S, Perry's Victory and Int'l Peace Memorial (OH) (a)	1,425,860	260	66.4	100%		$1	$8	$12	$35
2013-S, Perry's Victory and Int'l Peace Memorial (OH), Proof	947,815	1,841	69.5				$3	$4.50	$15
2013-S, Perry's Victory and Int'l Peace Memorial (OH), Proof, Silver	467,691	4,859	69.7				$8	$9	$20
2013-P, Great Basin National Park (NV)	122,400,000	215	66.9	100%	$0.45	$0.50	$1	$10	$30
2013-D, Great Basin National Park (NV)	141,400,000	442	66.5	100%	$0.45	$0.50	$1	$10	$30
2013-S, Great Basin National Park (NV) (a)	1,316,500	296	66.9	100%		$1	$8	$12	$35
2013-S, Great Basin National Park (NV), Proof	945,777	1,841	69.5				$3	$4.50	$15
2013-S, Great Basin National Park (NV), Proof, Silver	467,691	5,031	69.7				$8	$9	$20
2013-P, Ft. McHenry Nat'l Monument / Historic Shrine (MD)	120,000,000	486	66.5	100%	$0.45	$0.50	$1	$10	$30
2013-D, Ft. McHenry Nat'l Monument / Historic Shrine (MD)	151,400,000	299	67.2	100%	$0.45	$0.50	$1	$10	$30
2013-S, Ft. McHenry Nat'l Monument / Historic Shrine (MD) (a)	1,313,680	498	67.1	100%		$1	$8	$12	$35
2013-S, Ft. McHenry Nat'l Monument / Historic Shrine (MD), Proof	946,380	1,839	69.5				$3	$4.50	$15
2013-S, Ft. McHenry National Monument / Historic Shrine (MD), Proof, Silver	467,691	4,989	69.7				$8	$9	$20
2013-P, Mount Rushmore National Memorial (SD)	231,800,000	191	66.9	100%	$0.45	$0.50	$1	$10	$30
2013-D, Mount Rushmore National Memorial (SD)	272,400,000	438	66.3	100%	$0.45	$0.50	$1	$10	$30
2013-S, Mount Rushmore National Memorial (SD) (a)	1,373,260	445	66.9	100%		$1	$8	$12	$35
2013-S, Mount Rushmore National Memorial (SD), Proof	958,853	1,840	69.5				$3	$4.50	$15
2013-S, Mount Rushmore National Memorial (SD), Proof, Silver	467,691	4,999	69.7				$8	$9	$20

a. Not issued for circulation. From 2012 to date, the San Francisco Mint has made Uncirculated S-mintmark quarters of each design in the National Park series. These can be purchased by collectors directly from the U.S. Mint, in bags of 100 or rolls of 40 coins, for a premium above face value.

	Mintage	Cert	Avg	%MS	AU-50	MS-63	MS-65	MS-66	MS-67
							PF-65	PF-66DC	PF-69DC
2014-P, Great Smoky Mountains National Park (TN)	73,200,000	413	66.6	100%	$0.45	$0.50	$1	$10	$30
2014-D, Great Smoky Mountains National Park (TN)	99,400,000	259	67.4	100%	$0.45	$0.50	$1	$10	$30
2014-S, Great Smoky Mountains National Park (TN) (a)	1,360,780	485	66.7	100%		$1	$8	$12	$35
2014-S, Great Smoky Mountains National Park (TN), Proof	881,896	2,081	69.5				$3	$4.50	$15
2014-S, Great Smoky Mountains National Park (TN), Proof, Silver	472,107	4,286	69.7				$8	$9	$20
2014-P, Shenandoah National Park (VA)	112,800,000	413	66.4	100%	$0.45	$0.50	$1	$10	$30
2014-D, Shenandoah National Park (VA)	197,800,000	236	67.4	100%	$0.45	$0.50	$1	$10	$30
2014-S, Shenandoah National Park (VA) (a)	1,266,720	695	66.9	100%		$1	$8	$12	$35
2014-S, Shenandoah National Park (VA), Proof	846,441	2,075	69.5				$3	$4.50	$15
2014-S, Shenandoah National Park (VA), Proof, Silver	472,107	4,291	69.7				$8	$9	$20
2014-P, Arches National Park (UT)	214,200,000	252	67.3	100%	$0.45	$0.50	$1	$10	$30
2014-D, Arches National Park (UT)	251,400,000	295	67.4	100%	$0.45	$0.50	$1	$10	$30
2014-S, Arches National Park (UT) (a)	1,235,940	575	66.8	100%		$1	$8	$12	$35
2014-S, Arches National Park (UT), Proof	844,775	2,078	69.4				$3	$4.50	$15
2014-S, Arches National Park (UT), Proof, Silver	472,107	4,418	69.7				$8	$9	$20
2014-P, Great Sand Dunes National Park (CO)	159,600,000	186	67.4	100%	$0.45	$0.50	$2	$10	$30
2014-D, Great Sand Dunes National Park (CO)	171,800,000	224	67.6	100%	$0.45	$0.50	$1.50	$10	$30
2014-S, Great Sand Dunes National Park (CO) (a)	1,176,760	822	67.1	100%		$1	$8	$12	$35
2014-S, Great Sand Dunes National Park (CO), Proof	843,238	2,074	69.5				$3	$4.50	$15
2014-S, Great Sand Dunes National Park (CO), Proof, Silver	472,107	4,284	69.7				$8	$9	$20
2014-P, Everglades National Park (FL)	157,601,200	198	67.3	100%	$0.45	$0.50	$1	$10	$30
2014-D, Everglades National Park (FL)	142,400,000	286	67.6	100%	$0.45	$0.50	$1	$10	$30
2014-S, Everglades National Park (FL) (a)	1,180,900	0	n/a			$1	$8	$12	$35
2014-S, Everglades National Park (FL), Proof	856,139	2,076	69.5				$3	$4.50	$15
2014-S, Everglades National Park (FL), Proof, Silver	472,107	4,283	69.7				$8	$9	$20
2015-P, Homestead National Monument of America (NE)	214,780,456	2,383	64.8	100%	$0.50	$0.75	$1	$10	$30
2015-D, Homestead National Monument of America (NE)	248,980,456	129	66.8	100%	$0.50	$0.75	$1	$10	$30
2015-S, Homestead National Monument of America (NE) (a)	1,153,840	1,022	67.0	100%		$2	$8	$12	$35
2015-S, Homestead National Monument of America (NE), Proof	778,319	1,666	69.6				$3	$4.50	$15
2015-S, Homestead National Monument of America (NE), Proof, Silver	490,621	3,892	69.5				$8	$9	$20
2015-P, Kisatchie National Forest (LA)	397,579,544	228	67.3	100%	$0.50	$0.75	$1	$10	$30
2015-D, Kisatchie National Forest (LA)	379,979,544	178	67.0	100%	$0.50	$0.75	$1	$10	$30
2015-S, Kisatchie National Forest (LA) (a)	1,099,380	596	67.0	100%		$2	$8	$12	$35
2015-S, Kisatchie National Forest (LA), Proof	777,407	1,600	69.6				$3	$4.50	$15
2015-S, Kisatchie National Forest (LA), Proof, Silver	490,621	3,911	69.5				$8	$9	$20
2015-P, Blue Ridge Parkway (NC)	326,947,055	132	66.8	100%	$0.50	$0.75	$1	$10	$30
2015-D, Blue Ridge Parkway (NC)	506,529,955	165	66.9	100%	$0.50	$0.75	$1	$10	$30
2015-S, Blue Ridge Parkway (NC) (a)	1,096,620	356	66.5	100%		$2	$8	$12	$35
2015-S, Blue Ridge Parkway (NC), Proof	779,338	1,599	69.6				$3	$4.50	$15
2015-S, Blue Ridge Parkway (NC), Proof, Silver	490,621	3,884	69.5				$8	$9	$20
2015-P, Bombay Hook National Wildlife Refuge (DE)	275,377,747	189	67.1	100%	$0.50	$0.75	$1	$10	$30
2015-D, Bombay Hook National Wildlife Refuge (DE)	206,777,747	239	67.2	100%	$0.50	$0.75	$1	$10	$30
2015-S, Bombay Hook National Wildlife Refuge (DE) (a)	1,013,920	270	66.7	100%		$2	$8	$12	$35
2015-S, Bombay Hook National Wildlife Refuge (DE), Proof	775,610	1,603	69.5				$3	$4.50	$15
2015-S, Bombay Hook National Wildlife Refuge (DE), Proof, Silver	490,621	3,908	69.5				$8	$9	$20
2015-P, Saratoga National Historical Park (NY)	223,379,266	130	67.0	100%	$0.50	$0.75	$1	$10	$30
2015-D, Saratoga National Historical Park (NY)	216,179,266	179	67.0	100%	$0.50	$0.75	$1	$10	$30
2015-S, Saratoga National Historical Park (NY) (a)	1,045,500	276	66.9	100%		$2	$8	$12	$35

a. Not issued for circulation. From 2012 to date, the San Francisco Mint has made Uncirculated S-mintmark quarters of each design in the National Park series. These can be purchased by collectors directly from the U.S. Mint, in bags of 100 or rolls of 40 coins, for a premium above face value.

	Mintage	Cert	Avg	%MS	AU-50	MS-63	MS-65	MS-66	MS-67
							PF-65	PF-66DC	PF-69DC
2015-S, Saratoga National Historical Park (NY), Proof	777,129	1,604	69.5				$3	$4.50	$15
2015-S, Saratoga National Historical Park (NY), Proof, Silver	490,621	3,892	69.5				$8	$9	$20

a. Not issued for circulation. From 2012 to date, the San Francisco Mint has made Uncirculated S-mintmark quarters of each design in the National Park series. These can be purchased by collectors directly from the U.S. Mint, in bags of 100 or rolls of 40 coins, for a premium above face value.

In 2016 a special .9999 fine gold striking of Hermon A. MacNeil's Standing Liberty quarter was created to celebrate the 100th anniversary of its introduction. It is smaller than the silver strikings, with a diameter of 22 mm and weighing 7.776 grams. Struck at West Point, it has a reeded edge. Similar strikings were made for the 1916 dime and half dollar designs.

	Mintage	Cert	Avg	%MS	SP-67	SP-70
2016-W, Standing Liberty Centennial Gold Coin	91,752				$450	$550

Normally scheduled production of clad and silver America the Beautiful quarters, in the same standards and specifications as previously, continued in 2016 and beyond, and was not disrupted by the gold Standing Liberty quarter.

	Mintage	Cert	Avg	%MS	AU-50	MS-63	MS-65	MS-66	MS-67
							PF-65	PF-66DC	PF-69DC
2016-P, Shawnee National Forest (IL)	155,600,000	216	67.0	100%	$0.50	$0.75	$1	$10	$30
2016-D, Shawnee National Forest (IL)	151,800,000	244	66.9	100%	$0.50	$0.75	$1	$10	$30
2016-S, Shawnee National Forest (IL) (a)	1,066,440	241	66.8	100%		$2	$3	$12	$35
2016-S, Shawnee National Forest (IL), Proof	732,039	1,134	69.7				$3	$4.50	$15
2016-S, Shawnee National Forest (IL), Proof, Silver	515,205	3,965	69.7				$8	$9	$20
2016-P, Cumberland Gap National Historical Park (KY)	215,400,000	260	67.1	100%	$0.50	$0.75	$1	$10	$30
2016-D, Cumberland Gap National Historical Park (KY)	223,200,000	349	67.3	100%	$0.50	$0.75	$1	$10	$30
2016-S, Cumberland Gap National Historical Park (KY) (a)	1,021,120	259	66.6	100%		$2	$3	$12	$35
2016-S, Cumberland Gap National Historical Park (KY), Proof	701,831	1,131	69.7				$3	$4.50	$15
2016-S, Cumberland Gap National Historical Park (KY), Proof, Silver	515,205	3,984	69.7				$8	$9	$20
2016-P, Harpers Ferry National Historical Park (WV)	434,630,000	191	66.7	100%	$0.50	$0.75	$1	$10	$30
2016-D, Harpers Ferry National Historical Park (WV)	424,000,000	209	67.0	100%	$0.50	$0.75	$1	$10	$30
2016-S, Harpers Ferry National Historical Park (WV) (a)	1,035,840	269	66.7	100%		$2	$3	$12	$35
2016-S, Harpers Ferry National Historical Park (WV), Proof	701,203	1,142	69.7				$3	$4.50	$15
2016-S, Harpers Ferry National Historical Park (WV), Proof, Silver	515,205	4,023	69.7				$8	$9	$20
2016-P, Theodore Roosevelt National Park (ND)	231,600,000	202	66.9	100%	$0.50	$0.75	$1	$10	$30
2016-D, Theodore Roosevelt National Park (ND)	223,200,000	231	66.9	100%	$0.50	$0.75	$1	$10	$30
2016-S, Theodore Roosevelt National Park (ND) (a)	1,057,020	1	66.0	100%		$2	$3	$12	$35
2016-S, Theodore Roosevelt National Park (ND), Proof	702,930	1,130	69.7				$3	$4.50	$15
2016-S, Theodore Roosevelt National Park (ND), Proof, Silver	515,205	3,967	69.7				$8	$9	$20
2016-P, Fort Moultrie (Fort Sumter National Monument) (SC)	154,400,000	225	67.0	100%	$0.50	$0.75	$1	$10	$30
2016-D, Fort Moultrie (Fort Sumter National Monument) (SC)	142,200,000	260	67.1	100%	$0.50	$0.75	$1	$10	$30
2016-S, Fort Moultrie (Fort Sumter National Monument) (SC) (a)	966,260	1	67.0	100%		$2	$3	$12	$35
2016-S, Fort Moultrie (Fort Sumter National Monument) (SC), Proof	717,049	1,128	69.7				$3	$4.50	$15

a. Not issued for circulation. From 2012 to date, the San Francisco Mint has made Uncirculated S-mintmark quarters of each design in the National Park series. These can be purchased by collectors directly from the U.S. Mint, in bags of 100 or rolls of 40 coins, for a premium above face value.

	Mintage	Cert	Avg	%MS	AU-50	MS-63	MS-65 / PF-65	MS-66 / PF-66DC	MS-67 / PF-69DC
2016-S, Fort Moultrie (Fort Sumter National Monument) (SC), Proof, Silver	515,205	4,061	69.7				$8	$9	$20
2017-P, Effigy Mounds National Monument (IA)	271,200,000				$0.50	$0.75	$1	$10	$30
2017-D, Effigy Mounds National Monument (IA)	210,800,000				$0.50	$0.75	$1	$10	$30
2017-S, Effigy Mounds National Monument (IA) (a)	931,340					$2	$3	$12	$35
2017-S, Effigy Mounds National Monument (IA), Enhanced Uncirculated							$3	$4.50	$15
2017-S, Effigy Mounds National Monument (IA), Proof	706,042						$3	$4.50	$15
2017-S, Effigy Mounds National Monument (IA), Proof, Silver	496,626						$8	$9	$20
2017-P, Frederick Douglass National Historic Site (DC)	184,800,000				$0.50	$0.75	$1	$10	$30
2017-D, Frederick Douglass National Historic Site (DC)	185,800,000							$30	
2017-S, Frederick Douglass National Historic Site (DC) (a)	934,940					$2	$3	$12	$35
2017-S, Frederick Douglass National Historic Site (DC), Enhanced Uncirculated							$3	$4.50	$15
2017-S, Frederick Douglass National Historic Site (DC), Proof	672,188						$3	$4.50	$15
2017-S, Frederick Douglass National Historic Site (DC), Proof, Silver	496,626						$8	$9	$20
2017-P, Ozark National Scenic Riverways (MO)	203,000,000				$0.50	$0.75	$1	$10	$30
2017-D, Ozark National Scenic Riverways (MO)	200,000,000				$0.50	$0.75	$1	$10	$30
2017-S, Ozark National Scenic Riverways (MO) (a)	906,840					$2	$3	$12	$35
2017-S, Ozark National Scenic Riverways (MO), Enhanced Uncirculated							$3	$4.50	$15
2017-S, Ozark National Scenic Riverways (MO), Proof	671,902						$3	$4.50	$15
2017-S, Ozark National Scenic Riverways (MO), Proof, Silver	496,626						$8	$9	$20
2017-P, Ellis Island (Statue of Liberty National Monument) (NJ)	234,000,000				$0.50	$0.75	$1	$10	$30
2017-D, Ellis Island (Statue of Liberty National Monument) (NJ)	254,000,000							$30	
2017-S, Ellis Island (Statue of Liberty National Monument) (NJ) (a)	956,200					$2	$3	$12	$35
2017-S, Ellis Island (Statue of Liberty National Monument) (NJ), Enhanced Uncirculated							$3	$4.50	$15
2017-S, Ellis Island (Statue of Liberty National Monument) (NJ), Proof	674,537						$3	$4.50	$15
2017-S, Ellis Island (Statue of Liberty National Monument) (NJ), Proof, Silver	496,626						$8	$9	$20
2017-P, George Rogers Clark National Historical Park (IN)	191,600,000				$0.50	$0.75	$1	$10	$30
2017-D, George Rogers Clark National Historical Park (IN)	180,800,000				$0.50	$0.75	$1	$10	$30
2017-S, George Rogers Clark National Historical Park (IN) (a)	919,060					$2	$3	$12	$35
2017-S, George Rogers Clark National Historical Park (IN), Enhanced Uncirculated							$3	$4.50	$15
2017-S, George Rogers Clark National Historical Park (IN), Proof	689,235						$3	$4.50	$15
2017-S, George Rogers Clark National Historical Park (IN), Proof, Silver	496,626						$8	$9	$20
2018-P, Pictured Rocks National Lakeshore (MI)	186,714,000				$0.50	$0.75	$1	$10	$30
2018-D, Pictured Rocks National Lakeshore (MI)	182,600,000				$0.50	$0.75	$1	$10	$30
2018-S, Pictured Rocks National Lakeshore (MI) (a)	917,580					$2	$3	$12	$35
2018-S, Pictured Rocks National Lakeshore (MI), Proof	688,538						$3	$4.50	$15
2018-S, Pictured Rocks National Lakeshore (MI), Proof, Silver	350,820						$8	$9	$20
2018-P, Apostle Islands National Lakeshore (WI)	223,200,000				$0.50	$0.75	$1	$10	$30
2018-D, Apostle Islands National Lakeshore (WI)	216,600,000				$0.50	$0.75	$1	$10	$30
2018-S, Apostle Islands National Lakeshore (WI) (a)	871,820					$2	$3	$12	$35

a. Not issued for circulation. From 2012 to date, the San Francisco Mint has made Uncirculated S-mintmark quarters of each design in the National Park series. These can be purchased by collectors directly from the U.S. Mint, in bags of 100 or rolls of 40 coins, for a premium above face value.

	Mintage	Cert	Avg	%MS	AU-50	MS-63	MS-65 / PF-65	MS-66 / PF-66DC	MS-67 / PF-69DC
2018-S, Apostle Islands National Lakeshore (WI), Proof	659,633						$3	$4.50	$15
2018-S, Apostle Islands National Lakeshore (WI), Proof, Silver	350,820						$8	$9	$20
2018-P, Voyageurs National Park (MN)	237,400,000				$0.50	$0.75	$1	$10	$30
2018-D, Voyageurs National Park (MN)	197,800,000				$0.50	$0.75	$1	$10	$30
2018-S, Voyageurs National Park (MN) (a)	831,560					$2	$3	$12	$35
2018-S, Voyageurs National Park (MN), Proof	659,448						$3	$4.50	$15
2018-S, Voyageurs National Park (MN), Proof, Silver	350,820						$8	$9	$20
2018-P, Cumberland Island National Seashore (GA)	138,000,000				$0.50	$0.75	$1	$10	$30
2018-D, Cumberland Island National Seashore (GA)	151,600,000				$0.50	$0.75	$1	$10	$30
2018-S, Cumberland Island National Seashore (GA) (a)	816,660					$2	$3	$12	$35
2018-S, Cumberland Island National Seashore (GA), Proof	658,438						$3	$4.50	$15
2018-S, Cumberland Island National Seashore (GA), Proof, Silver	350,820						$8	$9	$20
2018-P, Block Island National Wildlife Refuge (RI)	159,600,000				$0.50	$0.75	$1	$10	$30
2018-D, Block Island National Wildlife Refuge (RI)	159,600,000				$0.50	$0.75	$1	$10	$30
2018-S, Block Island National Wildlife Refuge (RI) (a)	764,660					$2	$3	$12	$35
2018-S, Block Island National Wildlife Refuge (RI), Proof	675,567						$3	$4.50	$15
2018-S, Block Island National Wildlife Refuge (RI), Proof, Silver	350,820						$8	$9	$20
2019-P, Lowell National Historical Park (MA)					$0.50	$0.75	$1	$10	$30
2019-D, Lowell National Historical Park (MA)					$0.50	$0.75	$1	$10	$30
2019-S, Lowell National Historical Park (MA) (a)						$2	$3	$12	$35
2019-S, Lowell National Historical Park (MA), Proof							$3	$4.50	$15
2019-S, Lowell National Historical Park (MA), Proof, Silver							$8	$9	$20
2019-W, Lowell National Historical Park (MA) (b)									
2019-P, American Memorial Park (Northern Mariana Islands)					$0.50	$0.75	$1	$10	$30
2019-D, American Memorial Park (Northern Mariana Islands)					$0.50	$0.75	$1	$10	$30
2019-S, American Memorial Park (Northern Mariana Islands) (a)						$2	$3	$12	$35
2019-S, American Memorial Park (Northern Mariana Islands), Proof							$3	$4.50	$15
2019-S, American Memorial Park (Northern Mariana Islands), Proof, Silver							$8	$9	$20
2019-W, American Memorial Park (Northern Mariana Islands) (b)									
2019-P, San Antonio Missions National Historical Park (TX)					$0.50	$0.75	$1	$10	$30
2019-D, San Antonio Missions National Historical Park (TX)					$0.50	$0.75	$1	$10	$30
2019-S, San Antonio Missions National Historical Park (TX) (a)						$2	$3	$12	$35
2019-S, San Antonio Missions Nat'l Historical Park (TX), Proof							$3	$4.50	$15
2019-S, San Antonio Missions Nat'l Historical Park (TX), Proof, Silver							$8	$9	$20
2019-W, San Antonio Missions National Historical Park (TX) (b)									
2019-P, War in the Pacific National Historical Park (Guam)					$0.50	$0.75	$1	$10	$30
2019-D, War in the Pacific National Historical Park (Guam)					$0.50	$0.75	$1	$10	$30
2019-S, War in the Pacific National Historical Park (Guam) (a)						$2	$3	$12	$35
2019-S, War in the Pacific National Historical Park (Guam), Proof							$3	$4.50	$15
2019-S, War in the Pacific Nat'l Historical Park (Guam), Proof, Silver							$8	$9	$20
2019-W, War in the Pacific National Historical Park (Guam) (b)									
2019-P, Frank Church River of No Return Wilderness (ID)					$0.50	$0.75	$1	$10	$30
2019-D, Frank Church River of No Return Wilderness (ID)					$0.50	$0.75	$1	$10	$30
2019-S, Frank Church River of No Return Wilderness (ID) (a)						$2	$3	$12	$35
2019-S, Frank Church River of No Return Wilderness (ID), Proof							$3	$4.50	$15
2019-S, Frank Church River of No Return Wilderness (ID), Proof, Silver							$8	$9	$20
2019-W, Frank Church River of No Return Wilderness (ID) (b)									

a. Not issued for circulation. From 2012 to date, the San Francisco Mint has made Uncirculated S-mintmark quarters of each design in the National Park series. These can be purchased by collectors directly from the U.S. Mint, in bags of 100 or rolls of 40 coins, for a premium above face value. **b.** Coinciding with National Coin Week (April 21–27, 2019), the United States Mint released into circulation 10 million 2019 quarters struck at the West Point Mint, each bearing a W mintmark. The coins were mixed into bulk bags of quarters at the Philadelphia and Denver mints and shipped and distributed to banks and financial institutions by the Federal Reserve starting in early April.

Half Dollars
1794 to Date
AN OVERVIEW OF HALF DOLLARS

Many hobbyists consider a collection of half dollars to be one of the most satisfying in the American series. The panorama of designs is extensive, ranging from the early Flowing Hair issues of 1794 and 1795 down to classic 20th-century motifs and the presidential portrait of the present day. The large size of half dollar coins makes them convenient to view and easy to enjoy.

Among the types, the 1794–1795 Flowing Hair half dollar is readily available in circulated grades and rare in Mint State, but at any level is hard to find well struck and without adjustment marks (evidence of where a Mint worker filed an overweight planchet down to proper weight). Most on the market are dated 1795. Careful selection for quality is advised.

The next type, dated 1796–1797 with a Draped Bust obverse and Small Eagle reverse, is the scarcest in the American silver series excepting the 1839 Gobrecht dollar. (However, the latter is available in Proof restrike form, yielding choice and gem examples, so it can be considered in a different category from the circulation-strike 1796–1797 half dollar type.) It might not be possible to be particular, but, finances permitting, a collector should take some time and endeavor to find an example that is sharply struck on both sides. Needle-sharp striking is more of a theory than a practicality, and some compromise in this regard may be necessary.

Half dollars of the 1801–1807 type, with the obverse as preceding but now with the Heraldic Eagle reverse, are plentiful enough in worn grades but somewhat scarce in Mint State. Striking is seldom needle-sharp and ranges from average to very poor. However, there are enough coins in the marketplace that collectors can afford to take their time and seek a sharp strike.

Capped Bust half dollars with a lettered edge, 1807–1836, abound in just about any grade desired. Again, striking is a consideration, and some searching is needed for a high-quality strike. Generally, those in the late 1820s and the 1830s are better struck than are those of earlier dates, the earlier coins being scarcer and more expensive in any event.

The short-lived type of 1836–1837, Capped Bust with a reeded edge and with the denomination spelled as 50 CENTS, is available easily enough through the high-mintage 1837, but most have problems with the quality of striking. Then comes the 1838–1839 type of the same obverse style, its reverse modified with a slightly different eagle and with the denomination as HALF DOL. Generally these are fairly well struck.

Liberty Seated half dollars of the several styles within the series, 1839–1891, admit of no great rarities for the type collector, save for the 1839, No Drapery, in levels of MS-63 and finer. However, among the earlier types in particular, sharply struck pieces are in the minority. Curiously, the most readily available Mint State Liberty Seated half dollars also are the lowest-mintage issues, the dates 1879 and later, as these were recognized as desirable at the time of issue and were widely saved.

Barber half dollars were not popular in their time, and while Proofs exist in proportion to their production figures, few circulation-strike coins were saved by collectors and Mint State examples are quite scarce today. In fact, as a type, a Barber half dollar dated 1900 or later in Mint State is the scarcest of all silver issues of that century. Well-struck MS-63 and better Barber half dollars, with the upper-right corner of the shield and the leg at lower right showing full details, are significantly scarcer than generally realized.

Liberty Walking half dollars, minted from 1916 to 1947, are plentiful in all grades. Again, some attention should be made to striking sharpness, which makes the search become more intense. Fortunately there are countless thousands of MS-63 and finer coins of the 1940s on the market, giving collectors a wide choice. Then come Franklin half dollars, made only from 1948 to 1963, with representative coins easy enough to acquire in about any grade desired. Kennedy half dollars exist in several varieties, all of which are available without any problem. Among these and other modern coins care needs to be taken for value received versus price paid. Modern issues in, for example, MS–65 and 66, selected for quality, are for many collectors preferable to MS–69 or 70 coins offered at a much higher price.

The release of the Franklin half dollar was announced to the coin-collecting world on the front page of the *Numismatist*, June 1948.

FOR THE COLLECTOR AND INVESTOR: HALF DOLLARS AS A SPECIALTY

Many collectors over the years have pursued half dollars by date, mint, and variety. Except for the series of copper cents, half dollars are the most generally available coins over a nearly continuous span, making them possible to collect for reasonable cost. Also, enough die varieties exist that this can form another focus of interest and importance.

In general, the half dollars of the early era form a concentration in themselves. Die varieties can be attributed by Overton numbers, as listed by Al C. Overton in his immensely popular *Early Half Dollar Die Varieties 1794–1836*. Glenn R. Peterson's book, *The Ultimate Guide to Attributing Bust Half Dollars*, is also useful in this regard. The John Reich Collectors Society (www.jrcs.org) publishes the *John Reich Journal* and serves as a forum for the exchange of information, updates, news about die varieties, and the like.

Among rarities in the early years, the 1796 and 1797 half dollars with the Draped Bust obverse and Small Eagle reverse are perhaps the most famous, needed for variety collections as well as one example for a type set. Variety enthusiasts aspire to get two of 1796—one with 15 stars on the obverse and the other with 16 stars—plus the 1797.

Draped Bust half dollars from 1801 through 1807 have a number of rare die varieties (as listed by Overton), but the basic varieties are easy enough to find. The 1805, 5 Over 4, overdate is particularly popular, as there was no "perfect date" 1804, and this is the closest collectors can come to it.

A vast and interesting field in early American numismatics is that of the Capped Bust half dollar, 1807–1836, with a lettered edge. Several hundred different die combinations exist, and many collectors are active in their pursuit, using the Overton book as a road map. All the major varieties are readily collectible except the 1817, 7 Over 4, overdate, of which only about a half dozen exist. The 1815, 5 Over 2, is considered the key issue among the specific dates (rather than varieties of dates). The majority of these survive in VF grade, not often lower and not often higher either—an interesting situation. During the 1820s vast quantities of these were transferred among banks, not wearing down from as much hand-to-hand circulation as they might have otherwise. While many if not most of the varieties listed herein can be obtained in Mint State, most collectors opt for VF or EF, these grades showing the necessary details but also permitting a budget to be stretched to include more varieties, rather than just a few high-grade pieces. Choice and gem examples can be found here and there, and are most plentiful among the later dates.

Among the Capped Bust half dollars of reduced size, 1836–1837, the 1836 is a key date, with fewer than 5,000 believed to have been minted. The next type, 1838 and 1839, Capped Bust, reeded edge, with a modified eagle on the reverse, includes the famous 1838-O rarity, of which only 20 are said to have been struck (per a note published in 1894 in the catalog of the Friesner Collection). These have a prooflike surface. Interestingly, they were not struck until 1839. In the same year, 1839-O half dollars were also struck, to the extensive quantity of 178,976 pieces; they are unusual as the mintmark is on the obverse, an odd placement for the era.

Within the series of Liberty Seated half dollars, collectors generally seek the varieties listed herein, although certain dedicated specialists will consult the *Complete Guide to Liberty Seated Half Dollars*, by Randy Wiley and Bill Bugert—a volume that delineates many interesting features, including the number of different reeds on the edges of certain coins.

Among Liberty Seated half dollars there is just one "impossible" rarity, that being the 1853-O coin without arrows at the date. Only three exist, and each shows extensive wear. At the San Francisco Mint, half dollars were first struck in 1855, and at the Carson City Mint in 1870. Generally, large quantities were minted of most dates and mintmark varieties of Liberty Seated half dollars, making them readily obtainable today. Except for the later dates, 1879 to 1891, Mint State pieces are generally scarce, gems especially so. Many specialists in half dollars belong to the Liberty Seated Collectors Club (LSCC, at www.lsccweb.org) and receive its magazine, *The Gobrecht Journal*.

Proof Liberty Seated halves can be collected by date sequence from 1858 onward. Survivors exist in proportion to their mintage quantities. Generally those before the mid-1870s often are found cleaned or hairlined, and more care is needed in selecting choice examples than is necessary for the later dates.

Barber half dollars were made continuously from 1892 through 1915, in such quantities that today there are no great rarities in the series. However, a number of issues are quite scarce, even in well-worn grades, and in MS-63 and better many are difficult to find. These coins had little honor in the era in which they were issued, and few numismatists saved them. Proofs were made each year from 1892 to 1915 and today can be obtained in proportion to their mintages. However, those of 1914 and 1915 are hard to find with choice, original surfaces—decades ago a collector hoarded these two dates and polished the ones in his possession.

Liberty Walking half dollars are popular to collect by date and mint. Scarce varieties include the 1917-S with obverse mintmark, the three issues of 1921, and the low mintage 1938-D, although the latter is not inordinately expensive. Mint State pieces are most readily available for 1916 and 1917, and then especially so in the 1930s and 1940s. Striking quality can be a problem, particularly for issues of the mid-1920s and also the later dates. For example, with a needle-sharp strike the 1923-S is an extreme rarity. Among later coins the 1940-S and 1941-S often are weakly struck.

Franklin half dollars minted from 1948 through 1963 have been very popular in recent decades. The complete series of dates and mintmarks is short and contains no scarce or rare pieces in higher grades such as MS–63 and 64. However, if you consider the element of sharp striking, usually defined as Full Bell Lines (FBL) on the reverse, certain otherwise common dates become elusive. Proofs of most years can also be readily collected.

Kennedy half dollars are easily enough collected, and so many have been made by this time that nearly 200 date-and-mintmark combinations extend from 1964 to present, including a gold version that marks the design's 50th anniversary. The wise collector will select coins that have a meeting point between a high grade such as MS–65 or 66 (or equivalent Proofs) and a reasonable price.

FLOWING HAIR (1794–1795)

Designer: *Robert Scot.* **Weight:** *13.48 grams.*
Composition: *.8924 silver, .1076 copper.* **Diameter:** *Approximately 32.5 mm.*
Edge: *FIFTY CENTS OR HALF A DOLLAR with decorations between the words.* **Mint:** *Philadelphia.*

Overton-104

History. The Flowing Hair design inaugurated the half-dollar denomination. They were immediately popular, as was evident in 1795, when many depositors of silver at the Philadelphia Mint asked for half dollars in return. The same motif was used on half dimes and silver dollars of the same years. Early half dollars have been extensively collected by die varieties, of which many exist for most dates. Valuations given below are in each case for the most readily available variety; scarcer ones, as listed by Overton, generally command higher prices.

Striking and Sharpness. Many have problems of one sort or another, including adjustment marks from the planchet being filed down to proper weight and mushy denticles. On the obverse, check the hair details and the stars. On the reverse, check the breast of the eagle in particular. As with other silver coins of this design, it may not be possible to find a *needle-sharp* example, but with some extensive searching a fairly decent strike can be obtained. Sharp striking and excellent eye appeal add to the value dramatically. However, very few 1794 and 1795 halves are uniformly sharp on both sides.

Availability. Probably 3,500 to 6,000 circulated Flowing Hair half dollars exist. Most are dated 1795, the 1794 being considered a rare date (though not among the great U.S. coin rarities). Typical grades are Good to Fine. EF and AU grades are elusive in regard to the total population. Probably 100 or so could be graded MS (nearly all of them 1795). Unlike half dollars of the 1796–1797 type, none of these are known to have been made with prooflike surfaces.

GRADING STANDARDS

MS-60 to 70 (Mint State). *Obverse:* At MS-60, some abrasion and contact marks are evident, most noticeably on the cheek and in the fields. This denomination, heavier than the half dime of the same design, was more susceptible to contact and other outside influences. A typical half dollar certified at MS–60 or 61 today might well have been designated as About Uncirculated a generation ago. Luster is present, but may be dull or lifeless, and

1795; Overton-110a. Graded MS-63.

interrupted in patches, perhaps as much from old cleaning as from contact the coin may have received. At MS-63, contact marks are very few, and abrasion is present, but not as noticeable. An MS-65 coin has no abrasion, and contact marks are very few. Luster should be full and rich. Higher grades are seldom seen in this type, but are defined in theory by having fewer marks as perfection is approached. ***Reverse:*** Comments apply as for the obverse, except that abrasion and contact marks are most noticeable on the eagle at the center. This area is often lightly struck, so in all grades do not mistake weak striking for actual wear. Knowledge of specific die varieties is helpful in this regard. The field area is small and is protected by lettering and the wreath, and in any given grade shows fewer marks than on the obverse.

Illustrated coin: This is a well-struck example with superb eye appeal.

AU-50, 53, 55, 58 (About Uncirculated).
Obverse: Light wear is seen on the hair area immediately to the left of the face and above the forehead, on the cheek, and, to a lesser extent, on the top of the neck truncation, more so at AU-50 than at AU-53 or 55. An AU-58 coin has minimal traces of wear. An AU-50 coin has luster in protected areas among the stars and letters, with little in the open fields or on the portrait. At AU-58,

1795; O-116. Graded AU-55.

much luster is present in the fields but is worn away on the highest parts of the motifs. ***Reverse:*** Light wear is seen on the eagle's body and the upper part of both wings. On well-struck pieces the details of the wing features are excellent. At AU-50, detail is lost in some feathers in this area. However, striking can play a part, as some coins were weakly struck to begin with. Light wear is seen on the wreath and lettering, but is harder to discern. Luster is the best key to actual wear. This will range from perhaps 20% remaining in protected areas (at AU-50) to nearly full mint bloom (at AU-58), although among certified coins the amounts of luster can vary widely.

Illustrated coin: Significant luster remains in protected areas on this attractive early half dollar.

EF-40, 45 (Extremely Fine). ***Obverse:*** More
wear is evident on the portrait, especially on the hair to the left of and above the forehead, and in the back below the LI of LIBERTY. The tip of the neck truncation shows flatness, and the cheek is worn. Excellent detail remains in low-relief areas of the hair. The stars show wear, as do the date and letters. Luster, if present at all, is minimal and in pro-tected areas. ***Reverse:*** The eagle shows more

1794; O-101. Graded EF-40.

wear on the body and on the tops of the wings. Interior wing detail is good on most coins (depending on the variety and the striking), and the tail feathers can be discerned. Additional wear is on the wreath and letters, but many details are present. Some luster may be seen in protected areas and if present is slightly more abundant than on the obverse.

Illustrated coin: Note some lightness of the stars at the right and at the reverse center, as struck. The scrape on the reverse below the ribbon knot was mentioned by the cataloger in an auction offering.

VF-20, 30 (Very Fine). *Obverse:* The hair is well worn at VF-20, less so at VF-30, and is most noticeable in the upper part of the head, the area above the level of the eye, and extending to the back. The strands are blended as to be heavy. The cheek shows only slight relief, and the tip of the neck truncation is flat. The stars have more wear, making them appear larger (an optical illusion). Scattered marks are common on half dollars at this level

1795; O-109. Graded VF-20.

and below, and should be mentioned if particularly serious. *Reverse:* The body of the eagle shows few if any feathers, while the wings have perhaps a quarter or a third of the feathers visible depending on the strike, with sharper strikes having up to half visible (as PCGS suggests). *Photograde* and the ANA grading standards suggest half of the feathers on all, which may be the case on coins that were well struck to begin with. The leaves lack detail and are in outline form. Scattered, non-disfiguring marks are normal for this and lower grades. Any major defects should be noted separately.

Illustrated coin: On this variety in this grade, the denticles are especially prominent on each side. Such aspects vary from coin to coin.

F-12, 15 (Fine). *Obverse:* Wear is more extensive than on the preceding, with less hair visible. The ear position can be seen, as can the eye. The cheek is nearly flat, and the stars appear larger. The rim is distinct and most denticles remain visible. *Reverse:* Wear is more extensive. Now, feather details are fewer, mostly remaining on the wing to the left. The wreath and lettering are more worn, and the rim is usually weak in areas, although most denticles can be seen.

1795; O-107. Graded F-12.

VG-8, 10 (Very Good). *Obverse:* The portrait is mostly seen in outline form, with most hair strands gone save for an area centered behind the neck. The hair tips at the lower left are clear. The eye location is barely discernible. The stars appear larger still and often quite bold, again an illusion. The rim is weak in areas. LIBERTY and the date are readable and usually full, although some letters may be weak at their tops. *Reverse:* The

1795; O-109. Graded VG-8.

eagle is mostly an outline, although traces of the separation between the body and the right wing can sometimes be seen. The rim is worn, as are the letters, with some weak, but the motto is readable. On many coins the rim remains fairly prominent.

Illustrated coin: Note a spot, a tiny edge bruise, and some adjustment marks. A cataloger mentioned that "the top of the obverse is slightly soft due to axial misalignment"—a technical note. On any half dollar of this era, knowledge of the varieties and peculiarities of striking is useful.

G-4, 6 (Good). *Obverse:* Wear is more extensive, and some stars may be missing or only partially visible. The head is an outline, although a few elements of thick hair strands may be seen. The rim is well worn or even missing. LIBERTY is worn, and parts of some letters may be missing, but elements of all should be readable. The date is readable, but worn. *Reverse:* The eagle is flat and discernible in outline form. The wreath is well

1794; O-106. Graded G-6.

worn. Some of the letters may be partly missing. At this level some "averaging" can be done. If the letters are stronger than usual in one area, but some are missing in another area, the coin can still qualify as G-4. Often on this type in lower grades the reverse is more detailed than the obverse.

AG-3 (About Good). *Obverse:* Wear is very extensive. The head is in outline form (perhaps partly blended into the field). LIBERTY is mostly gone. The date, while readable, may be partially worn away. Some stars are missing. *Reverse:* The reverse is well worn, with parts of the wreath and lettering very weak or even missing. The details that remain and those that do not is often dependent on the particular die variety.

1795; O-116. Graded AG-3.

| 1795, Normal Date | 1795, Recut Date | 1795, Two Leaves Under Each Wing | 1795, Three Leaves Under Each Wing |

	Mintage	Cert	Avg	%MS	AG-3	G-4	VG-8	F-12	VF-20	EF-40	AU-50	AU-55	MS-60
1794	23,464	342	21.7	2%	$2,500	$4,500	$7,000	$12,000	$23,000	$40,000	$65,000	$105,000	$225,000
Auctions: $152,750, MS-61, June 2014; $19,975, VF-30, March 2016; $18,800, VF-30, August 2014; $12,925, VF-20, August 2014													
1795, All kinds (a)	299,680												
1795, Normal Date		1,203	23.3	4%	$650	$1,100	$1,500	$2,750	$3,900	$11,000	$17,500	$21,000	$45,000
Auctions: $129,250, MS-62, November 2013; $1,998, F-12, March 2015; $881, G-6, September 2015; $705, AG-3, June 2015													
1795, Recut Date		29	22.9	0%	$650	$1,150	$1,550	$2,750	$4,250	$11,000	$20,500	$25,000	$45,000
Auctions: $1,651, F-12, March 2014; $1,645, VG-8, September 2014													
1795, 3 Leaves Under Each Wing		16	24.4	0%	$1,100	$2,350	$3,250	$4,600	$8,500	$20,000	$40,000	$42,000	$65,000
Auctions: $8,519, VF, March 2014													

a. Varieties of 1795 are known with the final S in STATES over a D; with the A in STATES over an E; and with the Y in LIBERTY over a star. All are scarce. Some 1794 and 1795 half dollars were weight-adjusted by insertion of a silver plug in the center of the blank planchet before the coin was struck.

DRAPED BUST, SMALL EAGLE REVERSE (1796–1797)

Designer: *Robert Scot.* **Weight:** *13.48 grams.*
Composition: *.8924 silver, .1076 copper.* **Diameter:** *Approximately 32.5 mm.*
Edge: *FIFTY CENTS OR HALF A DOLLAR with decorations between words.* **Mint:** *Philadelphia.*

O-101a.

History. Robert Scot's Draped Bust design is similar to that used on the half dime, dime, quarter, and silver dollar of this era. In 1796 and 1797 there was little demand for half dollars and the combined mintage for the two years was therefore low. Among design types of U.S. silver coins made in circulation-strike format this is the Holy Grail—a classic rarity, with no common date in the series.

Striking and Sharpness. On the obverse, check the hair details and the stars. On the reverse, first check the breast of the eagle, but examine other areas as well. Also check the denticles on both sides. Look especially for coins that do not have significant adjustment marks (from an overweight planchet being filed down to correct specifications). Coins of this denomination are on average better struck than are half dimes, dimes, quarters (which have reverse problems), and dollars in the Draped Bust suite.

Availability. Examples are rare in any grade—survivors likely number only in the hundreds of coins. MS examples are particularly rare, and when seen are nearly always dated 1796. Some of these have partially prooflike surfaces. Any half dollar of this type has strong market demand.

Grading Standards

MS-60 to 70 (Mint State). *Obverse:* At MS-60, some abrasion and contact marks are evident, most noticeably on the cheek, the drapery at the shoulder, and the right field. Also check the hair to the left of the forehead. Luster is present, but may be dull or lifeless, and interrupted in patches. At MS-63, contact marks are few, and abrasion is hard to detect, although this type is sometimes graded liberally due to its rarity. An MS-65 coin has

1797; O-101a. Graded MS-66.

no abrasion, and contact marks are so minute as to require magnification. Luster should be full and rich. Coins graded above MS-65 are more theoretical than actual for this type, although some notable pieces have crossed the auction block. These are defined by having fewer marks as perfection is approached. *Reverse:* Comments apply as for the obverse, except that abrasion and contact marks are most noticeable on the eagle at the center, a situation that should be evaluated by considering the original striking (which can be quite sharp, but with many exceptions). The field area is small and is protected by lettering and the wreath, and in any given grade shows fewer marks than on the obverse.

Illustrated coin: This superb gem has prooflike surfaces.

AU-50, 53, 55, 58 (About Uncirculated). *Obverse:* Light wear is seen on the hair area above the ear and extending to the left of the forehead, on the ribbon, and on the drapery at the shoulder, more so at AU-50 than at AU–53 or 55. An AU-58 coin has minimal traces of wear. An AU-50 coin has luster in protected areas among the stars and letters, with little in the open fields or on the portrait. At AU-58, most luster is present in the fields, but is worn

1797; O-101a. Graded AU-50.

away on the highest parts of the motifs. *Reverse:* Light wear is seen on the eagle's body and the edges of the wings. Light wear is seen on the wreath and lettering. Luster is the best key to actual wear. This ranges from perhaps 20% remaining in protected areas (at AU-50) to nearly full mint bloom (at AU-58).

EF-40, 45 (Extremely Fine). *Obverse:* More wear is evident on the upper hair area, particularly to the left of the forehead and also below the LI of LIBERTY, in the ribbon, and on the drapery and bosom. Excellent detail remains in low-relief areas of the hair. The stars show wear as do the date and letters. Luster, if present at all, is minimal and in protected areas. *Reverse:* The eagle shows more wear, this being the focal point to

1796, 15 Stars; O-101. Graded EF-40.

check. Many feathers remain on the interior areas of the wings. Additional wear is on the wreath and letters, but many details are present. Some luster may be seen in protected areas and if present is slightly more abundant than on the obverse.

VF-20, 30 (Very Fine). *Obverse:* The higher-relief areas of hair are well worn at VF-20, less so at VF-30. The drapery and bosom show extensive wear. The stars have more wear. *Reverse:* The body of the eagle shows few if any feathers, while the wings have about half or more of the feathers visible, depending on the strike. The leaves lack most detail and are outlined. Scattered, non-disfiguring marks are normal for this and lower grades; major defects should be noted separately.

1796, 16 Stars; O-103. Graded VF-20.

F-12, 15 (Fine). *Obverse:* Wear is more extensive than on a Very Fine coin, particularly noticeable on the hair, face, and bosom. The stars appear larger (an optical illusion). About half the hair detail remains, most noticeably behind the neck and shoulder. The rim may be partially worn away and blend into the field, but on many coins it remains intact. *Reverse:* Wear is more extensive. Now, feather details are diminished,

1797; O-101a. Graded F-15.

with fewer than half remaining on the wings. The wreath and lettering are worn further, and the rim is usually weak in areas, but most denticles can be seen.

VG-8, 10 (Very Good). *Obverse:* The portrait is mostly seen in outline form, with most hair strands gone, although there is some definition at the back of the hair and behind the shoulder. The ear is barely discernible and the eye is fairly distinct. The stars appear larger still, again an illusion. The rim is weak in areas, but shows most denticles. LIBERTY and the date are readable and usually full, although some letters may be weak at their

1796, 16 Stars; O-102. Graded VG-10.

tops. *Reverse:* The eagle is mostly an outline, with parts blending into the field (on lighter strikes). The rim is worn, as are the letters, with some weak, but the motto is readable.

G-4, 6 (Good). *Obverse:* Wear is more extensive, and some stars may be partly missing. The head is an outline. The eye is visible only in outline form. The rim is well worn or even missing in areas, but many denticles remain. LIBERTY is worn. The letters and date are weak but fully readable. *Reverse:* The eagle is flat and discernible in outline form, and may be blending into the field. The wreath is well worn. Some of the letters may

1797. Graded G-4.

be partly missing. At this level some "averaging" can be done. If the letters are stronger than usual in one area, but some are missing in another area, the coin can still qualify as G-4.

AG-3 (About Good). *Obverse:* Wear is so extensive that the coin is barely identifiable. The head is in outline form. LIBERTY is mostly gone; same for the stars. The date, while readable, may be partially worn away. *Reverse:* The reverse is well worn, with parts of the wreath and lettering missing. On most coins the reverse shows more wear than the obverse.

1797. Graded AG-3.

1796, 15 Stars

1796, 16 Stars

	Mintage	Cert	Avg	%MS	AG-3	G-4	VG-8	F-12	VF-20	EF-40	AU-50	AU-58	MS-60
1796, 15 Stars †	(a)	20	40.6	35%	$23,000	$35,000	$43,500	$52,000	$75,000	$125,000	$165,000	$235,000	$290,000
Auctions: No auction records available.													
1796, 16 Stars †	(a)	14	34.2	29%	$23,000	$36,500	$45,000	$56,000	$71,000	$125,000	$170,000	$250,000	$300,000
Auctions: $470,000, MS-63, November 2013													
1797, 15 Stars †	3,918	56	27.2	5%	$23,000	$37,500	$47,500	$57,500	$75,000	$125,000	$165,000	$225,000	$300,000
Auctions: $17,625, MS-64, August 2015; $8,225, AU-53, November 2015; $4,406, EF-40, August 2015; $329, VF-20, September 2016													

† All Draped Bust, Small Eagle Reverse Half Dollars are ranked in the *100 Greatest U.S. Coins* (fourth edition). **a.** Included in 1797, 15 Stars, mintage figure.

DRAPED BUST, HERALDIC EAGLE REVERSE (1801–1807)

Designer: *Robert Scot.* **Weight:** *13.48 grams.*
Composition: *.8924 silver, .1076 copper.* **Diameter:** *Approximately 32.5 mm.*
Edge: *FIFTY CENTS OR HALF A DOLLAR with decorations between words.* **Mint:** *Philadelphia.*

O-101.

History. The half dollar's Draped Bust, Heraldic Eagle design is similar to that of other silver coins of the era. While dies were prepared for the 1804 half dollar, none were minted in that year, despite Mint reports that state otherwise.

hair details and, in particular, the star centers. On the reverse, check the stars above the eagle, the clouds, the details of the shield, and the eagle's wings. Check the denticles on both sides. Adjustment marks are sometimes seen, from overweight planchets being filed down to correct weight, but not as often as on earlier half dollar types. Typically, the earlier years are better struck; many of 1806 and nearly all of 1807 are poorly struck. Sharp striking and excellent eye appeal add to the value dramatically, this being particularly true for those of 1805 to 1807, which are often weak (particularly 1807).

Availability. Earlier years are scarce in the marketplace, beginning with the elusive 1801 and including the 1802, after which they are more readily available. Some die varieties are scarce. Most MS coins are dated 1806 and 1807, but all are scarce. Finding sharply struck high-grade coins is almost impossible, a goal more than a reality.

GRADING STANDARDS

MS-60 to 70 (Mint State). *Obverse:* At MS-60, some abrasion and contact marks are evident, most noticeably on the cheek, the drapery at the shoulder, and the right field. Luster is present, but may be dull or lifeless, and interrupted in patches. At MS-63, contact marks are very few, and abrasion is hard to detect except under magnification. An MS-65 coin has no abrasion, and contact marks are so minute as to require magnification.

1803, Large 3; O-101. Graded MS-63.

Luster should be full and rich. Coins grading above MS-65 are more theoretical than actual for this type—but they do exist, and are defined by having fewer marks as perfection is approached. Later years usually have areas of flat striking. *Reverse:* Comments apply as for the obverse, except that abrasion and contact marks are most noticeable on the eagle's neck, the tips of the wing, and the tail. The field area is complex, without much open space, given the stars above the eagle, the arrows and olive branch, and other features. Accordingly, marks are not as noticeable as on the obverse.

Illustrated coin: This is an extraordinary strike with superb eye appeal. A connoisseur might prefer this coin to an MS-65 example with flat striking.

AU-50, 53, 55, 58 (About Uncirculated). *Obverse:* Light wear is seen on the hair area above the ear and extending to left of the forehead, on the ribbon, and on the bosom, more so at AU-50 than at AU–53 or 55. An AU-58 coin has minimal traces of wear. An AU-50 coin has luster in protected areas among the stars and letters, with little in the open fields or on the portrait. At AU-58, most luster is present in the fields, but is worn

1806, Pointed 6, No Stem; O-109. Graded AU-50.

away on the highest parts of the motifs. *Reverse:* Comments as preceding, except that the eagle's neck, the tips and top of the wings, the clouds, and the tail now show noticeable wear, as do other features. Luster ranges from perhaps 20% remaining in protected areas (at AU-50) to nearly full mint bloom (at AU-58). Often the reverse of this type retains much more luster than the obverse.

Illustrated coin: This example has gray and lilac toning.

EF-40, 45 (Extremely Fine). *Obverse:* More wear is evident on the upper hair area and the ribbon, and on the drapery and bosom. Excellent detail remains in low-relief areas of the hair. The stars show wear, as do the date and letters. Luster, if present at all, is minimal and in protected areas. *Reverse:* Wear is greater than on an About Uncirculated coin, overall. The neck lacks feather detail on its highest points. Feathers have lost some detail

1807; O-105. Graded EF-40.

near the edges of the wings, and some areas of the horizontal lines in the shield may be blended together. Some traces of luster may be seen, more so at EF-45 than at EF-40.

Illustrated coin: Light striking at the obverse center is normal for this die variety.

VF-20, 30 (Very Fine). *Obverse:* The higher-relief areas of hair are well worn at VF-20, less so at VF-30. The drapery on the shoulder and the bosom show extensive wear. The stars have more wear, making them appear larger (an optical illusion seen on most worn silver coins of this era). *Reverse:* Wear is greater, including on the shield and wing feathers. Half to two-thirds of the feathers are visible. Star centers are flat. Other areas have lost detail as well.

1806, 6 Over Inverted 9; O-111a. Graded VF-30.

Illustrated coin: Note the cud break on the reverse rim over the E in UNITED.

F-12, 15 (Fine). *Obverse:* Wear is more extensive than on a Very Fine coin, particularly noticeable on the hair, face, and bosom. The stars appear larger. About half the hair detail remains, most noticeably behind the neck and shoulder, but the fine hair is now combined into thicker tresses. The rim may be partially worn away and blend into the field. *Reverse:* Wear is even more extensive, with the shield and wing feathers being

1805; O-109. Graded F-15.

points to observe. The incuse E PLURIBUS UNUM may have half or more of the letters worn away (depending on striking). The clouds all appear connected. The stars are weak. Parts of the border and lettering may be weak.

VG-8, 10 (Very Good). *Obverse:* The portrait is mostly seen in outline form, with most hair strands gone, although there is some definition at the back of the hair and behind the shoulder. The ear is discernible as is the eye. The stars appear larger still, again an illusion. The rim is weak in areas. LIBERTY and the date are readable and usually full, although some letters may be weak at their tops. *Reverse:* Wear is more extensive. Half

1805, 5 Over 4; O-103. Graded VG-8.

or more of the letters in the motto are worn away. Most feathers are worn away, although separation of some of the lower feathers may be seen. Some stars are faint (depending on the strike). The border blends into the field in areas and some letters are weak.

G-4, 6 (Good). *Obverse:* Wear is more extensive, and some stars may be partly missing. The head is mostly an outline, although some hair strand outlines may be visible on some strikings. The rim is well worn or even missing in areas. LIBERTY is worn, and parts of some letters may be missing, but elements should be readable. The date is readable, but worn. *Reverse:* Wear is more extensive. The upper part of the eagle is flat. Feathers are

1805; O-111. Graded G-4.

noticeable only at the lower edge of the wings, and do not have detail. The upper part of the shield is flat or mostly so (depending on the strike). Only a few letters of the motto can be seen. The rim is worn extensively, and a few letters may be missing.

AG-3 (About Good). *Obverse:* Wear is so extensive that the coin is barely identifiable. The head is in outline form. LIBERTY is mostly gone; same for the stars. The date, while readable, may be partially worn away. *Reverse:* Extensive wear is seen overall, with the rim worn away and some areas worn smooth. The eagle can be discerned in outline form, but not necessarily completely. A few stray motto letters may remain.

1801. Graded AG-3.

	Mintage	Cert	Avg	%MS	G-4	VG-8	F-12	VF-20	EF-40	AU-50	AU-55	MS-60	MS-63
1801	30,289	149	27.1	1%	$875	$1,350	$2,400	$3,500	$6,000	$15,000	$25,000	$75,000	$160,000
	Auctions: $329,000, MS-64, November 2013; $4,700, EF-40, March 2015; $576, G-4, October 2014; $517, AG-3, July 2015												
1802	29,890	103	31.0	0%	$1,000	$1,500	$2,650	$3,500	$7,500	$17,000	$26,500	$60,000	
	Auctions: $70,500, AU-58, August 2013; $3,173, VF-20, August 2014; $2,115, F-15, August 2014												

1803, Small 3

1803, Large 3

1805, 5 Over 4

1805, Normal Date

1806, 6 Over 5

1806, 6 Over Inverted 6

1806, Stem Not Through Claw

1806, Stem Through Claw

1806, Knobbed-Top 6, Large Stars
With traces of overdate.

1806, Knobbed-Top 6, Small Stars

	Mintage	Cert	Avg	%MS	G-4	VG-8	F-12	VF-20	EF-40	AU-50	AU-55	MS-60	MS-63
1803, All kinds	188,234												
1803, Small 3		43	37.2	2%	$350	$475	$650	$1,000	$2,750	$5,500	$9,500	$25,000	$115,000
Auctions: $49,938, MS-62, June 2014													
1803, Large 3		125	32.1	4%	$275	$425	$500	$900	$2,000	$5,000	$7,000	$22,500	$65,000
Auctions: $1,763, EF-40, March 2015; $881, VF-30, June 2015; $752, VF-25, March 2015; $552, VF-20, March 2015													
1805, All kinds	211,722												
1805, 5 Over 4		118	33.2	2%	$400	$800	$1,000	$1,650	$3,500	$7,500	$12,750	$35,000	$85,000
Auctions: $3,055, EF-40, March 2016; $2,233, VF-30, August 2015; $999, F-12, June 2015; $9,106, VG-8, March 2015													
1805, Normal Date		418	32.4	2%	$260	$350	$475	$850	$2,250	$5,000	$6,500	$22,500	$35,000
Auctions: $4,406, AU-50, March 2015; $2,350, EF-45, May 2015; $1,528, VF-25, September 2015; $617, F-15, August 2015													
1806, All kinds	839,576												
1806, 6 Over 5		210	32.6	3%	$300	$400	$600	$900	$2,350	$5,000	$6,500	$13,500	$45,000
Auctions: $21,150, MS-61, November 2013; $881, VF-30, September 2014; $794, VF-25, January 2015; $764, VF-20, July 2014													
1806, 6 Over Inverted 6		74	26.4	1%	$350	$500	$925	$1,500	$3,500	$8,500	$12,500	$27,500	$50,000
Auctions: $28,200, MS-61, November 2013; $999, F-12, September 2014; $940, F-12, August 2014; $999, Fair-2, August 2014													
1806, Knobbed 6, Large Stars (Traces of Overdate)		37	29.5	0%	$225	$275	$400	$700	$2,000	$5,000	$7,000		
Auctions: $2,364, EF-40, August 2013													
1806, Knobbed 6, Small Stars		41	30.7	0%	$250	$325	$500	$700	$2,000	$5,000	$7,000	$12,000	$35,000
Auctions: $2,350, EF-45, January 2014; $435, F-15, July 2014													
1806, Knobbed 6, Stem Not Through Claw		1	25.0	0%	$65,000	$80,000	$85,000	$95,000	$125,000				
Auctions: $126,500, EF-40, January 2009													
1806, Pointed 6, Stem Through Claw		285	32.8	6%	$225	$275	$400	$700	$1,750	$4,500	$5,750	$9,500	$20,000
Auctions: $35,250, MS-64, November 2013; $7,638, AU-53, August 2014; $447, F-12, October 2015; $327, VG-10, February 2015													
1806, Pointed 6, Stem Through Claw, E Over A in STATES		8	21.3	0%	$400	$900	$1,600	$3,200	$7,500	$20,000			
Auctions: $4,465, VF-20, January 2015; $2,280, VG-8, February 2018													
1806, Pointed 6, Stem Not Through Claw		113	36.1	6%	$225	$275	$400	$700	$2,000	$4,500	$5,750	$9,500	$20,000
Auctions: $12,925, MS-62, November 2013; $3,840, AU-55, August 2014; $1,293, EF-40, January 2015; $881, VF-30, July 2015													
1807	301,076	1,154	33.5	7%	$225	$275	$400	$700	$1,850	$4,750	$5,500	$9,500	$20,000
Auctions: $1,528, EF-40, March 2015; $588, VF-20, February 2015; $400, F-12, August 2015; $306, VG-10, May 2015													

CAPPED BUST, LETTERED EDGE (1807–1836)

Designer: *John Reich.* **Weight:** *13.48 grams.*
Composition: *.8924 silver, .1076 copper.* **Diameter:** *Approximately 32.5 mm.*
Edge: *1807–1814—FIFTY CENTS OR HALF A DOLLAR;*
1814–1831—star added between DOLLAR and FIFTY;
1832–1836—vertical lines added between words. **Mint:** *Philadelphia.*

First Style (1807–1808)
O-104.

Remodeled Portrait and Eagle
(1809–1836)
O-109.

Remodeled Portrait and Eagle, Proof
O-103.

History. The Capped Bust design was created by Mint assistant engraver John Reich; the motif was widely used, in several variations, on much of the era's coinage. Reich was the first artist to consistently include the denomination in his designs for U.S. gold and silver coins. The half dollar, minted continuously from 1807 to 1836, except 1816, was the largest silver coin of the realm at the time (silver dollars had not been struck since 1804).

Striking and Sharpness. On the obverse, check the hair and broach details. The stars are often flatly struck on Capped Bust half dollars, much more so than on other denominations. On the reverse, check the motto band and the eagle's head, and the wing to the left, as well as other areas (the neck feathers, often lightly struck on other denominations of Capped Bust silver, are usually fairly sharp on half dollars). The E PLURIBUS UNUM band is often weak in the area left of its center; this does not normally occur on other Capped Bust silver coins. Inspect the denticles on both sides. Generally, later dates are better struck than are earlier ones. Many half dollars have semi-prooflike surfaces, or patches of mirror-like character interspersed with luster. Others can have nearly full prooflike surfaces, with patches of luster being in the minority (and often in the left obverse field); some of these have been mischaracterized as "Proofs." Some issues from the early 1830s have little digs or "bite marks" on the portrait, possibly from some sort of a gadget used to eject them from the press. Unlike the Capped Bust half dime, dime, and quarter dollar, the half dollar is particularly subject to very wide variations in striking quality.

True Proofs have deeply mirrored surfaces. Impostors are often seen, with deeply toned surfaces or with patches of mint luster. This situation is more prevalent with half dollars than with any other Capped Bust denomination. Proceed slowly, and be careful. There are some crushed-lettered-edge ("CLE")

Proofs of the 1833 to 1835 era that are especially beautiful and are more deeply mirrorlike than original issues. Some of these are restrikes (not necessarily an important consideration, but worth mentioning), believed to have been made at the Mint beginning in the spring of 1859.

Availability. Examples of most dates and overdates are easily found in just about any grade desired, from Fine and VF to MS. (As the largest silver coin struck between 1803 and 1836, these half dollars spent much of their time in bags, transferred from bank to bank, rather than wearing down in circulation.) The later years are the most readily available and are also seen in higher average grades. Many die varieties range from scarce to rare. Proofs were made in limited numbers for presentation purposes and for distribution to numismatists.

GRADING STANDARDS

MS-60 to 70 (Mint State). *Obverse:* At MS-60, some abrasion and contact marks are evident, most noticeably on the cheek, the hair below the left part of LIBERTY, the cap, and the front part of the bosom and drapery. These areas also coincide with the highest parts of the coin and are thus susceptible to lightness of strike. Complicating matters is that when an area is lightly struck, and the planchet is not forced into the deepest parts

1827, Square Base 2; O-104. Graded MS-60.

of the die, the *original planchet surface* (which may exhibit scuffing and nicks) is visible. A lightly struck coin can have virtually perfect luster in the fields, deep and rich, and yet appear to be "worn" on the higher parts, due to the lightness of strike. This is a very sophisticated concept and is hard to quantify. In practice, the original planchet surface will usually be considered as wear on the finished coin, which of course is not true. Such grades as high About Uncirculated and low Mint State levels are often assigned to pieces that, if well struck, would be MS–64 and 65. As a matter of practicality, but not of logic, you will need to do the same. If a coin has original planchet abrasions, but otherwise is a Gem, those abrasions must be taken into consideration. Apart from this, on well-struck coins in lower Mint State grades, luster is present, but may be dull or lifeless, and interrupted in patches. At MS-63, on a well-struck coin, contact marks are very few, and abrasion is hard to detect except under magnification. A well-struck MS-65 coin has no abrasion, and contact marks are so minute as to require magnification. Luster should be full and rich. Grades above MS-65 are seen now and again and are defined by having fewer marks as perfection is approached. *Reverse:* Comments apply as for the obverse, except that nearly all coins with weak striking on the obverse (so as to reveal original planchet surface) do not show such original surface on the reverse, except perhaps on the motto ribbon. Accordingly, market grading is usually by the obverse only, even if the reverse seems to be in much better preservation. On well-struck coins, abrasion and contact marks are most noticeable on the eagle's head, the top of the wings, the claws, and the flat band that surrounds the incuse motto. The field is mainly protected by design elements and does not show abrasion as much as does the obverse on a given coin.

 Illustrated coin: This is an exceptional coin at the low Mint State level.

AU-50, 53, 55, 58 (About Uncirculated).
Obverse: Light wear is seen on the cheek, the hair below the left part of LIBERTY, the cap, and the front part of the bosom and drapery. Some of this apparent "wear" may be related to the original planchet surface (as noted under Mint State, above), but at the About Uncirculated level the distinction is less important. On a well-struck coin, at AU-58 the luster is extensive except in the open area of the field, espe-

1820, Curl Base 2, Small Date; O-103. Graded AU-55.

cially to the right. At AU–50 and 53, luster remains only in protected areas. *Reverse:* Wear is evident on the eagle's head, the top of the wings, the claws, and the flat band above the eagle. An AU-58 coin has nearly full luster. At AU–50 and 53, there still is significant luster, more than on the obverse.

Illustrated coin: An attractive coin by any measure, this has light toning and ample areas of original luster.

EF-40, 45 (Extremely Fine). *Obverse:* Wear is more extensive, most noticeably on the higher areas of the hair. The cap shows more wear, as does the cheek. Luster, if present, is in protected areas among the star points and close to the portrait. *Reverse:* The wings show wear on the higher areas of the feathers, and some details are lost. The top of the head and the beak are flat. The eagle's claws and the leaves show wear. Luster may be present

1810; O-110. Graded EF-45.

in protected areas, even if there is little or none on the obverse.

Illustrated coin: This coin probably was lightly cleaned years ago so as to give a light silver color, which added some hairlines, but now it has halo toning around the borders that adds attractiveness.

VF-20, 30 (Very Fine). *Obverse:* Wear is more extensive, and most of the hair is combined into thick tresses without delicate features. The curl on the neck is flat. The cap shows significant wear at its top, and the left part of the drapery and bosom is nearly flat. Stars are flat at their centers (even if sharply struck to begin with). *Reverse:* Wear is most evident on the eagle's head, the tops of the wings, and the leaves and claws. Nearly all feathers in the wing remain distinct.

1815, 5 Over 2; O-101. Graded VF-30.

Illustrated coin: The areas of wear appear exaggerated due to the light toning, a feature often observed on half dollars of this date but not as often among other years.

F-12, 15 (Fine). *Obverse:* Wear is more extensive, with much of the hair blended together. The drapery is indistinct on most of its upper edge. The stars are flat at their centers. LIBERTY remains bold. *Reverse:* Wear is more extensive, now with only about half of the feathers remaining on the wings, more on the right wing. The head shows the eye, nostril, and beak but no details. The claws show more wear. Other features are worn as well, but not as noticeable as the key points mentioned.

1827, Square Base 2; O-122. Graded F-12.

VG-8, 10 (Very Good). *Obverse:* The hair is less distinct, with the forehead blended into the hair above. LIBERTY is complete, but may be slightly weak in areas. The stars are flat. The rim is distinct, with most if not all denticles visible. *Reverse:* Feathers are fewer and mostly on the right wing, although sharp strikes can show detail in both wings. Other details are weaker. All lettering remains easily readable.

1831; O-120. Graded VG-8.

Illustrated coin: This coin was cleaned and partially retoned. It is sharply struck on the reverse.

G-4, 6 (Good). *Obverse:* The portrait is mostly in outline, with few interior details discernible. LIBERTY may still be readable or may be partially worn away, depending on the variety. The rim is weak, but distinct in most areas. *Reverse:* The eagle is mostly in outline form, although some feathers can be seen in the right wing. All letters around the border are clear. E PLURIBUS UNUM may be weak. Overall, a typical coin has the reverse in a slightly higher grade than the obverse.

1808. Graded G-4.

AG-3 (About Good). *Obverse:* The portrait is an outline, although some of LIBERTY can still be seen. The rim is worn down, and some stars are blended into it. The date remains clear, but is weak at the bottom (on most but not all). *Reverse:* At this level the reverse shows more wear overall than the obverse, with the rim indistinct in areas and many letters worn away. This is an interesting turnabout from the situation of most G-4 coins.

1824. Graded AG-3.

PF-60 to 70 (Proof). *Obverse and Reverse:* Proofs of this type have confused experts for a long time (as have large copper cents of the same era). Proofs that were extensively cleaned and therefore have many hairlines, or that are dull and grainy, are lower level, such as PF–60 to 62. While any early Proof half dollar will generate interest among collectors, lower levels are not of great interest to specialists unless they are of rare die varieties. With medium

1836; O-108. Graded PF-64 Cameo.

hairlines, an assigned grade of PF-64 may be in order and with relatively few, Gem PF-65. PF-66 should have hairlines so delicate that magnification is needed to see them. Above that, a Proof should be free of such lines. Grading is highly subjective with early Proofs, with eye appeal being a major factor.

1807, Small Stars   **1807, Large Stars**

1807, Large Stars,   **1807, "Bearded" Liberty**   **1808, 8 Over 7**
50 Over 20

	Mintage	Cert	Avg	%MS	G-4	F-12	VF-20	EF-40	AU-50	AU-55	MS-60	MS-63	MS-65
											PF-63	PF-64	PF-65
1807, All kinds	750,500												
1807, Small Stars		37	34.0	5%	$225	$650	$1,000	$2,400	$5,500	$6,500	$20,000	$35,000	$75,000
	Auctions: $28,200, MS-61, January 2014; $999, EF-40, August 2014; $1,058, VF-30, March 2016; $823, VF-25, January 2015												
1807, Large Stars		37	38.5	8%	$175	$500	$750	$2,000	$3,500	$6,000	$15,000	$32,500	$150,000
	Auctions: $152,750, MS-65, November 2013; $646, VF-25, September 2016; $1,080, VF-35, March 2018												
1807, Large Stars, 50 Over 20		146	39.3	6%	$185	$450	$700	$1,400	$2,700	$3,750	$5,750	$11,000	$125,000
	Auctions: $1,293, EF-45, January 2015; $940, VF-35, February 2015; $764, VF-35, January 2015; $282, VG-10, February 2015												
1807, "Bearded" Liberty (a)		38	30.6	0%	$700	$2,000	$3,500	$6,500	$12,500	$20,000			
	Auctions: $5,405, EF-45, February 2015; $4,700, VF-30, March 2015												
1808, All kinds	1,368,600												
1808, 8 Over 7		202	41.3	10%	$100	$185	$350	$650	$1,500	$2,250	$4,500	$10,000	$25,000
	Auctions: $21,150, MS-65, November 2013; $676, EF-45, January 2015; $705, EF-40, July 2014; $388, VF-35, October 2014												
1808		606	41.1	14%	$75	$150	$250	$450	$1,150	$1,850	$3,250	$6,000	$19,000
	Auctions: $1,175, AU-50, August 2015; $705, EF-45, March 2015; $259, VF-20, April 2015; $212, F-15, March 2015; $660, EF-45, March 2018												

a. Also called the Bearded Goddess variety; a die crack gives the illusion of long whiskers growing from Miss Liberty's chin.

1809, xxxx Edge
Experimental edge has
"xxxx" between the words.

1809, | | | | | Edge
Experimental edge has
"| | | | |" between the words.

1811, (18.11), 11 Over 10
The date is "punctuated" with a period.

1811, Small 8

1811, Large 8

1812, 2 Over 1, Small 8

1812, 2 Over 1, Large 8

1812, Two Leaves
Below Wing

1812, Single Leaf
Below Wing

	Mintage	Cert	Avg	%MS	G-4	F-12	VF-20	EF-40	AU-50	AU-55	MS-60	MS-63	MS-65
											PF-63	PF-64	PF-65
1809, All kinds	1,405,810												
1809, Normal Edge		638	42.9	14%	$100	$175	$250	$500	$900	$1,500	$3,000	$8,500	$22,500
	Auctions: $764, AU-55, February 2015; $494, EF-40, April 2015; $353, VF-35, August 2015; $165, F-15, January 2015; $900, AU-50, April 2018												
1809, xxxx Edge		62	36.3	3%	$150	$250	$425	$1,100	$1,750	$4,000	$8,500	$15,000	
	Auctions: $1,645, AU-50, April 2014; $411, VF-25, July 2014												
1809, IIIII Edge		140	38.8	8%	$100	$150	$250	$650	$1,200	$2,500	$4,750	$12,500	$37,500
	Auctions: $38,188, MS-66, April 2014; $780, EF-40, January 2018												
1810	1,276,276	721	42.8	13%	$75	$135	$200	$400	$800	$1,400	$2,750	$6,500	$22,500
	Auctions: $646, AU-53, January 2015; $505, AU-50, June 2015; $447, EF-40, June 2015; $282, VF-35, October 2015; $1,200, AU-55, February 2018												
1811, All kinds	1,203,644												
1811, (18.11), 11 Over 10		128	41.8	10%	$100	$250	$400	$650	$1,400	$2,750	$5,500	$10,000	
	Auctions: $9,988, MS-63, February 2016; $6,463, AU-58, January 2014; $423, VF-35, August 2015; $494, VF-30, June 2015												
1811, Small 8		225	44.3	16%	$75	$135	$200	$385	$800	$1,200	$2,500	$4,000	$17,000
	Auctions: $999, AU-55, January 2015; $1,175, AU-53, February 2015; $494, VF-35, March 2015; $188, VF-20, June 2015												
1811, Large 8		63	46.2	3%	$75	$125	$170	$325	$800	$1,500	$3,000	$5,000	$17,250
	Auctions: $1,880, AU-58, January 2015; $329, EF-45, June 2015; $494, EF-40, October 2015; $282, VF-35, March 2015												
1812, All kinds	1,628,059												
1812, 2 Over 1, Small 8		124	43.0	18%	$115	$200	$300	$650	$1,200	$2,000	$3,500	$8,500	$25,000
	Auctions: $1,293, AU-55, July 2014; $306, VF-30, March 2015; $248, VF-25, October 2015; $182, F-15, October 2015; $1,320, AU-53, January 2018												
1812, 2 Over 1, Large 8		17	36.0	0%	$2,000	$5,500	$10,000	$13,000	$24,000	$30,000			
	Auctions: $14,100, AU-58, August 2013; $8,225, VF-30, August 2014												
1812		1024	46.7	25%	$75	$135	$175	$450	$750	$1,100	$2,200	$4,000	$15,000
	Auctions: $44,063, MS-65, November 2013; $441, AU-50, October 2014; $470, EF-45, August 2014; $324, EF-40, October 2014												
1812, Single Leaf Below Wing		2	31.5	0%	$750	$1,300	$2,400	$3,750	$7,000	$12,000	$17,000	$30,000	
	Auctions: No auction records available.; $31,200, AU-53, February 2018												

1813, 50 C. Over UNI.

1814, 4 Over 3

1814, E Over A in STATES

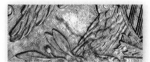

**1814, Two Leaves
Below Wing**

**1814, Single Leaf
Below Wing**

1815, 5 Over 2

1817, 7 Over 3

1817, 7 Over 4

1817, Dated 181.7
*The date is "punctuated"
with a period between
the second 1 and the 7.*

**1817, Two Leaves
Below Wing**

**1817, Single Leaf
Below Wing**

	Mintage	Cert	Avg	%MS	G-4	F-12	VF-20	EF-40	AU-50	AU-55	MS-60	MS-63	MS-65
											PF-63	PF-64	PF-65
1813, All kinds	1,241,903												
1813		676	45.0	17%	$75	$115	$160	$400	$750	$1,250	$2,500	$4,500	$16,000
	Auctions: $881, AU-53, September 2015; $423, EF-45, January 2015; $353, EF-40, May 2015; $212, VF-30, October 2015												
1813, 50 C. Over UNI		76	47.9	21%	$115	$250	$400	$800	$1,400	$2,100	$3,500	$6,000	
	Auctions: $24,675, MS-64, June 2014												
1814, All kinds	1,039,075												
1814, 4 Over 3		109	41.4	12%	$135	$250	$400	$800	$2,000	$2,650	$4,500	$8,500	$35,000
	Auctions: $1,175, EF-45, June 2015; $823, EF-40, September 2015; $353, VF-35, March 2015; $482, VF-25, February 2015												
1814, E Over A in STATES		36	39.0	6%	$135	$300	$500	$1,500	$3,500	$6,500	$8,500	$12,500	
	Auctions: $4,700, AU-55, January 2014; $505, VF-35, July 2014												
1814		609	47.5	23%	$85	$150	$225	$600	$800	$1,300	$2,250	$4,500	$14,000
	Auctions: $22,325, MS-65, November 2013; $3,290, MS-62, August 2014; $705, AU-50, October 2014; $382, EF-45, September 2014												
1814, Single Leaf Below Wing		25	34.3	0%	$85	$150	$225	$550	$1,750	$2,250	$3,200	$6,000	
	Auctions: $3,408, AU-50, August 2014; $705, EF-40, November 2013; $159, VF-20, October 2014												
1815, 5 Over 2	47,150	263	42.3	10%	$1,450	$3,250	$4,500	$5,500	$10,000	$13,000	$18,500	$50,000	
	Auctions: $117,500, MS-64, November 2013; $7,931, EF-45, August 2016; $5,581, EF-40, March 2015												
1817, All kinds	1,215,567												
1817, 7 Over 3		158	40.0	14%	$165	$450	$650	$1,250	$3,000	$4,750	$8,500	$14,500	$42,500
	Auctions: $28,200, MS-64, November 2013; $823, AU-50, January 2015; $541, F-15, October 2015; $499, F-15, July 2014												
1817, 7 Over 4 † (b)		1	35.0	0%	$67,500	$150,000	$200,000	$275,000	$375,000				
	Auctions: $184,000, VF-20, August 2010												
1817, Dated 181.7		32	44.1	9%	$100	$200	$300	$650	$1,750	$2,500	$3,500	$7,500	$22,000
	Auctions: $3,055, AU-58, August 2013; $529, VF-30, July 2014; $540, VF-35, March 2018												
1817		580	43.1	14%	$100	$145	$200	$400	$750	$1,100	$2,500	$4,000	$17,500
	Auctions: $508, AU-53, January 2015; $541, AU-50, June 2015; $325, EF-45, May 2015; $153, F-12, August 2015												
1817, Single Leaf Below Wing		13	38.6	8%	$100	$150	$200	$475	$1,000	$1,650	$2,750	$4,500	
	Auctions: $3,055, AU-55, April 2013												

† Ranked in the *100 Greatest U.S. Coins* (fourth edition). **b.** 8 examples are known.

| 1818, First 8 Small, Second 8 Over 7 | 1818, First 8 Large, Second 8 Over 7 | 1819, Small 9 Over 8 | 1819, Large 9 Over 8 |

| 1820, 20 Over 19, Square Base 2 | 1820, 20 Over 19, Curl Base 2 | 1820, Curl Base, No Knob 2, Small Date | 1820, Square Base, Knob 2, Large Date |

1820, Square Base, No Knob 2, Large Date

1820, Broken Serifs on E's
Compare with normal serifs on 1834, Large Letters, reverse.

	Mintage	Cert	Avg	%MS	G-4	F-12	VF-20	EF-40	AU-50	AU-55	MS-60 / PF-63	MS-63 / PF-64	MS-65 / PF-65
1818, All kinds	1,960,322												
1818, 8 Over 7, Small 8		59	45.6	12%	$90	$145	$250	$500	$1,350	$1,900	$2,900	$8,500	$20,000
Auctions: $881, AU-53, August 2014; $499, EF-40, September 2014; $270, VF-35, March 2015; $165, F-15, October 2015													
1818, 8 Over 7, Large 8		77	43.2	9%	$90	$145	$225	$475	$1,250	$1,800	$3,250	$7,000	$25,000
Auctions: $1,645, AU-55, January 2015; $999, AU-50, September 2014; $764, EF-40, August 2014; $212, VF-25, October 2015													
1818		743	46.6	16%	$70	$100	$155	$300	$600	$1,250	$2,200	$4,250	$14,000
Auctions: $2,174, MS-62, May 2015; $1,528, AU-55, January 2015; $353, EF-45, January 2015; $235, EF-40, May 2015													
1818, Proof	3–5	4	65.5								$45,000	$55,000	$65,000
Auctions: $100,625, PF-65, April 2011													
1819, All kinds	2,208,000												
1819, Small 9 Over 8		63	39.5	3%	$75	$120	$200	$375	$825	$1,350	$2,250	$5,500	$20,000
Auctions: $588, AU-50, July 2015; $353, EF-45, May 2015; $235, VF-35, May 2015; $141, VF-20, May 2015; $432, EF-40, March 2018													
1819, Large 9 Over 8		148	45.5	8%	$75	$120	$175	$350	$750	$1,400	$4,000	$7,500	$25,000
Auctions: $734, AU-53, October 2014; $1,763, AU-50, September 2015; $329, EF-40, January 2015; $206, Fair-2, October 2014													
1819		543	44.0	17%	$75	$100	$150	$325	$650	$1,150	$2,000	$4,500	$20,000
Auctions: $823, AU-55, February 2015; $646, AU-53, July 2015; $259, EF-40, May 2015; $400, VF-35, October 2015													
1820, All kinds	751,122												
1820, 20 Over 19, Square 2		49	40.7	12%	$100	$150	$250	$650	$1,250	$2,000	$2,650	$8,500	$35,000
Auctions: $15,863, MS-63, January 2014; $3,819, AU-58, August 2014; $382, VF-30, July 2014													
1820, 20 Over 19, Curl Base 2		63	42.8	3%	$100	$150	$250	$600	$1,100	$2,250	$3,250	$10,000	$35,000
Auctions: $8,225, MS-63, January 2014; $1,028, AU-50, January 2015; $940, AU-50, March 2015; $470, VF-35, May 2015													
1820, Curl Base 2, Small Dt		36	50.4	14%	$100	$200	$275	$500	$1,000	$1,750	$4,500	$10,500	$25,000
Auctions: $823, AU-50, January 2015; $705, AU-53, January 2015; $376, VF-35, March 2015; $165, F-12, August 2015													
1820, Sq Base, Knob 2, Lg Dt		61	49.3	11%	$100	$175	$250	$500	$950	$1,600	$3,250	$6,000	$20,000
Auctions: $18,800, MS-64, January 2014; $517, MS-60, August 2015; $1,880, AU-55, October 2014; $411, EF-40, March 2015													
1820, Sq Base, No Knob 2, Large Date		62	47.1	11%	$100	$175	$250	$500	$850	$1,600	$3,250	$6,500	$20,000
Auctions: $61,688, MS-65, June 2014; $1,293, AU-53, March 2015; $259, AU-50, August 2015; $1,058, EF-45, July 2014													
1820, Broken Serifs on E's		10	40.4	20%	$500	$1,250	$3,250	$6,500	$10,000	$13,500	$25,000		
Auctions: $4,888, VF-35, December 2011													
1820, Proof	3–5	1	63.0								$45,000	$55,000	$65,000
Auctions: No auction records available.													

1822, So-Called 2 Over 1

1823, Normal Date

1823, Broken 3

1823, Patched 3

1823, Ugly 3

1824, Normal Date

1824, 4 Over 1

**1824, 4 Over
Various Dates**
Probably 4 Over 2 Over 0.

1824, 4 Over 4
*4 Over 4 varieties are
easily mistaken for the
scarcer 4 Over 1. Note
the distance between
the 2's and 4's in each.*

	Mintage	Cert	Avg	%MS	G-4	F-12	VF-20	EF-40	AU-50	AU-55	MS-60	MS-63	MS-65
											PF-63	PF-64	PF-65
1821	1,305,797	699	46.4	17%	$70	$100	$145	$275	$650	$850	$1,650	$3,250	$15,000
	Auctions: $447, AU-50, May 2015; $282, EF-45, March 2015; $306, EF-40, August 2015; $84, VG-10, February 2015												
1821, Proof	3–5	3	64.0								$50,000	$65,000	$80,000
	Auctions: No auction records available.												
1822, All kinds	1,559,573												
1822		765	48.1	25%	$70	$100	$155	$300	$500	$800	$1,350	$2,850	$14,000
	Auctions: $823, AU-55, February 2015; $282, EF-40, April 2015; $153, VF-35, May 2015; $94, F-15, February 2015												
1822, So-Called 2 Over 1		108	48.8	22%	$100	$140	$225	$600	$1,100	$1,650	$2,500	$5,500	$20,000
	Auctions: $1,410, MS-60, November 2013; $1,645, EF-45, September 2014; $306, VF-30, October 2014												
1822, Proof	3–5	1	64.0								$45,000	$55,000	$95,000
	Auctions: $55,813, PF-64, June 2014												
1823, All kinds	1,694,200												
1823, Broken 3		51	39.9	14%	$120	$225	$400	$750	$2,250	$3,000	$5,500	$11,000	$40,000
	Auctions: $23,500, MS-64, November 2013; $720, VF-35, February 2018												
1823, Patched 3		52	48.8	31%	$100	$150	$275	$700	$1,600	$2,250	$4,250	$6,500	$22,500
	Auctions: $4,113, MS-63, March 2015; $1,410, AU-50, January 2015; $353, EF-45, February 2015; $165, VF-25, May 2015												
1823, Ugly 3		25	46.6	16%	$100	$150	$250	$650	$2,250	$3,500	$5,500	$10,000	$30,000
	Auctions: $4,113, AU-55, January 2014; $900, EF-45, February 2018												
1823, Normal		931	47.3	21%	$70	$100	$130	$250	$500	$800	$1,250	$2,850	$12,500
	Auctions: $94,000, MS-67, November 2013; $3,290, MS-64, August 2014; $2,115, MS-62, August 2014; $1,410, MS-62, August 2014												
1823, Proof	3–5	1	63.0								$50,000	$60,000	$75,000
	Auctions: $80,500, PF-63, April 2011												
1824, All kinds	3,504,954												
1824, 4 Over Various Dates		77	42.6	9%	$70	$145	$175	$350	$1,250	$1,750	$3,250	$5,500	$15,000
	Auctions: $11,163, MS-64, June 2014; $1,116, AU-53, August 2015; $306, VF-25, February 2015; $129, F-15, September 2015												
1824, 4 Over 1		95	49.4	35%	$75	$115	$175	$350	$750	$1,200	$2,250	$6,500	$20,000
	Auctions: $799, AU-53, September 2014; $529, AU-53, September 2014; $517, AU-50, January 2015; $353, EF-40, October 2015												
1824, 4 Over 4 (c)		156	47.9	19%	$75	$110	$140	$210	$700	$1,200	$1,500	$2,950	$12,000
	Auctions: $558, AU-50, August 2014; $558, AU-50, July 2014; $458, AU-50, January 2015; $235, VF-30, October 2015												
1824, Normal		1,168	47.0	22%	$75	$100	$115	$175	$500	$850	$1,150	$2,000	$14,000
	Auctions: $10,575, MS-65, January 2015; $2,820, MS-63, March 2015; $223, EF-45, March 2015; $94, F-15, August 2015												

c. 2 varieties.

| 1827, 7 Over 6 | 1827, Square Base 2 | 1827, Curl Base 2 |

| 1828, Curl Base, No Knob 2 | 1828, Curl Base, Knob 2 | 1828, Square Base 2, Large 8's | 1828, Square Base 2, Small 8's |

1828, Large Letters   1828, Small Letters

	Mintage	Cert	Avg	%MS	G-4	F-12	VF-20	EF-40	AU-50	AU-55	MS-60 PF-63	MS-63 PF-64	MS-65 PF-65
1825	2,943,166	1,299	50.6	26%	$75	$100	$115	$175	$425	$500	$1,150	$2,250	$12,000
Auctions: $541, AU-58, January 2015; $176, EF-45, March 2015; $188, EF-40, March 2015; $112, VF-30, July 2015													
1825, Proof	3–5	1	66.0								$50,000	$60,000	$75,000
Auctions: $32,200, PF-62, May 2008													
1826	4,004,180	1,937	50.8	26%	$75	$100	$115	$175	$350	$525	$1,150	$2,000	$9,500
Auctions: $1,058, MS-61, January 2015; $881, AU-55, September 2015; $182, EF-40, March 2015; $89, VF-30, January 2015													
1826, Proof	3–5	1	65.0								$50,000	$60,000	$75,000
Auctions: $76,375, PF-65, September 2013													
1827, All kinds	5,493,400												
1827, 7 Over 6		180	50.7	23%	$100	$150	$200	$450	$1,000	$1,500	$2,350	$4,250	$15,000
Auctions: $18,800, MS-65, November 2013; $764, AU-55, October 2014; $810, AU-55, February 2018													
1827, Square Base 2		704	49.0	17%	$75	$100	$115	$175	$400	$525	$1,200	$2,500	$10,000
Auctions: $764, MS-60, June 2015; $494, AU-55, January 2015; $329, AU-50, May 2015; $165, EF-40, July 2015													
1827, Curl Base 2		56	49.7	11%	$75	$100	$130	$300	$550	$850	$1,500	$3,250	$17,500
Auctions: $8,813, MS-64, January 2014; $192, VF-30, March 2018													
1827, Proof	5–8	3	64.7								$50,000	$60,000	$75,000
Auctions: $21,150, PF-62, September 2013													
1828, All kinds	3,075,200												
1828, Curl Base, No Knob 2		82	51.0	17%	$70	$100	$130	$200	$450	$650	$1,350	$2,250	$10,000
Auctions: $5,875, MS-65, March 2015; $940, AU-58, June 2015; $764, AU-55, October 2015; $247, EF-45, April 2015													
1828, Curl Base, Knob 2		37	52.5	24%	$70	$115	$150	$250	$700	$950	$2,000	$4,500	$12,000
Auctions: $19,975, MS-65, April 2013; $382, AU-58, July 2014; $259, EF-45, May 2015													
1828, Square Base 2, Large 8's		53	49.2	11%	$70	$95	$115	$165	$350	$550	$1,150	$2,000	$11,000
Auctions: $32,900, MS-66, November 2013; $306, AU-50, October 2014; $112, EF-45, October 2014; $204, EF-45, March 2018													
1828, Square Base 2, Small 8's, Large Letters		310	49.6	17%	$65	$90	$115	$165	$350	$550	$1,150	$2,000	$9,000
Auctions: $329, AU-50, October 2015; $223, EF-45, January 2015; $192, VF-35, May 2015; $188, VF-30, October 2015													
1828, Square Base 2, Small 8's and Letters		26	49.5	4%	$75	$105	$150	$250	$600	$750	$1,500	$3,000	$11,000
Auctions: $30,550, MS-65, April 2014; $411, AU-50, July 2014; $1,020, AU-53, March 2018													

1829, 9 Over 7　　　**1830, Small 0**　　　**1830, Large 0**

1830, Large Letters

Experimental Edge of 1830
Raised segment lines angled to the right.

Experimental Edge of 1830–1831
Raised segment lines angled to the left.

Edge Adopted for Coinage, 1830–1836
Straight vertical lines.

1832, Large Letters Reverse
O-101a. Note the prominent die crack.

	Mintage	Cert	Avg	%MS	G-4	F-12	VF-20	EF-40	AU-50	AU-55	MS-60 / PF-63	MS-63 / PF-64	MS-65 / PF-65
1829, All kinds	3,712,156												
1829, 9 Over 7		231	51.3	24%	$70	$120	$165	$350	$750	$1,000	$1,500	$3,500	$22,500
Auctions: $2,115, MS-61, January 2015; $558, AU-53, September 2014; $353, EF-45, July 2014; $141, VF-25, October 2015													
1829		1108	48.1	22%	$60	$80	$110	$180	$400	$500	$1,150	$2,000	$10,000
Auctions: $16,450, MS-66, March 2015; $1,058, AU-55, January 2015; $306, AU-50, June 2015; $153, EF-45, March 2015													
1829, Large Letters		30	54.4	27%	$65	$90	$120	$200	$400	$550	$1,200	$2,500	$10,500
Auctions: $194, AU-50, September 2013; $408, AU-55, May 2018													
1829, Proof	6–9	5	64.2								$50,000	$60,000	$75,000
Auctions: $102,813, PF-64, January 2014													
1830, All kinds	4,764,800												
1830, Small 0		551	47.7	13%	$65	$90	$120	$180	$375	$550	$1,100	$2,100	$10,000
Auctions: $1,410, MS-61, January 2015; $589, AU-58, August 2015; $217, EF-45, July 2015; $100, VF-25, September 2015													
1830, Large 0		143	50.7	16%	$65	$90	$120	$180	$375	$550	$1,000	$2,100	$10,000
Auctions: $41,125, MS-66, November 2013; $588, AU-58, July 2014; $482, AU-55, July 2014; $353, AU-53, July 2014; $2,280, AU-58, April 2018													
1830, Large Letters		12	33.3	8%	$1,400	$2,950	$3,800	$4,800	$9,000	$14,000	$17,500	$22,000	
Auctions: $2,990, VF-35, October 2011													
1830, Proof	3–5	2	64.5								$50,000	$60,000	$75,000
Auctions: $41,400, PF-64, January 2005													
1831	5,873,660	1,961	51.3	25%	$65	$90	$110	$180	$375	$500	$1,100	$2,000	$10,000
Auctions: $922, MS-61, January 2015; $541, AU-58, August 2015; $306, AU-53, October 2015; $153, EF-40, February 2015													
1831, Proof	3–5	2	64.5								$50,000	$60,000	$75,000
Auctions: $79,313, PF-65, April 2013													
1832, All kinds	4,797,000												
1832		1,802	50.8	23%	$65	$90	$110	$180	$375	$500	$1,100	$2,000	$10,000
Auctions: $999, MS-62, January 2015; $764, AU-58, January 2015; $212, EF-45, March 2015; $112, VF-35, October 2015													
1832, Large Letters		79	50.6	14%	$65	$90	$110	$180	$375	$500	$1,100	$2,000	$10,000
Auctions: $4,406, MS-64, November 2013; $364, AU-55, July 2014; $382, AU-50, August 2014; $420, AU-55, January 2018													
1832, Proof	6–9	3	64.7								$50,000	$60,000	$75,000
Auctions: $29,900, PF-63, January 2008													

1834, Large Date **1834, Small Date** **1834, Large Letters** **1834, Small Letters**

1836, Over 1336

| | Mintage | Cert | Avg | %MS | G-4 | F-12 | VF-20 | EF-40 | AU-50 | AU-55 | MS-60 | MS-63 | MS-65 |
											PF-63	PF-64	PF-65
1833	5,206,000	1,762	50.8	22%	$65	$90	$110	$180	$375	$500	$1,100	$2,000	$10,000
Auctions: $353, AU-55, February 2015; $317, AU-53, August 2015; $270, AU-50, May 2015; $188, EF-45, April 2015													
1833, Proof	1–2	4	63.8										
Auctions: No auction records available.													
1833, Crushed Lettered Edge, Proof	3–5	2	64.5								$55,000	$75,000	$115,000
Auctions: No auction records available.													
1834, All kinds	6,412,004												
1834, Large Date and Letters		144	50.3	18%	$60	$80	$110	$180	$375	$500	$1,100	$2,000	$9,000
Auctions: $564, AU-58, January 2015; $135, EF-45, May 2015; $159, EF-40, July 2015; $153, VF-35, February 2015													
1834, Large Date, Small Letters		220	50.6	18%	$60	$80	$110	$180	$375	$500	$1,100	$2,000	$9,000
Auctions: $823, AU-58, January 2015; $447, AU-55, August 2015; $376, AU-53, June 2015; $200, EF-45, April 2015													
1834, Small Date, Stars, Letters		429	49.1	13%	$60	$80	$110	$180	$375	$500	$1,100	$2,000	$9,000
Auctions: $764, AU-58, February 2015; $350, AU-55, May 2015; $120, EF-40, January 2015; $94, VF-35, September 2015													
1834, Proof	8–12	7	64.6								$40,000	$60,000	$75,000
Auctions: $23,710, PF-63, November 2013													
1834, Crushed Lettered Edge, Proof	3–5	1	55.0								$40,000	$65,000	$95,000
Auctions: No auction records available.													
1835	5,352,006	1092	49.1	20%	$60	$80	$110	$180	$375	$500	$1,100	$2,000	$9,000
Auctions: $881, AU-58, August 2015; $350, AU-55, February 2015; $212, EF-45, August 2015; $141, VF-35, October 2015													
1835, Proof	5–8	2	63.0								$40,000	$65,000	$95,000
Auctions: $43,125, PF-64, August 2007													
1835, Crushed Lettered Edge, Proof	3–5	2	65.0								$40,000	$65,000	$95,000
Auctions: No auction records available.													
1836, All kinds	6,545,000												
1836		1,603	48.6	20%	$60	$80	$110	$180	$375	$500	$1,100	$2,000	$9,000
Auctions: $823, AU-58, August 2015; $282, AU-50, January 2015; $100, VF-30, August 2015; $94, VF-25, October 2015													
1836, 1836 Over 1336		65	48.7	12%	$80	$100	$130	$225	$475	$700	$1,200	$2,500	$10,000
Auctions: $2,703, MS-64, August 2014; $499, AU-53, July 2014; $270, AU-50, March 2015; $194, VF-35, December 2014													
1836, 50 Over 00		50	50.7	20%	$125	$200	$350	$500	$925	$1,500	$2,500	$5,000	$30,000
Auctions: $1,645, AU-55, February 2013; $384, EF-45, February 2018													
1836, Beaded Border on Reverse (d)		44	43.9	16%	$85	$120	$140	$250	$525	$675	$1,300	$2,400	$9,500
Auctions: $494, AU-53, May 2015; $212, EF-45, February 2015; $153, VF-35, September 2015 $112, EF-40, November 2014													
1836, Lettered Edge, Proof	8–12	5	64.4								$40,000	$65,000	$85,000
Auctions: $96,938, PF-66, November 2013													
1836, 50 Over 00, Proof	3–5	2	64.5								$50,000	$80,000	$115,000
Auctions: $81,937, PF-65, October 2006													

d. The same beaded-border reverse die was used for Proofs of 1833, 1834, and 1835 with the crushed edge lettering; all are very rare.

CAPPED BUST, REEDED EDGE (1836–1839)

Designer: *Christian Gobrecht.* **Weight:** *13.36 grams.* **Composition:** *.900 silver, .100 copper.*
Diameter: *30 mm.* **Edge:** *Reeded.* **Mint:** *Philadelphia.*

Reverse 50 CENTS (1836–1837)   **Reverse 50 CENTS, Proof**

Reverse HALF DOL. (1838–1839)   *Mintmark location is on the obverse, above the date.*   **Reverse HALF DOL., Proof**

History. This half dollar type features a slight restyling of John Reich's Capped Bust design, modified by Christian Gobrecht. It is of smaller diameter than the preceding type, and made with a reeded edge. The reverse is of two variations: the 1836–1837, with 50 CENTS; and the 1838–1839, with HALF DOL.

Striking and Sharpness. The key points for observation are the stars on the obverse. On the reverse, check the border letters and the details of the eagle. The 1839-O nearly always shows die cracks, often extensive (these have no effect on desirability or market value).

Availability. The 1836 is rare. The 1838-O is a famous rarity, and the 1839-O is scarce. The others are easily available in nearly any grade desired, with 1837 being the most common. Proofs are occasionally encountered of the year 1836 and are quite rare. Authentic Proofs of 1837 exist but for all practical purposes are unobtainable. Most 1838-O (a rarity) and a few 1839-O coins have been called branch-mint Proofs.

GRADING STANDARDS

MS-60 to 70 (Mint State). *Obverse and Reverse:* Grading guidelines are the same as for the 1807–1836 type, except on this type the rims are more uniform. On the 1836–1837 dates the reverse rim is generally lower than the obverse, causing the reverse to wear slightly more quickly. On the 1838–1839 type (with slightly different lettering) the wear occurs evenly on both sides, and light striking showing areas of the original planchet on the obverse does not occur here.

1837. Graded MS-62.

Illustrated coin: This example displays light gray toning with a sprinkling of gold over fully lustrous surfaces.

AU-50, 53, 55, 58 (About Uncirculated). *Obverse and Reverse:* Grading guidelines are the same as for the 1807–1836 type, except on this type the rims are more uniform. On the 1836–1837 dates the reverse rim is generally lower than the obverse, causing the reverse to wear slightly more quickly. On the 1838–1839 type (with slightly different lettering) the wear occurs evenly on both sides.

1836. Graded AU-53.

EF-40, 45 (Extremely Fine). *Obverse and Reverse:* Grading guidelines are the same as for the 1807–1836 type, except on this type the rims are more uniform. On the 1836–1837 dates the reverse rim is generally lower than the obverse, causing the reverse to wear slightly more quickly. On the 1838–1839 type (with slightly different lettering) the wear occurs evenly on both sides.

1836. Graded EF-40.

VF-20, 30 (Very Fine). *Obverse and Reverse:* Grading guidelines are the same as for the 1807–1836 type, except on this type the rims are more uniform. On the 1836–1837 dates the reverse rim is generally lower than the obverse, causing the reverse to wear slightly more quickly. On the 1838–1839 type (with slightly different lettering) the wear occurs evenly on both sides.

1836. Graded VF-20.

F-12, 15 (Fine). *Obverse and Reverse:* Grading guidelines are the same as for the 1807–1836 type, except on this type the rims are more uniform. On the 1836–1837 dates the reverse rim is generally lower than the obverse, causing the reverse to wear slightly more quickly. On the 1838–1839 type (with slightly different lettering) the wear occurs evenly on both sides.

1839-O. Graded F-15.

VG-8, 10 (Very Good). *Obverse and Reverse:* Grading guidelines are the same as for the 1807–1836 type, except on this type the rims are more uniform. On the 1836–1837 dates the reverse rim is generally lower than the obverse, causing the reverse to wear slightly more quickly. On the 1838–1839 type (with slightly different lettering) the wear occurs evenly on both sides.

1836. Graded VG-10.

G-4, 6 (Good). *Obverse and Reverse:* Grading guidelines are the same as for the 1807–1836 type, except on this type the rims are more uniform. On the 1836–1837 dates the reverse rim is generally lower than the obverse, causing the reverse to wear slightly more quickly. On the 1838–1839 type (with slightly different lettering) the wear occurs evenly on both sides.

1838. Graded G-4.

AG-3 (About Good). *Obverse and Reverse:* Grading guidelines are the same as for the 1807–1836 type, except on this type the rims are more uniform. On the 1836–1837 dates the reverse rim is generally lower than the obverse, causing the reverse to wear slightly more quickly. On the 1838–1839 type (with slightly different lettering) the wear occurs evenly on both sides.

1836. Graded AG-3.

PF-60 to 70 (Proof). *Obverse and Reverse:* Proofs in grades of PF–60 to 62 show extensive hairlines and cloudiness. At PF-63, hairlines are obvious, but the mirrored fields are attractive. PF–64 and 65 coins have fewer hairlines, but they still are obvious when the coin is slowly turned while held at an angle to the light. PF-66 coins require a magnifier to discern hairlines, and higher grades should have no hairlines.

1836. Graded PF-64 Cameo.

1839, Regular Letters Reverse

1839, Small Letters Reverse

	Mintage	Cert	Avg	%MS	G-4	F-12	VF-20	EF-40	AU-50	AU-55	MS-60	MS-63	MS-65
											PF-60	PF-63	PF-65
1836	1,200+	208	48.2	16%	$1,000	$1,750	$2,150	$3,500	$5,000	$6,000	$9,500	$20,000	$65,000
	Auctions: $38,188, MS-64, October 2014; $423, AU-58, September 2015; $4,113, AU-53, March 2015; $3,290, EF-45, March 2015												
1836, Reeded Edge, Proof	10–15	10	63.7								$30,000	$45,000	$90,000
	Auctions: $32,900, PF-63, April 2013												
1837	3,629,820	1,523	53.3	34%	$65	$100	$125	$220	$450	$625	$1,150	$2,750	$17,500
	Auctions: $11,456, MS-64, March 2015; $1,645, MS-62, January 2015; $425, AU-55, June 2015; $247, EF-45, August 2015												
1837, Proof	4–6	2	63.5								$50,000	$100,000	
	Auctions: $32,200, PF-62, July 2008												
1838	3,546,000	1,139	52.3	27%	$65	$100	$125	$220	$450	$675	$1,150	$2,750	$18,000
	Auctions: $17,625, MS-66, May 2015; $1,645, MS-62, January 2015; $588, AU-55, January 2015; $235, EF-45, June 2015												
1838, Proof	3–5	0	n/a								$50,000	$115,000	
	Auctions: $129,250, PF-64, April 2014												
1838-O								$350,000	$400,000		$500,000		
1838-O, Proof † (a)	20	4	59.0								$350,000	$450,000	
	Auctions: $193,875, PF-65, March 2015; $646,250, PF-64, May 2015; $293,750, PF-50, August 2015												
1839	1,392,976	525	50.7	24%	$75	$110	$140	$275	$500	$750	$1,400	$3,100	$30,000
	Auctions: $5,288, MS-64, March 2015; $470, AU-55, January 2015; $259, EF-45, June 2015; $235, EF-40, June 2015; $600, AU-58, February 2018												
1839, Small Letters Reverse		2	52.5	0%	$15,000	$40,000	$55,000	$60,000	$75,000			$150,000	
	Auctions: $50,025, AU-50, January 2010												
1839, Reeded Edge, Proof (b)	n/a	0	n/a								—		
	Auctions: No auction records available.												
1839-O	116,000	290	46.2	18%	$425	$950	$1,200	$2,000	$2,500	$3,500	$6,500	$12,500	$42,500
	Auctions: $52,875, MS-65, July 2015; $1,528, VF-25, June 2015; $2,585, EF-40, August 2016; $1,293, F-12, August 2016												
1839-O, Proof	5–10	4	62.8								$85,000	$125,000	$225,000
	Auctions: $92,000, PF-63, March 2012												

† Ranked in the *100 Greatest U.S. Coins* (fourth edition). **a.** The 1838-O, Proof, was the first branch-mint half dollar, though it was not mentioned in the Mint director's report. The New Orleans chief coiner stated that only 20 were struck. **b.** Unverified.

LIBERTY SEATED (1839–1891)

Variety 1, No Motto Above Eagle (1839–1853): **Designer:** *Christian Gobrecht.*
Weight: *13.36 grams.* **Composition:** *.900 silver, .100 copper.* **Diameter:** *30.6 mm.*
Edge: *Reeded.* **Mints:** *Philadelphia and New Orleans.*

Mintmark
location is
on the reverse,
below the eagle,
for all varieties.

Variety 1 (1839–1853)　　　　　　　　　　**Variety 1, Proof**

Variety 2, Arrows at Date, Rays Around Eagle (1853): **Designer:** *Christian Gobrecht.*
Weight: *12.44 grams.* **Composition:** *.900 silver, .100 copper.* **Diameter:** *30.6 mm.*
Edge: *Reeded.* **Mints:** *Philadelphia and New Orleans.*

Variety 2 (1853)　　　　　　　　　　**Variety 2, Proof**

Variety 3, Arrows at Date, No Rays (1854–1855): **Designer:** *Christian Gobrecht.*
Weight: *12.44 grams.* **Composition:** *.900 silver, .100 copper.* **Diameter:** *30.6 mm.*
Edge: *Reeded.* **Mints:** *Philadelphia, New Orleans, and San Francisco.*

Variety 3 (1854–1855)　　　　　　　　　　**Variety 3, Proof**

Variety 1 Resumed, With Weight Standard of Variety 2 (1856–1866):
Designer: *Christian Gobrecht.* **Weight:** *12.44 grams.* **Composition:** *.900 silver, .100 copper.*
Diameter: *30.6 mm.* **Edge:** *Reeded.* **Mints:** *Philadelphia, New Orleans, and San Francisco.*

Variety 1 Resumed, Weight Standard
of Variety 2 (1856–1866)　　　　　　　**Variety 1 Resumed, Weight Standard**
of Variety 2, Proof

Variety 4, Motto Above Eagle (1866–1873): Designer: *Christian Gobrecht.*
Weight: *12.44 grams.* **Composition:** *.900 silver, .100 copper.* **Diameter:** *30.6 mm.*
Edge: *Reeded.* **Mints:** *Philadelphia, San Francisco, and Carson City.*

Variety 4 (1866–1873)

Variety 4, Proof

Variety 5, Arrows at Date (1873–1874): Designer: *Christian Gobrecht.*
Weight: *12.50 grams.* **Composition:** *.900 silver, .100 copper.* **Diameter:** *30.6 mm.*
Edge: *Reeded.* **Mints:** *Philadelphia, San Francisco, and Carson City.*

Variety 5 (1873–1874)

Variety 5, Proof

Variety 4 Resumed, With Weight Standard of Variety 5 (1875–1891): Designer: *Christian Gobrecht.*
Weight: *12.50 grams.* **Composition:** *.900 silver, .100 copper.* **Diameter:** *30.6 mm.*
Edge: *Reeded.* **Mints:** *Philadelphia, San Francisco, and Carson City.*

Variety 4 Resumed, Weight Standard
of Variety 5 (1875–1891)

Variety 4 Resumed, Weight Standard
of Variety 5, Proof

History. Half dollars of the Liberty Seated type were struck every year from 1839 to 1891. The designs varied slightly over the years, but with the basic obverse and reverse motifs remaining the same (e.g., from 1842 to 1853 the coins bore a modified reverse with large letters in the legend, and in 1846 the date size was enlarged). Large quantities were made until 1879, at which time there was a glut of silver coins in commerce. After that mintages were reduced.

The earliest Liberty Seated half dollars, dated 1839, lacked drapery at Miss Liberty's elbow. In that year Robert Ball Hughes modified Christian Gobrecht's design by adding drapery, a feature that continued for the rest of the series.

Striking and Sharpness. On the obverse, first check the head of Miss Liberty and the star centers. On coins of the Arrows at Date variety, especially 1855, the word LIBERTY tends to wear faster compared to earlier and later varieties. On the reverse, check the eagle at the lower left. Afterward, check all other features. Generally, the higher-mintage issues are the least well struck, and many New Orleans Mint coins can be lightly struck, particularly those of the 1850s. The luster on MS coins usually is very attractive. Resurfaced dies often are prooflike, some with the drapery polished away (as with 1877-S, in particular). Above and beyond issues of strike, the Small Letters coins of 1839 to 1842 have narrower, lower rims that afforded less protection to the central devices of the reverse. In contrast, the No Motto, Large Letters, coins have wider, higher rims that tend to better protect the central devices. Many pre–Civil War dates, particularly of the 1840s, show evidence of extensive die polishing in the fields (especially evident in the open expanses of the obverse). From grades of EF downward, sharpness of strike of the stars and the head does not matter to connoisseurs. Quality is often lacking, with lint marks seen on some issues of the late 1850s and early 1860s. Light striking is occasionally seen on the star centers and the head of Miss Liberty; connoisseurs avoid coins with this detraction, but most buyers will not be aware. Slide marks (usually seen on the right knee) from coin albums can be a problem, more so on Liberty Seated halves than on lower denominations of this design.

Availability. Collecting these coins is a popular pursuit with many enthusiasts. Examples of the higher-mintage dates are readily available, with earlier years being much scarcer than later ones. Most often seen among MS coins are issues from the mid-1870s onward. Circulated coins from well worn through AU can be found of most dates and mintmarks; these are avidly sought. Proofs were made in most years, with production beginning in a particularly significant way in 1858, when an estimated 210 silver sets were sold. Today, Proofs from 1858 through 1891 are readily available.

GRADING STANDARDS

MS-60 to 70 (Mint State). *Obverse:* At MS-60, some abrasion and contact marks are evident, most noticeably on the bosom and thighs and knees. Luster is present, but may be dull or lifeless. At MS-63, contact marks are very few, and abrasion is hard to detect except under magnification. An MS-65 coin has no abrasion, and contact marks are sufficiently minute as to require magnification. Check the knees of Liberty and the right field. Luster

1856-O. Graded MS-63.

should be full and rich. Most Mint State coins of the 1861 to 1865 years, Philadelphia issues, have extensive die striae (from dies not being completely finished); note that these are *raised* (whereas cleaning hairlines are incuse). *Reverse:* Comments as preceding, except that in lower Mint State grades abrasion and contact marks are most noticeable on the eagle's head, neck, and claws, and the top of the wings (harder to see there, however). At MS-65 or higher there are no marks visible to the unaided eye. The field is mainly protected by design elements and does not show abrasion as much as does the obverse on a given coin.

AU-50, 53, 55, 58 (About Uncirculated). *Obverse:* Light wear is seen on the thighs and knees, bosom, and head. At AU-58, the luster is extensive, but incomplete, especially in the right field. At AU–50 and 53, luster is less. *Reverse:* Wear is evident on the eagle's neck, the claws, and the top of the wings. An AU-58 coin has nearly full luster, more so than on the obverse, as the design elements protect the small field areas. At AU–50 and 53, there still are traces of luster.

1841-O. Graded AU-55.

Illustrated coin: Gray toning is evident on this coin. The reverse is lightly struck, a characteristic that should not be mistaken for wear.

EF-40, 45 (Extremely Fine). *Obverse:* Further wear is seen on all areas, especially the thighs and knees, bosom, and head. Little or no luster is seen on most coins. From this grade downward, sharpness of strike of stars and the head does not matter to connoisseurs. *Reverse:* Further wear is evident on the eagle's neck, claws, and wings.

1839, No Drapery From Elbow. Graded EF-40.

VF-20, 30 (Very Fine). *Obverse:* Further wear is seen. Most details of the gown are worn away, except in the lower-relief areas above and to the right of the shield. Hair detail is mostly or completely gone. *Reverse:* Wear is more extensive, with some of the feathers blended together.

1839, No Drapery From Elbow. Graded VF-20.

F-12, 15 (Fine). *Obverse:* The seated figure is well worn, but with some detail above and to the right of the shield. LIBERTY is readable but weak in areas, perhaps with a letter missing (a slightly looser interpretation than the demand for full LIBERTY a generation ago). *Reverse:* Wear is extensive, with about a third to half of the feathers flat or blended with others.

1842-O, Small Date. Graded F-12.

VG-8, 10 (Very Good). *Obverse:* The seated figure is more worn, but some detail can be seen above and to the right of the shield. The shield is discernible, but the upper-right section may be flat and blended into the seated figure. In LIBERTY at least the equivalent of two or three letters (can be a combination of partial letters) must be readable, possibly very weak at VG-8, with a few more visible at VG-10. In the marketplace and among certified coins, parts of

1873-CC, Arrows at Date. Graded VG-8.

two letters seem to be allowed. Per PCGS, "localized weakness may obscure some letters." LIBERTY is *not* an infallible guide: some varieties have the word in low relief on the die, so it wore away slowly. *Reverse:* Further wear has flattened all but a few feathers, and many if not most horizontal lines of the shield are indistinct. The leaves are only in outline form. The rim is visible all around, as are the ends of most denticles.

G-4, 6 (Good). *Obverse:* The seated figure is worn nearly smooth. At G-4 there are no letters in LIBERTY remaining on most (but not all) coins; some coins, especially of the early 1870s, are exceptions. At G-6, traces of one or two can barely be seen and more details can be seen in the figure. *Reverse:* The eagle shows only a few details of the shield and feathers. The rim is worn down, and the tops of the border letters are weak or worn away, although the inscription can still be read.

1873, No Arrows, Open 3. Graded G-6.

AG-3 (About Good). *Obverse:* The seated figure is visible in outline form. Much or all of the rim is worn away. The date remains clear. *Reverse:* The border letters are partially worn away. The eagle is mostly in outline form, but with a few details discernible. The rim is weak or missing.

1873, No Arrows, Open 3. Graded AG-3.

PF-60 to 70 (Proof). *Obverse and Reverse:* Proofs that are extensively cleaned and have many hairlines, or that are dull and grainy, are lower level, such as PF-60 to 62. These are not widely desired, save for the low mintage (in circulation-strike format) years from 1879 to 1891. With medium hairlines and good reflectivity, an assigned grade of PF-64 is appropriate, and with relatively few hairlines, Gem PF-65. In various grades hairlines are

1889. Graded PF-65.

most easily seen in the obverse field. PF-66 should have hairlines so delicate that magnification is needed to see them. Above that, a Proof should be free of such lines.

No Drapery From Elbow (1839) 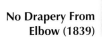 Drapery From Elbow (Starting 1839)

	Mintage	Cert	Avg	%MS	G-4	VG-8	F-12	VF-20	EF-40	AU-50	MS-60 / PF-60	MS-63 / PF-63	MS-65 / PF-65
1839, No Drapery From Elbow	(a)	174	45.9	13%	$125	$250	$500	$750	$2,000	$2,700	$6,500	$27,500	$150,000
Auctions: $2,180, EF-40, January 2015; $881, VF-30, June 2015; $705, VF-25, August 2015; $595, VF-20, February 2015													
1839, No Drapery, Proof	4–6	6	63.2								$100,000	$135,000	$250,000
Auctions: $223,250, PF-64, November 2013													
1839, Drapery From Elbow	1,972,400	170	51.1	32%	$50	$75	$100	$200	$300	$450	$1,300	$2,300	$17,500
Auctions: $4,230, MS-64, January 2015; $541, AU-55, January 2015; $564, AU-53, January 2015; $541, AU-50, May 2015													
1839, Drapery, Proof	1–2	1	64.0									$95,000	$200,000
Auctions: $184,000, PF-64, April 2008													
1840, Small Letters	1,435,008	236	51.2	26%	$50	$75	$100	$200	$300	$450	$800	$1,400	$7,500
Auctions: $5,640, MS-65, October 2015; $329, AU-50, February 2015													

a. Included in circulation-strike 1839, Drapery From Elbow, mintage figure.

| Small Letters in Legend (1839–1841) | 1840 (Only), Medium Letters, Large Eagle | Large Letters in Legend (1842–1853) |

| 1842, Small Date | 1842, Medium Date |

	Mintage	Cert	Avg	%MS	G-4	VG-8	F-12	VF-20	EF-40	AU-50	MS-60	MS-63	MS-65
											PF-60	PF-63	PF-65
1840, Medium Letters (b)	(c)	53	41.9	15%	$200	$300	$500	$800	$1,200	$2,000	$4,000	$8,750	$45,000
Auctions: $2,233, MS-62, February 2015; $1,028, AU-58, January 2015; $259, EF-45, May 2015; $188, VF-30, September 2015
1840, Small Letters, Proof	4–8	7	64.0										$65,000
Auctions: $49,350, PF-65, May 2015; $30,550, PF-63, November 2013
1840-O	855,100	130	48.0	25%	$60	$75	$100	$200	$350	$500	$1,650	$4,500	
Auctions: $2,350, MS-62, January 2015; $1,410, MS-60, June 2015; $212, EF-45, June 2015; $141, VF-30, June 2015
1841	310,000	77	54.9	32%	$65	$110	$150	$300	$450	$600	$1,400	$2,800	$9,000
Auctions: $11,750, MS-65, May 2015; $4,230, MS-64, January 2015; $857, AU-58, June 2015; $364, EF-45, August 2015
1841, Proof	4–8	6	64.5								$15,000	$20,000	$37,500
Auctions: $30,550, PF-64, September 2013
1841-O	401,000	116	51.1	25%	$50	$75	$115	$200	$350	$500	$1,250	$3,500	$12,000
Auctions: $27,025, MS-66, May 2015; $447, AU-53, July 2015; $259, EF-45, May 2015; $153, VF-30, July 2015
1842, Sm Date, Sm Letters	(d)	1	64.0	100%	$15,000		$30,000		$40,000				
Auctions: $99,875, MS-64, June 2014
1842, Medium Date	2,012,764	137	49.4	15%	$50	$75	$100	$200	$300	$400	$975	$2,000	$7,000
Auctions: $2,585, MS-64, October 2015; $353, MS-60, August 2015; $360, AU-58, May 2015; $129, EF-40, September 2015
1842, Sm Date, Lg Letters	(d)	56	51.7	27%	$65	$110	$150	$300	$450	$600	$1,300	$3,300	$23,000
Auctions: $21,150, MS-65, April 2014; $2,585, MS-63, January 2015; $306, EF-45, May 2015; $176, VF-25, August 2015
1842, Sm Date, Lg Ltrs, Proof	4–8	5	64.2								$15,000	$25,000	$45,000
Auctions: $44,063, PF-66, June 2014
1842-O, Sm Date, Sm Letters	203,000	37	34.9	3%	$700	$1,000	$1,500	$2,250	$4,000	$8,000	$16,500	$32,500	
Auctions: $35,250, MS-62, January 2014; ; $3,760, EF-40, January 2015; $764, VG-10, November 2014; $823, VG-8, September 2014
1842-O, Med Date, Lg Letters	754,000	64	47.8	20%	$65	$75	$100	$200	$300	$450	$1,800	$4,500	$20,000
Auctions: $19,975, MS-65, January 2015; $517, AU-50, July 2015; $282, EF-45, July 2015; $212, VF-35, January 2015
1843	3,844,000	235	50.6	28%	$50	$75	$100	$175	$250	$400	$900	$1,800	$7,750
Auctions: $4,935, MS-65, January 2015; $201, AU-50, January 2015; $212, EF-45, August 2015; $89, VF-25, March 2015
1843, Proof	4–8	3	63.7								$15,000	$27,500	$60,000
Auctions: $70,500, PF-65Cam, August 2013; $44,063, PF-64, October 2014
1843-O	2,268,000	112	50.6	38%	$50	$75	$100	$200	$300	$450	$1,400	$3,250	$25,000
Auctions: $3,290, MS-63, January 2015; $764, AU-58, August 2015; $646, AU-55, June 2015; $223, EF-40, January 2015

b. The 1840, Medium Letters, half dollars were struck at the New Orleans Mint from a reverse die of the previous style, without mintmark. c. Included in circulation-strike 1840, Small Letters, mintage figure. d. Included in 1842, Medium Date, mintage figure.

1846, Medium Date

1844-O, Doubled Date
FS-50-1844o-301.

1846, Tall Date

1846-O, Medium Date

1846-O, Tall Date

1847, 7 Over 6
FS-50-1847-301.

	Mintage	Cert	Avg	%MS	G-4	VG-8	F-12	VF-20	EF-40	AU-50	MS-60 / PF-60	MS-63 / PF-63	MS-65 / PF-65
1844	1,766,000	149	53.4	33%	$50	$75	$100	$175	$250	$450	$700	$1,700	$8,750
Auctions: $12,338, MS-65, May 2015; $223, AU-50, August 2015; $129, EF-45, May 2015; $247, EF-40, February 2015													
1844, Proof	3–6	1	62										$75,000
Auctions: $149,500, PF-66Cam, January 2008; $31,725, PF-64, May 2015													
1844-O	2,005,000	111	46.3	31%	$50	$75	$100	$200	$300	$475	$1,350	$3,000	$13,500
Auctions: $10,575, MS-64, May 2015; $764, AU-58, January 2015; $295, AU-50, October 2015; $376, EF-45, October 2015													
1844-O, Doubled Date (e)	(f)	20	41.2	5%	$600	$1,000	$1,500	$1,900	$4,000	$6,000	$8,500		
Auctions: $6,463, AU-55, February 2013; $115, VG-8, July 2014; $235, Fair-2, October 2014													
1845	589,000	56	49.8	21%	$100	$150	$200	$350	$500	$700	$1,000	$3,500	
Auctions: $3,055, MS-64, January 2015; $447, AU-55, June 2015; $536, AU-53, January 2015; $235, VF-30, January 2015													
1845, Proof	3–6	3	65.0								$15,000	$30,000	$65,000
Auctions: $57,500, PF-64, May 2008													
1845-O	2,094,000	120	45.9	22%	$50	$75	$100	$200	$300	$400	$850	$3,000	$9,000
Auctions: $329, AU-50, November 2015; $259, AU-50, November 2015; $353, EF-45, May 2015; $223, EF-40, August 2015													
1845-O, No Drapery (g)	(h)	19	49.3	21%	$100	$125	$150	$180	$480	$800	$1,400	$4,500	
Auctions: $6,463, MS-64, June 2014													
1846, All kinds	2,210,000												
1846, Medium Date		79	50.9	27%	$50	$75	$100	$200	$300	$450	$1,000	$1,550	$12,000
Auctions: $1,293, MS-63, January 2015; $705, AU-58, June 2015; $223, AU-50, May 2015; $165, EF-40, August 2015													
1846, Tall Date		107	52.8	27%	$80	$110	$200	$300	$400	$500	$1,300	$2,750	
Auctions: $881, AU-58, September 2015; $588, AU-53, October 2015; $423, AU-53, May 2015; $317, EF-45, April 2015													
1846, 6 Over Horizontal 6 (i)		38	47.4	16%	$225	$300	$500	$1,000	$1,650	$2,500	$4,750	$10,000	$20,000
Auctions: $7,050, MS-62, June 2014; $1,440, VF-30, February 2018													
1846, Med Letters, Proof	15–20	11	63.5								$11,000	$21,000	$50,000
Auctions: $28,200, PF-64, October 2014; $23,500, PF-63, January 2014; $14,100, PF-63, March 2015													
1846-O, Medium Date	2,304,000	101	43.1	19%	$75	$110	$200	$300	$400	$500	$1,500	$3,600	$20,000
Auctions: $2,820, MS-62, January 2015; $588, AU-55, January 2015; $376, AU-53, July 2015; $153, VF-35, March 2015													
1846-O, Tall Date	(j)	29	37.8	7%	$250	$500	$1,000	$1,750	$2,500	$3,500	$9,500	$15,000	
Auctions: $1,528, EF-45, January 2015; $881, VF-30, June 2015; $306, F-15, June 2015; $360, VG-10, January 2015													
1847, 7 Over 6 (k)	(l)	4	46.8	25%	$1,500	$2,250	$3,250	$4,250	$10,000	$13,500	$27,500		
Auctions: $17,038, AU-55, May 2015; $5,875, AU-50, August 2014; $8,225, VF-35, August 2014; $5,640, VF-35, January 2015													
1847	1,156,000	114	51.8	23%	$50	$75	$100	$200	$300	$450	$1,000	$1,650	$7,000
Auctions: $8,813, MS-65, May 2015; $1,410, MS-63, February 2015; $235, AU-53, May 2015; $165, EF-40, October 2015													
1847, Proof	15–20	10	63.5								$10,000	$20,000	$45,000
Auctions: $12,338, PF-63, August 2013													
1847-O	2,584,000	97	49.6	30%	$50	$75	$100	$200	$300	$450	$1,000	$2,750	$15,000
Auctions: $30,550, MS-66, May 2015; $1,880, MS-62, January 2015; $378, AU-53, February 2015; $176, EF-40, October 2015													

e. This rare variety shows all four numerals protruding from the rock above the primary date. **f.** Included in 1844-O mintage figure. **g.** The drapery is missing because of excessive polishing of the die. **h.** Included in 1845-O mintage figure. **i.** This variety can be detected in low grades. **j.** Included in 1846-O, Medium Date, mintage figure. **k.** Remains of an underlying 6 are visible below and between the primary 4 and 7. "The overdate might not be evident on later die states" (*Cherrypickers' Guide to Rare Die Varieties*, sixth edition, volume II). **l.** Included in circulation-strike 1847 mintage figure.

	Mintage	Cert	Avg	%MS	G-4	VG-8	F-12	VF-20	EF-40	AU-50	MS-60	MS-63	MS-65
											PF-60	PF-63	PF-65
1848	580,000	69	54.2	45%	$100	$150	$200	$350	$500	$700	$1,200	$2,500	$14,000
	Auctions: $7,638, MS-64, January 2015; $617, AU-55, March 2015; $341, EF-45, August 2015; $235, VF-35, May 2015												
1848, Proof	4–8	2	66.0								$10,000	$20,000	$45,000
	Auctions: $34,075, PF-64, June 2014												
1848-O	3,180,000	109	48.3	22%	$50	$75	$100	$200	$300	$500	$1,200	$2,200	$24,500
	Auctions: $940, AU-58, January 2015; $999, AU-55, June 2015; $306, EF-45, July 2015; $141, VF-35, August 2015												
1849	1,252,000	104	56.1	38%	$100	$150	$200	$350	$500	$700	$1,000	$2,250	$13,500
	Auctions: $10,575, MS-65, January 2015; $517, AU-58, June 2015; $400, AU-53, August 2015; $294, EF-45, March 2015												
1849, Proof	4–8	4	65.0								$10,000	$20,000	$45,000
	Auctions: $70,500, PF-66, January 2014; $38,188, PF-66, October 2014; $18,800, PF-63, October 2015												
1849-O	2,310,000	81	48.9	26%	$50	$75	$100	$200	$300	$850	$1,600	$2,700	$17,000
	Auctions: $793, AU-55, January 2015; $564, AU-53, January 2015; $153, VF-35, January 2015; $129, VF-30, August 2015												
1850	227,000	89	54.0	34%	$275	$375	$600	$800	$1,200	$1,500	$2,500	$4,000	$19,500
	Auctions: $117,500, MS-67, May 2015; $15,275, MS-65, November 2013; $764, EF-40, August 2015; $447, Fair-2, October 2014												
1850, Proof	4–8	4	63.8								$13,000	$27,500	$60,000
	Auctions: $20,125, PF-64, July 2009												
1850-O	2,456,000	90	52.9	40%	$50	$75	$100	$200	$300	$450	$1,000	$1,500	$15,000
	Auctions: $28,200, MS-66, May 2015; $329, AU-50, May 2015; $259, EF-40, November 2015; $165, VF-35, August 2015												
1851	200,750	49	58.2	61%	$750	$1,000	$1,500	$1,750	$2,500	$3,000	$3,500	$5,000	$12,500
	Auctions: $49,938, MS-66, June 2014; $2,820, AU-58, January 2015; $1,645, EF-45, September 2014; $881, Fair-2, October 2014												
1851-O	402,000	58	53.0	45%	$65	$110	$150	$300	$450	$600	$1,400	$3,000	$10,000
	Auctions: $999, AU-55, January 2015; $940, AU-53, September 2015; $588, EF-45, November 2015; $376, VF-35, August 2015												
1852	77,130	74	56.4	53%	$500	$750	$1,000	$1,500	$2,000	$2,500	$3,000	$4,500	$11,000
	Auctions: $12,338, MS-66, October 2014; $3,525, MS-62, January 2015; $2,115, AU-58, January 2015; $1,410, AU-53, July 2014												
1852, Proof	3–6	3	62.7									$35,000	$55,000
	Auctions: $74,750, PF-65, July 2008												
1852-O	144,000	48	45.5	10%	$275	$450	$600	$800	$1,100	$1,800	$3,500	$10,000	$35,000
	Auctions: $1,116, EF-40, June 2015; $940, VF-20, February 2015; $823, F-15, July 2015; $764, F-15, September 2015												
1852-O, Proof	2–3	1	62.0									$37,500	
	Auctions: $24,150, PF-62, May 2001												
1853-O, Variety 1 † (m)		1	40.0	0%	$200,000	$250,000	$350,000	$500,000					
	Auctions: $368,000, VF-35, October 2006; $199,750, VG-8, August 2015												
1853, Variety 2	3,532,708	1,148	49.9	24%	$50	$75	$100	$140	$300	$600	$1,500	$3,500	$22,000
	Auctions: $73,438, MS-66, January 2015; $28,200, MS-66, May 2015; $282, EF-45, October 2015; $165, VF-35, August 2015												
1853, Variety 2, Proof	5–10	4	65.0									$50,000	$150,000
	Auctions: $117,500, PF-65, October 2014; $184,000, PF-65, January 2012; $94,000, PF-64, October 2014												
1853-O, Variety 2	1,328,000	218	43.6	15%	$60	$75	$95	$180	$400	$750	$2,750	$5,500	$40,000
	Auctions: $12,338, MS-64, January 2015; $1,058, AU-55, August 2015; $259, EF-40, January 2015; $176, VF-25, June 2015												
1854	2,982,000	503	52.3	27%	$50	$75	$100	$140	$200	$375	$625	$1,500	$8,750
	Auctions: $1,645, MS-63, February 2015; $282, AU-55, June 2015; $153, EF-40, January 2015; $79, VF-30, January 2015												
1854, Proof	15–20	14	64.8			·					$8,500	$13,500	$30,000
	Auctions: $70,500, PF-67, November 2013												
1854-O	5,240,000	761	50.5	30%	$50	$75	$100	$140	$200	$350	$650	$1,500	$7,500
	Auctions: $5,405, MS-65, January 2015; $470, MS-61, September 2015; $494, AU-58, August 2015; $94, VF-35, January 2015												

† Ranked in the *100 Greatest U.S. Coins* (fourth edition). **m.** 4 examples are known.

1855, 1855 Over 854
FS-50-1855-301.

	Mintage	Cert	Avg	%MS	G-4	VG-8	F-12	VF-20	EF-40	AU-50	MS-60	MS-63	MS-65
											PF-60	PF-63	PF-65
1855, All kinds	759,500												
1855, 1855 Over 1854		54	48.0	28%	$75	$90	$175	$360	$500	$1,200	$2,250	$3,600	$11,500
Auctions: $353, AU-50, November 2014; $588, EF-45, January 2015; $423, EF-45, July 2015; $411, VF-35, December 2014													
1855, Normal Date		152	54.3	38%	$50	$75	$100	$140	$200	$400	$800	$1,750	$12,500
Auctions: $881, AU-58, June 2015; $329, AU-53, January 2015; $176, EF-45, January 2015; $118, VF-35, August 2015													
1855, 55 Over 54, Proof	1–2	0	n/a								$10,000	$22,000	$60,000
Auctions: $30,550, PF-64, June 2014													
1855, Proof	15–20	8	64.5								$7,500	$12,500	$35,000
Auctions: $41,125, PF-66Cam, June 2014													
1855-O	3,688,000	532	52.2	29%	$50	$75	$100	$140	$200	$350	$650	$1,500	$9,500
Auctions: $705, MS-62, September 2015; $423, AU-58, May 2015; $172, EF-45, March 2015; $100, VF-35, May 2015													
1855-S	129,950	54	33.5	6%	$450	$1,000	$1,350	$1,750	$3,500	$7,600	$35,000	$50,000	
Auctions: $41,125, MS-61, October 2014; $14,688, AU-55, January 2015; $8,225, AU-53, July 2014; $423, G-4, October 2015													
1855-S, Proof	2–3	1	65.0									$150,000	
Auctions: $276,000, PF-65, August 2011													
1856	938,000	133	52.2	31%	$50	$75	$100	$140	$250	$350	$600	$1,200	$5,750
Auctions: $16,450, MS-66, May 2015; $376, AU-58, November 2015; $188, AU-50, March 2015; $176, EF-45, March 2015													
1856, Proof	20–30	20	64.3								$4,000	$6,500	$23,000
Auctions: $17,625, PF-65, October 2014; $17,625, PF-65, November 2013													
1856-O	2,658,000	270	52.6	39%	$50	$75	$100	$140	$250	$350	$500	$1,100	$6,000
Auctions: $4,818, MS-65, January 2015; $470, MS-61, September 2015; $282, AU-53, May 2015; $141, EF-45, July 2015													
1856-S	211,000	37	40.7	11%	$95	$150	$240	$450	$1,100	$2,100	$5,000	$13,000	
Auctions: $12,925, MS-63, May 2015; $3,055, AU-58, January 2015; $881, VF-35, August 2015; $499, VF-35, October 2014													
1857	1,988,000	243	52.5	33%	$50	$75	$100	$140	$250	$350	$600	$1,100	$4,800
Auctions: $3,525, MS-65, January 2015; $764, MS-63, September 2015; $400, AU-58, July 2015; $282, AU-55, August 2015													
1857, Proof	30–50	37	63.8								$3,000	$4,500	$23,000
Auctions: $23,500, PF-66, June 2013													
1857-O	818,000	79	48.3	11%	$50	$75	$100	$175	$300	$500	$1,350	$3,500	$12,000
Auctions: $517, AU-58, June 2015; $259, AU-53, May 2015; $212, EF-45, August 2015; $182, EF-40, June 2015													
1857-S	158,000	37	44.2	14%	$150	$180	$250	$425	$1,400	$2,000	$3,600	$10,000	$35,000
Auctions: $61,688, MS-66, June 2014; $400, EF-40, August 2014; $176, VG-8, October 2014													
1858	4,225,700	608	52.4	30%	$50	$75	$100	$140	$250	$350	$600	$1,100	$5,000
Auctions: $1,058, MS-63, January 2015; $423, AU-58, August 2015; $259, AU-55, October 2015; $147, EF-45, February 2015													
1858, Proof	300+	56	63.7								$1,400	$2,250	$6,500
Auctions: $7,050, PF-65, February 2015; $6,756, PF-65, January 2015; $6,463, PF-64, October 2015; $1,821, PF-63, October 2015													
1858-O	7,294,000	507	47.0	19%	$50	$75	$100	$140	$250	$350	$600	$1,200	$8,500
Auctions: $411, MS-61, June 2015; $470, AU-58, January 2015; $141, EF-45, September 2015; $123, EF-40, March 2015													
1858-S	476,000	68	47.9	19%	$60	$100	$200	$300	$450	$675	$1,700	$4,000	$13,500
Auctions: $505, AU-53, March 2015; $423, AU-50, August 2015; $400, EF-45, November 2015; $235, VF-30, February 2015													

1861-O, Cracked Obverse Die
FS-50-1861o-401.

	Mintage	Cert	Avg	%MS	G-4	VG-8	F-12	VF-20	EF-40	AU-50	MS-60 / PF-60	MS-63 / PF-63	MS-65 / PF-65
1859	747,200	192	53.9	33%	$50	$75	$100	$140	$250	$350	$500	$1,100	$5,250
	Auctions: $18,213, MS-67, May 2015; $1,293, MS-61, January 2015; $329, AU-55, October 2015; $153, EF-40, August 2015												
1859, Proof	800	147	63.5								$1,150	$1,600	$5,500
	Auctions: $12,925, PF-67, October 2015; $7,050, PF-66, January 2015; $4,004, PF-65, September 2015; $4,700, PF-64, August 2015												
1859-O	2,834,000	249	47.4	20%	$50	$75	$100	$140	$250	$350	$650	$1,800	$7,500
	Auctions: $9,988, MS-66, May 2015; $541, MS-62, September 2015; $376, AU-55, February 2015; $141, EF-40, September 2015												
1859-S	566,000	70	55.9	51%	$60	$100	$200	$300	$400	$600	$1,300	$3,000	$8,500
	Auctions: $47,000, MS-68, May 2015; $646, AU-55, February 2015; $329, EF-40, May 2015; $306, EF-40, August 2015												
1860	302,700	81	55.5	42%	$60	$75	$100	$175	$300	$500	$875	$1,100	$5,000
	Auctions: $940, MS-62, January 2015; $423, AU-55, October 2015; $400, AU-55, May 2015; $247, EF-45, March 2015												
1860, Proof	1,000	131	63.9								$750	$1,600	$5,000
	Auctions: $29,375, PF-67, May 2015; $2,585, PF-64, January 2015; $1,998, PF-63, July 2015; $1,410, PF-63, June 2015												
1860-O	1,290,000	256	52.2	37%	$50	$75	$100	$140	$250	$350	$650	$1,300	$5,000
	Auctions: $940, MS-63, January 2015; $306, AU-55, May 2015; $235, AU-50, May 2015; $206, EF-45, August 2015												
1860-S	472,000	73	52.0	34%	$60	$100	$200	$300	$400	$600	$1,400	$3,750	$15,000
	Auctions: $1,116, AU-58, July 2015; $646, AU-55, October 2014; $165, AU-50, November 2014; $282, EF-40, April 2015												
1861	2,887,400	482	55.5	46%	$50	$75	$100	$140	$250	$350	$575	$1,200	$5,000
	Auctions: $10,575, MS-66, January 2015; $306, AU-53, May 2015; $165, EF-45, February 2015; $112, VF-35, October 2015												
1861, Proof	1,000	102	63.6								$750	$1,600	$5,000
	Auctions: $1,351, PF-63, September 2015; $823, PF-61, July 2014; $764, PF-60, January 2015												
1861-O (n)	2,532,633	315	50.0	37%	$70	$90	$120	$180	$300	$900	$1,500	$2,800	$6,500
	Auctions: $2,820, MS-64, January 2015; $1,528, AU-53, June 2015; $259, EF-45, March 2015; $212, F-15, October 2015												
1861-O, Cracked Obv (o)	(p)	99	49.5	30%	$360	$550	$775	$1,450	$3,000	$4,500	$14,000		
	Auctions: $16,450, MS-62, October 2014; $11,750, AU-58, September 2013; $4,700, EF-40, August 2014; $3,525, EF-40, August 2014												
1861-S	939,500	119	43.3	16%	$60	$100	$200	$300	$400	$700	$1,200	$2,700	$20,000
	Auctions: $3,760, MS-64, January 2015; $588, AU-55, June 2015; $259, EF-40, September 2015; $112, VF-20, August 2015												
1862	253,000	78	54.2	58%	$100	$150	$200	$350	$500	$650	$1,250	$1,750	$6,000
	Auctions: $18,800, MS-66, May 2015; $881, MS-62, July 2015; $282, EF-45, August 2015; $259, EF-40, February 2015												
1862, Proof	550	199	63.6								$750	$1,600	$5,000
	Auctions: $9,988, PF-65Cam, February 2015; $4,935, PF-65, February 2015; $4,230, PF-65, October 2015; $4,113, PF-65, March 2015												
1862-S	1,352,000	129	52.7	38%	$60	$100	$175	$225	$350	$450	$1,100	$2,700	$25,000
	Auctions: $42,300, MS-66, May 2015; $1,058, MS-61, February 2015; $793, AU-55, January 2015; $223, EF-40, August 2015												
1863	503,200	95	55.6	55%	$100	$150	$200	$350	$500	$650	$1,250	$1,750	$7,500
	Auctions: $24,675, MS-67, January 2015; $212, AU-50, February 2015; $329, EF-45, February 2015; $270, VF-30, December 2014												
1863, Proof	460	135	63.5								$750	$1,600	$5,000
	Auctions: $7,638, PF-66, October 2015; $4,700, PF-65, February 2015; $2,468, PF-64, March 2015; $2,233, PF-64, January 2015												
1863-S	916,000	72	40.9	19%	$60	$100	$175	$225	$350	$550	$1,300	$2,500	$12,000
	Auctions: $3,408, MS-64, January 2015; $588, AU-55, January 2015; $165, EF-40, September 2015; $84, VF-20, October 2015												

n. The 1861-O mintage includes 330,000 half dollars struck by the United States government; 1,240,000 struck for the State of Louisiana after it seceded from the Union; and 962,633 struck after Louisiana joined the Confederate States of America. All of these coins were made from federal dies, rendering it impossible to distinguish one from another with but one exception. **o.** In 1861, the New Orleans Mint used a federal obverse die and a Confederate reverse die to strike a handful of Confederate half dollars. That particular obverse die was also paired with a regular federal reverse die to strike some 1861-O half dollars, which today are popular among collectors, especially in higher grades. Their identifying feature is a die crack running from the denticles to the right of the sixth star down to Miss Liberty's nose (and to her shoulder below her jaw). **p.** Included in 1861-O mintage figure.

	Mintage	Cert	Avg	%MS	G-4	VG-8	F-12	VF-20	EF-40	AU-50	MS-60 PF-60	MS-63 PF-63	MS-65 PF-65
1864	379,100	97	56.6	60%	$100	$150	$200	$350	$450	$800	$1,300	$1,800	$7,500
Auctions: $999, MS-62, July 2015; $646, AU-53, August 2015; $376, AU-50, September 2015; $306, EF-40, February 2015													
1864, Proof	470	155	63.7								$750	$1,600	$5,000
Auctions: $2,233, PF-64, September 2015; $1,175, PF-62, June 2015; $940, PF-62, September 2015; $676, PF-60, October 2015													
1864-S	658,000	68	43.7	18%	$100	$150	$200	$350	$450	$750	$1,800	$4,250	$15,000
Auctions: $4,700, MS-63, February 2015; $940, AU-55, January 2015; $247, VF-30, August 2015; $235, VF-25, May 2015													
1865	511,400	78	52.3	45%	$100	$150	$200	$350	$500	$700	$1,400	$2,100	$5,500
Auctions: $32,900, MS-67, May 2015; $3,290, MS-64, February 2015; $764, AU-53, June 2015; $282, EF-40, August 2015													
1865, Proof	500	201	64.0								$750	$1,600	$5,000
Auctions: $7,050, PF-66, July 2015; $4,465, PF-65Cam, June 2015; $4,700, PF-65, January 2015; $2,115, PF-64, October 2015													
1865-S	675,000	68	43.7	18%	$100	$150	$200	$350	$500	$650	$2,000	$3,500	$50,000
Auctions: $42,300, MS-65, May 2015; $705, AU-53, June 2015; $282, EF-40, May 2015; $247, VF-35, August 2015													
1866-S, Variety 1	60,000	74	27.5	11%	$450	$600	$875	$1,250	$2,300	$3,000	$9,500	$20,000	$70,000
Auctions: $164,500, MS-67, November 2013; $2,585, EF-45, August 2014; $1,410, VF-35, July 2014; $676, F-12, July 2014													
1866, Variety 4	744,900	110	51.1	47%	$60	$100	$175	$225	$350	$600	$1,000	$2,100	$5,850
Auctions: $5,170, MS-66, January 2015; $282, AU-53, May 2015; $200, EF-45, May 2015; $118, VF-25, August 2015													
1866, Variety 4, Proof	725	118	63.7								$700	$1,500	$3,200
Auctions: $3,643, PF-66, January 2015; $3,525, PF-66, July 2015; $2,115, PF-64Cam, November 2014; $1,116, PF-63, October 2015													
1866, No Motto, Proof † (q)	1	1	62.0									—	
Auctions: No auction records available.													
1866-S, Variety 4	994,000	78	44.9	24%	$60	$100	$175	$225	$350	$400	$700	$2,250	$12,000
Auctions: $881, AU-55, January 2015; $259, EF-45, May 2015; $223, EF-40, August 2015; $176, VF-30, January 2015													
1867	449,300	61	50.2	38%	$100	$150	$200	$350	$500	$700	$1,000	$1,600	$5,000
Auctions: $999, AU-58, January 2015; $235, EF-45, May 2015; $329, EF-40, May 2015; $259, VF-35, July 2015													
1867, Proof	625	168	64.0								$700	$1,500	$3,200
Auctions: $8,225, PF-66Cam, October 2015; $3,995, PF-65Cam, February 2015; $3,290, PF-64Cam, January 2015; $793, PF-62, July 2015													
1867-S	1,196,000	98	48.9	26%	$60	$100	$175	$225	$350	$650	$1,250	$3,000	$12,500
Auctions: $1,116, AU-58, January 2015; $306, AU-53, January 2015; $176, EF-45, October 2015; $188, VF-30, June 2015													
1868	417,600	51	49.6	33%	$100	$150	$200	$350	$500	$700	$1,000	$2,000	$7,000
Auctions: $9,988, MS-65, May 2015; $1,175, MS-63, January 2015; $494, AU-55, July 2015; $259, VF-30, May 2015													
1868, Proof	600	161	63.8								$700	$1,500	$3,200
Auctions: $4,230, PF-66, February 2015; $2,585, PF-65, August 2015; $823, PF-62, July 2015; $564, PF-61, March 2015													
1868-S	1,160,000	81	48.8	15%	$60	$100	$175	$225	$350	$500	$1,000	$2,100	$12,500
Auctions: $17,625, MS-66, May 2015; $564, AU-55, January 2015; $353, AU-53, November 2015; $349, AU-53, March 2015													
1869	795,300	138	53.8	33%	$60	$100	$175	$225	$350	$500	$1,000	$1,600	$10,000
Auctions: $1,293, MS-62, June 2015; $376, AU-55, October 2015; $200, EF-45, May 2015; $200, EF-40, May 2015; $408, AU-55, March 2018													
1869, Proof	600	154	63.6								$700	$1,500	$3,200
Auctions: $7,638, PF-67, May 2015; $6,169, PF-67, September 2015; $1,410, PF-64, January 2015; $1,293, PF-64, February 2015													
1869-S	656,000	61	47.9	34%	$60	$100	$175	$225	$350	$475	$1,000	$2,600	$7,500
Auctions: $259, AU-50, November 2015; $189, AU-50, August 2015; $141, EF-40, May 2015; $94, EF-40, February 2015													
1870	633,900	82	50.4	33%	$60	$100	$175	$225	$350	$475	$725	$1,500	$8,000
Auctions: $1,058, MS-62, January 2015; $376, AU-53, November 2015; $212, EF-40, August 2015; $165, VF-30, January 2015													
1870, Proof	1,000	131	63.2								$700	$1,350	$3,400
Auctions: $1,645, PF-64, March 2015; $1,528, PF-64, May 2015; $1,175, PF-63, September 2015; $1,058, PF-63, January 2015													
1870-CC	54,617	72	25.1	6%	$1,750	$2,750	$4,750	$6,500	$12,000	$32,000	$85,000	—	
Auctions: $28,200, AU-50, August 2016; $17,625, EF-45, January 2015; $11,750, EF-45, January 2015; $7,050, VF-30, January 2015													
1870-S	1,004,000	50	45.1	18%	$100	$150	$200	$400	$500	$750	$2,300	$4,000	$32,000
Auctions: $1,293, AU-55, January 2015; $376, EF-45, January 2015; $306, EF-40, May 2015; $176, VF-25, February 2015													

† Ranked in the *100 Greatest U.S. Coins* (fourth edition). **q.** Classified as Judd-538 (*United States Pattern Coins*, tenth edition). This fantasy piece was deliberately struck for pharmacist and coin collector Robert Coulton Davis, likely around 1869 or in the early 1870s, along with the No Motto Proof quarter and dollar of the same date.

1873, Close 3　　　　**1873, Open 3**

	Mintage	Cert	Avg	%MS	G-4	VG-8	F-12	VF-20	EF-40	AU-50	MS-60 PF-60	MS-63 PF-63	MS-65 PF-65
1871	1,203,600	163	52.9	37%	$60	$100	$150	$200	$300	$500	$1,000	$1,300	$4,750
	Auctions: $3,525, MS-64, May 2015; $223, AU-50, March 2015; $176, EF-45, October 2015; $91, VF-30, March 2015												
1871, Proof	960	167	63.3								$700	$1,300	$3,400
	Auctions: $4,230, PF-66, January 2015; $2,703, PF-65, January 2015; $1,410, PF-64, June 2015; $1,058, PF-63, January 2015												
1871-CC	153,950	63	26.5	5%	$525	$750	$1,250	$1,750	$3,250	$6,000	$30,000	$55,000	
	Auctions: $76,375, MS-64, May 2015; $3,055, EF-45, January 2015; $1,998, VF-30, January 2015; $259, AG-3, November 2015												
1871-S	2,178,000	127	47.1	20%	$60	$100	$150	$200	$300	$500	$1,000	$1,850	$8,000
	Auctions: $2,611, MS-64, May 2015; $294, AU-53, July 2015; $165, EF-45, November 2015; $112, EF-40, August 2015												
1872	880,600	86	50.1	28%	$60	$100	$150	$200	$300	$500	$1,000	$1,400	$5,500
	Auctions: $1,528, MS-62, February 2015; $329, AU-55, August 2015; $223, AU-50, May 2015; $153, AU-50, January 2015												
1872, Proof	950	160	63.6								$700	$1,300	$2,800
	Auctions: $5,523, PF-65Cam, June 2015; $4,935, PF-65Cam, January 2015; $4,465, PF-65Cam, February 2015												
1872-CC	257,000	118	27.0	1%	$300	$600	$800	$1,250	$2,500	$5,000	$25,000	$70,000	
	Auctions: $4,230, AU-53, January 2015; $2,115, EF-45, August 2016; $447, F-12, October 2015; $282, VG-8, May 2015												
1872-S	580,000	50	47.8	28%	$100	$150	$200	$400	$500	$700	$1,750	$3,000	$13,500
	Auctions: $2,820, MS-63, February 2015; $1,028, AU-55, June 2015; $353, EF-45, April 2015; $306, VF-30, May 2015												
1873, Close 3, Variety 4	587,000	81	48.6	23%	$60	$100	$175	$225	$350	$600	$1,000	$1,500	$6,000
	Auctions: $1,410, AU-58, July 2015; $212, AU-53, May 2015; $176, EF-45, July 2015; $94, EF-40, May 2015												
1873, Open 3, Variety 4	214,200	14	31.2	0%	$3,250	$4,500	$5,500	$6,750	$8,000	$13,500	$50,000	$95,000	
	Auctions: $55,813, MS-61, October 2014; $21,150, AU-58, January 2015; $4,230, VG-8, January 2015; $3,290, VG-8, August 2014												
1873, Variety 4, Proof	600	179	63.8								$700	$1,300	$2,800
	Auctions: $8,813, PF-66, June 2015; $3,290, PF-65, February 2015; $1,410, PF-64, September 2015; $618, PF-61, June 2015												
1873-CC, Variety 4	122,500	53	31.5	13%	$400	$750	$1,200	$1,750	$4,000	$6,500	$12,000	$32,500	$80,000
	Auctions: $5,053, AU-50, January 2015; $423, G-6, August 2015; $306, G-6, October 2015; $206, AG-3, November 2015												
1873-S, Variety 4 (r)	5,000	0	n/a										
	Auctions: No auction records available.												
1873, Variety 5	1,815,200	301	50.5	36%	$50	$60	$75	$150	$300	$475	$950	$1,800	$15,000
	Auctions: $1,293, AU-58, January 2015; $259, EF-45, November 2015; $159, VF-35, August 2015; $107, VF-25, February 2015												
1873, Variety 5, Proof	800	142	63.7								$1,000	$2,200	$9,000
	Auctions: $12,925, PF-66, September 2014; $6,463, PF-65, March 2015; $2,174, PF-63, June 2015; $1,763, PF-63, January 2015												
1873-CC, Variety 5	214,560	121	34.1	12%	$250	$500	$850	$1,150	$2,250	$3,750	$8,750	$20,000	$50,000
	Auctions: $2,497, EF-45, January 2015; $764, VF-20, June 2015; $376, VG-10, October 2015; $176, AG-3, November 2015												
1873-S, Variety 5	228,000	49	46.8	18%	$100	$150	$200	$350	$500	$750	$2,500	$8,000	$35,000
	Auctions: $705, AU-50, May 2015; $364, AU-50, November 2015; $208, EF-40, October 2015; $165, VF-20, May 2015												
1874	2,359,600	372	52.9	41%	$50	$60	$75	$150	$300	$450	$950	$1,875	$15,000
	Auctions: $25,850, MS-66, May 2015; $200, MS-60, October 2015; $364, AU-53, June 2015; $259, EF-45, August 2015												
1874, Proof	700	203	63.3								$1,000	$2,200	$9,000
	Auctions: $11,750, PF-66, January 2015; $6,169, PF-65, June 2015; $4,465, PF-64Cam, June 2015; $1,469, PF-62, August 2015												
1874-CC	59,000	72	32.2	15%	$1,250	$1,750	$2,250	$3,500	$6,000	$9,000	$15,000	$30,000	$95,000
	Auctions: $94,000, MS-65, May 2015; $44,650, MS-64, January 2015; $1,293, VG-10, October 2014; $1,410, VG-8, September 2014												
1874-S	394,000	54	51.5	44%	$100	$180	$225	$250	$375	$700	$1,700	$3,000	$25,000
	Auctions: $15,275, MS-65, January 2015; $4,406, MS-64, March 2015; $1,116, AU-55, June 2015; $282, VF-35, August 2015												

r. The 1873-S, No Arrows, half dollar is unknown in any collection.

1877, 7 Over 6
FS-50-1877-301.

	Mintage	Cert	Avg	%MS	G-4	VG-8	F-12	VF-20	EF-40	AU-50	MS-60	MS-63	MS-65
											PF-60	PF-63	PF-65
1875	6,026,800	386	53.9	49%	$50	$75	$100	$140	$200	$300	$475	$800	$3,000
	Auctions: $1,410, MS-64, January 2015; $1,116, MS-63, August 2015; $376, AU-58, April 2015; $129, EF-45, March 2015												
1875, Proof	700	136	63.7								$600	$1,150	$2,700
	Auctions: $12,925, PF-67, May 2015; $4,465, PF-66, February 2015; $3,055, PF-65Cam, January 2015; $810, PF-62, March 2015												
1875-CC	1,008,000	161	45.0	37%	$75	$125	$225	$325	$550	$1,000	$1,750	$2,850	$8,500
	Auctions: $881, AU-55, July 2015; $999, AU-53, January 2015; $881, AU-50, January 2015; $353, VF-30, May 2015												
1875-S	3,200,000	269	57.9	68%	$50	$75	$100	$140	$200	$300	$475	$800	$3,000
	Auctions: $2,820, MS-65, January 2015; $646, MS-63, August 2015; $329, AU-55, November 2015; $165, EF-45, August 2015												
1876	8,418,000	436	52.9	45%	$50	$75	$100	$140	$200	$300	$475	$800	$3,800
	Auctions: $3,055, MS-65, March 2015; $588, MS-62, February 2015; $176, AU-53, January 2015; $94, VF-35, January 2015												
1876, Proof	1,150	212	63.5								$600	$1,150	$2,700
	Auctions: $3,055, PF-65Cam, February 2015; $1,410, PF-64, November 2014; $1,116, PF-62Cam, August 2014; $646, PF-61, September 2014												
1876-CC	1,956,000	214	47.8	41%	$85	$110	$165	$200	$400	$700	$1,600	$2,400	$5,500
	Auctions: $1,528, AU-58, January 2015; $212, VF-35, August 2015; $212, VF-25, February 2015; $69, VG-10, March 2015												
1876-S	4,528,000	216	53.2	49%	$40	$45	$65	$80	$120	$225	$450	$800	$3,600
	Auctions: $3,173, MS-65, January 2015; $212, AU-55, July 2015; $176, AU-50, May 2015; $118, EF-45, June 2015												
1877	8,304,000	368	52.9	51%	$40	$60	$70	$80	$120	$225	$450	$800	$3,200
	Auctions: $6,463, MS-67, May 2015; $376, AU-58, July 2015; $200, EF-45, November 2015; $71, EF-40, March 2015												
1877, 7 Over 6 (s)	(t)	0	n/a		$275	$450	$625	$1,200	$2,200	$3,750	$12,000		
	Auctions: $3,335, MS-62, August 2009												
1877, Proof	510	171	63.4								$600	$1,150	$2,700
	Auctions: $11,750, PF-66Cam, February 2015; $3,290, PF-66, October 2015; $1,528, PF-64, January 2015; $881, PF-62, March 2015												
1877-CC	1,420,000	241	52.3	61%	$85	$135	$150	$200	$375	$450	$1,150	$2,250	$5,000
	Auctions: $7,931, MS-66, May 2015; $960, AU-58, January 2015; $212, VF-20, May 2015; $100, VG-10, June 2015												
1877-S	5,356,000	528	55.5	55%	$40	$45	$65	$80	$100	$225	$475	$800	$3,000
	Auctions: $19,975, MS-67, May 2015; $353, AU-58, March 2015; $206, AU-50, January 2015; $153, EF-45, August 2015												
1878	1,377,600	109	53.4	48%	$45	$90	$120	$135	$150	$240	$425	$1,100	$5,200
	Auctions: $705, MS-62, January 2015; $259, AU-50, November 2015; $119, VF-35, June 2015; $84, F-12, May 2015												
1878, Proof	800	226	64.1								$600	$1,150	$2,700
	Auctions: $35,250, PF-68, May 2015; $4,935, PF-66Cam, October 2015; $1,998, PF-64, January 2015; $969, PF-63, January 2015												
1878-CC	62,000	53	23.5	11%	$1,050	$1,350	$2,250	$3,000	$4,250	$6,500	$12,000	$24,000	$50,000
	Auctions: $64,625, MS-65, June 2014; $1,763, VG-10, September 2014; $881, G-4, November 2014												
1878-S	12,000	13	37.3	46%	$30,000	$40,000	$45,000	$55,000	$67,500	$70,000	$100,000	$150,000	$250,000
	Auctions: $199,750, MS-64, June 2014; $58,750, AU-50, August 2014												
1879	4,800	253	60.6	82%	$350	$450	$550	$650	$750	$900	$1,050	$1,300	$3,250
	Auctions: $2,938, MS-65, January 2015; $940, AU-55, June 2015; $881, AU-53, June 2015; $705, EF-40, January 2015												
1879, Proof	1,100	319	63.7								$600	$1,150	$2,700
	Auctions: $8,225, PF-67Cam, February 2015; $2,468, PF-65, March 2015; $1,410, PF-64, January 2015; $911, PF-62, March 2015												
1880	8,400	104	59.0	77%	$350	$450	$550	$650	$750	$900	$1,050	$1,500	$4,000
	Auctions: $8,225, PF-67, May 2015; $4,230, MS-66, January 2015; $1,293, AU-58, June 2015; $1,087, AU-55, June 2015												
1880, Proof	1,355	385	63.8								$600	$1,150	$2,700
	Auctions: $7,050, PF-66Cam, August 2015; $2,938, PF-66, January 2015; $1,645, PF-64, July 2015												

s. The top portion of a 6 is visible on the upper surface of the last 7. **t.** Included in circulation-strike 1877 mintage figure.

	Mintage	Cert	Avg	%MS	G-4	VG-8	F-12	VF-20	EF-40	AU-50	MS-60	MS-63	MS-65
											PF-60	PF-63	PF-65
1881	10,000	106	55.9	74%	$350	$450	$550	$650	$750	$900	$1,050	$1,500	$4,000
	Auctions: $9,400, MS-67, June 2014												
1881, Proof	975	335	63.9								$600	$1,150	$2,700
	Auctions: $9,400, PF-68, May 2015; $6,698, PF-67, July 2014; $2,820, PF-65Cam, July 2014; $2,938, PF-65, September 2014												
1882	4,400	77	58.0	74%	$350	$450	$550	$650	$750	$900	$1,050	$1,600	$4,750
	Auctions: $4,700, MS-65, January 2015; $2,291, MS-64, January 2015; $646, VF-25, October 2015; $470, VG-8, October 2015												
1882, Proof	1,100	318	64.0								$600	$1,150	$2,700
	Auctions: $15,275, PF-67Cam, November 2013; $6,463, PF-66DCam, August 2014; $6,169, PF-65DCam, August 2014; $1,763, PF-63DCam, August 2015												
1883	8,000	92	54.9	66%	$350	$450	$550	$650	$750	$900	$1,050	$1,500	$4,250
	Auctions: $5,640, MS-66, May 2015; $1,116, MS-61, June 2015; $911, AU-58, June 2015; $306, AG-3, October 2015												
1883, Proof	1,039	333	64.0								$600	$1,150	$2,700
	Auctions: $11,163, PF-67Cam, October 2014; $7,638, PF-67Cam, November 2014; $1,998, PF-64Cam, March 2015; $1,528, PF-63Cam, June 2015												
1884	4,400	98	60.6	87%	$425	$475	$550	$650	$775	$925	$1,100	$1,500	$4,500
	Auctions: $21,150, MS-67, January 2015; $15,275, MS-67, June 2014; $1,234, EF-45, July 2015; $517, VG-10, October 2015												
1884, Proof	875	223	63.9								$600	$1,150	$2,700
	Auctions: $7,931, PF-67, May 2015; $2,233, PF-65, September 2015; $1,528, PF-64, August 2015; $764, PF-61, January 2015												
1885	5,200	77	55.8	69%	$500	$550	$625	$725	$800	$900	$1,050	$1,500	$4,250
	Auctions: $4,230, MS-66, January 2015; $1,998, MS-63, January 2015; $1,058, AU-55, February 2015; $1,410, EF-45, January 2015												
1885, Proof	930	301	64.1								$600	$1,150	$2,700
	Auctions: $5,758, PF-67, September 2015; $2,585, PF-65Cam, September 2015; $1,351, PF-63Cam, March 2015; $823, PF-61, July 2015												
1886	5,000	91	56.9	77%	$500	$550	$625	$725	$800	$900	$1,100	$1,500	$4,250
	Auctions: $25,850, MS-67, May 2015; $617, AU-50, June 2015; $646, VG-10, August 2015; $517, VG-8, October 2015												
1886, Proof	886	248	63.9								$600	$1,150	$2,700
	Auctions: $11,163, PF-67Cam, August 2015; $3,290, PF-66, June 2015; $2,585, PF-65, January 2015; $1,116, PF-62, June 2015												
1887	5,000	115	57.4	73%	$525	$575	$650	$750	$950	$1,000	$1,100	$1,400	$4,250
	Auctions: $24,675, MS-67, June 2014; $1,116, AU-50, August 2014; $734, EF-40, October 2014												
1887, Proof	710	186	64.2								$600	$1,150	$2,700
	Auctions: $29,375, PF-68DCam, November 2013												
1888	12,001	127	56.3	69%	$350	$450	$550	$650	$750	$900	$1,000	$1,350	$4,000
	Auctions: $8,813, MS-67, January 2015; $4,230, MS-66, January 2015; $852, AU-50, March 2015; $447, VG-10, October 2015												
1888, Proof	832	219	63.8								$600	$1,150	$2,700
	Auctions: $8,225, PF-67, July 2015; $3,760, PF-66, February 2015; $2,820, PF-65, October 2015; $2,350, PF-64Cam, January 2015												
1889	12,000	112	55.4	68%	$350	$450	$550	$650	$750	$900	$1,000	$1,250	$4,000
	Auctions: $8,225, MS-66, May 2015; $2,115, MS-64, January 2015; $823, AU-55, June 2015; $588, VF-25, October 2015												
1889, Proof	711	195	63.8								$600	$1,150	$2,700
	Auctions: $2,820, PF-66, August 2015; $2,115, PF-65, March 2015; $2,233, PF-64, January 2015; $1,175, PF-63, June 2015												
1890	12,000	105	57.1	76%	$350	$450	$550	$650	$750	$900	$1,000	$1,150	$4,000
	Auctions: $676, MS-60, February 2015; $705, AU-50, September 2015; $676, AU-50, June 2015; $411, VG-8, October 2015												
1890, Proof	590	209	64.4								$600	$1,150	$2,700
	Auctions: $9,988, PF-67Cam, May 2015; $2,585, PF-65, January 2015; $1,645, PF-64Cam, February 2015; $823, PF-62Cam, January 2015												
1891	200,000	176	56.5	68%	$100	$150	$200	$350	$500	$700	$800	$1,200	$3,800
	Auctions: $423, AU-55, November 2015; $541, AU-53, May 2015; $141, VF-35, August 2015; $125, VF-30, October 2015												
1891, Proof	600	194	64.2								$600	$1,150	$2,700
	Auctions: $5,405, PF-67, January 2015; $4,230, PF-66, February 2015; $1,410, PF-64, January 2015; $1,175, PF-63, June 2015												

BARBER OR LIBERTY HEAD (1892–1915)

Designer: *Charles E. Barber.* **Weight:** *12.50 grams.* **Composition:** *.900 silver, .100 copper.*
Diameter: *30.6 mm.* **Edge:** *Reeded.* **Mints:** *Philadelphia, Denver, New Orleans, and San Francisco.*

Mintmark
location is
on the reverse,
below the eagle.

Circulation Strike   **Proof**

History. Charles E. Barber, chief engraver of the U.S. Mint, crafted the eponymous "Barber" or Liberty Head half dollars along with similarly designed dimes and quarters of the same era. His initial, B, is at the truncation of Miss Liberty's neck. Production of the coins was continuous from 1892 to 1915, stopping a year before the dime and quarter of the same design.

Striking and Sharpness. On the obverse, check Miss Liberty's hair details and other features. On the reverse, the eagle's leg at the lower right and the arrows often are weak, and there can be weakness at the upper right of the shield and the nearby wing area. At EF and below, sharpness of strike on the reverse is not important. Most Proofs are sharply struck, although many are weak on the eagle's leg at the lower right and on certain parts of the arrows and/or the upper-right area of the shield and the nearby wing. The Proofs of 1892 to 1901 usually have cameo contrast between the designs and the mirror fields. Those of 1914 and 1915 are often with extensive hairlines or other problems.

Availability. Most examples seen in the marketplace are well worn. There are no rarities in the Barber half dollar series, although some are scarcer than others. Coins that are Fine or better are much scarcer—in particular the San Francisco Mint issues of 1901, 1904, and 1907. MS coins are available of all dates and mints, but some are very elusive. Proofs exist in proportion to their mintages. Choicer examples tend to be of later dates, similar to other Barber coins.

GRADING STANDARDS

MS-60 to 70 (Mint State). *Obverse:* At MS-60, some abrasion and contact marks are evident, most noticeably on the cheek and the obverse field to the right. Luster is present, but may be dull or lifeless. Many Barber coins have been cleaned, especially of the earlier dates. At MS-63, contact marks are very few; abrasion still is evident but less than at lower levels. Indeed, the cheek of Miss Liberty virtually showcases abrasion. This is even more evident on a half dollar than on lower denominations. An

1909. Graded MS-62.

MS-65 coin may have minor abrasion, but contact marks are so minute as to require magnification. Luster should be full and rich. *Reverse:* Comments apply as for the obverse, except that in lower Mint State grades abrasion and contact marks are most noticeable on the head and tail of the eagle and on the tips of the wings. At MS-65 or higher there are no marks visible to the unaided eye. The field is mainly protected by design elements, so the reverse often appears to grade a point or two higher than the obverse.

    Illustrated coin: On this example, mottled light-brown toning appears over lustrous surfaces.

AU-50, 53, 55, 58 (About Uncirculated).
Obverse: Light wear is seen on the head, especially on the forward hair under LIBERTY. At AU-58, the luster is extensive but incomplete, especially on the higher parts and in the right field. At AU–50 and 53, luster is less. *Reverse:* Wear is seen on the head and tail of the eagle and on the tips of the wings. At AU–50 and 53, there still is significant luster. An AU-58 coin (as determined by the obverse) can have the reverse appear to be full Mint State.

1915-D. Graded AU-53.

  Illustrated coin: Areas of original Mint luster can be seen on this coin, more so on the reverse than on the obverse.

EF-40, 45 (Extremely Fine). *Obverse:* Further wear is seen on the head. The hair above the forehead lacks most detail. LIBERTY shows wear but still is strong. *Reverse:* Further wear is seen on the head and tail of the eagle and on the tips of the wings, most evident at the left and right extremes of the wings At this level and below, sharpness of strike on the reverse is not important.

1908. Graded EF-45.

VF-20, 30 (Very Fine). *Obverse:* The head shows more wear, now with nearly all detail gone in the hair above the forehead. LIBERTY shows wear, but is complete. The leaves on the head all show wear, as does the upper part of the cap. *Reverse:* Wear is more extensive, particularly noticeable on the outer parts of the wings, the head, the shield, and the tail.

  Illustrated coin: This coin is seemingly lightly cleaned.

1897-S. Graded VF-30.

F-12, 15 (Fine). *Obverse:* The head shows extensive wear. LIBERTY, the key place to check, is weak, especially at ER, but is fully readable. The ANA grading standards and *Photograde* adhere to this. PCGS suggests that lightly struck coins "may have letters partially missing." Traditionally, collectors insist on full LIBERTY. *Reverse:* More wear is seen on the reverse, in the places as above. E PLURIBUS UNUM is light, with one to several letters worn away.

1909-O. Graded F-12.

VG-8, 10 (Very Good). *Obverse:* A net of three letters in LIBERTY must be readable. Traditionally LI is clear, and after that there is a partial letter or two. *Reverse:* Further wear has smoothed more than half of the feathers in the wing. The shield is indistinct except for a few traces of interior lines. The motto is partially worn away. The rim is full, and many if not most denticles can be seen.

1915-S. Graded VG-8.

G-4, 6 (Good). *Obverse:* The head is in outline form, with the center flat. Most of the rim is there and all letters and the date are full. *Reverse:* The eagle shows only a few feathers, and only a few scattered letters remain in the motto. The rim may be worn flat in some or all of the area, but the peripheral lettering is clear.

   Illustrated coin: On this coin the obverse is perhaps G-6 and the reverse AG-3. The grade might be averaged as G-4.

1892-O. Graded G-4.

AG-3 (About Good). *Obverse:* The stars and motto are worn, and the border may be indistinct. Distinctness varies at this level. The date is clear. Grading is usually determined by the reverse. *Reverse:* The rim is gone and the letters are partially worn away. The eagle is mostly flat, perhaps with a few hints of feathers. Usually, the obverse appears to be in a slightly higher grade than the reverse.

1896-S. Graded AG-3.

PF-60 to 70 (Proof). *Obverse and Reverse:* Proofs that are extensively cleaned and have many hairlines, or that are dull and grainy, are lower level, such as PF–60 to 62; these are not widely desired. With medium hairlines and good reflectivity, an assigned grade of PF-64 is appropriate. Tiny horizontal lines on Miss Liberty's cheek, known as slide marks, from National and other album slides scuffing the relief of the cheek, are endemic on all Barber

1914. Graded PF-61.

silver coins. With noticeable marks of this type, the highest grade assignable is PF-64. With relatively few hairlines, a rating of PF-65 can be given. PF-66 should have hairlines so delicate that magnification is needed to see them. Above that, a Proof should be free of any hairlines or other problems.

   Illustrated coin: This is an attractive coin at the relatively low PF-61 grade.

1892-O, Normal O **1892-O, Micro O**
FS-50-1892o-501.

	Mintage	Cert	Avg	%MS	G-4	VG-8	F-12	VF-20	EF-40	AU-50	MS-60 / PF-60	MS-63 / PF-63	MS-65 / PF-65
1892	934,000	999	58.7	73%	$27	$35	$70	$135	$210	$350	$600	$925	$2,000
Auctions: $39,950, MS-68, October 2015; $1,116, MS-64, January 2015; $353, AU-55, May 2015; $247, EF-45, September 2015													
1892, Proof	1,245	371	64.4								$525	$1,100	$2,250
Auctions: $7,639, PF-68, January 2015; $9,400, PF-67UCam, October 2015; $4,700, PF-66, January 2015; $2,585, PF-64DCam, August 2015													
1892-O	390,000	470	33.0	32%	$300	$475	$600	$675	$700	$850	$1,100	$1,850	$3,250
Auctions: $47,000, MS-68, August 2015; $588, AU-55, October 2015; $725, AU-53, January 2015; $200, G-4, February 2015													
1892-O, Micro O (a)	(b)	17	22.3	24%	$3,650	$7,500	$10,000	$12,500	$15,500	$20,000	$32,500	$45,000	$85,000
Auctions: $36,014, MS-63, June 2014; $3,055, G-4, March 2016; $3,055, AG-3, September 2016													
1892-S	1,029,028	326	27.5	22%	$275	$340	$400	$550	$750	$925	$1,200	$2,250	$5,500
Auctions: $30,550, MS-67, October 2015; $646, EF-40, January 2015; $259, VG-8, June 2015; $188, G-6, November 2015													
1893	1,826,000	291	54.1	53%	$25	$30	$80	$160	$210	$400	$600	$1,000	$3,000
Auctions: $28,200, MS-67, August 2015; $1,058, MS-64, October 2015; $212, EF-40, September 2015; $306, VF-35, January 2015													
1893, Proof	792	280	64.4								$525	$1,100	$2,250
Auctions: $18,800, PF-68Cam, August 2015; $4,530, PF-67, February 2015; $1,265, PF-63Cam, June 2015; $564, PF-61, September 2015													
1893-O	1,389,000	219	49.7	58%	$40	$75	$135	$250	$350	$500	$900	$1,250	$8,500
Auctions: $18,800, MS-66, July 2015; $1,880, MS-64, March 2015; $505, MS-60, September 2015; $588, AU-53, July 2015													
1893-S	740,000	262	21.9	18%	$150	$210	$550	$800	$1,200	$1,600	$2,250	$4,000	$17,000
Auctions: $12,925, MS-65, February 2015; $1,763, AU-58, August 2015; $388, F-12, October 2015; $212, VG-10, February 2015													
1894	1,148,000	237	46.2	51%	$30	$50	$115	$200	$300	$375	$600	$1,100	$2,500
Auctions: $17,625, MS-67, October 2015; $306, AU-55, May 2015; $223, EF-40, May 2015; $188, VF-30, January 2015													
1894, Proof	972	313	64.2								$525	$1,100	$2,250
Auctions: $4,406, PF-67, June 2015; $4,113, PF-66, May 2015; $1,293, PF-64, July 2015; $3,055, PF-63, January 2015													
1894-O	2,138,000	200	48.6	56%	$25	$35	$90	$170	$300	$375	$600	$1,150	$5,000
Auctions: $14,100, MS-66, August 2015; $999, AU-58, June 2015; $194, VF-20, August 2015; $106, F-15, January 2015													
1894-S	4,048,690	235	45.3	46%	$22	$25	$70	$140	$215	$400	$650	$1,400	$6,500
Auctions: $8,813, MS-66, May 2015; $1,175, MS-63, June 2015; $329, AU-50, September 2015; $212, VF-25, June 2015													
1895	1,834,338	212	48.8	53%	$18	$25	$70	$140	$210	$400	$600	$900	$2,650
Auctions: $5,170, MS-66, October 2015; $1,058, MS-64, January 2015; $517, AU-55, October 2015; $306, AU-50, May 2015													
1895, Proof	880	354	64.5								$525	$1,100	$2,250
Auctions: $3,819, PF-67, March 2015; $3,290, PF-66, June 2015; $2,100, PF-65, November 2014; $1,755, PF-65, October 2015													
1895-O	1,766,000	166	37.9	36%	$40	$60	$130	$180	$260	$385	$750	$1,450	$5,000
Auctions: $25,850, MS-67, October 2015; $541, AU-50, July 2015; $176, EF-45, January 2015; $79, VG-10, February 2015													
1895-S	1,108,086	179	49.8	61%	$30	$65	$140	$250	$300	$385	$625	$1,250	$5,000
Auctions: $11,163, MS-66, August 2015; $794, AU-55, July 2015; $355, VF-30, January 2015; $94, F-12, May 2015													
1896	950,000	138	49.6	53%	$35	$45	$90	$160	$240	$365	$600	$1,000	$3,600
Auctions: $25,850, MS-67, October 2015; $1,293, MS-64, September 2015; $852, MS-63, January 2015; $176, VF-25, January 2015													
1896, Proof	762	265	64.4								$525	$1,100	$2,250
Auctions: $7,050, PF-67Cam, October 2015; $1,880, PF-64, August 2015; $940, PF-63, February 2015; $881, PF-62, June 2015													
1896-O	924,000	124	25.6	15%	$50	$70	$210	$500	$2,200	$3,300	$6,000	$10,500	$24,000
Auctions: $88,125, MS-67, August 2015; $3,525, AU-55, July 2016; $3,525, AU-55, October 2015; $646, VF-30, January 2015													
1896-S	1,140,948	212	22.3	20%	$115	$165	$240	$425	$959	$1,450	$2,500	$3,750	$8,000
Auctions: $23,500, MS-66, May 2015; $1,528, EF-45, September 2015; $881, VF-35, October 2015; $212, VG-8, February 2015													

a. This variety "was created when an O mintmark punch for quarters was used in place of the regular, larger mintmark intended for use on half dollar dies. . . . Many examples show strong strike doubling on reverse" (*Cherrypickers' Guide to Rare Die Varieties*, sixth edition, volume II). **b.** Included in 1892-O mintage figure.

	Mintage	Cert	Avg	%MS	G-4	VG-8	F-12	VF-20	EF-40	AU-50	MS-60	MS-63	MS-65
											PF-60	PF-63	PF-65
1897	2,480,000	251	51.9	52%	$20	$22	$45	$95	$200	$375	$600	$950	$3,250
	Auctions: $19,388, MS-67, August 2015; $212, EF-45, January 2015; $141, VF-30, May 2015; $52, F-15, September 2015												
1897, Proof	731	328	64.8								$525	$1,100	$2,250
	Auctions: $61,688, PF-69UCam, August 2015; $18,800, PF-68DCam, January 2015; $5,875, PF-67Cam, October 2015; $4,465, PF-65Cam, January 2015												
1897-O	632,000	339	15.1	9%	$160	$230	$500	$750	$1,050	$1,300	$2,000	$4,000	$8,000
	Auctions: $25,850, MS-67, October 2015; $8,813, MS-66, October 2016; $940, VF-25, January 2015; $259, VG-10, August 2015												
1897-S	933,900	297	21.2	19%	$150	$220	$350	$550	$900	$1,450	$2,750	$3,750	$6,750
	Auctions: $35,250, MS-67, May 2015; $4,230, AU-58, August 2015; $282, F-12, November 2015; $176, VG-8, May 2015												
1898	2,956,000	252	48.5	46%	$18	$20	$45	$95	$200	$375	$600	$900	$3,000
	Auctions: $37,600, MS-67, October 2015; $5,170, MS-66, January 2015; $482, AU-58, June 2015; $353, AU-53, January 2015												
1898, Proof	735	268	64.9								$525	$1,100	$2,250
	Auctions: $15,275, PF-68Cam, January 2015; $12,925, PF-67Cam, August 2015; $2,938, PF-66Cam, September 2015; $1,528, PF-64Cam, January 2015												
1898-O	874,000	135	32.5	27%	$38	$90	$240	$400	$540	$775	$1,500	$2,600	$6,500
	Auctions: $22,325, MS-67, October 2015; $2,233, AU-50, January 2015; $553, VF-30, July 2015; $212, F-12, August 2015												
1898-S	2,358,550	145	40.2	25%	$30	$48	$90	$185	$340	$500	$1,500	$3,600	$8,000
	Auctions: $4,700, MS-64, January 2015; $3,564, MS-64, September 2015; $823, AU-55, August 2015; $247, VF-30, January 2015												
1899	5,538,000	388	47.9	43%	$18	$20	$45	$95	$200	$375	$600	$1,000	$2,250
	Auctions: $19,975, MS-67, August 2015; $400, AU-58, April 2015; $376, AU-55, September 2015; $112, VF-30, February 2015												
1899, Proof	846	212	64.4								$525	$1,100	$2,250
	Auctions: $11,163, PF-68, August 2015; $3,290, PF-66Cam, October 2015; $1,234, PF-64Cam, March 2015; $646, PF-62, July 2015												
1899-O	1,724,000	139	40.4	40%	$25	$35	$80	$165	$275	$400	$700	$1,600	$4,500
	Auctions: $11,750, MS-66, May 2015; $3,760, MS-65, August 2015; $2,820, AU-58, January 2015; $141, VF-30, November 2015												
1899-S	1,686,411	136	46.7	37%	$25	$40	$90	$175	$300	$400	$850	$2,000	$4,500
	Auctions: $17,625, MS-67, August 2015; $764, AU-58, January 2015; $259, EF-45, June 2015; $141, VF-25, November 2015												
1900	4,762,000	377	51.7	52%	$17	$19	$45	$95	$200	$375	$600	$850	$2,250
	Auctions: $19,975, MS-67, October 2015; $4,700, MS-66, May 2015; $376, AU-58, August 2015; $147, VF-35, December 2015												
1900, Proof	912	296	64.6								$525	$1,100	$2,250
	Auctions: $10,869, PF-68Cam, October 2015; $7,638, PF-67Cam, August 2015; $2,115, PF-65, February 2015; $940, PF-63, January 2015												
1900-O	2,744,000	112	38.5	29%	$18	$25	$60	$170	$325	$550	$1,200	$3,400	$10,000
	Auctions: $37,600, MS-67, May 2015; $30,550, MS-66, August 2015; $5,170, MS-64, January 2015; $376, AU-50, May 2015												
1900-S	2,560,322	131	44.6	26%	$17	$19	$45	$100	$210	$375	$650	$2,400	$10,000
	Auctions: $22,325, MS-67, May 2015; $14,100, MS-66, October 2015; $470, AU-58, January 2015; $353, AU-53, February 2015												
1901	4,268,000	346	50.2	42%	$17	$18	$45	$95	$200	$375	$550	$850	$2,350
	Auctions: $17,625, MS-67, August 2015; $376, AU-58, January 2015; $165, VF-30, October 2015; $123, VF-25, April 2015												
1901, Proof	813	267	64.5								$525	$1,100	$2,250
	Auctions: $32,900, PF-69Cam, August 2015; $9,106, PF-68, September 2015; $1,175, PF-64, January 2015; $881, PF-63, March 2015												
1901-O	1,124,000	87	42.2	43%	$17	$26	$80	$230	$1,100	$1,500	$2,400	$4,000	$13,500
	Auctions: $6,169, MS-64, August 2015; $1,528, AU-55, September 2015; $470, VF-35, July 2015; $317, VF-20, August 2015												
1901-S	847,044	108	24.1	16%	$32	$55	$165	$400	$1,250	$1,600	$3,500	$6,500	$12,000
	Auctions: $11,750, MS-65, August 2015; $9,694, MS-65, October 2016; $2,703, AU-55, September 2015												
1902	4,922,000	308	48.7	42%	$17	$18	$45	$95	$200	$375	$550	$900	$2,250
	Auctions: $14,100, MS-67, October 2015; $517, MS-62, February 2015; $541, AU-58, February 2015; $84, VF-25, January 2015												
1902, Proof	777	238	64.1								$525	$1,100	$2,250
	Auctions: $4,113, PF-67, March 2015; $4,230, PF-66Cam, February 2015; $2,233, PF-65, January 2015; $1,293, PF-64, January 2015												
1902-O	2,526,000	142	43.7	37%	$17	$20	$55	$105	$220	$400	$900	$2,500	$7,500
	Auctions: $16,450, MS-67, August 2015; $1,763, MS-63, October 2015; $1,528, AU-58, June 2015; $129, VF-30, April 2015												
1902-S	1,460,670	83	42.9	42%	$19	$28	$65	$150	$250	$400	$900	$2,400	$4,250
	Auctions: $28,200, MS-67+, August 2015; $10,575, MS-66, October 2015; $5,170, MS-65, August 2015; $5,170, MS-64, October 2015												

	Mintage	Cert	Avg	%MS	G-4	VG-8	F-12	VF-20	EF-40	AU-50	MS-60 PF-60	MS-63 PF-63	MS-65 PF-65
1903	2,278,000	124	48.3	45%	$17	$18	$45	$95	$200	$375	$550	$1,500	$7,200
	Auctions: $12,925, MS-66, May 2015; $4,230, MS-65, June 2015; $588, AU-58, June 2015; $165, VF-30, January 2015												
1903, Proof	755	256	64.5								$525	$1,100	$2,250
	Auctions: $12,925, PF-68, May 2015; $4,348, PF-66Cam, January 2015; $2,938, PF-66, June 2015; $1,382, PF-64, February 2015												
1903-O	2,100,000	186	50.4	53%	$17	$18	$55	$125	$210	$400	$800	$1,700	$4,500
	Auctions: $9,988, MS-66, May 2015; $4,230, MS-65, August 2015; $646, AU-55, January 2015; $353, EF-45, January 2015												
1903-S	1,920,772	121	44.6	50%	$17	$19	$60	$130	$230	$450	$950	$1,700	$3,500
	Auctions: $17,625, MS-67, May 2015; $1,763, AU-58, July 2015; $308, EF-40, January 2015; $153, VF-25, February 2015												
1904	2,992,000	212	48.5	43%	$17	$18	$35	$85	$200	$375	$600	$1,000	$4,000
	Auctions: $4,465, MS-66, August 2015; $250, AU-55, May 2015; $259, EF-45, May 2015; $89, VF-25, January 2015												
1904, Proof	670	262	64.3								$525	$1,100	$2,250
	Auctions: $12,925, PF-68, October 2015; $3,878, PF-67, October 2015; $2,820, PF-66, July 2015; $2,291, PF-65, January 2015												
1904-O	1,117,600	95	39.5	24%	$22	$35	$95	$235	$400	$800	$1,700	$3,750	$10,750
	Auctions: $12,925, MS-66, October 2015; $2,233, MS-60, June 2015; $705, AU-55, June 2015; $881, EF-45, January 2015												
1904-S	553,038	251	18.0	8%	$48	$150	$350	$900	$3,000	$7,000	$12,500	$20,000	$39,000
	Auctions: $91,063, MS-67, August 2015; $28,200, MS-64, March 2016; $3,055, EF-45, July 2015; $2,820, VF-35, January 2015												
1905	662,000	128	45.9	45%	$25	$29	$85	$185	$265	$425	$700	$1,600	$4,800
	Auctions: $16,450, MS-67, October 2015; $4,583, MS-65, January 2015; $823, AU-58, July 2015; $223, EF-45, February 2015												
1905, Proof	727	212	64.1								$525	$1,100	$2,250
	Auctions: $9,106, PF-68, August 2015; $2,585, PF-66, October 2015; $2,350, PF-65, March 2015; $1,645, PF-64, January 2015												
1905-O	505,000	133	46.9	61%	$30	$45	$125	$225	$350	$525	$850	$1,750	$4,500
	Auctions: $56,400, MS-68, January 2015; $8,813, MS-67, October 2015; $2,233, AU-58, June 2015; $118, F-12, January 2015												
1905-S	2,494,000	134	39.7	36%	$16	$19	$53	$140	$240	$400	$700	$1,600	$7,500
	Auctions: $14,100, MS-67, August 2015; $1,410, AU-58, August 2015; $259, EF-45, April 2015; $179, VF-30, May 2015												
1906	2,638,000	375	50.9	53%	$16	$17	$45	$95	$200	$375	$550	$950	$2,100
	Auctions: $15,275, MS-67, August 2015; $2,703, MS-65, March 2015; $329, AU-53, January 2015; $188, EF-45, May 2015												
1906, Proof	675	257	64.5								$525	$1,100	$2,250
	Auctions: $10,869, PF-68, May 2015; $4,230, PF-67, October 2015; $2,938, PF-66, July 2015; $2,176, PF-65, January 2015												
1906-D	4,028,000	306	46.9	44%	$16	$17	$45	$95	$200	$375	$550	$950	$2,600
	Auctions: $47,000, MS-67, May 2015; $423, AU-58, June 2015; $223, EF-45, August 2015; $118, VF-30, February 2015												
1906-O	2,446,000	139	39.1	31%	$16	$19	$42	$95	$200	$400	$900	$1,400	$5,500
	Auctions: $18,800, MS-67, May 2015; $7,050, MS-66, October 2015; $282, EF-45, September 2015; $94, F-15, June 2015												
1906-S	1,740,154	131	48.4	48%	$16	$19	$53	$115	$210	$375	$625	$1,400	$3,000
	Auctions: $15,275, MS-67, May 2015; $940, MS-62, February 2015; $1,058, AU-55, January 2015; $212, VF-25, January 2015												
1907	2,598,000	323	52.9	60%	$16	$17	$45	$95	$200	$375	$550	$950	$2,100
	Auctions: $3,995, MS-66, January 2015; $881, MS-63, October 2015; $282, AU-53, May 2015; $165, VF-35, February 2015												
1907, Proof	575	191	64.2								$525	$1,100	$2,250
	Auctions: $18,800, PF-68, June 2014												
1907-D	3,856,000	355	47.8	46%	$16	$17	$45	$95	$200	$375	$550	$950	$2,100
	Auctions: $3,055, MS-66, October 2015; $1,116, MS-63, August 2015; $353, AU-53, April 2015; $112, VF-30, May 2015												
1907-O	3,946,600	301	48.4	53%	$16	$17	$45	$95	$200	$375	$550	$950	$2,100
	Auctions: $16,450, MS-67, August 2015; $306, AU-50, January 2015; $153, EF-40, August 2015; $212, VF-35, May 2015												
1907-S	1,250,000	99	36.1	31%	$18	$30	$85	$185	$425	$725	$2,500	$6,000	$11,000
	Auctions: $17,625, MS-67, October 2015; $2,585, AU-53, January 2015; $450, VF-35, May 2015; $165, F-15, May 2015												
1908	1,354,000	203	51.0	58%	$16	$17	$45	$95	$200	$375	$550	$950	$2,100
	Auctions: $12,925, MS-67, August 2015; $2,233, MS-65, June 2015; $1,058, MS-64, March 2015; $911, MS-63, January 2015												
1908, Proof	545	178	64.3								$525	$1,100	$2,250
	Auctions: $7,050, PF-68, October 2015; $2,115, PF-65, June 2015; $823, PF-63, September 2015; $764, PF-62, June 2015												
1908-D	3,280,000	391	45.4	41%	$16	$17	$45	$95	$200	$375	$550	$950	$2,300
	Auctions: $22,325, MS-68, October 2015; $2,350, MS-65, March 2015; $306, AU-55, January 2015; $176, EF-45, September 2015												
1908-O	5,360,000	307	45.0	46%	$16	$17	$45	$95	$200	$375	$550	$950	$2,100
	Auctions: $15,275, MS-67, August 2015; $793, MS-63, June 2015; $646, AU-58, January 2015; $646, AU-53, May 2015												
1908-S	1,644,828	110	35.6	36%	$16	$25	$75	$160	$400	$600	$1,100	$2,750	$8,500
	Auctions: $7,050, MS-66, August 2015; $3,819, MS-65, March 2015; $3,055, MS-64, January 2015; $2,585, AU-58, August 2015												

1909-S, Inverted Mintmark
FS-50-1909S-501.

1911-S, Repunched Mintmark
FS-50-1911S-501.

	Mintage	Cert	Avg	%MS	G-4	VG-8	F-12	VF-20	EF-40	AU-50	MS-60 PF-60	MS-63 PF-63	MS-65 PF-65
1909	2,368,000	501	47.4	50%	$16	$17	$45	$95	$200	$375	$550	$950	$2,100
Auctions: $3,760, MS-66, May 2015; $447, AU-55, February 2015; $306, AU-53, October 2015; $165, EF-40, January 2015													
1909, Proof	650	287	64.5								$525	$1,100	$2,250
Auctions: $11,163, PF-68Cam, May 2015; $1,880, PF-64, January 2015; $940, PF-63, October 2015; $881, PF-62, June 2015													
1909-O	925,400	157	35.6	36%	$18	$22	$65	$175	$375	$650	$1,100	$1,650	$4,500
Auctions: $$16,450, MS-66, May 2015; $2,820, MS-64, September 2015; $705, AU-50, July 2015; $106, F-15, August 2015													
1909-S	1,764,000	165	33.9	29%	$16	$17	$45	$110	$250	$475	$750	$1,300	$3,500
Auctions: $17,625, MS-67, May 2015; $3,525, MS-65, January 2015; $329, EF-45, January 2015; $259, EF-40, February 2015													
1909-S, Inverted Mintmark (c)	**(d)**	0	n/a							$425	$675	$1,550	
Auctions: $11,750, MS-67, October 2015; $4,406, MS-66, November 2014; $141, VF-35, June 2015; $206, VF-30, August 2014													
1910	418,000	168	46.6	50%	$20	$30	$95	$175	$320	$410	$600	$1,100	$3,200
Auctions: $8,225, MS-66, August 2015; $646, MS-61, September 2015; $764, AU-58, October 2015; $188, VF-25, May 2015													
1910, Proof	551	256	64.5								$525	$1,100	$2,250
Auctions: $15,275, PF-68, October 2015; $5,875, PF-67Cam, January 2015; $1,175, PF-64, August 2015													
1910-S	1,948,000	149	35.4	30%	$18	$20	$35	$95	$200	$375	$700	$2,000	$4,000
Auctions: $15,275, MS-67, October 2015; $376, AU-50, January 2015; $147, VF-35, October 2015; $141, VF-30, May 2015													
1911	1,406,000	346	52.4	59%	$16	$17	$45	$95	$200	$375	$550	$950	$2,100
Auctions: $4,702, MS-66, August 2015; $494, MS-62, January 2015; $306, AU-55, January 2015; $129, VF-30, January 2015													
1911, Proof	543	240	64.5								$525	$1,100	$2,250
Auctions: $16,450, PF-67, October 2015; $1,175, PF-64, October 2015; $588, PF-62, September 2015; $541, PF-61, June 2015													
1911-D	695,080	154	51.3	58%	$16	$17	$45	$95	$200	$375	$550	$950	$2,100
Auctions: $15,275, MS-67, October 2015; $2,115, MS-65, September 2015; $1,704, MS-64, June 2015; $1,177, MS-64, July 2015													
1911-S	1,272,000	125	34.9	28%	$18	$20	$40	$120	$240	$425	$700	$1,500	$4,000
Auctions: $42,300, MS-67, August 2015; $3,532, MS-65, August 2015; $118, VF-30, April 2015; $106, VF-25, February 2015													
1911-S, Repunched Mintmark (e)	**(f)**	0	n/a							$475	$750	$1,600	$5,400
Auctions: $4,888, MS-65, December 2009													
1912	1,550,000	403	50.8	55%	$16	$17	$45	$95	$200	$375	$550	$950	$2,100
Auctions: $15,275, MS-66, May 2015; $2,233, MS-65, January 2015; $1,116, MS-64, January 2015; $423, AU-58, September 2015													
1912, Proof	700	193	64.0								$525	$1,100	$2,250
Auctions: $8,813, PF-68, May 2015; $4,465, PF-67, January 2015; $1,763, PF-65, October 2015; $881, PF-63, June 2015													
1912-D	2,300,800	607	49.3	52%	$16	$17	$45	$95	$200	$375	$550	$950	$2,100
Auctions: $4,700, MS-66, October 2015; $353, AU-58, February 2015; $176, EF-40, May 2015; $94, VF-20, July 2015													
1912-S	1,370,000	239	40.6	44%	$16	$18	$45	$100	$200	$425	$600	$1,000	$3,250
Auctions: $12,338, MS-67, August 2015; $376, AU-50, October 2015; $200, EF-40, January 2015; $129, VF-25, January 2015													
1913	188,000	468	17.4	11%	$75	$90	$210	$425	$800	$1,200	$1,750	$2,100	$4,000
Auctions: $8,225, MS-66, October 2015; $494, VF-20, June 2015; $79, VG-8, February 2015; $59, G-6, August 2015													
1913, Proof	627	199	64.0								$600	$1,100	$2,250
Auctions: $3,055, PF-66, October 2015; $1,293, PF-64, August 2015; $940, PF-63, June 2015; $541, PF-62, June 2015													
1913-D	534,000	281	51.9	51%	$16	$17	$45	$95	$200	$375	$550	$950	$3,700
Auctions: $7,050, MS-66, August 2015; $282, AU-55, July 2015; $353, AU-53, April 2015; $306, EF-40, November 2015													
1913-S	604,000	163	41.6	48%	$16	$25	$55	$120	$275	$400	$800	$1,700	$4,000
Auctions: $21,150, MS-67, October 2015; $12,925, MS-66, September 2015; $1,763, MS-64, January 2015													

c. The S mintmark was punched into the die upside-down (with the top slightly wider than the base). **d.** Included in 1909-S mintage figure. **e.** The lower serif of the underlying mintmark is visible protruding from the primary serif. **f.** Included in 1911-S mintage figure.

	Mintage	Cert	Avg	%MS	G-4	VG-8	F-12	VF-20	EF-40	AU-50	MS-60	MS-63	MS-65
											PF-60	PF-63	PF-65
1914	124,230	600	18.6	15%	$125	$140	$325	$550	$1,000	$1,150	$1,500	$2,100	$7,000
Auctions: $9,988, MS-65, January 2015; $2,585, AU-58, September 2015; $294, F-15, May 2015; $129, VG-8, February 2015													
1914, Proof	380	174	64.4								$650	$1,200	$2,250
Auctions: $5,875, PF-67, October 2015; $4,700, PF-66, June 2015; $2,056, PF-64, October 2015; $423, PF-58, June 2015													
1914-S	992,000	193	40.3	41%	$16	$20	$40	$100	$200	$400	$600	$1,150	$3,500
Auctions: $22,325, MS-66, February 2015; $235, EF-40, January 2015; $118, VF-25, May 2015; $79, F-15, March 2015													
1915	138,000	632	14.7	6%	$85	$135	$285	$375	$650	$1,000	$1,400	$2,250	$5,750
Auctions: $11,750, MS-66, August 2015; $6,463, MS-66, October 2016; $4,230, MS-65, July 2016													
1915, Proof	450	175	64.5								$700	$1,200	$2,750
Auctions: $15,275, PF-68, May 2015; $2,703, PF-66, January 2015; $3,290, PF-65, October 2015; $1,528, PF-64, August 2015													
1915-D	1,170,400	685	52.0	56%	$16	$17	$45	$95	$200	$375	$550	$850	$2,000
Auctions: $4,465, MS-66, July 2015; $188, AU-50, February 2015; $188, EF-45, October 2015; $165, EF-40, May 2015													
1915-S	1,604,000	529	48.0	53%	$16	$17	$45	$95	$200	$375	$550	$850	$2,000
Auctions: $8,225, MS-67, August 2015; $588, AU-58, October 2015; $112, VF-25, May 2015; $52, F-12, February 2015													

LIBERTY WALKING (1916–1947)

Designer: *Adolph A. Weinman.* **Weight:** *12.50 grams.*
Composition: *.900 silver, .100 copper (net weight .36169 oz. pure silver).*
Diameter: *30.6 mm.* **Edge:** *Reeded.* **Mints:** *Philadelphia, Denver, and San Francisco.*

Circulation Strike   Proof

Mintmark location,   Mintmark location,
1916–1917, is on the   1917–1947, is on the
obverse, below the motto.   reverse, below the branch.

History. The Liberty Walking half dollar was designed by Adolph A. Weinman, the sculptor who also created the Mercury or Winged Liberty Head dime. His monogram appears under the tips of the eagle's wing feathers. Mintage was intermittent from 1916 to 1947, with none struck in 1922, 1924, 1925, 1926, 1930, 1931, and 1932. On the 1916 coins and some of the 1917 coins, the mintmark is located on the obverse, below IN GOD WE TRUST. Other coins of 1917, and those through 1947, have the mint-mark on the reverse, under the pine branch. The Mint also created a 2016 gold Liberty Walking half dollar at a smaller dimension. See page 819.

Striking and Sharpness. Most circulation-strike Liberty Walking half dollars are lightly struck. In this respect they are similar to Standing Liberty quarters of the same era. On the obverse, the key points to check are Miss Liberty's left hand, the higher parts and lines in the skirt, and her head; after that, check all other areas. *Very few* coins are sharply struck in these areas, and for some issues sharp strikes might not exist at all. On the reverse, check the breast of the eagle.

Proofs were made beginning in 1936 and continuing through 1942. The entire die was polished (including the figure of Miss Liberty and the eagle), generating coins of low contrast. Proofs are usually fairly well struck. Most Proofs of 1941 are from over-polished dies, with the AW monogram of the designer no longer present. Striking sharpness can vary. Seek coins with full head and left-hand details.

Availability. All dates and mintmarks are readily collectible, although some, such as 1917-S (obverse mintmark), 1919-D, the three issues of 1921, and 1938-D, are scarce. Earlier years are often seen with extensive wear. MS coins are most often seen of the three issues of 1916, the 1917, and those of 1933 to 1947. Collectors saved the issues of the 1940s in large quantities, making the coins common today. As noted, coins with Full Details can range from scarce to extremely rare for certain dates. Half dollars dated 1928-D are counterfeit.

Note: Values of common-date silver coins have been based on the current bullion price of silver, $17 per ounce, and may vary with the prevailing spot price.

GRADING STANDARDS

MS-60 to 70 (Mint State). *Obverse:* At MS-60, some abrasion and contact marks are evident on the higher areas, which are also the areas most likely to be weakly struck. This includes Miss Liberty's left arm, her hand, and the areas of the skirt covering her left leg. The luster may not be complete in those areas on weakly struck coins (even those certified above MS-65)—the *original planchet surface* may be revealed, as it was not smoothed out by strik-

1917. Graded MS-65.

ing. Accordingly, grading is best done by evaluating abrasion as it is observed *in the right field*, plus evaluating the mint luster. Luster may be dull or lifeless at MS–60 to 62, but should have deep frost at MS-63 or better, particularly in the lower-relief areas. At MS-65 or better, it should be full and rich. Sometimes, to compensate for flat striking, certified coins with virtually flawless luster in the fields, evocative of an MS–65 or 66 grade, are called MS-63 or a lower grade. Such coins would seem to offer a lot of value for the money, if the variety is one that is not found with Full Details (1923-S is one of many examples). *Reverse:* Striking is usually better, permitting observation of luster in all areas except the eagle's body, which may be lightly struck. Luster may be dull or lifeless at MS–60 to 62, but should have deep frost at MS-63 or better, particularly in the lower-relief areas. At MS-65 or better, it should be full and rich.

Illustrated coin: This is a lustrous gem example.

AU-50, 53, 55, 58 (About Uncirculated). *Obverse:* Light wear is seen on the higher-relief areas of Miss Liberty, the vertical area from her head down to the date. At AU-58, the luster in the field is extensive, but is interrupted by friction and light wear. At AU–50 and 53, luster is less. *Reverse:* Wear is most evident on the eagle's breast immediately under the neck feathers, the left leg, and the top of the left wing. Luster is nearly complete at AU-58, but at AU-50 half or more is gone.

1921. Graded AU-50.

EF-40, 45 (Extremely Fine). *Obverse:* Wear is more extensive, with the higher parts of Miss Liberty now without detail, and with no skirt lines visible directly over her left leg. Little or no luster is seen. *Reverse:* The eagle shows more wear overall, with the highest parts of the body and left leg worn flat.

1919. Graded EF-40.

VF-20, 30 (Very Fine). *Obverse:* Wear is more extensive, and Miss Liberty is worn mostly flat in the line from her head to her left foot. Her skirt is worn, but most lines are seen, except over the leg and to the left and right. The lower part of her cape (to the left of her waist) is worn. *Reverse:* The eagle is worn smooth from the head to the left leg, and the right leg is flat at the top. Most feathers in the wings are delineated, but weak.

1921-S. Graded VF-20.

F-12, 15 (Fine). *Obverse:* Wear is more extensive, now with only a few light lines visible in the skirt. The rays of the sun are weak below the cape, and may be worn away at their tips. *Reverse:* Wear is more extensive, with most details now gone on the eagle's right leg. Delineation of the feathers is less, and most in the upper area and right edge of the left wing are blended together.

1918-S. Graded F-12.

VG-8, 10 (Very Good). *Obverse:* Wear is slightly more extensive, but the rim still is defined all around. The tops of the date numerals are worn and blend slightly into the ground above. *Reverse:* Wear is more extensive. On the left wing only a few feathers are delineated, and on the shoulder of the right wing most detail is gone. Detail in the pine branch is lost and it appears as a clump.

1921-D. Graded VG-8.

G-4, 6 (Good). *Obverse:* Miss Liberty is worn flat, with her head, neck, and arms all blended together. Folds can be seen at the bottom of the skirt, and nearly all gown lines are visible. The rim is worn done into the tops of some of the letters. *Reverse:* All areas show more wear. The rim is worn down into the tops of some of the letters, particularly at the top border.

1917-S, Obverse Mintmark. Graded G-4.

AG-3 (About Good). *Obverse:* Wear is more extensive. The sun's rays are nearly all gone, the motto is very light and sometimes incomplete, and the rim is worn down into more of the letters. *Reverse:* Wear is more extensive, with the eagle essentially worn flat. The rim is worn down into more of the letters.

1918. Graded AG-3.

PF-60 to 70 (Proof). *Obverse and Reverse:* Proofs that are extensively cleaned and have many hairlines, or that are dull and grainy, are lower level, such as PF–60 to 62. These are not widely desired, and represent coins that have been mistreated. With medium hairlines and good reflectivity, assigned grades of PF–63 or 64 are appropriate. Tiny horizontal lines on Miss Liberty's leg, known as slide marks, from National and other album slides scuffing the relief of the cheek, are common; coins with such marks should not be graded higher than PF-64, but sometimes are. With relatively few hairlines and no noticeable slide marks, a rating of PF-65 can be given. PF-66 should have hairlines so delicate that magnification is needed to see them. Above that, a Proof should be free of any hairlines or other problems.

1939. Graded PF-65.

Illustrated coin: This example is a brilliant gem Proof.

	Mintage	Cert	Avg	%MS	G-4	VG-8	F-12	VF-20	EF-40	AU-50	MS-60 PF-64	MS-63 PF-65	MS-65 PF-67
1916	608,000	1,661	51.3	65%	$50	$55	$90	$160	$250	$265	$450	$650	$2,600
	Auctions: $35,250, MS-67, August 2015; $588, MS-61, August 2015; $329, AU-55, May 2015; $118, F-15, February 2015												
1916-D, Obverse Mintmark	1,014,400	1,898	50.7	61%	$50	$60	$85	$135	$215	$240	$450	$725	$2,600
	Auctions: $4,935, MS-66, August 2015; $400, AU-58, October 2015; $200, EF-45, February 2015; $141, VF-25, February 2015												
1916-S, Obverse Mintmark	508,000	1,221	32.1	36%	$100	$140	$250	$450	$650	$950	$1,600	$2,500	$6,750
	Auctions: $9,988, MS-65, June 2015; $1,821, AU-58, August 2015; $411, VF-25, January 2015; $160, VG-10, December 2015												

	Mintage	Cert	Avg	%MS	G-4	VG-8	F-12	VF-20	EF-40	AU-50	MS-60	MS-63	MS-65
											PF-64	PF-65	PF-67
1917	12,292,000	2,263	61.7	83%	$18	$19	$19.50	$21	$40	$70	$150	$210	$1,100
Auctions: $2,233, MS-66, June 2015; $353, MS-64, August 2015; $118, MS-61, April 2015; $94, AU-58, February 2015
1917-D, Obverse Mintmark	765,400	989	53.2	59%	$25	$35	$80	$150	$240	$325	$800	$1,150	$7,500
Auctions: $32,900, MS-66, August 2015; $5,640, MS-65, September 2015; $705, AU-58, February 2015; $282, EF-45, April 2015
1917-S, Obverse Mintmark	952,000	556	43.8	42%	$18	$19	$45	$145	$280	$515	$1,200	$2,200	$16,000
Auctions: $152,750, MS-67, August 2015; $21,150, MS-65, August 2015; $376, VF-35, February 2015; $112, F-12, January 2015
1917-D, Reverse Mintmark	1,940,000	603	53.7	49%	$27	$50	$140	$375	$750	$1,300	$3,250	$5,500	$26,000
Auctions: $28,200, MS-66, August 2015; $1,410, AU-58, February 2015; $470, AU-53, November 2015; $141, VF-30, June 2015
1917-S, Reverse Mintmark	5,554,000	874	57.7	67%	$18	$19	$20	$35	$70	$170	$700	$1,800	$15,000
Auctions: $37,600, MS-66, August 2015; $10,869, MS-65, January 2015; $541, AU-58, October 2015; $212, EF-45, February 2015
1918	6,634,000	795	58.3	67%	$18	$19	$20	$65	$155	$265	$625	$1,250	$4,500
Auctions: $32,900, MS-66, August 2015; $4,230, MS-65, June 2015; $306, AU-55, May 2015; $84, VF-35, August 2015
1918-D	3,853,040	764	54.3	58%	$18	$19	$38	$100	$250	$475	$1,500	$3,500	$30,000
Auctions: $99,875, MS-66, August 2015; $35,250, MS-65, August 2015; $84, VF-30, January 2015; $40, F-15, September 2015
1918-S	10,282,000	907	57.0	64%	$18	$19	$20	$35	$80	$200	$600	$2,150	$20,000
Auctions: $18,800, MS-65, August 2015; $4,700, MS-64, March 2015; $376, AU-55, May 2015; $123, EF-45, January 2015
1919	962,000	571	43.0	41%	$25	$32	$78	$265	$515	$950	$2,350	$3,500	$8,500
Auctions: $54,050, MS-67, August 2015; $32,900, MS-66, May 2015; $4,113, MS-64, January 2015; $1,116, AU-53, October 2015
1919-D	1,165,000	603	40.6	37%	$26	$40	$115	$345	$825	$1,900	$4,750	$13,000	$225,000
Auctions: $32,900, MS-64, August 2016; $30,550, MS-64, August 2015; $5,170, MS-62, November 2016; $1,939, AU-50, July 2015
1919-S	1,552,000	498	39.7	28%	$20	$30	$85	$275	$815	$1,600	$4,000	$8,750	$27,500
Auctions: $44,650, MS-66, August 2016; $42,300, MS-66, August 2015; $11,750, MS-64, January 2015; $2,233, AU-50, June 2015
1920	6,372,000	854	59.7	75%	$18	$19	$20	$45	$80	$160	$425	$700	$4,200
Auctions: $7,050, MS-66, January 2015; $564, MS-63, August 2015; $329, AU-58, April 2015; $123, EF-45, August 2015
1920-D	1,551,000	359	44.1	44%	$18	$20	$75	$250	$450	$925	$3,000	$4,500	$17,500
Auctions: $54,050, MS-66, August 2015; $2,585, AU-58, June 2015; $823, EF-45, June 2015; $235, VF-25, March 2015
1920-S	4,624,000	517	52.0	52%	$18	$18.50	$23	$90	$230	$600	$1,200	$3,000	$15,000
Auctions: $58,750, MS-66, August 2015; $999, AU-58, January 2015; $376, EF-45, August 2015; $141, VF-35, April 2015
1921	246,000	1,471	18.1	13%	$135	$200	$325	$775	$2,000	$2,900	$6,000	$7,500	$25,000
Auctions: $54,050, MS-66, August 2015; $10,575, MS-64, January 2015; $1,410, VF-35, August 2015; $176, VG-8, January 2015
1921-D	208,000	1,763	15.8	10%	$200	$350	$550	$850	$2,850	$5,500	$9,250	$14,000	$47,500
Auctions: $94,000, MS-66, August 2015; $37,600, MS-65, August 2016; $3,290, EF-40, March 2015; $1,175, VF-20, January 2015
1921-S	548,000	1,233	19.7	9%	$48	$80	$250	$800	$4,500	$8,000	$20,000	$32,000	$110,000
Auctions: $117,500, MS-65, August 2015; $70,500, MS-64, August 2016; $8,813, AU-53, March 2015; $3,055, EF-40, January 2015
1923-S	2,178,000	451	49.8	50%	$13	$15	$30	$110	$365	$1,400	$2,750	$4,250	$16,000
Auctions: $25,850, MS-66, August 2015; $2,233, MS-62, September 2015; $1,645, AU-55, February 2015; $376, EF-40, September 2015
1927-S	2,392,000	620	56.9	70%	$13	$15	$18	$50	$160	$450	$1,200	$2,050	$11,000
Auctions: $44,650, MS-66, August 2015; $969, AU-55, August 2015; $707, AU-53, June 2015; $259, EF-45, October 2015
1928-S (a,b)	1,940,000	498	54.7	62%	$13	$15	$19	$75	$180	$500	$1,250	$3,000	$9,000
Auctions: $25,850, MS-66, August 2015; $8,813, MS-65, September 2015; $1,410, AU-58, June 2015; $940, AU-55, January 2015
1929-D	1,001,200	893	57.8	60%	$12	$15	$18	$30	$100	$190	$450	$800	$3,000
Auctions: $5,405, MS-66, May 2015; $646, MS-63, August 2015; $282, AU-55, January 2015; $118, EF-45, August 2015
1929-S	1,902,000	800	57.6	67%	$12	$15	$18	$35	$115	$230	$500	$1,200	$3,500
Auctions: $3,290, MS-66, January 2015; $1,293, MS-64, October 2015; $400, AU-58, September 2015; $106, EF-45, May 2015
1933-S	1,786,000	996	57.3	56%	$12	$15	$18	$20	$60	$240	$750	$1,500	$3,250
Auctions: $25,850, MS-67, June 2015; $1,410, MS-63, September 2015; $705, AU-58, January 2015; $282, AU-55, May 2015
1934	6,964,000	2,542	63.4	90%	$9	$10	$11	$16	$19	$26	$75	$100	$350
Auctions: $5,405, MS-67, August 2015; $118, MS-64, October 2015; $94, MS-63, August 2015; $79, MS-61, March 2015
1934-D (a)	2,361,000	1,393	62.6	88%	$9	$10	$11	$16	$35	$85	$140	$250	$1,200
Auctions: $3,819, MS-66, August 2015; $306, MS-64, June 2015; $223, MS-63, September 2015; $141, AU-50, October 2015
1934-S	3,652,000	895	60.5	70%	$9	$10	$11	$16	$30	$90	$365	$750	$2,750
Auctions: $30,550, MS-67, August 2015; $2,585, MS-65, July 2015; $1,001, MS-64, January 2015; $79, AU-53, January 2015

a. Large and small mintmark varieties exist. **b.** Half dollars dated 1928-D are counterfeit.

1936, Doubled Die Obverse
FS-50-1936-101.

	Mintage	Cert	Avg	%MS	G-4	VG-8	F-12	VF-20	EF-40	AU-50	MS-60	MS-63	MS-65
											PF-64	PF-65	PF-67
1935	9,162,000	2,544	63.5	92%	$9	$10	$11	$16	$19	$25	$40	$70	$275
	Auctions: $11,750, MS-68, October 2015; $4,935, MS-67, August 2015; $200, MS-65, August 2015; $89, MS-64, February 2015												
1935-D	3,003,800	1,022	62.4	87%	$9	$10	$11	$16	$30	$65	$140	$300	$1,750
	Auctions: $8,225, MS-66, May 2015; $1,821, MS-65, August 2015; $259, MS-62, January 2015; $100, MS-60, November 2015												
1935-S	3,854,000	877	61.9	84%	$9	$10	$11	$16	$26	$95	$275	$465	$2,250
	Auctions: $5,640, MS-66, January 2015; $1,293, MS-64, October 2015; $564, MS-63, August 2015; $259, AU-58, March 2015												
1936	12,614,000	3,574	63.9	94%	$9	$10	$11	$16	$18	$25	$45	$75	$210
	Auctions: $1,528, MS-67, June 2015; $306, MS-66, September 2015; $212, MS-65, January 2015; $89, MS-64, August 2015												
1936, DblDie Obv (c)	(d)	0	n/a		$500	$600							
	Auctions: $235, MS-65, January 2015; $940, MS-65, December 2013												
1936, Proof	3,901	1,356	64.7								$2,400	$3,200	$9,000
	Auctions: $14,689, PF-67, June 2015; $4,348, PF-66, July 2015; $2,820, PF-65, January 2015; $2,820, PF-64, October 2016												
1936-D	4,252,400	1,748	63.5	94%	$9	$10	$11	$16	$20	$50	$85	$120	$400
	Auctions: $4,935, MS-67, August 2015; $2,585, MS-66, February 2015; $212, MS-64, September 2015; $79, MS-63, June 2015												
1936-S	3,884,000	1,312	63.4	94%	$9	$10	$11	$16	$22	$60	$130	$200	$650
	Auctions: $19,975, MS-67, August 2015; $881, MS-65, January 2015; $329, MS-64, May 2015; $217, MS-63, September 2015												
1937	9,522,000	3,234	63.8	93%	$9	$10	$11	$16	$18	$25	$40	$70	$150
	Auctions: $1,528, MS-67, June 2015; $270, MS-66, July 2015; $259, MS-65, January 2015; $84, MS-64, August 2015												
1937, Proof	5,728	1,538	65.2								$650	$850	$1,600
	Auctions: $5,640, PF-68, January 2015; $2,115, PF-67, August 2015; $564, PF-64, January 2015; $470, PF-63, October 2015												
1937-D	1,676,000	1,189	63.0	88%	$9	$10	$11	$18	$32	$100	$215	$265	$700
	Auctions: $5,170, MS-67, August 2015; $482, MS-65, October 2015; $235, MS-63, January 2015; $153, AU-58, January 2015												
1937-S	2,090,000	1,270	63.6	94%	$9	$10	$11	$16	$25	$60	$165	$210	$625
	Auctions: $8,813, MS-67, August 2015; $353, MS-65, October 2015; $247, MS-64, February 2015; $129, MS-62, July 2015												
1938	4,110,000	2,301	63.4	92%	$9	$10	$11	$18	$20	$45	$70	$160	$300
	Auctions: $2,585, MS-67, January 2015; $212, MS-65, September 2015; $123, MS-63, May 2015; $46, AU-55, May 2015												
1938, Proof	8,152	1,834	65.4								$500	$675	$1,100
	Auctions: $14,100, PF-68, January 2015; $764, PF-66, August 2015; $734, PF-65, June 2015; $430, PF-64, October 2015												
1938-D	491,600	3,109	40.8	37%	$55	$65	$90	$100	$160	$225	$475	$650	$1,200
	Auctions: $5,640, MS-67, June 2015; $1,410, MS-65, July 2015; $400, AU-58, February 2015; $176, EF-45, January 2015												
1939	6,812,000	3,705	64.3	94%	$9	$10	$11	$16	$18	$26	$40	$65	$155
	Auctions: $8,225, MS-68, August 2015; $194, MS-66, September 2015; $118, MS-65, January 2015; $84, MS-64, September 2015												
1939, Proof	8,808	2,008	65.6								$450	$600	$900
	Auctions: $4,935, PF-68, August 2015; $570, PF-66, March 2015; $646, PF-65, February 2015; $388, PF-64, July 2015												
1939-D	4,267,800	2,944	64.2	96%	$9	$10	$11	$16	$18	$25	$43	$75	$145
	Auctions: $4,700, MS-67, January 2015; $270, MS-66, October 2015; $165, MS-65, August 2015; $94, MS-64, February 2015												
1939-S	2,552,000	1,975	64.4	96%	$9	$10	$11	$16	$26	$70	$150	$180	$240
	Auctions: $12,925, MS-68, September 2015; $564, MS-66, October 2015; $153, MS-64, April 2015; $74, AU-58, June 2015												
1940	9,156,000	4,152	64.2	95%	$9	$10	$11	$16	$18	$22	$35	$55	$120
	Auctions: $7,050, MS-68, August 2015; $294, MS-66, January 2015; $89, MS-65, September 2015; $94, MS-64, April 2015												
1940, Proof	11,279	2,322	65.5								$450	$500	$825
	Auctions: $3,290, PF-68, January 2015; $517, PF-66, June 2015; $423, PF-65, October 2015; $376, PF-64, February 2015												
1940-S	4,550,000	3,089	63.8	97%	$9	$10	$11	$16	$18	$35	$45	$80	$280
	Auctions: $27,025, MS-67, June 2015; $823, MS-66, October 2015; $235, MS-65, August 2015; $112, MS-64, February 2015												

c. No examples have yet been discovered grading better than Fine. "Extremely strong doubling is evident on the date. Less doubling is evident on IN GOD WE TRUST, the skirt, and some other elements" (*Cherrypickers' Guide to Rare Die Varieties*, sixth edition, volume II). Several varieties exist; this one is FS-50-1936-101. d. Included in circulation-strike 1936 mintage figure.

1945, Missing Designer's Initials
FS-50-1945-901.

	Mintage	Cert	Avg	%MS	G-4	VG-8	F-12	VF-20	EF-40	AU-50	MS-60 PF-64	MS-63 PF-65	MS-65 PF-67
1941	24,192,000	11,273	64.2	94%	$9	$10	$11	$16	$18	$22	$35	$55	$100
Auctions: $2,938, MS-68, January 2015; $588, MS-67, August 2015; $79, MS-65, February 2015; $46, MS-64, October 2015													
1941, Proof (e)	15,412	2,596	65.3								$450	$500	$800
Auctions: $7,050, PF-68, August 2015; $646, PF-67, October 2015; $400, PF-65, September 2015; $400, PF-64, February 2015													
1941-D	11,248,400	5,982	64.3	96%	$9	$10	$11	$16	$18	$22	$38	$65	$125
Auctions: $881, MS-67, January 2015; $176, MS-66, November 2015; $118, MS-65, July 2015; $67, MS-64, May 2015													
1941-S	8,098,000	5,875	63.2	91%	$9	$10	$11	$16	$18	$26	$75	$120	$600
Auctions: $35,250, MS-67, August 2015; $1,293, MS-66, January 2015; $141, MS-64, April 2015; $64, MS-61, June 2015													
1942	47,818,000	16,804	63.9	93%	$9	$10	$11	$16	$18	$22	$40	$60	$100
Auctions: $3,290, MS-67+, February 2015; $129, MS-66, July 2015; $84, MS-65, August 2015; $46, MS-64, October 2015													
1942, Proof	21,120	4,374	65.6								$450	$500	$800
Auctions: $4,465, PF-68, June 2015; $1,528, PF-67+, August 2015; $400, PF-65, October 2015; $470, PF-64, January 2015													
1942-D	10,973,800	4,349	64.3	96%	$9	$10	$11	$16	$18	$20	$40	$80	$200
Auctions: $834, MS-67, June 2015; $212, MS-66, January 2015; $165, MS-65, October 2015; $84, MS-64, February 2015													
1942-S (a)	12,708,000	4,584	63.7	96%	$9	$10	$11	$16	$18	$22	$40	$80	$330
Auctions: $1,116, MS-66, February 2015; $306, MS-65, January 2015; $94, MS-64, November 2015; $118, MS-63, February 2015													
1943	53,190,000	17,109	63.9	93%	$9	$10	$11	$16	$18	$20	$35	$50	$100
Auctions: $21,150, MS-68, August 2015; $1,293, MS-67+, January 2015; $74, MS-64+, April 2015; $40, MS-63, February 2015													
1943-D	11,346,000	5,189	64.6	96%	$9	$10	$11	$16	$18	$24	$48	$75	$190
Auctions: $4,935, MS-68, June 2015; $646, MS-67, February 2015; $94, MS-64, August 2015; $40, MS-62, October 2015													
1943-S	13,450,000	5,258	64.0	97%	$9	$10	$11	$16	$18	$25	$42	$60	$240
Auctions: $6,463, MS-67, August 2015; $4,465, MS-66+, February 2015; $200, MS-65, August 2015; $69, MS-64, May 2015													
1944	28,206,000	9,975	63.8	94%	$9	$10	$11	$16	$18	$20	$35	$50	$105
Auctions: $3,525, MS-67, August 2015; $76, MS-65, March 2015; $56, MS-64, October 2015; $32, MS-60, March 2015													
1944-D	9,769,000	6,228	64.6	97%	$9	$10	$11	$16	$18	$20	$40	$60	$105
Auctions: $1,528, MS-67+, September 2015; $183, MS-66, January 2015; $118, MS-65, March 2015; $89, MS-64, February 2015													
1944-S	8,904,000	6,200	63.9	98%	$9	$10	$11	$16	$18	$24	$40	$63	$325
Auctions: $3,290, MS-66+, June 2015; $376, MS-65, July 2015; $84, MS-64, February 2015; $44, MS-62, October 2015													
1945	31,502,000	13,832	63.9	95%	$9	$10	$11	$16	$18	$20	$35	$50	$100
Auctions: $1,645, MS-67, July 2015; $89, MS-65, October 2015; $94, MS-64, August 2015; $44, MS-63, February 2015													
1945, Missing Initials	(f)	28	55.8	64%						$100	$150	$250	
Auctions: $705, MS-64, January 2014													
1945-D	9,966,800	9,046	64.8	98%	$9	$10	$11	$17.50	$18	$20	$35	$60	$120
Auctions: $14,100, MS-68, August 2015; $4,465, MS-67+, August 2015; $94, MS-65, May 2015; $64, MS-64, February 2015													
1945-S	10,156,000	7,582	64.3	98%	$9	$10	$11	$17.50	$18	$24	$38	$55	$120
Auctions: $6,463, MS-67, January 2015; $212, MS-66, August 2015; $106, MS-65, April 2015; $74, MS-64, February 2015													

a. Large and small mintmark varieties exist. **e.** The variety without the designer's initials was created by the over-polishing of dies. **f.** Included in 1945 mintage figure.

1946, Doubled Die Reverse
FS-50-1946-801.

	Mintage	Cert	Avg	%MS	G-4	VG-8	F-12	VF-20	EF-40	AU-50	MS-60	MS-63	MS-65
											PF-64	PF-65	PF-67
1946	12,118,000	7,064	63.9	96%	$9	$10	$11	$17.50	$18	$20	$37	$50	$120
	Auctions: $3,525, MS-67, August 2015; $176, MS-66, April 2015; $112, MS-65, April 2015; $94, MS-64, September 2015												
1946, DblDie Rev (g)	(h)	201	51.5	36%	$20	$24	$28	$40	$65	$125	$275	$550	$2,500
	Auctions: $2,233, MS-64, January 2015; $188, AU-58, April 2015; $84, EF-45, August 2015; $79, F-15, April 2015												
1946-D	2,151,000	13,296	64.8	100%	$9	$10	$11	$17.50	$22	$32	$47	$60	$105
	Auctions: $3,760, MS-67, August 2015; $141, MS-66, January 2015; $60, MS-64, October 2015; $42, MS-62, October 2015												
1946-S	3,724,000	8,727	64.7	99%	$9	$10	$11	$17.50	$18	$25	$43	$58	$100
	Auctions: $8,225, MS-67, October 2015; $217, MS-66, February 2015; $100, MS-65, July 2015; $89, MS-64, May 2015												
1947	4,094,000	7,657	64.3	98%	$9	$10	$11	$17.50	$18	$25	$48	$60	$110
	Auctions: $9,400, MS-67, February 2015; $188, MS-66, November 2015; $123, MS-65, July 2015; $64, MS-64, October 2015												
1947-D	3,900,600	8,537	64.6	99%	$9	$10	$11	$17.50	$18	$30	$45	$60	$105
	Auctions: $5,640, MS-67, August 2015; $182, MS-66, April 2015; $129, MS-65, September 2015; $69, MS-64, July 2015												

g. Very strong doubling is visible on E PLURIBUS UNUM, the eagle's wing feathers and left wing, and the branch. **h.** Included in 1946 mintage figure.

FRANKLIN (1948–1963)

Designer: *John R. Sinnock.* **Weight:** *12.50 grams.*
Composition: *.900 silver, .100 copper (net weight .36169 oz. pure silver).*
Diameter: *30.6 mm.* **Edge:** *Reeded.* **Mints:** *Philadelphia, Denver, and San Francisco.*

Circulation Strike

Mintmark location is on the reverse, above the beam.

Proof

History. U.S. Mint chief engraver John R. Sinnock developed a motif for a silver half dime in 1942; it was proposed but never adopted for regular coinage. In 1948, the year after Sinnock died, his Franklin half dollar was introduced, its design an adaptation of his earlier half dime motif. The Liberty Bell is similar to that used by Sinnock on the 1926 Sesquicentennial commemorative half dollar modeled from a sketch by John Frederick Lewis. The designs were finished by Sinnock's successor, chief engraver Gilroy Roberts. The coin-collecting community paid little attention to the Franklin half dollar at the time, but today the coins are widely collected.

Striking and Sharpness. Given the indistinct details of the obverse, sharpness of strike usually is ignored. On the reverse, if the bottom lines of the Liberty Bell are complete the coin may be designated as Full Bell Lines (FBL). Virtually all Proofs are well struck.

Availability. All dates and mintmarks are easily available in grades from VF upward. Lower-level MS coins can be unattractive due to contact marks and abrasion, particularly noticeable on the obverse.

High-quality gems are generally inexpensive, although varieties that are rare with FBL can be costly amid much competition in the marketplace. Most collectors seek MS coins. Grades below EF are not widely desired. Proofs were made from 1950 to 1963 and are available today in proportion to their mint-ages. Those with cameo-frosted devices are in the minority and often sell for strong premiums.

Note: Values of common-date silver coins have been based on the current bullion price of silver, $17 per ounce, and may vary with the prevailing spot price.

Grading Standards

MS-60 to 70 (Mint State). *Obverse:* At MS-60, some abrasion and contact marks are evident on the cheek, on the hair left of the ear, and the neck. At MS-63, abrasion is slight at best, less so for MS-64. An MS-65 coin should display no abrasion or contact marks except under magnification, and MS-66 and higher coins should have none at all. Luster should be full and rich. As details are shallow on this design, the amount and "depth" of luster is important to grading.

1951-S. Graded MS-65.

Reverse: General comments apply as for the obverse. The points to check are the bell harness, the words PASS AND STOW on the upper area of the Liberty Bell, and the bottom of the bell.

　Illustrated coin: Satiny brilliance is seen on the obverse of this coin, light golden toning on the reverse.

AU-50, 53, 55, 58 (About Uncirculated). *Obverse:* At AU-50, medium wear is evident on the portrait, and most of the luster in the field is gone. At AU-53, wear is less and luster is more extensive. AU–55 and 58 coins show much luster. Wear is noticeable on the portrait and, to a lesser extent, in the field. *Reverse:* At AU-50, medium wear is evident on most of the Liberty Bell, and most of the luster in the field is gone. At AU-53, wear is

1949-D. Graded AU-50.

slightly less. AU–55 and 58 coins show much luster. Light wear is seen on the higher areas of the bell.

EF-40, 45 (Extremely Fine). *Obverse:* Wear is more extensive, and some hair detail (never strong to begin with) is lost. There is no luster. *Reverse:* Wear is seen overall. The inscription on the bell is weak, and the highest parts of the bottom horizontal lines are worn away. There is no luster.

　The Franklin half dollar is seldom collected in grades lower than EF-40.

1955. Graded EF-40.

PF-60 to 70 (Proof). *Obverse and Reverse:* Proofs that are extensively cleaned and have many hairlines, or that are dull and grainy, are lower level, such as PF–60 to 62. These are not widely desired, and represent coins that have been mistreated. Fortunately, only a few Proof Franklin half dollars are in this category. With medium hairlines and good reflectivity, assigned grades of PF–63 or 64 are appropriate. PF-66 should have hairlines so delicate that magnification is needed to see them. Above that, a Proof should be free of any hairlines or other problems.

1950. Graded PF-65 Cameo.

Full Bell Lines

1948, Doubled Die Reverse
FS-50-1948-801.

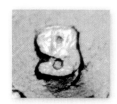
1949-S, Repunched Mintmark
FS-50-1949S-501.

	Mintage	Cert	Avg	%MS	VF-20	EF-40	MS-60	MS-63	MS-64	MS-65	MS-65FBL	MS-66	MS-66FBL
											PF-64	PF-65	PF-65DC
1948	3,006,814	4,368	64.1	97%	$9	$11	$20	$27	$35	$70	$135	$265	$325
Auctions: $3,760, MS-67FBL, September 2015; $1,410, MS-66FBL+, June 2015; $84, MS-65FBL, August 2015; $46, MS-64FBL, August 2015
1948, Doubled Die Reverse (a)	(b)	33	63.8	100%				$75	$125	$190	$285	$235	
Auctions: No auction records available.
1948-D	4,028,600	4,100	64.0	98%	$9	$11	$20	$24	$30	$135	$145	$475	$475
Auctions: $19,975, MS-67FBL, January 2015; $12,925, MS-67FBL, July 2015; $135, MS-65FBL, February 2015; $74, MS-64, January 2015
1949	5,614,000	2,875	63.1	89%	$12	$18	$40	$75	$85	$130	$155	$315	$415
Auctions: $1,469, MS-66FBL+, September 2015; $212, MS-65FBL, November 2015; $188, MS-65FBL, July 2015; $62, MS-64FBL, January 2015
1949-D	4,120,600	3,201	63.2	95%	$12	$18	$45	$75	$90	$325	$500	$1,300	$1,550
Auctions: $1,116, MS-66, July 2016; $1,058, MS-66, August 2016; $1,058, MS-66, September 2016; $5,640, MS-66, October 2016
1949-S	3,744,000	3,360	63.9	95%	$12	$20	$65	$95	$115	$165	$350	$265	$575
Auctions: $6,463, MS-67FBL, June 2015; $259, MS-66, September 2015; $200, MS-65FBL, May 2015; $74, MS-64, January 2015
1949-S, Doubled Mintmark (c)	(d)	9	60.7	67%				$120	$170	$280	$350	$575	
Auctions: $223, MS-65, January 2014
1950	7,742,123	2,486	63.6	93%	$9	$11	$30	$35	$55	$100	$145	$275	$525
Auctions: $18,213, MS-67FBL, August 2015; $1,528, MS-66FBL, January 2015; $259, MS-65, February 2015; $56, MS-64FBL, November 2015
1950, Proof	51,386	3,960	64.8								$425	$575	$15,000
Auctions: $4,230, PF-67, January 2015; $7,638, PF-66Cam, October 2015; $1,645, PF-65Cam, July 2015; $376, PF-64, June 2015
1950-D	8,031,600	2,578	63.4	95%	$9	$11	$26	$40	$70	$200	$290	$850	$1,450
Auctions: $2,585, MS-66FBL, January 2015; $1,058, MS-66FBL, June 2015; $235, MS-65FBL, May 2015; $46, MS-64FBL, August 2015

a. Doubling is visible on E PLURIBUS UNUM, UNITED, HALF DOLLAR, the dots, and the Liberty Bell's clapper. "There are several similar, yet lesser, DDRs for this date" (*Cherrypickers' Guide to Rare Die Varieties*, sixth edition, volume II). The variety listed and pictured is FS-50-1948-801. **b.** Included in 1948 mintage figure. **c.** The secondary mintmark is visible south of the primary. CONECA lists two other repunched mintmarks for this date; the one illustrated and listed here is FS-50-1949S-501. **d.** Included in 1949-S mintage figure.

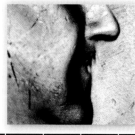

1955, Clashed Obverse Die "Bugs Bunny" variety
FS-50-1955-401.

1951-S, Doubled Die Reverse
FS-50-1951S-801.

	Mintage	Cert	Avg	%MS	VF-20	EF-40	MS-60	MS-63	MS-64	MS-65	MS-65FBL PF-64	MS-66 PF-65	MS-66FBL PF-65DC
1951	16,802,102	2,719	63.9	95%	$9	$11	$14	$24	$35	$55	$190	$240	$500
	Auctions: $1,410, MS-66FBL, July 2015; $200, MS-66, July 2015; $235, MS-65FBL, September 2015; $44, MS-65, January 2015												
1951, Proof	57,500	3,563	64.9								$300	$400	$3,000
	Auctions: $4,465, PF-68, June 2015; $3,290, PF-67Cam, February 2015; $494, PF-65Cam, July 2015; $259, PF-64, March 2015												
1951-D	9,475,200	2,117	63.6	96%	$9	$11	$30	$45	$70	$140	$200	$585	$700
	Auctions: $764, MS-66FBL, January 2015; $141, MS-65FBL, July 2015; $84, MS-64FBL, April 2015; $28, MS-63FBL, July 2015												
1951-S	13,696,000	2,801	64.1	97%	$9	$11	$25	$35	$45	$55	$350	$185	$950
	Auctions: $1,645, MS-67, October 2015; $588, MS-66FBL, July 2015; $176, MS-64FBL, January 2015; $46, MS-63, May 2015												
1951-S, DblDie Rev (e)	(f)	9	64.4	100%			$80	$110	$265	$685	$800		
	Auctions: $188, MS-65, January 2014												
1952	21,192,093	2,753	64.0	96%	$9	$11	$14	$23	$35	$55	$110	$185	$335
	Auctions: $4,935, MS-67FBL, July 2015; $200, MS-66FBL, February 2015; $94, MS-65FBL, February 2015; $48, MS-64FBL, November 2015												
1952, Proof	81,980	4,114	65.3								$190	$275	$4,500
	Auctions: $3,821, PF-67Cam, August 2015; $8,813, PF-66DCam, June 2015; $260, PF-66, October 2015; $118, PF-64, January 2015												
1952-D	25,395,600	2,580	63.8	97%	$9	$11	$14	$23	$32	$115	$145	$550	$600
	Auctions: $564, MS-66FBL, January 2015; $176, MS-65FBL, September 2015; $129, MS-65FBL, February 2015; $40, MS-64FBL, February 2015												
1952-S	5,526,000	2,634	64.5	99%	$12	$17	$50	$70	$80	$110	$725	$200	$1,850
	Auctions: $21,150, MS-67FBL, February 2015; $1,645, MS-67, January 2015; $129, MS-66, July 2015; $423, MS-64FBL, January 2015												
1953	2,668,120	2,264	64.0	98%	$9	$10	$14	$27	$40	$110	$575	$325	$1,400
	Auctions: $2,233, MS-66FBL, January 2015; $306, MS-66, March 2015; $646, MS-65FBL, October 2015; $129, MS-64FBL, May 2015												
1953, Proof	128,800	5,535	65.6								$125	$190	$1,400
	Auctions: $4,230, PF-68Cam, August 2015; $2,585, PF-66DCam, January 2015; $165, PF-66, February 2015; $84, PF-64, May 2015												
1953-D	20,900,400	3,341	63.9	98%	$9	$10	$14	$23	$38	$105	$145	$500	$625
	Auctions: $494, MS-66FBL, February 2015; $112, MS-65FBL, February 2015; $74, MS-65, May 2015; $56, MS-64FBL, October 2015												
1953-S	4,148,000	5,297	64.8	100%	$9	$10	$25	$35	$48	$55	$23,500	$275	$36,500
	Auctions: $2,233, MS-67, January 2015; $447, MS-66, June 2015; $21,150, MS-65FBL, September 2015; $100, MS-65, September 2015												
1954	13,188,202	4,393	64.2	99%	$9	$10	$14	$20	$30	$45	$110	$300	$550
	Auctions: $1,880, MS-66FBL, July 2015; $823, MS-66FBL, October 2015; $153, MS-65FBL, January 2015; $38, MS-64FBL, July 2015												
1954, Proof	233,300	7,574	66.3								$65	$85	$425
	Auctions: $14,100, PF-68DCam, October 2015; $270, PF-67, May 2015; $129, PF-66Cam, May 2015; $34, PF-64, August 2015												
1954-D	25,445,580	5,361	64.1	99%	$9	$10	$14	$24	$28	$75	$130	$400	$750
	Auctions: $588, MS-66FBL, June 2015; $353, MS-66, February 2015; $89, MS-65FBL, January 2015; $54, MS-65, May 2015												
1954-S	4,993,400	8,322	64.7	100%	$12	$14	$16	$24	$30	$35	$235	$185	$950
	Auctions: $1,763, MS-67, July 2015; $194, MS-66, November 2015; $188, MS-65FBL, September 2015; $56, MS-64FBL, February 2015												
1955	2,498,181	7,767	64.1	99%MS	$18	$22	$25	$30	$40	$42	$95	$135	$325
	Auctions: $1,763, MS-66FBL, January 2015; $52, MS-65, September 2015; $38, MS-64FBL, April 2015; $40, MS-63FBL, April 2015												
1955, Clashed Obverse Die (g)	(h)	673	62.7	100%			$48	$65	$120	$325	$235	$750	
	Auctions: $423, MS-66FBL, February 2013; $129, MS-64FBL, September 2014; $76, MS-64FBL, September 2014												
1955, Proof	378,200	12,490	66.9								$65	$75	$425
	Auctions: $4,700, PF-68DCam, October 2015; $212, PF-68, January 2015; $165, PF-67Cam, March 2015; $141, PF-66, August 2015												

e. Doubling is evident on the eagle's tail feathers and left wing, as well as on E PLURIBUS UNUM. This variety is FS-50-1951S-801.
f. Included in 1951-S mintage figure. **g.** This variety, popularly known as the "Bugs Bunny," has evidence of clash marks that appear as two buckteeth on Benjamin Franklin. **h.** Included in circulation-strike 1955 mintage figure.

1957, Tripled Die Reverse, Proof *FS-50-1957-801.*			**1959, Doubled Die Reverse** *FS-50-1959-801.*		

	Mintage	Cert	Avg	%MS	VF-20	EF-40	MS-60	MS-63	MS-64	MS-65	MS-65FBL / PF-64	MS-66 / PF-65	MS-66FBL / PF-65DC
1956	4,032,000	9,997	64.3	100%	$9	$10	$14	$25	$28	$32	$90	$85	$215
Auctions: $353, MS-67, January 2015; $176, MS-66FBL, September 2015; $106, MS-66, July 2015; $60, MS-65FBL, December 2015													
1956, Proof	669,384	4,612	67.1								$35	$45	$100
Auctions: $2,820, PF-69DCam, September 2015; $329, PF-69, February 2015; $118, PF-68, February 2015; $376, PF-67, July 2015													
1957	5,114,000	4,753	64.7	100%	$9	$10	$14	$19	$25	$32	$95	$85	$250
Auctions: $$1,763, MS-67FBL, October 2015; $329, MS-67, January 2015; $94, MS-66FBL, October 2015; $48, MS-66, October 2015													
1957, Proof	1,247,952	18,370	67.0								$25	$28	$250
Auctions: $2,585, PF-69Cam, September 2015; $112, PF-68, June 2015; $90, PF-67, July 2015; $84, PF-66Cam, February 2015													
1957, Tripled Die Reverse, Proof (i)	(j)	7	66.4								$75	$90	$800
Auctions: No auction records available.													
1957-D	19,966,850	5,288	64.4	99%	$9	$10	$14	$19	$23	$33	$75	$80	$300
Auctions: $3,055, MS-67FBL, October 2015; $764, MS-67, October 2015; $212, MS-66FBL, February 2015; $123, MS-65, August 2015													
1958	4,042,000	6,558	64.6	99%	$9	$10	$14	$19	$24	$33	$90	$70	$265
Auctions: $4,700, MS-67FBL, January 2015; $400, MS-67, February 2015; $353, MS-67, September 2015; $44, MS-66, April 2015													
1958, Proof	875,652	13,547	66.8								$18	$30	$675
Auctions: $705, PF-69Cam, July 2015; $2,115, PF-67UCam, July 2015; $153, PF-67Cam, March 2015; $20, PF-63, September 2015													
1958-D	23,962,412	6,508	64.5	99%	$9	$10	$14	$18	$19	$33	$75	$80	$400
Auctions: $$1,175, MS-67FBL, October 2015; $588, MS-67, January 2015; $153, MS-66FBL, February 2015; $20, MS-64, May 2015													
1959	6,200,000	4,894	64.3	99%	$9	$10	$14	$18	$20	$60	$135	$550	$1,400
Auctions: $1,763, MS-66FBL, January 2015; $154, MS-65FBL, May 2015; $84, MS-65, November 2015; $46, MS-64, May 2015													
1959, Doubled Die Reverse (k)	(l)	60	64.0	98%			$85	$90	$150	$450	$1,125	$1,250	
Auctions: $1,528, MS-66, October 2016; $431, MS-65FBL, March 2011													
1959, Proof	1,149,291	15,291	66.8								$18	$25	$2,000
Auctions: $1,529, PF-68Cam, January 2015; $423, PF-67Cam, February 2015; $341, PF-67Cam, March 2015; $235, PF-66Cam, October 2015													
1959-D	13,053,750	4,874	64.3	99%	$9	$10	$14	$18	$22	$75	$115	$600	$1,250
Auctions: $1,528, MS-66FBL, August 2015; $470, MS-66, January 2015; $118, MS-65FBL, February 2015; $89, MS-65FBL, September 2015													
1960	6,024,000	4,563	64.2	100%	$9	$10	$14	$18	$19	$80	$210	$575	$1,350
Auctions: $1,293, MS-66FBL, January 2015; $1,058, MS-66FBL, September 2015; $176, MS-65FBL, February 2015; $153, MS-65FBL, November 2014													
1960, Proof	1,691,602	17,161	66.8								$18	$25	$100
Auctions: $646, PF-69, January 2015; $1,369, PF-68UCam, July 2015; $176, PF-68Cam, March 2015; $46, PF-66, August 2015													
1960, Doubled Die Obverse, Proof (m)	(n)	72	66.2								$80	$95	$400
Auctions: $160, PF-67, May 2012													
1960-D	18,215,812	3,908	64.0	99%	$9	$10	$14	$18	$30	$160	$400	$600	$1,400
Auctions: $1,645, MS-66FBL, February 2015; $331, MS-65FBL, August 2015; $112, MS-65, July 2015; $28, MS-64FBL, January 2015													

i. A closely tripled image is evident on E PLURIBUS UNUM, portions of UNITED STATES OF AMERICA, and HALF DOLLAR. j. Included in 1957, Proof, mintage figure. k. Strong doubling is evident on the eagle; doubling is also visible on E PLURIBUS UNUM, UNITED, and portions of the Liberty Bell. l. Included in circulation-strike 1959 mintage figure. m. Doubling is visible on LIBERTY, TRUST, and the date. n. Included in 1960, Proof, mintage figure.

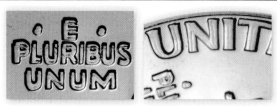

1961, Doubled Die Reverse, Proof
FS-50-1961-801.

	Mintage	Cert	Avg	%MS	VF-20	EF-40	MS-60	MS-63	MS-64	MS-65	MS-65FBL PF-64	MS-66 PF-65	MS-66FBL PF-65DC
1961	8,290,000	4,713	64.2	99%	$9	$10	$14	$18	$25	$50	$925	$500	$4,900
	Auctions: $8,225, MS-66FBL, July 2015; $881, MS-66, September 2015; $40, MS-65, July 2015; $84, MS-64FBL, May 2015												
1961, Proof	3,028,244	22,375	66.8								$18	$25	$125
	Auctions: $1,880, PF-68DCam, January 2015; $306, PF-68Cam, January 2015; $129, PF-68, July 2015; $84, PF-67Cam, May 2015												
1961, Doubled Die Reverse, Proof (o)	(p)	91	65.6								$2,200	$2,900	
	Auctions: $4,935, PF-67, August 2015; $5,405, PF-67, July 2016; $2,350, PF-65, June 2014; $1,880, PF-64, July 2014												
1961-D	20,276,442	3,652	64.0	99%	$9	$10	$14	$18	$25	$100	$465	$575	$2,750
	Auctions: $3,302, MS-66FBL, February 2015; $1,175, MS-66, January 2015; $423, MS-65FBL, January 2015; $79, MS-65, October 2015												
1962	9,714,000	3,957	64.1	99%	$9	$10	$14	$18	$25	$80	$1,250	$800	$7,500
	Auctions: $7,638, MS-66FBL, October 2015; $1,645, MS-65FBL, January 2015; $200, MS-64FBL, February 2015; $36, MS-63FBL, July 2015												
1962, Proof	3,218,019	28,342	66.7								$18	$25	$60
	Auctions: $153, PF-68Cam, July 2015; $212, PF-67UCam, April 2015; $26, PF-67, September 2015; $56, PF-66Cam, April 2015												
1962, Doubled Die Obverse, Proof (q)	(r)	0	n/a								$25	$30	$150
	Auctions: No auction records available.												
1962-D	35,473,281	4,426	64.0	99%	$9	$10	$14	$18	$25	$80	$435	$800	$2,750
	Auctions: $4,230, MS-66FBL, January 2015; $60, MS-65, March 2015; $22, MS-64, October 2015; $38, MS-63FBL, March 2015												
1963	22,164,000	12,017	64.3	99%	$9	$10	$14	$18	$19	$30	$1,500	$625	$17,500
	Auctions: $$17,625, MS-66FBL, October 2015; $1,880, MS-65FBL, January 2015; $1,116, MS-65FBL, October 2015; $330, MS-64FBL, January 2015												
1963, Proof	3,075,645	27,551	66.9								$18	$25	$52
	Auctions: $364, PF-69, February 2015; $1,998, PF-68DCam, September 2015; $118, PF-68Cam, January 2015; $129, PF-67Cam, June 2015												
1963-D	67,069,292	9,338	64.1	98%	$9	$10	$14	$18	$19	$30	$160	$400	$950
	Auctions: $1,175, MS-66FBL, July 2015; $282, MS-65FBL, September 2015; $153, MS-65FBL, March 2015; $36, MS-64FBL, April 2015												

o. Other reverse doubled dies exist for this date. The variety pictured and listed here (FS-50-1961-801) is by far the most dramatic. Very strong doubling is evident on the reverse lettering. **p.** Included in 1961, Proof, mintage figure. **q.** Doubling is visible on the 62 of the date and on WE TRUST. **r.** Included in 1962, Proof, mintage figure.

KENNEDY (1964 TO DATE)

Designers: *Gilroy Roberts and Frank Gasparro.* **Weight:** *1964, modern silver Proofs, and 2014 silver—12.50 grams; 1965–1970—11.50 grams; 1971 to date—11.34 grams.* **Composition:** *1964 and modern silver Proofs—.900 silver, .100 copper (net weight .36169 oz. pure silver); 1965–1970—outer layers of .800 silver and .200 copper bonded to inner core of .209 silver, .791 copper (net weight .1479 oz. pure silver); 1971 to date—outer layers of copper-nickel (.750 copper, .250 nickel) bonded to inner core of pure copper; 2014 gold—.9999 gold (net weight .75 oz. pure gold).* **Diameter:** *30.6 mm.* **Edge:** *Reeded.* **Mints:** *Philadelphia, Denver, and San Francisco.*

Circulation Strike   **Proof**

Mintmark location, 1964, is on the reverse, below the claw holding the branch.   Mintmark location, 1968 to date, is on the obverse, above the date.

Bicentennial variety: **Designers:** *Gilroy Roberts and Seth Huntington.* **Weight:** *Silver clad—11.50 grams; copper-nickel clad—11.34 grams.* **Composition:** *Silver clad—outer layers of .800 silver, .200 copper bonded to inner core of .209 silver, .791 copper (net weight .14792 oz. pure silver); copper-nickel clad—outer layers of copper-nickel (.750 copper, .250 nickel) bonded to inner core of pure copper.* **Diameter:** *30.6 mm.* **Edge:** *Reeded.* **Mints:** *Philadelphia, Denver, and San Francisco.*

Bicentennial variety   **Bicentennial variety, Proof**

50th Anniversary varieties: **Designers:** *Gilroy Roberts and Frank Gasparro.*
Weight: *Gold—23.33 grams; silver Proofs and Unc.—12.50 grams; copper-nickel clad—*
11.34 grams. **Composition:** *Gold—.9999 gold (net weight .75 oz. pure gold); silver—.900 silver,*
.100 copper (net weight .36169 oz. pure silver); copper-nickel clad—outer layers of copper-nickel
(.750 copper, .250 nickel) bonded to inner core of pure copper. **Diameter:** *30.6 mm.*
Edge: *Reeded.* **Mints:** *Philadelphia, Denver, San Francisco, and West Point.*

50th Anniversary variety, gold

50th Anniversary variety, Uncirculated

50th Anniversary variety,
Enhanced Uncirculated

50th Anniversary variety, Proof

50th Anniversary variety, Reverse Proof

History. Kennedy half dollars, minted from 1964 to date, were struck in 90% silver the first year, then with 40% silver content through 1970, and in later years in copper-nickel (except for special silver issues made for collectors and a gold issue in 2014). The obverse, by Chief Engraver Gilroy Roberts, features a portrait of President John F. Kennedy, while the reverse, by Frank Gasparro, displays a modern version of a heraldic eagle.

The 1976 Bicentennial coin shows Philadelphia's Independence Hall, a design by Seth G. Huntington. The obverse was unchanged except for the dual dating 1776–1976. The Bicentennial half dollars were struck during 1975 and 1976 and were used for general circulation as well as being included in Proof and Uncirculated sets for 1975 and 1976.

The year 2014 brought several special issues to mark the 50th year of the Kennedy half dollar: a .9999 fine gold version containing three-quarters of an ounce of pure gold; a Proof in silver; a Reverse Proof in silver; an Enhanced Uncirculated in silver; and an Uncirculated in silver. These coins are dual-dated 1964–2014 on the obverse. They were offered for sale by the U.S. Mint in a number of packages and options.

Striking and Sharpness. Nearly all are well struck. Check the highest points of the hair on the obverse and the highest details on the reverse.

Availability. All issues are common in high circulated grades as well as MS and Proof.

Proofs and Special Mint Set Coins. Proofs of 1964 were struck at the Philadelphia Mint. Those from 1968 to date have been made in San Francisco. All are easily obtained. Most from the 1970s to date have cameo contrast. Special Mint Set (SMS) coins were struck in lieu of Proofs from 1965 to 1967; in some instances, these closely resemble Proofs. Silver Proofs have been struck in recent years, for Silver Proof sets and for the 2014 50th Anniversary issue (which also includes a Reverse Proof). In 1998, a special Matte Proof silver Kennedy half dollar was struck for inclusion in the Robert F. Kennedy commemorative coin set.

Note: Values of common-date silver coins have been based on the current bullion price of silver, $17 per ounce, and may vary with the prevailing spot price.

GRADING STANDARDS

MS-60 to 70 (Mint State). *Obverse:* At MS-60, some abrasion and contact marks are evident on the cheek, and on the hair to the right of the forehead and temple. At MS-63, abrasion is slight at most, and less so for MS-64. An MS-65 coin should display no abrasion or contact marks except under magnification, and MS-66 and higher coins should have none at all. Luster should be full and rich. *Reverse:* Comments apply as for the obverse, except that the highest parts of the eagle at the center are the key places to check.

1964-D. Graded MS-66.

AU-50, 53, 55, 58 (About Uncirculated). *Obverse:* Light wear is seen on the cheek and higher-relief area of the hair below the part, high above the ear. At AU-58, the luster is extensive but incomplete, especially on the higher parts and in the field. At AU-50 and 53, luster is less. *Reverse:* Light wear is seen on the higher parts of the eagle. At AU-50 and 53 there still is significant luster.

1964. Graded AU-55.

EF-40, 45 (Extremely Fine). *Obverse:* Further wear is seen on the head. More details are gone on the higher parts of the hair. *Reverse:* Further wear is seen on the eagle in particular, but also on other areas in high relief (including the leaves, arrowheads, and clouds).

The Kennedy half dollar is seldom collected in grades lower than EF-40.

1964. Graded EF-45.

PF-60 to 70 (Proof). *Obverse and Reverse:* Proofs that are extensively cleaned and have many hairlines, or that are dull and grainy, are lower level, such as PF–60 to 62. There are not many of these in the marketplace. With medium hairlines and good reflectivity, assigned grades of PF–63 or 64 are appropriate. With relatively few hairlines a rating of PF-65 can be given. PF-66 should have hairlines so delicate that magnification is needed to see them. Above that, a Proof should be free of any hairlines or other problems.

1964. Graded PF-66.

1964, Doubled Die Obverse
FS-50-1964-102.

1964, Heavily Accented Hair, Proof
FS-50-1964-401.

1964-D, Doubled Die Obverse
FS-50-1964D-101.

1964-D, Repunched Mintmark
FS-50-1964D-502.

	Mintage	Cert	Avg	%MS	MS-60	MS-63	MS-65 PF-65	MS-66 PF-67Cam	MS-67 PF-68DC
1964	273,304,004	11,561	64.5	99%	$11	$12	$24	$75	$700
	Auctions: $1,234, MS-67, October 2015; $118, MS-66, January 2015; $34, MS-65, April 2015; $37, MS-64, April 2015								
1964, Doubled Die Obverse (a)	(b)	19	64.6	100%			$35	$70	$275
	Auctions: $69, MS-65, June 2015; $52, MS-64, August 2015; $34, MS-64, August 2015								
1964, Proof	3,950,762	31,246	67.5				$20	$60	$400
	Auctions: $4,700, PF-70, August 2015; $4,230, PF-69DCam, August 2015; $364, PF-68DCam, January 2015								
1964, Heavily Accented Hair, Proof †† (c)	(d)	14,953	64.9				$75	$400	$10,000
	Auctions: $1,645, PF-69, June 2015; $212, PF-67, April 2015; $89, PF-65, September 2015; $40, PF-63, October 2015								
1964-D	156,205,446	5,138	64.4	99%	$11	$12	$26	$135	$1,100
	Auctions: $2,291, MS-67, February 2015; $1,880, MS-67, January 2015; $69, MS-65, January 2015; $60, MS-65, August 2015								
1964-D, Doubled Die Obverse (e)	(f)	32	61.9	69%			$45	$110	$325
	Auctions: $60, MS-66, November 2011; $89, MS-65, June 2015; $36, MS-64, August 2015								
1964-D, Repunched Mintmark (g)	(f)	26	63.4	92%			$45	$160	$850
	Auctions: $130, AU-55, June 2010								

†† Ranked in the *100 Greatest U.S. Modern Coins* (fourth edition). **a.** There are several doubled-die obverses for the 1964 Kennedy half dollar. The one pictured and listed is FS-50-1964-102. **b.** Included in circulation-strike 1964 mintage figure. **c.** This variety "is identifiable by the enhanced hairline in the central area of the hair, just below the part. However, the easiest way to identify the variety is the weak or broken lower left serif of the I (in LIBERTY)" (*Cherrypickers' Guide to Rare Die Varieties*, sixth edition, volume II). **d.** Included in 1964, Proof, mintage figure. **e.** Doubling on this variety is evident on the date, IN GOD WE TRUST, the designer's initials, and the LI and TY of LIBERTY. "This is a very popular variety. It is extremely rare above MS-65" (*Cherrypickers' Guide to Rare Die Varieties*, sixth edition, volume II). There are other doubled-die obverses for 1964-D. The one pictured and listed is FS-50-1964D-101. **f.** Included in 1964-D mintage figure. **g.** There are several repunched mintmarks for 1964-D. The one listed is FS-50-1964D-502.

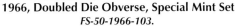

1966, Doubled Die Obverse, Special Mint Set
FS-50-1966-103.

1967, Quintupled Die Obverse, Special Mint Set
FS-50-1967-101.

	Mintage	Cert	Avg	%MS	MS-63	MS-65	MS-66	MS-67
						PF-65	PF-67Cam	PF-68DC
1965	65,879,366	1,406	64.7	99%	$6	$30	$200	$1,500
	Auctions: $470, MS-67, January 2015; $282, MS-67, October 2015; $259, MS-66, July 2015							
1965, Special Mint Set	2,360,000	11,583	66.6			$9	$400	
	Auctions: $999, MS-67, September 2016; $2,350, MS-66, October 2015; $823, MS-65, July 2015							
1966	108,984,932	1,386	64.7	98%	$6	$35	$235	$2,500
	Auctions: No auction records available.							
1966, Special Mint Set	2,261,583	12,871	66.8			$9	$100	
	Auctions: $376, MS-68, September 2015; $1,410, MS-67, October 2015; $94, MS-67, July 2015							
1966, Special Mint Set, Doubled Die Obverse (a)	**(b)**	197	66.7			$65	$250	
	Auctions: $176, MS-67, October 2015; $153, MS-67, September 2015; $940, MS-67, August 2016							
1967	295,046,978	1,476	64.5	96%	$6	$33	$150	$1,450
	Auctions: $17,625, MS-68, August 2015; $3,525, MS-67, October 2015; $100, MS-67, October 2015							
1967, Special Mint Set	1,863,344	11,949	66.7			$9	$90	
	Auctions: $200, PF-68, September 2014; $734, PF-67DCam, November 2014							
1967, Special Mint Set, Quintupled Die Obverse (c)	**(d)**	32	66.4			$135	$600	
	Auctions: $19,975, MS-69, August 2016; $176, MS-68, March 2016; $705, MS-67, July 2016							
1968-D	246,951,930	2,702	64.8	99%	$6	$18	$48	$950
	Auctions: $1,763, MS-67, January 2015; $1,293, MS-67, October 2015; $46, MS-66, April 2015							
1968-S, Proof	3,041,506	7,305	67.7			$8	$22	$50
	Auctions: $10,575, PF-70DCam, August 2015; $329, PF-69DCam, August 2015							
1969-D	129,881,800	1,903	64.6	99%	$6	$30	$225	$1,800
	Auctions: $1,116, MS-66, March 2016; $30,550, MS-65, August 2016; $823, MS-63, December 2015							
1969-S, Proof	2,934,631	10,568	67.9			$8	$23	$45
	Auctions: $224, PF-69DCam, January 2014							
1970-D ††	2,150,000	4,523	64.3	100%	$20	$45	$300	$1,500
	Auctions: $622, MS-66, November 2016; $235, MS-66, September 2015; $74, MS-65, October 2015							
1970-S, Proof	2,632,810	9,407	67.9			$15	$30	$50
	Auctions: $306, PF-69DCam, January 2015; $282, PF-69DCam, January 2015							
1971	155,164,000	220	64.3	95%	$3	$15	$45	$200
	Auctions: $170, MS-66, May 2014							
1971-D	302,097,424	981	65.1	96%	$3	$10	$22	$70
	Auctions: $235, MS-67, January 2015; $112, MS-67, March 2015; $100, MS-66, July 2015							
1971-S, Proof	3,220,733	5,483	67.8			$4	$20	$100
	Auctions: $1,821, PF-67, July 2013							

†† Ranked in the *100 Greatest U.S. Modern Coins* (fourth edition). **a.** There are several doubled-die obverse varieties of the 1966, Special Mint Set, half dollar. The one listed is FS-50-1966-103, with strong doubling evident on the profile, IN GOD WE TRUST, the eye, the hair, and the designer's initials. **b.** Included in 1966, Special Mint Set, mintage figure. **c.** "A prominent quintupled (at least) spread is evident on RTY of LIBERTY, with strong multiple images on all obverse lettering and portions of the hair" (*Cherrypickers' Guide to Rare Die Varieties*, sixth edition, volume II). **d.** Included in 1967, Special Mint Set, mintage figure.

**1972, Doubled Die
Obverse**
FS-50-1972-101.

**1972-D, Missing
Designer's Initials**
FS-50-1972D-901.

	Mintage	Cert	Avg	%MS	MS-63 / PF-65	MS-65 / PF-67Cam	MS-66 / PF-68DC	MS-67
1972	153,180,000	341	64.9	96%	$3	$15	$50	$290
Auctions: $36, MS-66, July 2014								
1972, Doubled Die Obverse (e)	(f)	2	58.0	0%	$140	$165	$225	$450
Auctions: $90, AU-50, March 2011								
1972-D	141,890,000	573	65.2	98%	$3	$10	$23	$100
Auctions:$153, MS-67, November 2015; $94, MS-67, October 2015; $17, MS-66, July 2015								
1972-D, Missing Designer's Initials	(g)	5	58.2	20%	$60	$80	$150	$250
Auctions: $380, EF-45, October 2009								
1972-S, Proof	3,260,996	4,189	68.0			$4	$16	$25
Auctions: $92, PF-69DCam, June 2014								
1973	64,964,000	240	64.7	97%	$3	$15	$45	$155
Auctions: $282, MS-67, August 2014; $153, MS-67, October 2015; $38, MS-66, October 2015								
1973-D	83,171,400	410	65.1	98%	$3	$11	$20	$170
Auctions: $329, MS-67, July 2014; $206, MS-67, October 2015								
1973-S, Proof	2,760,339	825	68.2			$3	$16	$25
Auctions: $2,350, PF-70DCam, December 2011								
1974	201,596,000	203	64.3	96%	$3	$20	$35	$145
Auctions: $3,290, MS-67, October 2015; $2,350, MS-67, August 2014; $37, MS-66, March 2008								
1974-D	79,066,300	307	64.7	94%	$3	$15	$35	$175
Auctions: $382, MS-67, August 2014; $259, MS-67, October 2015; $65, MS-65, June 2014								
1974-D, Doubled Die Obverse (h)	(i)	484	63.9	95%	$40	$100	$200	$450
Auctions: $411, MS-66, July 2014; $135, MS-65, July 2014; $28, MS-63, October 2014								
1974-S, Proof	2,612,568	872	68.1			$4	$9	$18
Auctions: $4,406, PF-70DCam, March 2014								
1776–1976, Copper-Nickel Clad	234,308,000	457	64.2	95%	$3	$15	$50	$125
Auctions: $1,998, MS-67, August 2014; $2,350, MS-62, February 2014								
1776–1976-D, Copper-Nickel Clad	287,565,248	854	64.9	98%	$3	$15	$25	$375
Auctions: $1,116, MS-67, October 2015; $79, MS-65, August 2015; $999, AU-58, August 2015								
1776–1976-S, Silver Clad	11,000,000	1,403	66.0	100%	$8	$10	$15	$30
Auctions: $217, MS-68, July 2014; $188, MS-68, October 2015; $153, MS-68, September 2015; $141, MS-68, May 2015								
1776–1976-S, Proof, Copper-Nickel Clad	7,059,099	1,976	67.8			$4	$13	$18
Auctions: $3,290, PF-70DCam, January 2015; $2,585, PF-70DCam, July 2015; $2,233, PF-70DCam, August 2015								
1776–1976-S, Proof, Silver Clad (j)	4,000,000	3,545	68.2			$12	$15	$25
Auctions: $881, PF-70DCam, January 2015; $881, PF-70DCam, July 2015; $750, PF-70DCam, August 2015								
1977	43,598,000	386	65.3	99%	$3	$12	$28	$120
Auctions: $1,116, MS-67, November 2014; $764, MS-67, June 2014; $259, MS-67, August 2014								
1977-D	31,449,106	191	65.1	98%	$3	$15	$22	$85
Auctions: $176, MS-67, August 2014; $153, MS-67, October 2015; $21, MS-66, August 2007								
1977-S, Proof	3,251,152	1,338	68.7			$4	$9	$15
Auctions: $141, PF-70DCam, February 2015; $129, PF-70DCam, March 2015; $106, PF-70DCam, August 2015								

e. Doubling is strongly evident on IN GOD WE TRUST and on the date. This variety is very rare above MS-65. **f.** Included in 1972 mintage figure. **g.** Included in 1972-D mintage figure. **h.** Strong doubling is visible on IN GOD WE TRUST, the date, and LIBERTY. **i.** Included in 1974-D mintage figure. **j.** Mintage figures for 1976-S silver coins are approximate. Many were melted in 1982.

| 1979-S, Filled S (Type 1), Proof | 1979-S, Clear S (Type 2), Proof | 1981-S, Rounded S (Type 1), Proof | 1981-S, Flat S (Type 2), Proof |

	Mintage	Cert	Avg	%MS	MS-63 / PF-65	MS-65 / PF-67Cam	MS-66 / PF-68DC	MS-67
1978	14,350,000	262	65.2	99%	$3	$12	$20	$150
	Auctions: $411, MS-67, August 2014; $212, MS-67, October 2015; $19, MS-66, July 2008							
1978-D	13,765,799	225	65.1	100%	$3	$10	$23	$150
	Auctions: $881, MS-67, August 2014; $18, MS-66, September 2008							
1978-S, Proof	3,127,781	1,487	68.8			$3	$12	$18
	Auctions: $106, PF-70DCam, February 2015; $89, PF-70DCam, June 2015; $84, PF-70DCam, October 2015; $74, PF-70DCam, May 2015							
1979	68,312,000	339	65.2	98%	$3	$10	$25	$150
	Auctions: $423, MS-67, July 2014; $306, MS-67, October 2015; $188, MS-64, September 2015; $764, AU-58, July 2015							
1979-D	15,815,422	299	65.2	100%	$3	$12	$25	$160
	Auctions: $823, MS-67, October 2015; $764, MS-67, August 2014; $11, MS-66, September 2008							
1979-S, Proof, All kinds (k)	3,677,175							
1979-S, Type 1, Proof		2,115	68.9			$3	$11	$14
	Auctions: $200, PF-70DCam, April 2012							
1979-S, Type 2, Proof		1,703	69.0			$25	$27	$30
	Auctions: $588, PF-70DCam, February 2013							
1980-P	44,134,000	368	65.5	99%	$3	$10	$17	$35
	Auctions: $129, MS-67, July 2014; $129, MS-67, October 2015; $42, MS-67, October 2015							
1980-D	33,456,449	192	64.8	98%	$3	$15	$55	$175
	Auctions: $4,935, MS-68, October 2015; $212, MS-67, October 2015; $138, MS-66, September 2008; $65, MS-66, October 2015							
1980-S, Proof	3,554,806	2,089	68.8			$3	$12	$15
	Auctions: $135, PF-70DCam, July 2015; $106, PF-70DCam, November 2015; $100, PF-70DCam, October 2015; $60							
1981-P	29,544,000	339	65.3	99%	$3	$12	$25	$260
	Auctions: No auction records available.							
1981-D	27,839,533	134	64.2	99%	$3	$18	$40	$350
	Auctions: $1,880, MS-67, August 2014; $50, MS-66, June 2014							
1981-S, Proof, All kinds (l)	4,063,083							
1981-S, Type 1, Proof		2,458	68.8			$3	$12	$15
	Auctions: $259, PF-70DCam, June 2013							
1981-S, Type 2, Proof		1,157	68.9			$25	$29	$33
	Auctions: $2,585, PF-70DCam, November 2013							
1982-P	10,819,000	212	64.8	98%	$7	$23	$70	$425
	Auctions: $153, MS-66, October 2015; $74, MS-65, October 2015; $69, MS-65, August 2015; $42, MS-64, October 2015							
1982-D	13,140,102	297	65.3	99%	$7	$18	$40	$325
	Auctions: $3,290, MS-67, November 2013; $999, MS-67, August 2014; $823, MS-67, October 2015; $141, MS-66, October 2015							
1982-S, Proof	3,857,479	1,517	69.0			$4	$12	$15
	Auctions: $529, PF-70DCam, June 2013							

k. The mintmark style of 1979-S, Proof, coins was changed during production, resulting in two distinct types. The scarcer, well-defined Type 2 is easily distinguished from the more common blob-like Type 1. l. The mintmark style of the 1981-S, Proof, coins was changed during production, creating two different types. The scarcer Type 2 is not easily distinguished from the common Type 1. Type 2 is flat on the top curve of the S, compared to Type 1, which has a more rounded top. The surface of Type 2 is frosted, and the openings in the loops are slightly larger.

1988-S, Doubled Die
Obverse, Proof
FS-50-1988S-101.

	Mintage	Cert	Avg	%MS	MS-63 / PF-65	MS-65 / PF-67Cam	MS-66 / PF-68DC	MS-67
1983-P	34,139,000	358	65.2	98%	$8	$22	$45	$200
Auctions: $147, MS-65, April 2014								
1983-D	32,472,244	211	64.9	98%	$7	$15	$30	$330
Auctions: $1,645, MS-67, August 2014; $646, MS-67, October 2015; $13, MS-66, October 2008								
1983-S, Proof	3,279,126	1,487	69.0			$4	$12	$15
Auctions: $115, PF-70DCam, August 2013								
1984-P	26,029,000	225	65.5	99%	$3	$12	$38	$250
Auctions: $1,116, MS-67, August 2014; $940, MS-67, October 2015; $98, MS-66, September 2008								
1984-D	26,262,158	211	65.1	100%	$3	$17	$40	$350
Auctions: $3,290, MS-67, October 2015; $2,820, MS-67, August 2014; $11, MS-66, September 2008								
1984-S, Proof	3,065,110	1,086	69.0			$4	$12	$15
Auctions: $382, PF-70DCam, June 2013								
1985-P	18,706,962	271	65.9	100%	$5	$15	$25	$90
Auctions: $123, MS-67, July 2014; $62, MS-67, October 2015								
1985-D	19,814,034	378	66.1	100%	$5	$12	$15	$45
Auctions: $159, MS-67, July 2014; $112, MS-67, October 2015								
1985-S, Proof	3,362,821	1,286	69.0			$4	$12	$15
Auctions: $135, PF-70DCam, November 2015; $106, PF-70DCam, August 2013								
1986-P	13,107,633	297	66.0	100%	$6	$13	$28	$70
Auctions: $282, MS-67, July 2014; $118, MS-67, October 2015; $112, MS-67, August 2015								
1986-D	15,336,145	396	66.1	100%	$5	$11	$20	$45
Auctions: $57, MS-67, July 2014								
1986-S, Proof	3,010,497	976	69.0			$4	$12	$15
Auctions: $106, PF-70DCam, October 2015; $94, PF-70DCam, March 2015; $94, PF-70DCam, July 2015								
1987-P (m)	2,890,758	464	65.6	100%	$5	$15	$30	$100
Auctions: $4,113, MS-68, October 2015; $3,290, MS-68, August 2014; $223, MS-67, October 2015								
1987-D (m)	2,890,758	618	66.0	100%	$5	$12	$23	$50
Auctions: $3,055, MS-68, October 2015; $2,585, MS-68, August 2014; $21, MS-67, October 2008								
1987-S, Proof	4,227,728	1,586	69.1			$4	$12	$15
Auctions: $96, PF-70DCam, August 2013								
1988-P	13,626,000	223	65.8	100%	$5	$15	$28	$90
Auctions: $282, MS-67, July 2014; $153, MS-67, October 2015								
1988-D	12,000,096	357	66.2	100%	$4	$12	$25	$40
Auctions: $57, MS-67, July 2014								
1988-S, Proof	3,262,948	1,139	69.1			$4	$12	$15
Auctions: $113, PF-70DCam, May 2013								
1988-S, Doubled Die Obverse, Proof (n)	(o)	12	68.8			$110	$160	
Auctions: $260, PF-68UCam, February 2011								

m. Not issued for circulation; included with Mint and Souvenir sets. **n.** Clear doubling is visible on IN GOD WE TRUST, the date, and the mintmark. Some doubling is also evident on LIBERTY and the mintmark. **o.** Included in 1988-S, Proof, mintage figure.

| | Mintage | Cert | Avg | %MS | MS-63 | MS-65 | MS-66 | MS-67 |
						PF-65	PF-67Cam	PF-68DC
1989-P	24,542,000	277	65.7	99%	$4	$15	$23	$90
	Auctions: $282, MS-67, October 2015; $259, MS-67, July 2014							
1989-D	23,000,216	347	66.0	100%	$3	$11	$18	$60
	Auctions: $129, MS-67, July 2014; $74, MS-67, October 2015							
1989-S, Proof	3,220,194	1,049	69.0			$5	$12	$20
	Auctions: $123, PF-70Cam, May 2013							
1990-P	22,278,000	196	65.8	100%	$3	$11	$22	$150
	Auctions: $259, MS-67, October 2015; $200, MS-66, November 2015; $153, MS-66, November 2015; $106, MS-65, November 2014							
1990-D	20,096,242	236	65.6	100%	$3	$16	$32	$200
	Auctions: $31, MS-66, October 2008							
1990-S, Proof	3,299,559	1,204	69.1			$5	$12	$18
	Auctions: $82, PF-70DCam, May 2013							
1991-P	14,874,000	236	66.0	100%	$4	$12	$25	$200
	Auctions: $217, MS-67, July 2014; $165, MS-67, October 2015							
1991-D	15,054,678	260	65.8	100%	$4	$15	$30	$300
	Auctions: $920, MS-67, September 2008; $329, MS-67, August 2014; $294, MS-67, October 2015							
1991-S, Proof	2,867,787	1,104	69.3			$10	$14	$20
	Auctions: $68, PF-70DCam, July 2013							
1992-P	17,628,000	211	65.9	100%	$3	$11	$22	$25
	Auctions: $2,350, MS-68, August 2014; $11, MS-67, October 2008							
1992-D	17,000,106	156	66.1	100%	$3	$10	$18	$30
	Auctions: $147, MS-67, August 2014; $30, MS-67, August 2014; $46, MS-67, July 2014							
1992-S, Proof	2,858,981	706	69.2			$5	$14	$20
	Auctions: $35, PF-70DCam, May 2013							
1992-S, Proof, Silver	1,317,579	2,363	69.1			$17	$20	$25
	Auctions: $92, PF-70DCam, July 2013							
1993-P	15,510,000	348	66.4	99%	$3	$11	$20	$40
	Auctions: $58, MS-67, July 2014							
1993-D	15,000,006	619	66.0	100%	$3	$10	$22	$60
	Auctions: $2,585, MS-68, August 2014; $11, MS-66, October 2008							
1993-S, Proof	2,633,439	766	69.3			$8	$17	$23
	Auctions: $31, PF-70DCam, May 2013							
1993-S, Proof, Silver	761,353	1,796	69.1			$27	$30	$37
	Auctions: $99, PF-70DCam, May 2014							
1994-P	23,718,000	431	65.8	100%	$3	$10	$20	$55
	Auctions: $2,115, MS-68, August 2014; $10, MS-66, October 2008							
1994-D	23,828,110	205	65.8	100%	$3	$10	$20	$75
	Auctions: $364, MS-67, July 2014; $141, MS-67, October 2015							
1994-S, Proof	2,484,594	728	69.3			$8	$17	$23
	Auctions: $45, PF-70DCam, May 2013							
1994-S, Proof, Silver	785,329	1,711	69.1			$26	$33	$35
	Auctions: $206, PF-70DCam, February 2013							
1995-P	26,496,000	251	66.1	99%	$3	$10	$17	$40
	Auctions: $55, MS-67, July 2014							
1995-D	26,288,000	308	66.2	100%	$3	$10	$20	$50
	Auctions: $2,585, MS-68, August 2014; $13, MS-67, October 2008							
1995-S, Proof	2,117,496	674	69.3			$16	$20	$25
	Auctions: $66, PF-70DCam, August 2013							
1995-S, Proof, Silver	679,985	2,039	69.1			$38	$40	$45
	Auctions: $135, PF-70DCam, May 2014							

	Mintage	Cert	Avg	%MS	MS-63 / PF-65	MS-65 / PF-67Cam	MS-66 / PF-68DC	MS-67
1996-P	24,442,000	354	66.2	99%	$3	$10	$17	$35
	Auctions: $247, MS-68, July 2014; $165, MS-68, October 2015							
1996-D	24,744,000	348	66.0	99%	$3	$10	$17	$35
	Auctions: $1,293, MS-68, August 2014; $999, MS-68, January 2015; $11, MS-67, October 2008							
1996-S, Proof	1,750,244	666	69.2			$10	$15	$22
	Auctions: $66, PF-70DCam, August 2013							
1996-S, Proof, Silver	775,021	1,685	69.1			$30	$35	$40
	Auctions: $135, PF-70DCam, August 2013							
1997-P	20,882,000	174	66.2	99%	$3	$12	$30	$80
	Auctions: $60, MS-67, July 2014							
1997-D	19,876,000	281	65.9	100%	$3	$13	$30	$90
	Auctions: $646, MS-68, June 2013; $123, MS-67, July 2014; $79, MS-67, October 2015							
1997-S, Proof	2,055,000	575	69.3			$12	$20	$25
	Auctions: $76, PF-70DCam, August 2013							
1997-S, Proof, Silver	741,678	1,779	69.2			$30	$40	$50
	Auctions: $96, PF-70DCam, August 2013							
1998-P	15,646,000	220	66.3	100%	$3	$15	$35	$70
	Auctions: $76, MS-67, July 2014							
1998-D	15,064,000	210	65.8	100%	$3	$11	$20	$70
	Auctions: $62, MS-67, July 2014							
1998-S, Proof	2,086,507	685	69.4			$10	$17	$23
	Auctions: $56, PF-70DCam, August 2013							
1998-S, Proof, Silver	878,792	2,008	69.3			$18	$25	$35
	Auctions: $88, PF-70DCam, August 2013							
1998-S, Matte Finish Proof, Silver †† (p)	62,000	2,386	3.5			$125		
	Auctions: $113, PF-69, November 2014; $170, PF-69, March 2015; $165, PF-69, March 2015							
1999-P	8,900,000	243	66.4	100%	$3	$10	$20	$30
	Auctions: $2,115, MS-69, June 2013; $823, MS-68, August 2014							
1999-D	10,682,000	247	66.2	100%	$3	$10	$16	$23
	Auctions: $1,998, MS-68, August 2014; $10, MS-66, October 2008							
1999-S, Proof	2,543,401	3,436	69.3			$13	$16	$20
	Auctions: $90, PF-70DCam, May 2013							
1999-S, Proof, Silver	804,565	5,731	69.1			$25	$30	$32
	Auctions: $147, PF-70DCam, August 2013							
2000-P	22,600,000	134	66.0	100%	$3	$10	$17	$35
	Auctions: $764, MS-68, August 2014; $48, MS-67, October 2008							
2000-D	19,466,000	229	66.0	100%	$3	$10	$20	$40
	Auctions: $123, MS-67, July 2014; $94, MS-67, October 2015							
2000-S, Proof	3,082,483	2,712	69.3			$5	$12	$16
	Auctions: $58, PF-70DCam, May 2013							
2000-S, Proof, Silver	965,421	6,556	69.2			$14	$18	$20
	Auctions: $78, PF-70DCam, May 2013							
2001-P	21,200,000	407	65.5	100%	$3	$8	$15	$28
	Auctions: $176, MS-68, September 2015; $60, MS-68, October 2015							
2001-D	19,504,000	451	65.8	100%	$3	$8	$13	$28
	Auctions: $247, MS-68, July 2014; $153, MS-68, October 2015							
2001-S, Proof	2,294,909	2,061	69.3			$6	$10	$13
	Auctions: $76, PF-70DCam, May 2013							
2001-S, Proof, Silver	889,697	4,931	69.2			$15	$21	$23
	Auctions: $90, PF-70DCam, May 2013							

†† Ranked in the *100 Greatest U.S. Modern Coins* (fourth edition). **p.** Minted for inclusion in the Robert F. Kennedy commemorative set (along with an RFK commemorative dollar).

	Mintage	Cert	Avg	%MS	MS-63	MS-65	MS-66	MS-67
						PF-65	PF-67Cam	PF-68DC
2002-P (q)	3,100,000	225	65.6	100%	$3	$8	$15	$30
	Auctions: $182, MS-68, June 2014; $135, MS-68, January 2015; $129, MS-68, October 2015; $118, MS-68, July 2014							
2002-D (q)	2,500,000	240	65.8	100%	$3	$9	$20	$40
	Auctions: $2,115, MS-69, June 2013							
2002-S, Proof	2,319,766	2,103	69.2			$5	$13	$16
	Auctions: $60, PF-70DCam, May 2013							
2002-S, Proof, Silver	892,229	5,089	69.3			$14	$18	$20
	Auctions: $61, PF-70DCam, May 2013							
2003-P (q)	2,500,000	279	65.8	100%	$3	$9	$20	$30
	Auctions: $59, MS-67, July 2014							
2003-D (q)	2,500,000	262	65.8	100%	$3	$8	$16	$25
	Auctions: $51, MS-67, July 2014							
2003-S, Proof	2,172,684	4,126	69.2			$5	$12	$16
	Auctions: $62, PF-70DCam, August 2015; $35, PF-70DCam, May 2013							
2003-S, Proof, Silver	1,125,755	6,033	69.2			$14	$18	$20
	Auctions: $76, PF-70DCam, November 2014; $82, PF-70DCam, May 2014							
2004-P (q)	2,900,000	254	66.2	100%	$3	$8	$17	$30
	Auctions: $100, MS-67, October 2015; $86, MS-67, July 2014							
2004-D (q)	2,900,000	404	66.3	100%	$3	$8	$16	$25
	Auctions: $423, MS-68, July 2014; $235, MS-68, October 2015							
2004-S, Proof	1,789,488	1,883	69.2			$13	$17	$24
	Auctions: $66, PF-70DCam, August 2013							
2004-S, Proof, Silver	1,175,934	5,879	69.2			$20	$22	$23
	Auctions: $69, PF-70DCam, January 2013							
2005-P (q)	3,800,000	232	66.0	100%	$4	$18	$25	$75
	Auctions: $470, MS-67, October 2015; $42, MS-66, July 2014							
2005-P, Satin Finish (q)	1,160,000	2,518	67.0	100%			$8	$15
	Auctions: No auction records available.							
2005-D (q)	3,500,000	265	66.3	100%	$4	$15	$23	$40
	Auctions: $1,116, MS-68, August 2014; $11, MS-66, October 2008							
2005-D, Satin Finish (q)	1,160,000	2,189	66.7	100%			$8	$15
	Auctions: No auction records available.							
2005-S, Proof	2,275,000	7,128	69.2			$5	$12	$16
	Auctions: $66, PF-70DCam, August 2013							
2005-S, Proof, Silver	1,069,679	7,291	69.3			$12	$18	$20
	Auctions: $74, PF-70DCam, January 2013							
2006-P (q)	2,400,000	204	66.7	100%	$2	$9	$22	$26
	Auctions: $42, MS-69, January 2009; $764, MS-68, August 2014; $376, MS-68, October 2015							
2006-P, Satin Finish (q)	847,361	1,371	66.8	100%			$8	$15
	Auctions: No auction records available.							
2006-D (q)	2,000,000	197	66.3	100%	$2	$7	$15	$28
	Auctions: $82, MS-67, July 2014; $60, MS-67, October 2015							
2006-D, Satin Finish (q)	847,361	1,363	66.8	100%			$8	$15
	Auctions: No auction records available.							
2006-S, Proof	2,000,428	2,780	69.3			$5	$12	$16
	Auctions: $46, PF-70DCam, August 2013							
2006-S, Proof, Silver	1,054,008	4,165	69.4			$12	$18	$20
	Auctions: $76, PF-70DCam, August 2013							
2007-P (q)	2,400,000	173	66.5	100%	$2	$6	$11	$17
	Auctions: $270, MS-68, July 2014; $100, MS-68, October 2015							

q. Not issued for circulation. Sold directly to the public in rolls and small bags.

	Mintage	Cert	Avg	%MS	MS-63	MS-65	MS-66	MS-67
						PF-65	PF-67Cam	PF-68DC
2007-P, Satin Finish (q)	895,628	360	66.8	100%			$8	$15
	Auctions: No auction records available.							
2007-D (q)	2,400,000	137	66.1	100%	$2	$6	$15	$30
	Auctions: $15, MS-69, January 2009							
2007-D, Satin Finish (q)	895,628	382	66.9	100%			$8	$15
	Auctions: No auction records available.							
2007-S, Proof	1,702,116	2,849	69.3			$5	$12	$16
	Auctions: $64, PF-70DCam, January 2013							
2007-S, Proof, Silver	875,050	3,719	69.4			$14	$19	$22
	Auctions: $86, PF-70DCam, August 2013							
2008-P (q)	1,700,000	213	66.3	100%	$2	$8	$20	$40
	Auctions: $1,410, MS-68, August 2014; $12, SP-67, April 2012							
2008-P, Satin Finish (q)	745,464	100	67.1	100%			$8	$15
	Auctions: No auction records available.							
2008-D (q)	1,700,000	104	65.8	100%	$2	$8	$20	$45
	Auctions: $24, MS-66, June 2011							
2008-D, Satin Finish (q)	745,464	77	67.0	100%			$8	$15
	Auctions: No auction records available.							
2008-S, Proof	1,405,674	1,793	69.3			$5	$12	$16
	Auctions: $71, PF-70DCam, November 2013							
2008-S, Proof, Silver	763,887	3,781	69.4			$14	$20	$23
	Auctions: $66, PF-70DCam, August 2013							
2009-P (q)	1,900,000	191	66.2	100%	$2	$6	$12	$25
	Auctions: $1,998, MS-68, August 2014; $6, MS-66, November 2011							
2009-P, Satin Finish (q)	784,614	236	67.1	100%			$8	$15
	Auctions: No auction records available.							
2009-D (q)	1,900,000	148	66.2	100%	$2	$6	$12	$30
	Auctions: $27, MS-66, February 2012							
2009-D, Satin Finish (q)	784,614	272	67.5	100%			$8	$15
	Auctions: No auction records available.							
2009-S, Proof	1,482,502	3,626	69.3			$5	$12	$16
	Auctions: $31, PF-70DCam, May 2013							
2009-S, Proof, Silver	697,365	4,592	69.3			$14	$18	$20
	Auctions: $41, PF-70DCam, May 2013							
2010-P (q)	1,800,000	256	66.6	100%	$2	$6	$12	$25
	Auctions: $23, MS-67, July 2014							
2010-P, Satin Finish (q)	583,897	244	67.1	100%			$8	$15
	Auctions: No auction records available.							
2010-D (q)	1,700,000	174	66.3	100%	$2	$6	$12	$30
	Auctions: $3,995, MS-68, August 2015; $101, MS-67, July 2014; $48, MS-67, October 2015							
2010-D, Satin Finish (q)	583,897	330	67.6	100%			$8	$15
	Auctions: No auction records available.							
2010-S, Proof	1,103,815	1,294	69.3			$5	$12	$16
	Auctions: $48, PF-70DCam, August 2013							
2010-S, Proof, Silver	585,401	4,205	69.6			$14	$18	$20
	Auctions: $48, PF-70DCam, May 2013							
2011-P (q)	1,750,000	465	66.7	100%	$3	$6	$12	$25
	Auctions: $229, MS-68, July 2014; $176, MS-68, October 2015							
2011-D (q)	1,700,000	401	66.5	100%	$3	$6	$12	$25
	Auctions: $1,116, MS-68, August 2014; $1,058, MS-68, August 2014; $33, MS-67, January 2012							

q. Not issued for circulation. Sold directly to the public in rolls and small bags.

	Mintage	Cert	Avg	%MS	MS-63	MS-65 / PF-65	MS-66 / PF-67Cam	MS-67 / PF-68DC
2011-S, Proof	1,098,835	2,318	69.4			$5	$12	$16
Auctions: $21, PF-70UCam, March 2012								
2011-S, Proof, Silver	574,175	4,990	69.7			$14	$18	$20
Auctions: $39, PF-70DCam, August 2014; $36, PF-70DCam, April 2012								
2012-P (q)	1,800,000	247	66.8	100%	$3	$6	$12	$25
Auctions: No auction records available.								
2012-D (q)	1,700,000	285	66.7	100%	$3	$6	$12	$25
Auctions: No auction records available.								
2012-S, Proof	843,705	1,895	69.3			$5	$12	$16
Auctions: $51, PF-70DCam, May 2013								
2012-S, Proof, Silver	445,612	2,067	69.6			$14	$18	$20
Auctions: No auction records available.								
2013-P (q)	5,000,000	298	66.8	100%	$3	$6	$12	$25
Auctions: No auction records available.								
2013-D (q)	4,600,000	326	66.9	100%	$3	$6	$12	$25
Auctions: No auction records available.								
2013-S, Proof	*854,785*	1,906	69.3			$5	$12	$16
Auctions: No auction records available.								
2013-S, Proof, Silver	467,691	2,232	69.6			$14	$18	$20
Auctions: No auction records available.								
2014-P (q)	2,500,000	434	66.4	100%	$3	$6	$12	$25
Auctions: No auction records available.								
2014-P, High Relief ✝✝ (r)		10,086	65.9	100%	$15	$20		
Auctions: No auction records available.								
2014-P, Proof, Silver ✝✝ (s)	*219,173*	17,120	1.1			$15	$35	$40
Auctions: No auction records available.								
2014-D (q)	*2,100,000*	673	62.5	100%	$3	$6	$12	$25
Auctions: No auction records available.								
2014-D, High Relief ✝✝ (r)		9,589	66.0	100%	$15	$20		
Auctions: No auction records available.								
2014-D, Silver ✝✝ (s)	*219,173*	16,827	1.2	100%	$10	$15	$20	$23
Auctions: No auction records available.								
2014-S, Enhanced Uncirculated, Silver ✝✝ (s)	*219,173*	17,673	1.2	100%	$10	$15	$20	$25
Auctions: No auction records available.								
2014-S, Proof	*767,977*	2,575	1.1			$15	$18	$20
Auctions: No auction records available.								
2014-S, Proof, Silver	472,107	5,457	2.0			$15	$20	$23
Auctions: No auction records available.								
2014-W, Reverse Proof, Silver ✝✝ (s)	*219,173*	17,460	1.2			$20	$25	$35
Auctions: No auction records available.								
2014-W, 50th Anniversary, Proof, Gold ✝✝ (t)	73,772	10,132	69.7			$900	$1,000	$1,200
Auctions: No auction records available.								

✝✝ All 2014 Kennedy 50th Anniversary Half Dollars are ranked in the *100 Greatest U.S. Modern Coins* (fourth edition), as a single entry. **q.** Not issued for circulation. Sold directly to the public in rolls and small bags. **r.** To celebrate the 50th anniversary of the Kennedy half dollar, in 2014 the U.S. Mint issued an Uncirculated two-coin set featuring a Kennedy half dollar from Philadelphia and one from Denver. **s.** Featured in the 2014 half dollar silver-coin collection released by the U.S. Mint to commemorate the 50th anniversary of the Kennedy half dollar. **t.** First gold half dollar offered by the U.S. Mint. It commemorates the 50th anniversary of the first release of the Kennedy half dollar in 1964. Dual-dated 1964–2014.

| | Mintage | Cert | Avg | %MS | MS-63 | MS-65 | MS-66 | MS-67 |
						PF-65	PF-67Cam	PF-68DC
2015-P (q)	2,300,000	416	66.3	100%	$3	$6	$12	$25
Auctions: No auction records available.								
2015-D (q)	2,300,000	521	66.4	100%	$3	$6	$12	$25
Auctions: No auction records available.								
2015-S, Proof	662,854	2,917	69.4			$5	$12	$16
Auctions: No auction records available.								
2015-S, Proof, Silver	387,310	3,034	69.5			$14	$18	$20
Auctions: No auction records available.								

q. Not issued for circulation. Sold directly to the public in rolls and small bags.

In 2016 a special .9999 fine gold striking of Adolf A. Weinman's Liberty Walking half dollar was created to celebrate the 100th anniversary of its introduction. It is smaller than the silver strikings, with a diameter of 27 mm and weighing 15.552 grams. Struck at West Point, it has a reeded edge. Similar strikings were made for the 1916 dime and quarter designs.

	Mintage	Cert	Avg	%MS	SP-67	SP-70
2016-W, Liberty Walking Centennial Gold Coin ††	65,509				$850	$1,000

†† 2016 Centennial Gold Coins in all denominations are ranked in the *100 Greatest U.S. Modern Coins* (fourth edition), as a single entry.

Normally scheduled production of clad and silver Kennedy half dollars, in the same standards and specifications as previously, continued in 2016 and beyond, and was not disrupted by the gold Liberty Walking half dollar.

| | Mintage | Cert | Avg | %MS | MS-63 | MS-65 | MS-66 | MS-67 |
						PF-65	PF-67Cam	PF-68DC
2016-P (q)	2,100,000	64	67.0	100%	$3	$6	$12	$25
2016-D (q)	2,100,000	0	n/a		$2	$6	$12	$25
2016-S, Proof	641,775	891	69.5			$5	$12	$16
2016-S, Proof, Silver	419,256	2,580	69.6			$14	$18	$20
2017-P (q)	1,800,000				$2	$6	$12	$25
2017-D (q)	2,900,000				$2	$6	$12	$25
2017-S, Proof	(621,384)					$5	$12	$16
2017-S, Proof, Silver	(406,994)					$14	$18	$20
2018-P (q)	4,800,000				$2	$6	$12	$25
2018-D (q)	6,100,000				$2	$6	$12	$25
2018-S, Proof	(535,221)					$5	$12	$16
2018-S, Proof, Silver	(350,820)					$14	$18	$20
2019-P (q)					$2	$6	$12	$25
2019-D (q)					$2	$6	$12	$25
2019-S, Proof						$5	$12	$16
2019-S, Proof, Silver (s)						$14	$18	$20
2019-S, Enhanced Reverse Proof (t)								

q. Not issued for circulation. Sold directly to the public in rolls and small bags. **s.** Beginning in 2019, the Mint changed its composition for silver Proofs to .999 fine. **t.** Included in the Apollo 11 50th Anniversary Proof Half Dollar Set.

Silver Dollars
1794–1935

AN OVERVIEW OF SILVER DOLLARS

The silver dollar was authorized by Congress on April 2, 1792, and first coined in 1794. This denomination includes some of the most popular series in American numismatics.

The first coin of the denomination, the Flowing Hair dollar, is easy enough to obtain (given the proper budget) in grades from VF through low Mint State. Striking usually ranges from poor to barely acceptable, and adjustment marks (from an overweight planchet being filed down to correct weight) are often seen. Accordingly, careful examination is needed to find a good example.

The silver dollar with the Draped Bust obverse in combination with the Small Eagle reverse was made from 1795 through 1798, with most examples being dated 1796 or 1797. Today both the 1796 and 1797 exist in about the same numbers. Although mintage figures refer to the quantities produced in the given calendar year, these do not necessarily refer to the dates on the coins themselves, as Mint workers would use coinage dies into the next calendar year. Silver dollars of this type are fairly scarce. Sharpness of strike presents a challenge to the collector, and usually there are weaknesses in details, particularly on the reverse eagle.

The 1798 to 1804 type features a Draped Bust obverse and Heraldic Eagle reverse. Many such coins exist, mostly in grades from VF through lower Mint State levels. Striking can be indifferent, but the population of surviving coins is such that collectors have more to choose from, and can select for quality.

The Gobrecht silver dollars of 1836 (starless obverse, stars on reverse, plain edge) and 1839 (stars on obverse, starless reverse, reeded edge) present a special challenge in the formation of a type set. For quite a few years these were considered by numismatists to be *patterns*, and thus anyone forming a type set of regular-issue U.S. coins did not have to notice them. However, in recent decades, research by R.W. Julian (in particular), Walter Breen, and others, has revealed that the vast majority of 1836 and 1839 silver dollars originally produced were put into circulation at face value. Accordingly, they were coins of the realm at the time, were spent as currency, and are deserving of a place among regular coinage types.

The 1836 Gobrecht dollar is easy enough to find in today's marketplace, although expensive. The original production amounted to 1,600 coins, to which an unknown number of restrikes can be added. The main problem arises with the 1839, made only to the extent of 300 pieces. Those that exist today nearly always have abundant signs of circulation. This is the rarest of all major U.S. coin design types, even outclassing the 1796–1797 half dollar and the 1808 quarter eagle.

In 1840 the regular Liberty Seated dollar made its appearance, with the reverse depicting a perched eagle holding an olive branch and arrows. This style was continued through 1873, with minor modifications over the years; for example, in 1866 the motto IN GOD WE TRUST was added to the reverse.

Generally, Liberty Seated dollars can be easily enough found in circulated grades from VF up, as well as low Mint State levels. MS-63 and higher pieces are in the minority, particularly of the 1840–1865 type.

Morgan silver dollars, made by the hundreds of millions from 1878 through 1921, are easily found, with the 1881-S being at once the most common of all varieties existing today in gem condition and also usually seen with sharp strike and nice appearance.

Peace silver dollars of 1921 through 1935 exist in large quantities. Some collectors select the first year of issue, 1921, as a separate type, as the design is in high relief. The 1921 is plentiful in Mint State, but rarely is found sharply struck at the obverse and reverse center. Later Peace dollars with shallow relief abound in MS-63 and finer grades, although strike quality can be a problem.

The Peace dollar was the last of the United States' circulating .900 fine silver dollars. One final type of dollar coin was produced in the large 38.1 mm format—the Eisenhower dollar, often colloquially called a "silver dollar" even though its regular issues were made of copper and nickel. Since the Eisenhower dollar, U.S. coins of this denomination have been produced in smaller diameters and in base metals. These modern dollars are explored in detail in the next chapter. The U.S. Mint has also produced various *commemorative* silver dollars from 1900 to date, and the one-ounce American Silver Eagle bullion coin has a denomination of one dollar. These coins are covered in the Commemoratives and Bullion sections, respectively.

FOR THE COLLECTOR AND INVESTOR: SILVER DOLLARS AS A SPECIALTY

Generally, silver dollars of the 1794–1803 years are collected by dates and major types.

Although the 1794, of which an estimated 135 or so exist today, is famous and expensive, other varieties are eminently affordable in such grades as VF and EF. Beyond the listings herein there is a rich panorama of die varieties, most extensively delineated in the 1993 two-volume study *Silver Dollars and Trade Dollars of the United States: A Complete Encyclopedia*. This built upon earlier works, including J.W. Haseltine's *Type Table of United States Dollars, Half Dollars and Quarter Dollars*, and, especially, the long-term standard work by M.H. Bolender, *The United States Early Silver Dollars from 1794 to 1803*. In many instances among early dollars the number of aficionados desiring a particularly rare die combination may be even smaller than the population of coins available—with the result that not much premium has to be paid.

The 1804 silver dollar is a study in itself. None were actually produced in the year 1804. Several were made in 1834 as presentation pieces for foreign dignitaries, and even later examples were made for private collectors. Only a handful exist of this classic rarity, the "King of American Coins."

After 1803 it is a long jump to 1836, when silver dollars (of the Gobrecht design) were again struck for circulation. In 1839 more Gobrecht dollars were struck, with the design modified. In addition to the listings in this book are a number of other die combinations, edge and metal varieties, etc., including pieces of the year 1838, most of which are pattern restrikes (studied in *United States Pattern Coins*). These are avidly desired and collected.

Forming a specialized collection of Liberty Seated dollars from 1840 through 1873 has been a pursuit of many collectors over the years. Generally, the Philadelphia Mint dates are available without difficulty, although the 1851 and 1852 are typically acquired as Proof restrikes—originals of both years being prohibitively rare. Most difficult to find in higher grades are coins of the branch mints, including the famous 1870-S, of which only 10 are known to exist and for which no mintage quantity figure was ever listed in official reports. Branch-mint pieces, starting with the 1846-O, were placed into circulation and used extensively. Beginning in 1870, dollars of this type were struck at Carson City; these also are seen with evidence of circulation. The only exceptions to this are certain dollars of 1859-O and 1860-O which turned up in very "baggy" Mint State preservation (showing contact marks from other coins) among Treasury hoards, to the extent of several thousand pieces of both dates combined.

Morgan silver dollars from 1878 through 1921 are one of the most active and popular series in American numismatics. Approximately 100 different major varieties can be collected, although certain unusual varieties (not basic dates and mintmarks) can be dropped from a collection or added as desired. The vast majority of Morgan dollars can be found in Mint State. When these coins were first minted there was little need for them in circulation, and hundreds of millions of coins piled up in Treasury and other vaults. Although many were melted in 1918, enough remained that untold millions exist today in the hands of the public.

Varieties such as the 1881-S are common and are normally seen in high grades with sharp strike, but others with high mintages, the 1886-O and 1896-O being examples, are quite rare in MS-63 and finer, and when seen usually have rather poor eye appeal. Accordingly, quite a bit of discernment is recommended for the savvy collector.

Peace silver dollars, minted from 1921 to 1935, include the High Relief style of 1921, and the shallow-relief motif of 1922 to 1935. A basic set of 24 different dates and mintmarks is easily enough obtained, including in Mint State. The most elusive is the 1934-S.

Anthony de Francisci, designer of the Peace dollar, used his wife Teresa (ranked in the *100 Greatest Women on Coins*) as the model for his Miss Liberty.

FLOWING HAIR (1794–1795)

Engraver: *Robert Scot.* **Weight:** *26.96 grams.* **Composition:** *.900 silver, .100 copper (net weight 0.78011 oz. pure silver).* **Diameter:** *Approximately 39–40 mm.* **Edge:** *HUNDRED CENTS ONE DOLLAR OR UNIT with decorations between words.* **Mint:** *Philadelphia.*

Bowers-Borckardt–24, Bolender-13.

History. The first U.S. silver dollars were of the Flowing Hair design. In 1794 only 1,758 were released for circulation (slightly fewer than were struck), and the next year nearly 100 times that amount. These coins were popular in their time and circulated for decades afterward. Many were used in international trade, particularly in the Caribbean.

Striking and Sharpness. On the obverse, check the hair details. It is essential to check the die variety, as certain varieties were struck with very little detail at the center. Accordingly, high-grade examples can appear to be well worn on the hair. Check the star centers, as well. On the reverse, check the breast and wings of the eagle. All 1794 dollars are lightly struck at the lower left of the obverse (often at portions of the date) and to a lesser extent the corresponding part of the reverse. Many coins of both dates have planchet adjustment marks (from overweight blanks being filed down to proper weight before striking), often heavy and sometimes even disfiguring; these are not noted by the certification services. Expect weakness in some areas on dollars of this type; a coin with Full Details on both sides is virtually unheard of. Sharp striking and excellent eye appeal add to the value dramatically. These coins are very difficult to find problem-free, even in MS.

Availability. The 1794 is rare in all grades, with an estimated 125 to 135 known, including a handful in MS. The 1795 is easily available, with an estimated 4,000 to 7,500 still existing, although some die varieties range from scarce to rare. Many if not most have been dipped at one time or another, and many have been retoned, often satisfactorily. The existence of *any* luster is an exception between EF-40 and AU-58. MS coins are quite scarce (perhaps 150 to 250 existing, most dated 1795), especially at MS-63 or above.

Varieties listed herein are those most significant to collectors, but numerous minor variations may be found because each of the early dies was made individually. (Values of varieties not listed in this guide depend on collector interest and demand.) Blanks were weighed before the dollars were struck and overweight pieces were filed to remove excess silver. Coins with old adjustment marks from this filing process may be worth less than the values shown here. Some Flowing Hair dollars were weight-adjusted through insertion of a small (8 mm) silver plug in the center of the blank planchet before the coin was struck.

GRADING STANDARDS

MS-60 to 70 (Mint State). *Obverse:* At MS-60, some abrasion and contact marks are evident, most noticeably on the cheek and in the fields. Luster is present, but may be dull or lifeless, and interrupted in patches. At MS-63, contact marks are very few, and abrasion is light and not obvious. An MS-65 coin has little or, better yet, no abrasion, and contact marks are minute. Luster should be full

1794; BB-1, Bolender-1. Graded MS-64.
Fully brilliant and highly lustrous.

and rich. Coins graded above MS-65 are more theoretical than actual for this type—but they do exist, and are defined by having fewer marks as perfection is approached. *Reverse:* Comments apply as for the obverse, except that abrasion and contact marks are most noticeable on the eagle at the center, although most dollars of this type are lightly struck in the higher points of that area. The field area is small and is protected by lettering and the wreath and in any given grade shows fewer marks than on the obverse.

Illustrated coin: Like all 1794 dollars, this coin is weak at the left obverse and the corresponding part of the reverse. Planchet flaws are seen at stars 3 and 5. The center obverse is very well struck.

AU-50, 53, 55, 58 (About Uncirculated).
Obverse: Light wear is seen on the hair area immediately to the left of the face and neck (except for those flatly struck there), on the cheek, and on the top of the neck truncation, more so at AU-50 than at AU–53 or 55. An AU-58 coin has minimal traces of wear. An AU-50 coin has luster in protected areas among the stars and letters, with little luster in the open fields or the portrait. Some certified coins have

1795, Two Leaves; BB-21, Bolender-1. Graded AU-58.

virtually no luster, but are considered high quality in other aspects. At AU-58, most luster is partially present in the fields. On any high-grade dollar, luster is often a better key to grading than is the appearance of wear. *Reverse:* Light wear is seen on the eagle's body and the upper edges of the wings. At AU-50, detail is lost for some of the feathers in this area. However, some coins are weak to begin with. Light wear is seen on the wreath and lettering. Again, luster is the best key to actual wear. This ranges from perhaps 20% remaining in protected areas (at AU-50) to two-thirds or more (at AU-58). Generally, the reverse has more luster than the obverse.

Illustrated coin: This coin shows above-average striking sharpness on the obverse.

EF-40, 45 (Extremely Fine). *Obverse:* More wear is evident on the portrait, especially on the hair to the left of the face and neck (again, remember that some varieties were struck with flatness in this area), the cheek, and the tip of the neck truncation. Excellent detail remains in low-relief areas of the hair. The stars show wear, as do the date and letters. Luster, if present at all, is minimal and in protected areas. *Reverse:* The eagle shows more

1795, Three Leaves; BB-26, Bolender-12a. Graded EF-40.

wear, this being the focal point to check. Most or nearly all detail is well defined. These aspects should be reviewed in combination with knowledge of the die variety, to determine the sharpness of the coin when it was first struck. Most silver dollars of this type were flat at the highest area of the center at the time they were made, as this was opposite the highest point of the hair in the press when the coins were struck. Additional wear is on the wreath and letters, but many details are present. Some luster may be seen in protected areas, and if present is slightly more abundant than on the obverse.

Illustrated coin: On the obverse, a massive die crack extends upward through the 7 of the date.

VF-20, 30 (Very Fine). *Obverse:* The hair is well worn at VF-20, less so at VF-30. On well-struck varieties the weakness is in the area left of the temple and cheek. The strands are blended as to be heavy. The cheek shows only slight relief. The stars have more wear, making them appear larger (an optical illusion). *Reverse:* The body of the eagle shows few if any feathers, while the wings have a third to half of the feathers visible, depending on the strike. The leaves

1795, Two Leaves; BB-21, Bolender-1. Graded VF-20.

lack most detail, but veins can be seen on a few. Scattered, non-disfiguring marks are normal for this and lower grades. Any major defects should be noted separately.

Illustrated coin: Light rim bumps should be noted. This coin features attractive medium toning.

F-12, 15 (Fine). *Obverse:* Wear is more extensive than on the preceding, reducing the definition of the thick strands of hair. The cheek has less detail, but the eye is usually well defined. On most coins, the stars appear larger. The rim is distinct in most areas, and many denticles remain visible. *Reverse:* Wear is more extensive. Now, feather details are fewer, mostly remaining on the wing to the left and at the extreme tip of the wing on the

1795, Three Leaves; BB-27, Bolender-5. Graded F-12.

right. As always, the die variety in question can have an influence on this. The wreath and lettering are worn further. The rim is usually complete, with most denticles visible.

Illustrated coin: This variety is flatly struck on the head, and examples in higher grades show no detail at the center. Note the smooth, even wear with some marks.

VG-8, 10 (Very Good). *Obverse:* The portrait is mostly seen in outline form, with most hair strands gone, although some are visible left of the neck, and the tips at the lower left are clear. The eye is distinct. The stars appear larger still, again an illusion. LIBERTY and the date are readable and usually full, although some letters may be weak at their tops. The rim is usually complete, and many denticles can be seen. *Reverse:* The eagle is mostly an

1795, Two Leaves; BB-11, Bolender-3. Graded VG-10.

outline, although some traces of feathers may be seen in the tail and the lower part of the inside of the right wing. The rim is worn, as are the letters, with some weak, but the motto is readable.

Illustrated coin: This coin shows some microscopic granularity overall. It is an interesting variety with a silver plug inserted at the center of the planchet prior to minting, to slightly increase the weight; this feature can barely be seen in outline form.

G-4, 6 (Good). *Obverse:* Wear is more extensive. LIBERTY and the stars are all there, but weak. The head is an outline, although the eye can still be seen. The rim is well worn or even missing. LIBERTY is worn, and parts of some letters may be missing, but elements of all should be readable. The date is readable, but worn. *Reverse:* The eagle is flat and discernible in outline form. The wreath is well worn. Some of the letters may be partly miss-

1795, Two Leaves; BB-11, Bolender-1. Graded G-6.

ing. At this level some "averaging" can be done. If the letters are stronger than usual in one area, but some are missing in another area, the coin can still qualify as G-4.

Illustrated coin: This is an attractive example with smooth, even wear and a few defects.

AG-3 (About Good). *Obverse:* Wear is extensive, but some stars and letters can usually be discerned. The head is in outline form. The date, while readable, may be partially worn away. *Reverse:* The reverse is well worn, with parts of the wreath and lettering missing.

1795, Three Leaves. Graded AG-3.

**1795, Two Leaves
Beneath Each Wing**

**1795, Three Leaves
Beneath Each Wing**

1795, Silver Plug
BB-15, Bolender-7.

	Mintage	Cert	Avg	%MS	AG-3	G-4	VG-8	F-12	VF-20	EF-40	AU-50	MS-60	MS-63
1794 †	1,758	36	37.1	17%	$40,000	$67,500	$105,000	$135,000	$165,000	$325,000	$525,000	$1,000,000	$1,600,000
Auctions: $305,500, EF-40, January 2014; $223,250, VF-35, August 2014
1794, Silver Plug (a)	**(b)**	1	66.0	100%									
Auctions: No auction records available.
1795, All kinds	160,295												
1795, Two Leaves		195	31.6	5%	$1,100	$2,250	$2,600	$4,150	$6,000	$13,500	$20,000	$70,000	$175,000
Auctions: $25,850, AU-55, August 2013; $9,400, EF-40, November 2015; $4,994, VF-35, August 2014; $5,993, VF-30, August 2014
1795, Three Leaves		178	34.2	2%	$1,100	$2,250	$2,500	$4,100	$5,500	$12,000	$19,500	$65,000	$160,000
Auctions: $31,725, AU-55, July 2015; $11,750, AU-50, August 2015; $14,100, EF-40, March 2016 $3,819, F-15, March 2015
1795, Silver Plug		35	32.1	3%	$1,500	$3,250	$5,250	$8,500	$16,000	$22,500	$45,000	$130,000	
Auctions: $99,875, AU-55, August 2013; $10,575, VG-10, August 2016

† Ranked in the *100 Greatest U.S. Coins* (fourth edition). **a.** This unique piece, graded SP-66, shows evidence of planchet adjustment marks, as well as traces of a silver plug that was added to bring the coin's weight up to specification. **b.** Included in 1794 mintage figure.

DRAPED BUST, SMALL EAGLE REVERSE (1795–1798)

Designer: *Robert Scot.* **Weight:** *26.96 grams.* **Composition:** *.8924 silver, .1076 copper (net weight .77352 oz. pure silver).* **Diameter:** *Approximately 39–40 mm.* **Edge:** *HUNDRED CENTS ONE DOLLAR OR UNIT with decorations between words.* **Mint:** *Philadelphia.*

BB-51, Bolender-14.

History. The Draped Bust silver dollar with the Small Eagle reverse, inaugurated in 1795, brought the first appearance of this popular obverse portrait—a depiction of Miss Liberty that later was used on other silver denominations as well as copper half cents and cents. The motif was continued into 1798. Production of the Draped Bust silver dollars started at the end of the year on a new mint press that was first used for striking Flowing Hair dollars that summer. Draped Bust dollars circulated widely, especially outside the United States, and in the Caribbean in particular.

Striking and Sharpness. On the obverse, check the highest areas of the hair, the bust line, and the centers of the stars. On the reverse, check the feathers on the eagle's breast and wings. Examine the denticles. Planchet adjustment marks (from the filing down of overweight blanks) are common and should be avoided. Studying die varieties can be helpful for accurate grading. For example, the Small Letters reverse, a long-lived die design used from 1795 to 1798, has shallow relief and is usually seen with a low rim, with the result that its grade is lower than that of the obverse. On some reverse dies the eagle has very little detail. Fairly sharp striking (not necessarily Full Details) and excellent eye appeal add to the value dramatically.

Availability. These silver dollars are readily available as a type, although certain varieties range from scarce to very rare. MS coins are elusive and when seen are usually of the 1795 date, sometimes with prooflike surfaces. Most coins have been dipped and/or retoned, some successfully. These coins acquired marks more readily than did smaller denominations, and such are to be expected (but should be noted along with the grade, if distracting). Careful buying is needed to obtain coins with good eye appeal. Many AU examples are deeply toned and recolored.

The Smithsonian's National Numismatic Collection includes a unique Specimen 1794 dollar, plugged, and a unique Specimen 1797 10 Stars Left, 6 Stars Right, dollar.

GRADING STANDARDS

MS-60 to 70 (Mint State). *Obverse:* At MS-60, some abrasion and contact marks are evident, most noticeably on the cheek, the drapery at the shoulder, and the right field. Luster is present, but may be dull or lifeless, and interrupted in patches. At MS-63, contact marks are few, and abrasion is harder to detect. Many coins listed as Mint State are deeply toned, making it impossible to evaluate abrasion and even light wear; these are best avoided completely. An MS-65 coin has

1796, Small Date, Large Letters; BB-61, Bolender-2. Graded MS-60.

no abrasion, and contact marks are so minute as to require magnification. Luster should be full and rich. Coins grading above MS-65 are more theoretical than actual for this type—but they do exist, and are defined by having fewer marks as perfection is approached. *Reverse:* Comments apply as for the obverse, except that abrasion and contact marks are most noticeable on the eagle at the center, a situation complicated by the fact that this area was often flatly struck, not only on the famous Small Letters dies used from 1795 to 1798, but on some others as well. Grading is best done by the obverse, then verified by the reverse. In the Mint State category the amount of luster is usually a good key to grading. The field area is small and is protected by lettering and the wreath, and in any given grade shows fewer marks than on the obverse.

Illustrated coin: Note the tiny dig near Miss Liberty's ear. This coin is fairly well struck overall, but with some lightness on the eagle's body and leg on the right. It has excellent eye appeal.

AU-50, 53, 55, 58 (About Uncirculated). *Obverse:* Light wear is seen on the hair area above the ear and extending to left of the forehead, on the ribbon, and on the drapery at the shoulder, more so at AU-50 than at AU–53 or 55. An AU-58 coin has minimal traces of wear. An AU-50 coin has luster in protected areas among the stars and letters, with little in the open fields or on the portrait. At AU-58, most luster is present in the fields, but is worn away on the highest parts of the motifs. At this level

1797, Stars 9x7, Large Letters; BB-73, Bolender-1. Graded AU-50.

there are many deeply toned and recolored coins, necessitating caution when buying. *Reverse:* Light wear is seen on the eagle's body (keep in mind this area might be lightly struck) and edges of the wings. Light wear is seen on the wreath and lettering. Luster is the best key to actual wear. This ranges from perhaps 20% remaining in protected areas (at AU-50) to nearly full mint bloom (at AU-58).

Illustrated coin: This coin has some lightness of strike, but is better than average. It has some dings and marks, but these are not immediately obvious; without them, the coin might grade higher. This illustrates the many variables on these large, heavy coins. No single rule fits all.

EF-40, 45 (Extremely Fine). *Obverse:* More wear is evident on the upper hair area and the ribbon, and on the drapery and bosom. Excellent detail remains in low-relief areas of the hair. The stars show wear, as do the date and letters. Luster, if present at all, is minimal and in protected areas. For any and all dollars of this type, knowledge of die variety characteristics is essential to grading. Once again, one rule does not fit all. *Reverse:* The eagle, this being the focal point to check, shows more wear. On most strikings, the majority of feathers remain on the interior areas of the wings. Additional wear is on the wreath and letters, but many details are present. Some luster may be seen in protected areas and if present is slightly more abundant than on the obverse.

1796, Small Date, Large Letters; BB-61, Bolender-4. Graded EF-40.

Illustrated coin: Some marks are on the neck and a small pit is above the eagle's beak.

VF-20, 30 (Very Fine). *Obverse:* The higher-relief areas of hair are well worn at VF-20, less so at VF-30. The drapery and bosom show extensive wear, usually resulting in loss of most detail below the neck. The stars have more wear, making them appear larger. *Reverse:* The body of the eagle shows few if any feathers, while the wings have about half of the feathers visible, depending on the strike. The leaves lack most detail and are in outline form. Scattered, non-disfiguring marks are normal for this and lower grades. Any major defects should be noted separately.

1797, Stars 9x7, Small Letters; BB-72, Bolender-2. Graded VF-20.

Illustrated coin: This is the particularly famous Small Letters die (one of three Small Letters dies used for this type) first used in 1795 and last used in 1798. Used on 1795 BB-51, later 1796 BB-62, BB-63, and BB-66 now relapped, 1797 BB-72, and 1798 BB-81. The rims are low, and the eagle is in low relief. For coins struck from this particular reverse die, grading must be done by the obverse only.

F-12, 15 (Fine). *Obverse:* Wear is more extensive than on a Very Fine coin, particularly noticeable on the hair, face, and bosom. The stars appear larger. About half the hair detail remains, most noticeably behind the neck and shoulder. The rim shows wear but is complete or nearly so, with most denticles visible. *Reverse:* Wear is more extensive. Now, feather details are diminished, with relatively few remaining on the wings. The wreath and lettering are worn further, and the rim is usually weak in areas, although most denticles can be seen.

1796, Large Date, Small Letters; BB-65, Bolender-5. Graded F-12.

Illustrated coin: This is not the long-lived Small Letters die discussed above; this Small Letters die was used only in 1796. It is distinguished by a piece out of the die at the lower right of the reverse.

VG-8, 10 (Very Good). *Obverse:* The portrait is worn further, with much detail lost in the area above the level of the ear, although the curl over the forehead is delineated. There is some definition at the back of the hair and behind the shoulder, with the hair now combined to form thick strands. The ear is discernible, as is the eye. The stars appear larger still, again an illusion. The rim is weak in areas. LIBERTY and the date are readable and usually full. The rim is worn away in areas, although many denticles can still be discerned. *Reverse:* The eagle is mostly an outline, with parts blending into the field (on lighter strikes). The rim is worn, as are the letters, with some weak, but the motto is readable.

1796, Small Date, Large Letters; BB-61, Bolender-4. Graded VG-10.

Illustrated coin: Note the vertical scratches on the cheek.

G-4, 6 (Good). *Obverse:* Wear is more extensive, and some stars may be partly missing. The head is an outline. The eye is visible only in outline form. The rim is well worn or even missing in areas. LIBERTY is worn, and parts of some letters may be missing, but elements of all should be readable. The date is readable, but worn. Usually the date is rather bold. *Reverse:* The eagle is flat and discernible in outline form, and may be blending into the field. The wreath is well worn. Some of the letters may be partly missing (for some shallow-relief dies with low rims). At this level some "averaging" can be done. If the letters are stronger than usual in one area, but some are missing in another area, the coin can still qualify as G-4. This general rule is applicable to most other series as well.

1797, Stars 9x7, Large Letters; BB-73, Bolender-1. Graded G-4.

Illustrated coin: This is a well-circulated coin with several edge bumps.

AG-3 (About Good). *Obverse:* Wear is very extensive, but most letters and stars should be discernible. The head is in outline form. The date, while readable, may be partially worn away. *Reverse:* The reverse is well worn, with parts of the wreath and lettering missing. At this level, the reverse usually gives much less information than does the obverse.

1796, Large Date, Small Letters; BB-65, Bolender-5a. Graded AG-3.

1795, Off-Center Bust

1795, Centered Bust

1796, Small Date

1796, Large Date

Small Letters

Large Letters

1797, 10 Stars Left, 6 Right

1797, 9 Stars Left, 7 Right

1798, 15 Stars on Obverse

1798, 13 Stars on Obverse

	Mintage	Cert	Avg	%MS	AG-3	G-4	VG-8	F-12	VF-20	EF-40	AU-50	MS-60	MS-63
1795, All kinds	42,738												
1795, Off-Center Bust		102	38.3	8%	$960	$1,850	$2,350	$3,500	$5,100	$9,500	$14,500	$60,000	$150,000
Auctions: $763,750, MS-66, May 2016; $30,550, AU-58, February 2015; $12,925, EF-45, August 2014; $1,528, G-4, July 2015													
1795, Centered Bust		36	37.3	11%	$960	$1,850	$2,150	$3,500	$5,100	$9,500	$15,500	$55,000	$150,000
Auctions: $12,925, AU-55, March 2016; $17,625, AU-50, March 2013; $13,513, AU-50, February 2015; $7,638, EF-45, August 2014													
1796, All kinds	79,920												
1796, Small Date, Small Letters (a)		24	40.5	4%	$825	$1,850	$2,100	$3,800	$5,500	$9,500	$14,000	$62,500	$150,000
Auctions: $1,175,000, MS-65, April 2013; $4,406, VF-30, August 2014; $3,290, F-12, October 2014; $4,560, VF-25, May 2018													
1796, Small Date, Large Letters		49	36.8	2%	$825	$1,850	$2,100	$3,800	$5,500	$9,500	$14,000	$75,000	$200,000
Auctions: $352,500, MS-63, November 2013; $10,575, AU-53, August 2016; $14,100, AU-50, November 2015; $7,638, EF-45, August 2014													
1796, Large Date, Small Letters		52	33.1	6%	$825	$1,850	$2,100	$3,400	$5,250	$9,500	$14,000	$62,500	$160,000
Auctions: $12,338, AU-50, August 2014; $13,513, AU-50, August 2013; $9,988, AU-50, February 2016; $6,463, EF-45, August 2016													
1797, All kinds	7,776												
1797, 10 Stars Left, 6 Right		117	38.2	7%	$850	$1,850	$2,000	$3,000	$5,000	$9,000	$13,750	$62,000	$125,000
Auctions: $440,625, MS-64, November 2013; $182,267, MS-64, July 2015; $5,170, VF-30, March 2016; $4,406, VF-25, August 2014													
1797, 9 Stars Left, 7 Right, Large Letters		84	35.5	5%	$850	$1,850	$2,000	$3,100	$6,000	$9,500	$13,500	$63,000	$135,000
Auctions: $381,875, MS-64, November 2013; $5,288, VF-30, August 2014; $2,820, F-12, August 2014													
1797, 9 Stars Left, 7 Right, Small Letters		33	31.6	0%	$1,200	$2,100	$2,750	$3,900	$8,200	$15,000	$32,500	$110,000	
Auctions: $164,500, MS-62, November 2013; $7,638, VF-20, August 2014; $1,763, G-4, March 2015													
1798, All kinds (b)	327,536												
1798, 15 Stars on Obverse		33	37.8	6%	$1,100	$2,150	$2,650	$3,800	$8,000	$14,500	$24,500	$84,000	$155,000
Auctions: $258,500, MS-63, November 2013; $7,050, VF-35, August 2015; $6,169, VF-35, August 2014; $9,988, VF-25, August 2014													
1798, 13 Stars on Obverse		30	38.4	7%	$1,000	$1,850	$2,100	$3,500	$7,750	$13,000	$20,000	$150,000	
Auctions: $37,600, AU-58, August 2015; $9,988, EF-40, August 2016; $9,106, EF-40, August 2014; $3,525, VF-25, March 2016													

a. 3 varieties. **b.** The Mint struck 327,536 silver dollars in 1798, but did not record how many of each type (Small Eagle reverse and Heraldic Eagle reverse).

DRAPED BUST, HERALDIC EAGLE REVERSE (1798–1804)

Designer: *Robert Scot.* **Weight:** *26.96 grams.* **Composition:** *.8924 silver, .1076 copper (net weight .77352 oz. pure silver).* **Diameter:** *Approximately 39–40 mm.* **Edge:** *HUNDRED CENTS ONE DOLLAR OR UNIT with decorations between words.* **Mint:** *Philadelphia.*

Circulation Strike
BB-241, Bolender-6.

Proof (Restrike)
BB-302.

History. The design of the silver dollar closely follows that of other silver coins of the era. The two earliest reverse dies of 1798 have five vertical lines in the stripes in the shield. All dollar dies thereafter have four vertical lines. Production of the Draped Bust dollar continued through early 1804, but in that year the coins were struck from earlier-dated dies.

1804 silver dollars were first struck in 1834 from 1804-dated dies prepared at that time. (As a class these can be called *novodels*, rather than *restrikes*, as no originals were ever made in 1804.) The 1804 dollars were produced in Proof format. Later, probably circa 1859, a new reverse die was made up and combined with the earlier 1804 obverse (made in 1834). Those coins made in 1834 and around that time are today known as Class I dollars, whereas those made with a different reverse, beginning in 1859 and continuing perhaps through the 1870s, are known as Class III. An intermediate variety, from the Class III die combination but with a plain instead of lettered edge, is in the Smithsonian Institution's National Numismatic Collection and is known as Class II. All varieties combined comprise 15 different specimens. The 1804 dollar has been called the "King of American Coins" for well over a century and has achieved great fame. Interested numismatists are directed to *The Fantastic 1804 Dollar, Tribute Edition* (2009).

Striking and Sharpness. Very few of these coins have Full Details. On the obverse, check the highest points of the hair, the details of the drapery, and the centers of the stars. On the reverse, check the shield, the eagle, the stars above the eagle, and the clouds. Examine the denticles on both sides. Planchet adjustment marks are often seen, from overweight blanks being filed down to proper specifications, but they usually are lighter than on the earlier silver dollar types. The relief of the dies and the height of the rims can vary, affecting sharpness. Sharp striking and excellent eye appeal add to the value dramatically. Top-grade MS coins, when found, usually are dated 1800.

Availability. This is the most readily available type among the early silver dollars. Most often seen are the dates 1798 and 1799. Many varieties are available in any grade desired, although MS–63 and 65 coins are elusive. Other die varieties are rare at any level. As with other early dollars, connoisseurship is needed to acquire high-quality coins. These silver dollars usually have problems. To evaluate one for the market it is necessary to grade it, determine its quality of striking, and examine the characteristics of its surface. Nearly all have been dipped or cleaned.

Proofs. There were no Proofs coined in the era this type was issued. Years later, in 1834, the U.S. Mint made up new dies with the 1804 date and struck an unknown number of Proofs, perhaps a dozen or so, for inclusion in presentation Proof sets for foreign dignitaries. Today these are called Class I 1804 dollars. Eight examples are known, one of which shows circulation. The finest by far is the Sultan of Muscat coin, which approaches perfection. Circa 1858 or 1859 the Mint prepared a new obverse die dated 1804 and struck an unknown number of examples for private sale to collectors and dealers—the Class III dollars. No records were kept. These were artificially worn to give them the appearance of original dollars struck in 1804.

Sometime between circa 1858 and the 1870s, the Mint prepared new obverse dies dated 1801, 1802, and 1803, and struck Proof dollars for secret sale to the numismatic market. Many if not most were distributed through J.W. Haseltine, a Philadelphia dealer who had close connections with Mint officials. Today these are known as "Proof restrikes." All are rare, the 1801 being particularly so.

Class I 1804 dollars typically show hairlines and light abrasion. Grading is usually very liberal, in view of the fame of this rarity (not that this is logical). Circulated examples of Class I and Class III 1804 dollars have been graded using prefixes such as EF and AU. Proof restrikes of 1801 to 1803 generally survive in much higher grades, PF-64 or finer.

GRADING STANDARDS

MS-60 to 70 (Mint State). *Obverse:* At MS-60, some abrasion and contact marks are evident, most noticeably on the cheek, the drapery, and the right field. Luster is present, but may be dull or lifeless, and interrupted in patches. At MS-63, contact marks are very few, and abrasion is hard to detect except under magnification. Knowledge of the die variety is desirable, but on balance the portraits on this type are usually quite well struck. An MS-65 coin has no abrasion, and contact marks are so minute as to require magnification.

1798, 10 Arrows; BB-108, Bolender-13. Graded MS-63.

Luster should be full and rich. Coins grading above MS-65 are more theoretical than actual for this type—but they do exist and are defined by having fewer marks as perfection is approached. *Reverse:* Comments apply as for the obverse, except that abrasion and contact marks are most noticeable on the eagle's neck, the tips of the wing, and the tail. The field area is complex, without much open space, given the stars above the eagle, the arrows and olive branch, and other features. Accordingly, marks will not be as noticeable as on the obverse.

Illustrated coin: This coin is well struck, essentially problem free, and with superb eye appeal.

AU-50, 53, 55, 58 (About Uncirculated). *Obverse:* Light wear is seen on the hair area above the ear and extending to left of the forehead, on the ribbon, and on the drapery and bosom, more so at AU-50 than AU-53 or 55. An AU-58 coin has minimal traces of wear. An AU-50 coin has luster in protected areas among the stars and letters, with little in the open fields or on the portrait. At AU-58, much luster is present in the fields, but is worn away on the highest parts of the

1799, Irregular Date, 13-Star Reverse; BB-152, Bolender-15. Graded AU-50.

motifs. *Reverse:* Comments as preceding, except that the eagle's neck, the tips and top of the wings, the clouds, and the tail now show noticeable wear, as do other features. Luster ranges from perhaps 20% remaining in protected areas (at AU-50) to nearly full mint bloom (at AU-58). Sometimes the reverse of this type retains much more luster than the obverse, this being dependent on the height of the rim and the depth of the strike (particularly at the center).

Illustrated coin: This is an attractive and problem-free coin.

EF-40, 45 (Extremely Fine). *Obverse:* More wear is evident on the upper hair area and the ribbon, and on the drapery and bosom. The shoulder is a key spot to check for wear. Excellent detail remains in low-relief areas of the hair. The stars show wear, as do the date and letters. Luster, if present at all, is minimal and in protected areas. *Reverse:* Wear is greater than on an AU coin, overall. The neck has lost its feather detail on the highest points. Feathers have lost some detail near the edges of the wings. Some traces of luster may be seen, more so at EF-45 than at EF-40.

1802, Narrow Normal Date; BB-241, Bolender-6. Graded EF-45.

Illustrated coin: This is an attractive example retaining some mint luster. It has above-average striking sharpness.

VF-20, 30 (Very Fine). *Obverse:* The higher-relief areas of hair are well worn at VF-20, less so at VF-30. The drapery at the shoulder and the bosom show extensive wear. The stars have more wear, making them appear larger (an optical illusion seen on most worn silver coins of this era). *Reverse:* Wear is greater, including on the shield and the wing feathers. Most of the feathers on the wings are clear. The star centers are flat. Other areas have lost detail as well.

1799; BB-157, Bolender-5. Graded VF-20.

Illustrated coin: Some scratches appear on the portrait. This coin was cleaned long ago and now is retoned. It is a typical early dollar at this grade.

F-12, 15 (Fine). *Obverse:* Wear is more extensive than on a Very Fine coin, particularly on the hair, face, and bosom. The stars appear larger. About half the hair detail remains, most noticeably behind the neck and shoulder. The rim may be partially worn away and blend into the field. *Reverse:* Wear is even more extensive, with the shield and wing feathers being points to observe. Half or slightly more of the feathers will remain clear. The incuse E PLURIBUS UNUM

1798, Pointed 9, Close Date; BB-122, Bolender-14. Graded F-12.

may have a few letters worn away. The clouds all seem to be connected except on varieties in which they are spaced apart. The stars are weak. Parts of the border and lettering may be weak.

Illustrated coin: This coin was cleaned long ago. Cleaning and retoning is common on dollars of this era, but often is not noted by the grading services.

VG-8, 10 (Very Good). *Obverse:* The portrait is mostly seen in outline form, with most hair strands gone, although there is some definition at the back of the hair and behind the shoulder. The ear is discernible, as is the eye. The stars appear larger still, again an illusion. The rim is weak in areas. LIBERTY and the date are readable and usually full, although some letters may be weak at their tops. *Reverse:* Wear is more extensive. Half

1799. Graded VG-8.

or more of the letters in the motto are worn away. Most feathers are worn away, although separation of some of the lower feathers may be seen at the edges of the wings. Some stars are faint or missing. The border blends into the field in areas and some letters are weak. As always, a particular die variety can vary in areas of weakness.

G-4, 6 (Good). *Obverse:* Wear is more extensive, and some stars may be partly missing. The head is an outline. The eye is visible only in outline form. The rim is well worn or even missing in areas. LIBERTY is worn, and parts of some letters may be missing, but elements of all should be readable. The date is readable, but worn. *Reverse:* Wear is more extensive. The upper part of the eagle is flat. The feathers are noticeable only at the lower

1799; BB-169, Bolender-21. Graded G-4.

edge of the wings, sometimes incompletely, and do not have detail. The upper part of the shield is mostly flat. Only a few letters of the motto can be seen, if any at all. The rim is worn extensively, and the letters are well worn, but the inscription should be readable.

Illustrated coin: This coin has some marks, but is respectable for the grade.

AG-3 (About Good). *Obverse:* Wear is so extensive that the coin is barely identifiable. The head is in outline form. LIBERTY is mostly gone; same for the stars. The date, while readable, may be partially worn away. *Reverse:* Extensive wear is seen overall, with the rim worn away and some areas worn smooth. The eagle can be discerned in outline form, but not necessarily completely. A few stray motto letters may remain.

1799. Graded AG-3.

PF-60 to 70 (Proof). *Obverse and Reverse:* For lower Proof levels, extensive abrasion is seen in the fields, or even evidence of circulation (the Mickley example of the 1804 Class I, earlier graded as AU-50, was certified as PF-62 by a leading certification service in 2008). Numbers assigned by grading services have been erratic. No rules are known, and grading has not been consistent.

1804, Class I. Proof.

1798, Knob 9

1798, Pointed 9

1798, Pointed 9, Close Date

1798, Pointed 9, Wide Date

Five Vertical Lines in Shield's Stripes

Four Vertical Lines in Shield's Stripes

1798, Pointed 9, 10 Arrows

1798, Pointed 9, 4 Berries

1799, 99 Over 98, 15-Star Reverse

1799, 99 Over 98, 13-Star Reverse

1799, Irregular Date, 15-Star Reverse

1799, Irregular Date, 13-Star Reverse

1799, Irregular Date

1799, Normal Date

1800, Very Wide Date, Low 8

1800, "Dotted Date"

1799, 8 Stars Left, 5 Stars Right

1800, Only 12 Arrows

1800, AMERICAI

	Mintage	Cert	Avg	%MS	G-4	VG-8	F-12	VF-20	EF-40	AU-50	MS-60 / PF-63	MS-63 / PF-64	MS-65 / PF-65
1798, Knob 9, 5 Vertical Lines	(a)	8	34.4	0%	$850	$1,050	$1,450	$2,600	$4,500	$7,500	$22,000	$70,000	—
Auctions: $10,063, AU-50, September 2011													
1798, Knob 9, 4 Vertical Lines	(a)	8	50.9	25%	$850	$1,050	$1,450	$2,600	$4,500	$7,500	—		
Auctions: $9,775, AU-50, September 2011													
1798, Knob 9, 10 Arrows	(a)	8	34.4	0%	$850	$1,050	$1,450	$2,600	$4,500	$7,500	—		
Auctions: $7,175, AU-53, September 2013													
1798, Pointed 9, Close Date	(a)	150	37.6	3%	$850	$1,050	$1,450	$2,600	$4,500	$7,500	$22,000	$70,000	$155,000
Auctions: $5,302, AU-50, October 2014; $4,348, EF-45, July 2015; $3,290, EF-40, March 2015; $940, VG-10, January 2015													
1798, Pointed 9, Wide Date	(a)	163	36.0	6%	$850	$1,050	$1,450	$2,600	$4,500	$7,500	$22,000	$70,000	$155,000
Auctions: $3,290, EF-45, October 2015; $3,525, EF-40, August 2015; $2,115, VF-30, June 2015; $911, VF-20, September 2015													
1798, Pointed 9, 5 Vertical Lines	(a)	53	37.2	2%	$850	$1,050	$1,450	$2,600	$4,500	$7,500	$25,000	—	—
Auctions: $8,225, AU-53, September 2013													
1798, Pointed 9, 10 Arrows	(a)	56	32.2	4%	$900	$1,100	$1,750	$3,100	$4,900	$9,250	$23,500	$80,000	—
Auctions: $13,513, AU-53, August 2016; $4,700, EF-45, September 2016; $1,880, VF-25, July 2016; $4,560, AU-53, January 2018													
1798, Pointed 9, 4 Berries	(a)	36	29.0	0%	$900	$1,050	$1,650	$2,800	$4,700	$8,500	$21,500	$67,500	$155,000
Auctions: $4,465, AU-53, September 2015; $3,290, EF-40, September 2015; $2,233, VF-30, January 2015													
1799, All kinds	423,515												
1799, 99 Over 98, 15-Star Reverse (b)		47	43.8	17%	$960	$1,250	$1,800	$2,850	$5,200	$8,700	$23,000	$57,000	—
Auctions: $88,125, MS-64, October 2015; $29,375, MS-62, August 2014; $4,406, EF-45, September 2014; $3,055, EF-40, March 2016													
1799, 99 Over 98, 13-Star Reverse		34	36.4	6%	$950	$1,150	$1,750	$2,700	$4,700	$8,500	$22,400	$56,500	—
Auctions: $852, F-12, November 2014; $646, AG-3, July 2015													
1799, Irregular Date, 15-Star Reverse		14	32.2	0%	$950	$1,050	$1,550	$2,550	$4,700	$8,500	$23,000	—	—
Auctions: $3,055, VF-35, September 2013													
1799, Irregular Date, 13-Star Reverse		28	37.3	7%	$950	$1,050	$1,550	$2,550	$4,700	$8,250	$22,000	$56,500	$185,000
Auctions: $99,875, MS-64, August 2013; $2,409, VF-30, October 2014; $1,320, F-12, March 2018													
1799, Normal Date		1,977	35.5	4%	$900	$1,050	$1,550	$2,550	$4,700	$8,250	$22,400	$56,500	$185,000
Auctions: $5,875, AU-53, March 2015; $1,998, VF-25, May 2015; $1,998, VF-20, November 2015; $1,645, F-15, August 2015													
1799, 8 Stars Left, 5 Right		39	38.8	5%	$1,000	$1,250	$1,900	$3,100	$5,750	$13,500	$32,500	$92,500	—
Auctions: $5,640, EF-45, May 2016; $3,290, EF-45, August 2016; $4,113, EF-40, February 2015; $646, VG-8, November 2014													
1800, All kinds	220,920												
1800, Very Wide Date, Low 8		19	39.1	0%	$900	$1,050	$1,600	$2,350	$4,500	$8,500	$24,500	$60,000	—
Auctions: $11,750, AU-53, January 2014; $8,813, AU-53, August 2014; $2,233, VF-30, March 2015; $1,763, F-15, August 2014													
1800, "Dotted Date" (c)		34	39.2	12%	$900	$1,050	$1,650	$2,500	$5,200	$8,500	$24,500	$59,000	$185,000
Auctions: $11,750, AU-55, August 2014; $9,988, AU-53, August 2013; $2,350, VF-30, October 2014; $999, VF-20, January 2015													
1800, Only 12 Arrows		31	40.5	13%	$900	$1,050	$1,600	$2,400	$4,600	$8,500	$24,500	$60,000	—
Auctions: $6,463, AU-50, September 2013; $2,938, EF-40, March 2015; $1,880, VF-25, August 2014													
1800, Normal Dies		843	36.6	2%	$900	$1,050	$1,600	$2,400	$4,600	$8,500	$24,000	$55,000	$185,000
Auctions: $17,625, AU-58, August 2014; $12,925, AU-55, August 2014; $2,233, VF-30, November 2015; $494, VG-8, July 2015													
1800, AMERICAI (d)		41	38.5	10%	$900	$1,050	$1,600	$2,400	$4,600	$8,000	$26,500	—	—
Auctions: $223,250, MS-65, November 2013													

Note: The two earliest reverse dies of 1798 have five vertical lines in the stripes in the shield. All dollar dies thereafter have four vertical lines. **a.** The Mint struck 327,536 silver dollars in 1798, but did not record how many of each type (Small Eagle reverse and Heraldic Eagle reverse). **b.** The engraver of the reverse die accidentally engraved 15 stars, instead of the 13 needed to represent the original Colonies. He attempted to cover the two extra stars under the leftmost and rightmost clouds, but their points stick out slightly. **c.** The "dotted" date is the result of die breaks. **d.** A reverse-die flaw resulted in what appears to be a sans-serif letter I after AMERICA. "Perhaps from a punch or from a stray piece of metal during the die making process" (Bowers, *Silver Dollars & Trade Dollars of the United States*).

1802, 2 Over 1,
Narrow Date

1802, 2 Over 1,
Wide Date

1802, Narrow
Normal Date

1802, Wide Normal Date

1803, Small 3

1803, Large 3

	Mintage	Cert	Avg	%MS	G-4	VG-8	F-12	VF-20	EF-40	AU-50	MS-60 / PF-63	MS-63 / PF-64	MS-65 / PF-65
1801	54,454	304	37.7	5%	$900	$1,050	$1,600	$2,400	$4,900	$8,350	$29,500	$82,500	$235,000
Auctions: $329,000, MS-65, November 2013; $3,525, EF-40, October 2014; $764, VG-8, January 2015													
1801, Restrike, Proof † (e)	2 known	1	66.0								650,000	850,000	—
Auctions: No auction records available.													
1802, All kinds	41,650												
1802, 2 Over 1, Narrow Date		22	37.8	9%	$950	$1,100	$1,800	$2,500	$5,000	$9,100	$30,000	$65,000	—
Auctions: $11,750, AU-58, February 2013; $2,115, VF-30, January 2015; $2,820, VF-20, October 2014; $3,240, VF-30, January 2018													
1802, 2 Over 1, Wide Date		35	34.2	6%	$1,000	$1,150	$1,900	$2,600	$5,250	$9,500	$32,000	$70,000	—
Auctions: $6,463, AU-53, January 2015; $4,465, EF-40, February 2015; $2,820, VF-25, January 2015; $2,585, VF-25, October 2015													
1802, Narrow Normal Date		57	41.5	16%	$950	$1,100	$1,700	$2,400	$4,900	$8,000	$23,500	$65,000	$240,000
Auctions: $54,050, MS-63, January 2015; $25,850, MS-61, May 2015; $12,925, AU-55, June 2015; $2,350, VF-25, January 2015													
1802, Wide Normal Date		8	40.4	0%	$1,000	$1,050	$1,850	$2,650	$5,000	$9,500	$36,000	$72,500	$300,000
Auctions: $10,869, AU-55, August 2013; $2,350, VF-35, August 2015; $3,525, VF-30, January 2015													
1802, Restrike, Proof † (e)	4 known	3	64.0								250,000	450,000	750,000
Auctions: $920,000, PF-65Cam, April 2008													
1803, All kinds	85,634												
1803, Small 3		69	37.7	7%	$1,000	$1,050	$1,800	$2,650	$5,250	$9,000	$27,000	$70,000	—
Auctions: $117,500, MS-63, November 2013; $2,585, VF-35, October 2014; $2,350, VF-30, August 2014; $999, F-12, July 2014													
1803, Large 3		72	38.0	4%	$1,000	$1,050	$1,800	$2,650	$5,250	$9,000	$27,000	$70,000	—
Auctions: $6,463, EF-45, August 2014; $2,174, VF-20, March 2015; $1,410, VF-20, August 2015; $646, VF-20, August 2015													
1803, Restrike, Proof † (e)	3 known	7	65.6								250,000	450,000	750,000
Auctions: $851,875, PF-66, January 2013													

† Proof Restrikes of the 1801, 1802, and 1803 Draped Bust dollars are ranked in the *100 Greatest U.S. Coins* (fourth edition), as a single entry. **e.** "The Proof silver dollars of 1801, 1802, and 1803 are all extremely rare, valuable, and desirable, although none of them were made anywhere near the dates on the coins, nor do they share any die characteristics with any real silver dollars made from 1801 to 1803" (*100 Greatest U.S. Coins*, fourth edition).

| 1804 Dollar, Proof | 1804, First Reverse, Proof | 1804, Second Reverse, Proof |

Note the position of the words STATES OF in relation to the clouds.

	Mintage	Cert	Avg	%MS	G-4	VG-8	F-12	VF-20	EF-40	AU-50	MS-60 / PF-63	MS-63 / PF-64	MS-65 / PF-65
1804, First Reverse, Class I, Proof †	8 known	6	50.0								2,750,000	3,250,000	4,000,000
Auctions: $3,877,500, PF-62, August 2013													
1804, Second Reverse, Restrike, Class III, Proof †	6 known	4	59.3										
Auctions: $2,300,000, PF-58, April 2009; $1,880,000, PF-55, August 2014													
1804, Second Reverse, Restrike, Plain Edge, Class II, Proof † (f)	1	0	n/a										
Auctions: No auction records available.													
1804, Electrotype of Unique Plain-Edge Specimen † (g)	4	0	n/a										
Auctions: No auction records available.													

† All 1804 Draped Bust dollars are ranked in the *100 Greatest U.S. Coins* (fourth edition), as a single entry. **f.** The plain-edge restrike is in the Smithsonian's National Numismatic Collection. **g.** These electrotypes were made by the U.S. Mint.

GOBRECHT (1836–1839)

No Stars on Obverse, Stars on Reverse (1836):
Designer: *Christian Gobrecht.* **Weight:** *26.96 grams.*
Composition: *.8924 silver, .1076 copper (net weight .77352 oz. pure silver).*
Diameter: *39–40 mm.* **Edge:** *Plain.*

No Stars on Obverse, Stars on Reverse

Stars on Obverse, No Stars on Reverse (1838–1839): **Designer:** *Christian Gobrecht.*
Weight: *26.73 grams.* **Composition:** *.900 silver, .100 copper*
(net weight .77345 oz. pure silver). **Diameter:** *39–40 mm.* **Edge:** *Reeded.*

Stars on Obverse, No Stars on Reverse

History. Suspension of silver dollar coinage was lifted in 1831, but it was not until 1835 that steps were taken to resume their production. Late that year, Mint Director R.M. Patterson had engraver Christian Gobrecht prepare a pair of dies based on motifs by Thomas Sully and Titian Peale. The first obverse die, dated 1836, bore the seated figure of Miss Liberty with the inscription C. GOBRECHT F. ("F." for the Latin word *Fecit*, or "made it") in the field above the date. On the reverse die was a large eagle flying left, surrounded by 26 stars and the legend UNITED STATES OF AMERICA • ONE DOLLAR •. It is unknown whether coins were struck from these dies at that time. A new obverse die with Gobrecht's name on the base of Liberty was prepared, and in December 1836, a thousand plain-edged pieces were struck for circulation. These coins weighed 416 grains, the standard enacted in 1792.

The feeder mechanism that was used, apparently designed for coins of half dollar size or smaller, damaged the reverse die's rim. Attempts were made to solve the problem by rotating the reverse die at various times during the striking run, but this only extended the damage to both sides of the rim. The original 1836 issue is thus known in multiple die alignments:

Die Alignment I—head of Liberty opposite DO in DOLLAR; eagle flying upward.

Die Alignment II—head of Liberty opposite ES in STATES; eagle flying upward.

Die Alignment III—head of Liberty opposite N of ONE; eagle flying level.

Die Alignment IV—head of Liberty opposite F in OF; eagle flying level.

Original 1836 die orientation using
either "coin" or "medal" turn.

Die alignment of original issues
dated 1838 and 1839.

Restrikes were made from the late 1850s through the early 1870s. They were struck using the original obverse die and a different reverse die with cracks through NITED STATES O and OLLA, and in Die Alignment III.

In January 1837, the standard weight for the dollar was lowered to 412-1/2 grains, and on January 8, 1837, Benjamin Franklin Peale wrote an internal memorandum to Mint Director Patterson noting, among other things, that the new dollar had received much criticism for looking too medallic, rather than like a coin. Peale felt this was due to the "smooth" edge and suggested striking with a segmented, lettered-edge collar like one he had seen in France. In March 1837, the dies of 1836 were used to strike 600 pieces (whether with plain or reeded edge is unknown). According to reports, the results were unsatisfactory and the coins were destroyed—although a single example, with a reeded edge, is known. It is unclear whether it was part of the March striking, from an earlier 1837 striking caused by the Peale memo, or struck at some later period.

Pattern pieces were struck in 1838 using modified dies with Gobrecht's name removed from the base, 13 stars added to the obverse, and the 26 stars removed from the reverse. These were struck in alignment IV using a reeded-edge collar. In 1839, 300 pieces were struck for circulation, also in alignment IV. Both of these were restruck in alignment III and possibly alignment IV in the late 1850s through early 1870s.

Striking and Sharpness. Striking is usually very good. Check the details on Miss Liberty's head and the higher parts of the eagle. Note that the word LIBERTY is raised.

Availability. 1836 Gobrecht dollars are available in grades from so-called Very Fine upward (the coins were struck as Proofs, and worn examples are properly designated as PF-30, PF-40, and so on; however, sometimes they are found graded as Fine, VF, and EF for levels below PF-50). Most in the marketplace range from PF–50 to 62. Most have contact marks. Truly pristine PF-65 and better examples are very elusive. The demand for these coins is intense. For the 1839, circulated grades typically are PF-50 or higher, often with damage. Pristine Proofs are available, but virtually all are restrikes.

GRADING STANDARDS

PF-60 to 70 (Proof). *Obverse and Reverse:* Many Proofs have been extensively cleaned and have many hairlines and dull fields. This is more applicable to 1836 than to 1839. Grades are PF–60 to 61 or 62. With medium hairlines and good reflectivity, an assigned grade of PF-64 is appropriate, and with relatively few hairlines, Gem PF-65. In various grades hairlines are most easily seen in the obverse field. PF-66 should have hairlines so

1839. Graded PF-65.

delicate that magnification is needed to see them. Above that, a Proof should be free of such lines.

Illustrated coin: This is a restrike made at the Mint in or after spring 1859.

PF-50, 53, 55, 58 (Proof). *Obverse:* Light wear is seen on the thighs and knees, bosom, and head. At PF-58, the Proof surface is extensive, but the open fields show abrasion. At PF–50 and 53, most if not all mirror surface is gone and there are scattered marks. *Reverse:* Wear is most evident on the eagle's breast and the top of the wings. Mirror surface ranges from perhaps 60% complete (at PF-58) to none (at PF-50).

1836. Graded PF-58.

Illustrated coin: This original 1836 Gobrecht dollar, of which 1,000 were coined in 1836, is nicely toned and has excellent eye appeal.

PF-40 to 45 (Proof). *Obverse:* Further wear is seen on all areas, especially the thighs and knees, bosom, and head. The center of LIBERTY, which is in relief, is weak. Most at this level and lower are the 1836 issues. *Reverse:* Further wear is evident on the eagle, including the back edge of the closest wing, the top of the farthest wing, and the tail.

1836. Graded PF-45.

PF-20, 25, 30, 35 (Proof). *Obverse:* Further wear is seen. Many details of the gown are worn away, but the lower-relief areas above and to the right of the shield remain well defined. Hair detail is mostly or completely gone. LIBERTY is weak at the center. *Reverse:* Even more wear is evident on the eagle, with only about 60% of the feathers visible.

1836. Graded PF-20.

	Cert	Avg	%MS	PF-20	PF-40	PF-50	PF-60	PF-62	PF-63	PF-64	PF-65
1836. C. GOBRECHT F. on base. Judd-60. Plain edge, no stars on obverse, stars in field on reverse. Die alignment I, ↑↓. Circulation issue. 1,000 struck † (a)	209	55.7		$12,500	$15,000	$18,000	$25,000	$27,000	$40,000	$75,000	$125,000
	Auctions: $82,250, PF-64, May 2016										
1836. As above. Plain edge. Judd-60. Die alignment II, ↑↑, and die alignment IV, ↑↑. Circulation issue struck in 1837. 600 struck † (a)	**(b)**			$13,000	$16,000	$21,000	$25,000	$30,000	$45,000	$75,000	$125,000
	Auctions: $12,338, PF-50, October 2016; $9,988, PF-50, June 2015										

† All Gobrecht dollars are ranked in the *100 Greatest U.S. Coins* (fourth edition), as a single entry. **a.** Originals. Although these are listed in Judd as patterns, they are considered circulation strikes. **b.** Included in 1836, C. GOBRECHT F. on base, certified population.

	Cert	Avg	%MS	PF-20	PF-40	PF-50	PF-60	PF-62	PF-63	PF-64	PF-65
1838. Obverse stars added around border, reeded edge. Judd-84. Designer's name removed. Reverse, eagle flying in plain field. Die alignment IV, ↑↑. †	28	62.3					$55,000	$65,000	$75,000	$85,000	$150,000
Auctions: $83,375, PF-64, July 2008											
1839. As above. Reeded edge. Judd-104. Die alignment IV, ↑↑. Circulation issue. 300 struck †	47	62.6		$15,000	$17,500	$22,500	$29,000	$38,500	$55,000	$80,000	$150,000
Auctions: $18,975, PF-45, November 2011											

† All Gobrecht dollars are ranked in the *100 Greatest U.S. Coins* (fourth edition), as a single entry.

Restrike

	Cert	Avg	%MS	PF-20	PF-40	PF-50	PF-60	PF-62	PF-63	PF-64	PF-65
1836. Name below base; eagle in starry field; plain edge. Judd-58. Die alignment III, ↑↓, and die alignment IV, ↑↑. † (a)	12 (b)	64.0		$17,500	$30,000	$70,000	$75,000	$80,000	$85,000	$100,000	$125,000
Auctions: $34,500, PF-63, April 2012											
1836. Name on base; plain edge. Judd-60. Die alignment III, ↑↓. † (a,c)	(d)			$15,000	$20,000	$23,500	$26,000	$35,000	$45,000	$55,000	$90,000
Auctions: $18,975, PF-61, September 2010											
1836. C. GOBRECHT F. on base. Judd-61. Reeded edge. No stars on obverse, stars in field on reverse. Die alignment IV, ↑↑. † (a)	0	n/a		*(extremely rare)*	$18,000	$25,000					—
Auctions: $195,000, PF-63, May 2003											
1838. Designer's name removed; reeded edge. Judd-84. Die alignment III, ↑↓, and die alignment IV, ↑↑. † (a)	(d)			$25,000	$30,000	$35,000	$47,500	$62,500	$75,000	$85,000	$125,000
Auctions: $83,375, PF-64, March 2012											
1839. Designer's name removed; eagle in plain field; reeded edge. Judd-104. Die alignment III, ↑↓, and die alignment IV, ↑↑. † (a)	(d)			$20,000	$25,000	$37,500	$42,500	$50,000	$60,000	$70,000	$100,000
Auctions: $51,750, PF-64, April 2012											

Note: Restrikes were produced from the late 1850s to the 1870s, and are not official Mint issues. They were all oriented in either die alignment III (coin turn) or die alignment IV (medal turn), with the eagle flying level. Almost all were struck from a cracked reverse die. For detailed analysis of these pieces, consult *United States Pattern Coins*, tenth edition. † All Gobrecht dollars are ranked in the *100 Greatest U.S. Coins* (fourth edition), as a single entry. **a.** Restrikes. Listed in Judd as patterns. **b.** Many originals were certified as restrikes in years past. This figure includes some of these originals. **c.** 30 to 40 are known. **d.** Included in figure for first listing with this Judd number, as the grading services do not consistently distinguish between originals and restrikes.

LIBERTY SEATED (1840–1873)

No Motto (1840–1865): **Designer:** *Christian Gobrecht.* **Weight:** *26.73 grams.*
Composition: *.900 silver, .100 copper (net weight .77344 oz. pure silver).*
Diameter: *38.1 mm.* **Edge:** *Reeded.* **Mints:** *Philadelphia, New Orleans, and San Francisco.*

Mintmark location
is on the reverse,
below the eagle,
for all varieties.

No Motto
(1840–1865)

No Motto, Proof

With Motto IN GOD WE TRUST (1866–1873): **Designer:** *Christian Gobrecht.*
Weight: *26.73 grams.* **Composition:** *.900 silver, .100 copper (net weight .77344 oz. pure silver).*
Diameter: *38.1 mm.* **Edge:** *Reeded.* **Mints:** *Philadelphia, Carson City, and San Francisco.*

With Motto
IN GOD
WE TRUST
(1866–1873)

With Motto
IN GOD
WE TRUST,
Proof

History. The Liberty Seated dollar was minted every year from 1840 to 1873, with an obverse design modified from that of the 1839 Gobrecht dollar. On the reverse, the flying eagle of the Gobrecht dollar was replaced with a perched eagle similar to that of contemporary quarter and half dollars. The dollars, minted in modest numbers, circulated in the United States through 1850. In that year the rising value of silver on the international markets brought the cost of minting each coin to more than $1. Production continued for the international, rather than domestic, market, through 1873, when the trade dollar took the Liberty Seated dollar's place.

Striking and Sharpness. On the obverse, check the head of Miss Liberty and the centers of the stars. On the reverse, check the feathers of the eagle. The denticles usually are sharp. Dollars of 1857 usually are weakly struck, but have semi-prooflike surfaces. The word LIBERTY is in a high-relief area on the coin, with the result that it wore away quickly. Therefore this feature cannot be used as the only guide to grading an obverse. From EF downward, strike sharpness in the stars and the head does not matter to connoisseurs. Proof coins were made for all dates. All of 1851 and 1853 are restrikes, as are most of 1852. In 1858 only Proofs were struck, to the extent of an estimated 210 pieces, with no related circulation strikes. Most early dates were restruck at the Mint, augmenting the supply of originals. Nearly all Proofs are very well struck.

Availability. All issues from 1840 to 1850 are available in proportion to their mintages. Those of 1851 to the late 1860s are either scarce or rare in circulated grades, and in MS they range from rare to extremely rare, despite generous mintages in some instances. The later-date coins were shipped to China and later melted. Coins of the 1870s are more readily available, although some are scarce to rare. Today, Proofs from 1858 to 1873 are readily available, but high-quality examples with superb eye appeal are in the minority. Most Proofs prior to 1860 survive only in grades below PF-65 if strict grading is applied.

GRADING STANDARDS

MS-60 to 70 (Mint State). *Obverse:* At MS-60, some abrasion and contact marks are evident, most noticeably on the bosom and thighs and knees. Luster is present, but may be dull or lifeless. At MS-63, contact marks are very few, and abrasion is minimal. An MS-65 coin has no abrasion in the fields (but may have a hint on the knees), and contact marks are trivial. Check the knees of Liberty and the right field. Luster should be full and

1864. Graded MS-65.

rich on later issues, not necessarily so for dates in the 1840s. Most Mint State coins of the 1861 to 1865 years, Philadelphia issues, have extensive die striae (from not completely finishing the die). *Reverse:* Comments apply as for the obverse, except that in lower Mint State grades, abrasion and marks are most noticeable on the eagle's head, the neck, the claws, and the top of the wings (harder to see there, however). At MS-65 or higher, there are no marks visible to the unaided eye. The field is mainly protected by design elements and does not show abrasion as much as does the obverse on a given coin.

Illustrated coin: The fields show striations from incomplete polishing of the dies, but this does not affect the grade.

AU-50, 53, 55, 58 (About Uncirculated). *Obverse:* Light wear is seen on the thighs and knees, bosom, and head. At AU-58, the luster is extensive but incomplete, especially in the right field. At AU–50 and 53, luster is less. *Reverse:* Wear is visible on the eagle's neck, the claws, and the top of the wings. An AU-58 coin has nearly full luster. At AU–50 and 53, there still are traces of luster.

Illustrated coin: This is an attractive example with much of the original luster.

1842. Graded AU-58.

EF-40, 45 (Extremely Fine). *Obverse:* Further wear is seen on all areas, especially the thighs and knees, bosom, and head. Little or no luster is seen on most coins. From this grade downward, strike sharpness in the stars and the head does not matter to connoisseurs. *Reverse:* Further wear is evident on the eagle's neck, claws, and the wings, although on well-struck coins nearly all details are sharp.

1846. Graded EF-40.

VF-20, 30 (Very Fine). *Obverse:* Further wear is seen. Many details of the gown are worn away, but the lower-relief areas above and to the right of the shield remain well defined. Hair detail is mostly or completely gone. The word LIBERTY is weak at BE (PCGS allows BER to be missing "on some coins"). *Reverse:* Wear is more extensive, with some feathers blended together, especially on the neck for a typical coin. Detail remains quite good overall.

1854. Graded VF-20.

F-12, 15 (Fine). *Obverse:* The seated figure is well worn, but with some detail above and to the right of the shield. BER in LIBERTY is visible only in part or missing entirely. *Reverse:* Wear is extensive, with about a third to half of the feathers flat or blended with others.

Illustrated coin: The reverse is stronger than the obverse on this coin.

1872-CC. Graded F-12.

VG-8, 10 (Very Good). *Obverse:* The seated figure is more worn, but some detail can be seen above and to the right of the shield. The shield is discernible, but the upper-right section may be flat and blended into the seated figure. In LIBERTY two or three letters, or a combination totaling that, are readable. *Reverse.* Further wear has flattened half or slightly more of the feathers (depending on the strike). The rim is visible all around,

1871-CC. Graded VG-8.

as are the ends of the denticles. A Very Good Liberty Seated dollar usually has more detail overall than a lower-denomination coin of the same design.

G-4, 6 (Good). *Obverse:* The seated figure is worn nearly smooth. The stars and date are complete, but may be weak toward the periphery. *Reverse:* The eagle shows only a few details of the shield and feathers. The rim is worn down. The tops of the border letters are weak or worn away, although the inscription can still be read.

1850-O. Graded G-6.

AG-3 (About Good). *Obverse:* The seated figure is visible in outline form. Much or all of the rim is worn away. The stars are weak and some may be missing. The date remains clear. *Reverse:* The border letters are partially worn away. The eagle is mostly in outline form, but with a few details discernible. The rim is weak or missing.

1872. Graded AG-3.

PF-60 to 70 (Proof). *Obverse and Reverse:* Proofs that are extensively cleaned and have many hairlines, or that are dull and grainy, are lower level, such as PF–60 to 62. These are not widely desired, except for use as fillers for the dates (most circulation-strike dollars are rare after 1849 and before 1870). The rarities of 1851, 1852, and 1858 are in demand no matter what the grade. With medium hairlines and good reflectivity, an assigned

1861. Graded PF-63.

grade of PF-64 is appropriate, and with relatively few hairlines, gem PF-65. In various grades hairlines are most easily seen in the obverse field. PF-66 should have hairlines so delicate that magnification is needed to see them. Above that, a Proof should be free of such lines.

Illustrated coin: The frosty cameo motifs on this example contrast with the deeply mirrored fields.

1851, Original,
High Date

1851, Restrike,
Proof
Date is centered.

1852, Original

1852, Restrike,
Proof

	Mintage	Cert	Avg	%MS	VG-8	F-12	VF-20	EF-40	AU-50	MS-60 PF-60	MS-63 PF-63	MS-65 PF-65
1840	61,005	268	49.4	20%	$450	$500	$575	$850	$1,500	$5,500	$14,500	—
Auctions: $12,925, MS-63, October 2015; $1,240, EF-45, January 2015; $705, VF-35, August 2015; $517, VF-25, January 2015												
1840, Proof	*40–60*	27	63.3							1$2,500	$22,500	$75,000
Auctions: $85,188, PF-64Cam, April 2013; $30,000, PF-66, January 2018												
1841	173,000	272	49.9	18%	$400	$475	$550	$700	$1,050	$2,750	$8,000	$90,000
Auctions: $2,820, MS-62, January 2015; $1,528, AU-58, January 2015; $541, EF-45, August 2015; $400, VF-35, February 2015												
1841, Proof	*10–15*	4	63.0							$30,000	$70,000	$250,000
Auctions: $94,000, PF-64, October 2014; $141,000, PF-64, April 2013												
1842	184,618	623	48.6	14%	$400	$475	$550	$600	$950	$2,400	$5,000	$90,000
Auctions: $19,975, MS-64, September 2016; $11,163, MS-64, May 2015; $7,344, MS-64, July 2016; $1,528, AU-58, June 2015												
1842, Proof	*10–15*	8	63.3							$15,000	$35,000	$80,000
Auctions: $57,281, PF-65, August 2013												
1843	165,100	514	48.0	11%	$400	$475	$550	$600	$950	$2,400	$7,000	$100,000
Auctions: $3,055, MS-62, June 2015; $940, AU-55, August 2015; $517, EF-45, January 2015; $411, F-15, June 2015												
1843, Proof	*10–15*	8	63.4							$15,000	$30,000	1$10,000
Auctions: $52,875, PF-64, August 2013												
1844	20,000	161	51.0	13%	$450	$500	$575	$800	$1,250	$5,000	$14,000	$100,000
Auctions: $3,055, AU-58, January 2015; $940, AU-50, July 2015; $541, VF-30, January 2015; $541, VF-25, March 2015												
1844, Proof	*10–15*	8	63.9							$12,500	$30,000	$90,000
Auctions: $70,500, PF-65, April 2013; $44,063, PF-64, October 2014												
1845	24,500	188	50.0	11%	$450	$500	$575	$800	$1,500	$9,000	$25,000	$150,000
Auctions: $31,725, MS-63, May 2015; $5,170, MS-61, June 2015; $2,350, AU-58, January 2015; $676, VF-30, January 2015												
1845, Proof	*10–15*	10	63.8							$12,500	$30,000	$70,000
Auctions: $141,000, PF-67, August 2013; $30,000, PF-64, January 2018												

	Mintage	Cert	Avg	%MS	VG-8	F-12	VF-20	EF-40	AU-50	MS-60 / PF-60	MS-63 / PF-63	MS-65 / PF-65
1846	110,600	513	50.1	16%	$450	$475	$525	$650	$1,000	$2,500	$5,500	$90,000
	Auctions: $6,463, MS-64, October 2015; $2,585, MS-61, January 2015; $1,175, AU-55, June 2015; $570, EF-40, July 2015											
1846, Proof	10–15	14	62.9							$12,500	$30,000	$105,000
	Auctions: $94,000, PF-66, April 2013											
1846-O	59,000	179	46.7	11%	$450	$500	$575	$800	$1,400	$7,250	$17,000	$100,000
	Auctions: $70,501, MS-64, January 2015; $4,230, MS-60, January 2015; $881, EF-40, January 2015; $505, VF-20, March 2015											
1847	140,750	526	50.5	16%	$450	$500	$575	$600	$850	$2,700	$5,500	$90,000
	Auctions: $5,875, MS-64, October 2015; $4,700, MS-63, October 2015; $2,115, AU-58, August 2015; $793, EF-45, October 2015											
1847, Proof	10–15	16	63.9							$12,500	$22,000	$55,000
	Auctions: $35,250, PF-65, October 2014; $41,125, PF-65, April 2013											
1848	15,000	98	49.0	10%	$450	$650	$750	$1,100	$1,500	$4,750	$13,000	$90,000
	Auctions: $47,000, MS-64, May 2015; $5,993, MS-61, September 2014; $2,350, AU-55, January 2015; $646, EF-40, January 2015											
1848, Proof	10–15	10	64.2							$12,500	$30,000	$65,000
	Auctions: $117,500, PF-67, August 2013											
1849	62,600	304	53.3	25%	$450	$500	$575	$700	$1,000	$2,600	$6,750	$90,000
	Auctions: $2,585, MS-62, June 2015; $1,763, AU-58, January 2015; $588, EF-40, August 2015; $400, VF-35, March 2015											
1849, Proof	10–15	9	63.9							$13,500	$34,000	$65,000
	Auctions: $129,250, PF-67, April 2013											
1850	7,500	116	54.9	34%	$550	$750	$1,100	$1,800	$2,500	$6,500	$14,000	$90,000
	Auctions: $7,638, MS-61, July 2015; $3,995, MS-60, January 2015; $4,230, AU-58, February 2015; $2,996, AU-53, February 2015											
1850, Proof	20–30	15	63.8							$12,500	$25,000	$50,000
	Auctions: $51,406, PF-66, August 2013; $19,975, PF-64, October 2014											
1850-O	40,000	145	43.1	10%	$450	$500	$750	$1,450	$3,200	$11,500	$25,000	$120,000
	Auctions: $3,055, AU-50, July 2015; $2,350, EF-45, January 2015; $823, VF-30, January 2015; $646, F-15, October 2015											
1851, Original, High Date † (a)	1,300	27	60.9	70%	$10,000	$12,500	$13,500	$20,000	$27,500	$35,000	$65,000	$140,000
	Auctions: $70,500, MS-64, January 2015; $42,300, MS-63, May 2015; $28,200, AU-58, September 2015											
1851, Restrike, Proof (a)	35–50	18	62.9							$20,000	$30,000	$75,000
	Auctions: $99,875, PF-65Cam, April 2014											
1852, Original † (a)	1,100	20	60.0	70%	$5,500	$10,000	$13,500	$17,500	$27,500	$40,000	$60,000	$140,000
	Auctions: $70,500, MS-63, January 2015; $34,075, AU-58, June 2014; $23,500, AU-50, September 2014											
1852, Original, Proof (a)	20–30	3	64.3							$27,500	$43,500	$75,000
	Auctions: $57,500, PF-65Cam, January 2009											
1852, Restrike, Proof (a)	20–30	17	63.6							$17,500	$30,000	$70,000
	Auctions: $70,500, PF-65, June 2014											
1853	46,110	153	57.6	54%	$350	$450	$650	$1,100	$1,300	$3,200	$7,250	$85,000
	Auctions: $12,925, MS-64, August 2016; $11,163, MS-64, March 2016; $2,350, AU-58, February 2015; $1,680, AU-55, January 2018											
1853, Restrike, Proof (b)	15–20	6	63.7							$20,000	$37,000	$110,000
	Auctions: $152,750, PF-66Cam, August 2013; $105,750, PF-66, October 2014; $16,318, PF-58, October 2015											
1854	33,140	46	55.6	43%	$1,500	$2,500	$4,000	$5,000	$6,000	$9,000	$13,000	$95,000
	Auctions: $21,738, MS-64, May 2015; $6,169, AU-58, January 2015; $5,053, EF-45, June 2015; $4,465, VF-35, August 2015											
1854, Proof	40–60	16	63.7							$12,500	$16,500	$45,000
	Auctions: $49,938, PF-66, April 2013; $21,150, PF-64, May 2015; $15,275, PF-62, August 2014; $13,200, PF-62, April 2018											
1855	26,000	57	53.9	32%	$1,250	$2,500	$4,000	$5,000	$6,500	$8,000	$30,000	—
	Auctions: $7,050, AU-58, October 2015; $4,700, AU-50, January 2015; $4,465, AU-50, August 2015; $5,640, EF-45, August 2015											

† Original circulation strikes of 1851 and 1852 Liberty Seated dollars are ranked in the *100 Greatest U.S. Coins* (fourth edition), as a single entry. **a.** Silver dollars of 1851 are found in two formats: originals struck for circulation and Proof restrikes made years later. Silver dollars of 1852 are found in these formats and also as original Proofs. "As part of [Mint Director] James Ross Snowden's restriking activities in 1859, Proof examples of certain rare silver dollars of earlier dates were made, including the 1851 and 1852. For the 1851 dollar, the original die (with four-date digit logotype slanting slightly upward and the date close to the base of Liberty) probably could not be located in 1859. In any event, a different die, not originally used in 1851, with the date horizontal and centered, was employed. Whether this die was created new in 1859 and given an 1851 date, or whether it was made in 1851 and not used at that time, is not known" (*United States Pattern Coins*, tenth edition). **b.** Made at the Mint from postdated dies circa 1862.

	Mintage	Cert	Avg	%MS	VG-8	F-12	VF-20	EF-40	AU-50	MS-60 PF-60	MS-63 PF-63	MS-65 PF-65
1855, Proof	*40–60*	21	64.0							$12,500	$16,000	$40,000
	Auctions: $45,531, PF-66, August 2013											
1856	$63,500	$54	$52	$0	$500	$700	$900	$2,300	$3,500	$5,000	$15,000	$85,000
	Auctions: $4,230, AU-58, January 2015; $3,290, EF-45, January 2015; $1,763, VF-20, June 2015; $1,234, F-15, October 2015											
1856, Proof	*40–60*	$38	$64							$5,500	$13,000	$30,000
	Auctions: $30,550, PF-65, October 2014; $27,025, PF-65, April 2013; $23,500, PF-65, May 2015; $13,513, PF-64, January 2015											
1857	$94,000	$89	$59	$1	$500	$625	$850	$2,200	$2,500	$3,250	$9,500	$85,000
	Auctions: $76,375, MS-66, May 2015; $10,575, MS-64, October 2015; $5,405, AU-58, January 2015; $2,233, EF-45, January 2015											
1857, Proof	*50–70*	$28	$64							$7,000	$13,500	$30,000
	Auctions: No auction records available.											
1858					$4,000	$5,000	$6,000	$7,000	$9,000			
1858, Proof (c)	$300	$78	$62							$10,000	$14,000	$35,000
	Auctions: $11,456, PF-63, October 2014; $11,163, PF-63, September 2015; $14,100, PF-62, August 2015; $9,400, PF-61, January 2015											
1859	$255,700	$79	$56	$0	$400	$425	$525	$750	$1,225	$2,500	$6,000	$85,000
	Auctions: $8,813, MS-64, January 2015; $5,170, MS-63, July 2015; $3,290, MS-61, June 2015; $1,880, AU-55, February 2015											
1859, Proof	$800	$154	$64							$2,400	$4,750	$12,000
	Auctions: $5,640, PF-64, January 2015; $5,405, PF-64, June 2015; $3,258, PF-62, January 2015; $2,088, PF-60, January 2015											
1859-O	$360,000	$652	$53	$0	$400	$425	$475	$600	$850	$2,050	$5,000	$65,000
	Auctions: $2,820, MS-62, February 2015; $764, AU-53, September 2015; $329, VF-25, February 2015; $259, F-15, September 2015											
1859-S	$20,000	$143	$45	$0	$500	$550	$850	$1,700	$3,350	$13,000	$29,000	
	Auctions: $30,550, MS-63, August 2016; $17,625, MS-63, September 2015; $10,575, MS-62, October 2015; $9,400, MS-62, March 2016											
1860	$217,600	$120	$57	$1	$450	$500	$575	$700	$900	$2,100	$5,000	$75,000
	Auctions: $6,463, MS-64, August 2015; $1,175, AU-53, July 2015; $823, AU-50, January 2015; $564, EF-40, January 2015											
1860, Proof	$1,330	$149	$64							$2,400	$4,750	$12,000
	Auctions: $64,625, PF-67, April 2013; $24,675, PF-66, May 2015; $22,325, PF-66, October 2015; $4,230, PF-63, July 2015											
1860-O	$515,000	$924	$54	$1	$400	$425	$475	$600	$785	$1,900	$3,750	$60,000
	Auctions: $6,169, MS-64, January 2015; $853, AU-55, June 2015; $541, EF-45, January 2015; $494, EF-40, June 2015											
1861	$77,500	$76	$56	$1	$775	$1,100	$1,650	$2,750	$3,000	$3,750	$5,850	$65,000
	Auctions: $50,525, MS-65, May 2015; $8,225, MS-64, November 2014; $2,585, MS-60, June 2015; $3,055, EF-45, January 2015											
1861, Proof	$1,000	$99	$63							$2,400	$4,750	$12,000
	Auctions: $4,994, PF-63Cam+, September 2014; $76,375, PF-66, June 2014; $19,200, PF-65, February 2018											
1862	$11,540	$94	$55	$1	$900	$1,300	$1,900	$2,750	$3,750	$5,500	$9,000	$65,000
	Auctions: $31,725, MS-64, June 2014; $12,925, MS-64, November 2014; $5,405, AU-53, January 2015; $3,525, EF-40, November 2014											
1862, Proof	$550	$168	$63							$2,400	$4,750	$11,500
	Auctions: $38,775, PF-67, January 2015; $35,250, PF-67, August 2015; $6,169, PF-64, January 2015; $2,820, PF-62, January 2015											
1863	$27,200	$81	$55	$1	$900	$1,300	$1,900	$2,200	$2,500	$3,575	$7,000	$50,000
	Auctions: $9,988, MS-64, August 2015; $8,813, MS-64, January 2015; $3,055, AU-53, July 2015; $1,763, EF-40, January 2015											
1863, Proof	$460	$141	$64							$2,400	$4,750	$11,500
	Auctions: $129,250, PF-69, April 2013; $18,800, PF-66, May 2015; $9,988, PF-65, August 2014; $3,760, PF-63, January 2015											
1864	$30,700	$89	$48	$0	$475	$550	$700	$1,300	$2,000	$3,575	$7,500	$60,000
	Auctions: $47,000, MS-65, May 2015; $1,058, AU-50, January 2015; $1,998, EF-45, October 2015; $1,528, EF-45, March 2015											
1864, Proof	$470	$160	$64							$2,400	$4,750	$11,500
	Auctions: $52,875, PF-68, April 2013; $3,840, PF-62, February 2018											
1865 (d)	$46,500	$77	$51	$0	$425	$450	$650	$1,600	$2,100	$3,000	$7,500	$80,000
	Auctions: $5,405, MS-61, October 2015; $3,408, AU-55, January 2015; $1,116, AU-50, January 2015; $1,763, EF-40, February 2015											
1865, Proof	$500	$190	$64							$2,400	$4,750	$11,500
	Auctions: $19,975, PF-66, August 2015; $10,575, PF-65, June 2015; $4,600, PF-63Cam, August 2015; $3,995, PF-63, July 2015											

c. Proof only. d. There is a common doubled-die reverse variety for 1865, which does not command a premium in today's market. "Doubling is evident only on the U of UNITED. . . . This is probably the most common variety for this date" (*Cherrypickers' Guide to Rare Die Varieties*, sixth edition, volume II).

1869, Repunched Date
FS-S1-1869-302.
Other varieties exist.

	Mintage	Cert	Avg	%MS	VG-8	F-12	VF-20	EF-40	AU-50	MS-60 / PF-60	MS-63 / PF-63	MS-65 / PF-65
1866	48,900	113	52.0	35%	$425	$450	$600	$1,000	$1,400	$2,300	$5,500	$65,000
	Auctions: $4,230, MS-63, January 2015; $2,291, MS-61, January 2015; $1,293, AU-50, August 2015; $823, EF-45, January 2015										
1866, Proof	725	228	62.9							$2,100	$3,800	$11,500
	Auctions: $19,975, PF-66Cam, October 2015; $17,625, PF-66Cam, May 2015; $6,463, PF-64, October 2015; $3,525, PF-62Cam, June 2015										
1866, No Motto, Proof † (e)	2 known	2	64.0								—	
	Auctions: No auction records available.										
1867	46,900	72	49.4	35%	$425	$450	$600	$1,000	$1,200	$2,200	$5,300	$70,000
	Auctions: $$11,163, MS-64, June 2015; $8,813, MS-64, October 2015; $881, AU-50, February 2015; $881, EF-40, January 2015										
1867, Proof	625	217	63.4							$2,100	$3,900	$11,500
	Auctions: $56,400, PF-65, May 2015; $47,588, PF-65, October 2015; $5,405, PF-64Cam, January 2015; $2,938, PF-63, June 2015										
1868	162,100	115	48.0	17%	$425	$450	$500	$800	$1,150	$2,400	$7,000	$65,000
	Auctions: $705, AU-50, January 2015; $764, EF-45, September 2015; $764, EF-40, January 2015; $423, EF-40, September 2015										
1868, Proof	600	209	63.7							$2,100	$3,800	$11,500
	Auctions: $3,290, PF-63, September 2015; $2,291, PF-62, August 2015; $2,115, PF-62, January 2015; $1,763, PF-61, October 2014										
1869	423,700	135	50.1	33%	$425	$450	$500	$750	$1,050	$2,300	$5,250	$65,000
	Auctions: $3,995, MS-63, September 2015; $4,230, MS-62, January 2015; $494, VF-30, June 2015; $423, VF-25, May 2015										
1869, Repunched Date (f)	(g)	0	n/a						$1,100	$2,750	$7,000	
	Auctions: $4,406, MS-62, October 2014										
1869, Proof	600	207	63.5							$2,100	$3,800	$11,500
	Auctions: $9,988, PF-64DCam, October 2014; $6,463, PF-64Cam, October 2014; $5,875, PF-64Cam, November 2014										
1870	415,000	244	48.7	26%	$425	$450	$525	$600	$950	$2,100	$4,750	$55,000
	Auctions: $56,400, MS-65+, May 2015; $1,175, AU-55, March 2015; $470, VF-35, January 2015; $400, VF-25, August 2015										
1870, Proof	1,000	212	63.3							$2,100	$3,800	$11,500
	Auctions: $17,625, PF-66Cam, September 2015; $9,106, PF-65, October 2015; $5,405, PF-64Cam, August 2015										
1870-CC	11,758	237	40.0	8%	$1,000	$1,500	$2,500	$4,500	$5,500	$25,000	$42,500	—
	Auctions: $19,975, AU-58+, August 2015; $10,575, AU-55, July 2016; $9,988, AU-55, November 2016; $6,463, AU-50, January 2015										
1870-S †	(h)	4	47.0	0%	$200,000	$250,000	$400,000	$525,000	$800,000	$1,750,000	—	—
	Auctions: $763,750, EF-40, January 2014										
1871	1,073,800	805	45.3	20%	$400	$450	$500	$600	$1,050	$2,100	$4,650	$50,000
	Auctions: $50,525, MS-65, January 2015; $705, AU-50, March 2015; $470, EF-45, June 2015; $306, VF-20, December 2015										
1871, Proof	960	203	62.9							$2,100	$3,800	$11,500
	Auctions: $21,150, PF-66, January 2015; $15,863, PF-66, October 2015; $4,700, PF-64, September 2015; $1,998, PF-61, October 2015										
1871-CC	1,376	45	41.7	9%	$3,750	$5,500	$6,750	$13,000	$20,000	$75,000	$175,000	—
	Auctions: $5,640, AU-50, January 2015; $11,163, VF-35, January 2015; $4,935, VF-25, January 2015; $3,760, F-12, January 2015										

† Ranked in the *100 Greatest U.S. Coins* (fourth edition). **e.** The 1866, No Motto, dollar is classified as Judd-540 (*United States Pattern Coins*). Two examples of this fantasy piece are known; at least one was deliberately struck for pharmacist and coin collector Robert Coulton Davis, likely around 1869 or in the early 1870s, along with the No Motto Proof quarter and half dollar of the same date. The three-coin set is on display at the American Numismatic Association's Edward C. Rochette Money Museum in Colorado Springs. "A second 1866 'No Motto' silver dollar resurfaced in the 1970s before entering a private Midwestern collection in the early 1980s. After not meeting its auction reserve price in September 2003, the coin was sold privately for nearly a million dollars some time later" (*100 Greatest U.S. Coins*, fourth edition). **f.** There are several repunched dates known for 1869. The one listed is FS-S1-1869-302. The top flag of a secondary 1 is evident midway between the primary 1 and the 8. **g.** Included in circulation-strike 1869 mintage figure. **h.** The Mint shows no record of 1870-S dollars being struck, but about a dozen are known to exist. The 1870-S silver dollars may have been struck as mementos of the laying of the cornerstone of the San Francisco Mint (May 25, 1870).

	Mintage	Cert	Avg	%MS	VG-8	F-12	VF-20	EF-40	AU-50	MS-60	MS-63	MS-65
										PF-60	PF-63	PF-65
1872	1,105,500	593	43.6	16%	$400	$450	$500	$600	$950	$2,050	$4,700	$50,000
	Auctions: $14,100, MS-64, August 2015; $940, AU-53, January 2015; $329, F-15, August 2015; $176, G-4, February 2015; $4,560, MS-64, March 2018											
1872, Proof	950	178	63.1							$2,100	$3,800	$11,500
	Auctions: $9,988, PF-65, August 2015; $8,813, PF-65, March 2015; $7,638, PF-64, May 2015; $1,410, PF-60, January 2015											
1872-CC	3,150	88	41.1	16%	$2,850	$3,750	$4,200	$6,000	$10,000	$28,000	$100,000	$300,000
	Auctions: $28,200, MS-62, October 2015; $11,750, AU-53, February 2015; $5,640, EF-45, August 2015; $2,468, VG-10, February 2015											
1872-S	9,000	112	42.9	11%	$500	$675	$950	$1,975	$3,500	$12,000	$37,500	
	Auctions: $7,050, MS-61, October 2015; $6,463, AU-58, January 2015; $1,528, EF-40, October 2015; $1,410, VF-35, January 2015											
1873	293,000	184	52.0	39%	$475	$500	$550	$650	$975	$2,100	$4,850	$60,000
	Auctions: $58,750, MS-65, May 2015; $11,750, MS-64+, January 2015; $881, EF-45, October 2015; $646, VF-35, February 2015											
1873, Proof	600	185	63.3							$2,100	$3,800	$11,500
	Auctions: $16,450, PF-65Cam+, August 2014; $9,988, PF-65, June 2015; $16,450, PF-64, August 2015; $940, PF-60, January 2015											
1873-CC	2,300	28	44.0	18%	$9,000	$13,000	$19,000	$30,000	$42,500	$115,000	$190,000	$500,000
	Auctions: $105,750, MS-61, May 2015; $56,400, AU-55, August 2015; $35,250, EF-45, November 2014; $11,163, EF-40, January 2015											
1873-S (i)	700	0	n/a									
	Auctions: No auction records available.											

i. The 1873-S is unknown in any collection, public or private, despite Mint records indicating that 700 were struck. None have ever been seen.

MORGAN (1878–1921)

Designer: *George T. Morgan.* **Weight:** *26.73 grams.* **Composition:** *.900 silver, .100 copper (net weight .77344 oz. pure silver).* **Diameter:** *38.1 mm.*
Edge: *Reeded.* **Mints:** *Philadelphia, New Orleans, Carson City, Denver, and San Francisco.*

Mintmark location is on the reverse, below the bow.

Circulation Strike

Proof

History. The Morgan dollar, named for English-born designer George T. Morgan, was struck every year from 1878 to 1904, and again in 1921. The coin's production benefited Western silver interests by creating an artificial federal demand for the metal, whose market value had dropped sharply by 1878. Hundreds of millions of the coins, stored in cloth bags of 1,000 each, piled up in government vaults. In the 1900s some were melted, but immense quantities were bought by collectors and investors; today they are the most widely collected of all coins of their era.

Striking and Sharpness. On coins of 1878 to 1900, check the hair above Miss Liberty's ear and, on the reverse, the breast feathers of the eagle. These are weak on many issues, particularly those of the New Orleans Mint. From 1900 to 1904 a new reverse hub was used, and breast feathers, while discernible, are not as sharp. In 1921 new dies were made in lower relief, with certain areas indistinct. Many Morgan dollars have partially or fully prooflike surfaces. These are designated as Prooflike (PL), Deep Prooflike (DPL), or Deep Mirror Prooflike (DMPL). Certification practices can be erratic, and some DMPL-certified coins are not fully mirrored. All prooflike coins tend to emphasize contact marks, with the result that lower MS levels can be unattractive. *A Guide Book of Morgan Silver Dollars* (Bowers) and other references furnish information as to which dates and mintmarks are easily found with Full Details and which usually are weak, as well as the availability of the various levels of prooflike surface.

Proofs were struck from 1878 to 1904, with those of 1878 to 1901 generally having cameo contrast, and 1902 to 1904 having the portrait lightly polished in the die. Some are lightly struck; check the hair above Liberty's ear (in particular), and the eagle's breast feathers. In 1921 many so-called Zerbe Proofs (named thus after numismatic entrepreneur Farran Zerbe), with many microscopic die-finish lines, were made. A very few deeply mirrored 1921 coins were made, called Chapman Proofs (after coin dealer Henry Chapman, who started marketing them shortly after their production). Some Zerbe Proofs have been miscertified as Chapman Proofs.

Availability. All dates and mints of Morgan dollars are available in grades from well worn to MS. Some issues such as certain Carson City coins are rare if worn and common in MS. Other issues such as the 1901 Philadelphia coins are common if worn and are rarities at MS-65. The 1889-CC and 1893-S, and the Proof 1895, are considered to be the key issues. Varieties listed herein are some of those most significant to collectors. Numerous other variations exist, studied in the *Cherrypickers' Guide to Rare Die Varieties* and other specialized texts. Values shown herein are for the most common pieces. Values of varieties not listed in this guide depend on collector interest and demand.

Note: Values of common-date silver coins have been based on the current bullion price of silver, $17 per ounce, and may vary with the prevailing spot price.

GRADING STANDARDS

MS-60 to 70 (Mint State). *Obverse:* At MS-60, some abrasion and contact marks are evident, most noticeably on the cheek and on the hair above the ear. The left field also shows such marks. Luster is present, but may be dull or lifeless. At MS-63, contact marks are extensive but not distracting. Abrasion still is evident, but less than at lower levels. Indeed, the cheek of Miss Liberty showcases abrasion. An MS-65 coin may have minor abrasion, but

1895-O. Graded MS-61.

contact marks are so minute as to require magnification. Luster should be full and rich. Coins with prooflike surfaces such as PL, DPL, and DMPL display abrasion and contact marks much more noticeably than coins with frosty surfaces; in grades below MS-64 many are unattractive. With today's loose and sometimes contradictory interpretations, many at MS-64 appear to have extensive marks as well. *Reverse:* Comments apply as for the obverse, except that in lower Mint State grades abrasion and contact marks are most noticeable on the eagle's breast. At MS-65 or higher there are no marks visible to the unaided eye. The field is mainly protected by design elements, so the reverse often appears to grade a point or two higher than the obverse. A Morgan dollar can have an MS-63 obverse and an MS-65 reverse, as was indeed the nomenclature used prior to the single-number system. A careful cataloger may want to describe each side separately for a particularly valuable or rare Morgan dollar. An example with an MS-63 obverse and an MS-65 reverse should have an overall grade of MS-63, as the obverse is traditionally given prominence.

Illustrated coin: This is a lustrous and attractive example.

AU-50, 53, 55, 58 (About Uncirculated). *Obverse:* Light wear is seen on the cheek and, to a lesser extent, on the hair below the coronet. Generally, the hair details mask friction and wear and it is not as easy to notice as on the cheek and in the fields. At AU-58, the luster is extensive, but incomplete, especially on the higher parts and in the left field. At AU–50 and 53, luster is less, but still is present. PL, DPL, and DMPL coins are not widely desired

1889-CC. Graded AU-58.

at these levels, as the marks are too distracting. *Reverse:* Wear is evident on the head, breast, wing tips, and, to a lesser extent, in the field. An AU-58 coin (as determined by the obverse) can have a reverse that appears to be full Mint State. (Incidentally, this is also true of Barber quarter dollars and half dollars.)

Illustrated coin: This is a lustrous example of the rarest Carson City Morgan dollar. As is typical of AU-58 dollars of this design, the reverse appears to be full Mint State, as the field is protected by the design elements.

EF-40, 45 (Extremely Fine). *Obverse:* Further wear is seen on the cheek in particular. The hair near the forehead and temple has flatness in areas, most noticeable above the ear. Some luster can be seen in protected areas on many coins, but is not needed to define the EF-40 and 45 grades. *Reverse:* Further wear is seen on the breast of the eagle (most noticeably), the wing tips, and the leaves.

1879-CC. Graded EF-40.

VF-20, 30 (Very Fine). *Obverse:* The head shows more wear, now with most of the detail gone in the areas adjacent to the forehead and temple. The lower area has most hair fused into large strands. *Reverse:* Wear is more extensive on the breast and on the feathers in the upper area of the wings, especially the right wing, and on the legs. The high area of the leaves has no detail.

1889-CC. Graded VF-20.

F-12, 15 (Fine). *Obverse:* The head shows more wear, with most hair detail gone, and with a large flat area above the ear. Less detail is seen in the lower curls. *Reverse:* More wear is seen on the reverse, with the eagle's breast and legs flat and about a third of the feather detail gone, mostly near the tops of the wings.

1893-S. Graded F-15.

VG-8, 10 (Very Good). *Obverse:* More hair details are gone, especially from the area from the top of the head down to the ear. The details of the lower part of the cap are gone. The rim is weak in areas, and some denticles are worn away. *Reverse:* Further wear has smoothed more than half of the feathers in the wing. The leaves are flat except for the lowest areas. The rim is weak in areas.

1892-CC. Graded VG-8.

G-4, 6 (Good). *Obverse:* The head is in outline form, with most details gone. LIBERTY still is readable. The eye position and lips are discernible. Most of the rim is worn away. *Reverse:* The eagle shows some feathers near the bottom of the wings, but nearly all others are gone. The leaves are seen in outline form. The rim is mostly worn away. Some letters have details toward the border worn away.

The Morgan dollar is seldom collected in grades lower than G-4.

Illustrated coin: Here is a well-worn example of this key issue.

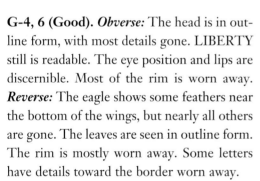

1893-S. Graded G-4.

PF-60 to 70 (Proof). *Obverse and Reverse:* Dull, grainy Proofs, or extensively cleaned ones with many hairlines, are lower level (PF–60 to 62). Only the 1895 is desirable at such low grades. Those with medium hairlines and good reflectivity may grade at about PF-64, and with relatively few hairlines, Gem PF-65. Hairlines are most easily seen in the obverse field. Horizontal slide marks on Miss Liberty's cheek, caused by clear slides on some coin albums, are common. PF-66 may have hairlines so delicate that magnification is needed to see them. Above that, a Proof should be free of such lines, including slide marks.

1898. Graded PF-64.

First Reverse
Eight tail feathers.

Second Reverse
Parallel top arrow feather, concave breast.

Third Reverse
Slanted top arrow feather, convex breast.

1878, Doubled Tail Feathers
FS-S1-1878-032.

1878, 8 Feathers, Obverse Die Gouge
The "Wild Eye" variety.
VAM-14.11. FS-S1-1878-014.11.

1878, 7 Over 8 Tail Feathers, Tripled Leaves
VAM-44. FS-S1-1878-044.

	Mintage	Cert	Avg	%MS	VF-20	EF-40	AU-50	MS-60	MS-63	MS-64	MS-64DMPL PF-60	MS-65 PF-63	MS-65DMPL PF-65
1878, 8 Feathers	749,500	13,390	61.8	93%	$85	$100	$120	$200	$250	$425	$4,000	$1,050	$21,000
Auctions: $1,586, MS-65, January 2015; $212, MS-62, May 2015; $125, AU-55, February 2015; $89, EF-45, May 2015													
1878, 8 Feathers, Obverse Die Gouge (a)	(b)	7	60.4	71%				$10,000	$13,000	$20,000			
Auctions: $16,100, MS-62, August 2011													
1878, 7 Feathers, All kinds	9,759,300												
1878, 7 Over 8, Clear Doubled Feathers	(c)	2,480	61.5	91%	$50	$55	$75	$200	$275	$500	$5,200	$1,500	$16,000
Auctions: $1,410, MS-64, January 2015; $223, MS-63, August 2015; $188, MS-62, June 2015; $52, EF-45, February 2015													
1878, 7 Over 8, Tripled Leaves (d)	(c)	22	50.8	23%				$4,500	$10,000	$23,000			
Auctions: $820, MS-65, September 2015; $206, MS-64, January 2015; $106, MS-62, June 2015; $62, AU-58, February 2015													
1878, 7 Feathers, 2nd Reverse (e)	(c)	15,210	62.3	95%	$45	$48	$60	$90	$150	$250	$2,200	$900	$11,000
Auctions: $3,760, MS-66, January 2015; $176, MS-63, June 2015; $84, MS-61, February 2015; $62, AU-55, April 2015													
1878, 7 Feathers, 3rd Reverse (e)	(c)	5,474	61.5	90%	$45	$48	$50	$110	$250	$450	$5,500	$1,750	$23,000
Auctions: $11,163, MS-66, August 2015; $5,760, MS-66, January 2018													

a. Two spikes protrude from the front of Liberty's eye. "Fewer than a dozen specimens are known of this Top 100 variety and any sale is a landmark event" (*Cherrypickers' Guide to Rare Die Varieties*, sixth edition, volume II). b. Included in circulation-strike 1878, 8 Feathers, mintage figure. c. Included in circulation-strike 1878, 7 Feathers, mintage figure. d. Called the "King of VAMs" (Van Allen / Mallis varieties), this variety shows three to five weak tail feathers under the seven primary feathers. On the obverse, tripling is evident on the cotton bolls and the leaves, and doubling on LIBERTY. Values are fluid for this popular variety. e. The Second Reverse is sometimes known as "Concave Breast" or "Reverse of 1878." The Third Reverse is sometimes known as "Round Breast" or "Reverse of 1879."

1880, 80 Over 79
VAM-6. FS-S1-1880-006.

	Mintage	Cert	Avg	%MS	VF-20	EF-40	AU-50	MS-60	MS-63	MS-64	MS-64DMPL / PF-60	MS-65 / PF-63	MS-65DMPL / PF-65
1878, 8 Feathers, Proof	500	135	64.2								$1,500	$3,500	$11,500
Auctions: $70,500, PF-67, January 2015; $11,163, PF-65Cam, January 2015; $14,100, PF-64Cam+, August 2015; $5,053, PF-64, August 2015													
1878, 7 Feathers, 2nd Reverse, Proof	250	100	63.6								$2,750	$3,750	$12,500
Auctions: $8,225, PF-63, March 2015; $6,463, PF-63, August 2015; $4,700, PF-63, October 2014; $6,463, PF-62, September 2014													
1878, 7 Feathers, 3rd Reverse, Proof (e)	(f)	5	62.4								$16,500	$85,000	$200,000
Auctions: $155,250, PF-64, November 2004													
1878-CC	2,212,000	26,131	60.4	88%	$125	$150	$240	$400	$440	$500	$2,800	$1,350	$10,000
Auctions: $17,625, MS-66, August 2016; $14,100, MS-66, November 2016; $12,925, MS-66, October 2016; $6,463, MS-66, January 2015													
1878-S	9,774,000	46,773	63.1	98%	$45	$47	$48	$65	$85	$110	$2,000	$280	$10,000
Auctions: $8,225, MS-67, January 2015; $306, MS-65, November 2015; $79, MS-63, May 2015; $2,703, EF-45, February 2015													
1879	14,806,000	12,467	62.6	94%	$30	$33	$50	$55	$85	$130	$2,100	$500	$15,000
Auctions: $2,468, MS-66, January 2015; $617, MS-65, November 2015; $141, MS-64, February 2015; $118, MS-60, August 2015													
1879, Proof	1,100	322	64.2								$1,300	$3,200	$5,500
Auctions: $14,100, PF-67Cam, August 2015; $4,583, PF-64Cam, January 2015; $2,585, PF-63, January 2015; $1,763, PF-62, August 2015													
1879-CC, CC Over CC	756,000	2,056	46.3	46%	$335	$800	$1,925	$4,200	$6,500	$8,500	$40,000	$40,000	$60,000
Auctions: $4,700, MS-62, March 2015; $1,058, EF-45, January 2015; $541, VF-35, September 2015; $176, VG-10, February 2015													
1879-CC, Clear CC	(g)	4,048	47.9	57%	$375	$950	$2,500	$4,500	$7,300	$9,500	$23,500	$21,000	$47,500
Auctions: $21,150, MS-65, September 2015; $9,694, MS-64, January 2015; $705, EF-40, July 2015; $481, VF-35, July 2015													
1879-O	2,887,000	9,058	61.3	84%	$42	$45	$47	$90	$240	$525	$4,250	$2,450	$22,000
Auctions: $17,625, MS-66, August 2015; $3,525, MS-65, January 2015; $112, MS-61, May 2015; $56, AU-55, March 2015													
1879-O, Proof (h)	4–8	5	64.4										$275,000
Auctions: $176,250, PF-64, August 2013													
1879-S, 2nd Reverse	9,110,000	2,418	60.3	80%	$65	$75	$90	$190	$1,000	$1,750	$8,000	$6,000	$21,000
Auctions: $3,290, MS-65, January 2015; $1,704, MS-64, January 2015; $84, AU-55, August 2015; $200, AU-53, May 2015													
1879-S, 3rd Reverse	(i)	104,060	64.2	100%	$32	$35	$39	$55	$65	$75	$500	$130	$1,300
Auctions: $5,758, MS-68, June 2015; $1,351, MS-67, January 2015; $112, MS-64, September 2015; $282, MS-63, November 2015													
1880	12,600,000	14,112	62.7	96%	$40	$42	$46	$50	$85	$130	$1,150	$550	$6,000
Auctions: $4,230, MS-66, June 2015; $588, MS-65, October 2015; $141, MS-64, July 2015; $194, AU-53, February 2015													
1880, 80 Over 79 (j)	(k)	1	45.0	0%	$35	$37	$48	$150	$600	$2,500		$4,000	
Auctions: $764, AU-58, January 2015; $200, AU-55, February 2015; $176, AU-53, November 2014; $153, AU-50, January 2015													
1880, Proof	1,355	428	64.8								$1,300	$3,000	$5,500
Auctions: $10,575, PF-67Cam, August 2015; $9,988, PF-66Cam+, June 2015; $6,169, PF-65, August 2015; $2,585, PF-62, March 2015													

e. The Second Reverse is sometimes known as "Concave Breast" or "Reverse of 1878." The Third Reverse is sometimes known as "Round Breast" or "Reverse of 1879." **f.** Included in 1878, 7 Feathers, Proof, mintage figure. **g.** Included in 1879-CC, CC Over CC, mintage figure. **h.** Some numismatists classify these as Deep Mirror Prooflike circulation strikes, rather than as Proofs. **i.** Included in 1879-S, 2nd Reverse, mintage figure. **j.** Several die varieties exist; values shown are for the most common. **k.** Included in circulation-strike 1880 mintage figure.

1880-CC, 80 Over 79
VAM-4. FS-S1-1880CC-004.

1880-CC, 8 Over High 7
VAM-5. FS-S1-1880CC-005.

1880-CC, 8 Over Low 7
VAM-6. FS-S1-1880CC-006.

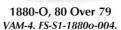 

1880-O, 80 Over 79
VAM-4. FS-S1-1880o-004.

1880-O, Die Gouge
The "Hangnail" variety.
VAM-49. FS-S1-1880o-049.

	Mintage	Cert	Avg	%MS	VF-20	EF-40	AU-50	MS-60	MS-63	MS-64	MS-64DMPL / PF-60	MS-65 / PF-63	MS-65DMPL / PF-65
1880-CC, All kinds	591,000												
1880-CC, 80 Over 79, 2nd Reverse (l)		1,323	62.8	99%	$220	$285	$350	$500	$650	$1,150	$5,000	$2,500	$20,000
Auctions: $8,225, MS-66, March 2015; $1,058, MS-64, January 2015; $734, MS-63, March 2015; $129, G-4, January 2015													
1880-CC, 8 Over 7, 2nd Reverse		328	63.4	100%	$210	$285	$325	$550	$600	$1,000	$5,000	$2,000	$20,000
Auctions: $1,998, MS-64, August 2015; $881, MS-64, July 2015; $588, MS-62, August 2015; $235, VG-10, August 2015													
1880-CC, 8 Over High 7, 3rd Reverse (m)		588	63.5	100%	$210	$275	$325	$500	$575	$700	$2,450	$1,000	$9,000
Auctions: $852, MS-64+, March 2015; $588, MS-64, January 2015; $541, MS-63, September 2015; $529, MS-63, December 2015													
1880-CC, 8 Over Low 7, 3rd Reverse (n)		475	63.5	100%	$270	$365	$475	$600	$650	$750	$2,700	$1,000	$9,000
Auctions: $1,763, MS-65, March 2015; $905, MS-64, September 2015; $764, MS-64, June 2015; $494, MS-63, August 2015													
1880-CC, 3rd Reverse		0	n/a		$225	$260	$325	$500	$575	$700	$2,450	$1,000	$9,000
Auctions: $18,800, MS-67, January 2015; $259, EF-45, February 2015; $200, VF-25, September 2015; $112, G-6, July 2015													
1880-O, All kinds	5,305,000												
1880-O, 80 Over 79 (o)		248	59.5	66%	$40	$42	$50	$150	$600	$2,500	$8,000		
Auctions: $353, MS-63, January 2015; $341, MS-63, September 2015; $353, AU-58, January 2015; $165, AU-58, March 2015													
1880-O		10,302	60.5	75%	$40	$42	$45	$90	$350	$1,350	$7,250	$14,000	$62,500
Auctions: $14,100, MS-65, January 2015; $329, MS-63, November 2015; $64, AU-58, August 2015; $48, AU-55, February 2015													
1880-O, Die Gouge (p)		214	56.0	36%	$200	$450	$900	$2,000	—				
Auctions: $15,275, MS-65, January 2015; $94, AU-58, March 2015; $74, AU-58, January 2015; $69, AU-58, February 2015													
1880-S, All kinds	8,900,000												
1880-S, 80 Over 79		814	63.9	99%	$30	$40	$46	$55	$75	$125	$450	$275	$1,500
Auctions: $435, MS-66, January 2015; $188, MS-65, October 2015; $112, MS-64, April 2015; $94, MS-64, February 2015													
1880-S, 0 Over 9		937	64.0	100%	$35	$40	$46	$63	$75	$125	$450	$275	$1,500
Auctions: $1,058, MS-66+, January 2015; $176, MS-65, April 2015; $129, MS-64, May 2015; $89, MS-63, September 2015													
1880-S		153,690	64.2	100%	$30	$33	$39	$45	$50	$70	$450	$125	$1,000
Auctions: $12,925, MS-68, February 2015; $3,525, MS-65, January 2015; $282, MS-64, November 2015; $182, MS-63, May 2015													

l. The top crossbar and diagonal stem of an underlying 79 are clearly seen within the 8. Extensive polishing marks are visible within the 0. m. An almost complete 7 is visible inside the last 8 of the date. The top edge of the 7 touches the top inside of the 8. n. A complete 7 is visible inside the last 8 of the date. The crossbar of the underlying 7 can be seen in the top loop and the diagonal of the 7 is visible in the lower loop. o. The crossbar of the underlying 7 is visible within the upper loop of the second 8. The 1 and the first 8 are slightly doubled to the right. p. On the reverse of the "Hangnail" variety, a die gouge runs from the bottom of the arrow feather, across the feathers, and out the eagle's rightmost tail feather. On the obverse, the top-left part of the second 8 has a spike.

1881-O, Repunched Mintmark
VAM-5. FS-S1-1881o-005.

1882-O, O Over S
VAM-4. FS-S1-1882o-004.

	Mintage	Cert	Avg	%MS	VF-20	EF-40	AU-50	MS-60	MS-63	MS-64	MS-64DMPL / PF-60	MS-65 / PF-63	MS-65DMPL / PF-65
1881	9,163,000	11,333	63.1	98%	$30	$37	$45	$53	$80	$140	$1,375	$500	$19,500
Auctions: $2,350, MS-66, August 2015; $588, MS-65, June 2015; $118, MS-64, October 2015; $79, MS-63, January 2015													
1881, Proof	984	265	64.2								$1,300	$3,000	$5,500
Auctions: $5,581, PF-65Cam, July 2014; $8,813, PF-67, August 2014; $14,100, PF-67, October 2014; $2,468, PF-63, January 2015													
1881-CC	296,000	23,772	63.1	98%	$400	$425	$440	$500	$550	$575	$1,200	$800	$3,000
Auctions: $7,050, MS-67+, October 2015; $517, MS-64, January 2015; $470, MS-61, April 2015; $306, VF-20, March 2015													
1881-O	5,708,000	17,947	62.6	95%	$40	$42	$45	$50	$75	$160	$900	$925	$18,000
Auctions: $10,575, MS-66, June 2015; $3,290, MS-65+, August 2015; $129, MS-64, July 2015; $48, AU-58, June 2015													
1881-O, Repunched Mintmark (q)	(r)	84	61.8	99%			$80	$110	$400	$1,000	$1,450	$1,500	
Auctions: $218, MS-64, March 2012													
1881-O, Doubled Die Obverse (s)	(r)	32	56.7	25%			$175	$400	$2,500	$4,000		$6,000	
Auctions: $150, AU-50, September 2011													
1881-S	12,760,000	252,423	64.1	100%	$30	$33	$39	$45	$50	$70	$475	$125	$1,000
Auctions: $5,405, MS-68+, January 2015; $129, MS-65, September 2015; $74, MS-64+, May 2015; $188, MS-63, November 2015													
1882	11,100,000	20,122	63.2	98%	$30	$33	$39	$50	$75	$115	$1,000	$350	$6,500
Auctions: $3,173, MS-66+, August 2015; $112, MS-64+, March 2015; $61, MS-63, June 2015; $294, AU-58, January 2015													
1882, Proof	1,100	358	64.4								$1,300	$3,000	$5,500
Auctions: $14,688, PF-67Cam, October 2015; $9,400, PF-66DCam, August 2015; $4,935, PF-65, January 2015; $4,465, PF-64, January 2015													
1882-CC	1,133,000	41,072	63.2	99%	$110	$130	$150	$210	$225	$250	$625	$450	$1,900
Auctions: $6,463, MS-67, January 2015; $129, AU-53, May 2015; $112, EF-40, June 2015; $84, VG-8, February 2015													
1882-O	6,090,000	18,312	62.8	96%	$37	$39	$45	$50	$75	$125	$1,300	$750	$5,200
Auctions: $4,583, MS-66, July 2015; $84, MS-64, February 2015; $56, MS-62, February 2015; $54, AU-55, July 2015													
1882-O, O Over S (t)	(u)	4,227	56.4	40%	$57	$63	$80	$235	$550	$1,750	$8,500	$48,000	$62,500
Auctions: $1,528, MS-64, March 2016; $911, MS-63, March 2015; $376, MS-62, July 2015; $94, AU-58, January 2015; $42, VF-35, April 2015													
1882-S	9,250,000	80,981	64.2	100%	$30	$33	$39	$45	$50	$70	$950	$125	$3,800
Auctions: $4,465, MS-68, October 2015; $1,058, MS-67, July 2015; $176, MS-65, August 2015; $84, MS-64, January 2015													
1883	12,290,000	23,890	63.6	99%	$30	$33	$39	$50	$75	$85	$450	$150	$1,600
Auctions: $5,875, MS-67+, October 2015; $188, MS-65, May 2015; $89, MS-64, January 2015; $60, MS-63, August 2015													
1883, Proof	1,039	296	64.1								$1,300	$3,000	$5,500
Auctions: $16,450, PF-67, January 2015; $8,225, PF-66Cam, January 2015; $2,468, PF-63, June 2015; $1,410, PF-61, September 2015													
1883-CC	1,204,000	54,155	63.5	99%	$100	$125	$145	$210	$215	$250	$525	$400	$1,300
Auctions: $3,760, MS-67, January 2015; $4,230, MS-66+, January 2015; $423, MS-65, November 2015; $229, MS-61, July 2015													
1883-O	8,725,000	144,587	63.4	100%	$30	$33	$39	$45	$50	$70	$500	$125	$1,450
Auctions: $2,585, MS-67, January 2015; $129, MS-65, October 2015; $74, MS-64, August 2015; $79, MS-62, February 2015													
1883-O, Proof (v)	4–8	2	64.0										$200,000
Auctions: $270,250, PF-67Cam, April 2013													
1883-S	6,250,000	5,646	55.4	33%	$30	$50	$115	$750	$2,200	$4,500	$75,000	$30,000	$125,000
Auctions: $17,625, MS-65, September 2015; $1,351, MS-61, June 2015; $341, AU-58, January 2015; $50, EF-45, May 2015													

q. A diagonal image, the remains of one or two additional O mintmark punches, is visible within the primary O. **r.** Included in 1881-O mintage figure. **s.** Clear doubling is evident on the back outside of Liberty's ear **t.** Several varieties exist. **u.** Included in 1882-O mintage figure. **v.** "A numismatic tradition exists, dating back well over a century, that 12 full Proofs were struck of the 1883-O Morgan dollar. And, they may have been, although the differentiation between a cameo DMPL and a 'branch mint Proof' would be difficult to explain" (*A Guide Book of Morgan Silver Dollars*, sixth edition).

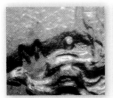 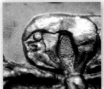

1884, Large Dot
VAM-3. FS-S1-1884-003.

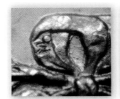 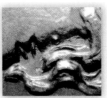

1884, Small Dot
VAM-4. FS-S1-1884-004.

1885, Die Chip
VAM-8. FS-S1-1885-008.

1886, Repunched Date
VAM-20. FS-S1-1886-020.

	Mintage	Cert	Avg	%MS	VF-20	EF-40	AU-50	MS-60	MS-63	MS-64	MS-64DMPL / PF-60	MS-65 / PF-63	MS-65DMPL / PF-65
1884, All kinds	14,070,000												
1884		18,410	63.3	98%	$30	$33	$39	$50	$75	$95	$850	$250	$5,000
Auctions: $25,850, MS-68, January 2015; $1,880, MS-66, October 2015; $94, MS-64, February 2015; $64, MS-63, July 2015													
1884, Large Dot (w)		98	55.2	44%			$55	$100	$400	$700			
Auctions: $80, MS-62, May 2014; $74, AU-55, September 2014													
1884, Small Dot (w)		245	61.9	91%			$65	$110	$450	—			
Auctions: $182, MS-63, September 2014; $153, MS-63, February 2015; $141, MS-63, September 2014; $123, MS-63, July 2015													
1884, Proof	875	210	64.4								$1,300	$3,000	$5,500
Auctions: $8,813, PF-66Cam, July 2015; $4,259, PF-65, March 2015; $4,406, PF-64Cam, March 2015; $3,760, PF-63Cam, January 2015													
1884-CC	1,136,000	62,237	63.6	100%	$150	$160	$165	$210	$215	$250	$550	$400	$1,300
Auctions: $5,170, MS-67, June 2015; $423, MS-65, November 2015; $306, MS-64, February 2015; $223, MS-62, March 2015													
1884-O	9,730,000	212,636	63.5	100%	$30	$33	$39	$50	$50	$70	$450	$125	$1,000
Auctions: $2,585, MS-67, January 2015; $188, MS-65, June 2015; $74, MS-64, September 2015; $188, MS-63, February 2015													
1884-S	3,200,000	8,459	52.2	5%	$32	$75	$200	$7,800	$38,000	$130,000	$135,000	$225,000	$275,000
Auctions: $123,375, MS-64, January 2015; $41,125, MS-63, November 2016; $22,325, MS-62, August 2015; $17,625, MS-62, March 2016													
1885	17,787,000	79,158	63.7	99%	$30	$33	$39	$50	$50	$70	$450	$125	$1,000
Auctions: $2,174, MS-67, October 2015; $147, MS-65, August 2015; $764, MS-64, October 2015; $329, MS-63, November 2015													
1885, Die Chip (x)	(y)	14	62.4	93%			$70	$95	$400	$800			
Auctions: No auction records available.													
1885, Proof	930	249	64.3								$1,300	$3,000	$5,500
Auctions: $9,400, PF-66Cam, June 2015; $7,050, PF-65, July 2015; $4,935, PF-64Cam, August 2015; $2,938, PF-63, July 2015													
1885-CC	228,000	23,515	63.5	99%	$575	$600	$625	$675	$700	$750	$1,300	$950	$2,400
Auctions: $14,100, MS-67, October 2015; $2,468, MS-66+, January 2015; $676, MS-62, July 2015; $423, F-12, February 2015													
1885-O	9,185,000	207,615	63.7	100%	$30	$33	$39	$50	$50	$70	$450	$125	$1,000
Auctions: $37,600, MS-68, January 2015; $329, MS-66, November 2015; $118, MS-64, November 2015; $74, MS-63, February 2015													
1885-S	1,497,000	6,578	60.8	82%	$45	$60	$95	$270	$325	$600	$5,000	$1,600	$45,000
Auctions: $4,700, MS-66, June 2015; $1,645, MS-65, May 2015; $212, MS-60, April 2015; $79, AU-50, January 2015													
1886	19,963,000	135,282	63.8	100%	$30	$33	$39	$50	$50	$70	$475	$125	$1,300
Auctions: $4,465, MS-68, June 2015; $1,293, MS-67, August 2015; $176, MS-65, November 2015; $62, MS-64, May 2015													
1886, RPD (z)	(aa)	10	60.1	70%			$600	$1,000	$4,000	$8,500			
Auctions: $3,819, MS-64, September 2013													
1886, Proof	886	240	64.1								$1,300	$3,000	$5,500
Auctions: $8,813, PF-67, October 2014; $5,875, PF-66, October 2014; $5,405, PF-66, January 2015; $1,939, PF-62, July 2015													

w. A raised dot, either Large or Small, is visible after the designer's initial and on the reverse ribbon. "These dots varieties are thought to have been used as some sort of identifier" (*Cherrypickers' Guide to Rare Die Varieties*, sixth edition, volume II). **x.** A large, raised die chip is evident below the second 8. **y.** Included in circulation-strike 1885 mintage figure. **z.** Repunching is especially evident in the base of the 1, and the lower loop of the 6. **aa.** Included in circulation-strike 1886 mintage figure.

1887, 7 Over 6
VAM-2.
FS-S1-1887-002.

1887-O, 7 Over 6
VAM-3. FS-S1-1887o-003.

1888-O, Obverse Die Break
The "Scarface" variety.
VAM-1B. FS-S1-1888o-001b.

1888-O, Doubled Die Obverse
The "Hot Lips" variety.
VAM-4. FS-S1-1888o-004.

	Mintage	Cert	Avg	%MS	VF-20	EF-40	AU-50	MS-60	MS-63	MS-64	MS-64DMPL / PF-60	MS-65 / PF-63	MS-65DMPL / PF-65
1886-O	10,710,000	6,610	55.5	28%	$42	$45	$80	$875	$2,700	$9,000	$70,000	$150,000	$300,000
Auctions: $12,338, MS-64, January 2015; $1,293, MS-61, June 2015; $317, AU-58, July 2015; $282, AU-50, April 2015													
1886-O, Clashed Die (bb)	(cc)	11	51.5	0%			$225	$1,400	$5,500	—			
Auctions: $282, AU-58, July 2015; $176, AU-55, August 2015; $89, AU-50, January 2015; $31, EF-45, March 2015													
1886-S	750,000	4,763	59.9	74%	$78	$115	$150	$460	$450	$700	$8,500	$1,800	$27,000
Auctions: $5,875, MS-66, August 2015; $423, MS-63, May 2015; $188, AU-58, March 2015; $90, EF-45, January 2015													
1887, 7 Over 6	(dd)	1,035	62.5	94%	$45	$50	$165	$350	$450	$600	$4,750	$1,600	$26,000
Auctions: $764, MS-64, August 2015; $400, MS-63, January 2015; $376, MS-62, December 2015; $353, MS-61, January 2015													
1887	20,290,000	195,124	63.7	100%	$30	$33	$39	$50	$50	$70	$450	$125	$1,000
Auctions: $1,087, MS-67, August 2015; $2,585, MS-66, January 2015; $69, MS-63, February 2015; $40, AU-58, September 2015													
1887, Proof	710	223	64.3								$1,300	$3,000	$5,500
Auctions: $17,038, PF-67, May 2015; $3,055, PF-64, October 2015; $3,408, PF-63, January 2015; $823, PF-60, January 2015													
1887-O, 7 Over 6	(ee)	595	60.5	82%	$48	$70	$175	$450	$1,800	$4,000		$35,000	
Auctions: $5,581, MS-64, January 2014; $1,586, MS-63, January 2015; $705, MS-60, October 2014; $447, MS-60, January 2015													
1887-O	11,550,000	10,051	62.2	94%	$30	$33	$42	$70	$140	$340	$1,700	$1,700	$13,500
Auctions: $2,585, MS-65, January 2015; $306, MS-64, August 2015; $129, MS-63, October 2015; $94, MS-62, March 2015													
1887-S	1,771,000	7,084	61.2	81%	$30	$33	$43	$135	$230	$575	$7,000	$1,650	$27,500
Auctions: $4,465, MS-66, August 2015; $3,525, MS-65+, September 2015; $176, MS-62, September 2015; $79, AU-58, February 2015													
1888	19,183,000	48,563	63.6	99%	$30	$33	$39	$50	$65	$80	$450	$175	$2,400
Auctions: $4,935, MS-67, July 2015; $376, MS-66, October 2015; $166, MS-65, August 2015; $96, MS-64+, January 2015													
1888, Proof	833	194	63.9								$1,300	$3,000	$5,500
Auctions: $24,675, PF-66Cam, April 2013; $5,288, PF-65, October 2015													
1888-O	12,150,000	25,562	63.1	99%	$30	$33	$45	$50	$75	$105	$500	$380	$4,500
Auctions: $4,583, MS-66, January 2015; $94, MS-64, September 2015; $69, MS-63, November 2015; $517, AU-58, January 2015													
1888-O, Obverse Die Break (ff)	(gg)	68	62.0	99%			$2,250	$4,750	$8,500	$22,000			
Auctions: $14,688, MS-64, December 2013													
1888-O, Doubled Die Obverse (hh)	(gg)	935	32.2	1%	$145	$290	$900	$15,000	$35,000	—			
Auctions: $6,169, MS-66, January 2015; $764, MS-64, August 2015; $235, AU-58, December 2015; $141, EF-45, March 2015													
1888-S	657,000	5,362	58.6	70%	$125	$140	$150	$315	$450	$750	$2,850	$2,750	$15,500
Auctions: $6,169, MS-66, January 2015; $764, MS-64, August 2015; $235, AU-58, December 2015; $141, EF-45, March 2015													

bb. Clashing of the E of LIBERTY is evident between the eagle's tail feathers and the bow on the wreath **cc.** Included in 1886-O mintage figure. **dd.** Included in circulation-strike 1887 mintage figure. **ee.** Included in 1887-O mintage figure. **ff.** A major die break runs from the rim between E and P, through the field, and all the way across Liberty's face and neck. This variety is nicknamed "Scarface." **gg.** Included in 1888-O mintage figure. **hh.** Doubling is visible on the lips (especially), nose, eye, chin, entire profile, and part of the hair. This variety is nicknamed "Hot Lips."

1889, Die Break
The "Bar Wing" variety.
VAM-22. FS-S1-1889-022.

1889-O, Clashed Die
VAM-1A. FS-S1-1889o-001a.

1890-CC, Die Gouge
The "Tailbar" variety.
VAM-4. FS-S1-1890CC-004.

1890-O, Die Gouges
The "Comet" variety.
VAM-10. FS-S1-1890o-010.

	Mintage	Cert	Avg	%MS	VF-20	EF-40	AU-50	MS-60	MS-63	MS-64	MS-64DMPL	MS-65	MS-65DMPL
											PF-60	PF-63	PF-65
1889	21,726,000	48,862	63.1	98%	$30	$33	$39	$50	$60	$70	$700	$225	$3,600
Auctions: $5,004, MS-66+, January 2015; $235, MS-65, September 2015; $84, MS-64, February 2015; $64, MS-63, July 2015													
1889, Die Break (ii)	(jj)	304	59.6	67%			$80	$150	$275	$300		$2,500	
Auctions: $182, MS-63, September 2014; $106, MS-62, February 2015; $89, MS-62, September 2014; $84, MS-61, September 2014													
1889, Proof	811	192	64.2								$1,300	$3,000	$5,500
Auctions: $12,925, PF-66Cam, August 2015; $3,290, PF-64Cam, January 2015; $3,055, PF-64, January 2015; $3,290, PF-63, January 2015													
1889-CC	350,000	5,195	31.6	10%	$1,150	$2,750	$7,500	$24,000	$45,000	$75,000	$95,000	$300,000	$350,000
Auctions: $16,450, MS-61, January 2015; $7,344, AU-53, February 2015; $705, VG-10, June 2015; $376, AG-3, August 2015													
1889-O	11,875,000	4,795	60.1	82%	$30	$37	$57	$185	$350	$750	$6,500	$3,500	$17,500
Auctions: $8,813, MS-65+, January 2015; $646, MS-64, July 2015; $200, MS-61, October 2015; $64, AU-55, January 2015													
1889-O, Clashed Die (kk)	(ll)	42	37.9	2%			$975	$2,000	—	—			
Auctions: $4,465, MS-61, August 2015; $940, AU-58, August 2015; $740, AU-55, January 2015; $217, VF-35, March 2015													
1889-S	700,000	6,637	60.8	77%	$60	$75	$95	$275	$340	$550	$5,500	$1,500	$37,500
Auctions: $3,055, MS-66, August 2015; $223, MS-61, March 2015; $135, AU-58, January 2015; $94, AU-53, December 2015													
1890	16,802,000	18,431	62.8	97%	$30	$33	$40	$53	$75	$130	$2,500	$900	$20,000
Auctions: $2,820, MS-65+, June 2015; $194, MS-64+, March 2015; $141, MS-64, January 2015; $74, MS-63, August 2015													
1890, Proof	590	230	64.8								$1,300	$3,000	$5,500
Auctions: $88,125, PF-69DCam, April 2013; $12,925, PF-66Cam, July 2014; $4,259, PF-64Cam, November 2014													
1890-CC	2,309,041	8,403	55.2	73%	$110	$150	$230	$540	$900	$1,250	$2,800	$3,000	$13,750
Auctions: $70,500, MS-64, August 2016; $58,750, MS-63, August 2016; $36,425, MS-62, September 2016; $25,850, MS-61, February 2016													
1890-CC, Die Gouge (mm)	(nn)	454	46.4	47%			$650	$1,150	$2,950	$5,000	$16,000		
Auctions: $3,760, MS-63, January 2015; $911, AU-55, January 2015; $470, EF-45, January 2015; $223, F-12, November 2015													
1890-O	10,701,000	9,759	62.4	96%	$30	$33	$49	$75	$110	$280	$1,500	$1,400	$9,250
Auctions: $2,585, MS-65, June 2015; $376, MS-64+, July 2015; $94, MS-63, December 2015; $79, MS-62, January 2015													
1890-O, Die Gouges (oo)	(pp)	63	61.0	84%			$65	$90	$250	$500		$2,000	
Auctions: $2,233, MS-65, February 2015; $1,410, MS-64+, July 2015; $306, MS-64, September 2015; $188, MS-63, January 2015													
1890-S	8,230,373	10,150	62.2	91%	$30	$33	$43	$70	$120	$250	$3,200	$950	$9,250
Auctions: $4,230, MS-66+, January 2015; $1,087, MS-65, September 2015; $329, MS-64+, August 2015; $84, MS-62, February 2015													

ii. A die break is visible on the top of the eagle's right wing. This variety is nicknamed the "Bar Wing." Different obverse die pairings exist. **jj.** Included in circulation-strike 1889 mintage figure. **kk.** The E of LIBERTY is visible in the field below the eagle's tail feathers and slightly left of the bow. This variety is extremely rare in Mint State, and unknown above MS-61. **ll.** Included in 1889-O mintage figure. **mm.** A heavy die gouge extends from between the eagle's first tail feather and the lowest arrow feather to the leaves in the wreath below. "This is an extremely popular and highly marketable variety, especially in Mint State" (*Cherrypickers' Guide to Rare Die Varieties*, sixth edition, volume II). This variety is nicknamed the "Tailbar." **nn.** Included in 1890-CC mintage figure. **oo.** Die gouges are evident to the right of the date. This variety is nicknamed the "Comet." **pp.** Included in 1890-O mintage figure.

1891-O, Clashed Die
VAM-1A. FS-S1-1891o-001a.

1891-O, Pitted Reverse Die
VAM-1B. FS-S1-1891o-001b.

	Mintage	Cert	Avg	%MS	VF-20	EF-40	AU-50	MS-60	MS-63	MS-64	MS-64DMPL / PF-60	MS-65 / PF-63	MS-65DMPL / PF-65
1891	8,693,556	7,594	61.6	91%	$30	$33	$45	$75	$180	$550	$6,900	$3,300	$23,000
Auctions: $12,925, MS-65+, October 2015; $564, MS-64, July 2015; $89, MS-62, December 2015; $50, AU-58, January 2015													
1891, Proof	650	224	64.4								$1,300	$3,000	$5,500
Auctions: $4,583, PF-65, October 2015; $3,525, PF-64Cam, January 2015; $3,408, PF-64Cam, January 2015; $2,938, PF-63, August 2015													
1891-CC	1,618,000	11,458	59.5	84%	$110	$140	$240	$490	$770	$1,050	$4,500	$3,750	$32,000
Auctions: $4,935, MS-65, August 2015; $881, MS-63, January 2015; $282, AU-58, December 2015; $206, EF-45, March 2015													
1891-O	7,954,529	4,830	61.1	89%	$30	$33	$40	$240	$390	$610	$7,250	$5,000	$36,500
Auctions: $8,225, MS-65, June 2015; $517, MS-64, September 2015; $235, MS-62, January 2015; $79, AU-58, February 2015													
1891-O, Clashed Die (qq)	(rr)	156	36.4	1%			$235	$400	$1,350	—			
Auctions: $517, AU-53, January 2015; $153, AU-50, June 2015; $79, AU-50, November 2014; $48, F-12, November 2014													
1891-O, Pitted Reverse Die (ss)	(rr)	10	51.2	0%			$370		—	—			
Auctions: $4,700, MS-65, June 2014; $3,055, MS-65, October 2014; $3,290, MS-65, November 2014; $2,585, MS-64, October 2014													
1891-S	5,296,000	6,797	62.3	91%	$30	$33	$43	$70	$175	$340	$3,200	$1,150	$20,000
Auctions: $5,640, MS-66, June 2015; $1,234, MS-65, September 2015; $118, MS-63, December 2015; $46, AU-58, May 2015													
1892	1,036,000	4,833	59.9	72%	$45	$55	$85	$320	$450	$1,000	$3,200	$3,200	$18,000
Auctions: $4,230, MS-65+, January 2015; $1,704, MS-64, August 2015; $84, AU-53, December 2015; $46, VF-35, May 2015													
1892, Proof	1,245	367	64.3								$1,300	$3,000	$5,500
Auctions: $14,100, PF-67, January 2015; $6,169, PF-65Cam, October 2015; $3,878, PF-64, August 2015; $2,350, PF-63, September 2015													
1892-CC	1,352,000	6,450	54.2	69%	$250	$450	$700	$1,400	$2,150	$3,000	$9,000	$6,000	$36,000
Auctions: $22,913, MS-66, August 2015; $7,638, MS-65, September 2015; $588, AU-53, February 2015; $458, EF-45, December 2015													
1892-O	2,744,000	5,367	60.6	83%	$35	$42	$85	$275	$425	$775	$20,000	$3,250	$50,000
Auctions: $3,525, MS-65, January 2015; $1,763, MS-64+, August 2015; $306, MS-62, September 2015; $259, MS-61, March 2015													
1892-S	1,200,000	4,270	39.7	1%	$125	$275	$1,450	$41,000	$95,000	$175,000		$225,000	
Auctions: $82,250, MS-62, August 2016; $39,950, MS-61, November 2016; $21,150, AU-58, November 2016; $20,563, AU-58, August 2015													
1893	378,000	5,043	51.5	44%	$225	$250	$350	$875	$1,150	$2,100	$32,500	$4,300	$67,500
Auctions: $10,313, MS-65+, June 2015; $350, AU-55, December 2015; $235, EF-45, January 2015; $147, VG-10, February 2015													
1893, Proof	792	249	64.0								$1,300	$3,000	$5,500
Auctions: $35,250, PF-68, May 2015; $3,995, PF-64, October 2015; $1,763, PF-62, January 2015; $911, PF-58, February 2015													
1893-CC	677,000	4,570	39.0	39%	$625	$1,350	$2,500	$4,900	$7,250	$17,000	$46,000	$85,000	$125,000
Auctions: $25,850, MS-64+, July 2015; $5,170, MS-62, August 2015; $2,350, AU-50, January 2015; $705, VF-30, February 2015													
1893-CC, Proof (tt)	4–8	10	63.8										$200,000
Auctions: $149,500, PF-65, August 2011													
1893-O	300,000	3,768	40.9	19%	$300	$475	$775	$3,500	$7,000	$16,500	$100,000	$175,000	$275,000
Auctions: $11,163, MS-64, March 2015; $5,170, MS-62, January 2015; $1,351, AU-55, February 2015; $235, VF-20, June 2015													
1893-S † (uu,vv)	100,000	3,196	19.9	1%	$5,200	$8,500	$20,750	$145,000	$275,000	$330,000		$600,000	
Auctions: $282,000, MS-63, July 2015; $88,125, MS-61, November 2016; $25,850, AU-55, January 2015; $23,500, AU-53, August 2016													

† Ranked in the *100 Greatest U.S. Coins* (fourth edition). **qq.** The evidence of a clashed die is visible below the eagle's tail feathers and slightly left of the bow, where the E in LIBERTY has been transferred from the obverse die. **rr.** Included in 1891-O mintage figure. **ss.** Pitting on the reverse is visible around the ONE and on the bottom of the wreath above and between ONE and DOLLAR. This variety is rare in circulated grades, and unknown in Mint State. **tt.** Some numismatists classify these as Deep Mirror Prooflike circulation strikes, rather than as Proofs. **uu.** "All 1893-S Morgan dollars were struck from a single die pairing. Genuine 1893-S silver dollars display a diagonal die scratch in the top of the T in LIBERTY. This diagnostic can be seen even on very low-grade examples" (*100 Greatest U.S. Coins*, fourth edition). **vv.** Beware of altered or otherwise fraudulent mintmarks.

1899-O, Micro O
VAM-4, 5, 6, 31, and
32. FS-S1-1899o-501.

	Mintage	Cert	Avg	%MS	VF-20	EF-40	AU-50	MS-60	MS-63	MS-64	MS-64DMPL	MS-65	MS-65DMPL
											PF-60	PF-63	PF-65
1894 (vv)	110,000	3,906	45.8	25%	$925	$1,000	$1,050	$3,100	$4,700	$7,400	$60,000	$37,000	$90,000
	Auctions: $28,200, MS-65, January 2015; $881, VF-35, July 2015; $823, F-15, February 2015; $541, G-6, October 2015												
1894, Proof	972	349	64.1								$2,500	$3,500	$6,500
	Auctions: $44,063, PF-67Cam, April 2013; $14,100, PF-66Cam, October 2014												
1894-O	1,723,000	5,060	50.6	21%	$55	$95	$160	$1,375	$4,500	$8,750	$29,000	$58,000	$65,000
	Auctions: $19,388, MS-64+, June 2015; $2,104, MS-62, July 2015; $212, AU-55, February 2015; $56, VF-30, May 2015												
1894-S	1,260,000	3,427	55.4	63%	$95	$175	$425	$850	$1,275	$2,300	$22,000	$6,300	$35,000
	Auctions: $18,800, MS-66, March 2015; $8,225, MS-65, August 2015; $411, AU-55, February 2015; $212, EF-45, April 2015												
1895, Proof † (ww)	880	376	61.6								$45,000	$50,000	$75,000
	Auctions: $58,750, PF-65Cam, January 2015; $58,750, PF-64Cam, November 2014; $42,300, PF-63Cam, January 2015												
1895-O	450,000	6,078	38.7	2%	$350	$500	$1,100	$16,000	$55,000	$85,000	$140,000	$195,000	$240,000
	Auctions: $79,313, MS-64, January 2015; $24,675, MS-62, July 2015; $16,450, MS-61, November 2016; $852, AU-50, February 2015; $353												
1895-O, Proof (tt)	2–3	5	64.0										
	Auctions: $528,750, PF-66, June 2013												
1895-S	400,000	3,241	35.6	25%	$675	$1,000	$1,500	$4,500	$6,500	$9,000	$19,500	$20,000	$40,000
	Auctions: $11,750, MS-64+, January 2015; $3,055, AU-58, August 2015; $1,087, EF-45, October 2015; $400, F-12, December 2015												
1896	9,976,000	56,047	63.5	99%	$30	$33	$39	$40	$50	$70	$450	$150	$1,200
	Auctions: $3,055, MS-67, January 2015; $764, MS-66+, July 2015; $80, MS-64, March 2015; $94, MS-63, October 2015												
1896, Proof	762	281	64.9								$1,300	$3,000	$5,500
	Auctions: $39,950, PF-68DCam, February 2015; $19,975, PF-68, October 2014; $3,672, PF-63DCam, November 2014; $1,528, PF-60, July 2014												
1896-O	4,900,000	6,926	54.1	20%	$42	$45	$125	$1,700	$6,500	$36,000	$60,000	$160,000	$200,000
	Auctions: $17,038, MS-63, August 2015; $1,500, MS-61, June 2015; $176, AU-55, January 2015; $58, EF-45, October 2015												
1896-S	5,000,000	1,760	48.3	41%	$70	$250	$850	$2,300	$3,750	$5,400	$57,500	$14,000	$100,000
	Auctions: $15,275, MS-65, July 2015; $9,106, MS-64, June 2015; $1,293, AU-55, January 2015; $200, EF-40, December 2015												
1897	2,822,000	17,954	63.3	98%	$30	$33	$39	$50	$70	$90	$500	$240	$3,700
	Auctions: $6,463, MS-67, July 2015; $1,533, MS-66+, January 2015; $235, MS-65, October 2015; $79, MS-64, December 2015												
1897, Proof	731	217	64.4								$1,300	$3,000	$5,500
	Auctions: $7,050, PF-66, June 2015; $4,935, PF-65, February 2015; $2,056, PF-62, September 2014; $881, PF-60, November 2014												
1897-O	4,004,000	6,890	55.2	22%	$30	$50	$85	$975	$4,000	$15,000	$37,500	$62,000	$75,000
	Auctions: $9,988, MS-64, October 2015; $4,700, MS-63, August 2015; $1,182, MS-61, July 2015; $259, AU-58, December 2015												
1897-S	5,825,000	8,512	62.8	93%	$30	$33	$48	$85	$145	$200	$1,100	$525	$3,000
	Auctions: $5,170, MS-67, August 2015; $1,293, MS-66, January 2015; $306, MS-64, October 2015; $46, AU-58, September 2015												
1898	5,884,000	22,920	63.5	98%	$30	$33	$39	$50	$65	$80	$450	$190	$1,300
	Auctions: $5,170, MS-67, January 2015; $206, MS-65, November 2015; $84, MS-64, August 2015; $142, MS-63, May 2015												
1898, Proof	735	254	64.7								$1,300	$3,000	$5,500
	Auctions: $25,850, PF-68Cam, January 2015; $21,150, PF-68, May 2015; $9,400, PF-65DCam, January 2015; $3,055, PF-63, August 2015												
1898-O	4,440,000	73,216	63.9	100%	$30	$33	$39	$50	$70	$80	$450	$130	$1,025
	Auctions: $2,820, MS-67, June 2015; $470, MS-66+, August 2015; $129, MS-65, August 2015; $84, MS-64, January 2015												
1898-S	4,102,000	3,473	59.5	67%	$45	$50	$90	$275	$500	$675	$3,250	$1,500	$13,750
	Auctions: $15,275, MS-66+, August 2015; $764, MS-64, January 2015; $282, MS-61, September 2015; $129, AU-58, March 2015												

† Ranked in the *100 Greatest U.S. Coins* (fourth edition). **tt.** Some numismatists classify these as Deep Mirror Prooflike circulation strikes, rather than as Proofs. **vv.** Beware of altered or otherwise fraudulent mintmarks. **ww.** Mint records indicate that 12,000 1895 Morgan dollars were struck for circulation; however, none have ever been seen. In order to complete their collections, date-by-date collectors are forced to acquire one of the 880 Proofs struck that year, causing much competition for this, "The King of the Morgan Dollars."

**1900-O, Obverse
Die Crack**
VAM-29A. FS-S1-1900o-029a.

1900-O, O Over CC
Various VAMs.
FS-S1-1900o-501.

1901, Doubled Die Reverse
The "Shifted Eagle" variety. VAM-3. FS-S1-1901-003.

	Mintage	Cert	Avg	%MS	VF-20	EF-40	AU-50	MS-60	MS-63	MS-64	MS-64DMPL	MS-65	MS-65DMPL
											PF-60	PF-63	PF-65
1899	330,000	10,468	61.3	87%	$175	$185	$195	$260	$280	$350	$1,200	$820	$2,300
	Auctions: $4,465, MS-66, August 2015; $259, MS-63, October 2015; $141, AU-53, December 2015; $165, EF-45, March 2015												
1899, Proof	846	226	64.2								$1,300	$3,000	$5,500
	Auctions: $22,325, PF-68, June 2015; $9,988, PF-67, June 2015; $2,820, PF-63, January 2015; $1,410, PF-61, July 2015												
1899-O	12,290,000	58,451	63.7	100%	$30	$33	$39	$50	$65	$75	$500	$130	$1,650
	Auctions: $4,230, MS-67, August 2015; $940, MS-66+, January 2015; $282, MS-66, September 2015; $79, MS-64, November 2015												
1899-O, Micro O (xx)	(yy)	614	37.1	3%			$250	$2,500	$4,000	$10,000		$25,000	
	Auctions: $306, AU-55, September 2015; $200, AU-53, October 2015; $69, AU-50, January 2015; $84, EF-45, January 2015												
1899-S	2,562,000	3,112	60.1	74%	$45	$65	$180	$425	$575	$820	$3,800	$1,900	$23,000
	Auctions: $37,600, MS-67, August 2015; $3,995, MS-66, January 2015; $411, MS-61, August 2015; $121, AU-55, February 2015												
1900	8,830,000	33,625	63.6	98%	$30	$33	$39	$45	$50	$70	$9,000	$125	$40,000
	Auctions: $8,225, MS-67, February 2015; $3,290, MS-66+, February 2015; $223, MS-65, October 2015; $63, MS-63, June 2015												
1900, Proof	912	275	64.3								$1,300	$3,000	$5,500
	Auctions: $8,813, PF-67, January 2015; $7,050, PF-65Cam, August 2015; $5,170, PF-65, January 2015; $2,174, PF-62, March 2015												
1900-O	12,590,000	44,969	63.7	99%	$30	$33	$39	$45	$50	$70	$1,100	$125	$5,750
	Auctions: $2,585, MS-67, January 2015; $1,175, MS-66+, September 2015; $135, MS-65, June 2015; $94, MS-63, November 2015												
1900-O, Obverse Die Crack (zz)	(aaa)	71	29.2	6%		$700		—	—				
	Auctions: $306, AU-58, January 2015; $153, EF-40, October 2014; $112, VF-30, February 2015; $94, VF-25, July 2015												
1900-O, O Over CC (bbb)	(aaa)	3,301	59.3	81%	$95	$140	$170	$340	$700	$925	$8,500	$2,050	$19,000
	Auctions: $1,293, MS-64, January 2015; $447, MS-62, December 2015; $235, AU-58, June 2015; $153, EF-40, February 2015												
1900-S	3,540,000	4,160	60.7	75%	$45	$55	$85	$290	$400	$575	$19,000	$1,400	$35,000
	Auctions: $2,233, MS-65+, January 2015; $306, MS-62, June 2015; $129, AU-58, March 2015; $50, EF-45, September 2015												
1901 (ccc)	6,962,000	5,207	53.5	14%	$55	$95	$225	$3,500	$13,000	$54,000	$70,000	$450,000	
	Auctions: $1,880, MS-62, August 2016; $1,058, AU-58, October 2016; $55,200, MS-64, January 2018												
1901, Doubled Die Reverse (ddd)	(eee)	125	41.5	2%	$350	$1,100	$1,900	$14,000	—				
	Auctions: $41,125, MS-62, August 2013												
1901, Proof	813	278	63.8								$1,600	$3,000	$5,500
	Auctions: $28,200, PF-68, May 2015; $12,925, PF-67, August 2015; $7,050, PF-65Cam, June 2015; $2,820, PF-62Cam, July 2015												
1901-O	13,320,000	38,645	63.6	100%	$40	$42	$48	$50	$55	$70	$1,200	$130	$8,500
	Auctions: $19,975, MS-67, March 2015; $4,465, MS-66+, January 2015; $223, MS-65, August 2015; $94, MS-64, June 2015												
1901-S	2,284,000	2,694	58.7	69%	$48	$65	$200	$550	$875	$1,225	$21,000	$2,150	$30,000
	Auctions: $42,300, MS-67, February 2015; $9,400, MS-66, August 2015; $282, AU-58, September 2015; $42, EF-40, January 2015												

xx. The O mintmark is smaller than normal; its punch was probably intended for a Barber half dollar. Five different dies are known, all scarce. **yy.** Included in 1899-O mintage figure. **zz.** A die break is visible from the rim through the date to just below the lower point of the bust. This variety is very rare in Mint State. **aaa.** Included in 1900-O mintage figure. **bbb.** An O mintmark was punched into the die over a previously punched CC mintmark. There are at least seven different dies involved; the one pictured is VAM-9. **ccc.** Beware of a fraudulently removed mintmark intended to make a less valuable 1901-O or 1901-S appear to be a 1901 dollar. **ddd.** Doubling is visible on the eagle's tail feathers, and also on IN GOD WE TRUST, as well as on the arrows, wreath, and bow. This variety is nicknamed the "Shifted Eagle." It is very rare in Mint State. **eee.** Included in circulation-strike 1901 mintage figure.

**1903-S,
Small S
Mintmark**
VAM-2.
FS-S1-1903S-002.

	Mintage	Cert	Avg	%MS	VF-20	EF-40	AU-50	MS-60	MS-63	MS-64	MS-64DMPL	MS-65	MS-65DMPL
											PF-60	PF-63	PF-65
1902	7,994,000	6,168	63.1	95%	$43	$50	$53	$55	$175	$225	$13,000	$350	$20,000
	Auctions: $5,405, MS-67, June 2015; $1,645, MS-66, September 2015; $129, MS-64, August 2015; $106, MS-63, January 2015												
1902, Proof	777	238	64.3								$1,300	$3,000	$5,500
	Auctions: $9,400, PF-67, January 2015; $11,750, PF-66, August 2015; $5,053, PF-65, February 2015; $2,820, PF-63, January 2015												
1902-O	8,636,000	70,628	63.6	100%	$40	$43	$45	$50	$55	$70	$2,800	$160	$13,500
	Auctions: $15,275, MS-67, February 2015; $3,055, MS-66+, June 2015; $200, MS-65+, September 2015; $89, MS-64, May 2015												
1902-S	1,530,000	3,605	57.3	69%	$140	$190	$250	$380	$610	$850	$8,000	$1,900	$14,000
	Auctions: $6,463, MS-66, August 2015; $646, MS-63, June 2015; $259, AU-58, December 2015; $79, F-12, January 2015												
1903	4,652,000	13,030	63.4	95%	$50	$53	$55	$78	$100	$120	$7,500	$225	$22,500
	Auctions: $3,526, MS-67, August 2015; $1,293, MS-66+, October 2015; $223, MS-65, February 2015; $89, MS-64, December 2015												
1903, Proof	755	264	64.2								$1,300	$3,000	$5,500
	Auctions: $3,995, PF-64, January 2015; $3,819, PF-64, March 2015; $3,055, PF-63, August 2015; $1,998, PF-62, January 2015												
1903-O	4,450,000	8,131	63.0	98%	$350	$375	$385	$415	$440	$450	$1,800	$635	$6,400
	Auctions: $3,760, MS-67, January 2015; $2,585, MS-66+, June 2015; $823, MS-65, September 2015; $376, MS-64, December 2015												
1903-S	1,241,000	2,962	32.3	10%	$275	$375	$1,600	$5,000	$7,300	$8,150	$15,000	$10,000	$38,000
	Auctions: $7,638, MS-64, January 2015; $6,770, MS-63, January 2015; $2,115, AU-55, October 2015; $188, VF-35, November 2015												
1903-S, Small S (fff)	(ggg)	144	23.5	1%			$6,400	$12,000	$25,000	$40,000		$60,000	
	Auctions: $588, VF-30, January 2015; $329, VF-20, January 2015; $112, VG-10, May 2015; $94, G-4, February 2015												
1904	2,788,000	4,753	61.8	89%	$40	$47	$50	$100	$250	$500	$42,500	$1,850	$60,000
	Auctions: $9,988, MS-66, August 2015; $2,233, MS-65, September 2015; $376, MS-64, January 2015; $79, AU-58, October 2015												
1904, Proof	650	291	63.9								$1,300	$3,000	$5,500
	Auctions: $22,325, PF-68, May 2015; $7,638, PF-66, March 2015; $3,995, PF-64+, February 2015; $2,820, PF-64, January 2015												
1904-O	3,720,000	137,541	63.7	100%	$43	$45	$48	$50	$65	$75	$450	$120	$1,150
	Auctions: $4,465, MS-67, January 2015; $400, MS-66, September 2015; $153, MS-65, July 2015; $74, MS-64+, February 2015												
1904-S	2,304,000	2,198	46.0	30%	$80	$200	$600	$2,600	$4,500	$5,000	$13,000	$8,000	$22,000
	Auctions: $16,450, MS-66, June 2015; $4,935, MS-64, August 2015; $2,350, AU-58, January 2015; $200, EF-45, December 2015												
1921	44,690,000	114,656	63.4	99%	$28	$30	$32	$35	$40	$55	$7,750	$120	$11,500
	Auctions: $3,055, MS-66+, January 2015; $182, MS-65, May 2015; $100, MS-64, September 2015; $129, MS-62, August 2015												
1921, Zerbe Proof (hhh)	150–250	75	64.0								$4,000	$5,500	$12,000
	Auctions: $29,375, PF-66, August 2015; $11,163, PF-65, June 2015; $11,163, PF-64, January 2015; $9,401, SP-63, August 2015												
1921, Chapman Proof (iii)	25–40	1	66.0								$20,000	$35,000	$75,000
	Auctions: $61,688, PF-65, April 2013												
1921-D	20,345,000	17,318	62.9	94%	$32	$34	$35	$50	$75	$140	$7,500	$265	$12,000
	Auctions: $3,760, MS-66, August 2015; $259, MS-65, August 2015; $112, MS-64, December 2015; $100, AU-53, January 2015												
1921-S	21,695,000	13,805	62.7	95%	$32	$34	$35	$50	$75	$110	$12,000	$685	$30,000
	Auctions: $3,819, MS-66, January 2015; $852, MS-65, February 2015; $84, MS-64, May 2015; $69, MS-63, October 2015												
1921-S, Zerbe Proof (hhh)	1–2	0	n/a										$140,000
	Auctions: $117,500, PF-65, August 2013												

fff. The S mintmark is smaller than normal, possibly intended to be punched into a Barber half dollar die. **ggg.** Included in 1903-S mintage figure. **hhh.** "Pieces called Zerbe Proofs are simply circulation strikes with a semi-prooflike character, not as nice as on the earlier-noted [mirrorlike] prooflike pieces, struck from dies that were slightly polished, but that retained countless minute striae and preparation lines. In the view of the writer [Bowers], Zerbe Proofs have no basis in numismatic fact or history, although opinions differ on the subject. It seems highly unlikely that these were produced as Proofs for collectors. If indeed they were furnished to Farran Zerbe, a leading numismatic entrepreneur of the era, it is likely that they were simply regular production pieces. Zerbe had a fine collection and certainly knew what a brilliant Proof should look like, and he never would have accepted such pieces as mirror Proofs" (*A Guide Book of Morgan Silver Dollars*, sixth edition). **iii.** Breen stated that 12 Chapman Proofs were minted (*Walter Breen's Encyclopedia of U.S. and Colonial Proof Coins, 1792–1977*); Bowers estimates fewer than 30 (*A Guide Book of Morgan Silver Dollars*, sixth edition). These are sometimes called *Chapman Proofs* because Philadelphia coin dealer Henry Chapman advertised them for sale within a few months of their production.

PEACE (1921–1935)

Designer: *Anthony de Francisci.* **Weight:** *26.73 grams.*
Composition: *.900 silver, .100 copper (net weight .77344 oz. pure silver).*
Diameter: *38.1 mm.* **Edge:** *Reeded.* **Mints:** *Philadelphia, Denver, and San Francisco.*

Mintmark location is on the reverse, to the left of the tail feathers.

Circulation Strike

Proof

History. In 1921, following the melting of more than 270 million silver dollars as legislated by the Pittman Act of 1918, the U.S. Treasury struck millions more silver dollars of the Morgan type while a new Peace dollar was in development. Sculptor and medalist Anthony de Francisci created the Peace design, originally intended as a commemorative of the end of the hostilities of the Great War. The obverse features a flowing-haired Miss Liberty wearing a spiked tiara, and the reverse an eagle perched before the rising sun. The designer's monogram is located in the field of the coin under the neck of Miss Liberty. Coins of 1921 were struck in high relief; this caused weakness at the centers, so the design was changed to low relief in 1922. The dollars were struck until 1928, then again in 1934 and 1935. Legislation dated August 3, 1964, authorized the coinage of 45 million silver dollars, and 316,076 dollars of the Peace design dated 1964 were struck at the Denver Mint in 1965. Plans for completing this coinage were subsequently abandoned and all of these coins were melted. None were preserved or released for circulation; details are found in *A Guide Book of Peace Dollars* (Burdette).

Striking and Sharpness. Peace dollars of 1921 are always lightly struck at the center of the obverse, with hair detail not showing in an area. The size of this flat spot can vary. For this and other Peace dollars, check the hair detail at the center and, on the reverse, the feathers on the eagle. Many coins are struck from overly used dies, giving a grainy appearance to the fields, particularly the obverse. On many Peace dollars tiny white "milk spots" are seen, left over from when they were struck; these are not as desirable in the marketplace as unspotted coins.

Availability. All dates and mintmarks are readily available. Although some are well worn, they are generally collected in EF and finer grades. MS coins are available for each, with the 1934-S considered to be the key date. San Francisco issues of the 1920s, except for 1926-S, are often heavily bagmarked from coming into contact with other coins during shipment, storage, and other handling. The appearance of luster varies from issue to issue and can be deeply frosty, or—in the instance of Philadelphia Mint coins of 1928, 1934, and 1935—satiny or "creamy."

Proofs. Some Sandblast Proofs were made in 1921 and a limited issue in 1922 in high relief. These are rare today. Seemingly, a few Satin Proofs were also made in 1921. Sandblast Proofs of 1922 have a peculiar whitish surface in most instances, sometimes interrupted by small dark flecks or spots. There are a number of impostors among certified "Proofs."

Note: Values of common-date silver coins have been based on the current bullion price of silver, $17 per ounce, and may vary with the prevailing spot price.

GRADING STANDARDS

MS-60 to 70 (Mint State). *Obverse:* At MS-60, some abrasion and contact marks are evident, most noticeably on the cheek and on the hair to the right of the face and forehead. Luster is present, but may be dull or lifeless. At MS-63, contact marks are extensive but not distracting. Abrasion still is evident, but less than at lower levels. MS-64 coins are slightly finer. Some Peace dollars have whitish "milk spots" in the field; while these are

1921. Graded MS-64.

not caused by handling, but seem to have been from liquid at the mint or in storage, coins with these spots are rarely graded higher than MS–63 or 64. An MS-65 coin may have minor abrasion, but contact marks are so minute as to require magnification. Luster should be full and rich on earlier issues, and either frosty or satiny on later issues, depending on the date and mint. *Reverse:* At MS-60 some abrasion and contact marks are evident, most noticeably on the eagle's shoulder and nearby. Otherwise, comments apply as for the obverse.

Illustrated coin: Note the scattered marks that are practically definitive of the grade. The high relief of this particular year results in light striking at the center; this is normal and not to be mistaken for wear.

AU-50, 53, 55, 58 (About Uncirculated). *Obverse:* Light wear is seen on the cheek and the highest-relief areas of the hair. The neck truncation edge also shows wear. At AU-58, the luster is extensive, but incomplete. At AU–50 and 53, luster is less but still present. *Reverse:* Wear is evident on the eagle's shoulder and back. Otherwise, comments apply as for the obverse.

1934-S. Graded AU-53.

Illustrated coin: This coin shows medium and somewhat mottled toning. Luster is still seen in protected areas.

EF-40, 45 (Extremely Fine). *Obverse:* Further wear is seen on the highest-relief areas of the hair, with many strands now blended together. Some luster can usually be seen in protected areas on many coins, but is not needed to define the EF-40 and 45 grades. *Reverse:* Further wear is seen on the eagle, and the upper 60% of the feathers have most detail gone, except for the delineation of the edges of rows of feathers. PEACE shows light wear.

1928. Graded EF-40.

VF-20, 30 (Very Fine). *Obverse:* More wear shows on the hair, with more tiny strands now blended into heavy strands. *Reverse:* Further wear has resulted in very little feather detail except on the neck and tail. The rock shows wear. PEACE is slightly weak.

1934-D. Graded VF-30.

F-12, 15 (Fine). *Obverse:* Most of the hair is worn flat, with thick strands blended together, interrupted by fewer divisions than on higher grades. The rim is full. *Reverse:* Fewer feather details show. Most of the eagle, except for the tail feathers and some traces of feathers at the neck, is in outline only. The rays between the left side of the eagle and PEACE are weak and some details are worn away.

The Peace dollar is seldom collected in grades lower than F-12.

1921. Graded F-12.

PF-60 to 70 (Proof). *Obverse and Reverse:* Proofs of both types usually display very few handling marks or defects. To qualify as Satin PF-65 or Sandblast PF-65 or finer, contact marks must be microscopic.

1921. Satin Finish Proof.

1921, Line Through L
VAM-3. FS-S1-1921-003.

| | Mintage | Cert | Avg | %MS | VF-20 | EF-40 | AU-50 | MS-60 | MS-62 | MS-63 | MS-64 | MS-65 | MS-66 |
											PF-60	PF-63	PF-65
1921, High Relief	1,006,473	15,809	58.8	74%	$110	$135	$150	$260	$350	$425	$800	$1,600	$5,000
	Auctions: $70,500, MS-67, August 2015; $5,875, MS-66, August 2016; $4,700, MS-66, January 2015; $2,820, MS-66, November 2016												
1921, High Relief, Line Through L (a)	**(b)**	57	60.7	79%			$225	$315	$400	$500	$900	$2,400	
	Auctions: $940, MS-63, June 2013												
1921, Satin Finish Proof	10–20	17	63.6								$15,000	$30,000	$75,000
	Auctions: $32,200, PF-64, July 2009												
1921, Sandblast Finish Proof	5–8	3	64.0										$85,000
	Auctions: $99,875, PF-66, January 2014; $129,250, PF-64, August 2014												

a. A ray runs through the first L in DOLLAR, instead of behind it. b. Included in 1921, High Relief, mintage figure.

1922, Die Break in Field
VAM-1F. FS-S1-1922-001f.

1922, Die Break at Ear
The "Ear Ring" variety.
VAM-2A. FS-S1-1922-002a.

1922, Die Break in Hair
The 1922 "Extra Hair" variety.
VAM-2C. FS-S1-1922-002c.

1922, Die Break on Cheek
The "Scar Cheek" variety.
VAM-5A. FS-S1-1922-005a.

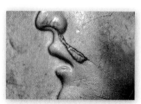

1922, Die Break at Nose
The "Moustache" variety.
VAM-12A. FS-S1-1922-012a.

	Mintage	Cert	Avg	%MS	VF-20	EF-40	AU-50	MS-60	MS-62	MS-63	MS-64 PF-60	MS-65 PF-63	MS-66 PF-65
1922, High Relief (c)	35,401	0	n/a				—						
Auctions: No auction records available.													
1922, Normal Relief	51,737,000	195	63.5	99%	$25	$27	$28	$30	$32	$33	$45	$110	$375
Auctions: $11,163, MS-67, August 2015; $1,175, MS-66, March 2015; $176, MS-65, February 2015; $188, MS-64, October 2015													
1922, Die Break in Field (d)	(e)	60	56.0	32%				$400	$800	$1,750	$2,500		
Auctions: $1,528, MS-64, December 2013; $646, MS-63, July 2016; $153, MS-61, July 2015; $58, AU-55, September 2014													
1922, Die Break at Ear (f)	(e)	64	58.5	52%				$290	$650	$1,400	$2,300		
Auctions: $306, MS-64, July 2016; $1,293, MS-63, December 2013													
1922, Die Break in Hair (g)	(e)	231	57.2	52%				$90	$180	$300	$385		
Auctions: $153, MS-64, February 2015; $76, MS-62, March 2015; $74, MS-62, October 2014; $69, MS-61, September 2014													
1922, Die Break on Cheek (h)	(e)	37	59.6	68%				$190	$400	$550			
Auctions: $259, MS-63, February 2015; $165, MS-63, February 2015; $165, MS-61, February 2015; $200, AU-58, September 2014													
1922, Die Break at Nose (i)	(e)	148	58.4	45%				$90	$200	$325	$500	$975	
Auctions: $223, MS-62, January 2015; $212, MS-62, March 2015; $129, AU-58, February 2015; $112, AU-58, September 2015													
1922, High Relief, Sandblast Finish Proof	10–15	11	65.0										$200,000
Auctions: $329,000, PF-67, January 2014													
1922, Low Relief, Sandblast Finish Proof	3–6	2	65.0										—
Auctions: $35,200, PF-65, November 1988													
1922, Low Relief, Satin Finish Proof	3–6	1	63.0										$150,000
Auctions: $44,850, PF-60, November 2009													
1922-D	15,063,000	7,380	63.0	94%	$28	$30	$33	$50	$55	$75	$125	$500	$1,500
Auctions: $39,950, MS-67, August 2015; $7,050, MS-66+, February 2015; $734, MS-65+, October 2015; $153, MS-64, January 2015													
1922-S	17,475,000	6,180	62.2	92%	$28	$30	$33	$50	$60	$90	$225	$1,400	$28,500
Auctions: $8,813, MS-66, January 2015; $4,230, MS-65+, August 2015; $259, MS-64, February 2015; $36, AU-58, September 2015													

c. 1 example is known. **d.** A die break is visible in the field above DOLLAR. "This variety has turned out to be much rarer than previously thought, and is very scarce in grades above EF" (*Cherrypickers' Guide to Rare Die Varieties*, sixth edition, volume II). **e.** Included in 1922, Normal Relief, mintage figure. **f.** A major die break near Liberty's ear, dangling down to her neck, gives this variety its nickname, the "Ear Ring." Several die states are known. **g.** An irregular line of raised metal runs along the back of Liberty's hair. This is called the "Extra Hair" variety. Several die states are known. **h.** Liberty's cheek has a raised, almost triangular chunk of metal along a vertical die break. Also, the reverse is lightly tripled. This variety, called the "Scarface," is very scarce in Mint State. **i.** A die break is visible running from Liberty's nose along the top of her mouth. This is known as the "Moustache" variety.

1923, Die Break at Jaw
The "Whisker Jaw" variety.
VAM-1A. FS-S1-1923-001a.

1923, Die Break in Hair
The 1923 "Extra Hair"
variety. VAM-1B.
FS-S1-1923-001b.

1923, Die Break on
O in DOLLAR
The "Tail on O" variety.
VAM-1C. FS-S1-1923-001c.

1923, Die Break on Cheek
The "Whisker Cheek" variety.
VAM-1D. FS-S1-1923-001d.

1923, Doubled Die Obverse
The "Double Tiara" variety. VAM-2. FS-S1-1923-002.

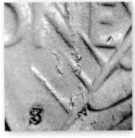

1923-S, Pitted Reverse
VAM-1C. FS-S1-1923S-001c.

1924, Die Break on Wing
The "Broken Wing" variety.
VAM-5A. FS-S1-1924-005a.

	Mintage	Cert	Avg	%MS	VF-20	EF-40	AU-50	MS-60	MS-62	MS-63	MS-64	MS-65	MS-66
											PF-60	PF-63	PF-65
1923	30,800,000	286,626	63.7	100%	$25	$27	$28	$30	$32	$33	$45	$110	$375
	Auctions: $4,465, MS-67, January 2015; $940, MS-66+, February 2015; $64, MS-64, May 2015; $40, MS-62, July 2015												
1923, Die Break at Jaw (j)	(k)	207	61.6	82%			$80	$125	$175	$265	$550		$1,250
	Auctions: $282, MS-65, February 2015; $141, MS-64, March 2015; $129, MS-64, January 2015; $76, MS-62, March 2015												
1923, Die Break in Hair (l)	(k)	80	61.7	88%			$125	$200	$300	$400	$600		
	Auctions: $400, MS-65, February 2015; $59, MS-64, September 2014; $115, MS-63, August 2014; $84, MS-63, September 2014												
1923, Die Break on O (m)	(k)	68	58.8	72%			$275	$650	$1,150	$1,800			
	Auctions: $2,468, MS-65, April 2014; $423, MS-64, July 2016												
1923, Die Break on Cheek (n)	(k)	103	60.3	67%			$165	$250	$350	$475	$875		
	Auctions: $206, MS-64, March 2015; $235, MS-63, February 2015; $165, MS-62, August 2015; $200, AU-55, June 2015												
1923, DblDie Obverse (o)	(k)	68	61.8	81%			$58	$75	$100	$160	$375		
	Auctions: $329, MS-65, February 2015; $129, MS-62, January 2015; $74, MS-62, July 2015; $129, AU-58, February 2015												
1923-D	6,811,000	3,620	62.1	89%	$28	$30	$40	$75	$90	$155	$350	$950	$3,500
	Auctions: $17,625, MS-66+, August 2015; $282, MS-64, September 2015; $123, MS-63, October 2015; $46, AU-55, January 2015												
1923-S	19,020,000	6,814	62.0	91%	$28	$30	$36	$50	$70	$85	$325	$2,500	$29,000
	Auctions: $4,230, MS-65, January 2015; $705, MS-64, February 2015; $112, MS-63, June 2015; $38, AU-58, November 2015												
1923-S, Pitted Reverse (p)	(q)	35	58.2	54%			$125	$250	—	$450	$975		
	Auctions: $282, MS-63, December 2013												
1924	11,811,000	46,403	63.8	99%	$25	$28	$29	$30	$32	$33	$45	$110	$375
	Auctions: $12,925, MS-67, August 2015; $1,293, MS-66+, January 2015; $217, MS-65, September 2015; $94, MS-64+, November 2015												
1924, Die Break on Wing (r)	(s)	52	61.3	79%			$130	$200	$375	$475			
	Auctions: $2,233, MS-67, January 2015; $423, MS-64, January 2015; $282, MS-63, February 2015; $106, MS-62, August 2014												
1924-S	1,728,000	4,350	60.4	72%	$28	$40	$60	$235	$325	$450	$950	$6,200	$41,000
	Auctions: $11,163, MS-65, June 2015; $9,400, MS-65, August 2015; $4,230, MS-64+, January 2015; $2,233, MS-64, July 2016												

j. A die break bridges Liberty's cheek and jaw. This is the "Whisker Jaw" variety. **k.** Included in 1923 mintage figure. **l.** A significant die break runs diagonally across the strands of Liberty's hair; die breaks may also be visible toward the back of her hair. This variety is nicknamed the 1923 "Extra Hair." **m.** A die break trails from the O of DOLLAR. This variety, called the "Tail on O," is very rare in any grade. **n.** A die break runs down Liberty's cheek toward the junction of the chin and neck. This is the "Whisker Cheek" variety. **o.** Doubling is most evident in the wide spread on the rays of Liberty's tiara, especially those under the BER of LIBERTY. This is the "Double Tiara" variety. **p.** "Pitting runs from the eagle's back tail-feathers, just to the right of the mintmark, upward to the N in ONE. . . . This is the most important Pitted Reverse variety in the Peace dollar series" (*Cherrypickers' Guide to Rare Die Varieties*, sixth edition, volume II). **q.** Included in 1923-S mintage figure. **r.** A dramatic die break runs down and across the entire width of the eagle's back. This is the "Broken Wing" variety. **s.** Included in 1924 mintage figure.

1925, Missing Ray
VAM-5. FS-S1-1925-005.

1926-S, Reverse Dot
The "Extra Berry" variety.
VAM-4. FS-S1-1926S-004.

1934-D, Doubled Die Obverse, Small D
VAM-4. FS-S1-1934D-004.

	Mintage	Cert	Avg	%MS	VF-20	EF-40	AU-50	MS-60	MS-62	MS-63	MS-64	MS-65	MS-66
											PF-60	PF-63	PF-65
1925	10,198,000	51,997	63.9	99%	$25	$28	$29	$30	$32	$35	$45	$110	$400
	Auctions: $5,405, MS-67, January 2015; $1,528, MS-66, June 2015; $123, MS-65+, March 2015; $74, MS-64, February 2015												
1925, Missing Ray (t)	(u)	96	62.8	92%			$65	$85	$100	$145	$250	$400	
	Auctions: $129, MS-64, December 2013; $200, MS-63, February 2015; $59, MS-62, September 2014; $47, MS-62, September 2014												
1925-S	1,610,000	6,315	61.6	84%	$28	$32	$45	$90	$180	$250	$625	$23,000	$70,000
	Auctions: $30,550, MS-65; $24,675, MS-65, January 2015; $12,925, MS-65, September 2016; $3,055, MS-64, January 2015												
1926	1,939,000	9,565	63.2	97%	$28	$32	$37	$50	$75	$100	$125	$425	$1,400
	Auctions: $3,760, MS-66, August 2015; $376, MS-65, September 2015; $106, MS-64, June 2015; $94, AU-58, January 2015												
1926-D	2,348,700	3,746	62.2	86%	$28	$32	$44	$100	$140	$220	$410	$1,000	$2,500
	Auctions: $47,000, MS-67, August 2015; $3,760, MS-66, August 2015; $1,528, MS-65, January 2015; $153, MS-63, May 2015												
1926-S	6,980,000	6,220	62.3	89%	$28	$32	$38	$60	$75	$100	$240	$775	$2,850
	Auctions: $6,463, MS-66, August 2015; $1,058, MS-65, September 2015; $206, MS-64, November 2015; $84, MS-63, January 2015												
1926-S, Reverse Dot (v)	(w)	46	57.0	54%			$55	$90	$140	$200	$360		
	Auctions: $165, MS-64, September 2014; $223, MS-63, February 2015; $129, MS-63, September 2015; $61, AU-58, November 2014												
1927	848,000	6,122	62.0	88%	$39	$42	$50	$80	$120	$185	$410	$1,300	$21,000
	Auctions: $23,500, MS-66, September 2015; $3,290, MS-65, January 2015; $79, MS-61, December 2015; $54, AU-58, March 2015												
1927-D	1,268,900	3,570	60.8	77%	$39	$45	$75	$200	$250	$390	$1,000	$3,300	$28,000
	Auctions: $9,988, MS-65+, January 2015; $793, MS-64, August 2015; $79, AU-55, March 2015; $74, AU-53, September 2015												
1927-S	866,000	4,076	61.0	80%	$39	$45	$75	$190	$265	$500	$900	$7,500	$43,000
	Auctions: $8,225, MS-65, January 2015; $4,700, MS-65, March 2016; $1,763, MS-64, June 2015; $470, MS-63+, October 2015												
1928	360,649	8,389	58.6	65%	$275	$320	$340	$425	$500	$625	$850	$3,200	$28,000
	Auctions: $39,950, MS-66, August 2015; $7,050, MS-65, January 2015; $400, AU-58, May 2015; $235, EF-40, February 2015												
1928-S	1,632,000	5,547	60.5	75%	$39	$48	$65	$210	$300	$400	$975	$1,600	$50,000
	Auctions: $42,300, MS-65+, August 2015; $2,585, MS-64+, February 2015; $470, MS-63, November 2015; $94, AU-55, May 2015												
1934	954,057	5,649	62.3	88%	$44	$45	$50	$120	$170	$200	$325	$650	$2,100
	Auctions: $11,750, MS-66+, January 2015; $1,175, MS-65, September 2015; $494, MS-64, May 2015; $69, AU-58, December 2015												
1934-D (x)	1,569,500	5,256	60.8	77%	$44	$45	$50	$130	$250	$325	$500	$1,200	$3,750
	Auctions: $10,575, MS-66, August 2015; $1,880, MS-64+, June 2015; $306, MS-63, November 2015; $64, AU-58, February 2015												
1934-D, DblDie Obv, Sm D (y)	(z)	37	53.5	27%	$115	$185	$375	$750	$900	$1,650			
	Auctions: $999, MS-63, January 2015; $306, MS-62, September 2015; $364, AU-58, January 2015; $353, AU-55, February 2015												
1934-S	1,011,000	3,923	50.1	33%	$80	$175	$500	$2,300	$3,200	$4,250	$6,300	$8,200	$26,000
	Auctions: $32,900, MS-66, August 2015; $9,988, MS-65+, January 2015; $6,463, MS-64, February 2015; $118, EF-40, October 2015												
1935	1,576,000	7,302	62.6	90%	$44	$45	$50	$80	$90	$120	$250	$625	$1,900
	Auctions: $9,988, MS-66+, June 2015; $517, MS-65, October 2015; $129, MS-63, February 2015; $94, MS-62, July 2015												
1935-S (aa)	1,964,000	3,651	60.9	79%	$44	$50	$88	$260	$325	$425	$525	$1,075	$2,650
	Auctions: $16,450, MS-66+, August 2015; $881, MS-64, February 2015; $400, MS-63, May 2015; $153, AU-58, September 2015												
1964-D (bb)	316,076	0	n/a										
	Auctions: No auction records available.												

t. This variety is the result of a reverse die polished with too much gusto. The partially effaced remains of bold clash marks are evident, but the topmost internal ray is missing. **u.** Included in 1925 mintage figure. **v.** A raised circular dot of metal is visible to the left of the bottom olive leaf. This is nicknamed the "Extra Berry" variety. **w.** Included in 1926-S mintage figure. **x.** Varieties exist with small and large mintmarks. **y.** The obverse shows strong doubling on most letters of IN GOD WE TRUST, the rays on the right, and especially on Liberty's profile. The mintmark is a small D, shaped much like that of the 1920s-era D punches. **z.** Included in 1934-D mintage figure. **aa.** Varieties exist with either three or four rays below ONE. They are valued equally in the marketplace. **bb.** The entire mintage of 1964-D Peace dollars was melted by government order. Deceptive reproductions exist.

Modern Dollars
1971 to Date

AN OVERVIEW OF MODERN DOLLARS

After the last Peace dollars rolled off the presses at the San Francisco and Philadelphia mints in 1935, there was a long lapse in silver dollar coinage until 1965. In that year the Denver Mint struck Peace dollars dated 1964—the start of production of 45 million coins authorized by legislation of August 3, 1964. This coinage ultimately was stopped after 316,076 of the new Peace dollars were made; they were held back from being released into circulation and melted. It would be another six years before the United States had a new dollar coin, and it would not be silver.

Production of the next dollar started in 1971. The coin was the size of the 20th century's earlier silver dollars, but made in copper-nickel for circulation (and, in much smaller quantities, in .400 fine silver for collectors). Its motifs honor the late President Dwight D. Eisenhower, and the Apollo 11 spaceflight that had landed the first men on the Moon in 1969.

Silver dollars had long since disappeared from circulation, but there was demand for dollar coins in Las Vegas, Reno, and other centers of legalized gambling. Casinos otherwise had to depend on gaming chips and tokens.

The Eisenhower dollar was minted from 1971 to 1978, with those made in 1975 and 1976 being dual-dated 1776–1976 for the national bicentennial. In 1979 the "Ike" dollar was replaced by a smaller-format coin, the Susan B. Anthony dollar, honoring the famous women's-rights leader. Its reverse design shows an eagle landing on the Moon, similar to that of its predecessor (this design had in turn been based on the official insignia of the Apollo 11 mission). The Anthony dollar was struck in 1979, 1980, and 1981; then, in 1999 an additional final mintage of more than 40 million coins was produced to meet the needs of the vending-machine industry until distribution of the next year's new-design dollars could begin.

Presidential golden dollars cover the span from the 1st president of the United States, George Washington, to the 40th president, Ronald Reagan.

The year 2000 marked the debut of the first of several types of "golden" dollars, so called for the lustrous color of their manganese-brass surfaces. First came the Sacagawea dollar, minted from 2000 to 2008, with its conceptualized portrait of the young Shoshone Native American interpreter and guide who assisted the Lewis and Clark expedition of the early 1800s. A series of Native American dollars, each celebrating a different aspect of Native culture and historical importance, which began in 2009 and is ongoing today, is an offshoot of the Sacagawea dollar. And, since 2007, the golden-dollar format has been the canvas for a series of presidential portrait dollars honoring the nation's chief executives.

FOR THE COLLECTOR AND INVESTOR: MODERN DOLLARS AS A SPECIALTY

Eisenhower dollars, Susan B. Anthony dollars, and the golden dollars of various types are all easily found in today's marketplace. Dealers often have an abundance on hand of every date, mint, and most varieties. Banks sometimes have small quantities of Eisenhower or Anthony dollars. The current series are available directly from the U.S. Mint in collector formats and in rolls and bags of circulation strikes.

Eisenhower dollars are easily obtained in choice Mint State, although some of the coins made for circulation, especially of the earlier years, tend to be blemished with contact marks from jostling other coins during minting, transportation, and storage. Gems can be elusive. The Mint issued many options for collectors, including Proofs and .400 fine silver issues. Specialists look for die varieties including modified features, doubled dies, changes in depth of relief in the design, and other popular anomalies and variations that increase the challenge of building an extensive collection in what is otherwise a fairly short coinage series. Some Denver Mint dollars of 1974 and 1977 are also known to be struck in error, in silver clad composition rather than the intended copper-nickel.

Anthony dollars, too, are easy to assemble into a complete, high-grade collection of dates and mints. Specialists can focus on both varieties of 1979-P (Narrow Rim and Wide Rim), and varieties of S mintmark styles among the Proofs. Even these are common enough to easily acquire. Those seeking a harder challenge can search for the elusive 1980-S, Repunched Mintmark, Proof.

The Sacagawea dollar series includes several uncommon varieties that make an otherwise easy-to-collect type more challenging. The 2000-P coins include popular die varieties as detailed herein. Later dates were struck in smaller quantities and not issued for circulation, but still are readily available in high grades in the numismatic marketplace.

Native American dollars of 2009 to date are readily available in high grades.

The Presidential dollar series includes some error varieties with plain edges, instead of the normal lettered edge. These can be added to a date-and-mintmark collection for reasonable premiums. Otherwise the entire series is readily collectible from the secondary market and, for the current year of issue, in quantity directly from the U.S. Mint.

EISENHOWER (1971–1978)

Designer: *Frank Gasparro.* **Weight:** *Silver issue—24.59 grams; copper-nickel issue—22.68 grams.*
Composition: *Silver issue—40% silver, 60% copper, consisting of outer layers of .800 silver,*
.200 copper bonded to inner core of .209 silver, .791 copper (net weight .3161 oz. pure silver);
copper-nickel issue—outer layers of .750 copper, .250 nickel bonded to inner core of pure copper.
Diameter: *38.1 mm.* **Edge:** *Reeded.* **Mints:** *Philadelphia, Denver, and San Francisco.*

Circulation Strike

Proof

Mintmark location is on the obverse, between the bust and the date.

Bicentennial variety: Designers: *Frank Gasparro and Dennis R. Williams.*
Weight: *Silver issue—24.59 grams; copper-nickel issue—22.68 grams.*
Composition: *Silver issue—outer layers of .800 silver, .200 copper bonded
to inner core of .209 silver, .791 copper (net weight .3161 oz. pure silver);
copper-nickel issue—outer layers of .750 copper, .250 nickel bonded to inner core of pure copper.*
Diameter: *38.1 mm.* **Edge:** *Reeded.* **Mints:** *Philadelphia, Denver, and San Francisco.*

Bicentennial
variety

Bicentennial
variety, Proof

History. Honoring both President Dwight D. Eisenhower and the first landing of man on the Moon, this coin is the work of Chief Engraver Frank Gasparro, whose initials are on the truncation of the president's neck and below the eagle. The reverse is an adaptation of the official Apollo 11 insignia. Collectors' coins were struck in 40% silver composition and sold by the Mint at a premium, and the circulation issue (for years a staple of the casino trade) was made in copper-nickel.

The dies for the Eisenhower dollar were modified several times by changing the relief, strengthening the design, and making Earth (above the eagle) more clearly defined.

Low-relief (Variety 1) dies, with a flattened Earth and three islands off the coast of Florida, were used for all copper-nickel issues of 1971, Uncirculated silver coins of 1971, and most copper-nickel coins of 1972.

High-relief (Variety 2) dies, with a round Earth and weak or indistinct islands, were used for all Proofs of 1971, all silver issues of 1972, and the reverse of some exceptional and scarce Philadelphia copper-nickel coins of 1972.

Improved high-relief reverse dies (Variety 3) were used for late-1972 Philadelphia copper-nickel coins and for all subsequent issues. Modified high-relief dies were also used on all issues beginning in 1973.

A few 1974-D and 1977-D dollars were made, in error, in silver clad composition.

A special reverse design was selected for the nation's Bicentennial. Nearly a thousand entries were submitted after the Treasury announced an open competition in October 1973. After the field was narrowed down to 12 semifinalists, the judges chose a rendition of the Liberty Bell superimposed on the Moon to appear on the dollar coins. The obverse remained unchanged except for the dual date 1776–1976, which appeared on all dollars made during 1975 and 1976. These dual-dated coins were included in the various offerings of Proof and Uncirculated coins made by the Mint. They were also struck for general circulation. The lettering was slightly modified early in 1975 to produce a more attractive design.

Striking and Sharpness. Striking generally is very good. For circulation strikes, on the obverse check the high parts of the portrait, and on the reverse, the details of the eagle. Nearly all Proofs are well struck and of high quality.

Availability. MS coins are common in the marketplace, although several early varieties are elusive at MS-65 or higher grades. Lower grades are not widely collected. Proofs were made of the various issues (both copper-nickel clad and silver clad from 1971 to 1976; copper-nickel only in 1977 and 1978). All are readily available in the marketplace today.

Note: Values of common-date silver coins have been based on the current bullion price of silver, $17 per ounce, and may vary with the prevailing spot price.

GRADING STANDARDS

MS-60 to 70 (Mint State). *Obverse:* At MS-60, some abrasion and contact marks are evident, most noticeably on the cheek, jaw, and temple. Luster is present, but may be dull or lifeless. At MS-63, contact marks are extensive but not distracting. Abrasion still is evident, but less than at lower levels. MS-64 coins are slightly finer. An MS-65 coin may have minor abrasion, but contact marks are so minute as to require magnification. Luster

1971-S. Graded MS-65.

should be full and rich. *Reverse:* At MS-60, some abrasion and contact marks are evident, most noticeably on the eagle's breast, head, and talons. Otherwise, the same comments apply as for the obverse.

AU-50, 53, 55, 58 (About Uncirculated). *Obverse:* Light wear is seen on the higher-relief areas of the portrait. At AU-58, the luster is extensive, but incomplete. At AU–50 and 53, luster is less but still present. *Reverse:* Further wear is evident on the eagle, particularly the head, breast, talons, and tops of the wings. Otherwise, the same comments apply as for the obverse.

The Eisenhower dollar is seldom collected in grades lower than AU-50.

1972. Graded AU-50.

PF-60 to 70 (Proof). *Obverse and Reverse:* Proofs that are extensively cleaned and have many hairlines, or that are dull and grainy, are lower level, such as PF–60 to 62. There are not many of these in the marketplace. With medium hairlines and good reflectivity, assigned grades of PF–63 or 64 are appropriate. With relatively few hairlines a rating of PF-65 can be given. PF-66 may have hairlines so delicate that magnification is needed

1776–1976-S, Bicentennial. Graded PF-68.

to see them. Above that, a Proof should be free of any hairlines or other problems.

1971-S, Silver Clad, Repunched Mintmark

1971-S, Silver Clad, Polished Die
The "Peg Leg R" variety.

1971-S, Silver Clad, Doubled Die Obverse, Proof

1972-S, Silver Clad, Doubled Die Obverse, Proof

1973-S, Silver Clad, Doubled Die Obverse, Proof

| | Mintage | Cert | Avg | %MS | EF-40 | MS-63 | MS-65 | MS-66 |
						PF-65	PF-67Cam	PF-68DC
1971, Copper-Nickel Clad, Reverse A †† (a)	47,799,000	1,537	64.0	97%	$2.25	$6	$120	$750
1971-D, Copper-Nickel Clad, Variety 1, Reverse A	68,587,424	2,842	64.7	97%	$3.50	$5	$100	$250
1971-D, Copper-Nickel Clad, Variety 2, Reverse B	(b)	0	n/a		$2	$5	$50	$130
1971-S, Silver Clad, Reverse A	6,868,530	4,099	65.2	100%		$13	$20	$60
1971-S, Silver Clad, Repunched Mintmark (c,d)	(e)	17	64.9	100%			$225	$350
1971-S, Silver Clad, Polished Die (f)	(e)	0	n/a				$125	$250
1971-S, Silver Clad, Proof, Reverse A	4,265,234	5,214	68.1			$14	$15	$25
1971-S, Silver Clad, Doubled Die Obverse, Proof (g,h)	(i)	42	67.6			$90	$150	
1972, Copper-Nickel Clad, All kinds	75,890,000							
1972, Copper-Nickel Clad, Variety 1, Reverse A (j)		1,284	63.9	98%	$2	$5	$140	$2,500
1972, Copper-Nickel Clad, Variety 2, Reverse D †† (k)		540	62.3	87%	$7	$80	$1,300	$8,500
1972, Copper-Nickel Clad, Variety 3, Reverse E (l)		1,006	64.2	98%	$2.50	$5	$125	$750
1972-D, Copper-Nickel Clad, Reverse A	92,548,511	1,692	64.5	97%	$2	$5	$30	$150
1972-S, Silver Clad	2,193,056	4,598	66.5	100%		$13	$15	$20
1972-S, Silver Clad, Proof	1,811,631	3,793	68.2			$14	$15	$25
1972-S, Silver Clad, Doubled Die Obverse, Proof (g)	(n)	21	67.9					—
1973, Copper-Nickel Clad †† (o)	2,000,056	1,087	64.5	100%		$13	$65	$500
1973-D, Copper-Nickel Clad †† (p)	2,000,000	1,061	64.5	100%		$13	$50	$250
1973-S, Copper-Nickel Clad (q)	(r)	0	n/a					
1973-S, Silver Clad	1,883,140	3,105	66.3	100%		$14	$18	$35
1973-S, Copper-Nickel Clad, Proof	2,760,339	1,207	68.1			$14	$16	$30
1973-S, Silver Clad, Proof	1,013,646	3,281	68.1			$35	$37	$50
1973-S, Silver Clad, DblDie Obv, Proof (m)	(k)	8	68.0					—

†† 1973 and 1973-D Copper-Nickel Clad Eisenhower dollars are ranked in the *100 Greatest U.S. Modern Coins* (fourth edition), as a single entry. Only issued in Mint sets. **a.** Auction: $823, MS-66, August 2015. **b.** Included in 1971-D, Copper-Nickel Clad, Variety 1, mintage figure. **c.** A secondary S is visible protruding northwest of the primary S. "This is one of fewer than a half dozen RPMs known for the entire series" (*Cherrypickers' Guide to Rare Die Varieties*, sixth edition, volume II). **d.** Auction: $253, MS-66, July 2011. **e.** Included in circulation-strike 1971-S, Silver Clad, mintage figure. **f.** The left leg of the R in LIBERTY was overpolished. This is popularly known as the "Peg Leg R" variety. **g.** Strong doubling is visible on IN GOD WE TRUST, the date, and LIBER of LIBERTY. There are at least two doubled-die obverses for this date (valued similarly); the one listed is FS-S1-1971S-103. "This obverse is also paired with a minor doubled-die reverse" (*Cherrypickers' Guide to Rare Die Varieties*, sixth edition, volume II). **h.** Auction: $2,585, PF-69Cam, January 2016. **i.** Included in 1971-S, Proof, Silver Clad, mintage figure. **j.** Auction: $1,528, MS-66, August 2015. **k.** Auction: $329, MS-64+, May 2015. **l.** Auction: $2,820, MS-66, January 2015. **m.** A medium spread of doubling is evident on IN GOD WE TRUST, LIBERTY, and slightly on the date. **n.** Included in 1972-S, Proof, Silver Clad, mintage figure. **o.** Auction: $940, MS-66, January 2015. **p.** Auction: $12,925, MS-67, June 2013. **q.** Two reported to exist. **r.** Included in 1973-D, Copper-Nickel Clad, mintage figure. **s.** Included in 1973-S, Proof, Silver Clad, mintage figure.

	Mintage	Cert	Avg	%MS	EF-40	MS-63	MS-65	MS-66
						PF-65	PF-67Cam	PF-68DC
1974, Copper-Nickel Clad	27,366,000	1,288	64.5	99%	$2	$6	$25	$280
1974-D, Copper-Nickel Clad	45,517,000	7,717	65	100%	$2	$6	$16	$70
1974-S, Silver Clad	1,900,156	4,067	66.5	100%		$13	$18	$24
1974-S, Copper-Nickel Clad, Proof	2,612,568	1,017	68			$7	$10	$20
1974-S, Silver Clad, Proof	1,306,579	3,707	68.3			$15	$16	$30
1776–1976, Copper-Nickel Clad, Variety 1 (t)	4,019,000	889	64.2	100%	$2	$8	$160	$1,500
1776–1976, Copper-Nickel Clad, Variety 2	113,318,000	3,111	64.8	99%	$2	$5	$30	$125
1776–1976-D, Copper-Nickel Clad, Variety 1	21,048,710	1,967	64.8	99%	$2	$5	$50	$185
1776–1976-D, Copper-Nickel Clad, Variety 2	82,179,564	5,546	65	100%	$2	$5	$28	$60
1776–1976-S, Copper-Nickel Clad, Variety 1, Proof (u)	2,845,450	1,282	67.9			$12	$15	$30
1776–1976-S, Copper-Nickel Clad, Variety 2, Proof	4,149,730	1,731	68.1			$8	$12	$30
1776–1976, Silver Clad, Variety 2		0	n/a					
1776–1976, Silver Clad, Variety 2, Proof		0	n/a			—		
1776–1976-S, Silver Clad, Variety 1	11,000,000	2,904	66.2	100%		$17	$20	$30
1776–1976-S, Silver Clad, Variety 1, Proof	4,000,000	4,281	68.1			$19	$20	$35
1977, Copper-Nickel Clad	12,596,000	2,502	65	100%	$2	$6	$35	$135
1977-D, Copper-Nickel Clad	32,983,006	15,438	65.1	100%	$2	$6	$35	$170
1977-S, Copper-Nickel Clad, Proof	3,251,152	1,790	68.4			$5	$7	$15
1978, Copper-Nickel Clad	25,702,000	1,066	64.8	99%	$2	$6	$45	$160
1978-D, Copper-Nickel Clad	33,012,890	4,968	65	100%	$2	$5.50	$40	$125
1978-S, Copper-Nickel Clad, Proof	3,127,781	1,891	68.5			$5	$7	$15

t. Auction: $129, MS-65, January 2015. **u.** Only issued in Mint sets. Auction: $2,820, PF-70DCam, October 2015.

SUSAN B. ANTHONY (1979–1999)

Designer: *Frank Gasparro.* **Weight:** *8.1 grams.*
Composition: *Outer layers of copper-nickel (.750 copper, .250 nickel)
bonded to inner core of pure copper.* **Diameter:** *26.5 mm.*
Edge: *Reeded.* **Mints:** *Philadelphia, Denver, and San Francisco.*

Circulation Strike

Mintmark location
is on the obverse,
above the left
tip of the bust.

Proof

History. The Susan B. Anthony dollar was designed by Frank Gasparro, chief engraver of the U.S. Mint, following a congressional mandate. It features a portrait of the famous suffragette, along with an eagle-and-Moon motif reduced from the coin's larger predecessor, the Eisenhower dollar. Legislators hoped that these so-called mini-dollars would be an efficient substitute for paper dollars, which wear much more quickly in circulation. A large mintage in 1979 was followed by smaller quantities in 1980 and 1981, and then a hiatus of almost 20 years. The coins were not popular in circulation, with some members of the public complaining that they were too easily confused with the similarly sized quarter dollar. A final coinage of Anthony dollars was struck in 1999—a stopgap measure to ensure the Treasury's supply of dollar coins before the Sacagawea dollar was launched in 2000.

Striking and Sharpness. Most are well struck, but check the highest areas of both sides.

Availability. Susan B. Anthony dollars are readily available in MS, although those of 1981 are less common than those of 1979 and 1980. Circulated coins are not widely sought by collectors. Proofs were made of all issues and are readily available today.

GRADING STANDARDS

MS-60 to 70 (Mint State). *Obverse:* At MS-60, some abrasion and contact marks are evident, most noticeably on the cheek and upper center of the hair. Luster is present, but may be dull or lifeless. At MS-63, contact marks are extensive but not distracting. Abrasion still is evident, but less than at lower levels. MS-64 coins are slightly finer. An MS-65 coin may have minor abrasion, but contact marks are so minute as to require magnification. Luster should be full and rich. *Reverse:* At MS-60, some abrasion and contact marks are evident, most noticeably on the eagle's breast, head, and talons. Otherwise, the same comments apply as for the obverse.

1980-D. Graded MS-65.

AU-50, 53, 55, 58 (About Uncirculated). *Obverse:* Light wear is seen on the higher-relief areas of the portrait. At AU-58, the luster is extensive but incomplete. At AU–50 and 53, luster is less but still present. *Reverse:* Further wear is evident on the eagle, particularly the head, breast, talons, and tops of the wings. Otherwise, the same comments apply as for the obverse.

The Susan B. Anthony dollar is seldom collected in grades lower than AU-50.

1979-D. Graded AU-50.

PF-60 to 70 (Proof). *Obverse and Reverse:* Proofs that are extensively cleaned and have many hairlines, or that are dull and grainy, are lower level, such as PF–60 to 62. This comment is more theoretical than practical, as nearly all Proofs have been well kept. With medium hairlines and good reflectivity, assigned grades of PF–63 or 64 are appropriate. With relatively few hairlines a rating of PF-65 can be given. PF-66 may have hairlines so delicate that magnification is needed to see them. Above that, all the way to PF-70, a Proof should be free of any hairlines or other problems under strong magnification.

1979-S, Type 2. Graded PF-70 Deep Cameo.

| 1979-P, Narrow Rim | 1979-P, Wide Rim |
| *The "Far Date" variety.* | *The "Near Date" variety.* |

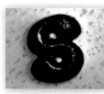

1979-S, Filled S (Type 1), Proof	1979-S, Clear S (Type 2), Proof	1981-S, Rounded S (Type 1), Proof	1981-S, Flat S (Type 2), Proof	1980-S, Repunched Mintmark, Proof *FS-C1-1980S-501*

	Mintage	Cert	Avg	%MS	MS-63	MS-64	MS-65 PF-65	MS-66 PF-68DC
1979-P, Narrow Rim (a)	360,222,000	984	64.8	97%	$6	$8	$14.50	$22
1979-P, Wide Rim †† (a,b)	(c)	1,634	64.6	96%	$38	$40	$45	$90
1979-D	288,015,744	1,017	65.3	99%	$7	$9	$10	$18
1979-S	109,576,000	844	65.3	99%	$6	$8	$10	$15
1979-S, Type 1, Proof (d)	3,677,175	4,266	9.2				$7	$10
1979-S, Type 2, Proof (d,e)	(f)	3,348	10.8				$45	$60
1980-P	27,610,000	1,224	65.8	100%	$5	$8	$12	$18.50
1980-D	41,628,708	1,091	65.6	100%	$5	$8	$13	$22
1980-S	20,422,000	1,142	65.2	100%	$10	$12	$15	$35
1980-S, Proof	3,554,806	3,904	68.9				$6	$10
1980-S, RPM, Proof (g)		0	n/a				—	—
1981-P (h)	3,000,000	879	65.6	100%	$12	$15	$17.50	$35
1981-D (h)	3,250,000	1,046	65.7	100%	$10	$12	$15	$50
1981-S (h)	3,492,000	762	64.6	100%	$20	$25	$35	$220
1981-S, Type 1, Proof	4,063,083	4,801	11.5				$6	$10
1981-S, Type 2, Proof †† (i)	(j)	2,894	16.1				$125	$145
1999-P (k)	29,592,000	736	66.2	100%	$3	$5	$10	$22
1999-D (k)	11,776,000	941	66.5	100%	$3	$5	$10	$22
1999-P, Proof (l)	750,000	5,283	69.3				$22	$27.50

†† Ranked in the *100 Greatest U.S. Modern Coins* (fourth edition). **a.** The obverse design was modified in 1979 to widen the border rim. Late issues of 1979-P and subsequent issues have the wide rim. The 1979-P Wide Rim dollar is nicknamed the "Near Date" because the numerals are closer to the rim. **b.** Auction: $259, MS-67, January 2015. **c.** Included in 1979-P, Narrow Rim, mintage figure. **d.** The S mintmark punch was changed in 1979 to create a clearer mintmark. **e.** Auction: $188, PF-70DCam, June 2015. **f.** Included in 1979-S, Variety 1, Proof, mintage figure. **g.** "The remnants of a previously punched S appear left of the primary S. . . . Very few specimens of this variety have surfaced to date" (*Cherrypickers' Guide to Rare Die Varieties*, sixth edition, volume II). **h.** 1981-P, -D, and -S dollars were issued only in Mint Sets. **i.** Auction: $764, PF-70DCam, February 2015. **j.** Included in 1981-S, Variety 1, Proof, mintage figure. **k.** Dies for the 1999 dollars were further modified to strengthen details on the reverse. **l.** The mintage reflects the total for the Proof coins dated 1999, which were sold through 2003.

SACAGAWEA (2000–2008)

Designers: *Glenna Goodacre (obverse), Thomas D. Rogers Sr. (reverse).*
Weight: *8.1 grams.* **Composition:** *Pure copper core with outer layers of manganese brass (.770 copper, .120 zinc, .070 manganese, and .040 nickel).*
Diameter: *26.5 mm.* **Edge:** *Plain.* **Mints:** *Philadelphia, Denver, and San Francisco; 22-karat gold experimental specimens dated 2000-W were struck at West Point in 1999.*

Circulation Strike

Mintmark location is on the obverse, below the date.

Proof

History. The Sacagawea dollar was launched in 2000, with a distinctive golden color and a plain edge to distinguish it from other denominations or coins of similar size. (One complaint leveled against the Susan B. Anthony dollar was that it too closely resembled the quarter dollar; both were silvery, with reeded edges, and with only about two millimeters' difference in diameter.) The new coinage alloy and the change in appearance were mandated by the United States Dollar Coin Act of 1997. The core of the coin is pure copper, and the golden outer layer is of manganese brass. The obverse shows a modern artist's conception of Sacagawea, the Shoshone Indian who assisted the Lewis and Clark expedition, and her infant son, Jean Baptiste. (No known contemporary portraits of them exist.) The reverse shows an eagle in flight.

In 1999, about a dozen Sacagawea dollars were struck in 22-karat gold at the West Point Mint, as experimental or presentation pieces. These featured a prototype reverse design with boldly detailed tail feathers on the eagle. The following year, a small number of early circulation strikes from the Philadelphia Mint also featured that same prototype design. These are popularly called "Cheerio" dollars, as the coins were packaged as a promotion in boxes of Cheerios cereal (their unusual nature was not recognized at the time). Today collectors seek them as rare and desirable varieties.

In addition to the regular Uncirculated or Mint State coins produced in large quantities, smaller numbers of Satin Finish dollars were made of the 2005 to 2008 years, Philadelphia and Denver mints. Sold at an additional premium, most of these exist today in grades of MS-67 and upward and are designated SP (Specimen) or SMS (Special Mint Set) by the commercial grading services.

Several distinct finishes can be identified on the Sacagawea dollars as a result of the Mint's attempts to adjust the dies, blanks, strikes, or finishing to produce coins with minimal spotting and better surface color. One group of 5,000 pieces, dated 2000 and with a special finish, was presented to sculptor Glenna Goodacre in payment for the obverse design. These have since entered the numismatic market and command a significant premium.

Another peculiarity in the Sacagawea series is a numismatic mule (a coin made from mismatched dies)—the combination of an undated State quarter obverse and a Sacagawea dollar reverse. Examples of this error are extremely rare.

Striking and Sharpness. Most are very well struck. Weakness sometimes is evident on the higher design points. Special issues are uniformly sharply struck.

Availability. These coins are common in high grades, and are usually collected in MS and Proof.

GRADING STANDARDS

MS-60 to 70 (Mint State). *Obverse:* At MS-60, some abrasion and contact marks are evident, most noticeably on the cheekbone and the drapery near the baby's head. Luster is present, but may be dull or lifeless. At MS-63, contact marks are extensive but not distracting. Abrasion still is evident, but less than at lower levels. MS-64 coins are slightly finer. An MS-65 coin may have minor abrasion, but contact marks are so minute as to require magnification. Luster should be full and rich. *Reverse:* At MS-60, some abrasion and contact marks are evident, most noticeably on the eagle's breast. Otherwise, the same comments apply as for the obverse.

2006-D. Graded MS-65.

AU-50, 53, 55, 58 (About Uncirculated).

Obverse: Light wear is seen on cheekbone, drapery, and elsewhere. At AU-58, the luster is extensive, but incomplete. At AU–50 and 53, luster is less but still present. *Reverse:* Further wear is evident on the eagle. Otherwise, the same comments apply as for the obverse.

The Sacagawea dollar is seldom collected in grades lower than AU-50.

2000-P. Graded AU-55.

PF-60 to 70 (Proof). *Obverse and Reverse:*

Proofs that are extensively cleaned and have many hairlines, or that are dull and grainy, are lower level, such as PF–60 to 62. This comment is more theoretical than practical, as nearly all Proofs have been well kept. With medium hairlines and good reflectivity, assigned grades of PF–63 or 64 are appropriate. With relatively few hairlines a rating of PF-65 can be given. PF-66 may have hair-

2002-S. Graded PF-69.

lines so delicate that magnification is needed to see them. Above that, all the way to PF-70, a Proof should be free of any hairlines or other problems under strong magnification.

2000-P, Reverse Die Aberrations *The "Speared Eagle" variety.*	2000-P, Normal Feathers	2000-P, Boldly Detailed Tail Feathers

	Mintage	Cert	Avg	%MS	MS-64	MS-65 PF-65	MS-66 PF-69DC
2000-P	767,140,000	5,787	66.7	100%	$2.50	$5	$12
2000-P, Reverse Die Aberrations (a,b)	(c)	74	67.4	100%		$700	$1,250
2000-P, Boldly Detailed Tail Feathers †† (d,e)	5,500	2	64	100%	$2,750	$3,000	$4,000
2000-P, Goodacre Presentation Finish †† (f,g)	5,000	294	66.8	100%	$400	$500	$650
2000-D	518,916,000	7,517	66.4	100%	$4	$8	$15
2000-S, Proof	4,047,904	15,879	2.3			$6	$15
2001-P	62,468,000	682	67.1	100%	$2	$4	$6
2001-D	70,939,500	401	65.9	100%	$2	$4	$6
2001-S, Proof	3,183,740	11,255	69.2			$6	$20
2002-P (h)	3,865,610	393	67.1	100%	$2	$4	$10
2002-D (h)	3,732,000	363	66.3	100%	$2	$4	$8
2002-S, Proof	3,211,995	9,298	69.2			$6	$15
2003-P (h)	3,080,000	689	66.7	100%	$3	$5	$8

†† Ranked in the *100 Greatest U.S. Modern Coins* (fourth edition). **a.** Two spike-like die aberrations appear through the breast of the eagle. This variety is nicknamed the "Speared Eagle." **b.** Auction: $2,012, MS-67, January 2012. **c.** Included in 2000-P mintage figure. **d.** The feathers of the eagle are finely enhanced. This is nicknamed the "Cheerios" variety, as the coins were included as a promotion in boxes of Cheerios cereal. **e.** Auction: $8,195, MS-67, September 2008. **f.** A group of 5,000 coins, dated 2000 and with a special finish, were presented to sculptor Glenna Goodacre in payment for the obverse design. **g.** Auction: $541, MS-68, June 2015. **h.** Not issued for circulation.

	Mintage	Cert	Avg	%MS	MS-64	MS-65 PF-65	MS-66 PF-69DC
2003-D (h)	3,080,000	605	66.1	100%	$3	$5	$8
2003-S, Proof	3,298,439	12,608	69.2			$6	$15
2004-P (h)	2,660,000	578	66.8	100%	$2	$4	$8
2004-D (h)	2,660,000	703	66.6	100%	$2	$4	$8
2004-S, Proof	2,965,422	12,090	69.2			$6	$15
2005-P (h)	2,520,000	351	66.3	100%	$7	$10	$20
2005-P, Satin Finish (h)	1,160,000	4,012	67	100%		$5	$12
2005-D (h)	2,520,000	594	66.1	100%	$7	$10	$20
2005-D, Satin Finish (h)	1,160,000	3,707	66.6	100%		$5	$12
2005-S, Proof	3,344,679	17,543	69.2			$6	$15
2006-P (h)	4,900,000	378	66.1	100%	$2	$4	$8
2006-P, Satin Finish (h)	847,631	1,560	66.9	100%		$5	$12
2006-D (h)	2,800,000	580	65.9	100%	$2	$4	$8
2006-D, Satin Finish (h)	847,631	1,503	66.9	100%		$5	$12
2006-S, Proof	3,054,436	8,553	69.3			$6	$15
2007-P (h)	3,640,000	569	66.7	100%	$3	$5	$8
2007-P, Satin Finish (h)	895,628	569	67	100%		$5	$12
2007-D (h)	3,920,000	882	66.5	100%	$3	$5	$8
2007-D, Satin Finish (h)	895,628	621	66.9	100%		$5	$12
2007-S, Proof	2,577,166	8,763	69.2			$6	$15
2008-P (h)	1,820,000	242	66.4	100%	$3	$5	$8
2008-P, Satin Finish (h)	745,464	284	67.1	100%		$5	$12
2008-D (h)	1,820,000	678	66.8	100%	$3	$5	$8
2008-D, Satin Finish (h)	745,464	363	67.3	100%		$5	$12
2008-S, Proof	2,169,561	6,342	69.2			$6	$15

h. Not issued for circulation.

PRESIDENTIAL (2007–2016)

Designers: *Various (obverse); Don Everhart (reverse).* **Weight:** *8.1 grams.*
Composition: *Pure copper core with outer layers of manganese brass (.770 copper, .120 zinc, .070 manganese, and .040 nickel).* **Diameter:** *26.5 mm.* **Edge:** *Lettered.* **Mints:** *Philadelphia, Denver, and San Francisco.*

Obverse Style,
2007–2008,
Circulation Strike
No motto on obverse.

Obverse Style,
2009–2016,
Circulation Strike
Motto beneath portrait.

Common Reverse,
Circulation Strike

Proof

Date, Mintmark, and
Mottos Incused on Edge
*IN GOD WE TRUST
moved to obverse in 2009.*

History. Presidential dollars debuted in 2007 and were issued at the rate of four designs per year through 2015, with the program's three final coins issued in 2016. The series started with George Washington and continued in order of office. Living presidents were ineligible, so the program ended with Ronald Reagan. Each coin has a common reverse showing the Statue of Liberty. The series began with the date, mintmark, and mottos IN GOD WE TRUST and E PLURIBUS UNUM incused on the edge of the coins; in 2009 IN GOD WE TRUST was moved from the edge to the obverse after some public criticism of the "Godless dollars."

In December 2011, Secretary of the Treasury Timothy Geithner directed that the U.S. Mint suspend minting and issuing circulating Presidential dollars. "Regular circulating demand for the coins will be met through the Federal Reserve Bank's existing inventory of circulating coins minted prior to 2012," the Mint announced. Collector formats, however, continued to be issued.

In addition to the regular Uncirculated or Mint State coins produced in large quantities, smaller numbers of Satin Finish dollars were made of the 2007 to 2010 years, Philadelphia and Denver Mints. Sold at an additional premium, most of these exist today in grades of MS-67 and upward and are designated SP (Specimen) or SMS (Special Mint Set) by the commercial grading services. Catching collectors, dealers, and others by surprise, the Coin and Chronicles sets of Presidential dollars were introduced in 2015. A small number of additional (to the regular Uncirculated) coins were made with Reverse Proof finish and sold at a sharp premium as part of Coin and Chronicles sets, which also included a brochure and a medal. Most collectors desired only the dollar. The Eisenhower and Truman sets, the first offered, sold out quickly, leaving many Mint clients disappointed. Letters of protest filled the columns of Coin World and Numismatic News when the only option to secure them seemed to be paying double or triple issue price on eBay and other venues. These were carefully produced, and nearly all grade MS–68 to 70. "First strike" and other notations on holders add little or nothing to the resale value of these or other modern coins.

Some Presidential dollars were inadvertently struck with the edge lettering missing. A 2009-D, John Tyler, variety has the wrong date, 2010, on the edge.

Striking and Sharpness. These usually are well struck, but check the higher-relief parts of each side. Special issues are uniformly sharp.

Availability. Presidential dollars are very common in MS. Most have from a few to many bagmarks, with true MS-65 and better coins in the minority.

GRADING STANDARDS

MS-60 to 70 (Mint State). *Obverse:* At MS-60, some abrasion and contact marks are evident, most noticeably on the highest-relief areas of the portrait, the exact location varying with the president depicted. Luster is present, but may be dull or lifeless. At MS-63, contact marks are extensive but not distracting. Abrasion still is evident, but less than at lower levels. MS-64 coins are slightly finer. An MS-65

2007-P, Washington. Graded MS-68.

coin may have minor abrasion, but contact marks are so minute as to require magnification. Luster should be full and rich. *Reverse:* At MS-60, some abrasion and contact marks are evident, most noticeably on the cheek and arm. Otherwise, the same comments apply as for the obverse.

AU-50, 53, 55, 58 (About Uncirculated). *Obverse:* Light wear is seen on the portrait, most prominently on the higher-relief areas. At AU-58, the luster is extensive, but incomplete. At AU–50 and 53, luster is less, but still is present. *Reverse:* Further wear is evident on statue. Otherwise, the same comments apply as for the obverse.

Presidential dollars are seldom collected in grades lower than AU-50.

2007-P, Madison. Graded AU-53.

PF-60 to 70 (Proof). *Obverse and Reverse:* Proofs that are extensively cleaned and have many hairlines, or that are dull and grainy, are lower level, such as PF–60 to 62. This comment is more theoretical than practical, as nearly all Proofs have been well kept. With medium hairlines and good reflectivity, assigned grades of PF–63 or 64 are appropriate. With relatively few hairlines a rating of PF-65 can be given. PF-66 may have hairlines so del-

2007-S, Madison. Graded PF-65.

icate that magnification is needed to see them. Above that, all the way to PF-70, a Proof should be free of any hairlines or other problems under strong magnification.

| 2007, Washington | 2007, J. Adams | 2007, Jefferson | 2007, Madison |

	Mintage	Cert	Avg	%MS	MS-64	MS-65 / PF-65	MS-66 / PF-69DC
2007-P, Washington	176,680,000	17,800	65.0	100%	$1.50	$3	$6
2007-P, Washington, Satin Finish (a)	895,628	761	66.3	100%		$5	$12
2007-P, Washington, Plain Edge †† (b,c)	(d)	43,472	64.7	100%	$30	$40	$65
2007-D, Washington	163,680,000	14,557	65.1	100%	$1.50	$3	$6
2007-D, Washington, Satin Finish (a)	895,628	929	66.9	100%		$5	$12
2007-S, Washington, Proof	3,965,989	45,159	69.2			$4	$15
2007-P, J. Adams	112,420,000	20,141	64.6	100%	$1.50	$3	$6
2007-P, J. Adams, Satin Finish (a)	895,628	827	66.4	100%		$5	$12
2007-D, J. Adams	112,140,000	5,851	65.0	100%	$1.50	$3	$6
2007-D, J. Adams, Satin Finish (a)	895,628	911	67.0	100%		$5	$12
2007-S, J. Adams, Proof	3,965,989	44,915	69.2			$4	$15
2007-P, Jefferson	100,800,000	4,988	65.3	100%	$1.50	$3	$6
2007-P, Jefferson, Satin Finish (a)	895,628	894	66.5	100%		$5	$12
2007-D, Jefferson	102,810,000	5,651	65.3	100%	$1.50	$3	$6
2007-D, Jefferson, Satin Finish (a)	895,628	921	66.9	100%		$5	$12
2007-S, Jefferson, Proof	3,965,989	45,007	69.2			$4	$15
2007-P, Madison	84,560,000	2,678	65.4	100%	$1.50	$3	$6
2007-P, Madison, Satin Finish (a)	895,628	868	66.6	100%		$5	$12
2007-D, Madison	87,780,000	3,015	65.4	100%	$1.50	$3	$6
2007-D, Madison, Satin Finish (a)	87,780,000	883	66.9	100%		$5	$12
2007-S, Madison, Proof	3,965,989	45,269	69.2			$4	$15

†† Ranked in the *100 Greatest U.S. Modern Coins* (fourth edition). **a.** Not issued for circulation. **b.** Some circulation-strike Washington dollars are known without the normal edge lettering (date, mintmark, IN GOD WE TRUST, and E PLURIBUS UNUM). **c.** Auction: $235, MS-67, September 2015. **d.** Included in 2007-P, Washington, mintage figure.

| 2008, Monroe | 2008, J.Q. Adams | 2008, Jackson | 2008, Van Buren |

	Mintage	Cert	Avg	%MS	MS-64	MS-65	MS-66
						PF-65	PF-69DC
2008-P, Monroe	64,260,000	2,269	65.6	100%	$1.50	$3	$6
2008-P, Monroe, Satin Finish (a)	745,464	400	67.0	100%		$5	$12
2008-D, Monroe	60,230,000	1,799	65.3	100%	$1.50	$3	$6
2008-D, Monroe, Satin Finish (a)	745,464	421	67.1	100%		$5	$12
2008-S, Monroe, Proof	3,083,940	24,174	69.2			$4	$15
2008-P, J.Q. Adams	57,540,000	2,607	65.9	100%	$1.50	$3	$6
2008-P, J.Q. Adams, Satin Finish (a)	745,464	418	66.9	100%		$5	$12
2008-D, J.Q. Adams	57,720,000	2,057	65.7	100%	$1.50	$3	$6
2008-D, J.Q. Adams, Satin Finish (a)	745,464	426	67.2	100%		$5	$12
2008-S, J.Q. Adams, Proof	3,083,940	24,180	69.3			$4	$15
2008-P, Jackson	61,180,000	3,044	65.7	100%	$1.50	$3	$6
2008-P, Jackson, Satin Finish (a)	745,464	387	67.1	100%		$5	$12
2008-D, Jackson	61,070,000	1,932	65.2	100%	$1.50	$3	$6
2008-D, Jackson, Satin Finish (a)	745,464	420	67.3	100%		$5	$12
2008-S, Jackson, Proof	3,083,940	24,151	69.2			$4	$15
2008-P, Van Buren	51,520,000	1,405	65.8	100%	$1.50	$3	$6
2008-P, Van Buren, Satin Finish (a)	745,464	393	66.8	100%		$5	$12
2008-D, Van Buren	50,960,000	933	65.2	100%	$1.50	$3	$6
2008-D, Van Buren, Satin Finish (a)	745,464	389	67.0	100%		$5	$12
2008-S, Van Buren, Proof	3,083,940	24,214	69.3			$4	$15

a. Not issued for circulation.

| 2009, W.H. Harrison | 2009, Tyler | 2009, Polk | 2009, Taylor |

	Mintage	Cert	Avg	%MS	MS-64	MS-65	MS-66
						PF-65	PF-69DC
2009-P, W.H. Harrison	43,260,000	1,122	65.5	100%	$1.50	$3	$6
2009-P, W.H. Harrison, Satin Finish (a)	784,614	494	67.3	100%		$5	$12
2009-D, W.H. Harrison	55,160,000	1,154	65.2	100%	$1.50	$3	$6
2009-D, W.H. Harrison, Satin Finish (a)	784,614	461	67.5	100%		$5	$12
2009-S, W.H. Harrison, Proof	2,809,452	17,982	69.2			$4	$15
2009-P, Tyler	43,540,000	1,020	65.3	100%	$1.50	$3	$6
2009-P, Tyler, Satin Finish (a)	784,614	340	67.1	100%		$5	$12
2009-D, Tyler	43,540,000	1002	65.2	100%	$1.50	$3	$6
2009-D, Tyler, Satin Finish (a)	784,614	283	67.0	100%		$5	$12
2009-D, Tyler, 2010 Edge	(e)	10	66.0	100%	—	—	—
2009-S, Tyler, Proof	2,809,452	17,950	69.2			$4	$15

a. Not issued for circulation. e. Included in 2009-D, Tyler, mintage figure.

	Mintage	Cert	Avg	%MS	MS-64	MS-65 PF-65	MS-66 PF-69DC
2009-P, Polk	46,620,000	1,035	66.0	100%	$1.50	$3	$6
2009-P, Polk, Satin Finish (a)	784,614	408	67.3	100%		$5	$12
2009-D, Polk	41,720,000	770	65.4	100%	$1.50	$3	$6
2009-D, Polk, Satin Finish (a)	784,614	377	67.3	100%		$5	$12
2009-S, Polk, Proof	2,809,452	17,957	69.2			$4	$15
2009-P, Taylor	41,580,000	781	65.7	100%	$1.50	$3	$6
2009-P, Taylor, Satin Finish (a)	784,614	481	67.6	100%		$5	$12
2009-D, Taylor	36,680,000	784	65.6	100%	$1.50	$3	$6
2009-D, Taylor, Satin Finish (a)	784,614	424	67.4	100%		$5	$12
2009-S, Taylor, Proof	2,809,452	18,115	69.3			$4	$15

a. Not issued for circulation.

2010, Fillmore

2010, Pierce

2010, Buchanan

2010, Lincoln

	Mintage	Cert	Avg	%MS	MS-64	MS-65 PF-65	MS-66 PF-69DC
2010-P, Fillmore	37,520,000	862	65.6	100%	$1.50	$3	$6
2010-P, Fillmore, Satin Finish (a)	583,897	418	67.3	100%		$5	$12
2010-D, Fillmore	36,960,000	603	65.2	100%	$1.50	$3	$6
2010-D, Fillmore, Satin Finish (a)	583,897	567	67.5	100%		$5	$12
2010-S, Fillmore, Proof	2,224,827	15,324	69.2			$6	$15
2010-P, Pierce	38,220,000	760	65.6	100%	$1.50	$3	$6
2010-P, Pierce, Satin Finish (a)	583,897	434	67.4	100%		$5	$12
2010-D, Pierce	38,360,000	692	65.5	100%	$1.50	$3	$6
2010-D, Pierce, Satin Finish (a)	583,897	583	67.6	100%		$5	$12
2010-S, Pierce, Proof	2,224,827	15,274	69.2			$6	$15
2010-P, Buchanan	36,820,000	355	65.6	100%	$1.50	$3	$6
2010-P, Buchanan, Satin Finish (a)	583,897	433	67.2	100%		$5	$12
2010-D, Buchanan	36,540,000	496	65.3	100%	$1.50	$3	$6
2010-D, Buchanan, Satin Finish (a)	583,897	562	67.5	100%		$5	$12
2010-S, Buchanan, Proof	2,224,827	15,347	69.2			$6	$15
2010-P, Lincoln	49,000,000	724	65.5	100%	$1.50	$3	$6
2010-P, Lincoln, Satin Finish (a)	583,897	681	67.1	100%		$5	$12
2010-D, Lincoln	48,020,000	376	65.2	100%	$1.50	$3	$6
2010-D, Lincoln, Satin Finish (a)	583,897	922	67.4	100%		$5	$12
2010-S, Lincoln, Proof	2,224,827	16,054	69.2			$6	$15

a. Not issued for circulation.

2011, A. Johnson

2011, Grant

2011, Hayes

2011, Garfield

	Mintage	Cert	Avg	%MS	MS-64	MS-65	MS-66
						PF-65	PF-69DC
2011-P, A. Johnson	35,560,000	390	66.7	100%	$1.50	$3	$6
2011-D, A. Johnson	37,100,000	374	67.0	100%	$1.50	$3	$6
2011-S, A. Johnson, Proof	1,972,863	8,118	69.2			$8	$15
2011-P, Grant	38,080,000	427	66.8	100%	$1.50	$3	$6
2011-D, Grant	37,940,000	394	67.0	100%	$1.50	$3	$6
2011-S, Grant, Proof	1,972,863	8,180	69.2			$8	$15
2011-P, Hayes	37,660,000	388	66.5	100%	$1.50	$3	$6
2011-D, Hayes	36,820,000	395	67.1	100%	$1.50	$3	$6
2011-S, Hayes, Proof	1,972,863	8,259	69.3			$8	$15
2011-P, Garfield	37,100,000	339	66.4	100%	$1.50	$3	$6
2011-D, Garfield	37,100,000	348	67.0	100%	$2	$3	$6
2011-S, Garfield, Proof	1,972,863	8,251	69.2			$8	$15

| 2012, Arthur | 2012, Cleveland, First Term | 2012, B. Harrison | 2012, Cleveland, Second Term |

	Mintage	Cert	Avg	%MS	MS-64	MS-65	MS-66
						PF-65	PF-69DC
2012-P, Arthur (a)	6,020,000	709	66.8	100%	$2	$3	$6
2012-D, Arthur (a)	4,060,000	282	67.1	100%	$2	$3	$6
2012-S, Arthur, Proof	1,438,743	5,123	69.3			$17	$35
2012-P, Cleveland, First Term (a)	5,460,000	739	66.7	100%	$2	$3	$6
2012-D, Cleveland, First Term (a)	4,060,000	252	66.9	100%	$2	$3	$6
2012-S, Cleveland, First Term, Proof	1,438,743	5,147	69.3			$17	$35
2012-P, B. Harrison (a)	5,640,001	727	66.6	100%	$2	$3	$6
2012-D, B. Harrison (a)	4,200,000	252	67.1	100%	$2	$3	$6
2012-S, B. Harrison, Proof	1,438,743	5,118	69.3			$17	$35
2012-P, Cleveland, Second Term (a)	10,680,000	693	66.6	100%	$2	$3	$6
2012-D, Cleveland, Second Term (a)	3,920,000	259	67.1	100%	$2	$3	$6
2012-S, Cleveland, Second Term, Proof	1,438,743	5,084	69.3			$17	$35

a. Not issued for circulation.

| 2013, McKinley | 2013, T. Roosevelt | 2013, Taft | 2013, Wilson |

	Mintage	Cert	Avg	%MS	MS-64	MS-65	MS-66
						PF-65	PF-69DC
2013-P, McKinley (a)	4,760,000	746	67.1	100%	$2	$3	$6
2013-D, McKinley (a)	3,365,100	155	67.0	100%	$2	$3	$6
2013-S, McKinley, Proof	1,488,798	4,953	69.5			$7	$16

a. Not issued for circulation.

	Mintage	Cert	Avg	%MS	MS-64	MS-65	MS-66
						PF-65	PF-69DC
2013-P, T. Roosevelt (a)	5,310,700	1,009	67.1	100%	$2	$3	$6
2013-D, T. Roosevelt (a)	3,920,000	292	66.6	100%	$2	$3	$6
2013-S, T. Roosevelt, Proof	1,503,943	4,990	69.5			$7	$16
2013-P, Taft (a)	4,760,000	877	67.1	100%	$2	$3	$6
2013-D, Taft (a)	3,360,000	212	67.0	100%	$2	$3	$6
2013-S, Taft, Proof	1,488,798	4,903	69.5			$7	$16
2013-P, Wilson (a)	4,620,000	950	67.4	100%	$2	$3	$6
2013-D, Wilson (a)	3,360,000	197	67.2	100%	$2	$3	$6
2013-S, Wilson, Proof	1,488,798	4,899	69.5			$7	$16

a. Not issued for circulation.

2014, Harding

2014, Coolidge

2014, Hoover

2014, F.D. Roosevelt

	Mintage	Cert	Avg	%MS	MS-64	MS-65	MS-66
						PF-65	PF-69DC
2014-P, Harding (a)	6,160,000	264	66.8	100%	$2	$3	$6
2014-D, Harding (a)	3,780,000	221	67.0	100%	$2	$3	$6
2014-S, Harding, Proof	1,373,569	4,188	69.5			$7	$16
2014-P, Coolidge (a)	4,480,000	308	67.2	100%	$2	$3	$6
2014-D, Coolidge (a)	3,780,000	192	67.2	100%	$2	$3	$6
2014-S, Coolidge, Proof	1,373,569	4,208	69.5			$7	$16
2014-P, Hoover (a)	4,480,000	251	67.0	100%	$2	$3	$6
2014-D, Hoover (a)	3,780,000	201	67.1	100%	$2	$3	$6
2014-S, Hoover, Proof	1,373,569	4,190	69.4			$7	$16
2014-P, F.D. Roosevelt (a)	4,760,000	296	67.1	100%	$2	$3	$6
2014-D, F.D. Roosevelt (a)	3,920,000	163	67.2	100%	$2	$3	$6
2014-S, F.D. Roosevelt, Proof	1,392,619	4,214	69.5			$7	$16

a. Not issued for circulation.

2015, Truman

2015, Eisenhower

2015, Kennedy

2015, L.B. Johnson

	Mintage	Cert	Avg	%MS	MS-64	MS-65	MS-66
						PF-65	PF-69DC
2015-P, Truman (a)	4,900,000	1,058	66.9	100%	$2	$3	$5
2015-P, Truman, Reverse Proof ††	16,812	1,471	69.0			$175	$225
2015-D, Truman (a)	3,500,000	173	67.1	100%	$2	$3	$5
2015-S, Truman, Proof	1,272,462	5,286	69.4			$6	$15
2015-P, Eisenhower (a)	4,900,000	974	66.8	100%	$2	$3	$5
2015-P, Eisenhower, Reverse Proof ††	16,744	1,179	68.9			$150	$180
2015-D, Eisenhower (a)	3,645,998	161	67.0	100%	$2	$3	$5

†† Ranked in the *100 Greatest U.S. Modern Coins* (fourth edition), combined in a single entry. **a.** Not issued for circulation.

	Mintage	Cert	Avg	%MS	MS-64	MS-65	MS-66
						PF-65	PF-69DC
2015-S, Eisenhower, Proof	1,272,462	5,295	69.4			$6	$15
2015-P, Kennedy (a)	6,160,000	1,389	66.7	100%	$2	$3	$5
2015-P, Kennedy, Reverse Proof	49,051	2,757	69.0			$80	$125
2015-D, Kennedy (a)	5,180,000	230	67.2	100%	$2	$3	$5
2015-S, Kennedy, Proof	1,272,462	5,404	69.4			$6	$15
2015-P, L.B. Johnson (a)	7,840,000	987	66.8	100%	$2	$3	$5
2015-P, L.B. Johnson, Reverse Proof	23,905	1,385	68.8			$75	$90
2015-D, L.B. Johnson (a)	4,200,000	169	66.9	100%	$2	$3	$5
2015-S, L.B. Johnson, Proof	1,272,462	5,289	69.4			$6	$15

†† Ranked in the *100 Greatest U.S. Modern Coins* (fourth edition), in a single entry with 2015-P, Truman Presidential Dollar, Reverse Proof. **a.** Not issued for circulation.

2016, Nixon	2016, Ford	2016, Reagan

	Mintage	Cert	Avg	%MS	MS-64	MS-65	MS-66
						PF-65	PF-69DC
2016-P, Richard M. Nixon (a)	5,460,000	146	66.7	100%	$2	$3	$5
2016-D, Richard M. Nixon (a)	4,340,000	304	67.0	100%	$2	$3	$5
2016-S, Richard M. Nixon, Proof	1,196,582	4,910	69.5			$8	$15
2016-P, Gerald Ford (a)	5,460,000	124	66.5	100%	$2	$3	$5
2016-D, Gerald Ford (a)	5,040,000	302	66.8	100%	$2	$3	$5
2016-S, Gerald Ford, Proof	1,196,582	4,904	69.5			$8	$15
2016-P, Ronald Reagan (a)	7,140,000	155	66.7	100%	$2	$3	$5
2016-D, Ronald Reagan (a)	5,880,000	302	67.0	100%	$2	$3	$5
2016-S, Ronald Reagan, Proof	1,196,582	4,910	69.5			$8	$15
2016-P, Ronald Reagan, Reverse Proof	47,447	1,142	69.1			$60	$80

a. Not issued for circulation.

NATIVE AMERICAN (2009 TO DATE)

Designers: *Glenna Goodacre (obverse); see image captions for reverse designers.*
Weight: *8.1 grams.* **Composition:** *Pure copper core with outer layers of manganese brass (.770 copper, .120 zinc, .070 manganese, and .040 nickel).*
Diameter: *26.5 mm.* **Edge:** *Lettered.* **Mints:** *Philadelphia, Denver, and San Francisco.*

Circulation Strike   **Mintmark location is on the rim.**   **Proof**

History. Since 2009, the reverse of the golden dollar has featured an annually changing design that memorializes Native Americans and, in the words of the authorizing legislation, "the important contributions made by Indian tribes and individual Native Americans to the development [and history] of the

United States." The coins are marked (incuse) on their edges with the year of minting, the mintmark, and the legend E PLURIBUS UNUM. The Native American $1 Coin Act also specified that at least 20% of the total mintage of dollar coins in any given year (including Presidential dollars) will be Native American dollars. Production of all dollar coins minted after 2011 has been limited to numismatic sales (Proofs and other collector formats, and circulation strikes in rolls and bags available directly from the U.S. Mint); none are issued for circulation, as they have proven unpopular in commerce.

The obverse of the Native American dollar coin is a modified version of the Sacagawea dollar, featuring that coin's central portraits (of Sacagawea and Jean Baptiste), and the legends LIBERTY and IN GOD WE TRUST. The date and mintmark, as noted above, are on the coin's edge. Each new reverse design is chosen by the secretary of the Treasury following consultation with the Senate Committee on Indian Affairs, the Congressional Native American Caucus of the House of Representatives, the Commission of Fine Arts, and the National Congress of American Indians. Design proposals are also reviewed by the Citizens Coinage Advisory Committee.

In addition to the regular Uncirculated or Mint State coins produced in large quantities, smaller numbers of Satin Finish dollars were made of the 2009-P, 2009-D, 2010-P, and 2010-D issues. Sold at an additional premium, most of these exist today in grades of MS-67 and upward and are designated SP (Specimen) or SMS (Special Mint Set) by the commercial grading services. 50,000 2014-D coins were made with Enhanced Uncirculated finish and were sold at an extra premium. Most of these grade MS–68 to 70. In 2015 at the West Point Mint 90,000 2015-W dollars were struck with Enhanced Uncirculated finish. These are unique up to this time as the only collectible West Point dollars in any of the three "golden dollar" series (Sacagawea, Native American, and Presidential). Nearly all are in grades MS–68 to 70.

Some error coins have been discovered without edge lettering.

Striking and Sharpness. Most examples are very well struck. Check the higher points of the design. Special issues are uniformly sharply struck.

Availability. Native American dollars are common in high grades, and are usually collected in MS and Proof. Distribution for public circulation has been slow despite Mint efforts such as the $1 Coin Direct Ship program (intended "to make $1 coins readily available to the public, at no additional cost [including shipping], so they can be easily introduced into circulation—particularly by using them for retail transactions, vending, and mass transit"). Proofs have been made each year and are readily available.

GRADING STANDARDS

MS-60 to 70 (Mint State). *Obverse:* At MS-60, some abrasion and contact marks are evident, most noticeably on the cheekbone and the drapery near the baby's head. Luster is present, but may be dull or lifeless. At MS-63, contact marks are extensive but not distracting. Abrasion still is evident, but less than at lower levels. MS-64 coins are slightly finer. An MS-65 coin may have minor abrasion, but contact marks are so minute as to

2009-P, Three Sisters. Graded MS-68.

require magnification. Luster should be full and rich. *Reverse:* At MS-60, some abrasion and contact marks are evident, most noticeably on the eagle's breast. Otherwise, the same comments apply as for the obverse.

Native American dollars are seldom collected in grades lower than MS-60.

PF-60 to 70 (Proof). *Obverse and Reverse:* Proofs that are extensively cleaned and have many hairlines, or that are dull and grainy, are lower level, such as PF–60 to 62. This comment is more theoretical than practical, as nearly all Proofs have been well kept. With medium hairlines and good reflectivity, assigned grades of PF–63 or 64 are appropriate. With relatively few hairlines a rating of PF-65 can be given. PF-66 may have hairlines so delicate that magnification is needed to see them. Above that, all the way to PF-70, a Proof should be free of any hairlines or other problems under strong magnification.

2009-S, Three Sisters. Graded PF-70 Deep Cameo.

Three Sisters (2009)
Reverse designer:
Norman E. Nemeth.

Great Law of Peace (2010)
Reverse designer:
Thomas Cleveland.

Wampanoag Treaty (2011)
Reverse designer:
Richard Masters.

Trade Routes in the 17th Century (2012)
Reverse designer:
Thomas Cleveland.

Treaty With the Delawares (2013)
Reverse designer:
Susan Gamble.

Native Hospitality (2014)
Reverse designer:
Chris Costello.

Mohawk Ironworkers (2015)
Reverse designer:
Ronald D. Sanders.

Code Talkers (2016)
Reverse designer:
Thomas D. Rogers Sr.

Sequoyah (2017)
Reverse designer:
Chris Costello.

Jim Thorpe (2018)
Reverse designer:
Michael Gaudioso.

American Indians in Space (2019)
Reverse designer:
Glenna Goodacre.

	Mintage	Cert	Avg	%MS	MS-64	MS-65	MS-66
						PF-65	PF-69DC
2009-P, Three Sisters	39,200,000	344	66.1	100%	$3	$5	$8
2009-P, Three Sisters, Satin Finish (a)	784,614	587	67.3	100%		$5	$12
2009-D, Three Sisters	35,700,000	268	65.4	100%	$3	$5	$8
2009-D, Three Sisters, Satin Finish (a)	784,614	441	67.2	100%		$5	$12
2009-S, Three Sisters, Proof	2,179,867	9,860	69.2			$8	$15

a. Not issued for circulation.

	Mintage	Cert	Avg	%MS	MS-64	MS-65	MS-66
						PF-65	PF-69DC
2010-P, Great Law	32,060,000	463	66.0	100%	$3	$5	$8
2010-P, Great Law, Satin Finish (a)	583,897	301	67.4	100%		$5	$12
2010-D, Great Law	48,720,000	365	65.8	100%	$3	$5	$8
2010-D, Great Law, Satin Finish (a)	583,897	375	67.5	100%		$5	$12
2010-S, Great Law, Proof	1,689,216	6,209	69.2			$8	$15
2011-P, Wampanoag Treaty	29,400,000	371	66.7	100%	$3	$5	$8
2011-D, Wampanoag Treaty	48,160,000	416	67.0	100%	$3	$5	$8
2011-S, Wampanoag Treaty, Proof	1,673,010	7,764	69.2			$8	$15
2012-P, Trade Routes	2,800,000	224	67.2	100%	$3	$5	$8
2012-D, Trade Routes	3,080,000	1,333	67.3	100%	$3	$5	$8
2012-S, Trade Routes, Proof	1,189,445	4,635	69.3			$15	$20
2013-P, Treaty With the Delawares	1,820,000	327	67.0	100%	$3	$5	$8
2013-D, Treaty With the Delawares	1,820,000	1,266	67.1	100%	$3	$5	$8
2013-S, Treaty With the Delawares, Proof	1,222,180	4,198	69.5			$8	$15
2014-P, Native Hospitality	3,080,000	206	67.0	100%	$3	$6	$9
2014-D, Native Hospitality	2,800,000	535	67.2	100%	$3	$6	$9
2014-D, Native Hospitality, Enhanced Unc. ††	50,000	5,184	68.9	100%		$10	$15
2014-S, Native Hospitality, Proof	1,144,154	6,363	69.3			$8	$15
2015-P, Mohawk Ironworkers	2,800,000	181	66.6	100%	$3	$5	$6
2015-D, Mohawk Ironworkers	2,240,000	1,513	66.9	100%	$3	$5	$6
2015-S, Mohawk Ironworkers, Proof	1,050,164	5,743	69.4			$8	$15
2015-W, Mohawk Ironworkers, Enhanced Unc.	88,805					$20	$30
2016-P, Code Talkers	2,800,000	14	65.4	100%	$3	$5	$6
2016-D, Code Talkers	2,100,000	22	66.5	100%	$3	$5	$6
2016-S, Code Talkers, Enhanced Uncirculated	50,737					$20	$30
2016-S, Code Talkers, Proof	965,033	2,689	69.5			$8	$15
2017-P, Sequoyah	1,820,000				$3	$5	$6
2017-D, Sequoyah	1,540,000				$3	$5	$6
2017-S, Sequoyah, Proof	926,774					$8	$15
2017-S, Sequoyah, Enhanced Uncirculated						$20	$30
2018-P, Jim Thorpe	1,400,000				$3	$5	$6
2018-D, Jim Thorpe	1,400,000				$3	$5	$6
2018-S, Jim Thorpe, Proof	799,413					$8	$15
2019-P, American Indians in Space					$3	$5	$6
2019-D, American Indians in Space					$3	$5	$6
2019-S, American Indians in Space, Proof						$8	$15

†† Ranked in the *100 Greatest U.S. Modern Coins* (fourth edition). **a.** Not issued for circulation.

AMERICAN INNOVATION (2018–2032)

Designers: *Justin Kunz (obverse); see image captions for reverse designers.*
Weight: *8.1 grams.* **Composition:** *Pure copper core with outer layers of manganese brass (.770 copper, .120 zinc, .070 manganese, and .040 nickel).*
Diameter: *26.5 mm.* **Edge:** *Lettered.* **Mints:** *Philadelphia, Denver, and San Francisco.*

  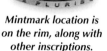  

Circulation Strike

Mintmark location is on the rim, along with other inscriptions.

Proof

History. In 2018, the U.S. Mint issued the first coin in a new, 15-year series: the American Innovation $1 Coin Program. Authorized by Public Law 115-197, each of the golden dollars in the program features a reverse design that "symbolizes quintessentially American traits—the willingness to explore, to discover, and to create one's own destiny." Four new designs, in Uncirculated and Proof finishes, are issued each year from 2019 through 2032—one for each state, in the order in which the states ratified the Constitution or were admitted to the Union, and then for the District of Columbia and each of the five U.S. territories (Puerto Rico, Guam, American Samoa, the U.S. Virgin Islands, and the Northern Mariana Islands). Like all dollar coins minted after 2011, they are issued for numismatic sales only; none are distributed for circulation.

Design concepts that showcase "an innovation, innovator or group of innovators from each State or Territory" are submitted to the Mint by official state/territorial liaisons. The secretary of the Treasury selects the concepts deemed most appropriate for $1 coin designs, and the Mint—working in concert with its artists, the state liaisons, the U.S. Commission of Fine Arts (CFA), the Citizens Coinage Advisory Committee (CCAC), and technical and historical consultants (as needed)—produces the final design candidates. The Treasury secretary makes the final selection from the resulting designs.

Coins in the series bear the following required inscriptions: on the obverse, IN GOD WE TRUST and the denomination; on the reverse, the name of the state, the District of Columbia, or territory (as appropriate), along with UNITED STATES OF AMERICA; and incused into the edge, the date, the mintmark, and the inscription E PLURIBUS UNUM. The common obverse depicts a left-facing profile of the Statue of Liberty, as designed by Justin Kunz and sculpted by Phebe Hemphill.

While each issue from 2019 through 2032 represents an individual state, district, or territory, the 2018 inaugural issue (designed by Donna Weaver and sculpted by Renata Gordon) represents the program in general. A pattern of gears and cogs represents American industry; below, a facsimile of George Washington's signature with SIGNED FIRST PATENT beneath it together represent the presidential signature on the first-ever U.S. patent, issued July 31, 1790. On a cartouche at the right, an eagle crouches on an angled shield, its wings spread behind it, with tools representing innovation (hammer, plow, wheel, etc.) below it.

Striking and Sharpness. Most examples are very well struck; check the higher points of the design.

Availability. American Innovation dollars are common in high grades, and are collected in MS and Proof. Proofs are been as well and are readily available.

GRADING STANDARDS

MS-60 to 70 (Mint State). *Obverse:* At MS-60, some abrasion and contact marks are evident, most noticeably on Liberty's cheek and in the wide, empty field. Luster is present but may be dull or lifeless. At MS-63, contact marks are extensive but not distracting. Abrasion still is evident, but less than at lower levels. MS-64 coins are slightly finer. An MS-65 coin may have minor abrasion, but contact marks are so minute as to require magnification. Luster should be full and rich. *Reverse:* At MS-60, some abrasion and contact marks are evident, most noticeably on the gear wheels. Otherwise, the same comments apply as for the obverse.

American Innovation dollars are seldom collected in grades lower than MS-60.

PF-60 to 70 (Proof). *Obverse and Reverse:* With medium hairlines and good reflectivity, assigned grades of PF–63 or 64 are appropriate. With relatively few hairlines a rating of PF-65 can be given. PF-66 may have hairlines so delicate that magnification is needed to see them. Above that, all the way to PF-70, a Proof should be free of any hairlines or other problems under strong magnification.

American Innovators
(2018)
Reverse designer:
Donna Weaver.

	Mintage	Cert	Avg	%MS	MS-64	MS-65	MS-66
						PF-65	PF-69DC
2018-P, American Innovators					$3	$5	$8
2018-D, American Innovators					$3	$5	$8
2018-S, American Innovators, Proof						$8	$15
2019-P, Delaware					$3	$5	$8
2019-D, Delaware					$3	$5	$8
2019-S, Delaware, Proof						$8	$15
2019-P, Pennsylvania					$3	$5	$8
2019-D, Pennsylvania					$3	$5	$8
2019-S, Pennsylvania, Proof						$8	$15
2019-P, New Jersey					$3	$5	$8
2019-D, New Jersey					$3	$5	$8
2019-S, New Jersey, Proof						$8	$15
2019-P, Georgia					$3	$5	$8
2019-D, Georgia					$3	$5	$8
2019-S, Georgia, Proof						$8	$15

Trade Dollars
1873–1885

AN OVERVIEW OF TRADE DOLLARS

A new denomination, the silver trade dollar, was authorized by the Coinage Act of 1873. This provided that a coin weighing 420 grains, of .900 fine silver, be struck for use in the export trade. By comparison, contemporary Liberty Seated silver dollars weighed 412.5 grains. Produced in quantity from 1873 through 1878, the trade dollars were a great success, particularly in China, where merchants preferred silver to gold and would not accept paper money of any kind. Coinage would have continued except for passage of the Bland-Allison Act of February 28, 1878, which authorized the government to buy millions of ounces of silver each year and resume the production of standard silver dollars (which had not been minted since 1873). The trade dollar was discontinued forthwith; however, Proof impressions were made for numismatists through 1883, plus a small quantity of Proofs distributed privately in 1884 and 1885, coins of these last two issues being great rarities today.

Choosing a trade dollar for a type set is easy enough to do, the choices being a circulation strike, which requires some connoisseurship, or a Proof, most of which are sharply struck and attractive. Enough exist in both formats that collectors will easily find a nice example, except that MS-65 and better pieces are elusive.

FOR THE COLLECTOR AND INVESTOR: TRADE DOLLARS AS A SPECIALTY

There are two great rarities among trade dollars: the Proof-only 1884, of which just ten are known, and the Proof-only 1885, of which only five are known. Neither was produced openly, and examples were sold for the private profit of Mint officials, going to John W. Haseltine, a Philadelphia dealer who was a favored outlet for such things. The existence of these coins was not generally known to numismatists until 1907–1908, when examples began to appear on the market. As to the mintage figures, the numbers five and ten have no official origin, but are said to represent the number once held by Haseltine. Relatively few numismatists have been able to afford examples of these two dates.

William Barber's Amazonian design, featuring a seated Columbia with eagle and sword, was rejected by Mint authorities for being too militaristic.

Beyond the above, a complete collection of trade dollars of the 1873 to 1883 years can be formed with some effort. Proofs were made of each year during this span, and after 1878 *only* Proofs were made, at the Philadelphia Mint, with no branch-mint issues. Proofs had greater appeal than Mint State circulation strikes to collectors of an earlier era, and more were saved, with the result that Proofs of the otherwise common dates 1873 to 1877 are much harder to find today, especially in choice condition.

Circulation strikes were regularly minted from 1873 through 1878, with production greatest at the San Francisco and Carson City mints, these being closest to eastern Asia, where the coins were used in commerce. Some trade dollars (but not many) went into domestic circulation (they were legal tender until that status was repealed on July 22, 1876). Later, after 1876, they traded widely in the United States but were valued by their silver content, not their face value. In 1878 the 412.5-grain Morgan dollar was worth $1.00 in circulation, while the heavier 420-grain trade dollar was worth only its melt-down value of about $0.90.

Very few of the circulating issues were saved by numismatists, with the result today that assembling a collection in choice or gem Mint State can be a great challenge. The key issue is the 1878-CC, with the lowest mintage by far in the series—scarce in any and all grades. As trade dollars became numismatically popular in the United States, thousands were repatriated from China, often bearing Chinese characters called *chopmarks*, which were applied by bankers and merchants. More often than not the imported coins had been harshly cleaned in China, as the owners thought shiny coins were more desirable. However, many choice and undamaged pieces were imported as well. The pieces with chopmarks are collectible in their own right in view of their historical significance.

Collectors are warned that many modern counterfeit trade dollars lurk in the marketplace.

TRADE DOLLAR (1873–1885)

Designer: *William Barber.* **Weight:** *27.22 grams.*
Composition: *.900 silver, .100 copper (net weight .7874 oz. pure silver).*
Diameter: *38.1 mm.* **Edge:** *Reeded.* **Mints:** *Philadelphia, Carson City, and San Francisco.*

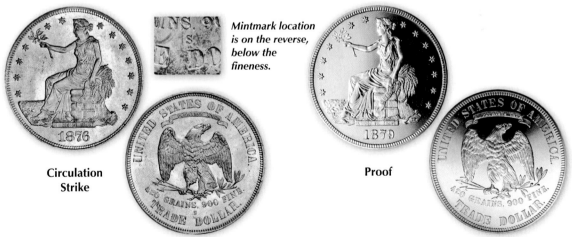

Mintmark location is on the reverse, below the fineness.

Circulation Strike

Proof

History. Trade dollars were minted under the Coinage Act of 1873. Containing 420 grains of .900 fine silver, they were heavier than the Liberty Seated dollar (of 412.5 grains). They were made for use in the China export trade and proved to be a great success. Some circulated at par in the United States, until they were demonetized by the Act of July 22, 1876, after which they circulated at their silver value, which was slightly lower than their face value. The Bland-Allison Act of 1878 provided for the new "Morgan" silver dollar, and trade dollars were discontinued, although Proofs continued to be made through 1885. Modifications to the trade dollar design are distinguished as follows.

Reverse 1: With a berry under the eagle's left talon; the lowest arrowhead ends over the 0 in 420. (Used on all coins from all mints in 1873 and 1874, and occasionally in 1875 and 1876.)

Reverse 2: Without an extra berry under the talon; the lowest arrowhead ends over the 2 in 420. (Used occasionally at all mints from 1875 through 1876, and on all coins from all mints 1877 through 1885.)

Obverse 1: The ends of the scroll point to the left; the extended hand has only three fingers. (Used on coins at all mints, 1873 through 1876.)

Obverse 2: The ends of the scroll point downward; the extended hand has four fingers. (Used in combination with Reverse 2 on one variety of 1876-S, and on all coins at all mints from 1877 through 1885.)

Striking and Sharpness. Weakness is often seen. On the obverse, check Miss Liberty's head and the star centers first. On the reverse, check the feathers on the eagle, particularly on the legs. Luster can range from dull to deeply frosty. In EF and lower grades, strike sharpness on the stars and the head does not matter to connoisseurs. Some Proofs are lightly struck on the head and the stars on the obverse and the leg feathers of the eagle on the reverse.

Availability. The 1878-CC is a rarity. Other dates and mintmarks are readily collected in grades from EF to MS. Lower grades are not often seen, for these coins did not circulate for a long time. Many used in China have counterstamps, called *chopmarks*, which are of interest to collectors. On an MS-63 or better coin a chopmark will decrease its value, but on EF and AU coins specialists eagerly seek them. MS coins are mostly in the lower ranges, often with unsatisfactory surfaces. True gems are very scarce. Proofs for collectors were made from 1873 to 1883 in quantity to supply the demand. In addition, a few were secretly made in 1884 and 1885. Most survivors are of high quality today, although gems of the 1873 to 1877 years are much harder to find than are those of 1878 to 1883.

Note: In recent years a flood of modern counterfeit trade dollars, many coming from China, has deluged the market.

GRADING STANDARDS

MS-60 to 70 (Mint State). *Obverse:* At MS-60, some abrasion and contact marks are evident, most noticeably on the left breast, left arm, and left knee. Luster is present, but may be dull or lifeless. Many of these coins are light in color or even brilliant, having been repatriated from China, and have been cleaned to remove sediment and discoloration. At MS-63, contact marks are very few, and abrasion is minimal. An MS-65 coin has

1875-S, Reverse 1. Graded MS-61.

no abrasion in the fields (but may have a hint on the higher parts of the seated figure), and contact marks are trivial. Luster should be full and rich. *Reverse:* Comments apply as for the obverse, except that in lower Mint State grades abrasion and contact marks are most noticeable on the eagle's head, the claws, and the top of the wings. At MS-65 or higher there are no marks visible to the unaided eye. The field is mainly protected by design elements and does not show abrasion as much as does the obverse on a given coin.

Illustrated coin: Some friction in the fields is seen, but much of the original luster remains.

AU-50, 53, 55, 58 (About Uncirculated). *Obverse:* Light wear is seen on the knees, bosom, and head. At AU-58, the luster is extensive but incomplete. At AU–50 and 53, luster is less. *Reverse:* Wear is visible on the eagle's head, the claws, and the top of the wings. An AU-58 coin will have nearly full luster. At AU–50 and 53, there still are traces of luster.

1876, Reverse 2. Graded AU-53.

Illustrated coin: This example shows light, even wear. Most of the luster is gone, except in protected areas, but it has excellent eye appeal for the grade.

EF-40, 45 (Extremely Fine). *Obverse:* Further wear is seen on all areas, especially the head, the left breast, the left arm, the left leg, and the bale on which Miss Liberty is seated. Little or no luster is seen on most coins. From this grade downward, strike sharpness on the stars and the head does not matter to connoisseurs. *Reverse:* Further wear is evident on the eagle's head, legs, claws, and wings, although on well-struck coins nearly all feather details on the wings are sharp.

1876-CC, Reverse 1. Graded EF-40.

VF-20, 30 (Very Fine). *Obverse:* Further wear is seen on the seated figure, although more than half the details of her dress are visible. Details of the wheat sheaf are mostly intact. IN GOD WE TRUST and LIBERTY are clear. *Reverse:* Wear is more extensive; some feathers are blended together, with two-thirds or more still visible.

1877-S. Graded VF-30.

F-12, 15 (Fine). *Obverse:* The seated figure is further worn, with fewer details of the dress visible. Most details in the wheat sheaf are clear. Both mottos are readable, but some letters may be weak. *Reverse:* Wear is extensive, with about half to nearly two-thirds of the feathers flat or blended with others. The eagle's left leg is mostly flat. Wear is seen on the raised E PLURIBUS UNUM, and one or two letters may be missing.

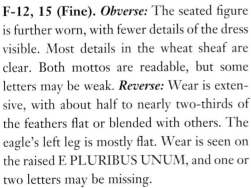

1873-CC. Graded F-12.

The trade dollar is seldom collected in grades lower than F-12.

PF-60 to 70 (Proof). *Obverse and Reverse:* Proofs that are extensively cleaned and have many hairlines, or that are dull and grainy, are lower level, such as PF–60 to 62. These are not widely desired. With medium hairlines and good reflectivity, an assigned grade of PF-64 is appropriate, and with relatively few hairlines, gem PF-65. In various grades hairlines are most easily seen in the obverse field. PF-66 may have hairlines so delicate

1882. Graded PF-62.

that magnification is needed to see them. Above that, a Proof should be free of such lines.

Illustrated coin: This coin has medium-gray toning overall.

Chopmarked Trade Dollar

Examples of chopmarks.

	Mintage	Cert	Avg	%MS	VG-8	F-12	VF-20	EF-40	AU-50	MS-60	MS-63	MS-64	MS-65
										PF-60	PF-63	PF-65
1873	396,900	183	57.5	65%	$170	$185	$225	$325	$650	$1,100	$3,000	$4,000	$9,000
	Auctions: $3,760, MS-64, August 2015; $3,668, MS-64, January 2015; $646, AU-55, September 2015; $588, AU-50, March 2015												
1873, Proof	600	159	63.1							$1,500	$3,000	$7,000
	Auctions: $8,225, PF-65, March 2015; $3,055, PF-64, September 2015; $3,055, PF-63Cam, June 2015; $2,720, PF-62Cam, July 2015												
1873-CC	124,500	131	52.9	27%	$375	$675	$900	$1,650	$2,750	$8,000	$25,000	$55,000	$110,000
	Auctions: $11,763, MS-62, October 2016; $5,288, AU-58, August 2015; $3,290, AU-58, February 2015; $3,290, AU-55, February 2015												
1873-S	703,000	109	59.6	71%	$175	$200	$300	$450	$675	$1,600	$3,800	$4,250	$22,500
	Auctions: $3,995, MS-63, July 2015; $2,820, MS-63, June 2015; $646, AU-55, March 2015; $165, VF-30, September 2015												

Reverse 1
Arrowheads end over 0;
berry under eagle's left talon.

Reverse 2
Arrowheads end over 2;
no berry under talon.

Obverse 1
Hand has three fingers;
scroll points left.

Obverse 2
Hand has four fingers;
scroll points downward.

1875-S, S Over CC
FS-T1-1875S-501.

	Mintage	Cert	Avg	%MS	VG-8	F-12	VF-20	EF-40	AU-50	MS-60	MS-63	MS-64	MS-65
										PF-60	PF-63	PF-65	
1874	987,100	146	57.6	62%	$170	$185	$225	$300	$425	$1,200	$2,400	$3,900	$13,000
	Auctions: $9,400, MS-65, August 2015; $2,350, MS-63, January 2015; $823, AU-58, September 2015; $400, EF-45, October 2015												
1874, Proof	700	206	63.2							$1,500	$3,000	$6,500	
	Auctions: $8,813, PF-66, January 2015; $11,456, PF-65Cam, October 2015; $3,878, PF-64Cam, August 2015; $2,468, PF-62, October 2015												
1874-CC	1,373,200	238	57.8	62%	$300	$425	$525	$700	$1,150	$3,000	$5,750	$17,500	$35,000
	Auctions: $17,038, MS-64, August 2016; $14,100, MS-64, October 2015; $12,925, MS-64, August 2015; $7,050, MS-63, August 2015												
1874-S	2,549,000	321	59.6	68%	$170	$185	$200	$300	$325	$875	$1,900	$3,250	$15,000
	Auctions: $1,645, MS-63, July 2015; $1,129, MS-62, September 2015; $911, MS-61, July 2015; $376, AU-53, July 2015												
1875	218,200	106	58.0	70%	$350	$450	$650	$950	$1,300	$2,500	$4,500	$7,500	$15,000
	Auctions: $1,175, AU-53, September 2015; $541, AU-50, June 2015; $353, EF-40, April 2015; $1,763, VF-30, January 2015												
1875, Reverse 2	(a)	1	64.0	100%	$240	$375	$525	$750	$1,250	$2,600	$4,650	$9,000	$21,000
	Auctions: $4,888, MS-64, April 2012												
1875, Proof	700	228	63.3							$1,500	$3,000	$8,500	
	Auctions: $28,200, PF-66, May 2015; $7,638, PF-65, August 2015; $3,290, PF-64Cam, June 2015; $2,233, PF-62, July 2015												
1875-CC, All kinds	1,573,700												
1875-CC		325	55.0	48%	$275	$375	$475	$575	$850	$2,500	$5,750	$11,500	$35,000
	Auctions: $8,813, MS-64, August 2016; $823, MS-60, June 2015; $969, AU-53, December 2015; $646, EF-40, June 2015												
1875-CC, Reverse 2		0	n/a		$275	$375	$475	$650	$925	$2,500	$5,500	$10,500	$33,500
	Auctions: $1,610, AU-58, January 2012												
1875-S, All kinds	4,487,000												
1875-S		973	60.1	76%	$165	$185	$225	$300	$350	$875	$1,600	$2,900	$8,500
	Auctions: $1,058, MS-62, August 2015; $881, MS-61, September 2015; $447, AU-58, April 2015; $282, EF-45, December 2015												
1875-S, Reverse 2		5	61.4	80%	$165	$185	$200	$325	$400	$1,175	$2,350	$3,400	$11,000
	Auctions: $69,000, MS-67, January 2012; $1,020, MS-62, January 2018												
1875-S, S Over CC (b)		57	58.6	49%	$265	$400	$525	$1,000	$1,700	$5,000	$14,500	$25,000	$45,000
	Auctions: $24,675, MS-64, May 2015; $11,750, MS-64, March 2016; $4,113, MS-61, January 2015; $2,585, AU-58, October 2015												

a. Included in circulation-strike 1875 mintage figure. **b.** A weak C from the underlying CC mintmark is visible to the right of the S mintmark.

1876-CC, Doubled Die Reverse
FS-T1-1876CC-801.

1876-S, Doubled Die Obverse
FS-T1-1876S-101.

	Mintage	Cert	Avg	%MS	VG-8	F-12	VF-20	EF-40	AU-50	MS-60	MS-63	MS-64	MS-65
											PF-60	PF-63	PF-65
1876	455,000	465	59.2	75%	$165	$185	$200	$300	$335	$1,050	$1,850	$3,200	$9,000
	Auctions: $400, MS-60, May 2015; $494, AU-55, August 2015; $212, AU-50, February 2015; $212, EF-45, June 2015; $504, AU-50, March 2018												
1876, Obverse 2, Reverse 2 (c)	(d)	0	n/a							—			
	Auctions: No auction records available.												
1876, Reverse 2	(d)	0	n/a		$165	$185	$225	$300	$335	$900	$2,000	$3,200	$11,000
	Auctions: $2,760, MS-64, April 2012												
1876, Reverse 2, Proof	1,150	283	62.8								$1,500	$3,000	$6,500
	Auctions: $15,275, PF-66Cam, October 2015; $3,760, PF-64Cam, June 2015; $2,703, PF-63, January 2015; $1,410, PF-60, February 2015												
1876-CC, All kinds	509,000												
1876-CC		138	54.5	38%	$350	$450	$575	$775	$2,000	$6,250	$25,000	$37,500	$80,000
	Auctions: $2,820, AU-58, February 2015; $2,585, AU-55, February 2015; $1,528, AU-53, March 2016; $646, AU-50, September 2014; $1,293												
1876-CC, Reverse 1	1	53.0	0%	$325	$450	$600	$875	$2,350	$7,250	$27,500	$40,000	$115,000	
	Auctions: $3,220, MS-60, February 2006												
1876-CC, Doubled Die Reverse (e)		33	54.9	27%	$500	$650	$1,150	$1,550	$2,100	$10,000	$25,000		
	Auctions: $2,350, MS-60, February 2014; $1,087, AU-50, June 2015; $382, AU-50, September 2014; $3,030, AU-58, February 2018												
1876-S, All kinds	5,227,000												
1876-S		883	57.0	56%	$165	$185	$200	$300	$350	$900	$1,600	$3,000	$11,000
	Auctions: $1,175, MS-62, January 2015; $705, AU-58, May 2015; $400, AU-55, October 2015; $200, EF-40, October 2015												
1876-S, Doubled Die Obverse (f)		0	n/a					$1,400	$1,750	$2,200			
	Auctions: No auction records available.												
1876-S, Reverse 2		3	57.0	0%	$165	$185	$200	$300	$350	$900	$1,600	$3,000	$11,000
	Auctions: $1,506, MS-63, September 2011												
1876-S, Obverse 2, Reverse 2		1	58.0	0%	$165	$200	$300	$500	$850	$1,500	$2,650	$3,700	$13,500
	Auctions: $1,495, MS-60 CAC, August 2011												

c. Extremely rare. **d.** Included in circulation-strike 1876 mintage figure. **e.** Doubling is visible on the branches on the right, the eagle's talons, the right wing tip, and the eagle's beak; and is very strong on E PLURIBUS UNUM. Weaker doubling is seen on UNITED STATES OF AMERICA. "Considered by most to be the strongest reverse doubled die in the series, this variety is one of the highlights of the trade dollar varieties and is thought to be extremely rare in grades above AU" (*Cherrypickers' Guide to Rare Die Varieties*, sixth edition, volume II). **f.** Doubling is visible on Liberty's hand, chin, and left foot, and on the olive branch. "This DDO is easily the rarest doubled die in the series, and is considered extremely rare in grades above AU. Most known examples are cleaned. The variety is known as the king of the trade dollar varieties" (*Cherrypickers' Guide to Rare Die Varieties*, sixth edition, volume II).

1877, Doubled Die Obverse
FS-T1-1877-101.

1877-S, Repunched Date
FS-T1-1877S-301.

1877-S, Doubled Die Reverse
FS-T1-1877S-801.

1877-S, Doubled Die Reverse
FS-T1-1877S-802.

1878-S, Doubled Die Reverse
FS-T1-1878S-801.

	Mintage	Cert	Avg	%MS	VG-8	F-12	VF-20	EF-40	AU-50	MS-60 / PF-60	MS-63 / PF-63	MS-64	MS-65 / PF-65
1877	3,039,200	654	51.6	44%	$165	$200	$225	$325	$350	$950	$1,650	$3,400	$9,000
Auctions: $16,450, MS-65, October2015; $12,925, MS-65, October 2015; $1,528, MS-63, January 2015; $1,058, MS-62, March 2016; $999													
1877, DblDie Obv (g)	(h)	2	60.0	50%				$300	$400	$1,250			
Auctions: No auction records available.													
1877, Proof	510	202	63.5							$1,650	$3,500		$7,000
Auctions: $3,055, PF-64, March 2015; $3,290, PF-63Cam, June 2015; $1,528, PF-60, January 2015; $1,293, PF-60, June 2015													
1877-CC	534,000	137	54.5	53%	$285	$425	$550	$725	$1,000	$4,000	$10,000	$23,500	$65,000
Auctions: $25,850, MS-64, August 2015; $14,100, MS-64, March 2015; $7,638, MS-63, August 2016; $7,638, MS-63, February 2015													
1877-S	9,519,000	1,543	54.7	50%	$165	$185	$200	$300	$325	$1,000	$1,600	$3,100	$9,000
Auctions: $6,463, MS-65, January 2015; $1,351, MS-63, October 2015; $212, EF-45, March 2015; $136, VF-30, June 2015													
1877-S, Repunched Date (i)	(j)	0	n/a					$550	$800	$1,600			
Auctions: $250, EF-45, May 2010													
1877-S, DblDie Rev (k)	(j)	2	55.5	0%				$300	$425	$1,300			
Auctions: No auction records available.													
1877-S, DblDie Rev (l)	(j)	6	52.7	50%				$300	$400	$1,200			
Auctions: $1,323, MS-62, April 2011													
1878	0	n/a							$1,500				
Auctions: No auction records available.													
1878, Proof	900	340	63.7							$1,500	$3,000		$7,000
Auctions: $12,338, PF-66, May 2015; $6,463, PF-65Cam, August 2015; $8,813, PF-64DCam, September 2015; $2,820, PF-63Cam, August 2015													
1878-CC (m)	97,000	91	47.3	29%	$700	$1,175	$1,675	$3,750	$5,000	$13,500	$35,000	$75,000	$130,000
Auctions: $18,800, MS-62, May 2015; $12,338, MS-61, February 2015; $11,163, AU-58, August 2015; $10,575, AU-58, June 2015													
1878-S	4,162,000	1118	51.8	40%	$165	$185	$200	$300	$350	$900	$1,600	$3,000	$9,000
Auctions: $28,200, MS-66, May 2015; $2,703, MS-64, August 2015; $329, AU-55, January 2015; $200, EF-40, October 2015													
1878-S, DblDie Rev (n)	(o)	14	53.6	36%				$450	$550	$1,300			
Auctions: $1,000, MS-62, August 2011													

g. Doubling on this rare variety is evident on the wheat stalks, LIBERTY, IN GOD WE TRUST, and stars 11, 12, and 13. **h.** Included in circulation-strike 1877 mintage figure. **i.** A secondary 7 protrudes prominently south from the last 7. **j.** Included in 1877-S mintage figure. **k.** Doubling is visible on E PLURIBUS UNUM, the ribbon, and UNITED STATES OF AMERICA. There are at least two different doubled-die reverses for 1877-S; this one is FS-T1-1877S-801. "Considered a highlight of the trade dollar varieties" (*Cherrypickers' Guide to Rare Die Varieties*, sixth edition, volume II). **l.** Minor doubling is visible on nearly all reverse lettering, especially on 420 GRAINS. This reverse doubled die is more common than the preceding; it is listed as FS-T1-1877S-802. **m.** On July 19, 1878, a quantity of 44,148 trade dollars was melted by the Mint. Many of these may have been 1878-CC. **n.** Strong doubling is visible on the entire lower left of the reverse, on the arrow points and shafts, and on 420 GRAINS; slight doubling is evident on the motto. Rare in AU and higher grades. There are at least two doubled-die reverses for this date; the one listed is FS-T1-1878S-801. **o.** Included in 1878-S mintage figure.

	Mintage	Cert	Avg	%MS	VG-8	F-12	VF-20	EF-40	AU-50	MS-60 PF-40	MS-63 PF-60	MS-64 PF-63	MS-65 PF-65
1879, Proof	1,541	554	63.7							$1,250	$1,500	$3,000	$6,500
Auctions: $15,863, PF-67Cam, January 2015; $8,813, PF-66Cam, September 2015; $5,053, PF-65+, September 2015; $1,763, PF-62, January 2015													
1880, Proof	1,987	700	63.5							$1,250	$1,500	$3,000	$6,500
Auctions: $15,275, PF-67, August 2015; $11,750, PF-66UCam, January 2015; $3,408, PF-64Cam, January 2015; $2,585, PF-63, January 2015													
1881, Proof	960	419	63.7							$1,250	$1,500	$3,000	$6,500
Auctions: $$8,225, PF-66, May 2015; $4,818, PF-65, October 2015; $4,700, PF-64Cam+, September 2015; $1,763, PF-62, January 2015													
1882, Proof	1,097	517	63.9							$1,250	$1,500	$3,000	$6,500
Auctions: $19,975, PF-66DCam, August 2015; $5,405, PF-65, August 2015; $3,760, PF-64Cam, October 2015; $3,055, PF-63Cam, August 2015													
1883, Proof	979	493	63.7							$1,250	$1,500	$3,000	$6,500
Auctions: $14,100, PF-66Cam, August 2015; $7,638, PF-65, August 2015; $4,935, PF-64Cam, June 2015; $2,374, PF-63, January 2015													
1884, Proof † (p)	10	7	64.0							$1,250		$650,000	$1,100,000
Auctions: $998,750, PF-65, January 2014													
1885, Proof † (p)	5	2	62.0									$2,000,000	$3,500,000
Auctions: $1,006,250, PF-62, November 2004													

† Ranked in the *100 Greatest U.S. Coins* (fourth edition). **p.** Trade dollars of 1884 and 1885 were unknown to the numismatic community until 1907 and 1908. None are listed in the Mint director's report, and numismatists believe that they are not a part of the regular Mint issue but were produced secretly for private sale to collectors.

Gold Dollars
1849–1889

AN OVERVIEW OF GOLD DOLLARS

Coinage of the gold dollar was authorized by the Act of March 3, 1849, after the start of the California Gold Rush.

Although a case could be made for designating the Small Head, Open Wreath, gold dollar as a separate type, it is not generally collected as such. Instead, pieces dated from 1849 through 1854 (whether Open Wreath or Close Wreath) are collectively designated as Type 1. Examples today are readily available in all grades, although truly choice and gem Mint State pieces are in the minority.

In contrast, the Type 2 design, produced at the Philadelphia Mint in part of 1854, and at the Philadelphia, Charlotte, Dahlonega, and New Orleans mints in 1855, and only at the San Francisco Mint in 1856, is a great challenge. Examples are scarcer in all grades than are those of types 1 and 3. Choice and gem coins are especially rare. Striking is a great problem, and while some sharp pieces exist, probably 80% or more have areas of weakness, typically at the 85 (center two digits) of the date, but also often on the headdress and elsewhere. Further, the borders are sometimes imperfect.

Type 3 gold dollars, made from 1856 through 1889, are easier to acquire in nearly any grade desired, including choice and gem Mint State. Most are well struck and in Mint State have excellent eye appeal. Among Type 3 gold dollars the dates from 1879 through 1889 inclusive are most often seen, as these were widely saved by coin dealers and collectors at the time and did not circulate to any appreciable extent. Gold dollar coins also were popular as Christmas gifts in the late 1800s. Some of these have very low mintage figures, making them very appealing to today's collectors.

FOR THE COLLECTOR AND INVESTOR: GOLD DOLLARS AS A SPECIALTY

North Carolina Representative James Iver McKay was among the proponents for the introduction of a gold dollar coin. He introduced a bill to authorize the denomination into the House of Representatives on February 20, 1849.

Forming a specialized collection of gold dollars is a fascinating pursuit, one that has drawn the attention of many numismatists over the years. A complete run of date-and-mintmark issues from 1849 through 1889 includes no impossible rarities, although the 1875, with just 20 Proofs and 400 circulation strikes made, is the key date and can challenge collectors. While the dollars of 1879 through 1889 often have remarkably low mintages, they were saved in quantity, and certain of these dates are easily obtainable (although not necessarily inexpensive).

The branch-mint gold dollars of the early years present a special challenge. Among the Charlotte Mint varieties the 1849 comes with an Open Wreath (of which just five are presently known, with a rumor of a sixth) and with a Close Wreath, the latter being scarce but available. Later Charlotte gold dollars, extending through 1859, range from scarce to rare. The 1857-C is notorious for its poor striking.

Gold dollars were struck at the Dahlonega Mint from 1849 through 1861. In the latter year the facility was under the control of the Confederate States of America, and thus the 1861-D gold dollars, rare in any event, are even more desirable as true Confederate coins. The New Orleans Mint also produced gold dollars, which in general are better struck than those of the Charlotte and Dahlonega mints. From 1854 intermittently to 1860, and then in 1870, gold dollars were struck in San Francisco. These Western issues are usually sharply defined and range from scarce to rare. In particular, choice and gem Mint State pieces are elusive.

LIBERTY HEAD (1849–1854)

Designer: *James B. Longacre.* **Weight:** *1.672 grams.*
Composition: *.900 gold, .100 copper (net weight .04837 oz. pure gold).*
Diameter: *13 mm.* **Edge:** *Reeded.* **Mints:** *Philadelphia,*
Charlotte, Dahlonega, New Orleans, and San Francisco.

| Open Wreath Reverse | Close Wreath Reverse | Proof | Mintmark location is on the reverse, below the wreath. |

History. U.S. Mint chief engraver James Barton Longacre designed the nation's gold dollars. This first type measured 13 mm in diameter, which proved to be inconvenient, and the two later types were enlarged to 15 mm.

Striking and Sharpness. As a rule, Type 1 gold dollars struck in Philadelphia are sharper than those of the Charlotte and Dahlonega mints. On the obverse, check the highest areas of the hair below the coronet. On the reverse, check the wreath and the central two figures in the date. On both sides check the denticles, which can be mushy or indistinct (particularly on Charlotte and Dahlonega coins, which often have planchet roughness as well).

Availability. All dates and mintmarks are readily collectible, save for the 1849-C, Open Wreath, variety. MS coins often are found for the Philadelphia issues but can be elusive for the branch mints. Charlotte and Dahlonega coins often have striking problems. The few gold dollars of this type that are less than VF in grade usually are damaged or have problems. Although a few Proofs were coined in the early years, they are for all practical purposes unobtainable. Only about a dozen are known.

GRADING STANDARDS

MS-60 to 70 (Mint State). *Obverse:* At MS–60 to 62, there is abrasion on the hair below the coronet (an area that can be weakly struck as well) and on the cheeks. Marks may be seen. At MS-63, there may be slight abrasion. Luster is irregular. At MS-64, abrasion is less. Luster is rich on most coins, less so on Charlotte and Dahlonega varieties. At MS-65 and above, luster is deep and frosty. At MS-66 and higher, no marks at all are visible

1854, Close Wreath. Graded MS-62.

without magnification. *Reverse:* On MS–60 to 62 coins, there is abrasion on the 1, the highest parts of the leaves, and the ribbon. Otherwise, the same comments apply as for the obverse.

Illustrated coin: Some friction is visible on the portrait and in the fields.

AU-50, 53, 55, 58 (About Uncirculated). *Obverse:* Light wear on the hair below the coronet and the cheek is very noticeable at AU-50, and progressively less at higher levels to AU-58. Luster is minimal at AU-50 and scattered and incomplete at AU-58. Some tiny nicks and contact marks are to be expected and should be mentioned if they are distracting. *Reverse:* Light wear on the 1, the wreath, and the ribbon characterize an AU-50 coin,

1853-D. Graded AU-58.

progressively less at higher levels to AU-58. Otherwise, the same comments apply as for the obverse.

Illustrated coin: Much of the luster remains, especially in protected areas.

EF-40, 45 (Extremely Fine). *Obverse:* Medium wear is seen on the hair below the coronet, extending to near the bun, and on the curls below. Detail is partially gone on the hair to the right of the coronet. Luster is gone on most coins. *Reverse:* Light wear is seen overall, and the highest parts of the leaves are flat. Luster is gone.

1849-C, Close Wreath. Graded EF-45.

VF-20, 30 (Very Fine). *Obverse:* Most hair detail is gone, except in the lower-relief areas and on the lower curls. Star centers are flat. *Reverse:* The wreath and other areas show more wear. Most detail is gone on the higher-relief leaves.

This gold dollar is seldom collected in grades lower than VF-20.

1851-D. Graded VF-25.

PF-60 to 70 (Proof). *Obverse and Reverse:* PF–60 to 62 coins have extensive hairlines and may have nicks and contact marks. At PF-63, hairlines are prominent, but the mirror surface is very reflective. PF-64 coins have fewer hairlines. At PF-65, hairlines should be minimal and mostly seen only under magnification. One cannot be "choosy" with Proofs of this type, as only a few exist.

1849, Open Wreath. Proof.

1849, With L   1849, No L

	Mintage	Cert	Avg	%MS	VF-20	EF-40	AU-50	AU-55	AU-58	MS-60	MS-63	MS-64	MS-65
													PF-60
1849, Open Wreath, So-Called Small Head, With L (a)	688,567	963	60.9	74%	$225	$250	$275	$300	$325	$350	$1,500	$2,100	$4,250
Auctions: $1,763, MS-64, June 2015; $705, MS-62, January 2015; $188, AU-58, January 2015; $235, AU-50, July 2015													
1849, Open Wreath, So-Called Small Head, No L (a)	(b)	390	62.2	86%	$225	$275	$300	$325	$400	$800	$1,750	$2,100	$4,250
Auctions: $4,935, MS-65, July 2015; $1,293, MS-63, January 2015; $881, MS-61, February 2015; $823, MS-60, October 2015													
1849, Open Wreath, So-Called Large Head (a)	(b)	0	n/a		$225	$250	$275	$300	$325	$350	$1,250	$1,900	$4,250
Auctions: $3,760, MS-65, January 2015; $1,495, MS-64, April 2012													
1849, Close Wreath	(b)	482	61.6	80%	$215	$250	$275	$295	$325	$650	$1,500	$1,950	$5,500
Auctions: $25,850, MS-66, August 2015; $705, MS-62, August 2015; $376, AU-58, August 2015; $329, AU-50, March 2015													
1849, Open Wreath, So-Called Small Head, No L, Proof (c)	unknown	3	62.7										
Auctions: No auction records available.													
1849-C, Open Wreath † (d)	(b)	2	32.5	0%	$200,000	$225,000	$250,000	$300,000	$365,000	$450,000	$650,000		
Auctions: $3,220, AU-58, April 2012													
1849-C, Close Wreath	11,634	97	55.7	31%	$1,300	$1,800	$2,500	$4,000	$6,000	$9,000	$17,500	$45,000	
Auctions: $49,350, MS-64, August 2015; $10,281, MS-62, September 2013; $1,058, AU-50, January 2015; $2,820, EF-45, July 2014													
1849-D, Open Wreath	21,588	0	n/a		$1,500	$2,100	$2,600	$3,250	$4,000	$5,500	$11,500	$22,500	$55,000
Auctions: $22,325, MS-64, April 2013; $4,465, MS-62, January 2015; $3,760, MS-61, January 2015; $2,585, AU-55, September 2014													
1849-O, Open Wreath	215,000	0	n/a		$265	$325	$400	$485	$600	$1,000	$3,500	$7,000	$12,500
Auctions: $11,750, MS-65, March 2015; $999, MS-61, September 2015; $423, AU-58, June 2015; $259, EF-45, November 2015													

† Ranked in the *100 Greatest U.S. Coins* (fourth edition). **a.** It is now well known that the so-called Small Head and Large Head coins are from the same punch. **b.** Included in 1849, Open Wreath, So-Called Small Head, With L, mintage figure. **c.** 2 to 3 examples are known. **d.** This coin is extremely rare.

	Mintage	Cert	Avg	%MS	VF-20	EF-40	AU-50	AU-55	AU-58	MS-60	MS-63	MS-64	MS-65 PF-60
1850	481,953	542	59.9	67%	$215	$250	$265	$285	$300	$425	$850	$1,350	$4,000
	Auctions: $32,900, MS-67, August 2015; $2,585, MS-64, October 2015; $447, MS-61, June 2015; $235, AU-55, January 2015												
1850, Proof (e)	*unknown*	0	n/a										$100,000
	Auctions: No auction records available.												
1850-C	6,966	90	54.8	26%	$1,450	$1,850	$3,000	$4,000	$4,750	$8,000	$23,500		
	Auctions: $24,675, MS-63, February 2015; $19,975, MS-63, January 2014; $17,625, MS-63, November 2014; $11,163, MS-61, September 2016												
1850-D	8,382	98	55.0	23%	$1,500	$2,200	$3,400	$5,000	$6,750	$10,500	$25,000	$37,500	
	Auctions: $3,290, AU-55, January 2015; $3,204, AU-50, July 2014												
1850-O	14,000	197	58.2	43%	$300	$500	$900	$1,150	$1,850	$3,000	$6,500	$13,500	
	Auctions: $2,532, MS-61, April 2012												
1851	3,317,671	4,468	61.1	80%	$200	$225	$240	$250	$275	$325	$500	$750	$2,250
	Auctions: $3,995, MS-66, July 2015; $329, MS-61, January 2015; $229, AU-55, April 2015; $1,528, EF-45, September 2015												
1851-C	41,267	398	57.2	34%	$1,350	$1,650	$2,000	$2,250	$2,550	$3,200	$6,250	$13,500	$25,000
	Auctions: $5,376, MS-63, January 2015; $3,525, MS-62, June 2015; $2,468, AU-58, March 2015; $2,056, AU-55, January 2015												
1851-D	9,882	141	57.9	40%	$1,500	$2,000	$2,500	$3,000	$4,000	$5,000	$14,500	$22,500	$45,000
	Auctions: $14,688, MS-64, October 2014; $7,638, MS-62, February 2015; $4,113, AU-58, October 2014; $2,233, AU-50, March 2015												
1851-O	290,000	900	58.5	46%	$225	$265	$325	$425	$450	$800	$2,000	$4,000	$9,500
	Auctions: $12,925, MS-65, August 2015; $764, MS-61, January 2015; $270, AU-55, November 2015; $194, EF-45, January 2015												
1852	2,045,351	4,023	61.2	80%	$200	$225	$240	$250	$275	$325	$500	$750	$2,250
	Auctions: $4,700, MS-66, July 2015; $470, MS-63, August 2015; $259, AU-58, May 2015; $235, AU-55, August 2015												
1852-C	9,434	150	57.2	41%	$1,400	$1,850	$2,250	$2,750	$3,500	$4,600	$10,500	$16,500	$30,000
	Auctions: $15,863, MS-64, February 2013; $2,128, AU-55, October 2014; $2,585, AU-53, July 2014; $1,880, EF-40, July 2015												
1852-D	6,360	109	56.4	29%	$1,500	$2,250	$2,750	$3,750	$5,000	$8,500	$30,000		
	Auctions: $4,230, AU-58, February 2015; $4,994, AU-55, July 2014; $4,230, EF-45, January 2015												
1852-O	140,000	475	56.9	33%	$225	$265	$400	$600	$750	$1,300	$4,200	$12,500	$35,000
	Auctions: $37,600, MS-65, August 2015; $2,497, MS-63, January 2015; $541, AU-58, January 2015; $237, AU-53, June 2015												
1853	4,076,051	10,644	61.2	81%	$200	$225	$240	$250	$275	$325	$500	$750	$2,250
	Auctions: $20,575, MS-67, August 2015; $881, MS-64, February 2015; $353, MS-61, August 2015; $235, AU-55, November 2015												
1853-C	11,515	130	57.0	37%	$1,350	$1,600	$2,100	$2,600	$3,500	$4,750	$13,000	$22,000	$45,000
	Auctions: $14,100, MS-64, January 2014; $4,406, MS-62, August 2014; $9,988, MS-62, October 2014; $1,593, EF-40, July 2014												
1853-D	6,583	129	57.5	29%	$1,500	$2,000	$2,500	$4,250	$5,500	$8,500	$22,000	$32,500	$50,000
	Auctions: $17,038, MS-63, June 2015; $8,225, MS-62, June 2015; $6,933, MS-61, January 2015; $3,055, AU-55, October 2014												
1853-O	290,000	1,285	59.5	57%	$225	$255	$335	$425	$450	$700	$2,000	$2,750	$8,000
	Auctions: $23,500, MS-66, August 2015; $1,058, MS-62, January 2015; $259, AU-55, June 2015; $212, AU-50, February 2015												
1854	855,502	3,749	61.5	86%	$200	$225	$240	$250	$275	$325	$500	$750	$2,250
	Auctions: $19,975, MS-67, August 2015; $5,170, MS-66, August 2015; $376, MS-62, November 2015; $282, AU-55, October 2015												
1854, Proof	*unknown*	0	n/a										
	Auctions: No auction records available.												
1854-D	2,935	75	56.1	33%	$2,000	$2,500	$5,250	$6,500	$7,750	$11,000	$30,000	$65,000	
	Auctions: $7,638, MS-61, October 2015; $6,465, AU-58, July 2015; $5,640, AU-58, January 2015; $4,465, EF-45, September 2016												
1854-S	14,632	148	58.5	39%	$450	$650	$1,000	$1,400	$2,000	$2,600	$6,500	$16,000	$35,000
	Auctions: $56,400, MS-65, August 2015; $2,820, MS-62, January 2015; $1,528, AU-58, January 2015; $1,058, AU-53, February 2015												

e. 2 examples are known.

INDIAN PRINCESS HEAD, SMALL HEAD (1854–1856)

Designer: *James B. Longacre.* **Weight:** *1.672 grams.*
Composition: *.900 gold, .100 copper (net weight .04837 oz. pure gold).* **Diameter:** *15 mm.*
Edge: *Reeded.* **Mints:** *Philadelphia, Charlotte, Dahlonega, New Orleans, San Francisco.*

Circulation Strike

Mintmark location is on the reverse, below the wreath.

Proof

History. The Type 2 gold dollar, with the diameter increased from 13 mm to 15 mm, was first made in 1854. The headdress is decorated with *ostrich* plumes, which would not have been used in any genuine Native American headgear. The design proved difficult to strike, leading to its modification in 1856.

Striking and Sharpness. On the obverse, check the highest area of the hair below the coronet and the tips of the feathers. Check the letters. On the reverse, check the ribbon bow knot and in particular the two central digits of the dates. Examine the digits on both sides. Nearly all have problems. This type is often softly struck in the centers, with weak hair detail and the numerals 85 in the date sometimes faint—this should not be confused with wear. The 1855-C and 1855-D coins are often poorly struck and on rough planchets.

Availability. All Type 2 gold dollars are collectible, but the Charlotte and Dahlonega coins are rare. With patience, Full Details coins are available of 1854, 1855, and 1856-S, but virtually impossible to find for the branch-mint issues of 1855. The few gold dollars of this type that are less than VF in grade usually are damaged or have problems. Proofs exist of the 1854 and 1855 issues, but were made in very small quantities.

GRADING STANDARDS

MS-60 to 70 (Mint State). *Obverse:* At MS–60 to 62, there is abrasion on the hair below the band lettered LIBERTY (an area that can be weakly struck as well), on the tips of the feather plumes, and throughout the field. Contact marks may also be seen. At MS-63, there should be only slight abrasions. Luster is irregular. At MS-64, abrasions and marks are less. Luster is rich on most coins, less so on Charlotte and Dahlonega issues. At

1854. Graded MS-61.

MS-65 and above, luster is deep and frosty, with no marks at all visible without magnification at MS-66 and higher. *Reverse:* At MS–60 to 62, there may be abrasions on the 1, on the highest parts of the leaves, on the ribbon knot, and in the field. Otherwise, the same comments apply as for the obverse.

  Illustrated coin: Some loss of luster is evident in the fields, but strong luster remains among the letters and in other protected areas. Good eye appeal is elusive for this type.

AU-50, 53, 55, 58 (About Uncirculated). *Obverse:* Light wear on the hair below the coronet, the cheek, and the tips of the feather plumes is very noticeable at AU-50, progressively less at higher levels to AU-58. Luster is minimal at AU-50 and scattered and incomplete at AU-58. Some tiny nicks and contact marks are to be expected and should be mentioned if they are distracting. *Reverse:* Light wear on the 1, the wreath, and the ribbon knot characterize an AU-50 coin, progressively less at higher levels to AU-58. Otherwise, the same comments apply as for the obverse.

1855. Graded AU-55.

Illustrated coin: This coin was lightly struck at the center. Clash marks appear on both sides, most prominent within the wreath on the reverse.

EF-40, 45 (Extremely Fine). *Obverse:* Medium wear is seen on the hair below the coronet and on the feather plume tips. Detail is partially gone on the hair, although the usual light striking may make this moot. Luster is gone on most coins. *Reverse:* Light wear is seen overall, and the highest parts of the leaves are flat. Luster is gone on most coins.

Illustrated coin: This coin was lightly struck at the centers, but overall has extraordinary quality.

1855-C. Graded EF-40.

VF-20, 30 (Very Fine). *Obverse:* Most hair detail is gone, except at the back of the lower curls. The feather plume ends are flat. *Reverse:* The wreath and other areas show more wear. Most detail is gone on the higher-relief leaves.

This gold dollar is seldom collected in grades lower than VF-20.

Illustrated coin: This coin is well worn, but has an exceptionally bold date, indicating that it must have been a very sharp strike.

1854. Graded VF-25.

PF-60 to 70 (Proof). *Obverse and Reverse:* PF–60 to 62 coins have extensive hairlines and may have nicks and contact marks. At PF-63, hairlines are prominent, but the mirror surface is very reflective. PF-64 coins have fewer hairlines. At PF-65, hairlines should be minimal and mostly seen only under magnification. There should be no nicks or marks. PF-66 and higher coins have no marks or hairlines visible to the unaided eye.

1854. Graded PF-66.

1854, Doubled Die Obverse
FS-G1-1854-1101.

	Mintage	Cert	Avg	%MS	VF-20	EF-40	AU-50	AU-55	MS-60	MS-62	MS-63 / PF-63	MS-64 / PF-64	MS-65 / PF-65
1854	783,943	5,943	57.3	27%	$325	$425	$500	$625	$1,250	$2,250	$5,750	$7,750	$25,000
Auctions: $51,700, MS-66, August 2015; $1,880, MS-62, January 2015; $402, AU-53, October 2015; $329, EF-40, August 2015													
1854, Doubled Die Obverse (a)	**(b)**	18	56.2	6%					$2,500	$5,500	$7,500	$12,500	
Auctions: $3,738, MS-62, December 2011													
1854, Proof †	*4 known*	5	64.6								$200,000	$300,000	$425,000
Auctions: $218,500, PF-64DCam, March 2009													
1855	758,269	5,486	57.1	28%	$325	$425	$500	$625	$1,250	$2,250	$5,750	$7,750	$25,000
Auctions: $54,050, MS-66, August 2015; $4,230, MS-63, January 2015; $640, AU-58, February 2015; $529, EF-40, April 2015													
1855, Proof †	*unknown*	6	64.8								$165,000	$225,000	$325,000
Auctions: $397,800, PF, September 2013													
1855-C	9,803	190	51.5	9%	$2,350	$4,750	$6,500	$10,000	$25,000	$35,000			
Auctions: $24,675, MS-61, January 2015; $7,638, AU-55, June 2015; $5,611, AU-50, June 2015; $4,230, EF-40, June 2015													
1855-D	1,811	42	54.4	12%	$12,500	$25,000	$35,000	$40,000	$60,000	$70,000	$100,000	$175,000	
Auctions: $164,500, MS-64, August 2015; $28,200, AU-55, September 2016; $8,225, AU-50, July 2015; $52,875, EF-45, July 2014													
1855-O	55,000	508	54.7	13%	$775	$1,300	$1,850	$3,000	$8,000	$15,000	$30,000	$45,000	
Auctions: $3,525, AU-58, June 2015; $2,585, AU-55, January 2015; $1,998, AU-50, July 2015; $705, VF-25, January 2015													
1856-S	24,600	227	54.5	14%	$850	$1,500	$2,250	$3,500	$7,500	$15,000	$25,000	$45,000	
Auctions: $52,875, MS-64, February 2013; $5,640, AU-58, January 2015; $3,290, AU-58, January 2015; $282, VF-20, August 2015													

† 1854 and 1855 Proof Indian Princess Head, Large Head Gold Dollars are ranked in the *100 Greatest U.S. Coins* (fourth edition), as a single entry. **a.** Check for strong doubling on UNITED STATES OF AMERICA, the beads in the headdress, the feathers, and portions of LIBERTY. **b.** Included in circulation-strike 1854 mintage figure.

INDIAN PRINCESS HEAD, LARGE HEAD (1856–1889)

Designer: *James B. Longacre.* **Weight:** *1.672 grams.*
Composition: *.900 gold, .100 copper (net weight .04837 oz. pure gold).* **Diameter:** *15 mm.*
Edge: *Reeded.* **Mints:** *Philadelphia, Charlotte, Dahlonega, and San Francisco.*

Circulation Strike   **Proof**

History. The design of the Indian Princess Head was modified in 1856. The new Type 3 portrait is larger and in shallower relief. After this change, most (but not all) gold dollars were struck with strong detail. Gold dollars of this type did not circulate extensively after 1861, except in the West. As they did not see heavy use, today most pieces are EF or better. MS coins are readily available, particularly of the dates 1879 through 1889 (during those years the coins were popular among investors and speculators, and many were saved). These gold dollars were very popular with jewelers, who would purchase them at a price of $1.50 for use in a variety of ornaments.

Striking and Sharpness. These dollars usually are well struck, but many exceptions exist. Charlotte and Dahlonega coins are usually weak in areas and can have planchet problems. On all coins, check the hair details on the obverse. The word LIBERTY may be only partially present or missing completely, as the dies were made this way for some issues, particularly in the 1870s; this does not affect their desirability. On the reverse, check the ribbon knot and the two central date numerals. Check the denticles on both sides. Copper stains are sometimes seen on issues of the 1880s due to incomplete mixing of the alloy. Many coins of the 1860s onward have highly prooflike surfaces.

Availability. All Type 3 gold dollars are collectible, but many issues are scarce. Most MS-65 or finer coins are dated from 1879 to 1889. The few gold dollars of this type that are less than VF usually are damaged or have problems. Proofs were made of all years. Most range from rare to very rare, some dates in the 1880s being exceptions. Some later dates have high Proof mintages, but likely many of these coins were sold to the jewelry trade (as the Mint was reluctant to release circulation strikes to this market sector). Such coins were incorporated into jewelry and no longer exist as collectible coins.

GRADING STANDARDS

MS-60 to 70 (Mint State). *Obverse:* At MS–60 to 62, there is abrasion on the hair below the band lettered LIBERTY (an area that can be weakly struck as well), on the tips of the feather plumes, and throughout the field. Contact marks may also be seen. At MS-63, there should be only slight abrasions. Luster is irregular. At MS-64, abrasions and marks are less. Luster is rich on most coins, less so on Charlotte and Dahlonega issues. At

1878. Graded MS-67.

MS-65 and above, luster is deep and frosty, with no marks at all visible without magnification at MS-66 and higher. *Reverse:* At MS–60 to 62, there may be abrasions on the 1, on the highest parts of the leaves, on the ribbon knot, and in the field. Otherwise, the same comments apply as for the obverse.

Illustrated coin: This exceptionally high-grade coin has superb eye appeal.

AU-50, 53, 55, 58 (About Uncirculated). *Obverse:* Light wear on the hair below the coronet, the cheek, and the tips of the feather plumes is very noticeable at AU-50, progressively less at higher levels to AU-58. Luster is minimal at AU-50 and scattered and incomplete at AU-58. Some tiny nicks and contact marks are to be expected and should be mentioned if they are distracting. *Reverse:* Light wear on the 1, the wreath, and the ribbon

1857-C. Graded AU-58.

knot characterize an AU-50 coin, progressively less at higher levels to AU-58. Otherwise, the same comments apply as for the obverse.

Illustrated coin: The obverse field is slightly bulged. This coin is lightly struck at the center, unusual for most Type 3 gold dollars, but sometimes seen on Charlotte and Dahlonega varieties. Among 1857-C gold dollars this coin is exceptional. Most have poor striking and/or planchet problems.

EF-40, 45 (Extremely Fine). *Obverse:* Medium wear is seen on the hair below the coronet and on the feather plume tips. Detail is partially gone on the hair, although the usual light striking may make this moot. Luster is gone on most coins. *Reverse:* Light wear is seen overall, and the highest parts of the leaves are flat. Luster is gone on most coins.

1859-S. Graded EF-40.

VF-20, 30 (Very Fine). *Obverse:* Most hair detail is gone, except at the back of the lower curls. The feather plume ends are flat. *Reverse:* The wreath and other areas show more wear. Most detail is gone on the higher-relief leaves.

This gold dollar is seldom collected in grades lower than VF-20.

Illustrated coin: This coin is lightly struck at the center obverse, as well as at the U and IC in the border lettering. It is lightly struck at the center of the reverse.

1859-D. Graded VF-20.

PF-60 to 70 (Proof). *Obverse and Reverse:* PF-60 to 62 coins have extensive hairlines and may have nicks and contact marks. At PF-63, hairlines are prominent, but the mirror surface is very reflective. PF-64 coins have fewer hairlines. At PF-65, hairlines should be minimal and mostly seen only under magnification. There should be no nicks or marks. PF-66 and higher coins have no marks or hairlines visible to the unaided eye.

1884. Graded PF-68.

Illustrated coin: This splendid cameo Proof is one of the finest graded.

	Mintage	Cert	Avg	%MS	VF-20	EF-40	AU-50	AU-55	MS-60	MS-62	MS-63	MS-64	MS-65
											PF-63	PF-64	PF-65
1856, All kinds	1,762,936												
1856, Upright 5		338	58.9	49%	$275	$300	$375	$450	$650	$850	$1,500	$2,100	$9,500
	Auctions: $16,450, MS-66, July 2015; $1,998, MS-64, September 2015; $447, MS-61, September 2015; $259, AU-55, September 2015												
1856, Slant 5		1,508	59.2	53%	$245	$250	$265	$285	$475	$600	$750	$1,100	$2,500
	Auctions: $42,300, MS-68, August 2015; $400, MS-62, January 2015; $306, AU-58, June 2015; $212, AU-50, November 2015												
1856, Slant 5, Proof	*unknown*	5	66.0								$30,000	$35,000	$65,000
	Auctions: $30,550, PF, January 2013												
1856-D	1,460	35	55.5	11%	$5,000	$8,000	$9,500	$12,000	$27,500	$45,000	$80,000		
	Auctions: $15,275, AU-58, September 2016; $11,750, AU-58, September 2013; $8,225, AU-50, September 2016; $7,050, EF-45, July 2014												

**1862, Doubled
Die Obverse**
FS-G1-1862-101.

	Mintage	Cert	Avg	%MS	VF-20	EF-40	AU-50	AU-55	MS-60	MS-62	MS-63	MS-64	MS-65
											PF-63	PF-64	PF-65
1857	774,789	1,321	60.0	63%	$245	$250	$265	$285	$475	$650	$800	$1,200	$2,850
	Auctions: $51,700, MS-68, August 2015; $823, MS-64, October 2015; $353, MS-61, September 2015; $329, AU-50, October 2015												
1857, Proof	*unknown*	6	64.8								$20,000	$24,000	$45,000
	Auctions: $16,100, PF-63Cam, June 2008												
1857-C	13,280	153	53.8	8%	$1,350	$1,750	$3,250	$5,000	$11,000	$16,500			
	Auctions: $8,813, MS-61, January 2015; $3,290, AU-55, March 2015; $3,102, AU-55, January 2015; $3,055, EF-45, January 2015												
1857-D	3,533	98	55.4	19%	$1,500	$2,400	$3,750	$5,000	$10,500	$17,500			
	Auctions: $5,581, AU-58, April 2013; $3,525, AU-53, October 2014; $2,238, EF-45, July 2014												
1857-S	10,000	114	54.1	15%	$450	$750	$1,250	$2,000	$5,750	$8,500	$20,000	$35,000	
	Auctions: $3,995, MS-61, January 2015; $3,775, MS-61, June 2015; $2,350, AU-55, July 2014; $999, AU-53, January 2015												
1858	117,995	251	60.1	61%	$245	$250	$265	$285	$400	$650	$950	$1,750	$4,750
	Auctions: $51,700, MS-68, August 2015; $1,410, MS-63, September 2015; $282, AU-55, July 2015; $235, AU-53, January 2015												
1858, Proof	*unknown*	15	64.7								$13,500	$15,000	$30,000
	Auctions: $32,900, PF-66Cam+, November 2014; $79,313, PF, March 2014												
1858-D	3,477	113	55.4	27%	$1,500	$2,250	$3,750	$4,750	$8,500	$12,500	$21,500	$37,500	$60,000
	Auctions: $7,638, MS-61, December 2013; $4,230, AU-58, February 2015; $1,439, AU-50, September 2014; $1,998, EF-45, July 2014												
1858-S	10,000	101	54.3	12%	$425	$750	$1,300	$1,750	$5,500	$9,000	$15,000	$25,000	$40,000
	Auctions: $25,850, MS-64, August 2015; $7,050, MS-62, June 2015; $4,348, MS-61, August 2015; $852, AU-50, January 2015												
1859	168,244	420	60.6	71%	$245	$250	$255	$285	$325	$400	$800	$1,100	$2,500
	Auctions: $37,600, MS-68, August 2015; $1,998, MS-65, August 2015; $376, MS-61, August 2015; $282, AU-58, January 2015												
1859, Proof	80	13	64.8								$10,000	$14,000	$22,500
	Auctions: $22,325, PF-64, August 2013												
1859-C	5,235	89	56.9	26%	$2,000	$3,250	$4,000	$5,000	$7,000	$13,500	$25,000		
	Auctions: $15,275, MS-63, June 2015; $5,640, AU-58, June 2015; $4,465, AU-55, July 2015; $2,585, AU-50, August 2015												
1859-D	4,952	115	57.1	28%	$1,600	$2,250	$3,250	$4,750	$8,750	$12,500	$21,500	$32,500	$55,000
	Auctions: $11,750, MS-62, June 2013; $3,290, AU-55, July 2014; $3,055, AU-53, February 2015; $911, AU-50, November 2014												
1859-S	15,000	154	52.2	10%	$300	$575	$1,250	$1,900	$4,750	$8,000	$14,500	$24,000	
	Auctions: $6,169, MS-62, February 2013; $3,760, MS-61, January 2015; $1,469, AU-58, June 2015; $306, EF-40, September 2015												
1860	36,514	168	61.2	81%	$245	$250	$275	$300	$525	$675	$1,250	$2,250	$7,500
	Auctions: $10,869, MS-65, August 2015; $881, MS-63, September 2015; $646, MS-61, August 2015; $329, AU-55, February 2015												
1860, Proof	154	18	64.7								$8,000	$10,000	$20,000
	Auctions: $27,600, PF-66, January 2012												
1860-D	1,566	63	55.2	22%	$3,750	$6,500	$10,000	$12,000	$20,000	$30,000	$50,000	$65,000	
	Auctions: $42,300, MS-64, February 2013; $11,750, AU-50, June 2015; $6,463, EF-40, July 2014												
1860-S	13,000	149	56.2	26%	$350	$500	$775	$1,100	$2,650	$4,000	$6,000	$11,000	$30,000
	Auctions: $31,725, MS-65, August 2015; $1,998, MS-61, January 2015; $1,116, AU-55, January 2015; $317, AU-50, October 2015												
1861	527,150	1,478	61.3	83%	$245	$250	$265	$285	$575	$675	$800	$1,500	$3,000
	Auctions: $32,900, MS-67, August 2015; $2,585, MS-65, September 2015; $494, MS-61, January 2015; $212, EF-45, January 2015												
1861, Proof	349	15	64.7								$8,000	$11,000	$20,000
	Auctions: $17,625, PF-65Cam, October 2014												
1861-D †	1,250	26	58.2	38%	$25,000	$30,000	$40,000	$57,500	$75,000	$85,000	$125,000	$160,000	$200,000
	Auctions: $111,625, MS-63, June 2013; $70,500, MS-61, January 2015; $30,550, EF-45, July 2014												
1862	1,361,355	3,087	61.7	88%	$245	$250	$265	$285	$485	$525	$750	$875	$2,000
	Auctions: $25,850, MS-67, August 2015; $4,230, MS-66, August 2015; $353, MS-61, April 2015; $223, AU-55, January 2015												
1862, DblDie Obv (a)	**(b)**	18	61.6	83%	$750	$1,500	$2,000	$2,500	$4,000	$4,750	$5,750		
	Auctions: $675, MS-62, February 2011; $447, AU-50, April 2015												

†† Ranked in the *100 Greatest U.S. Modern Coins* (fourth edition). **a.** Doubling, visible on the entire obverse, is most evident on the tops of the hair curls and the feathers. **b.** Included in circulation-strike 1862 mintage figure.

| | Mintage | Cert | Avg | %MS | VF-20 | EF-40 | AU-50 | AU-55 | MS-60 | MS-62 | MS-63 | MS-64 | MS-65 |
											PF-63	PF-64	PF-65
1862, Proof	35	19	64.9								$8,000	$11,000	$20,000
Auctions: $7,475, PF-63UCam, April 2008; $28,850, PF-65, April 2018													
1863	6,200	36	61.5	75%	$1,350	$2,000	$3,250	$4,250	$6,000	$7,500	$10,000	$13,500	$22,500
Auctions: $193,875, MS-68, August 2015; $10,575, MS-64, October 2014; $8,813, MS-63, April 2013; $5,434, AU-55, July 2014													
1863, Proof	50	18	65.2								$10,000	$17,500	$25,000
Auctions: $58,750, PF, February 2013													
1864	5,900	70	61.3	79%	$650	$850	$1,250	$1,300	$1,500	$2,500	$3,750	$6,500	$8,750
Auctions: $70,500, MS-68, August 2015; $705, MS-60, October 2014; $1,293, AU-55, July 2014; $235, AU-50, March 2015													
1864, Proof	50	13	64.2								$10,000	$17,500	$25,000
Auctions: $32,200, PF-66UCam, October 2011													
1865	3,700	36	62.2	83%	$750	$1,000	$1,100	$1,350	$2,000	$2,750	$4,500	$7,000	$11,500
Auctions: $15,275, MS-66, August 2015; $12,925, MS-65, July 2015; $3,055, MS-61, October 2014; $1,116, EF-45, July 2014													
1865, Proof	25	13	65.2								$10,000	$17,500	$25,000
Auctions: $25,300, PF-65, August 2011													
1866	7,100	76	62.4	84%	$450	$600	$750	$825	$1,250	$1,550	$2,500	$3,500	$5,750
Auctions: $23,500, MS-67, August 2015; $4,700, MS-66, January 2015; $1,175, MS-62, January 2015; $646, AU-55, January 2015													
1866, Proof	30	19	65.4								$10,000	$17,500	$25,000
Auctions: $27,600, PF-67UCam, August 2007													
1867	5,200	77	61.5	71%	$450	$625	$750	$850	$1,200	$1,500	$2,500	$3,000	$6,500
Auctions: $9,400, MS-66, August 2015; $1,763, MS-63, January 2015; $1,058, MS-61, January 2015; $823, MS-60, February 2015													
1867, Proof	50	13	63.5								$10,000	$17,500	$25,000
Auctions: $19,975, PF-66Cam, August 2014													
1868	10,500	127	60.9	76%	$450	$600	$700	$800	$1,000	$1,500	$2,000	$3,000	$6,500
Auctions: $35,250, MS-68, August 2015; $5,940, MS-66, June 2015; $881, MS-61, October 2015; $329, MS-60, May 2015													
1868, Proof	25	9	64.4								$10,000	$17,500	$25,000
Auctions: $29,900, PF-66UCam+, August 2011													
1869	5,900	89	61.6	82%	$450	$600	$700	$800	$1,150	$1,600	$2,000	$2,500	$5,500
Auctions: $42,300, MS-68, August 2015; $2,115, MS-64, January 2015; $1,293, MS-62, September 2015; $940, AU-58, January 2015													
1869, Proof	25	10	64.0								$10,000	$17,500	$25,000
Auctions: $19,975, PF-65Cam, April 2014													
1870	6,300	113	61.6	77%	$450	$600	$700	$800	$1,000	$1,500	$2,000	$2,750	$4,500
Auctions: $18,800, MS-67, August 2015; $1,410, MS-63, January 2015; $676, MS-61, July 2015; $588, AU-58, September 2015													
1870, Proof	35	9	62.6								$10,000	$17,500	$25,000
Auctions: $17,625, PF-64, January 2014													
1870-S	3,000	56	60.0	61%	$700	$875	$1,250	$1,750	$2,750	$4,000	$8,000	$12,500	$35,000
Auctions: $35,250, MS-68, August 2015; $3,878, MS-62, January 2015; $3,525, AU-58, September 2015; $1,293, AU-50, January 2015													
1871	3,900	123	62.2	89%	$350	$450	$575	$675	$900	$1,100	$1,600	$2,250	$4,250
Auctions: $35,250, MS-68, August 2015; $823, MS-61, October 2014; $412, MS-60, September 2014; $852, AU-58, July 2014													
1871, Proof	30	4	66.3								$10,000	$17,500	$25,000
Auctions: $27,600, PF-65DCam, November 2011													
1872	3,500	69	60.6	72%	$350	$425	$575	$700	$1,000	$1,250	$2,250	$3,000	$5,500
Auctions: $14,100, MS-67, August 2015; $1,528, MS-63, October 2015; $764, AU-58, January 2015; $517, AU-55, June 2015													
1872, Proof	30	15	64.2								$10,000	$17,500	$25,000
Auctions: $4,888, PF-61, March 2011													
1873, Close 3	1,800	115	60.4	70%	$425	$750	$1,100	$1,150	$1,700	$2,500	$4,000	$8,000	$15,000
Auctions: $1,529, MS-62, August 2015; $1,293, MS-61, April 2015; $1,183, MS-61, September 2015; $832, AU-58, June 2015													
1873, Open 3	123,300	2,258	61.8	91%	$245	$250	$265	$285	$350	$450	$575	$800	$1,500
Auctions: $35,250, MS-68, August 2015; $1,410, MS-64, January 2015; $541, MS-63, August 2015; $353, MS-60, June 2015													
1873, Close 3, Proof	25	6	63.0								$15,000	$22,500	$35,000
Auctions: $30,550, PF-65, August 2014													
1874	198,800	3999	62.2	93%	$245	$250	$265	$285	$350	$425	$525	$750	$1,200
Auctions: $10,575, MS-68, October 2015; $940, MS-65, January 2015; $341, MS-61, June 2015; $259, AU-53, June 2015													

	Mintage	Cert	Avg	%MS	VF-20	EF-40	AU-50	AU-55	MS-60	MS-62	MS-63 / PF-63	MS-64 / PF-64	MS-65 / PF-65
1874, Proof	20	7	64.4								$12,000	$15,000	$27,500
Auctions: $12,650, PF-64UC+, August 2010													
1875	400	30	61.5	83%	$3,500	$5,000	$6,000	$6,500	$10,000	$12,000	$16,000	$25,000	$42,500
Auctions: $76,375, MS-66, August 2015; $22,325, MS-64, April 2013; $2,820, MS-60, October 2014; $5,875, AU-53, July 2014													
1875, Proof	20	10	63.9								$18,500	$30,000	$45,000
Auctions: $55,813, PF-66DCam, November 2013													
1876	3,200	145	61.5	79%	$325	$375	$500	$600	$750	$1,000	$1,350	$1,650	$4,250
Auctions: $28,200, MS-67, October 2015; $940, MS-62, July 2014; $588, AU-55, September 2014; $646, AU-50, October 2014													
1876, Proof	45	17	64.7								$7,000	$14,000	$20,000
Auctions: $34,075, PF-66DCam, June 2013; $16,450, PF-65DCam, September 2014													
1877	3,900	178	62.1	83%	$300	$375	$525	$600	$800	$1,000	$1,400	$1,550	$3,500
Auctions: $12,338, MS-67, August 2015; $541, AU-58, June 2015; $423, AU-55, August 2015; $329, AU-55, January 2015													
1877, Proof	20	16	64.8								$8,000	$14,000	$20,000
Auctions: $7,638, PF, February 2014													
1878	3,000	153	61.8	88%	$300	$350	$400	$500	$775	$1,000	$1,500	$1,750	$4,750
Auctions: $32,900, MS-67, August 2015; $2,849, MS-65, August 2015; $1,175, MS-62, October 2014; $764, MS-61, July 2014													
1878, Proof	20	13	64.3								$7,500	$14,000	$20,000
Auctions: $19,550, PF-65DCam, January 2012													
1879	3,000	204	63.3	92%	$265	$300	$325	$350	$650	$800	$1,150	$1,300	$2,750
Auctions: $5,640, MS-67, July 2015; $4,113, MS-66, August 2015; $1,175, MS-64, January 2015; $270, AU-55, January 2015													
1879, Proof	30	9	64.3								$6,500	$14,000	$20,000
Auctions: $8,225, PF, August 2013													
1880	1,600	293	65.4	99%	$265	$300	$325	$350	$575	$700	$900	$1,050	$2,350
Auctions: $8,813, MS-68, January 2015; $7,050, MS-68, June 2015; $2,849, MS-67, August 2015; $2,585, MS-66, January 2015													
1880, Proof	36	29	64.4								$5,500	$10,500	$12,000
Auctions: $18,800, PF-65DCam, February 2013													
1881	7,620	383	64.7	97%	$250	$285	$325	$350	$575	$700	$900	$1,050	$1,800
Auctions: $12,925, MS-68, August 2015; $2,644, MS-67, October 2015; $1,645, MS-66, October 2015; $517, MS-63, March 2015													
1881, Proof	87	28	64.7								$5,000	$8,500	$12,500
Auctions: $2,820, PF-60, September 2014; $19,975, PF, March 2014													
1882	5,000	217	64.2	96%	$250	$285	$325	$350	$575	$700	$900	$1,050	$1,500
Auctions: $16,450, MS-68, August 2015; $1,998, MS-66, September 2015; $1,645, MS-66, August 2015; $646, MS-62, July 2014													
1882, Proof	125	35	65.3								$5,000	$8,500	$11,500
Auctions: $20,563, PF-67UCam, January 2015; $8,813, PF-64DCam, November 2014; $15,275, PF, August 2013; $5,760, PF-64, January 2018													
1883	10,800	491	64.1	97%	$250	$285	$325	$350	$575	$700	$900	$1,050	$1,500
Auctions: $18,800, MS-68, August 2015; $4,230, MS-67, September 2015; $3,055, MS-64, January 2015; $564, MS-62, January 2015													
1883, Proof	207	47	65.0								$5,000	$8,000	$11,500
Auctions: $9,400, PF-65Cam, February 2013													
1884	5,230	229	63.4	97%	$250	$285	$325	$350	$575	$700	$900	$1,050	$1,500
Auctions: $8,225, MS-68, July 2015; $3,995, MS-67, June 2015; $705, MS-64, January 2015; $588, MS-62, June 2015													
1884, Proof	1,006	62	65.3								$5,000	$7,000	$10,500
Auctions: $29,250, PF, September 2013; $10,200, PF-65, January 2018													
1885	11,156	455	63.7	96%	$250	$285	$325	$350	$575	$700	$900	$1,050	$1,500
Auctions: $7,638, MS-68, June 2015; $1,763, MS-66, June 2015; $1,175, MS-65, October 2015; $235, AU-55, January 2015													
1885, Proof	1,105	110	64.9								$5,000	$7,000	$10,500
Auctions: $16,450, PF-66, August 2015; $9,400, PF-65Cam, July 2014; $28,200, PF, August 2013													
1886	5,000	318	63.1	97%	$250	$285	$325	$350	$575	$700	$900	$1,050	$1,500
Auctions: $4,113, MS-67, January 2015; $1,645, MS-65, February 2015; $470, MS-61, July 2015; $282, AU-50, January 2015													
1886, Proof	1,016	72	64.4								$5,000	$7,000	$10,500
Auctions: $18,800, PF-67Cam, August 2014; $13,513, PF-67Cam, January 2015; $14,100, PF-66Cam, January 2015; $12,925, PF-66Cam, November 2014													

	Mintage	Cert	Avg	%MS	VF-20	EF-40	AU-50	AU-55	MS-60	MS-62	MS-63 PF-63	MS-64 PF-64	MS-65 PF-65
1887	7,500	484	63.8	99%	$250	$285	$300	$315	$575	$675	$900	$1,050	$1,500
	Auctions: $35,250, MS-68, August 2015; $1,645, MS-66, October 2015; $494, MS-63, January 2015; $306, MS-60, November 2015												
1887, Proof	1,043	63	64.7								$5,000	$7,000	$10,500
	Auctions: $10,575, PF-65DCam, September 2013; $10,288, PF-65Cam+, October 2014; $4,700, PF-64Cam, January 2015												
1888	15,501	738	63.7	97%	$250	$285	$300	$315	$575	$600	$650	$800	$1,200
	Auctions: $15,275, MS-68, August 2015; $2,961, MS-67, July 2015; $1,645, MS-66, January 2015; $881, MS-64, February 2015												
1888, Proof	1,079	94	64.5								$5,000	$7,000	$10,500
	Auctions: $18,800, PF-66DCam, April 2013; $7,814, PF-65, April 2018												
1889	28,950	2,009	64.2	98%	$250	$265	$275	$285	$575	$600	$650	$800	$1,200
	Auctions: $8,225, MS-68, August 2015; $3,055, MS-67, July 2015; $764, MS-64, January 2015; $400, MS-62, October 2015												
1889, Proof	1,779	35	64.2								$5,000	$7,000	$10,500
	Auctions: $12,925, PF-66Cam, April 2013												

Gold Quarter Eagles ($2.50) 1796–1929

AN OVERVIEW OF GOLD QUARTER EAGLES

The quarter eagle, denominated at one-fourth of an eagle, or $2.50, was authorized by the Act of April 2, 1792. Early types in the series range from rare to very rare. The first, the 1796 without stars on the obverse, Heraldic Eagle motif on the reverse, is a classic, one of the most desired of all pieces needed for a type set, and accordingly expensive. Most examples are in such grades as EF and AU.

Quarter eagles with stars on the obverse and with the Heraldic Eagle reverse were produced from 1796 intermittently through 1807. Today they exist in modest numbers, particularly in grades such as EF and AU, but on an absolute basis are fairly rare.

The standalone 1808 Draped Bust type, by John Reich, of which only 2,710 were minted, is the rarest single type coin in the entire American copper, nickel, silver, and gold series, possibly excepting the 1839 Gobrecht dollar (in a different category, as Proof restrikes were made). Examples of the 1808 can be found in various grades from VF through AU, and only rarely higher.

The next style of quarter eagle, from 1821 through 1827, is scarce, but when seen is usually in grades such as EF, AU, or even the low levels of Mint State. The same can be said for the modified quarter eagle of 1829 through early 1834.

Finally, with the advent of the Classic Head in late 1834, continuing through 1839, quarter eagles become more readily available. Examples can be found in nearly any grade from VF into the lower levels of Mint State. Then come the Liberty Head quarter eagles, minted continuously from 1840 through 1907, in sufficient numbers and for such a long time that it is not difficult to obtain an example to illustrate the type, with choice and gem Mint State coins being plentiful for the dates of the early 20th century.

The last quarter eagles are of the Indian Head type, minted from 1908 through 1929. These pieces are plentiful today, but grading can be difficult, as they were struck in sunken relief and the highest part on the coin is the field (this area was immediately subject to contact marks and wear). Although many opportunities exist in the marketplace, a collector should approach a purchase with care, seeking an example that has frosty, lustrous fields.

FOR THE COLLECTOR AND INVESTOR: GOLD QUARTER EAGLES AS A SPECIALTY

Collecting quarter eagles by dates, mintmarks, and major varieties is a very appealing pursuit. Although many are scarce and rare—this description applies to any variety from 1796 through early 1834—none are truly impossible to obtain. Among the Classic Head issues of 1834–1839, branch-mint coins are especially scarce in higher grades.

Liberty Head quarter eagles, produced continuously from 1840 through 1907, include a number of key issues, such as the famous 1854-S (usually seen in well-circulated grades), the Proof-only 1863 (of which only 30 were struck), and a number of elusive mintmarks. Of particular interest is the 1848 coin with CAL. counterstamped on the reverse, signifying that the coin was made from gold bullion brought to the Philadelphia Mint in a special shipment from California.

CAPPED BUST TO RIGHT (1796–1807)

Designer: *Robert Scot.* **Weight:** *4.37 grams.* **Composition:** *.9167 gold, .0833 silver and copper.* **Diameter:** *Approximately 20 mm.* **Edge:** *Reeded.* **Mint:** *Philadelphia.*

No Stars on Obverse (1796)
Bass-Dannreuther–2.

Stars on Obverse (1796–1807)
Bass-Dannreuther–3.

History. The first quarter eagles were struck intermittently during the late 1790s and early 1800s, with consistently small mintages. The earliest issues of 1796 lack obverse stars. They likely circulated domestically, rather than being exported in international trade.

Striking and Sharpness. Most have light striking in one area or another. On the obverse, check the hair details and the stars. On the reverse, check the shield, stars, and clouds. Examine the denticles on both sides. Planchet adjustment marks (from a coin's overweight planchet being filed down to correct specifications) are seen on many coins and are not noted by the certification services. On high-grade coins the luster usually is very attractive. Certain reverse dies of this type were also used to make dimes of the era, which were almost exactly the same diameter.

Availability. Most Capped Bust to Right quarter eagles in the marketplace are EF or AU. MS coins are elusive; when seen, they usually are of later dates.

GRADING STANDARDS

MS-60 to 70 (Mint State). *Obverse:* At MS-60, some abrasion and contact marks are evident, most noticeably on the hair to the left of Miss Liberty's forehead and on the higher-relief areas of the cap. On the No Stars quarter eagles, there is some abrasion in the field—more so than the With Stars coins, on which the field is more protected. Luster is present, but may be dull or lifeless, and

1802, 2 Over 1. Graded MS-61.

interrupted in patches. At MS-63, contact marks are few, and abrasion is very light. An MS-65 coin will have hardly any abrasion, and contact marks are so minute as to require magnification. Luster should be full and rich. Coins grading above MS-65 exist more in theory than in reality for this type—but they do exist, and are defined by having fewer marks as perfection is approached. *Reverse:* Comments apply as for the obverse, except that abrasion and contact marks are most noticeable on the upper part of the eagle and the clouds. The field area is complex; there is not much open space, with stars above the eagle, the arrows and olive branch, and other features. Accordingly, marks are not as noticeable as on the obverse.

Illustrated coin: Some friction appears on the higher areas of this example, but the fields retain nearly full luster, and the coin overall has nice eye appeal.

AU-50, 53, 55, 58 (About Uncirculated). *Obverse:* Light wear is seen on the cheek, the hair immediately to the left of the face, and the cap, more so at AU-50 than at AU–53 or 55. An AU-58 coin has minimal traces of wear. An AU-50 coin has luster in protected areas among the stars and letters, with little in the open fields or on the portrait. At AU-58 most luster is present in the fields, but is worn away on the highest parts of the motifs. The 1796 No Stars type has less luster in any given grade. *Reverse:* Comments as for Mint State, except that the eagle's neck, the tips and top of the wings, the clouds, and the tail now show noticeable wear, as do other features. Luster ranges from perhaps 40% remaining in protected areas at AU-50 to nearly full mint bloom at AU-58. Often the reverse of this type retains much more luster than does the obverse.

1796, No Stars; BD-2. Graded AU-58.

EF-40, 45 (Extremely Fine). *Obverse:* Wear is evident all over the portrait, with some loss of detail in the hair to the left of Miss Liberty's face. Excellent detail remains in low-relief areas of the hair, such as the front curl and the back of the head. The stars show wear, as do the date and letters. Luster, if present at all, is minimal and in protected areas. *Reverse:* Wear is greater than at the About Uncirculated level. The neck lacks feather detail on its highest points. Feathers have lost some detail near the edges of the wings, and some areas of the horizontal lines in the shield may be blended together. Some traces of luster may be seen, more so at EF-45 than at EF-40. Overall, the reverse appears to be in a slightly higher grade than the obverse.

1802; BD-1. Graded EF-45.

VF-20, 30 (Very Fine). *Obverse:* The higher-relief areas of hair are well worn at VF-20, less so at VF-30. The stars are flat at their centers. *Reverse:* Wear is greater, including on the shield and wing feathers. The star centers are flat. Other areas have lost detail as well. E PLURIBUS UNUM is easy to read.

The Capped Bust to Right quarter eagle is seldom collected in grades lower than VF-20.

1796, With Stars; BD-3. Graded VF-30.

	Mintage	Cert	Avg	%MS	F-12	VF-20	EF-40	AU-50	AU-55	AU-58	MS-60	MS-63	MS-64
1796, No Stars on Obverse †	963	38	56.0	29%	$57,500	$75,000	$95,000	$130,000	$170,000	$200,000	$250,000	$850,000	$1,000,000 (a)
	Auctions: $352,500, MS-61, October 2015; $123,375, AU-58, February 2016; $82,250, EF-40, October 2015; $94,000, VF-30, December 2013												
1796, Stars on Obverse	432	23	58.2	48%	$52,500	$65,000	$85,000	$100,000	$135,000	$170,000	$200,000	$500,000	$650,000
	Auctions: $111,625, AU-58, February 2016; $102,813, AU-58, March 2014; $223,250, AU-58, November 2014												
1797	427	16	49.5	13%	$15,000	$22,500	$37,500	$65,000	$125,000	$165,000	$185,000	$350,000	$500,000
	Auctions: $105,750, AU-53, April 2013												

† Ranked in the *100 Greatest U.S. Coins* (fourth edition). **a.** Value in MS-65 is $2,000,000.

| 1798, Close Date | 1798, Wide Date | 1804, 13-Star Reverse | 1804, 14-Star Reverse |

	Mintage	Cert	Avg	%MS	F-12	VF-20	EF-40	AU-50	AU-55	AU-58	MS-60	MS-63	MS-64
1798, All kinds	1,094												
1798, Close Date		20	57.1	30%				$30,000	$43,500	$55,000	$85,000	$135,000	
Auctions: $18,800, AU-50, August 2014													
1798, Wide Date	(b)							$30,000	$43,500	$55,000	$75,000	$135,000	
Auctions: $70,500, AU-58, November 2014; $44,063, AU-50, June 2014													
1802	3,035	73	56.6	34%	$5,500	$7,500	$14,500	$17,500	$20,000	$23,500	$32,500	$75,000	$200,000
Auctions: $20,563, AU-58, August 2014; $21,150, AU-58, March 2013; $16,450, AU-50, August 2014; $15,275, EF-45, August 2014													
1804, 13-Star Reverse †	(c)	3	50.0	0%	$65,000	$95,000	$150,000	$200,000	$350,000	$500,000			
Auctions: $322,000, AU-58, July 2009													
1804, 14-Star Reverse	3,327	61	52.8	18%	$6,750	$9,500	$15,000	$18,000	$21,000	$25,000	$35,000	$165,000	
Auctions: $44,063, MS-62, April 2014; $70,501, MS-62, November 2014; $21,738, AU-58, November 2014; $19,975, AU-55, August 2014													
1805	1,781	53	54.9	30%	$5,250	$8,500	$14,000	$18,000	$21,000	$23,500	$32,500	$135,000	
Auctions: $32,900, MS-60, March 2015; $20,563, AU-58, August 2014; $23,500, AU-55, November 2014; $14,100, AU-53, October 2014													
1806, 6 Over 4, 8 Stars Left, 5 Right	1,136	26	53.6	35%	$5,250	$8,750	$14,000	$18,000	$22,500	$27,500	$35,000	$150,000	
Auctions: $30,550, MS-61, June 2014; $22,325, AU-58, August 2014; $21,150, AU-58, August 2014; $20,563, AU-58, October 2014													
1806, 6 Over 5, 7 Stars Left, 6 Right	480	14	57.5	50%	$8,500	$11,500	$25,000	$35,000	$50,000	$60,000	$85,000	$300,000	
Auctions: $67,563, AU-About Uncirculated, February 2014													
1807	6,812	118	55.7	35%	$5,750	$7,500	$13,250	$17,000	$20,000	$25,000	$32,500	$85,000	$200,000
Auctions: $44,063, MS-62, March 2014; $24,675, AU-58, March 2015; $17,625, AU-55, August 2014; $11,750, AU-50, November 2014													

† Ranked in the *100 Greatest U.S. Coins* (fourth edition). **b.** Included in certified population for 1798, Close Date. **c.** Included in 1804, 14-Star Reverse, mintage figure.

DRAPED BUST TO LEFT, LARGE SIZE (1808)

Designer: *John Reich.* **Weight:** *4.37 grams.* **Composition:** *.9167 gold, .0833 silver and copper.*
Diameter: *Approximately 20 mm.* **Edge:** *Reeded.*

History. John Reich's Draped Bust was an adaptation of the design introduced in 1807 on the half dollar. On the quarter eagle it was used for a single year only, with fewer than 3,000 coins struck, making it the rarest of the major gold coin types (indeed, the rarest of any U.S. coin type).

Striking and Sharpness. All examples are lightly struck on one area or another, particularly the stars and rims. The rims are low and sometimes missing or nearly so (on the obverse), causing quarter eagles of this type to wear more quickly than otherwise might be the case. Sharpness of strike is overlooked by most buyers.

Availability. Examples are rare in any grade. Typical grades are EF and AU. Lower grades are seldom seen, as the coins did not circulate to any great extent. Gold coins of this era were not seen in circulation after 1821, so they did not get a chance to acquire significant wear.

GRADING STANDARDS

MS-60 to 70 (Mint State). *Obverse:* At MS-60, some abrasion and contact marks are seen on the cheek, on the hair below the LIBERTY inscription, and on the highest-relief folds of the cap. Luster is present, but may be dull or lifeless, and interrupted in patches. At MS-63, contact marks are few, and abrasion is very light. Abrasion is even less at MS-64. (Discussion of such high grades in these early coins starts to enter the realm of

1808; BD-1. Graded MS-63.

theory.) Quarter eagles of this type are almost, but not quite, non-existent in a combination of high grade and nice eye appeal. *Reverse:* Comments apply as for the obverse, except that abrasion is most noticeable on the eagle's neck and highest area of the wings.

   Illustrated coin: Superbly struck, this coin is a "poster example" with few peers.

AU-50, 53, 55, 58 (About Uncirculated). *Obverse:* Light wear is seen on the cheek and higher-relief areas of the hair and cap. Friction and scattered marks are in the field, ranging from extensive at AU-50 to minimal at AU-58. The low rim affords little protection to the field of this coin, but the stars in relief help. Luster may be seen in protected areas, minimal at AU-50, but less so at AU-58. At AU-58 the field retains some lus-

1808. Graded AU-50.

ter as well. *Reverse:* Comments are as for a Mint State coin, except that the eagle's neck, the top of the wings, the leaves, and the arrowheads now show noticeable wear, as do other features. Luster ranges from perhaps 40% remaining in protected areas at AU-50 to nearly full mint bloom at AU-58. Often the reverse of this type retains much more luster than does the obverse, as on this type the motto, eagle, and lettering protect the surrounding flat areas.

   Illustrated coin: Note some lightness of strike.

EF-40, 45 (Extremely Fine). *Obverse:* More wear is seen on the portrait, the hair, the cap, and the drapery near the clasp. Luster is likely to be absent on the obverse due to the low rim. *Reverse:* Wear is more extensive on the eagle, including the top of the wings, the head, the top of the shield, and the claws. Some traces of luster may be seen in protected areas, more so at EF-45 than at EF-40.

1808. Graded EF-40.

VF-20, 30 (Very Fine). *Obverse:* Wear on the portrait has reduced the hair detail, especially to the right of the face and the top of the head, but much can still be seen. *Reverse:* Wear on the eagle is greater, and details of feathers near the shield and near the top of the wings are weak or missing. All other features show wear, but most are fairly sharp. Generally, Draped Bust gold coins at this grade level lack eye appeal.

1808. Graded VF-20.

The Draped Bust to Left, Large Size, quarter eagle is seldom collected in grades lower than VF-20.

Illustrated coin: This is a nice, problem-free example of a lower but very desirable grade for this rare issue.

	Mintage	Cert	Avg	%MS	F-12	VF-20	EF-40	AU-50	AU-55	AU-58	MS-60	MS-62	MS-63	MS-64
1808 †	2,710	46	54.4	28%	$27,500	$40,000	$65,000	$90,000	$105,000	$130,000	$175,000	$275,000	$450,000	$750,000
	Auctions: $223,250, MS-61, March 2016; $126,900, MS-60, January 2013; $80,781, AU-55, August 2014													

† Ranked in the *100 Greatest U.S. Coins* (fourth edition).

CAPPED HEAD TO LEFT (1821–1834)

Designer: *John Reich.* **Weight:** *4.37 grams.* **Composition:** *.9167 gold, .0833 silver and copper.*
Diameter: *1821–1827—18.5 mm; 1829–1834—approximately 18.2 mm.*
Edge: *Reeded.* **Mint:** *Philadelphia.*

Large Diameter, Circulation Strike
BD-1.

Large Diameter, Proof

Small Diameter, Circulation Strike
BD-1.

Small Diameter, Proof

History. Capped Head to Left quarter eagles dated 1821 through 1827 have a larger diameter and larger letters, dates, and stars than those of 1829 to 1834. The same grading standards apply to both. Gold coins of this type did not circulate in commerce, because their face value was lower than their bullion value. Many legislators, who had the option to draw their pay in specie (silver and gold coinage), took advantage of this fact to sell their salaries at a premium for paper money. Most wear was due to use as pocket pieces, or from minor handling.

Striking and Sharpness. Most Capped Head to Left quarter eagles are well struck. On the obverse, check the hair details (which on the Large Diameter style can be light in areas) and the stars. On the reverse, check the eagle. On both sides inspect the denticles. Fields are often semi-prooflike on higher grades.

Availability. All Capped Head to Left quarter eagles are rare. Grades typically range from EF to MS, with choice examples in the latter category being scarce, and gems being very rare. Proof coins were made on a limited basis for presentation and for sale to numismatists. All Proof examples are exceedingly rare today, and are usually encountered only when great collections are dispersed.

GRADING STANDARDS

MS-60 to 70 (Mint State). *Obverse:* At MS-60, some abrasion and contact marks are seen on the cheek, on the hair below the LIBERTY inscription, and on the highest-relief folds of the cap. Luster is present, but may be dull or lifeless, and interrupted in patches. At MS-63, contact marks are few, and abrasion is very light. Abrasion is even less at MS-64. (Discussion of such high grades in these early coins starts to enter the realm of theory.) Quarter eagles of this type are almost, but not quite, non-existent in a combination of high grade and nice eye appeal. *Reverse:* Comments apply as for the obverse, except that abrasion is most noticeable on the eagle's neck and highest area of the wings.

1827, BD-1. Graded MS-65.

  Illustrated coin: This is a well-struck lustrous gem.

AU-50, 53, 55, 58 (About Uncirculated). *Obverse:* Light wear is seen on the cheek and higher-relief areas of the hair and cap. Friction and scattered marks are in the field, ranging from extensive at AU-50 to minimal at AU-58. The low rim affords little protection to the field of this coin, but the stars in relief help. Luster may be seen in protected areas, minimal at AU-50, but less so at AU-58. At AU-58 the field retains some luster as well.

1833; BD-1. Graded AU-53.

Reverse: Comments are as for a Mint State coin, except that the eagle's neck, the top of the wings, the leaves, and the arrowheads now show noticeable wear, as do other features. Luster ranges from perhaps 40% remaining in protected areas at AU-50 to nearly full mint bloom at AU-58. Often the reverse of this type retains much more luster than does the obverse, as on this type the motto, eagle, and lettering protect the surrounding flat areas.

EF-40, 45 (Extremely Fine). *Obverse:* More wear is seen on the portrait, the hair, the cap, and the drapery near the clasp. Luster is likely to be absent on the obverse due to the low rim. *Reverse:* Wear is more extensive on the eagle, including the top of the wings, the head, the top of the shield, and the claws. Some traces of luster may be seen in protected areas, more so at EF-45 than at EF-40.

1821; BD-1. Graded EF-40.

  The Capped Head to Left quarter eagle is seldom collected in grades lower than EF-40.

PF-60 to 70 (Proof). *Obverse and Reverse:*
PF-60 to 62 coins have extensive hairlines and may have nicks and contact marks. At PF-63, hairlines are prominent, but the mirror surface is very reflective. PF-64 coins have fewer hairlines. At PF-65, hairlines should be minimal and mostly seen only under magnification. There should be no nicks or marks. PF-66 and higher coins should have no marks or hairlines visible to the unaided eye.

1824, 4 Over 1. Proof.

	Mintage	Cert	Avg	%MS	F-12	VF-20	EF-40	AU-50	AU-55	AU-58	MS-60	MS-63 / PF-63	MS-65 / PF-64
1821	6,448	20	57.4	40%	$6,750	$9,000	$14,500	$16,000	$17,500	$23,500	$35,000	$85,000	
Auctions: $44,063, MS-62, March 2014													
1821, Proof	*3–5*	3	64.7									$275,000	$450,000
Auctions: $241,500, PF-64Cam, January 2007													
1824, 4 Over 1	2,600	29	56.7	38%	$6,750	$9,500	$14,000	$16,500	$18,750	$25,000	$35,000	$80,000	
Auctions: $18,800, AU-58, August 2013													
1824, 4 Over 1, Proof	*3–5*	0	n/a	*(unique, in the Smithsonian's National Numismatic Collection)*									
Auctions: No auction records available.													
1825	4,434	50	58.8	56%	$6,750	$8,000	$13,000	$15,500	$17,500	$23,500	$32,500	$65,000	
Auctions: $141,000, MS-65, November 2014; $105,750, MS-64, March 2014; $38,188, MS-62, July 2014; $32,900, MS-61, August 2014													
1825, Proof (a)	*unknown*	0	n/a										
Auctions: No auction records available.													
1826, 6 Over 6	760	9	56.0	11%	$10,000	$12,500	$16,500	$25,000	$37,500	$50,000	$67,500		
Auctions: $44,063, AU-58, August 2014; $27,025, AU-55, November 2014; $45,531, AU-55, September 2013													
1826, 6 Over 5, Proof (b)	*unknown*	0	n/a										
Auctions: No auction records available.													
1827	2,800	25	58.4	60%	$6,500	$9,500	$13,100	$17,500	$19,500	$32,500	$35,000	$65,000	
Auctions: $58,750, MS-63, September 2014; $21,150, AU-58, August 2014; $28,200, AU-55, February 2013													
1827, Proof (c)	*unknown*	0	n/a										
Auctions: No auction records available.													
1829	3,403	44	60.0	64%	$6,000	$7,500	$9,500	$13,000	$17,000	$18,500	$22,500	$35,000	$115,000
Auctions: $41,125, MS-63, June 2013; $12,925, AU-55, August 2014													
1829, Proof	*2–4*	0	n/a	*(extremely rare; 2–3 known)*									
Auctions: No auction records available.													
1830	4,540	46	60.1	52%	$6,000	$7,500	$9,500	$13,000	$17,000	$18,500	$22,500	$35,000	$85,000
Auctions: $29,375, MS-63, November 2013; $24,675, MS-62, November 2014; $22,913, MS-62, November 2014													
1830, Proof (d)	*unknown*	0	n/a										
Auctions: No auction records available.													
1831	4,520	61	60.2	66%	$6,000	$7,500	$9,500	$13,000	$17,000	$18,500	$22,500	$35,000	$85,000
Auctions: $28,200, MS-63, September 2014; $18,800, AU-58, February 2013; $15,863, AU-58, August 2014													
1831, Proof	*6–10*	2	64.5									$100,000	$150,000
Auctions: $30,550, PF-60, September 2013													
1832	4,400	40	57.5	43%	$6,000	$7,500	$9,500	$13,000	$17,000	$18,500	$22,500	$37,500	
Auctions: $21,150, MS-61, March 2014; $22,913, MS-61, August 2014; $15,275, AU-58, August 2014; $12,338, AU-55, August 2014													
1832, Proof	*2–4*	0	n/a	*(unique, in the Bass Foundation Collection)*									
Auctions: No auction records available.													

a. The 1825 quarter eagle might not exist in Proof; see the *Encyclopedia of U.S. Gold Coins, 1795–1933.* b. Proofs have been reported, but none have been authenticated. c. Proof 1827 quarter eagles almost certainly were made, but none are known to exist. d. Examples identified as Proofs are extremely rare, many are impaired, and none have been certified.

	Mintage	Cert	Avg	%MS	F-12	VF-20	EF-40	AU-50	AU-55	AU-58	MS-60	MS-63	MS-65
												PF-63	PF-64
1833	4,160	45	59.2	53%	$6,000	$7,500	$9,500	$13,000	$17,000	$18,500	$22,500	$35,000	$95,000
	Auctions: $41,125, MS-63, August 2013; $15,275, AU-58, August 2014												
1833, Proof	2–4	0	n/a		*(extremely rare; 3–4 known)*								
	Auctions: No auction records available.												
1834, With Motto	4,000	8	54.4	13%	$22,500	$27,500	$55,000	$90,000	$135,000	$145,000	$200,000	$275,000	
	Auctions: $19,975, AU-50, November 2014												
1834, With Motto, Proof	4–8	0	n/a		*(extremely rare; 3–5 known)*								
	Auctions: No auction records available.												

CLASSIC HEAD, NO MOTTO ON REVERSE (1834–1839)

Designer: *William Kneass.* **Weight:** *4.18 grams.*
Composition: *.8992 gold, .1008 silver and copper (changed to .900 gold in 1837).*
Diameter: *18.2 mm.* **Edge:** *Reeded.* **Mints:** *Philadelphia, Charlotte, Dahlonega, and New Orleans.*

Circulation Strike
Breen-6143.

Mintmark location
is on the obverse,
above the date.

Proof

History. Gold quarter eagles had not circulated at face value in the United States since 1821, as the price of bullion necessitated more than $2.50 worth of gold to produce a single coin. Accordingly, they traded at their bullion value. The Act of June 28, 1834, provided lower weights for gold coins, after which the issues (of new designs to differentiate them from the old) circulated effectively. The Classic Head design by William Kneass is an adaptation of the head created by John Reich for the cent of 1808. The reverse illustrates a perched eagle. The motto E PLURIBUS UNUM, seen on earlier gold coins, no longer is present. These coins circulated widely until mid-1861 (for this reason, many show extensive wear). After that, they were hoarded by the public because of financial uncertainty during the Civil War.

Striking and Sharpness. Weakness is often seen on the higher areas of the hair curls. Also check the star centers. On the reverse, check the rims. The denticles usually are well struck.

Availability. Most coins range from VF to AU or lower ranges of MS. Most MS coins are of the first three years. MS-63 to 65 examples are rare. Good eye appeal can be elusive. Proofs were made in small quantities, and today probably only a couple dozen or so survive, most bearing the 1834 date.

GRADING STANDARDS

MS-60 to 70 (Mint State). *Obverse:* At MS-60, some abrasion and contact marks are seen on the portrait, most noticeably on the cheek, as the hair details are complex on this type. Luster is present, but may be dull or lifeless, and interrupted in patches. Many low-level Mint State coins have grainy surfaces. At MS-63, contact marks are few, and abrasion is very light. Abrasion is even less at MS-64. An MS-65 coin has hardly any abrasion, and contact marks are minute. Luster should be full and rich and is often more intense on the

1834. Graded MS-65.

obverse. Grades above MS-65 are defined by having fewer marks as perfection is approached. *Reverse:* Comments apply as for the obverse, except that abrasion is most noticeable on the eagle's neck and the highest area of the wings.

Illustrated coin: This coin is especially well struck.

AU-50, 53, 55, 58 (About Uncirculated).

1837. Graded AU-55.

Obverse: Friction is seen on the higher parts, particularly the cheek and hair (under magnification) of Miss Liberty. Friction and scattered marks are in the field, ranging from extensive at AU-50 to minimal at AU-58. Luster may be seen in protected areas, minimal at AU-50 but more visible at AU-58. On an AU-58 coin the field retains some luster as well. *Reverse:* Comments as for Mint State, except that the eagle's neck, the top of the wings, the leaves, and the arrowheads now show noticeable wear, as do other features. Luster ranges from perhaps 40% remaining in protected areas at AU-50 to nearly full mint bloom at AU-58. Often the reverse of this type retains much more luster than does the obverse.

Illustrated coin: The coin has light wear overall, but traces of luster can be seen here and there.

EF-40, 45 (Extremely Fine).

1834. Graded EF-40.

Obverse: Wear is seen on the portrait overall, with reduction or elimination of some separation of hair strands, especially in the area close to the face. The cheek shows light wear. Luster is minimal or nonexistent at EF-40, and may survive in among the letters of LIBERTY at EF-45. *Reverse:* Wear is greater than on an About Uncirculated coin. On most (but not all) coins the eagle's neck lacks some feather detail on its highest points. Feathers have lost some detail near the edges and tips of the wings. Some areas of the horizontal lines in the shield may be blended together. Some traces of luster may be seen, more so at EF-45 than at EF-40.

Illustrated coin: This coin is well struck.

VF-20, 30 (Very Fine).

1836. Graded VF-30.

Obverse: Wear on the portrait has reduced the hair detail, especially to the right of the face and the top of the head, but much can still be seen. *Reverse:* Wear is greater, including on the shield and wing feathers. Generally, Classic Head gold at this grade level lacks eye appeal.

The Classic Head quarter eagle is seldom collected in grades lower than VF-20.

Illustrated coin: This coin was lightly cleaned. It is lightly struck at the centers, although at this grade level that is not important.

PF-60 to 70 (Proof). *Obverse and Reverse:* PF–60 to 62 coins have extensive hairlines and may have nicks and contact marks. At PF-63, hairlines are prominent, but the mirror surface is very reflective. PF-64 coins have fewer hairlines. At PF-65, hairlines should be minimal and mostly seen only under magnification. There should be no nicks or marks. PF-66 and higher coins should have no marks or hairlines visible to the unaided eye.

1836. Graded PF-65 Cameo.

1836, Script 8

1836, Block 8

	Mintage	Cert	Avg	%MS	F-12	VF-20	EF-40	AU-50	AU-55	AU-58	MS-60 / PF-60	MS-63 / PF-63	MS-65 / PF-65
1834, No Motto	112,234	1,017	56.2	31%	$365	$600	$800	$1,250	$1,650	$2,100	$3,250	$9,500	$50,000
	Auctions: $3,525, MS-61, February 2015; $1,645, AU-58, June 2015; $1,293, AU-50, June 2015; $794, EF-40, January 2015												
1834, No Motto, Proof	15–25	6	64.3								$35,000	$100,000	$275,000
	Auctions: $138,000, PF-64Cam, January 2011												
1835	131,402	318	54.1	29%	$365	$600	$800	$1,250	$1,650	$2,100	$3,250	$10,000	$50,000
	Auctions: $7,050, MS-63, January 2015; $1,770, AU-58, August 2015; $1,528, AU-55, June 2015; $1,116, AU-53, July 2015												
1835, Proof	5–8	1	65.0								$35,000	$100,000	$300,000
	Auctions: No auction records available.												
1836, All kinds	547,986												
1836, Script 8 (a)		529	51.4	20%	$365	$600	$800	$1,250	$1,650	$2,100	$3,250	$9,500	$42,500
	Auctions: $7,638, MS-63, September 2015; $3,055, MS-61, October 2015; $1,424, AU-50, June 2015; $423, VF-30, January 2015												
1836, Block 8		488	50.1	16%	$365	$600	$800	$1,250	$1,650	$2,100	$3,250	$9,500	$42,500
	Auctions: $9,400, MS-64, January 2015; $3,290, MS-61, September 2015; $999, AU-50, October 2015; $764, EF-45, January 2015												
1836, Proof	5–8	7	65.0								$35,000	$115,000	$300,000
	Auctions: $195,500, PF-64Cam, April 2012												
1837	45,080	265	52.2	17%	$450	$750	$1,200	$1,750	$2,000	$2,500	$4,500	$13,500	$55,000
	Auctions: $11,750, MS-63, January 2014; $2,585, MS-60, August 2014; $3,055, AU-58, November 2014; $1,528, AU-50, October 2014												
1837, Proof (b)	3–5	2	64.5								$32,500	$125,000	$350,000
	Auctions: No auction records available.												
1838	47,030	295	53.3	22%	$385	$625	$1,000	$1,500	$1,750	$2,600	$4,250	$11,500	$47,500
	Auctions: $2,468, AU-58, August 2015; $1,469, AU-55, August 2015; $1,058, AU-50, January 2015; $541, VF-35, January 2015												
1838, Proof	2–4	0	n/a	*(unique, in the Bass Foundation Collection)*									
	Auctions: No auction records available.												
1838-C	7,880	71	55.4	15%	$2,500	$4,500	$7,500	$10,000	$12,500	$17,500	$26,500	$50,000	
	Auctions: $8,225, AU-53, October 2016; $3,055, AU-50, June 2015; $6,463, EF-45, August 2016; $6,756, EF-40, January 2015												

Note: So-called 9 Over 8 varieties for Philadelphia, Charlotte, and Denver mints were made from defective punches. **a.** Also known as the "Head of 1835." **b.** Two Proofs of 1837 are known; one is in the Smithsonian's National Numismatic Collection. A third example has been rumored, but its existence is not verified.

| | Mintage | Cert | Avg | %MS | F-12 | VF-20 | EF-40 | AU-50 | AU-55 | AU-58 | MS-60 | MS-63 | MS-65 |
											PF-60	PF-63	PF-65
1839	27,021	91	52.5	15%	$650	$1,000	$1,650	$3,000	$4,000	$6,000	$9,500	$35,000	
	Auctions: $28,200, MS-61, August 2013; $4,700, AU-58, January 2015; $3,701, AU-58, January 2015; $1,116, AU-50, June 2015												
1839, Proof (c)	4–6	1	62.0						*(extremely rare)*				
	Auctions: $136,679, PF-62, August 2006												
1839-C	18,140	214	52.5	8%	$1,750	$3,500	$5,500	$9,000	$10,000	$15,000	$25,000	$65,000	
	Auctions: $44,063, MS-62, September 2015; $21,150, MS-61, August 2016; $7,403, MS-60, January 2015; $7,050, AU-55, June 2015												
1839-D	13,674	123	48.7	10%	$2,500	$4,500	$6,750	$9,000	$14,000	$20,000	$30,000	$55,000	
	Auctions: $105,750, MS-64, January 2013; $19,975, AU-58, November 2014; $18,800, AU-58, August 2015; $9,988, AU-55, July 2015												
1839-O	17,781	335	52.6	18%	$1,000	$1,650	$3,000	$4,250	$7,000	$8,750	$10,000	$30,000	
	Auctions: $32,900, MS-64, September 2015; $11,163, AU-58, August 2015; $3,995, AU-53, July 2015; $2,350, EF-45, August 2015												

c. Three Proofs of 1839 are reported to exist; only two are presently accounted for.

LIBERTY HEAD (1840–1907)

Designer: *Christian Gobrecht.* **Weight:** *4.18 grams.*
Composition: *.900 gold, .100 copper (net weight .12094 oz. pure gold).* **Diameter:** *18 mm.*
Edge: *Reeded.* **Mints:** *Philadelphia, Charlotte, Dahlonega, New Orleans, and San Francisco.*

Circulation Strike

Mintmark location is on the reverse, above the denomination.

Proof

History. The Liberty Head quarter eagle debuted in 1840 and was a workhorse of American commerce for decades, being minted until 1907. Christian Gobrecht's design closely follows those used on half eagles and eagles of the same era.

In 1848, about 230 ounces of gold were sent to Secretary of War William L. Marcy by Colonel R.B. Mason, military governor of California. The gold was turned over to the Philadelphia Mint and made into quarter eagles. The distinguishing mark CAL. was punched above the eagle on the reverse of these coins, while they were in the die. Several pieces with prooflike surfaces are known.

A modified reverse design (with smaller letters and arrowheads) was used on Philadelphia quarter eagles from 1859 through 1907, and on San Francisco issues of 1877, 1878, and 1879. A few Philadelphia Mint pieces were made in 1859, 1860, and 1861 with the old Large Letters reverse design.

Striking and Sharpness. On the obverse, check the highest points of the hair, and the star centers. On the reverse, check the eagle's neck, and the area to the lower left of the shield and the lower part of the eagle. Examine the denticles on both sides. Branch-mint coins struck before the Civil War often are lightly struck in areas and have weak denticles. Often, a certified EF coin from the Dahlonega or Charlotte mint will not appear any sharper than a VF coin from Philadelphia. There are exceptions, and some C and D coins are sharp. The careful study of photographs is useful in acquainting you with the peculiarities of a given date or mint. Most quarter eagles from the 1880s to 1907 are sharp in all areas. Tiny copper staining spots (from improperly mixed alloy) can be a problem. Cameo contrast is the rule for Proofs prior to 1902, when the portrait was polished in the die (a few years later cameo-contrast coins were again made).

Availability. Early dates and mintmarks are generally scarce to rare in MS and very rare in MS–63 to 65 or finer, with only a few exceptions. Coins of Charlotte and Dahlonega (all of which are especially avidly collected) are usually EF or AU, or overgraded low MS. Rarities for the type include 1841, 1854-S, and 1875. Coins of the 1860s onward generally are seen with sharper striking and in higher average grades. Typically, San Francisco quarter eagles are in lower average grades than are those from the Philadelphia Mint, as Philadelphia coins did not circulate at par in the East and Midwest from late December 1861 until December 1878, and thus did not acquire as much wear. MS coins are readily available for the early-1900s years, and usually have outstanding eye appeal. Proofs exist relative to their original mintages; all prior to the 1890s are rare.

Note: Values of common-date gold coins have been based on the current bullion price of gold, $1,300 per ounce, and may vary with the prevailing spot price.

GRADING STANDARDS

MS-60 to 70 (Mint State). *Obverse:* At MS-60, some abrasion and contact marks are evident, most noticeably on the hair to the right of Miss Liberty's forehead, and on the jaw. Luster is present, but may be dull or lifeless, and interrupted in patches. At MS-63, contact marks are few, and abrasion is very light. An MS-65 coin has hardly any abrasion, and contact marks are so minute as to require magnification. Luster should be full and rich.

1859-S. Graded MS-65.

Grades above MS-65 are usually found late in the series and are defined by having fewer marks as perfection is approached. *Reverse:* Comments apply as for the obverse, except that abrasion and contact marks are most noticeable on the eagle's neck and to the lower left of the shield.

Illustrated coin: Sharply struck, bright, and with abundant luster and great eye appeal, this is a "just right" coin for the connoisseur.

AU-50, 53, 55, 58 (About Uncirculated). *Obverse:* Light wear is seen on the face, the hair to the right of the face, and the highest area of the hair bun, more so at AU-50 than at AU–53 or 55. An AU-58 coin has minimal traces of wear. An AU-50 coin has luster in protected areas among the stars and letters, with little in the open fields or on the portrait. At AU-58, most luster is present in the fields, but is worn away on the highest parts

1855-D. Graded AU-55.

of the motifs. *Reverse:* Comments apply as for the preceding, except that the eagle shows wear in all of the higher areas, as well as the leaves and arrowheads. Luster ranges from perhaps 40% remaining in protected areas at AU-50 to nearly full mint bloom at AU-58. Often the reverse of this type retains more luster than the obverse.

Illustrated coin: The example has the bold rims often seen on Dahlonega Mint coins of this denomination.

EF-40, 45 (Extremely Fine). *Obverse:* Wear is evident on all high areas of the portrait, including the hair to the right of the forehead, the tip of the coronet, and the hair bun. The stars show light wear at their centers. Luster, if present at all, is minimal and in protected areas such as between the star points. *Reverse:* Wear is greater than on an AU coin. The eagle's neck is nearly smooth, much detail is lost on the right wing, and there is flatness at

1860-C. Graded EF-40.

the lower left of the shield, and on the leaves and arrowheads. Traces of luster may be seen, more so at EF-45 than at EF-40. Overall, the reverse appears to be in a slightly higher grade than the obverse.

Illustrated coin: This is an attractive coin with medium wear.

VF-20, 30 (Very Fine). *Obverse:* The higher-relief areas of hair are worn flat at VF-20, less so at VF-30. The hair to the right of the coronet is merged into heavy strands. The stars are flat at their centers. *Reverse:* Much of the eagle is flat, with less than 50% of the feather detail remaining. The vertical shield stripes, being deeply recessed, remain bold.

The Liberty Head quarter eagle is seldom collected in grades lower than VF-20.

1843-O, Small Date, Crosslet 4. Graded VF-20.

PF-60 to 70 (Proof). *Obverse and Reverse:* PF–60 to 62 coins have extensive hairlines and may have nicks and contact marks. At PF-63, hairlines are prominent, but the mirror surface is very reflective. PF-64 coins have fewer hairlines; PF-65, minimal hairlines mostly seen only under magnification, and no nicks or marks. PF-66 and higher coins should have no marks or hairlines visible to the unaided eye.

1895. Graded PF-66.

Illustrated coin: This is an exceptional gem in rich yellow-orange gold.

	Mintage	Cert	Avg	%MS	VF-20	EF-40	AU-50	AU-55	AU-58	MS-60	MS-62	MS-63
												PF-63
1840	18,859	103	50.1	12%	$850	$1,100	$2,400	$3,250	$4,250	$6,500	$8,000	$12,000 (a)
	Auctions: $2,468, AU-58, April 2013; $1,777, AU-53, October 2014; $564, AU-50, July 2015; $999, VF-30, June 2015; $1,440, EF-45, January 2018											
1840, Proof	*3–6*	0	n/a					(extremely rare; 3 known)				
	Auctions: No auction records available.											
1840-C	12,822	152	52.2	10%	$1,750	$3,250	$4,250	$5,750	$7,500	$10,000	$16,500	$24,000
	Auctions: $3,525, AU-58, March 2015; $1,087, AU-50, February 2015; $2,115, EF-45, October 2014; $1,645, VF-25, June 2015											
1840-D	3,532	44	48.8	7%	$3,250	$8,500	$11,000	$18,000	$25,000	$35,000	$75,000	
	Auctions: $28,200, MS-60, August 2016; $11,163, AU-55, November 2016											
1840-O	33,580	111	51.4	13%	$500	$1,100	$2,000	$3,250	$5,000	$9,000	$14,000	$25,000
	Auctions: $14,100, MS-62, April 2014; $7,344, MS-61, October 2014; $4,113, AU-58, July 2015; $270, VF-20, August 2014											

a. Value in MS-64 is $22,500.

1843-C, Small Date, Crosslet 4	1843-C, Large Date, Plain 4	1843-O, Small Date, Crosslet 4	1843-O, Large Date, Plain 4

	Mintage	Cert	Avg	%MS	VF-20	EF-40	AU-50	AU-55	AU-58	MS-60	MS-62	MS-63 / PF-63
1841 † (b)	unknown	0	n/a		$75,000	$100,000	$125,000	$140,000	$160,000	$225,000		
	Auctions: $149,500, PF-55, April 2012											
1841, Proof †	15–20	5	57.0									$250,000
	Auctions: $149,500, PF-55, April 2012											
1841-C	10,281	104	51.5	6%	$1,500	$2,250	$4,500	$6,000	$8,500	$15,000	$25,000	
	Auctions: $28,200, MS-62, March 2014; $5,875, AU-58, November 2014; $3,055, AU-50, June 2015; $2,468, EF-45, January 2015											
1841-D	4,164	55	46.9	5%	$2,500	$4,750	$9,000	$12,000	$15,000	$26,500	$40,000	$55,000
	Auctions: $23,500, MS-60, August 2015; $10,575, AU-55, September 2016; $8,225, AU-55, October 2015; $7,638, AU-55, April 2013											
1842	2,823	22	49.9	5%	$1,250	$3,250	$6,000	$8,000	$10,000	$17,500	$35,000	
	Auctions: $15,275, MS-60, January 2014; $7,931, AU-55, August 2015; $7,050, AU-55, July 2014; $3,819, EF-40, November 2014											
1842, Proof	2–3	0	n/a		(unique, in the Smithsonian's National Numismatic Collection)							
	Auctions: No auction records available.											
1842-C	6,729	59	47.5	5%	$2,000	$3,250	$6,750	$9,250	$10,500	$22,500	$37,500	
	Auctions: $8,813, AU-55, September 2014; $5,581, AU, February 2014; $3,760, EF-45, January 2015; $1,645, VF-20, January 2015											
1842-D	4,643	69	48.6	6%	$2,500	$5,500	$8,500	$11,000	$17,500	$32,500	$55,000	
	Auctions: $25,850, AU-58, August 2015; $15,275, AU-58, August 2015; $13,513, AU-58, September 2015; $9,400, AU-55, June 2015											
1842-O	19,800	151	48.9	9%	$525	$1,350	$2,250	$4,000	$6,500	$8,500	$12,500	$25,000
	Auctions: $7,638, MS-61, August 2015; $3,760, AU-58, October 2015; $1,293, EF-45, September 2015; $259, F-12, November 2015											
1843	100,546	197	54.3	11%	$350	$450	$700	$900	$1,250	$2,500	$4,000	$6,500
	Auctions: $3,231, MS-62, January 2015; $764, AU-58, January 2015; $470, AU-53, July 2015; $376, AU-50, January 2015											
1843, Proof	4–8	3	64.3		(extremely rare; 5–6 known)							
	Auctions: No auction records available.											
1843-C, Small Date, Crosslet 4	2,988	54	52.0	11%	$2,500	$5,250	$7,500	$10,000	$12,500	$22,500	$30,000	
	Auctions: $4,406, MS-63, August 2014; $499, MS-60, July 2014; $646, AU-55, July 2014; $441, AU-55, October 2014											
1843-C, Large Date, Plain 4	23,076	204	48.2	9%	$1,500	$2,000	$3,000	$4,250	$5,500	$8,000	$12,500	$18,500
	Auctions: $4,230, AU-58, August 2015; $3,525, AU-53, January 2015; $2,115, EF-45, January 2015; $764, VF-20, January 2015											
1843-D, Small Date, Crosslet 4	36,209	273	50.0	8%	$2,000	$2,250	$3,250	$4,500	$5,500	$6,500	$15,000	$25,000
	Auctions: $4,406, MS-63, August 2014; $499, MS-60, July 2014; $646, AU-55, July 2014; $441, AU-55, October 2014											
1843-O, Small Date, Crosslet 4	288,002	527	53.0	16%	$350	$375	$475	$750	$1,000	$1,750	$3,000	$6,500
	Auctions: $4,465, MS-63, June 2015; $764, AU-58, September 2015; $317, AU-50, October 2015; $259, F-15, August 2015											
1843-O, Large Date, Plain 4	76,000	132	53.8	14%	$400	$600	$1,750	$2,750	$4,000	$6,250	$13,000	$20,000
	Auctions: $15,275, MS-62, February 2014; $5,875, MS-61, June 2015; $3,525, AU-55, August 2015; $4,320, AU-58, January 2018											
1844	6,784	52	51.6	10%	$450	$800	$2,000	$3,000	$4,250	$8,500	$13,500	$22,500
	Auctions: $15,275, MS-61, January 2014											
1844, Proof	3–6	1	66.0		(extremely rare; 4–5 known)							
	Auctions: No auction records available.											
1844-C	11,622	120	48.7	10%	$1,500	$2,500	$5,500	$6,500	$8,500	$15,000	$22,500	$40,000
	Auctions: $14,100, MS-61, January 2014; $6,756, AU-58, July 2015; $2,350, AU-50, August 2014; $3,055, VF-30, June 2015											
1844-D	17,332	159	52.2	13%	$1,650	$2,500	$3,250	$4,250	$5,250	$7,000	$12,500	$22,500
	Auctions: $17,038, MS-63, April 2014; $1,645, AU-50, January 2015; $2,585, EF-45, August 2014											

† Both varieties of 1841 Liberty Head Quarter Eagles are ranked in the *100 Greatest U.S. Coins* (fourth edition). **b.** Values are for circulated Proofs; existence of circulation strikes is unclear.

	Mintage	Cert	Avg	%MS	VF-20	EF-40	AU-50	AU-55	AU-58	MS-60	MS-62	MS-63
												PF-63
1845	91,051	252	55.3	27%	$375	$400	$500	$600	$625	$1,250	$2,250	$4,750 **(a)**
	Auctions: $18,800, MS-65, January 2014; $14,100, MS-65, October 2014; $1,410, MS-61, March 2015; $235, AU-50, May 2015											
1845, Proof	4–8	2	67.0		*(extremely rare; 4–5 known)*							
	Auctions: No auction records available.											
1845-D	19,460	169	51.4	5%	$1,650	$2,350	$3,250	$4,250	$5,750	$10,000	$22,500	$40,000
	Auctions: $35,250, MS-63, January 2014											
1845-O	4,000	62	50.9	3%	$1,250	$2,500	$6,500	$8,750	$11,500	$22,500	$30,000	$50,000
	Auctions: $5,875, AU-50, January 2014; $10,800, AU-58, February 2018											
1846	21,598	134	55.6	19%	$360	$550	$900	$1,100	$2,250	$5,000	$13,500	$20,000
	Auctions: $3,760, MS-61, August 2015; $1,293, AU-58, July 2015; $734, AU-53, October 2015; $646, AU-50, January 2015											
1846, Proof	4–8	1	64.0		*(extremely rare; 4–5 known)*							
	Auctions: $106,375, PF-64Cam, January 2011											
1846-C	4,808	71	51.1	10%	$1,700	$3,000	$6,000	$8,500	$11,500	$16,000	$20,000	$35,000
	Auctions: $15,275, MS-62, April 2014; $4,084, AU-58, February 2018											
1846-D	19,303	178	51.7	9%	$1,750	$2,500	$3,250	$4,500	$6,250	$9,500	$13,500	$28,500
	Auctions: $7,638, MS-61, June 2013; $1,528, AU-50, August 2014; $3,055, EF-45, February 2015; $3,408, EF-40, July 2015											
1846-D, D Over D	**(d)**	4	52.0	0%		$2,750	$3,750	$5,500	$7,500	$15,000		
	Auctions: $5,175, AU-55, November 2011; $4,800, AU-53, January 2018											
1846-O	62,000	287	51.1	8%	$400	$525	$1,100	$1,900	$3,000	$5,500	$9,500	$18,500
	Auctions: $4,700, MS-61, February 2013; $423, AU-50, August 2015; $552, EF-45, June 2015; $400, EF-40, June 2015											
1847	29,814	125	55.0	19%	$375	$450	$850	$1,200	$1,750	$3,000	$5,000	$8,500
	Auctions: $3,055, MS-61, November 2014; $1,175, AU-58, June 2013											
1847, Proof	2–3	0	n/a		*(unique, in the Smithsonian's National Numismatic Collection)*							
	Auctions: No auction records available.											
1847-C	23,226	248	52.4	14%	$1,500	$2,250	$3,000	$3,500	$4,500	$5,750	$8,000	$15,000
	Auctions: $3,525, AU-58, August 2015; $2,820, AU-50, July 2015; $2,364, AU-50, September 2015; $1,821, AU-50, January 2015											
1847-D	15,784	165	52.6	13%	$1,650	$2,500	$3,250	$4,500	$5,500	$8,750	$13,500	$24,000
	Auctions: $9,404, MS, February 2014; $2,820, AU-53, August 2014; $2,350, AU-50, January 2015; $3,000, AU-55, February 2018											
1847-O	124,000	326	50.0	10%	$375	$425	$1,000	$1,650	$2,750	$4,000	$10,000	$16,000
	Auctions: $1,645, AU-55, January 2015; $764, AU-53, February 2015; $376, EF-40, May 2015; $259, VF-20, January 2015											

c. Value in MS-64 is $8,500. **d.** Included in 1846-D mintage figure.

1848, CAL. Above Eagle

	Mintage	Cert	Avg	%MS	VF-20	EF-40	AU-50	AU-55	MS-60	MS-62	MS-63	MS-64	MS-65
											PF-60	PF-63	PF-65
1848	6,500	59	54.6	27%	$550	$950	$2,250	$3,250	$5,500	$8,500	$15,000	$25,000	
	Auctions: $5,640, AU-55, September 2015; $2,585, AU-50, February 2014; $823, AU-50, July 2014												
1848, CAL. Above Eagle †	1,389	46	56.2	41%	$37,500	$45,000	$55,000	$60,000	$80,000	$100,000	$125,000	$150,000	$200,000
	Auctions: $55,813, AU-58, October 2015; $32,900, VF-25, September 2016												
1848, Proof	3–6	0	n/a		*(extremely rare; 3–4 known)*							$55,000	
	Auctions: $96,600, PF-64, January 2008												
1848-C	16,788	158	50.4	9%	$1,500	$2,500	$3,500	$4,500	$11,500	$20,000	$32,500		
	Auctions: $15,275, MS-62, March 2014; $3,120, AU-55, January 2018												
1848-D	13,771	150	53.6	13%	$1,650	$2,650	$3,750	$4,250	$8,000	$12,500	$28,000		
	Auctions: $25,850, MS-63, April 2014												

† Ranked in the *100 Greatest U.S. Coins* (fourth edition).

	Mintage	Cert	Avg	%MS	VF-20	EF-40	AU-50	AU-55	MS-60	MS-62	MS-63 PF-60	MS-64 PF-63	MS-65 PF-65
1849	23,294	136	55.1	16%	$450	$700	$950	$1,250	$2,750	$4,000	$7,500	$14,000	
	Auctions: $3,525, MS-62, March 2014; $3,055, MS-62, January 2015; $999, AU-55, July 2014; $764, AU-55, October 2015												
1849-C	10,220	103	51.1	10%	$1,650	$2,500	$5,000	$7,500	$15,000	$42,500	$60,000		
	Auctions: $15,275, MS-62, August 2015; $15,275, MS-61, January 2014; $12,338, MS-60, September 2016; $6,463, AU-58, November 2016												
1849-D	10,945	142	52.8	6%	$2,000	$2,750	$3,750	$5,500	$14,000	$23,500	—		
	Auctions: $4,348, AU-55, September 2016; $2,820, AU-50, November 2016; $2,468, EF-40, August 2016; $1,800, VF-30, April 2018												
1850	252,923	470	56.3	24%	$360	$375	$400	$500	$1,000	$1,750	$3,500	$7,500	
	Auctions: $940, MS-61, January 2015; $423, AU-58, September 2015; $376, AU-53, May 2015; $259, EF-40, July 2015												
1850, Proof	2–4	0	n/a					*(extremely rare; 1–2 known)*					
	Auctions: $41,250, PF-62, June 1995												
1850-C	9,148	138	51.2	13%	$1,500	$2,500	$3,500	$5,000	$12,500	$18,500	$35,000		
	Auctions: $8,879, MS-61, August 2014; $8,813, MS-61, October 2014; $12,925, MS-60, March 2014; $881, EF-40, January 2015												
1850-D	12,148	140	52.6	9%	$1,600	$2,750	$3,750	$5,500	$12,500	$25,000	$45,000		
	Auctions: $23,500, MS-62, April 2014; $18,800, MS-62, March 2016; $10,575, MS-61, January 2015; $5,434, AU-55, August 2015												
1850-O	84,000	333	50.8	3%	$350	$550	$1,250	$1,500	$4,000	$7,500	$15,000		
	Auctions: $1,645, AU-58, March 2015; $1,410, AU-58, June 2015; $764, EF-45, August 2015; $447, EF-45, February 2015; $990, AU-55, March 2018												
1851	1,372,748	854	58.9	54%	$325	$350	$375	$400	$550	$750	$1,100	$2,000	$5,500
	Auctions: $9,400, MS-66, February 2015; $376, MS-61, October 2015; $400, AU-58, March 2015; $266, AU-53, May 2015												
1851-C	14,923	114	50.9	15%	$1,500	$2,450	$3,750	$5,000	$8,500	$15,000	$35,000		
	Auctions: $5,640, MS-61, September 2015; $3,290, AU-53, January 2015; $2,820, AU-53, January 2015; $2,115, EF-40, July 2015												
1851-D	11,264	86	51.5	6%	$1,650	$2,500	$4,000	$5,500	$10,500	$15,000	$32,500	$50,000	$75,000
	Auctions: $7,638, AU-58, December 2013; $2,115, AU-50, September 2014; $5,520, AU-58, January 2018												
1851-O	148,000	448	53.4	9%	$400	$450	$800	$1,500	$4,500	$7,000	$11,500	$23,500	
	Auctions: $3,539, MS-61, February 2015; $2,143, AU-58, January 2015; $823, AU-55, October 2015; $646, AU-50, January 2015												
1852	1,159,681	1,047	59.7	59%	$325	$350	$375	$400	$550	$800	$1,100	$2,250	$5,500
	Auctions: $4,818, MS-65, June 2015; $1,998, MS-64, February 2015; $588, MS-62, June 2015; $329, AU-58, July 2015												
1852-C	9,772	98	52.5	9%	$1,500	$2,500	$4,000	$5,750	$11,000	$21,000	$32,500		
	Auctions: $6,463, AU-58, August 2015; $4,465, AU-55, July 2015; $3,525, AU-53, October 2015; $4,935, AU-50, February 2015												
1852-D	4,078	52	53.5	6%	$1,850	$3,250	$6,000	$8,000	$15,750	$30,000	$42,500	$65,000	
	Auctions: $8,813, AU-53, August 2013; $6,300, AU-58, April 2018												
1852-O	140,000	518	52.7	6%	$400	$450	$950	$1,300	$4,750	$8,000	$11,000		
	Auctions: $4,465, MS-61, August 2015; $1,410, AU-58, July 2015; $764, AU-55, January 2015; $617, AU-53, July 2015; $3,240, MS-60, March 2018												
1853	1,404,668	1,502	59.7	58%	$300	$325	$350	$365	$475	$600	$1,000	$1,500	$5,000
	Auctions: $9,988, MS-66, June 2015; $676, MS-62, March 2015; $306, AU-58, June 2015; $247, AU-50, January 2015												
1853-D	3,178	49	52.1	14%	$2,000	$3,500	$5,000	$6,000	$15,000	$30,000	$50,000		
	Auctions: $25,850, MS-62, January 2014; $12,338, MS-61, October 2014; $13,513, MS-61, November 2014; $4,113, AU-50, July 2014												
1854	596,258	720	59.1	50%	$300	$325	$350	$365	$550	$750	$1,250	$2,500	$6,000
	Auctions: $4,230, MS-65, January 2015; $470, MS-61, January 2015; $294, AU-55, August 2015; $376, AU-50, February 2015												
1854, Proof	2–4	0	n/a					*(unique, in the Bass Foundation Collection)*					
	Auctions: No auction records available.												
1854-C	7,295	113	54.1	17%	$1,500	$2,600	$5,000	$6,500	$12,000	$22,500	$37,500		
	Auctions: $9,988, MS-61, June 2013; $4,994, AU-58, August 2014; $4,230, AU-53, August 2015; $3,525, EF-45, January 2015												
1854-D	1,760	23	48.9	17%	$3,500	$7,500	$10,000	$12,500	$27,500	$40,000	$75,000		
	Auctions: $5,405, EF-40, November 2016; $2,938, VF-30, September 2016; $84,000, MS-64, April 2018												
1854-O	153,000	519	53.6	8%	$385	$425	$575	$800	$1,500	$4,500	$9,000	$15,000	
	Auctions: $2,585, MS-61, February 2015; $435, MS-60, September 2015; $329, AU-53, January 2015; $329, EF-45, October 2015												
1854-S †	246	6	35.3	0%	$275,000	$400,000	$450,000	$500,000					
	Auctions: $282,000, EF-35, October 2013; $264,000, VF-35, April 2018												
1855	235,480	401	59.4	54%	$300	$325	$350	$365	$550	$1,100	$1,600	$3,250	$7,000
	Auctions: $2,585, MS-64, October 2015; $764, MS-62, July 2015; $447, MS-61, July 2015; $329, AU-58, April 2015												

† Ranked in the *100 Greatest U.S. Coins* (fourth edition).

Old Reverse (Pre-1859)	New Reverse

	Mintage	Cert	Avg	%MS	VF-20	EF-40	AU-50	AU-55	MS-60	MS-62	MS-63	MS-64	MS-65
									PF-60		PF-63		PF-65
1855-C	3,677	71	54.6	23%	$2,250	$4,250	$6,000	$8,500	$20,000	$27,500	$42,500	$65,000	$100,000
	Auctions: $23,500, MS-62, January 2014; $81,000, MS-65, April 2018												
1855-D	1,123	25	53.5	12%	$4,500	$8,000	$13,500	$20,000	$50,000	$70,000	$100,000		
	Auctions: $25,850, AU-55, July 2014; $8,225, EF-45, March 2015												
1856	384,240	628	59.4	54%	$300	$325	$350	$365	$450	$850	$1,250	$3,000	$5,500
	Auctions: $3,995, MS-65, July 2015; $1,234, MS-63, July 2015; $376, AU-58, March 2015; $282, AU-53, May 2015												
1856, Proof	6–8	0	n/a						$35,000		$55,000		$145,000
	Auctions: No auction records available.												
1856-C	7,913	95	52.5	17%	$1,650	$2,750	$4,000	$6,000	$11,500	$20,000	$25,000		
	Auctions: $6,463, AU-58, April 2013; $4,465, AU-58, August 2015; $4,230, AU-55, August 2015; $1,410, AU-50, October 2014												
1856-D	874	17	52.7	24%	$10,000	$15,000	$30,000	$37,500	$75,000				
	Auctions: $55,813, AU-58, March 2014												
1856-O	21,100	145	53.5	10%	$385	$800	$1,650	$2,250	$8,250	$35,000			
	Auctions: $7,050, MS-61, August 2013; $1,320, AU-55, January 2018												
1856-S	72,120	206	51.6	14%	$385	$450	$850	$1,250	$5,000	$8,000	$12,000	$13,500	$27,500
	Auctions: $2,585, AU-58, September 2015; $1,821, AU-58, September 2015; $1,410, AU-58, June 2015; $1,058, AU-50, January 2015												
1857	214,130	465	59.5	55%	$300	$325	$350	$365	$450	$850	$1,250	$2,500	$6,500
	Auctions: $5,904, MS-65, July 2015; $423, MS-61, January 2015; $282, MS-60, November 2015; $282, AU-55, May 2015												
1857, Proof	6–8	0	n/a						$35,000		$57,500		$125,000
	Auctions: No auction records available.												
1857-D	2,364	64	56.6	28%	$1,750	$2,800	$4,000	$5,500	$12,000	$22,000	$30,000		
	Auctions: $18,800, MS-62, April 2014; $4,935, AU-55, June 2015; $1,586, AU-50, January 2015; $1,528, AU-50, July 2014												
1857-O	34,000	270	55.1	19%	$385	$400	$1,250	$1,700	$4,250	$7,500	$13,500	$22,500	
	Auctions: $6,463, MS-62, April 2014; $4,113, MS-61, November 2014; $1,998, AU-58, January 2015; $823, AU-53, January 2015												
1857-S	69,200	184	51.7	11%	$385	$475	$1,200	$2,000	$5,500	$7,500	$13,500	$25,000	
	Auctions: $5,875, MS-61, June 2015; $1,775, AU-58, July 2015; $1,293, AU-55, January 2015; $317, VF-35, July 2014												
1858	47,377	192	58.2	36%	$375	$390	$450	$500	$1,100	$1,850	$3,000	$6,000	$13,500
	Auctions: $999, MS-61, January 2015; $564, AU-58, October 2015; $376, AU-55, February 2015; $353, AU-53, May 2015												
1858, Proof	6–8	3	65.3						$25,000		$45,000		$115,000
	Auctions: $82,250, PF, March 2014												
1858-C	9,056	142	54.5	25%	$1,500	$2,250	$3,500	$4,250	$8,000	$13,500	$25,000		
	Auctions: $11,163, MS-62, January 2014; $4,113, AU-58, November 2014; $3,525, AU-58, November 2014												
1859, Old Reverse	39,364	130	57.8	34%	$375	$550	$850	$1,000	$2,000	$3,500	$6,000	$10,000	
	Auctions: $1,102, AU, February 2014; $456, AU-50, November 2014; $411, EF-40, August 2014												
1859, New Reverse	(a)	50	57.9	18%	$360	$370	$500	$650	$1,200	$1,750	$3,000	$7,250	$11,000
	Auctions: $3,290, MS-63, October 2014; $3,055, MS-63, August 2015; $1,998, MS-62, November 2014; $2,879, MS, January 2014												
1859, Old Reverse Proof (b)	80	8	64.9						$15,000		$30,000		$75,000
1859, New Reverse Proof (b)		(c)									—		
	Auctions: $80,500, PF-66, July 2005												

a. Included in circulation-strike 1859, Old Reverse, mintage figure. **b.** Nearly all 1859 Proofs are of the Old Reverse style. **c.** Included in figures for 1859, Old Reverse, Proof

| 1862, 2 Over 1 | 1873, Close 3 | 1873, Open 3 |

	Mintage	Cert	Avg	%MS	VF-20	EF-40	AU-50	AU-55	MS-60	MS-62	MS-63 / PF-60	MS-64 / PF-63	MS-65 / PF-65
1859-D	2,244	93	55.0	15%	$2,200	$3,250	$4,250	$5,750	$17,500	$37,500			
	Auctions: $44,063, MS-62, August 2015; $24,675, MS-62, August 2015; $13,513, MS-60, September 2015; $14,100, AU-58, September 2016												
1859-S	15,200	97	49.5	9%	$475	$1,000	$2,000	$2,750	$5,500	$9,000	$17,500	$25,000	
	Auctions: $4,994, MS-61, April 2014; $4,847, MS-61, August 2014; $3,290, AU-58, October 2014; $2,585, AU-58, July 2014												
1860, Old Reverse	22,563	33	56.2	33%	$1,250	$2,000	$2,750	$4,000	$5,000	$6,000	$10,000	$12,500	
	Auctions: $6,463, MS-62, April 2013												
1860, New Reverse	(d)	53	58.5	43%	$350	$370	$500	$600	$1,100	$1,850	$2,750	$7,500	$12,500
	Auctions: $1,763, MS-60, August 2013												
1860, Proof (e)	112	9	63.8								$14,000	$22,500	$40,000
	Auctions: $11,550, PF-64Cam, October 1993												
1860-C	7,469	119	51.5	9%	$1,850	$2,500	$3,250	$6,000	$15,000	$20,000	$30,000		
	Auctions: $25,850, MS-63, January 2014; $14,100, MS-61, June 2015; $12,925, MS-61, August 2015; $8,813, AU-58, September 2015												
1860-S	35,600	122	47.2	8%	$425	$675	$1,250	$1,750	$3,750	$7,500	$15,000	$30,000	
	Auctions: $6,756, MS-62, August 2013; $317, EF-40, November 2014												
1861, Old Reverse	1,283,788	131	58.2	37%	$525	$1,000	$1,500	$1,850	$3,750	$6,500	$10,000		
	Auctions: $11,163, MS-64, October 2015; $8,225, MS-63, August 2016; $3,760, MS-61, September 2016; $2,849, MS-61, July 2016												
1861, New Reverse	(f)	1,472	59.5	56%	$300	$325	$350	$365	$700	$1,000	$1,750	$3,000	$4,500
	Auctions: $9,400, MS-66, January 2015; $646, MS-61, July 2015; $353, AU-55, September 2015; $329, AU-50, September 2015												
1861, Proof (g)	90	3	65.3								$12,000	$20,000	$40,000
	Auctions: $44,850, PF-65DCam, September 2005												
1861-S	24,000	94	46.6	7%	$500	$900	$3,250	$4,750	$7,250	$20,000			
	Auctions: $5,875, AU-58, April 2013												
1862, 2 Over 1	(h)	55	54.5	15%	$1,000	$1,850	$3,000	$4,750	$8,500	$15,000	$32,500		
	Auctions: $9,400, MS-61, January 2014; $558, AU-50, July 2014; $10,800, MS-61, January 2018												
1862	98,508	196	56.3	30%	$400	$600	$1,350	$2,250	$4,750	$6,500	$11,000	$30,000	
	Auctions: $8,225, MS-63, August 2015; $4,700, MS-62, October 2015; $2,381, AU-58, January 2015; $1,116, AU-50, January 2015												
1862, Proof	35	11	64.7								$12,000	$20,000	$40,000
	Auctions: $46,000, PF-65UCam, February 2007												
1862-S	8,000	134	46.7	8%	$1,650	$2,250	$4,250	$6,000	$16,000	$25,000	$35,000		
	Auctions: $23,500, MS-62, January 2014												
1863, Proof † (i)	30	7	64.4								$50,000	$75,000	$125,000
	Auctions: $45,531, PF-58, April 2014; $78,000, PF-63, January 2018												
1863-S	10,800	76	46.1	9%	$700	$2,000	$4,500	$6,500	$15,000	$20,000	$30,000		
	Auctions: $3,290, EF-45, March 2013												
1864	2,824	8	53.4	25%	$6,500	$12,500	$22,500	$37,500	$75,000				
	Auctions: $48,469, AU-55, March 2014												
1864, Proof	50	15	64.7								$12,000	$25,000	$55,000
	Auctions: $30,550, PF-64Cam, April 2014; $78,000, PF-65, January 2018												
1865	1,520	17	53.5	0%	$4,500	$10,000	$20,000	$27,500	$40,000	$45,000	$60,000		
	Auctions: $15,891, AU-55, June 2013; $16,450, AU-50, November 2016; $11,163, EF-45, August 2015; $4,113, VF-20, November 2014												
1865, Proof	25	13	63.9								$13,500	$20,000	$55,000
	Auctions: $48,875, PF-65UCam, January 2012												
1865-S	23,376	97	45.0	4%	$750	$1,300	$2,000	$2,500	$4,500	$12,500	$15,000	$27,500	
	Auctions: $1,998, AU-53, March 2014												

† Ranked in the *100 Greatest U.S. Coins* (fourth edition). **d.** Included in 1860, Old Reverse, mintage figure. **e.** All known 1860 Proofs are of the New Reverse style. **f.** Included in 1861, Old Reverse, mintage figure. **g.** All 1861 Proofs were struck in the New Reverse style. **h.** Included in circulation-strike 1862 mintage figure. **i.** Proof only.

	Mintage	Cert	Avg	%MS	VF-20	EF-40	AU-50	AU-55	MS-60	MS-62	MS-63	MS-64	MS-65
											PF-60	PF-63	PF-65
1866	3,080	37	51.5	16%	$1,150	$3,000	$5,250	$7,500	$12,500	$20,000	$25,000	$35,000	
	Auctions: $7,050, AU-58, February 2013												
1866, Proof	30	14	64.0								$10,000	$17,500	$45,000
	Auctions: $23,500, PF-64Cam, April 2014												
1866-S	38,960	195	47.1	5%	$450	$750	$1,500	$2,250	$6,500	$12,500	$22,500		
	Auctions: $7,050, MS-61, August 2015; $1,880, AU-58, July 2015; $470, EF-45, January 2015; $376, VF-25, January 2015												
1867	3,200	37	54.9	27%	$350	$750	$1,350	$1,700	$5,000	$6,500	$12,000	$25,000	$35,000
	Auctions: $1,544, AU-55, July 2014; $1,645, AU-55, May 2013												
1867, Proof	50	11	64.1								$10,000	$16,000	$35,000
	Auctions: $35,250, PF-65DCam, October 2015; $18,800, PF-64DCam, October 2014; $99,875, PF, August 2013; $21,600, PF-64, April 2018												
1867-S	28,000	167	47.1	6%	$350	$650	$1,250	$1,600	$4,000	$5,500	$12,000	$15,000	
	Auctions: $1,163, AU-50, September 2015; $940, EF-45, August 2015; $541, EF-45, January 2015; $306, VF-30, November 2015												
1868	3,600	145	56.9	23%	$375	$450	$700	$850	$2,250	$5,000	$8,000	$13,500	
	Auctions: $3,290, MS-61, August 2014; $1,998, MS-61, November 2014; $1,880, AU-58, July 2015; $881, AU-58, February 2015												
1868, Proof	25	5	63.4								$9,500	$16,500	$45,000
	Auctions: $43,700, PF-65Cam, January 2009												
1868-S	34,000	248	51.8	7%	$350	$425	$700	$1,000	$3,000	$5,500	$8,500	$13,500	
	Auctions: $2,820, AU-58, August 2015; $999, AU-55, January 2015; $529, AU-50, July 2015; $447, EF-45, June 2015; $1,140, AU-58, January 2018												
1869	4,320	143	56.7	23%	$375	$450	$800	$1,150	$3,000	$5,000	$10,000	$22,500	
	Auctions: $19,975, MS-64, August 2014; $1,058, AU-58, January 2015; $881, AU-55, July 2015; $940, AU-50, June 2015												
1869, Proof	25	17	64.1								$8,500	$15,000	$40,000
	Auctions: $12,650, PF-63, October 2011												
1869-S	29,500	224	51.6	8%	$325	$475	$700	$1,350	$3,500	$5,500	$9,250	$13,000	
	Auctions: $3,525, MS-62, October 2015; $1,645, AU-58, January 2015; $1,528, AU-58, August 2015; $1,528, AU-58, June 2015												
1870	4,520	91	56.8	20%	$325	$400	$750	$1,250	$3,250	$5,000	$8,000		
	Auctions: $4,994, MS-61, January 2014; $3,525, MS-61, January 2015; $3,760, MS-60, August 2015; $1,645, AU-58, August 2015												
1870, Proof	35	5	63.8								$8,500	$15,000	$40,000
	Auctions: $70,500, PF-66DCam, January 2014												
1870-S	16,000	142	51.0	9%	$325	$400	$900	$1,500	$4,000	$8,500	$12,500	$20,000	
	Auctions: $8,225, MS-62, January 2014; $1,528, AU-58, July 2014; $1,645, AU-50, October 2015; $447, AU-50, September 2015												
1871	5,320	118	56.3	24%	$325	$400	$750	$1,000	$2,000	$2,750	$4,000	$8,000	
	Auctions: $999, AU-58, July 2015; $705, AU-55, October 2015; $646, AU-55, July 2015; $306, AU-50, January 2015												
1871, Proof	30	9	64.4								$8,500	$15,000	$40,000
	Auctions: $19,975, PF-64DCam, August 2014; $14,400, PF-63, April 2018												
1871-S	22,000	203	52.5	11%	$325	$400	$550	$1,000	$2,000	$3,000	$4,350	$9,000	$17,500
	Auctions: $1,087, AU-55, August 2015; $517, AU-53, June 2015; $423, AU-53, February 2015; $282, VF-30, November 2015												
1872	3,000	65	56.0	15%	$400	$700	$1,100	$2,000	$4,350	$9,000	$15,000	$25,000	
	Auctions: $2,596, AU-58, March 2014												
1872, Proof	30	9	64.8								$8,500	$15,000	$37,500
	Auctions: $34,075, PF-65Cam, March 2013												
1872-S	18,000	189	50.6	8%	$325	$400	$950	$1,250	$4,000	$6,000	$10,500	$13,500	
	Auctions: $3,594, MS-61, April 2012												
1873, Close 3	55,200	601	59.9	62%	$325	$375	$400	$425	$500	$650	$1,250	$1,750	$4,500
	Auctions: $3,525, MS-65, June 2015; $1,763, MS-64, June 2015; $1,293, MS-64, September 2015; $705, MS-63, July 2015												
1873, Open 3	122,800	518	60.7	74%	$300	$350	$375	$385	$500	$600	$825	$1,250	$4,250
	Auctions: $11,750, MS-66, July 2015; $1,116, MS-64, October 2015; $400, MS-62, August 2015; $329, AU-58, July 2015												
1873, Close 3, Proof	25	11	62.7								$8,500	$15,000	$40,000
	Auctions: $23,500, PF-63Cam, August 2014; $19,388, PF, August 2013												
1873-S	27,000	254	50.0	7%	$325	$400	$975	$1,000	$2,000	$4,000	$6,500	$13,500	
	Auctions: $11,750, MS-64, August 2015; $3,525, MS-62, October 2015; $620, AU-55, February 2015; $447, EF-45, May 2015												

	Mintage	Cert	Avg	%MS	VF-20	EF-40	AU-50	AU-55	MS-60	MS-62	MS-63 PF-60	MS-64 PF-63	MS-65 PF-65
1874	3,920	113	56.9	26%	$325	$375	$650	$1,050	$2,000	$4,000	$6,000	$9,500	$25,000
	Auctions: $3,525, MS-62, August 2013; $2,280, MS-61, April 2018												
1874, Proof	20	11	64.4								$8,500	$17,500	$50,000
	Auctions: $38,188, PF-64DCam, August 2014												
1875	400	25	57.1	20%	$5,500	$7,500	$12,500	$15,000	$27,500	$32,500	$45,000		
	Auctions: $25,850, MS-61, January 2015; $25,850, MS-61, August 2013; $28,200, MS-60, October 2016; $15,275, AU-58, October 2014												
1875, Proof	20	11	63.7								$25,000	$50,000	$125,000
	Auctions: $94,000, PF, October 2013												
1875-S	11,600	184	54.0	16%	$325	$375	$650	$1,100	$3,500	$5,000	$7,250	$12,000	
	Auctions: $5,581, MS-63, October 2014; $1,087, AU-58, July 2015; $999, AU-58, June 2015; $676, AU-53, August 2014												
1876	4,176	133	53.9	14%	$350	$600	$950	$1,750	$3,250	$5,500	$7,500	$12,000	
	Auctions: $5,581, MS-62, March 2014; $3,055, MS-61, September 2015; $2,350, MS-60, October 2015; $823, AU-53, October 2015												
1876, Proof	45	16	64.4								$7,500	$15,000	$40,000
	Auctions: $39,950, PF, January 2013												
1876-S	5,000	140	54.1	16%	$325	$525	$950	$1,350	$3,000	$4,000	$8,500		
	Auctions: $8,225, MS-63, January 2014; $2,820, MS-61, August 2014; $1,880, AU-58, November 2015; $734, AU-53, June 2015												
1877	1,632	108	56.7	31%	$400	$750	$1,000	$1,500	$3,000	$4,750	$9,500	$15,000	
	Auctions: $4,406, MS-62, April 2014; $3,055, MS-61, August 2014; $1,763, AU-58, June 2015; $884, AU-50, March 2015												
1877, Proof	20	6	64.0								$7,500	$15,000	$40,000
	Auctions: $8,050, PF-55, November 2011												
1877-S	35,400	405	58.7	45%	$325	$350	$375	$400	$650	$1,250	$2,350	$4,000	$10,000
	Auctions: $376, AU-58, June 2015; $259, AU-58, January 2015; $282, AU-53, May 2015; $329, AU-50, May 2015; $1,140, MS-62, January 2018												
1878	286,240	2,402	60.8	74%	$300	$325	$350	$375	$450	$500	$700	$1,000	$2,000
	Auctions: $12,925, MS-67, July 2015; $999, MS-64, August 2015; $541, MS-62, February 2015; $329, AU-58, June 2015												
1878, Proof	20	11	64.4								$7,500	$15,000	$40,000
	Auctions: $50,313, PF-65DCam, April 2012; $52,800, PF-65, April 2018												
1878-S	178,000	734	59.2	52%	$300	$365	$375	$385	$500	$850	$1,500	$3,500	$12,000
	Auctions: $12,925, MS-66, January 2015; $423, MS-61, June 2015; $353, AU-58, October 2015; $353, AU-53, September 2015												
1879	88,960	965	60.7	73%	$300	$365	$375	$425	$525	$550	$800	$1,000	$3,000
	Auctions: $7,638, MS-66, September 2015; $940, MS-64, January 2015; $423, MS-61, October 2015; $282, AU-58, May 2015												
1879, Proof	30	8	65.0								$7,500	$13,000	$35,000
	Auctions: $40,250, PF-67Cam, January 2011; $37,200, PF-65, April 2018												
1879-S	43,500	224	54.2	9%	$300	$365	$550	$850	$1,750	$3,500	$4,500	$17,500	
	Auctions: $423, MS-60, January 2015; $400, MS-60, February 2015; $617, AU-58, July 2015; $259, EF-45, January 2015												
1880	2,960	145	58.7	46%	$375	$425	$650	$800	$1,500	$2,150	$3,750	$6,000	$12,500
	Auctions: $2,820, MS-62, October 2013; $1,410, MS-61, February 2015; $1,410, AU-58, November 2014; $999, AU-58, January 2015												
1880, Proof	36	15	63.4								$6,500	$12,500	$35,000
	Auctions: $3,244, PF-55, January 2011; $13,214, PF-63, April 2018												
1881	640	75	56.9	29%	$2,000	$3,000	$5,000	$6,000	$10,000	$15,000	$20,000	$25,000	$45,000
	Auctions: $12,925, MS-61, November 2016; $11,750, MS-61, August 2016; $7,931, MS-60, June 2013; $5,875, AU-58, August 2014												
1881, Proof	51	22	64.1								$6,500	$13,500	$30,000
	Auctions: $34,075, PF-65DCam, August 2013; $14,100, PF-64DCam, July 2014												
1882	4,000	166	59.6	52%	$375	$425	$550	$700	$1,250	$2,000	$2,750	$5,500	$12,500
	Auctions: $9,400, MS-66, November 2014; $1,058, AU-58, July 2015; $282, AU-50, July 2015; $259, AU-50, July 2015; $1,148, MS-61, March 2018												
1882, Proof	67	13	65.3								$4,500	$9,500	$25,000
	Auctions: $9,487, PF-64, May 2006												
1883	1,920	61	58.1	33%	$1,000	$1,750	$2,750	$4,500	$5,500	$6,000	$7,500	$10,000	$15,000
	Auctions: $4,994, MS-61, June 2014; $5,040, AU-58, January 2018												
1883, Proof	82	22	64.8								$4,500	$9,500	$25,000
	Auctions: $28,200, PF, March 2014												

1891, Doubled Die Reverse
FS-G2.5-1891-801.

	Mintage	Cert	Avg	%MS	VF-20	EF-40	AU-50	AU-55	MS-60	MS-62	MS-63	MS-64	MS-65
											PF-60	PF-63	PF-65
1884	1,950	120	60.0	63%	$375	$500	$800	$1,000	$2,000	$2,500	$3,500	$6,500	$20,000
	Auctions: $18,800, MS-65, June 2015; $2,468, MS-62, June 2014; $1,645, MS-61, June 2015; $1,058, AU-58, August 2014												
1884, Proof	73	25	64.0								$4,500	$9,500	$25,000
	Auctions: $82,250, PF, August 2013												
1885	800	50	58.4	44%	$950	$2,000	$2,750	$3,250	$5,500	$7,000	$10,000	$15,000	$25,000
	Auctions: $13,513, MS-63, March 2014; $1,423, AU-50, July 2014												
1885, Proof	87	22	64.2								$5,000	$9,000	$27,500
	Auctions: $56,160, PF, September 2013												
1886	4,000	146	59.5	53%	$375	$400	$550	$600	$1,250	$2,000	$3,500	$6,750	$11,000
	Auctions: $1,528, MS-62, July 2014; $823, AU-58, September 2015; $823, AU-58, July 2015; $518, AU-53, June 2015												
1886, Proof	88	32	64.3								$4,500	$9,500	$25,000
	Auctions: $40,538, PF, August 2013												
1887	6,160	210	60.0	66%	$375	$400	$450	$500	$800	$1,250	$1,500	$4,000	$15,000
	Auctions: $15,275, MS-65, August 2015; $881, MS-62, February 2015; $764, AU-58, January 2015; $329, AU-50, October 2015												
1887, Proof	122	25	64.0								$4,500	$9,500	$30,000
	Auctions: $58,750, PF, August 2013; $26,400, PF-64, April 2018												
1888	16,001	465	61.9	88%	$325	$365	$375	$385	$450	$650	$900	$1,850	$4,500
	Auctions: $8,225, MS-66, August 2015; $1,234, MS-64, January 2015; $541, MS-62, January 2015; $376, MS-61, August 2015												
1888, Proof	97	30	64.5								$4,500	$8,500	$25,000
	Auctions: $25,850, PF-65Cam, February 2013; $6,463, PF-63, November 2014; $5,288, PF-62, August 2014												
1889	17,600	404	61.5	87%	$325	$365	$375	$385	$450	$650	$950	$1,650	$5,500
	Auctions: $6,463, MS-65, July 2014; $441, MS-61, August 2014; $341, AU-58, October 2014; $329, AU-58, July 2015												
1889, Proof	48	17	64.9								$4,500	$8,500	$25,000
	Auctions: $31,792, PF-65DCam, August 2014												
1890	8,720	233	60.8	69%	$325	$375	$385	$400	$650	$800	$1,500	$3,000	$9,000
	Auctions: $9,400, MS-65, July 2015; $940, MS-62, August 2015; $646, AU-58, May 2015; $400, AU-55, June 2015												
1890, Proof	93	52	64.6								$4,500	$8,500	$20,000
	Auctions: $19,388, PF-65DCam, June 2014; $29,458, PF-65, October 2014												
1891	10,960	321	60.9	75%	$350	$385	$400	$425	$550	$700	$1,450	$1,850	$6,000
	Auctions: $2,233, MS-64, November 2014; $1,645, MS-64, June 2015; $447, MS-61, February 2015; $411, AU-58, May 2015												
1891, Doubled Die Reverse	(j)	0	n/a					$500	$850	$1,500	$2,500	$3,000	$5,500
	Auctions: $823, MS-63, November 2014												
1891, Proof	80	26	65.5								$4,500	$8,000	$20,000
	Auctions: $30,550, PF, April 2013; $8,419, PF-63, April 2018												
1892	2,440	137	61.2	81%	$350	$400	$475	$525	$900	$1,100	$2,250	$4,000	$8,000
	Auctions: $21,150, MS-67, November 2013; $8,527, MS-66, August 2014; $7,931, MS-66, November 2014; $1,998, MS-63, October 2014												
1892, Proof	105	30	64.5								$4,500	$8,000	$20,000
	Auctions: $111,625, PF, February 2013; $24,000, PF-65, April 2018												
1893	30,000	908	62.3	91%	$325	$350	$375	$385	$550	$800	$1,250	$1,350	$1,750
	Auctions: $7,050, MS-67, January 2015; $3,290, MS-66, January 2015; $494, MS-62, April 2015; $259, MS-60, January 2015												
1893, Proof	106	38	65.1								$4,500	$7,500	$20,000
	Auctions: $21,150, PF-66DCam, September 2014; $44,063, PF, August 2013; $10,800, PF-64+, February 2018												

j. Included in circulation-strike 1891 mintage figure.

	Mintage	Cert	Avg	%MS	VF-20	EF-40	AU-50	AU-55	MS-60	MS-62	MS-63 / PF-60	MS-64 / PF-63	MS-65 / PF-65
1894	4,000	243	61.9	86%	$360	$365	$375	$475	$750	$900	$1,350	$1,750	$5,500
	Auctions: $3,525, MS-65, January 2015; $1,410, MS-62, July 2015; $833, MS-61, January 2015; $823, MS-61, August 2015												
1894, Proof	122	66	64.5								$4,500	$7,500	$20,000
	Auctions: $21,150, PF-66DCam, September 2014; $44,063, PF, August 2013; $20,400, PF-65, January 2018												
1895	6,000	266	62.4	92%	$360	$365	$375	$385	$575	$725	$1,100	$1,650	$3,750
	Auctions: $8,519, MS-66, March 2013												
1895, Proof	119	72	65.0								$4,500	$7,500	$20,000
	Auctions: $23,500, PF-66DCam, January 2014; $28,200, PF-66DCam, August 2014; $9,400, PF-64DCam, January 2015												
1896	19,070	716	62.6	94%	$300	$325	$375	$385	$500	$600	$800	$1,000	$2,000
	Auctions: $7,344, MS-67, March 2014; $1,998, MS-65, September 2014; $940, MS-64, March 2015; $306, AU-58, July 2015												
1896, Proof	132	66	64.7								$4,500	$7,500	$20,000
	Auctions: $3,819, PF-62, March 2015; $3,055, PF-62, November 2014; $21,150, PF, October 2013; $3,480, PF-61, April 2018												
1897	29,768	1,055	62.8	95%	$300	$325	$375	$385	$500	$525	$700	$900	$1,750
	Auctions: $7,638, MS-67, January 2015; $3,055, MS-66, July 2015; $881, MS-64, October 2015; $447, MS-62, January 2015												
1897, Proof	136	84	64.8								$4,500	$7,500	$20,000
	Auctions: $27,025, PF, March 2014; $38,400, PF-68, January 2018												
1898	24,000	791	63.2	97%	$300	$315	$325	$350	$475	$525	$675	$800	$1,500
	Auctions: $7,638, MS-67, January 2015; $2,879, MS-66, August 2015; $364, MS-61, September 2015; $294, MS-60, April 2015												
1898, Proof	165	115	64.3								$4,500	$7,500	$20,000
	Auctions: $25,850, PF-66DCam, September 2014; $25,850, PF-66DCam, September 2014; $5,941, PF-64Cam, June 2015												
1899	27,200	817	62.8	97%	$275	$300	$325	$350	$425	$475	$575	$625	$1,650
	Auctions: $2,585, MS-66, June 2015; $1,998, MS-65, July 2015; $1,414, MS-65, June 2015; $969, MS-64, June 2015												
1899, Proof	150	137	64.4								$4,500	$7,500	$20,000
	Auctions: $36,425, PF, August 2013												
1900	67,000	2,029	63.0	96%	$275	$285	$300	$325	$400	$425	$475	$575	$850
	Auctions: $3,290, MS-67, June 2015; $940, MS-65, January 2015; $705, MS-64, October 2015; $541, MS-62, July 2015												
1900, Proof	205	193	64.0								$4,500	$7,500	$17,500
	Auctions: $56,400, PF-68DCam+, October 2015; $37,600, PF-68UCam, June 2015; $64,625, PF-68DCam, November 2014												
1901	91,100	2,364	62.9	96%	$275	$285	$300	$325	$400	$425	$475	$575	$850
	Auctions: $4,700, MS-67, August 2014; $1,351, MS-65, January 2015; $541, MS-63, January 2015; $447, MS-62, January 2015												
1901, Proof	223	136	64.3								$4,500	$7,500	$17,500
	Auctions: $28,200, PF-67DCam, October 2014; $16,450, PF-66Cam+, June 2015; $11,750, PF-64Cam, September 2014												
1902	133,540	3,451	63.0	97%	$275	$285	$300	$325	$400	$425	$475	$575	$850
	Auctions: $5,405, MS-67, January 2015; $646, MS-64, August 2015; $329, MS-61, April 2015; $282, MS-60, January 2015												
1902, Proof	193	104	64.0								$4,500	$7,500	$17,500
	Auctions: $5,640, PF-64, June 2015; $3,290, PF-62, June 2015; $2,585, PF-61, January 2015; $1,528, PF-50, August 2015												
1903	201,060	6,151	63.1	97%	$275	$285	$300	$325	$400	$425	$475	$575	$850
	Auctions: $9,400, MS-68, January 2015; $2,350, MS-67, January 2015; $376, MS-62, February 2015; $235, MS-60, June 2015												
1903, Proof	197	123	63.0								$4,500	$7,500	$17,500
	Auctions: $12,925, PF-65, January 2015; $7,050, PF-64, August 2014; $3,173, PF-62, November 2014; $3,055, PF-62, March 2015												
1904	160,790	4,664	63.0	96%	$275	$285	$300	$325	$400	$425	$475	$575	$850
	Auctions: $28,200, MS-68, January 2013; $3,290, MS-67, July 2015; $2,585, MS-67, November 2014; $1,351, MS-66, November 2014												
1904, Proof	170	114	64.1								$4,500	$7,500	$17,500
	Auctions: $4,700, PF-63, January 2015; $1,293, MS-66, October 2015; $270, MS-60, January 2015; $259, AU-55, January 2015												
1905 (k)	217,800	6,509	63.1	96%	$275	$285	$300	$325	$400	$425	$475	$575	$850
	Auctions: $3,995, MS-67, August 2015; $1,528, MS-66, August 2015; $329, MS-62, July 2015; $282, AU-58, February 2015												
1905, Proof	144	122	63.6								$4,500	$7,500	$17,500
	Auctions: $8,225, PF-64, October 2014; $6,463, PF-64, July 2015; $6,463, PF-64, February 2015; $1,058, PF, March 2015												

k. Pieces dated 1905-S are counterfeit.

	Mintage	Cert	Avg	%MS	VF-20	EF-40	AU-50	AU-55	MS-60	MS-62	MS-63	MS-64	MS-65
											PF-60	PF-63	PF-65
1906	176,330	5,489	63.0	97%	$275	$285	$300	$325	$400	$425	$475	$575	$850
Auctions: $21,150, MS-68, October 2015; $1,528, MS-66, January 2015; $353, MS-61, June 2015; $306, AU-58, June 2015													
1906, Proof	160	136	64.5								$4,500	$7,500	$17,500
Auctions: $7,638, PF-64Cam, August 2014; $8,225, PF-64Cam, September 2014; $44,063, PF, August 2013; $7,200, PF-64, February 2018													
1907	336,294	9,201	63.1	97%	$275	$285	$300	$325	$400	$425	$475	$575	$850
Auctions: $12,925, MS-68, January 2015; $1,351, MS-66, June 2015; $494, MS-62, January 2015; $282, MS-60, June 2015													
1907, Proof	154	113	64.7								$4,500	$7,500	$17,500
Auctions: $32,900, PF-68, April 2013; $21,738, PF-65+, January 2015; $4,700, PF-63Cam, September 2014; $31,200, PF-67, January 2018													

INDIAN HEAD (1908–1929)

Designer: *Bela Lyon Pratt.* **Weight:** *4.18 grams.*
Composition: *.900 gold, .100 copper (net weight .12094 oz. pure gold).*
Diameter: *18 mm.* **Edge:** *Reeded.* **Mints:** *Philadelphia and Denver.*

Circulation Strike   *Mintmark is on the reverse, to the left of arrows.*   **Sandblast Finish Proof**   **Satin Finish Proof**

History. The Indian Head design—used on both the quarter eagle and the half eagle—is unusual in that the lettering and motifs are in sunken relief. (The design sometimes is erroneously described as incuse.) The designer, sculptor Bela Lyon Pratt, was chosen by President Theodore Roosevelt after Augustus Saint-Gaudens died before beginning his own design. Pratt modeled the head on Chief Hollow Horn Bear of the Lakota. The "standing eagle" reverse design was based on the reverse of Saint-Gaudens's Indian Head $10 gold coin of 1907; Pratt was a pupil of the famous sculptor.

Some Americans worried that the sunken designs of the Indian Head quarter eagle would accumulate dirt and germs—an unfounded fear. As the smallest gold denomination of the era, these coins were popular for use as souvenirs and gifts, but they did not circulate as money except in the West.

Striking and Sharpness. The striking quality of Indian Head quarter eagles varies. On many early issues the rims are flat, while on others, including most of the 1920s, they are slightly raised. Some have traces of a wire rim, usually on the reverse. Look for weakness on the high parts of the Indian's bonnet (particularly the garland of flowers) and in the feather details in the headdress. On the reverse, check the feathers on the highest area of the wing, the top of the shoulder. On some issues of the 1911-D, the D mintmark can be weak.

Availability. This design was not popular with collectors, and they saved relatively few of the coins. However, many coins were given as gifts and preserved in high quality. The survival of MS-63 and better coins is a matter of chance, especially for the issues dated from 1909 to 1915. The only scarce issue is 1911-D. Luster can range from deeply frosty to grainy. As the fields are the highest areas of the coin, luster diminished quickly as examples were circulated or jostled with others in bags. The Indian Head quarter eagle is one of the most challenging series for professional graders, and opinions can vary widely.

Proofs. Sandblast (also called Matte) Proofs were made in 1908 and 1911 to 1915, while Satin (also called Roman Finish) Proofs were made in 1909 and 1910. The Sandblast issues are usually somewhat dull, while the Satin Proofs are usually of a light-yellow gold. In their time the Proofs of both styles, made for all gold series, were not popular with numismatists. Today, they are in strong demand. As a class these are significantly more readily available than half eagles of the same date and style of finish.

Most are in grades from PF-63 upward. At lower levels coins can show light contact marks. Some microscopic bright flecks may have been caused by the sandblasting process and, although they do not represent handling, usually result in a coin being assigned a slightly lower grade.

Note: Values of common-date gold coins have been based on the current bullion price of gold, $1,300 per ounce, and may vary with the prevailing spot price.

GRADING STANDARDS

MS-60 to 70 (Mint State). *Obverse:* On MS–60 to 62 coins there is abrasion in the field, this representing the highest part of the coin. Abrasion is also evident on the headdress. Marks and, occasionally, a microscopic pin scratch may be seen. At MS-63, there may be some abrasion and some tiny marks. Luster is irregular. At MS-64, abrasion is less. Luster is rich. At MS-65 and above, luster is deep and frosty. No marks at all are visible

1911-D. Graded MS-64.

without magnification at MS-66 and higher. *Reverse:* At MS–60 to 62, there is abrasion in the field, this representing the highest part of the coin. Abrasion is also evident on the eagle's wing. Otherwise, the same comments apply as for the obverse.

Illustrated coin: This lustrous example has excellent eye appeal.

AU-50, 53, 55, 58 (About Uncirculated). *Obverse:* Friction on the cheek is very noticeable at AU-50, progressively less at higher levels to AU-58. The headdress shows light wear, most evident on the ribbon above the forehead and on the garland. Luster is minimal at AU-50 and scattered and incomplete at AU-58. Nicks and contact marks are to be expected. *Reverse:* Friction on the wing and neck is very noticeable at AU-50, increasingly

1911-D. Graded AU-55.

less at higher levels to AU-58. Otherwise, the same comments apply as for the obverse.

Illustrated coin: Much of the original luster remains in the incuse areas but not in the fields, which are the highest points on this design.

EF-40, 45 (Extremely Fine). *Obverse:* Light wear characterizes the portrait and headdress. Luster is gone. Marks and tiny scratches are to be expected, but not distracting. *Reverse:* Light wear is most evident on the eagle's head and wing, although other areas are lightly worn as well. Luster is gone. Marks and tiny scratches are to be expected, but not distracting.

1911-D. Graded EF-40.

VF-20, 30 (Very Fine). *Obverse:* Many details of the ribbon above the forehead and the garland are worn away. Many feather vanes are blended together. The field is dull and has contact marks. *Reverse:* The neck and the upper part of the wing show extensive wear, other areas less so. The field is dull and has contact marks.

The Indian Head quarter eagle is seldom collected in grades lower than VF-20.

PF-60 to 70 (Proof). *Obverse and Reverse:* At PF–60 to 63, there is light abrasion and some contact marks; the lower the grade, the higher the quantity. On Sandblast Proofs these show up as visually unappealing bright spots. At PF-64 and higher levels, marks are fewer, with magnification needed to see any at PF-65. At PF-66, there should be none at all.

Illustrated coin: This is a Sandblast Proof of exceptionally high quality.

1912. Graded VF-20.

1913, Sandblast Finish. Graded PF-66.

	Mintage	Cert	Avg	%MS	VF-20	EF-40	AU-50	MS-60	MS-62	MS-63 / PF-60	MS-64 / PF-63	MS-65 / PF-65
1908	564,821	9,673	61.5	84%	$300	$325	$350	$400	$550	$700	$1,200	$2,500
	Auctions: $7,931, MS-66, August 2015; $1,645, MS-64, July 2015; $353, MS-61, February 2015; $235, AU-50, August 2015											
1908, Sandblast Finish Proof	236	134	65.2							4,500	$10,000	$25,000
	Auctions: $49,938, PF-68, April 2014; $70,500, PF-67, January 2015; $38,188, PF-66, August 2014; $5,170, PF-58, February 2015											
1909	441,760	7,604	61.2	79%	$300	$325	$350	$385	$550	$1,150	$1,750	$4,000
	Auctions: $11,750, MS-66, October 2015; $2,115, MS-64, January 2015; $317, MS-60, August 2015; $282, AU-58, January 2015											
1909, Satin Finish Proof	139	46	64.3							4,000	$11,000	$35,000
	Auctions: $57,500, PF-67, January 2011											
1910	492,000	8,777	61.4	85%	$300	$325	$350	$385	$500	$900	$1,300	$3,250
	Auctions: $2,938, MS-65, August 2015; $1,293, MS-64, June 2015; $376, MS-62, July 2015; $282, AU-58, March 2015											
1910, Satin Finish Proof	682	111	65.2							4,000	$11,000	$27,500
	Auctions: $64,625, PF-67, January 2015; $23,500, PF-65, July 2015; $27,600, PF-64+, September 2011											
1910, Sandblast Finish Proof (a)	unknown	0	n/a					*(unique)*				
	Auctions: $47,000, PF-66, August 2014											
1911	704,000	13,164	61.2	81%	$300	$325	$350	$385	$500	$700	$1,000	$3,250
	Auctions: $3,525, MS-65, January 2015; $470, MS-62, June 2015; $423, AU-58, March 2015; $306, AU-55, June 2015											
1911, Sandblast Finish Proof	191	98	65.8							4,500	$10,000	$25,000
	Auctions: $27,025, PF-66, January 2014											
1911-D (b)	55,680	5,093	59.8	57%	$2,750	$3,500	$4,500	$7,750	$10,000	$13,500	$20,000	$50,000
	Auctions: $52,875, MS-65, August 2015; $37,600, MS-65, February 2016; $3,525, MS-65, January 2015; $25,850, MS-64, October 2016											
1911-D, Weak D	(c)	219	54.0	3%	$1,000	$1,500	$2,250	$4,000				
	Auctions: $2,645, AU-55, April 2012											

a. The sole known example is part of a complete 1910 Sandblast Finish Proof gold set. Other examples may exist, but have not yet been confirmed. **b.** Beware of counterfeit and altered pieces. **c.** Included in 1911-D mintage figure.

	Mintage	Cert	Avg	%MS	VF-20	EF-40	AU-50	MS-60	MS-62	MS-63 PF-60	MS-64 PF-63	MS-65 PF-65
1912	616,000	9,309	60.7	74%	$325	$350	$375	$400	$550	$1,250	$2,250	$10,000
Auctions: $14,100, MS-65, October 2015; $2,350, MS-64, September 2015; $400, MS-61, July 2015; $282, AU-55, February 2015												
1912, Sandblast Finish Proof	197	48	65.6							4,500	$10,000	$30,000
Auctions: $35,250, PF-66, October 2014; $41,125, PF-66, September 2013												
1913	722,000	12,688	61.1	80%	$325	$350	$375	$400	$525	$625	$1,000	$4,000
Auctions: $3,290, MS-65, January 2015; $499, MS-62, February 2015; $264, AU-58, February 2015; $259, AU-50, February 2015												
1913, Sandblast Finish Proof	165	56	65.9							4,500	$11,500	$35,000
Auctions: $31,050, PF-67, January 2012												
1914	240,000	7,893	60.7	74%	$350	$375	$450	$550	$1,100	$2,000	$4,500	$15,000
Auctions: $24,675, MS-65, January 2015; $23,500, MS-65, December 2015; $18,800, MS-65, August 2016; $16,450, MS-65, August 2015												
1914, Sandblast Finish Proof	117	77	65.2							4,500	$10,000	$27,500
Auctions: $12,650, PF-64, April 2012												
1914-D	448,000	10,893	61.1	79%	$325	$350	$375	$450	$550	$1,250	$2,000	$12,500
Auctions: $15,275, MS-65, August 2015; $2,233, MS-64, June 2015; $376, MS-61, September 2015; $282, AU-55, November 2015												
1915	606,000	12,062	61.3	82%	$300	$325	$350	$400	$500	$600	$1,250	$3,000
Auctions: $25,850, MS-66, October 2015; $1,058, MS-64, January 2015; $376, AU-58, March 2015; $259, AU-50, June 2015												
1915, Sandblast Finish Proof	100	43	65.2							6,000	$12,500	$35,000
Auctions: $41,688, PF-66, January 2012												
1925-D	578,000	20,999	62.3	93%	$300	$325	$350	$400	$425	$475	$675	$1,500
Auctions: $6,500, MS-66, January 2015; $881, MS-64, January 2015; $329, MS-61, June 2015; $376, AU-58, March 2015												
1926	446,000	18,950	62.3	95%	$300	$325	$350	$400	$425	$475	$675	$1,500
Auctions: $5,875, MS-66, January 2015; $705, MS-64, January 2015; $329, MS-61, January 2015; $259, MS-60, June 2015												
1927	388,000	15,518	62.3	95%	$300	$325	$350	$400	$425	$475	$675	$1,500
Auctions: $14,688, MS-66, October 2015; $447, MS-63, November 2015; $306, MS-61, March 2015; $311, AU-58, July 2015												
1928	416,000	16,856	62.4	97%	$300	$325	$350	$400	$425	$475	$675	$1,500
Auctions: $8,225, MS-66, September 2015; $764, MS-64, July 2015; $376, MS-62, March 2015; $247, AU-50, March 2015												
1929	532,000	20,603	62.4	98%	$300	$325	$350	$400	$475	$500	$800	$2,750
Auctions: $7,638, MS-65, October 2015; $764, MS-64, August 2015; $376, MS-62, August 2015; $353, MS-60, October 2015												

Three-Dollar Gold Pieces
1854–1889

AN OVERVIEW OF THREE-DOLLAR GOLD PIECES

The three-dollar gold coin denomination was conceived in 1853 and first produced for circulation in 1854. Although there were high hopes for it at the outset, and mintages were generous, the value was redundant given the $2.50 quarter eagle then in circulation. Mintages declined, and although pieces were struck each year through 1889, very few actually circulated after the 1850s.

Although many different three-dollar dates are available at reasonable prices, most numismatists opt to acquire either a circulated or Mint State 1854 (significant as the first year of issue; also, in this year the word DOLLARS is in smaller letters than on later issues) or a Mint State coin from the low-mintage era of 1879–1889. Similar to the situation for gold dollars, although the mintages of these later pieces were low, they were popularly saved at the time, and many more have survived in high quality than might otherwise be the case.

Some numismatists have observed that $3 gold pieces might have been commonly used to purchase sheets of 100 3¢ stamps.

FOR THE COLLECTOR AND INVESTOR: THREE-DOLLAR GOLD PIECES AS A SPECIALTY

Collecting three-dollar pieces by date and mint would at first seem to be daunting, but it is less challenging than expected, outside of a handful of pieces. The 1870-S is unique (in the Harry W. Bass Jr. Collection on loan to the American Numismatic Association), the 1875 and 1876 were made only in Proof format to the extent of 20 and 45 pieces respectively, and the 1873 is quite rare. Beyond that, examples of coins in grades such as EF and AU (including some varieties with very low mintages) can be purchased for reasonable prices.

Choice examples can be elusive, this being particularly true of branch-mint issues of the 1854–1860 years. Generally, Mint State Philadelphia pieces are rare after 1855, but then come on the market with frequency for 1861 and later, with dates in the 1860s being scarcer than later issues. Coins of the years 1878 and 1879 were made in larger quantities, with the 1878 in particular being easy to find today, although examples usually are quite bag-marked. The low-mintage three-dollar pieces of 1879 through 1889 were popular at the time of issue, many were saved, and today Mint State pieces exist to a greater extent than would otherwise be the case.

INDIAN PRINCESS HEAD (1854–1889)

Designer: *James B. Longacre.* **Weight:** *5.015 grams.*
Composition: *.900 gold, .100 copper (net weight .14512 oz. pure gold).* **Diameter:** *20.5 mm.*
Edge: *Reeded.* **Mints:** *Philadelphia, Dahlonega, New Orleans, and San Francisco.*

Circulation Strike

Mintmark location is on the reverse, below the wreath.

Proof

History. The three-dollar gold coin was designed by U.S. Mint chief engraver James B. Longacre, and first struck in 1854. The quarter eagle and half eagle had already been in use for a long time, and the reason for the creation of this odd new denomination is uncertain, although some numismatists note it could have been used to buy a sheet of current 3¢ postage stamps or a group of 100 silver trimes. After a large initial mintage in 1854, the coins were struck in smaller annual quantities. These coins were more popular on the West Coast, but, even in that region, use of this denomination dropped off sharply by the 1870s.

Striking and Sharpness. Points to observe on the obverse include the tips of the feathers in the headdress, and the hair details below the band inscribed LIBERTY. Focal points on the reverse are the wreath details (especially the vertical division in the ribbon knot), and the two central date numerals. Many of the later issues—particularly those of the early 1880s—are prooflike.

Availability. In circulated grades the issues of 1854 to 1860 survive in approximate proportion to their mintages. MS coins are plentiful for the first-year Philadelphia issue, 1854, but are scarce to rare for other years and for all branch-mint issues. For the 1860s and 1870s most are in grades such as EF, AU, and low MS, except for 1874 and in particular 1878, easily found in MS. Dates from 1879 to 1889 have a higher survival ratio and are mostly in MS, often at MS-65.

Proofs. Proofs were struck of all years. All prior to the 1880s are very rare today, with issues of the 1850s being exceedingly so. Coins of 1875 and 1876 were made only in Proof format, with no related circulation strikes. Most often seen in the marketplace are the higher-mintage Proofs of the 1880s. Some have patches of graininess or hints of non-Proof surface on the obverse, or an aura or "ghosting" near the portrait, an artifact of striking.

GRADING STANDARDS

MS-60 to 70 (Mint State). *Obverse:* On MS–60 to 62 coins there is abrasion on the hair below the band lettered LIBERTY (an area that can be weakly struck as well) and on tips of the feather plumes. At MS-63, there may be slight abrasion. Luster can be irregular. At MS-64, abrasion is less. Luster is rich on most coins, less so on the 1854-D (which is often overgraded). At MS-65 and above,

1879. Graded MS-64.

luster is deep and frosty, with no marks at all visible without magnification at MS-66 and higher. *Reverse:* On MS–60 to 62 coins there is abrasion on the 1, the highest parts of the leaves, and the ribbon knot. Otherwise, the same comments apply as for the obverse.

Illustrated coin: Satiny luster and partial mirror surfaces yield excellent eye appeal.

AU-50, 53, 55, 58 (About Uncirculated). *Obverse:* Light wear on the hair below the coronet, the cheek, and the tips of the feather plumes is very noticeable at AU-50, increasingly less at higher levels to AU-58. Luster is minimal at AU-50 and scattered and incomplete at AU-58. Some tiny nicks and contact marks are to be expected and should be mentioned if they are distracting. *Reverse:* Light wear on the 1, the wreath, and the ribbon knot characterize an AU-50 coin, increasingly less at higher levels to AU-58. Otherwise, the same comments apply as for the obverse.

1854. Graded AU-55.

Illustrated coin: Most of the original luster is gone, but perhaps 15% remains in the protected areas.

EF-40, 45 (Extremely Fine). *Obverse:* Medium wear is seen on the hair below the coronet and on the feather plume tips. Detail is partially gone on the hair. Luster is gone on most coins. *Reverse:* Light wear is seen overall, and the highest parts of the leaves are flat, but detail remains elsewhere. Luster is gone on most coins.

1854-D. Graded EF-40.

Illustrated coin: Note the mushy denticles (as seen on all but one specimen of this, the only Dahlonega variety in the series).

VF-20, 30 (Very Fine). *Obverse:* Most hair detail is gone, except at the back of the lower curls. The feather plume ends are flat. *Reverse:* The wreath and other areas show more wear. Most detail is gone on the higher-relief leaves.

Three-dollar gold pieces are seldom collected in grades lower than VF-20.

1874. Graded VF-20.

PF-60 to 70 (Proof). *Obverse and Reverse:* PF–60 to 62 coins have extensive hairlines and may have nicks and contact marks. At PF-63, hairlines are prominent, but the mirror surface is very reflective. PF-64 coins have fewer hairlines. At PF-65, hairlines should be minimal and mostly seen only under magnification. There should be no nicks or marks. PF-66 and higher coins should have no marks or hairlines visible to the unaided eye.

1876. Graded PF-61.

Illustrated coin: Extensive friction is visible in the fields, but the mirror surface can be seen in protected areas. This is still a desirable example of a date of which only 45 were minted.

	Mintage	Cert	Avg	%MS	VF-20	EF-40	AU-50	AU-55	MS-60	MS-62	MS-63	MS-65
										PF-60	PF-63	PF-65
1854	138,618	4,101	55.4	22%	$850	$1,000	$1,100	$1,250	$2,250	$2,750	$4,000	$13,000
	Auctions: $17,050, MS-66, January 2015; $1,293, AU-58, January 2015; $999, EF-45, January 2015; $18,000, MS-65, April 2018											
1854, Proof	*15–20*	7	62.0							$35,000	$80,000	$175,000
	Auctions: $164,500, PF-64Cam, November 2013; $30,550, PF-61, January 2015											
1854-D	1,120	99	51.1	9%	$20,000	$27,500	$45,000	$50,000	$100,000	$200,000		
	Auctions: $188,000, MS-62, February 2016; $39,950, AU-53, September 2016; $52,875, EF-35, March 2013; $52,801, AU-55, April 2018											
1854-O	24,000	854	49.6	3%	$2,000	$3,250	$3,750	$8,000	$40,000	$75,000	$110,000	
	Auctions: $76,375, MS-62; $58,750, MS-62, March 2016; $23,500, AU-58, March 2016; $12,338, AU-55, September 2016; $8,225, AU-55, July 2015											
1855	50,555	1,262	54.2	19%	$950	$1,000	$1,150	$1,250	$2,250	$3,500	$5,000	$30,000
	Auctions: $5,170, MS-63, July 2015; $1,645, AU-58, October 2015; $794, EF-40, January 2015; $541, VF-20, June 2015											
1855, Proof	*4–8*	0	n/a							$35,000	$75,000	$200,000
	Auctions: $75,900, PF-64Cam, November 2003											
1855-S	6,600	163	42.5	2%	$1,500	$3,000	$6,000	$12,000	$32,500	$55,000	$100,000	
	Auctions: $55,225, MS-62, February 2016; $17,625, AU-58, November 2013; $2,820, EF-45, August 2015; $1,763, EF-40, March 2015											
1855-S, Proof	*unknown*	1	64.0									
	Auctions: $1,322,500, PF-64Cam, August 2011											
1856	26,010	781	55.0	19%	$850	$1,000	$1,150	$1,300	$3,000	$4,250	$7,500	$37,500
	Auctions: $1,645, AU-58, August 2015; $999, AU-50, June 2015; $823, EF-45, October 2015; $494, VG-10, September 2015											
1856, Proof	*8–10*	2	63.5							$19,500	$45,000	$125,000
	Auctions: $28,750, PF-62Cam, March 2011											
1856-S (a)	34,500	549	45.5	5%	$1,000	$1,500	$2,750	$4,000	$12,000	$18,500	$30,000	
	Auctions: $2,115, AU-55, October 2015; $1,116, AU-50, July 2015; $1,175, EF-40, July 2015; $552, VF-20, July 2015											
1857	20,891	639	54.8	18%	$850	$1,100	$1,350	$1,500	$3,500	$4,500	$8,500	$35,000
	Auctions: $14,100, MS-64, August 2015; $7,050, MS-63, June 2015; $1,175, AU-50, June 2015; $617, EF-40, October 2015											
1857, Proof	*8–12*	1	64.0							$17,500	$30,000	$125,000
	Auctions: No auction records available.											
1857-S	14,000	198	43.3	2%	$1,300	$2,250	$5,000	$9,000	$21,500	$45,000	$60,000	$100,000
	Auctions: $12,925, AU-58, November 2014; $6,463, AU-55, April 2013; $2,115, EF-45, January 2015; $999, VF-25, October 2015											
1858	2,133	107	52.6	8%	$1,300	$2,250	$3,750	$5,500	$12,000	$15,000	$23,500	
	Auctions: $7,931, AU-58, August 2013											
1858, Proof	*8–12*	4	65.0							$15,000	$30,000	$100,000
	Auctions: $85,188, PF-65Cam, April 2013; $94,000, PF-65, October 2014; $91,063, PF-65, January 2015											
1859	15,558	588	55.5	21%	$1,000	$1,250	$1,350	$1,750	$3,250	$4,500	$7,500	$25,000
	Auctions: $38,188, MS-66, June 2013; $10,575, MS-64, July 2014; $9,988, MS-64, August 2014; $9,400, MS-64, September 2014											
1859, Proof	80	9	64.3							$8,500	$20,000	$65,000
	Auctions: $59,925, PF-65DCam, April 2014											
1860	7,036	326	55.4	22%	$1,000	$1,300	$1,800	$1,950	$3,500	$6,500	$7,500	$30,000
	Auctions: $5,875, MS-63, January 2015; $1,645, MS-60, October 2015; $1,763, AU-53, January 2015; $940, AU-50, June 2015											
1860, Proof	119	14	64.6							$8,000	$16,000	$60,000
	Auctions: $88,125, PF-67Cam, September 2014; $67,563, PF-66Cam, August 2013											
1860-S	7,000	148	42.4	3%	$1,300	$2,750	$7,000	$11,500	$25,000	$50,000		
	Auctions: $25,850, MS-61, February 2016; $21,150, AU-58, August 2015; $2,938, EF-45, March 2016; $999, F-15, October 2015											
1861	5,959	270	55.0	23%	$1,500	$2,500	$3,750	$4,500	$7,000	$11,000	$13,000	$32,500
	Auctions: $17,625, MS-64, September 2015; $6,169, AU-58, January 2015; $2,115, AU-50, August 2014; $2,585, VF-35, September 2015											
1861, Proof	113	5	64.8							$8,000	$16,000	$60,000
	Auctions: $37,375, PF-64Cam, January 2011											
1862	5,750	206	54.9	22%	$1,650	$2,750	$4,250	$4,750	$7,000	$11,000	$13,500	$40,000
	Auctions: $6,463, AU-58, August 2015; $4,230, AU-53, October 2015; $1,293, AU-50, January 2015; $423, VG-8, July 2015											
1862, Proof	35	9	64.9							$8,000	$16,000	$60,000
	Auctions: $74,750, PF-66UCam, August 2009											

a. Collectors recognize three mintmark sizes: Large (very rare); Medium (common), and Small (rare).

	Mintage	Cert	Avg	%MS	VF-20	EF-40	AU-50	AU-55	MS-60	MS-62 / PF-60	MS-63 / PF-63	MS-65 / PF-65
1863	5,000	244	55.7	25%	$1,500	$2,500	$4,000	$4,500	$8,000	$12,500	$15,000	$35,000
Auctions: $61,700, MS-67, July 2015; $28,200, MS-66, August 2015; $8,225, MS-61, June 2015; $3,055, AU-50, October 2015												
1863, Proof	39	10	63.4							$8,000	$16,000	$55,000
Auctions: $80,500, PF-66UCam, March 2011												
1864	2,630	157	56.2	28%	$1,650	$3,000	$4,750	$6,000	$8,000	$13,000	$15,000	$45,000
Auctions: $5,584, AU-58, June 2015; $4,935, AU-55, January 2015; $3,560, EF-45, October 2015; $588, VF-20, July 2015												
1864, Proof	50	18	62.8							$8,000	$16,000	$55,000
Auctions: $48,875, PF-64DCam, April 2012												
1865	1,140	76	56.1	36%	$2,750	$4,500	$7,500	$9,500	$15,000	$23,500	$30,000	$55,000
Auctions: $70,500, MS-66, January 2014; $3,290, VF-25, November 2014; $14,400, MS-61, January 2018												
1865, Proof	25	8	63.8							$8,500	$20,000	$55,000
Auctions: $46,000, PF-64Cam, March 2006												
1865, Proof Restrike (b)	5	0	n/a		*(extremely rare)*							
Auctions: No auction records available.												
1866	4,000	171	55.8	25%	$1,150	$1,350	$2,250	$2,500	$4,500	$7,500	$10,000	$35,000
Auctions: $12,925, MS-64, June 2015; $7,638, MS-63, November 2014; $2,115, AU-55, October 2015; $1,116, AU-50, August 2015												
1866, Proof	30	9	63.7							$8,000	$16,500	$55,000
Auctions: $46,000, PF-64DCam, April 2011												
1867	2,600	128	56.5	23%	$1,300	$1,650	$2,500	$3,250	$5,500	$11,000	$15,000	$35,000
Auctions: $141,000, MS-67, January 2014												
1867, Proof	50	10	62.8							$8,000	$16,500	$55,000
Auctions: $19,388, PF-63DCam, October 2014; $52,875, PF-66Cam, August 2014; $64,625, PF-66Cam, August 2013												
1868 (c)	4,850	366	56.8	26%	$1,150	$1,350	$2,000	$2,500	$4,250	$6,000	$10,000	$30,000
Auctions: $6,463, MS-63, January 2015; $3,290, AU-55, September 2015; $940, AU-50, August 2015; $823, VF-20, October 2015												
1868, Proof	25	9	64.3							$8,000	$16,500	$55,000
Auctions: $57,500, PF-65Cam, January 2011												
1869 (c)	2,500	178	54.6	17%	$1,150	$1,400	$2,200	$2,800	$4,750	$9,000	$13,500	$45,000
Auctions: $9,988, MS-63, August 2014; $3,525, MS-61, January 2015; $2,350, AU-55, March 2015; $1,763, AU-53, October 2015												
1869, Proof	25	4	64.5							$8,000	$16,500	$55,000
Auctions: $57,500, PF-65UCam, February 2009												
1870	3,500	280	54.3	12%	$1,150	$1,550	$2,250	$2,750	$4,500	$10,000	$15,000	$50,000
Auctions: $51,700, MS-65, January 2015; $2,820, AU-58, June 2015; $1,293, AU-50, January 2015; $823, EF-40, July 2015												
1870, Proof	35	10	62.9							$8,000	$16,500	$55,000
Auctions: $55,813, PF-64Cam, January 2014												
1870-S † (d)	0		n/a		$5,000,000							
Auctions: $687,500, EF-40, October 1982												
1871	1,300	190	56.6	22%	$1,150	$1,650	$2,250	$3,000	$4,750	$9,000	$12,750	$35,000
Auctions: $9,400, MS-63, November 2014; $6,463, MS-62, October 2014; $3,055, AU-58, October 2015; $1,880, AU-53, September 2015												
1871, Proof	30	5	62.2							$8,000	$16,500	$60,000
Auctions: $19,550, PF-63Cam, September 2007												
1872	2,000	201	56.5	24%	$1,150	$1,650	$2,500	$3,000	$4,750	$8,000	$12,500	
Auctions: $7,638, MS-62, August 2014; $7,050, MS-62, November 2014; $4,700, MS-62, February 2015; $3,290, AU-58, January 2015												
1872, Proof	30	22	62.8							$8,000	$16,500	$55,000
Auctions: $9,400, MS-62, November 2013; $7,638, AU-58, July 2014; $5,581, AU-58, November 2014; $2,115, AU-50, August 2014												

† Ranked in the *100 Greatest U.S. Coins* (fourth edition). **b.** Sometime around 1873, the Mint restruck a small number of 1865 three-dollar pieces using an obverse die of 1872 and a newly created reverse with the date slanting up to the right (previously listed in *United States Pattern Coins* as Judd-440). Two examples are known in gold. Versions were also made in copper (Judd-441) for interested collectors. **c.** Varieties showing traces of possible overdating include 1868, 8 Over 7; 1869, 9 Over 8; and 1878, 8 Over 7. **d.** A second example of the 1870-S is rumored to exist in the cornerstone of the San Francisco Mint, but the precise location of the cornerstone has long been unknown.

	Mintage	Cert	Avg	%MS	VF-20	EF-40	AU-50	AU-55	MS-60	MS-62 / PF-60	MS-63 / PF-63	MS-65 / PF-65
1873, Close 3	(e)	51	56.4	20%	$5,500	$9,500	$13,500	$18,000	$30,000	$40,000	$55,000	
Auctions: $51,700, MS-64, February 2016; $24,675, MS-61, May 2015												
1873, Open 3 (Original), Proof (f)	25	7	64.3							$25,000 (g)	$32,500	$100,000
Auctions: $212,750, PF-65DCam, September 2008; $164,500, PF-65, February 2016												
1873, Close 3, Proof	(h)	0	n/a							$25,000	$37,500	$75,000
Auctions: $37,375, PF-61, January 2011												
1874	41,800	2,929	56.5	28%	$850	$1,000	$1,050	$1,150	$2,150	$2,750	$4,000	$13,500
Auctions: $14,100, MS-66, October 2015; $1,998, MS-61, June 2015; $705, AU-50, July 2015; $564, F-15, September 2015												
1874, Proof	20	9	64.3							$12,500	$28,000	$60,000
Auctions: $54,625, PF-65Cam, January 2012												
1875, Proof † (i)	20	8	62.8							$95,000 (j)	$165,000	$275,000
Auctions: $329,000, PF-65, February 2016; $164,500, PF-64, January 2015												
1876, Proof (i)	45	28	63.9							$35,000 (k)	$50,000	$85,000
Auctions: $76,375, PF-65Cam, June 2013												
1877	1,468	36	56.9	25%	$4,500	$7,500	$12,500	$15,000	$30,000	$35,000	$50,000	
Auctions: $70,500, MS-64, February 2016; $22,325, MS-61, August 2013; $18,800, AU-58, September 2015; $18,000, AU-58, January 2018												
1877, Proof	20	14	63.1							$12,500	$30,000	$55,000
Auctions: $64,400, PF-65DCam, November 2011												
1878 (c)	82,304	5,388	59.3	57%	$850	$1,000	$1,050	$1,150	$2,150	$2,750	$4,000	$9,500
Auctions: $23,500, MS-66, January 2015; $999, AU-55, February 2015; $646, EF-40, September 2015; $423, AG-3, February 2015												
1878, Proof	20	8	63.8							$12,500	$27,500	$55,000
Auctions: $877, PF, June 2014												
1879	3,000	408	60.8	67%	$1,000	$1,300	$2,000	$2,750	$3,750	$5,500	$7,000	$13,500
Auctions: $19,975, MS-66, February 2015; $4,935, MS-64, July 2015; $2,233, AU-58, October 2015; $881, AU-50, September 2015												
1879, Proof	30	12	64.7							$10,000	$17,000	$42,500
Auctions: $14,375, PF-63Cam, October 2011												
1880	1,000	122	62.2	89%	$1,450	$2,000	$3,500	$3,750	$5,000	$7,000	$9,000	$20,000
Auctions: $16,450, MS-65, January 2015; $5,875, MS-62, June 2015; $3,995, MS-62, October 2015; $2,820, MS-60, October 2015												
1880, Proof	36	16	64.0							$10,000	$17,000	$42,500
Auctions: $51,113, PF, August 2013												
1881	500	107	57.8	39%	$3,000	$5,000	$8,000	$9,500	$14,000	$16,500	$22,500	$55,000
Auctions: $35,250, MS-64, September 2014; $14,100, MS-62, February 2015; $6,463, AU-55, January 2015; $3,290, EF-40, January 2015												
1881, Proof	54	27	64.1							$10,000	$17,000	$42,500
Auctions: $32,200, PF-64Cam, January 2011; $66,000, PF-66Cam, March 2018												
1882	1,500	266	59.0	55%	$1,250	$1,750	$2,500	$3,000	$4,000	$6,750	$10,000	$25,000
Auctions: $22,325, MS-65, August 2015; $3,643, MS-61, August 2015; $2,950, AU-58, September 2015; $705, AU-50, June 2015												
1882, Proof	76	33	63.2							$7,500	$13,500	$35,000
Auctions: $38,188, PF-65DCam, September 2014; $28,200, PF-64DCam, March 2014												
1883	900	136	58.6	57%	$1,500	$2,500	$3,000	$3,500	$4,500	$6,500	$8,500	$25,000
Auctions: $21,150, MS-65, June 2015; $3,760, MS-61, February 2015; $4,465, MS-60, July 2015; $2,820, AU-53, January 2015												
1883, Proof	89	39	64.3							$7,500	$13,500	$35,000
Auctions: $70,500, PF-66Cam+, November 2014; $38,188, PF-65Cam, April 2013												
1884	1,000	52	60.3	67%	$1,750	$2,500	$3,500	$4,000	$5,500	$7,500	$10,000	$25,000
Auctions: $7,931, MS-62, August 2013												
1884, Proof	106	40	64.0							$7,500	$13,500	$35,000
Auctions: $30,550, PF-65DCam, September 2014; $23,500, PF-64DCam, August 2013												

† Ranked in the *100 Greatest U.S. Coins* (fourth edition). **c.** Varieties showing traces of possible overdating include 1868, 8 Over 7; 1869, 9 Over 8; and 1878, 8 Over 7. **e.** The mintage figure for the 1873, Close 3, coins is unknown. Research suggests that only Proofs may have been struck (none for circulation), and those perhaps as late as 1879. **f.** Mint records report 25 Proof coins (with no reference to the style, Open or Close, of the number 3 in the date). The actual mintage may be as high as 100 to 1,000 coins. **g.** Value in PF-40, $17,500; in PF-50, $20,000. **h.** Included in 1873, Open 3 (Original), Proof, mintage figure. **i.** Proof only. **j.** Value in PF-50, $75,000. **k.** Value in PF-50, $22,500.

	Mintage	Cert	Avg	%MS	VF-20	EF-40	AU-50	AU-55	MS-60	MS-62	MS-63	MS-65
										PF-60	PF-63	PF-65
1885	800	154	59.5	56%	$1,650	$2,500	$3,750	$4,500	$6,000	$9,000	$13,500	$27,500
	Auctions: $27,025, MS-65, January 2015; $7,638, MS-62+, August 2014; $4,700, AU-58, January 2015; $3,995, AU-58, October 2015											
1885, Proof	110	54	63.5							$7,500	$13,500	$35,000
	Auctions: $10,281, PF-63, November 2014; $8,813, PF-62, October 2014; $76,050, PF, September 2013											
1886	1,000	163	58.0	44%	$1,500	$1,950	$2,750	$3,750	$5,000	$7,500	$13,500	$40,000
	Auctions: $11,163, MS-63, January 2015; $4,465, MS-61, September 2015; $2,233, MS-60, August 2015; $1,293, AU-50, January 2015											
1886, Proof	142	72	64.1							$7,500	$13,500	$35,000
	Auctions: $38,188, PF-65DCam, April 2013											
1887	6,000	220	60.5	67%	$1,000	$1,350	$2,000	$2,250	$3,000	$4,250	$5,500	$14,500
	Auctions: $11,750, MS-65, August 2015; $3,995, MS-63, January 2015; $1,410, AU-53, October 2015; $953, AU-50, September 2015											
1887, Proof	160	70	63.8							$7,500	$13,500	$35,000
	Auctions: $64,625, PF-67Cam, August 2013; $40,800, PF-66DC, January 2018											
1888	5,000	516	60.8	72%	$950	$1,250	$1,750	$1,850	$3,000	$4,250	$4,500	$11,500
	Auctions: $7,638, MS-65, October 2015; $4,935, MS-64, January 2015; $3,599, MS-63, January 2015; $3,055, MS-61, October 2015											
1888, Proof	291	97	64.1							$7,500	$12,500	$32,500
	Auctions: $38,188, PF-66Cam, November 2013; $15,863, PF-64Cam+, November 2014; $9,988, PF-63Cam, October 2015											
1889	2,300	317	60.6	68%	$850	$1,150	$1,450	$1,650	$3,000	$4,250	$4,500	$11,500
	Auctions: $15,275, MS-65, February 2015; $5,170, MS-63, January 2015; $3,760, MS-60, October 2015; $2,350, AU-58, October 2015											
1889, Proof	129	51	63.7							$7,500	$12,500	$35,000
	Auctions: $25,850, PF-65Cam, January 2014; $7,050, PF-62, November 2014											

Four-Dollar Gold Pieces
1879–1880

AN OVERVIEW OF FOUR-DOLLAR GOLD PIECES

The four-dollar pattern gold coin, or Stella, is not widely collected, simply because of its rarity. For type-set purposes some numismatists opt to acquire a single example of the only issue readily available, Charles Barber's 1879 Flowing Hair, although these are expensive. However, the Coiled Hair style is a different type, much rarer, and a collector with the means might acquire an example of that design as well.

FOR THE COLLECTOR AND INVESTOR: FOUR-DOLLAR GOLD PIECES AS A SPECIALTY

Over the past century perhaps two dozen numismatists have put together complete sets of one of each gold striking of the 1879 and 1880 Flowing Hair and Coiled Hair Stella, this being made possible by collections being dispersed and sold to others, as it is unlikely that even as many as 20 complete sets could exist at one time.

John A. Kasson, a former Iowa congressman, originally proposed the four-dollar gold piece, or "Stella."

STELLA, FLOWING HAIR AND COILED HAIR (1879–1880)

Designers: *Charles E. Barber (Flowing Hair, and common reverse); George T. Morgan (Coiled Hair).*
Weight: *7.0 grams.* **Composition:** *Approximately .857 gold, .042 silver, .100 copper.*
Diameter: *22 mm.* **Edge:** *Reeded.* **Mint:** *Philadelphia.*

Flowing Hair

Coiled Hair

History. The four-dollar gold Stellas of 1879 and 1880 are Proof-only patterns, not regular issues. How-ever, as they have been listed in popular references for decades, collectors have adopted them into the regular gold series. The obverse inscription notes the coins' metallic content in proportions of gold, silver, and copper in the metric system, intended to facilitate their use in foreign countries, where the value could be quickly determined. The Stella was proposed by John A. Kasson (formerly a U.S. repre-sentative from Iowa and chairman of the House Committee on Coinage, Weights, and Measures; in 1879 serving as envoy extraordinary and minister plenipotentiary to Austria-Hungary). It is believed that Charles E. Barber designed the Flowing Hair type (as well as the reverse common to both types), and George T. Morgan designed the Coiled Hair. Those dated 1879 were struck for congressional exam-ination; popular testimony of the era suggests that the Flowing Hair Stella became a favorite gift for congressmen's lovers in the Washington demimonde. The only issue produced in quantity was the 1879, Flowing Hair. The others were made in secret and sold privately by Mint officers and employees. The Coiled Hair Stella was not generally known to the numismatic community until they were illustrated in *The Numismatist* in the early 20th century. Stellas are cataloged by their Judd numbers, assigned in the standard reference, *United States Pattern Coins*.

Striking and Sharpness. On nearly all examples the high parts of the hair are flat, often with striations. The other areas of the coin are typically well struck. Tiny planchet irregularities are common.

Availability. The 1879 Flowing Hair is often available on the market—usually in PF–61 to 64, although higher-condition examples come on the market with regularity (as do lightly handled and impaired coins). The 1880 Flowing Hair is typically found in PF–63 or higher. Both years of Coiled Hair Stellas are great rarities; typical grades are PF–63 to 65, with a flat strike on the head and with some tiny plan-chet flaws.

GRADING STANDARDS

PF-60 to 70 (Proof). *Obverse and Reverse:* PF–60 to 62 coins have extensive hairlines and may have nicks and contact marks. At PF-63, hairlines are prominent, but the mirror sur-face is very reflective. PF-64 coins have fewer hairlines. At PF-65, hairlines should be mini-mal and mostly seen only under magnifi-cation. There should be no nicks or marks. PF-66 and higher coins should have no marks or hairlines visible to the unaided eye.

1879, Flowing Hair; J-1657. Graded PF-62.

Illustrated coin: A nick above the head and some light friction define the grade, but the coin has nice eye appeal overall.

PF-60 to 70 (Proof). *Obverse and Reverse:* PF–60 to 62 coins have extensive hairlines and may have nicks and contact marks. At PF-63, hairlines are prominent, but the mirror surface is very reflective. PF-64 coins have fewer hairlines. At PF-65, hairlines should be minimal and mostly seen only under magnification. There should be no nicks or marks. PF-66 and higher coins should have no marks or hairlines visible to the unaided eye.

1879, Coiled Hair; J-1660. Graded PF-65.

	Mintage	Cert	Avg	%MS	PF-40	PF-50	PF-60	PF-63	PF-64	PF-65	PF-66	PF-67
1879, Flowing Hair, Proof †	425+	235	63.7		$90,000	$95,000	$120,000	$165,000	$175,000	$225,000	$275,000	$400,000
Auctions: $305,500, MS-67, August 2016; $205,625, MS-65, August 2015; $199,750, MS-65, August 2015; $312,000, PF-67Cam, January 2018												
1879, Coiled Hair, Proof †	12–15 known	13	65.1				$300,000	$450,000	$550,000	$800,000	$1,100,000	$1,250,000
Auctions: $1,041,300, PF, September 2013; $1,050,000, PF-66Cam, January 2018												
1880, Flowing Hair, Proof †	17–20 known	20	64.9				$175,000	$325,000	$350,000	$450,000	$550,000	$750,000
Auctions: $417,125, MS-65, June 2015; $352,500, MS-65, August 2016; $959,400, PF, September 2013; $750,000, PF-67Cam, January 2018												
1880, Coiled Hair, Proof †	8–10 known	12	64.9				$600,000	$775,000	$875,000	$1,250,000	$1,750,000	$2,000,000
Auctions: $2,574,000, PF, September 2013; $1,116,250, PF-65, June 2015												

Note: Many individual high-value rare coins are submitted for certification and grading multiple times over the years, which can inflate the number of certifications above the number of coins actually minted. † All Stella 4 Dollar Gold pieces are ranked in the *100 Greatest U.S. Coins* (fourth edition), as a single entry.

Gold Half Eagles ($5)
1795–1929

AN OVERVIEW OF GOLD HALF EAGLES

The half eagle was the first gold coin actually struck for the United States. The five-dollar gold piece was authorized by the Act of April 2, 1792, and the first batch was minted in 1795.

Forming a type set of half eagles is a daunting but achievable challenge—if a collector has the finances and some determination. Examples of the first type, with Capped Bust to Right (conical cap obverse), and with an eagle on a palm branch on the reverse, regularly come up on the market, usually of the date 1795. Typical grades range from EF to lower Mint State levels. Such pieces are scarce, and the demand for them is strong. The next type, the Heraldic Eagle motif, first struck in 1798, but also known from a 1795-dated die used later, was produced through 1807, and is easily enough obtained today. Again, typical grades range from EF to Mint State. MS-63 and better coins are available, but are in the distinct minority.

The short-lived Capped Bust to Left style, 1807–1812, can be found in similar grades, although such pieces did not circulate as extensively, and AU and Mint State levels are the rule, with VF pieces being unusual. Then follows the era of rarities. The Capped Head to Left, stars surrounding head, large diameter, 1813–1829 style is available largely courtesy of the first date of issue, 1813. This is the only date seen with some frequency. When available, examples tend to be choice. The later stretch of this series includes some formidable rarities, among which are the famous 1815 and the even rarer 1822, along with a whole string of other seldom-seen varieties in the 1820s. The same style, but of reduced diameter, 1829–1834, also is rare; examples of the 1830s turn up with some regularity, but these often lack eye appeal. For some reason, half eagles of the early 1830s are often heavily marked and abraded, which is not true at all for coins of the 1820s.

William Woodin, secretary of the Treasury under Franklin D. Roosevelt, built upon the findings of J. Colvin Randall in his research of half eagle die varieties.

Classic Head half eagles, capless and without the motto E PLURIBUS UNUM, first minted in August 1834, are easily enough obtained. Those seen in today's marketplace are usually of the first several dates, and less frequently of 1837 or 1838.

Grades range from VF upward, reflecting their extensive use in circulation. Mint State coins can be found on occasion and are scarce. Choice and gem pieces are rare.

With just a few exceptions, Liberty Head half eagles of the 1839–1866 type without the motto IN GOD WE TRUST are very plentiful in worn grades, including certain of the higher-mintage issues from the popular Charlotte and Dahlonega mints (permitting interesting varieties to be added to a type set). Mint State coins are scarce, and when seen are usually in lower levels such as MS–60 and 62. Gems of any date are rare. Then follow the Liberty Head pieces with the motto IN GOD WE TRUST on the reverse, 1866 through 1908; the earlier years are mostly encountered in worn grades, the later ones are easy enough to find in Mint State. Proofs were made of all Liberty Head half eagle dates, and today they are generally collectible from about 1860 onward.

With two exceptions (1909-O and 1929), the Indian Head half eagles of 1908 to 1929 are common enough in worn grades as well as low Mint State levels, but true gems, accurately graded and with lustrous, frosty surfaces, are quite rare. The field is the highest area of the coin and thus is quite susceptible to scuffs and marks. Probably the most readily available dates in higher grades are 1908 and 1909, with the 1909-D being plentiful due to a hoard that came on the market a generation ago.

FOR THE COLLECTOR AND INVESTOR: GOLD HALF EAGLES AS A SPECIALTY

While in the annals of American numismatics dozens of old-time numismatists collected half eagles by date (or, less often, by date *and* mint), today rarities are so widely scattered and are so expensive that few collectors can rise to the challenge.

Early half eagles can be collected by dates and basic varieties, and also by die varieties. The year 1795 in particular is rich in the latter, and years ago several scholars described such varieties, beginning with J. Colvin Randall in the 1870s, continuing to William H. Woodin in the early 1900s, then Edgar H. Adams, Thomas Ollive Mabbott, and Walter Breen. In more recent times Robert Miller, Harry W. Bass Jr., John Dannreuther, and others have added their research to the literature.

Among early half eagles there are two unique varieties: the 1797 with a 16-star obverse, and the 1797 with a 15-star obverse, both with the Heraldic Eagle reverse, likely struck in 1798. Of the later 1822, just three are known, two of which are in the National Numismatic Collection at the Smithsonian Institution. Of all early half eagles the 1815 was far and away the most famous during the 19th century. (In the 1880s a publication on the Mint Collection stated that the two highlights there were the 1815 half eagle and the unique 1849 double eagle.) At the time the rarer 1822 was not recognized for its elusive nature. Today an estimated 11 examples of the 1815 half eagles exist, mostly in higher circulated grades, including those in museums. There are only two known of the 1825, 5 Over 4, overdate, but it is not at all famous, probably because it is an overdate variety, not a single date on its own. Half eagles of 1826 through 1829 all are rare, with the 1829 being particularly well known. The latter date includes early pieces with regular diameter and later ones with the diameter reduced. Generally, all half eagles from 1815 through 1834 are scarce, some of them particularly so.

Classic Head half eagles of 1834 to 1838 include the scarce 1838-C and 1838-D, the first of the Charlotte and Dahlonega mints respectively; none are prohibitively rare. Generally, the higher-grade pieces are found toward the beginning of the Classic Head series, especially bearing the date 1834.

Liberty Head half eagles are readily available of most dates and mints from 1839 to 1908, save for the one great rarity, the 1854-S, of which just three are known (one is in the Smithsonian). There is a vast panorama of Charlotte and Dahlonega issues through 1861, most of which were made in fairly large quantities, as this was the highest denomination ever struck at each of these mints (larger-capacity presses were not on hand). Accordingly, they are highly collectible today. Some varieties are scarce, but none are completely out of reach. Typical grades range from VF to EF and AU, occasionally Mint State, though not often MS-63 or higher.

Among San Francisco half eagles most of the early issues are scarce, as such pieces circulated extensively and there was no thought to saving numismatic examples. However, there are not many specialists in the field, and for some varieties it can be said that collectors are harder to find than are the coins themselves, yielding the opportunity to purchase truly rare pieces for significantly less than would otherwise be the case. Carson City half eagles were minted beginning in 1870 and continuing intermittently through 1893. Most of the early issues range from scarce to rare, the 1870-CC being particularly well known in this regard. Proofs of the Liberty Head type are generally collectible from the 1860s onward, with most on the market being of the higher-mintage issues of the 1890s and 1900s.

Among Indian Head half eagles, 1908 to 1929, the 1909-O is the rarest of the early coins, and when seen is usually worn. A choice or gem Mint State 1909-O is an incredible rarity. However, enough worn 1909-O half eagles exist, including many brought from overseas hoards in recent decades, that a piece in VF or so grade presents no problem. Half eagles of 1929, of which just 662,000 were minted, were mostly melted, it seems. A couple hundred or so exist today, nearly all of which are Mint State, but nicked and with bagmarks, MS–60 to 62 or 63. Truly high-quality gems are exceedingly rare.

CAPPED BUST TO RIGHT, SMALL EAGLE REVERSE (1795–1798)

Designer: *Robert Scot.* **Weight:** *8.75 grams.*
Composition: *.9167 gold, .0833 silver and copper.*
Diameter: *Approximately 25 mm.* **Edge:** *Reeded.* **Mint:** *Philadelphia.*

Bass-Dannreuther–6.

History. Half eagles of this style, the first federal gold coins, were introduced in July 1795. The obverse features Miss Liberty wearing a conical cap, a design generally called Capped Bust to Right. The reverse depicts a "small" eagle perched on a palm branch. The same motif was used on contemporary $10 gold coins. No Proofs or presentation strikes were made of this type.

Striking and Sharpness. On the obverse, check the star centers and the hair details. On the reverse, check the feathers of the eagle, particularly on the breast. Examine the denticles on both sides. Adjustment marks (from Mint workers filing down overweight planchets to acceptable standards) often are visible, but are not explicitly noted by the grading services.

Availability. Typical grades range from EF to AU and low MS. MS-63 and better coins are rare; when seen, they usually are of the 1795 date (of which many different die varieties exist). Certain varieties are rare, most famously the 1798 with Small Eagle reverse.

GRADING STANDARDS

MS-60 to 70 (Mint State). *Obverse:* At MS-60, some abrasion and contact marks are evident, most noticeably on the hair to the left of Miss Liberty's forehead and on the higher-relief areas of the cap. Luster is present, but may be dull or lifeless, and interrupted in patches. At MS-63, contact marks are few, and abrasion is very light. An MS-65 coin has hardly any abrasion, and contact marks are so minute as to require magnifica-

1795, S Over D in STATES; BD-6. Graded MS-63.

tion. Luster should be full and rich. Grades above MS-65 for this type are more often theoretical than actual—but they do exist and are defined by having fewer marks as perfection is approached. *Reverse:* Comments apply as for the obverse, except that abrasion and contact marks are most noticeable on the breast and head of the eagle. The field area is mainly protected by the eagle, branch, and lettering.

Illustrated coin: This is the error die with the second S over an erroneous D in STATES (which originally read as STATED).

AU-50, 53, 55, 58 (About Uncirculated). *Obverse:* Light wear is seen on the cheek, the hair immediately to the left of the face, and the cap, more at AU-50 than at AU–53 or 55. An AU-58 coin has minimal traces of wear. An AU-50 coin has luster in protected areas among the stars and letters, with little in the open fields or on the portrait. At AU-58, most luster is present in the fields but is worn away on the highest parts of the motifs.

1795; BD-7. Graded AU-58.

Reverse: Comments as preceding, except that the eagle shows light wear on the breast and head in particular, but also at the tip of the wing on the left and elsewhere. Luster ranges from perhaps 40% remaining in protected areas (at AU-50) to nearly full mint bloom (at AU-58).

EF-40, 45 (Extremely Fine). *Obverse:* Wear is evident all over the portrait, with some loss of detail in the hair to the left of Miss Liberty's face. Excellent detail remains in low-relief areas of the hair, such as the front curl and at the back of her head. The stars show wear, as do the date and letters. Luster, if present at all, is minimal and in protected areas. *Reverse:* Wear is greater than on an About Uncirculated coin. The breast, neck, and legs of the

1795; BD-4. Graded EF-40.

eagle lack nearly all feather detail. More wear is seen on the edges of the wing. Some traces of luster may be seen, more so at EF-45 than at EF-40.

VF-20, 30 (Very Fine). *Obverse:* The higher-relief areas of hair are well worn at VF-20, less so at VF-30. The stars are flat at their centers. *Reverse:* Wear is greater, the eagle is flat in most areas, and about 40% to 60% of the wing feathers can be seen.

The Capped Bust to Right half eagle with Small Eagle reverse is seldom collected in grades lower than VF-20.

Illustrated coin: While exhibiting typical wear for a VF-20 coin, this specimen also shows rim damage from having been mounted as jewelry at some point in time.

1795. Graded VF-20.

| 1796, 6 Over 5 | 1797, 15-Star Obverse | 1797, 16-Star Obverse |

	Mintage	Cert	Avg	%MS	F-12	VF-20	EF-40	AU-50	AU-55	MS-60	MS-62	MS-63	MS-64
1795	8,707	226	56.2	30%	$21,500	$25,000	$32,500	$40,000	$52,500	$75,000	$115,000	$165,000	$325,000 (a)
	Auctions: $587,500, MS-66H, January 2015; $64,625, MS-61, February 2013; $64,625, AU-58, August 2014; $52,875, AU-58, August 2014												
1795, S Over D in STATES (b)	(c)	1	51.0	0%				$42,000	$55,000	$77,500			
	Auctions: $345,000, MS-65PL, July 2009												
1796, 6 Over 5	6,196	36	57.4	42%	$22,500	$27,500	$40,000	$60,000	$75,000	$110,000	$165,000	$250,000	$350,000
	Auctions: $67,563, AU-58, February 2014; $45,531, AU-55, October 2014; $52,875, AU-53, August 2014												
1797, All kinds	3,609												
1797, 15-Star Obverse		5	56.8	20%	$27,000	$45,000	$65,000	$125,000	$155,000	$300,000			
	Auctions: $235,000, AU-58, August 2015: $152,750, AU-53, January 2014												
1797, 16-Star Obverse †		6	59.0	33%	$25,000	$40,000	$55,000	$100,000	$145,000	$275,000			
	Auctions: $411,250, MS-61, August 2013												
1798, Small Eagle † (d)	*unknown*	1	56.0	0%		$500,000	$600,000	$750,000	$1,250,000	—			
	Auctions: $1,175,000, AU-55, September 2015												

† Ranked in the *100 Greatest U.S. Coins* (fourth edition). **a.** Value in MS-65 is $550,000. **b.** The final S in STATES is punched over an erroneous D. **c.** Included in 1795, Small Eagle, mintage figure. **d.** The reverse of the 1798, Small Eagle, was from a 1795 die. The obverse has an arched die crack or flaw beneath the date. 7 examples are known, and the finest is an AU-55 from the collection of King Farouk of Egypt.

CAPPED BUST TO RIGHT, HERALDIC EAGLE REVERSE (1795–1807)

Designer: *Robert Scot.* **Weight:** *8.75 grams.*
Composition: *.9167 gold, .0833 silver and copper.*
Diameter: *Approximately 25 mm.* **Edge:** *Reeded.* **Mint:** *Philadelphia.*

BD-15.

History. For this type, the obverse design is the same as that of the preceding. The reverse features a heraldic eagle, as used on other silver and gold coins of the era. Some half eagles of the Heraldic Eagle Reverse design are dated 1795, but these were actually struck in 1798, from a leftover obverse coinage die. The *Encyclopedia of U.S. Gold Coins, 1795–1933* notes that "No Proofs were made, but one 1795 half eagle with a Heraldic Eagle reverse has been certified as a Specimen."

Striking and Sharpness. On the obverse, check the star centers and the hair details. On the reverse, check the upper part of the shield, the lower part of the eagle's neck, the eagle's wing, the stars above the eagle, and the clouds. Inspect the denticles on both sides. Adjustment marks (from overweight planchets being filed down to correct standards by Mint workers) can be an aesthetic problem and are not explicitly identified by the grading services.

Availability. Although there are many rare die varieties, as a type this half eagle is plentiful. Typical grades are EF to lower MS. MS-63 and higher coins are seen with some frequency and usually are dated from 1802 to 1807. Sharply struck coins without adjustment marks are in the minority.

GRADING STANDARDS

MS-60 to 70 (Mint State). *Obverse:* At MS-60, some abrasion and contact marks are evident, most noticeably on the hair to the left of Miss Liberty's forehead and on the higher-relief areas of the cap. Luster is present, but may be dull or lifeless, and interrupted in patches. At MS-63, contact marks are few, and abrasion is very light. An MS-65 coin has hardly any abrasion, and contact marks are so minute as to require magnifica-

1802, 2 Over 1. Graded MS-62.

tion. Luster should be full and rich. Grades above MS-65 are not often seen but are defined by having fewer marks as perfection is approached. *Reverse:* Comments apply as for the obverse, except that abrasion and contact marks are most noticeable on the upper part of the eagle and the clouds. The field area is complex, with not much open space, given the stars above the eagle, the arrows and olive branch, and other features. Accordingly, marks are not as noticeable as on the obverse.

Illustrated coin: This is an attractive coin with rich luster. Some friction is visible on the higher points and in the obverse field.

AU-50, 53, 55, 58 (About Uncirculated).
Obverse: Light wear is seen on the cheek, the hair immediately to the left of the face, and the cap, more at AU-50 than at AU–53 or 55. An AU-58 coin has minimal traces of wear. An AU-50 coin has luster in protected areas among the stars and letters, with little in the open fields or on the portrait. At AU-58, most luster is present in the fields, but is worn away on the highest parts of the motifs.

1804. Graded AU-58.

Reverse: Comments as preceding, except that the eagle's neck, the tips and top of the wings, the clouds, and the tail now show noticeable wear, as do other features. Luster ranges from perhaps 40% remaining in protected areas (at AU-50) to nearly full mint bloom (at AU-58). Often the reverse of this type retains much more luster than the obverse.

Illustrated coin: An abrasion in the left obverse field keeps this otherwise lustrous and attractive coin below the Mint State level.

EF-40, 45 (Extremely Fine). *Obverse:* Wear is evident all over the portrait, with some loss of detail in the hair to the left of Miss Liberty's face. Excellent detail remains in low-relief areas of the hair, such as the front curl and at the back of her head. The stars show wear, as do the date and letters. Luster, if present at all, is minimal and in protected areas. *Reverse:* Wear is greater than on an About Uncirculated coin. The neck lacks feather detail on its

1804, Small 8 Over Large 8; BD-7. Graded EF-45.

highest points. Feathers have lost some detail near the edges of the wings, and some areas of the horizontal lines in the shield may be blended together. Some traces of luster may be seen, more so at EF-45 than at EF-40. Overall, the reverse appears to be in a slightly higher grade than the obverse.

VF-20, 30 (Very Fine). *Obverse:* The higher-relief areas of hair are well worn at VF-20, less so at VF-30. The stars are flat at their centers. *Reverse:* Wear is greater, including on the shield and wing feathers. The star centers are flat. Other areas have lost detail as well. E PLURIBUS UNUM may be light or worn away in areas.

The Capped Bust to Right half eagle with Heraldic Eagle reverse is seldom collected in grades lower than VF-20.

1798, Large 8, 13-Star Reverse; BD-4. Graded VF-20.

1797, 16-Star Obverse   1797, 15-Star Obverse

1797, 7 Over 5   1798, Small 8   1798, Large 8

1798, 13-Star Reverse   1798, 14-Star Reverse   1799, Small Reverse Stars   1799, Large Reverse Stars

	Mintage	Cert	Avg	%MS	F-12	VF-20	EF-40	AU-50	AU-55	MS-60	MS-62	MS-63	MS-64
1795	(a)	21	60.8	62%	$15,000	$25,000	$35,000	$60,000	$80,000	$115,000	$165,000	$250,000	$300,000
Auctions: No auction records available.													
1797, 7 Over 5	(a)	3	61.0	67%	$22,500	$35,000	$45,000	$75,000	$115,000	$200,000			
Auctions: $126,500, AU-58, September 2005													
1797, 16-Star Obverse	(a)	0	n/a		*(unique, in Smithsonian collection)*		—						
Auctions: No auction records available.													
1797, 15-Star Obverse	(a)	0	n/a		*(unique, in Smithsonian collection)*		—						
Auctions: No auction records available.													
1798, All kinds	24,867												
1798, Small 8		24	56.3	25%	$6,000	$8,000	$12,500	$18,500	$22,000	$32,500	$50,000	$77,500	
Auctions: $18,800, AU-53, April 2014													
1798, Large 8, 13-Star Reverse		185	59.3	57%	$5,000	$6,000	$10,000	$16,000	$20,000	$30,000	$40,000	$60,000	
Auctions: $21,150, AU-55, August 2014; $19,975, AU-55, November 2014; $16,450, AU-53, August 2014; $12,925, AU-50, January 2014													
1798, Large 8, 14-Star Reverse		185	59.3	57%	$5,500	$7,000	$15,000	$25,000	$35,000	$115,000			
Auctions: $32,900, AU-55, August 2014; $25,850, AU-55, October 2014; $25,850, AU, February 2014													
1799, All kinds	7,451												
1799, Small Reverse Stars		10	59.7	50%	$5,000	$7,000	$10,000	$14,000	$18,000	$27,500	$37,500	$65,000	$100,000
Auctions: $47,000, MS-62, February 2013; $19,975, AU-58, August 2014; $13,513, AU-55, September 2014; $4,711, EF-40, August 2014													
1799, Large Reverse Stars		17	58.1	59%	$5,000	$7,000	$10,000	$14,000	$18,000	$27,500	$37,500	$65,000	$100,000
Auctions: $70,500, MS-63, January 2014; $16,450, AU-55, August 2014; $11,750, AU-53, August 2014													

a. The 1795 and 1797 Heraldic Eagle half eagles are thought to have been struck in 1798 and are included in that year's mintage figure of 24,867.

| 1800, Pointed 1 | 1800, Blunt 1 | 1800, 8 Arrows | 1800, 9 Arrows |

| 1802, 2 Over 1 FS-G5-1802/1-301. | 1803, 3 Over 2 | 1804, Small 8 | 1804, Small 8 Over Large 8 |

| 1806, Pointed-Top 6, Stars 8 and 5 | Closeup of Pointed-Top 6 | 1806, Round-Top 6, Stars 7 and 6 | Closeup of Round-Top 6 |

	Mintage	Cert	Avg	%MS	F-12	VF-20	EF-40	AU-50	AU-55	MS-60	MS-62	MS-63	MS-64
1800	37,628	258	56.7	40%	$4,500	$5,500	$7,750	$11,000	$12,500	$17,500	$22,500	$40,000	$85,000
Auctions: $16,100, MS-62, April 2012; $11,750, AU-55, January 2015; $8,425, AU-53, March 2018													
1800, Pointed 1 (b)	(c)	1	56.0	0%				$21,000	$24,000	$28,000			
Auctions: $25,850, MS-63, November 2014; $21,150, MS-62, November 2013; $12,338, MS-61, October 2014													
1800, 9 Arrows (d)	(c)	0	n/a					$17,500	$21,500				
Auctions: No auction records available.													
1802, 2 Over 1	53,176	274	57.5	39%	$4,000	$5,000	$7,000	$10,000	$12,000	$16,000	$18,500	$35,000	$57,500 (e)
Auctions: $58,750, MS-64, January 2014; $16,450, MS-62, October 2014; $11,750, AU-58, September 2014; $5,141, AU, March 2015													
1803, 3 Over 2	33,506	320	57.4	44%	$4,000	$5,000	$7,000	$10,000	$12,500	$19,500	$25,000	$42,500	$80,000 (f)
Auctions: $12,925, MS-62, October 2014; $14,100, MS-62, November 2014; $20,563, MS-62, October 2013; $10,575, AU-58, August 2014													
1804, All kinds	30,475												
1804, Small 8		36	60.2	67%	$4,000	$5,000	$7,000	$10,000	$11,500	$16,500	$22,000	$32,500	$60,000
Auctions: $18,800, MS-62, January 2014; $10,575, AU-58, August 2014; $12,925, AU-55, August 2014; $5,875, AU-50, August 2014													
1804, Small 8 Over Large 8 (g)		64	59.4	56%	$4,000	$5,000	$7,000	$10,500	$12,500	$19,000	$25,000	$42,500	$75,000
Auctions: $32,900, MS-63, January 2014; $8,813, AU-53, August 2014; $8,813, AU-53, November 2014; $5,581, AU-50, September 2014													
1805	33,183	185	59.3	57%	$4,500	$5,500	$7,750	$11,000	$12,500	$16,000	$21,000	$35,000	$60,000 (h)
Auctions: $15,275, MS-62, August 2014; $14,688, MS-61, November 2014; $16,450, MS, February 2014; $12,925, AU-58, November 2014													
1806, Pointed-Top 6	9,676	75	57.4	51%	$4,000	$5,000	$7,000	$10,000	$12,000	$16,500	$20,000	$36,500	$60,000
Auctions: $15,275, MS-61, August 2014; $15,275, MS-60, August 2014; $12,925, MS-60, February 2016; $4,406, AU, March 2015													
1806, Rounded-Top 6	54,417	182	58.5	53%	$4,000	$5,000	$7,000	$10,000	$11,500	$15,500	$19,000	$32,500	$47,500 (i)
Auctions: $111,625, MS-65, March 2013; $48,469, MS-64, August 2014; $19,388, MS-62, August 2014; $4,440, VF-30, February 2018													

b. 4 to 6 examples are known. **c.** Included in 1800 mintage figure. **d.** 18 to 25 examples are known. **e.** Value in MS-65 is $135,000. **f.** Value in MS-65 is $145,000. **g.** Created when the engraver mistakenly used an 8 punch intended for $10 gold coins, then corrected the error by overpunching with a much smaller 8. **h.** Value in MS-65 is $165,000. **i.** Value in MS-65 is $125,000.

| 1807, Small Reverse Stars | 1807, Large Reverse Stars |

	Mintage	Cert	Avg	%MS	F-12	VF-20	EF-40	AU-50	AU-55	MS-60	MS-62	MS-63	MS-64
1807, All kinds	32,488												
1807, Small Reverse Stars		0	n/a		$5,000	$6,500	$8,000	$10,000	$11,500	$15,500	$18,000	$32,500	$47,500
Auctions: $44,563, MS-64, January 2012													
1807, Large Reverse Stars		0	n/a		$5,000	$6,500	$8,000	$10,000	$11,500	$15,500	$18,000	$32,500	$47,500
Auctions: $21,850, MS-63, January 2012; $1,880, F-12, October 2015													

DRAPED BUST TO LEFT (1807–1812)

Designer: *John Reich.* **Weight:** *8.75 grams.*
Composition: *.9167 gold, .0833 silver and copper.*
Diameter: *Approximately 25 mm.* **Edge:** *Reeded.* **Mint:** *Philadelphia.*

BD-8.

History. This half eagle motif, designed by John Reich and stylistically related to his Capped Bust half dollar of 1807, was used for several years in the early 1800s. Quantities minted were high, and the coins saw wide circulation. No Proof examples were made of this type.

Striking and Sharpness. The striking usually is quite good and is significantly better than on earlier half eagle types. Adjustment marks (from overweight planchets being filed down to acceptable weight) are seen only occasionally. On the obverse, check the star centers and the hair details. On the reverse, check the eagle, particularity at the shield and the lower left. Examine the denticles on both sides.

Availability. After 1821 gold coins of this standard no longer circulated, as their bullion value exceeded their face value. Accordingly, they never sustained extensive wear, and nearly all examples are in EF or higher grades (coins used as pocket pieces or incorporated into jewelry are exceptions). As a type this issue is readily available in grades up to MS-63, although MS–64 and 65 coins are seen on occasion. Most have excellent eye appeal.

GRADING STANDARDS

MS-60 to 70 (Mint State). *Obverse:* At MS-60, some abrasion and contact marks are seen on the cheek, the hair below the LIBERTY inscription, and the highest-relief folds of the cap. Luster is present, but may be dull or lifeless, and interrupted in patches. At MS-63, contact marks are few, and abrasion is very light. At MS-64, abrasion is even less. An MS-65 coin has hardly any abrasion, and contact marks are minute. Luster should be

1808. Graded MS-60.

full and rich and is often more intense on the obverse. Grades above MS-65 are defined by having fewer marks as perfection is approached. *Reverse:* Comments apply as for the obverse, except that abrasion is most noticeable on the eagle's neck and the highest area of the wings.

Illustrated coin: This attractive Draped Bust to Left half eagle has nice luster.

AU-50, 53, 55, 58 (About Uncirculated). *Obverse:* Light wear is seen on the cheek and the higher-relief areas of the hair and cap. Friction and scattered marks are in the field, ranging from extensive at AU-50 to minimal at AU-58. Luster may be seen in protected areas, minimal at AU-50 but more evident at AU-58. On an AU-58 coin the field retains some luster as well. *Reverse:* Comments as preceding, except that the eagle's neck, the

1811, Tall 5. Graded AU-58.

top of the wings, the leaves, and the arrowheads now show noticeable wear, as do other features. Luster ranges from perhaps 40% remaining in protected areas (at AU-50) to nearly full mint bloom (at AU-58). Often the reverse of this type retains much more luster than the obverse, as the motto, eagle, and lettering protect the surrounding flat areas.

Illustrated coin: This lustrous example is well struck.

EF-40, 45 (Extremely Fine). *Obverse:* More wear is seen on the portrait, the hair, the cap, and the drapery near the clasp. Luster is minimal or nonexistent at EF-40, and may be slight at EF-45. *Reverse:* Wear is more extensive on the eagle, including the top of the wings, the head, the top of the shield, and the claws. Some traces of luster may be seen, more so at EF-45 than at EF-40.

1807; BD-8. Graded EF-40.

VF-20, 30 (Very Fine). *Obverse:* Wear on the portrait has reduced the hair detail, especially to the right of the face and the top of the head, but much can still be seen. *Reverse:* Wear on the eagle is greater, and details of feathers near the shield and near the top of the wings are weak or missing. All other features show wear, but most are fairly sharp. Generally, Draped Bust gold coins at this grade level lack eye appeal.

1807; BD-8. Graded VF-20.

The Draped Bust to Left half eagle is seldom collected in grades lower than VF-20.

1808, 8 Over 7   1808, Normal Date   1809, 9 Over 8

 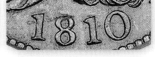

1810, Small Date   1810, Large Date

Small 5   Large 5   Tall 5

	Mintage	Cert	Avg	%MS	F-12	VF-20	EF-40	AU-50	AU-55	MS-60	MS-62	MS-63	MS-64
1807	51,605	248	58.6	52%	$3,250	$4,750	$5,750	$8,250	$9,750	$14,000	$16,500	$26,000	$35,000 **(a)**
Auctions: $76,375, MS-65, April 2013; $19,975, MS-63, October 2014; $11,750, MS-62, August 2014; $12,338, MS-62, November 2014													
1808, All kinds	55,578												
1808, 8 Over 7		48	58.6	56%	$3,250	$5,000	$6,500	$9,000	$11,500	$18,500	$25,000	$35,000	$60,000
Auctions: $24,675, MS-62, August 2014; $19,388, MS-61, June 2014; $6,463, EF-45, November 2015													
1808		181	58.1	52%	$3,000	$4,500	$5,500	$8,000	$9,500	$13,500	$15,500	$28,500	$35,500 **(b)**
Auctions: $25,850, MS-63, March 2013; $12,925, MS-60, October 2014; $4,113, MS, March 2015; $7,638, AU-58, November 2014													
1809, 9 Over 8	33,875	184	58.6	55%	$3,000	$4,500	$5,500	$9,250	$10,500	$14,000	$16,500	$27,500	$52,500
Auctions: $51,406, MS-64, January 2014; $11,750, MS-61, August 2014; $8,001, AU-53, August 2014													
1810, All kinds	100,287												
1810, Small Date, Small 5		5	55.8	40%	$20,000	$40,000	$55,000	$75,000	$80,000	$100,000	$125,000		
Auctions: $19,388, 88, November 2015: $18,800, AU-50, January 2014													
1810, Small Date, Tall 5		80	57.6	51%	$3,000	$4,500	$5,500	$8,000	$9,500	$14,000	$16,000	$29,000	$55,000
Auctions: $58,750, MS-64, August 2016; $12,925, MS-62, January 2014; $12,925, MS-62, August 2014; $12,925, AU-58, September 2014													
1810, Large Date, Small 5		83	57.7	53%	$30,000	$55,000	$75,000	$110,000	$130,000	$200,000			
Auctions: No auction records available.													
1810, Large Date, Large 5		258	59.2	63%	$3,000	$4,500	$5,500	$8,000	$9,500	$13,000	$14,500	$26,000	$36,500 **(c)**
Auctions: $32,900, MS-64, January 2014; $11,750, MS-62, November 2014; $8,813, AU-58, August 2014; $9,988, AU-55, March 2015													

a. Value in MS-65 is $125,000. **b.** Value in MS-65 is $95,000. **c.** Value in MS-65 is $115,000.

	Mintage	Cert	Avg	%MS	F-12	VF-20	EF-40	AU-50	AU-55	MS-60	MS-62	MS-63	MS-64
1811, All kinds	99,581												
1811, Small 5		27	55.7	44%	$3,000	$4,500	$5,500	$8,000	$9,500	$13,000	$14,500	$26,000	$36,500 (c)
	Auctions: $64,625, MS-64, August 2013; $10,575, MS-61, July 2014; $4,994, MS-60, October 2014; $3,836, AU-50, September 2014												
1811, Tall 5		45	60.1	62%	$3,000	$4,500	$5,500	$8,000	$9,500	$13,000	$14,500	$26,000	$36,500 (c)
	Auctions: $76,375, MS-65, August 2013; $9,400, AU-58, August 2014; $1,880, EF-40, July 2014; $3,055, EF-40, September 2014												
1812	58,087	222	59.0	64%	$3,000	$4,500	$5,500	$8,000	$9,500	$13,000	$14,500	$26,000	$36,500
	Auctions: $30,550, MS-64, November 2014; $61,688, MS-64, August 2013; $4,465, MS-60, August 2015												

c. Value in MS-65 is $115,000.

CAPPED HEAD TO LEFT (1813–1834)

Designer: *John Reich (design modified by William Kneass in 1829).*
Weight: *8.75 grams.* **Composition:** *.9167 gold, .0833 silver and copper.*
Diameter: *25 mm (reduced to 23.8 mm in 1829).* **Edge:** *Reeded.* **Mint:** *Philadelphia.*

Circulation Strike
BD-1.

Proof
BD-3.

History. Half eagles of the Capped Head to Left design are divided into issues of 1813 to 1829 (with a larger diameter), and issues of 1829 to 1834 (with a smaller diameter, and smaller letters, dates, and stars). Those dated 1813 to 1815 are in bold relief and sometimes collected as a separate variety.

Striking and Sharpness. On the obverse, check the star centers and the hair details (these details are usually less distinct on the 1829–1834 smaller-diameter coins). On the reverse, check the eagle. Most examples are well struck. Adjustment marks (from overweight planchets being filed down to acceptable specifications at the mint) are not often encountered. Proof coins were struck on a limited basis for inclusion in sets and for numismatists. Over the years some prooflike Mint State pieces have been classified as Proofs.

Availability. The 1813 and 1814, 4 Over 3, are seen with some frequency and constitute the main supply available for assembling type sets. Other dates range from very rare to extremely rare, with the 1822 topping the list (just three are known, two of which are in the Smithsonian Institution). As gold coins did not circulate after 1821, issues of 1813 to 1820 are usually seen in high-level AU or in MS, and those of the 1820s in MS. The half eagles of the early 1830s are exceptions; these usually show light wear and are much rarer in high-level MS. All Proofs are exceedingly rare.

GRADING STANDARDS

MS-60 to 70 (Mint State). *Obverse:* At MS-60, some abrasion and contact marks are seen on the cheek, the hair below the LIBERTY inscription, and the highest-relief folds of the cap. Luster is present, but may be dull or lifeless, and interrupted in patches. At MS-63, contact marks are few, and abrasion is very light. At MS-64, abrasion is even less. An MS-65 coin has hardly any abrasion, and

1832, 13 Obverse Stars; BD-1. Graded MS-63.

contact marks are minute. Luster should be full and rich and is often more intense on the obverse. Grades above MS-65 are defined by having fewer marks as perfection is approached. *Reverse:* Comments apply as for the obverse, except that abrasion is most noticeable on the eagle's neck and the highest area of the wings.

AU-50, 53, 55, 58 (About Uncirculated). *Obverse:* Light wear is seen on the cheek and the higher-relief areas of the hair and cap. Friction and scattered marks are in the field, ranging from extensive at AU-50 to minimal at AU-58. Luster may be seen in protected areas, minimal at AU-50 but more evident at AU-58. On an AU-58 coin the field retains some luster as well. *Reverse:* Comments as preceding, except that the eagle's neck, the

1813; BD-1. Graded AU-50.

top of the wings, the leaves, and the arrowheads now show noticeable wear, as do other features. Luster ranges from perhaps 40% remaining in protected areas (at AU-50) to nearly full mint bloom (at AU-58). Often the reverse of this type retains much more luster than the obverse, as the motto, eagle, and lettering protect the surrounding flat areas.

EF-40, 45 (Extremely Fine). *Obverse:* More wear is seen on the portrait, the hair, the cap, and the drapery near the clasp. Luster is minimal or nonexistent at EF-40, and may be slight at EF-45. *Reverse:* Wear is more extensive on the eagle, including the top of the wings, the head, the top of the shield, and the claws. Some traces of luster may be seen, more so at EF-45 than at EF-40.

The Capped Head half eagle is seldom collected in grades lower than EF-40.

1813; BD-1. Graded EF-45.

PF-60 to 70 (Proof). *Obverse and Reverse:* PF–60 to 62 coins have extensive hairlines and may have nicks and contact marks. At PF-63, hairlines are prominent, but the mirror surface is very reflective. PF-64 coins have fewer hairlines. At PF-65, hairlines should be minimal and mostly seen only under magnification. There should be no nicks or marks. PF-66 and higher coins should have no marks or hairlines visible to the unaided eye.

1829, Small Date, Reduced Diameter; BD-2. Proof.

| 1820, Curved-Base 2 | 1820, Square-Base 2 | 1820, Small Letters | 1820, Large Letters |

	Mintage	Cert	Avg	%MS	F-12	VF-20	EF-40	AU-50	AU-55	MS-60	MS-62	MS-63	MS-64
											PF-63	PF-64	PF-65
1813	95,428	281	58.7	56%	$4,750	$5,750	$7,000	$10,000	$11,000	$15,000	$17,500	$28,500	$36,500 (a)
Auctions: $49,350, MS-64, January 2013; $15,863, MS-62, August 2014; $6,463, MS-60, September 2014; $9,400, AU-55, October 2014													
1814, 4 Over 3	15,454	62	59.8	66%	$5,500	$7,000	$9,000	$12,000	$13,000	$20,000	$27,500	$40,000	$55,000
Auctions: $14,688, AU-58, January 2014; $11,764, AU-55, November 2014													
1815 † (b)	635	4	57.8	50%			$200,000	$275,000	$325,000	$400,000	$500,000	$600,000	
Auctions: $822,500, MS-65, February 2016; $460,000, MS-64, January 2009													
1818, All kinds	48,588												
1818		38	59.5	61%	$5,000	$6,000	$7,500	$15,500	$18,500	$25,000	$30,000	$45,000	$60,000 (c)
Auctions: $38,188, MS-62, November 2014; $19,388, MS-62, November 2014; $15,863, AU-50, September 2013													
1818, STATESOF one word		41	60.3	71%	$5,500	$7,000	$9,000	$14,000	$17,000	$22,500	$30,000	$45,000	$65,000
Auctions: $23,500, MS-62, January 2014; $4,994, AU-50, September 2014													
1818, I Over O		6	62.5	100%	$5,000	$6,500	$8,000	$11,000	$15,000	$30,000	$35,000	$50,000	$65,000 (d)
Auctions: $135,125, MS-65, January 2014													
1819, All kinds †	51,723												
1819 †		3	51.7	33%			$65,000	$80,000	$95,000	$150,000	$200,000		
Auctions: $38,188, AU-50, August 2014													
1819, I Over O †		7	55.6	29%			$50,000	$65,000	$80,000	$125,000	$180,000	$225,000	
Auctions: $67,563, AU-55, January 2014													
1820, All kinds	263,806												
1820, Curved-Base 2, Small Letters		1	62.0	100%	$5,250	$7,000	$11,000	$14,000	$20,000	$27,500	$32,500	$85,000	$170,000
Auctions: $172,500, MS-64, January 2012													
1820, Curved-Base 2, Large Letters		1	64.0	100%	$5,000	$6,750	$8,500	$12,500	$17,500	$25,000	$27,500	$40,000	$75,000
Auctions: $19,975, MS-60, January 2014; $11,750, MS-60, September 2014													
1820, Square-Base 2		5	62.2	100%	$5,500	$7,000	$11,000	$16,000	$20,000	$27,500	$32,500	$45,000	$65,000
Auctions: $31,725, MS-63, January 2014													
1820, Square-Base 2, Proof (e)	2–3	1	64.0		*(unique, in the Bass Foundation Collection)*								
Auctions: No auction records available.													
1821	34,641	6	55.5	33%	$25,000	$35,000	$60,000	$100,000	$150,000	$215,000	$265,000	$400,000	
Auctions: $540,000, MS-63+, January 2015; $141,000, AU-55, January 2014													
1821, Proof (f)	3–5	0	n/a		*(extremely rare)*								
Auctions: No auction records available.													
1822 † (g)	17,796	2	45.0	0%					$8,000,000				
Auctions: No auction records available.													
1822, Proof (h)	unknown	0	n/a		*(extremely rare)*								
Auctions: No auction records available.													

† Ranked in the *100 Greatest U.S. Coins* (fourth edition); both 1819 Capped Bust Half Eagle varieties as a single entry. **a.** Value in MS-65 is $105,000. **b.** 11 examples are known. **c.** Value in MS-65 is $135,000. **d.** Value in MS-65 is $140,000. **e.** Some experts have questioned the Proof status of this unique piece; the surface of the coin is reflective, but it is not as convincing as other true Proofs of the type. Prior claims that as many as four Proofs exist of this date have not been substantiated. **f.** 2 examples are known. One is in the Harry W. Bass Jr. Foundation Collection, and another is in the Smithsonian's National Numismatic Collection. **g.** 3 examples are known. **h.** 3 examples are known, though the Proof status of these pieces has been questioned.

1825, 5 Over Partial 4

1825, 5 Over 4

1828, 8 Over 7

1829, Large Date
BD-1.

1829, Small Date
BD-2.

	Mintage	Cert	Avg	%MS	F-12	VF-20	EF-40	AU-50	AU-55	MS-60	MS-62 / PF-63	MS-63 / PF-64	MS-64 / PF-65
1823	14,485	25	56.8	44%	$8,500	$10,000	$15,000	$20,000	$25,000	$30,000	$35,000	$50,000	$75,000
Auctions: $82,250, MS-64, January 2014; $29,375, MS-62, August 2014													
1823, Proof (i)	unknown	0	n/a										
Auctions: No auction records available.													
1824	17,340	16	60.4	63%	$14,000	$20,000	$30,000	$37,500	$50,000	$75,000	$95,000	$130,000	$150,000 (j)
Auctions: $199,750, MS-65, January 2014													
1824, Proof (k)	unknown	0	n/a										
Auctions: No auction records available.													
1825, 5 Over Partial 4 † (l)	29,060	7	61.4	86%	$14,000	$20,000	$30,000	$37,500	$47,500	$75,000	$100,000	$130,000	$150,000
Auctions: $99,875, MS-61, January 2014													
1825, 5 Over 4 † (m)	(n)	2	56.5	50%			$500,000	$700,000					$1,000,000
Auctions: $940,000, MS-64, May 2016: $690,000, AU-50, July 2008													
1825, 5 Over Partial 4, Proof † (o)	1–2	0	n/a		*(unique, in the Smithsonian's National Numismatic Collection)*									
Auctions: No auction records available.													
1826	18,069	6	63.8	100%	$10,000	$15,000	$20,000	$30,000	$40,000	$70,000	$80,000	$115,000	$140,000
Auctions: $546,000, MS-66, January 2015; $763,750, MS-66, January 2014													
1826, Proof	2–4	0	n/a		*(unique, in the Smithsonian's National Numismatic Collection)*									
Auctions: No auction records available.													
1827	24,913	14	62.9	93%	$20,000	$25,000	$30,000	$40,000	$50,000	$65,000	$75,000	$125,000	$150,000
Auctions: $141,000, MS-64, January 2014													
1827, Proof (p)	unknown	0	n/a										
Auctions: No auction records available.													
1828, 8 Over 7 (q)	(r)	3	63.3	100%				$100,000	$175,000	$300,000	$400,000	$450,000	$850,000
Auctions: $632,500, MS-64, January 2012													
1828	28,029	3	60.7	67%	$50,000	$70,000	$80,000	$100,000	$200,000	$225,000	$325,000	$450,000	
Auctions: $499,375, MS-64, April 2013													
1828, Proof	1–2	0	n/a		*(unique, in the Smithsonian's National Numismatic Collection)*									
Auctions: No auction records available.													
1829, Large Date †	57,442	2	66.0	100%			—	—		$225,000	$300,000	$425,000	$600,000
Auctions: $763,750, MS-66+, May 2016													
1829, Large Date, Proof †	2–4	0	n/a								$1,400,000		
Auctions: $1,380,000, PF-64, January 2012													

† Ranked in the *100 Greatest U.S. Coins* (fourth edition); all 1825, 5 Over 4 Capped Bust Half Eagle varieties are a single entry, as are all 1829 Capped Bust Half Eagle varieties. **i.** The only auction references for a Proof 1823 half eagle are from 1885 and 1962. Neither coin (assuming they are not the same specimen) has been examined by today's standards to confirm its Proof status. **j.** Value in MS-65 is $150,000. **k.** No 1824 Proof half eagles are known to exist, despite previous claims that the Smithsonian's Mint collection specimen (actually an MS-62 circulation strike) is a Proof. **l.** Sometimes called 1825, 5 Over 1. **m.** 2 examples are known. **n.** Included in circulation-strike 1825, 5 Over Partial 4, mintage figure. **o.** The Smithsonian's example is a PF-67 with a mirrored obverse and frosty reverse. A second example, reported to have resided in King Farouk's collection, has not been confirmed. **p.** Two purported 1827 Proofs have been revealed to be circulation strikes: the Smithsonian's example is an MS-64, and the Bass example is prooflike. **q.** 5 examples are known. **r.** Included in circulation-strike 1828 mintage figure.

Small 5 D.

Large 5 D.

1832, Curved-Base 2,
12-Star Obverse

1832, Square-Base 2,
13-Star Obverse

1833, Large Date

1833, Small Date

1834, Plain 4

1834, Crosslet 4

	Mintage	Cert	Avg	%MS	F-12	VF-20	EF-40	AU-50	AU-55	MS-60 / PF-63	MS-62 / PF-64	MS-63 / PF-65
1829, Sm Dt, Reduced Diameter †	(a)	2	62.5	100%	$75,000	$100,000	$150,000	$200,000	$250,000	$375,000	$450,000	$500,000
Auctions: $881,250, MS-65+, May 2016; $431,250, MS-61, January 2012												
1829, Small Date, Proof † (b)	2–4	0	n/a				*(extremely rare)*					
Auctions: $881,250, MS-65, May 2016												
1830, Small or Large 5 D. (c)	126,351	21	60.0	71%	$20,000	$27,500	$40,000	$45,000	$52,500	$75,000	$85,000	$100,000
Auctions: $73,438, MS-63, January 2014; $47,000, AU-58, August 2014; $41,125, AU-58, October 2014												
1830, Proof (d)	2–4	2	63.5				*(extremely rare)*			$450,000	$750,000	
Auctions: No auction records available.												
1831, Small or Large 5 D. (e)	140,594	11	60.6	64%	$20,000	$27,500	$40,000	$45,000	$52,500	$75,000	$85,000	$100,000
Auctions: $82,250, MS-61, January 2014												
1832, Curved-Base 2, 12 Stars † (f)	(g)	2	60.5	50%		$300,000	$350,000	$450,000	$500,000			
Auctions: $822,500, MS-63, May 2016												
1832, Square-Base 2, 13 Stars	157,487	12	61.8	75%	$20,000	$27,500	$40,000	$45,000	$55,000	$95,000	$110,000	$125,000 (h)
Auctions: $176,250, MS-65, January 2014												
1832, Square-Base 2, 13 Stars, Proof	2–3	0	n/a				*(extremely rare)*			$750,000		
Auctions: No auction records available.												
1833, Large Date	196,630	2	63.0	100%	$20,000	$27,500	$40,000	$45,000	$52,500	$75,000	$80,000	$100,000 (h)
Auctions: $29,375, AU-50, April 2014												
1833, Small Date (i)	(j)	1	61.0	100%	$20,000	$27,500	$40,000	$45,000	$52,500	$70,000	$100,000	$125,000 (k)
Auctions: $126,500, MS-63 PQ, May 2006												
1833, Proof † (l)	4–6	4	61.3				*(extremely rare)*			$500,000	$750,000	
Auctions: $977,500, PF-67, January 2005												
1834, All kinds	50,141											
1834, Plain 4		18	59.5	56%	$20,000	$27,500	$40,000	$45,000	$52,500	$75,000	$80,000	$100,000
Auctions: $143,750, MS-65, August 2011												
1834, Crosslet 4		9	58.6	56%	$21,500	$30,000	$40,000	$47,500	$57,000	$85,000	$110,000	$140,000
Auctions: $49,350, MS-63, May 2016: $45,531, AU-55, January 2014												

† Ranked in the *100 Greatest U.S. Coins* (fourth edition); all 1829 Capped Bust Half Eagle varieties are a single entry. **a.** Included in circulation-strike 1829, Large Date, mintage figure (see chart on page 981). **b.** 2 examples are known. One is in the Harry W. Bass Jr. Foundation Collection, and another of equal quality (PF-66) is in the Smithsonian's National Numismatic Collection. **c.** The 1830, Small 5 D. is slightly rarer than the Large 5 D. Certified population reports are unclear, and auction-lot catalogers typically do not differentiate between the two varieties. **d.** 2 examples are known. One is in the Byron Reed collection at the Durham Museum, Omaha, Nebraska. **e.** The 1831, Small 5 D. is estimated to be three to four times rarer than the Large 5 D. Both are extremely rare. **f.** 5 examples are known. **g.** Included in circulation-strike 1832, Square-Base 2, 13 Stars, mintage figure. **h.** Value in MS-64 is $145,000. **i.** The 1833 Small Date is slightly scarcer than the Large Date. **j.** Included in 1833, Large Date, mintage figure. **k.** Value in MS-64 is $175,000. **l.** 4 or 5 examples are known.

CLASSIC HEAD, NO MOTTO ON REVERSE (1834–1838)

Designer: *William Kneass.* **Weight:** *8.36 grams.*
Composition: *(1834–1836) .8992 gold, .1008 silver and copper; (1837–1838) .900 gold.*
Diameter: *22.5 mm.* **Edge:** *Reeded.* **Mints:** *Philadelphia, Charlotte, and Dahlonega.*

Circulation Strike
McCloskey-2.

*Mintmark location is on the
obverse, above the date.*

Proof
McCloskey-5.

History. U.S. Mint chief engraver William Kneass based the half eagle's Classic Head design on John Reich's cent of 1808. Minted under the Act of June 28, 1834, the coins' reduced size and weight encouraged circulation over melting or export, and they served American commerce until hoarding became extensive during the Civil War. Accordingly, many show considerable wear.

Striking and Sharpness. On the obverse, weakness is often seen on the higher areas of the hair curls. Also check the star centers. On the reverse, check the rims. The denticles are usually well struck.

Availability. Most coins range from VF to AU or lower grades of MS. Most MS coins are dated 1834. MS-63 and better examples are rare. Good eye appeal can be elusive. Proofs of the Classic Head type were made in small quantities, and today probably only a couple dozen or so survive, most bearing the 1834 date.

GRADING STANDARDS

MS-60 to 70 (Mint State). *Obverse:* At MS-60, some abrasion and contact marks are seen on the portrait, most noticeably on the cheek, as the hair details are complex on this type. Luster is present, but may be dull or lifeless, and interrupted in patches. Many low-level Mint State coins have grainy surfaces. At MS-63, contact marks are few, and abrasion is very light. Abrasion is even less at MS-64. An MS-65 coin will have hardly any

1834, Plain 4. Graded MS-65.

abrasion, and contact marks are minute. Luster should be full and rich and is often more intense on the obverse. Grades above MS-65 are defined by having fewer marks as perfection is approached. *Reverse:* Comments apply as for the obverse, except that abrasion is most noticeable in the field, on the eagle's neck, and on the highest area of the wings. Most Mint State coins in the marketplace are graded liberally, with slight abrasion on both sides of MS-65 coins.

Illustrated coin: This well-struck coin has some light abrasion, most evident in the reverse field.

AU-50, 53, 55, 58 (About Uncirculated). *Obverse:* Friction is seen on the higher parts, particularly the cheek and the hair (under magnification) of Miss Liberty. Friction and scattered marks are in the field, ranging from extensive at AU-50 to minimal at AU-58. Luster may be seen in protected areas, minimal at AU-50, more evident at AU-58. On an AU-58 coin the field retains some luster as well. *Reverse:* Comments as preceding, except

1834, Crosslet 4. Graded AU-50.

that the eagle's neck, the top of the wings, the leaves, and the arrowheads now show noticeable wear, as do other features. Luster ranges from perhaps 40% remaining in protected areas (at AU-50) to nearly full mint bloom (at AU-58). Often the reverse of this type retains much more luster than the obverse.

EF-40, 45 (Extremely Fine). *Obverse:* Wear is seen on the portrait overall, with reduction or elimination of some separation of hair strands, especially in the area close to the face. The cheek shows light wear. Luster is minimal or nonexistent at EF-40, and may survive in among the letters of LIBERTY at EF-45. *Reverse:* Wear is greater than on an About Uncirculated coin. On most (but not all) coins the neck lacks some feather detail

1837, Script 8. Graded EF-40.

on its highest points. Feathers have lost some detail near the edges and tips of the wings, and some areas of the horizontal lines in the shield may be blended together. Some traces of luster may be seen, more so at EF-45 than at EF-40.

VF-20, 30 (Very Fine). *Obverse:* Wear on the portrait has reduced the hair detail, especially to the right of the face and the top of the head, but much can still be seen. *Reverse:* Wear is greater, including on the shield and the wing feathers. Generally, Classic Head gold at this grade level lacks eye appeal.

The Classic Head half eagle is seldom collected in grades lower than VF-20.

1835, Block 8. Graded VF-30.

PF-60 to 70 (Proof). *Obverse and Reverse:* PF–60 to 62 coins have extensive hairlines and may have nicks and contact marks. At PF-63, hairlines are prominent, but the mirror surface is very reflective. PF-64 coins have fewer hairlines. At PF-65, hairlines should be minimal and mostly seen only under magnification. There should be no nicks or marks. PF-66 and higher coins should have no marks or hairlines visible to the unaided eye.

1834, Plain 4. Graded PF-65.

1834, Plain 4   **1834, Crosslet 4**

	Mintage	Cert	Avg	%MS	VF-20	EF-40	AU-50	AU-55	MS-60	MS-62 / PF-63	MS-63 / PF-64	MS-64 / PF-65
1834, Plain 4 (a)	657,460	2,166	51.2	13%	$625	$850	$1,350	$1,750	$4,500	$6,500	$11,500	$22,500
Auctions: $4,230, MS-61, February 2015; $1,704, AU-55, September 2015; $824, EF-45, July 2015; $447, VF-20, May 2015
1834, Crosslet 4	(b)	87	46.1	10%	$2,250	$4,000	$6,000	$9,500	$23,500	$27,500	$55,000	$100,000
Auctions: $14,688, MS-61, January 2015; $6,463, AU-55, January 2015; $5,581, AU-50, January 2015; $3,995, EF-45, September 2015
1834, Plain 4, Proof †	8–12	4	64.3							$100,000	$150,000	$225,000
Auctions: $109,250, PF-63Cam, January 2011
1835 (a)	371,534	716	51.2	13%	$625	$825	$1,350	$1,800	$4,500	$6,500	$11,000	$22,500
Auctions: $9,988, MS-63, September 2015; $2,115, AU-58, September 2015; $1,058, AU-53, August 2015; $517, F-12, November 2015
1835, Proof † (c)	4–6	1	68.0							$125,000	$175,000	$275,000
Auctions: $690,000, PF-67, January 2005
1836 (a)	553,147	1,215	50.0	12%	$625	$825	$1,450	$1,900	$4,500	$6,500	$11,000	$22,500
Auctions: $3,353, MS-61, January 2015; $1,175, AU-55, October 2015; $631, EF-40, March 2015; $588, VF-30, August 2015
1836, Proof † (d)	4–6	2	67.0							$125,000	$175,000	
Auctions: No auction records available.
1837 (a)	207,121	448	50.7	12%	$625	$850	$1,550	$2,100	$5,500	$8,500	$20,000	$37,500
Auctions: $21,738, MS-63, October 2013; $3,525, MS-61, October 2015; $1,763, AU-55, August 2014; $999, EF-45, January 2015
1837, Proof †	4–6	0	n/a		*(unique, in the Smithsonian's National Numismatic Collection)*							
Auctions: No auction records available.
1838	286,588	689	51.8	13%	$675	$850	$1,500	$2,050	$4,500	$8,500	$12,500	$35,000
Auctions: $2,233, AU-58, August 2015; $1,645, AU-55, January 2015; $940, EF-45, June 2015; $447, EF-40, January 2015
1838, Proof	2–3	1	65.0		*(unique, in the Bass Foundation Collection)*							
Auctions: No auction records available.
1838-C	17,179	112	44.9	4%	$6,000	$10,000	$15,000	$22,500	$75,000	$125,000	$250,000	
Auctions: $235,000, MS-63, May 2016; $8,813, EF-45, September 2016; $10,575, EF-40, August 2013; $5,405, EF-40, June 2015
1838-D	20,583	134	49.5	8%	$6,500	$8,500	$12,500	$20,000	$35,000	$50,000	$85,000	
Auctions: $94,000, MS-63, May 2016; $21,150, MS-60, January 2014; $21,150, AU-58, October 2016; $21,738, AU-55, August 2014

† All Classic Head Half Eagle Proof strikes from 1834–1837 are ranked in the *100 Greatest U.S. Coins* (fourth edition), as a single entry. **a.** Varieties have either a script 8 or block-style 8 in the date. (See illustrations of similar quarter eagles on page 939.) **b.** Included in circulation-strike, 1838, Plain 4, mintage figure. **c.** 3 or 4 examples are known. **d.** 3 or 4 examples are known.

LIBERTY HEAD (1839–1908)

Designer: *Christian Gobrecht.* **Weight:** *8.359 grams.*
Composition: *.900 gold, .100 copper (net weight .24187 oz. pure gold).*
Diameter: *(1839–1840) 22.5 mm; (1840–1908) 21.6 mm.* **Edge:** *Reeded.*
Mints: *Philadelphia, Charlotte, Dahlonega, Denver, New Orleans, San Francisco, and Carson City.*

Large Diameter, Without Motto, Circulation Strike (1839–1840)
McCloskey–1-A.

Mintmark location, 1839, is on the obverse, above the date.

Large Diameter, Without Motto, Proof

Reduced Diameter, Without Motto, Circulation Strike (1840–1865)

Mintmark location, 1840–1908, is on the reverse, below the eagle.

Reduced Diameter, Without Motto, Proof

With Motto, Circulation Strike (1866–1908)

With Motto, Proof

History. Christian Gobrecht's Liberty Head half eagle design was introduced in 1839. The mintmark (for branch-mint coins) in that year was located on the obverse; for all later issues it was relocated to the reverse. The motto IN GOD WE TRUST was added to the reverse in 1866.

Striking and Sharpness. On the obverse, check the highest points of the hair and the star centers; the reverse, the eagle's neck, the area to the lower left of the shield, and the lower part of the eagle. Generally, the eagle on the $5 coins is better struck than on quarter eagles. Examine the denticles on both sides. Branch-mint coins struck before the Civil War are often lightly struck in areas. San Francisco half eagles are in lower average grades than are those from the Philadelphia Mint, as Philadelphia coins did not circulate at par in the East and Midwest from late December 1861 until December 1878, thus acquiring less wear. Most late 19th- and early 20th-century coins are sharp in all areas; for these issues, tiny copper staining spots (from improperly mixed coinage alloy) can be a problem. Cameo contrast is the rule for Proofs prior to 1902. Beginning that year the portrait was polished in the die, although a few years later cameo-contrast coins were again made.

Availability. Early dates and mintmarks are typically scarce to rare in MS, very rare in MS–63 to 65. Charlotte and Dahlonega coins are usually EF or AU, or overgraded as low MS, as seen with quarter eagles. The 1854-S and several varieties in the 1860s and 1870s are rare. Coins from 1880 onward are seen in higher than average grades. Proof coins exist in relation to their original mintages; issues prior to the 1890s are rare.

Note: Values of common-date gold coins have been based on the current bullion price of gold, $1,300 per ounce, and may vary with the prevailing spot price.

GRADING STANDARDS

MS-60 to 70 (Mint State). *Obverse:* At MS-60, some abrasion and contact marks are evident, most noticeably on the hair to the right of Miss Liberty's forehead and on the jaw. Luster is present, but may be dull or lifeless, and interrupted in patches. At MS-63, contact marks are few, and abrasion is very light. An MS-65 coin has only slight abrasion, and contact marks are so minute as to require

1848-C. Graded MS-63.

magnification. Luster should be full and rich. Grades above MS-65 are defined by having fewer marks as perfection is approached. *Reverse:* Comments apply as for the obverse, except that abrasion and contact marks are most noticeable on the eagle's neck and to the lower left of the shield.

    Illustrated coin: Friction is seen in the obverse fields amid luster; on the reverse, luster is nearly complete.

AU-50, 53, 55, 58 (About Uncirculated). *Obverse:* Light wear is seen on the face, the hair to the right of the face, and the highest area of the hair bun, more so at AU-50 than at AU–53 or 55. An AU-58 coin has minimal traces of wear. An AU-50 coin has luster in protected areas among the stars and letters, with little in the open fields or on the portrait. At AU-58, most luster is present in the fields, but is worn away on the highest parts

1840. Graded AU-55.

of the motifs. Striking must be taken into consideration, for a lightly struck coin can be About Uncirculated, but be weak in the central areas. *Reverse:* Comments as preceding, except that the eagle shows wear in all of the higher areas, as well as the leaves and arrowheads. From 1866 to 1908 the motto IN GOD WE TRUST helped protect the field, with the result that luster is more extensive on this side in comparison to the obverse. Luster ranges from perhaps 50% remaining in protected areas (at AU-50) to nearly full mint bloom (at AU-58).

EF-40, 45 (Extremely Fine). *Obverse:* Wear is evident on all high areas of the portrait, including the hair to the right of the forehead, the tip of the coronet, the back of the head, and the hair bun. The stars show light wear at their centers (unless protected by a high rim). Luster, if present at all, is minimal and in protected areas such as between the star points. *Reverse:* Wear is greater than on an About Uncirculated coin, and flatness is

1844. Graded EF-40.

seen on the feather ends, the leaves, and elsewhere. Some traces of luster may be seen, more so at EF-45 than at EF-40. Overall, the reverse appears to be in a slightly higher grade than the obverse on coins from 1866 to 1908 (With Motto).

    Illustrated coin: This coin is well struck on both sides.

VF-20, 30 (Very Fine). *Obverse:* The higher-relief areas of hair are worn flat at VF-20, less so at VF-30. The hair to the right of the coronet is merged into heavy strands. The stars are flat at their centers. *Reverse:* Feather detail is mostly worn away on the neck and legs, less so on the wings. The vertical shield stripes, being deeply recessed, remain bold.

The Liberty Head half eagle is seldom collected in grades lower than VF-20.

1858-C. Graded VF-20.

PF-60 to 70 (Proof). *Obverse and Reverse:* PF–60 to 62 coins have extensive hairlines and may have nicks and contact marks. At PF-63, hairlines are prominent, but the mirror surface is very reflective. PF-64 coins have fewer hairlines. At PF-65, hairlines should be minimal and mostly seen only under magnification. There should be no nicks or marks. PF-66 and higher coins should have no marks or hairlines visible to the unaided eye.

1872. Graded PF-55.

	Mintage	Cert	Avg	%MS	VF-20	EF-40	AU-50	AU-55	MS-60	MS-63 PF-63	MS-64 PF-64	MS-65 PF-65
1839	118,143	238	51.3	14%	$700	$1,150	$1,800	$2,500	$7,000	$27,500	$50,000	
	Auctions: $11,764, MS-62, January 2015; $3,760, AU-58, August 2015; $1,528, AU-55, January 2015; $1,410, AU-50, September 2015											
1839, Proof (a)	2–3	1	61.0		*(extremely rare)*							
	Auctions: $184,000, PF-61, January 2010											
1839-C	17,205	90	50.2	17%	$2,750	$4,750	$9,500	$14,000	$25,000	$65,000	$135,000	
	Auctions: $111,625, MS-64, May 2016; $42,300, MS-63, March 2016: $23,500, MS-61, January 2014; $16,450, MS-60, January 2015											
1839-D	18,939	119	47.2	5%	$3,000	$5,500	$9,500	$16,000	$30,000			
	Auctions: $9,400, AU-53, September 2013; $4,700, AU-50, July 2015; $4,700, EF-45, February 2015; $2,350, EF-40, November 2014											
1840 (b)	137,382	331	51.2	8%	$550	$650	$1,000	$1,350	$3,250	$9,000	$25,000	
	Auctions: $2,585, AU-58, October 2015; $2,115, AU-58, June 2015; $999, AU-53, January 2015; $646, EF-45, January 2015											
1840, Proof	2–3	0	n/a		*(unique, in the Smithsonian's National Numismatic Collection)*							
	Auctions: No auction records available.											
1840-C	18,992	93	48.0	11%	$2,000	$4,000	$6,000	$7,000	$20,000	$55,000	$75,000	
	Auctions: $28,200, MS-62, January 2014; $5,581, AU-55, February 2015; $4,700, AU-50, August 2015; $1,645, VF-20, August 2014											
1840-D	22,896	72	50.7	19%	$2,250	$3,500	$5,750	$7,250	$14,000	$45,000		
	Auctions: $14,100, MS-61, December 2013; $881, F-12, August 2014											
1840-O (b)	40,120	156	51.4	11%	$600	$1,200	$2,250	$3,000	$9,500	$37,500		
	Auctions: $5,405, AU-58, June 2015; $2,350, AU-55, October 2015; $1,763, AU-55, January 2015; $764, AU-50, January 2015											
1841	15,833	69	52.9	26%	$550	$950	$1,600	$1,850	$4,500	$12,000	$18,500	$37,500
	Auctions: $1,763, AU-55, December 2013											
1841, Proof (c)	2–3	1	63.0		*(extremely rare)*							
	Auctions: No auction records available.											
1841-C	21,467	92	48.7	9%	$1,850	$2,500	$4,500	$5,750	$15,000	$40,000	$65,000	
	Auctions: $5,581, AU-58, January 2014; $4,230, AU-55, September 2015; $1,939, EF-40, January 2015; $1,705, VF-35, August 2014											

a. 2 or 3 examples are known. b. Scarce varieties of the 1840 coins have the fine edge-reeding and wide rims of the 1839 issues. This is referred to as the broad-mill variety. c. 2 examples are known. One is in the Smithsonian's National Numismatic Collection; the other is ex Eliasberg Collection.

Small Letters	Large Letters	Small Date	Large Date

	Mintage	Cert	Avg	%MS	VF-20	EF-40	AU-50	AU-55	MS-60	MS-63	MS-64	MS-65
										PF-63	PF-64	PF-65
1841-D	27,492	101	49.6	22%	$2,250	$3,000	$4,500	$5,250	$12,500	$22,000	$45,000	
	Auctions: $9,988, MS-61, January 2014; $8,578, MS-60, August 2014											
1841-O (d)	50	0	n/a									
	Auctions: No auction records available.											
1842, All kinds	27,578											
1842, Small Letters		25	53.4	16%	$650	$1,250	$2,500	$4,000	$11,000	$22,000	$32,500	$60,000
	Auctions: $15,275, MS-62, January 2014											
1842, Large Letters		21	48.6	0%	$725	$1,600	$3,750	$5,500	$11,500	$25,000		
	Auctions: $4,113, AU-55, April 2014; $4,700, AU-55, August 2014											
1842, Small Letters, Proof (e)	4–6	1	64.0		*(extremely rare)*							
	Auctions: $172,500, PF-64CamH, January 2009											
1842-C, All kinds	27,432											
1842-C, Small Date		25	51.6	20%	$9,000	$17,500	$25,000	$35,000	$75,000	$125,000		
	Auctions: $111,625, MS-63, January 2015; $49,938, AU-58, July 2014; $20,563, AU-53, January 2015; $16,450, EF-45, August 2016											
1842-C, Large Date		103	50.7	14%	$2,000	$2,550	$4,000	$5,000	$12,500	$30,000	$45,000	
	Auctions: $25,850, MS-63, September 2013; $11,750, MS-61, November 2014											
1842-D, All kinds	59,608											
1842-D, Small Date		158	46.1	5%	$2,000	$2,600	$4,250	$5,000	$13,000	$30,000		
	Auctions: $16,450, MS-62, April 2014; $3,995, AU-55, October 2015; $2,350, EF-45, July 2014; $764, F-12, January 2015											
1842-D, Large Date		25	44.7	8%	$3,500	$7,500	$11,000	$18,500	$45,000			
	Auctions: $7,050, MS-60, January 2014; $16,200, AU-55, April 2018											
1842-O	16,400	49	45.1	4%	$2,500	$4,000	$9,500	$12,500	$22,500	$45,000		
	Auctions: $7,638, AU-53, January 2014; $734, VF-20, January 2015; $646, VF-20, August 2014; $823, F-12, January 2015											
1843	611,205	559	53.5	14%	$500	$525	$575	$650	$1,400	$9,500	$20,000	$37,500
	Auctions: $1,410, MS-61, January 2015; $1,175, MS-60, September 2015; $535, AU-55, January 2015; $447, EF-45, September 2015											
1843, Proof (f)	4–8	4	64.0		*(extremely rare)*							
	Auctions: $34,500, PF-58, August 2009											
1843-C	44,277	159	44.9	9%	$1,800	$2,500	$3,750	$4,500	$9,500	$27,500	$55,000	
	Auctions: $8,813, MS-61, October 2015; $3,084, AU-53, February 2015; $2,838, AU-50, November 2014; $2,233, EF-45, January 2015											
1843-D	98,452	233	46.3	9%	$2,000	$2,500	$3,500	$4,250	$10,000	$22,500	$50,000	
	Auctions: $19,975, MS-63, April 2013; $4,406, MS-60, November 2014; $5,434, AU-58, September 2014; $1,998, AU-50, August 2015											
1843-D, Proof (g)	*unknown*	1	65.0									
	Auctions: No auction records available.											
1843-O, Small Letters	19,075	73	46.9	8%	$850	$1,650	$2,250	$4,500	$17,500	$35,000	$50,000	$65,000
	Auctions: $5,940, AU-58, January 2015; $2,585, AU-50, October 2014; $3,760, EF-45, September 2015; $1,116, EF-40, November 2014											
1843-O, Large Letters	82,000	111	49.8	19%	$650	$1,250	$2,000	$3,500	$10,000	$25,000	$35,000	
	Auctions: $19,975, MS-62, January 2014; $5,875, AU-58, March 2015; $5,170, AU-58, July 2015; $797, EF-40, August 2014											

d. Official Mint records report 8,350 coins struck at the New Orleans Mint in 1841. However, most—if not all—were actually dated 1840. No 1841-O half eagle has ever appeared on the market. **e.** Of the examples known today, one is in the Smithsonian's National Numismatic Collection, and another is ex Pittman Collection. **f.** 4 or 5 examples are known. **g.** One non-circulation example of the 1843-D half eagle, probably a presentation strike of some sort, has been certified by NGC as a Specimen (rated Specimen-65).

**1846-D, High
Second D Over D**

	Mintage	Cert	Avg	%MS	VF-20	EF-40	AU-50	AU-55	MS-60	MS-63	MS-64	MS-65
										PF-63	PF-64	PF-65
1844	340,330	338	53.1	12%	$500	$525	$575	$625	$1,950	$10,000	$18,000	$55,000
Auctions: $3,525, MS-62, October 2015; $564, AU-53, June 2015; $494, AU-50, January 2015; $12,000, MS-63, April 2018												
1844, Proof (h)	3–5	1	64.0		*(extremely rare)*							
Auctions: No auction records available.												
1844-C	23,631	88	46.3	7%	$2,250	$3,250	$5,000	$7,000	$14,000	$30,000		
Auctions: $4,230, AU-55, January 2015; $3,290, AU-55, January 2015; $2,957, VF-35, March 2015; $999, G-6, October 2015												
1844-D	88,982	249	46.4	8%	$2,000	$2,750	$3,750	$4,000	$8,500	$25,000	$45,000	
Auctions: $7,638, MS-61, June 2015; $6,000, MS-60, January 2015; $5,405, EF-40, July 2015; $1,763, VF-35, September 2015												
1844-O	364,600	674	50.3	9%	$550	$600	$875	$1,350	$4,500	$17,500	$25,000	$45,000
Auctions: $1,880, AU-58, June 2015; $646, EF-45, July 2015; $494, EF-45, September 2015; $400, EF-40, October 2015												
1844-O, Proof † (i)	1	0	n/a		*(unique)*							
Auctions: No auction records available.												
1845	417,099	382	53.7	13%	$500	$550	$625	$700	$2,000	$8,000	$16,000	
Auctions: $12,925, MS-64, July 2015; $1,235, AU-58, July 2015; $447, AU-53, January 2015; $470, EF-45, July 2015												
1845, Proof (j)	5–8	3	64.7		*(extremely rare)*							
Auctions: $149,500, PF-66UCam, August 2004												
1845-D	90,629	284	49.7	8%	$2,000	$2,500	$3,500	$4,500	$9,000	$22,500	$37,500	$85,000
Auctions: $7,050, MS-61, June 2015; $4,230, AU-58, January 2015; $2,056, EF-45, January 2015; $1,058, VG-8, October 2015												
1845-O	41,000	141	50.8	13%	$750	$1,200	$2,500	$4,500	$10,000	$27,500		
Auctions: $6,463, AU-58, December 2013												
1846, All kinds	395,942											
1846, Large Date		214	53.2	12%	$450	$500	$650	$700	$2,000	$13,000	$18,500	
Auctions: $16,450, MS-63, January 2015; $11,456, MS-63, September 2015; $1,058, MS-60, September 2015; $400, EF-45, June 2015												
1846, Small Date		92	54.1	15%	$500	$650	$850	$1,100	$3,500	$13,500	$20,000	
Auctions: $3,055, MS-61, October 2015; $2,585, MS-60, January 2015; $1,528, AU-58, July 2014; $388, EF-40, July 2014												
1846, Proof (k)	6–10	1	64.0		*(extremely rare)*							
Auctions: $161,000, PF-64Cam, January 2011												
1846-C	12,995	69	48.9	10%	$2,000	$3,750	$5,000	$7,000	$15,000	$60,000	$80,000	
Auctions: $12,925, MS-60, October 2015: $10,575, MS-60, January 2014												
1846-D, All kinds	80,294											
1846-D (l)		129	47.6	3%	$2,000	$2,750	$3,750	$4,750	$12,000			
Auctions: $3,055, AU-53, August 2014; $5,640, AU-50, July 2015; $2,350, EF-45, September 2015; $1,058, EF-40, August 2014												
1846-D, High Second D Over D		127	49.6	6%	$2,250	$2,500	$4,000	$5,000	$11,000	$27,500		
Auctions: $21,150, MS-63, January 2014; $2,115, EF-45, August 2014; $2,115, EF-40, January 2015; $1,763, VF-25, January 2015												
1846-O	58,000	147	49.4	5%	$675	$1,000	$3,250	$4,750	$11,000	$25,000		
Auctions: $9,400, MS-61, January 2014; $4,230, AU-55, October 2015; $1,528, EF-45, July 2015; $881, EF-40, July 2014												

† Ranked in the *100 Greatest U.S. Coins* (fourth edition), grouped with 1844-O Proof Liberty Head Eagles, as a single entry. **j.** 4 or 5 examples are known. **k.** 4 or 5 examples are known. Of the 20 or so Proof sets made in 1846, experts believe only 4 or 5 contained the year's gold coinage. **l.** The 1846-D half eagle with a normal mintmark actually is rarer than the variety with a boldly repunched D Over D mintmark.

1847, Top of Extra 7	1848-D, D Over D	1850-C, Normal C	1850-C, Weak C
Very Low at Border			
FS-G5-1847-301.			

	Mintage	Cert	Avg	%MS	VF-20	EF-40	AU-50	AU-55	MS-60	MS-63	MS-64	MS-65
										PF-63	PF-64	PF-65
1847, All kinds	915,981											
1847		775	54.4	18%	$450	$550	$600	$625	$1,650	$6,000	$12,000	
	Auctions: $2,820, MS-62, June 2015; $940, AU-58, September 2015; $517, AU-53, September 2015; $388, EF-45, January 2015											
1847, Top of Extra 7 Very Low at Border		164	55.1	16%	$525	$575	$675	$1,100	$2,150	$8,500	$13,000	
	Auctions: $3,173, MS-62, October 2013; $1,998, MS-61, November 2014; $705, AU-53, October 2015											
1847, Proof	2–3	0	n/a		*(unique, in the Smithsonian's National Numismatic Collection)*							
	Auctions: No auction records available.											
1847-C	84,151	258	46.2	6%	$2,000	$2,350	$3,500	$4,500	$9,500	$27,500	$37,500	$75,000
	Auctions: $4,406, AU-58, April 2014; $3,525, AU-55, October 2015; $2,350, EF-45, July 2014; $1,763, EF-40, August 2014											
1847-D	64,405	156	48.4	10%	$2,000	$2,500	$3,500	$5,000	$8,500	$16,500		
	Auctions: $3,995, AU-55, October 2015; $3,995, AU-55, January 2015; $4,261, AU-50, January 2015; $2,056, EF-45, January 2015											
1847-O	12,000	47	44.3	4%	$3,000	$7,500	$11,500	$13,500	$27,000			
	Auctions: $14,100, AU-53, January 2014; $11,163, AU-53, January 2015; $4,113, AU-50, August 2014											
1848	260,775	338	53.4	11%	$450	$525	$600	$700	$1,750	$9,500	$25,000	
	Auctions: $1,058, MS-60, April 2013; $705, AU-58, August 2015; $564, AU-53, September 2015; $515, EF-45, July 2014											
1848, Proof (m)	6–10	0	n/a		*(extremely rare)*							
	Auctions: No auction records available.											
1848-C	64,472	188	46.3	4%	$2,000	$2,500	$3,500	$5,500	$15,000	$40,000	$65,000	
	Auctions: $3,055, AU-53, January 2015; $2,115, AU-50, June 2015; $1,880, AU-50, June 2015; $1,586, VF-30, January 2015											
1848-D	47,465	117	48.5	5%	$1,850	$2,750	$3,500	$5,500	$12,500	$25,000	$65,000	
	Auctions: $5,640, AU-58, February 2015; $4,113, AU-55, April 2014; $2,241, EF-45, August 2014; $2,115, EF-40, July 2014											
1848-D, D Over D	(n)	0	n/a					$9,000	$20,000			
	Auctions: $29,900, MS-62, May 2008											
1849	133,070	210	52.9	14%	$450	$525	$675	$825	$2,750	$10,000	$15,000	
	Auctions: $2,585, MS-61, August 2014; $5,288, MS-61, April 2013; $911, AU-55, August 2014; $705, AU-53, November 2014											
1849-C	64,823	223	50.0	10%	$2,000	$2,500	$3,250	$4,750	$8,500	$23,500	$40,000	
	Auctions: $4,230, AU-55, September 2015; $2,585, AU-53, February 2015; $1,645, AU-50, February 2015; $2,233, EF-45, August 2015											
1849-D	39,036	141	49.1	4%	$2,000	$2,750	$3,500	$4,500	$11,500	$35,000		
	Auctions: $5,288, AU-58, April 2013; $2,233, AU-50, September 2015; $2,585, EF-45, August 2014											
1850	64,491	142	49.9	4%	$450	$525	$975	$1,250	$3,000	$12,500	$32,000	$75,000
	Auctions: $1,293, AU-58, October 2014; $1,028, AU-55, April 2014; $705, AU-50, October 2015; $499, EF-40, August 2014											
1850-C	63,591	165	48.0	12%	$2,000	$2,350	$3,250	$4,250	$10,000	$18,500	$40,000	
	Auctions: $8,813, MS-61, February 2013; $3,995, AU-50, January 2015; $2,056, AU-50, August 2015; $1,763, VF-35, August 2015											
1850-C, Weak C (o)	(p)	45	49.7	9%	$1,200	$1,500	$2,000	$2,500	$4,500			
	Auctions: $3,819, MS-61, August 2014; $1,293, EF-45, July 2014; $1,116, EF-45, October 2015; $1,058, VF-35, January 2015											
1850-D	43,984	135	48.6	3%	$2,000	$2,750	$3,950	$5,000	$23,500			
	Auctions: $5,640, AU-58, October 2015; $5,170, AU-53, February 2015; $1,293, AU-50, August 2015; $2,115, EF-45, August 2014											

m. 2 examples are known. One is in the Smithsonian's National Numismatic Collection; the other is ex Pittman Collection. **n.** Included in 1848-D mintage figure **o.** Several branch-mint half eagles of the early 1850s can exhibit weak (sometimes very weak or almost invisible) mintmarks; such coins generally trade at deep discounts. **p.** Included in 1850-C mintage figure.

1851-D, Normal D **1851-D, Weak D** **1854, Doubled Die Obverse**
FS-G5-1854-101.

1854-C, Normal C **1854-C, Weak C** **1854-D, Normal D** **1854-D, Weak D**

	Mintage	Cert	Avg	%MS	VF-20	EF-40	AU-50	AU-55	MS-60	MS-63	MS-64	MS-65
										PF-63	PF-64	PF-65
1851	377,505	414	54.6	15%	$450	$525	$600	$650	$2,500	$8,500	$22,500	
Auctions: $2,820, MS-61, February 2015; $705, AU-55, June 2015; $447, AU-53, February 2015; $353, EF-40, July 2015												
1851-C	49,176	141	48.5	11%	$2,000	$2,500	$3,500	$4,500	$11,000	$37,500	$55,000	
Auctions: $30,550, MS-63, April 2013; $3,760, AU-55, January 2015; $2,820, AU-53, February 2015; $2,468, AU-50, September 2016												
1851-D	62,710	118	49.5	7%	$2,000	$2,500	$3,750	$5,500	$12,000	$25,000	$45,000	
Auctions: $16,450, MS-62, January 2014												
1851-D, Weak D (o)	(q)	10	56.9	40%	$1,200	$1,500	$2,000	$2,500				
Auctions: $2,185, AU-50, July 2009												
1851-O	41,000	134	47.1	1%	$850	$1,500	$4,750	$5,750	$12,000	$25,000	$60,000	
Auctions: $11,163, MS-61, October 2014; $6,463, AU-58, June 2013; $3,055, AU-50, July 2014; $447, EF-40, January 2015												
1852	573,901	737	54.8	15%	$450	$500	$575	$600	$1,500	$6,500	$12,500	$27,500
Auctions: $9,400, MS-64, January 2015; $3,055, MS-62, August 2015; $646, AU-55, October 2015; $477, AU-55, May 2015												
1852-C	72,574	244	49.5	16%	$2,000	$2,500	$3,500	$4,250	$6,500	$20,000	$27,500	
Auctions: $28,200, MS-64, August 2013; $9,694, MS-62, January 2015; $2,585, MS-60, November 2014; $2,468, EF-45, January 2015												
1852-D	91,584	271	48.8	8%	$2,000	$2,600	$3,750	$5,000	$9,500	$25,000		
Auctions: $3,290, AU-55, June 2015; $3,290, AU-53, August 2015; $2,233, EF-45, June 2015; $1,645, VF-25, January 2015												
1853	305,770	558	54.4	15%	$450	$500	$575	$600	$1,500	$5,750	$16,000	$60,000
Auctions: $15,863, MS-64, October 2015; $2,115, MS-62, March 2015; $1,528, MS-61, June 2015; $423, EF-40, January 2015												
1853-C	65,571	164	48.9	12%	$2,000	$2,500	$3,500	$4,250	$6,750	$21,500	$55,000	
Auctions: $8,225, MS-62, January 2015; $1,998, MS-60, January 2015; $4,406, AU-58, August 2014; $852, VF-20, February 2015												
1853-D	89,678	343	51.1	12%	$2,000	$2,400	$3,400	$4,500	$6,750	$15,000	$55,000	
Auctions: $13,513, MS-63, October 2015; $6,463, MS-61, January 2015; $3,290, AU-55, June 2015; $2,233, EF-45, October 2015												
1854	160,675	348	54.6	16%	$450	$500	$575	$850	$2,000	$8,500	$15,000	
Auctions: $764, AU-58, August 2015; $530, AU-55, June 2015; $470, AU-50, June 2015; $423, AU-50, April 2015												
1854, Doubled Die Obverse	(r)	38	55.2	11%					$1,350	$2,500		
Auctions: $1,998, AU-55, October 2014												
1854, Proof (s)	*unknown*	0	n/a									
Auctions: No auction records available.												
1854-C	39,283	102	48.8	8%	$2,000	$2,500	$4,000	$5,000	$12,000	$37,500		
Auctions: $35,250, MS-63, April 2014; $3,819, AU-50, March 2015; $1,998, AU-50, January 2015; $2,115, EF-40, January 2015												
1854-C, Weak C (o)	(t)	41	49.8	15%	$1,200	$1,500	$1,750	$2,500	$6,500	$12,000		
Auctions: $12,338, MS-63, January 2014; $4,584, MS-60, September 2014												
1854-D	56,413	222	53.3	22%	$2,000	$2,500	$3,750	$4,500	$8,000	$23,500	$42,500	$75,000
Auctions: $8,813, MS-62, June 2013; $3,825, AU-55, March 2015; $3,055, EF-45, January 2015; $940, VF-30, January 2015												
1854-D, Weak D (o)	(u)	15	50.9	7%	$1,200	$1,500	$1,750	$2,500	$4,500			
Auctions: $5,581, MS-61, September 2014; $1,998, AU-55, April 2014												

o. Several branch-mint half eagles of the early 1850s can exhibit weak (sometimes very weak or almost invisible) mintmarks; such coins generally trade at deep discounts. **q.** Included in 1851-D mintage figure. **r.** Included in circulation-strike 1854 mintage figure **s.** According to Walter Breen, a complete 1854 Proof set was presented to dignitaries of the sovereign German city of Bremen who visited the Philadelphia Mint. The set resided in Bremen until it disappeared almost 100 years later, during World War II. **t.** Included in 1854-C mintage figure. **u.** Included in 1854-D mintage figure.

	Mintage	Cert	Avg	%MS	VF-20	EF-40	AU-50	AU-55	MS-60	MS-63 / PF-63	MS-64 / PF-64	MS-65 / PF-65
1854-O	46,000	180	51.0	6%	$550	$800	$1,350	$2,250	$6,500	$22,500		
	Auctions: $2,585, AU-58, October 2015; $1,234, AU-53, June 2015; $764, EF-40, January 2015; $494, VF-30, January 2015											
1854-S † (v)	268	1	58.0	0%	$2,500,000							
	Auctions: No auction records available.											
1855	117,098	261	53.8	12%	$450	$550	$600	$650	$1,650	$7,500	$16,500	
	Auctions: $2,115, MS-61, October 2015; $588, AU-58, October 2015; $470, AU-53, August 2014; $388, AU-53, November 2014											
1855-C	39,788	144	50.1	10%	$2,250	$2,500	$3,750	$4,500	$12,000	$45,000	$65,000	
	Auctions: $11,163, MS-61, August 2016: $9,694, MS-61, April 2013; $7,638, AU-58, January 2015; $1,763, AU-50, January 2015											
1855-D	22,432	79	50.9	9%	$2,000	$2,750	$3,600	$5,000	$13,500	$35,000		
	Auctions: $15,275, MS-61, January 2014; $3,819, MS-60, August 2014; $2,820, EF-45, July 2014; $5,640, VF-30, July 2015											
1855-O	11,100	55	49.5	4%	$1,250	$2,750	$4,500	$7,000	$20,000			
	Auctions: $8,225, AU-58, January 2015; $4,700, AU-50, September 2014; $3,290, AU-50, November 2014; $3,525, EF-40, January 2015											
1855-S	61,000	109	48.4	3%	$750	$1,250	$2,250	$4,000	$12,500			
	Auctions: $3,055, AU-58, September 2015; $2,115, AU-53, July 2014; $940, AU-50, August 2014; $1,351, EF-45, July 2014											
1856	197,990	403	54.0	11%	$475	$525	$600	$650	$2,000	$8,000	$17,000	$55,000
	Auctions: $6,182, MS-63, October 2015; $2,115, MS-61, September 2015; $470, AU-55, August 2015; $317, AU-50, June 2015											
1856-C	28,457	139	51.2	9%	$2,000	$2,500	$3,750	$5,000	$13,500	$45,000		
	Auctions: $17,625, MS-62, January 2014; $3,055, AU-50, September 2015; $2,820, AU-50, February 2015; $1,351, AU-50, January 2015											
1856-D	19,786	106	49.6	12%	$2,000	$2,500	$3,750	$5,750	$8,500	$27,500	$50,000	
	Auctions: $12,925, MS-62, January 2014; $3,878, AU-53, August 2015; $3,878, AU-53, January 2015; $1,880, VF-25, July 2014											
1856-O	10,000	48	49.5	10%	$1,000	$1,850	$4,250	$6,500	$12,500			
	Auctions: $10,575, MS-60, April 2014											
1856-S	105,100	155	47.9	4%	$575	$750	$1,250	$2,000	$7,500	$25,000	$40,000	
	Auctions: $4,700, AU-58, January 2014; $1,763, AU-55, January 2015; $1,116, AU-55, November 2014; $951, AU-53, July 2014											
1857	98,188	303	55.3	14%	$450	$475	$575	$625	$1,850	$6,000	$15,000	
	Auctions: $5,170, MS-63, January 2015; $1,528, MS-61, January 2015; $1,293, MS-61, September 2015; $705, AU-58, October 2015											
1857, Proof (w)	*3–6*	1	65.0		*(extremely rare)*							
	Auctions: $230,000, PF-65Cam, January 2007											
1857-C	31,360	171	53.0	16%	$2,000	$2,500	$3,500	$4,250	$7,500	$27,500		
	Auctions: $22,325, MS-63, January 2014; $8,813, MS-61, August 2015; $6,756, AU-55, July 2015; $2,115, EF-45, July 2014											
1857-D	17,046	100	52.1	14%	$2,000	$2,600	$3,750	$5,000	$10,000	$40,000		
	Auctions: $9,988, MS-61, January 2014; $5,581, AU-58, October 2014; $5,405, AU-58, January 2015; $1,586, VF-25, August 2014											
1857-O	13,000	82	48.8	4%	$1,000	$1,700	$4,000	$5,500	$13,500	$47,500		
	Auctions: $41,125, MS-63, April 2014; $3,672, AU-53, October 2014											
1857-S	87,000	123	47.3	4%	$600	$800	$1,100	$2,250	$10,500	$25,000		
	Auctions: $2,820, AU-58, September 2015; $2,350, AU-58, September 2015; $881, AU-55, August 2014; $1,528, AU-55, September 2014											
1858	15,136	80	53.6	19%	$550	$575	$800	$1,250	$3,250	$8,000	$12,500	$35,000
	Auctions: $14,100, MS-64, June 2015; $4,935, MS-62, August 2015; $1,410, AU-55, August 2014; $881, EF-40, August 2015											
1858, Proof (x)	*4–6*	5	65.6							$75,000	$100,000	$150,000
	Auctions: $195,500, PF-66UCamH, March 2006											
1858-C	38,856	191	51.5	13%	$2,000	$2,500	$3,750	$4,500	$9,000	$30,000		
	Auctions: $9,400, MS-61, August 2013; $3,055, AU-55, August 2014; $2,585, EF-40, January 2015; $1,175, EF-40, August 2015											
1858-D	15,362	121	51.4	8%	$2,000	$2,500	$3,750	$4,750	$10,500	$32,500	$45,000	
	Auctions: $17,625, MS-61, June 2013; $9,988, MS-61, February 2015; $7,638, MS-61, August 2014; $3,525, AU-55, June 2015											
1858-S	18,600	55	47.0	0%	$1,500	$3,000	$5,250	$9,000	$27,500			
	Auctions: $7,050, AU-55, March 2014											

† Ranked in the *100 Greatest U.S. Coins* (fourth edition). **v.** 3 examples are known. **w.** 2 examples are known. **x.** 4 or 5 examples are known today. One resides in the Smithsonian's National Numismatic Collection, another in the collection of the American Numismatic Society. In recent decades the collections of Eliasberg, Trompeter, and Bass have included examples.

	Mintage	Cert	Avg	%MS	VF-20	EF-40	AU-50	AU-55	MS-60	MS-63	MS-64	MS-65
										PF-63	PF-64	PF-65
1859	16,734	98	50.6	8%	$550	$750	$1,650	$1,750	$6,000	$18,000		
	Auctions: $17,625, MS-63 Prooflike, June 2014; $21,150, MS-62, April 2015; $2,585, AU-58, August 2015; $2,115, AU-55, October 2015											
1859, Proof	80	5	63.8							$45,000	$85,000	$125,000
	Auctions: $158,625, PF-66UCam, August 2015											
1859-C	31,847	157	50.7	9%	$2,000	$2,500	$3,500	$5,000	$10,500	$35,000		
	Auctions: $8,225, MS-61, January 2014; $4,113, AU-55, August 2014; $1,645, AU-50, July 2014; $1,469, VF-25, August 2014											
1859-D	10,366	104	51.9	13%	$2,000	$2,750	$3,750	$5,000	$10,000	$35,000		
	Auctions: $19,975, MS-62, January 2014; $2,938, MS-60, July 2014; $7,050, AU-58, June 2015; $2,115, AU-50, January 2015											
1859-S	13,220	31	47.5	3%	$1,500	$3,500	$5,000	$6,500	$25,000			
	Auctions: $8,695, AU-58, October 2013; $6,463, AU-53, August 2014; $4,230, EF-45, October 2015											
1860	19,763	120	52.8	6%	$600	$1,000	$1,500	$2,000	$3,500	$17,500	$25,000	
	Auctions: $4,700, AU-58, January 2014; $2,233, AU-58, August 2014; $646, AU-50, July 2014											
1860, Proof	62	5	64.6							$37,500	$75,000	$115,000
	Auctions: $103,500, PF-66CamH, January 2012											
1860-C	14,813	119	53.2	18%	$2,000	$2,750	$4,250	$6,500	$11,000	$27,500	$50,000	
	Auctions: $20,124, MS-63, April 2013; $4,113, AU-50, August 2014; $3,525, AU-50, June 2015; $2,585, EF-40, October 2014											
1860-D	14,635	133	51.3	13%	$2,250	$3,500	$4,500	$6,500	$13,000	$40,000	$65,000	
	Auctions: $14,100, MS-62, March 2014; $5,405, AU-58, June 2015; $3,760, AU-53, February 2015; $3,760, EF-45, September 2015											
1860-S	21,200	57	45.7	2%	$2,000	$3,500	$6,500	$9,500	$29,500			
	Auctions: $19,975, AU-58, April 2014; $4,994, AU-53, October 2014; $2,585, EF-45, September 2014											
1861	688,084	1,813	55.5	16%	$450	$475	$575	$675	$1,750	$6,000	$10,500	$35,000
	Auctions: $32,900, MS-65, January 2015; $2,820, MS-62, January 2015; $1,528, AU-55, January 2015; $376, EF-40, June 2015											
1861, Proof	66	2	65.0							$35,000	$75,000	$115,000
	Auctions: $117,500, PF-66Cam, August 2015											
1861-C	6,879	81	52.2	9%	$6,000	$9,500	$13,000	$15,500	$30,000	$85,000		
	Auctions: $25,850, MS-61, January 2014; $6,463, AU-50, January 2015; $3,290, AU-50, August 2014; $9,694, EF-45, January 2015											
1861-D	1,597	40	53.7	10%	$25,000	$40,000	$45,000	$60,000	$90,000	$200,000		
	Auctions: $99,875, MS-62, January 2014; $42,314, AU-53, August 2016; $42,300, AU-50, September 2016; $51,002, AU-55, April 2018											
1861-S	18,000	45	43.3	0%	$3,250	$6,500	$8,500	$12,000				
	Auctions: $11,163, AU-53, March 2014; $9,988, AU-53, January 2015; $8,813, AU-53, January 2015; $4,259, VF-35, August 2014											
1862	4,430	36	51.7	3%	$2,500	$5,000	$8,500	$13,500	$30,000			
	Auctions: $14,702, AU-58, August 2014; $17,625, AU-55, April 2013											
1862, Proof	35	8	64.5							$35,000	$75,000	$115,000
	Auctions: $92,000, PF-65UCam, August 2011											
1862-S	9,500	42	40.8	5%	$4,250	$8,500	$10,500	$17,500	$40,000			
	Auctions: $15,275, AU-53, March 2014; $4,406, VF-25, August 2014											
1863	2,442	18	53.1	11%	$3,500	$8,500	$18,500	$27,500	$55,000			
	Auctions: $35,250, AU-58, September 2016; $32,900, AU-58, August 2016: $30,550, AU-58, January 2014; $15,275, AU-50, March 2016											
1863, Proof	30	3	65.3							$35,000	$75,000	$115,000
	Auctions: $69,000, PF-64DCam, November 2005											
1863-S	17,000	50	41.4	0%	$3,500	$5,000	$12,500	$17,500	$40,000			
	Auctions: $16,450, AU-55, March 2014											
1864	4,170	53	50.9	8%	$2,500	$4,000	$8,500	$11,000	$20,000			
	Auctions: $12,925, AU-55, January 2014; $10,575, AU-55, June 2015; $10,281, AU-55, October 2015											
1864, Proof	50	18	64.6							$35,000	$75,000	$115,000
	Auctions: $103,500, PF-65UCam, October 2011											
1864-S	3,888	9	39.3	0%	$16,000	$37,500	$60,000	$75,000	$100,000			
	Auctions: $79,313, EF-45, March 2014											

	Mintage	Cert	Avg	%MS	VF-20	EF-40	AU-50	AU-55	MS-60	MS-63 / PF-63	MS-64 / PF-64	MS-65 / PF-65
1865	1,270	25	54.1	12%	$6,500	$12,000	$20,000	$25,000	$35,000			
	Auctions: $17,626, AU-55, August 2014; $18,800, AU-53, January 2014; $17,625, AU-53, August 2015											
1865, Proof	25	13	64.5							$35,000	$75,000	$115,000
	Auctions: $86,250, PF-65UCam, April 2012											
1865-S	27,612	87	43.4	6%	$2,750	$4,250	$7,000	$8,000	$14,500	$35,000	$60,000	
	Auctions: $8,813, AU-55, March 2014; $5,875, EF-45, August 2014											
1866-S, No Motto	9,000	53	37.8	0%	$2,250	$5,000	$8,500	$11,000	$30,000			
	Auctions: $14,688, AU-58, March 2014; $14,100, AU-58, January 2015; $5,581, AU-50, August 2014; $2,350, VF-20, August 2014											
1866, Motto Above Eagle	6,700	44	54.9	11%	$1,000	$2,000	$3,000	$4,250	$11,500	$40,000		
	Auctions: $34,075, MS-63, February 2013; $12,338, MS-61, January 2015; $3,290, AU-55, August 2014; $3,055, EF-40, September 2015											
1866, Motto Above Eagle, Proof	30	6	61.8							$25,000	$40,000	$65,000
	Auctions: $80,500, PF-66UCamH, August 2010											
1866-S, Motto Above Eagle	34,920	47	38.0	2%	$1,250	$2,750	$7,000	$10,000	$25,000			
	Auctions: $4,994, AU-50, June 2013; $2,585, EF-45, August 2014; $1,469, VF-30, October 2014											
1867	6,870	55	49.6	2%	$1,000	$1,750	$3,000	$4,000	$10,000			
	Auctions: $16,450, MS-61, September 2014; $8,813, MS-60, January 2014; $881, AU-50, August 2014											
1867, Proof	50	4	63.3							$25,000	$40,000	$60,000
	Auctions: $21,150, PF-63Cam, August 2014											
1867-S	29,000	81	39.2	0%	$1,100	$2,000	$5,500	$10,000				
	Auctions: $1,351, EF-40, January 2015; $1,293, VF-30, October 2015; $1,058, VF-20, June 2015; $458, F-12, January 2015											
1868	5,700	51	51.2	4%	$600	$1,000	$2,500	$4,750	$10,000			
	Auctions: $16,450, MS-61, April 2013; $5,405, AU-58, October 2015; $4,935, AU-55, July 2015; $2,233, AU-50, August 2014											
1868, Proof	25	3	64.7							$25,000	$40,000	$60,000
	Auctions: $69,000, PF-64DCam, June 2008											
1868-S	52,000	111	43.7	5%	$525	$1,250	$2,750	$4,250	$20,000			
	Auctions: $18,213, MS-61, June 2015; $23,500, MS-60, March 2014; $1,645, AU-53, October 2014; $1,827, AU-50, July 2014											
1869	1,760	38	52.3	8%	$1,100	$2,750	$5,000	$7,500	$15,000	$27,000	$37,500	
	Auctions: $9,400, AU-55, April 2014; $4,700, AU-53, February 2015; $4,700, EF-45, September 2016; $2,267, EF-40, August 2014											
1869, Proof	25	6	64.0							$25,000	$40,000	$60,000
	Auctions: $69,000, PF-65Cam, April 2012											
1869-S	31,000	121	41.9	3%	$600	$1,500	$3,000	$5,000	$20,000			
	Auctions: $17,625, MS-61, July 2014; $2,233, AU-50, September 2015; $1,998, EF-45, August 2014											
1870	4,000	45	48.8	2%	$900	$2,000	$3,250	$5,000	$15,000			
	Auctions: $7,640, AU-58, September 2014; $8,225, AU-55, January 2014; $2,180, VF-30, October 2015; $1,410, VF-30, October 2014											
1870, Proof	35	1	66.0							$25,000	$40,000	$75,000
	Auctions: $82,250, PF-64, January 2014											
1870-CC	7,675	45	36.3	2%	$22,500	$30,000	$45,000	$65,000	$110,000			
	Auctions: $47,000, AU-53, January 2014											
1870-S	17,000	97	39.6	0%	$1,000	$2,350	$5,500	$8,500	$25,000			
	Auctions: $12,925, AU-58, August 2014; $1,763, AU-50, September 2015; $2,115, EF-40, July 2014; $1,116, VF-25, August 2014											
1871	3,200	48	53.3	8%	$1,150	$1,600	$2,650	$4,500	$10,000			
	Auctions: $15,275, MS-61, September 2013; $3,525, AU-55, August 2014; $2,820, AU-53, August 2014											
1871, Proof	30	7	61.4							$25,000	$40,000	$60,000
	Auctions: $73,438, PF-66Cam, August 2015; $70,500, PF-65Cam, September 2014											
1871-CC	20,770	89	37.2	2%	$4,750	$9,500	$13,500	$25,000	$55,000	$75,000		
	Auctions: $48,469, MS-61, April 2013; $2,115, EF-40, July 2014; $5,288, EF-40, September 2014; $3,173, VF-30, August 2014											
1871-S	25,000	104	45.5	2%	$525	$1,100	$2,500	$4,000	$13,500			
	Auctions: $35,250, MS-63, August 2014; $25,850, MS-61, March 2014; $2,364, AU-50, August 2015; $2,585, VF-25, August 2014											

1873, Close 3   **1873, Open 3**

	Mintage	Cert	Avg	%MS	VF-20	EF-40	AU-50	AU-55	MS-60	MS-63	MS-64	MS-65
										PF-63	PF-64	PF-65
1872	1,660	26	54.3	15%	$1,000	$2,000	$4,500	$5,500	$10,500	$20,000	$25,000	
Auctions: $5,434, AU-58, April 2014												
1872, Proof	30	6	62.5							$22,500	$40,000	$60,000
Auctions: $7,188, PF-55, March 2012												
1872-CC	16,980	70	34.7	0%	$3,500	$7,500	$15,000	$25,000				
Auctions: $28,200, AU-58, March 2014; $11,764, AU-50, August 2014; $1,175, F-12, November 2014												
1872-S	36,400	114	42.5	2%	$750	$1,100	$2,600	$4,000	$12,000			
Auctions: $3,055, AU-55, October 2014; $2,233, AU-50, August 2015; $1,998, AU-50, February 2015; $1,880, AU-50, October 2015												
1873, Close 3	112,480	306	55.7	24%	$350	$375	$475	$550	$950	$4,000	$7,500	$17,500
Auctions: $5,875, MS-64, December 2013; $3,055, MS-63, July 2015; $852, MS-61, September 2014; $470, AU-58, August 2014												
1873, Open 3	112,505	338	55.8	25%	$350	$375	$450	$500	$1,000	$3,500	$8,000	$20,000
Auctions: $5,875, MS-64, September 2013; $2,703, MS-63, May 2015; $363, AU-58, August 2015; $317, EF-40, October 2014												
1873, Close 3, Proof	25	9	64.4							$22,500	$40,000	$60,000
Auctions: $24,675, PF-63Cam, August 2014; $12,338, PF-58, January 2014												
1873-CC	7,416	37	35.7	3%	$7,500	$15,000	$25,000	$35,000	$75,000	$180,000		
Auctions: $11,750, AU-50, August 2014; $21,150, AU-50, January 2013; $14,688, EF-45, September 2016; $5,581, F-12, August 2014												
1873-S	31,000	109	42.2	1%	$600	$1,100	$2,250	$4,250	$18,500			
Auctions: $2,233, AU-55, August 2014; $3,173, AU-53, January 2014; $823, VF-35, January 2015; $376, VF-20, November 2015												
1874	3,488	57	49.9	7%	$850	$1,400	$2,250	$3,000	$10,000	$22,500		
Auctions: $4,700, AU-58, January 2014; $3,290, AU-55, August 2014												
1874, Proof	20	3	66.0							$27,500	$50,000	$75,000
Auctions: $54,625, PF-65CamH, August 2011												
1874-CC	21,198	131	38.4	1%	$2,750	$4,500	$10,000	$17,000	$35,000			
Auctions: $21,738, AU-58, August 2014; $14,100, AU-55, August 2015; $4,348, VF-35, February 2015; $734, F, March 2015												
1874-S	16,000	88	41.8	0%	$800	$1,650	$3,000	$4,750				
Auctions: $3,760, AU-55, August 2015; $2,820, AU-55, January 2015; $2,820, AU-53, September 2015; $1,645, EF-45, October 2015												
1875	200	2	51.0	0%	$85,000	$100,000	$150,000	$225,000				
Auctions: $211,500, AU-55, April 2014												
1875, Proof (y)	20	6	62.2							$150,000	$175,000	$250,000
Auctions: $176,250, PF-65Cam, January 2014												
1875-CC	11,828	88	37.5	0%	$3,750	$6,500	$14,500	$25,000	$45,000	$115,000		
Auctions: $17,625, AU-58, January 2014												
1875-S	9,000	67	42.3	3%	$1,250	$2,500	$4,250	$7,500	$18,500			
Auctions: $8,813, AU-58, August 2014; $3,819, AU-55, August 2014; $2,585, AU-50, August 2014; $3,055, AU-50, August 2013												
1876	1,432	25	55.6	16%	$1,750	$4,500	$5,500	$7,500	$14,000	$25,000	$32,500	$45,000
Auctions: $19,975, MS-63, March 2013												
1876, Proof	45	18	64.0							$20,000	$25,000	$47,500
Auctions: $48,469, PF-65Cam, February 2013												
1876-CC	6,887	75	38.8	1%	$4,500	$8,000	$13,500	$17,500	$40,000			
Auctions: $21,150, AU-58, March 2014; $4,113, VF-25, July 2014												
1876-S	4,000	23	39.3	4%	$3,250	$5,500	$10,000	$12,500	$30,000			
Auctions: $18,800, AU-58, March 2014												

y. The mintages of only 200 circulation strikes and 20 Proofs for the year 1875 combine to make the Proof a high-demand coin; hence its strong market value.

1881, Final 1 Over 0
FS-G5-1881-301.

1881, Recut 1881 Over 1881
FS-G5-1881-303.

	Mintage	Cert	Avg	%MS	VF-20	EF-40	AU-50	AU-55	MS-60	MS-63 PF-63	MS-64 PF-64	MS-65 PF-65
1877	1,132	47	54.5	23%	$2,250	$3,750	$5,000	$6,000	$12,500			
	Auctions: $7,638, AU-58, April 2014; $1,645, AU-50, June 2015; $1,469, AU-50, August 2015; $3,525, EF-45, July 2014											
1877, Proof	20	3	65.0							$22,500	$32,500	$57,500
	Auctions: $51,750, PF-63, June 2005											
1877-CC	8,680	100	40.7	0%	$3,000	$5,500	$12,000	$20,000	$50,000			
	Auctions: $14,688, AU-55, November 2014; $11,163, AU-53, July 2014; $8,871, AU-50, January 2015; $3,760, AU-50, August 2015											
1877-S	26,700	125	44.9	1%	$500	$650	$1,500	$3,000	$8,500	$20,000	$30,000	
	Auctions: $1,645, AU-55, February 2015; $1,293, AU-53, August 2014; $1,175, EF-45, August 2014; $411, EF-40, June 2015											
1878	131,720	410	58.8	52%	$350	$365	$375	$385	$575	$1,750	$4,000	$8,500
	Auctions: $8,813, MS-65, January 2015; $8,225, MS-65, September 2015; $3,525, MS-64, August 2014; $400, AU-58, March 2015											
1878, Proof	20	8	64.1							$22,500	$32,500	$57,500
	Auctions: $31,725, PF-63DCam, June 2014											
1878-CC	9,054	53	45.3	4%	$5,500	$11,000	$17,500	$32,000	$75,000			
	Auctions: $47,000, AU-58, March 2014; $7,344, VF-25, September 2016											
1878-S	144,700	496	56.2	23%	$350	$365	$375	$385	$650	$4,000	$7,000	$20,000
	Auctions: $423, AU-58, August 2015; $400, AU-55, March 2015; $323, AU-50, September 2015; $341, EF-45, August 2015											
1879	301,920	705	59.2	56%	$350	$365	$375	$385	$450	$1,500	$3,600	$8,500
	Auctions: $6,463, MS-65, September 2014; $4,406, MS-64, September 2014; $2,115, MS-64, March 2015; $458, MS-60, February 2015											
1879, Proof	30	6	64.2							$22,500	$30,000	$55,000
	Auctions: $63,250, PF-65Cam, April 2012											
1879-CC	17,281	160	44.1	4%	$1,750	$2,750	$4,000	$7,500	$25,000			
	Auctions: $21,150, MS-60, March 2014; $8,813, AU-58, August 2014; $1,116, VG-8, June 2015; $764, G-6, July 2014											
1879-S	426,200	733	57.1	26%	$350	$365	$375	$385	$600	$1,750	$6,000	$25,000
	Auctions: $1,058, MS-63, January 2015; $541, MS-61, February 2015; $376, AU-58, January 2015; $282, AU-50, July 2015											
1880	3,166,400	3,043	59.8	73%	$350	$365	$375	$385	$450	$650	$1,050	$1,850
	Auctions: $10,575, MS-66, October 2015; $4,348, MS-65, August 2015; $705, MS-63, July 2015; $376, EF-40, February 2015											
1880, Proof	36	8	65.5							$17,500	$30,000	$52,500
	Auctions: $72,702, PF-67Cam, August 2006											
1880-CC	51,017	318	46.1	4%	$1,250	$1,500	$2,000	$4,500	$12,500	$45,000		
	Auctions: $14,100, MS-61, September 2016: $11,750, MS-61, January 2014; $705, VF-20, January 2015; $1,058, F-15, January 2015											
1880-S	1,348,900	2,282	61.0	84%	$350	$365	$375	$385	$450	$650	$1,100	$8,500
	Auctions: $1,410, MS-64, January 2015; $940, MS-64, January 2015; $400, MS-62, January 2015; $329, AU-55, February 2015											
1881, Final 1 Over 0 (z)	(aa)	110	58.3	52%	$475	$500	$550	$675	$1,350	$2,500	$8,000	
	Auctions: $2,233, MS-63, January 2014; $646, AU-55, August 2014; $499, EF-40, July 2014											
1881, Recut 1881 Over 1881	(aa)	0	n/a					$535	$625	$1,325		
	Auctions: $705, MS-63, August 2014; $1,528, MS-62, April 2014											
1881	5,708,760	17,235	61.5	92%	$350	$365	$375	$385	$450	$600	$750	$2,000
	Auctions: $1,058, MS-64, June 2015; $435, MS-62, March 2015; $423, MS-61, July 2015; $329, AU-55, July 2015											
1881, Proof	42	10	65.8							$16,500	$25,000	$40,000
	Auctions: $37,375, PF-65Cam, January 2011											
1881-CC	13,886	84	45.3	8%	$1,750	$3,500	$7,000	$10,500	$25,000	$55,000		
	Auctions: $32,900, MS-62, May 2013; $11,750, AU-58, September 2016; $3,055, EF-40, August 2014; $1,763, VF-30, July 2014											
1881-S	969,000	1,960	61.3	89%	$350	$365	$375	$385	$450	$650	$1,250	$3,250
	Auctions: $1,058, MS-64, January 2015; $969, MS-64, February 2015; $687, MS-63, January 2015; $494, MS-62, January 2015											

z. The last digit of the date is repunched over the remnants of a zero; this is easily visible with the naked eye, making the 1 Over 0 a popular variety. **aa.** Included in circulation-strike 1881 mintage figure.

	Mintage	Cert	Avg	%MS	VF-20	EF-40	AU-50	AU-55	MS-60	MS-63 PF-63	MS-64 PF-64	MS-65 PF-65
1882	2,514,520	7,857	61.5	91%	$350	$365	$375	$385	$450	$650	$800	$3,500
	Auctions: $2,468, MS-65, May 2015; $999, MS-64, August 2015; $588, MS-63, August 2015; $454, MS-62, February 2015											
1882, Proof	48	12	64.3							$15,500	$25,000	$40,000
	Auctions: $9,085, PF-63Cam, February 2010											
1882-CC	82,817	568	50.9	5%	$1,000	$1,500	$2,000	$4,000	$11,500	$35,000		
	Auctions: $18,800, MS-62, February 2015; $1,175, AU-50, February 2015; $1,116, AU-50, January 2015; $734, EF-40, February 2015											
1882-S	969,000	2,434	61.6	92%	$350	$365	$375	$385	$500	$600	$800	$1,750
	Auctions: $3,408, MS-65, January 2015; $999, MS-64, January 2015; $823, MS-64, January 2015; $447, MS-62, January 2015											
1883	233,400	485	60.3	71%	$350	$365	$375	$385	$500	$1,250	$2,250	$12,500
	Auctions: $17,625, MS-67, February 2013; $1,410, MS-64, September 2015; $1,116, MS-63, June 2015; $411, AU-58, August 2014											
1883, Proof	61	8	64.1							$15,500	$25,000	$40,000
	Auctions: $5,288, PF-55, September 2014											
1883-CC	12,598	126	49.9	6%	$2,000	$3,000	$4,500	$6,750	$18,500	$50,000		
	Auctions: $18,213, MS-61, August 2014; $7,638, AU-58, August 2015; $5,875, AU-55, January 2015; $3,305, AU-50, September 2016											
1883-S	83,200	257	58.4	55%	$350	$365	$375	$385	$700	$1,650	$7,000	
	Auctions: $7,050, MS-64, August 2013; $706, MS-61, July 2015; $382, AU-58, January 2015; $1,058, AU-53, August 2014											
1884	191,030	462	59.1	58%	$350	$365	$375	$385	$550	$1,650	$2,750	$9,000
	Auctions: $2,468, MS-64, February 2013; $881, MS-62, July 2015; $588, MS-62, November 2015; $588, MS-61, August 2015											
1884, Proof	48	7	64.4							$15,500	$25,000	$40,000
	Auctions: $39,100, PF-66UCam, November 2010											
1884-CC	16,402	177	49.3	3%	$1,100	$1,500	$4,500	$6,500	$20,000			
	Auctions: $8,225, AU-58, January 2014; $8,519, AU-58, October 2014; $4,994, AU-55, August 2014											
1884-S	177,000	460	59.8	68%	$350	$365	$375	$385	$450	$1,150	$3,500	$9,500
	Auctions: $999, MS-63, August 2015; $940, MS-63, June 2015; $588, MS-62, October 2015; $541, MS-62, August 2015											
1885	601,440	1,402	61.2	84%	$350	$365	$375	$385	$450	$600	$1,250	$4,500
	Auctions: $1,528, MS-64, July 2015; $676, MS-63, July 2015; $517, MS-62, May 2015; $400, AU-53, February 2015											
1885, Proof	66	19	64.6							$15,500	$25,000	$40,000
	Auctions: $70,500, PF-67UCam, August 2015; $56,400, PF-66UCam, January 2015; $31,725, PF-65DCam, August 2014											
1885-S	1,211,500	4,444	61.9	94%	$350	$365	$375	$385	$450	$600	$800	$2,000
	Auctions: $5,170, MS-66, January 2015; $705, MS-63, August 2015; $458, MS-61, January 2015; $376, AU-55, July 2015											
1886	388,360	724	60.2	70%	$350	$365	$375	$385	$450	$700	$2,500	$5,500
	Auctions: $5,288, MS-65, June 2013; $573, MS-63, August 2014; $499, MS-61, July 2014											
1886, Proof	72	10	64.2							$15,500	$25,000	$40,000
	Auctions: $57,281, PF, March 2014											
1886-S	3,268,000	8,625	61.4	93%	$350	$365	$375	$385	$450	$550	$800	$1,750
	Auctions: $2,350, MS-65, January 2015; $823, MS-64, October 2015; $458, MS-62, January 2015; $400, MS-60, October 2015											
1887, Proof (bb)	87	18	63.6							$65,000	$80,000	$115,000
	Auctions: $54,050, PF, August 2013											
1887-S	1,912,000	3,473	61.1	91%	$350	$365	$375	$385	$450	$600	$1,100	$4,000
	Auctions: $1,410, MS-64, January 2015; $940, MS-64, July 2015; $881, MS-64, July 2015; $470, MS-62, June 2015											
1888	18,201	169	59.8	68%	$350	$365	$375	$385	$650	$1,750	$3,000	$12,500
	Auctions: $1,775, MS-63, January 2014; $764, MS-61, January 2015; $588, MS-60, August 2014											
1888, Proof	95	18	64.7							$13,500	$20,000	$32,500
	Auctions: $34,500, PF-65DCam, October 2008											
1888-S	293,900	347	55.0	22%	$350	$365	$375	$450	$1,000	$3,500		
	Auctions: $2,350, MS-64, August 2013; $1,116, MS-63, October 2014; $470, AU-53, July 2014; $368, EF-40, August 2014											
1889	7,520	158	58.1	42%	$500	$600	$700	$950	$1,250	$4,500	$6,000	
	Auctions: $4,406, MS-63, June 2014; $1,763, MS-62, September 2015; $1,058, AU-55, July 2015; $1,175, AU-53, August 2014											
1889, Proof	45	13	64.3							$14,000	$22,500	$35,000
	Auctions: $29,900, PF-65Cam, January 2011											

bb. Proof only.

	Mintage	Cert	Avg	%MS	VF-20	EF-40	AU-50	AU-55	MS-60	MS-63 / PF-63	MS-64 / PF-64	MS-65 / PF-65
1890	4,240	75	55.6	28%	$550	$675	$850	$1,250	$2,250	$6,000	$10,000	$15,000
Auctions: $5,581, MS-62, June 2014; $1,000, AU-55, July 2014; $823, AU-50, August 2014												
1890, Proof	88	31	64.7							$14,000	$22,500	$35,000
Auctions: $24,675, PF-64DCam, January 2014												
1890-CC	53,800	628	57.2	47%	$800	$950	$1,100	$1,450	$2,250	$8,500	$15,000	$45,000
Auctions: $11,750, MS-64, June 2015; $9,400, MS-63, October 2015; $5,640, MS-63, March 2016; $2,820, MS-62, June 2015												
1891	61,360	384	60.5	78%	$350	$365	$375	$385	$500	$1,250	$3,250	$12,000
Auctions: $4,700, MS-64, February 2013; $499, MS-61, August 2014; $400, AU-58, August 2015; $353, AU-53, September 2015												
1891, Proof	53	14	65.0							$13,500	$20,000	$32,500
Auctions: $19,550, PF-64DCam, January 2010												
1891-CC	208,000	2,111	57.9	52%	$875	$950	$1,150	$1,350	$2,000	$4,500	$7,500	$32,500
Auctions: $5,875, MS-64, January 2015; $1,175, AU-58, June 2015; $823, EF-45, July 2015; $764, VF-30, October 2015												
1892	753,480	2,118	61.5	92%	$350	$365	$375	$385	$450	$600	$1,100	$1,750
Auctions: $3,760, MS-66, July 2015; $2,585, MS-65, September 2015; $823, MS-63, January 2015; $329, AU-50, September 2015												
1892, Proof	92	16	64.5							$13,500	$18,000	$32,500
Auctions: $6,325, PF-62Cam, December 2011												
1892-CC	82,968	764	53.8	20%	$750	$850	$1,100	$1,250	$2,500	$9,000	$22,500	$42,500
Auctions: $2,511, MS-61, February 2015; $1,058, AU-55, January 2015; $881, EF-45, January 2015; $541, VG-8, January 2015												
1892-O	10,000	40	58.3	38%	$1,750	$2,250	$2,500	$3,500	$5,500	$18,500		
Auctions: $8,225, MS-62, December 2013; $3,290, AU-58, July 2014; $3,290, AU-58, August 2014												
1892-S	298,400	452	57.8	45%	$350	$365	$375	$385	$450	$1,800	$4,250	$7,500
Auctions: $4,230, MS-64, January 2015; $2,350, MS-63, April 2013; $823, MS-62, August 2015; $400, MS-60, October 2015												
1893	1,528,120	8,415	62.0	97%	$350	$365	$375	$385	$450	$575	$800	$2,150
Auctions: $4,230, MS-66, June 2015; $3,995, MS-66, January 2015; $940, MS-64, September 2015; $852, MS-64, January 2015												
1893, Proof	77	19	64.7							$13,500	$18,000	$32,500
Auctions: $70,500, PF, August 2013												
1893-CC	60,000	706	56.7	26%	$950	$1,100	$1,300	$1,800	$3,000	$10,000	$22,500	$30,000
Auctions: $24,675, MS-64, August 2015; $2,115, AU-58, June 2015; $1,410, AU-53, July 2015; $969, EF-40, February 2015												
1893-O	110,000	453	58.8	50%	$400	$450	$500	$550	$1,000	$5,000	$9,500	
Auctions: $7,638, MS-64, January 2014; $1,880, MS-62, July 2015; $541, MS-60, August 2015; $529, AU-58, August 2014												
1893-S	224,000	1,074	61.0	84%	$350	$365	$375	$385	$450	$600	$1,750	$8,500
Auctions: $1,645, MS-64, October 2015; $999, MS-64, July 2015; $482, MS-62, October 2015; $447, MS-61, October 2015												
1894	957,880	3,624	61.8	96%	$350	$365	$375	$385	$450	$600	$900	$3,300
Auctions: $3,760, MS-65, January 2015; $1,058, MS-64, June 2015; $458, MS-62, August 2015; $329, MS-60, July 2015												
1894, Proof	75	25	64.1							$13,500	$18,500	$32,500
Auctions: $58,750, PF-67DCam, October 2014; $37,600, PF-66UCam, August 2015; $29,375, PF-64UCam, August 2015												
1894-O	16,600	329	57.6	34%	$425	$450	$550	$800	$2,000	$8,500		
Auctions: $3,525, MS-62, June 2014; $1,888, MS-61, July 2014; $1,175, AU-58, September 2015; $823, AU-55, November 2014												
1894-S	55,900	232	53.3	13%	$400	$425	$450	$650	$2,500	$9,000	$16,000	
Auctions: $3,819, MS-62, March 2015; $2,938, MS-62, July 2015; $2,350, MS-60, February 2015; $881, AU-58, August 2014												
1895	1,345,855	8,387	61.8	95%	$350	$365	$375	$385	$425	$600	$800	$1,750
Auctions: $19,975, MS-67, January 2015; $7,931, MS-66, February 2015; $564, MS-63, July 2015; $423, MS-61, May 2015												
1895, Proof	81	24	64.8							$12,500	$18,000	$30,000
Auctions: $6,233, PF-60, February 2014												
1895-S	112,000	317	53.4	8%	$375	$425	$450	$650	$1,500	$5,000	$8,000	$18,500
Auctions: $2,350, MS-62, September 2015; $1,645, MS-61, September 2015; $1,586, MS-61, June 2015; $447, AU-53, October 2015												
1896	58,960	508	61.8	93%	$350	$365	$375	$385	$425	$600	$1,500	$7,500
Auctions: $1,410, MS-64, August 2015; $1,293, MS-64, June 2015; $1,293, MS-64, January 2015; $382, AU-55, August 2014												
1896, Proof	103	25	65.0							$12,500	$18,000	$30,000
Auctions: $35,250, PF-65DCam, September 2014												
1896-S	155,400	391	54.5	19%	$350	$365	$375	$385	$1,100	$5,500	$8,500	$20,000
Auctions: $7,064, MS-64, January 2015; $4,230, MS-63, July 2015; $3,525, MS-63, August 2015; $2,233, MS-62, January 2015												

1901-S, Final 1 Over 0
FS-G5-1901S-301.

	Mintage	Cert	Avg	%MS	VF-20	EF-40	AU-50	AU-55	MS-60	MS-63 PF-63	MS-64 PF-64	MS-65 PF-65
1897	867,800	4,328	61.6	92%	$350	$365	$375	$385	$425	$600	$800	$1,850
Auctions: $8,225, MS-66, January 2015; $1,175, MS-64, August 2015; $505, MS-62, July 2015; $388, AU-58, July 2015											
1897, Proof	83	24	64.5							$12,500	$18,000	$30,000
Auctions: $9,988, PF-63, June 2014											
1897-S	354,000	425	56.1	26%	$350	$365	$375	$385	$800	$4,500	$7,000	
Auctions: $15,275, MS-66, March 2015; $1,645, MS-62, July 2014; $499, MS-61, August 2014; $388, AU-58, November 2015											
1898	633,420	2,532	61.6	93%	$350	$365	$375	$385	$425	$600	$1,500	$3,500
Auctions: $8,225, MS-66, June 2015; $3,643, MS-65, June 2015; $1,028, MS-64, June 2015; $447, MS-62, August 2015											
1898, Proof	75	38	64.7							$12,500	$18,000	$30,000
Auctions: $105,750, PF-67UCam, August 2015; $29,375, PF-65DCam, September 2014; $18,800, PF-64DCam+, August 2015											
1898-S	1,397,400	701	59.2	67%	$350	$365	$375	$385	$450	$1,100	$2,750	$8,000
Auctions: $70,500, MS-68, June 2015; $5,434, MS-65, June 2014; $7,050, MS-65, October 2014; $4,406, MS-64, August 2014											
1899	1,710,630	13,285	62.5	98%	$350	$365	$375	$385	$425	$600	$800	$1,800
Auctions: $2,938, MS-66, June 2015; $2,585, MS-65, January 2015; $447, MS-62, January 2015; $388, AU-55, June 2015											
1899, Proof	99	30	64.5							$12,500	$18,000	$30,000
Auctions: $134,550, PF, September 2013											
1899-S	1,545,000	987	59.5	70%	$350	$365	$375	$385	$450	$1,000	$1,750	$7,500
Auctions: $1,410, MS-64, January 2015; $764, MS-63, January 2015; $734, MS-62, August 2015; $447, MS-62, March 2015											
1900	1,405,500	16,718	62.1	96%	$350	$365	$375	$385	$425	$575	$800	$1,750
Auctions: $5,875, MS-66, January 2015; $2,820, MS-65, September 2015; $423, MS-62, July 2015; $329, MS-60, July 2015											
1900, Proof	230	64	64.2							$12,500	$18,000	$30,000
Auctions: $35,250, PF-65DCam, September 2013											
1900-S	329,000	525	60.2	70%	$350	$365	$375	$385	$450	$850	$900	$9,500
Auctions: $1,293, MS-64, March 2013; $940, MS-64, January 2015; $705, MS-63, August 2014; $529, MS-62, August 2014											
1901	615,900	5,491	61.9	93%	$350	$365	$375	$385	$425	$575	$700	$1,750
Auctions: $16,450, MS-67, January 2015; $881, MS-64, July 2015; $823, MS-64, June 2015; $423, MS-62, May 2015											
1901, Proof	140	44	64.2							$12,500	$18,000	$30,000
Auctions: $28,200, PF-65DCam, August 2014											
1901-S, All kinds	3,648,000											
1901-S, Final 1 Over 0		372	60.5	69%	$350	$365	$475	$500	$550	$1,250	$1,750	$3,750
Auctions: $1,645, MS-64, January 2015; $1,116, MS-63, August 2014; $470, MS-62, October 2014; $401, AU-55, March 2015											
1901-S		7,540	62.0	92%	$350	$365	$375	$385	$425	$575	$700	$1,750
Auctions: $2,585, MS-66, January 2015; $999, MS-64, June 2015; $705, MS-64, June 2015; $564, MS-63, August 2015											
1902	172,400	1,528	61.8	94%	$350	$365	$375	$385	$425	$575	$700	$1,750
Auctions: $18,800, MS-67, October 2015; $2,820, MS-65, August 2015; $646, MS-63, June 2015; $535, MS-63, August 2015											
1902, Proof	162	28	63.3							$12,500	$18,000	$30,000
Auctions: $12,925, PF-64, April 2013											
1902-S	939,000	2,665	62.1	92%	$350	$365	$375	$385	$425	$575	$700	$1,750
Auctions: $23,500, MS-67, January 2014; $1,998, MS-65, January 2015; $588, MS-63, July 2015; $436, MS-62, March 2015											
1903	226,870	1,898	61.6	92%	$350	$365	$375	$385	$425	$575	$700	$1,750
Auctions: $3,290, MS-66, July 2014; $3,819, MS-65, February 2014; $2,820, MS-65, September 2015; $423, MS-62, August 2015											
1903, Proof	154	55	63.9							$12,500	$18,000	$30,000
Auctions: $32,900, PF-65, October 2014; $30,550, PF-65, August 2015; $66,975, PF, March 2014											
1903-S	1,855,000	4,442	62.0	92%	$350	$365	$375	$385	$425	$575	$700	$1,750
Auctions: $2,585, MS-66, June 2015; $1,763, MS-65, January 2015; $764, MS-64, February 2015; $881, MS-63, September 2015											

	Mintage	Cert	Avg	%MS	VF-20	EF-40	AU-50	AU-55	MS-60	MS-63 / PF-63	MS-64 / PF-64	MS-65 / PF-65
1904	392,000	4,119	62.0	95%	$350	$365	$375	$385	$425	$575	$700	$1,750
Auctions: $5,170, MS-66, August 2015; $2,128, MS-65, July 2015; $482, MS-63, October 2015; $353, AU-58, June 2015												
1904, Proof	136	58	64.0							$12,500	$18,000	$30,000
Auctions: $31,725, PF-66Cam, June 2013												
1904-S	97,000	279	57.4	35%	$350	$365	$400	$450	$800	$3,000	$4,500	$8,500
Auctions: $4,113, MS-64, April 2013; $2,056, MS-63, January 2015; $423, AU-58, August 2015; $470, AU-55, October 2015												
1905	302,200	2,832	61.9	94%	$350	$365	$375	$385	$425	$575	$700	$1,750
Auctions: $2,350, MS-65, July 2015; $1,880, MS-65, February 2015; $999, MS-64, January 2015; $793, MS-64, June 2015												
1905, Proof	108	33	62.9							$12,500	$18,000	$30,000
Auctions: $23,000, PF-65Cam, October 2010												
1905-S	880,700	947	57.4	32%	$350	$365	$400	$475	$650	$1,500	$3,000	$8,000
Auctions: $764, MS-62, July 2015; $411, MS-61, March 2015; $347, AU-58, April 2015; $341, AU-53, March 2015												
1906	348,735	2,928	61.8	93%	$350	$365	$375	$385	$425	$575	$700	$1,750
Auctions: $7,050, MS-66, January 2015; $1,293, MS-64, September 2015; $517, MS-61, June 2015; $447, AU-55, January 2015												
1906, Proof	85	57	63.8							$12,500	$18,000	$30,000
Auctions: $64,625, PF-66Cam, August 2013												
1906-D	320,000	2,748	62.1	94%	$350	$365	$375	$385	$425	$575	$700	$1,750
Auctions: $4,935, MS-66, January 2015; $940, MS-64, August 2015; $823, MS-64, August 2015; $423, MS-60, February 2015												
1906-S	598,000	695	60.0	71%	$350	$365	$400	$450	$500	$1,000	$1,650	$4,500
Auctions: $793, MS-63, January 2015; $646, MS-63, February 2015; $470, MS-62, January 2015; $517, MS-61, June 2015												
1907	626,100	9,264	62.2	96%	$350	$365	$375	$385	$425	$575	$700	$1,750
Auctions: $7,638, MS-67, June 2015; $4,230, MS-66, August 2015; $1,175, MS-64, August 2015; $1,058, MS-64, August 2015												
1907, Proof	92	43	64.0							$12,500	$18,000	$30,000
Auctions: $24,675, PF-65Cam, April 2014												
1907-D	888,000	4,620	62.0	94%	$350	$365	$375	$385	$425	$575	$700	$1,750
Auctions: $1,704, MS-65, February 2015; $1,410, MS-64, September 2015; $423, MS-62, February 2015; $396, MS-61, July 2015												
1908	421,874	6,524	62.4	96%	$350	$365	$375	$385	$425	$575	$700	$1,750
Auctions: $4,465, MS-66, January 2015; $2,585, MS-65, August 2015; $999, MS-64, January 2015; $617, MS-63, January 2015												

INDIAN HEAD (1908–1929)

Designer: *Bela Lyon Pratt.* **Weight:** *8.359 grams.*
Composition: *.900 gold, .100 copper (net weight .24187 oz. pure gold).* **Diameter:** *21.6 mm.*
Edge: *Reeded.* **Mints:** *Philadelphia, Denver, New Orleans, and San Francisco.*

Circulation Strike   **Sandblast Finish Proof**   **Satin Finish Proof**

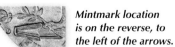

Mintmark location is on the reverse, to the left of the arrows.

History. The Indian Head half eagle made its first appearance in 1908; it was minted continuously through 1916, and again in 1929. Its design elements are in sunken relief (sometimes imprecisely called "incuse"), like those of the similar quarter eagle; the mintmark is raised. On most examples the rims are flat, while on others they are slightly raised. These coins saw limited circulation in the West, and were rarely encountered elsewhere.

Striking and Sharpness. Striking quality of Indian Head half eagles varies. Look for weakness on the high parts of the Indian's bonnet and in the feather details in the headdress. On the reverse, check the feathers on the highest area of the wing.

Proofs. Sandblast (also called Matte) Proofs were made in 1908 and from 1911 to 1915, while Satin (also called Roman Finish) Proofs were made in 1909 and 1910. At lower levels, these coins can show light contact marks. Some microscopic bright flecks may be caused by the sandblasting process and, although they do not represent handling, usually result in a coin being assigned a slightly lower grade.

Availability. Indian Head half eagles were not popular with numismatists of the time, who saved very few. Rare issues include the 1909-O, which usually is seen with evidence of circulation (often extensive) and the 1929, most of which are in MS. Luster can range from deeply frosty to grainy. Because the fields are the highest areas of the coin, luster diminished quickly as the coins were circulated or jostled with others in bags. When Proof examples are seen, they are usually in higher Proof grades, PF-64 and above. As a class these half eagles are rarer than quarter eagles of the same date and style of finish.

Note: Values of common-date gold coins have been based on the current bullion price of gold, $1,300 per ounce, and may vary with the prevailing spot price.

GRADING STANDARDS

MS-60 to 70 (Mint State). *Obverse:* At MS–60 to 62, there is abrasion in the field, this representing the highest part of the coin. Abrasion is also evident on the headdress. Marks and, occasionally, a microscopic pin scratch may be seen. At MS-63, there may be some abrasion and some tiny marks. Luster is irregular. At MS-64, abrasion is less. Luster is rich. At MS-65 and above, luster is deep and frosty, with no marks at all visible with-

1911-D. Graded MS-62.

out magnification at MS-66 and higher. *Reverse:* At MS–60 to 62 there is abrasion in the field, this representing the highest part of the coin. Abrasion is also evident on the eagle's wing. Otherwise, the same comments apply as for the obverse.

   Illustrated coin: This example is lustrous and attractive. Most of the luster in the fields (the highest-relief area of this unusual design) is still intact.

AU-50, 53, 55, 58 (About Uncirculated). *Obverse:* Friction on the cheek is very notice-able at AU-50, increasingly less at higher lev-els to AU-58. The headdress shows light wear, most evident on the ribbon above the forehead and on the garland. Luster is mini-mal at AU-50 and scattered and incomplete at AU-58. Nicks and contact marks are to be expected. *Reverse:* Friction on the wing and neck is very noticeable at AU-50, increasingly

1911. Graded AU-50.

less noticeable at higher levels to AU-58. Otherwise, the same comments apply as for the obverse.

EF-40, 45 (Extremely Fine). *Obverse:* Light wear will characterize the portrait and head-dress. Luster is gone. Marks and tiny scratches are to be expected, but not distracting. *Reverse:* Light wear is most evident on the eagle's head and wing, although other areas are lightly worn as well. Luster is gone. Marks and tiny scratches are to be expected, but not distracting.

1909-O. Graded EF-40.

VF-20, 30 (Very Fine). *Obverse:* Many details of the garland and of the ribbon above the forehead are worn away. Many feather vanes are blended together. The field is dull and has contact marks. *Reverse:* The neck and the upper part of the wing show extensive wear, other areas less so. The field is dull and has contact marks.

The Indian Head half eagle is seldom collected in grades lower than VF-20.

1909. Graded VF-25.

Illustrated coin: Some bumps are seen on the top obverse rim and should be mentioned in a description.

PF-60 to 70 (Proof). *Obverse and Reverse:* At PF–60 to 63, there is light abrasion and some contact marks (the lower the grade, the higher the quantity). On Sandblast Proofs these show up as visually unappealing bright spots. At PF-64 and higher levels, marks are fewer, with magnification needed to see any at PF-65. At PF-66, there should be none at all.

Illustrated coin: This is a particularly nice example.

1911, Sandblast Finish. Graded PF-67.

	Mintage	Cert	Avg	%MS	VF-20	EF-40	AU-50	AU-55	AU-58	MS-60	MS-62	MS-63	MS-65
											PF-63	PF-64	PF-65
1908	577,845	7,651	61.4	85%	$400	$420	$440	$460	$475	$500	$650	$1,250	$8,000
	Auctions: $51,700, MS-67, January 2015; $911, MS-62, August 2015; $558, AU-58, February 2015; $376, AU-55, March 2015												
1908, Sandblast Finish Proof	167	86	65.2								$15,000	$25,000	$45,000
	Auctions: $152,750, PF, August 2013												
1908-D	148,000	2,796	62.3	94%	$400	$420	$440	$460	$475	$650	$800	$1,250	$25,000
	Auctions: $3,290, MS-64, September 2015; $1,351, MS-63, June 2015; $705, MS-61, August 2015; $470, AU-58, July 2015												
1908-S	82,000	539	57.7	42%	$575	$700	$1,000	$1,350	$1,750	$2,750	$5,500	$9,000	$16,000
	Auctions: $47,000, MS-67, August 2014; $17,625, MS-65, January 2015; $7,344, MS-63, January 2015; $1,175, AU-55, July 2015												

	Mintage	Cert	Avg	%MS	VF-20	EF-40	AU-50	AU-55	AU-58	MS-60	MS-62 / PF-63	MS-63 / PF-64	MS-65 / PF-65
1909	627,060	6,960	61.0	83%	$400	$420	$440	$460	$475	$525	$650	$1,250	$8,500
Auctions: $7,638, MS-65, February 2015; $2,115, MS-64, October 2015; $676, MS-62, October 2015; $764, MS-61, July 2015
1909, Satin Finish Proof	78	36	65.3								$17,500	$30,000	$50,000
Auctions: $82,250, PF-67, August 2014; $55,813, PF-66, August 2014; $99,875, PF-66, February 2013
1909, Sandblast Finish Proof (a)	unknown	1	67.0										
Auctions: No auction records available.
1909-D	3,423,560	32,146	61.5	87%	$400	$420	$440	$460	$475	$525	$650	$1,250	$8,000
Auctions: $2,350, MS-64, March 2015; $764, MS-62, June 2015; $552, MS-61, September 2015; $353, EF-40, April 2015
1909-O (b)	34,200	984	55.5	14%	$4,750	$7,500	$11,000	$16,500	$25,000	$40,000	$65,000	$85,000	$400,000
Auctions: $56,400, MS-62, December 2015: $35,250, MS-61, August 2015; $32,900, MS-61, March 2016
1909-S	297,200	711	56.7	29%	$425	$450	$475	$550	$725	$2,250	$5,500	$10,000	$47,500
Auctions: $5,640, MS-62, January 2015; $3,410, MS-61, January 2015; $529, AU-55, March 2015; $400, EF-40, February 2015
1910	604,000	7,071	60.9	80%	$400	$420	$440	$460	$475	$525	$650	$1,250	$8,000
Auctions: $17,625, MS-65, August 2015; $1,998, MS-64, February 2015; $999, MS-63, October 2015; $447, MS-60, May 2015
1910, Satin Finish Proof	250	48	65.3								$17,500	$25,000	$45,000
Auctions: $146,250, PF, September 2013
1910, Sandblast Finish Proof (c)	unknown	0	n/a										
Auctions: No auction records available.
1910-D	193,600	1,189	60.4	75%	$400	$420	$440	$460	$475	$525	$1,200	$2,500	$26,000
Auctions: $7,050, MS-64, January 2015; $1,029, MS-62, January 2015; $617, MS-61, June 2015; $400, AU-55, May 2015
1910-S	770,200	1,532	57.0	27%	$425	$450	$475	$500	$800	$1,500	$3,500	$9,500	$75,000
Auctions: $3,290, MS-62, March 2015; $2,056, MS-61, January 2015; $676, AU-58, August 2015; $517, AU-55, August 2015
1911	915,000	10,914	60.7	77%	$400	$420	$440	$460	$475	$525	$650	$1,250	$8,500
Auctions: $8,225, MS-65, January 2015; $1,880, MS-64, January 2015; $529, MS-61, September 2015
1911, Sandblast Finish Proof	139	54	65.7								$15,000	$25,000	$45,000
Auctions: $99,875, PF-67, April 2013
1911-D	72,500	1,459	56.9	15%	$750	$1,000	$1,750	$3,000	$4,500	$8,500	$20,000	$37,500	$225,000
Auctions: $36,425, MS-63, December 2015: $12,925, MS-62, August 2015; $8,813, MS-61, January 2015
1911-S	1,416,000	2,757	57.2	36%	$425	$450	$475	$500	$600	$900	$2,000	$4,500	$42,500
Auctions: $12,925, MS-64, January 2015; $1,175, MS-61, July 2015; $494, AU-55, June 2015; $376, EF-45, March 2015
1912	790,000	10,394	60.9	81%	$400	$420	$440	$460	$475	$525	$650	$1,250	$8,500
Auctions: $7,050, MS-65, January 2015; $2,820, MS-64, June 2015; $447, MS-61, October 2015; $482, AU-58, July 2015
1912, Sandblast Finish Proof	144	38	66.4								$15,000	$25,000	$45,000
Auctions: $58,750, PF-66, September 2013
1912-S	392,000	1,544	56.1	17%	$425	$450	$475	$600	$900	$1,850	$5,500	$15,000	$180,000
Auctions: $5,405, MS-62, August 2015; $2,820, MS-61, October 2015; $1,293, AU-58, August 2015; $449, AU-53, March 2015
1913	915,901	11,984	60.9	82%	$400	$420	$440	$460	$475	$525	$650	$1,250	$8,000
Auctions: $2,585, MS-64, March 2015; $1,058, MS-63, October 2015; $764, MS-61, June 2015; $423, AU-58, July 2015
1913, Sandblast Finish Proof	99	25	66.2								$15,000	$25,000	$45,000
Auctions: $51,750, PF-67, July 2011
1913-S	408,000	1,881	56.4	23%	$525	$575	$625	$800	$875	$2,500	$6,000	$15,000	$120,000
Auctions: $4,600, MS-62, January 2015; $823, AU-58, July 2015; $470, AU-53, February 2015; $340, EF-40, February 2015
1914	247,000	2,842	60.8	77%	$400	$420	$440	$460	$475	$525	$800	$1,750	$12,500
Auctions: $9,400, MS-65, January 2015; $5,170, MS-64, August 2015; $1,028, MS-62, June 2015; $541, MS-61, March 2015
1914, Sandblast Finish Proof	125	33	65.8								$15,000	$25,000	$45,000
Auctions: $93,600, PF, September 2013
1914-D	247,000	2,618	60.5	72%	$400	$420	$440	$460	$475	$600	$900	$2,250	$20,000
Auctions: $3,760, MS-64, October 2015; $1,880, MS-63, July 2015; $1,058, MS-61, February 2015; $470, AU-58, February 2015
1914-S	263,000	1,500	57.8	35%	$425	$450	$475	$525	$850	$1,750	$4,500	$8,000	$125,000
Auctions: $16,450, MS-63, August 2015; $2,115, AU-58, September 2015; $470, AU-53, May 2015; $382, VF-35, June 2015

a. This unique coin is certified by NGC as PF-67. **b.** Beware spurious "O" mintmark. **c.** This unique coin is part of the unique complete 1910 Sandblast Finish Proof gold set.

	Mintage	Cert	Avg	%MS	VF-20	EF-40	AU-50	AU-55	AU-58	MS-60	MS-62	MS-63	MS-65
											PF-63	PF-64	PF-65
1915 (d)	588,000	6,448	60.8	76%	$400	$420	$440	$460	$475	$525	$650	$1,250	$8,000
Auctions: $9,988, MS-65, August 2015; $3,760, MS-64, September 2015; $764, MS-62, August 2015; $646, MS-61, June 2015													
1915, Sandblast Finish Proof	75	22	65.2								$17,500	$25,000	$55,000
Auctions: $47,000, PF-66, June 2014													
1915-S	164,000	1,319	56.3	21%	$425	$450	$500	$700	$1,250	$2,500	$7,500	$12,500	$130,000
Auctions: $5,640, MS-62, January 2015; $3,525, MS-61, January 2015; $1,116, AU-58, October 2015; $364, AU-50, March 2015													
1916-S	240,000	2,069	58.9	48%	$450	$485	$525	$625	$850	$1,250	$2,500	$5,000	$32,500
Auctions: $41,126, MS-65, August 2015; $1,410, MS-61, October 2015; $400, AU-55, March 2015; $376, AU-50, October 2015													
1929	662,000	225	63.3	90%	$18,500	$20,000	$23,500	$25,000	$30,000	$35,000	$40,000	$42,500	$115,000
Auctions: $54,050, MS-64, January 2015; $51,700, MS-64, January 2015; $47,000, MS-64, September 2016; $37,600, MS-62, August 2015													

d. Pieces dated 1915-D are counterfeit.

Gold Eagles ($10)
1795–1933

AN OVERVIEW OF GOLD EAGLES

The ten-dollar gold coin, or *eagle*, was first produced in 1795. Coinage authority for the denomination, including its weight and fineness, had been specified by the Act of April 2, 1792.

The Capped Bust to Right with Small Eagle reverse is the rarest of the early ten-dollar coin types. However, when seen they tend to be in higher grades such as EF, AU, or low levels of Mint State. The Heraldic Eagle reverse issues from 1797 through 1804 are much more readily available and in slightly higher average grade.

The Liberty Head eagles without the motto IN GOD WE TRUST, minted from 1838 through 1865, are elusive in any Mint State grade, although VF and EF pieces are plentiful, and there are enough AU coins to easily satisfy collector demands. Some collectors have considered the 1838 and 1839, 9 Over 8, with the head of Miss Liberty tilted forward in relation to the date, to be a separate type. Eagles with IN GOD WE TRUST on the reverse, produced from 1866 to 1907, are plentiful in high grades, including choice and gem Mint State. Some of these were repatriated from overseas bank vaults beginning in the second half of the 20th century.

The Saint-Gaudens eagles of 1907, of the style with periods between and flanking the words E PLURIBUS UNUM, exist in the Wire Rim and Rounded Rim varieties. These can be collected as a distinct type, or not. Most readily available is the Wire Rim style, of which somewhat more than 400 are likely to exist today, nearly all in Mint State, often choice or gem. These coins were made as regular issues but soon became numismatic delicacies for Treasury officials to distribute as they saw fit. Some were to have gone to museums, but in reality most were secretly filtered out through favored coin dealers. Then comes the 1907–1908 style, without periods, easily available in EF, AU, and lower Mint State levels, although gems are elusive.

The final eagle type, the 1908–1933 style with IN GOD WE TRUST on the reverse, is readily obtained in grades from EF through MS-63. Higher-grade pieces are elusive, and

This pattern eagle of 1878, struck in copper and designated J-1580, was designed by George Morgan and strongly resembles the silver dollar design that bears his name.

when seen are often dated 1932, a year in which 4,463,000 were struck—more than any other coin in the history of the denomination.

For the Collector and Investor: Gold Eagles as a Specialty

Collecting ten-dollar gold coins by die varieties is unusual, as the series includes so many scarce and rare coins. However, unlike other denominations, none is in the "impossible" category, and with some patience a full set of significant varieties, as listed in this book, can be obtained.

The early issues with a Small Eagle reverse, minted from 1795 through 1797, and those with the Heraldic Eagle reverse of 1797 through 1804, can be collected and studied by die varieties, with *United States Ten Dollar Gold Eagles 1795–1804*, by Anthony Teraskza, being one useful guide. *Early U.S. Gold Coin Varieties: A Study of Die States, 1795–1834*, by John W. Dannreuther and Harry W. Bass Jr., offers an abundance of information and enlarged photographs for study. In addition to the regular issues, a few 1804 restrike ten-dollar pieces exist from 1804-dated dies newly created in 1834.

Liberty Head eagles from 1838 through 1866 (without the motto IN GOD WE TRUST) comprise many scarce dates and mintmarks. Years ago the 1858, of which only 2,521 were minted, was highly acclaimed as a landmark issue, but since then the publicity has faded. In any event, although certain date-and-mintmark varieties are rare, the number of numismatists collecting them by date sequence is very small, and thus opportunities exist to acquire very elusive pieces at a much smaller proportionate premium than would be possible in, say, the gold dollar series. No full set of Mint State early eagles has ever been formed; probably none ever will be. EF and AU are typically the grades of choice, with Mint State pieces added when available.

Later Liberty Head eagles of the 1866–1907 style (with the motto IN GOD WE TRUST) include some low-mintage issues, but again these are not impossible to collect. The most famous is the 1875 Philadelphia coin, of which just 100 circulation strikes were made. Although smaller numbers exist for Proof-only mintages, in terms of those made for commerce the 1875 sets a record. The low-mintage 1879-O (1,500 made) and 1883-O (800) also have attracted much attention. Again, these pieces, while rare, are available to the specialist, as there is not a great deal of competition.

Among Indian Head eagles the 1907, With Periods, Wire Rim, is famous, popular, and rare. Examples come on the market with regularity but are expensive due to the demand they attract. The Rounded Rim style is much rarer and when seen is usually in choice Mint State.

The regular without-periods 1907 and 1908 eagles are easy enough to obtain in Mint State, although gems are elusive. The varieties from 1908 through 1916 include no great rarities, although some are scarcer than others. Not many such pieces were saved at the time they were issued, and, accordingly, gems are elusive. However, grades such as AU and low Mint State will present no problem. Among later eagles, the 1920-S, 1930-S, and 1933 are rarities. In particular the 1920-S is difficult to find in choice and gem Mint State. The 1933 eagle is usually found in Mint State, but is expensive due to the publicity given to it. Readily available at reasonable prices are the 1926 and 1932.

CAPPED BUST TO RIGHT, SMALL EAGLE REVERSE (1795–1797)

Designer: *Robert Scot.* **Weight:** *17.50 grams.*
Composition: *.9167 gold, .0833 silver and copper.*
Diameter: *Approximately 33 mm.* **Edge:** *Reeded.* **Mint:** *Philadelphia.*

Bass-Dannreuther–1.

History. Eagles of this style, the first in the denomination, debuted in the autumn of 1795. The obverse features Miss Liberty dressed in a conical cap. The reverse shows a "small" eagle perched on a palm branch and holding a laurel in his beak. The same motif was used on contemporary gold half eagles.

Striking and Sharpness. On the obverse, check the star centers and the hair details. On the reverse, check the feathers of the eagle. In particular, the breast feathers often are weakly struck. Examine the denticles on both sides. Adjustment marks (from a Mint worker filing an overweight planchet down to the correct weight) often are visible, but are not noted by the grading services.

Availability. Typical grades range from EF to AU and low MS. MS-63 and higher coins are rare; when seen, they usually are of the 1795 or 1796 dates. Certain varieties are rare. While no Proofs of this type were made, certain eagles of 1796 have prooflike surfaces and are particularly attractive if in high grades.

GRADING STANDARDS

MS-60 to 70 (Mint State). *Obverse:* At MS-60, some abrasion and contact marks are evident, most noticeably on the hair to the left of Miss Liberty's forehead and on the higher-relief areas of the cap. Luster is present, but may be dull or lifeless, and interrupted in patches. At MS-63, contact marks are few, and abrasion is very light. An MS-65 coin has hardly any abrasion, and contact marks are so minute as to require magnifica-

1795, 13 Leaves; BD-5. Graded MS-63.

tion. Luster should be full and rich. On prooflike coins in any Mint State grade, abrasion and surface marks are much more noticeable. Coins above MS-65 exist more in theory than in reality for this type—but they do exist, and are defined by having fewer marks as perfection is approached. *Reverse:* Comments apply as for the obverse, except that abrasion and contact marks are most noticeable on the breast and head of the eagle. The field area is mainly protected by the eagle, branch, and lettering.

AU-50, 53, 55, 58 (About Uncirculated).
Obverse: Light wear is seen on the cheek, the hair immediately to the left of the face, and the cap, more so at AU-50 than at AU–53 or 55. An AU-58 coin has minimal traces of wear. An AU-50 coin has luster in protected areas among the stars and letters, with little in the open fields or on the portrait. At AU-58, most luster is present in the fields, but is worn away on the highest parts of the motifs.

1796. Graded AU-58.

Reverse: Comments as preceding, except that the eagle shows light wear on the breast and head in particular, but also at the tip of the wing on the left and elsewhere. Luster ranges from perhaps 40% remaining in protected areas (at AU-50) to nearly full mint bloom (at AU-58).

Illustrated coin: This example shows light wear overall, with hints of original luster in protected areas.

EF-40, 45 (Extremely Fine). *Obverse:* Wear is evident all over the portrait, with some loss of detail in the hair to the left of Miss Liberty's face. Excellent detail remains in low-relief areas of the hair, such as the front curl and at the back of her head. The stars show wear, as do the date and letters. Luster, if present at all, is minimal and in protected areas. *Reverse:* Wear is greater than on an About Uncirculated coin. The breast, neck, and legs of the

1795, 9 Leaves; BD-3. Graded EF-45.

eagle lack nearly all feather detail. More wear is seen on the edges of the wing. Some traces of luster may be seen, more so at EF-45 than at EF-40.

VF-20, 30 (Very Fine). *Obverse:* The higher-relief areas of hair are well worn at VF-20, less so at VF-30. The stars are flat at their centers. *Reverse:* Wear is greater, the eagle is flat in most areas, and about 40% to 60% of the wing feathers can be seen.

The Capped Bust to Right eagle coin with Small Eagle reverse is seldom collected in grades lower than VF-20.

1795, 13 Leaves; BD-2. Graded VF-30.

1795, 13 Leaves **1795, 9 Leaves**

	Mintage	Cert	Avg	%MS	F-12	VF-20	EF-40	AU-50	AU-55	MS-60	MS-62	MS-63
1795, 13 Leaves Below Eagle	5,583	64	55.7	23%	$27,500	$35,000	$50,000	$57,500	$72,500	$105,000	$150,000	$300,000 (a)
Auctions: $152,750, MS-62, November 2014; $64,625, AU-55, August 2016; $49,938, EF-45, August 2014; $822,500, MS-64+, March 2019												
1795, 9 Leaves Below Eagle †	(b)	14	57.4	14%	$75,000	$85,000	$95,000	$140,000	$180,000	$250,000	$350,000	$750,000
Auctions: $146,875, EF-45, August 2014; $47,000, EF-40, January 2014												
1796	4,146	67	57.8	27%	$32,500	$37,500	$55,000	$60,000	$75,000	$125,000	$225,000	$425,000
Auctions: $164,500, MS-62, April 2014; $82,250, AU-55, August 2014												
1797, Small Eagle	3,615	27	56.1	33%	$40,000	$55,000	$80,000	$115,000	$130,000	$225,000	$400,000	$500,000
Auctions: $164,500, AU-58, August 2014; $91,063, EF-45, August 2016; $47,000, EF-40, August 2014												

† Ranked in the *100 Greatest U.S. Coins* (fourth edition). **a.** Value in MS-64 is $475,000. **b.** Included in 1795, 13 Leaves Below Eagle, mintage figure.

CAPPED BUST TO RIGHT, HERALDIC EAGLE REVERSE (1797–1804)

Designer: *Robert Scot.* **Weight:** *17.50 grams.*
Composition: *.9167 gold, .0833 silver and copper.*
Diameter: *Approximately 33 mm.* **Edge:** *Reeded.* **Mint:** *Philadelphia.*

Circulation Strike
BD-2.

Proof

History. Gold eagles of this type combine the previous obverse style with the Heraldic Eagle—a modification of the Great Seal of the United States—as used on other silver and gold coins of the era. Regarding the Proofs dated 1804: There were no Proofs coined in the era in which this type was issued, and all eagle and silver dollar production was suspended by President Thomas Jefferson in 1804. Years later, in 1834, the Mint made up new dies with the 1804 date (this time featuring a Plain 4 rather than a Crosslet 4) and struck a number of Proofs (the quantity unknown today, but perhaps a dozen or so) for inclusion in presentation Proof sets for foreign dignitaries.

Striking and Sharpness. On the obverse, check the star centers and the hair details. On the reverse, check the upper part of the shield, the lower part of the eagle's neck, the eagle's wing, the stars above the eagle, and the clouds. Inspect the denticles on both sides. Adjustment marks (from where an over-weight planchet was filed down to correct specifications) can be problematic; these are not identified by the grading services.

Availability. Mintages of this type were erratic. Eagles of 1797 appear in the market with some regularity, while those of 1798 are rare. Usually seen are the issues of 1799 through 1803. Typical grades range from EF to lower MS. MS-62 and higher coins are seen with some frequency and usually are dated 1799 and later. The 1804 circulation strike is rare in true MS. Sharply struck coins without planchet adjustment marks are in the minority. Only a handful of the aforementioned 1804 Proofs survive today.

GRADING STANDARDS

MS-60 to 70 (Mint State). *Obverse:* At MS-60, some abrasion and contact marks are evident, most noticeably on the hair to the left of Miss Liberty's forehead and on the higher-relief areas of the cap. Luster is present, but may be dull or lifeless, and interrupted in patches. At MS-63, contact marks are few, and abrasion is very light. An MS-65 coin has even less abrasion (most observable in the right field), and contact marks are so

1799, Large Stars; BD-10. Graded MS-65.

minute as to require magnification. Luster should be full and rich. Coins graded above MS-65 are more theoretical than actual for this type—but they do exist, and are defined by having fewer marks as perfection is approached. Large-size eagles are usually graded with slightly less strictness than the lower gold denominations of this type. *Reverse:* Comments apply as for the obverse, except that abrasion and contact marks are most noticeable on the upper part of the eagle and the clouds. The field area is complex, without much open space, given the stars above the eagle, the arrows and olive branch, and other features. Accordingly, marks are not as noticeable as on the obverse.

Illustrated coin: This coin has an exceptionally sharp strike overall, but with some lightness on the eagle's dexter (viewer's left) talon. Note some trivial abrasion in the right obverse field.

AU-50, 53, 55, 58 (About Uncirculated). *Obverse:* Light wear is seen on the cheek, the hair immediately to the left of the face, and the cap, more so at AU-50 than at AU–53 or 55. An AU-58 coin has minimal traces of wear. An AU-50 coin has luster in protected areas among the stars and letters, with little in the open fields or on the portrait. At AU-58, most luster is present in the fields, but is worn away on the highest parts of the

1799, Small Stars; BD-7. Graded AU-50.

motifs. *Reverse:* Comments as preceding, except that the eagle's neck, the tips and top of the wings, the clouds, and the tail now show noticeable wear, as do other features. Luster ranges from perhaps 40% remaining in protected areas (at AU-50) to nearly full mint bloom (at AU-58). Often the reverse of this type retains much more luster than the obverse.

Illustrated coin: Note some lightness of strike at the center of the obverse. Significant luster remains.

EF-40, 45 (Extremely Fine). *Obverse:* Wear is evident all over the portrait, with some loss of detail in the hair to the left of Miss Liberty's face. Excellent detail remains in low-relief areas of the hair, such as the front curl and at the back of her head. The stars show wear as do the date and letters. Luster, if present at all, is minimal and in protected areas. *Reverse:* Wear is greater than on the preceding. The neck lacks some feather detail on its highest

1801; BD-2. Graded EF-45.

points. Feathers have lost some detail near the edges of the wings, and some areas of the horizontal lines in the shield may be blended together. Some traces of luster may be seen, more so at EF-45 than at EF-40. Overall, the reverse appears to be in a slightly higher grade than the obverse.

VF-20, 30 (Very Fine). *Obverse:* The higher-relief areas of hair are well worn at VF-20, less so at VF-30. *Reverse:* Wear is greater, including on the shield and wing feathers. The star centers are flat. Other areas have lost detail as well. E PLURIBUS UNUM may be faint in areas, but is usually sharp.

The Capped Bust to Right eagle coin with Heraldic Eagle reverse is seldom collected in grades lower than VF-20.

1799, Small Stars; BD-7. Graded VF-30.

PF-60 to 70 (Proof). *Obverse and Reverse:* PF–60 to 62 coins have extensive hairlines and may have nicks and contact marks. At PF-63, hairlines are prominent, but the mirror surface is very reflective. PF-64 coins have fewer hairlines. At PF-65, hairlines should be minimal and mostly seen only under magnification. There should be no nicks or marks.

1804, Plain 4; BD-2. Proof.

| 1798, 8 Over 7, 9 Stars Left, 4 Right | 1798, 8 Over 7, 7 Stars Left, 6 Right | 1799, Small Obverse Stars | 1799, Large Obverse Stars |

| 1803, Small Reverse Stars | 1803, Large Reverse Stars |

	Mintage	Cert	Avg	%MS	F-12	VF-20	EF-40	AU-50	AU-55	MS-60	MS-62	MS-63	MS-64
											PF-63	PF-64	PF-65
1797	10,940	168	56.5	29%	$11,000	$15,000	$20,000	$32,500	$40,000	$55,000	$100,000	$150,000	$225,000
	Auctions: $117,500, MS-63, April 2014; $44,063, MS-61, November 2014; $41,125, AU-58, August 2014; $34,075, AU-58, August 2014												
1798, 8 Over 7, 9 Stars Left, 4 Stars Right †	900	27	57.6	30%	$22,500	$27,500	$40,000	$55,000	$72,500	$125,000	$225,000	$325,000	
	Auctions: $176,250, MS-62, April 2014; $76,375, AU-55, August 2016												
1798, 8 Over 7, 7 Stars Left, 6 Stars Right †	842	4	52.5	25%	$45,000	$60,000	$95,000	$175,000	$250,000	$425,000	$650,000		
	Auctions: $352,500, AU-58, August 2016; $161,000, AU-55, January 2005; $176,250, AU-50, August 2014												
1799, Small Obverse Stars	37,449	34	57.6	44%	$9,500	$12,500	$16,000	$20,000	$23,500	$32,500	$42,500	$67,500	$135,000
	Auctions: $9,988, AU-58, September 2014; $25,850, AU-58, August 2014; $24,675, AU-55, January 2014; $15,275, AU-50, August 2014												
1799, Large Obverse Stars	(a)	31	58.9	58%	$9,500	$12,500	$16,000	$20,000	$23,500	$32,500	$42,500	$67,500	$115,000
	Auctions: $32,900, MS-62, October 2014; $19,975, AU-58, August 2014; $16,450, AU-53, November 2014; $9,400, AU, March 2015												
1800	5,999	107	57.3	41%	$9,500	$13,000	$16,500	$21,500	$24,500	$35,000	$47,500	$87,500	$175,000
	Auctions: $117,500, MS-64, January 2014; $32,900, MS-61, August 2014; $15,275, AU-50, August 2014; $7,638, AU-50, July 2014												
1801	44,344	412	58.6	52%	$9,500	$11,000	$15,500	$18,500	$21,000	$30,000	$40,000	$65,000	$125,000
	Auctions: $88,125, MS-64, March 2013; $48,763, MS-63, August 2014; $45,535, MS-63, August 2014; $29,375, MS-61, October 2014												
1803, Small Reverse Stars	15,017	22	57.1	45%	$10,000	$12,000	$16,000	$21,500	$23,500	$37,500	$50,000	$65,000	$135,000
	Auctions: $28,200, MS-61, January 2014; $15,875, AU-55, November 2014; $17,625, AU-55, August 2014; $13,513, AU-55, August 2014												
1803, Large Reverse Stars (b)	(c)	9	58.2	44%	$10,000	$12,000	$16,000	$21,500	$23,500	$37,500	$55,000	$65,000	$135,000
	Auctions: $99,875, MS-64, January 2014; $42,594, MS-62, August 2014; $24,675, AU-53, August 2014												
1804, Crosslet 4	3,757	53	59.9	49%	$20,000	$25,000	$37,500	$50,000	$65,000	$85,000	$100,000	$185,000	
	Auctions: $73,438, MS-61, January 2014; $64,625, MS-60, August 2014; $58,750, AU-58, August 2014												
1804, Plain 4, Proof † (d)	5–8	2	65.0								$4,000,000	$4,500,000	$5,000,000
	Auctions: $73,438, MS-61, January 2014												

† Ranked in the *100 Greatest U.S. Coins* (fourth edition); both 1798, 8 Over 7 Capped Bust to Right, Heraldic Eagle Reverse Eagle varieties as a single entry. **a.** Included in 1799, Small Obverse Stars, mintage figure. **b.** A variety without the tiny 14th star in the cloud is very rare; 6 or 7 examples are known. It does not command a significant premium. **c.** Included in 1803, Small Reverse Stars, mintage figure. **d.** These coins were minted in 1834 (from newly created dies with the date 1804) for presentation sets for foreign dignitaries. 3 or four 4 are known today.

LIBERTY HEAD (1838–1907)

Designer: *Christian Gobrecht.* **Weight:** *16.718 grams.*
Composition: *.900 gold, .100 copper (net weight: .48375 oz. pure gold).* **Diameter:** *27 mm.*
Edge: *Reeded.* **Mints:** *Philadelphia, Carson City, Denver, New Orleans, and San Francisco.*

No Motto Above Eagle (1838–1866)

No Motto Above Eagle, Proof

Motto Above Eagle (1866–1907)

Motto Above Eagle, Proof

History. Production of the gold eagle, suspended after 1804, started up again in 1838 with the Liberty Head design. The coin's weight and diameter was reduced from the specifications of the earlier type. For the first time in the denomination's history, its value, TEN D., was shown. Midway through 1839 the style was modified slightly, including in the letters (made smaller) and in the tilt of Miss Liberty's portrait. In 1866 the motto IN GOD WE TRUST was placed on a banner above the eagle's head.

Striking and Sharpness. On the obverse, check the highest points of the hair and the star centers. On the reverse, check the eagle's neck, and the area to the lower left of the shield and the lower part of the eagle. Examine the denticles on both sides. Branch-mint coins issued before the Civil War often are lightly struck in areas, and some Carson City coins of the early 1870s can have areas of lightness. Most late 19th-century and early 20th-century coins are sharp in all areas. Tiny copper staining spots (from improperly mixed alloy) can be a problem for those issues. Cameo contrast is the rule for Proofs prior to 1902. Beginning that year the portrait was polished in the die, imparting a mirror finish across the entire design, although a few years later cameo-contrast coins were again made.

Availability. Early dates and mintmarks are generally scarce to rare in MS and very rare in MS-63 and better grades, with only a few exceptions. These were workhorse coins in commerce; VF and EF grades are the rule for dates through the 1870s, and for some dates the finest known grade can be AU. In MS, Liberty Head eagles as a type are rarer than either quarter eagles or half eagles of the same design. Indeed, the majority of Mint State examples were only discovered in recent decades, resting in European banks, and some varieties are not known to exist at this level. Eagles of the 1880s onward generally are seen in higher average grades. Proof coins exist in relation to their original mintages, with all issues prior to the 1890s being very rare.

Note: Values of common-date gold coins have been based on the current bullion price of gold, $1,300 per ounce, and may vary with the prevailing spot price.

GRADING STANDARDS

MS-60 to 70 (Mint State). *Obverse:* At MS-60, some abrasion and contact marks are evident, most noticeably on the hair to the right of Miss Liberty's forehead and on the jaw. Luster is present, but may be dull or lifeless, and interrupted in patches. At MS-63, contact marks are few, and abrasion is very light. An MS-65 coin has hardly any abrasion, and contact marks are so minute as to require magnification. Luster should be full and rich.

1880. Graded MS-63.

For most dates, coins graded above MS-65 exist more in theory than in actuality—but they do exist, and are defined by having fewer marks as perfection is approached. *Reverse:* Comments apply as for the obverse, except that abrasion and contact marks are most noticeable on the eagle's neck and to the lower left of the shield.

   Illustrated coin: This coin is brilliant and lustrous with scattered marks in the field, as is typical for this grade.

AU-50, 53, 55, 58 (About Uncirculated). *Obverse:* Light wear is seen on the face, the hair to the right of the face, and the highest area of the hair bun, more so at AU-50 than at AU–53 or 55. An AU-58 coin has minimal traces of wear. An AU-50 coin has luster in protected areas among the stars and letters, with little in the open fields or on the portrait. At AU-58 most luster is present in the fields, but is worn away on the highest parts

1839, Large Letters, 9 Over 8. Graded AU-53.

of the motifs. *Reverse:* Comments as preceding, except that the eagle shows wear in all of the higher areas, as well as the leaves and arrowheads. Luster ranges from perhaps 40% remaining in protected areas (at AU-50) to nearly full mint bloom (at AU-58). Often the reverse of this type retains more luster than the obverse.

EF-40, 45 (Extremely Fine). *Obverse:* Wear is evident on all high areas of the portrait, including the hair to the right of the forehead, the tip of the coronet, and the hair bun. The stars show light wear at their centers. Luster, if present at all, is minimal and in protected areas such as between the star points. *Reverse:* Wear is greater than on an About Uncirculated coin. On the $10 coins (in contrast to the $2.50 and $5 of the same design), most of the details on

1868. Graded EF-40.

the eagle are sharp. There is flatness on the leaves and arrowheads. Some traces of luster may be seen, more so at EF-45 than at EF-40.

   Illustrated coin: Note the many contact marks on both sides.

VF-20, 30 (Very Fine). *Obverse:* The higher-relief areas of hair are worn flat at VF-20, less so at VF-30. The hair to the right of the coronet is merged into heavy strands. The stars are flat at their centers. *Reverse:* The eagle is worn further, with most neck feathers gone and with the feathers in the wing having flat tips. The branch leaves have little or no detail. The vertical shield stripes, being deeply recessed, remain bold.

1838. Graded VF-25.

The Liberty Head eagle is seldom collected in grades lower than VF-20.

PF-60 to 70 (Proof). *Obverse and Reverse:* PF–60 to 62 coins have extensive hairlines and may have nicks and contact marks. At PF-63, hairlines are prominent, but the mirror surface is very reflective. PF-64 coins have fewer hairlines. At PF-65, hairlines should be minimal and mostly seen only under magnification. There should be no nicks or marks. PF-66 and higher coins should have no marks or hairlines visible to the unaided eye.

1862. Graded PF-65.

Illustrated coin: This is a museum-quality gem, with cameo-contrast motifs and mirror fields.

**1839, Large Letters
(Type of 1838)**   **1839, Small Letters
(Type of 1840)**

	Mintage	Cert	Avg	%MS	VF-20	EF-40	AU-50	AU-55	AU-58	MS-60	MS-63	MS-65
										PF-63	PF-64	PF-65
1838	7,200	60	49.4	2%	$4,000	$10,000	$20,000	$30,000	$62,500	$75,000	$125,000	
	Auctions: $105,750, MS-63, May 2016; $64,625, AU-58, August 2016: $41,125, AU-58, August 2014; $7,638, EF-40, August 2015											
1838, Proof † (a)	4–6	1	65.0		*(extremely rare)*							
	Auctions: $500,000, ChPF, May 1998											
1839, Large Letters (b)	25,801	163	50.5	10%	$2,000	$5,000	$6,500	$11,500	$15,000	$32,500	$85,000	$350,000
	Auctions: $10,575, AU-58, September 2015; $9,694, AU-55, August 2015; $9,400, AU-55, August 2016; $4,759, AU-50, August 2015											
1839, Small Letters	12,447	41	48.1	2%	$3,500	$9,500	$13,500	$20,000	$27,500	$45,000	$135,000	
	Auctions: $47,000, AU-58, February 2014; $9,988, AU-50, September 2015; $3,995, 35, September 2016											
1839, Large Letters, Proof (c)	4–6	1	67.0		*(extremely rare)*							
	Auctions: $1,610,000, PF-67UCam, January 2007											

† Ranked in the *100 Greatest U.S. Coins* (fourth edition). **a.** 3 examples are known. **b.** The Large Letters style is also known as the "Type of 1838," because of the distinct style of the 1838 Liberty Head motif. The Small Letters style (or "Type of 1840") was used on subsequent issues. **c.** 3 examples are known.

1842, Small Date   **1842, Large Date**

	Mintage	Cert	Avg	%MS	VF-20	EF-40	AU-50	AU-55	AU-58	MS-60 / PF-63	MS-63 / PF-64	MS-65 / PF-65
1840	47,338	177	49.3	3%	$1,150	$1,500	$1,850	$2,750	$6,000	$9,500		
Auctions: $35,250, MS-62, August 2014; $15,275, MS-61, June 2015; $1,528, AU-53, June 2015; $1,645, EF-40, September 2015												
1840, Proof (d)	1–2	0	n/a		*(unique, in the Smithsonian's National Numismatic Collection)*							
Auctions: No auction records available.												
1841	63,131	207	49.9	7%	$1,000	$1,100	$1,350	$2,500	$4,500	$8,000	$45,000	
Auctions: $9,400, MS-61, February 2014; $4,230, AU-58, August 2015; $1,645, AU-55, February 2015; $1,116, AU-53, June 2015												
1841, Proof (e)	4–6	1	61.0		*(extremely rare)*							
Auctions: No auction records available.												
1841-O	2,500	47	45.6	0%	$7,000	$12,500	$27,500	$60,000	$85,000			
Auctions: $25,850, AU-53, January 2014; $21,150, AU-50, September 2016; $14,688, AU-50, October 2014												
1842, Small Date	18,623	97	51.4	6%	$1,000	$1,150	$1,750	$3,000	$5,000	$12,500	$40,000	
Auctions: $12,925, MS-61, June 2015; $2,115, AU-55, January 2015; $1,175, AU-50, February 2015; $940, AU-50, January 2015												
1842, Large Date	62,884	118	51.7	4%	$1,000	$1,150	$1,650	$2,750	$5,000	$15,000	$35,000	$125,000
Auctions: $2,233, MS-60, January 2014												
1842, Small Date, Proof (f)	2	0	n/a		*(extremely rare)*							
Auctions: No auction records available.												
1842-O	27,400	269	49.1	2%	$1,250	$1,650	$3,500	$7,500	$17,500	$65,000	$250,000	
Auctions: $8,825, AU-55, March 2014; $4,230, AU-53, August 2015; $2,115, AU-50, July 2016; $999, AU-50, July 2015												
1843	75,462	200	49.6	3%	$1,050	$1,150	$1,850	$4,000	$8,500	$14,500		
Auctions: $3,055, AU-55, October 2015; $1,763, AU-50, August 2015; $1,058, EF-40, January 2015; $1,011, VF-30, March 2015												
1843, Doubled Die	(g)	0	n/a									
Auctions: No auction records available.												
1843, Proof (h)	6–8	3	62.7		*(extremely rare)*							
Auctions: No auction records available.												
1843-O	175,162	426	49.6	2%	$1,050	$1,200	$1,800	$3,250	$5,500	$12,000	$55,000	
Auctions: $7,050, AU-58, February 2015; $2,585, AU-53, July 2015; $1,175, AU-50, January 2015; $1,058, VF-35, January 2015												
1844	6,361	39	50.5	8%	$2,500	$4,500	$5,500	$13,500	$20,000	$25,000	$75,000	
Auctions: $24,170, AU-55, January 2014												
1844, Proof (i)	6–8	1	63.0		*(extremely rare)*							
Auctions: No auction records available.												
1844-O	118,700	380	50.9	5%	$1,050	$1,350	$1,850	$4,750	$8,500	$15,000		
Auctions: $7,931, AU-58, June 2013; $2,585, AU-53, July 2015; $2,585, AU-53, March 2015; $1,293, EF-45, November 2014												
1844-O, Proof †	1	1	65.0									
Auctions: No auction records available.												
1845	26,153	114	48.8	3%	$1,000	$1,450	$2,750	$4,000	$7,500	$15,000		
Auctions: $4,994, AU-55, April 2013												
1845, Proof (j)	6–8	1	65.0		*(extremely rare)*							
Auctions: $120,750, PF-64, August 1999												
1845-O	47,500	230	49.7	5%	$1,050	$1,650	$3,250	$7,500	$11,000	$15,000	$50,000	
Auctions: $2,820, AU-53, November 2014; $881, AU-50, October 2014; $3,819, AU, March 2014; $764, EF-40, January 2015												

† Ranked in the *100 Greatest U.S. Coins* (fourth edition), grouped with 1844-O Proof Liberty Head Half Eagles, as a single entry. **d.** While there is only one known example known of this coin, it is possible that other 1840 Proof eagles were made, given that duplicates are known of the quarter eagle and half eagle denominations. **e.** 3 examples are known. **f.** 2 examples are known. **g.** Included in circulation-strike 1843 mintage figure. **h.** 5 examples are known. **i.** 3 or 4 examples are known. **j.** 4 or 5 examples are known.

| 1846-O, 6 Over 5 | 1850, Large Date | 1850, Small Date |

	Mintage	Cert	Avg	%MS	VF-20	EF-40	AU-50	AU-55	AU-58	MS-60	MS-63	MS-65
										PF-63	PF-64	PF-65
1846	20,095	90	47.6	4%	$1,150	$1,350	$4,250	$7,000	$10,000	$20,000		
	Auctions: $4,994, AU-55, September 2014; $4,406, AU-55, September 2014; $8,225, AU-55, January 2014; $3,760, AU-50, June 2015											
1846, Proof (k)	6–8	1	64.0			*(extremely rare)*						
	Auctions: $161,000, PF-64Cam, January 2011											
1846-O, All kinds	81,780											
1846-O		149	45.9	1%	$1,200	$2,000	$3,500	$6,000	$9,000	$13,500		
	Auctions: $2,820, AU-50, January 2014											
1846-O, 6 Over 5		13	55.3	8%	$1,300	$2,250	$4,000	$7,500	$17,500	$35,000		
	Auctions: $3,525, AU-50, January 2014											
1847	862,258	1,340	52.3	5%	$900	$1,000	$1,050	$1,100	$1,650	$3,500	$21,500	
	Auctions: $894, AU-55, June 2015; $823, AU-53, February 2015; $764, AU-50, January 2015; $881, EF-40, July 2015											
1847, Proof	1–2	0	n/a		*(unique, in the Smithsonian's National Numismatic Collection)*							
	Auctions: No auction records available.											
1847-O	571,500	1,068	50.2	2%	$950	$1,050	$1,150	$1,600	$2,500	$6,000	$30,000	
	Auctions: $2,056, AU-58, August 2015; $1,528, AU-55, October 2015; $1,058, AU-50, July 2015; $881, VF-30, January 2015											
1848	145,484	403	51.8	7%	$850	$950	$1,050	$1,350	$1,750	$6,000	$23,500	
	Auctions: $64,625, MS-64, October 2014; $3,760, MS-60, June 2015; $940, AU-53, June 2015; $881, EF-45, January 2015											
1848, Proof (l)	3–5	1	64.0			*(extremely rare)*						
	Auctions: No auction records available.											
1848-O	35,850	182	49.0	4%	$1,500	$3,250	$4,000	$6,500	$11,000	$15,000	$35,000	$95,000
	Auctions: $51,700, MS-64, January 2015; $2,820, MS-60, October 2014; $3,525, AU-50, September 2015; $2,820, AU-50, June 2015											
1849	653,618	1,191	50.7	4%	$850	$1,100	$1,300	$1,400	$1,850	$3,750	$15,000	
	Auctions: $4,467, MS-61, June 2015; $999, AU-55, August 2015; $1,058, EF-45, August 2015; $676, VF-25, October 2015											
1849, Recut 1849 Over 849	(m)	39	49.8	8%				$4,000	$6,000			
	Auctions: $978, EF-40, May 2011											
1849-O	23,900	105	47.8	2%	$1,750	$3,500	$5,500	$9,500	$13,500	$25,000		
	Auctions: $5,875, AU-53, October 2013											
1850, All kinds	291,451											
1850, Large Date		526	50.8	4%	$900	$1,000	$1,100	$1,250	$1,850	$4,500	$27,500	
	Auctions: $3,525, MS-60, September 2015; $1,116, AU-55, February 2015; $1,058, AU-53, August 2015; $940, AU-50, October 2015											
1850, Small Date		145	49.6	5%	$950	$1,200	$1,850	$2,750	$4,500	$8,000	$35,000	
	Auctions: $10,575, MS-61, August 2015; $1,528, AU-53, October 2015; $1,058, EF-45, July 2015; $999, EF-40, February 2015											
1850-O	57,500	208	47.6	1%	$1,350	$2,000	$3,500	$6,500	$11,000	$20,000		
	Auctions: $6,169, AU-58, November 2014; $3,967, AU-55, March 2015; $1,293, VF-35, January 2015; $1,293, VF-30, September 2015											
1851	176,328	344	52.3	6%	$875	$1,000	$1,100	$1,250	$1,850	$4,250	$32,500	
	Auctions: $852, AU-50, September 2014; $881, AU-50, August 2014; $3,819, MS-61, September 2013; $734, VF-30, October 2014											
1851-O	263,000	993	50.9	2%	$1,000	$1,200	$1,750	$2,750	$6,500	$9,500	$32,500	
	Auctions: $18,800, MS-61, January 2015; $2,820, AU-55, January 2015; $1,293, EF-45, August 2015; $705, VF-20, January 2015											
1852	263,106	744	53.0	6%	$875	$1,000	$1,050	$1,250	$1,650	$4,250	$25,000	
	Auctions: $3,995, MS-61, July 2015; $1,146, AU-55, July 2015; $940, AU-50, July 2015; $823, VF-35, February 2015											
1852-O	18,000	101	49.7	2%	$1,650	$2,500	$6,000	$11,000	$27,500	$85,000		
	Auctions: $7,638, AU-55, August 2015; $3,290, AU-53, November 2014; $18,800, AU, February 2014; $12,925, AU-50, November 2016											

k. 4 examples are known. **l.** 2 examples are known. **m.** Included in circulation-strike 1849 mintage figure.

1853, 3 Over 2	**1854-O, Large Date**	**1854-O, Small Date**

	Mintage	Cert	Avg	%MS	VF-20	EF-40	AU-50	AU-55	AU-58	MS-60 / PF-63	MS-63 / PF-64	MS-65 / PF-65
1853, All kinds	201,253											
1853, 3 Over 2		164	52.3	2%	$1,000	$1,500	$2,000	$3,250	$6,500	$15,000		
Auctions: $14,688, MS-61, June 2015; $11,779, MS-60, August 2015; $5,875, AU-58, October 2014; $2,350, AU-55, June 2015												
1853		778	53.8	6%	$875	$1,000	$1,050	$1,150	$1,650	$3,500	$17,000	
Auctions: $34,075, MS-64, October 2014; $3,819, MS-61, November 2014; $999, AU-55, January 2015; $793, AU-53, January 2015												
1853-O	51,000	260	51.1	3%	$1,200	$1,600	$2,250	$4,500	$10,000	$15,000		
Auctions: $16,450, MS-61, November 2014; $9,400, MS-60, June 2015; $6,463, AU-58, October 2014; $881, AU-50, January 2015												
1853-O, Proof (n)	*1*	1	61.0									
Auctions: No auction records available.												
1854	54,250	296	52.7	4%	$900	$1,050	$1,250	$1,650	$2,750	$6,500	$27,500	
Auctions: $2,350, AU-58, September 2015; $2,115, AU-58, August 2015; $1,410, AU-55, June 2015; $1,293, AU-55, May 2015												
1854, Proof (o)	*unknown*	1	55.0									
Auctions: No auction records available.												
1854-O, Large Date (p)	52,500	161	53.7	9%	$1,150	$1,350	$2,000	$3,250	$6,000	$10,500		
Auctions: $10,869, MS-60, August 2013; $1,998, AU-53, November 2014; $2,585, EF-40, September 2015												
1854-O, Small Date (q)	(r)	116	53.1	1%	$1,150	$1,500	$2,250	$3,500	$4,750	$11,500		
Auctions: $1,821, AU-55, August 2013												
1854-S	123,826	498	50.4	2%	$1,150	$1,400	$2,000	$3,250	$6,500	$12,500		
Auctions: $4,935, AU-58, June 2015; $3,290, AU-55, June 2015; $1,998, AU-53, January 2015; $1,293, AU-50, August 2015												
1855	121,701	629	54.3	11%	$900	$1,100	$1,200	$1,350	$1,850	$4,750	$17,500	
Auctions: $7,115, MS-62, September 2015; $2,233, AU-58, August 2015; $1,058, AU-53, August 2015; $881, EF-45, January 2015												
1855, Proof (s)	*unknown*	0	n/a									
Auctions: No auction records available.												
1855-O	18,000	110	49.3	0%	$1,250	$3,500	$5,500	$10,000	$20,000	$27,500		
Auctions: $17,625, AU-58, January 2014												
1855-S	9,000	32	49.9	0%	$2,750	$3,500	$7,000	$11,000	$22,500			
Auctions: $17,625, AU-58, March 2014												
1856	60,490	344	53.9	11%	$900	$1,000	$1,150	$1,250	$1,500	$4,000	$15,000	
Auctions: $3,995, MS-61, January 2015; $2,242, AU-58, January 2015; $881, AU-53, February 2015; $793, EF-45, February 2015												
1856, Proof (s)	*unknown*	0	n/a									
Auctions: No auction records available.												
1856-O	14,500	114	50.0	4%	$1,350	$2,500	$4,500	$7,000	$12,500	$27,500		
Auctions: $10,869, AU-58, September 2016; $4,406, AU-55, January 2014; $4,700, AU-53, August 2016												
1856-S	68,000	279	50.3	1%	$900	$1,150	$1,500	$2,750	$4,750	$11,500	$27,500	
Auctions: $9,988, MS-61, April 2014; $3,290, AU-58, November 2014; $1,763, AU-55, October 2015; $1,116, AU-53, June 2015												

n. The 1853-O Proof listed here is not a Proof from a technical standpoint. This unique coin has in the past been called a presentation piece and a branch-mint Proof. "Although the piece does not have the same convincing texture as the 1844-O Proof eagle, it is clearly different from the regular-issue eagles found for the year and mint" (*Encyclopedia of U.S. Gold Coins, 1795–1933,* second edition).
o. According to Walter Breen, in July 1854 a set of Proof coins was given by the United States to representatives of the sovereign German city of Bremen. Various Proof 1854 gold dollars, quarter eagles, and three-dollar gold pieces have come to light, along with a single gold eagle. **p.** The Large Date variety was made in error, when the diesinker used a date punch for a silver dollar on the much smaller ten-dollar die. **q.** The Small Date variety is scarce in AU. Only 3 or 4 MS examples are known, none finer than MS-60.
r. Included in 1854-O, Large Date, mintage figure. **s.** No Proof 1855 or 1856 eagles have been confirmed, but Wayte Raymond claimed to have seen one of each some time prior to 1949.

	Mintage	Cert	Avg	%MS	VF-20	EF-40	AU-50	AU-55	AU-58	MS-60	MS-63	MS-65
										PF-63	PF-64	PF-65
1857	16,606	128	52.0	6%	$900	$1,000	$1,650	$3,000	$5,500	$12,000		
	Auctions: $4,406, AU-58, April 2014; $1,293, EF-45, September 2014											
1857, Proof	2–3	1	66.0									
	Auctions: No auction records available.											
1857-O	5,500	60	51.7	0%	$2,500	$4,500	$8,500	$12,500	$25,000	—		
	Auctions: $22,325, AU-58, August 2014; $8,225, AU-55, February 2014											
1857-S	26,000	71	47.5	3%	$1,350	$1,850	$2,500	$4,500	$7,500	$11,000	$27,500	
	Auctions: $8,225, AU-58, July 2014; $5,875, AU-55, January 2015; $3,378, EF-45, August 2014; $4,465, EF-40, September 2015											
1858 (t)	2,521	36	49.9	8%	$5,500	$7,500	$12,500	$17,500	$25,000	$35,000		
	Auctions: $15,275, AU-53, February 2014											
1858, Proof (u)	4–6	2	64.0		*(extremely rare)*							
	Auctions: No auction records available.											
1858-O	20,000	193	51.4	4%	$1,250	$1,600	$2,750	$3,750	$7,000	$11,000	$35,000	
	Auctions: $6,463, AU-58, January 2015; $2,585, AU-55, January 2015; $1,293, AU-50, October 2015; $1,645, EF-45, January 2015											
1858-S	11,800	51	51.2	0%	$1,600	$3,250	$7,000	$12,000	$20,000			
	Auctions: $15,275, AU-58, April 2013; $3,055, EF-45, November 2014; $2,820, EF-40, October 2015; $2,115, EF-40, November 2014											
1859	16,013	169	51.9	6%	$1,000	$1,250	$1,500	$2,250	$4,000	$17,500	$70,000	
	Auctions: $41,125, MS-62, November 2014; $47,000, MS-62, April 2014; $1,175, EF-45, July 2015; $734, VF-20, January 2015											
1859, Proof	80	5	64.6							$75,000	$150,000	$200,000
	Auctions: No auction records available.											
1859-O	2,300	22	51.5	5%	$6,000	$12,500	$25,000	$30,000	$50,000			
	Auctions: $28,200, AU-50, December 2013											
1859-S	7,000	37	43.6	3%	$3,000	$5,000	$18,500	$22,500	$27,500	$50,000		
	Auctions: $14,100, AU-53, October 2014; $3,525, AU-50, June 2015; $6,463, EF-45, October 2015; $3,290, EF-40, August 2014											
1860	15,055	146	51.9	8%	$900	$1,100	$1,750	$2,500	$3,000	$7,500	$25,000	
	Auctions: $70,500, MS-64, February 2013; $14,100, MS-62, June 2015; $1,645, AU-50, September 2014; $1,293, EF-45, January 2015											
1860, Proof	50	5	63.6							$50,000	$100,000	$135,000
	Auctions: $142,175, PF-64DCam, April 2014											
1860-O	11,100	126	51.4	6%	$1,450	$2,750	$4,000	$6,000	$8,000	$17,500		
	Auctions: $8,814, AU-About Uncirculated, March 2014											
1860-S	5,000	21	48.0	10%	$4,750	$12,500	$17,500	$27,500	$35,000	$50,000		
	Auctions: $28,200, AU-55, March 2014; $25,850, AU-55, May 2016; $9,400, VF-35, August 2016; $7,050, VF-30, September 2016											
1861	113,164	751	54.9	13%	$925	$1,050	$1,500	$2,500	$4,000	$6,500	$20,000	
	Auctions: $8,225, MS-62, August 2015; $7,652, MS-62, January 2015; $4,113, AU-58, July 2014; $940, AU-50, January 2015											
1861, Proof	69	6	64.2							$45,000	$85,000	$125,000
	Auctions: $129,250, PF-64Cam, March 2013											
1861-S	15,500	75	51.1	1%	$4,000	$8,500	$12,500	$17,500	$25,000	$47,500		
	Auctions: $25,850, AU-58, March 2014; $9,400, AU-53, August 2015; $7,638, AU-53, September 2014; $6,463, EF-40, June 2015											
1862	10,960	88	51.4	13%	$1,000	$2,250	$5,500	$6,500	$12,000	$18,500	$37,500	
	Auctions: $18,800, MS-61, October 2015; $7,050, AU-55, January 2015; $6,169, AU-53, July 2015; $4,935, AU-50, September 2015											
1862, Proof	35	5	64.4							$42,500	$85,000	$125,000
	Auctions: $152,750, PF-65DCam, August 2013											
1862-S	12,500	46	45.8	0%	$2,500	$5,000	$10,000	$22,500	$35,000	$100,000		
	Auctions: $21,150, AU-58, October 2014; $5,581, EF-35, February 2014											
1863	1,218	16	52.0	19%	$12,500	$32,500	$45,000	$60,000	$70,000	$85,000	—	
	Auctions: $49,938, AU-53, January 2014; $42,300, EF-45, September 2016; $35,250, EF-45, August 2016											
1863, Proof	30	12	64.2							$42,500	$85,000	$125,000
	Auctions: $299,000, PF-65DCam, August 2011											
1863-S	10,000	32	46.0	3%	$5,500	$13,000	$20,000	$32,500	$45,000	$100,000		
	Auctions: $32,900, AU-53, February 2014; $12,925, AU-50, October 2015; $15,275, EF-45, October 2014; $5,875, F-12, November 2014											

t. Beware of fraudulently removed mintmark. **u.** 4 or 5 examples are known.

**1865-S, 865
Over Inverted 186**

	Mintage	Cert	Avg	%MS	VF-20	EF-40	AU-50	AU-55	AU-58	MS-60	MS-63	MS-65
										PF-63	PF-64	PF-65
1864	3,530	24	50.0	17%	$6,500	$10,000	$22,500	$35,000	$50,000	$75,000		
Auctions: $41,125, AU-55, October 2014; $28,200, AU-55, January 2014												
1864, Proof	50	17	63.8							$42,500	$85,000	$125,000
Auctions: $138,000, PF-64UCam, October 2011												
1864-S	2,500	7	43.9	0%	$45,000	$85,000	$145,000	$175,000				
Auctions: $146,875, AU-53, March 2014												
1865	3,980	31	50.5	6%	$4,500	$9,000	$15,000	$20,000	$27,500	$47,500	$90,000	
Auctions: $15,275, AU-53, October 2014; $18,800, AU-53, January 2014; $13,513, AU-50, October 2014; $12,925, AU-50, August 2015												
1865, Proof	25	13	64.1							$42,500	$85,000	$125,000
Auctions: $528,750, PF, August 2013												
1865-S, All kinds	16,700											
1865-S		32	40.2	3%	$6,500	$12,500	$19,500	$27,500	$45,000	$85,000		
Auctions: $5,170, VF-25, September 2016; $4,230, VF-20, September 2016; $6,756, F-12, February 2013												
1865-S, 865 Over Inverted 186		39	43.2	3%	$7,500	$10,000	$17,500	$25,000	$35,000	$45,000		
Auctions: $20,563, AU-55, January 2015; $27,025, AU-53, March 2014; $9,400, EF-45, October 2015; $1,880, VG-8, August 2014												
1866-S, No Motto	8,500	33	47.1	3%	$5,000	$15,000	$20,000	$25,000	$30,000	$50,000		
Auctions: $14,950, EF-45, August 2011												
1866, With Motto	3,750	46	49.5	13%	$1,500	$3,000	$5,000	$10,000	$25,000	$42,500		
Auctions: $32,900, MS-61, January 2015; $14,100, AU-55, September 2013; $4,054, AU-50, August 2015; $1,763, EF-40, January 2015												
1866, Proof	30	8	64.1							$35,000	$55,000	$85,000
Auctions: $66,125, PF-64UCam+H, January 2012												
1866-S, With Motto	11,500	40	49.0	0%	$2,500	$4,500	$7,250	$10,000	$17,500	$30,000		
Auctions: $15,275, AU-58, March 2014; $9,988, AU-55, August 2014; $4,230, EF-45, July 2015; $4,230, VF-35, January 2015												
1867	3,090	61	49.3	3%	$2,000	$3,000	$6,500	$11,500	$22,500	$40,000		
Auctions: $30,550, AU-58, August 2013												
1867, Proof	50	4	64.8							$35,000	$55,000	$85,000
Auctions: $64,625, PF-65Cam, August 2014; $64,625, PF-64Cam+, February 2015; $54,344, PF-64Cam, October 2014												
1867-S	9,000	37	47.5	0%	$4,000	$6,500	$9,000	$15,000	$40,000			
Auctions: $12,925, AU-55, July 2016; $9,988, AU-53, June 2013; $6,463, AU-50, September 2016												
1868	10,630	158	50.9	5%	$850	$1,250	$1,850	$3,500	$8,000	$17,500		
Auctions: $5,875, AU-58, February 2015; $4,700, AU-58, July 2015; $1,645, AU-50, January 2015; $2,350, EF-45, September 2015												
1868, Proof	25	4	64.8							$35,000	$55,000	$85,000
Auctions: $24,150, PF-62Cam, June 2005												
1868-S	13,500	71	48.3	0%	$1,750	$2,500	$4,000	$10,000	$17,500			
Auctions: $5,875, AU-58, August 2014; $4,700, AU-55, July 2015; $1,469, AU-50, August 2015; $2,115, EF-40, August 2014												
1869	1,830	39	50.6	8%	$1,650	$4,000	$5,500	$11,500	$18,500	$35,000		
Auctions: $14,100, AU-58, August 2013												
1869, Proof	25	8	63.8							$35,000	$55,000	$80,000
Auctions: $161,000, PF-67UCam+H, February 2012												
1869-S	6,430	37	47.2	3%	$2,200	$3,500	$6,000	$11,000	$20,000	$27,500		
Auctions: $16,450, AU-58, January 2015; $11,163, AU-55, August 2015; $7,638, AU-55, January 2015; $1,528, EF-40, October 2015												

	Mintage	Cert	Avg	%MS	VF-20	EF-40	AU-50	AU-55	AU-58	MS-60	MS-63	MS-65
										PF-63	PF-64	PF-65
1870	3,990	68	49.0	1%	$1,100	$1,750	$3,000	$10,000	$15,000	$25,000		
Auctions: $10,575, AU-55, January 2014												
1870, Proof	35	4	64.5							$35,000	$55,000	$80,000
Auctions: $97,750, PF-65UCam, January 2010												
1870-CC	5,908	33	41.7	0%	$40,000	$60,000	$85,000	$150,000	$185,000			
Auctions: $135,125, AU-55, March 2014; $36,719, VF-35, August 2014; $28,200, VG-10, August 2015												
1870-S	8,000	60	42.0	0%	$1,650	$4,000	$5,500	$11,000	$18,500	$32,500		
Auctions: $12,925, AU-58, March 2014												
1871	1,790	49	50.7	0%	$1,400	$3,000	$5,500	$8,500	$15,000	$45,000		
Auctions: $15,275, AU-58, September 2013; $9,400, AU-55, March 2015; $4,583, AU-50, July 2015; $3,290, EF-40, August 2014												
1871, Proof	30	5	63.2							$35,000	$55,000	$80,000
Auctions: $76,375, PF-64DCam, August 2013												
1871-CC	8,085	71	46.1	3%	$5,500	$15,000	$22,500	$32,500	$45,000	$75,000		
Auctions: $35,250, AU-58, October 2014; $14,100, AU-53, January 2015; $5,170, AU-50, June 2015; $19,975, EF-45, August 2016												
1871-S	16,500	84	42.8	0%	$1,500	$2,250	$4,500	$8,250	$12,500			
Auctions: $10,281, AU-58, March 2014; $2,115, AU-50, July 2014; $1,116, AU-50, October 2015; $2,231, EF-45, February 2015												
1872	1,620	21	51.0	5%	$2,250	$4,250	$9,000	$11,000	$15,000	$17,500		
Auctions: $38,188, AU-58, August 2014; $16,450, AU-55, August 2015; $16,450, AU-55, February 2015; $6,169, EF-45, July 2015												
1872, Proof	30	7	64.7							$35,000	$55,000	$80,000
Auctions: $48,875, PF-64DCam, June 2012												
1872-CC	4,600	54	44.5	2%	$8,500	$15,000	$27,500	$42,500	$62,500			
Auctions: $47,000, AU, February 2014, $9,988, EF-40, August 2014												
1872-S	17,300	140	47.3	1%	$975	$1,500	$2,000	$4,250	$8,500	$25,000		
Auctions: $8,225, AU-58, October 2014; $7,050, AU-58, March 2014; $5,640, AU-58, January 2015; $1,645, EF-45, July 2015												
1873	800	21	50.0	0%	$10,000	$20,000	$35,000	$47,500	$65,000	$75,000		
Auctions: $64,625, AU-58, May 2016: $55,813, AU-55, January 2014; $30,550, AU-53, September 2016; $21,738, AU-53, January 2015												
1873, Proof	25	9	63.7							$37,500	$65,000	$85,000
Auctions: $74,750, PF-65Cam+, February 2012												
1873-CC	4,543	39	42.1	0%	$12,500	$25,000	$50,000	$75,000	$100,000			
Auctions: $58,750, AU-53, March 2014; $44,650, AU-50, August 2016												
1873-S	12,000	83	42.8	0%	$1,250	$2,500	$4,250	$7,000	$13,500	$27,500		
Auctions: $4,700, AU-53, March 2013												
1874	53,140	347	56.1	21%	$750	$850	$900	$925	$1,000	$1,650	$10,000	$45,000
Auctions: $1,410, MS-61, September 2014; $1,058, AU-58, August 2015; $940, AU-58, September 2015; $999, AU-50, October 2014												
1874, Proof	20	1	62.0							$35,000	$65,000	$85,000
Auctions: $29,500, PF-64Cam, September 2006												
1874-CC	16,767	154	42.3	1%	$3,500	$6,000	$12,500	$20,000	$40,000	$70,000	$200,000	
Auctions: $30,550, AU-58, May 2013; $3,643, VF-35, June 2015; $2,585, F-15, January 2015; $1,410, VG-8, February 2015												
1874-S	10,000	96	42.3	0%	$1,500	$2,250	$4,750	$8,000	$17,500			
Auctions: $12,338, AU-58, July 2014; $2,644, EF-45, August 2014; $940, VF-20, February 2015												
1875	100	7	46.4	0%	$125,000	$165,000	$300,000	$450,000				
Auctions: $211,500, AU-50, February 2014												
1875, Proof	20	4	65.5							$155,000	$200,000	$275,000
Auctions: $164,500, PF-50, January 2014												
1875-CC	7,715	73	39.4	3%	$6,000	$10,000	$17,500	$35,000	$75,000	$100,000	$175,000	
Auctions: $8,225, EF-45, February 2014												

	Mintage	Cert	Avg	%MS	VF-20	EF-40	AU-50	AU-55	AU-58	MS-60 PF-63	MS-63 PF-64	MS-65 PF-65
1876	687	20	51.1	5%	$5,000	$10,000	$27,500	$35,000	$55,000	$80,000		
	Auctions: $70,500, AU-58, January 2015; $28,200, AU-55, June 2015; $22,325, AU-53, August 2015; $18,800, AU-53, July 2014											
1876, Proof	45	14	63.7							$32,500	$45,000	$75,000
	Auctions: $100,625, PF-65Cam, April 2011											
1876-CC	4,696	95	41.7	0%	$5,500	$13,500	$22,500	$35,000	$60,000			
	Auctions: $14,100, AU-50, October 2013											
1876-S	5,000	48	45.0	0%	$2,000	$4,500	$8,500	$20,000	$35,000			
	Auctions: $22,325, AU-55, October 2013											
1877	797	30	54.0	0%	$4,250	$7,000	$10,000	$13,500	$17,500	$55,000		
	Auctions: $64,625, MS-61, March 2015; $11,163, AU-55, July 2014; $11,163, AU-55, January 2014; $3,290, EF-40, February 2015											
1877, Proof	20	3	64.7							$35,000	$45,000	$75,000
	Auctions: $39,100, PF-64Cam, April 2002											
1877-CC	3,332	43	41.5	0%	$8,500	$12,500	$25,000	$50,000	$100,000			
	Auctions: $10,575, EF-45, April 2014											
1877-S	17,000	167	46.7	2%	$850	$1,350	$2,000	$4,500	$11,000	$30,000		
	Auctions: $3,290, AU-55, September 2015; $881, AU-50, September 2015; $1,116, EF-45, September 2015; $1,116, EF-45, June 2015											
1878	73,780	361	57.9	43%	$700	$715	$725	$750	$850	$975	$5,500	
	Auctions: $1,410, MS-62, July 2015; $881, MS-61, September 2015; $852, MS-61, September 2015; $823, MS-61, January 2015											
1878, Proof	20	4	63.8							$27,500	$45,000	$75,000
	Auctions: $25,300, PF-63, August 2011											
1878-CC	3,244	38	47.9	3%	$7,500	$20,000	$40,000	$65,000	$100,000	$135,000		
	Auctions: $64,625, AU-55, September 2016: $28,200, AU-55, March 2014; $19,388, AU-50, August 2016											
1878-S	26,100	221	47.8	2%	$850	$950	$1,350	$2,000	$3,500	$11,500	$25,000	
	Auctions: $2,938, AU-58, October 2015; $1,410, AU-55, February 2015; $1,293, AU-50, October 2015; $646, EF-40, September 2014											
1879	384,740	928	58.8	53%	$700	$715	$725	$775	$850	$900	$3,000	
	Auctions: $2,585, MS-63, July 2015; $940, MS-61, August 2015; $711, MS-60, October 2015; $646, AU-58, January 2015											
1879, Proof	30	6	63.2							$25,000	$37,500	$65,000
	Auctions: $52,875, PF-65Cam, February 2013											
1879-CC	1,762	39	43.7	3%	$17,500	$25,000	$40,000	$55,000	$75,000			
	Auctions: $41,125, AU-50, March 2014											
1879-O	1,500	48	49.4	4%	$10,000	$17,500	$25,000	$35,000	$60,000	$85,000		
	Auctions: $88,125, MS-61, June 2014; $23,500, EF-45, August 2016; $14,688, VF-30, September 2016											
1879-S	224,000	466	56.9	25%	$700	$715	$725	$800	$850	$1,200	$6,000	
	Auctions: $1,410, MS-62, January 2015; $881, MS-60, June 2015; $999, AU-58, August 2015; $705, AU-55, October 2015											
1880	1,644,840	2,153	59.9	81%	$700	$715	$725	$800	$825	$900	$1,500	
	Auctions: $19,975, MS-65, August 2013; $764, MS-61, June 2015; $705, VF-35, February 2015; $646, AG-3, January 2015											
1880, Proof	36	5	64.2							$22,500	$35,000	$60,000
	Auctions: $32,200, PF-64, October 1999											
1880-CC	11,190	187	50.6	6%	$2,000	$2,750	$4,000	$6,500	$10,000	$37,500		
	Auctions: $2,761, AU-53, August 2013; $1,175, EF-40, July 2014											
1880-O	9,200	186	51.9	5%	$1,500	$2,500	$4,250	$5,500	$10,500	$20,000		
	Auctions: $3,760, AU-55, August 2015; $4,230, AU-50, September 2015; $2,233, AU-50, August 2015; $4,113, EF-40, June 2014											
1880-S	506,250	1,036	60.2	78%	$700	$715	$725	$775	$825	$900	$2,000	
	Auctions: $4,465, MS-64, October 2015; $1,293, MS-63, July 2015; $1,175, MS-62, August 2015; $764, MS-61, September 2015											
1881	3,877,220	12,760	60.9	94%	$700	$715	$725	$775	$800	$850	$1,000	$15,000
	Auctions: $2,115, MS-64, February 2015; $999, MS-63, January 2015; $705, MS-62, October 2014; $676, MS-61, January 2015											
1881, Proof	40	5	65.2							$22,500	$32,500	$55,000
	Auctions: $56,063, PF-65, October 2011											
1881-CC	24,015	344	52.3	13%	$1,750	$2,500	$3,500	$4,500	$5,000	$8,500		
	Auctions: $12,925, MS-62, April 2013; $4,113, AU-58, January 2015; $1,116, AU-50, July 2014; $1,763, EF-40, January 2015											
1881-O	8,350	177	52.1	7%	$1,150	$1,500	$3,000	$5,000	$7,000	$15,000		
	Auctions: $12,338, MS-60, January 2014											
1881-S	970,000	2,556	60.7	91%	$700	$715	$725	$750	$800	$850	$1,500	
	Auctions: $2,585, MS-63, January 2015; $1,763, MS-63, October 2015; $764, MS-62, January 2015; $734, MS-62, June 2015											

	Mintage	Cert	Avg	%MS	VF-20	EF-40	AU-50	AU-55	AU-58	MS-60	MS-63	MS-65
										PF-63	PF-64	PF-65
1882	2,324,440	13,788	61.2	96%	$700	$715	$725	$750	$800	$850	$1,000	
	Auctions: $1,175, MS-63, August 2015; $823, MS-62, August 2015; $881, MS-61, June 2015; $777, MS-61, September 2015											
1882, Proof	40	9	64.2							$20,000	$32,500	$55,000
	Auctions: $43,125, PF-65Cam, October 2009											
1882-CC	6,764	144	52.4	2%	$2,000	$3,500	$5,500	$11,500	$22,500	$35,000		
	Auctions: $25,850, MS-60, July 2014; $7,344, AU-55, February 2015; $4,935, EF-45, July 2015; $1,645, EF-40, January 2015											
1882-O	10,820	195	52.5	10%	$1,150	$1,500	$2,500	$4,500	$7,500	$12,500	$45,000	
	Auctions: $30,550, MS-62, January 2014; $2,389, AU-53, September 2014; $1,410, VF-35, September 2015											
1882-S	132,000	343	60.6	86%	$700	$715	$725	$750	$800	$850	$2,500	
	Auctions: $1,880, MS-63, January 2015; $1,293, MS-62, October 2015; $1,234, MS-62, August 2015; $1,087, MS-62, October 2015											
1883	208,700	1,431	61.2	95%	$700	$715	$725	$750	$800	$850	$1,350	
	Auctions: $3,995, MS-64, January 2015; $1,880, MS-63, October 2015; $1,293, MS-63, August 2015; $881, MS-62, July 2015											
1883, Proof	40	9	64.3							$20,000	$32,500	$55,000
	Auctions: $8,813, PF-60, July 2014											
1883-CC	12,000	344	49.3	4%	$1,650	$2,500	$4,500	$8,500	$18,500	$37,500		
	Auctions: $41,125, MS-61, October 2014; $3,055, AU-50, October 2015; $2,820, EF-40, June 2015; $1,586, VF-20, January 2015											
1883-O	800	20	52.2	5%	$12,500	$27,500	$55,000	$80,000	$100,000	$125,000		
	Auctions: $82,250, AU-58, August 2014; $70,500, AU-58, January 2015; $70,500, AU-55, February 2014; $47,000, AU-50, October 2014											
1883-S	38,000	138	56.0	40%	$700	$715	$725	$750	$800	$1,150	$8,500	
	Auctions: $11,163, MS-63, February 2013; $2,056, MS-62, January 2015; $1,293, MS-61, August 2015; $823, AU-58, November 2014											
1884	76,860	354	58.3	44%	$700	$715	$725	$750	$800	$950	$4,250	
	Auctions: $846, MS-61, July 2014; $823, AU-55, February 2014											
1884, Proof	45	7	64.6							$20,000	$32,500	$55,000
	Auctions: $37,375, PF-64DCam, March 2012											
1884-CC	9,925	174	50.7	6%	$1,750	$3,000	$5,500	$7,500	$13,500	$17,500	$65,000	
	Auctions: $17,625, AU-58, September 2016: $17,625, AU-58, February 2014; $9,988, AU-58, August 2016; $3,760, AU-55, August 2015											
1884-S	124,250	538	59.4	67%	$700	$715	$725	$750	$800	$850	$4,500	
	Auctions: $4,994, MS-63, July 2014; $1,175, MS-62, September 2015; $1,116, MS-62, September 2015; $1,175, MS-61, October 2015											
1885	253,462	655	60.5	84%	$700	$715	$725	$750	$800	$850	$2,000	$20,000
	Auctions: $1,880, MS-63, October 2013; $1,528, MS-63, November 2014; $1,410, MS-63, July 2015; $823, MS-60, August 2014											
1885, Proof	65	12	63.5							$20,000	$32,500	$52,500
	Auctions: $57,500, PF-66UCam, January 2012											
1885-S	228,000	849	60.8	87%	$700	$715	$725	$750	$800	$850	$1,150	
	Auctions: $5,875, MS-64, August 2014; $4,406, MS-63, August 2013; $705, MS-62, October 2014; $881, MS-62, July 2014											
1886	236,100	639	59.3	64%	$700	$715	$725	$750	$800	$850	$2,000	
	Auctions: $1,998, MS-63, June 2015; $764, MS-61, October 2015; $823, AU-58, June 2015; $564, VF-30, October 2015											
1886, Proof	60	18	62.7							$18,500	$32,500	$52,500
	Auctions: $39,656, PF-64DCam, April 2014											
1886-S	826,000	3,054	61.3	95%	$700	$715	$725	$750	$800	$850	$1,000	
	Auctions: $1,116, MS-63, January 2015; $999, MS-63, January 2015; $969, MS-63, May 2015; $852, MS-63, July 2015											
1887	53,600	280	57.8	43%	$700	$715	$725	$750	$800	$1,000	$4,500	
	Auctions: $4,465, MS-63, June 2015; $1,351, MS-62, February 2015; $881, MS-61, January 2015; $999, AU-58, August 2015											
1887, Proof	80	17	63.9							$18,500	$32,500	$52,500
	Auctions: $64,625, PF-65DCam, April 2014											
1887-S	817,000	1,526	60.9	90%	$700	$715	$725	$750	$800	$850	$1,500	
	Auctions: $3,819, MS-64, January 2015; $1,293, MS-63, January 2015; $1,234, MS-63, February 2015; $1,116, MS-63, January 2015											
1888	132,921	472	58.8	57%	$700	$715	$725	$750	$800	$850	$3,250	
	Auctions: $2,820, MS-63, January 2015; $1,175, MS-62, February 2015; $1,028, MS-62, August 2015; $940, MS-61, September 2015											
1888, Proof	75	12	64.1							$18,500	$32,500	$52,500
	Auctions: $17,250, PF-63DCam, February 2009											
1888-O	21,335	643	60.2	80%	$750	$800	$850	$1,000	$1,100	$1,250	$7,500	
	Auctions: $21,150, MS-64, August 2013; $999, MS-62, October 2014; $1,293, MS-61, July 2014; $734, MS-60, January 2015											
1888-S	648,700	1,930	60.8	90%	$700	$715	$725	$750	$800	$850	$1,200	
	Auctions: $1,763, MS-63, August 2015; $1,528, MS-63, July 2015; $881, MS-62, January 2015; $764, AU-58, January 2015											

1889-S, Repunched Mintmark
FS-G10-1889S-501.

	Mintage	Cert	Avg	%MS	VF-20	EF-40	AU-50	AU-55	AU-58	MS-60	MS-63	MS-65
										PF-63	PF-64	PF-65
1889	4,440	114	58.7	54%	$900	$925	$950	$1,350	$2,500	$4,250	$10,000	
	Auctions: $4,935, MS-62, June 2015; $3,995, MS-61, August 2015; $1,998, AU-58, June 2015; $1,528, AU-50, January 2015											
1889, Proof	45	4	64.3							$18,000	$32,500	$52,500
	Auctions: $23,500, PF-64Cam, August 2014; $4,994, PF-60, April 2013											
1889-S	425,400	1,284	60.8	89%	$700	$715	$725	$750	$800	$850	$1,250	
	Auctions: $999, MS-63, January 2015; $764, MS-62, February 2015; $823, MS-61, July 2015; $676, AU-55, June 2015											
1889-S, Repunched Mintmark	(v)	1	45.0	0%				$900	$975	$1,025	$1,850	
	Auctions: $1,035, MS-63, August 2006											
1890	57,980	443	59.0	63%	$700	$715	$725	$750	$800	$900	$3,500	$15,000
	Auctions: $2,820, MS-63, July 2014; $1,058, MS-62, November 2014; $1,116, MS-62, September 2014; $764, MS-60, October 2015											
1890, Proof	63	23	63.8							$16,500	$25,000	$47,500
	Auctions: $29,900, PF-64UCam, January 2012											
1890-CC	17,500	388	57.8	39%	$1,250	$1,550	$2,250	$2,750	$3,750	$4,500	$20,000	
	Auctions: $15,863, MS-63, August 2016; $9,400, MS-62, August 2016; $7,050, MS-62, August 2015; $4,935, MS-61, June 2015											
1891	91,820	720	61.2	95%	$700	$715	$725	$750	$800	$900	$2,500	
	Auctions: $7,344, MS-64, November 2013; $1,998, MS-63, August 2014; $1,410, MS-62, July 2014; $716, MS-62, October 2015											
1891, Proof	48	20	64.2							$16,500	$25,000	$47,500
	Auctions: $54,625, PF-65Cam, February 2012											
1891-CC	103,732	2,542	59.4	58%	$1,250	$1,450	$1,650	$2,250	$2,650	$2,850	$8,500	
	Auctions: $14,688, MS-64, June 2015; $2,115, MS-61, July 2015; $1,763, AU-55, August 2015; $1,410, AU-50, August 2015											
1892	797,480	8,644	61.4	98%	$700	$715	$725	$750	$800	$850	$1,000	$7,500
	Auctions: $6,756, MS-65, October 2013; $1,028, MS-63, July 2014; $652, MS-62, October 2014; $852, MS-62, August 2014											
1892, Proof	72	12	63.7							$16,500	$25,000	$47,500
	Auctions: $4,406, PF-55, January 2014											
1892-CC	40,000	497	53.5	7%	$1,250	$1,500	$2,000	$2,750	$3,500	$5,500	$35,000	
	Auctions: $1,763, AU-53, August 2014; $1,528, EF-45, February 2015; $823, EF-40, October 2015; $1,528, VF-35, January 2015											
1892-O	28,688	712	60.2	79%	$750	$800	$850	$900	$1,000	$1,300	$8,000	
	Auctions: $1,998, MS-62, August 2015; $1,763, MS-62, September 2015; $1,410, MS-60, July 2015; $764, AU-55, January 2015											
1892-S	115,500	315	59.1	65%	$700	$715	$725	$750	$950	$1,050	$2,000	
	Auctions: $940, MS-62, July 2015; $852, MS-62, January 2015; $764, MS-61, January 2015; $764, AU-58, January 2015											
1893	1,840,840	35,775	61.8	99%	$700	$715	$725	$750	$800	$850	$950	$6,500
	Auctions: $1,645, MS-64, August 2015; $1,528, MS-63, July 2015; $734, MS-62, August 2015; $705, MS-61, June 2015											
1893, Proof	55	16	63.2							$16,500	$25,000	$47,500
	Auctions: $30,550, PF-64DCam, August 2014; $58,750, PF, March 2014											
1893-CC	14,000	243	52.2	6%	$1,650	$2,000	$3,500	$5,500	$9,500	$20,000	—	
	Auctions: $18,800, MS-61, January 2014; $6,463, AU-58, July 2015; $4,465, AU-55, September 2015; $4,465, AU-55, July 2015											
1893-O	17,000	448	59.7	70%	$725	$800	$850	$975	$1,000	$1,350	$5,000	
	Auctions: $4,465, MS-63, June 2015; $1,293, MS-61, September 2014; $4,406, AU-58, September 2013; $823, AU-53, January 2015											
1893-S	141,350	633	60.2	79%	$700	$715	$725	$750	$800	$850	$2,000	
	Auctions: $999, MS-62, July 2015; $940, MS-62, July 2015; $881, MS-62, February 2015; $823, MS-62, March 2015											

v. Included in 1889-S mintage figure.

	Mintage	Cert	Avg	%MS	VF-20	EF-40	AU-50	AU-55	AU-58	MS-60	MS-63	MS-65
										PF-63	PF-64	PF-65
1894	2,470,735	37,487	61.7	99%	$700	$715	$725	$750	$800	$850	$1,000	$10,000
	Auctions: $5,942, MS-65, October 2015; $1,528, MS-64, October 2015; $705, MS-62, June 2015; $650, MS-60, January 2015											
1894, Proof	43	11	64.1							$16,500	$25,000	$47,500
	Auctions: $105,750, PF-65, January 2014											
1894-O	107,500	900	57.4	35%	$750	$800	$850	$975	$1,000	$1,250	$5,500	
	Auctions: $1,410, MS-61, July 2015; $940, AU-58, August 2015; $823, AU-53, June 2015; $705, AU-50, January 2015											
1894-S	25,000	160	53.6	13%	$750	$775	$950	$1,100	$1,800	$3,500		
	Auctions: $9,988, MS-61, March 2014; $1,058, AU-55, September 2014; $1,293, AU-50, September 2015											
1895	567,770	11,493	61.7	99%	$700	$715	$725	$750	$800	$850	$1,000	$11,000
	Auctions: $9,400, MS-65, June 2015; $1,410, MS-64, January 2015; $1,058, MS-63, November 2015; $764, AU-58, June 2015											
1895, Proof	56	18	63.8							$16,000	$25,000	$47,500
	Auctions: $51,750, PF-65UCam, January 2012											
1895-O	98,000	721	58.8	49%	$725	$775	$850	$975	$1,000	$1,200	$6,500	
	Auctions: $9,400, MS-63, February 2013; $940, AU-55, July 2015; $764, AU-55, January 2015; $705, EF-45, January 2015											
1895-S	49,000	226	52.6	9%	$850	$925	$975	$1,000	$1,150	$2,000	$8,000	
	Auctions: $5,875, MS-62, October 2014; $4,700, MS-62, November 2014; $966, AU-55, May 2015; $846, AU-55, September 2014											
1896	76,270	1,454	61.7	98%	$700	$715	$725	$750	$800	$850	$1,200	$12,000
	Auctions: $1,293, MS-63, July 2015; $911, MS-63, May 2015; $881, MS-62, July 2015; $823, MS-62, October 2015											
1896, Proof	78	18	64.1							$16,000	$25,000	$47,500
	Auctions: $89,125, PF-66DCam, April 2012; $70,500, PF-66, September 2014											
1896-S	123,750	468	54.1	14%	$725	$750	$775	$850	$900	$1,850	$8,000	
	Auctions: $2,233, MS-62, January 2015; $823, AU-55, September 2015; $617, AU-50, October 2015; $705, EF-45, June 2015											
1897	1,000,090	10,028	61.6	97%	$700	$715	$725	$750	$800	$850	$925	$4,000
	Auctions: $5,875, MS-65, August 2015; $2,233, MS-64, September 2015; $1,528, MS-64, October 2015; $764, MS-62, February 2015											
1897, Proof	69	12	64.3							$16,000	$25,000	$47,500
	Auctions: $19,975, PF, August 2013											
1897-O	42,500	394	58.7	47%	$725	$750	$775	$900	$1,150	$1,500	$6,500	$27,500
	Auctions: $6,169, MS-63, March 2013; $2,350, MS-62, June 2015; $1,880, AU-58, July 2014; $999, AU-55, January 2015											
1897-S	234,750	362	57.2	35%	$700	$715	$725	$750	$800	$850	$5,500	$25,000
	Auctions: $1,058, MS-62, February 2015; $823, MS-61, July 2015; $823, MS-60, October 2015; $734, AU-55, September 2015											
1898	812,130	4,160	61.3	94%	$700	$715	$725	$750	$800	$850	$950	$6,500
	Auctions: $5,599, MS-65, August 2015; $2,056, MS-64, August 2015; $1,293, MS-63, February 2015; $999, MS-63, January 2015											
1898, Proof	67	27	65.2							$16,000	$25,000	$47,500
	Auctions: $58,750, PF-66DCam, September 2014; $85,188, PF-66DCam, April 2013											
1898-S	473,600	458	60.2	85%	$700	$715	$725	$750	$800	$850	$2,000	$15,000
	Auctions: $3,290, MS-63, January 2014; $1,116, MS-62, October 2015; $870, MS-61, July 2014; $764, MS-61, October 2015											
1899	1,262,219	21,409	62.1	98%	$700	$715	$725	$750	$800	$850	$950	$2,750
	Auctions: $25,850, MS-67, June 2015; $17,625, MS-66, January 2015; $1,175, MS-63, September 2015; $764, MS-62, October 2015											
1899, Proof	86	37	64.4							$15,000	$25,000	$45,000
	Auctions: $76,375, PF-67DCam, September 2014; $56,400, PF, March 2014											
1899-O	37,047	231	59.1	48%	$750	$775	$800	$950	$1,000	$1,450	$7,500	
	Auctions: $7,638, MS-63, October 2015; $2,115, MS-62, July 2015; $1,763, MS-62, January 2015; $940, AU-55, July 2014											
1899-S	841,000	699	60.1	79%	$700	$715	$725	$750	$800	$850	$1,750	$15,000
	Auctions: $3,525, MS-64, January 2015; $1,293, MS-63, May 2015; $1,028, MS-63, July 2015; $764, EF-40, July 2015											
1900	293,840	6,671	62.1	99%	$700	$715	$725	$750	$800	$825	$950	$3,500
	Auctions: $3,643, MS-65, January 2015; $2,500, MS-65, January 2015; $1,351, MS-64, July 2015; $940, MS-63, August 2014											
1900, Proof	120	49	64.4							$15,000	$25,000	$45,000
	Auctions: $1,880, PF, February 2014											
1900-S	81,000	187	58.0	39%	$700	$715	$725	$750	$800	$1,000	$5,500	$20,000
	Auctions: $6,169, MS-63, September 2013; $658, AU-58, November 2014; $705, AU-58, July 2014											

	Mintage	Cert	Avg	%MS	VF-20	EF-40	AU-50	AU-55	AU-58	MS-60 PF-63	MS-63 PF-64	MS-65 PF-65
1901	1,718,740	24,650	62.3	98%	$700	$715	$725	$750	$800	$825	$950	$2,750
	Auctions: $7,931, MS-66, October 2015; $3,200, MS-65, January 2015; $999, MS-63, January 2015; $940, MS-62, June 2015											
1901, Proof	85	49	63.8							$15,000	$25,000	$45,000
	Auctions: $48,875, PF-66Cam, January 2012											
1901-O	72,041	444	60.0	68%	$750	$775	$800	$925	$975	$1,150	$3,250	$15,000
	Auctions: $6,169, MS-64, June 2014											
1901-S	2,812,750	18,193	62.9	99%	$700	$715	$725	$750	$800	$825	$950	$2,750
	Auctions: $19,975, MS-67, January 2015; $3,290, MS-65, August 2015; $1,146, MS-64, March 2015; $1,251, MS-63, August 2015											
1902	82,400	726	61.2	90%	$700	$715	$725	$750	$800	$850	$1,300	$9,000
	Auctions: $1,528, MS-63, June 2015; $1,293, MS-63, September 2015; $1,645, MS-62, August 2015; $712, AU-58, February 2015											
1902, Proof	113	27	63.7							$15,000	$25,000	$45,000
	Auctions: $61,688, PF-67, February 2013											
1902-S	469,500	2,908	62.8	99%	$700	$715	$725	$750	$800	$825	$950	$2,750
	Auctions: $8,519, MS-66, February 2014; $1,058, MS-63, September 2014; $1,058, MS-63, August 2014											
1903	125,830	1,039	61.3	91%	$700	$715	$725	$750	$800	$850	$950	$7,000
	Auctions: $1,116, MS-64, October 2014; $6,463, MS-65, January 2014; $1,058, MS-63, October 2014; $1,058, MS-63, August 2014											
1903, Proof	96	43	64.4							$15,000	$25,000	$45,000
	Auctions: $39,950, PF, October 2013											
1903-O	112,771	1,196	60.2	72%	$725	$750	$800	$925	$1,000	$1,200	$2,500	$17,500
	Auctions: $1,645, MS-62, September 2016: $1,175, MS-62, January 2015; $999, MS-61, January 2015; $940, AU-58, September 2015											
1903-S	538,000	993	62.3	92%	$700	$715	$725	$750	$800	$850	$950	$2,750
	Auctions: $9,106, MS-66, September 2015; $4,935, MS-66, July 2015; $4,935, MS-65, January 2015; $2,350, MS-64, June 2015											
1904	161,930	1,188	61.3	92%	$700	$715	$725	$750	$800	$850	$1,500	$8,500
	Auctions: $1,763, MS-64, October 2015; $1,293, MS-64, July 2015; $999, MS-63, June 2015; $999, MS-63, April 2015											
1904, Proof	108	35	63.3							$15,000	$25,000	$45,000
	Auctions: $64,625, PF-66Cam, June 2013											
1904-O	108,950	678	60.1	69%	$725	$750	$800	$925	$1,000	$1,200	$3,000	$20,000
	Auctions: $19,975, MS-65, January 2015; $1,410, MS-62, July 2015; $734, AU-58, January 2015; $764, AU-55, February 2015											
1905	200,992	2,307	61.7	94%	$700	$715	$725	$750	$800	$850	$1,200	$5,500
	Auctions: $24,675, MS-67, September 2015; $1,880, MS-64, June 2015; $1,880, MS-64, February 2015; $1,528, MS-64, June 2015											
1905, Proof	86	35	63.6							$15,000	$25,000	$45,000
	Auctions: $76,050, PF, September 2013											
1905-S	369,250	592	57.0	27%	$700	$715	$725	$750	$800	$850	$3,500	$30,000
	Auctions: $1,645, MS-62, July 2015; $940, MS-61, July 2015; $705, AU-58, January 2015; $617, AU-55, October 2015											
1906	165,420	1,560	61.2	91%	$700	$715	$725	$750	$800	$850	$1,250	$8,000
	Auctions: $1,998, MS-64, July 2015; $1,058, MS-63, July 2015; $1,058, MS-63, December 2014; $652, MS-61, October 2014											
1906, Proof	77	35	64.2							$15,000	$25,000	$45,000
	Auctions: $41,125, PF, February 2013											
1906-D	981,000	3,918	61.4	91%	$700	$715	$725	$750	$800	$850	$1,000	$6,500
	Auctions: $2,938, MS-64, June 2015; $1,058, MS-63, August 2015; $881, MS-62, September 2015; $764, MS-61, January 2015											
1906-O	86,895	358	60.3	68%	$725	$750	$800	$925	$1,000	$1,100	$4,750	$20,000
	Auctions: $21,150, MS-65, October 2014; $5,875, MS-64, August 2014; $1,645, MS-62, January 2015; $1,175, MS-62, October 2014											
1906-S	457,000	582	58.1	45%	$700	$715	$725	$750	$800	$850	$2,500	$16,500
	Auctions: $12,925, MS-64, February 2015; $1,998, MS-63, January 2015; $1,880, MS-63, January 2015; $1,528, MS-63, June 2015											
1907	1,203,899	24,710	62.0	98%	$700	$715	$725	$750	$800	$850	$950	$2,750
	Auctions: $3,525, MS-65, October 2015; $1,645, MS-64, October 2015; $764, MS-62, June 2015; $913, MS-61, July 2015											
1907, Proof	74	56	64.0							$15,000	$25,000	$45,000
	Auctions: $54,050, PF-65Cam, January 2015; $33,638, PF-65Cam, March 2012; $29,375, PF-64Cam, August 2014											
1907-D	1,030,000	557	61.4	89%	$700	$715	$725	$750	$800	$850	$1,650	$13,500
	Auctions: $2,585, MS-64, August 2015; $2,233, MS-64, January 2015; $1,821, MS-63, November 2014; $823, MS-61, August 2014											
1907-S	210,500	374	58.9	55%	$700	$715	$725	$750	$800	$850	$3,500	$20,000
	Auctions: $1,880, MS-62, September 2015; $969, MS-62, August 2015; $881, MS-61, January 2015; $823, MS-61, February 2015											

INDIAN HEAD (1907–1933)

Designer: *Augustus Saint-Gaudens.* **Weight:** *16.718 grams.*
Composition: *.900 gold, .100 copper (net weight: .48375 oz. pure gold).*
Diameter: *27 mm.* **Edge:** *1907–1911—46 raised stars; 1912–1933—48 raised stars.*
Mints: *Philadelphia, Denver, and San Francisco.*

Mintmark location, 1908-D (No Motto), is on the reverse, at the tip of the branch.

Mintmark location, 1908 (With Motto)–1930, is on the reverse, to the left of the arrows.

No Motto (1907–1908)

With Motto (1908–1933)

With Motto, Sandblast Finish Proof   **With Motto, Satin Finish Proof**

History. The Indian Head eagle, designed by sculptor Augustus Saint-Gaudens and championed by President Theodore Roosevelt, was struck from 1907 to 1916, and again in intermittent issues through the 1920s and early 1930s. Saint-Gaudens's original design proved impractical to strike and thus was modified slightly by Charles Barber before any large quantities were produced. Not long after (in July 1908), the motto IN GOD WE TRUST was added to the reverse, where it remained to the end of the series. These coins were widely used until 1918, in circulation in the American West and for export.

Striking and Sharpness. On the obverse, check the hair details and the vanes in the feathers. On the reverse, check the shoulder of the eagle. As well-struck coins are available for all varieties, avoid those that are weakly struck. Some examples may exhibit a pink-green color or rust-red "copper spots." Luster varies, but is often deeply frosty. On other coins, particularly from 1910 to 1916, it may be grainy.

Proofs. Sandblast (also called Matte) Proofs were made each year from 1907 through 1915. These have dull surfaces, much like fine-grained sandpaper. Satin (also called Roman Finish) Proofs were made in 1908, 1909, and 1910; they have satiny surfaces and are bright yellow.

Availability. Key rarities in this series are the rolled (or round) rim and wire rim 1907 coins, and the 1920-S, 1930-S, and 1933. Others are generally more readily available. MS-63 and higher coins are generally scarce to rare for the mintmarked issues. The Indian Head eagle is a very popular series. Most such coins in collectors' hands were exported in their time, then brought back to America after World War II. All of the Proofs are rare today.

Note: Values of common-date gold coins have been based on the current bullion price of gold, $1,300 per ounce, and may vary with the prevailing spot price.

GRADING STANDARDS

MS-60 to 70 (Mint State). *Obverse:* At MS-60, some abrasion and contact marks are evident, most noticeably on the hair to the left of Miss Liberty's forehead and in the left field. Luster is present, but may be dull or lifeless, and interrupted in patches. At MS-63, contact marks are few, and abrasion is very light. An MS-65 coin has hardly any abrasion, and contact marks are minute. Luster should be full and rich. Grades above MS-65 are defined by

1907. Graded MS-62.

having fewer marks as perfection is approached. *Reverse:* Comments apply as for the obverse, except that abrasion and contact marks are most noticeable on the front of the left wing and in the left field.

Illustrated coin: This is a brilliant and lustrous example.

AU-50, 53, 55, 58 (About Uncirculated). *Obverse:* Light wear is seen on the cheek, the hair to the right of the face, and the headdress, more so at AU-50 coin than at AU–53 or 55. An AU-58 coin has minimal traces of wear. An AU-50 coin has luster in protected areas among the stars and in the small field area to the right. At AU-58, most luster is present in the fields but is worn away on the highest parts of the Indian. *Reverse:* Com-

1908-D. Graded AU-58.

ments as preceding, except that the eagle's left wing, left leg, neck, and leg show light wear. Luster ranges from perhaps 40% (at AU-50) to nearly full mint bloom (at AU-58).

Illustrated coin: With nearly full original luster, this coin has remarkable eye appeal.

EF-40, 45 (Extremely Fine). *Obverse:* More wear is evident on the hair to the right of the face, and the feather vanes lack some details, although most are present. Luster, if present at all, is minimal. *Reverse:* Wear is greater than on the preceding. The front edge of the left wing is worn and blends into the top of the left leg. Some traces of luster may be seen, more so at EF-45 than at EF-40.

1907. Graded EF-40.

VF-20, 30 (Very Fine). *Obverse:* The Indian's forehead blends into the hair to the right. Feather-vane detail is gone except in the lower areas. *Reverse:* Wear is greater on the eagle, with only a few details remaining on the back of the left wing and the tail.

The Indian Head eagle is seldom collected in grades lower than VF-20.

1908-S. Graded VF-25.

PF-60 to 70 (Proof). *Obverse and Reverse:* At PF–60 to 63, there is light abrasion and some contact marks (the lower the grade, the higher the quantity). On Sandblast Proofs these show up as visually unappealing bright spots. At PF-64 and higher levels, marks are fewer, with magnification needed to see any at PF-65. At PF-66, there should be none at all.

1915. Sandblast Finish. Graded PF-65.

No Periods   Periods

	Mintage	Cert	Avg	%MS	VF-20	EF-40	AU-50	AU-55	MS-60	MS-62 / PF-63	MS-63 / PF-64	MS-65 / PF-65
1907, Wire Rim, Periods	500	177	64.0	92%		$25,000	$27,500	$29,500	$35,000	$40,000	$45,000	$75,000
Auctions: $82,250, MS-65, August 2016; $67,563, MS-65, October 2015; $58,750, MS-65, August 2015; $56,400, MS-65, May 2016												
1907, Rounded Rim, Periods Before and After •E•PLURIBUS•UNUM• † (a)	50	30	62.7	83%		$60,000	$65,000	$70,000	$85,000	$100,000	$165,000	$300,000
Auctions: $470,000, MS-67, August 2013												
1907, No Periods	239,406	7,719	61.6	85%	$750	$800	$850	$900	$1,250	$1,850	$2,500	$7,000
Auctions: $35,250, MS-67, August 2015; $5,170, MS-64, June 2015; $1,293, AU-58, January 2015; $999, AU-50, February 2015												
1907, Wire Rim, Periods, Plain Edge, Proof (b)	*unknown*	0	n/a									
Auctions: $359,375, PF-62, August 2010												
1907, Rounded Rim, Periods, Satin Finish Proof	*unknown*	0	n/a					*(extremely rare)*				
Auctions: $2,185,000, PF-67, January 2011												
1907, Sandblast Finish Proof (c)	*unknown*	0	n/a					*(extremely rare)*				
Auctions: No auction records available.												

† Ranked in the *100 Greatest U.S. Coins* (fourth edition). **a.** All but 50 of the 31,500 coins were melted at the mint. **b.** According to the *Encyclopedia of U.S. Gold Coins, 1795–1933*, the only confirmed example may be from the Captain North set of 1907 and 1908 gold coins sold by Stack's in the 1970s. **c.** 2 or 3 examples are known.

	Mintage	Cert	Avg	%MS	VF-20	EF-40	AU-50	AU-55	MS-60	MS-62	MS-63	MS-65
											PF-63	PF-64	PF-65
1908, No Motto	33,500	813	61.0	78%	$800	$850	$875	$925	$1,500	$3,000	$5,500	$15,000
Auctions: $19,975, MS-66, October 2015; $7,050, MS-64, January 2015; $3,055, MS-62, October 2015; $1,763, AU-58, June 2015												
1908-D, No Motto	210,000	1,020	59.5	55%	$750	$825	$850	$875	$1,500	$3,000	$6,500	$45,000
Auctions: $13,513, MS-64, January 2015; $2,233, MS-61, February 2015; $1,234, AU-58, August 2015; $734, EF-45, October 2015												
1908, With Motto	341,370	4,734	60.8	80%	$700	$725	$750	$775	$1,000	$1,150	$1,450	$5,500
Auctions: $32,900, MS-66, October 2015; $1,998, MS-63, March 2015; $1,058, AU-58, August 2015; $764, EF-45, February 2015												
1908, With Motto, Sandblast Finish Proof	116	53	65.2							$20,000	$32,500	$55,000
Auctions: $69,000, PF-66, January 2012; $79,313, PF-65, August 2014; $61,688, PF-65, January 2015												
1908, With Motto, Satin Finish Proof (d)	(e)	1	64.0		*(extremely rare)*							
Auctions: No auction records available.												
1908-D, With Motto	836,500	824	59.0	55%	$700	$725	$750	$775	$1,200	$2,500	$4,500	$25,000
Auctions: $5,640, MS-63, January 2015; $3,525, MS-62, October 2015; $1,293, MS-61, January 2015; $999, AU-58, August 2015												
1908-S	59,850	824	55.4	20%	$975	$1,100	$1,200	$1,500	$4,500	$8,500	$14,500	$25,000
Auctions: $35,251, MS-66, October 2015; $14,100, MS-64, March 2015; $4,113, AU-58, September 2015; $999, EF-45, February 2015												
1909	184,789	2,225	60.6	74%	$700	$725	$750	$775	$900	$1,000	$1,750	$17,500
Auctions: $5,640, MS-64, June 2015; $3,290, MS-63, January 2015; $1,058, MS-62, March 2015; $940, MS-61, June 2015												
1909, Satin Finish Proof	74	43	66.1							$22,500	$35,000	$70,000
Auctions: $48,875, PF-65, July 2011												
1909, Sandblast Finish Proof (f)	(g)	0	n/a		*(extremely rare)*							
Auctions: No auction records available.												
1909-D	121,540	1,065	59.4	57%	$800	$850	$925	$975	$1,250	$2,500	$3,000	$30,000
Auctions: $4,113, MS-63, January 2015; $2,115, MS-62, March 2015; $999, AU-58, August 2015; $940, AU-55, August 2015												
1909-S	292,350	873	57.3	34%	$700	$725	$750	$775	$1,500	$3,000	$4,500	$17,500
Auctions: $7,638, MS-64, October 2015; $1,880, MS-61, September 2015; $1,116, AU-58, June 2015; $800, AU-53, August 2015												
1910	318,500	6,605	61.6	89%	$700	$725	$750	$775	$850	$900	$1,200	$6,500
Auctions: $17,625, MS-66, January 2015; $1,645, MS-64, January 2015; $940, MS-61, September 2015; $676, MS-60, October 2015												
1910, Satin Finish Proof	204	27	65.4							$20,000	$35,000	$75,000
Auctions: $80,500, PF-67, January 2012												
1910, Sandblast Finish Proof (h)	(i)	1	66.0									
Auctions: No auction records available.												
1910-D	2,356,640	13,069	61.6	90%	$700	$725	$750	$775	$850	$900	$1,000	$6,500
Auctions: $13,513, MS-66, October 2015; $1,998, MS-64, January 2015; $837, MS-60, June 2015; $705, AU-58, October 2015												
1910-S	811,000	1,902	57.0	31%	$700	$725	$750	$775	$1,000	$2,250	$6,500	$45,000
Auctions: $12,925, MS-64, January 2015; $1,645, MS-61, August 2015; $1,410, AU-58, January 2015; $823, AU-58, August 2015												
1911	505,500	10,468	61.5	87%	$700	$725	$750	$775	$850	$950	$1,050	$6,000
Auctions: $30,550, MS-67, August 2015; $9,988, MS-66, September 2015; $1,293, MS-63, February 2015; $705, AU-55, August 2015												
1911, Sandblast Finish Proof	95	24	66.3							$20,000	$32,500	$60,000
Auctions: $152,750, PF-67, November 2013; $76,375, PF-66, August 2015; $74,025, PF-66, October 2014												
1911-D	30,100	942	55.7	17%	$1,250	$1,750	$2,750	$3,500	$11,500	$14,500	$30,000	$250,000
Auctions: $23,500, MS-63, October 2015; $22,325, MS-63, August 2016; $30,550, MS-62, January 2015; $6,169, AU-58, January 2015												
1911-S	51,000	383	56.8	28%	$800	$850	$1,100	$1,125	$3,000	$6,500	$11,000	$25,000
Auctions: $24,793, MS-65, October 2015; $3,525, MS-61, October 2015; $2,820, AU-58, September 2015; $1,645, AU-50, February 2015												

d. 3 or 4 examples are known. **e.** Included in 1908, With Motto, Matte Proof, mintage figure. **f.** 2 or 3 examples are known.
g. Included in 1909, Satin Finish Proof, mintage figure. **h.** The only example known is part of the unique complete 1910 Matte Proof gold set. **i.** Included in 1910, Satin Finish Proof, mintage figure.

	Mintage	Cert	Avg	%MS	VF-20	EF-40	AU-50	AU-55	MS-60	MS-62	MS-63	MS-65
										PF-63	PF-64	PF-65
1912	405,000	7,142	61.3	86%	$700	$725	$750	$775	$875	$1,000	$1,100	$8,000
	Auctions: $54,050, MS-67, January 2015; $3,290, MS-64, January 2015; $881, MS-61, September 2015; $705, AU-55, August 2015											
1912, Sandblast Finish Proof	83	21	65.6							$20,000	$32,500	$60,000
	Auctions: $99,875, PF, March 2014											
1912-S	300,000	1,192	57.2	27%	$725	$750	$775	$825	$1,250	$2,500	$6,000	$35,000
	Auctions: $12,402, MS-64, October 2015; $1,116, AU-58, August 2015; $734, AU-50, February 2015; $705, EF-45, January 2015											
1913	442,000	6,312	61.1	83%	$700	$725	$750	$775	$875	$1,000	$1,250	$6,500
	Auctions: $14,100, MS-66, January 2015; $3,408, MS-64, February 2015; $881, MS-62, June 2015; $705, AU-58, July 2015											
1913, Sandblast Finish Proof	71	25	65.4							$20,000	$32,500	$60,000
	Auctions: $63,250, PF-66, January 2012											
1913-S	66,000	974	55.0	13%	$1,000	$1,100	$1,200	$2,250	$7,000	$12,500	$22,500	$165,000
	Auctions: $22,325, MS-63, January 2015; $4,243, AU-58, February 2015; $1,528, AU-53, June 2015; $852, EF-40, January 2015											
1914	151,000	2,346	61.1	82%	$700	$725	$750	$775	$875	$975	$1,650	$8,500
	Auctions: $10,869, MS-65, October 2015; $2,832, MS-64, January 2015; $1,998, MS-63, January 2015; $881, MS-62, May 2015											
1914, Sandblast Finish Proof	50	32	65.7							$20,000	$32,500	$60,000
	Auctions: $96,938, PF, October 2013											
1914-D	343,500	2,898	60.7	75%	$700	$725	$750	$775	$875	$1,000	$1,500	$12,500
	Auctions: $9,988, MS-65, October 2015; $1,998, MS-63, January 2015; $887, MS-61, June 2015; $764, AU-55, October 2015											
1914-S	208,000	1,095	58.3	40%	$700	$725	$750	$825	$2,000	$3,250	$5,500	$40,000
	Auctions: $16,450, MS-64, October 2015; $1,645, AU-58, January 2015; $705, AU-53, August 2015; $709, EF-45, August 2015											
1915	351,000	4,544	61.1	80%	$700	$725	$750	$775	$900	$975	$1,650	$6,500
	Auctions: $6,463, MS-65, January 2015; $2,350, MS-63, January 2015; $823, MS-60, September 2015; $823, AU-58, September 2015											
1915, Sandblast Finish Proof	75	17	65.7							$22,500	$32,500	$70,000
	Auctions: $94,000, PF, August 2013											
1915-S	59,000	430	57.3	26%	$900	$1,000	$1,500	$1,750	$5,500	$12,500	$20,000	$65,000
	Auctions: $19,975, MS-62, September 2015; $6,611, MS-61, August 2015; $3,408, AU-58, January 2015; $1,058, AU-50, January 2015											
1916-S	138,500	927	59.0	49%	$950	$985	$1,000	$1,100	$1,500	$2,750	$6,500	$25,000
	Auctions: $7,050, MS-63, August 2015; $1,763, MS-61, October 2015; $1,528, AU-58, August 2015; $764, AU-50, September 2015											
1920-S	126,500	53	59.5	55%	$20,000	$25,000	$32,500	$40,000	$60,000	$75,000	$105,000	$225,000
	Auctions: $70,500, MS-62, September 2015; $70,500, MS-61, June 2015; $64,625, MS-61, October 2015; $47,000, AU-58, January 2015											
1926	1,014,000	41,128	62.5	99%	$700	$725	$750	$775	$875	$900	$950	$2,750
	Auctions: $7,638, MS-66, October 2015; $1,469, MS-64, October 2015; $823, MS-61, June 2015; $646, MS-60, July 2015											
1930-S	96,000	63	63.6	95%	$20,000	$22,500	$25,000	$30,000	$40,000	$45,000	$55,000	$100,000
	Auctions: $85,188, MS-65, September 2014; $70,500, MS-64, March 2014; $17,625, MS-60, January 2015											
1932	4,463,000	60,919	62.9	100%	$700	$725	$750	$775	$875	$900	$950	$2,750
	Auctions: $10,869, MS-66, January 2015; $2,482, MS-65, March 2015; $1,528, MS-63, August 2015; $793, MS-60, July 2015											
1933 † (j)	312,500	11	64.4	100%					$300,000	$325,000	$400,000	$750,000
	Auctions: $587,500, MS-65, June 2015: $367,188, MS-64, August 2013											

† Ranked in the *100 Greatest U.S. Coins* (fourth edition). **j.** Nearly all were melted at the mint.

Gold Double Eagles ($20)
1850–1933

AN OVERVIEW OF GOLD DOUBLE EAGLES

Congress authorized the double eagle, or twenty-dollar coin—the largest denomination of all regular U.S. coinage issues—by the Act of March 3, 1849, in response to the huge amounts of gold coming from California.

Double eagles are at once large and impressive to own. Many gold collectors form a type set of the six major double eagle designs (with the 1861 Paquet added as a sub-type if desired). Thanks to overseas hoards repatriated since the 1950s, finding choice and gem Mint State examples is no problem at all for the later types.

The first double eagle type, the Liberty Head of 1850 to 1866 without the motto IN GOD WE TRUST, is generally available in grades from VF up. Mint State pieces were elusive prior to the 1990s, but the market supply was augmented by more than 5,000 pieces—including some gems—found in the discovery of the long-lost treasure ship SS *Central America*. The SS *Brother Jonathan*, lost at sea in 1865, was recovered in the 1990s and yielded hundreds of Mint State 1865-S double eagles, along with some dated 1864 and a few earlier. The wreck of the SS *Republic*, lost in 1865 while on a voyage from New York City to New Orleans and salvaged in 2003, also yielded some very attractive Mint State double eagles of this first Liberty Head type.

The Liberty Head type from 1866 through 1876, with the motto IN GOD WE TRUST above the eagle and with the denomination expressed as TWENTY D., is the rarest in MS-63 and higher grades. Many EF and AU coins have been repatriated from overseas holdings, as have quite a few in such grades as MS–60 through 62. However, true gems are hardly ever seen.

Liberty Head double eagles of the 1877–1907 type with the IN GOD WE TRUST motto and with the denomination spelled out as TWENTY DOLLARS are exceedingly plentiful in just about any grade desired, with gems being readily available of certain issues of the early 20th century. While it is easy to obtain a gem of a common date, some collectors of type coins have opted to acquire a coin of special historical interest, such as a Carson City issue.

The famous Saint-Gaudens MCMVII High Relief double eagle of 1907 was saved in quantity by the general public as well as by numismatists, and today it is likely that at least 5,000 to 6,000 exist, representing about half of the mintage. Most of these are in varying degrees of Mint State, with quite a few graded as MS–64 and 65. Those in lower grades such as VF and EF often were used for jewelry or were polished, or have other problems. This particular design is a great favorite with collectors, and although the coins are not rarities, they are hardly inexpensive.

The so-called Arabic Numerals 1907–1908 Saint-Gaudens design is available in nearly any grade desired, with MS-60 through MS-63 or MS-64 pieces being plentiful and inexpensive. Double eagles of the final type, 1908–1933, are abundant in any grade desired, with choice and gem coins being plentiful.

FOR THE COLLECTOR AND INVESTOR: GOLD DOUBLE EAGLES AS A SPECIALTY

Collecting double eagles by date and mint is more popular than one might think. Offhand, one might assume that these high denominations, laden with a number of rare dates, would attract few enthusiasts. However, over a long period of years more collectors have specialized in double eagles than have specialized in five-dollar or ten-dollar pieces.

Two particularly notable collections of double eagles by date and mint, from the earliest times to the latest, were formed by Louis E. Eliasberg of Baltimore, and Jeff Browning of Dallas. Both have been dispersed across the auction block. The first was cataloged by Bowers and Ruddy in 1982, and the second was offered by Stack's and Sotheby's in 2001. In addition, dozens of other collections over the years have had large numbers of double eagles, some specializing in the Liberty Head types of 1850–1907, others only with the Saint-Gaudens types from 1907 onward, and others addressing the entire range.

Among rarities in the double eagle series are the 1854-O and 1856-O, each known only to the extent of a few dozen pieces; the 1861 Philadelphia Mint coins with Paquet reverse (two known); the Proof-only issues of 1883, 1884, and 1887; several other low-mintage varieties of this era; the famous Carson City issue of 1870-CC; and various issues from 1920 onward, including 1920-S, 1921, mintmarked coins after 1923, and all dates after 1928. Punctuating these rarities is a number of readily available pieces, including the very common Philadelphia issues from 1922 through 1928 inclusive.

LIBERTY HEAD (1849–1907)

Designer: *James B. Longacre.* **Weight:** *33.436 grams.*
Composition: *.900 gold, .100 copper (net weight: .96750 oz. pure gold).* **Diameter** *34 mm.*
Edge: *Reeded.* **Mints:** *Philadelphia, Carson City, Denver, New Orleans, and San Francisco.*

No Motto (1849–1866)　　　　　No Motto, Proof

*Mintmark location is on
the reverse, below the eagle.*

With Motto (1866–1907)　　　　　With Motto, Proof

History. The twenty-dollar denomination was introduced to circulation in 1850 (after a unique pattern, which currently resides in the Smithsonian's National Numismatic Collection, was minted in 1849). The large new coin was ideal for converting the flood of California gold rush bullion into federal legal tender. U.S. Mint chief engraver James B. Longacre designed the coin. A different reverse, designed by Anthony Paquet with taller letters than Longacre's design, was tested in 1861 but ultimately not used past that date. In 1866 the motto IN GOD WE TRUST was added to the reverse. In 1877 the denomination on the reverse, formerly given as TWENTY D., was changed to TWENTY DOLLARS. The double eagle denomination proved to be very popular, especially for export. By 1933, more than 75 percent of the American gold used to strike coins from the 1850s onward had been used to make double eagles. Oddly, some of the coins of 1850 to 1858 appear to have the word LIBERTY misspelled as LLBERTY.

Striking and Sharpness. On the obverse, check the star centers and the hair details. As made, the hair details are less distinct on many coins of 1859 (when a slight modification was made) through the 1890s, and knowledge of this is important. Later issues usually have exquisite detail. The reverse usually is well struck, but check the eagle and other features. The denticles are sharp on nearly all coins, but should be checked. Proofs were made in all years from 1858 to 1907, and a few were made before then. Proofs of 1902 onward, particularly 1903, have the portrait polished in the die, imparting a mirror finish across the design, and lack the cameo contrast of earlier dates.

Availability. Basic dates and mintmarks are available in proportion to their mintages. Key issues include the 1854-O, 1856-O, 1861 Paquet Reverse, 1861-S Paquet Reverse, 1866 No Motto, 1870-CC, 1879-O, and several Philadelphia Mint dates of the 1880s The vast majority of others are readily collectible. Among early coins, MS examples from about 1854 to 1857 are available, most notably the 1857-S and certain varieties of the 1860s. Most varieties of the 1880s onward, and particularly of the 1890s and 1900s, are easily available in MS, due to the repatriation of millions of coins that had been exported overseas. Proofs dated through the 1870s are all very rare today; those of the 1880s are less so; and those of the 1890s and 1900s are scarce. Many Proofs have been mishandled. Dates that are Proof-only (and those that are very rare in circulation-strike form) are in demand even if impaired. These include 1883, 1884, 1885, 1886, and 1887.

Note: Values of common-date gold coins have been based on the current bullion price of gold, $1,300 per ounce, and may vary with the prevailing spot price.

GRADING STANDARDS

MS-60 to 70 (Mint State). *Obverse:* At MS-60, some abrasion and contact marks are evident, most noticeably on the hair to the right of Miss Liberty's forehead and on the cheek. Luster is present, but may be dull or lifeless, and interrupted in patches. At MS-63, contact marks are few, and abrasion is light. An MS-65 coin has little abrasion, and contact marks are minute. Luster should be full and rich. Grades above MS-65 are defined by

1876-S. Graded MS-64.

having fewer marks as perfection is approached. *Reverse:* Comments apply as for the obverse, except that abrasion and contact marks are most noticeable on eagle's neck, wingtips, and tail.

AU-50, 53, 55, 58 (About Uncirculated).
Obverse: Light wear is seen on the face, the hair to the right of the face, and the highest area of the hair behind the coronet, more so at AU-50 than at AU–53 or 55. An AU-58 coin has minimal traces of wear. An AU-50 coin has luster in protected areas among the stars and letters, with little in the open fields or on the portrait. At AU-58 most luster is present in the fields, but is worn away on the

1856-S. Graded AU-53.

highest parts of the motifs. *Reverse:* Comments as preceding, except that the eagle and ornaments show wear in all of the higher areas. Luster ranges from perhaps 40% remaining in protected areas (at AU-50) to nearly full mint bloom (at AU-58). Often the reverse of this type retains more luster than the obverse.

Illustrated coin: Much of the original luster still remains at this grade level, especially on the reverse.

EF-40, 45 (Extremely Fine). *Obverse:* Wear is evident on all high areas of the portrait, including the hair to the right of the forehead, the tip of the coronet, and hair behind the coronet. The curl to the right of the neck is flat on its highest-relief area. Luster, if present at all, is minimal and in protected areas such as between the star points. *Reverse:* Wear is greater than on an About Uncirculated coin. The eagle's neck and wingtips

1855-S. Graded EF-45.

show wear, as do the ornaments and rays. Some traces of luster may be seen, more so at EF-45 than at EF-40. Overall, the reverse appears to be in a slightly higher grade than the obverse.

VF-20, 30 (Very Fine). *Obverse:* The higher-relief areas of hair are worn flat at VF-20, less so at VF-30. The hair to the right of the coronet is merged into heavy strands and is flat at the back, as is part of the bow. The curl to the right of the neck is flat. *Reverse:* The eagle shows further wear on the head, the tops of the wings, and the tail. The ornament has flat spots.

The Liberty Head double eagle is seldom collected in grades lower than VF-20.

1857-S. Graded VF-20.

Illustrated coin: Note the small test cut or mark on the top rim.

PF-60 to 70 (Proof). *Obverse and Reverse:* PF–60 to 62 coins have extensive hairlines and may have nicks and contact marks. At PF-63, hairlines are prominent, but the mirror surface is very reflective. PF-64 coins have fewer hairlines. At PF-65, hairlines should be relatively few. These large and heavy coins reveal hairlines more readily than do the lower denominations, mostly seen only under magnification. PF-66 and higher coins should have no marks or hairlines visible to the unaided eye.

1903. Graded PF-64.

Illustrated coin: A beautiful Proof, this is just a few hairlines away from a higher level.

Value TWENTY D. (1849–1876)	Value TWENTY DOLLARS (1877–1907)	1853, So-called 3 Over 2 *Note rust under LIBERTY.* FS-G20-1853-301.

	Mintage	Cert	Avg	%MS	VF-20	EF-40	AU-50	AU-55	MS-60	MS-62 PF-63	MS-63 PF-64	MS-65 PF-65
1849, Proof † (a)	1	0	n/a		*(unique; in the Smithsonian's National Numismatic Collection)*							
	Auctions: No auction records available.											
1850	1,170,261	1,514	50.3	5%	$2,500	$3,500	$5,000	$7,000	$16,500	$40,000	$60,000	$200,000
	Auctions: $42,300, MS-62, August 2015; $7,344, AU-55, August 2015; $4,465, AU-50, June 2015; $2,585, EF-40, January 2015											
1850, Proof (b)	1–2	0	n/a									
	Auctions: No auction records available.											
1850-O	141,000	345	48.2	2%	$5,500	$7,250	$15,000	$24,500	$75,000			
	Auctions: $58,750, MS-61, January 2015; $21,150, AU-55, January 2015; $9,400, EF-45, August 2015; $4,465, VF-25, August 2015											
1851	2,087,155	1,161	51.4	7%	$2,000	$2,250	$2,600	$3,000	$6,500	$14,500	$25,000	
	Auctions: $14,100, MS-62, July 2015; $5,170, AU-55, August 2015; $1,645, EF-40, January 2015; $1,772, VF-35, June 2015											
1851-O	315,000	762	50.7	2%	$2,750	$4,500	$7,000	$12,500	$28,500	$60,000	$125,000	
	Auctions: $13,513, AU-58, August 2015; $7,638, AU-53, October 2015; $6,463, AU-50, January 2015; $4,818, EF-45, October 2015											
1852	2,053,026	1,912	51.6	6%	$2,000	$2,250	$2,600	$3,500	$6,500	$14,500	$22,500	
	Auctions: $10,600, MS-62, October 2015; $3,819, AU-58, March 2015; $1,704, AU-50, January 2015; $1,998, EF-40, January 2015											
1852-O	190,000	584	51.3	4%	$2,500	$4,500	$7,500	$12,500	$37,500	$55,000	$95,000	
	Auctions: $27,061, AU-58, August 2015; $5,640, AU-50, September 2015; $3,408, EF-40, July 2015; $2,291, VF-20, August 2015											
1853, All kinds	1,261,326											
1853, So-called 3 Over 2 (c)		210	52.5	3%	$3,000	$4,000	$6,500	$12,500	$42,500	$55,000		
	Auctions: $28,200, AU-58, August 2014; $28,200, AU-58, October 2014: $17,625, AU-58, April 2014											
1853		1,307	52.5	5%	$2,000	$2,250	$2,600	$3,000	$6,500	$16,000	$30,000	
	Auctions: $7,638, MS-61, February 2015; $6,169, AU-58, January 2015; $2,848, AU-53, January 2015; $1,880, EF-40, August 2015											
1853-O	71,000	240	50.7	3%	$3,000	$7,000	$12,500	$17,500	$37,500			
	Auctions: $14,100, AU-55, August 2015; $11,750, AU-55, January 2015; $10,575, AU-50, January 2015; $7,638, EF-45, August 2015											

† Ranked in the *100 Greatest U.S. Coins* (fourth edition). **a.** An unknown quantity of Proof 1849 double eagles was struck as patterns; all but two were melted. One (current location unknown) was sent to Treasury secretary W.M. Meredith; the other was placed in the Mint collection in Philadelphia, and transferred with that collection to the Smithsonian in 1923. **b.** Although no examples currently are known, it is likely that a small number of Proof 1850 double eagles were struck. For the years 1851 to 1857, no Proofs are known. **c.** Although overlaid photographs indicate this is not a true overdate, what appear to be remnants of a numeral are visible beneath the 3 in the date. This variety also shows a rust spot underneath the R of LIBERTY.

1854, Small Date   **1854, Large Date**

	Mintage	Cert	Avg	%MS	VF-20	EF-40	AU-50	AU-55	MS-60	MS-62 PF-63	MS-63 PF-64	MS-65 PF-65
1854, All kinds	757,899											
1854, Small Date		635	52.3	4%	$2,000	$2,250	$2,850	$3,750	$9,500	$18,000	$35,000	
Auctions: $11,163, MS-61, January 2015; $4,714, AU-55, January 2015; $2,233, EF-45, October 2015; $1,645, VF-30, August 2015												
1854, Large Date		127	52.9	8%	$3,500	$4,250	$10,000	$16,000	$37,500	$50,000	$65,000	
Auctions: $55,813, MS-61, August 2014; $19,975, AU-58, October 2014; $9,988, AU-53, September 2015; $9,400, AU-50, August 2015												
1854-O † (d)	3,250	17	53.6	0%	$135,000	$215,000	$350,000	$425,000	—			
Auctions: $440,625, AU-55, April 2014; $340,750, AU-55, August 2015; $329,000, AU-50, August 2014												
1854-S	141,468	218	52.5	23%	$3,000	$4,250	$10,500	$17,500	$30,000	$40,000	$50,000	$90,000
Auctions: $16,450, AU-55, August 2015; $16,450, AU-55, September 2016; $21,738, AU-53, February 2015; $14,688, AU-53, July 2015												
1854-S, Proof † (e)	*unknown*	0	n/a		*(unique; in the Smithsonian's National Numismatic Collection)*							
Auctions: No auction records available.												
1855	364,666	402	53.0	5%	$2,000	$2,250	$3,000	$4,500	$12,000	$25,000	$60,000	
Auctions: $5,170, AU-58, September 2015; $3,878, AU-55, February 2015; $2,820, AU-53, August 2015; $2,350, AU-50, January 2015												
1855-O	8,000	48	51.3	8%	$13,500	$35,000	$50,000	$67,500	$125,000			
Auctions: $141,000, MS-61, January 2014; $70,500, AU-58, August 2015; $58,750, AU-55, August 2014; $28,200, AU-50, October 2014												
1855-S	879,675	1,097	51.6	3%	$2,000	$2,250	$2,600	$3,750	$8,000	$17,500	$25,000	
Auctions: $11,163, MS-61, July 2015; $3,819, AU-58, March 2015; $1,704, EF-40, June 2015; $1,528, VF-20, August 2015												
1856	329,878	367	52.5	6%	$2,150	$2,250	$3,250	$4,500	$10,000	$20,000	$35,000	
Auctions: $7,050, AU-58, October 2015; $4,465, AU-55, June 2015; $3,290, AU-53, January 2015; $3,995, AU-50, August 2015												
1856-O † (f)	2,250	10	52.2	0%	$145,000	$225,000	$350,000	$385,000				
Auctions: $340,750, AU-55, August 2015; $425,938, AU-53, August 2014; $164,500, AU-50, August 2014; $381,875, EF-45, January 2014												
1856-O, Proof † (g)	*unknown*	1	63.0									
Auctions: $1,437,500, SP-63, May 2009												
1856-S	1189750	1,249	51.5	4%	$2,000	$2,350	$2,750	$3,500	$7,000	$12,500	$16,500	$45,000
Auctions: $7,344, MS-61, June 2015; $4,935, AU-58, September 2015; $5,170, AU-53, January 2015; $2,115, EF-40, September 2015												
1857	439,375	521	53.4	10%	$2,000	$2,500	$2,750	$3,500	$8,000	$14,500	$40,000	
Auctions: $5,875, MS-60, January 2015; $3,760, AU-58, January 2015; $2,350, AU-53, September 2015; $2,585, EF-45, January 2015												
1857-O	30,000	149	52.4	6%	$4,750	$9,500	$15,000	$25,000	$50,000	$165,000	$250,000	
Auctions: $21,150, AU-53, August 2015; $11,163, AU-50, January 2015; $7,050, EF-40, October 2015; $2,585, VF-20, September 2015												
1857-S † (h)	970,500	1,499	54.6	27%	$2,000	$2,250	$2,500	$3,250	$5,500	$7,000	$8,500	$14,500
Auctions: $15,863, MS-65, September 2015; $5,405, AU-58, August 2015; $2,233, AU-53, July 2015; $2,233, EF-40, January 2015												
1858	211,714	461	52.4	7%	$2,150	$2,500	$3,500	$4,500	$9,000	$30,000	$45,000	
Auctions: $19,975, MS-62, January 2015; $4,935, AU-58, October 2015; $2,820, AU-53, October 2015; $3,055, EF-45, August 2015												
1858, Proof (i)	*unknown*	0	n/a		*(extremely rare)*							
Auctions: No auction records available.												
1858-O	35,250	145	51.4	6%	$5,000	$9,500	$20,000	$32,500	$60,000	$75,000		
Auctions: $164,500, MS-63, January 2015; AU-58, August 2015; $9,988, AU-50, August 2015; $7,050, AU-50, January 2015												
1858-S	846,710	1,107	51.1	2%	$2,000	$2,250	$3,000	$3,750	$10,000	$15,000	$45,000	
Auctions: $8,225, MS-60, October 2015; $7,638, AU-58, January 2015; $2,879, AU-53, June 2015; $1,528, EF-40, January 2015												

† Ranked in the *100 Greatest U.S. Coins* (fourth edition); both 1856-O Liberty Head Double Eagles as a single entry. **d.** Probably fewer than 35 exist, most in VF and EF. **e.** This unique coin, perhaps more accurately described as a presentation strike than a Proof, was sent to the Mint collection in Philadelphia by San Francisco Mint superintendent Lewis A. Birdsall. It may have been the first coin struck for the year, set aside to recognize the opening of the San Francisco Mint. **f.** Probably fewer than 25 exist, most in VF and EF. **g.** This prooflike presentation strike is unique. **h.** The treasure of the shipwrecked SS *Central America* included thousands of 1857-S double eagles in high grades. Different size mintmark varieties exist; the Large S variety is rarest. **i.** 3 or 4 examples are known.

1861-S, Normal Reverse　　　　**1861-S, Paquet Reverse**
Note taller letters.

	Mintage	Cert	Avg	%MS	VF-20	EF-40	AU-50	AU-55	MS-60	MS-62	MS-63	MS-65
										PF-63	PF-64	PF-65
1859	43,597	131	51.6	5%	$3,250	$6,500	$12,500	$15,000	$32,000	$47,500		
	Auctions: $17,625, AU-55, August 2015; $12,925, AU-50, August 2015; $3,290, AU-50, August 2014; $7,050, EF-40, October 2015											
1859, Proof (j)	80	6	63.7							$250,000	$400,000	$500,000
	Auctions: $210,600, PF, June 2014											
1859-O	9,100	59	51.3	2%	$9,500	$25,000	$47,500	$65,000	$125,000			
	Auctions: $28,200, MS-60, August 2014: $105,750, AU-58, September 2016; $76,375, AU-58, August 2014											
1859-S	636,445	842	50.9	3%	$2,000	$2,250	$2,800	$4,500	$14,000	$30,000	$57,500	
	Auctions: $9,400, AU-58, August 2015; $3,995, AU-55, July 2015; $2,820, AU-53, October 2015; $2,585, EF-45, September 2015											
1860	577,611	975	53.9	11%	$2,000	$2,150	$2,500	$3,000	$6,500	$12,000	$20,000	
	Auctions: $10,575, MS-61, August 2015; $3,301, AU-58, January 2015; $2,644, AU-55, June 2015; $2,585, AU-53, January 2015											
1860, Proof (k)	59	9	65.3							$125,000	$250,000	$400,000
	Auctions: $367,188, PF-66Cam, August 2014											
1860-O	6,600	62	51.5	3%	$12,500	$37,500	$55,000	$67,500				
	Auctions: $64,625, AU-58, August 2015; $55,813, AU-53, August 2014; $30,550, EF-40, January 2015											
1860-S	544,950	767	51.4	3%	$2,000	$2,250	$2,750	$4,000	$10,000	$20,000	$35,000	
	Auctions: $7,050, AU-58, January 2015; $3,673, AU-55, January 2015; $3,760, AU-53, August 2015; $1,528, VF-20, February 2015											
1861	2,976,387	3,462	54.3	16%	$2,000	$2,150	$2,500	$3,000	$5,500	$8,750	$18,500	$57,500
	Auctions: $8,813, MS-62, July 2015; $4,465, AU-58, February 2015; $1,998, AU-50, July 2015; $2,115, EF-40, January 2015											
1861, Proof (l)	66	2	65.0							$125,000	$250,000	$375,000
	Auctions: $44,850, PF-65DCam, September 2005											
1861-O	17,741	112	49.4	5%	$15,000	$35,000	$55,000	$67,500	$165,000			
	Auctions: $51,406, AU-50, March 2015; $44,650, AU-50, August 2015; $16,450, AU, March 2015; $11,163, AU-50, January 2015											
1861-S	768,000	857	50.8	3%	$2,000	$2,250	$3,250	$5,000	$16,000	$32,500	$47,500	
	Auctions: $3,525, MS-60, October 2015; $4,935, AU-58, January 2015; $2,350, AU-50, July 2015; $2,115, EF-45, August 2015											
1861, Paquet Rev (Tall Ltrs) † (m)	*unknown*	1	67.0	100%					$2,000,000			
	Auctions: $1,645,000, MS-61, August 2014											
1861-S, Paquet Rev (Tall Ltrs) † (n)	19,250	78	49.8	0%	$35,000	$65,000	$90,000	$115,000				
	Auctions: $223,250, AU-58, April 2014; $164,500, AU-58, August 2015; $152,750, AU-58, August 2015; $105,750, 0, August 2016											
1862	92,098	100	52.0	15%	$4,500	$12,000	$15,000	$20,000	$40,000	$60,000	$70,000	
	Auctions: $70,500, MS-62, August 2014; $49,938, MS-62, August 2014; $28,200, AU-58, August 2015											
1862, Proof (o)	35	6	64.2							$125,000	$250,000	$375,000
	Auctions: $381,875, PF-65Cam, April 2014											
1862-S	854,173	1,105	51.2	4%	$2,000	$2,500	$3,500	$5,000	$13,500	$30,000	$50,000	
	Auctions: $9,400, AU-58, January 2015; $3,995, AU-55, October 2015; $2,470, AU-50, August 2015; $2,585, EF-45, February 2015											

† Ranked in the *100 Greatest U.S. Coins* (fourth edition). **j.** 7 or 8 examples are known. **k.** Fewer than 10 examples are known. **l.** 5 or 6 examples are known. **m.** Once thought to be a pattern; now known to have been intended for circulation. 2 examples are known. **n.** Approximately 100 examples are known, most in VF and EF. **o.** Approximately 12 examples are known.

| | Mintage | Cert | Avg | %MS | VF-20 | EF-40 | AU-50 | AU-55 | MS-60 | MS-62 | MS-63 | MS-65 |
										PF-63	PF-64	PF-65
1863	142,760	204	52.8	12%	$3,000	$5,500	$11,500	$15,000	$32,500	$55,000	$85,000	
Auctions: $85,188, MS-63, January 2015; $21,150, AU-58, September 2015; $20,563, AU-58, January 2015; $17,625, AU-55, August 2015												
1863, Proof (p)	30	8	64.3							$125,000	$250,000	$375,000
Auctions: $381,875, PF-66Cam, August 2014; $345,150, PF, September 2013												
1863-S	966,570	1,456	51.6	9%	$2,150	$2,500	$3,000	$4,250	$10,000	$21,000	$35,000	
Auctions: $5,405, AU-58, August 2015; $4,230, AU-55, August 2015; $2,115, EF-45, August 2015; $1,880, VF-30, January 2015												
1864	204,235	307	52.5	9%	$3,250	$5,500	$9,000	$11,000	$25,000	$47,500	$75,000	
Auctions: $282,000, MS-65, April 2014; $8,813, AU-53, August 2015; $4,230, EF-40, August 2015; $3,760, EF-40, January 2015												
1864, Proof (q)	50	10	64.4							$125,000	$250,000	$375,000
Auctions: $199,750, PF-64Cam, April 2014												
1864-S	793,660	1,017	51.4	12%	$2,000	$2,250	$2,750	$3,500	$11,000	$20,000	$45,000	$110,000
Auctions: $19,975, MS-62, August 2015; $4,935, AU-53, February 2015; $1,998, EF-45, August 2015; $1,763, VF-35, July 2015												
1865	351,175	791	56.9	42%	$2,250	$2,750	$3,000	$3,750	$7,500	$14,500	$22,500	$57,500
Auctions: $45,825, MS-65, October 2015; $3,290, AU-55, March 2015; $2,350, AU-50, January 2015; $2,115, EF-45, August 2015												
1865, Proof (r)	25	7	64.9							$125,000	$250,000	$375,000
Auctions: $440,625, PF-66DCam, April 2014												
1865-S	1,042,500	1,415	53.8	33%	$2,000	$2,150	$2,750	$3,500	$7,250	$11,000	$13,500	$30,000
Auctions: $25,850, MS-65, September 2015; $10,588, MS-62, August 2015; $2,233, AU-53, January 2015; $2,350, EF-45, August 2015												
1866-S, No Motto	120,000	166	49.1	4%	$10,000	$22,500	$37,500	$60,000	$155,000	$250,000		
Auctions: $30,550, AU-50, October 2015; $28,200, AU-50, July 2015; $35,250, EF-45, August 2015; $8,225, VF-20, October 2015												

p. Approximately 12 examples are known. **q.** 12 to 15 examples are known. **r.** Fewer than 10 examples are known.

**1866, With Motto,
Doubled Die Reverse**
FS-G20-1866-801.

| | Mintage | Cert | Avg | %MS | VF-20 | EF-40 | AU-50 | AU-55 | MS-60 | MS-62 | MS-63 | MS-64 |
										PF-63	PF-64	PF-65
1866, With Motto	698,745	595	53.5	9%	$1,600	$1,850	$2,500	$5,000	$12,000	$32,500	$65,000	$125,000
Auctions: $25,850, MS-61, January 2015; $9,400, AU-58, August 2015; $3,995, AU-55, January 2015; $3,055, AU-50, September 2015												
1866, With Motto, Doubled Die Reverse	(a)	0	n/a				$4,000	$6,000				
Auctions: $12,650, MS-61, August 2010												
1866, With Motto, Proof (b)	30	7	64.6							$57,500	$125,000	$275,000
Auctions: $126,500, PF-64, May 2007												
1866-S, With Motto	842,250	795	49.7	3%	$1,950	$2,250	$4,000	$8,000	$22,500	$45,000		
Auctions: $15,275, AU-58, August 2015; $9,400, AU-55, February 2015; $3,760, AU-50, January 2015; $2,820, EF-40, August 2015												
1867	251,015	391	56.9	41%	$1,600	$1,750	$1,800	$3,750	$7,000	$10,000	$35,000	
Auctions: $258,500, MS-66, November 2014; $9,400, MS-61, August 2015; $7,638, MS-61, August 2015; $6,492, AU-58, August 2015												
1867, Proof (c)	50	5	65.0							$57,500	$125,000	$225,000
Auctions: $129,250, PF-64DCam, January 2015; $129,250, PF-64DCam, August 2014; $38,188, PF-61Cam, August 2014												
1867-S	920,750	1,196	50.9	3%	$1,500	$1,700	$2,250	$4,500	$13,500	$32,500		
Auctions: $17,038, MS-61, January 2015; $8,225, AU-58, July 2015; $2,115, AU-53, January 2015; $1,763, EF-45, August 2015												

a. Included in circulation-strike 1866 mintage figure. **b.** Approximately 15 examples are known. **c.** 10 to 12 examples are known.

Open 3 **Close 3**

	Mintage	Cert	Avg	%MS	VF-20	EF-40	AU-50	AU-55	MS-60	MS-62 / PF-63	MS-63 / PF-64	MS-64 / PF-65
1868	98,575	201	52.6	5%	$2,000	$2,500	$4,000	$7,000	$22,500	$45,000	$70,000	
Auctions: $44,063, MS-62, August 2014; $18,800, AU-58, August 2015; $8,813, AU-53, June 2015; $4,113, EF-45, August 2014												
1868, Proof (d)	25	7	64.3							$65,000	$125,000	$225,000
Auctions: $149,500, PF-64DCam Plus, August 2011												
1868-S	837,500	1,477	51.8	3%	$1,500	$1,650	$1,800	$3,250	$11,000	$32,500		
Auctions: $16,450, MS-61, January 2015; $7,050, AU-58, January 2015; $1,645, AU-50, February 2015; $1,410, EF-45, January 2015												
1869	175,130	347	53.0	3%	$1,500	$1,650	$1,800	$4,000	$11,000	$20,000	$37,500	$77,500
Auctions: $108,688, MS-64, January 2014; $9,988, MS-60, January 2015; $2,115, AU-53, February 2015; $3,290, AU-50, August 2015												
1869, Proof (e)	25	7	65.0							$65,000	$125,000	$225,000
Auctions: $106,375, PF-64DCam, February 2009												
1869-S	686,750	1,442	52.3	5%	$1,500	$1,750	$1,850	$3,000	$8,500	$25,000	$42,500	$75,000
Auctions: $37,600, MS-62, August 2015; $7,638, AU-58, June 2015; $2,705, AU-55, February 2015; $1,880, AU-53, July 2015												
1870	155,150	270	54.0	15%	$1,500	$1,650	$2,500	$5,500	$16,000	$30,000	$52,500	
Auctions: $22,325, MS-61, June 2015; $14,688, MS-60, June 2015; $7,638, AU-58, August 2015; $6,463, AU-55, August 2015												
1870, Proof (f)	35	5	65.2							$65,000	$175,000	$275,000
Auctions: $503,100, PF, September 2013												
1870-CC † (g)	3,789	32	41.3	0%	$200,000	$250,000	$350,000	$475,000				
Auctions: $411,250, AU-53, March 2014; $58,815, EF-40, August 2014; $188,000, VF-30, October 2014; $182,125, VF-30, August 2015												
1870-S	982,000	1,463	52.3	5%	$1,500	$1,650	$1,750	$2,500	$7,000	$22,500	$55,000	
Auctions: $10,869, MS-61, September 2015; $2,000, AU-55, January 2015; $1,528, AU-50, January 2015; $1,410, EF-40, September 2015												
1871	80,120	277	53.4	5%	$1,650	$1,750	$2,500	$4,500	$8,500	$25,000	$45,000	$70,000
Auctions: $4,935, AU-58, January 2015; $4,848, AU-55, August 2015; $2,585, AU-50, September 2015; $2,820, EF-45, July 2015												
1871, Proof (h)	30	6	63.8							$65,000	$125,000	$225,000
Auctions: $26,450, PF-62Cam, August 2004												
1871-CC	17,387	175	49.8	3%	$25,000	$37,500	$55,000	$70,000	$125,000			
Auctions: $111,625, MS-60, August 2015; $64,625, AU-55, October 2016; $56,400, AU-53, January 2015; $30,550, AU-50, September 2015												
1871-S	928,000	1,796	54.2	11%	$1,500	$1,600	$1,750	$2,250	$4,500	$10,000	$22,500	$50,000
Auctions: $10,575, MS-62, August 2015; $6,463, MS-61, March 2016; $3,525, MS-60, March 2016; $2,471, AU-58, July 2015												
1872	251,850	725	55.2	12%	$1,500	$1,600	$1,750	$2,200	$5,500	$15,000	$22,500	$65,000
Auctions: $28,200, MS-63, January 2015; $2,820, AU-58, October 2015; $2,291, AU-53, January 2015; $1,528, EF-40, October 2015												
1872, Proof (i)	30	4	63.5							$65,000	$125,000	$225,000
Auctions: $135,125, PF-64, October 2014												
1872-CC	26,900	417	50.6	3%	$5,500	$9,500	$15,500	$22,500	$75,000			
Auctions: $94,000, MS-61, August 2015; $54,050, AU-58, January 2015; $13,513, AU-50, August 2015; $7,050, EF-40, January 2015												
1872-S	780,000	1,655	54.3	10%	$1,500	$1,600	$1,750	$1,850	$3,750	$13,500	$30,000	
Auctions: $25,850, MS-63, February 2015; $4,700, MS-61, March 2015; $1,880, AU-55, August 2015; $1,645, EF-45, August 2015												
1873, Close 3	1,709,800	400	54.5	12%	$1,500	$1,600	$1,750	$2,000	$4,250	$14,000		
Auctions: $3,525, MS-60, July 2015; $2,115, AU-55, January 2015; $1,880, AU-55, August 2015; $1,586, AU-55, October 2015												
1873, Open 3	(j)	8,330	58.6	52%	$1,500	$1,550	$1,600	$1,650	$1,850	$2,500	$7,500	$35,000
Auctions: $6,463, MS-63, January 2015; $1,645, AU-58, August 2015; $1,322, AU-53, September 2015; $1,234, EF-45, May 2015												
1873, Close 3, Proof (k)	25	7	63.9							$65,000	$125,000	$225,000
Auctions: $230,000, PF-65UCam, April 2011												

† Ranked in the *100 Greatest U.S. Coins* (fourth edition). **d.** Approximately 12 examples are known. **e.** Approximately 12 examples are known. **f.** Approximately 12 examples are known. **g.** An estimated 35 to 50 examples are believed to exist; most are in VF with extensive abrasions. **h.** Fewer than 10 examples are known. **i.** Fewer than 12 examples are known. **j.** Included in circulation-strike 1873, Close 3, mintage figure. **k.** 10 to 12 examples are known.

| | Mintage | Cert | Avg | %MS | VF-20 | EF-40 | AU-50 | AU-55 | MS-60 | MS-62 | MS-63 | MS-64 |
										PF-63	PF-64	PF-65
1873-CC, Close 3	22,410	396	52.1	5%	$4,000	$8,000	$17,500	$25,000	$50,000	$85,000	$135,000	
	Auctions: $25,850, AU-55, August 2015; $18,800, AU-55, January 2015; $15,863, AU-53, August 2015; $7,050, EF-40, October 2015											
1873-S, Close 3	1,040,600	1,791	54.8	14%	$1,500	$1,600	$1,675	$1,750	$2,650	$9,500	$20,000	
	Auctions: $7,638, MS-61, August 2015; $2,115, AU-58, February 2015; $1,410, AU-53, October 2015; $1,528, EF-45, September 2015											
1873-S, Open 3	(l)	894	54.4	11%	$1,500	$1,725	$1,775	$2,750	$7,000	$27,500		
	Auctions: $14,100, MS-61, September 2015; $4,230, AU-58, August 2015; $1,528, AU-53, June 2015; $1,293, EF-45, September 2015											
1874	366,780	1,156	57.0	27%	$1,500	$1,550	$1,600	$1,650	$3,000	$13,000	$20,000	$47,500
	Auctions: $39,950, MS-64, August 2015; $3,760, MS-60, January 2015; $2,585, AU-55, August 2015; $1,351, AU-50, January 2015											
1874, Proof (m)	20	5	63.6							$75,000	$135,000	$275,000
	Auctions: $218,500, PF-64UCamH, January 2012											
1874-CC	115,085	1,337	49.0	1%	$3,500	$4,500	$6,500	$10,000	$27,500	$60,000		
	Auctions: $21,150, AU-58, August 2015; $5,640, AU-53, October 2015; $3,760, EF-45, July 2015; $2,350, VF-30, January 2015											
1874-S	1,214,000	3,644	56.0	19%	$1,500	$1,550	$1,600	$1,700	$2,250	$5,500	$28,500	
	Auctions: $7,050, MS-62, June 2015; $1,998, MS-60, January 2015; $1,645, AU-55, February 2015; $1,293, EF-45, January 2015											
1875	295,720	1,555	59.2	58%	$1,500	$1,550	$1,600	$1,700	$2,250	$2,850	$8,000	$40,000
	Auctions: $8,225, MS-63, September 2015; $2,585, MS-60, August 2015; $1,528, AU-58, January 2015; $1,351, AU-55, January 2015											
1875, Proof (n)	20	5	64.8							$100,000	$175,000	$350,000
	Auctions: $94,300, PF-63Cam, August 2009											
1875-CC	111,151	1,719	53.4	28%	$3,500	$4,000	$4,500	$6,000	$12,500	$20,000	$37,500	$75,000
	Auctions: $28,200, MS-63, January 2015; $7,344, AU-58, July 2015; $2,585, AU-50, January 2015; $2,820, EF-45, March 2015											
1875-S	1,230,000	4,442	56.8	27%	$1,500	$1,550	$1,600	$1,700	$2,000	$3,500	$11,000	$35,000
	Auctions: $16,450, MS-63, July 2015; $1,645, AU-58, August 2015; $1,410, AU-53, October 2015; $1,293, VF-35, January 2015											
1876	583,860	2,775	57.9	38%	$1,500	$1,550	$1,600	$1,700	$1,850	$3,750	$10,000	$35,000
	Auctions: $3,995, MS-62, January 2015; $1,410, AU-55, September 2015; $1,351, AU-53, January 2015; $1,528, EF-40, September 2015											
1876, Proof (o)	45	13	63.8							$55,000	$75,000	$135,000
	Auctions: $152,750, PF-64DCam, February 2013											
1876-CC	138,441	2,048	52.2	12%	$3,000	$4,000	$5,500	$6,000	$12,500	$25,000	$35,000	
	Auctions: $12,925, MS-60, October 2015; $8,813, AU-58, August 2015; $3,995, AU-50, October 2015; $2,585, VF-20, August 2015											
1876-S	1,597,000	7,018	57.0	31%	$1,500	$1,550	$1,600	$1,700	$2,000	$2,750	$8,500	$32,500
	Auctions: $42,300, MS-64, August 2015; $2,291, MS-61, August 2015; $1,528, AU-55, September 2015; $1,528, AU-50, October 2015											

l. Included in 1873-S, Close 3, mintage figure. **m.** Fewer than 10 examples are known. **n.** 10 to 12 examples are known.
o. Approximately 15 examples are known.

| | Mintage | Cert | Avg | %MS | VF-20 | EF-40 | AU-50 | AU-55 | MS-60 | MS-62 | MS-63 | MS-65 |
										PF-63	PF-64	PF-65
1877	397,650	1,044	59.3	66%	$1,400	$1,450	$1,550	$1,600	$2,100	$4,500	$15,000	
	Auctions: $3,995, MS-62, January 2015; $3,055, MS-61, August 2015; $2,000, MS-61, January 2015; $1,880, MS-61, July 2015											
1877, Proof (a)	20	8	63.5							$40,000	$75,000	$135,000
	Auctions: $21,150, PF-58, February 2013											
1877-CC	42,565	865	49.1	3%	$3,000	$4,000	$7,000	$12,500	$30,000	$65,000		
	Auctions: $24,675, AU-58, September 2015; $9,400, AU-55, August 2015; $4,700, AU-50, August 2015; $3,525, EF-40, January 2015											
1877-S	1,735,000	2,287	58.9	60%	$1,400	$1,425	$1,475	$1,500	$1,850	$4,750	$16,000	$45,000
	Auctions: $5,170, MS-62, February 2015; $1,998, MS-61, December 2015; $1,528, MS-60, February 2015; $1,645, AU-58, August 2015											
1878	543,625	1,618	59.8	70%	$1,400	$1,425	$1,475	$1,500	$1,750	$3,750	$11,000	
	Auctions: $9,400, MS-63, September 2015; $1,998, MS-61, July 2015; $1,645, AU-58, August 2015; $1,645, AU-55, August 2015											
1878, Proof (b)	20	8	64.5							$40,000	$65,000	$135,000
	Auctions: $69,000, PF-64Cam, April 2011											
1878-CC	13,180	342	48.0	3%	$5,500	$10,000	$14,500	$25,000	$47,500	$75,000		
	Auctions: $19,975, AU-55, August 2015; $9,400, EF-45, August 2015; $7,638, EF-40, July 2015; $6,169, VF-35, January 2015											
1878-S	1,739,000	1,592	58.1	56%	$1,400	$1,425	$1,475	$1,500	$1,750	$5,500	$16,500	
	Auctions: $6,169, MS-62, September 2015; $1,763, MS-60, August 2015; $1,763, AU-58, July 2015; $1,351, AU-55, January 2015											

a. 10 to 12 examples are known. **b.** Fewer than 10 examples are known.

| | Mintage | Cert | Avg | %MS | VF-20 | EF-40 | AU-50 | AU-55 | MS-60 | MS-62 | MS-63 | MS-65 |
										PF-63	PF-64	PF-65
1879	207,600	611	58.3	45%	$1,400	$1,425	$1,475	$1,500	$2,150	$6,500	$17,500	
	Auctions: $3,290, MS-61, September 2015; $2,585, MS-61, February 2015; $2,350, MS-60, August 2015; $2,115, AU-58, September 2015											
1879, Proof (c)	30	4	64.0							$40,000	$65,000	$135,000
	Auctions: $57,500, PF-64, July 2009											
1879-CC	10,708	325	50.9	3%	$6,750	$12,000	$22,500	$28,500	$60,000	$85,000		
	Auctions: $28,200, AU-55, July 2015; $4,230, AU-50, August 2015; $11,899, EF-45, January 2015; $3,055, EF-40, October 2015											
1879-O	2,325	83	50.6	11%	$25,000	$45,000	$50,000	$65,000	$140,000	$175,000	$200,000	
	Auctions: $135,125, MS-60, January 2014; $70,500, AU-58, August 2015; $35,250, AU-50, August 2014; $37,600, VF-25, September 2016											
1879-S	1,223,800	1,335	57.4	30%	$1,400	$1,425	$1,475	$1,500	$2,250	$16,500	$40,000	
	Auctions: $4,714, MS-61, January 2015; $2,585, AU-58, July 2015; $1,316, AU-55, January 2015; $1,539, AU-53, August 2015											
1880	51,420	393	55.3	15%	$1,475	$1,500	$1,575	$1,750	$8,500	$25,000	$32,500	
	Auctions: $15,275, MS-61, August 2015; $3,525, AU-58, February 2015; $3,760, AU-55, August 2015; $2,820, AU-53, September 2015											
1880, Proof (d)	36	4	64.3							$40,000	$65,000	$135,000
	Auctions: $217,375, PF-65DCam, August 2014; $235,000, PF, March 2014											
1880-S	836,000	922	58.0	39%	$1,375	$1,425	$1,475	$1,500	$1,800	$8,500	$22,500	
	Auctions: $5,405, MS-62, January 2015; $4,700, MS-61, August 2015; $1,645, AU-58, June 2015; $1,645, AU-53, August 2015											
1881	2,199	31	53.7	16%	$17,500	$27,500	$45,000	$60,000	$125,000			
	Auctions: $141,000, MS-61, August 2015; $141,000, MS-61, January 2015; $82,290, AU-58, September 2016; $56,400, AU-58, August 2015											
1881, Proof (e)	61	7	63.7							$40,000	$75,000	$135,000
	Auctions: $172,500, PF-65Cam, January 2011											
1881-S	727,000	776	58.5	53%	$1,375	$1,385	$1,400	$1,425	$2,000	$6,500	$22,500	
	Auctions: $10,575, MS-62, January 2015; $1,998, MS-61, February 2015; $2,233, AU-58, August 2015; $3,055, AU-55, September 2015											
1882	571	15	55.9	13%	$30,000	$50,000	$90,000	$100,000	$135,000	$175,000	$225,000	
	Auctions: $94,000, AU-58, January 2014; $129,250, AU-55, August 2014											
1882, Proof (f)	59	6	63.7							$40,000	$75,000	$125,000
	Auctions: $161,000, PF-64Cam, January 2011											
1882-CC	39,140	990	54.2	7%	$3,000	$4,000	$5,000	$7,500	$15,000	$32,500	$100,000	
	Auctions: $12,925, AU-58, July 2015; $7,050, AU-55, January 2015; $5,288, AU-53, September 2015; $3,055, EF-45, February 2015											
1882-S	1,125,000	1,446	59.0	61%	$1,375	$1,385	$1,400	$1,425	$1,750	$3,500	$14,000	
	Auctions: $12,925, MS-63, June 2015; $3,995, MS-62, September 2015; $1,528, MS-60, July 2015; $1,552, AU-58, October 2015											
1883, Proof (g)	92	11	65.1							$115,000	$150,000	$275,000
	Auctions: $282,000, PF-65DCam, January 2014; $158,625, PF-64DCam, August 2014											
1883-CC	59,962	1,321	53.4	7%	$3,000	$3,500	$5,250	$7,000	$13,500	$27,500	$40,000	
	Auctions: $19,975, MS-61, January 2015; $11,750, AU-58, June 2015; $5,875, AU-53, August 2015; $2,820, EF-45, February 2015											
1883-S	1,189,000	2,202	59.7	72%	$1,375	$1,385	$1,400	$1,425	$1,750	$2,250	$5,500	
	Auctions: $14,100, MS-64, June 2015; $1,528, MS-61, March 2015; $1,469, AU-55, January 2015; $1,293, EF-45, January 2015											
1884, Proof (h)	71	10	63.1							$110,000	$150,000	$275,000
	Auctions: $246,750, PF-65DCam, January 2015; $235,000, PF-65DCam, August 2014; $246,750, PF-66Cam, April 2014											
1884-CC	81,139	1,698	54.1	18%	$2,750	$3,500	$5,000	$7,000	$11,500	$22,500	$45,000	
	Auctions: $28,200, MS-62, June 2015; $5,244, AU-55, August 2015; $3,290, EF-40, July 2015; $3,525, VG-10, August 2015											
1884-S	916,000	2,622	60.5	82%	$1,375	$1,385	$1,400	$1,425	$1,850	$2,000	$4,500	$45,000
	Auctions: $3,761, MS-63, January 2015; $1,998, MS-61, August 2015; $1,396, MS-60, January 2015; $1,351, AU-58, January 2015											
1885	751	57	57.0	33%	$22,500	$30,000	$47,500	$65,000	$85,000	$105,000	$135,000	
	Auctions: $82,250, MS-62, October 2014; $14,100, MS-60, November 2014; $58,750, AU-58, January 2014											
1885, Proof (i)	77	11	64.1							$50,000	$100,000	$135,000
	Auctions: $35,250, PF-61DCam, September 2014											
1885-CC	9,450	300	51.8	6%	$6,500	$12,000	$16,500	$22,500	$42,500	$65,000	$125,000	
	Auctions: $61,688, MS-62, March 2015; $37,600, MS-61, January 2015; $23,500, AU-55, August 2015; $3,055, AU-50, June 2015											
1885-S	683,500	2,278	60.8	86%	$1,375	$1,385	$1,400	$1,425	$1,800	$2,250	$3,250	
	Auctions: $3,995, MS-63, January 2015; $1,998, MS-62, August 2015; $1,998, MS-61, August 2015; $1,528, AU-58, August 2015											

c. 10 to 12 examples are known. d. 10 to 12 examples are known. e. Fewer than 20 examples are known. f. 12 to 15 examples are known. g. Proof only. Approximately 20 examples are known. h. Proof only. Approximately 20 examples are known. i. 15 to 20 examples are known.

1888, Doubled Die Reverse
FS-G20-1888-801.

	Mintage	Cert	Avg	%MS	VF-20	EF-40	AU-50	AU-55	MS-60	MS-62	MS-63	MS-65
										PF-63	PF-64	PF-65
1886	1,000	28	54.9	7%	$40,000	$75,000	$85,000	$100,000	$135,000	$145,000	$165,000	
Auctions: $129,250, MS-60, January 2014; $111,625, AU-58, August 2014; $76,375, AU-53, August 2015; $73,438, EF-45, August 2015												
1886, Proof (j)	106	18	64.4							$45,000	$75,000	$115,000
Auctions: $19,975, PF-60, January 2014												
1887, Proof (k)	121	10	65.1							$67,500	$85,000	$125,000
Auctions: $258,500, PF-66, January 2014; $123,375, PF-65Cam, August 2014; $117,500, PF-65Cam, August 2015												
1887-S	283,000	927	60.0	73%	$1,375	$1,385	$1,400	$1,425	$1,800	$4,750	$12,500	
Auctions: $9,694, MS-63, January 2015; $4,935, MS-62, January 2015; $4,700, MS-62, August 2015; $2,585, MS-61, October 2015												
1888	226,161	1,086	60.1	73%	$1,375	$1,385	$1,400	$1,425	$2,100	$3,000	$12,000	$30,000
Auctions: $4,465, MS-62, June 2015; $2,115, MS-61, September 2015; $1,763, MS-60, August 2015; $1,469, AU-55, January 2015												
1888, Doubled Die Reverse	(l)	21	60.0	76%					$3,000	$3,750		
Auctions: $3,819, MS-62, April 2013												
1888, Proof (m)	105	20	64.3							$30,000	$45,000	$85,000
Auctions: $126,500, PF-65DCam, April 2012												
1888-S	859,600	2,592	60.7	84%	$1,375	$1,385	$1,400	$1,425	$1,750	$2,100	$4,000	
Auctions: $5,640, MS-63, August 2015; $2,291, MS-62, February 2015; $1,998, MS-61, August 2015; $1,557, AU-58, August 2015												
1889	44,070	533	60.5	82%	$1,375	$1,385	$1,400	$1,425	$2,150	$4,250	$15,000	
Auctions: $5,405, MS-62, August 2015; $2,585, MS-61, February 2015; $1,880, AU-55, August 2015; $1,645, AU-50, September 2015												
1889, Proof (n)	41	10	63.5							$30,000	$45,000	$85,000
Auctions: $352,500, PF-65, January 2014												
1889-CC	30,945	858	52.5	8%	$3,500	$4,000	$6,500	$8,500	$13,500	$30,000	$45,000	
Auctions: $16,450, MS-61, January 2015; $14,688, MS-60, June 2015; $7,638, AU-55, August 2015; $5,699, AU-53, August 2015												
1889-S	774,700	1,974	60.6	83%	$1,375	$1,385	$1,400	$1,425	$1,800	$2,500	$3,250	
Auctions: $21,150, MS-65, January 2015; $2,115, MS-62, July 2015; $1,998, MS-61, September 2015; $1,410, AU-50, January 2015												
1890	75,940	649	60.6	81%	$1,375	$1,385	$1,400	$1,425	$1,750	$3,250	$10,000	$35,000
Auctions: $7,931, MS-63, January 2015; $2,820, MS-62, October 2015; $2,115, AU-58, August 2015; $2,115, AU-50, September 2015												
1890, Proof (o)	55	13	65.2							$30,000	$45,000	$85,000
Auctions: $92,000, PF-65UCam, August 2011												
1890-CC	91,209	2,214	52.9	9%	$3,000	$4,000	$5,000	$7,000	$13,000	$20,000	$45,000	
Auctions: $25,850, MS-62, June 2015; $10,575, AU-58, August 2015; $5,875, AU-50, February 2015; $3,055, EF-40, October 2015												
1890-S	802,750	1,791	60.0	73%	$1,375	$1,385	$1,400	$1,425	$1,600	$2,000	$4,500	
Auctions: $21,150, MS-65, January 2015; $3,995, MS-63, June 2015; $2,056, MS-62, June 2015; $1,586, MS-61, September 2015												
1891	1,390	41	56.2	12%	$15,000	$22,500	$40,000	$50,000	$85,000	$102,500		
Auctions: $82,250, MS-61, January 2014; $52,889, AU-58, November 2016; $52,875, AU-58, August 2014												
1891, Proof (p)	52	27	63.7							$30,000	$45,000	$85,000
Auctions: $655,200, PF, September 2013												
1891-CC	5,000	259	55.0	14%	$8,500	$15,000	$22,000	$27,500	$45,000	$65,000	$90,000	
Auctions: $41,125, MS-61, March 2015; $38,775, MS-60, January 2015; $28,200, AU-55, October 2016; $23,500, AU-55, July 2015												
1891-S	1,288,125	5,553	61.1	91%	$1,375	$1,385	$1,400	$1,425	$1,600	$1,650	$2,750	
Auctions: $4,935, MS-64, July 2015; $2,468, MS-63, January 2015; $1,998, MS-62, July 2015; $1,880, MS-62, August 2015												

j. 20 to 25 examples are known. **k.** Proof only. More than 30 examples are known. **l.** Included in circulation-strike 1888 mintage figure. **m.** 20 to 30 examples are known. **n.** 10 to 12 examples are known. **o.** Approximately 15 examples are known. **p.** 20 to 25 examples are known.

	Mintage	Cert	Avg	%MS	VF-20	EF-40	AU-50	AU-55	MS-60	MS-62	MS-63	MS-65
										PF-63	PF-64	PF-65
1892	4,430	124	57.1	31%	$4,500	$6,500	$10,000	$13,500	$22,500	$35,000	$40,000	$85,000
	Auctions: $32,900, MS-62, August 2015; $23,500, MS-61, March 2016; $5,640, MS-60, July 2015; $11,788, AU-55, August 2014											
1892, Proof (q)	93	15	64.3							$30,000	$45,000	$85,000
	Auctions: $188,000, PF-66DCam, January 2014											
1892-CC	27,265	871	55.3	21%	$2,850	$4,000	$5,000	$8,500	$15,000	$32,500	$55,000	
	Auctions: $35,250, MS-63, August 2015; $28,200, MS-62, February 2016; $9,988, AU-58, July 2015; $4,465, AU-53, July 2015											
1892-S	930,150	4,477	61.1	91%	$1,375	$1,385	$1,400	$1,425	$1,525	$1,650	$2,500	$22,500
	Auctions: $17,625, MS-65, January 2015; $8,225, MS-64, August 2015; $1,592, MS-62, August 2015; $1,351, AU-55, January 2015											
1893	344,280	5,966	61.6	98%	$1,375	$1,385	$1,400	$1,425	$1,525	$1,575	$2,500	
	Auctions: $3,643, MS-63, February 2015; $2,826, MS-63, October 2015; $1,998, MS-62, August 2015; $1,410, MS-60, October 2015											
1893, Proof (r)	59	5	63.4							$30,000	$45,000	$85,000
	Auctions: $15,525, PF-60Cam, August 2011											
1893-CC	18,402	775	58.7	49%	$3,500	$4,500	$6,500	$8,500	$14,000	$22,500	$50,000	
	Auctions: $19,975, MS-62, August 2015; $17,625, MS-62, July 2015; $28,200, MS-61, September 2016; $14,688, MS-61, June 2015											
1893-S	996,175	5,267	61.1	92%	$1,450	$1,475	$1,485	$1,500	$1,650	$1,675	$3,250	
	Auctions: $3,290, MS-63, February 2015; $2,820, MS-63, January 2015; $1,763, MS-62, August 2015; $1,645, MS-62, July 2015											
1894	1,368,940	15,435	61.4	97%	$1,375	$1,385	$1,400	$1,425	$1,525	$1,575	$2,000	$25,000
	Auctions: $22,325, MS-65, January 2015; $4,700, MS-64, February 2015; $1,645, MS-62, September 2015; $1,351, AU-55, January 2015											
1894, Proof (s)	50	13	63.8							$30,000	$45,000	$85,000
	Auctions: $54,625, PF-64Cam, January 2005											
1894-S	1,048,550	5,673	61.2	93%	$1,375	$1,385	$1,400	$1,425	$1,525	$1,575	$2,750	$23,000
	Auctions: $4,935, MS-64, January 2015; $2,585, MS-63, February 2015; $1,763, MS-62, August 2015; $1,351, MS-61, January 2015											
1895	1,114,605	22,087	61.7	98%	$1,375	$1,385	$1,400	$1,425	$1,525	$1,575	$2,100	$20,000
	Auctions: $3,055, MS-64, January 2015; $1,880, MS-63, August 2015; $1,528, MS-62, August 2015; $1,293, AU-58, February 2015											
1895, Proof	51	11	64.2							$30,000	$45,000	$85,000
	Auctions: $82,250, PF-65Cam, September 2014											
1895-S	1,143,500	7,363	61.3	94%	$1,375	$1,385	$1,400	$1,425	$1,525	$1,650	$2,000	$12,500
	Auctions: $9,583, MS-65, January 2015; $3,878, MS-64, February 2015; $1,763, MS-62, October 2015; $1,293, MS-60, June 2015											
1896	792,535	10,297	61.7	97%	$1,375	$1,385	$1,400	$1,425	$1,525	$1,575	$2,000	$18,000
	Auctions: $3,290, MS-64, September 2015; $2,056, MS-63, January 2015; $1,763, MS-62, July 2015; $1,704, MS-62, September 2015											
1896, Proof (t)	128	38	64.0							$30,000	$45,000	$85,000
	Auctions: $97,750, PF-65DCam, April 2012											
1896-S	1,403,925	9,274	61.3	94%	$1,375	$1,385	$1,400	$1,425	$1,525	$1,575	$2,000	$25,000
	Auctions: $3,055, MS-63, January 2015; $2,468, MS-63, February 2015; $1,645, MS-62, September 2015; $1,528, MS-61, January 2015											
1897	1,383,175	18,096	61.7	98%	$1,375	$1,385	$1,400	$1,425	$1,525	$1,575	$2,000	$20,000
	Auctions: $2,585, MS-64, January 2015; $2,115, MS-63, August 2015; $1,763, MS-62, September 2015; $1,351, MS-61, January 2015											
1897, Proof (u)	86	23	64.1							$30,000	$45,000	$85,000
	Auctions: $73,438, PF-64Cam, August 2014; $30,550, PF-62Cam, April 2013											
1897-S	1,470,250	12,894	61.6	95%	$1,375	$1,385	$1,400	$1,425	$1,525	$1,650	$2,250	$18,000
	Auctions: $16,450, MS-65, January 2015; $3,643, MS-64, June 2015; $1,763, MS-62, August 2015; $1,351, MS-61, January 2015											
1898	170,395	1,728	61.2	89%	$1,375	$1,385	$1,400	$1,425	$2,000	$2,250	$3,250	
	Auctions: $4,818, MS-63, October 2015; $2,585, MS-62, August 2015; $1,410, MS-61, January 2015; $1,410, AU-58, January 2015											
1898, Proof (v)	75	35	64.2							$30,000	$45,000	$85,000
	Auctions: $52,875, PF-64DCam, September 2014; $117,500, PF-65Cam, April 2013											
1898-S	2,575,175	22,750	61.7	96%	$1,375	$1,385	$1,400	$1,425	$1,525	$1,575	$2,000	$8,500
	Auctions: $9,400, MS-65, June 2015; $1,645, MS-62, September 2015; $1,351, AU-58, January 2015; $1,351, AU-55, January 2015											

q. Approximately 25 examples are known. **r.** 15 to 20 examples are known. **s.** 15 to 20 examples are known. **t.** 45 to 50 examples are known. **u.** 20 to 25 examples are known. **v.** 35 to 40 examples are known.

	Mintage	Cert	Avg	%MS	VF-20	EF-40	AU-50	AU-55	MS-60	MS-62	MS-63	MS-65
										PF-63	PF-64	PF-65
1899	1,669,300	24,341	62.0	98%	$1,375	$1,385	$1,400	$1,425	$1,525	$1,575	$1,750	$8,500
	Auctions: $7,638, MS-65, September 2015; $4,113, MS-64, June 2015; $1,410, MS-61, October 2015; $1,528, AU-58, August 2015											
1899, Proof (w)	84	29	64.2							$30,000	$45,000	$85,000
	Auctions: $76,375, PF, March 2014											
1899-S	2,010,300	9,282	61.3	91%	$1,375	$1,385	$1,400	$1,425	$1,525	$1,575	$2,500	$20,000
	Auctions: $2,291, MS-63, September 2015; $1,939, MS-63, February 2015; $1,763, MS-62, August 2015; $1,645, MS-62, August 2015											
1900	1,874,460	53,270	62.4	99%	$1,375	$1,385	$1,400	$1,425	$1,525	$1,575	$1,650	$5,500
	Auctions: $7,344, MS-65, August 2015; $2,820, MS-64, August 2015; $1,821, MS-62, June 2015; $1,293, MS-60, July 2015											
1900, Proof (x)	124	30	64.6							$30,000	$45,000	$85,000
	Auctions: $88,125, PF, March 2014											
1900-S	2,459,500	7,801	61.1	93%	$1,375	$1,385	$1,400	$1,425	$1,525	$1,575	$2,250	$22,500
	Auctions: $3,055, MS-63, August 2015; $1,763, MS-62, August 2015; $1,422, MS-60, August 2015; $1,410, AU-58, October 2015											
1901	111,430	5,438	62.9	99%	$1,375	$1,385	$1,400	$1,425	$1,525	$1,575	$1,750	$3,000
	Auctions: $3,290, MS-65, January 2015; $2,115, MS-64, August 2015; $1,880, MS-63, February 2015; $1,645, MS-62, August 2015											
1901, Proof (y)	96	41	62.9							$30,000	$45,000	$85,000
	Auctions: $68,150, PF, February 2013											
1901-S	1,596,000	3,119	61.1	93%	$1,375	$1,385	$1,400	$1,425	$1,525	$1,575	$3,750	$22,500
	Auctions: $3,525, MS-63, February 2015; $2,938, MS-63, September 2015; $2,115, MS-62, August 2015; $2,350, MS-61, August 2015											
1902	31,140	511	59.9	67%	$1,375	$1,385	$1,400	$1,425	$2,500	$6,000	$10,000	
	Auctions: $4,700, MS-62, July 2015; $3,995, MS-61, August 2015; $2,350, MS-61, January 2015; $2,820, AU-58, August 2015											
1902, Proof (z)	114	29	63.1							$30,000	$45,000	$85,000
	Auctions: $9,400, PF-50, January 2014											
1902-S	1,753,625	4,507	61.0	93%	$1,375	$1,385	$1,400	$1,425	$1,525	$1,575	$3,250	$30,000
	Auctions: $28,200, MS-65, October 2015; $3,525, MS-63, January 2015; $1,410, MS-60, January 2015; $1,351, AU-58, June 2015											
1903	287,270	12,579	62.9	100%	$1,375	$1,385	$1,400	$1,425	$1,525	$1,575	$1,650	$3,000
	Auctions: $3,290, MS-65, January 2015; $2,585, MS-64, August 2015; $1,645, MS-63, August 2015; $1,410, MS-61, January 2015											
1903, Proof (aa)	158	38	62.9							$30,000	$45,000	$85,000
	Auctions: $63,450, PF, March 2014											
1903-S	954,000	6,473	61.8	98%	$1,375	$1,385	$1,400	$1,425	$1,525	$1,575	$2,250	$14,500
	Auctions: $3,290, MS-64, September 2015; $2,174, MS-63, June 2015; $1,481, MS-62, August 2015; $1,422, AU-55, August 2015											
1904	6,256,699	225,037	62.6	99%	$1,375	$1,385	$1,400	$1,425	$1,525	$1,575	$1,650	$2,750
	Auctions: $5,875, MS-66, October 2015; $4,818, MS-65, March 2015; $1,528, MS-62, August 2015; $1,351, MS-60, June 2015											
1904, Proof (bb)	98	41	63.7							$30,000	$45,000	$85,000
	Auctions: $146,875, PF-67Cam, August 2013											
1904-S	5,134,175	24,431	62.4	98%	$1,375	$1,385	$1,400	$1,425	$1,525	$1,575	$1,650	$2,750
	Auctions: $4,465, MS-65, January 2015; $2,350, MS-64, January 2015; $1,645, MS-62, August 2015; $1,293, AU-58, January 2015											
1905	58,919	799	59.3	59%	$1,375	$1,385	$1,400	$1,425	$2,500	$6,500	$15,000	$85,000
	Auctions: $6,463, MS-62, August 2015; $5,405, MS-62, July 2015; $1,763, AU-58, June 2015; $1,763, AU-53, August 2015											
1905, Proof (cc)	92	26	62.8							$30,000	$45,000	$85,000
	Auctions: $10,005, PF-58, January 2012											
1905-S	1,813,000	2,324	61.1	89%	$1,375	$1,385	$1,400	$1,425	$1,525	$1,575	$3,500	$20,000
	Auctions: $4,935, MS-64, July 2015; $3,525, MS-63, January 2015; $2,468, MS-62, August 2015; $1,645, MS-61, September 2015											

w. Fewer than 30 examples are known. **x.** Approximately 50 examples are known. **y.** 40 to 50 examples are known. **z.** Fewer than 50 examples are known. **aa.** 40 to 50 examples are known. **bb.** Approximately 50 examples are known. **cc.** 30 to 40 examples are known.

	Mintage	Cert	Avg	%MS	VF-20	EF-40	AU-50	AU-55	MS-60	MS-62 PF-63	MS-63 PF-64	MS-65 PF-65
1906	69,596	691	60.4	75%	$1,400	$1,475	$1,500	$1,600	$1,800	$5,000	$8,500	$32,500
	Auctions: $14,361, MS-64, August 2015; $4,230, MS-62, August 2015; $3,760, MS-61, August 2015; $3,055, AU-58, August 2015											
1906, Proof (dd)	94	45	63.4							$30,000	$45,000	$85,000
	Auctions: $85,188, PF, August 2013											
1906-D	620,250	1,870	61.8	96%	$1,375	$1,385	$1,400	$1,425	$1,525	$1,575	$4,000	$20,000
	Auctions: $10,575, MS-64, August 2015; $3,525, MS-63, January 2015; $3,760, MS-62, August 2015; $1,410, MS-61, January 2015											
1906-D, Proof (ee)	6	0	n/a				*(extremely rare)*					
	Auctions: No auction records available.											
1906-S	2,065,750	4,555	61.5	95%	$1,375	$1,385	$1,400	$1,425	$1,525	$1,575	$2,250	$25,000
	Auctions: $25,850, MS-65, January 2015; $4,935, MS-64, October 2015; $1,645, MS-62, August 2015; $1,645, EF-45, August 2015											
1907	1,451,786	32,059	61.9	99%	$1,375	$1,385	$1,400	$1,425	$1,525	$1,575	$1,650	$7,500
	Auctions: $2,820, MS-64, July 2015; $1,471, MS-62, August 2015; $1,351, MS-60, January 2015; $1,351, AU-55, January 2015											
1907, Proof (ff)	78	49	63.6							$30,000	$45,000	$85,000
	Auctions: $40,250, PF-64Cam, January 2012											
1907-D	842,250	2,295	62.4	96%	$1,375	$1,385	$1,400	$1,425	$1,525	$1,575	$3,500	$8,500
	Auctions: $8,813, MS-65, March 2015; $4,230, MS-64, January 2015; $1,998, MS-62, September 2015; $1,528, MS-61, January 2015											
1907-D, Proof (gg)	*unknown*	1	62.0									
	Auctions: $71,875, PF-62, January 2004											
1907-S	2,165,800	3,487	61.8	95%	$1,375	$1,385	$1,400	$1,425	$1,525	$1,575	$3,000	$22,500
	Auctions: $17,625, MS-65, June 2015; $5,875, MS-64, March 2015; $2,820, MS-63, August 2015; $1,410, MS-61, January 2015											

dd. 45 to 50 examples are known. **ee.** Six 1906-D presentation strikes were made to commemorate the first coinage of double eagles at the Denver Mint. The coins were well documented at the time; however, at present only two are accounted for. **ff.** 25 to 50 examples are known. **gg.** Believed to have once been part of the collection of King Farouk of Egypt; cleaned.

SAINT-GAUDENS, HIGH RELIEF AND ULTRA HIGH RELIEF, MCMVII (1907)

Designer: *Augustus Saint-Gaudens.* **Weight:** *33.436 grams.*
Composition: *.900 gold, .100 copper (net weight: .96750 oz. pure gold).*
Diameter *34 mm.* **Edge:** *E PLURIBUS UNUM with words divided by stars*
(one specimen of the high-relief variety with plain edge is known). **Mint:** *Philadelphia.*

Circulation Strike   Proof, Ultra High Relief Pattern

History. Created by famous artist Augustus Saint-Gaudens under a commission arranged by President Theodore Roosevelt, this double eagle was first made (in pattern form) with ultra high relief, sculptural in its effect, on both sides and the date in Roman numerals. The story of its production is well known and has been described in several books, notably *Renaissance of American Coinage, 1905–1908* (Burdette) and *Striking Change: The Great Artistic Collaboration of Theodore Roosevelt and August Saint-Gaudens* (Moran). After the Ultra High Relief patterns of 1907, a modified High Relief version was developed to facilitate production. Each coin required three blows of the press to strike up properly. Most featured a flat rim (now known as the Flat Rim variety), but planchet metal would occasionally be squeezed up between the collar and the die, resulting in the Wire Rim variety; this can exist around part of or the entire circumference of the coin. The coins were made on a medal press in December 1907 and January 1908, to the extent of fewer than 13,000 pieces. In the meantime, production was under way for low-relief coins, easier to mint in quantities sufficient for commerce—these dated 1907 rather than MCMVII. Today the MCMVII double eagle is a favorite among collectors, and when surveys are taken of beautiful and popular designs (as in *100 Greatest U.S. Coins*, by Garrett and Guth), it always ranks near the top.

Striking and Sharpness. The striking usually is good. Check the left knee of Miss Liberty, which sometimes shows lightness of strike and, most often, shows flatness or wear (sometimes concealed by postmint etching or clever tooling). Check the Capitol at the lower left. On the reverse, check the high points at the top of the eagle. The surface on all is a delicate matte texture, grainy rather than deeply frosty. Under examination the fields show myriad tiny raised curlicues and other die-finish marks. There is no record of any MCMVII double eagles being made as *Proofs*, nor is there any early numismatic record of any being sold as Proofs. Walter Breen in the 1960s made up some guidelines for Proofs, which some graders have adopted. Some homemade "Proofs" have been made by pickling or sandblasting the surface of regular coins—*caveat emptor.*

Availability. Half or more of the original mintage still exist today, as many were saved, and these grade mostly from AU-50 to MS-62. Circulated examples often have been cleaned, polished, or used in jewelry. Higher-grade coins are seen with some frequency, up to MS-65. Overgrading is common.

GRADING STANDARDS

MS-60 to 70 (Mint State). *Obverse:* At MS-60, some abrasion and contact marks are seen on Liberty's chest. The left knee is flat on lower Mint State coins and all circulated coins. Scattered marks and abrasion are in the field. Satiny luster is present, but may be dull or lifeless, and interrupted in patches. Many coins at this level have been cleaned. At MS-63, contact marks are fewer, and abrasion is light, but the knee still has a flat spot. An MS-65 coin

MCMVII (1907), High Relief. Graded MS-63.

has little abrasion and few marks. Grades above MS-65 are defined by having fewer marks as perfection is approached. *Reverse:* Comments apply as for the obverse, except that abrasion and contact marks are most noticeable on the side of the eagle's body and the top of the left wing.

Illustrated coin: This is a splendid choice striking.

AU-50, 53, 55, 58 (About Uncirculated). *Obverse:* Light wear is seen on the chest, the left leg, and the field, more so at AU-50 than at AU–53 or 55. An AU-58 coin has fewer traces of wear. An AU-50 coin has satiny luster in protected areas among the rays, with little in the open field above. At AU-58, most luster is present. *Reverse:* Comments as preceding, except that the side of the eagle below the front of the wing, the top of the wing, and the field

MCMVII (1907), High Relief. Graded AU-55.

show light wear. Satiny luster ranges from perhaps 40% (at AU-50) to nearly full mint bloom (at AU-58).

EF-40, 45 (Extremely Fine). *Obverse:* Wear is seen on all the higher-relief areas of the standing figure and on the rock at the lower right. Luster is minimal, if present at all. Eye appeal is apt to be lacking. Nearly all Extremely Fine coins have been cleaned. *Reverse:* The eagle shows more wear overall, especially at the bottom and on the tops of the wings.

MCMVII (1907), High Relief. Graded EF-45.

VF-20, 30 (Very Fine). *Obverse:* Most details of the standing figure are flat, her face is incomplete, and the tips of the rays are weak. Eye appeal is usually poor. As these coins did not circulate to any extent, a Very Fine coin was likely carried as a pocket piece. *Reverse:* Wear is greater overall, but most evident on the eagle. Detail is good at the center of the left wing, but worn away in most other areas of the bird.

MCMVII (1907), High Relief. Graded VF-30.

The MCMVII (1907) High Relief double eagle is seldom collected in grades lower than VF-20.

	Mintage	Cert	Avg	%MS	VF-20	EF-40	AU-50	AU-55	MS-60 / PF-63	MS-62 / PF-64	MS-63 / PF-65	MS-65 / PF-67
1907, High Relief, MCMVII, Wire Rim † (a)	12,367	1,423	63.2	89%	$9,000	$11,000	$12,000	$13,000	$15,000	$19,500	$24,000	$45,000
	Auctions: $71,675, MS-66, October 2015; $44,650, MS-65, November 2016; $18,800, AU-55, August 2015; $11,163, AU-55, October 2016											
1907, High Relief, MCMVII, Flat Rim †	(b)	581	63.3	86%	$9,000	$11,000	$12,000	$13,500	$15,000	$20,000	$24,000	$47,500
	Auctions: $117,500, MS-67, January 2015; $70,500, MS-66, August 2016; $16,450, AU-58, September 2015											
1907, High Relief, MCMVII, Wire or Flat Rim, Proof	unknown	0	n/a						$30,000	$42,500	$75,000	
	Auctions: $32,900, PF-64, February 2013											
1907, Ultra High Relief, Plain Edge, Proof	(c)	0	n/a									
	Auctions: No auction records available.											
1907, Ultra High Relief, Inverted Edge, Proof	(c)	0	n/a									
	Auctions: No auction records available.											
1907, Ultra High Relief, Lettered Edge, Proof †	16–22	3	67.3								$2,250,000	$2,500,000
	Auctions: $2,115,000, PF-68, January 2015; $1,840,000, PF-68, January 2007											

† Ranked in the *100 Greatest U.S. Coins* (fourth edition); all 1907 High Relief and 1907 Ultra High Relief Saint-Gaudens Roman Numeral Double Eagles as single entries, respectively. **a.** The Wire Rim and Flat Rim varieties were the result of different collars used in the minting process. The Flat Rim is considered slightly scarcer, but this has not led to large value differentials, as both varieties are very popular among collectors. **b.** Included in 1907, High Relief, MCMVII, Wire Rim, mintage figure. **c.** Included in 1907, Ultra High Relief, Lettered Edge, Proof, mintage figure.

SAINT-GAUDENS, FLAT RELIEF, ARABIC NUMERALS (1907–1933)

Designer: *Augustus Saint-Gaudens.* **Weight:** *33.436 grams.*
Composition: *.900 gold, .100 copper (net weight: .96750 oz. pure gold).*
Diameter: *34 mm.* **Edge:** *E PLURIBUS UNUM with words divided by stars.*
Mints: *Philadelphia, Denver, and San Francisco.*

No Motto (1907–1908)

Mintmark location is on
the obverse, above the date.

With Motto (1908–1933)　　　　　　　　With Motto, Proof

History. In autumn 1907 U.S. Mint chief engraver Charles E. Barber modified Augustus Saint-Gaudens's design by lowering its relief and substituting Arabic (not Roman) numerals. Coins of this type were struck in large quantities from 1907 to 1916 and again from 1920 to 1933. In July 1908 the motto IN GOD WE TRUST was added to the reverse. Coins dated 1907 to 1911 have 46 stars on the obverse; coins of 1912 to 1933 have 48 stars. Sandblast (also called Matte) Proofs were made in 1908 and from 1911 to 1915; Satin (also called Roman Finish) Proofs were made in 1909 and 1910.

The vast majority of these coins were exported. Since World War II millions have been repatriated, supplying most of those in numismatic hands today.

Striking and Sharpness. The details are often light on the obverse. Check the bosom of Miss Liberty, the covering of which tends to be weak on 1907 and, especially, 1908 No Motto coins. Check the Capitol building and its immediate area at the lower left. The reverse usually is well struck, but check the feathers on the eagle and the top of the wings. The Matte Proofs have dull surfaces, much like fine-grained sandpaper, while the Satin Proofs have satiny surfaces and are bright yellow.

Availability. Most dates and mintmarks range from very common to slightly scarce, punctuated with scarce to very rare issues such as 1908-S, 1920-S, 1921, mintmarked coins from 1924 to 1927, and all issues of 1929 to 1933. From their initial mintages, most of the double eagles of the 1920s were returned to the Mint and melted in the 1930s. Some, however, were unofficially saved by Treasury employees. Estimates of the quantities saved range from a few dozen to several hundred thousand, depending on the date; this explains the high values for coins that, judged only by their initial mintages, should otherwise be more common. Probably a million or more MS coins exist of certain dates, most notably 1908 No Motto, 1924, 1925, 1926, and 1928 (especially common). Quality varies, as many have contact marks.

Philadelphia Mint coins from 1922 onward usually are seen with excellent eye appeal. Common varieties are not usually collected in grades below MS. All of the Proofs are rare today.

Note: Values of common-date gold coins have been based on the current bullion price of gold, $1,300 per ounce, and may vary with the prevailing spot price.

GRADING STANDARDS

MS-60 to 70 (Mint State). *Obverse:* At MS-60, some abrasion and contact marks are seen on Liberty's chest and left knee, and scattered marks and abrasion are in the field. Luster is present, but may be dull or lifeless, and interrupted in patches. At MS-63, contact marks are fewer, and abrasion is light. An MS-65 coin has little abrasion and few marks, although quality among certified coins can vary. On a conservatively graded coin the lus-

1924. Graded MS-65.

ter should be full and rich. Grades above MS-65 are defined by having fewer marks as perfection is approached. Generally, Mint State coins of 1922 onward are choicer and more attractive than the earlier issues. *Reverse:* Comments apply as for the obverse, except that abrasion and contact marks are most noticeable on the eagle's left wing.

AU-50, 53, 55, 58 (About Uncirculated). *Obverse:* Light wear is seen on the chest, the left knee, the midriff, and across the field, more so at AU-50 than at AU–53 or 55. An AU-58 coin has minimal traces of wear. An AU-50 coin has luster in protected areas among the rays, with little in the open field above. At AU-58, most luster is present. *Reverse:* Comments as preceding, except that the side of the eagle below the front of the wing, the top of

1909, 9 Over 8. Graded AU-50.

the wing, and the field show light wear. Luster ranges from perhaps 40% (at AU-50) to nearly full mint bloom (at AU-58).

EF-40, 45 (Extremely Fine). *Obverse:* Wear is seen on all the higher-relief areas of the standing figure and on the rock at the lower right. Luster is minimal, if present at all. Eye appeal is apt to be lacking. *Reverse:* The eagle shows more wear overall, especially at the bottom and on the tops of the wings.

1908-S. Graded EF-40.

VF-20, 30 (Very Fine). *Obverse:* Most details of the standing figure are flat, her face is incomplete, and the tips of the rays are weak. Eye appeal is usually poor. *Reverse:* Wear is greater overall, but most evident on the eagle. Detail is good at the center of the left wing, but worn away in most other areas of the bird.

The Saint-Gaudens double eagle is seldom collected in grades lower than VF-20.

1914. Graded VF-20.

PF-60 to 70 (Proof). *Obverse and Reverse:* At PF–60 to 63, there is light abrasion and some contact marks (the lower the grade, the higher the quantity). On Sandblast Proofs these show up as visually unappealing bright spots. At PF-64 and higher levels, marks are fewer, with magnification needed to see any at PF-65. At PF-66, there should be none at all.

1909, Satin Finish. Graded PF-66.

| | Mintage | Cert | Avg | %MS | VF-20 | EF-40 | AU-50 | AU-55 | MS-60 | MS-62 | MS-63 | MS-65 |
										PF-63	PF-64	PF-65
1907, Arabic Numerals	361,667	11,226	63.7	97%	$1,400	$1,450	$1,475	$1,500	$1,850	$1,875	$2,000	$3,750
	Auctions: $5,170, MS-66, January 2015; $4,113, MS-65, January 2015; $2,585, MS-64, August 2015; $1,645, MS-62, February 2015											
1907, Proof (a)	*unknown*	0	n/a		*(extremely rare)*							
	Auctions: $70,500, MS-64, January 2015; $47,000, MS-64, August 2015											
1908, No Motto	4,271,551	139,212	63.3	100%	$1,350	$1,365	$1,375	$1,385	$1,400	$1,425	$1,450	$1,750
	Auctions: $6,463, MS-67, June 2015; $4,700, MS-66, February 2015; $1,763, MS-63, September 2015; $1,469, MS-61, September 2015											
1908-D, No Motto	663,750	4,360	62.4	97%	$1,350	$1,365	$1,375	$1,385	$1,600	$1,700	$1,750	$7,500
	Auctions: $9,400, MS-65, August 2015; $2,820, MS-64, August 2015; $1,586, MS-63, February 2015; $1,528, MS-62, September 2015											
1908, With Motto	156,258	2,105	62.0	95%	$1,400	$1,550	$1,650	$1,750	$1,875	$1,900	$2,250	$13,500
	Auctions: $5,170, MS-64, January 2015; $2,233, MS-63, March 2015; $1,645, MS-62, October 2015; $1,645, MS-60, July 2015											
1908, With Motto, Sandblast Finish Proof	101	77	65.3							$30,000	$50,000	$75,000
	Auctions: $57,500, PF-66+, June 2012											
1908, With Motto, Satin Finish Proof (b)	*unknown*	0	n/a		*(extremely rare)*							
	Auctions: $152,750, PF, August 2013											
1908-D, With Motto	349,500	2,237	62.5	93%	$1,350	$1,365	$1,375	$1,385	$1,400	$1,425	$2,000	$4,500
	Auctions: $21,150, MS-66, June 2015; $7,050, MS-65, January 2015; $3,525, MS-64, October 2015; $1,880, MS-62, July 2015											
1908-S, With Motto	22,000	518	56.9	31%	$2,500	$3,750	$6,000	$7,000	$11,500	$14,000	$22,500	$50,000
	Auctions: $21,150, MS-63, August 2015; $4,935, AU-53, July 2015; $3,878, EF-45, February 2015; $3,055, VF-35, August 2015											

a. 2 or 3 examples are known. **b.** 3 or 4 examples are known.

1909, 9 Over 8

	Mintage	Cert	Avg	%MS	VF-20	EF-40	AU-50	AU-55	MS-60	MS-62 PF-63	MS-63 PF-64	MS-65 PF-65
1909, All kinds	161,282											
1909, 9 Over 8 (c)		1,676	59.2	56%	$1,500	$1,550	$1,600	$1,650	$2,000	$3,000	$4,500	$40,000
Auctions: $14,153, MS-64, July 2015; $4,700, MS-63, January 2015; $1,880, AU-58, September 2015; $1,645, AU-50, August 2015												
1909		1,375	60.7	76%	$1,350	$1,365	$1,375	$1,385	$1,550	$1,850	$2,750	$37,500
Auctions: $35,250, MS-65, June 2015; $1,586, MS-61, April 2015; $1,469, AU-58, January 2015; $1,593, AU-53, July 2015												
1909, Satin Finish Proof	67	29	64.1							$32,500	$50,000	$85,000
Auctions: $184,860, PF, September 2013												
1909-D	52,500	502	60.7	60%	$1,600	$1,700	$1,750	$1,950	$3,250	$4,000	$6,000	$32,500
Auctions: $11,750, MS-64, July 2015; $5,640, MS-63, February 2015; $2,820, AU-58, September 2015; $1,528, AU-50, July 2015												
1909-S	2,774,925	5,776	62.6	96%	$1,350	$1,365	$1,375	$1,385	$1,400	$1,425	$1,650	$4,500
Auctions: $22,913, MS-66, July 2015; $2,938, MS-64, January 2015; $1,763, MS-63, June 2015; $1,645, MS-62, January 2015												
1910	482,000	8,352	62.3	98%	$1,350	$1,365	$1,375	$1,385	$1,400	$1,425	$1,650	$6,500
Auctions: $6,463, MS-65, September 2015; $3,055, MS-64, January 2015; $1,704, MS-63, August 2015; $1,704, MS-62, January 2015												
1910, Satin Finish Proof	167	0	n/a							$32,500	$50,000	$85,000
Auctions: $76,375, PF-65, August 2014; $56,063, PF-65, June 2012												
1910, Sandblast Finish Proof (d)	*unknown*	37	65.6		*(unique)*							
Auctions: No auction records available.												
1910-D	429,000	6,916	62.9	97%	$1,350	$1,365	$1,375	$1,385	$1,400	$1,425	$1,600	$2,600
Auctions: $9,400, MS-66, January 2015; $2,350, MS-65, July 2015; $1,763, MS-64, October 2015; $1,469, MS-62, September 2015												
1910-S	2,128,250	4,440	61.7	90%	$1,350	$1,365	$1,375	$1,385	$1,400	$1,425	$1,700	$6,000
Auctions: $88,125, MS-67, January 2015; $3,760, MS-64, January 2015; $1,998, MS-63, August 2015; $1,528, MS-62, October 2015												
1911	197,250	2,778	61.9	90%	$1,350	$1,365	$1,375	$1,385	$1,500	$1,600	$2,500	$15,000
Auctions: $17,038, MS-66, January 2015; $4,935, MS-64, June 2015; $1,763, MS-62, August 2015; $1,528, EF-45, September 2015												
1911, Sandblast Finish Proof	100	45	66.1							$30,000	$45,000	$80,000
Auctions: $157,950, PF, September 2013												
1911-D	846,500	12,034	63.4	98%	$1,350	$1,365	$1,375	$1,385	$1,400	$1,425	$1,600	$2,450
Auctions: $3,760, MS-66, January 2015; $2,644, MS-64, August 2015; $1,586, MS-63, July 2015; $1,469, MS-62, September 2015												
1911-S	775,750	5,417	62.8	97%	$1,350	$1,365	$1,375	$1,385	$1,400	$1,425	$1,650	$4,000
Auctions: $11,221, MS-66, October 2015; $5,758, MS-65, January 2015; $1,880, MS-63, February 2015; $1,469, MS-62, September 2015												
1912	149,750	2,463	61.5	88%	$1,350	$1,365	$1,375	$1,385	$1,500	$1,600	$2,250	$22,500
Auctions: $19,975, MS-65, September 2015; $5,640, MS-64, January 2015; $1,528, MS-61, February 2015; $1,469, AU-58, January 2015												
1912, Sandblast Finish Proof	74	54	66.0							$30,000	$45,000	$80,000
Auctions: $211,500, PF-67, August 2013												
1913	168,780	2,707	61.4	89%	$1,350	$1,365	$1,375	$1,385	$1,550	$1,800	$2,500	$55,000
Auctions: $11,750, MS-64, January 2015; $1,763, MS-62, July 2015; $1,645, MS-61, October 2015; $1,410, AU-58, January 2015												
1913, Sandblast Finish Proof	58	51	65.5							$30,000	$45,000	$80,000
Auctions: $79,313, PF, August 2013												
1913-D	393,500	3,990	62.5	95%	$1,350	$1,365	$1,375	$1,385	$1,450	$1,600	$1,750	$5,500
Auctions: $22,325, MS-66, February 2015; $6,463, MS-65, August 2015; $2,585, MS-64, October 2015; $2,350, MS-63, September 2015												
1913-S	34,000	1,153	61.6	86%	$1,750	$1,850	$2,000	$2,100	$2,350	$3,000	$4,500	$30,000
Auctions: $9,400, MS-64, January 2015; $3,055, MS-62, January 2015; $2,233, MS-61, July 2015; $2,585, AU-58, September 2015												

c. This is one of the few Saint-Gaudens double eagle die varieties that commands a premium over the regular coin. **d.** Part of the unique complete 1910 Sandblast Finish Proof gold set.

1922, Doubled Die Reverse

	Mintage	Cert	Avg	%MS	VF-20	EF-40	AU-50	AU-55	MS-60	MS-62 / PF-63	MS-63 / PF-64	MS-65 / PF-65
1914	95,250	1,754	62.0	91%	$1,400	$1,405	$1,415	$1,425	$1,500	$1,600	$2,750	$18,500
Auctions: $7,638, MS-64, January 2015; $7,050, MS-64, January 2015; $2,585, MS-63, August 2015; $2,115, MS-62, July 2015											
1914, Sandblast Finish Proof	70	28	65.5							$30,000	$45,000	$80,000
Auctions: $60,375, PF-66, June 2012											
1914-D	453,000	6,833	63.0	97%	$1,350	$1,365	$1,375	$1,385	$1,400	$1,425	$1,650	$2,750
Auctions: $3,055, MS-65, August 2015; $2,140, MS-64, September 2015; $1,788, MS-64, January 2015; $1,645, MS-63, October 2015											
1914-S	1,498,000	21,779	63.1	99%	$1,350	$1,365	$1,375	$1,385	$1,400	$1,425	$1,600	$2,500
Auctions: $4,583, MS-66, December 2015; $1,763, MS-64, September 2015; $1,410, MS-61, September 2015; $1,293, MS-60, June 2015											
1915	152,000	2,255	61.8	89%	$1,350	$1,365	$1,375	$1,385	$1,500	$1,650	$2,000	$16,500
Auctions: $5,170, MS-64, January 2015; $3,055, MS-63, September 2015; $1,586, MS-61, July 2015; $1,410, AU-55, January 2015											
1915, Sandblast Finish Proof	50	41	64.8							$32,500	$50,000	$100,000
Auctions: $63,250, PF-66, August 2011											
1915-S	567,500	16,062	63.3	99%	$1,350	$1,365	$1,375	$1,385	$1,400	$1,425	$1,600	$2,250
Auctions: $4,700, MS-66, June 2015; $1,528, MS-64, October 2015; $1,528, MS-63, June 2015; $1,410, MS-62, September 2015											
1916-S	796,000	4,284	63.4	97%	$1,350	$1,365	$1,375	$1,385	$1,400	$1,425	$1,800	$3,000
Auctions: $4,935, MS-66, January 2015; $2,233, MS-64, January 2015; $1,763, MS-63, September 2015; $1,469, AU-58, January 2015											
1920	228,250	6,913	62.1	99%	$1,350	$1,365	$1,375	$1,385	$1,400	$1,425	$1,700	$55,000
Auctions: $5,170, MS-64, January 2015; $4,348, MS-64, August 2015; $2,233, MS-63, January 2015; $1,528, MS-62, September 2015											
1920-S	558,000	73	61.8	73%	$16,500	$20,000	$25,000	$32,500	$50,000	$67,500	$85,000	$275,000
Auctions: $517,000, MS-65, November 2016; $99,875, MS-64, January 2015; $70,500, MS-63, January 2015; $44,650, AU-58, May 2016											
1921	528,500	72	60.2	58%	$25,000	$37,500	$55,000	$65,000	$100,000	$125,000	$225,000	$600,000
Auctions $199,750, MS-63, August 2016; $164,500, MS-63, January 2014; $105,750, MS-62, August 2014; $94,000, MS-62, January 2015											
1921, Proof † (e)	*unknown*	1	64.0		*(extremely rare)*							
Auctions: $1,495,000, PF-64+, 2006; $203,500, PF, 2000											
1922	1,375,500	55,035	62.6	100%	$1,350	$1,365	$1,375	$1,385	$1,400	$1,425	$1,650	$3,750
Auctions: $11,750, MS-66, August 2015; $3,290, MS-65, January 2015; $2,585, MS-64, August 2015; $1,351, MS-61, September 2015											
1922, DblDie Rev	(f)	4	63.3	100%			$2,000	$2,200	$2,500	$2,750	$3,500	
Auctions: $2,115, MS-64, December 2013											
1922-S	2,658,000	916	62.6	97%	$1,850	$1,900	$2,000	$2,150	$2,650	$3,000	$4,500	$35,000
Auctions: $9,988, MS-64, July 2015; $3,408, MS-63, January 2015; $3,290, MS-62, January 2015; $3,290, MS-61, July 2015											
1923	566,000	30,609	62.5	100%	$1,350	$1,365	$1,375	$1,385	$1,400	$1,425	$1,500	$4,000
Auctions: $3,760, MS-65, January 2015; $2,350, MS-64, August 2015; $2,115, MS-64, June 2015; $1,528, MS-63, July 2015											
1923-D	1,702,250	5,981	64.3	100%	$1,350	$1,365	$1,375	$1,385	$1,400	$1,425	$1,500	$2,150
Auctions: $11,750, MS-67, February 2015; $2,585, MS-66, October 2015; $2,350, MS-65, February 2015; $1,469, MS-62, March 2015											
1924	4,323,500	313,684	63.4	100%	$1,350	$1,365	$1,375	$1,385	$1,400	$1,425	$1,450	$1,750
Auctions: $6,463, MS-67, January 2015; $3,760, MS-66, June 2015; $1,528, MS-62, October 2015; $1,293, MS-60, February 2015											
1924-D	3,049,500	450	62.0	89%	$2,200	$2,500	$2,650	$3,250	$4,250	$5,500	$7,500	$70,000
Auctions: $12,925, MS-64, August 2015; $3,290, MS-60, July 2015; $1,998, AU-53, August 2015; $1,763, AU-50, January 2015											
1924-S	2,927,500	478	62.5	93%	$2,200	$2,500	$2,650	$3,250	$4,500	$6,000	$9,500	$65,000
Auctions: $16,450, MS-64, January 2015; $9,106, MS-63, January 2015; $3,173, MS-60, January 2015; $2,233, MS-60, January 2015											

† Ranked in the *100 Greatest U.S. Coins* (fourth edition). **e.** Prior to the first public auction of a 1921 presentation-strike double eagle (a lightly cleaned specimen) in summer 2000, this variety was unknown to the numismatic community at large. That example reportedly was struck in 1921 to celebrate the birth of Joseph Baker, nephew of U.S. Mint director Raymond T. Baker. In 2006 a second example (this one with original, uncleaned surfaces) was discovered and subsequently auctioned. **f.** Included in 1922 mintage figure.

1925, Doubled Die Reverse   **1933 Saint-Gaudens Double Eagle**

	Mintage	Cert	Avg	%MS	VF-20	EF-40	AU-50	AU-55	MS-60	MS-62 PF-63	MS-63 PF-64	MS-65 PF-65
1925	2,831,750	54,298	63.2	100%	$1,350	$1,365	$1,375	$1,385	$1,400	$1,425	$1,450	$1,750
Auctions: $4,230, MS-66, August 2015; $1,528, MS-64, June 2015; $1,293, MS-62, June 2015; $1,421, MS-60, October 2015												
1925, Doubled Die Reverse (g)	(h)	20	63.9	100%			$2,000	$2,500	$2,750	$3,000	$3,500	
Auctions: $3,055, MS-65, December 2013												
1925-D	2,938,500	308	62.6	98%	$2,600	$3,200	$3,750	$4,250	$5,500	$7,500	$10,000	$75,000
Auctions: $64,625, MS-65, June 2015; $12,925, MS-64, August 2014; $7,638, MS-62, June 2015; $4,465, MS-61, August 2015												
1925-S	3,776,500	422	59.3	57%	$2,250	$3,000	$4,000	$5,500	$9,500	$12,000	$15,500	$125,000
Auctions: $11,456, MS-63, August 2015; $8,225, MS-61, January 2015; $5,170, AU-58, January 2015; $5,405, AU-55, August 2015												
1926	816,750	23,575	63.6	100%	$1,350	$1,365	$1,375	$1,385	$1,400	$1,425	$1,450	$1,750
Auctions: $1,821, MS-65, August 2015; $1,645, MS-64, June 2015; $1,528, MS-64, October 2015; $1,469, MS-63, March 2015												
1926-D	481,000	106	62.2	89%	$8,000	$11,000	$12,500	$13,500	$14,500	$20,000	$25,000	$150,000
Auctions: $47,000, MS-64, March 2014; $22,325, MS-63, June 2015; $14,100, MS-62, September 2015; $11,163, AU-58, September 2015												
1926-S	2,041,500	678	63.1	97%	$2,150	$2,450	$2,750	$2,950	$3,500	$4,000	$5,500	$25,000
Auctions: $18,277, MS-65, October 2015; $8,226, MS-64, June 2015; $5,170, MS-63, February 2015; $2,115, MS-60, January 2015												
1927	2,946,750	143,922	63.5	100%	$1,350	$1,365	$1,375	$1,385	$1,400	$1,425	$1,450	$1,750
Auctions: $3,525, MS-66, September 2015; $2,585, MS-65, June 2015; $1,351, MS-61, September 2015; $1,410, MS-60, October 2015												
1927-D †	180,000	5	65.0	80%			$500,000	$550,000	$750,000	$850,000	$1,300,000	$1,750,000
Auctions: $1,997,500, MS-66, January 2014												
1927-S	3,107,000	121	61.3	75%			$14,000	$16,000	$26,000	$37,500	$45,000	$110,000
Auctions: $105,750, MS-65, March 2014; $42,300, MS-63, August 2016; $25,850, MS-62, June 2015; $17,625, AU-55, January 2015												
1928	8,816,000	49,431	63.3	100%	$1,350	$1,365	$1,375	$1,385	$1,400	$1,425	$1,450	$1,750
Auctions: $18,800, MS-67, August 2015; $4,818, MS-66, September 2015; $1,998, MS-64, June 2015; $1,379, MS-60, August 2015												
1929	1,779,750	126	63.1	96%			$13,500	$15,500	$20,000	$30,000	$35,000	$75,000
Auctions: $57,281, MS-65, August 2014; $37,600, MS-64, January 2015; $32,900, MS-63, September 2015; $15,863, MS-60, August 2014												
1930-S	74,000	21	64.1	100%			$42,000	$45,000	$65,000	$75,000	$90,000	$175,000
Auctions: $176,382, MS-65, March 2014; $164,500, MS-65, September 2014; $146,875, MS-64, November 2016; $164,500, MS-63, August 2014												
1931	2,938,250	34	64.3	100%			$22,500	$25,000	$35,000	$50,000	$65,000	$100,000
Auctions: $105,751, MS-65, September 2014; $105,750, MS-65, August 2016; $76,375, MS-65, March 2014; $64,625, MS-64, August 2014												
1931-D	106,500	42	63.3	98%			$22,500	$25,000	$35,000	$50,000	$65,000	$100,000
Auctions: $129,250, MS-65, September 2014; $99,875, MS-64, January 2014; $94,000, MS-64, November 2016; $64,625, MS-62, August 2014												
1932	1,101,750	70	63.9	100%			$22,500	$25,000	$35,000	$50,000	$65,000	$100,000
Auctions: $108,688, MS-66, March 2014; $99,875, MS-66, August 2014; $94,000, MS-64, August 2014												
1933 † (i)	445,500	0	n/a		(extremely rare)	—						
Auctions: $7,590,000, Gem BU, July 2002												

† Ranked in the *100 Greatest U.S. Coins* (fourth edition). **g.** Doubling is evident on the eagle's feathers, the rays, and IN GOD WE TRUST. **h.** Included in 1925 mintage figure. **i.** All but a few 1933 double eagles were to have been melted at the mint. Today 13 examples are known to have survived. Only one, said to have previously been in the collection of King Farouk of Egypt, has ever been sold at auction. The federal government has ruled that others are illegal to own privately.

U.S. Commemoratives
1892–1954 and 1982 to Date

AN OVERVIEW OF CLASSIC COMMEMORATIVES

Commemorative coins have been popular since the time of ancient Greece and Rome. In the beginning they recorded and honored important events and passed along the news of the day. Today commemorative coins, which are highly esteemed by collectors, have been issued by many modern nations—none of which has surpassed the United States when it comes to these impressive mementoes.

The unique position occupied by commemoratives in the United States coinage is largely due to the fact that, with few exceptions, all commemorative coins have real historical significance. The progress and advance of people in the New World are presented in an interesting and instructive manner on our commemorative coins. Such a record of history artistically presented on U.S. gold, silver, and other memorial issues appeals strongly to the collector who favors the romantic, storytelling side of numismatics. It is the historical features of our commemoratives, in fact, that create interest among many people who would otherwise have little interest in coins, and would not otherwise consider themselves collectors.

Proposed coin programs are considered by two congressional committees: the Senate Committee on Banking, Housing, and Urban Affairs; and the House Financial Services Committee. Once a program is approved by Congress, the independent Citizens Coinage Advisory Committee (ccac.gov) and the U.S. Commission of Fine Arts (cfa.gov) advise the secretary of the Treasury on its coin designs.

These special coins are usually issued either to commemorate events or to help pay for monuments, programs, or celebrations that commemorate historical persons, places, or things. Pre-1982 commemorative coins were offered in most instances by a commission in charge of the event to be commemorated and sold at a premium over face value.

Commemorative coins are popularly collected either by major types or in sets with mintmark varieties. The pieces covered in this section of the *Guide Book of United States Coins, Deluxe Edition*, are those of the "classic" era of U.S. commemoratives, 1892 to 1954. All commemoratives are of the standard weight and fineness of their regular-issue 20th-century gold and silver counterparts, and all are legal tender.

A note about mintages and distribution numbers: Unless otherwise stated, the coinage figures given in each "Distribution" column represent the total released mintage: the total mintage (including assay coins), minus the quantity of unsold coins. In many cases, larger quantities were minted but not all were sold. Unsold coins usually were returned to the mint and melted, although sometimes quantities were placed in circulation at face value. A limited number of Proof strikings or presentation pieces were made for some of the classic commemorative issues.

A note about price performance: It has mostly been in recent decades that the general public has learned about commemorative coins. They have long been popular with coin collectors who enjoy the artistry and history associated with them, as well as the profit to be made from owning these rare pieces. Very few of them ever reached circulation because they were all originally sold above face value, and because they are all so rare. Most of the early issues were of the half dollar denomination, often made in quantities of fewer than 20,000 pieces. This is minuscule when compared to the regular half dollar coins that are made by the millions each year, and still rarely seen in circulation.

At the beginning of 1988, prices of classic commemoratives in MS-65 condition had risen so high that most collectors had to content themselves with pieces in lower grades. Investors continued to apply pressure to the high-quality pieces, driving prices even higher, while the collector community went after coins in grades from AU to MS-63. For several months the pressure from both influences caused prices to rise very rapidly (for all issues and grades) without even taking the price-adjustment breather that usually goes along with such activity.

By 1990, prices dropped to the point that several of the commemoratives began to look like bargains once again. Many of the MS-65 pieces held firm at price levels above the $3,000 mark, but others were still available at under $500 even for coins of similar mintage. Coins in MS–63 or 64 were priced at but a fraction of the MS-65 prices, which would seem to make them reasonably priced because the demand for these pieces is universal, and not keyed simply to grade, rarity, or speculator pressure.

Historically, the entire series of commemorative coins has frequently undergone a roller-coaster cycle of price adjustments. These cycles have usually been of short duration, lasting from months to years, with prices always recovering and eventually exceeding previous levels.

See pages 1109 and 1110 for discussion of modern commemorative coins of 1982 to date, page 1210 for pricing of government commemorative sets, and page 1502 for an alphabetical cross-reference list of all commemoratives.

WORLD'S COLUMBIAN EXPOSITION HALF DOLLAR (1892–1893)

Designers: *Charles E. Barber (obverse), George T. Morgan (reverse).* **Weight:** *12.50 grams.*
Composition: *.900 silver, .100 copper (net weight .3617 oz. pure silver).*
Diameter: *30.6 mm.* **Edge:** *Reeded.* **Mint:** *Philadelphia.*

The first U.S. commemorative coin was the Columbian half dollar sold at the World's Columbian Exposition—also known as the Chicago World's Fair—during 1893. The event celebrated the 400th anniversary of Christopher Columbus's arrival in the New World. A great many of the coins remained unsold and a substantial quantity was later released for circulation at face value or melted.

Designs. *Obverse:* Charles Barber's conception of Christopher Columbus, derived from a plaster model by Olin Levi Warner, taken from the explorer's portrait on an 1892 Spanish medal. The medal's portrait was inspired by a statue by Jeronimo Suñel, which itself was from an imagined likeness by Charles Legrand. *Reverse:* A sailing ship atop two globes representing the Old World and the New World. The vessel is from a plaster model by Olin Levi Warner, taken from a model made in Spain of Columbus's flagship, the *Santa Maria.*

Mintage and Melting Data. *Maximum authorized*—5,000,000 (both years combined). *Number minted*—1892: 950,000 (including an unknown number of assay coins; approximately 100 Proofs were struck as well); 1893: 4,052,105 (including 2,105 assay coins). *Number melted*—1893: 2,501,700. *Net distribution*—1892: 950,000; 1893: 1,550,405.

Original Cost and Issuer. Sale price $1. Issued by the Exposition.

Key to Collecting. Both dates are common in all grades through MS-65, and are often available in MS-66 and higher. The typical high-grade coin is lustrous and frosty; some have attractive, original light-blue or iridescent toning. Well-worn examples are very common, as the Treasury Department eventually released large quantities into circulation at face value. Striking usually is good. Some coins can be weak at the center—on the higher areas of the portrait and, on the reverse, in the details of the ship's sails. Most have contact marks from handling and distribution. High-grade 1892 coins typically are better struck than those of 1893. Approximately 100 brilliant Proofs were struck for each date; they vary widely in quality and eye appeal.

First Points of Wear. *Obverse:* The eyebrow, the cheek, and the hair at the back of the forehead. (The hair area sometimes is flatly struck.) *Reverse:* The top of the rear sail, and the right side of the Eastern Hemisphere.

	Distribution	Cert	Avg	%MS	AU-50	MS-60	MS-62	MS-63	MS-64 / PF-63	MS-65 / PF-64	MS-66 / PF-65
1892	950,000	5,661	63.2	95%	$20	$27	$45	$70	$100	$310	$675
	Auctions: $2,350, MS-67, August 2016; $1,410, MS-66, September 2016										
1892, Proof	*100*	38	64.0						$5,750	$7,000	$13,000
	Auctions: $8,225, PF-65, November 2013										
1893	1,550,405	6,101	62.3	88%	$20	$27	$45	$70	$100	$310	$675
	Auctions: $8,229, MS-67, June 2015; $1,293, MS-66, July 2015; $400, MS-65, January 2015; $118, MS-64, August 2015										
1893, Proof	*3–5*	1	63.0								
	Auctions: $15,275, PF-66, January 2014; $5,830, PF-64, September 1993										

Note: Various repunched dates exist for both dates; these command little or no premium in the marketplace. For more information, see the *Cherrypickers' Guide to Rare Die Varieties*, sixth edition, volume II.

World's Columbian Exposition Isabella Quarter (1893)

Designer: *Charles E. Barber.* **Weight:** *6.25 grams.* **Composition:** *.900 silver, .100 copper (net weight .18084 oz. pure silver).* **Diameter:** *24.3 mm.* **Edge:** *Reeded.* **Mint:** *Philadelphia.*

In 1893 the Board of Lady Managers of the World's Columbian Exposition (also known as the Chicago World's Fair) petitioned for a souvenir quarter dollar. Authority was granted March 3, 1893, for the coin, which is known as the *Isabella quarter.*

Designs. *Obverse:* Crowned profile portrait of Spain's Queen Isabella, who sponsored Christopher Columbus's voyages to the New World. *Reverse:* A lady kneeling with a distaff and spindle, symbolic of the industry of American women.

Mintage and Melting Data. Authorized on March 3, 1893. *Maximum authorized*—40,000. *Number minted*—40,023 (including 23 assay coins). *Number melted*—15,809. *Net distribution*—24,214.

Original Cost and Issuer. Sale price $1. Issued by the Board of Lady Managers, World's Columbian Exposition.

Key to Collecting. Most examples in the marketplace are in Mint State, including many choice and gem pieces. Most are well struck and show full details, with richly lustrous fields. Connoisseurs avoid darkly toned, stained, and recolored coins. Many lower-grade Mint State examples have marks on Isabella's cheek and on the higher parts of the reverse design. The left obverse field often has marks made from contact with other coins during minting, storage, and distribution. The certification services have classified some coins with mirrored fields as Proofs, although no official records exist for the production of such.

First Points of Wear. *Obverse:* Isabella's cheekbone, and the center of the lower part of the crown. *Reverse:* The strand of wool at the lower-left thigh.

	Distribution	Cert	Avg	%MS	AU-50	MS-60	MS-62	MS-63	MS-64	MS-65	MS-66
									PF-63	PF-64	PF-65
1893	24,214	3,771	62.4	88%	$325	$375	$475	$500	$925	$1,600	$2,500
	Auctions: $17,625, MS-67, January 2015; $329, AU-58, February 2015; $306, EF-40, July 2015; $235, VF-30, February 2015										
1893, Proof	*100–105*	46	63.8						$4,750	$7,750	$13,000
	Auctions: $6,463, PF-64, July 2015; $5,640, PF-64, June 2015; $5,288, PF-64, October 2014										

LAFAYETTE DOLLAR (1900)

Designer: *Charles E. Barber.* **Weight:** *26.73 grams.* **Composition:** *.900 silver, .100 copper (net weight .7736 oz. pure silver).* **Diameter:** *38.1 mm.* **Edge:** *Reeded.* **Mint:** *Philadelphia.*

This issue—which was the first commemorative coin of one-dollar denomination, as well as the first authorized U.S. coin to bear a portrait of a U.S. president—commemorated the erection of a statue of Marquis de Lafayette in Paris in connection with the 1900 Paris Exposition (Exposition Universelle).

Designs. *Obverse:* Conjoined portraits of the marquis de Lafayette and George Washington. *Reverse:* Side view of the equestrian statue erected by the youth of the United States in honor of Lafayette. This view was based on an early model of the statue; the final version that was erected in Paris is slightly different.

Mintage and Melting Data. Authorized on March 3, 1899. *Maximum authorized—50,000. Number minted—50,026 (including 26 assay coins). Number melted—14,000. Net distribution—36,026.*

Original Cost and Issuer. Sale price $2. Issued by the Lafayette Memorial Commission through the American Trust & Savings Bank of Chicago.

Key to Collecting. Most surviving examples show evidence of circulation or other mishandling. The typical grade is AU. In Mint State, most are MS–60 to 63, and many are dull or unattractive, having been dipped or cleaned multiple times. Many have marks and dings. Properly graded MS-64 coins are very scarce, and MS-65 or higher gems are very rare, especially if with good eye appeal. Several die varieties exist and are collected by specialists.

Varieties. *Obverse varieties:* (1) Small point on the bust of Washington. The tip of Lafayette's bust is over the top of the L in DOLLAR. The AT in STATES is cut high. (2) The left foot of the final A in AMERICA is recut, and the A in STATES is high. The second S in STATES is repunched (this is diagnostic). (3) The AT in STATES is recut and the final S is low. The letter F in OF and in LAFAYETTE is broken from the lower tip of the crossbar and to the right base extension, and AMERICA is spaced A ME RI C A. The period after OF is close to the A of AMERICA. The tip of Lafayette's vest falls to the right of the top of the first L in DOLLAR. (4) The C in AMERICA is repunched at the inside top (this is diagnostic). The CA in AMERICA is spaced differently from the obverses previously described. *Reverse varieties:* (A) There are 14 long leaves and a long stem. The tip of the lowest leaf is over the 1 in 1900. (B) There are 14 shorter leaves and a short stem. The tip of the lowest leaf is over the space between the 1 and 9 in 1900. (C) There are 14 medium leaves and a short, bent stem. The tip of the lowest leaf is over the 9 in 1900. (D) There are 15 long leaves and a short, bent stem. The tip of the lowest leaf is over the 9 in 1900. (E) The tip of the lowest leaf is over the space to the left of the 1 in 1900.

First Points of Wear. *Obverse:* Washington's cheekbone, and Lafayette's lower hair curl. *Reverse:* The fringe of Lafayette's epaulet, and the horse's blinder and left rear leg bone.

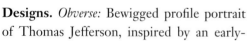

	Distribution	Cert	Avg	%MS	AU-50	MS-60	MS-62	MS-63	MS-64	MS-65	MS-66
1900	36,026	2,580	61.9	87%	$450	$775	$1,200	$1,400	$2,750	$5,500	$11,000
	Auctions: $73,438, MS-67, January 2015; $564, AU-58, January 2015; $376, EF-40, November 2015; $329, VF-30, July 2015										

LOUISIANA PURCHASE EXPOSITION JEFFERSON GOLD DOLLAR (1903)

Designer: *Charles E. Barber (assisted by George T. Morgan).* **Weight:** *1.672 grams.*
Composition: *.900 gold, .100 copper (net weight .04837 oz. pure gold).*
Diameter: *15 mm.* **Edge:** *Reeded.* **Mint:** *Philadelphia.*

The first commemorative U.S. gold coins were authorized for the Louisiana Purchase Exposition, held in St. Louis in 1904. The event commemorated the 100th anniversary of the United States' purchase of the Louisiana Territory from France, an acquisition overseen by President Thomas Jefferson.

Designs. *Obverse:* Bewigged profile portrait of Thomas Jefferson, inspired by an early-1800s medal by John Reich, after Jean-Antoine Houdon's bust. *Reverse:* Inscription and branch.

Mintage and Melting Data. Authorized on June 28, 1902. *Maximum authorized*—250,000 (both types combined). *Number minted*—250,258 (125,000 of each type; including 258 assay coins comprising both types). *Number melted*—215,250 (total for both types; no account was kept of the portraits; 250 assay coins were melted). *Net distribution*—35,000 (estimated at 17,500 of each type).

Original Cost and Issuer. Sale price $3. Issued by the Louisiana Purchase Exposition Company, St. Louis, Missouri (sales through Farran Zerbe). Some were sold as mounted in spoons, brooches, and stick pins; 100 certified Proofs of each design were made, mounted in an opening in a rectangular piece of imprinted cardboard.

Key to Collecting. Market demand is strong, from collectors and investors alike, as most surviving examples are in choice or gem Mint State, with strong eye appeal. Most specimens are very lustrous and frosty. An occasional coin is prooflike. Avoid any with copper stains (from improper mixing of the gold/copper alloy). Proofs enter the market rarely and garner much publicity.

First Points of Wear. *Obverse:* Portrait's cheekbone and sideburn. *Reverse:* Date and denomination.

	Distribution	Cert	Avg	%MS	AU-50	MS-60	MS-62	MS-63	MS-64	MS-65	MS-66
									PF-63	PF-64	PF-65
1903	17,500	2,262	63.9	94%	$550	$625	$700	$800	$925	$1,350	$1,675
	Auctions: $5,993, MS-67, July 2015; $1,293, MS-64, July 2015; $470, AU-58, January 2015; $329, AU-50, January 2015										
1903, Proof (a)	100	31	64.9								
	Auctions: $37,375, PF-67UCamH, January 2012										

a. The first 100 Jefferson gold dollars were struck in brilliant Proof format. True Proofs exhibit deeply mirrored fields and are sharply struck. Many also have frosted devices, giving them a cameo appearance. "Although many of the coins seen today have been certified and lack original packaging, they were originally housed in cardboard holders certifying each coin as having been one of the first 100 impressions from the dies. The original holders are quite interesting, with the coin covered by a small piece of wax paper and a piece of string sealed by dark red wax. The coins are difficult to see behind the wax paper, and the author has seen holders with a circulation-strike example substituted for the Proof piece. Caution should be used when purchasing an example of this extreme rarity" (*Encyclopedia of U.S. Gold Coins, 1795–1933*, second edition).

LOUISIANA PURCHASE EXPOSITION McKINLEY GOLD DOLLAR (1903)

Designer: *Charles E. Barber (assisted by George T. Morgan).* **Weight:** *1.672 grams.*
Composition: *.900 gold, .100 copper (net weight .04837 oz. pure gold).*
Diameter: *15 mm.* **Edge:** *Reeded.* **Mint:** *Philadelphia.*

President William McKinley—who had been assassinated while in office two years before the Louisiana Purchase Exposition—was remembered on a gold dollar issued alongside the aforementioned coin featuring Thomas Jefferson. Like Jefferson, McKinley oversaw expansion of U.S. territory, with the acquisition of Puerto Rico, Guam, and the Philippines, as well as the annexation of Hawaii.

Designs. *Obverse:* Bareheaded profile portrait of William McKinley, derived from his presidential medal (designed, like this coin, by Charles Barber). *Reverse:* Inscriptions and branch.

Mintage and Melting Data. Authorized on June 28, 1902. *Maximum authorized*—250,000 (both types combined). *Number minted*—250,258 (125,000 of each type; including 258 assay coins comprising both types). *Number melted*—215,250 (total for both types; no account was kept of the portraits; 250 assay coins were melted). *Net distribution*—35,000 (estimated at 17,500 of each type).

Original Cost and Issuer. Sale price $3. Issued by the Louisiana Purchase Exposition Company, St. Louis, Missouri (sales through Farran Zerbe). Some were sold as mounted in spoons, brooches, and stick pins; 100 certified Proofs of each design were made, mounted in an opening in a rectangular piece of imprinted cardboard.

Key to Collecting. Market demand is strong, from collectors and investors alike, as most surviving examples are in choice or gem Mint State, with strong eye appeal. Most specimens are very lustrous and frosty. An occasional coin is prooflike. Avoid any with copper stains (from improper mixing of the gold/copper alloy). Proofs enter the market rarely and garner much publicity.

First Points of Wear. *Obverse:* Portrait's cheekbone and sideburn. *Reverse:* Date and denomination.

	Distribution	Cert	Avg	%MS	AU-50	MS-60	MS-62	MS-63	MS-64	MS-65	MS-66
									PF-63	PF-64	PF-65
1903	17,500	2,143	63.9	96%	$550	$600	$625	$700	$850	$1,275	$1,700
	Auctions: $8,813, MS-68, January 2015; $1,763, MS-66, January 2015; $517, MS-63, January 2015; $376, AU-58, August 2015										
1903, Proof (a)	100	27	64.3								
	Auctions: $14,950, PF-65Cam, April 2012										

a. Like the Jefferson issue, the first 100 McKinley gold dollars were struck as Proofs, and packaged as such. "Prooflike circulation strikes are quite common for the issue, and true Proofs can be distinguished by deeply mirrored surfaces and cameo devices. Certification is highly recommended" (*Encyclopedia of U.S. Gold Coins, 1795–1933*, second edition).

LEWIS AND CLARK EXPOSITION GOLD DOLLAR (1904–1905)

Designer: *Charles E. Barber.* **Weight:** *1.672 grams.* **Composition:** *.900 gold, .100 copper (net weight .04837 oz. pure gold).* **Diameter:** *15 mm.* **Edge:** *Reeded.* **Mint:** *Philadelphia.*

A souvenir issue of gold dollars was struck to mark the Lewis and Clark Centennial Exposition, held in Portland, Oregon, in 1905. The sale of these coins financed the erection of a bronze memorial of the Shoshone Indian guide Sacagawea, who assisted in the famous expedition.

Designs. *Obverse:* Bareheaded profile portrait of Meriwether Lewis. *Reverse:* Bareheaded profile portrait of William Clark. These portraits were inspired by works of Charles Willson Peale.

Mintage and Melting Data. Authorized on April 13, 1904. *Maximum authorized*—250,000 (both years combined). *Number minted*—1904: 25,028 (including 28 assay coins); 1905: 35,041 (including 41 assay coins). *Number melted*—1904: 15,003; 1905: 25,000. *Net distribution*—1904: 10,025; 1905: 10,041.

Original Cost and Issuer. Sales price $2 (some at $2.50); many were probably discounted further. Issued by the Lewis and Clark Centennial and American Pacific Exposition and Oriental Fair Company, Portland, Oregon (sales through Farran Zerbe and others).

Key to Collecting. Most surviving examples show evidence of handling. Some exhibit die problems (a rough raised area of irregularity at the denticles). Most range from AU–50 to 58, with an occasional MS–60 to 63. MS-64 coins are scarce, and MS-65 rare. Pristine examples are very rare. Most MS coins have areas of prooflike finish; some are deeply lustrous and frosty. The 1905-dated issue is noticeably scarcer than the 1904.

First Points of Wear. *Obverse:* Lewis's temple. *Reverse:* Clark's temple.

	Distribution	Cert	Avg	%MS	AU-50	MS-60	MS-62	MS-63	MS-64	MS-65	MS-66
									PF-63	PF-64	PF-65
1904	10,025	1,263	63.4	95%	$750	$900	$950	$1,000	$2,150	$3,500	$6,500
	Auctions: $15,275, MS-67, January 2015; $6,580, MS-66, January 2015; $734, MS-61, February 2015; $400, AU-50, May 2015										
1904, Proof	2–3	2	63.5								
	Auctions: $30,550, PF-64, August 2015										
1905	10,041	1,250	62.8	92%	$750	$900	$1,100	$1,200	$2,875	$5,000	$9,500
	Auctions: $35,250, MS-67, January 2015; $19,388, MS-66, January 2015; $1,880, MS-63, January 2015; $705, MS-60, June 2015										

PANAMA-PACIFIC INTERNATIONAL EXPOSITION HALF DOLLAR (1915)

Designers: *Charles E. Barber (obverse), George T. Morgan (assisting Barber on reverse).*
Weight: *12.50 grams.* **Composition:** *.900 silver, .100 copper (net weight .3617 oz. pure silver).*
Diameter: *30.6 mm.* **Edge:** *Reeded.* **Mint:** *San Francisco.*

The Panama-Pacific International Exposition held in San Francisco in 1915 celebrated the opening of the Panama Canal, as well as the revival of the Bay Area following the 1906 earthquake and fire. Five commemorative coins in four different denominations, including a half dollar, were issued in conjunction with the event.

Designs. *Obverse:* Columbia scattering flowers, alongside a child holding a cornucopia, representing the bounty of the American West; the Golden Gate in the background. *Reverse:* A spread-winged eagle perched on a shield, with branches of oak and olive.

Mintage and Melting Data. Authorized by the Act of January 16, 1915. *Maximum authorized*—200,000. *Number minted*—60,030 (including 30 assay coins). *Number melted*—32,896 (including the 30 assay coins; 29,876 were melted on September 7, 1916 and the balance on October 30, 1916). *Net distribution*—27,134.

Original Cost and Issuer. Sale price $1. Issued by the Coin and Medal Department (Farran Zerbe), Panama-Pacific International Exposition, San Francisco, California (combination offers included a set of four coins, including the buyer's choice of one $50, in a leather case, for $100; and a set of five coins in a copper frame for $200).

Key to Collecting. The half dollar does not have the typical deep mint frost associated with earlier silver issues. Most are satiny in appearance with the high parts in particular having a microscopically grainy finish. Many pieces have an inner line around the perimeter near the rim, a die characteristic. On the reverse of all known coins, the eagle's breast feathers are indistinct, which sometimes gives MS coins the appearance of having light wear. Most surviving coins grade from AU-50 to MS-63.

First Points of Wear. *Obverse:* Columbia's left shoulder. *Reverse:* The eagle's breast.

	Distribution	Cert	Avg	%MS	AU-50	MS-60	MS-62	MS-63	MS-64	MS-65	MS-66
1915-S	27,134	2,718	63.3	93%	$375	$500	$650	$700	$925	$1,325	$2,500

Auctions: $13,513, MS-67, August 2015; $646, MS-61, October 2015; $247, AU-50, July 2015; $165, VF-25, February 2015

PANAMA-PACIFIC INTERNATIONAL EXPOSITION GOLD DOLLAR (1915)

Designer: *Charles Keck.* **Weight:** *1.672 grams.* **Composition:** *.900 gold, .100 copper (net weight .04837 oz. pure gold).* **Diameter:** *15 mm.* **Edge:** *Reeded.* **Mint:** *San Francisco.*

Coin dealer and entrepreneur Farran Zerbe conceived of a program of five different commemorative coins across four denominations (including the gold dollar) in conjunction with the Panama-Pacific International Exposition in 1915. The event was held in what eventually constituted a miniature city, whose sculptures and impressive architecture were intended to remind one of Rome or some other distant and romantic place, but which at night was more apt to resemble Coney Island.

Designs. *Obverse:* Capped profile portrait of a Panama Canal laborer. *Reverse:* Two dolphins, symbolizing the Atlantic and Pacific oceans, and legends.

Mintage and Melting Data. Authorized by the Act of January 16, 1915. *Maximum authorized*—25,000. *Number minted*—25,034 (including 34 assay coins). *Number melted*—10,034 (including the 34 assay coins; melted at the San Francisco Mint on October 30, 1916). *Net distribution*—15,000.

Original Cost and Issuer. Sale price $2 (and a few at $2.25). Issued by the Coin and Medal Department (Farran Zerbe), Panama-Pacific International Exposition, San Francisco, California (combination offers included, among others, a set of four coins, with the buyer's choice of one fifty-dollar coin, in a leather case, for $100; and a set of five coins in a copper frame for $200).

Key to Collecting. Most examples are in Mint State. Many exhibit deep mint frost. Friction is common, especially on the obverse.

First Points of Wear. *Obverse:* The peak of the laborer's cap. *Reverse:* The heads of the dolphins, and the denomination.

	Distribution	Cert	Avg	%MS	AU-50	MS-60	MS-62	MS-63	MS-64	MS-65	MS-66
1915-S	15,000	3,767	63.6	94%	$450	$550	$615	$650	$825	$1,200	$1,600
	Auctions: $3,538, MS-67, January 2015; $1,733, MS-64, August 2015; $441, AU-55, April 2015; $329, EF-40, April 2015										

PANAMA-PACIFIC INTERNATIONAL EXPOSITION QUARTER EAGLE (1915)

Designer: *Charles E. Barber (obverse), George T. Morgan (reverse).* **Weight:** *4.18 grams.*
Composition: *.900 gold, .100 copper (net weight .12094 oz. pure gold).*
Diameter: *18 mm.* **Edge:** *Reeded.* **Mint:** *San Francisco.*

The 1915 Panama-Pacific International Exposition—a name chosen to reflect the recently completed Panama Canal, as well as Pacific Ocean commerce—was planned to be the ultimate world's fair. Foreign countries, domestic manufacturers, artists, concessionaires, and others were invited to the 10-month event, which drew an estimated 19 million visitors. This quarter eagle was among the five coins issued to commemorate the celebration.

Designs. *Obverse:* Columbia seated on a hippocampus, holding a caduceus, symbolic of Medicine's triumph over yellow fever in Panama during the canal's construction. *Reverse:* An eagle, standing on a plaque inscribed E PLURIBUS UNUM, with raised wings.

Mintage and Melting Data. Authorized by the Act of January 16, 1915. *Maximum authorized*—10,000. *Number minted*—10,017 (including 17 assay coins). *Number melted*—3,268 (including the 17 assay coins; melted at the San Francisco Mint on October 30, 1916). *Net distribution*—6,749.

Original Cost and Issuer. Sale price $4. Issued by the Coin and Medal Department (Farran Zerbe), Panama-Pacific International Exposition, San Francisco, California (combination offers included, among others, a set of four coins, with the buyer's choice of one fifty-dollar coin, in a leather case, for $100; and a set of five coins in a copper frame for $200).

Key to Collecting. Most grade from AU-55 to MS-63. MS-64 coins are elusive, and MS-65 rare. Most MS pieces show a satiny, sometimes grainy luster.

First Points of Wear. *Obverse:* Columbia's head, breast, and knee. *Reverse:* The torch band and the eagle's leg.

	Distribution	Cert	Avg	%MS	AU-50	MS-60	MS-62	MS-63	MS-64	MS-65	MS-66
									PF-63	PF-64	PF-65
1915-S	6,749	1,987	64.5	96%	$1,550	$2,000	$2,850	$3,800	$4,750	$5,250	$5,500
	Auctions: $12,925, MS-67, January 2015; $6,463, MS-66, February 2015; $5,405, MS-64, January 2015; $2,233, AU-50, August 2015										
1915-S, Proof (a)	*unique*	0	n/a								
	Auctions: No auction records available.										

a. This unique Satin Finish Proof resides in the National Numismatic Collection of the Smithsonian Institution.

PANAMA-PACIFIC INTERNATIONAL EXPOSITION FIFTY-DOLLAR GOLD PIECE (1915)

Designer: *Robert Aitken.* **Weight:** *83.59 grams.* **Composition:** *.900 gold, .100 copper (net weight 2.4186 oz. pure gold).* **Diameter:** *43 mm (round), 44.9 mm (octagonal, measured point to point).* **Edge:** *Reeded.* **Mint:** *San Francisco.*

Both round and octagonal $50 gold pieces were struck as part of the series commemorating the Panama-Pacific International Exposition in 1915. These coins, along with the half dollars in the same series, were the first U.S. commemoratives to feature the motto IN GOD WE TRUST.

Designs. Round: *Obverse:* Helmeted profile portrait of Minerva, with shield and armor. *Reverse:* An owl, symbolic of wisdom, vigilant on a pine branch, with pinecones. Octagonal: *Obverse and reverse:* Same as the round coin, but with dolphins in the eight angled exergues on obverse and reverse.

Mintage and Melting Data. Authorized by the Act of January 16, 1915. Round: *Maximum authorized*—Round: 1,500; Octagonal:

1,500. *Number minted* (including 10 assay coins)—Round: 1,510 (including 10 assay coins); Octagonal: 1,509 (including 9 assay coins). *Number melted*—Round: 1,027; Octagonal: 864. *Net distribution*—Round: 483; Octagonal: 645.

Original Cost and Issuer. Round and octagonal: Sale price, each, $100. Coin and Medal Department (Farran Zerbe), Panama-Pacific International Exposition, San Francisco, California. Combination offers included a set of four coins (buyer's choice of one fifty-dollar coin) in a leather case for $100, and a set of five coins in a copper frame for $200, this issued after the Exposition closed.

Key to Collecting. Because such small quantities were issued, these hefty gold commemoratives today are rare in any grade. The round coins trade hands slightly less frequently than the octagonal. Typical grades are MS–63 or 64 for coins kept in an original box or frame over the years, or AU-58 to MS-63 if removed. Coins that have been cleaned or lightly polished exhibit a multitude of tiny hairlines; such pieces are avoided by connoisseurs.

First Points of Wear. *Obverse:* Minerva's cheek. *Reverse:* The owl's upper breast.

	Distribution	Cert	Avg	%MS	AU-50	MS-60	MS-62	MS-63	MS-64	MS-65	MS-66
1915-S, Round †	483	414	63.4	95%	$55,000	$67,500	$80,000	$90,000	$120,000	$190,000	$245,000
	Auctions: $176,250, MS-65, August 2015; $79,313, MS-63, January 2015; $64,625, MS-61, July 2015; $51,700, MS-60, January 2015										
1915-S, Octagonal †	645	458	63.1	95%	$55,000	$67,500	$77,500	$90,000	$110,000	$190,000	$245,000
	Auctions: $258,500, MS-67, January 2015; $123,375, MS-65, August 2015; $70,500, MS-62, September 2015; $55,225, AU-55, September 2015										

† Both 1915 Panama-Pacific $50 Gold Pieces are ranked in the *100 Greatest U.S. Coins* (fourth edition), as a single entry.

McKINLEY MEMORIAL GOLD DOLLAR (1916–1917)

Designers: *Charles E. Barber (obverse) and George T. Morgan (reverse).* **Weight:** *1.672 grams.*
Composition: *.900 gold, .100 copper (net weight .04837 oz. pure gold).*
Diameter: *15 mm.* **Edge:** *Reeded.* **Mint:** *Philadelphia.*

The sale of the William McKinley dollars aided in paying for a memorial building at Niles, Ohio, the martyred president's birthplace.

Designs. *Obverse:* Bareheaded profile portrait of William McKinley. *Reverse:* Artist's rendition of the proposed McKinley Birthplace Memorial intended to be erected in Niles, Ohio.

Mintage and Melting Data. Authorized on February 23, 1916. *Maximum authorized*—100,000 (both years combined). *Number minted*—1916: 20,026 (including 26 assay coins); 1917: 10,014 (including 14 assay coins). *Number melted*—1916: 5,000 (estimated); 1917: 5,000 (estimated). *Net distribution*—1916: 15,000 (estimated); 1917: 5,000 (estimated).

Original Cost and Issuer. Sale price $3. Issued by the National McKinley Birthplace Memorial Association, Youngstown, Ohio.

Key to Collecting. The obverse of the 1916 issue often displays friction while its reverse can appear as choice Mint State. Prooflike fields are common. Some are highly prooflike on both sides. The 1917 issue is much harder to find than the 1916; examples usually are in higher grades with rich luster on both sides, and often exhibit a pale yellow color.

First Points of Wear. *Obverse:* McKinley's temple area, and the hair above his ear. *Reverse:* The pillar above the second 1 in the date; and the bottom of the flagpole.

| | Distribution | Cert | Avg | %MS | AU-50 | MS-60 | MS-62 | MS-63 | MS-64 | MS-65 | MS-66 |
									PF-63	PF-64	PF-65
1916	15,000	2,602	63.7	96%	$450	$500	$550	$575	$685	$1,000	$1,500
	Auctions: $4,465, MS-67, August 2015; $1,528, MS-66, July 2015; $376, MS-61, January 2015; $447, AU-58, October 2015										
1916, Proof	3–6	1	63.0								
	Auctions: $37,375, PF-63, January 2012										
1917	5,000	1,516	63.6	94%	$500	$550	$575	$600	$950	$1,200	$1,600
	Auctions: $7,344, MS-67, January 2015; $2,585, MS-66, July 2015; $541, MS-62, October 2015; $306, MS-60, May 2015										

ILLINOIS CENTENNIAL HALF DOLLAR (1918)

Designers: *George T. Morgan (obverse) and John R. Sinnock (reverse).* **Weight:** *12.50 grams.*
Composition: *.900 silver, .100 copper (net weight .3617 oz. pure silver).*
Diameter: *30.6 mm.* **Edge:** *Reeded.* **Mint:** *Philadelphia.*

This coin was authorized to commemorate the 100th anniversary of the admission of Illinois into the Union, and was the first souvenir piece for such an event. The head of Abraham Lincoln on the obverse was based on that of a statue of the celebrated president by Andrew O'Connor in Springfield, Illinois.

Designs. *Obverse:* Bareheaded, beardless profile portrait of Abraham Lincoln, facing right.
Reverse: A fierce eagle atop a crag, clutching a shield and carrying a banner; from the Illinois state seal.

Mintage Data. Authorized on June 1, 1918. *Maximum authorized*—100,000. *Number minted*—100,000 (plus 58 assay coins).

Original Cost and Issuer. Sale price $1. Issued by the Illinois Centennial Commission, through various outlets.

Key to Collecting. Examples were struck with deep, frosty finishes, giving Mint State pieces an unusually attractive appearance. The obverse typically shows contact marks or friction on Lincoln's cheek and on other high parts of his portrait. The field typically shows contact marks. The reverse usually grades from one to three points higher than the obverse, due to the protective nature of its complicated design. Most examples are lustrous and frosty, although a few are seen with partially prooflike fields.

First Points of Wear. *Obverse:* The hair above Lincoln's ear. *Reverse:* The eagle's breast. (Note that the breast was sometimes flatly struck; look for differences in texture or color of the metal.)

	Distribution	Cert	Avg	%MS	AU-50	MS-60	MS-62	MS-63	MS-64	MS-65	MS-66
1918	100,058	4,323	63.9	98%	$130	$150	$160	$170	$225	$325	$685
	Auctions: $5,640, MS-67, January 2015; $823, MS-66, January 2015; $212, MS-64, February 2015; $84, AU-55, February 2015										

MAINE CENTENNIAL HALF DOLLAR (1920)

Designer: *Anthony de Francisci.* **Weight:** *12.50 grams.* **Composition:** *.900 silver, .100 copper (net weight .3617 oz. pure silver).* **Diameter:** *30.6 mm.* **Edge:** *Reeded.* **Mint:** *Philadelphia.*

Congress authorized the Maine Centennial half dollar on May 10, 1920, to be sold at the centennial celebration at Portland. They were received too late for this event and were sold by the state treasurer for many years.

Designs. *Obverse:* Arms of the state of Maine, with the Latin word DIRIGO ("I Direct"). *Reverse:* The centennial inscription enclosed by a wreath.

Mintage Data. Authorized on May 10, 1920. *Maximum authorized*—100,000. *Number minted*—50,028 (including 28 assay coins).

Original Cost and Issuer. Sale price $1. Issued by the Maine Centennial Commission.

Key to Collecting. Relatively few Maine half dollars were sold to the hobby community; the majority of coins distributed saw careless handling by the general public. Most examples show friction or handling marks on the center of the shield on the obverse. The fields were not completely finished in the dies and always show tiny raised lines or die-finishing marks; at first glance these may appear to be hairlines or scratches, but they have no effect on the grade. Appealing examples in higher Mint State levels are much more elusive than the high mintage might suggest.

First Points of Wear. *Obverse:* The left hand of the scythe holder; the right hand of the anchor holder. (Note that the moose and the pine tree are weakly struck.) *Reverse:* The bow knot.

	Distribution	Cert	Avg	%MS	AU-50	MS-60	MS-62	MS-63	MS-64	MS-65	MS-66
1920	50,028	2,940	64.1	98%	$120	$140	$155	$160	$200	$395	$525
	Auctions: $10,575, MS-68, January 2015; $3,290, MS-67, September 2015; $200, MS-64, January 2015; $74, EF-40, September 2015										

PILGRIM TERCENTENARY HALF DOLLAR (1920–1921)

Designer: *Cyrus E. Dallin.* **Weight:** *12.50 grams.* **Composition:** *.900 silver, .100 copper (net weight .3617 oz. pure silver).* **Diameter:** *30.6 mm.* **Edge:** *Reeded.* **Mint:** *Philadelphia.*

To commemorate the landing of the Pilgrims at Plymouth, Massachusetts, in 1620, Congress authorized a special half dollar on May 12, 1920. The first issue had no date on the obverse. The coins struck in 1921 show that date in addition to 1620–1920.

Designs. *Obverse:* Artist's conception of a partial standing portrait of Governor William Bradford holding a book. *Reverse:* The *Mayflower* in full sail.

Mintage and Melting Data. Authorized on May 12, 1920. *Maximum authorized*—300,000 (both years combined). *Number minted*—1920: 200,112 (including 112 assay coins); 1921: 100,053 (including 53 assay coins). *Number melted*—1920: 48,000; 1921: 80,000. *Net distribution*—1920: 152,112; 1921: 20,053.

Original Cost and Issuer. Sale price $1. Issued by the Pilgrim Tercentenary Commission.

Key to Collecting. The 1920 issue is common, and the 1921 slightly scarce. Coins grading MS-64 and higher usually have excellent eye appeal, though many exceptions exist. Most coins have scattered contact marks, particularly on the obverse. Nearly all 1921 coins are this way. Many coins (particularly coins which are early impressions from the dies) show tiny raised lines in the obverse field, representing die finish marks; these are not to be confused with hairlines or other evidences of friction (which are recessed).

First Points of Wear. *Obverse:* Cheekbone, hair over ear, and the high areas of Governor Bradford's hat. *Reverse:* The ship's rigging and stern, the crow's nest, and the rim.

	Distribution	Cert	Avg	%MS	AU-50	MS-60	MS-62	MS-63	MS-64	MS-65	MS-66
1920	152,112	4,843	63.8	97%	$80	$90	$95	$100	$125	$200	$475
	Auctions: $6,756, MS-67, September 2015; $543, MS-66, October 2015; $153, MS-64, September 2015; $80, MS-62, September 2015										
1921, With Added Date	20,053	2,107	64.2	99%	$165	$180	$185	$195	$215	$275	$650
	Auctions: $5,876, MS-67, January 2015; $1,880, MS-66, July 2015; $447, MS-64, February 2015; $141, AU-58, March 2015										

MISSOURI CENTENNIAL HALF DOLLAR (1921)

Designer: *Robert Aitken.* **Weight:** *12.50 grams.* **Composition:** *.900 silver, .100 copper (net weight .3617 oz. pure silver).* **Diameter:** *30.6 mm.* **Edge:** *Reeded.* **Mint:** *Philadelphia.*

The 100th anniversary of the admission of Missouri to the Union was celebrated in the city of Sedalia during August 1921. To mark the occasion, Congress authorized the coinage of a fifty-cent piece.

Designs. *Obverse:* Coonskin-capped profile portrait of a frontiersman. One variety has 2★4 in the field; the other is plain. *Reverse:* Standing figures of a frontiersman and an Indian looking westward, against a starry field; SEDALIA (the location of the Missouri centennial exposition) incused below.

Mintage and Melting Data. Authorized on March 4, 1921. *Maximum authorized*—250,000 (both varieties combined). *Number minted*—50,028 (both varieties combined; including 28 assay coins). *Number melted*—29,600. *Net distribution*—20,428 (estimated; 9,400 for 1921 2★4 and 11,400 for 1921 Plain).

Original Cost and Issuer. Sale price $1. Issued by the Missouri Centennial Committee, through the Sedalia Trust Company.

Key to Collecting. Most grade from AU-55 to MS-63; have friction and contact marks on the higher areas of the design; and are lightly struck at the center of the portrait of Boone on the obverse, and at the torsos of the two figures on the reverse. MS-65 and higher coins with sharply struck centers are rarities.

First Points of Wear. *Obverse:* The hair in back of the ear. *Reverse:* The frontiersman's arm and shoulder.

	Distribution	Cert	Avg	%MS	AU-50	MS-60	MS-62	MS-63	MS-64	MS-65	MS-66
									PF-63	PF-64	PF-65
1921, "2★4" in Field	9,400	1,640	63.7	98%	$575	$625	$850	$950	$1,100	$2,100	$5,400
	Auctions: $6,169, MS-66, January 2015; $2,291, MS-65, August 2015; $705, MS-62, September 2015; $646, AU-58, September 2015										
1921, "2★4" in Field, Matte Proof	1–2	0	n/a								
	Auctions: No auction records available.										
1921, Plain	11,400	1,987	63.2	95%	$400	$525	$650	$675	$900	$2,000	$4,900
	Auctions: $5,640, MS-66, September 2015; $2,468, MS-65, January 2015; $353, AU-58, January 2015; $259, AU-50, November 2015										

ALABAMA CENTENNIAL HALF DOLLAR (1921)

Designer: *Laura Gardin Fraser.* **Weight:** *12.50 grams.* **Composition:** *.900 silver, .100 copper (net weight .3617 oz. pure silver).* **Diameter:** *30.6 mm.* **Edge:** *Reeded.* **Mint:** *Philadelphia.*

The Alabama half dollars were authorized in 1920 and struck until 1921 for the statehood centennial, which was celebrated in 1919. The coins were offered first during President Warren Harding's visit to Birmingham, October 26, 1921. T.E. Kilby's likeness on the obverse was first instance of a living person's portrait on a United States coin.

Designs. *Obverse:* Conjoined bareheaded profile portraits of William Wyatt Bibb, the first governor of Alabama, and Thomas Kilby, governor at the time of the centennial. *Reverse:* A dynamic eagle perched on a shield, clutching arrows and holding a banner; from the Alabama state seal.

Mintage and Melting Data. Authorized on May 10, 1920. *Maximum authorized*—100,000. *Number minted*—70,044 (including 44 assay coins). *Number melted*—5,000. *Net distribution*—2X2: estimated as 30,000; Plain: estimated as 35,000.

Original Cost and Issuer. Sale price $1. Issued by the Alabama Centennial Commission.

Key to Collecting. Most of these coins were sold to citizens of Alabama, and of those, few were acquired by numismatists. Many are in circulated grades (typical being EF or AU), with most surviving pieces grading MS-63 or less. Those grading MS-65 or finer are rare. Nearly all show friction or contact marks on Governor Kilby's cheek on the obverse, and many are flatly struck on the eagle's left leg and talons on the reverse. These coins were produced carelessly, and many lack sharpness and luster (sharply struck examples are very rare). Nicks and marks from the original planchets are often found on the areas of light striking. The eagle's upper leg is often lightly struck, particularly on the plain variety. The 2X2 coins usually are better struck than the plain variety.

First Points of Wear. *Obverse:* Kirby's forehead and the area to the left of his earlobe. *Reverse:* The eagle's lower neck and the top of its wings.

	Distribution	Cert	Avg	%MS	AU-50	MS-60	MS-62	MS-63	MS-64	MS-65	MS-66
1921, "2X2" in Field	6,006	1,706	63.4	95%	$285	$325	$375	$400	$550	$1,200	$2,650
	Auctions: $11,750, MS-67, August 2015; $3,525, MS-66, July 2015; $411, MS-63, September 2015; $188, AU-50, February 2015										
1921, Plain	16,014	2,029	62.7	90%	$160	$200	$300	$385	$460	$975	$1,600
	Auctions: $19,975, MS-67, January 2015; $5,405, MS-66, January 2015; $235, MS-62, March 2015; $141, AU-58, August 2015										

Grant Memorial Half Dollar (1922)

Designer: *Laura Gardin Fraser.* **Weight:** *12.50 grams.* **Composition:** *.900 silver, .100 copper (net weight .3617 oz. pure silver).* **Diameter:** *30.6 mm.* **Edge:** *Reeded.* **Mint:** *Philadelphia.*

This half dollar (along with the Grant Memorial gold dollar) was struck during 1922 as a centenary souvenir of Ulysses S. Grant's birth. The Ulysses S. Grant Centenary Memorial Association originally planned celebrations in Clermont County, Ohio; the construction of community buildings in Georgetown and Bethel; and the laying of a five-mile highway from New Richmond to Point Pleasant in addition to the coins, but the buildings and highway never came to fruition.

Designs. *Obverse:* Bareheaded profile portrait of Ulysses S. Grant in a military coat. One variety has a star above GRANT. *Reverse:* View of the house Grant was born in (Point Pleasant, Ohio), amidst a wooded setting.

Mintage Data. Authorized on February 2, 1922. *Number minted*—With Star: 5,016 (including 16 assay coins); No Star: 5,000. *Net distribution*—10,016 (both varieties combined).

Original Cost and Issuer. Sale price $3 for either variety. Issued by the U.S. Grant Centenary Memorial Commission (mail orders were serviced by Hugh L. Nichols, chairman, Batavia, Ohio).

Key to Collecting. Almost all known specimens are MS–63 to 65 or better. MS–66 and 67 examples are easy to find. Some lower-grade coins show friction on Grant's cheek and hair. Some specimens have dull surfaces; these are avoided by connoisseurs.

First Points of Wear. *Obverse:* Grant's cheekbone and hair. *Reverse:* The leaves of the tree under the U in TRUST.

	Distribution	Cert	Avg	%MS	AU-50	MS-60	MS-62	MS-63	MS-64	MS-65	MS-66
1922, Star in Obverse Field	4,256	1,306	63.6	97%	$900	$1,200	$1,450	$1,675	$2,675	$5,000	$8,000
	Auctions: $37,600, MS-67, January 2015; $12,926, MS-66, July 2015; $764, AU-53, August 2015; $646, EF-40, August 2015										
1922, No Star in Obverse Field	67,405	3,614	63.7	97%	$110	$120	$135	$150	$250	$550	$900
	Auctions: $3,760, MS-67, September 2015; $2,115, MS-66, August 2015; $165, MS-61, February 2015; $60, AU-58, February 2015										

GRANT MEMORIAL GOLD DOLLAR (1922)

Designer: *Laura Gardin Fraser.* **Weight:** *1.672 grams.* **Composition:** *.900 gold, .100 copper (net weight .04837 oz. pure gold).* **Diameter:** *15 mm.* **Edge:** *Reeded.* **Mint:** *Philadelphia.*

The Ulysses S. Grant Centenary Memorial Association, incorporated in 1921, marked the 100th birth anniversary of the Civil War general and U.S. president with this gold dollar (as well as a commemorative half dollar).

Designs. *Obverse:* Bareheaded profile portrait of Ulysses S. Grant in a military coat. One variety has a star above GRANT. *Reverse:* View of the house Grant was born in (Point Pleasant, Ohio), amidst a wooded setting.

Mintage Data. Authorized on February 2, 1922. *Number minted*—With Star: 5,016 (including 16 assay coins); No Star: 5,000. *Net distribution*—10,016 (both varieties combined).

Original Cost and Issuer. Sale price $3 for either type. Issued by the U.S. Grant Centenary Memorial Commission (mail orders were serviced by Hugh L. Nichols, chairman, Batavia, Ohio).

Key to Collecting. Almost all known specimens are MS–63 to 65 or better. MS–66 and 67 examples are easy to find. Some lower-grade coins show friction on Grant's cheek and hair. Some specimens have dull surfaces; these are avoided by connoisseurs.

First Points of Wear. *Obverse:* Grant's cheekbone and hair. *Reverse:* The leaves of the tree under the U in TRUST.

	Distribution	Cert	Avg	%MS	AU-50	MS-60	MS-62	MS-63	MS-64	MS-65	MS-66
1922, With Star	5,016	1,307	64.8	99%	$1,200	$1,300	$1,575	$1,600	$1,800	$2,100	$2,350
	Auctions: $12,925, MS-68, January 2015; $6,463, MS-67, June 2015; $1,410, MS-64, October 2015; $646, AU-50, May 2015										
1922, No Star	5,016	1,228	64.4	97%	$1,000	$1,200	$1,325	$1,400	$1,650	$2,000	$2,250
	Auctions: $3,760, MS-67, August 2015; $3,055, MS-66, July 2015; $1,586, MS-64, February 2015; $764, MS-60, October 2015										

MONROE DOCTRINE CENTENNIAL HALF DOLLAR (1923)

Designer: *Chester Beach.* **Weight:** *12.50 grams.* **Composition:** *.900 silver, .100 copper (net weight .3617 oz. pure silver).* **Diameter:** *30.6 mm.* **Edge:** *Reeded.* **Mint:** *San Francisco.*

The California film industry promoted this issue in conjunction with a motion-picture exposition held in June 1923. The coin purportedly commemorated the 100th anniversary of the Monroe Doctrine, which warned that European countries that interfered with countries in the Western Hemisphere or established new colonies there would be met with disapproval or worse from the U.S. government.

Designs. *Obverse:* Conjoined bareheaded profile portraits of presidents James Monroe and John Quincy Adams. *Reverse:* Stylized depiction of the continents of North and South America as female figures in the outlines of the two land masses.

Mintage Data. Authorized on January 24, 1923. *Maximum authorized*—300,000. *Number minted*—274,077 (including 77 assay coins). *Net distribution*—274,077.

Original Cost and Issuer. Sale price $1. Issued by the Los Angeles Clearing House, representing backers of the First Annual American Historical Revue and Motion Picture Industry Exposition.

Key to Collecting. Most examples show friction or wear. MS coins are common. Evaluating the numerical grade of MS-60 to 63 coins is difficult because of the design's weak definition. Low-magnification inspection usually shows nicks and graininess at the highest point of the obverse center; these flaws are from the original planchets. Many examples of this coin have been doctored and artificially toned in attempts to earn higher grades upon certification; these are avoided by connoisseurs.

First Points of Wear. *Obverse:* Adams's cheekbone. *Reverse:* The upper figure, underneath the CT in DOCTRINE.

	Distribution	Cert	Avg	%MS	AU-50	MS-60	MS-62	MS-63	MS-64	MS-65	MS-66
1923-S	274,077	3,675	63.1	96%	$50	$75	$100	$120	$225	$850	$2,500
	Auctions: $11,163, MS-67, August 2015; $5,640, MS-66, January 2015; $1,645, MS-65, January 2015; $84, MS-62, July 2015										

HUGUENOT-WALLOON TERCENTENARY HALF DOLLAR (1924)

Designer: *George T. Morgan (with model modifications by James Earle Fraser).*
Weight: *12.50 grams.* **Composition:** *.900 silver, .100 copper (net weight .3617 oz. pure silver).*
Diameter: *30.6 mm.* **Edge:** *Reeded.* **Mint:** *Philadelphia.*

Settling of the Huguenots and Walloons in the New World was the occasion commemorated by this issue. New Netherland, now New York, was founded in 1624 by this group of Dutch colonists. Interestingly, the persons represented on the obverse were not directly concerned with the occasion; both Admiral Gaspard de Coligny and Prince William the Silent were dead long before the settlement.

Designs. *Obverse:* Hat-clad profile portraits representing Admiral Gaspard de Coligny and Prince William the Silent, first stadtholder of the Netherlands. *Reverse:* The ship *Nieuw Nederland* in full sail.

Mintage Data. Authorized on February 26, 1923. *Maximum authorized—*300,000. *Number minted—*142,080 (including 80 assay coins). *Net distribution—*142,080.

Original Cost and Issuer. Sale price $1. Issued by the Huguenot-Walloon New Netherland Commission, Inc., and designated outlets.

Key to Collecting. This coin is readily available on the market, with most examples in MS–60 to 63. Those grading MS–64 and 65 are also found quite often; MS–66 coins are scarcer. Relatively few worn pieces exist. Friction and contact marks are sometimes seen on the cheek of Admiral Coligny on the obverse, and on the masts and ship's rigging on the reverse. Many coins have been cleaned or repeatedly dipped. Connoisseurs avoid deeply toned or stained coins, even those certified with high numerical grades. MS coins usually have satiny (rather than deeply lustrous or frosty) surfaces, and may have a gray appearance. High in the reverse field of most coins is a "bright" spot interrupting the luster, from a touch of polish in the die.

First Points of Wear. *Obverse:* Coligny's cheekbone. *Reverse:* The rim near the F in FOUNDING and over the RY in TERCENTENARY; the lower part of the highest sail; the center of the ship's stern.

	Distribution	Cert	Avg	%MS	AU-50	MS-60	MS-62	MS-63	MS-64	MS-65	MS-66
1924	142,080	3,330	64.2	98%	$125	$130	$140	$160	$175	$240	$575
Auctions: $15,275, MS-68, August 2015; $6,756, MS-67, September 2015; $100, MS-60, January 2015; $89, AU-58, January 2015											

Lexington-Concord Sesquicentennial Half Dollar (1925)

Designer: *Chester Beach.* **Weight:** *12.50 grams.* **Composition:** *.900 silver, .100 copper (net weight .3617 oz. pure silver).* **Diameter:** *30.6 mm.* **Edge:** *Reeded.* **Mint:** *Philadelphia.*

The Battle of Lexington and Concord—fought in 1775 just one day after Paul Revere's famous ride—is commemorated on this coin. Sculptor James Earle Fraser of the Commission of Fine Arts approved Beach's designs, but protested that the local committees had made a poor choice of subject matter.

Designs. *Obverse:* A view of *The Concord Minute Man of 1775* statue, by Daniel Chester French, located in Concord, Massachusetts. *Reverse:* Lexington's Old Belfry, whose tolling bell roused the Minute Men to action in 1775.

Mintage and Melting Data. Authorized on January 14, 1925. *Maximum authorized—*300,000. *Number minted—*162,099 (including 99 assay coins). *Number melted—*86. *Net distribution—*162,013.

Original Cost and Issuer. Sale price $1. Issued by the U.S. Lexington-Concord Sesquicentennial Commission, through local banks.

Key to Collecting. Examples are easily found in all grades, with most being in high AU or low MS grades, although eye appeal can vary widely. MS-65 coins are scarce in comparison to those in MS–60 through 64. Some specimens are deeply frosty and lustrous, whereas others have partially prooflike fields.

First Points of Wear. *Obverse:* The thighs of the Minuteman. *Reverse:* The top edge of the belfry.

	Distribution	Cert	Avg	%MS	AU-50	MS-60	MS-62	MS-63	MS-64	MS-65	MS-66
1925	162,013	4,173	63.6	97%	$75	$85	$90	$100	$135	$325	$600
	Auctions: $6,463, MS-67, July 2015; $1,645, MS-66, January 2015; $106, MS-63, June 2015; $69, AU-58, October 2015										

STONE MOUNTAIN MEMORIAL HALF DOLLAR (1925)

Designer: *Gutzon Borglum.* **Weight:** *12.50 grams.* **Composition:** *.900 silver, .100 copper (net weight .3617 oz. pure silver).* **Diameter:** *30.6 mm.* **Edge:** *Reeded.* **Mint:** *Philadelphia.*

The first of these half dollars were struck at Philadelphia on January 21, 1925, Confederate general Stonewall Jackson's birthday. Funds received from the sale of this large issue were devoted to the expense of carving figures of Confederate leaders and soldiers on Stone Mountain in Georgia. The coin's designer, Gutzon Borglum, was the original sculptor for that project, but left due to differences with the Stone Mountain Confederate Monumental Association. Augustus Lukeman took over in his stead, and the carving was completed and dedicated in 1970; Borglum would meanwhile go on to create the presidents' heads at Mount Rushmore.

Designs. *Obverse:* Equestrian portraits of Civil War generals Robert E. Lee and Thomas "Stonewall" Jackson. *Reverse:* An eagle perched on a cliff with wings in mid-spread.

Mintage and Melting Data. *Maximum authorized*—5,000,000. *Number minted*—2,314,709 (including 4,709 assay coins). *Number melted*—1,000,000. *Net distribution*—1,314,709.

Original Cost and Issuer. Sale price $1. Issued by the Stone Mountain Confederate Monumental Association through many outlets, including promotions involving pieces counterstamped with abbreviations for Southern states.

Key to Collecting. This is the most plentiful commemorative from the 1920s. Examples are easily found in grades ranging from lightly worn through gem Mint State (many with outstanding eye appeal). Circulated coins are also found, as well as those that were counterstamped for special fundraising sales. The typical coin has very lustrous and frosty surfaces, although the reverse field may be somewhat satiny.

First Points of Wear. *Obverse:* Lee's elbow and leg. *Reverse:* The eagle's breast.

	Distribution	Cert	Avg	%MS	AU-50	MS-60	MS-62	MS-63	MS-64	MS-65	MS-66
1925	1,314,709	8,572	63.9	96%	$55	$65	$70	$80	$135	$185	$300
	Auctions: $3,055, MS-67, January 2015; $564, MS-66, August 2015; $182, MS-64, March 2015; $50, AU-58, September 2015										

CALIFORNIA DIAMOND JUBILEE HALF DOLLAR (1925)

Designer: *Jo Mora.* **Weight:** *12.50 grams.* **Composition:** *.900 silver, .100 copper (net weight .3617 oz. pure silver).* **Diameter:** *30.6 mm.* **Edge:** *Reeded.* **Mint:** *San Francisco.*

The celebration for which these coins were struck marked the 75th anniversary of the admission of California into the Union. Notably, James Earle Fraser of the Commission of Fine Arts criticized Jo Mora's designs at the time. Art historian Cornelius Vermeule, however, called the coin "one of America's greatest works of numismatic art" in his book *Numismatic Art in America*.

Designs. *Obverse:* A rustic miner, squatting to pan for gold. *Reverse:* A grizzly bear, as taken from the California state flag.

Mintage and Melting Data. Authorized on February 24, 1925, part of the act also providing for the 1925 Fort Vancouver and 1927 Vermont half dollars. *Maximum authorized*—300,000. *Number minted*—150,200 (including 200 assay coins). *Number melted*—63,606. *Net distribution*—86,594.

Original Cost and Issuer. Sale price $1. Issued by the San Francisco Citizens' Committee through the San Francisco Clearing House Association and the Los Angeles Clearing House.

Key to Collecting. This coin's design is such that even a small amount of handling produces friction on the shoulder and high parts of the bear, in particular. As a result, most grade in the AU-55 to MS-62 range, and higher-level MS examples are rare. This issue exists in two finishes: frosty/lustrous, and the rarer "chrome-like" or prooflike. The frosty-finish pieces display some lack of die definition of the details. The prooflike pieces have heavily brushed and highly polished dies. Many specimens certified in high grades are toned, sometimes deeply, which can mask evidence of friction. Coins with no traces of friction are rarities.

First Points of Wear. *Obverse:* The folds of the miner's shirt sleeve. *Reverse:* The shoulder of the bear.

	Distribution	Cert	Avg	%MS	AU-50	MS-60	MS-62	MS-63	MS-64	MS-65	MS-66
									PF-63	PF-64	PF-65
1925-S	86,594	4,248	63.9	96%	$185	$200	$205	$210	$375	$450	$775
	Auctions: $12,925, MS-68, January 2015; $4,465, MS-67, September 2015; $165, MS-62, October 2015; $129, AU-55, March 2015										
1925-S, Matte Proof	*1–2*	1	65.0								
	Auctions: No auction records available.										

FORT VANCOUVER CENTENNIAL HALF DOLLAR (1925)

Designer: *Laura Gardin Fraser.* **Weight:** *12.50 grams.* **Composition:** *.900 silver, .100 copper (net weight .3617 oz. pure silver).* **Diameter:** *30.6 mm.* **Edge:** *Reeded.* **Mint:** *San Francisco.*

The sale of these half dollars at $1 each helped to finance the pageant staged for the celebration of the 100th anniversary of the construction of Fort Vancouver. As part of the publicity, pilot Oakley G. Kelly made a round-trip flight from Vancouver to San Francisco and back again to pick up and deliver the entire issue—which weighed 1,462 pounds.

Designs. *Obverse:* Bareheaded profile portrait of Dr. John McLoughlin, who built Fort Vancouver (Washington) on the Columbia River in 1825. *Reverse:* A pioneer in buckskin with a musket in his hands, with Fort Vancouver in the background.

Mintage and Melting Data. Authorized on February 24, 1925. *Maximum authorized*—300,000. *Number minted* (including 28 assay coins)—50,028. *Number melted*—35,034. *Net distribution*—14,994.

Original Cost and Issuer. Sale price $1. The Fort Vancouver Centennial Corporation, Vancouver, Washington.

Key to Collecting. This coin's design is such that even a small amount of handling produced friction on the higher spots. As a result, higher-level MS examples are rare.

First Points of Wear. *Obverse:* McLoughlin's temple area. *Reverse:* The pioneer's right knee.

	Distribution	Cert	Avg	%MS	AU-50	MS-60	MS-62	MS-63	MS-64	MS-65	MS-66
									PF-63	PF-64	PF-65
1925	14,994	2,274	64.0	96%	$300	$325	$350	$375	$450	$600	$900
	Auctions: $4,772, MS-67, September 2015; $2,115, MS-66, September 2015; $212, AU-53, March 2015; $129, EF-40, September 2015										
1925, Matte Proof	2–3	0	n/a								
	Auctions: $188,000, PF-66, April 2015										

SESQUICENTENNIAL OF AMERICAN INDEPENDENCE HALF DOLLAR (1926)

Designer: *John R. Sinnock.* **Weight:** *12.50 grams.* **Composition:** *.900 silver, .100 copper (net weight .3617 oz. pure silver).* **Diameter:** *30.6 mm.* **Edge:** *Reeded.* **Mint:** *Philadelphia.*

The 150th anniversary of the signing of the Declaration of Independence was the occasion for an international fair held in Philadelphia in 1926. To help raise funds for financing the fair, special issues of half dollars (as well as quarter eagles, below) were authorized by Congress. The use of Calvin Coolidge's likeness marked the first time a portrait of a president appeared on a coin struck during his own lifetime.

Designs. *Obverse:* Conjoined profile portraits of bewigged George Washington and bareheaded Calvin Coolidge. *Reverse:* The Liberty Bell.

Mintage and Melting Data. Authorized on March 23, 1925. *Maximum authorized*—1,000,000. *Number minted*—1,000,528 (including 528 assay coins). *Number melted*—859,408. *Net distribution*—141,120.

Original Cost and Issuer. Sale price $1. Issued by the National Sesquicentennial Exhibition Association.

Key to Collecting. Accurate grading can be problematic for this coin. Many examples certified at high grades have mottled or deeply toned surfaces that obfuscate examination, and others have been recolored. Most have graininess—marks from the original planchet—on the highest part of the portrait.

First Points of Wear. *Obverse:* Washington's cheekbone. *Reverse:* The area below the lower inscription on the Liberty Bell.

	Distribution	Cert	Avg	%MS	AU-50	MS-60	MS-62	MS-63	MS-64	MS-65	MS-66
1926	141,120	4,465	63.1	96%	$75	$90	$100	$130	$225	$1,600	$20,000
	Auctions: $5,288, MS-66, July 2015; $1,880, MS-65, January 2015; $112, MS-62, February 2015; $84, AU-55, July 2015										

SESQUICENTENNIAL OF AMERICAN INDEPENDENCE QUARTER EAGLE (1926)

Designer: *John R. Sinnock.* **Weight:** *4.18 grams.* **Composition:** *.900 gold, .100 copper (net weight .12094 oz. pure gold).* **Diameter:** *18 mm.* **Edge:** *Reeded.* **Mint:** *Philadelphia.*

This quarter eagle, along with a related half dollar, was sold to finance the National Sesquicentennial Exposition in Philadelphia (which marked the 150th anniversary of the signing of the Declaration of Independence). Note that though the issuer was known as the National Sesquicentennial *Exhibition* Association, the event was primarily billed with *Exposition* in its name.

Designs. *Obverse:* Miss Liberty standing, holding in one hand a scroll representing the Declaration of Independence and in the other, the Torch of Freedom. *Reverse:* A front view of Independence Hall in Philadelphia.

Mintage and Melting Data. Authorized on March 23, 1925. *Maximum authorized*—200,000. *Number minted*—200,226 (including 226 assay coins). *Number melted*—154,207. *Net distribution*—46,019.

Original Cost and Issuer. Sale price $4. National Sesquicentennial Exhibition Association.

Key to Collecting. Nearly all examples show evidence of handling and contact from careless production at the Mint, and from later indifference by their buyers. Most coins range from AU-55 to MS-62 in grade, and have scattered marks in the fields. MS-65 examples are rare. Well-struck coins are seldom seen. Some pieces show copper stains; connoisseurs avoid these.

First Points of Wear. *Obverse:* The bottom of the scroll held by Liberty. *Reverse:* The area below the top of the tower; and the central portion above the roof.

	Distribution	Cert	Avg	%MS	AU-50	MS-60	MS-62	MS-63	MS-64	MS-65	MS-66
									PF-63	PF-64	PF-65
1926	46,019	7,544	63.0	93%	$400	$450	$525	$550	$875	$1,800	$4,750
	Auctions: $25,850, MS-67, January 2015; $6,463, MS-66, January 2015; $494, MS-62, January 2015; $282, AU-55, September 2015										
1926, Matte Proof (a)	*unique*	1	65.0								
	Auctions: No auction records available.										

a. "The coin is unique and displays a matte surface similar to the Proof gold coins of 1908 to 1915. The coin was reportedly from the estate of the designer, John R. Sinnock, who is best known for his Roosevelt dime and Franklin half dollar designs. The piece was in the possession of coin dealer David Bullowa in the 1950s. Another example is rumored by Breen, but the whereabouts or existence of the coin is unknown" (*Encyclopedia of U.S. Gold Coins, 1795–1933*, second edition).

OREGON TRAIL MEMORIAL HALF DOLLAR (1926–1939)

Designers: *James Earle Fraser and Laura Gardin Fraser.* **Weight:** *12.50 grams.*
Composition: *.900 silver, .100 copper (net weight .3617 oz. pure silver).*
Diameter: *30.6 mm.* **Edge:** *Reeded.* **Mints:** *Philadelphia, San Francisco, and Denver.*

These coins—the longest-running series of commemoratives—were struck in commemoration of the Oregon Trail and in memory of the pioneers, many of whom lie buried along the famous 2,000-mile highway of history. This was the first commemorative to be struck at more than one Mint facility, and also the first commemorative to be struck at the Denver Mint.

Designs. *Obverse:* A pioneer family in a Conestoga wagon, heading west into the sunset. *Reverse:* A standing Indian with a bow, arm outstretched, and a map of the United States in the background.

Mintage and Melting Data. *Maximum authorized*—6,000,000 (for the entire series from 1926 onward). *Number minted*—1926: 48,030 (including 30 assay coins); 1926-S: 100,055 (including 55 assay coins); 1928: 50,028 (including 28 assay coins); 1933-D: 5,250 (including an unrecorded number of assay coins); 1934-D: 7,006 (including 6 assay coins); 1936: 10,006 (including 6 assay coins); 1936-S: 5,006 (including 6 assay coins); 1937-D: 12,008 (including 8 assay coins); 1938-P: 6,006 (including 6 assay coins); 1938-D: 6,005 (including 5 assay coins); 1938-S: 6,006 (including 6 assay coins). *Number melted*—1926: 75 (defective coins); 1926-S: 17,000; 1928: 44,000; 1933-D: 242 (probably defective coins). *Net distribution*—1926: 47,955; 1926-S: 83,055; 1928: 6,028; 1933-D: 5,008; 1934-D: 7,006; 1936: 10,006; 1936-S: 5,006; 1937-D: 12,008; 1938-P: 6,006; 1938-D: 6,005; 1938-S: 6,006.

Original Cost and Issuer. Sale price $1; later raised. Issued by the Oregon Trail Memorial Association, Inc.; some sold through Scott Stamp & Coin Co., Inc., and some sold through Whitman Centennial, Inc., Walla Walla, Washington. From 1937 onward, distributed solely by the Oregon Trail Memorial Association, Inc.

Key to Collecting. Although most of the later issues have low mintages, they are not rare in the marketplace, because the majority were originally sold to coin collectors and dealers. As a result, most surviving coins are in MS. The quality of the surface finish varies, with earlier issues tending to be frosty and lustrous and later issues (particularly those dated 1938 and 1939) having somewhat grainy or satiny fields. Grading requires care. Look for friction or contact marks on the high points of the Indian and the Conestoga wagon, but, more importantly, check both surfaces carefully for scattered cuts and marks. All three mints had difficulty in striking up the rims properly, causing many rejections. Those deemed acceptable and shipped out usually had full rims, but it is best to check when buying.

First Points of Wear. *Obverse:* The hip of the ox, and high points of the wagon (note that the top rear of the wagon was weakly struck in some years). *Reverse:* The Indian's left thumb and fingers (note that some pieces show flatness on the thumb and first finger, due to a weak strike).

	Distribution	Cert	Avg	%MS	AU-50	MS-60	MS-62	MS-63	MS-64	MS-65	MS-66
									PF-63	PF-64	PF-65
1926	47,955	2,188	64.4	98%	$135	$160	$170	$190	$210	$250	$325
Auctions: $999, MS-67, June 2015; $412, MS-66, November 2015; $235, MS-63, May 2015; $112, MS-61, February 2015											
1926, Matte Proof	1–2	1	65.0								
Auctions: No auction records available.											
1926-S	83,055	3,048	64.6	97%	$135	$160	$170	$190	$210	$260	$350
Auctions: $14,100, MS-68, January 2015; $1,998, MS-67, January 2015; $247, MS-65, June 2015; $129, MS-60, May 2015											
1928 (same as 1926)	6,028	1,311	65.3	100%	$160	$180	$185	$200	$240	$300	$435
Auctions: $1,410, MS-67, September 2015; $400, MS-66, September 2015; $306, MS-65, February 2015; $223, MS-64, January 2015											
1933-D	5,008	1,037	65.0	100%	$350	$370	$375	$400	$450	$475	$600
Auctions: $1,880, MS-67, June 2015; $564, MS-66, January 2015; $329, MS-65, August 2015; $329, MS-64, May 2015											
1934-D	7,006	1,337	64.8	100%	$190	$200	$205	$210	$215	$300	$450
Auctions: $1,175, MS-67, September 2015; $376, MS-66, August 2015; $212, MS-65, August 2015; $188, MS-63, October 2015											
1936	10,006	1,606	65.3	100%	$160	$180	$190	$200	$220	$260	$280
Auctions: $11,163, MS-68, September 2015; $1,293, MS-67, July 2015; $341, MS-66, February 2015; $200, MS-64, February 2015											
1936-S	5,006	1,138	65.5	100%	$170	$180	$190	$200	$225	$260	$335
Auctions: $1,763, MS-68, November 2014; $10,575, MS-68, January 2013; $670, MS-67+, October 2014; $425, MS-67, November 2014											
1937-D	12,008	2,356	65.9	100%	$165	$180	$185	$195	$225	$250	$315
Auctions: $4,935, MS-68, January 2015; $1,116, MS-67, September 2015; $353, MS-66, February 2015; $200, MS-64, February 2015											
1938 (same as 1926)	6,006	1,250	65.4	100%	$180	$190	$195	$200	$225	$265	$360
Auctions: $1,410, MS-67, January 2015; $306, MS-66, June 2015; $259, MS-65, February 2015; $153, MS-63, May 2015											
1938-D	6,005	1,427	65.8	100%	$180	$190	$195	$200	$225	$275	$340
Auctions: $5,405, MS-68, January 2015; $764, MS-67, August 2015; $306, MS-66, October 2015; $129, MS-63, May 2015											
1938-S	6,006	1,286	65.5	100%	$180	$190	$195	$200	$225	$300	$340
Auctions: $6,933, MS-68, March 2015; $1,293, MS-67, January 2015; $306, MS-66, January 2015; $182, MS-64, September 2015											
Set of 1938 P-D-S					$550	$575	$585	$600	$675	$850	$1,100
Auctions: $2,070, MS-67/67/67, February 2012; $617, MS-64/64/64, March 2015											
1939	3,004	769	65.5	100%	$450	$480	$500	$515	$535	$600	$650
Auctions: $2,350, MS-67, January 2015; $823, MS-66, January 2015; $564, MS-65, January 2015; $494, MS-64, October 2015											
1939-D	3,004	796	65.8	100%	$450	$480	$500	$515	$535	$575	$600
Auctions: $9,400, MS-68, January 2015; $1,880, MS-67, January 2015; $541, MS-65, January 2015; $353, AU-50, September 2015											
1939-S	3,005	788	65.5	100%	$450	$480	$500	$515	$535	$600	$650
Auctions: $4,230, MS-68, January 2015; $1,410, MS-67, August 2015; $881, MS-66, January 2015; $588, MS-64, October 2015											
Set of 1939 P-D-S					$1,350	$1,450	$1,500	$1,550	$1,625	$1,800	$2,200
Auctions: $5,175, MS-67/67/67, January 2012; $1,528, MS-65/65/65, March 2015											

VERMONT SESQUICENTENNIAL HALF DOLLAR (1927)

Designer: *Charles Keck.* **Weight:** *12.50 grams.* **Composition:** *.900 silver, .100 copper (net weight .3617 oz. pure silver).* **Diameter:** *30.6 mm.* **Edge:** *Reeded.* **Mint:** *Philadelphia.*

This souvenir issue commemorates the 150th anniversary of the Battle of Bennington and the independence of Vermont. Authorized in 1925, it was not coined until 1927. The Vermont Sesquicentennial Commission intended that funds derived would benefit the study of history.

Designs. *Obverse:* Profile portrait of a bewigged Ira Allen. *Reverse:* A catamount walking left.

Mintage and Melting Data. Authorized by the Act of February 24, 1925. *Maximum authorized*—40,000. *Number minted*—40,034 (including 34 assay coins). *Number melted*—11,892. *Net distribution*—28,142.

Original Cost and Issuer. Sale price $1. Issued by the Vermont Sesquicentennial Commission (Bennington Battle Monument and Historical Association).

Key to Collecting. The Vermont half dollar was struck with the highest relief of any commemorative issue to that date. Despite the depth of the work in the dies, nearly all of the coins were struck up properly and show excellent detail. Unfortunately, the height of the obverse portrait encourages evidence of contact at the central points, and nearly all coins show some friction on Allen's cheek. Most are in grades of MS–62 to 64 and are deeply lustrous and frosty. Cleaned examples are often seen—and are avoided by connoisseurs.

First Points of Wear. *Obverse:* Allen's cheek, and the hair above his ear and in the temple area. *Reverse:* The catamount's upper shoulder.

	Distribution	Cert	Avg	%MS	AU-50	MS-60	MS-62	MS-63	MS-64	MS-65	MS-66
1927	28,142	3,120	63.9	97%	$250	$265	$270	$275	$325	$460	$750
	Auctions: $3,290, MS-67, August 2015; $1,293, MS-66, January 2015; $282, MS-64, February 2015; $176, AU-53, January 2015										

Hawaiian Sesquicentennial Half Dollar (1928)

Designer: *Juliette M. Fraser.* **Weight:** *12.50 grams.* **Composition:** *.900 silver, .100 copper (net weight .3617 oz. pure silver).* **Diameter:** *30.6 mm.* **Edge:** *Reeded.* **Mint:** *Philadelphia.*

This issue was struck to commemorate the 150th anniversary of the arrival on the Hawaiian Islands of Captain James Cook in 1778. The coin's $2 price was the highest ever for a commemorative half dollar up to that point.

Designs. *Obverse:* Portrait of Captain James Cook. *Reverse:* A Hawaiian chieftain standing with arm outstretched and holding a spear.

Mintage Data. Authorized on March 7, 1928. *Maximum authorized*—10,000. *Number minted*—10,008 (including 8 assay coins and 50 Sandblast Proofs). *Net distribution*—10,008.

Original Cost and Issuer. Sale price $2. Issued by the Captain Cook Sesquicentennial Commission, through the Bank of Hawaii, Ltd.

Key to Collecting. This is the scarcest of classic U.S. commemorative coins. It is elusive in all grades, and highly prized. Most are AU-55 to MS-62 or slightly finer; those grading MS-65 or above are especially difficult to find. Most examples show contact or friction on the higher design areas. Some coins have a somewhat satiny surface, whereas others are lustrous and frosty. Many undipped pieces have a yellowish tint. Beware of coins which have been repeatedly dipped or cleaned. Problem-free examples are rarer even than the low mintage would suggest. Fake "Sandblast Proofs" exist; these are coins dipped in acid.

First Points of Wear. *Obverse:* Cook's cheekbone. *Reverse:* The chieftain's legs; his fingers and the hand holding the spear.

	Distribution	Cert	Avg	%MS	AU-50	MS-60	MS-62	MS-63	MS-64	MS-65	MS-66
									PF-63	PF-64	PF-65
1928	10,008	1,694	63.7	98%	$1,800	$2,100	$2,200	$2,475	$2,875	$3,750	$5,750
	Auctions: $17,625, MS-67, August 2015; $9,988, MS-66, January 2015; $4,230, MS-65, January 2015; $1,410, MS-60, June 2015										
1928, Proof (a)	*50*	27	64.1					$2,500	$20,000	$40,000	—
	Auctions: $25,300, PF-64, August 2004; $33,350, PF-64, January 2012; $21,850, PF-64, February 2000; $13,225, PF-63, January 2004										

a. Sandblast Proof presentation pieces. "Of the production figure, 50 were Sandblast Proofs, made by a special process which imparted a dull, grainy finish to the pieces, similar to that used on certain Mint medals of the era as well as on gold Proof coins circa 1908–1915" *(Guide Book of United States Commemorative Coins).*

MARYLAND TERCENTENARY HALF DOLLAR (1934)

Designer: *Hans Schuler.* **Weight:** *12.50 grams.* **Composition:** *.900 silver, .100 copper (net weight .3617 oz. pure silver).* **Diameter:** *30.6 mm.* **Edge:** *Reeded.* **Mint:** *Philadelphia.*

The 300th anniversary of the founding of the Maryland Colony by Cecil Calvert (known as Lord Baltimore) was the occasion for this special coin. The profits from the sale of this issue were used to finance the celebration in Baltimore during 1934. John Work Garrett, distinguished American diplomat and well-known numismatist, was among the citizens of Maryland who endorsed the commemorative half dollar proposal on behalf of the Maryland Tercentenary Commission of Baltimore.

Designs. *Obverse:* Three-quarter portrait of Cecil Calvert, Lord Baltimore. *Reverse:* The state seal and motto of Maryland.

Mintage Data. Authorized on May 9, 1934. *Maximum authorized—25,000. Number minted—25,015* (including 15 assay coins). *Net distribution—25,015.*

Original Cost and Issuer. Sale price $1. Issued by the Maryland Tercentenary Commission, through various outlets.

Key to Collecting. The coin's field has an unusual "rippled" appearance, similar to a sculptured plaque, so nicks and other marks that would be visible on a coin with flat fields are not as readily noticed. Most examples grade MS–62 to 64. Finer pieces, strictly graded, are elusive. This issue was not handled with care at the time of mintage and distribution, and nearly all show scattered contact marks. Some exist struck from a reverse die broken from the right side of the shield to a point opposite the upper right of the 4 in the date 1634.

First Points of Wear. *Obverse:* Lord Baltimore's nose (the nose usually appears flatly struck; also check the reverse for wear). *Reverse:* The top of the coronet on top of the shield, and the tops of the draperies.

	Distribution	Cert	Avg	%MS	AU-50	MS-60	MS-62	MS-63	MS-64	MS-65	MS-66
									PF-63	PF-64	PF-65
1934	25,015	3,466	64.7	100%	$130	$140	$150	$165	$175	$200	$300
	Auctions: $2,115, MS-67, January 2015; $447, MS-66, August 2015; $212, MS-65, January 2015; $119, MS-60, February 2015										
1934, Matte Proof	*2–4*	2	63.0								
	Auctions: $109,250, PF-64, March 2012										

TEXAS INDEPENDENCE CENTENNIAL HALF DOLLAR (1934–1938)

Designer: *Pompeo Coppini.* **Weight:** *12.50 grams.*
Composition: *.900 silver, .100 copper (net weight .3617 oz. pure silver).*
Diameter: *30.6 mm.* **Edge:** *Reeded.* **Mints:** *Philadelphia, Denver, and San Francisco.*

This issue commemorated the independence of Texas in 1836. Proceeds from the sale of the coin were intended to finance the Centennial Exposition, which was eventually held in Dallas. Sales were lower than expected, but the event was still held and attracted about 7 million visitors.

Designs. *Obverse:* A perched eagle with a large five-pointed star in the background.
Reverse: The goddess Victory kneeling, with medallions and portraits of General Sam Houston and Stephen Austin, founders of the republic and state of Texas, along with other Texan icons.

Mintage and Melting Data. Authorized on June 15, 1933. *Maximum authorized*—1,500,000 (for the entire series 1934 onward). 1934: *Number minted*—1934: 205,113 (including 113 assay coins); 1935-P: 10,008 (including 8 assay coins); 1935-D: 10,007 (including 7 assay coins); 1935-S: 10,008 (including 8 assay coins); 1936-P: 10,008 (including 8 assay coins); 1936-D: 10,007 (including 7 assay coins); 1936-S: 10,008 (including 8 assay coins); 1937-P: 8,005 (including 5 assay coins); 1937-D: 8,006 (including 6 assay coins); 1937-S: 8,007 (including 7 assay coins); 1938-P: 5,005 (including 5 assay coins); 1938-D: 5,005 (including 5 assay coins); 1938-S: 5,006 (including 6 assay coins). *Number melted*—1934: 143,650; 1935-P: 12 (probably defective coins); 1936-P: 12 (probably defective coins); 1937-P: 1,434; 1937-D: 1,401; 1937-S: 1,370; 1938-P: 1,225; 1938-D: 1,230; 1938-S: 1,192. *Net distribution*—1934: 61,463; 1935-P: 9,996; 1935-D: 10,007; 1935-S: 10,008; 1936-P: 9,996; 1936-D: 10,007; 1936-S: 10,008; 1937-P: 6,571; 1937-D: 6,605; 1937-S: 6,637; 1938-P: 3,780; 1938-D: 3,775; 1938-S: 3,814.

Original Cost and Issuer. Sale price $1; later raised. Issued by the American Legion Texas Centennial Committee, Austin, Texas, from 1934 through 1936; issued by the Texas Memorial Museum Centennial Coin Campaign in 1937 and 1938.

Key to Collecting. The typical example grades MS–64 or 65. Early issues are very lustrous and frosty; those produced toward the end of the series are more satiny.

First Points of Wear. *Obverse:* The eagle's upper breast and upper leg. *Reverse:* The forehead and knee of Victory.

	Distribution	Cert	Avg	%MS	AU-50	MS-60	MS-62	MS-63	MS-64	MS-65	MS-66
1934	61,463	2,537	64.5	98%	$130	$140	$145	$150	$165	$200	$300
	Auctions: $1,293, MS-67, July 2015; $306, MS-66, January 2015; $129, MS-64, September 2015; $100, MS-60, June 2015										
1935 (same as 1934)	9,996	1,590	65.6	100%	$130	$140	$145	$150	$160	$175	$290
	Auctions: $3,525, MS-68, January 2015; $1,998, MS-67, August 2015; $188, MS-65, September 2015; $106, MS-60, May 2015										
1935-D	10,007	1,607	65.5	100%	$130	$140	$145	$150	$160	$175	$290
	Auctions: $3,290, MS-68, September 2015; $1,410, MS-67, June 2015; $235, MS-66, May 2015; $153, MS-60, May 2015										
1935-S	10,008	1,356	65.2	100%	$130	$140	$145	$150	$160	$175	$290
	Auctions: $705, MS-67, January 2015; $259, MS-66, May 2015; $212, MS-65, August 2015; $129, MS-63, October 2015										
Set of 1935 P-D-S					$400	$425	$450	$465	$500	$600	$900
	Auctions: $940, MS-67/67/67, March 2015; $871, MS-66/66/66, December 2011; $470, MS-65/65/65, April 2015										

	Distribution	Cert	Avg	%MS	AU-50	MS-60	MS-62	MS-63	MS-64	MS-65	MS-66
1936 (same as 1934)	8,911	1,453	65.4	100%	$145	$150	$155	$165	$180	$225	$290
Auctions: $14,100, MS-68, July 2015; $823, MS-67, June 2015; $382, MS-66, January 2015; $141, MS-64, January 2015											
1936-D	9,039	1,650	65.7	100%	$145	$150	$160	$180	$190	$240	$300
Auctions: $2,820, MS-68, July 2015; $705, MS-67, August 2015; $329, MS-66, March 2015; $123, MS-64, May 2015											
1936-S	9,055	1,349	65.3	100%	$145	$150	$160	$180	$190	$240	$275
Auctions: $1,058, MS-67, October 2015; $282, MS-66, September 2015; $176, MS-65, September 2015; $123, MS-64, March 2015											
Set of 1936 P-D-S					$435	$450	$475	$525	$575	$725	$875
Auctions: $863, MS-66/66/66, December 2011; $705, MS-65/65/65, March 2015											
1937 (same as 1934)	6,571	1,184	65.2	100%	$140	$150	$160	$165	$175	$200	$300
Auctions: $12,925, MS-68, August 2015; $2,585, MS-67, August 2015; $200, MS-65, April 2015; $147, MS-63, October 2015											
1937-D	6,605	1,238	65.4	100%	$140	$150	$160	$165	$175	$200	$300
Auctions: $3,760, MS-68, January 2015; $1,175, MS-67, September 2015; $129, MS-62, October 2015; $89, MS-60, January 2015											
1937-S	6,637	1,250	65.3	100%	$140	$150	$160	$165	$175	$200	$300
Auctions: $1,880, MS-67, February 2015; $329, MS-66, February 2015; $259, MS-66, September 2015; $200, MS-65, October 2015											
Set of 1937 P-D-S					$435	$450	$500	$550	$600	$800	$1,000
Auctions: $625, MS-66/66/66, April 2012; $617, MS-66/66/66, March 2015; $541, MS-65/65/65, September 2015											
1938 (same as 1934)	3,780	847	65.1	100%	$300	$325	$335	$375	$415	$500	$750
Auctions: $1,645, MS-67, January 2015; $823, MS-66, January 2015; $400, MS-65, July 2015; $176, MS-63, October 2015											
1938-D	3,775	887	65.4	100%	$300	$325	$335	$375	$415	$500	$750
Auctions: $1,880, MS-67, August 2015; $447, MS-66, January 2015; $447, MS-66, January 2015; $294, MS-64, October 2015											
1938-S	3,814	881	65.3	100%	$300	$325	$335	$375	$385	$485	$850
Auctions: $2,233, MS-67, January 2015; $646, MS-66, January 2015; $329, MS-65, October 2015; $176, MS-63, October 2015											
Set of 1938 P-D-S					$725	$800	$850	$900	$1,125	$1,200	$1,900
Auctions: $604, MS-64/65/64, June 2012											

DANIEL BOONE BICENTENNIAL HALF DOLLAR (1934–1938)

Designer: *Augustus Lukeman.* **Weight:** *12.50 grams.*
Composition: *.900 silver, .100 copper (net weight .3617 oz. pure silver).*
Diameter: *30.6 mm.* **Edge:** *Reeded.* **Mints:** *Philadelphia, Denver, and San Francisco.*

This coin type, which was minted for five years, was first struck in 1934 to commemorate the 200th anniversary of the birth of Daniel Boone, famous frontiersman, trapper, and explorer. Coinage covered several years, similar to the schedule for the Texas issues; 1934 coins are the only examples with true bicentennial status.

Designs. *Obverse:* Artist's conception of Daniel Boone in a profile portrait. *Reverse:* Standing figures of Boone and Blackfish, war chief of the Chillicothe band of the Shawnee tribe. (In 1935 the date 1934 was added to the reverse design.)

Mintage and Melting Data. Authorized on May 26, 1934 and, with "1934" added to modify the design, on August 26, 1935. *Maximum authorized*—600,000 (for the entire series from 1934 onward). *Number minted*—1934: 10,007 (including 7 assay coins); 1935-P: 10,010 (including 10 assay coins); 1935-D: 5,005 (including 5 assay coins); 1935-S: 5,005 (including 5 assay coins); 1935-P, "Small 1934": 10,008 (including 8 assay coins); 1935-D, "Small 1934": 2,003; 1935-S, "Small 1934": 2,004; 1936-P: 12,012 (including 12 assay coins); 1936-D: 5,005 (including 5 assay coins); 1936-S: 5,006 (including 6 assay coins); 1937-P: 15,010 (including 10 assay coins); 1937-D: 7,506 (including 6 assay coins); 1937-S: 5,006 (including 6 assay coins); 1938-P: 5,005 (including 5 assay coins); 1938-D: 5,005 (including 5 assay coins); 1938-S: 5,006 (including 6 assay coins). *Number melted*—1937-P: 5,200; 1937-D: 5,000; 1937-S: 2,500; 1938-P: 2,905; 1938-D: 2,905; 1938-S: 2,906. *Net distribution*—1934: 10,007; 1935-P: 10,010; 1935-D: 5,005; 1935-S: 5,005; 1935-P, "Small 1934": 10,008 (including 8 assay coins); 1935-D, "Small 1934": 2,003; 1935-S, "Small 1934": 2,004; 1936-P: 12,012; 1936-D: 5,005; 1936-S: 5,006; 1937-P: 9,810; 1937-D: 2,506; 1937-S: 2,506; 1938-P: 2,100; 1938-D: 2,100; 1938-S: 2,100.

Original Cost and Issuer. Sale prices varied by mintmark, from a low of $1.10 per 1935-P coin to a high of $5.15 per 1937-S coin. Issued by Daniel Boone Bicentennial Commission (and its division, the Pioneer National Monument Association), Phoenix Hotel, Lexington, Kentucky (C. Frank Dunn, "sole distributor").

Key to Collecting. Most collectors desire just a single coin to represent the type, but there are enough specialists who want one of each date and mintmark to ensure a ready market whenever the scarcer sets come up for sale. Most surviving coins are in MS, with MS–64 to 66 pieces readily available for most issues. Early issues in the series are characterized by deep frosty mint luster, whereas issues toward the end of the run, particularly 1937 and 1938, often are seen with a satin finish and relatively little luster (because of the methods of die preparation and striking). The 1937-S is very often seen with prooflike surfaces, and the 1938-S occasionally so. In general, the Boone commemoratives were handled carefully at the time of minting and distribution, but scattered contact marks are often visible.

First Points of Wear. *Obverse:* The hair behind Boone's ear. *Reverse:* The left shoulder of the Indian.

	Distribution	Cert	Avg	%MS	AU-50	MS-60	MS-62	MS-63	MS-64	MS-65	MS-66
1934	10,007	1,050	64.8	100%	$130	$135	$140	$150	$160	$180	$275
	Auctions: $1,528, MS-67, January 2015; $569, MS-66, January 2015; $165, MS-65, September 2015; $94, MS-60, January 2015										
1935	10,010	1,201	64.7	100%	$130	$135	$140	$150	$175	$200	$250
	Auctions: $1,175, MS-67, January 2015; $200, MS-66, January 2015; $176, MS-65, January 2015; $94, MS-62, February 2015										
1935-D	5,005	676	64.6	100%	$130	$135	$140	$150	$200	$225	$350
	Auctions: $2,115, MS-67, January 2015; $201, MS-65, October 2015; $175, MS-65, March 2015; $153, MS-64, January 2015										
1935-S	5,005	848	65.0	100%	$130	$135	$140	$150	$175	$200	$275
	Auctions: $1,116, MS-67, October 2015; $376, MS-66, January 2015; $176, MS-65, February 2015; $106, MS-60, July 2015										
Set of 1935 P-D-S					$405	$420	$450	$525	$625	$875	
	Auctions: $380, MS-64/64/64, December 2011										
1935, With Small 1934	10,008	1,319	64.9	100%	$130	$140	$145	$150	$160	$180	$290
	Auctions: $1,528, MS-67, July 2015; $282, MS-66, January 2015; $188, MS-65, April 2015; $106, MS-60, May 2015										
1935-D, Same type	2,003	505	65.2	100%	$250	$265	$275	$325	$425	$775	$875
	Auctions: $6,463, MS-68, January 2015; $881, MS-66, January 2015; $646, MS-65, January 2015; $306, MS-64, January 2015										
1935-S, Same type	2,004	492	64.8	100%	$250	$265	$275	$325	$425	$650	$875
	Auctions: $4,230, MS-67, January 2015; $1,528, MS-66, September 2015; $541, MS-65, January 2015; $248, MS-64, April 2015										
Set of 1935 P-D-S, With Added Date					$650	$675	$700	$800	$1,025	$1,625	$2,050
	Auctions: $925, MS-65/63/64, May 2012										
1936	12,012	1,507	64.8	100%	$130	$135	$140	$150	$170	$215	$325
	Auctions: $7,050, MS-68, October 2015; $940, MS-67, January 2015; $306, MS-66, January 2015; $100, MS-63, February 2015										
1936-D	5,005	850	65.0	100%	$130	$135	$140	$150	$170	$215	$275
	Auctions: $1,293, MS-67, June 2015; $235, MS-66, September 2015; $188, MS-65, July 2015; $100, MS-63, February 2015										
1936-S	5,006	895	65.1	100%	$130	$135	$140	$150	$170	$215	$275
	Auctions: $11,163, MS-68, January 2015; $705, MS-67, August 2015; $353, MS-66, September 2015; $102, MS-63, August 2015										
Set of 1936 P-D-S					$400	$415	$425	$450	$525	$650	$875
	Auctions: $920, MS-66/66/66 Plus, November 2011										

	Distribution	Cert	Avg	%MS	AU-50	MS-60	MS-62	MS-63	MS-64	MS-65	MS-66
1937	9,810	1,391	64.9	100%	$130	$135	$140	$150	$170	$215	$360
Auctions: $2,585, MS-67, October 2015; $376, MS-66, March 2015; $200, MS-65, February 2015; $100, MS-60, September 2015											
1937-D	2,506	556	64.9	100%	$130	$135	$140	$150	$170	$215	$335
Auctions: $1,528, MS-67, October 2015; $376, MS-66, April 2015; $294, MS-65, January 2015; $212, MS-64, January 2015											
1937-S	2,506	677	65.0	100%	$130	$135	$140	$150	$170	$215	$275
Auctions: $1,645, MS-67, January 2015; $470, MS-66, May 2015; $353, MS-65, January 2015; $118, MS-63, August 2015											
Set of 1937 P-D-S					$400	$410	$425	$450	$525	$650	$1,000
Auctions: $564, MS-66/65/64, November 2011											
1938	2,100	462	64.8	100%	$220	$230	$240	$250	$275	$450	$600
Auctions: $2,585, MS-67, July 2015; $946, MS-66, January 2015; $306, MS-65, September 2015; $236, MS-63, February 2015											
1938-D	2,100	490	65.1	100%	$220	$230	$240	$250	$275	$425	$650
Auctions: $7,050, MS-67, January 2015; $823, MS-66, January 2015; $423, MS-65, February 2015; $259, MS-63, February 2015											
1938-S	2,100	492	64.9	100%	$220	$230	$240	$250	$275	$425	$600
Auctions: $1,410, MS-67, August 2015; $1,087, MS-66, January 2015; $235, MS-63, July 2015; $188, AU-50, November 2015											
Set of 1938 P-D-S					$725	$800	$900	$1,000	$1,150	$1,400	$2,000
Auctions: $4,312, MS-66/66/65, September 2011											

CONNECTICUT TERCENTENARY HALF DOLLAR (1935)

Designer: *Henry Kreis.* **Weight:** *12.50 grams.* **Composition:** *.900 silver, .100 copper (net weight .3617 oz. pure silver).* **Diameter:** *30.6 mm.* **Edge:** *Reeded.* **Mint:** *Philadelphia.*

In commemoration of the 300th anniversary of the founding of the colony of Connecticut, a souvenir half dollar was struck. According to legend, the Royal Charter of the colony was secreted in the Charter Tree (seen on the coin's reverse) during the reign of King James II, who wished to revoke it. The charter was produced after the king's overthrow in 1688, and the colony continued under its protection.

Designs. *Obverse:* A modernistic eagle, standing. *Reverse:* The Charter Oak.

Mintage Data. Authorized on June 21, 1934. *Maximum authorized—25,000. Number minted—25,018* (including 18 assay coins). *Net distribution—25,018.*

Original Cost and Issuer. Sale price $1. Issued by the Connecticut Tercentenary Commission.

Key to Collecting. Most examples survive in upper AU and lower MS grades. Higher-grade coins such as MS-65 are elusive. Friction and/or marks are often obvious on the broad expanse of wing on the obverse, and, in particular, at the ground or baseline of the oak tree on the reverse. Examples that are otherwise lustrous, frosty, and very attractive, often have friction on the wing.

First Points of Wear. *Obverse:* The top of the eagle's wing. *Reverse:* The ground above ON and TI in CONNECTICUT.

	Distribution	Cert	Avg	%MS	AU-50	MS-60	MS-62	MS-63	MS-64	MS-65	MS-66
									PF-63	PF-64	PF-65
1935	25,018	3,503	64.5	99%	$215	$220	$225	$235	$250	$400	$550
Auctions: $2,350, MS-67, January 2015; $823, MS-66, October 2015; $376, MS-65, January 2015; $188, MS-60, July 2015											
1935, Matte Proof	1–2	1	65.0								
Auctions: No auction records available.											

ARKANSAS CENTENNIAL HALF DOLLAR (1935–1939)

Designer: *Edward E. Burr.* **Weight:** *12.50 grams.*
Composition: *.900 silver, .100 copper (net weight .3617 oz. pure silver).*
Diameter: *30.6 mm.* **Edge:** *Reeded.* **Mints:** *Philadelphia, Denver, and San Francisco.*

This souvenir issue marked the 100th anniversary of the admission of Arkansas into the Union. The 1936 through 1939 issues were the same as those of 1935 except for the dates. The coin's four-year lifespan was intended to maximize profits, and sluggish sales contributed to the crash of the commemorative market and subsequent suspension of commemorative coinage in 1939.

Designs. *Obverse:* An eagle with outstretched wings, stars, and other elements of the Arkansas state seal. *Reverse:* Portraits of a Liberty in a Phrygian cap and an Indian chief of 1836.

Mintage and Melting Data. Authorized on May 14, 1934. *Maximum authorized*—500,000 (for the entire series from 1935 onward). *Number minted* (including 5, 5, and 6 assay coins)—1935-P: 13,012 (including 5 assay coins); 1935-D: 5,505 (including 5 assay coins); 1935-S: 5,506 (including 6 assay coins); 1936-P: 10,010 (including 10 assay coins); 1936-D: 10,010 (including 10 assay coins); 1936-S: 10,012 (including 12 assay coins); 1937-P: 5,505 (including 5 assay coins); 1937-D: 5,505 (including 5 assay coins); 1937-S: 5,506 (including 6 assay coins); 1938-P: 6,006 (including 6 assay coins); 1938-D: 6,005 (including 5 assay coins); 1938-S: 6,006 (including 6 assay coins); 1939-P: 2,140 (including 4 assay coins); 1939-D: 2,104 (including 4 assay coins); 1939-S: 2,105 (including 5 assay coins). *Number melted*—1936-P: 350; 1936-D: 350; 1936-S: 350; 1938-P: 2,850; 1938-D: 2,850; 1938-S: 2,850. *Net distribution*—1935-P: 13,012; 1935-D: 5,505; 1935-S: 5,506; 1936-P: 9,660; 1936-D: 9,660; 1936-S: 9,662; 1937-P: 5,505; 1937-D: 5,505; 1937-S: 5,506; 1938-P: 3,156; 1938-D: 3,155; 1938-S: 3,156; 1939-P: 2,104; 1939-D: 2,104; 1939-S: 2,105.

Original Cost and Issuer. Sale prices varied by mintmark, from a low of $1 per coin to $12 for a set of three. Issued by the Arkansas Centennial Commission in 1935, 1936, 1938, and 1939 (note that dealer B. Max Mehl bought quantities and retailed them at higher prices in 1935). Issued by Stack's of New York City in 1937.

Key to Collecting. The coin sets were produced with a satiny, almost "greasy" finish; even freshly minted coins appeared as if they had been dipped or repeatedly cleaned. Issues of 1937 to 1939 are usually more satisfactory but still are not deeply lustrous. The prominence of the girl's portrait on the center of the obverse renders that part of the coin prone to receiving bagmarks, scuffs, and other evidence of handling. As a result, relatively few pieces have great eye appeal. The obverse area where the ribbon crosses the eagle's breast is often very weak. Some examples are lightly struck on the eagle just behind its head.

First Points of Wear. *Obverse:* The eagle's head and the top of the left wing. *Reverse:* The band of the girl's cap, behind her eye.

	Distribution	Cert	Avg	%MS	AU-50	MS-60	MS-62	MS-63	MS-64	MS-65	MS-66
									PF-63	PF-64	PF-65
1935	13,012	1,167	64.4	100%	$90	$95	$105	$110	$120	$150	$425
	Auctions: $1,116, MS-67, September 2014; $1,528, MS-67 Plus, July 2014; $400, MS-66, December 2014; $558, MS-66, October 2014										
1935-D	5,505	849	64.7	100%	$90	$95	$105	$110	$120	$150	$425
	Auctions: $1,880, MS-67, January 2015; $400, MS-66, August 2015; $153, MS-65, January 2015; $100, MS-64, September 2015										
1935-S	5,506	857	64.6	100%	$90	$95	$105	$110	$120	$225	$550
	Auctions: $1,939, MS-67, January 2015; $705, MS-66, September 2015; $100, MS-64, January 2015; $74, MS-62, February 2015										
Set of 1935 P-D-S					$270	$300	$315	$330	$360	$525	$1,400
	Auctions: $322, MS-64/64/64 Plus, April 2012										
1936	9,660	1,011	64.3	100%	$90	$95	$105	$110	$120	$170	$550
	Auctions: $1,998, MS-67, September 2015; $1,116, MS-66, July 2015; $120, MS-64, September 2015; $79, MS-60, August 2015										
1936-D	9,660	970	64.5	100%	$90	$95	$105	$110	$120	$175	$575
	Auctions: $2,585, MS-67, January 2015; $353, MS-66, January 2015; $259, MS-65, July 2015; $100, MS-63, January 2015										
1936-S	9,662	990	64.4	100%	$90	$95	$105	$110	$120	$225	$775
	Auctions: $1,528, MS-67, January 2015; $282, MS-66, September 2015; $153, MS-65, September 2015; $94, MS-63, October 2015										
Set of 1936 P-D-S					$270	$285	$315	$330	$360	$475	$1,900
	Auctions: $300, MS-64/64/65, December 2011										
1937	5,505	749	64.3	100%	$110	$115	$120	$125	$130	$175	$485
	Auctions: $2,585, MS-67, June 2015; $541, MS-66, January 2015; $129, MS-64, January 2015; $118, MS-63, August 2015										
1937-D	5,505	797	64.5	100%	$110	$115	$120	$125	$130	$165	$550
	Auctions: $2,233, MS-67, January 2015; $494, MS-66, January 2015; $165, MS-64, September 2015; $79, MS-63, April 2015										
1937-S	5,506	654	64.2	100%	$110	$115	$120	$125	$130	$365	$825
	Auctions: $999, MS-66, September 2015; $940, MS-66, September 2015; $200, MS-65, May 2015; $79, MS-63, January 2015										
Set of 1937 P-D-S					$330	$345	$360	$375	$400	$725	$1,875
	Auctions: $600, MS-65/65/65, January 2012										
1938	3,156	535	64.4	100%	$135	$140	$150	$175	$215	$425	$1,075
	Auctions: $3,290, MS-67, August 2015; $705, MS-66, January 2015; $306, MS-65, February 2015; $106, MS-63, April 2015										
1938-D	3,155	562	64.4	100%	$135	$145	$145	$150	$215	$275	$775
	Auctions: $3,055, MS-67, January 2015; $881, MS-66, January 2015; $259, MS-64, June 2015; $123, MS-63, February 2015										
1938-S	3,156	510	64.3	100%	$140	$145	$150	$160	$215	$365	$950
	Auctions: $1,058, MS-66, July 2015; $999, MS-66, September 2015; $282, MS-65, January 2015; $153, MS-64, April 2015										
Set of 1938 P-D-S					$415	$435	$450	$500	$650	$1,075	$2,800
	Auctions: $2,900, MS-66/66/66, April 2012; $411, MS-63/63/63, October 2015										
Set of 1938 P-D-S, Matte Proof	1–2										
	Auctions: No auction records available.										
1939	2,104	439	64.2	100%	$230	$240	$250	$265	$300	$850	$3,250
	Auctions: $1,880, MS-66, June 2015; $1,763, MS-66, July 2015; $610, MS-65, January 2015; $306, MS-64, September 2015										
1939-D	2,104	464	64.4	100%	$230	$240	$250	$265	$300	$775	$1,150
	Auctions: $3,995, MS-67, August 2015; $1,146, MS-66, January 2015; $470, MS-65, January 2015; $270, MS-63, March 2015										
1939-S	2,105	502	64.5	100%	$240	$240	$250	$265	$300	$875	$1,325
	Auctions: $3,760, MS-67, August 2015; $1,939, MS-66, January 2015; $764, MS-65, January 2015; $294, MS-64, April 2015										
Set of 1939 P-D-S					$700	$725	$750	$800	$900	$2,200	$5,000
	Auctions: $1,610, MS-65/65/65, February 2012										

ARKANSAS CENTENNIAL—ROBINSON HALF DOLLAR (1936)

Designers: *Henry Kreis (obverse) and Edward E. Burr (reverse).* **Weight:** *12.50 grams*
(net weight .3617 oz. pure silver). **Composition:** *.900 silver, .100 copper.*
Diameter: *30.6 mm.* **Edge:** *Reeded.* **Mints:** *Philadelphia, Denver, San Francisco.*

A new reverse design for the Arkansas Centennial coin (see preceding coin) was authorized by the Act of June 26, 1936. Senator Joseph T. Robinson was still living at the time his portrait was used. Note that though it is normally true that portraits appear on the obverse of coins, the side bearing Robinson's likeness is indeed technically the reverse of this coin.

Designs. *Obverse:* An eagle with outstretched wings, stars, and other elements of the Arkansas state seal. *Reverse:* Bareheaded profile portrait of Senator Joseph T. Robinson.

Mintage Data. Authorized on June 26, 1936. *Maximum authorized*—50,000 (minimum 25,000). *Number minted*—25,265 (including 15 assay coins). *Net distribution*—25,265.

Original Cost and Issuer. Sale price $1.85. Issued by Stack's of New York City.

Key to Collecting. Most known coins are in MS, as most or all were originally sold to collectors and coin dealers. Examples are plentiful in the marketplace, usually grading MS–62 to 64. The coins were not handled with care during production, so many have contact marks on Robinson's portrait and elsewhere. Some examples are lightly struck on the eagle, just behind the head.

First Points of Wear. *Obverse:* The eagle's head and the top of the left wing. *Reverse:* Robinson's cheekbone.

	Distribution	Cert	Avg	%MS	AU-50	MS-60	MS-62	MS-63	MS-64	MS-65	MS-66
1936	25,265	2,738	64.3	100%	$105	$125	$130	$135	$160	$215	$375
	Auctions: $3,290, MS-67, August 2015; $617, MS-66, January 2015; $212, MS-65, February 2015; $112, MS-63, January 2015										

HUDSON, NEW YORK, SESQUICENTENNIAL HALF DOLLAR (1935)

Designer: *Chester Beach.* **Weight:** *12.50 grams.* **Composition:** *.900 silver, .100 copper*
(net weight .3617 oz. pure silver). **Diameter:** *30.6 mm.* **Edge:** *Reeded.* **Mint:** *Philadelphia.*

This souvenir half dollar marked the 150th anniversary of the founding of Hudson, New York, which was named after the explorer Henry Hudson. The area was actually settled in 1662, but not given its permanent name and formally incorporated until 1785. The distribution of these coins was widely criticized, as certain dealers were allowed to purchase large quantities at $1 or less and then resold them at dramatically inflated prices.

Designs. *Obverse:* The ship *Half Moon*, captained by Henry Hudson, in full sail. *Reverse:* The ocean god Neptune seated backward on a whale (derived from the seal of the city of Hudson); in the background, a mermaid blowing a shell.

Mintage Data. Approved May 2, 1935. *Maximum authorized*—10,000. *Number minted*—10,008 (including 8 assay coins). *Net distribution*—10,008.

Original Cost and Issuer. Sale price $1. Issued by the Hudson Sesquicentennial Committee, through the First National Bank & Trust Company of Hudson.

Key to Collecting. Examples are readily available in the marketplace. Note that deep or artificial toning, which can make close inspection impossible, has led some certified coins to certified grades that are higher than they should be. True gems are very rare. These coins were struck at high speed and with little care to preserve their quality; by the time they were originally distributed most pieces showed nicks, contact marks, and other evidence of handling. Most are lustrous and frosty (except on the central devices), and grade in the lower MS levels. MS–62 to 64 are typical. Carefully graded MS–65 coins are scarce, and anything higher is very rare.

First Points of Wear. *Obverse:* The center of the lower middle sail. *Reverse:* The motto on the ribbon, and the figure of Neptune (both of which may also be lightly struck).

	Distribution	Cert	Avg	%MS	AU-50	MS-60	MS-62	MS-63	MS-64	MS-65	MS-66
1935	10,008	1,995	64.1	98%	$650	$700	$765	$800	$900	$1,000	$1,400

Auctions: $8,519, MS-67, July 2015; $2,350, MS-66, September 2015; $1,087, MS-65, September 2015; $588, MS-60, January 2015

CALIFORNIA PACIFIC INTERNATIONAL EXPOSITION HALF DOLLAR (1935–1936)

Designer: *Robert Aitken.* **Weight:** *12.50 grams.* **Composition:** *.900 silver, .100 copper (net weight .3617 oz. pure silver).* **Diameter:** *30.6 mm.* **Edge:** *Reeded.* **Mints:** *San Francisco and Denver.*

Congress approved the coinage of souvenir half dollars for the California Pacific International Exposition on May 3, 1935. The event—held in San Diego's Balboa Park—was attended by only 4 million people, and interest in the coin was not particularly strong.

Designs. *Obverse:* Minerva seated, holding a spear and shield, with a grizzly bear to her right (from California's state seal). *Reverse:* The Chapel of St. Francis and the California Tower, at the California Pacific International Exposition in San Diego.

Mintage and Melting Data. Originally authorized on May 3, 1935; 1936-D issues authorized on May 6, 1936 (for recoinage of melted 1935-S issues). *Maximum authorized*—1935-S: 250,000; 1936-D: 180,000. *Number minted*—1935-S: 250,132 (including 132 assay coins); 1936-D: 180,092 (including 92 assay coins). *Number melted*—1935-S: 180,000; 1936-D: 150,000. *Net distribution*—1935-S: 70,132; 1936-D: 30,092.

Original Cost and Issuer. Sale prices $1 (1935-S; increased to $3 in 1937; dropped to $2 in 1938) and $1.50 (1936-D; increased to $3 in 1937; reduced to $1 in 1938). Issued by the California Pacific International Exposition Company.

Key to Collecting. Both the 1935-S and 1936-D issues were coined with deeply frosty and lustrous surfaces. The eye appeal usually is excellent. The design made these coins susceptible to bagmarks, and most survivors, even in higher MS grades, show evidence of handling. Minerva, in particular, usually displays some graininess or contact marks, even on coins given high numerical grades. Most coins are deeply lustrous and frosty. On the 1935 San Francisco coins the S mintmark usually is flat, and on the Denver coins the California Tower is often lightly struck at the top.

First Points of Wear. *Obverse:* The bosom and knees of Minerva. *Reverse:* The top right edge of the tower. (The 1936-D was flatly struck in this area; examine the texture of the surface to determine if actual wear exists.)

	Distribution	Cert	Avg	%MS	AU-50	MS-60	MS-62	MS-63	MS-64	MS-65	MS-66
1935-S	70,132	4,742	64.9	100%	$100	$105	$110	$115	$120	$135	$160
	Auctions: $2,115, MS-67, September 2015; $223, MS-66, September 2015; $153, MS-65, August 2015; $106, MS-60, February 2015										
1936-D	30,092	2,764	64.9	100%	$100	$105	$110	$115	$120	$140	$200
	Auctions: $1,528, MS-67, January 2015; $188, MS-66, September 2015; $176, MS-65, February 2015; $106, MS-64, September 2015										

OLD SPANISH TRAIL HALF DOLLAR (1935)

Designer: *L.W. Hoffecker.* **Weight:** *12.50 grams.* **Composition:** *.900 silver, .100 copper (net weight .3617 oz. pure silver).* **Diameter:** *30.6 mm.* **Edge:** *Reeded.* **Mint:** *Philadelphia.*

This coin commemorated the 400th anniversary of the overland trek of the Alvar Nuñez Cabeza de Vaca Expedition through the Gulf states in 1535. The coin's designer and distributor, L.W. Hoffecker, is known to have had his hands in many of this era's commemoratives (and the exploitative practices surrounding them).

Designs. *Obverse:* The head of a steer, inspired by the explorer's last name: Cabeza de Vaca translates to "head of cow." *Reverse:* A map of the Southeastern states and a yucca tree.

Mintage Data. Authorized on June 5, 1935. *Maximum authorized*—10,000. *Number minted*—10,008.

Original Cost and Issuer. Sale price $2. Issued by L.W. Hoffecker, trading as the El Paso Museum Coin Committee.

Key to Collecting. These coins were handled with care during their production and shipping—still, most show scattered contact marks. The typical grade is MS-65 and higher. The fields are usually somewhat satiny and gray, not deeply lustrous and frosty.

First Points of Wear. *Obverse:* The top of the cow's head. *Reverse:* The lettering at the top.

	Distribution	Cert	Avg	%MS	AU-50	MS-60	MS-62	MS-63	MS-64	MS-65	MS-66
1935	10,008	1,878	65.0	100%	$1,050	$1,100	$1,125	$1,150	$1,225	$1,275	$1,450
	Auctions: $2,468, MS-67, September 2015; $1,763, MS-66, January 2015; $1,410, MS-65, January 2015; $764, MS-60, June 2015										

PROVIDENCE, RHODE ISLAND, TERCENTENARY HALF DOLLAR (1936)

Designers: *Arthur G. Carey and John H. Benson.* **Weight:** *12.50 grams.*
Composition: *.900 silver, .100 copper (net weight .3617 oz. pure silver).*
Diameter: *30.6 mm.* **Edge:** *Reeded.* **Mints:** *Philadelphia, Denver, and San Francisco.*

The 300th anniversary of Roger Williams's founding of Providence was the occasion for this special half dollar in 1936. Interestingly, no mention of Providence is to be found on the coin. The distribution of this coin, like that of many other commemoratives of the 1930s, was wrapped in controversy—phony news releases reported that the coin was sold out when it was indeed not, and certain dealers procured large amounts at low prices only to resell for tidy profits.

Designs. *Obverse:* Roger Williams, the founder of Rhode Island, being welcomed by an Indian. *Reverse:* Elements from the Rhode Island state seal, including the anchor of Hope and a shield.

Mintage Data. Authorized on May 2, 1935. *Maximum authorized—50,000. Number minted—1936-P: 20,013 (including 13 assay coins); 1936-D: 15,010 (including 10 assay coins); 1936-S: 15,011 (including 11 assay coins). Net distribution—1936-P: 20,013; 1936-D: 15,010; 1936-S: 15,011.*

Original Cost and Issuer. Sale price $1. Issued by the Rhode Island and Providence Plantations Tercentenary Committee, Inc.

Key to Collecting. These coins are readily available singly and in sets, with typical grades being MS–63 to 65. Contact marks are common. Higher-level coins, such as MS–66 and 67, are not hard to find, but are elusive in comparison to the lesser-condition pieces. The 1936 (in particular) and 1936-S are sometimes found with prooflike surfaces. Most specimens have a combination of satiny/frosty surface. Many are light gray in color.

First Points of Wear. *Obverse:* The prow of the canoe, and the Indian's right shoulder. *Reverse:* The center of the anchor, and surrounding areas.

	Distribution	Cert	Avg	%MS	AU-50	MS-60	MS-62	MS-63	MS-64	MS-65	MS-66
1936	20,013	2,413	64.7	100%	$95	$105	$110	$120	$130	$150	$185
	Auctions: $823, MS-67, July 2015; $165, MS-66, August 2015; $212, MS-65, May 2015; $79, MS-60, February 2015										
1936-D	15,010	1,787	64.7	100%	$95	$105	$110	$120	$130	$150	$185
	Auctions: $969, MS-67, November 2015; $435, MS-66, January 2015; $176, MS-65, August 2015; $100, MS-64, May 2015										
1936-S	15,011	1,526	64.6	100%	$95	$105	$110	$120	$150	$185	$300
	Auctions: $2,820, MS-67, January 2015; $470, MS-66, November 2015; $112, MS-64, May 2015; $69, EF-45, September 2015										
Set of 1936 P-D-S					$300	$325	$345	$360	$410	$500	$675
	Auctions: $2,185, MS-66/66/66, January 2012										

CLEVELAND CENTENNIAL / GREAT LAKES EXPOSITION HALF DOLLAR (1936)

Designer: *Brenda Putnam.* **Weight:** *12.50 grams.* **Composition:** *.900 silver, .100 copper (net weight .3617 oz. pure silver).* **Diameter:** *30.6 mm.* **Edge:** *Reeded.* **Mint:** *Philadelphia.*

A special coinage of fifty-cent pieces was authorized in commemoration of the centennial celebration of Cleveland, Ohio, on the occasion of the Great Lakes Exposition held there in 1936. Numismatic entrepreneur Thomas G. Melish was behind the coins' production and distribution—though he served as the Cleveland Centennial Commemorative Coin Association's treasurer while based in Cincinnati.

Designs. *Obverse:* Bewigged profile portrait of Moses Cleaveland. *Reverse:* A map of the Great Lakes region with nine stars marking various cities, and a compass point at the city of Cleveland.

Mintage Data. Authorized on May 5, 1936. *Maximum authorized*—50,000 (minimum 25,000). *Number minted*—50,030 (including 30 assay coins). *Net distribution*—50,030.

Original Cost and Issuer. Sale prices: one coin for $1.65; two for $1.60 each; three for $1.58 each; five for $1.56 each; ten for $1.55 each; twenty for $1.54 each; fifty for $1.53 each; one hundred for $1.52 each. Issued by the Cleveland Centennial Commemorative Coin Association (Thomas G. Melish, Cincinnati).

Key to Collecting. The Cleveland half dollar is the most readily available issue from 1936—a bumper-crop year for U.S. commemoratives. Nearly all coins are in Mint State, typically from MS–63 to 65, and most are very lustrous and frosty. This issue was not handled with care at the Mint, and scattered contact marks are typically found on both obverse and reverse.

First Points of Wear. *Obverse:* The hair behind Cleaveland's ear. *Reverse:* The top of the compass, and the land (non-lake) areas of the map.

	Distribution	Cert	Avg	%MS	AU-50	MS-60	MS-62	MS-63	MS-64	MS-65	MS-66
1936	50,030	4,882	64.6	100%	$100	$110	$120	$130	$135	$150	$230
	Auctions: $3,995, MS-68, June 2015; $1,293, MS-67, September 2015; $247, MS-66, November 2015; $65, MS-62, March 2015										

WISCONSIN TERRITORIAL CENTENNIAL HALF DOLLAR (1936)

Designer: *David Parsons.* **Weight:** *12.50 grams.* **Composition:** *.900 silver, .100 copper (net weight .3617 oz. pure silver).* **Diameter:** *30.6 mm.* **Edge:** *Reeded.* **Mint:** *Philadelphia.*

The 100th anniversary of the Wisconsin territorial government was the occasion for this issue. Benjamin Hawkins, a New York artist, made changes to the original designs by University of Wisconsin student David Parsons so that the piece conformed to technical requirements.

Designs. *Obverse:* A badger on a log, from the state emblem; and arrows representing the Black Hawk War of the 1830s. *Reverse:* A miner's arm holding a pickaxe over a mound of lead ore, derived from Wisconsin's territorial seal.

Mintage Data. Authorized on May 15, 1936. *Minimum authorized*—25,000 (unlimited maximum). *Number minted*—25,015 (including 15 assay coins). *Net distribution*—25,015.

Original Cost and Issuer. Sale price $1.50 plus 7¢ postage for the first coin, 2¢ postage for each additional coin (later sold for $1.25 each in lots of 10 coins, and still later sold for $3 per coin). Issued by the Wisconsin Centennial Coin Committee (also known as the Coinage Committee of the Wisconsin Centennial Commission). Unsold remainders were distributed, into the 1950s, by the State Historical Society.

Key to Collecting. Examples are readily available in the marketplace. Most grade MS–62 to 64—although higher grades are not rare—and are very lustrous and frosty, except for the higher areas of the design (which often have a slightly polished appearance).

First Points of Wear. *Obverse:* The flank and shoulder of the badger. *Reverse:* The miner's hand.

	Distribution	Cert	Avg	%MS	AU-50	MS-60	MS-62	MS-63	MS-64	MS-65	MS-66
1936	25,015	3,843	65.3	100%	$175	$180	$185	$195	$210	$230	$250

Auctions: $3,055, MS-68, January 2015; $881, MS-67, January 2015; $235, MS-65, August 2015; $129, MS-60, November 2015

CINCINNATI MUSIC CENTER HALF DOLLAR (1936)

Designer: *Constance Ortmayer.* **Weight:** *12.50 grams.*
Composition: *.900 silver, .100 copper (net weight .3617 oz. pure silver).*
Diameter: *30.6 mm.* **Edge:** *Reeded.* **Mints:** *Philadelphia, Denver, and San Francisco.*

Although the head of Stephen Foster, "America's Troubadour," dominates the obverse of this special issue, the anniversary celebrated bears little to no relation to him. Foster did live in Cincinnati for a time, but never worked in music while there. The coins were supposedly struck to commemorate the 50th anniversary in 1936 of Cincinnati as a center of music, but the issue was really a personal project of numismatist Thomas G. Melish.

Designs. *Obverse:* Bareheaded profile portrait of Stephen Foster, "America's Troubadour." *Reverse:* A woman playing a lyre, personifying Music.

Mintage Data. Authorized on March 31, 1936. *Maximum authorized*—15,000. *Number minted*—1936-P: 5,005 (including 5 assay coins); 1936-D: 5,005 (including 5 assay coins); 1936-S: 5,006 (including 6 assay coins). *Net distribution*—1936-P: 5,005; 1936-D: 5,005; 1936-S: 5,006.

Original Cost and Issuer. Sale price $7.75 per set of three (actually $7.50 plus 25¢ for the display container with cellophane slide front). Issued by the Cincinnati Musical Center Commemorative Coin Association, Ohio (Thomas G. Melish).

Key to Collecting. Nearly all sets of these coins were bought by collectors and investors, thus most still exist in Mint State, primarily MS–63 to 65. Conservatively graded MS-65 and finer pieces are rare. Most coins were carelessly handled at the mints, and nearly all show scattered contact marks. This issue has a somewhat satiny or "greasy" surface, instead of fields with deep luster and frost. Denver Mint coins are typically found in slightly higher grades than their Philadelphia and San Francisco Mint companions.

First Points of Wear. *Obverse:* The hair at Foster's temple. *Reverse:* The left breast, and the skirt, of the female figure.

	Distribution	Cert	Avg	%MS	AU-50	MS-60	MS-62	MS-63	MS-64	MS-65	MS-66
1936	5,005	882	64.4	100%	$285	$300	$325	$360	$385	$450	$650
	Auctions: $4,700, MS-67, January 2015; $2,115, MS-66, January 2015; $423, MS-65, September 2015; $329, MS-64, January 2015										
1936-D	5,005	1,230	64.9	100%	$285	$300	$325	$360	$385	$450	$650
	Auctions: $3,290, MS-67, September 2015; $940, MS-66, January 2015; $705, MS-65, January 2015; $188, MS-60, November 2015										
1936-S	5,006	890	64.1	100%	$285	$300	$325	$360	$385	$475	$875
	Auctions: $3,055, MS-66, January 2015; $470, MS-65, January 2015; $329, MS-64, January 2015; $306, MS-63, January 2015										
Set of 1935 P-D-S					$875	$900	$975	$1,100	$1,125	$1,375	$2,600
	Auctions: $4,198, MS-66/66/66, February 2012										

LONG ISLAND TERCENTENARY HALF DOLLAR (1936)

Designer: *Howard K. Weinman.* **Weight:** *12.50 grams.* **Composition:** *.900 silver, .100 copper (net weight .3617 oz. pure silver).* **Diameter:** *30.6 mm.* **Edge:** *Reeded.* **Mint:** *Philadelphia.*

This souvenir issue was authorized to commemorate the 300th anniversary of the first white settlement on Long Island, which was made at Jamaica Bay by Dutch colonists. This was the first issue for which a date was specified (1936) irrespective of the year minted or issued, as a safeguard against extending the coinage over a period of years. This measure proved effective in preventing many of the profiteering problems that arose with other commemorative issues of the era.

Designs. *Obverse:* Conjoined profile portraits of a Dutch settler and an Algonquin Indian. *Reverse:* A Dutch vessel with full-blown sails.

Mintage and Melting Data. Authorized on April 13, 1936. *Maximum authorized*—100,000. *Number minted*—100,053 (including 53 assay coins). *Number melted*—18,227. *Net distribution*—81,826.

Original Cost and Issuer. Sale price $1. Issued by the Long Island Tercentenary Committee, through various banks and other outlets.

Key to Collecting. These are among the most plentiful survivors from the commemorative issues of the 1930s, and examples grading MS–64 to 66 are readily obtainable. The coins were minted and handled carelessly, and at the time of distribution most showed nicks, bagmarks, and other evidence of contact; these grade from AU-50 to MS-60. Most coins have, as struck, a satiny or slightly "greasy" luster and are not deeply frosty.

First Points of Wear. *Obverse:* The hair and the cheekbone of the Dutch settler. *Reverse:* The center of the lower middle sail.

	Distribution	Cert	Avg	%MS	AU-50	MS-60	MS-62	MS-63	MS-64	MS-65	MS-66
1936	81,826	4,562	64.2	99%	$85	$95	$100	$110	$115	$195	$375
	Auctions: $9,988, MS-67, September 2015; $1,293, MS-66, January 2015; $129, MS-64, February 2015; $52, EF-40, July 2015										

YORK COUNTY, MAINE, TERCENTENARY HALF DOLLAR (1936)

Designer: *Walter H. Rich.* **Weight:** *12.50 grams.* **Composition:** *.900 silver, .100 copper (net weight .3617 oz. pure silver).* **Diameter:** *30.6 mm.* **Edge:** *Reeded.* **Mint:** *Philadelphia.*

A souvenir half dollar was authorized by Congress upon the 300th anniversary of the founding of York County, Maine. While the commemorated event was considered somewhat obscure, the proposing and distributing group—the York County Tercentenary Commemorative Coin Commission, led by ardent numismatist Walter P. Nichols—was lauded for its diligence and proper handling of the release.

Designs. *Obverse:* Brown's Garrison, on the Saco River (site of the original settlement in York County in 1636). *Reverse:* An adaptation of the seal of York County.

Mintage Data. *Maximum authorized*—30,000. *Number minted*—25,015 (including 15 assay coins).

Original Cost and Issuer. Sale price $1.50 ($1.65 postpaid by mail to out-of-state buyers). Issued by the York County Tercentenary Commemorative Coin Commission, York National Bank, Saco, Maine.

Key to Collecting. This issue was well handled at the Mint and in distribution, so most examples are in higher grades and are relatively free of marks. On the reverse, the top of the shield is a key point. Some coins have been brushed and have a myriad of fine hairlines; these can be detected by examining the coin at various angles to the light. MS–64 and 65 coins are readily found in the marketplace.

First Points of Wear. *Obverse:* The mounted sentry near the corner of the fort; the stockade; and the rim of the coin. *Reverse:* The pine tree in the shield; the top-right area of the shield; and the rim.

	Distribution	Cert	Avg	%MS	AU-50	MS-60	MS-62	MS-63	MS-64	MS-65	MS-66
1936	25,015	3,467	65.4	100%	$160	$165	$170	$180	$195	$200	$220
	Auctions: $1,763, MS-68, August 2015; $881, MS-67, September 2015; $259, MS-66, January 2015; $121, MS-60, January 2015										

BRIDGEPORT, CONNECTICUT, CENTENNIAL HALF DOLLAR (1936)

Designer: *Henry Kreis.* **Weight:** *12.50 grams.* **Composition:** *.900 silver, .100 copper (net weight .3617 oz. pure silver).* **Diameter:** *30.6 mm.* **Edge:** *Reeded.* **Mint:** *Philadelphia.*

In commemoration of the 100th anniversary of the incorporation of the city of Bridgeport, a special fifty-cent piece was authorized on May 15, 1936. The city—actually originally founded in 1639—served as an important center in the 17th and 18th centuries.

Designs. *Obverse:* Bareheaded profile portrait of P.T. Barnum, Bridgeport's most famous citizen. *Reverse:* An art deco eagle, standing.

Mintage Data. Authorized on May 15, 1936. *Minimum authorized*—25,000 (unlimited maximum). *Number minted*—25,015 (including 15 assay coins). *Net distribution*—25,015.

Original Cost and Issuer. Sale price $2. Issued by Bridgeport Centennial, Inc., through the First National Bank and Trust Co. and other banks.

Key to Collecting. These coins are readily available in the marketplace. Most grade from MS–62 to 64. Many have been cleaned or lightly polished, but pristine MS-65 pieces are readily available. Obvious friction rub and/or marks are often seen. Some coins were struck from dies with lightly polished fields and have a prooflike or partially prooflike appearance in those areas.

First Points of Wear. *Obverse:* Barnum's cheek. *Reverse:* The eagle's wing.

	Distribution	Cert	Avg	%MS	AU-50	MS-60	MS-62	MS-63	MS-64	MS-65	MS-66
1936	25,015	3,128	64.6	100%	$120	$125	$130	$135	$145	$180	$280
	Auctions: $1,880, MS-67, September 2015; $353, MS-66, February 2015; $235, MS-65, August 2015; $106, MS-60, May 2015										

LYNCHBURG, VIRGINIA, SESQUICENTENNIAL HALF DOLLAR (1936)

Designer: *Charles Keck.* **Weight:** *12.50 grams.* **Composition:** *.900 silver, .100 copper (net weight .3617 oz. pure silver).* **Diameter:** *30.6 mm.* **Edge:** *Reeded.* **Mint:** *Philadelphia.*

The issuance of a charter to the city of Lynchburg in 1786 was commemorated in 1936 by a special coinage of half dollars. Interestingly, Lynchburg native Senator Carter Glass objected to the use of portraits of living persons on coins, but was featured on the issue anyway. It was considered that a portrait of John Lynch—for whom the city was named—would be used, but no such likeness existed.

Designs. *Obverse:* Bareheaded profile portrait of Senator Carter Glass, a native of Lynchburg and former secretary of the Treasury. *Reverse:* A figure of Miss Liberty standing before the old Lynchburg courthouse.

Mintage Data. Authorized on May 28, 1936. *Maximum authorized*—20,000. *Number minted*—20,013 (including 13 assay coins). *Net distribution*—20,013.

Original Cost and Issuer. Sale price $1. Issued by the Lynchburg Sesqui-Centennial Association.

Key to Collecting. Most of these half dollars are in higher grades; MS–65 and 66 examples are readily available in the marketplace. Some show graininess (from striking) on the high areas of the obverse portrait and on the bosom and skirt of Miss Liberty, or show evidences of handling or contact in the same areas. Surfaces are often somewhat satiny, instead of deeply lustrous and frosty. Often the reverse field is semi-prooflike. This issue must have been handled with particular care at the Mint.

First Points of Wear. *Obverse:* The hair above Glass's ear. *Reverse:* The hair of Miss Liberty, the folds of her gown, and her bosom.

	Distribution	Cert	Avg	%MS	AU-50	MS-60	MS-62	MS-63	MS-64	MS-65	MS-66
1936	20,013	2,620	64.8	100%	$220	$230	$235	$240	$260	$275	$350
	Auctions: $2,820, MS-67, January 2015; $294, MS-66, June 2015; $170, MS-63, October 2015; $118, AU-58, August 2015										

ELGIN, ILLINOIS, CENTENNIAL HALF DOLLAR (1936)

Designer: *Trygve Rovelstad.* **Weight:** *12.50 grams.* **Composition:** *.900 silver, .100 copper (net weight .3617 oz. pure silver).* **Diameter:** *30.6 mm.* **Edge:** *Reeded.* **Mint:** *Philadelphia.*

The 100th anniversary of the founding of Elgin, Illinois, was marked by a special issue of half dollars in 1936. The year 1673 (seen on the obverse) bears no relation to the event but refers to the year in which Louis Joliet and Jacques Marquette entered Illinois Territory.

Designs. *Obverse:* The fur-capped profile of a bearded pioneer (a close-up view of the statue depicted on the reverse). *Reverse:* The Pioneer Memorial statuary group, whose creation was financed by the sale of these coins.

Mintage and Melting Data. Authorized on June 16, 1936. *Maximum authorized—25,000. Number minted—25,015 (including 15 assay coins). Number melted—5,000. Net distribution—20,015.*

Original Cost and Issuer. Sale price $1.50. Issued by the Elgin Centennial Monumental Committee, El Paso, Texas (L.W. Hoffecker in charge), through banks in and near Elgin, including the First National Bank of Elgin, the Elgin National Bank, and the Union National Bank.

Key to Collecting. Elgin half dollars are fairly plentiful in today's marketplace. They seem to have been handled with particular care at the time of minting, as most have fewer bagmarks than many other commemoratives of the same era. Typical coins grade MS–64 to 66. The surfaces often have a matte-like appearance (seemingly a combination of a lustrous circulation strike and a Matte Proof) quite different from other commemorative issues of 1936. Some coins are fairly frosty. On many a bright spot is evident on the reverse below the A of AMERICA, the result of an inadvertent polishing on a small area of the die. Chief Engraver John Sinnock made a few Matte Proofs, perhaps as many as 10, by pickling coins in acid at the Mint.

First Points of Wear. *Obverse:* The cheek of the pioneer. *Reverse:* The rifleman's left shoulder. (Note that a lack of detailed facial features is the result of striking, not wear, and that the infant is always weakly struck.)

	Distribution	Cert	Avg	%MS	AU-50	MS-60	MS-62	MS-63	MS-64	MS-65	MS-66
1936	20,015	3,337	65.0	100%	$180	$190	$195	$200	$215	$230	$255

Auctions: $3,995, MS-68, January 2015; $1,880, MS-67, September 2015; $200, MS-65, April 2015; $165, MS-60, February 2015

ALBANY, NEW YORK, CHARTER HALF DOLLAR (1936)

Designer: *Gertrude K. Lathrop.* **Weight:** *12.50 grams.* **Composition:** *.900 silver, .100 copper (net weight .3617 oz. pure silver).* **Diameter:** *30.6 mm.* **Edge:** *Reeded.* **Mint:** *Philadelphia.*

The 250th anniversary of the granting of a charter to the city of Albany—an event of strictly local significance—was the occasion for this commemorative half dollar. Amusingly, designer Gertrude K. Lathrop kept a live beaver in her studio (courtesy of the state Conservation Department) during her work.

Designs. *Obverse:* A plump beaver gnawing on a maple branch—fauna and flora evocative of Albany and New York State, respectively. *Reverse:* A scene with Albany's first mayor, Peter Schuyler, and his secretary, Robert Livingston, accepting the city's charter in 1686 from Governor Thomas Dongan of New York.

Mintage and Melting Data. Authorized on June 16, 1936. *Maximum authorized—25,000. Number minted—25,013 (including 13 assay coins). Number melted—7,342. Net distribution—17,671.*

Original Cost and Issuer. Sale price $1. Issued by the Albany Dongan Charter Coin Committee.

Key to Collecting. This issue was fairly carefully handled during production and distribution, and most examples are relatively free of marks in the fields. Most specimens are lustrous and frosty, although the frost has satiny aspects. Albany half dollars are readily available on the market. The typical example grades from MS–63 to 65 and has at least minor friction and marks.

First Points of Wear. *Obverse:* The hip of the beaver (nearly all coins show at least minor evidence of contact here). *Reverse:* The sleeve of Dongan (the figure at left).

	Distribution	Cert	Avg	%MS	AU-50	MS-60	MS-62	MS-63	MS-64	MS-65	MS-66
1936	17,671	2,961	64.8	100%	$210	$230	$235	$240	$250	$285	$360
	Auctions: $1,293, MS-67, September 2015; $470, MS-66, February 2015; $282, MS-65, June 2015; $176, MS-60, September 2015										

SAN FRANCISCO–OAKLAND BAY BRIDGE OPENING HALF DOLLAR (1936)

Designer: *Jacques Schnier.* **Weight:** *12.50 grams.* **Composition:** *.900 silver, .100 copper (net weight .3617 oz. pure silver).* **Diameter:** *30.6 mm.* **Edge:** *Reeded.* **Mint:** *San Francisco.*

The opening of the San Francisco Bay Bridge was the occasion for a special souvenir fifty-cent piece. The bear depicted on the obverse was a composite of animals in local zoos.

Designs. *Obverse:* A stylized grizzly bear standing on all fours and facing the viewer. *Reverse:* A fading-to-the-horizon view of the San Francisco–Oakland Bay Bridge and part of San Francisco.

Mintage and Melting Data. Authorized on June 26, 1936. *Maximum authorized—200,000. Number minted—100,055 (including 55 assay coins). Number melted—28,631. Net distribution—71,424.*

Original Cost and Issuer. Sale price $1.50. Issued by the Coin Committee of the San Francisco–Oakland Bay Bridge Celebration.

Key to Collecting. These coins are readily available in today's marketplace, with most grading MS–62 to 64, typically with contact marks on the grizzly bear. The reverse design, being complex with many protective devices, normally appears free of marks, unless viewed at an angle under a strong light. The grade of the reverse for a given coin often is a point or two higher than that of the obverse. The fields of this coin often have a "greasy" appearance, rather than being deeply lustrous and frosty.

First Points of Wear. *Obverse:* The bear's body, in particular the left shoulder. *Reverse:* The clouds.

	Distribution	Cert	Avg	%MS	AU-50	MS-60	MS-62	MS-63	MS-64	MS-65	MS-66
1936-S	71,424	3,757	64.6	99%	$145	$150	$160	$175	$185	$215	$330
	Auctions: $1,763, MS-67, January 2015; $764, MS-66, September 2015; $153, MS-64, January 2015; $129, AU-58, January 2015										

COLUMBIA, SOUTH CAROLINA, SESQUICENTENNIAL HALF DOLLAR (1936)

Designer: *A. Wolfe Davidson.* **Weight:** *12.50 grams.*
Composition: *.900 silver, .100 copper (net weight .3617 oz. pure silver).*
Diameter: *30.6 mm.* **Edge:** *Reeded.* **Mints:** *Philadelphia, Denver, and San Francisco.*

Souvenir half dollars were authorized to help finance the extensive celebrations marking the sesquicentennial of the founding of Columbia, South Carolina, in 1786. The pieces had not been minted by the time of the actual celebrations, which took place in late March 1936, and only reached collectors (which the Columbia Sesqui-Centennial Commission expressed desire to sell to instead of to dealers) in December.

Designs. *Obverse:* Justice, with sword and scales, standing before the state capitol of 1786 and the capitol of 1936. *Reverse:* A palmetto tree, the state emblem, with stars encircling.

Mintage Data. Authorized on March 18, 1936. *Maximum authorized*—25,000. *Number minted*—1936-P: 9,007; 1936-D: 8,009; 1936-S: 8,007. *Net distribution*—1936-P: 9,007; 1936-D: 8,009; 1936-S: 8,007.

Original Cost and Issuer. Sale price $6.45 per set of three (single coins $2.15 each). Issued by the Columbia Sesqui-Centennial Commission.

Key to Collecting. These coins were widely distributed at the time of issue, and examples are readily obtainable today. Most grade from MS–63 to 65. They were treated carefully in their minting and distribution, so most coins exhibit lustrous surfaces with very few handling marks. Nearly all, however, show friction on the bosom of Justice and, to a lesser extent, on the high areas of the palmetto-tree foliage on the reverse.

First Points of Wear. *Obverse:* The right breast of Justice. *Reverse:* The top of the palmetto tree.

	Distribution	Cert	Avg	%MS	AU-50	MS-60	MS-62	MS-63	MS-64	MS-65	MS-66
1936	9,007	1,564	65.2	100%	$180	$215	$220	$225	$230	$245	$300
	Auctions: $2,585, MS-68, June 2015; $705, MS-67, May 2015; $235, MS-64, July 2015; $376, MS-62, October 2015										
1936-D	8,009	1,602	65.6	100%	$180	$215	$220	$225	$230	$245	$300
	Auctions: $705, MS-67, June 2015; $294, MS-66, February 2015; $212, MS-65, August 2015; $194, MS-63, July 2015										
1936-S	8,007	1,547	65.4	100%	$180	$215	$220	$225	$230	$245	$300
	Auctions: $7,638, MS-68, August 2015; $999, MS-67, September 2015; $306, MS-66, January 2015; $165, MS-63, October 2015										
Set of 1936 P-D-S					$540	$650	$660	$675	$700	$750	$900
	Auctions: $690, MS-65/66/65, February 2012										

DELAWARE TERCENTENARY HALF DOLLAR (1936)

Designer: *Carl L. Schmitz.* **Weight:** *12.50 grams.* **Composition:** *.900 silver, .100 copper (net weight .3617 oz. pure silver).* **Diameter:** *30.6 mm.* **Edge:** *Reeded.* **Mint:** *Philadelphia.*

The 300th anniversary of the landing of the Swedes in Delaware was the occasion for a souvenir issue of half dollars—as well as a two-krona coin issued in Sweden. The colonists landed on the spot that is now Wilmington and established a church, which is the oldest Protestant church in the United States still used for worship. Carl L. Schmitz's designs were chosen through a competition. These coins were authorized in 1936 and struck in 1937, but not released until 1938, as the Swedes' arrival was actually in 1638.

Designs. *Obverse:* Old Swedes Church. *Reverse:* The ship *Kalmar Nyckel*.

Mintage and Melting Data. Authorized on May 15, 1936. *Minimum authorized*—25,000 (unlimited maximum). *Number minted*—25,015 (including 15 assay coins). *Number melted*—4,022. *Net distribution*—20,993.

Original Cost and Issuer. Sale price $1.75. Issued by the Delaware Swedish Tercentenary Commission, through the Equitable Trust Company of Wilmington.

Key to Collecting. Most examples in today's marketplace grade MS–64 or 65, though they typically exhibit numerous original planchet nicks and marks. Most coins are very lustrous and frosty.

First Points of Wear. *Obverse:* The roof above the church entrance. (Note that the triangular section at the top of the entrance is weakly struck, giving an appearance of wear.) *Reverse:* The center of the lower middle sail (also often shows graininess and nicks from the original planchet).

	Distribution	Cert	Avg	%MS	AU-50	MS-60	MS-62	MS-63	MS-64	MS-65	MS-66
1936	20,993	2,984	64.7	100%	$210	$225	$235	$230	$240	$250	$350
	Auctions: $881, MS-67, January 2015; $541, MS-66, October 2015; $188, MS-63, September 2015; $176, MS-60, August 2015										

BATTLE OF GETTYSBURG ANNIVERSARY HALF DOLLAR (1936)

Designer: *Frank Vittor.* **weight:** *12.50 grams.* **Composition:** *.900 silver, .100 copper (net weight .3617 oz. pure silver).* **Diameter:** *30.6 mm.* **Edge:** *Reeded.* **Mint:** *Philadelphia.*

On June 16, 1936, Congress authorized a coinage of fifty-cent pieces in commemoration of the 75th anniversary of the 1863 Battle of Gettysburg. Similar to the previously mentioned Delaware Tercentenary coins, the coins were authorized two years before the event commemorated, and were minted a year early as well (in 1937). Paul L. Roy, secretary of the Pennsylvania State Commission, desired for the pieces to be struck at multiple mints—so as to sell more expensive sets of three coins, rather than just Philadelphia issues—but no coins were struck in Denver or San Francisco in the end.

Designs. *Obverse:* Uniformed profile portraits of a Union soldier and a Confederate soldier. *Reverse:* Union and Confederate shields separated by a fasces.

Mintage and Melting Data. Authorized on June 16, 1936. *Maximum authorized—50,000. Number minted—50,028* (including 28 assay coins). *Number melted—23,100. Net distribution—26,928.*

Original Cost and Issuer. Sale price $1.65. Issued by the Pennsylvania State Commission, Hotel Gettysburg, Gettysburg. The price was later raised to $2.65 for coins offered by the American Legion, Department of Pennsylvania.

Key to Collecting. Examples are fairly plentiful in the marketplace. The typical coin grades from MS–63 to 65, is deeply frosty and lustrous, and shows scattered contact marks, which are most evident on the cheeks of the soldiers on the obverse and, on the reverse, on the two shields (particularly at the top of the Union shield on the left side of the coin).

First Points of Wear. *Obverse:* The cheekbones of each soldier. *Reverse:* The three ribbons on the fasces, and the top of the Union shield.

	Distribution	Cert	Avg	%MS	AU-50	MS-60	MS-62	MS-63	MS-64	MS-65	MS-66
1936	26,928	3,377	64.4	99%	$435	$450	$480	$490	$600	$775	$1,200
	Auctions: $2,703, MS-67, January 2015; $1,763, MS-66, July 2015; $541, MS-64, September 2015; $423, AU-55, September 2015										

Norfolk, Virginia, Bicentennial Half Dollar (1936)

Designers: *William M. and Marjorie E. Simpson.* **Weight:** *12.50 grams.*
Composition: *.900 silver, .100 copper (net weight .3617 oz. pure silver).*
Diameter: *30.6 mm.* **Edge:** *Reeded.* **Mint:** *Philadelphia.*

To provide funds for the celebration of Norfolk's anniversary of its growth from a township in 1682 to a royal borough in 1736, Congress first passed a law for the striking of medals. The proponents, however, being dissatisfied, finally succeeded in winning authority for half dollars commemorating the 300th anniversary of the original Norfolk land grant and the 200th anniversary of the establishment of the borough. In a strange twist, none of the five dates on these coins actually reflects the year of the coins' actual striking (1937).

Designs. *Obverse:* The seal of the city of Norfolk, Virginia, with a three-masted ship at center. *Reverse:* The city's royal mace, presented by Lieutenant Governor Robert Dinwiddie in 1753.

Mintage and Melting Data. Authorized on June 28, 1937. *Maximum authorized—25,000. Number minted—25,013* (including 13 assay coins). *Number melted—8,077. Net distribution—16,936.*

Original Cost and Issuer. Sale price $1.50 locally ($1.65 by mail for the first coin, $1.55 for each additional). Issued by the Norfolk Advertising Board, Norfolk Association of Commerce.

Key to Collecting. Examples are fairly plentiful in today's marketplace, with most in high MS grades. The cluttered nature of the design had a positive effect: all of the lettering served to protect the fields and devices from nicks and marks, with the result that MS–65 and 66 coins are plentiful.

First Points of Wear. *Obverse:* The sails of the ship, especially the lower rear sail. *Reverse:* The area below the crown on the royal mace.

	Distribution	Cert	Avg	%MS	AU-50	MS-60	MS-62	MS-63	MS-64	MS-65	MS-66
1936	16,936	2,802	65.9	100%	$250	$280	$325	$300	$315	$340	$360
	Auctions: $1,175, MS-68, September 2015; $482, MS-67, August 2015; $388, MS-66, May 2015; $306, MS-64, August 2015										

ROANOKE ISLAND, NORTH CAROLINA, 350TH ANNIVERSARY HALF DOLLAR (1937)

Designer: *William M. Simpson.* **Weight:** *12.50 grams.* **Composition:** *.900 silver, .100 copper (net weight .3617 oz. pure silver).* **Diameter:** *30.6 mm.* **Edge:** *Reeded.* **Mint:** *Philadelphia.*

A celebration was held in Old Fort Raleigh in 1937 to commemorate the 350th anniversary of Sir Walter Raleigh's "Lost Colony" and the birth of Virginia Dare, the first white child born in British North America. Interestingly, Raleigh himself never actually visited America, but only sent ships of colonists who eventually founded a city in his name.

Designs. *Obverse:* Profile portrait of Sir Walter Raleigh in plumed hat and fancy collar. *Reverse:* Ellinor Dare and her baby, Virginia, the first white child born in the Americas to English parents.

Mintage and Melting Data. *Minimum authorized*—25,000 (unlimited maximum). *Number minted*—50,030 (including 30 assay coins). *Number melted*—21,000. *Net distribution*—29,030.

Original Cost and Issuer. Sale price $1.65. Issued by the Roanoke Colony Memorial Association of Manteo.

Key to Collecting. Most of these coins were handled with care during their minting, and today are in high grades. MS-65 pieces are plentiful. Most coins are lustrous and frosty. Partially prooflike pieces are occasionally seen (sometimes offered as "presentation pieces" or "prooflike presentation pieces").

First Points of Wear. *Obverse:* Raleigh's cheek and the brim of his hat. *Reverse:* The head of Ellinor Dare.

	Distribution	Cert	Avg	%MS	AU-50	MS-60	MS-62	MS-63	MS-64	MS-65	MS-66
1937	29,030	3,936	65.1	100%	$135	$150	$165	$185	$215	$230	$250

Auctions: $5,170, MS-68, October 2015; $940, MS-67, August 2015; $188, MS-64, September 2015; $112, AU-50, November 2015

BATTLE OF ANTIETAM ANNIVERSARY HALF DOLLAR (1937)

Designer: *William M. Simpson.* **Weight:** *12.50 grams.* **Composition:** *.900 silver, .100 copper (net weight .3617 oz. pure silver).* **Diameter:** *30.6 mm.* **Edge:** *Reeded.* **Mint:** *Philadelphia.*

A souvenir half dollar was struck in 1937 to commemorate the 75th anniversary of the famous Civil War battle to thwart Robert E. Lee's invasion of Maryland. The Battle of Antietam, which took place on September 17, 1862, was one of the bloodiest single-day battles of the war, with more than 23,000 men killed, wounded, or missing.

Designs. *Obverse:* Uniformed profile portraits of generals Robert E. Lee and George B. McClellan, opponent commanders during the Battle of Antietam. *Reverse:* Burnside Bridge, an important tactical objective of the battle.

Mintage and Melting Data. Authorized on June 24, 1937. *Maximum authorized*—50,000. *Number minted*—50,028 (including 28 assay coins). *Number melted*—32,000. *Net distribution*—18,028.

Original Cost and Issuer. Sale price $1.65. Issued by the Washington County Historical Society, Hagerstown, Maryland.

Key to Collecting. Antietam half dollars were handled with care during production. More often seen are scattered small marks, particularly on the upper part of the obverse. Most examples are very lustrous and frosty. MS-65 and finer coins are plentiful in the marketplace.

First Points of Wear. *Obverse:* Lee's cheekbone. *Reverse:* The leaves of the trees; the bridge; and the rim of the coin.

	Distribution	Cert	Avg	%MS	AU-50	MS-60	MS-62	MS-63	MS-64	MS-65	MS-66
1937	18,028	2,718	65.1	100%	$525	$550	$560	$575	$635	$600	$675
	Auctions: $4,935, MS-68, January 2015; $1,411, MS-67, February 2015; $705, MS-65, September 2015; $447, AU-50, January 2015										

NEW ROCHELLE, NEW YORK, 250TH ANNIVERSARY HALF DOLLAR (1938)

Designer: *Gertrude K. Lathrop.* **Weight:** *12.50 grams.* **Composition:** *.900 silver, .100 copper (net weight .3617 oz. pure silver).* **Diameter:** *30.6 mm.* **Edge:** *Reeded.* **Mint:** *Philadelphia.*

To observe the founding of New Rochelle in 1688 by French Huguenots, a special half dollar was issued in 1938. The title to the land that the Huguenots purchased from John Pell provided that a fattened calf be given away every year on June 20; this is represented the obverse of the coin.

Designs. *Obverse:* John Pell, who sold the French Huguenots the land for New Rochelle, and a fatted calf, an annual provision of the sale. *Reverse:* A fleur-de-lis, adapted from the seal of the city.

Mintage and Melting Data. Authorized on May 5, 1936. *Maximum authorized*—25,000. *Number minted*—25,015 (including 15 assay coins). *Number melted*—9,749. *Net distribution*—15,266.

Original Cost and Issuer. Sale price $2. Issued by the New Rochelle Commemorative Coin Committee, through the First National Bank of New Rochelle, New Rochelle, New York.

Key to Collecting. These half dollars received better-than-average care and handling during the minting and distribution process. The typical coin grades MS-64 or higher. Some examples show very light handling marks, but most are relatively problem-free. Some show areas of graininess or light striking on the high spots of the calf on the obverse, and on the highest area of the iris on the reverse. The majority of pieces have lustrous, frosty surfaces, and a few are prooflike (the latter are sometimes offered as "presentation pieces"). A total of 50 Specimen strikings were given to important people in New Rochelle, as well as to the Coinage Committee and some members of the Westchester County Coin Club.

First Points of Wear. *Obverse:* The hip of the calf. *Reverse:* The bulbous part of the fleur-de-lis. (Note that on the central petal the midrib is flatly struck.)

	Distribution	Cert	Avg	%MS	AU-50	MS-60	MS-62	MS-63	MS-64	MS-65	MS-66
									PF-63	PF-64	PF-65
1938	15,266	2,570	65.0	100%	$300	$310	$330	$325	$360	$375	$400
	Auctions: $1,410, MS-67, July 2015; $494, MS-66, September 2015; $400, MS-65, January 2015; $317, MS-64, January 2015										
1938, Proof	*1–2*	2	61.0								
	Auctions: No auction records available.										

IOWA CENTENNIAL HALF DOLLAR (1946)

Designer: *Adam Pietz.* **Weight:** *12.50 grams.* **Composition:** *.900 silver, .100 copper (net weight .3617 oz. pure silver).* **Diameter:** *30.6 mm.* **Edge:** *Reeded.* **Mint:** *Philadelphia.*

This half dollar, commemorating the 100th anniversary of Iowa's statehood, was sold first to the residents of Iowa and only a small remainder to others. Numismatists of the time, having largely forgotten the deceptions and hucksterism of the 1930s (and also seen the values of previously issued commemoratives rebound from a low point in 1941), were excited to see the first commemorative coin struck in some years. Nearly all of the issue was disposed of quickly, except for 500 that were held back to be distributed in 1996, and another 500 slated for 2046.

Designs. *Obverse:* The Old Stone Capitol building at Iowa City. *Reverse:* An eagle with wings spreading, adapted from the Iowa state seal.

Mintage Data. Authorized on August 7, 1946. *Maximum authorized*—100,000. *Number minted*—100,057 (including 57 assay coins).

Original Cost and Issuer. Sale price $2.50 to in-state buyers, $3 to those out of state. Issued by the Iowa Centennial Committee, Des Moines, Iowa.

Key to Collecting. Most coins are in varying degrees of Mint State, and are lustrous and frosty. MS–63 to 66 are typical grades. The nature of the design, without open field areas, is such that a slight amount of friction and contact is usually not noticeable.

First Points of Wear. *Obverse:* The clouds above the Capitol, and the shafts of the building near the upper-left and upper-right windows. *Reverse:* The back of the eagle's head and neck. (Note that the head sometimes is flatly struck.)

	Distribution	Cert	Avg	%MS	AU-50	MS-60	MS-62	MS-63	MS-64	MS-65	MS-66
1946	100,057	5,987	65.5	100%	$85	$90	$95	$100	$105	$110	$130

Auctions: $4,700, MS-68, January 2015; $270, MS-67, August 2015; $212, MS-66, October 2015; $84, MS-63, August 2015

BOOKER T. WASHINGTON MEMORIAL HALF DOLLAR (1946–1951)

Designer: *Isaac S. Hathaway.* **Weight:** *12.50 grams.*
Composition: *.900 silver, .100 copper (net weight .3617 oz. pure silver).*
Diameter: *30.6 mm.* **Edge:** *Reeded.* **Mints:** *Philadelphia, Denver, and San Francisco.*

This commemorative coin was issued to perpetuate the ideals and teachings of African-American educator and presidential advisor Booker T. Washington and to construct memorials to his memory. Issued from all mints, it received wide distribution from the start. Unfortunately, the provision that the coins could be minted over several years led to many of the same problems seen with the Arkansas, Boone, Oregon Trail, and Texas pieces from the prior decade.

Designs. *Obverse:* Bareheaded three-quarters profile portrait of Booker T. Washington. *Reverse:* The Hall of Fame at New York University and a slave cabin.

Mintage Data. Authorized on August 7, 1946. *Maximum authorized*—5,000,000 (for the entire series 1946 onward). *Number minted*—1946-P: 1,000,546 (including 546 assay coins); 1946-D: 200,113 (including 113 assay coins); 1946-S: 500,279 (including 279 assay coins); 1947-P: 100,017 (including 17 assay coins); 1947-D: 100,017 (including 17 assay coins); 1947-S: 100,017 (including 17 assay coins); 1948-P: 20,005 (including 5 assay coins); 1948-D: 20,005 (including 5 assay coins); 1948-S: 20,005 (including 5 assay coins); 1949-P: 12,004 (including 4 assay coins); 1949-D: 12,004 (including 4 assay coins); 1949-S: 12,004 (including 4 assay coins); 1950-P: 12,004 (including 4 assay coins); 1950-D: 12,004 (including 4 assay coins); 1950-S: 512,091 (including 91 assay coins); 1951-P: 510,082 (including 82 assay coins); 1951-D: 12,004 (including 4 assay coins); 1951-S: 12,004 (including 4 assay coins). *Net distribution*—1946-P: 700,546 (estimated); 1946-D: 50,000 (estimated); 1946-S: 500,279 (estimated); 1947-P: 6,000 (estimated); 1947-D: 6,000 (estimated); 1947-S: 6,000 (estimated); 1948-P: 8,005; 1948-D: 8,005; 1948-S: 8,005; 1949-P: 6,004; 1949-D: 6,004; 1949-S: 6,004; 1950-P: 6,004; 1950-D: 6,004; 1950-S: 62,091 (estimated); 1951-P: 210,082 (estimated); 1951-D: 7,004; 1951-S: 7,004.

Original Cost and Issuer. Original sale price $1 per coin for Philadelphia and San Francisco, $1.50 for Denver, plus 10¢ postage per coin. In 1946, issued by the Booker T. Washington Birthplace Memorial Commission, Inc., Rocky Mount, Virginia (Dr. S.J. Phillips in charge); Stack's of New York City; and Bebee Stamp & Coin Company (a.k.a. Bebee's). For later issues, costs and distributors varied.

Key to Collecting. Of all commemorative half dollar issues produced up to this point, the Booker T. Washington half dollars were made with the least amount of care during the coining process at the mints. At the time of release, nearly all were poorly struck on the obverse and were marked with abrasions and nicks. Many have graininess and marks on Washington's cheek, from the original planchet surface that did not strike up fully. Many coins grade from MS–60 to (liberally graded) 65. Some have natural or artificial toning that masks the true condition and facilitates gem certification. Prooflike coins are sometimes seen, including for 1947-S (in particular), 1948-S, 1949, and 1951-S. These are not at all mirror-like, but still have surfaces different from the normal mint frost.

First Points of Wear. *Obverse:* Washington's cheekbone. *Reverse:* The center lettering (FROM SLAVE CABIN TO HALL OF FAME, etc.).

	Distribution	Cert	Avg	%MS	AU-50	MS-60	MS-62	MS-63	MS-64	MS-65	MS-66
1946	700,546	2,887	64.6	99%	$18	$20	$21	$25	$35	$60	$125
Auctions: $1,293, MS-67, January 2015; $705, MS-67, March 2015; $141, MS-66, June 2015; $60, MS-65, March 2015											
1946-D	50,000	1,679	64.8	100%	$18	$20	$22	$25	$30	$60	$170
Auctions: $5,405, MS-68, July 2015; $1,410, MS-67, August 2015; $286, MS-66, October 2015; $32, MS-64, April 2015											
1946-S	500,279	2,432	64.9	99%	$18	$20	$22	$25	$30	$60	$115
Auctions: $4,113, MS-68, March 2015; $1,645, MS-67, August 2015; $123, MS-66, March 2015; $259, MS-64, November 2015											
Set of 1946 P-D-S					$55	$60	$70	$75	$100	$180	$425
Auctions: $110, MS-65/65/65, May 2012											
1947	6,000	881	64.9	100%	$18	$25	$40	$55	$60	$75	$300
Auctions: $3,525, MS-67, July 2015; $400, MS-66, January 2015; $259, MS-66, February 2015; $54, MS-65, January 2015											
1947-D	6,000	691	65.0	100%	$18	$30	$40	$55	$60	$85	$350
Auctions: $1,645, MS-67, June 2015; $494, MS-66, January 2015; $329, MS-66, August 2015; $84, MS-65, September 2015											
1947-S	6,000	904	65.1	100%	$18	$30	$40	$55	$60	$85	$160
Auctions: $2,585, MS-67, January 2015; $176, MS-66, November 2015; $64, MS-65, April 2015; $69, MS-64, January 2015											
Set of 1947 P-D-S					$55	$85	$120	$165	$180	$225	$700
Auctions: $196, MS-65/65/65, January 2012											

	Distribution	Cert	Avg	%MS	AU-50	MS-60	MS-62	MS-63	MS-64	MS-65	MS-66
1948	8,005	807	65.2	100%	$18	$25	$50	$65	$75	$80	$195
	Auctions: $999, MS-67, June 2015; $282, MS-66, September 2015; $235, MS-66, February 2015; $79, MS-65, February 2015										
1948-D	8,005	820	65.2	100%	$25	$30	$45	$60	$70	$85	$180
	Auctions: $1,028, MS-67, February 2015; $176, MS-66, November 2015; $94, MS-65, January 2015; $36, MS-64, April 2015										
1948-S	8,005	955	65.4	100%	$25	$30	$45	$60	$70	$90	$180
	Auctions: $1,293, MS-67, February 2015; $212, MS-66, February 2015; $70, MS-65, February 2015; $38, MS-64, April 2015										
Set of 1948 P-D-S					$70	$85	$150	$185	$215	$250	$525
	Auctions: $220, MS-66/65/65, June 2012										
1949	6,004	826	65.2	100%	$18	$20	$21	$25	$35	$100	$200
	Auctions: $2,233, MS-67, January 2015; $400, MS-66, February 2015; $141, MS-65, April 2015; $84, MS-64, January 2015										
1949-D	6,004	778	65.2	100%	$18	$20	$21	$25	$35	$100	$175
	Auctions: $1,058, MS-67, October 2015; $165, MS-66, April 2015; $112, MS-65, April 2015; $74, MS-64, January 2015										
1949-S	6,004	843	65.5	100%	$18	$20	$21	$25	$35	$100	$175
	Auctions: $940, MS-67, October 2015; $212, MS-66, September 2015; $188, MS-65, September 2015; $79, MS-64, February 2015										
Set of 1949 P-D-S					$54	$60	$63	$75	$105	$400	$525
	Auctions: $320, MS-65/66/66, May 2012										
1950	6,004	637	65.2	100%	$20	$20	$21	$25	$35	$60	$200
	Auctions: $541, MS-67, October 2015; $300, MS-66, May 2015; $200, MS-66, October 2015; $74, MS-65, May 2015										
1950-D	6,004	615	65.1	100%	$20	$20	$21	$25	$35	$60	$175
	Auctions: $1,763, MS-67, February 2015; $282, MS-66, August 2015; $212, MS-66, September 2015; $84, MS-65, January 2015										
1950-S	62,091	1,282	65.2	100%	$20	$20	$21	$25	$35	$60	$125
	Auctions: $940, MS-67, January 2015; $764, MS-67, August 2015; $141, MS-66, August 2015; $34, MS-65, April 2015										
Set of 1950 P-D-S					$60	$60	$65	$75	$135	$300	$500
	Auctions: $725, MS-66/66/66, April 2012										
1951	210,082	1,310	64.6	100%	$18	$25	$30	$40	$50	$50	$135
	Auctions: $1,528, MS-67, June 2015; $376, MS-66, January 2015; $147, MS-65, March 2015; $40, MS-64, April 2015										
1951-D	7,004	673	65.3	100%	$25	$40	$50	$60	$75	$100	$150
	Auctions: $764, MS-67, January 2015; $259, MS-66, September 2015; $141, MS-65, January 2015; $56, MS-63, April 2015										
1951-S	7,004	768	65.5	100%	$22	$30	$40	$60	$75	$100	$150
	Auctions: $764, MS-67, September 2015; $646, MS-67, September 2015; $170, MS-66, July 2015; $165, MS-66, November 2015										
Set of 1951 P-D-S					$65	$95	$120	$160	$200	$275	$450
	Auctions: $475, MS-66/66/66, May 2012; $153, MS-66/66/66, March 2015										

CARVER / WASHINGTON COMMEMORATIVE HALF DOLLAR (1951–1954)

Designer: *Isaac S. Hathaway.* **Weight:** *12.50 grams.*
Composition: *.900 silver, .100 copper (net weight .3617 oz. pure silver).*
Diameter: *30.6 mm.* **Edge:** *Reeded.* **Mints:** *Philadelphia, Denver, and San Francisco.*

Designed by Isaac Scott Hathaway, this coin portrays the conjoined busts of two prominent black Americans. Booker T. Washington was a lecturer, educator, and principal of Tuskegee Institute. He urged training to advance independence and efficiency for his race. George Washington Carver was an agricultural chemist who worked to improve the economy of the American South. He spent part of his life teaching crop improvement and new uses for soybeans, peanuts, sweet potatoes, and cotton waste. Controversy erupted when it came to light that money obtained from the sale of these commemoratives was to be used "to oppose the spread of communism among Negroes in the interest of national defense."

Designs. *Obverse:* Conjoined bareheaded profile portraits of George Washington Carver and Booker T. Washington. *Reverse:* A map of the United States, with legends.

Mintage Data. Signed into law by President Harry S Truman on September 21, 1951. *Maximum authorized*—3,415,631 (total for all issues 1951 onward; consisting of 1,581,631 undistributed Booker T. Washington coins which could be converted into Carver-Washington coins, plus the unused 1,834,000 earlier authorization for Booker T. Washington coins). The following include author's estimates: 1951-P-D-S: *Number minted* (including 18, 4, and 4 assay coins)—110,018; 10,004; 10,004. *Net distribution*—20,018 (estimated); 10,004 (estimated); 10,004 (estimated). 1952-P-D-S: *Number minted* (including 292, 6, and 6 assay coins)—2,006,292; 8,006; 8,006. *Net distribution*—1,106,292 (estimated); 8,006 (estimated); 8,006 (estimated). 1953-P-D-S: *Number minted* (including 3, 3, and 20 assay coins)—8,003; 8,003; 108,020. *Net distribution*—8,003 (estimated); 8,003 (estimated); 88,020 (estimated). 1954-P-D-S: *Number minted* (including 6, 6, and 24 assay coins)—12,006; 12,006; 122,024. *Net distribution*—12,006 (estimated); 12,006 (estimated); 42,024 (estimated).

Original Cost and Issuer. 1951-P-D-S: $10 per set. 1952-P-D-S: $10 per set; many Philadelphia coins were sold at or near face value through banks. 1953-P-D-S: $10 per set; some 1953-S coins were distributed at or near face value (Bebee's prices $9 until January 15, 1952, $10 after that date). 1954-P-D-S: Official sale price: $10 per set; some 1954-S coins were paid out at face value (Bebee's prices for sets $9 until January 20, 1954, $12 after that date). Issued mainly by the Carver-Washington Coin Commission acting for the Booker T. Washington Birthplace Memorial Foundation (Booker Washington Birthplace, Virginia) and the George Washington Carver National Monument Foundation (Diamond, Missouri). Also, for some issues, these dealers: Stack's, Bebee Stamp & Coin Company, Sol Kaplan, and R. Green.

Key to Collecting. Nearly all coins of this issue were handled casually at the mints and also during the distribution process. Most were not fully struck up, with the result that under magnification many tiny nicks and marks can be seen on the higher parts, originating from planchet marks that were not obliterated during the striking process. Many MS examples are available on the market.

First Points of Wear. *Obverse:* Carver's cheekbone. (Note that some pieces were struck poorly in this area; check the reverse also for wear.) *Reverse:* The lettering U.S.A. on the map.

	Distribution	Cert	Avg	%MS	AU-50	MS-60	MS-62	MS-63	MS-64	MS-65	MS-66
1951	20,018	1,032	64.1	100%	$18	$20	$21	$25	$60	$180	$600
Auctions: $940, MS-66, August 2015; $705, MS-66, January 2015; $141, MS-65, August 2015; $36, MS-64, April 2015											
1951-D	10,004	669	64.7	100%	$22	$25	$30	$40	$45	$80	$360
Auctions: $376, MS-66, February 2015; $89, MS-65, January 2015; $84, MS-65, January 2015; $79, MS-65, August 2015											
1951-S	10,004	834	65.1	100%	$22	$25	$30	$45	$55	$85	$180
Auctions: $1,763, MS-67, August 2015; $400, MS-66, August 2015; $275, MS-66, November 2015; $112, MS-65, August 2015											
Set of 1951 P-D-S					$65	$70	$85	$110	$160	$350	$1,150
Auctions: $140, MS-64/64/64, June 2012											
1952	1,106,292	4,015	64.2	98%	$18	$25	$26	$27	$30	$60	$200
Auctions: $2,820, MS-67, January 2015; $1,880, MS-67, August 2015; $306, MS-66, September 2015; $26, MS-60, August 2015											
1952-D	8,006	520	64.5	100%	$24	$30	$35	$45	$70	$135	$600
Auctions: $764, MS-66, January 2015; $517, MS-66, September 2015; $106, MS-65, August 2015; $30, MS-64, April 2015											
1952-S	8,006	686	65.1	100%	$24	$30	$35	$40	$50	$90	$210
Auctions: $3,200, MS-67, January 2015; $282, MS-66, September 2015; $84, MS-65, August 2015; $50, MS-64, August 2015											
Set of 1952 P-D-S					$70	$85	$100	$115	$150	$285	$1,025
Auctions: $230, MS-65/65/65, March 2012											

	Distribution	Cert	Avg	%MS	AU-50	MS-60	MS-62	MS-63	MS-64	MS-65	MS-66
1953	8,003	602	64.7	100%	$22	$30	$35	$40	$50	$95	$450
	Auctions: $259, MS-66, January 2015; $94, MS-65, September 2015; $89, MS-65, October 2015; $36, MS-64, May 2015										
1953-D	8,003	486	64.4	100%	$18	$40	$45	$50	$55	$110	$725
	Auctions: $376, MS-65, July 2015; $84, MS-65, May 2015; $48, MS-64, August 2015; $30, MS-64, August 2015										
1953-S	88,020	1,316	64.8	100%	$22	$25	$28	$30	$45	$60	$300
	Auctions: $3,290, MS-67, August 2015; $3,055, MS-67, March 2015; $282, MS-66, October 2015; $170, MS-65, May 2015										
Set of 1953 P-D-S					$65	$95	$110	$120	$150	$270	$1,500
	Auctions: $300, MS-65/65/65, May 2012										
1954	12,006	818	64.6	100%	$20	$25	$27	$30	$40	$60	$450
	Auctions: $282, MS-66, November 2015; $94, MS-65, July 2015; $79, MS-65, February 2015; $46, MS-64, April 2015										
1954-D	12,006	714	64.4	100%	$25	$30	$35	$40	$45	$85	$550
	Auctions: $676, MS-66, February 2015; $423, MS-66, August 2015; $100, MS-65, August 2015; $82, MS-65, January 2015										
1954-S	42,024	1,190	64.6	100%	$20	$25	$27	$30	$40	$60	$350
	Auctions: $1,998, MS-67, June 2015; $306, MS-66, August 2015; $84, MS-65, August 2015; $34, MS-64, August 2015										
Set of 1954 P-D-S					$65	$80	$90	$100	$125	$210	$1,350
	Auctions: $316, MS-65/65/65, March 2012										

AN OVERVIEW OF MODERN COMMEMORATIVES

No commemorative coins were made by the U.S. Mint from 1955 through 1981. As the years went by, the numismatic community missed having new commemoratives to collect, and many endorsements for events and subjects worthy of the honor were made through letters to congressmen and other officials, which were often reprinted in pages of *The Numismatist*, the *Numismatic Scrapbook Magazine*, *Numismatic News*, and *Coin World*.

Finally, in 1982, the Treasury Department issued the first commemorative coin since 1954—a silver half dollar celebrating the 250th anniversary of the birth of George Washington. This time around, distribution was placed in the hands of the Bureau of the Mint (today called the U.S. Mint) rather than with a commission or private individuals. The profits accrued to the Treasury Department and the U.S. government. The issue was well received in the numismatic community, with more than seven million of the half dollars sold nationwide.

Then came the 1983 and 1984 Los Angeles Olympiad coins, minted in the subject years for the Los Angeles Olympiad held in 1984. These comprised a diverse and somewhat experimental series, with dollars of two different designs and, for the first time, a commemorative ten-dollar gold coin. Sales were satisfactory, and the supply easily met the demand from collectors and investors.

The concept of a surcharge, or built-in fee, was introduced, with a certain amount per coin going to a congressionally designated beneficiary—in the instance of the Olympic coins, the Los Angeles Olympic Organizing Committee. These and related surcharges became controversial with collectors, some of whom resented making involuntary donations when they bought coins. Today the practice continues, though without as much controversy. Surcharges are the spark that has ignited most commemorative programs, as potential recipients of the earmarked profits launch intense lobbying campaigns in Congress.

In 1986 the 100th anniversary of the completion of the Statue of Liberty was commemorated by the issuance of a copper-nickel–clad half dollar (first of its kind in the commemorative series), a silver dollar, and a five-dollar gold coin, with varied motifs, each depicting on the obverse the Statue of Liberty or an element therefrom. Unprecedented millions of coins were sold.

Then followed a lull in commemorative purchases, although the Mint continued to issue coins celebrating more Olympic Games, various national anniversaries, and significant people, places, events, and other subjects. Some years saw four or five or more individual commemorative programs. Some were well received by the hobby community, but sales of most fell far short of projections. In certain cases these low sales would eventually prove beneficial for collectors who placed orders from the Mint. An example is the 1995 five-dollar commemorative honoring baseball star and Civil Rights hero Jackie Robinson. Only 5,174 Uncirculated pieces were sold, creating a modern rarity.

Most modern commemorative coins have seen only modest secondary-market appreciation, if any. Beyond their retail values, however, the coins will always have significant historical, cultural, and sentimental value. The 2001 American Buffalo silver dollar created a sensation with its bold design harkening back to the classic Buffalo nickel of 1913 to 1938; the issue sold out quickly and soon was commanding high premiums in the collector market. It remains popular and valuable today. In 2014, the National Baseball Hall of Fame commemoratives (a three-coin suite in copper-nickel, silver, and gold) captured mainstream-media headlines and national TV news coverage. Other modern commemoratives have honored American inventors and explorers, branches of the U.S. military, Boy Scouts and Girl Scouts, the Civil Rights Act of 1964, and other important themes, continuing a tradition of special coinage dating back to 1892 and giving today's collectors a broad spectrum of issues to study and cherish.

See page 1195 for pricing of government commemorative sets and page 1502 for an alphabetical cross-reference list of all commemoratives.

GEORGE WASHINGTON 250TH ANNIVERSARY OF BIRTH HALF DOLLAR (1982)

Designer: *Elizabeth Jones.* **Weight:** *12.50 grams.*
Composition: *.900 silver, .100 copper (net weight .3617 oz. pure silver).*
Diameter: *30.6 mm.* **Edge:** *Reeded.* **Mints:** *Denver (Uncirculated) and San Francisco (Proof).*

This coin, the first commemorative half dollar issued since 1954, celebrated the 250th anniversary of the birth of George Washington. It was also the first 90% silver coin produced by the U.S. Mint since 1964.

Designs. *Obverse:* George Washington on horseback. *Reverse:* Mount Vernon.

Mintage Data. Authorized by Public Law 97-014, signed by President Ronald Reagan on December 23, 1981. *Maximum authorized*—10,000,000. *Number minted*—1982-D: 478,716; 1982-S: 868,326. *Net distribution*—1982-D: 2,210,458 Uncirculated; 1982-S: 4,894,044 Proof.

Original Cost. Sale prices originally $8.50 (Uncirculated) and $10.50 (Proof), later raised to $10 and $12, respectively.

Key to Collecting. Today, Uncirculated 1982-D and Proof 1982-S Washington half dollars are plentiful on the market and are readily available in as-issued condition. They are popular and highly regarded as part of the modern commemorative series.

	Distribution	Cert	Avg	%MS	MS-67	
					PF-67	
1982-D ††	2,210,458	4,491	66.9	100%	$11	
	Auctions: $123, MS-69, June 2014					
1982-S, Proof	4,894,044	10,403	69.0		$11	
	Auctions: $110, PF-70, June 2014; $106, PF-70, September 2015; $106, PF-70, November 2014; $74, PF-70UCam, June 2015					

†† Ranked in the *100 Greatest U.S. Modern Coins* (fourth edition).

Los Angeles Olympiad Discus Thrower Silver Dollar (1983)

Designer: *Elizabeth Jones.* **Weight:** *26.73 grams.* **Composition:** *.900 silver, .100 copper (net weight .7736 oz. pure silver).* **Diameter:** *38.1 mm.* **Edge:** *Reeded.*
Mints: *Philadelphia and Denver (Uncirculated), San Francisco (Uncirculated and Proof).*

Three distinctive coins were issued to commemorate the 1984 Los Angeles Summer Olympic Games. The 1983 Discus Thrower dollar was the first commemorative silver dollar since the 1900 Lafayette issue.

Designs. *Obverse:* Representation of the traditional Greek discus thrower inspired by the ancient work of the sculptor Myron. *Reverse:* The head and upper body of an American eagle.

Mintage Data. Authorized by Public Law 97-220, signed by President Ronald Reagan on July 22, 1982. *Maximum authorized*—50,000,000 totally for 1983 and 1984. *Number minted*—1983-P: 294,543 Uncirculated; 1983-D: 174,014 Uncirculated; 1983-S: 174,014 Uncirculated and 1,577,025 Proof.

Original Cost. Sale prices $28 (Uncirculated) and $24.95 (Proof, ordered in advance); Proof raised later to $29, and still later to $32. Part of the $10 surcharge per coin went to the U.S. Olympic Committee and the Los Angeles Olympic Organizing Committee.

Key to Collecting. These pieces in both Uncirculated and Proof format can be found today for prices near their issue cost. The vast quantities issued (never mind that 52 million were not sold) made them common. Nearly all surviving coins are in superb gem preservation. Today the aftermarket is supported by coin collectors, not by Olympic sports enthusiasts.

	Distribution	Cert	Avg	%MS	MS-67	
					PF-67	
1983-P	294,543	2,375	69.0	100%	$22	
	Auctions: $499, MS-70, September 2014					
1983-D	174,014	1,747	69.0	100%	$22	
	Auctions: $7,638, MS-70, April 2013					
1983-S	174,014	1,824	69.0	100%	$22	
	Auctions: $8,813, MS-70, April 2013					
1983-S, Proof	1,577,025	5,014	69.0		$24	
	Auctions: $1,175, PF-70DCam, April 2014					

LOS ANGELES OLYMPIAD OLYMPIC COLISEUM SILVER DOLLAR (1984)

Designer: *John Mercanti.* **Weight:** *26.73 grams.* **Composition:** *.900 silver, .100 copper (net weight .7736 oz. pure silver).* **Diameter:** *38.1 mm.* **Edge:** *Reeded.*
Mints: *Philadelphia and Denver (Uncirculated), San Francisco (Uncirculated and Proof).*

This coin became a reality at the insistence of the Los Angeles Olympic Organizing Committee. The semi-nude figures on the obverse created some controversy.

Designs. *Obverse:* Robert Graham's headless torso sculptures at the entrance of the Los Angeles Memorial Coliseum. *Reverse:* Perched eagle looking back over its left wing.

Mintage Data. Authorized by Public Law 97-220, signed by President Ronald Reagan on July 22, 1982. *Maximum authorized*—50,000,000 totally for 1983 and 1984. *Number minted*—1984-P: 217,954 Uncirculated; 1984-D: 116,675 Uncirculated; 1984-S: 116,675 Uncirculated and 1,801,210 Proof.

Original Cost. Sales prices $28 (Uncirculated) and $32 (Proof); Proof later raised to $35. Part of the $10 surcharge per coin went to the U.S. Olympic Committee and the Los Angeles Olympic Organizing Committee.

Key to Collecting. These pieces in both Uncirculated and Proof format can be found today for close to what they cost at the time of issue. The vast quantities issued (never mind that 52 million were not sold) made them common. Nearly all surviving coins are in superb gem preservation. Today, the aftermarket is supported by coin collectors, not by Olympic sports enthusiasts.

	Distribution	Cert	Avg	%MS	MS-67 PF-67
1984-P	217,954	1,742	69.0	100%	$22
	Auctions: $705, MS-70, September 2013; $456, MS-70, September 2014; $447, MS-70, August 2015				
1984-D	116,675	1,246	68.9	100%	$23
	Auctions: $4,994, MS-70, April 2013				
1984-S	116,675	1,263	68.9	100%	$23
	Auctions: $9,400, MS-70, April 2013				
1984-S, Proof	1,801,210	4,323	68.9		$24
	Auctions: $411, PF-70DCam, September 2014; $558, PF-70DCam, April 2013				

Los Angeles Olympiad $10 Gold Coin (1984)

Designer: *John Mercanti.* **Weight:** *16.718 grams.* **Composition:** *.900 gold, .100 copper (net weight .4837 oz. pure gold).* **Diameter:** *27 mm.* **Edge:** *Reeded.*
Mints: *Philadelphia, Denver, and San Francisco (Proof); West Point (Uncirculated and Proof).*

This ten-dollar coin was the first commemorative to be struck in gold since the 1926 Sesquicentennial $2.50 gold pieces. Mint engraver John Mercanti based the obverse design on a sketch by James Peed of the Bureau of the Mint's Washington office.

Designs. *Obverse:* Two runners holding aloft the Olympic torch. *Reverse:* Adaptation of the Great Seal of the United States.

Mintage Data. Authorized by Public Law 97-220, signed by President Ronald Reagan on July 22, 1982. *Maximum authorized*—2,000,000. *Number minted*—1984-P: 33,309 Proof; 1984-D: 34,533 Proof; 1984-S: 48,551 Proof; 1984-W: 75,886 Uncirculated and 381,085 Proof.

Original Cost. Sales prices $339 (Uncirculated) and $353 (Proof). Part of the $35 surcharge per coin went to the U.S. Olympic Committee and the Los Angeles Olympic Organizing Committee.

Key to Collecting. These coins are necessarily expensive due to their gold content, but are still quite reasonable. Nearly all surviving coins are in superb gem preservation. Today, the aftermarket is supported by coin collectors, not by Olympic sports enthusiasts.

	Distribution	Cert	Avg	%MS	MS-67 PF-67
1984-P, Proof	33,309	1,876	69.0		$675
Auctions: $1,763, PF-70DCam, April 2013; $823, PF-70DCam, September 2014; $624, PF-69DCam, October 2014; $588, PF-69, June 2015					
1984-D, Proof	34,533	1,961	69.1		$675
Auctions: $1,116, PF-70DCam, April 2013; $617, PF-69DCam, October 2014; $611, PF-69DCam, October 2014; $564, PF-69, June 2015					
1984-S, Proof	48,551	1,844	69.2		$675
Auctions: $823, PF-70DCam, April 2013; $618, PF-69DCam, October 2014; $588, PF-69, June 2015					
1984-W ††	75,886	1,649	69.3	100%	$725
Auctions: $764, MS-70, September 2014; $893, MS-70, April 2013; $611, MS-69, October 2014					
1984-W, Proof ††	381,085	5,894	69.1		$675
Auctions: $646, PF-70UCam, January 2015; $646, PF-70UCam, July 2015; $646, PF-70UCam, July 2015; $588, PF-69, June 2015					

†† Both 1984-W Los Angeles Olympiad $10 Gold Coins are ranked in the *100 Greatest U.S. Modern Coins* (fourth edition), as a single entry.

Statue of Liberty Centennial Half Dollar (1986)

Designer: *Edgar Z. Steever IV (obverse), Sherl Winter (reverse).* **Weight:** *11.34 grams.*
Composition: *.9167 copper, .0833 nickel.* **Diameter:** *30.61 mm.*
Edge: *Reeded.* **Mints:** *Denver (Uncirculated) and San Francisco (Proof).*

The 100th anniversary of the dedication of the Statue of Liberty in New York City harbor in 1886 furnished the occasion for the issuance of three different commemorative coins in 1986. The clad half dollar was the first U.S. commemorative issued in copper-nickel format.

Designs. *Obverse:* Ship of immigrants steaming into New York harbor, with the Statue of Liberty greeting them in the foreground and the New York skyline in the distance. *Reverse:* Scene of an immigrant family with their belongings on the threshold of America.

Mintage Data. Authorized by the Act of July 9, 1985. *Maximum authorized—*25,000,000. *Number minted—* 1986-D: 928,008 Uncirculated; 1986-S: 6,925,627 Proof.

Original Cost. Sale prices $5 (Uncirculated, pre-order) and $6.50 (Proof, pre-order); Uncirculated later raised to $6, and Proof later raised to $7.50.

Key to Collecting. So many 1986 Statue of Liberty half dollars were issued that the aftermarket affords the possibility of purchasing the coins not much above the original offering price. Nearly all are superb gems.

	Distribution	Cert	Avg	%MS	MS-67 PF-67
1986-D	928,008	2,858	69.0	100%	$5
Auctions: $411, MS-70, April 2013					
1986-S, Proof ††	6,925,627	11,727	69.0		$5
Auctions: $84, PF-69DCam, January 2015; $129, PF-67, October 2015					

†† Ranked in the *100 Greatest U.S. Modern Coins* (fourth edition).

STATUE OF LIBERTY CENTENNIAL SILVER DOLLAR (1986)

Designer: *John Mercanti.* **Weight:** *26.73 grams.* **Composition:** *.900 silver, .100 copper (net weight .7736 oz. pure silver).* **Diameter:** *38.1 mm.* **Edge:** *Reeded.*
Mints: *Philadelphia (Uncirculated) and San Francisco (Proof).*

These coins, which are also known as Ellis Island silver dollars, feature an excerpt from Emma Lazarus's poem, *The New Colossus.*

Designs. *Obverse:* Statue of Liberty in the foreground, with the Ellis Island immigration center behind her. *Reverse:* Liberty's torch, along with the words GIVE ME YOUR TIRED, YOUR POOR, YOUR HUDDLED MASSES YEARNING TO BREATHE FREE.

Mintage Data. Authorized by the Act of July 9, 1985. *Maximum authorized—*10,000,000. *Number minted—* 1986-P: 723,635 Uncirculated; 1986-S: 6,414,638 Proof.

Original Cost. Sale prices $20.50 (Uncirculated, pre-order) and $22.50 (Proof, pre-order); Uncirculated later raised to $22, and Proof later raised to $24.

Key to Collecting. Nearly all coins of this issue are superb gems.

	Distribution	Cert	Avg	%MS	MS-67 PF-67
1986-P	723,635	4,000	69.0	100%	$24
Auctions: $170, MS-70, January 2013; $27, MS-69, August 2014					
1986-S, Proof	6,414,638	12,650	69.0		$25
Auctions: $141, PF-70DCam, April 2014; $106, PF-70DCam, April 2013; $70, PF-69DCam, August 2014; $188, PF-69DCam, November 2014					

Statue of Liberty Centennial $5 Gold Coin (1986)

Designer: *Elizabeth Jones.* **Weight:** *8.359 grams.* **Composition:** *.900 gold, .100 copper (net weight .242 oz. pure gold).* **Diameter:** *21.6 mm.* **Edge:** *Reeded.* **Mint:** *West Point.*

The designs on these five-dollar gold coins created a sensation in the numismatic community and were widely discussed, and the coin received Krause Publications' Coin of the Year Award. The entire authorization of a half million coins was spoken for—the only complete sellout of any commemorative coin of the 1980s.

Designs. *Obverse:* Face and crown of the Statue of Liberty. *Reverse:* American eagle in flight.

Mintage Data. Authorized by the Act of July 9, 1985. *Maximum authorized*—500,000. *Number minted*—95,248 Uncirculated and 404,013 Proof.

Original Cost. Sale prices $160 (Uncirculated, pre-order) and $170 (Proof, pre-order); Uncirculated later raised to $165, and Proof later raised to $175.

Key to Collecting. So many 1986 Statue of Liberty commemoratives were issued that the aftermarket affords the possibility of purchasing the coins at prices near bullion value. Nearly all coins of this issue are superb gems.

	Distribution	Cert	Avg	%MS	MS-67 PF-67
1986-W	95,248	3,869	69.5	100%	$325
	Auctions: $353, MS-70, August 2014; $329, MS-70, September 2014; $329, MS-70, November 2014; $441, MS-70, February 2013				
1986-W, Proof	404,013	10,817	69.3		$325
	Auctions: $306, PF-70, September 2015; $306, MS-70, April 2015; $282, PF-70, October 2015; $329, PF-69DCam, October 2014				

Constitution Bicentennial Silver Dollar (1987)

Designer: *Patricia Lewis Verani.* **Weight:** *26.73 grams.*
Composition: *.900 silver, .100 copper (net weight .7736 oz. pure silver).*
Diameter: *38.1 mm.* **Edge:** *Reeded.* **Mints:** *Philadelphia (Uncirculated) and San Francisco (Proof).*

In connection with the 200th anniversary of the U.S. Constitution, observed in 1987, Congress held a competition to design both a silver dollar and a five-dollar gold coin.

Designs. *Obverse:* Quill pen, a sheaf of parchment, and the words WE THE PEOPLE. *Reverse:* Cross-section of Americans from various periods representing various lifestyles.

Mintage Data. Authorized by Public Law 99-582, signed by President Ronald Reagan on October 29, 1986. *Maximum authorized*—1,000,000. *Number minted*—1987-P: 451,629 Uncirculated; 1987-S: 2,747,116 Proof.

Original Cost. Sale prices $22.50 (Uncirculated, pre-issue) and $24 (Proof, pre-issue); Uncirculated later raised to $26, and Proof later raised to $28. A $7 surcharge per coin went toward reducing the national debt.

Key to Collecting. Today, these coins remain inexpensive. Nearly all are superb gems.

	Distribution	Cert	Avg	%MS	MS-67
					PF-67
1987-P	451,629	3,463	69.1	100%	$22
	Auctions: $90, MS-70, January 2013				
1987-S, Proof	2,747,116	5,874	68.9		$22
	Auctions: $115, PF-70DCam, April 2013				

CONSTITUTION BICENTENNIAL $5 GOLD COIN (1987)

Designer: *Marcel Jovine.* **Weight:** *8.359 grams.* **Composition:** *.900 gold, .100 copper (net weight .242 oz. pure gold).* **Diameter:** *21.6 mm.* **Edge:** *Reeded.* **Mint:** *West Point.*

A modernistic design by Marcel Jovine was selected for the five-dollar gold coin honoring the bicentennial of the U.S. Constitution.

Designs. *Obverse:* Stylized eagle holding a massive quill pen. *Reverse:* Large quill pen with nine stars to the left (symbolizing the first colonies to ratify the Constitution) and four to the right (representing the remaining original states).

Mintage Data. Authorized by Public Law 99-582, signed by President Ronald Reagan on October 29, 1986. *Maximum authorized*—1,000,000. *Number minted*—214,225 Uncirculated and 651,659 Proof.

Original Cost. Sale prices $195 (Uncirculated, pre-issue) and $200 (Proof, pre-issue); Uncirculated later raised to $215, and Proof later raised to $225.

Key to Collecting. Nearly all coins of this issue are superb gems.

	Distribution	Cert	Avg	%MS	MS-67
					PF-67
1987-W	214,225	7,505	69.7	100%	$325
	Auctions: $353, MS-70, August 2015; $317, MS-70, August 2015; $306, MS-70, August 2015; $300, MS-70, September 2015				
1987-W, Proof	651,659	16,511	69.5		$325
	Auctions: $376, PF-70UCam, September 2015; $353, PF-70UCam, January 2015; $329, PF-70UCam, October 2015				

SEOUL OLYMPIAD SILVER DOLLAR (1988)

Designer: *Patricia Lewis Verani (obverse), Sherl Winter (reverse).* **Weight:** *26.73 grams.*
Composition: *.900 silver, .100 copper (net weight .7736 oz. pure silver).*
Diameter: *38.1 mm.* **Edge:** *Reeded.* **Mints:** *Denver (Uncirculated) and San Francisco (Proof).*

The holding of the 1988 Summer Olympic Games in Seoul, Republic of South Korea, furnished the opportunity for the issuance of this silver dollar (as well as a five-dollar gold coin; see next entry).

Designs. *Obverse:* One hand holding an Olympic torch as another hand holds another torch to ignite it. *Reverse:* Olympic rings surrounded by a wreath.

Mintage Data. Authorized by Public Law 100-141, signed by President Ronald Reagan on October 28, 1987. *Maximum authorized*—10,000,000. *Number minted*—1988-D: 191,368 Uncirculated; 1988-S: 1,359,366 Proof.

Original Cost. Sale prices $22 (Uncirculated, pre-issue) and $23 (Proof, pre-issue); Uncirculated later raised to $27, and Proof later raised to $29. The surcharge of $7 per coin went to the U.S. Olympic Committee.

Key to Collecting. These coins are inexpensive. The numismatic market, representing actual buyers and sellers, is not extensive enough to maintain large premiums over the price of hundreds of thousands of coins purchased by the non-numismatic public and then later sold when their novelty passed. Nearly all coins are superb gems.

	Distribution	Cert	Avg	%MS	MS-67 / PF-67
1988-D	191,368	2,099	69.0	100%	$22
Auctions: $247, MS-70, September 2014					
1988-S, Proof	1,359,366	4,762	68.9		$25
Auctions: $135, PF-70DCam, September 2014; $141, PF-70DCam, April 2013					

SEOUL OLYMPIAD $5 GOLD COIN (1988)

Designer: *Elizabeth Jones (obverse), Marcel Jovine (reverse).* **Weight:** *8.359 grams.*
Composition: *.900 gold, .100 copper (net weight .242 oz. pure gold).*
Diameter: *21.6 mm.* **Edge:** *Reeded.* **Mint:** *West Point.*

Elizabeth Jones's five-dollar obverse design is considered by many to be the high point of commemorative coinage art of the late 20th century. Some observers suggested that, because the event was not held in the United States, the Seoul Olympics were not an appropriate subject for American coinage; regardless, the gold coin was praised to the skies.

Designs. *Obverse:* Nike, goddess of Victory, wearing a crown of olive leaves. *Reverse:* Stylized Olympic flame.

Mintage Data. Authorized by Public Law 100-141, signed by President Ronald Reagan on October 28, 1987. *Maximum authorized*—1,000,000. *Number minted*—62,913 Uncirculated and 281,465 Proof.

Original Cost. Sale prices $200 (Uncirculated, pre-issue) and $205 (Proof, pre-issue); Uncirculated later raised to $225, and Proof later raised to $235. The surcharge of $35 per coin went to the U.S. Olympic Committee.

Key to Collecting. Examples are readily available today.

	Distribution	Cert	Avg	%MS	MS-67
					PF-67
1988-W	62,913	2,366	69.5	100%	$375
	Auctions: $306, MS-69, August 2014; $423, MS-69, March 2013				
1988-W, Proof	281,465	9,653	69.4		$325
	Auctions: $447, PF-70UCam, March 2015; $376, PF-70UCam, March 2015; $353, PF-70UCam, October 2015; $317, PF-70UCam, April 2015				

Congress Bicentennial Half Dollar (1989)

Designer: *Patricia Lewis Verani (obverse), William Woodward (reverse).*
Weight: *11.34 grams.* **Composition:** *.9167 copper, .0833 nickel.* **Diameter:** *30.61 mm.*
Edge: *Reeded.* **Mints:** *Denver (Uncirculated) and San Francisco (Proof).*

The 200th anniversary of the operation of Congress under the U.S. Constitution was observed in 1989, and a suite of commemorative coins was authorized to observe the bicentennial, among them this copper-nickel half dollar.

Designs. *Obverse:* The head of the *Freedom* statue (erected on top of the Capitol dome in 1863) is shown at the center, with inscriptions around, including LIBERTY in oversize letters at the bottom border. *Reverse:* A distant front view of the Capital is shown, with arcs of stars above and below, with appropriate lettering.

Mintage Data. Authorized by Public Law 100-673, signed by President Ronald Reagan on November 17, 1988. The coins were to be dated 1989 and could be minted through June 30, 1990. *Maximum authorized*—4,000,000. *Number minted*—1989-D: 163,753 Uncirculated; 1989-S: 767,897 Proof.

Original Cost. Sale prices $5 (Uncirculated, pre-issue) and $7 (Proof, pre-issue); Uncirculated later raised to $6, and Proof later raised to $8. The surcharge of $1 per coin went to the Capitol Preservation Fund.

Key to Collecting. Not popular with numismatists in 1989, these coins still languish in the marketplace. Exceptions are coins certified in ultra-high grades. The Uncirculated 1989-D half dollar exists with a misaligned reverse, oriented in the same direction as the obverse, instead of the usual 180 degree separation. These are rare and valuable, but are not widely known. Likely, some remain undiscovered in buyers' hands.

	Distribution	Cert	Avg	%MS	MS-67
					PF-67
1989-D	163,753	1,154	69.0	100%	$8
	Auctions: $4,113, MS-70, April 2013				
1989-S, Proof	767,897	2,737	69.0		$8
	Auctions: $382, PF-70, September 2014				

CONGRESS BICENTENNIAL SILVER DOLLAR (1989)

Designer: *William Woodward.* **Weight:** *26.73 grams.*
Composition: *.900 silver, .100 copper (net weight .7736 oz. pure silver).*
Diameter: *38.1 mm.* **Edge:** *Reeded.* **Mints:** *Denver (Uncirculated) and San Francisco (Proof).*

To inaugurate the Congress Bicentennial coins, four coining presses weighing seven tons each were brought from the Philadelphia Mint to the east front of the Capitol building, where in a special ceremony on June 14, 1989, the first silver dollars and five-dollar gold coins were struck (but no half dollars).

Designs. *Obverse:* The statue of *Freedom* full length, with a cloud and rays of glory behind. Lettering around the border. *Reverse:* The mace of the House of Representatives, which is in the House Chamber when that body is in session.

Mintage Data. Authorized by Public Law 100-673, signed by President Ronald Reagan on November 17, 1988. The coins were to be dated 1989 and could be minted through June 30, 1990. *Maximum authorized—3,000,000. Number minted—1989-D:* 135,203 Uncirculated; 1989-S: 762,198 Proof.

Original Cost. Sale prices $23 (Uncirculated, pre-issue) and $25 (Proof, pre-issue): Uncirculated later raised to $26, and Proof later raised to $29. Surcharge of $7 per coin went to the Capitol Preservation Fund.

Key to Collecting. Not popular with numismatists in 1989, these coins today can be found for prices close to bullion value. Exceptions are coins certified in ultra-high grades.

	Distribution	Cert	Avg	%MS	MS-67 / PF-67
1989-D	135,203	2,465	69.0	100%	$25
	Auctions: $646, MS-70, September 2014; $940, MS-70, April 2013				
1989-S, Proof	762,198	3,756	68.9		$27
	Auctions: $457, PF-70DCam, May 2013; $42, PF-69DCam, July 2014; $106, PF-69DCam, November 2014; $940, PF-70, March 2013				

CONGRESS BICENTENNIAL $5 GOLD COIN (1989)

Designer: *John Mercanti.* **Weight:** *8.359 grams.* **Composition:** *.900 gold, .100 copper (net weight .242 oz. pure gold).* **Diameter:** *21.6 mm.* **Edge:** *Reeded.* **Mint:** *West Point.*

To diversify the motifs of the three Congress Bicentennial commemorative coins, 11 artists from the private sector were invited to submit designs, as were members of the Mint's Engraving Department staff. The designs for this five-dollar gold coin were praised in the *Annual Report of the Director of the Mint*, 1989, which stated that the obverse displayed "a spectacular rendition of the Capitol dome," while the reverse "center[ed] around a dramatic portrait of the majestic eagle atop the canopy overlooking the Old Senate Chamber."

Designs. *Obverse:* The dome of the Capitol is shown, with lettering around. *Reverse:* The eagle in the old Senate chamber is depicted, with lettering surrounding.

Mintage Data. Authorized by Public Law 100-673, signed by President Ronald Reagan on November 17, 1988. The coins were to be dated 1989 and could be minted through June 30, 1990. *Maximum authorized*—1,000,000. *Number minted*—46,899 Uncirculated and 164,690 Proof.

Original Cost. Sale prices $185 (Uncirculated, pre-issue) and $195 (Proof, pre-issue); Uncirculated later raised to $200, and Proof later raised to $215. Surcharge of $35 per coin went to the Capitol Preservation Fund.

Key to Collecting. Not popular with numismatists in 1989, these coins today can be purchased in the secondary marketplace for prices close to their bullion value. Exceptions are coins certified in ultra-high grades.

	Distribution	Cert	Avg	%MS	MS-67 PF-67
1989-W	46,899	2,249	69.5	100%	$325
Auctions: $646, MS-70, September 2014; $376, MS-70, May 2015; $400, MS-69, April 2013					
1989-W, Proof	164,690	5,521	69.4		$325
Auctions: $341, PF-70UCam, October 2015; $341, PF-70, July 2015; $323, PF-70DCam, April 2015; $306, PF-70DCam, January 2015					

EISENHOWER CENTENNIAL SILVER DOLLAR (1990)

Designer: *John Mercanti (obverse), Marcel Jovine (reverse).* **Weight:** *26.73 grams.*
Composition: *.900 silver, .100 copper (net weight .7736 oz. pure silver).* **Diameter:** *38.1 mm.*
Edge: *Reeded.* **Mints:** *West Point (Uncirculated) and Philadelphia (Proof).*

Five outside artists as well as the artists on the Mint Engraving Department staff were invited to submit designs for this silver dollar. In August 1989, secretary of the Treasury Nicholas F. Brady made the final selections.

This is the only U.S. coin to feature two portraits of the same person on the same side. The reverse shows Eisenhower's retirement residence, identified as EISENHOWER HOME.

Designs. *Obverse:* Profile of President Eisenhower facing right, superimposed over his own left-facing profile as a five-star general. *Reverse:* Eisenhower retirement home at Gettysburg, a national historic site.

Mintage Data. Authorized by Public Law 100-467, signed by President Ronald Reagan on October 3, 1988. *Maximum authorized*—4,000,000. *Number minted*—1990-W: 241,669 Uncirculated; 1990-P: 1,144,461 Proof.

Original Cost. Sale prices $23 (Uncirculated, pre-issue) and $25 (Proof, pre-issue; Uncirculated later raised to $26, and Proof later raised to $29. Surcharge of $7 per coin went to reduce public debt.

Key to Collecting. Eisenhower Centennial dollars are appreciated as a fine addition to the commemorative series. Examples are plentiful and inexpensive in the marketplace. Nearly all are superb gems.

	Distribution	Cert	Avg	%MS	MS-67 PF-67
1990-W	241,669	2,174	69.1	100%	$27
Auctions: $206, MS-70, March 2013					
1990-P, Proof	1,144,461	4,180	69.0		$25
Auctions: $135, PF-70DCam, September 2014; $201, PF-70DCam, March 2013; $42, PF-69DCam, July 2014; $165, PF-68DCam, March 2015					

KOREAN WAR MEMORIAL SILVER DOLLAR (1991)

Designer: *John Mercanti (obverse), James Ferrell (reverse).* **Weight:** *26.73 grams.*
Composition: *.900 silver, .100 copper (net weight .7736 oz. pure silver).*
Diameter: *38.1 mm.* **Edge:** *Reeded.* **Mints:** *Denver (Uncirculated) and Philadelphia (Proof).*

In the annals of commemoratives, one of the more curious entries is the 1991 silver dollar observing the 38th anniversary of the end of the Korean War, struck to honor those who served there. The 38th anniversary was chosen—rather than the 50th or some other typical anniversary—because, during that war, the 38th degree of latitude on the map defined the division between North and South Korea.

Buyers reacted favorably to the coin, and more than 800,000 were produced.

Designs. *Obverse:* Two F-86 Sabrejet fighter aircraft flying to the right, a helmeted soldier carrying a backpack climbing a hill, and the inscriptions: THIRTY EIGHTH / ANNIVERSARY / COMMEMORATIVE / KOREA / IN GOD WE TRUST / 1953 / 1991. At the bottom of the coin are five Navy ships above the word LIBERTY. *Reverse:* Outline map of North and South Korea, divided. An eagle's head (representing the United States) is depicted to the right. Near the bottom is the symbol of Korea.

Mintage Data. Authorized by Public Law 101-495 of October 31, 1990. *Maximum authorized*—1,000,000. *Number minted*—1991-D: 213,049 Uncirculated; 1991-P: 618,488 Proof.

Original Cost. Sale prices $23 (Uncirculated, pre-issue) and $28 (Proof, pre-issue); Uncirculated later raised to $26, and Proof later raised to $31. A surcharge of $7 went to fund the Korean War Veterans Memorial.

Key to Collecting. Gem Uncirculated and Proof coins are readily available in the marketplace.

	Distribution	Cert	Avg	%MS	MS-67 PF-67
1991-D	213,049	2,346	69.1	100%	$25
	Auctions: $76, MS-70, July 2014; $106, MS-70, January 2013; $69, MS-70, May 2015				
1991-P, Proof	618,488	3,023	68.9		$23
	Auctions: $382, PF-70DCam, September 2014; $505, PF-70DCam, March 2013				

MOUNT RUSHMORE GOLDEN ANNIVERSARY HALF DOLLAR (1991)

Designer: *Marcel Jovine (obverse), T. James Ferrell (reverse).* **Weight:** *11.34 grams.*
Composition: *.9167 copper, .0833 nickel.* **Diameter:** *30.61 mm.* **Edge:** *Reeded.*
Mints: *Denver (Uncirculated) and San Francisco (Proof).*

This half dollar was part of a trio of coins struck to mark the Mount Rushmore National Memorial's 50th anniversary. Surcharges from their sale were divided between the Treasury Department and the Mount Rushmore National Memorial Society of Black Hills, North Dakota, with money going toward restoration work on the landmark.

Designs. *Obverse:* View of Mount Rushmore with rays of the sun behind. *Reverse:* An American bison with the words GOLDEN ANNIVERSARY.

Mintage Data. Authorized by the Mount Rushmore National Memorial Coin Act (Public Law 101-332, July 16, 1990). *Maximum authorized*—2,500,000. *Number minted*—1991-D: 172,754 Uncirculated; 1991-S: 753,257 Proof.

Original Cost. Sale prices $6 (Uncirculated) and $8.50 (Proof); Uncirculated later raised to $7, and Proof later raised to $9.50. Fifty percent of the surcharge of $1 per coin went to the Mount Rushmore National Memorial Society of Black Hills; the balance went to the U.S. Treasury.

Key to Collecting. Examples are easily available today. The coins were carefully struck, with the result that nearly all are superb gems.

	Distribution	Cert	Avg	%MS	MS-67
					PF-67
1991-D	172,754	1,708	69.1	100%	$13
	Auctions: $306, MS-70, September 2014; $823, MS-70, March 2013				
1991-S, Proof	753,257	3,190	69.1		$10
	Auctions: No auction records available.				

MOUNT RUSHMORE GOLDEN ANNIVERSARY SILVER DOLLAR (1991)

Designer: *Marika Somogyi (obverse), Frank Gasparro (reverse).* **Weight:** *26.73 grams.*
Composition: *.900 silver, .100 copper (net weight .7736 oz. pure silver).* **Diameter:** *38.1 mm.*
Edge: *Reeded.* **Mints:** *Philadelphia (Uncirculated) and San Francisco (Proof).*

The Mount Rushmore silver dollar displays the traditional portraits of presidents George Washington, Thomas Jefferson, Theodore Roosevelt, and Abraham Lincoln as sculpted on the mountain by Gutzon Borglum. The reverse was by former chief sculptor-engraver of the U.S. Mint Frank Gasparro.

Designs. *Obverse:* View of Mount Rushmore with an olive wreath prominently below. *Reverse:* The Great Seal of the United States, surrounded by a sunburst, above an outline map of the continental part of the United States inscribed SHRINE OF / DEMOCRACY.

Mintage Data. Authorized by the Mount Rushmore National Memorial Coin Act (Public Law 101-332, July 16, 1990). *Maximum authorized*—2,500,000. *Number minted*—1991-P: 133,139 Uncirculated; 1991-S: 738,419 Proof.

Original Cost. Sale prices $23 (Uncirculated, pre-issue) and $28 (Proof, pre-issue); Uncirculated later raised to $28, and Proof later raised to $31. Fifty percent of the surcharge of $7 per coin went to the Mount Rushmore National Memorial Society of Black Hills; the balance went to the U.S. Treasury.

Key to Collecting. Examples are easily available today. The coins were carefully struck, with the result that nearly all are superb gems.

	Distribution	Cert	Avg	%MS	MS-67
					PF-67
1991-P	133,139	1,849	69.3	100%	$30
	Auctions: $80, MS-70, July 2014; $92, MS-70, January 2013				
1991-S, Proof	738,419	3,793	69.0		$25
	Auctions: $194, PF-70DCam, September 2014; $176, PF-70DCam, June 2013; $174, PF-70DCam, February 2013; $53, PF-69DCam, July 2014				

Mount Rushmore Golden Anniversary $5 Gold Coin (1991)

Designer: *John Mercanti (obverse), William Lamb (reverse).* **Weight:** *8.359 grams.*
Composition: *.900 gold, .100 copper (net weight .242 oz. pure gold).*
Diameter: *21.6 mm.* **Edge:** *Reeded.* **Mint:** *West Point.*

The reverse of the five-dollar Mount Rushmore coin consisted solely of lettering, with no emblems or motifs, the first such instance in the history of U.S. commemorative coins.

Designs. *Obverse:* An American eagle flying above the monument with LIBERTY and date in the field. *Reverse:* MOUNT RUSHMORE NATIONAL MEMORIAL in script type.

Mintage Data. Authorized by the Mount Rushmore National Memorial Coin Act (Public Law 101-332, July 16, 1990). *Maximum authorized*—500,000. *Number minted*—31,959 Uncirculated and 111,991 Proof.

Original Cost. Sale prices $185 (Uncirculated, pre-issue) and $195 (Proof, pre-issue); Uncirculated later raised to $210, and Proof later raised to $225. Fifty percent of the surcharge of $35 per coin went to the Mount Rushmore National Memorial Society of Black Hills; the balance went to the U.S. Treasury.

Key to Collecting. Examples are easily available today. The coins were carefully struck, with the result that nearly all are superb gems.

	Distribution	Cert	Avg	%MS	MS-67 PF-67
1991-W	31,959	1,623	69.6	100%	$325
	Auctions: $653, MS-70, September 2014; $573, MS-70, November 2014; $353, MS-70, May 2015; $353, MS-70, April 2015				
1991-W, Proof	111,991	4,098	69.4		$325
	Auctions: $456, PF-70DCam, February 2013; $423, PF-70DCam, May 2015; $306, PF-69DCam, October 2014				

United Service Organizations Silver Dollar (1991)

Designer: *Robert Lamb (obverse), John Mercanti (reverse).* **Weight:** *26.73 grams.*
Composition: *.900 silver, .100 copper (net weight .7736 oz. pure silver).*
Diameter: *38.1 mm.* **Edge:** *Reeded.* **Mints:** *Denver (Uncirculated) and San Francisco (Proof).*

The United Service Organizations is a congressionally chartered nonprofit group that provides services, programs, and live entertainment to U.S. military troops and their families. The 50th anniversary of the USO was commemorated with this silver dollar in 1991.

Designs. *Obverse:* Consists entirely of lettering, except for a banner upon which appears USO. Inscriptions include IN GOD WE TRUST, 50th ANNIVERSARY (in script), USO (on a banner, as noted; with three stars to each side), and LIBERTY 1991. *Reverse:* Illustrates an eagle, facing right, with a ribbon inscribed USO in its beak, perched atop a world globe. An arc of 11 stars is in the space below the globe. The legends include FIFTY YEARS / SERVICE (on the left side of the coin), TO SERVICE / PEOPLE (on the right side of the coin).

Mintage Data. Authorized by Public Law 101-404, October 2, 1990. *Maximum authorized*—1,000,000. *Number minted*—1991-D: 124,958 Uncirculated; 1991-S: 321,275 Proof.

Original Cost. Sale prices $23 (Uncirculated, pre-issue) and $28 (Proof, pre-issue); Uncirculated later raised to $26, and Proof later raised to $31. Fifty percent of the surcharge of $7 per coin went to the USO; the balance went toward reducing the national debt.

Key to Collecting. Mintages were low compared to other recent commemorative silver dollars. Today these coins can be purchased for slightly more than their bullion value.

	Distribution	Cert	Avg	%MS	MS-67
					PF-67
1991-D	124,958	2,106	69.1	100%	$25
Auctions: $92, MS-70, March 2013; $86, MS-70, July 2014; $66, MS-70, May 2015					
1991-S, Proof	321,275	2,293	69.0		$23
Auctions: $881, PF-70DCam, September 2014; $235, PF-70DCam, September 2014; $382, PF-70DCam, April 2013					

CHRISTOPHER COLUMBUS QUINCENTENARY HALF DOLLAR (1992)

Designer: *T. James Ferrell.* **Weight:** *11.34 grams.* **Composition:** *.9167 copper, .0833 nickel.* **Diameter:** *30.61 mm.* **Edge:** *Reeded.* **Mints:** *Denver (Uncirculated) and San Francisco (Proof).*

The 500th anniversary of Christopher Columbus's first trip to the new world was observed in 1992 by a suite of commemoratives, including this clad half dollar. The numismatic tradition fit in nicely with the World's Columbian Exposition coins of a century earlier—the first commemorative half dollars issued in 1892 and 1893.

Designs. *Obverse:* A full-length figure of Columbus walking ashore, with a rowboat and the flagship *Santa Maria* in the background. *Reverse:* The reverse shows Columbus's three ships—the *Nina*, *Pinta*, and *Santa Maria*.

Mintage Data. Authorized by Public Law 102-281, signed by President George H.W. Bush on May 13, 1992. *Maximum authorized*—6,000,000. *Number minted*—1992-D: 135,702 Uncirculated; 1992-S: 390,154 Proof.

Original Cost. Sale prices $6.50 (Uncirculated, pre-issue) and $8.50 (Proof, pre-issue); Uncirculated later raised to $7.50, and Proof later raised to $9.50. A surcharge of $1 per coin went to the Christopher Columbus Quincentenary Coins and Fellowship Foundation.

Key to Collecting. Examples in the marketplace remain reasonably priced. Nearly all are superb gems.

	Distribution	Cert	Avg	%MS	MS-67
					PF-67
1992-D	135,702	956	69.2	100%	$12
Auctions: $86, MS-70, April 2013					
1992-S, Proof	390,154	2,569	69.1		$12
Auctions: No auction records available.					

CHRISTOPHER COLUMBUS QUINCENTENARY SILVER DOLLAR (1992)

Designer: *John Mercanti (obverse), Thomas D. Rogers Sr. (reverse).* **Weight:** *26.73 grams.*
Composition: *.900 silver, .100 copper (net weight .7736 oz. pure silver).*
Diameter: *38.1 mm.* **Edge:** *Reeded.* **Mints:** *Denver (Uncirculated) and Philadelphia (Proof).*

Representative Frank Annunzio, a Democrat from Illinois who was prominent in coin legislation for some time, introduced the bill that led to these commemoratives. Interestingly, on the approved sketch for this silver dollar's obverse design, Columbus was depicted holding a telescope—but after it was pointed out that such instrument had not been invented yet in 1492, it was changed to a scroll on the final coin.

Designs. *Obverse:* Columbus standing, holding a flag in his right hand, with a scroll in his left hand, and with a globe on a stand. Three ships are shown in the distance, in a panel at the top border. *Reverse:* A split image is shown, depicting exploration in 1492 at the left, with half of a sailing vessel, and in 1992 at the right, with most of a space shuttle shown in a vertical position, with the earth in the distance.

Mintage Data. Authorized by Public Law 102-281, signed by President George H.W. Bush on May 13, 1992. *Maximum authorized—4,000,000. Number minted—1992-D:* 106,949 Uncirculated; 1992-P: 385,241 Proof.

Original Cost. Sale prices $23 (Uncirculated, pre-issue) and $27 (Proof, pre-issue); Uncirculated later raised to $28, and Proof later raised to $31. A surcharge of $7 per coin went to the Christopher Columbus Quincentenary Coins and Fellowship Foundation.

Key to Collecting. Examples in the marketplace remain reasonably priced. Nearly all are superb gems.

	Distribution	Cert	Avg	%MS	MS-67
					PF-67
1992-D	106,949	1,761	69.2	100%	$30
	Auctions: $135, MS-70, March 2013; $86, MS-70, July 2014; $62, MS-70, September 2015				
1992-P, Proof	385,241	2,722	69.0		$25
	Auctions: $441, PF-70DCam, September 2014; $418, PF-70DCam, June 2013; $96, PF-70DCam, April 2013				

CHRISTOPHER COLUMBUS QUINCENTENARY $5 GOLD COIN (1992)

Designer: *T. James Ferrell (obverse), Thomas D. Rogers Sr. (reverse).* **Weight:** *8.359 grams.*
Composition: *.900 gold, .100 copper (net weight .242 oz. pure gold).*
Diameter: *21.6 mm.* **Edge:** *Reeded.* **Mint:** *West Point.*

No portrait from the life of Christopher Columbus is known to exist, so the five-dollar gold commemorative features T. James Ferrell's artistic imagining of the explorer's profile.

Designs. *Obverse:* The artist's conception of Columbus's face is shown gazing to the left toward an outline map of the New World. *Reverse:* The crest of the Admiral of the Ocean Sea and a chart dated 1492 are depicted.

Mintage Data. Authorized by Public Law 102-281, signed by President George H.W. Bush on May 13, 1992. *Maximum authorized*—1,000,000. *Number minted*—24,329 Uncirculated and 79,730 Proof.

Original Cost. Sale prices $180 (Uncirculated, pre-issue) and $190 (Proof, pre-issue); Uncirculated later raised to $210, and Proof later raised to $225. A surcharge of $35 per coin went to the Christopher Columbus Quincentenary Coins and Fellowship Foundation.

Key to Collecting. Examples in the marketplace remain reasonably priced. Nearly all are superb gems.

	Distribution	Cert	Avg	%MS	MS-67 PF-67
1992-W	24,329	1,330	69.6	100%	$325
	Auctions: $447, MS-70, June 2014; $646, MS-70, September 2014; $317, MS-69, August 2014; $306, MS-69, August 2014				
1992-W, Proof	79,730	2,837	69.5		$325
	Auctions: $353, PF-70DCam, May 2015; $329, PF-70DCam, May 2015; $435, PF-69DCam, April 2013; $306, PF-69DCam, August 2014				

XXV OLYMPIC GAMES HALF DOLLAR (1992)

Designer: *William Cousins (obverse), Steven M. Bieda (reverse).*
Weight: *11.34 grams.* **Composition:** *.9167 copper, .0833 nickel.* **Diameter:** *30.61 mm.*
Edge: *Reeded.* **Mints:** *Philadelphia (Uncirculated) and San Francisco (Proof).*

In 1992 the XXV Winter Olympic Games were held in Albertville and Savoie, France, while the Summer Games took place in Barcelona, Spain. Although the events did not take place in the United States, the rationale for a commemorative coin issue was, in part, to raise money to train American athletes. The same line of reasoning had been used for the coins made in connection with the 1988 Olympic Games held in Seoul, South Korea.

Designs. *Obverse:* A pony-tailed female gymnast doing the stretch against a background of stars and stripes. *Reverse:* The Olympic torch and an olive branch, with CITIUS / ALTIUS / FORTIUS nearby in three lines, Latin for "faster, higher, stronger."

Mintage Data. Authorized by the 1992 Olympic Commemorative Coin Act, Public Law 101-406, signed by President George H.W. Bush on October 3, 1990. *Maximum authorized*—6,000,000. *Number minted*—1992-P: 161,607 Uncirculated; 1992-S: 519,645 Proof.

Original Cost. Sale prices $6 (Uncirculated, pre-issue) and $8.50 (Proof, pre-issue); Uncirculated later raised to $7.50, and Proof later raised to $9.50. The surcharge of $1 per coin went to the U.S. Olympic Committee.

Key to Collecting. Examples are easily available today. Nearly all are gems.

	Distribution	Cert	Avg	%MS	MS-67 PF-67
1992-P	161,607	1,111	69.3	100%	$8
	Auctions: $59, MS-70, January 2013				
1992-S, Proof	519,645	2,547	69.2		$7
	Auctions: No auction records available.				

XXV Olympic Games Silver Dollar (1992)

Designer: *John R. Deecken (obverse), Marcel Jovine (reverse).* **Weight:** *26.73 grams.*
Composition: *.900 silver, .100 copper (net weight .7736 oz. pure silver).* **Diameter:** *38.1 mm.*
Edge: *Lettered (Uncirculated), reeded (Proof).* **Mints:** *Denver (Uncirculated) and San Francisco (Proof).*

The image on this coin's obverse fit closely that of Fleer's card showing popular baseball player Nolan Ryan, of the Texas Rangers, but the designer denied there was any connection when queried on the subject by the Treasury Department. The Denver Mint Uncirculated dollars have XXV OLYMPIAD incuse four times around the edge, alternately inverted, on a reeded background; these are the first lettered-edge U.S. coins since the 1933 double eagle.

Designs. *Obverse:* A pitcher is shown about to throw a ball to a batter. *Reverse:* A shield, intertwined Olympic rings, and olive branches make up the main design.

Mintage Data. Authorized by the 1992 Olympic Commemorative Coin Act, Public Law 101-406, signed by President George H.W. Bush on October 3, 1990. *Maximum authorized—4,000,000. Number minted—1992-D:* 187,552 Uncirculated; *1992-S:* 504,505 Proof.

Original Cost. Sale prices $24 (Uncirculated, pre-issue) and $28 (Proof, pre-issue); Uncirculated later raised to $28, and Proof later raised to $32. The surcharge of $1 per coin went to the U.S. Olympic Committee.

Key to Collecting. Examples are easily available today. Nearly all are gems.

	Distribution	Cert	Avg	%MS	MS-67 PF-67
1992-D ††	187,552	3,696	69.0	100%	$25
	Auctions: $247, MS-70, April 2013				
1992-S, Proof	504,505	2,927	69.0		$23
	Auctions: $588, PF-70DCam, September 2013; $84, PF-70, February 2013; $30, PF-69UCam, January 2015				

†† Ranked in the *100 Greatest U.S. Modern Coins* (fourth edition).

XXV Olympic Games $5 Gold Coin (1992)

Designer: *James Sharpe (obverse), James Peed (reverse).* **Weight:** *8.359 grams.*
Composition: *.900 gold, .100 copper (net weight .242 oz. pure gold).*
Diameter: *21.6 mm.* **Edge:** *Reeded.* **Mint:** *West Point.*

The five-dollar entry in the XXV commemorative coin program features a dynamic sprinter against a backdrop of the U.S. flag. Sales were relatively low compared to other recent gold commemoratives.

Designs. *Obverse:* A sprinter running forward with a vertical U.S. flag in the background. *Reverse:* A heraldic eagle with five Olympic rings and USA above.

Mintage Data. Authorized by the 1992 Olympic Commemorative Coin Act, Public Law 101-406, signed by President George H.W. Bush on October 3, 1990. *Maximum authorized*—500,000. *Number minted*—27,732 Uncirculated and 77,313 Proof.

Original Cost. Sale prices $185 (Uncirculated, pre-issue) and $195 (Proof, pre-issue); Uncirculated later raised to $215, and Proof later raised to $230. The surcharge of $35 per coin went to the U.S. Olympic Committee.

Key to Collecting. Examples are easily available today. Nearly all are gems.

	Distribution	Cert	Avg	%MS	MS-67
					PF-67
1992-W	27,732	1,569	69.7	100%	$325
	Auctions: $376, MS-70, May 2015; $364, MS-70, May 2015; $350, MS-70, April 2015; $329, MS-70, June 2015				
1992-W, Proof	77,313	3,117	69.5		$325
	Auctions: $423, PF-70UCam, March 2015; $364, PF-70UCam, April 2015; $358, PF-70UCam, March 2015; $333, PF-70UCam, May 2015				

WHITE HOUSE 200TH ANNIVERSARY SILVER DOLLAR (1992)

Designer: *Edgar Z. Steever IV (obverse), Chester Y. Martin (reverse).* **Weight:** *26.73 grams.*
Composition: *.900 silver, .100 copper (net weight .7736 oz. pure silver).*
Diameter: *38.1 mm.* **Edge:** *Reeded.* **Mints:** *Denver (Uncirculated) and West Point (Proof).*

This coin is one of few depicting Washington buildings that sold out its full authorized limit. Foliage, two trees, and a fountain were in the original sketch, but were removed at the suggestion of the Fine Arts Commission, yielding a clean and crisp design.

Designs. *Obverse:* The north portico of the White House is shown in a plan view, without shrubbery or background. *Reverse:* James Hoban, architect of the first White House, in a half-length portrait with the original entrance door.

Mintage Data. Authorized by Public Law 102-281, signed by President George H.W. Bush on May 13, 1992. *Maximum authorized*—500,000. *Number minted*—1992-D: 123,803 Uncirculated; 1992-W: 375,851 Proof.

Original Cost. Sale prices (pre-issue only) $23 (Uncirculated) and $28 (Proof). The surcharge of $10 per coin went towards the preservation of public rooms within the White House.

Key to Collecting. The White House dollar has remained popular ever since its issuance. Examples are readily available today and are nearly always found in superb gem preservation, as issued.

	Distribution	Cert	Avg	%MS	MS-67
					PF-67
1992-D	123,803	2,030	69.2	100%	$25
	Auctions: $108, MS-70, January 2013				
1992-W, Proof	375,851	2,904	69.0		$23
	Auctions: $194, PF-70DCam, April 2013				

BILL OF RIGHTS HALF DOLLAR (1993)

Designer: *T. James Ferrell (obverse), Dean McMullen (reverse).* **Weight:** *12.5 grams.*
Composition: *.900 silver, .100 copper.* **Diameter:** *30.6 mm.* **Edge:** *Reeded.*
Mints: *West Point (Uncirculated) and San Francisco (Proof).*

This silver half dollar, as well as the silver dollar and five-dollar gold coin issued alongside it, honored James Madison and the Bill of Rights, added to the Constitution in 1789 and intended to give basic rights and freedoms to all Americans. These were the first half dollars to be composed of 90% silver since the George Washington 250th Anniversary of Birth coins in 1982.

Designs. *Obverse:* James Madison seated at a desk, penning the Bill of Rights. Montpelier, Madison's Virginia home, is shown in the distance. *Reverse:* A hand holds a flaming torch, with inscriptions to each side.

Mintage Data. Authorized by Public Law 101-281, part of the White House Commemorative Coin Act, on May 13, 1992. *Maximum authorized*—1,000,000. *Number minted*—1993-W: 193,346 Uncirculated; 1993-S: 586,315 Proof.

Original Cost. Sale prices $9.75 (Uncirculated, pre-issue) and $12.50 (Proof, pre-issue); Uncirculated later increased in $11.50, and Proof later increased to $13.50. The surcharge went to the James Madison Memorial Scholarship Trust Fund.

Key to Collecting. Following the pattern of other commemoratives of the early 1990s, these coins are readily available on the market, typically in superb gem preservation.

	Distribution	Cert	Avg	%MS	MS-67 PF-67
1993-W	193,346	1,186	69.2	100%	$20
	Auctions: $82, MS-70, April 2013				
1993-S, Proof	586,315	2,761	69.0		$15
	Auctions: $441, PF-70DCam, April 2013; $382, PF-70DCam, April 2013				

BILL OF RIGHTS SILVER DOLLAR (1993)

Designer: *William Krawczewicz (obverse), Dean McMullen (reverse).* **Weight:** *26.73 grams.*
Composition: *.900 silver, .100 copper (net weight .7736 oz. pure silver).*
Diameter: *38.1 mm.* **Edge:** *Reeded.* **Mints:** *Denver (Uncirculated) and San Francisco (Proof).*

On June 1, 1992, U.S. Treasurer Catalina Vasquez Villalpando announced a nationwide competition seeking designs for the James Madison / Bill of Rights Commemorative Coin Program, with all entries to be received by August 31. Secretary of the Treasury Nicholas F. Brady selected his favorite motifs from 815 submissions, which were then sent to the Commission of Fine Arts for review. Many changes were suggested, including simplifying the appearance of Madison's residence, Montpelier.

Designs. *Obverse:* Portrait of James Madison facing right and slightly forward. *Reverse:* Montpelier.

Mintage Data. Authorized by Public Law 101-281, part of the White House Commemorative Coin Act, on May 13, 1992. *Maximum authorized*—900,000. *Number minted*—1993-D: 98,383 Uncirculated; 1993-S: 534,001 Proof.

Original Cost. Sale prices $22 (Uncirculated, pre-issue) and $25 (Proof, pre-issue); Uncirculated later raised to $27, and Proof later raised to $29. The surcharge went to the James Madison Memorial Scholarship Trust Fund.

Key to Collecting. Following the pattern of other commemoratives of the early 1990s, these coins are readily available on the market, typically in superb gem preservation.

	Distribution	Cert	Avg	%MS	MS-67
					PF-67
1993-D	98,383	1,411	69.1	100%	$35
Auctions: $182, MS-70, January 2013					
1993-S, Proof	534,001	2,421	68.9		$30
Auctions: No auction records available.					

BILL OF RIGHTS $5 GOLD COIN (1993)

Designer: *Scott R. Blazek (obverse), Joseph D. Peña (reverse).* **Weight:** *8.359 grams.* **Composition:** *.900 gold, .100 copper (net weight .242 oz. pure gold).* **Diameter:** *21.6 mm.* **Edge:** *Reeded.* **Mint:** *West Point.*

The coin project that resulted in this five-dollar gold coin (and the related half dollar and silver dollar) was encouraged by the Madison Foundation.

Designs. *Obverse:* Portrait of Madison, waist up, reading the Bill of Rights. *Reverse:* Quotation by Madison with an eagle above and small torch and laurel branch at the border below.

Mintage Data. Authorized by Public Law 101-281, part of the White House Commemorative Coin Act, on May 13, 1992. *Maximum authorized*—300,000. *Number minted*—23,266 Uncirculated and 78,651 Proof.

Original Cost. Sale prices $175 (Uncirculated, pre-issue) and $185 (Proof, pre-issue); Uncirculated later raised to $205, and Proof later raised to $220. The surcharge of $10 per coin went to the James Madison Memorial Scholarship Trust Fund.

Key to Collecting. Following the pattern of other commemoratives of the early 1990s, these coins are readily available on the market, typically in superb gem preservation.

	Distribution	Cert	Avg	%MS	MS-67
					PF-67
1993-W	23,266	1,344	69.6	100%	$325
Auctions: $329, MS-70, August 2014; $652, MS-70, September 2014; $400, MS-69, March 2013					
1993-W, Proof	78,651	3,272	69.4		$325
Auctions: $306, PF-70DCam, November 2014; $435, PF-70DCam, March 2013; $317, PF-69DCam, August 2014; $329, PF-69DCam, October 2014					

50TH ANNIVERSARY OF WORLD WAR II HALF DOLLAR (1991–1995)

Designer: *George Klauba (obverse), Bill J. Leftwich (reverse).* **Weight:** *11.34 grams.*
Composition: *.9167 copper, .0833 nickel.* **Diameter:** *30.61 mm.* **Edge:** *Reeded.* **Mint:** *Philadelphia.*

These half dollars and the other World War II 50th-anniversary coins were issued in 1993 and dated 1991–1995. Despite the importance of the war commemorated, the coins met with a lukewarm response by purchasers.

Designs. *Obverse:* The heads of a soldier, sailor, and airman are shown superimposed on a V (for victory), with a B-17 bomber flying overhead. *Reverse:* An American Marine is shown in action during the takeover of a Japanese-held island in the South Pacific. A carrier-based fighter plane flies overhead.

Mintage Data. Authorized by Public Law 102-414, signed by President William J. Clinton on October 14, 1992. *Maximum authorized*—2,000,000. *Number minted*—197,072 Uncirculated and 317,396 Proof.

Original Cost. Sale prices $8 (Uncirculated, pre-issue) and $9 (Proof, pre-issue); Uncirculated later raised to $9, and Proof later raised to $10. The surcharge of $2 per coin was split between the American Battle Monuments Commission (to aid in the construction of the World War II Monument in the nation's capital) and the Battle of Normandy Foundation (to assist in the erection of a monument in France).

Key to Collecting. Examples are easily enough found in the marketplace today and are nearly always of superb gem quality.

	Distribution	Cert	Avg	%MS	MS-67
					PF-67
1991–1995 (1993-P)	197,072	1,232	69.1	100%	$15
	Auctions: $165, MS-70Cam, September 2014; $529, MS-70Cam, April 2013; $153, MS-70, June 2013				
1991–1995 (1993-P), Proof	317,396	2,090	69.0		$15
	Auctions: No auction records available.				

50TH ANNIVERSARY OF WORLD WAR II SILVER DOLLAR (1991–1995)

Designer: *Thomas D. Rogers Sr.* **Weight:** *26.73 grams.*
Composition: *.900 silver, .100 copper (net weight .7736 oz. pure silver).*
Diameter: *38.1 mm.* **Edge:** *Reeded.* **Mints:** *Denver (Uncirculated) and West Point (Proof).*

The designs for these silver dollars and the related half dollars and five-dollar gold coins were the result of a competition. The works of five artists were selected (only one of them, Thomas D. Rogers Sr., being from the Mint staff). It was mandated that the dollar use the Battle of Normandy as a theme.

Designs. *Obverse:* An American soldier is shown as he runs ashore on the beach in Normandy during the D-Day invasion on June 6, 1944, which launched from England to liberate France. *Reverse:* The reverse illustrates the shoulder patch used on a uniform of Dwight D. Eisenhower's Supreme Headquarters Allied Expeditionary Force, with a quotation from Eisenhower.

Mintage Data. Authorized by Public Law 102-414, signed by President William J. Clinton on October 14, 1992. *Maximum authorized*—1,000,000. *Number minted*—1993-D: 107,240 Uncirculated; 1993-W: 342,041 Proof.

Original Cost. Sale prices $23 (Uncirculated, pre-issue) and $27 (Proof, pre-issue); Uncirculated later raised to $28, and Proof later raised to $31. The surcharge of $2 per coin was split between the American Battle Monuments Commission (to aid in the construction of the World War II Monument in the nation's capital) and the Battle of Normandy Foundation (to assist in the erection of a monument in France).

Key to Collecting. Examples are easily enough found in the marketplace today and are nearly always of superb gem quality.

	Distribution	Cert	Avg	%MS	MS-67 / PF-67
1991–1995 (1993-D)	107,240	1,996	69.3	100%	$35
Auctions: $118, MS-70, January 2013; $86, MS-70, July 2014; $74, MS-70, August 2015; $74, MS-70, May 2015					
1991–1995 (1993-W), Proof	342,041	3,201	69.0		$35
Auctions: $206, PF-70DCam, September 2014					

50TH ANNIVERSARY OF WORLD WAR II $5 GOLD COIN (1991–1995)

Designer: *Charles J. Madsen (obverse), Edward Southworth Fisher (reverse).*
Weight: *8.359 grams.* **Composition:** *.900 gold, .100 copper (net weight .242 oz. pure gold).*
Diameter: *21.6 mm.* **Edge:** *Reeded.* **Mint:** *West Point.*

The approval of the American Legion, Veterans of Foreign Wars of the United States, American Veterans of World War, Korea and Vietnam (AMVETS), and the Disabled American Veterans, was required for the designs of all three 50th Anniversary of World War II commemoratives. The five-dollar coin was mandated to reflect the Allied victory in the war.

Designs. *Obverse:* An American soldier holds his rifle and raises his arm to indicate victory. *Reverse:* A large V (for victory) is at the center, with three dots and a dash over it, the Morse code for that letter. Branches are to each side.

Mintage Data. Authorized by Public Law 102-414, signed by President William J. Clinton on October 14, 1992. *Maximum authorized*—300,000. *Number minted*—23,672 Uncirculated and 67,026 Proof.

Original Cost. Sale prices $170 (Uncirculated, pre-issue) and $185 (Proof, pre-issue); Uncirculated later raised to $185, and Proof later raised to $220. The surcharge of $35 per coin was split between the American Battle Monuments Commission (to aid in the construction of the World War II Monument in the nation's capital) and the Battle of Normandy Foundation (to assist in the erection of a monument in France).

Key to Collecting. Examples are easily enough found in the marketplace today and are nearly always of superb gem quality.

	Distribution	Cert	Avg	%MS	MS-67 PF-67
1991–1995 (1993-W)	23,672	1,421	69.6	100%	$375
	Auctions: $646, MS-70, September 2014; $411, MS-70, April 2013; $353, MS-69, August 2014				
1991–1995 (1993-W), Proof	67,026	2,540	69.3		$375
	Auctions: $458, PF-70DCam, April 2013; $382, PF-70DCam, April 2013; $333, PF-69DCam, August 2014				

THOMAS JEFFERSON SILVER DOLLAR (1993)

Designer: *T. James Ferrell.* **Weight:** *26.73 grams.*
Composition: *.900 silver, .100 copper (net weight .7736 oz. pure silver).*
Diameter: *38.1 mm.* **Edge:** *Reeded.* **Mints:** *Philadelphia (Uncirculated) and San Francisco (Proof).*

The 250th anniversary in 1993 of the birth of Thomas Jefferson in 1743 furnished the occasion for a commemorative silver dollar. The obverse portrait was based on an 1805 painting by Gilbert Stuart.

Designs. *Obverse:* Profile bust of President Thomas Jefferson. *Reverse:* Monticello, Jefferson's home.

Mintage Data. Authorized under Public Law 103-186, signed by President William J. Clinton on December 14, 1993. *Maximum authorized*—600,000. *Number minted*—1993-P: 266,927 Uncirculated; 1993-S: 332,891 Proof.

Original Cost. Sale prices $27 (Uncirculated, pre-issue) and $31 (Proof, pre-issue); Uncirculated later raised to $32, and Proof later raised to $35. The surcharge of $10 per coin went to the Jefferson Endowment Fund.

Key to Collecting. Although the Jefferson dollar was a popular sellout in its time, examples are easily found in the numismatic marketplace and are nearly always of superb gem quality. Most in demand, from the enthusiasm of five-cent piece collectors, are the special sets issued with the frosty Uncirculated 1994-P Jefferson nickel.

	Distribution	Cert	Avg	%MS	MS-67 PF-67
1993-P	266,927	3,064	69.2	100%	$28
	Auctions: $86, MS-70, January 2013				
1993-S, Proof	332,891	2,637	69.0		$23
	Auctions: $400, PF-70DCam, March 2013				

U.S. Capitol Bicentennial Silver Dollar (1994)

Designer: *William Cousins (obverse), John Mercanti (reverse).* **Weight:** *26.73 grams.*
Composition: *.900 silver, .100 copper (net weight .7736 oz. pure silver).*
Diameter: *38.1 mm.* **Edge:** *Reeded.* **Mints:** *Denver (Uncirculated) and San Francisco (Proof).*

These silver dollars commemorated the 200th anniversary of the U.S. Capitol in Washington, D.C. Although the Federal City, as it was called, was laid out in the 1790s, it was not until 1800 that the federal government relocated there from Philadelphia. In honor of the recently deceased first president, the name was changed to Washington City, or, in popular use, Washington. The Capitol building design represented the work of several architects and artists, among them Benjamin Latrobe, Charles Bulfinch, and Constantino Brumidi.

Designs. *Obverse:* Dome of the Capitol with stars surrounding the *Freedom* statue. *Reverse:* Shield with four American flags, branches, and surmounted by an eagle, a motif based on the center area of a stained-glass window near the House and Senate grand staircases (produced by J. & G. Gibson, of Philadelphia, in 1859 and 1860).

Mintage Data. Authorized by Public Law 103-186, signed by President William J. Clinton on December 14, 1993. *Maximum authorized*—500,000. *Number minted*—1994-D: 68,332 Uncirculated; 1994-S: 279,579 Proof.

Original Cost. Sale prices $32 (Uncirculated, pre-issue) and $36 (Proof, pre-issue; Uncirculated later raised to $37, and Proof later raised to $40. The surcharge of $15 per coin went to the United States Capitol Preservation Commission. A Mint announcement noted that this was to go "for the construction of the Capitol Visitor Center" (itself the subject of a 2001 commemorative dollar).

Key to Collecting. Superb gem Mint State and Proof coins are easily available.

	Distribution	Cert	Avg	%MS	MS-67
					PF-67
1994-D	68,332	1,570	69.4	100%	$34
	Auctions: $101, MS-70, January 2013; $100, MS-70, August 2015; $80, MS-70, July 2014				
1994-S, Proof	279,579	1,850	69.0		$34
	Auctions: $294, PF-70DCam, April 2013; $270, PF-70DCam, September 2014; $217, PF-70DCam, August 2014				

U.S. Prisoner of War Memorial Silver Dollar (1994)

Designer: *Tom Nielsen (obverse), Edgar Z. Steever IV (reverse).* **Weight:** *26.73 grams.*
Composition: *.900 silver, .100 copper (net weight .7736 oz. pure silver).*
Diameter: *38.1 mm.* **Edge:** *Reeded.* **Mints:** *West Point (Uncirculated) and Philadelphia (Proof).*

The proposed National Prisoner of War Museum set the stage for the issuance of a silver dollar observing the tribulations of prisoners held by foreign military powers. The obverse designer, Nielsen, was a decorated former prisoner of war employed by the Bureau of Veterans Affairs.

Designs. *Obverse:* An eagle with a chain on one leg flies through a circle of barbed wire, representing flight to freedom. *Reverse:* Plan view, with landscaping, of the proposed National Prisoner of War Museum.

Mintage Data. Authorized by Public Law 103-186, signed by President William J. Clinton on December 14, 1993. *Maximum authorized*—500,000. *Number minted*—1994-W: 54,893 Uncirculated; 1994-P: 224,449 Proof.

Original Cost. Sale prices $27 (Uncirculated, pre-issue) and $31 (Proof, pre-issue); Uncirculated later raised to $32, and Proof later raised to $35. The surcharge of $10 per coin went toward the construction of the museum.

Key to Collecting. The 1994-W dollar is in special demand due to its relatively low mintage. Both varieties are seen with frequency in the marketplace and are nearly always superb gems.

	Distribution	Cert	Avg	%MS	MS-67 PF-67
1994-W	54,893	1,909	69.4	100%	$50
	Auctions: $129, MS-70, January 2014; $100, MS-70, February 2015; $94, MS-70, January 2015; $87, MS-70, May 2015				
1994-P, Proof	224,449	2,439	68.9		$40
	Auctions: $1,116, PF-70DCam, September 2014; $999, PF-70DCam, September 2014; $1,763, PF-70DCam, January 2013				

Women in Military Service Memorial Silver Dollar (1994)

Designer: *T. James Ferrell.* **Weight:** *26.73 grams.*
Composition: *.900 silver, .100 copper (net weight .7736 oz. pure silver).*
Diameter: *38.1 mm.* **Edge:** *Reeded.* **Mints:** *West Point (Uncirculated) and Philadelphia (Proof).*

These coins were issued to honor women in the military and help fund the Women in Military Service for America Memorial at the ceremonial entrance to Arlington National Cemetery (which became a reality and opened in October 1997 on a 4.2-acre site).

Designs. *Obverse:* Servicewomen from the Army, Marine Corps, Navy, Air Force, and

Coast Guard, with the names of these branches around the border. *Reverse:* A diagonal view of the front of the proposed the Women in Military Service for America Memorial.

Mintage Data. Authorized by Public Law 103-186, signed by President William J. Clinton on December 14, 1993. *Maximum authorized*—500,000. *Number minted*—1994-W: 69,860 Uncirculated; 1994-P: 241,278 Proof.

Original Cost. Sale prices $27 (Uncirculated, pre-issue) and $31 (Proof, pre-issue); Uncirculated later raised to $32, and Proof later raised to $35. The surcharge of $10 per coin went towards the construction of the memorial.

Key to Collecting. Mirroring the situation for other commemoratives of the era, these are easily enough found on the market and are usually in superb gem grades.

	Distribution	Cert	Avg	%MS	MS-67 PF-67
1994-W	69,860	3,281	69.3	100%	$32
Auctions: $72, MS-70, April 2013					
1994-P, Proof	241,278	2,211	68.9		$38
Auctions: $646, PF-70DCam, April 2013					

Vietnam Veterans Memorial Silver Dollar (1994)

Designer: *John Mercanti (obverse), Thomas D. Rogers Sr. (reverse).* **Weight:** *26.73 grams.*
Composition: *.900 silver, .100 copper (net weight .7736 oz. pure silver).*
Diameter: *38.1 mm.* **Edge:** *Reeded.* **Mints:** *West Point (Uncirculated) and Philadelphia (Proof).*

In Washington, D.C., the Vietnam Veterans Memorial, often called the Memorial Wall, has been one of the city's prime attractions since it was dedicated in 1984.

Designs. *Obverse:* A hand touching the Wall. In the distance to the right is the Washington Monument. *Reverse:* Three military medals and ribbons surrounded with lettering.

Mintage Data. Authorized by Public Law 103-186, signed by President William J. Clinton on December 14, 1993. *Maximum authorized*—500,000. *Number minted*—1994-W: 57,290 Uncirculated; 1994-P: 227,671 Proof.

Original Cost. Sale prices $27 (Uncirculated) and $31 (Proof); Uncirculated later raised to $32, and Proof later raised to $35. The surcharge of $10 per coin went towards the construction of a visitor's center near the Memorial.

Key to Collecting. Gem specimens are easily available. The aftermarket price for this dollar is stronger than for most others of the early 1990s.

	Distribution	Cert	Avg	%MS	MS-67 PF-67
1994-W	57,290	1,780	69.3	100%	$55
Auctions: $141, MS-70, January 2013; $103, MS-70, July 2014; $84, MS-70, May 2015					
1994-P, Proof	227,671	3,033	68.9		$60
Auctions: $2,115, PF-70DCam, April 2013; $793, PF-70DCam, August 2015; $770, PF-70DCam, September 2014					

WORLD CUP TOURNAMENT HALF DOLLAR (1994)

Designer: *Richard T. LaRoche (obverse), Dean McMullen (reverse).* **Weight:** *11.34 grams.*
Composition: *.9167 copper, .0833 nickel.* **Diameter:** *30.61 mm.* **Edge:** *Reeded.*
Mints: *Denver (Uncirculated) and Philadelphia (Proof).*

The United States' hosting of the XV FIFA World Cup playoff—the culmination of soccer games among 141 nations—was commemorated with this copper-nickel half dollar, as well as a silver dollar and a five-dollar gold coin.

Designs. *Obverse:* A soccer player in action, on the run with a ball near his feet. *Reverse:* The World Cup USA logo at the center, flanked by branches.

Mintage Data. Authorized by Public Law 102-281, signed by President George H.W. Bush on May 13, 1992. *Maximum authorized*—5,000,000. *Number minted*—1994-D: 168,208 Uncirculated; 1994-P: 609,354 Proof.

Original Cost. Sale prices $8.75 (Uncirculated, pre-issue) and $9.75 (Proof, pre-issue); Uncirculated later raised to $9.50, and Proof later raised to $10.50. The surcharge of $1 per coin went to the World Cup Organizing Committee.

Key to Collecting. The World Cup coins are reasonably priced in the secondary market. Nearly all are superb gems.

	Distribution	Cert	Avg	%MS	MS-67 PF-67
1994-D	168,208	936	69.1	100%	$10
	Auctions: $212, MS-70, September 2014				
1994-P, Proof	609,354	2,882	69.0		$10
	Auctions: $411, PF-70, September 2014; $558, PF-70, April 2013				

WORLD CUP TOURNAMENT SILVER DOLLAR (1994)

Designer: *Dean McMullen.* **Weight:** *26.73 grams.*
Composition: *.900 silver, .100 copper (net weight .7736 oz. pure silver).*
Diameter: *38.1 mm.* **Edge:** *Reeded.* **Mints:** *Denver (Uncirculated) and San Francisco (Proof).*

In terms of mintage goals, this program was one of the greatest failures in the history of American commemorative coinage. The U.S. Mint stated it lost $3.5 million in the effort, noting that there simply were too many commemorative programs in progress, each with excessive mintage expectations. The only winner in the World Cup scenario seemed to be the recipient of the surcharge.

Designs. *Obverse:* Two competing soccer players converge on a soccer ball in play. *Reverse:* The World Cup USA logo at the center, flanked by branches.

Mintage Data. Authorized by Public Law 102-281, signed by President George H.W. Bush on May 13, 1992. *Maximum authorized*—5,000,000. *Number minted*—1994-D: 81,524 Uncirculated; 1994-S: 577,090 Proof.

Original Cost. Sale prices $23 (Uncirculated, pre-issue) and $27 (Proof, pre-issue); Uncirculated later raised to $28, and Proof later raised to $31. The surcharge of $7 per coin went to the World Cup Organizing Committee.

Key to Collecting. The World Cup coins are reasonably priced in the secondary market. Nearly all are superb gems.

	Distribution	Cert	Avg	%MS	MS-67
					PF-67
1994-D	81,524	1,329	69.0	100%	$45
Auctions: $329, MS-70, September 2014; $764, MS-70, April 2013					
1994-S, Proof	577,090	2,645	69.0		$35
Auctions: $170, PF-70DCam, September 2014; $294, PF-70DCam, April 2013					

WORLD CUP TOURNAMENT $5 GOLD COIN (1994)

Designer: *William J. Krawczewicz (obverse), Dean McMullen (reverse).* **Weight:** *8.359 grams.* **Composition:** *.900 gold, .100 copper (net weight .242 oz. pure gold).* **Diameter:** *21.6 mm.* **Edge:** *Reeded.* **Mint:** *West Point.*

The U.S. Mint's many recent commemoratives had caused buyer fatigue by the time the World Cup Tournament coins came out. Collectors blamed the Mint for creating coins that few people wanted. The complaints should have gone to Congress instead. Faced with so many coins to produce, often with very short deadlines, the Mint simply had no time to call for designs to be submitted from leading artists.

Designs. *Obverse:* The World Cup trophy. *Reverse:* The World Cup USA logo at the center, flanked by branches.

Mintage Data. Authorized by Public Law 102-281, signed by President George H.W. Bush on May 13, 1992. *Maximum authorized*—750,000. *Number minted*—22,447 Uncirculated and 89,614 Proof.

Original Cost. Sale prices $170 (Uncirculated, pre-issue) and $185 (Proof, pre-issue); Uncirculated later raised to $200, and Proof later raised to $220. The surcharge of $35 per coin went to the World Cup Organizing Committee.

Key to Collecting. The World Cup coins are reasonably priced in the secondary market. Nearly all are superb gems.

	Distribution	Cert	Avg	%MS	MS-67
					PF-67
1994-W	22,447	1,079	69.5	100%	$375
Auctions: $382, MS-70, September 2014; $382, MS-70, November 2014; $448, MS-70, April 2013; $306, MS-69, November 2014					
1994-W, Proof	89,614	2,179	69.3		$375
Auctions: $470, PF-70DCam, June 2013; $295, PF-69DCam, October 2014; $306, PF-68DCam, February 2015					

XXVI Olympiad Basketball Half Dollar (1995)

Designer: *Clint Hansen (obverse), T. James Ferrell (reverse).* **Weight:** *11.34 grams.*
Composition: *.9167 copper, .0833 nickel.* **Diameter:** *30.61 mm.* **Edge:** *Reeded.* **Mint:** *San Francisco.*

Men's basketball has been an Olympic sport since the 1936 Summer Games in Berlin. The 1996 U.S. team, also known as "Dream Team III," won the gold medal at the Summer Games in Atlanta.

Designs. *Obverse:* Three basketball players. *Reverse:* Symbol of the Atlanta Committee for the Olympic Games superimposed over the Atlantic Ocean as viewed from space.

Mintage Data. Authorized by Public Law 102-390, signed by President George H.W. Bush on October 6, 1992. *Maximum authorized—2,000,000. Number minted—171,001* Uncirculated and 169,655 Proof.

Original Cost. Sale prices $10.50 (Uncirculated, pre-issue) and $11.50 (Proof, pre-issue); Uncirculated later raised to $11.50, and Proof later raised to $12.50. The surcharge per coin went to the Atlanta Olympic Committee.

Key to Collecting. Enough 1995 and 1996 Olympics coins are on the aftermarket that finding designs of choice, or forming a set, will be no problem. The obverse designs are varied, and in total the collection is an excellent representation of this quadrennial worldwide competition.

	Distribution	Cert	Avg	%MS	MS-67
					PF-67
1995-S	171,001	1,436	69.3	100%	$18
	Auctions: $118, MS-70, July 2014; $76, MS-70, July 2013				
1995-S, Proof	169,655	2,014	69.1		$18
	Auctions: No auction records available.				

XXVI Olympiad Baseball Half Dollar (1995)

Designer: *Edgar Z. Steever IV (obverse), T. James Ferrell (reverse).* **Weight:** *11.34 grams.*
Composition: *.9167 copper, .0833 nickel.* **Diameter:** *30.61 mm.* **Edge:** *Reeded.* **Mint:** *San Francisco.*

Baseball was an official Olympic sport at each Summer Games between 1992 and 2008, but was voted out of the 2012 London Olympics and will remain off the docket until at least 2024 following a 2013 International Olympic Committee vote. The team representing Cuba took home the gold medal at the 1996 Atlanta Olympics.

Designs. *Obverse:* Batter at the plate with catcher and umpire. *Reverse:* Symbol of the Atlanta Committee for the Olympic Games superimposed over the Atlantic Ocean as viewed from space.

Mintage Data. Authorized by Public Law 102-390, signed by President George H.W. Bush on October 6, 1992. *Maximum authorized*—2,000,000. *Number minted*—164,605 Uncirculated and 118,087 Proof.

Original Cost. Sale prices $10.50 (Uncirculated, pre-issue) and $11.50 (Proof, pre-issue); Uncirculated later raised to $11.50, and Proof later raised to $12.50. The surcharge per coin went to the Atlanta Olympic Committee.

Key to Collecting. Enough 1995 and 1996 Olympics coins are on the aftermarket that finding designs of choice, or forming a set, will be no problem. The obverse designs are varied, and in total the collection is an excellent representation of this quadrennial worldwide competition.

	Distribution	Cert	Avg	%MS	MS-67
					PF-67
1995-S	164,605	1,098	69.3	100%	$16
Auctions: $130, MS-70, April 2013					
1995-S, Proof	118,087	1,593	69.1		$20
Auctions: $329, PF-70DCam, September 2014; $200, PF-70DCam, September 2014					

XXVI OLYMPIAD GYMNASTICS SILVER DOLLAR (1995)

Designer: *James C. Sharpe (obverse), William Krawczewicz (reverse).* **Weight:** *26.73 grams.*
Composition: *.900 silver, .100 copper (net weight .7736 oz. pure silver).*
Diameter: *38.1 mm.* **Edge:** *Reeded.* **Mints:** *Denver (Uncirculated) and Philadelphia (Proof).*

The men's gymnastics competition has been held at each Olympic Summer Games since the birth of the modern Olympic movement in 1896. Russia won the gold medal in the team all-around event at the 1996 Games in Atlanta.

Designs. *Obverse:* Men's gymnastics. *Reverse:* Clasped hands of two athletes with torch above.

Mintage Data. Authorized by Public Law 102-390, signed by President George H.W. Bush on October 6, 1992. *Maximum authorized*—750,000. *Number minted*—1995-D: 42,497 Uncirculated; 1995-P: 182,676 Proof.

Original Cost. Sale prices $27.95 (Uncirculated, pre-issue) and $30.95 (Proof, pre-issue); Uncirculated later raised to $31.95, and Proof later raised to $34.95. The surcharge per coin went to the Atlanta Olympic Committee.

Key to Collecting. Enough 1995 and 1996 Olympics coins are on the aftermarket that finding designs of choice, or forming a set, will be no problem. The obverse designs are varied, and in total the collection is an excellent representation of this quadrennial worldwide competition.

	Distribution	Cert	Avg	%MS	MS-67
					PF-67
1995-D	42,497	1,531	69.2	100%	$35
Auctions: $90, MS-70, April 2013					
1995-P, Proof	182,676	2,117	69.0		$30
Auctions: No auction records available.					

XXVI OLYMPIAD TRACK AND FIELD SILVER DOLLAR (1995)

Designer: *John Mercanti (obverse), William Krawczewicz (reverse).* **Weight:** *26.73 grams.*
Composition: *.900 silver, .100 copper (net weight .7736 oz. pure silver).*
Diameter: *38.1 mm.* **Edge:** *Reeded.* **Mints:** *Denver (Uncirculated) and Philadelphia (Proof).*

Track and field—grouped with road running and racewalking in the overarching "athletics" category—has been a part of the Olympics from the birth of the modern Games and traces its roots to the ancient Greek Olympics. At the 1996 Summer Games in Atlanta, the United States took home 13 gold medals between its men's and women's track and field teams, easily the most of any nation.

Designs. *Obverse:* Men competing in track and field. *Reverse:* Clasped hands of two athletes with torch above.

Mintage Data. Authorized by Public Law 102-390, signed by President George H.W. Bush on October 6, 1992. *Maximum authorized*—750,000. *Number minted*—1995-D: 24,976 Uncirculated; 1995-P: 136,935 Proof.

Original Cost. Sale prices $27.95 (Uncirculated, pre-issue) and $30.95 (Proof, pre-issue); Uncirculated later raised to $31.95, and Proof later raised to $34.95. The surcharge per coin went to the Atlanta Olympic Committee.

Key to Collecting. Enough 1995 and 1996 Olympics coins are on the aftermarket that finding designs of choice, or forming a set, will be no problem. The obverse designs are varied, and in total the collection is an excellent representation of this quadrennial worldwide competition.

	Distribution	Cert	Avg	%MS	MS-67 PF-67
1995-D	24,976	826	69.3	100%	$70
	Auctions: $159, MS-70, July 2014				
1995-P, Proof	136,935	1,479	69.0		$35
	Auctions: $411, PF-70DCam, September 2014				

XXVI OLYMPIAD CYCLING SILVER DOLLAR (1995)

Designer: *John Mercanti (obverse), William Krawczewicz (reverse).* **Weight:** *26.73 grams.*
Composition: *.900 silver, .100 copper (net weight .7736 oz. pure silver).*
Diameter: *38.1 mm.* **Edge:** *Reeded.* **Mints:** *Denver (Uncirculated) and Philadelphia (Proof).*

Part of the Summer Games from the inception of the modern Olympic movement in 1896, cycling has been expanded over the years to include more track races, mountain biking, and BMX racing. France dominated the podium at the 1996 Olympics in Atlanta, taking home the most gold medals (five) and total medals (nine).

Designs. *Obverse:* Men cycling. *Reverse:* Clasped hands of two athletes with torch above.

Mintage Data. Authorized by Public Law 102-390, signed by President George H.W. Bush on October 6, 1992. *Maximum authorized*—750,000. *Number minted*—1995-D: 19,662 Uncirculated; 1995-P: 118,795 Proof.

Original Cost. Sale prices $27.95 (Uncirculated, pre-issue) and $30.95 (Proof, pre-issue); Uncirculated later raised to $31.95, and Proof later raised to $34.95. The surcharge per coin went to the Atlanta Olympic Committee.

Key to Collecting. Enough 1995 and 1996 Olympics coins are on the aftermarket that finding designs of choice, or forming a set, will be no problem. The obverse designs are varied, and in total the collection is an excellent representation of this quadrennial worldwide competition.

	Distribution	Cert	Avg	%MS	MS-67
					PF-67
1995-D	19,662	913	69.3	100%	$85
Auctions: $206, MS-70, July 2014; $200, MS-70, April 2013; $112, MS-69, November 2014					
1995-P, Proof	118,795	1,469	69.0		$38
Auctions: $707, PF-70DCam, September 2014					

PARALYMPICS BLIND RUNNER SILVER DOLLAR (1995)

Designer: *James C. Sharpe (obverse), William Krawczewicz (reverse).* **Weight:** *26.73 grams.*
Composition: *.900 silver, .100 copper (net weight .7736 oz. pure silver).*
Diameter: *38.1 mm.* **Edge:** *Reeded.* **Mints:** *Denver (Uncirculated) and Philadelphia (Proof).*

Track and field events (under the umbrella of "athletics") have been a part of the Summer Paralympic Games since 1960. Spanish athletes took home a number of medals in the track events for visually impaired athletes at the 1996 Summer Paralympic Games, including the gold in two of the men's 100-meter dash events (Júlio Requena in the T-10 race, and Juan António Prieto in the T-11 race) and both of the women's 100-meter dash events (Purificación Santamarta in the T-10 race, and Beatríz Mendoza in the T-11 race).

Designs. *Obverse:* Blind runner tethered to a seeing companion in a race. *Reverse:* Clasped hands of two athletes with torch above.

Mintage Data. Authorized by Public Law 102-390, signed by President George H.W. Bush on October 6, 1992. *Maximum authorized*—750,000. *Number minted*—1995-D: 28,649 Uncirculated; 1995-P: 138,337 Proof.

Original Cost. Sale prices $27.95 (Uncirculated, pre-issue) and $30.95 (Proof, pre-issue); Uncirculated later raised to $31.95, and Proof later raised to $34.95. The surcharge per coin went to the Atlanta Olympic Committee.

Key to Collecting. Enough 1995 and 1996 Olympics coins are on the aftermarket that finding designs of choice, or forming a set, will be no problem. The obverse designs are varied, and in total the collection is an excellent representation of this quadrennial worldwide competition.

	Distribution	Cert	Avg	%MS	MS-67
					PF-67
1995-D	28,649	1,294	69.3	100%	$55
Auctions: No auction records available.					
1995-P, Proof	138,337	1,630	69.0		$30
Auctions: No auction records available.					

XXVI OLYMPIAD TORCH RUNNER $5 GOLD COIN (1995)

Designer: *Frank Gasparro.* **Weight:** *8.359 grams.*
Composition: *.900 gold, .100 copper (net weight .242 oz. pure gold).*
Diameter: *21.6 mm.* **Edge:** *Reeded.* **Mint:** *West Point.*

Whereas the concept of the Olympic flame dates from the ancient Games of ancient Greece, the torch relay has only been a tradition since 1936, when Carl Diem introduced the concept for the Berlin Summer Games. The 1996 Olympic torch relay spanned 112 days, approximately 18,030 miles, and 13,267 torch bearers before ending in Atlanta on July 19, 1996.

Designs. *Obverse:* Olympic runner carrying a torch. *Reverse:* Bald eagle with a banner in its beak with the Olympic Centennial dates 1896–1996.

Mintage Data. Authorized by Public Law 102-390, signed by President George H.W. Bush on October 6, 1992. *Maximum authorized*—175,000. *Number minted*—14,675 Uncirculated and 57,442 Proof.

Original Cost. Sale prices $229 (Uncirculated, pre-issue) and $239 (Proof, pre-issue); Uncirculated later raised to $249, and Proof later raised to $259. The surcharge per coin went to the Atlanta Olympic Committee.

Key to Collecting. Enough 1995 and 1996 Olympics coins are on the aftermarket that finding designs of choice, or forming a set, will be no problem. The obverse designs are varied, and in total the collection is an excellent representation of this quadrennial worldwide competition.

	Distribution	Cert	Avg	%MS	MS-67
					PF-67
1995-W	14,675	1,017	69.7	100%	$375
Auctions: $646, MS-70, February 2015; $447, MS-70, May 2015; $423, MS-70, May 2015; $353, MS-69, January 2015					
1995-W, Proof	57,442	1,841	69.3		$370
Auctions: No auction records available.					

XXVI Olympiad Stadium $5 Gold Coin (1995)

Designer: *Marcel Jovine (obverse), Frank Gasparro (reverse).* **Weight:** *8.359 grams.*
Composition: *.900 gold, .100 copper (net weight .242 oz. pure gold).*
Diameter: *21.6 mm.* **Edge:** *Reeded.* **Mint:** *West Point.*

Centennial Olympic Stadium was constructed in Atlanta for the 1996 Summer Games. The 85,000-seat venue hosted the track and field events, as well as the closing ceremony, and then was reconstructed into Turner Field, home of Major League Baseball's Atlanta Braves for two decades.

Designs. *Obverse:* Aerial view of the Olympic Stadium from a distance to the side. *Reverse:* Same as described for the Olympic Torch Runner $5 gold coin.

Mintage Data. Authorized by Public Law 102-390, signed by President George H.W. Bush on October 6, 1992. *Maximum authorized*—175,000. *Number minted*—10,579 Uncirculated and 43,124 Proof.

Original Cost. Sale prices $229 (Uncirculated, pre-issue) and $239 (Proof, pre-issue); Uncirculated later raised to $249, and Proof later raised to $259. The surcharge per coin went to the Atlanta Olympic Committee.

Key to Collecting. Enough 1995 and 1996 Olympics coins are on the aftermarket that finding designs of choice, or forming a set, will be no problem. The obverse designs are varied, and in total the collection is an excellent representation of this quadrennial worldwide competition.

	Distribution	Cert	Avg	%MS	MS-67 PF-67
1995-W	10,579	968	69.6	100%	$425
	Auctions: $823, MS-70, February 2015; $764, MS-70, January 2015; $823, MS-69, February 2015; $646, MS-69, February 2015				
1995-W, Proof	43,124	1,834	69.4		$370
	Auctions: $499, PF-70DCam, June 2014; $470, PF-70DCam, June 2014				

XXVI Olympiad Swimming Half Dollar (1996)

Designer: *William Krawczewicz (obverse), Malcolm Farley (reverse).* **Weight:** *11.34 grams.*
Composition: *.9167 copper, .0833 nickel.* **Diameter:** *30.61 mm.* **Edge:** *Reeded.* **Mint:** *San Francisco.*

Swimming—an Olympic sport since the modern Games began in 1896—was dominated by U.S. athletes at the 1996 Summer Games in Atlanta. Americans took home a total of 26 medals (more than double the 12 each of Russia and Germany, which come next on the list), and swept all six relay events across the men's and women's competitions.

Designs. *Obverse:* Male swimmer. *Reverse:* Symbols of the Olympic games, including flame, torch, rings, Greek column, and 100 (the latter to observe the 100th anniversary of the modern Olympic games inaugurated with the 1896 Games in Athens).

Mintage Data. Authorized by Public Law 102-390, signed by President George H.W. Bush on October 6, 1992. *Maximum authorized*—3,000,000. *Number minted*—49,533 Uncirculated and 114,315 Proof.

Original Cost. Sale prices $10.50 (Uncirculated, pre-issue) and $11.50 (Proof, pre-issue); Uncirculated later raised to $11.50, and Proof later raised to $12.50. The surcharge per coin went to the Atlanta Olympic Committee.

Key to Collecting. Enough 1995 and 1996 Olympics coins are on the aftermarket that finding designs of choice, or forming a set, will be no problem. The obverse designs are varied, and in total the collection is an excellent representation of this quadrennial worldwide competition.

	Distribution	Cert	Avg	%MS	MS-67 PF-67
1996-S ††	49,533	852	69.1	100%	$75
	Auctions: $499, MS-70, September 2013				
1996-S, Proof	114,315	984	69.1		$28
	Auctions: No auction records available.				

†† Ranked in the *100 Greatest U.S. Modern Coins* (fourth edition).

XXVI Olympiad Soccer Half Dollar (1996)

Designer: *Clint Hansen (obverse)*, *Malcolm Farley (reverse)*. **Weight:** *11.34 grams.* **Composition:** *.9167 copper, .0833 nickel.* **Diameter:** *30.61 mm.* **Edge:** *Reeded.* **Mint:** *San Francisco.*

Women's soccer debuted as an Olympic sport at the 1996 Summer Games in Atlanta. The host nation's team—featuring such names as Mia Hamm, Brandi Chastain, and Briana Scurry—was victorious in the gold medal game.

Designs. *Obverse:* Women playing soccer. *Reverse:* Symbols of the Olympic games, including flame, torch, rings, Greek column, and 100.

Mintage Data. Authorized by Public Law 102-390, signed by President George H.W. Bush on October 6, 1992. *Maximum authorized*—3,000,000. *Number minted*—52,836 Uncirculated and 112,412 Proof.

Original Cost. Sale prices $10.50 (Uncirculated, pre-issue) and $11.50 (Proof, pre-issue); Uncirculated later raised to $11.50, and Proof later raised to $12.50. The surcharge per coin went to the Atlanta Olympic Committee.

Key to Collecting. Enough 1995 and 1996 Olympics coins are on the aftermarket that finding designs of choice, or forming a set, will be no problem. The obverse designs are varied, and in total the collection is an excellent representation of this quadrennial worldwide competition.

	Distribution	Cert	Avg	%MS	MS-67 PF-67
1996-S	52,836	622	69.3	100%	$75
	Auctions: $147, MS-70, July 2014; $170, MS-70, August 2013				
1996-S, Proof	112,412	961	69.0		$60
	Auctions: $294, PF-70DCam, September 2014				

XXVI Olympiad Tennis Silver Dollar (1996)

Designer: *James C. Sharpe (obverse), Thomas D. Rogers Sr. (reverse).* **Weight:** *26.73 grams.*
Composition: *.900 silver, .100 copper (net weight .7736 oz. pure silver).*
Diameter: *38.1 mm.* **Edge:** *Reeded.* **Mints:** *Denver (Uncirculated) and Philadelphia (Proof).*

Women's tennis was first a part of the Olympics in 1900, and singles competition was regularly held for the Summer Games between 1908 and 1924. Subsequent disputes between the International Lawn Tennis Federation and the International Olympic Committee led to both men's and women's tennis being removed from the Games for more than 60 years, but the sport returned permanently in 1988. U.S. athletes took both the women's singles gold medal (Lindsay Davenport) and women's doubles gold medal (Gigi Fernandez and Mary Joe Fernandez) at the 1996 Games in Atlanta.

Designs. *Obverse:* Woman playing tennis. *Reverse:* Atlanta Committee for the Olympic Games logo with torch and flame.

Mintage Data. Authorized by Public Law 102-390, signed by President George H.W. Bush on October 6, 1992. *Maximum authorized—1,000,000. Number minted—*1996-D: 15,983 Uncirculated; 1996-P: 92,016 Proof.

Original Cost. Sale prices $27.95 (Uncirculated, pre-issue) and $30.95 (Proof, pre-issue); Uncirculated later raised to $31.95, and Proof later raised to $34.95. The surcharge per coin went to the Atlanta Olympic Committee.

Key to Collecting. Enough 1995 and 1996 Olympics coins are on the aftermarket that finding designs of choice, or forming a set, will be no problem. The obverse designs are varied, and in total the collection is an excellent representation of this quadrennial worldwide competition.

	Distribution	Cert	Avg	%MS	MS-67
					PF-67
1996-D ††	15,983	779	69.1	100%	$150
	Auctions: $206, MS-70, September 2014; $482, MS-70, April 2013; $170, MS-69, July 2014; $170, MS-69, November 2014				
1996-P, Proof	92,016	1,314	68.9		$65
	Auctions: $355, PF-69DCam, November 2014				

†† Ranked in the *100 Greatest U.S. Modern Coins* (fourth edition).

XXVI Olympiad Rowing Silver Dollar (1996)

Designer: *Bart Forbes (obverse), Thomas D. Rogers Sr. (reverse).* **Weight:** *26.73 grams.*
Composition: *.900 silver, .100 copper (net weight .7736 oz. pure silver).*
Diameter: *38.1 mm.* **Edge:** *Reeded.* **Mints:** *Denver (Uncirculated) and Philadelphia (Proof).*

Rowing has been an official Olympic sport from the first modern Games in 1896, though coincidentally the competition was cancelled for that event due to weather concerns. At the 1996 Summer Olympics in Atlanta, Australia won the most medals (six, two gold).

Designs. *Obverse:* Men rowing. *Reverse:* Atlanta Committee for the Olympic Games logo with torch and flame.

Mintage Data. Authorized by Public Law 102-390, signed by President George H.W. Bush on October 6, 1992. *Maximum authorized*—1,000,000. *Number minted*—1996-D: 16,258 Uncirculated; 1996-P: 151,890 Proof.

Original Cost. Sale prices $27.95 (Uncirculated, pre-issue) and $30.95 (Proof, pre-issue); Uncirculated later raised to $31.95, and Proof later raised to $34.95. The surcharge per coin went to the Atlanta Olympic Committee.

Key to Collecting. Enough 1995 and 1996 Olympics coins are on the aftermarket that finding designs of choice, or forming a set, will be no problem. The obverse designs are varied, and in total the collection is an excellent representation of this quadrennial worldwide competition.

	Distribution	Cert	Avg	%MS	MS-67 PF-67
1996-D	16,258	728	69.2	100%	$150
	Auctions: $382, MS-70, April 2013; $153, MS-69, November 2014; $147, MS-69, November 2014				
1996-P, Proof	151,890	1,294	68.9		$60
	Auctions: $6,169, PF-70DCam, September 2014				

XXVI Olympiad High Jump Silver Dollar (1996)

Designer: *Calvin Massey (obverse), Thomas D. Rogers Sr. (reverse).* **Weight:** *26.73 grams.*
Composition: *.900 silver, .100 copper (net weight .7736 oz. pure silver).*
Diameter: *38.1 mm.* **Edge:** *Reeded.* **Mints:** *Denver (Uncirculated) and Philadelphia (Proof).*

High jump has been one of the Olympic track and field program's events since the inaugural modern Games in 1896. At the 1996 Atlanta Olympics, the United States' Charles Austin won the gold medal in the men's competition with a height cleared of 2.39 meters.

Designs. *Obverse:* Athlete doing the "Fosbury Flop" maneuver. *Reverse:* Atlanta Committee for the Olympic Games logo with torch and flame.

Mintage Data. Authorized by Public Law 102-390, signed by President George H.W. Bush on October 6, 1992. *Maximum authorized*—1,000,000. *Number minted*—1996-D: 15,697 Uncirculated; 1996-P: 124,502 Proof.

Original Cost. Sale prices $27.95 (Uncirculated, pre-issue) and $30.95 (Proof, pre-issue); Uncirculated later raised to $31.95, and Proof later raised to $34.95. The surcharge per coin went to the Atlanta Olympic Committee.

Key to Collecting. Enough 1995 and 1996 Olympics coins are on the aftermarket that finding designs of choice, or forming a set, will be no problem. The obverse designs are varied, and in total the collection is an excellent representation of this quadrennial worldwide competition.

	Distribution	Cert	Avg	%MS	MS-67 PF-67
1996-D ††	15,697	723	69.1	100%	$150
	Auctions: $441, MS-70, April 2013; $147, MS-69, July 2014; $165, MS-69, November 2014				
1996-P, Proof	124,502	1,352	68.9		$45
	Auctions: No auction records available.				

†† Ranked in the *100 Greatest U.S. Modern Coins* (fourth edition).

PARALYMPICS WHEELCHAIR SILVER DOLLAR (1996)

Designer: *James C. Sharpe (obverse), Thomas D. Rogers Sr. (reverse).* **Weight:** *26.73 grams.*
Composition: *.900 silver, .100 copper (net weight .7736 oz. pure silver).*
Diameter: *38.1 mm.* **Edge:** *Reeded.* **Mints:** *Denver (Uncirculated) and Philadelphia (Proof).*

Wheelchair racing events have comprised part of the Paralympic track and field program since 1960. Several countries were represented on the podium, though the United States' Shawn Meredith (gold medals in the T-51 400-meter and 800-meter), France's Claude Issorat (gold medals in the T-53 200-meter and 800-meter), and Switzerland's Heinz Frei (gold medals in the T52-53 1,500-meter and 10,000-meter) had particularly strong showings.

Designs. *Obverse:* Athlete in a racing wheelchair competing in a track and field competition. *Reverse:* Atlanta Committee for the Olympic Games logo with torch and flame.

Mintage Data. Authorized by Public Law 102-390, signed by President George H.W. Bush on October 6, 1992. *Maximum authorized*—1,000,000. *Number minted*—1996-D: 14,497 Uncirculated; 1996-P: 84,280 Proof.

Original Cost. Sale prices $27.95 (Uncirculated, pre-issue) and $30.95 (Proof, pre-issue); Uncirculated later raised to $31.95, and Proof later raised to $34.95. The surcharge per coin went to the Atlanta Olympic Committee.

Key to Collecting. Enough 1995 and 1996 Olympics coins are on the aftermarket that finding designs of choice, or forming a set, will be no problem. The obverse designs are varied, and in total the collection is an excellent representation of this quadrennial worldwide competition.

	Distribution	Cert	Avg	%MS	MS-67
					PF-67
1996-D	14,497	1,294	69.3	100%	$150
	Auctions: $499, MS-70, April 2013; $223, MS-70, June 2015; $153, MS-69, November 2014; $129, MS-69, November 2014				
1996-P, Proof	84,280	1,630	69.0		$35
	Auctions: No auction records available.				

XXVI Olympiad Flag Bearer $5 Gold Coin (1996)

Designer: *Patricia Lewis Verani (obverse), William Krawczewicz (reverse).*
Weight: *8.359 grams.* **Composition:** *.900 gold, .100 copper (net weight .242 oz. pure gold).*
Diameter: *21.6 mm.* **Edge:** *Reeded.* **Mint:** *West Point.*

For the opening and closing ceremonies of each Olympic Games, each participating nation selects two flagbearers from among its athletes to lead its delegation in the Parade of Nations (opening) and Parade of Flags (closing). Wrestler Bruce Baumgartner served as the United States's flagbearer for the opening ceremony of the 1996 Summer Games, and show jumper Michael Matz was awarded the honor for the closing ceremony.

Designs. *Obverse:* Athlete with a flag followed by a crowd. *Reverse:* Atlanta Committee for the Olympic Games logo within laurel leaves.

Mintage Data. Authorized by Public Law 102-390, signed by President George H.W. Bush on October 6, 1992. *Maximum authorized*—300,000. *Number minted*—9,174 Uncirculated and 32,886 Proof.

Original Cost. Sale prices $229 (Uncirculated, pre-issue) and $239 (Proof, pre-issue); Uncirculated later raised to $249, and Proof later raised to $259. The surcharge per coin went to the Atlanta Olympic Committee.

Key to Collecting. Enough 1995 and 1996 Olympics coins are on the aftermarket that finding designs of choice, or forming a set, will be no problem. The obverse designs are varied, and in total the collection is an excellent representation of this quadrennial worldwide competition.

	Distribution	Cert	Avg	%MS	MS-67
					PF-67
1996-W ††	9,174	720	69.5	100%	$425
	Auctions: $881, MS-70, October 2015; $881, MS-70, February 2015; $494, MS-69, January 2015; $329, MS-69, September 2015				
1996-W, Proof	32,886	1,313	69.3		$370
	Auctions: No auction records available.				

†† Ranked in the *100 Greatest U.S. Modern Coins* (fourth edition).

XXVI Olympiad Cauldron $5 Gold Coin (1996)

Designer: *Frank Gasparro (obverse), William Krawczewicz (reverse).*
Weight: *8.359 grams.* **Composition:** *.900 gold, .100 copper (net weight .242 oz. pure gold).*
Diameter: *21.6 mm.* **Edge:** *Reeded.* **Mint:** *West Point.*

The tradition of maintaining an Olympic flame hearkens to the ancient Greek Olympics, during which a fire was kept burning to represent the theft of fire from Zeus by Prometheus. The concept became part of the modern Games in 1928 and now serves as the culmination of the Olympic torch relay. At the 1996 Summer Games in Atlanta, boxing legend and American icon Muhammad Ali (himself a gold medalist at the 1960 Olympics) was the final torch bearer and lit the cauldron.

Designs. *Obverse:* Lighting of the Olympic flame. *Reverse:* Atlanta Committee for the Olympic Games logo within laurel leaves.

Mintage Data. Authorized by Public Law 102-390, signed by President George H.W. Bush on October 6, 1992. *Maximum authorized*—300,000. *Number minted*—9,210 Uncirculated and 38,555 Proof.

Original Cost. Sale prices $229 (Uncirculated, pre-issue) and $239 (Proof, pre-issue); Uncirculated later raised to $249, and Proof later raised to $259. The surcharge per coin went to the Atlanta Olympic Committee.

Key to Collecting. Enough 1995 and 1996 Olympics coins are on the aftermarket that finding designs of choice, or forming a set, will be no problem. The obverse designs are varied, and in total the collection is an excellent representation of this quadrennial worldwide competition.

	Distribution	Cert	Avg	%MS	MS-67
					PF-67
1996-W	9,210	807	69.4	100%	$600
	Auctions: $1,116, MS-70, February 2015; $940, MS-70, October 2015; $823, MS-69, January 2015; $705, MS-69, November 2014				
1996-W, Proof	38,555	2,208	69.3		$370
	Auctions: $505, PF-70UCam, March 2015; $423, PF-70UCam, March 2015; $353, PF-70UCam, May 2015				

Civil War Battlefield Preservation Half Dollar (1995)

Designer: *Don Troiani (obverse), T. James Ferrell (reverse).* **Weight:** *11.34 grams.*
Composition: *.9167 copper, .0833 nickel.* **Diameter:** *30.61 mm.* **Edge:** *Reeded.* **Mint:** *San Francisco.*

Preserving battlefields associated with the Civil War (1861–1865) formed the topic for a suite of three commemorative coins, including this copper-nickel half dollar.

Designs. *Obverse:* Drummer standing. *Reverse:* Cannon overlooking battlefield with inscription above.

Mintage Data. Authorized by Public Law 102-379. *Maximum authorized—2,000,000. Number minted*—119,520 Uncirculated and 330,002 Proof.

Original Cost. Sale prices $9.50 (Uncirculated, pre-issue) and $10.75 (Proof, pre-issue); Uncirculated later raised to $10.25, and Proof later raised to $11.75. The surcharge of $2 per coin went to the Civil War Trust for the preservation of historically significant battlefields.

Key to Collecting. This coin, as well as those two issued alongside it, are readily available in the marketplace today. Most are superb gems.

	Distribution	Cert	Avg	%MS	MS-67
					PF-67
1995-S	119,520	992	69.3	100%	$40
Auctions: $206, MS-70, May 2014; $153, MS-70, July 2014; $112, MS-70, June 2015					
1995-S, Proof	330,002	1,828	69.0		$30
Auctions: $188, PF-68DCam, November 2014					

CIVIL WAR BATTLEFIELD PRESERVATION SILVER DOLLAR (1995)

Designer: *Don Troiani (obverse), John Mercanti (reverse).* **Weight:** *26.73 grams.*
Composition: *.900 silver, .100 copper (net weight .7736 oz. pure silver).*
Diameter: *38.1 mm.* **Edge:** *Reeded.* **Mints:** *Philadelphia (Uncirculated) and San Francisco (Proof).*

Civil War history attracts millions of followers, and books on the subject are always very popular. While total sales of the Civil War Battlefield Preservation silver dollar didn't approach the million coins authorized, sales of the Proof version were stronger than those of many recent silver dollars.

Designs. *Obverse:* Soldier offering canteen to a wounded comrade. *Reverse:* Gettysburg landscape with a quotation from Joshua Chamberlain, hero in that battle.

Mintage Data. Authorized by Public Law 102-379. *Maximum authorized—1,000,000. Number minted*—1995-P: 45,866 Uncirculated; 1995-S: 437,114 Proof.

Original Cost. Sale prices $27 (Uncirculated, pre-issue) and $30 (Proof, pre-issue); Uncirculated later raised to $30, and Proof later raised to $34. The surcharge of $7 per coin went to the Civil War Trust for the preservation of historically significant battlefields.

Key to Collecting. This coin, as well as those two issued alongside it, are readily available in the marketplace today. Most are superb gems.

	Distribution	Cert	Avg	%MS	MS-67
					PF-67
1995-P	45,866	1,259	69.1	100%	$65
Auctions: $247, MS-70, April 2013					
1995-S, Proof	437,114	3,135	69.0		$45
Auctions: $435, PF-70DCam, March 2013; $306, PF-70DCam, April 2013					

CIVIL WAR BATTLEFIELD PRESERVATION $5 GOLD COIN (1995)

Designer: *Don Troiani (obverse), Alfred F. Maletsky (reverse).* **Weight:** *8.359 grams.*
Composition: *.900 gold, .100 copper.* **Diameter:** *21.6 mm.* **Edge:** *Reeded.* **Mint:** *West Point.*

Troiani, the designer of this coin's obverse as well as those of the other two Civil War Battlefield Preservation commemoratives, is an artist in the private sector well known for his depictions of battle scenes.

Designs. *Obverse:* Bugler on horseback sounding a call. *Reverse:* Eagle perched on a shield.

Mintage Data. Authorized by Public Law 102-379. *Maximum authorized*—300,000. *Number minted*—12,735 Uncirculated and 55,246 Proof.

Original Cost. Sale prices $180 (Uncirculated, pre-issue) and $195 (Proof, pre-issue); Uncirculated later raised to $190, and Proof later raised to $225. The surcharge of $35 per coin went to the Civil War Trust for the preservation of historically significant battlefields.

Key to Collecting. This coin, as well as those two issued alongside it, are readily available in the marketplace today. Most are superb gems.

	Distribution	Cert	Avg	%MS	MS-67
					PF-67
1995-W	12,735	820	69.7	100%	$450
Auctions: $517, MS-70, January 2015; $494, MS-70, April 2015; $482, MS-70, January 2015; $329, MS-69, August 2015					
1995-W, Proof	55,246	1,945	69.3		$400
Auctions: $482, PF-70DCam, July 2015; $306, PF-69UCam, October 2015; $329, PF-69DCam, October 2015; $306, PF-69DCam, August 2015					

SPECIAL OLYMPICS WORLD GAMES SILVER DOLLAR (1995)

Designer: *T. James Ferrell from a portrait by Jamie Wyeth (obverse), Thomas D. Rogers Sr. (reverse).*
Weight: *26.73 grams.* **Composition:** *.900 silver, .100 copper (net weight .7736 oz. pure silver).*
Diameter: *38.1 mm.* **Edge:** *Reeded.* **Mints:** *West Point (Uncirculated) and Philadelphia (Proof).*

This silver dollar's subject, Eunice Kennedy Shriver, was not only the first living female on U.S. coinage, but also the sister of former president John F. Kennedy and the aunt of Joseph F. Kennedy II, the House representative who sponsored the bill that created the coin. She is credited on the silver dollar as the founder of the Special Olympics.

Designs. *Obverse:* Portrait of Eunice Shriver.
Reverse: Representation of a Special Olympics medal, a rose, and a quotation by Shriver.

Mintage Data. Authorized by Public Law 103-328, signed by President William J. Clinton on September 29, 1994. *Maximum authorized*—800,000. *Number minted*—1995-W: 89,301 Uncirculated; 1995-P: 351,764 Proof.

Original Cost. Sale prices $30 (Uncirculated, pre-issue) and $33 (Proof, pre-issue); Uncirculated later raised to $32, and Proof later raised to $37. The surcharge of $10 per coin went to the Special Olympics to support the 1995 World Summer Games.

Key to Collecting. These coins are plentiful in the marketplace. Most are superb gems.

	Distribution	Cert	Avg	%MS	MS-67
					PF-67
1995-W	89,301	965	69.2	100%	$30
Auctions: $135, MS-70, April 2013					
1995-P, Proof	351,764	1,499	69.0		$30
Auctions: $360, PF-70DCam, March 2013					

NATIONAL COMMUNITY SERVICE SILVER DOLLAR (1996)

Designer: *Thomas D. Rogers Sr. from a medal by Augustus Saint-Gaudens (obverse),*
William C. Cousins (reverse). **Weight:** *26.73 grams.* **Composition:** *.900 silver, .100 copper*
(net weight .7736 oz. pure silver). **Diameter:** *38.1 mm.* **Edge:** *Reeded.* **Mint:** *San Francisco.*

In 1996 the National Community Service dollar was sponsored by Representative Joseph D. Kennedy of Massachusetts, who also sponsored the Special Olympics World Games dollar.

Designs. *Obverse:* Standing figure of Liberty. *Reverse:* SERVICE FOR AMERICA in three lines, with a wreath around, and other lettering at the border.

Mintage Data. Authorized by Public Law 103-328, signed by President William J. Clinton on September 29, 1994. *Maximum authorized*—500,000. *Number minted*—23,500 Uncirculated and 101,543 Proof.

Original Cost. Sale prices $30 (Uncirculated, pre-issue) and $33 (Proof, pre-issue); Uncirculated later raised to $32, and Proof later raised to $37. The surcharge of $10 per coin went to the National Community Service Trust.

Key to Collecting. Uncirculated examples are scarce by virtue of their low mintage, but demand is scarce as well, with the result that they can be purchased easily enough. Both formats are usually seen in superb gem preservation.

	Distribution	Cert	Avg	%MS	MS-67
					PF-67
1996-S ††	23,500	1,094	69.3	100%	$85
Auctions: $153, MS-70, August 2014; $129, MS-70, June 2015; $88, MS-69, July 2014; $86, MS-69, November 2014					
1996-S, Proof	101,543	2,012	69.1		$34
Auctions: $195, PF-70DCam, April 2013					

†† Ranked in the *100 Greatest U.S. Modern Coins* (fourth edition).

SMITHSONIAN INSTITUTION 150TH ANNIVERSARY SILVER DOLLAR (1996)

Designer: *Thomas D. Rogers Sr. (obverse)*, *John Mercanti (reverse)*. **Weight:** *26.73 grams.*
Composition: *.900 silver, .100 copper (net weight .7736 oz. pure silver)*. **Diameter:** *38.1 mm.*
Edge: *Reeded.* **Mints:** *Denver (Uncirculated) and Philadelphia (Proof).*

This silver dollar, as well as a five-dollar gold coin, marked the 150th anniversary of Congress establishing the Smithsonian Institution in Washington, D.C., on August 10, 1846. Named for James Smithson—an English scientist whose will funded the entity—the institution quickly became America's national museum.

Designs. *Obverse:* The "Castle" building on the Mall in Washington, the original home of the Smithsonian Institution. Branches to each side. *Reverse:* Goddess of Knowledge sitting on top of a globe. In her left hand she holds a torch, in the right a scroll inscribed ART / HISTORY / SCIENCE. In the field to the right in several lines is FOR THE INCREASE AND DIFFUSION OF KNOWLEDGE.

Mintage Data. Authorized by Public Law 104-96, signed by President William J. Clinton on January 10, 1996. *Maximum authorized—650,000. Number minted—1996-D:* 31,320 Uncirculated; 1996-P: 129,152 Proof.

Original Cost. Sale prices $30 (Uncirculated, pre-issue) and $33 (Proof, pre-issue); Uncirculated later raised to $32, and Proof later raised to $37. The surcharge of $10 per coin went to the Smithsonian Board of Regents.

Key to Collecting. This silver dollar and the five-dollar gold coin issued alongside it have risen in value considerably since their release. Today examples can be found readily in the marketplace and are nearly always superb gems.

	Distribution	Cert	Avg	%MS	MS-67
					PF-67
1996-D	31,320	1,085	69.4	100%	$65
	Auctions: $119, MS-70, July 2014; $100, MS-70, February 2015; $89, MS-70, February 2015; $65, MS-69, October 2014				
1996-P, Proof	129,152	1,856	69.0		$40
	Auctions: $447, PF-70DCam, March 2013				

Smithsonian Institution 150th Anniversary $5 Gold Coin (1996)

Designer: *Alfred F. Maletsky (obverse), T. James Ferrell (reverse).* **Weight:** *8.359 grams.*
Composition: *.900 gold, .100 copper (net weight .242 oz. pure gold).*
Diameter: *21.6 mm.* **Edge:** *Reeded.* **Mint:** *West Point.*

The U.S. Mint offered the two 1996 Smithsonian commemorative coins via several new options, including the 50,000-set Young Collectors Edition and incorporated in jewelry items.

Designs. *Obverse:* Bust of James Smithson facing left. *Reverse:* Sunburst with SMITHSONIAN below.

Mintage Data. Authorized by Public Law 104-96, signed by President William J. Clinton on January 10, 1996. *Maximum authorized*—100,000. *Number minted*—9,068 Uncirculated and 21,772 Proof.

Original Cost. Sale prices $180 (Uncirculated, pre-issue) and $195 (Proof, pre-issue); Uncirculated later raised to $205, and Proof later raised to $225. The surcharge of $10 per coin went to the Smithsonian Board of Regents.

Key to Collecting. Both Smithsonian Institution 150th Anniversary coins have risen in value considerably since their release. Today examples can be found readily in the marketplace and are nearly always superb gems.

	Distribution	Cert	Avg	%MS	MS-67
					PF-67
1996-W ††	9,068	855	69.4	100%	$325
	Auctions: $646, MS-70, September 2014; $541, MS-70, January 2015; $447, MS-70, April 2015; $382, MS-69, August 2014				
1996-W, Proof	21,772	1,303	69.2		$325
	Auctions: $706, PF-70DCam, April 2013; $588, PF-70DCam, September 2014; $529, PF-70DCam, September 2014				

†† Ranked in the *100 Greatest U.S. Modern Coins* (fourth edition).

U.S. Botanic Garden Silver Dollar (1997)

Designer: *Edgar Z. Steever IV (obverse), William C. Cousins (reverse).* **Weight:** *26.73 grams.*
Composition: *Silver .900, copper .100 (net weight .7736 oz. pure silver).*
Diameter: *38.1 mm.* **Edge:** *Reeded.* **Mint:** *Philadelphia.*

These coins were purportedly struck to celebrate the 175th anniversary of the United States Botanic Garden (which would have been 1995), but they were dated on one side as 1997. The authorizing legislation that created the coins specified that the French façade of the U.S. Botanic Garden be shown on the obverse and a rose on the reverse.

Designs. *Obverse:* Façade of the United States Botanic Garden in plan view without landscaping. *Reverse:* A rose at the center with a garland of roses above. The inscription below includes the anniversary dates 1820–1995. Note that some listings designate the rose side as the obverse.

Mintage Data. Authorized by Public Law 103-328, signed by President William J. Clinton on September 29, 1994. *Maximum authorized*—500,000. *Number minted*—58,505 Uncirculated and 189,671 Proof.

Original Cost. Sale prices $30 (Uncirculated, pre-issue) and $33 (Proof, pre-issue); Uncirculated later raised to $33, and Proof later raised to $37. The surcharge of $10 per coin went to the National Fund for the Botanic Garden.

Key to Collecting. These coins are readily available on the market today. Nearly all are superb gems. Ironically, the most popular related item is the Mint package containing the 1997-P special-finish Jefferson nickel, the demand coming from collectors of five-cent pieces! Only 25,000 sets were sold. This is *déjà vu* of the 1993 Jefferson dollar offer.

	Distribution	Cert	Avg	%MS	MS-67 PF-67
1997-P	58,505	1,567	69.1	100%	$27
Auctions: $159, MS-70, July 2014; $170, MS-70, April 2013					
1997-P, Proof	189,671	1,515	69.0		$35
Auctions: $441, PF-70DCam, April 2013; $306, PF-70UCam, February 2015; $306, PF-70DCam, September 2014					

NATIONAL LAW ENFORCEMENT OFFICERS MEMORIAL SILVER DOLLAR (1997)

Designer: *Alfred F. Maletsky (obverse from a photograph by Larry Ruggieri).* **Weight:** *26.73 grams.*
Composition: *.900 silver, .100 copper (net weight .7736 oz. pure silver).*
Diameter: *38.1 mm.* **Edge:** *Reeded.* **Mint:** *Philadelphia.*

The National Law Enforcement Officers Memorial at Judiciary Square in Washington, D.C., dedicated on October 15, 1991, was the subject of this commemorative. The monument honors more than 14,000 men and women who gave their lives in the line of duty.

Designs. *Obverse:* United States Park Police officers Robert Chelsey and Kelcy Stefansson making a rubbing of a fellow officer's name.
Reverse: Shield with a rose across it, evocative of the sacrifices made by officers.

Mintage Data. Authorized by Public Law 104-329, signed by President William J. Clinton on October 20, 1996. *Maximum authorized*—500,000. *Number minted*—28,575 Uncirculated and 110,428 Proof.

Original Cost. Sale prices $30 (Uncirculated, pre-issue) and $33 (Proof, pre-issue); Uncirculated later raised to $32, and Proof later raised to $37.

Key to Collecting. Once the distribution figures were published, the missed opportunity was realized—collectors saw that these coins would be a modern rarity. The market price rose to a sharp premium, where it remains today. Nearly all coins approach perfection in quality.

	Distribution	Cert	Avg	%MS	MS-67 PF-67
1997-P ††	28,575	832	69.3	100%	$125
Auctions: $259, MS-70, May 2013; $206, MS-70, August 2014; $84, MS-69, February 2015					
1997-P, Proof	110,428	1,616	69.0		$65
Auctions: $353, PF-70DCam, April 2013; $243, PF-70DCam, September 2014; $60, PF-69DCam, January 2015					

†† Ranked in the *100 Greatest U.S. Modern Coins* (fourth edition).

JACKIE ROBINSON SILVER DOLLAR (1997)

Designer: *Alfred F. Maletsky (obverse), T. James Ferrell (reverse).* **Weight:** *26.73 grams.*
Composition: *.900 silver, .100 copper (net weight .7736 oz. pure silver).*
Diameter: *38.1 mm.* **Edge:** *Reeded.* **Mint:** *San Francisco.*

This silver dollar and a concurrently issued five-dollar gold coin commemorated the 50th anniversary of the first acceptance of a black player in a major league baseball game, Jack ("Jackie") Robinson being the hero. The watershed event took place at Ebbets Field on April 15, 1947.

Designs. *Obverse:* Robinson in game action stealing home plate, evocative of a 1955 World Series play in a contest between the New York Yankees and the Brooklyn Dodgers. *Reverse:* 50th anniversary logotype of the Jackie Robinson Foundation (a motif worn by all Major League Baseball players in the 1997 season) surrounded with lettering of two baseball accomplishments.

Mintage Data. Authorized on October 20, 1996, by Public Law 104-329, part of the United States Commemorative Coin Act of 1996, with a provision tied to Public Law 104-328 (for the Botanic Garden dollar). Coins could be minted for a full year beginning July 1, 1997. *Maximum authorized—200,000. Number minted—30,180 Uncirculated and 110,002 Proof.*

Original Cost. Sale prices $30 (Uncirculated, pre-issue) and $33 (Proof, pre-issue); Uncirculated later raised to $32, and Proof later raised to $37. The surcharge of $10 per coin went to the Jackie Robinson Foundation.

Key to Collecting. Although the Jackie Robinson coins were losers in the sales figures of the U.S. Mint, the small quantities issued made both coins winners in the return-on-investment sweepstakes. Today, each of these can be found without a problem, and nearly all are in superb gem preservation.

	Distribution	Cert	Avg	%MS	MS-67 / PF-67
1997-S	30,180	1,192	69.1	100%	$65
	Auctions: $411, MS-70, October 2014; $682, MS-70, January 2013				
1997-S, Proof	110,002	2,129	69.0		$55
	Auctions: $999, PF-70DCam, September 2014; $646, PF-70DCam, September 2013				

JACKIE ROBINSON $5 GOLD COIN (1997)

Designer: *William C. Cousins (obverse), James Peed (reverse).* **Weight:** *8.359 grams.*
Composition: *.900 gold, .100 copper (net weight .242 oz. pure gold).*
Diameter: *21.6 mm.* **Edge:** *Reeded.* **Mint:** *West Point.*

The U.S. Mint's marketing of the Jackie Robinson coins was innovative, as it had been in recent times. One promotion featured a reproduction of a rare baseball trading card, with the distinction of being the first such card ever issued by the U.S. government. But no matter how important Robinson's legacy was, buyers voted with their pocketbooks, and sales were low—making the Uncirculated gold coin a modern rarity.

Designs. *Obverse:* Portrait of Robinson in his later years as a civil-rights and political activist. *Reverse:* Detail of the seam on a baseball, Robinson's 1919–1972 life dates, and the inscription "Life of Courage."

Mintage Data. Authorized on October 20, 1996, by Public Law 104-329, part of the United States Commemorative Coin Act of 1996, with a provision tied to Public Law 104-328 (for the Botanic Garden dollar). Coins could be minted for a full year beginning July 1, 1997. *Maximum authorized*—100,000. *Number minted*—5,174 Uncirculated and 24,072 Proof.

Original Cost. Sale prices $180 (Uncirculated, pre-issue) and $195 (Proof, pre-issue); Uncirculated later raised to $205, and Proof later raised to $225. The surcharge of $35 per coin went to the Jackie Robinson Foundation.

Key to Collecting. The Jackie Robinson five-dollar gold coin takes top honors as the key issue among modern commemoratives. Especially rare and valuable is the Uncirculated version.

	Distribution	Cert	Avg	%MS	MS-67
					PF-67
1997-W ††	5,174	841	69.3	100%	$1,000
Auctions: $3,290, MS-70, February 2015; $3,055, MS-70, June 2015; $1,763, MS-69, February 2015; $1,645, MS-69, February 2015					
1997-W, Proof	24,072	1,524	69.3		$450
Auctions: $376, PF-69DCam, April 2015; $376, PF-69DCam, January 2015; $367, PF-69UCam, February 2015					

†† Ranked in the *100 Greatest U.S. Modern Coins* (fourth edition).

FRANKLIN D. ROOSEVELT $5 GOLD COIN (1997)

Designer: *T. James Ferrell (obverse), James Peed (reverse).* **Weight:** *8.359 grams.*
Composition: *.900 gold, .100 copper (net weight .242 oz. pure gold).*
Diameter: *21.6 mm.* **Edge:** *Reeded.* **Mint:** *West Point.*

Considering that newly inaugurated President Franklin D. Roosevelt suspended the mintage and paying out of U.S. gold coins in 1933, it was ironic that he should later have a gold coin commemorating his life. The year 1997 does not seem to have been a special anniversary date of any kind, as it was 115 years after his birth, 64 years after his inauguration, and 52 years after his death.

Designs. *Obverse:* Upper torso and head of Roosevelt facing right, based on one of the president's favorite photographs, taken when he was reviewing the U.S. Navy fleet in San Francisco Bay. *Reverse:* Presidential seal displayed at Roosevelt's 1933 inaugural.

Mintage Data. Authorized by Public Law 104-329, signed by President William J. Clinton on October 20, 1996. *Maximum authorized*—100,000. *Number minted*—11,894 Uncirculated and 29,474 Proof.

Original Cost. Sale prices $180 (Uncirculated, pre-issue) and $195 (Proof, pre-issue); Uncirculated later raised to $205, and Proof later raised to $225. A portion of the surcharge of $35 per coin went to the Franklin Delano Roosevelt Memorial Commission.

Key to Collecting. Since the mintages for both Uncirculated and Proof formats were low, their values rose substantially on the aftermarket. Examples are easily available today and are nearly always in superb gem preservation.

	Distribution	Cert	Avg	%MS	MS-67	
					PF-67	
1997-W	11,894	873	69.5	100%	$375	
	Auctions: $705, MS-70, August 2014; $611, MS-70, August 2014; $541, MS-70, April 2015; $535, MS-70, April 2015					
1997-W, Proof	29,474	1,763	69.3		$325	
	Auctions: $447, PF-69DCam, March 2013					

BLACK REVOLUTIONARY WAR PATRIOTS SILVER DOLLAR (1998)

Designer: *John Mercanti (obverse), Ed Dwight (reverse).* **Weight:** *26.73 grams.*
Composition: *.900 silver, .100 copper (net weight .7736 oz. pure silver).*
Diameter: *38.1 mm.* **Edge:** *Reeded.* **Mint:** *San Francisco.*

This coin commemorates black Revolutionary War patriots and the 275th anniversary of the birth of Crispus Attucks, the first patriot killed in the infamous Boston Massacre in 1770 (an event predating the Revolutionary War, one among many incidents that inflamed the pro-independence passions of Americans).

Designs. *Obverse:* U.S. Mint engraver John Mercanti's conception of Crispus Attucks.
Reverse: A black patriot family, a detail from the proposed Black Patriots Memorial.

Mintage Data. Authorized by Public Law 104-329, signed by President William J. Clinton on October 20, 1996. *Maximum authorized*—500,000. *Number minted*—37,210 Uncirculated and 75,070 Proof.

Original Cost. Sale prices $30 (Uncirculated, pre-issue) and $33 (Proof, pre-issue); Uncirculated later raised to $32, and Proof later raised to $37. A portion of the surcharge of $10 per coin went to the Black Revolutionary War Patriots Foundation to fund the construction of the Black Patriots Memorial in Washington, D.C.

Key to Collecting. These coins became highly desirable when the low mintage figures were published. Examples remain valuable today, and deservedly so. Nearly all are superb gems.

	Distribution	Cert	Avg	%MS	MS-67	
					PF-67	
1998-S	37,210	1,265	69.2	100%	$75	
	Auctions: $176, MS-70, April 2013					
1998-S, Proof	75,070	1,458	69.0		$50	
	Auctions: $353, PF-70DCam, April 2013					

ROBERT F. KENNEDY SILVER DOLLAR (1998)

Designer: *Thomas D. Rogers Sr.* **Weight:** *26.73 grams.*
Composition: *.900 silver, .100 copper (net weight .7736 oz. pure silver).*
Diameter: *38.1 mm.* **Edge:** *Reeded.* **Mint:** *San Francisco.*

These coins marked the 30th anniversary of the death of Robert F. Kennedy, attorney general of the United States appointed by his brother, President John F. Kennedy.

Designs. *Obverse:* Portrait of Robert F. Kennedy. *Reverse:* Eagle perched on a shield with JUSTICE above, Senate seal to lower left.

Mintage Data. Authorized by Public Law 103-328, signed by President William J. Clinton on September 29, 1994. *Maximum authorized—500,000. Number minted—106,422 Uncirculated and 99,020 Proof.*

Original Cost. Sale prices $30 (Uncirculated, pre-issue) and $33 (Proof, pre-issue); Uncirculated later raised to $32, and Proof later raised to $37. A portion of the surcharge of $10 per coin went to the Robert F. Kennedy Memorial.

Key to Collecting. Upon their publication the mintage figures were viewed as being attractively low from a numismatic viewpoint. Examples are easily found today and are usually superb gems.

	Distribution	Cert	Avg	%MS	MS-67
					PF-67
1998-S	106,422	3,057	69.3	100%	$30
	Auctions: $70, MS-70, July 2014; $129, MS-70, April 2013				
1998-S, Proof	99,020	1,511	69.0		$50
	Auctions: $282, PF-70DCam, September 2014; $270, PF-70DCam, September 2014				

DOLLEY MADISON SILVER DOLLAR (1999)

Designer: *Tiffany & Co.* **Weight:** *26.73 grams.*
Composition: *.900 silver, .100 copper (net weight .7736 oz. pure silver).*
Diameter: *38.1 mm.* **Edge:** *Reeded.* **Mint:** *Philadelphia.*

If the myth that Martha Washington was the subject for the 1792 silver half disme is discarded, Dolley Madison, wife of President James Madison, became the first of the first ladies to be depicted on a legal-tender U.S. coin with this silver dollar. The designs by Tiffany & Co. were modeled by T. James Ferrell (obverse) and Thomas D. Rogers Sr. (reverse). Note the T&Co. logo in a flower petal on the obverse and at the base of the trees to the right on the reverse.

Designs. *Obverse:* Portrait of Dolley Madison as depicted near the ice house (in the style of classic pergola) on the grounds of the family estate, Montpelier. A bouquet of cape jasmines is to the left. *Reverse:* Angular view of the front of Montpelier, complete with landscaping.

Mintage Data. Authorized by Public Law 104-329, signed by President William J. Clinton on October 20, 1996. *Maximum authorized*—500,000. *Number minted*—89,104 Uncirculated and 224,403 Proof.

Original Cost. Sale prices $30 (Uncirculated, pre-issue) and $33 (Proof, pre-issue); Uncirculated later raised to $32, and Proof later raised to $37. A portion of the surcharge of $10 per coin went to the National Trust for Historic Preservation.

Key to Collecting. The Dolley Madison dollars have been popular with collectors ever since they were first sold. Examples can be obtained with little effort and are usually superb gems.

	Distribution	Cert	Avg	%MS	MS-67 PF-67
1999-P	89,104	2,187	69.4	100%	$30
	Auctions: $90, MS-70, April 2013				
1999-P, Proof	224,403	2,629	69.1		$30
	Auctions: $106, PF-70DCam, April 2013				

GEORGE WASHINGTON DEATH BICENTENNIAL $5 GOLD COIN (1999)

Designer: *Laura Garden Fraser.* **Weight:** *8.359 grams.*
Composition: *.900 gold, .100 copper (net weight .242 oz. pure gold).*
Diameter: *21.6 mm.* **Edge:** *Reeded.* **Mint:** *West Point.*

The 200th anniversary of George Washington's death was commemorated with this coin. In 1932 Laura Garden Fraser's proposed Washington portrait for the quarter dollar had been rejected in favor of the portrait design by John Flanagan, but it was resurrected for this commemorative gold coin.

Designs. *Obverse:* A portrait of Washington inspired by the bust modeled in 1785 for French sculptor Jean Antoine Houdon. *Reverse:* A perched eagle with feathers widely separated at left and right.

Mintage Data. Authorized on October 20, 1996, by Public Law 104-329, part of the United States Commemorative Coin Act of 1996. *Maximum authorized*—100,000 pieces (both formats combined). *Number minted*—22,511 Uncirculated and 41,693 Proof.

Original Cost. Sale prices $180 (Uncirculated, pre-issue) and $195 (Proof, pre-issue); Uncirculated later raised to $195, and Proof later raised to $225. A portion of the surcharge went to the Mount Vernon Ladies' Association, which cares for Washington's home today.

Key to Collecting. This coin is readily available in any high grade desired.

	Distribution	Cert	Avg	%MS	MS-67 PF-67
1999-W	22,511	1,494	69.5	100%	$325
	Auctions: $423, MS-70, April 2015; $423, MS-70, April 2015; $400, MS-70, April 2015; $353, MS-70, April 2015				
1999-W, Proof	41,693	2,101	69.4		$325
	Auctions: $705, PF-70DCam, March 2013; $400, PF-70UCam, April 2015; $382, PF-69DCam, July 2014				

YELLOWSTONE NATIONAL PARK SILVER DOLLAR (1999)

Designer: *Edgar Z. Steever IV (obverse), William C. Cousins (reverse).* **Weight:** *26.73 grams.*
Composition: *.900 silver, .100 copper (net weight .7736 oz. pure silver).*
Diameter: *38.1 mm.* **Edge:** *Reeded.* **Mint:** *Philadelphia.*

This coin commemorated the 125th anniversary of the establishment of Yellowstone National Park. Technically, it came out and was dated two years later than it should have, as the park was founded in 1872 (and therefore the 125th anniversary would have been in 1997, not 1999).

Designs. *Obverse:* An unidentified geyser (not the famed Old Faithful, for the terrain is different) is shown in action. YELLOWSTONE is above, with other inscriptions to the left center and below, as illustrated. *Reverse:* A bison is shown, facing left. In the background is a mountain range with sun and resplendent rays (an adaptation of the seal of the Department of the Interior).

Mintage Data. Authorized on October 20, 1996, by Public Law 104-329, part of the United States Commemorative Coin Act of 1996. The catch-all legislation authorized seven commemoratives to be issued from 1997 to 1999. *Maximum authorized*—500,000 (both formats combined). *Number minted*—82,563 Uncirculated and 187,595 Proof.

Original Cost. Sale prices $30 (Uncirculated, pre-issue) and $33 (Proof, pre-issue); Uncirculated later raised to $32, and Proof later raised to $37.

Key to Collecting. Easily obtainable in the numismatic marketplace, nearly always in high grades. Investors are attracted to coins certified as MS-70 or PF-70, but few can tell the difference between these and coins at the 69 level. Only a tiny fraction of the mintage has ever been certified.

	Distribution	Cert	Avg	%MS	MS-67 PF-67
1999-P	82,563	1,872	69.3	100%	$38
	Auctions: No auction records available.				
1999-P, Proof	187,595	2,203	69.0		$40
	Auctions: $282, PF-70UCam, July 2015				

LIBRARY OF CONGRESS BICENTENNIAL SILVER DOLLAR (2000)

Designer: *Thomas D. Rogers Sr. (obverse), John Mercanti (reverse).* **Weight:** *26.73 grams.*
Composition: *.900 silver, .100 copper (net weight .7736 oz. pure silver).*
Diameter: *38.1 mm.* **Edge:** *Reeded.* **Mint:** *Philadelphia.*

The Library of Congress, located across the street from the U.S. Capitol in Washington, celebrated its 200th anniversary on April 24, 2000; these silver dollars and a ten-dollar bimetallic coin were issued to honor the milestone.

Designs. *Obverse:* An open book, with its spine resting on a closed book, with the torch of the Library of Congress dome behind. *Reverse:* The dome part of the Library of Congress.

Mintage Data. Authorized by Public Law 105-268, signed by President William J. Clinton on October 19, 1996. *Maximum authorized*—500,000. *Number minted*—53,264 Uncirculated and 198,503 Proof.

Original Cost. Sale prices $25 (Uncirculated, pre-issue) and $28 (Proof, pre-issue); Uncirculated later raised to $27, and Proof later raised to $32. A portion of the surcharges went to the Library of Congress Trust Fund Board.

Key to Collecting. The Library of Congress silver dollar (as well as the ten-dollar bimetallic coin issued alongside it) is readily available in the marketplace today, nearly always of the superb gem quality, as issued.

	Distribution	Cert	Avg	%MS	MS-67 PF-67
2000-P	53,264	1,616	69.4	100%	$22
	Auctions: $108, MS-70, April 2013; $76, MS-70, July 2014; $74, MS-70, October 2015				
2000-P, Proof	198,503	1,973	69.0		$27
	Auctions: $188, PF-70DCam, September 2014; $635, PF-70DCam, April 2013				

LIBRARY OF CONGRESS BICENTENNIAL $10 BIMETALLIC COIN (2000)

Designer: *John Mercanti (obverse), Thomas D. Rogers Sr. (reverse).*
Weight: *16.259 grams.* **Composition:** *.480 gold, .480 platinum, .040 alloy.*
Diameter: *27 mm.* **Edge:** *Reeded.* **Mint:** *West Point.*

This coin was the U.S. Mint's first gold/platinum bimetallic coin. The Library of Congress—the original location of which was burned by the British, but which was resurrected using Thomas Jefferson's personal book collection—is today a repository that includes 18 million books and more than 100 million other items, including periodicals, films, prints, photographs, and recordings.

Designs. *Obverse:* The torch of the Library of Congress dome. *Reverse:* An eagle surrounded by a wreath.

Mintage Data. Authorized by Public Law 105-268, signed by President William J. Clinton on October 19, 1996. *Maximum authorized*—200,000. *Number minted*—7,261 Uncirculated and 27,445 Proof.

Original Cost. Sale prices $380 (Uncirculated, pre-issue) and $395 (Proof, pre-issue); Uncirculated later raised to $405, and Proof later raised to $425. A portion of the surcharges went to the Library of Congress Trust Fund Board.

Key to Collecting. The Library of Congress ten-dollar bimetallic coin (as well as the silver dollar issued alongside it) is readily available in the marketplace today, nearly always of the superb gem quality as issued.

	Distribution	Cert	Avg	%MS	MS-67 PF-67
2000-W ††	7,261	1,420	69.7	100%	$1,200
	Auctions: $2,115, MS-70, June 2015; $1,998, MS-70, August 2015; $1,293, MS-69, October 2015; $1,175, MS-69, June 2015				
2000-W, Proof ††	27,445	3,176	69.2		$900
	Auctions: $2,115, PF-70DCam, September 2015; $1,763, PF-70UCam, October 2015; $823, PF-69UCam, October 2015				

†† Both 2000 Library of Congress $10 Bimetallic Coins are ranked in the *100 Greatest U.S. Modern Coins* (fourth edition), as a single entry.

LEIF ERICSON MILLENNIUM SILVER DOLLAR (2000)

Designer: *John Mercanti (obverse), T. James Ferrell (reverse).* **Weight:** *26.73 grams.*
Composition: *.900 silver, .100 copper (net weight .7736 oz. pure silver).*
Diameter: *38.1 mm.* **Edge:** *Reeded.* **Mint:** *Philadelphia.*

This silver dollar was issued in cooperation with a foreign government, the Republic of Iceland, which also sponsored its own coin, struck at the Philadelphia Mint (but with no mintmark), a silver 1,000 krónur. Both commemorated the millennium of the year 1000, the approximate departure date of Leif Ericson and his crew from Iceland to the New World.

Designs. *Obverse:* Portrait of Leif Ericson, an artist's conception, as no actual image survives—based on the image used on the Iceland 1 krónur coin. The helmeted head of the explorer is shown facing right. *Reverse:* A Viking long ship with high prow under full sail, FOUNDER OF THE NEW WORLD above, other inscriptions below.

Mintage Data. Authorized under Public Law 106-126. *Maximum authorized*—500,000. *Number minted*—28,150 Uncirculated and 144,748 Proof.

Original Cost. Sale prices $30 (Uncirculated, pre-issue) and $33 (Proof, pre-issue); Uncirculated later raised to $32, and Proof later raised to $37. The surcharge of $10 per coin went to the Leifur Eiriksson Foundation for funding student exchanges between the United States and Iceland.

Key to Collecting. These coins are readily available in the marketplace today.

	Distribution	Cert	Avg	%MS	MS-67 PF-67
2000-P	28,150	1,307	69.4	100%	$70
	Auctions: $223, MS-70, June 2015; $212, MS-70, January 2013; $176, MS-70, July 2014				
2000-P, Proof	144,748	2,212	69.0		$60
	Auctions: $999, PF-70DCam, September 2014; $999, PF-70DCam, April 2013				

AMERICAN BUFFALO SILVER DOLLAR (2001)

Designer: *James Earle Fraser.* **Weight:** *26.73 grams.*
Composition: *.900 silver, .100 copper (net weight .7736 oz. pure silver).*
Diameter: *38.1 mm.* **Edge:** *Reeded.* **Mints:** *Denver (Uncirculated) and Philadelphia (Proof).*

James Earle Fraser's design, originally used on nickels from 1913 to 1938, was modified slightly by Mint engravers for this silver dollar. Commonly called the "American Buffalo Commemorative," the coin debuted at the groundbreaking for the Smithsonian Institution's National Museum of the American Indian and was very well received.

Designs. *Obverse:* Portrait of a Native American facing right. *Reverse:* An American bison standing, facing left.

Mintage Data. Authorized by Public Law 106-375, October 27, 2000. *Maximum authorized*—500,000. *Number minted*—2001-D: 227,131 Uncirculated; 2001-P: 272,869 Proof.

Original Cost. Sale prices (pre-issue only) $30 (Uncirculated) and $33 (Proof). The surcharge of $10 per coin went to the National Museum of the American Indian.

Key to Collecting. Both the Uncirculated and Proof of the 2001 American Buffalo were carefully produced to high standards of quality. Nearly all examples today grade at high levels, including MS-70 and PF-70, these ultra-grades commanding a sharp premium for investors. Coins grading 68 or 69 often have little or any real difference in quality and would seem to be the best buys.

	Distribution	Cert	Avg	%MS	MS-67
					PF-67
2001-D ††	227,131	14,874	69.1	100%	$125
	Auctions: $259, MS-70, February 2015; $235, MS-70, July 2015; $259, MS-69, June 2015; $165, MS-69, January 2015				
2001-P, Proof ††	272,869	15,783	69.1		$120
	Auctions: $376, PF-70DCam, February 2015; $353, PF-70DCam, January 2015; $153, PF-69DCam, June 2015; $141, PF-69DCam, June 2015				

†† Both 2001 American Buffalo Silver Dollar varieties are ranked in the *100 Greatest U.S. Modern Coins* (fourth edition), as a single entry.

U.S. CAPITOL VISITOR CENTER HALF DOLLAR (2001)

Designer: *Dean McMullen (obverse), Alex Shagin and Marcel Jovine (reverse).* **Weight:** *11.34 grams.* **Composition:** *.9167 copper, .0833 nickel.* **Diameter:** *30.61 mm.* **Edge:** *Reeded.* **Mint:** *Philadelphia.*

In 1991 Congress voted on a Visitor Center to be established near the U.S. Capitol building. This copper-nickel half dollar, as well as a silver dollar and a ten-dollar gold coin, were decided upon to provide the funds through sale surcharges. The center and the coins did not become a reality until more than a decade later, though.

Designs. *Obverse:* The north wing of the original U.S. Capitol (burned by the British in 1814) is shown superimposed on a plan view of the present building. *Reverse:* Within a circle of 16 stars are inscriptions referring to the first meeting of the Senate and House.

Mintage Data. Authorized by Public Law 106-126, signed by President William J. Clinton on December 6, 1999. *Maximum authorized*—750,000. *Number minted*—99,157 Uncirculated and 77,962 Proof.

Original Cost. Sale prices $7.75 (Uncirculated, pre-issue) and $10.75 (Proof, pre-issue); Uncirculated later raised to $8.50, and Proof later raised to $11.50. The $3 surcharge per coin went towards the construction of the Visitor Center.

Key to Collecting. Today, this half dollar is readily available on the market, nearly always in the same gem quality as issued.

	Distribution	Cert	Avg	%MS	MS-67
					PF-67
2001-P	99,157	3,427	69.5	100%	$17
	Auctions: $153, MS-70, August 2013				
2001-P, Proof	77,962	1,359	69.0		$15
	Auctions: No auction records available.				

U.S. Capitol Visitor Center Silver Dollar (2001)

Designer: *Marika Somogyi (obverse), John Mercanti (reverse).* **Weight:** *26.73 grams.*
Composition: *.900 silver, .100 copper (net weight .7736 oz. pure silver).*
Diameter: *38.1 mm.* **Edge:** *Reeded.* **Mint:** *Philadelphia.*

The U.S. Capitol Visitor Center, as first proposed, was to offer free exhibits and films, and it was believed that the center would eliminate lengthy waits to view the Capitol proper. However, presumably many would still want to visit the Capitol itself, and no further plan to eliminate waiting time was presented. After the September 11, 2001, terrorist attack on the World Trade Center in New York City and the Pentagon in the District of Columbia, security at the Capitol was heightened—and the concept of the Visitor Center became even more important.

Designs. *Obverse:* The original Capitol is shown with the date 1800, and a much smaller later Capitol, with the date 2001—a variation on the same theme as used on the half dollar. *Reverse:* An eagle reminiscent of Mint engraver John Mercanti's reverse for the 1986 silver bullion "Eagle" dollar. In the present incarnation, the national bird wears a ribbon lettered U.S. CAPITOL VISITOR CENTER.

Mintage Data. Authorized by Public Law 106-126, signed by President William J. Clinton on December 6, 1999. *Maximum authorized*—500,000. *Number minted*—35,380 Uncirculated and 143,793 Proof.

Original Cost. Sale prices $27 (Uncirculated, pre-issue) and $29 (Proof, pre-issue); Uncirculated later raised to $29, and Proof later raised to $33. The $10 surcharge per coin went towards the construction of the Visitor Center.

Key to Collecting. Today, this silver dollar is readily available on the market, nearly always in the same gem quality as issued.

	Distribution	Cert	Avg	%MS	MS-67
					PF-67
2001-P	35,380	1,811	69.3	100%	$30
	Auctions: $129, MS-70, April 2013				
2001-P, Proof	143,793	2,203	69.0		$36
	Auctions: $294, PF-70DCam, February 2014; $4,113, PF-70DCam, April 2013				

U.S. Capitol Visitor Center $5 Gold Coin (2001)

Designer: *Elizabeth Jones.* **Weight:** *8.359 grams.* **Composition:** *.900 gold, .100 copper (net weight .242 oz. pure gold).* **Diameter:** *21.6 mm.* **Edge:** *Reeded.* **Mint:** *West Point.*

If there was a potential highlight for what proved to be yet another underperforming commemorative issue—with sales far below projections—it was that Elizabeth Jones, former chief engraver at the Mint, was tapped to do the obverse of the $5 gold coin in the Capitol Visitor Center series. The result might not be a showcase for her remarkable talent, given the nature of the subject, but it rounds out the suite of three commemorative coins with detailed architectural motifs.

Designs. *Obverse:* Section of a Corinthian column. *Reverse:* The 1800 Capitol (interestingly, with slightly different architectural details and proportions than seen on the other coins).

Mintage Data. Authorized by Public Law 106-126, signed by President William J. Clinton on December 6, 1999. *Maximum authorized*—100,000. *Number minted*—6,761 Uncirculated and 27,652 Proof.

Original Cost. Sale prices $175 (Uncirculated, pre-issue) and $177 (Proof, pre-issue); Uncirculated later raised to $200, and Proof later raised to $207. The $35 surcharge per coin went towards the construction of the Visitor Center.

Key to Collecting. Of all the Capitol Visitor Center commemoratives, the Uncirculated five-dollar gold coin is least often seen. After the distribution figure of only 6,761 was released for that coin, buyers clamored to acquire them, and the price rose sharply. Today, it still sells at one of the greatest premiums of any modern commemorative.

	Distribution	Cert	Avg	%MS	MS-67
					PF-67
2001-W ††	6,761	2,055	69.5	100%	$650
	Auctions: $1,087, MS-70, July 2014; $1,058, MS-70, August 2014; $881, MS-70, January 2015; $764, MS-70, June 2015				
2001-W, Proof	27,652	1,883	69.4		$325
	Auctions: No auction records available.				

†† Ranked in the *100 Greatest U.S. Modern Coins* (fourth edition).

Salt Lake City Olympic Winter Games Silver Dollar (2002)

Designer: *John Mercanti (obverse), Donna Weaver (reverse).* **Weight:** *26.73 grams.*
Composition: *.900 silver, .100 copper (net weight .7736 oz. pure silver).*
Diameter: *38.1 mm.* **Edge:** *Reeded.* **Mint:** *Denver (Uncirculated) and Philadelphia (Proof).*

In February 2002, Salt Lake City, Utah, was the focal point for the XIX Olympic Winter Games, a quadrennial event. Congress authorized both this silver dollar and a five-dollar gold coin to commemorate the competition.

Designs. *Obverse:* A stylized geometric figure representing an ice crystal. Five interlocked Olympic rings and inscriptions complete the picture, including XIX OLYMPIC WINTER GAMES. *Reverse:* The skyline of Salt Lake City is shown with exaggerated dimensions, with the rugged Wasatch Mountains in the distance. XIX OLYMPIC GAMES is repeated on the reverse.

Mintage Data. Authorized by Public Law 106-435, the Salt Lake Olympic Winter Games Commemorative Coin Act, signed by President William J. Clinton on November 6, 2000. *Maximum authorized*—400,000. *Number minted*—2002-D: 40,257 Uncirculated; 2002-P: 166,864 Proof.

Original Cost. Sale prices $30 (Uncirculated, pre-issue) and $33 (Proof, pre-issue); Uncirculated were later raised to $32, and Proof were later raised to $37. The surcharge of $10 per coin went to the Salt Lake Organizing Committee for the Olympic Winter Games of 2002 and the United States Olympic Committee.

Key to Collecting. As might be expected, coins encapsulated as MS-70 and PF-70 sell for strong prices to investors and Registry Set compilers. Most collectors are nicely satisfied with 68 and 69 grades, or the normal issue quality, since the coins are little different in actual appearance.

	Distribution	Cert	Avg	%MS	MS-67
					PF-67
2002-D	40,257	1,567	69.5	100%	$35
	Auctions: $94, MS-70, January 2013				
2002-P, Proof	166,864	2,175	69.1		$30
	Auctions: $217, PF-70DCam, April 2013				

SALT LAKE CITY OLYMPIC WINTER GAMES $5 GOLD COIN (2002)

Designer: *Donna Weaver.* **Weight:** *8.359 grams.*
Composition: *.900 gold, .100 copper (net weight .242 oz. pure gold).*
Diameter: *21.6 mm.* **Edge:** *Reeded.* **Mint:** *West Point.*

The design of the 2002 Olympic Winter Games commemoratives attracted little favorable notice outside of advertising publicity, and, once again, sales were low—all the more surprising, for Olympic coins often attract international buyers.

Designs. *Obverse:* An ice crystal dominates, superimposed over a geometric creation representing "Rhythm of the Land," but not identified. Also appearing are the date and SALT LAKE. *Reverse:* The outline of the Olympic cauldron is shown, with geometric sails above representing flames.

Mintage Data. Authorized by Public Law 106-435, the Salt Lake Olympic Winter Games Commemorative Coin Act, signed by President William J. Clinton on November 6, 2000. *Maximum authorized*—80,000. *Number minted*—10,585 Uncirculated and 32,877 Proof.

Original Cost. Sale prices $180 (Uncirculated, pre-issue) and $195 (Proof, pre-issue); Uncirculated were later raised to $205, and Proof were later raised to $225. The surcharge of $10 per coin went to the Salt Lake Organizing Committee for the Olympic Winter Games of 2002 and the United States Olympic Committee.

Key to Collecting. Although the mintage of the Uncirculated $5 in particular was quite low, there was not much interest in the immediate aftermarket. Coins graded MS-70 and PF-70 sell for strong prices to investors and Registry Set compilers.

	Distribution	Cert	Avg	%MS	MS-67
					PF-67
2002-W	10,585	1,197	69.5	100%	$325
	Auctions: $499, MS-70, August 2013; $397, MS-70, September 2014; $353, MS-70, April 2015				
2002-W, Proof	32,877	1,231	69.5		$325
	Auctions: $400, PF-70UCam, May 2015; $376, PF-70UCam, April 2015; $108, PF-70DCam, April 2013; $33, PF-69DCam, August 2014				

West Point (U.S. Military Academy) Bicentennial Silver Dollar (2002)

Designer: *T. James Ferrell (obverse), John Mercanti (reverse).* **Weight:** *26.73 grams.*
Composition: *.900 silver, .100 copper (net weight .7736 oz. pure silver).*
Diameter: *38.1 mm.* **Edge:** *Reeded.* **Mint:** *West Point.*

The 200th anniversary of the U.S. Military Academy at West Point, New York, was celebrated with this coin. The Cadet Chapel is shown on the obverse of the dollar.

Designs. *Obverse:* A fine depiction of the Academy color guard in a parade, with Washington Hall and the Cadet Chapel in the distance— and minimum intrusion of lettering—projects this to the forefront of commemorative designs of the era. *Reverse:* The West Point Bicentennial logotype is shown, an adaptation of the Academy seal, showing at the center an ancient Greek helmet with a sword and shield.

Mintage Data. Authorized several years earlier by Public Law 103-328, signed by President William J. Clinton on September 29, 1994. *Maximum authorized—*500,000. *Number minted—*103,201 Uncirculated and 288,293 Proof.

Original Cost. Sale prices $30 (Uncirculated, pre-issue) and $32 (Proof, pre-issue); Uncirculated later raised to $32, and Proof later raised to $37. The surcharge of $10 per coin went to the Association of Graduates.

Key to Collecting. The scenario is familiar: enough coins were struck to satisfy all comers during the period of issue, with the result that there was no unsatisfied demand. Coins certified at the MS-70 level appeal to a special group of buyers and command strong premiums.

	Distribution	Cert	Avg	%MS	MS-67
					PF-67
2002-W	103,201	4,472	69.5	100%	$25
	Auctions: No auction records available.				
2002-W, Proof	288,293	5,565	69.3		$35
	Auctions: No auction records available.				

First Flight Centennial Half Dollar (2003)

Designer: *John Mercanti (obverse), Norman E. Nemeth (reverse).* **Weight:** *11.34 grams.*
Composition: *.9167 copper, .0833 nickel.* **Diameter:** *30.61 mm.* **Edge:** *Reeded.* **Mint:** *Philadelphia.*

To celebrate the 100th anniversary of powered aircraft flight by Orville and Wilbur Wright in 1903, Congress authorized a set of 2003-dated commemoratives, including this copper-nickel half dollar.

Designs. *Obverse:* Wright Monument at Kill Devil Hill on the North Carolina seashore. *Reverse:* Wright Flyer biplane in flight.

Mintage Data. Authorized by Public Law 105-124, as an amendment and tag-on to the 50 States Commemorative Coin Program Act (which authorized the State quarters), signed by President William J. Clinton on December 1, 1997. *Maximum authorized*—750,000. *Number minted*—57,122 Uncirculated and 109,710 Proof.

Original Cost. Sale prices $9.75 (Uncirculated, pre-issue) and $12.50 (Proof, pre-issue); Uncirculated later raised to $10.75, and Proof later raised to $13.50. The surcharge of $1 per coin went to the First Flight Centennial Foundation, a private nonprofit group founded in 1995.

Key to Collecting. Values fell after sales concluded. In time, they recovered. Today, all the coins in this set sell for a premium. Superb gems are easily enough found.

	Distribution	Cert	Avg	%MS	MS-67
					PF-67
2003-P	57,122	2,186	69.5	100%	$15
Auctions: $50, MS-70, April 2013					
2003-P, Proof	109,710	2,093	69.1		$17
Auctions: No auction records available.					

FIRST FLIGHT CENTENNIAL SILVER DOLLAR (2003)

Designer: *T. James Ferrell (obverse), Norman E. Nemeth (reverse).* **Weight:** *26.73 grams.*
Composition: *.900 silver, .100 copper (net weight .7736 oz. pure silver).*
Diameter: *38.1 mm.* **Edge:** *Reeded.* **Mint:** *Philadelphia.*

The release of this coin and the two other First Flight Centennial commemoratives with it marked the third straight year that a coin featuring the Wrights' plane was featured on a U.S. coin. In 2001, the North Carolina State quarter had portrayed the Wright Flyer, and the Ohio State quarter did the same in 2002 (though an astronaut was also incorporated).

Designs. *Obverse:* Conjoined portraits of Orville and Wilbur Wright. *Reverse:* The Wright brothers' plane in flight.

Mintage Data. Authorized by Public Law 105-124, as an amendment and tag-on to the 50 States Commemorative Coin Program Act (which authorized the State quarters), signed by President William J. Clinton on December 1, 1997. *Maximum authorized*—500,000. *Number minted*—53,533 Uncirculated and 190,240 Proof.

Original Cost. Sale prices $31 (Uncirculated, pre-issue) and $33 (Proof, pre-issue); Uncirculated later raised to $33, and Proof later raised to $37. The surcharge of $1 per coin went to the First Flight Centennial Foundation, a private nonprofit group founded in 1995.

Key to Collecting. Values fell after sales concluded, but they did recover in time. Today, all the coins in this program sell for a premium. Superb gems are easily enough found.

	Distribution	Cert	Avg	%MS	MS-67
					PF-67
2003-P	53,533	3,154	69.4	100%	$40
Auctions: $94, MS-70, May 2013					
2003-P, Proof	190,240	3,133	69.0		$42
Auctions: $423, PF-70DCam, March 2013; $141, PF-70DCam, April 2013					

First Flight Centennial $10 Gold Coin (2003)

Designer: *Donna Weaver (obverse), Norman E. Nemeth (reverse).* **Weight:** *16.718 grams.*
Composition: *.900 gold, .100 copper (net weight .4837 oz. pure gold).*
Diameter: *27 mm.* **Edge:** *Reeded.* **Mint:** *West Point.*

None of the First Flight Centennial commemoratives sold particularly well. The redundancy of the motifs undoubtedly contributed to this: each had the same reverse motif of the Wright brothers' plane, and the two largest denominations each pictured the Wright brothers.

Designs. *Obverse:* Portraits of Orville and Wilbur Wright. *Reverse:* Wright Brothers' plane in flight with an eagle overhead.

Mintage Data. Authorized by Public Law 105-124, as an amendment and tag-on to the 50 States Commemorative Coin Program Act (which authorized the State quarters), signed by President William J. Clinton on December 1, 1997. *Maximum authorized*—100,000. *Number minted*—10,009 Uncirculated and 21,676 Proof.

Original Cost. Sale prices $340 (Uncirculated, pre-issue) and $350 (Proof, pre-issue); Uncirculated later raised to $365, and Proof later raised to $375. The surcharge of $1 per coin went to the First Flight Centennial Foundation, a private nonprofit group founded in 1995.

Key to Collecting. Values fell after sales concluded, but they did recover in time. Today, all the coins in this commemorative program sell for a premium. Superb gems are easily enough found.

	Distribution	Cert	Avg	%MS	MS-67
					PF-67
2003-W ††	10,009	1,914	69.8	100%	$700
Auctions: $823, MS-70, July 2015; $793, MS-70, January 2015; $617, MS-69, July 2015; $588, MS-69, June 2015					
2003-W, Proof	21,676	1,626	69.3		$700
Auctions: $823, PF-70DCam, July 2014; $1,293, PF-70DCam, April 2013					

†† Ranked in the *100 Greatest U.S. Modern Coins* (fourth edition).

Thomas Alva Edison Silver Dollar (2004)

Designer: *Donna Weaver (obverse), John Mercanti (reverse).* **Weight:** *26.73 grams.*
Composition: *.900 silver, .100 copper (net weight .7736 oz. pure silver).*
Diameter: *38.1 mm.* **Edge:** *Reeded.* **Mint:** *Philadelphia.*

The 125th anniversary of the October 21, 1879, demonstration by Thomas Edison of his first successful electric light bulb was the event commemorated with this silver dollar. Despite sales falling far short of the authorized amount, the Edison dollar was well received by collectors. Interestingly, several proposals had earlier been made for commemoratives to be issued in 1997 to observe the 150th anniversary of Edison's February 11, 1847, birth in Milan, Ohio.

Designs. *Obverse:* Waist-up portrait of Edison holding a light bulb in his right hand. *Reverse:* Light bulb of the 1879 style mounted on a base, with arcs surrounding.

Mintage Data. Authorized by Public Law 105-331, signed by President William J. Clinton on December 6, 1999. *Maximum authorized—*500,000. *Number minted—*92,510 Uncirculated and 211,055 Proof.

Original Cost. Sale prices $31 (Uncirculated, pre-issue) and $33 (Proof, pre-issue); Uncirculated later raised to $33, and Proof later raised to $37. The surcharge of $10 per coin was to be divided evenly among the Port Huron (Michigan) Museum of Arts and History, the Edison Birthplace Association, the National Park Service, the Edison Plaza Museum, the Edison Winter Home and Museum, the Edison Institute, the Edison Memorial Tower, and the Hall of Electrical History.

Key to Collecting. Examples are plentiful. Nearly all are superb gems. As was the situation for many other U.S. Mint issues of the period, promoters who had coins encased in certified holders marked MS-70 or PF-70 were able to persuade, or at least imply, to investors (but not to seasoned collectors) that coins of such quality were rarities, and obtained strong prices for them. Smart buyers simply purchased examples remaining in original Mint holders, of which many were just as nice as the "70" coins.

	Distribution	Cert	Avg	%MS	MS-67
					PF-67
2004-P	92,510	2,807	69.3	100%	$30
	Auctions: $90, MS-70, April 2013				
2004-P, Proof	211,055	3,402	69.1		$30
	Auctions: $78, PF-70DCam, July 2014; $141, PF-70DCam, March 2013				

LEWIS AND CLARK BICENTENNIAL SILVER DOLLAR (2004)

Designer: *Donna Weaver.* **Weight:** *26.73 grams.*
Composition: *.900 silver, .100 copper (net weight .7736 oz. pure silver).*
Diameter: *38.1 mm.* **Edge:** *Reeded.* **Mint:** *Philadelphia.*

This was one of the most successful commemorative programs, despite the fact that many events across the nation celebrating the bicentennial were flops. Note that the Lewis and Clark Expedition had previously been commemorated with gold dollars dated 1903 for the Louisiana Purchase Exposition (St. Louis World's Fair held in 1904) and those of 1904 and 1905 for the Lewis and Clark Exposition (Portland, Oregon, 1905).

Designs. *Obverse:* Meriwether Lewis and William Clark standing with a river and foliage in the distance as a separate motif. Lewis holds the barrel end of his rifle in one hand and a journal in the other and is looking at Clark, who is gazing to the distance in the opposite direction. *Reverse:* Copy of the reverse of the Jefferson Indian Peace medal designed by John Reich and presented to Indians on the expedition (the identical motif was also revived for use on one variety of the 2004 Jefferson nickel). Feathers are to the left and right, and 17 stars are above.

Mintage Data. Authorized by Public Law 106-136, signed by President William J. Clinton on December 6, 1999. *Maximum authorized—*500,000. *Number minted—*142,015 Uncirculated and 351,989 Proof.

Original Cost. Sale prices $33 (Uncirculated, pre-issue) and $35 (Proof, pre-issue); Uncirculated later raised to $35, and Proof later raised to $39. Two-thirds of the surcharge of $10 per coin went to the National Council of the Lewis and Clark Bicentennial, while one-third went to the National Park Service for the bicentennial celebration.

Key to Collecting. Superb gem coins are readily available.

	Distribution	Cert	Avg	%MS	MS-67
					PF-67
2004-P	142,015	4,128	69.4	100%	$30
	Auctions: $90, MS-70, April 2013				
2004-P, Proof	351,989	5,721	69.1		$35
	Auctions: $88, PF-70DCam, February 2013				

MARINE CORPS 230TH ANNIVERSARY SILVER DOLLAR (2005)

Designer: *Norman E. Nemeth (obverse), Charles L. Vickers (reverse).* **Weight:** *26.73 grams.*
Composition: *.900 silver, .100 copper (net weight .7736 oz. pure silver).*
Diameter: *38.1 mm.* **Edge:** *Reeded.* **Mint:** *Philadelphia.*

The widespread appreciation of the heritage of the Marine Corps plus the fame of the obverse design taken from Joe Rosenthal's photograph of the flag-raising at Iwo Jima, propelled this coin to remarkable success. For the first time in recent memory, pandemonium reigned in the coin market, as prices rose, buyers clamored to find all they could, and most dealers were sold out. Within a year, interest turned to other things, and the prices dropped, but not down to the issue levels.

Designs. *Obverse:* Marines raising the Stars and Stripes over Iwo Jima as shown on the famous photograph by Joe Rosenthal. *Reverse:* Eagle, globe, and anchor emblem of the Marine Corps.

Mintage Data. Authorized under Public Law 108-291, signed by President George W. Bush on August 6, 2004. *Maximum authorized*—500,000, later increased to 600,000. *Number minted*—49,671 Uncirculated and 548,810 Proof.

Original Cost. Sale prices $33 (Uncirculated, pre-issue) and $35 (Proof, pre-issue); Uncirculated later raised to $35, and Proof later raised to $39. The surcharge of $10 per coin went toward the construction of the Marine Corps Heritage Center at the base in Quantico, Virginia.

Key to Collecting. Superb gem coins are readily available.

	Distribution	Cert	Avg	%MS	MS-67
					PF-67
2005-P	49,671	12,110	69.6	100%	$45
	Auctions: $89, MS-70, January 2015; $76, MS-70, July 2014; $62, MS-70, August 2014				
2005-P, Proof	548,810	14,272	69.2		$43
	Auctions: $165, PF-70DCam, November 2013				

CHIEF JUSTICE JOHN MARSHALL SILVER DOLLAR (2005)

Designer: *John Mercanti (obverse), Donna Weaver (reverse).* **Weight:** *26.73 grams.*
Composition: *.900 silver, .100 copper (net weight .7736 oz. pure silver).*
Diameter: *38.1 mm.* **Edge:** *Reeded.* **Mint:** *Philadelphia.*

Chief Justice John Marshall, who served 34 years in that post in the U.S. Supreme Court, was the subject for this commemorative dollar. Mint engravers submitted designs for the coin, with six depictions of Marshall inspired by a painting by Saint-Mèmin, ten from an oil painting by Rembrandt Peale, and three from a statue by William W. Story. It was John Mercanti's interpretation of the Saint-Mèmin work that was selected.

Designs. *Obverse:* Portrait of Marshall, adapted from a painting made in March 1808 by Charles-Balthazar-Julien Fevret de Saint-Mèmin, of France. *Reverse:* The old Supreme Court Chamber within the Capitol.

Mintage Data. Authorized by Public Law 108-290, signed by President George W. Bush on August 9, 2004. *Maximum authorized*—400,000. *Number minted*—67,096 Uncirculated and 196,753 Proof.

Original Cost. Sale prices $33 (Uncirculated, pre-issue) and $35 (Proof, pre-issue); Uncirculated later raised to $35, and Proof later raised to $39. The surcharge of $10 per coin went to the Supreme Court Historical Society.

Key to Collecting. Superb gem coins are available in the marketplace.

	Distribution	Cert	Avg	%MS	MS-67
					PF-67
2005-P	67,096	2,353	69.6	100%	$37
	Auctions: $106, MS-70, January 2013				
2005-P, Proof	196,753	3,259	69.3		$35
	Auctions: $86, PF-70DCam, July 2014; $92, PF-70DCam, March 2013				

BENJAMIN FRANKLIN TERCENTENARY SCIENTIST SILVER DOLLAR (2006)

Designer: *Norman E. Nemeth (obverse), Charles L. Vickers (reverse).* **Weight:** *26.73 grams.*
Composition: *.900 silver, .100 copper (net weight .7736 oz. pure silver).*
Diameter: *38.1 mm.* **Edge:** *Reeded.* **Mint:** *Philadelphia.*

Two silver dollars were issued to commemorate the 300th anniversary of Benjamin Franklin's birth. This version celebrated Franklin's scientific accomplishments, which included discoveries in fields from electricity to oceanography to demographics.

Designs. *Obverse:* Franklin standing with a kite on a string, evocative of his experiments with lightning in June 1752. *Reverse:* Franklin's political cartoon, featuring a snake cut apart, titled "Join, or Die," reflecting the sentiment that the colonies should unite during the French and Indian War (and which had nothing to do with perceived offenses by the British, at this early time). This appeared in Franklin's *Pennsylvania Gazette* on May 9, 1754.

Mintage Data. Authorized by Public Law 104-463, the Benjamin Franklin Tercentenary Act, and signed by President George W. Bush on December 21, 2004. *Maximum authorized—250,000. Number minted*—58,000 Uncirculated, 142,000 Proof.

Original Cost. Sale prices $33 (Uncirculated, pre-issue) and $35 (Proof, pre-issue); Uncirculated later raised to $35, and Proof later raised to $39. The surcharge of $10 per coin went to the Franklin Institute.

Key to Collecting. Superb gems are easily found in the marketplace.

	Distribution	Cert	Avg	%MS	MS-67
					PF-67
2006-P	58,000	7,643	69.7	100%	$31
	Auctions: $76, MS-70, January 2013				
2006-P, Proof	142,000	9,868	69.4		$28
	Auctions: No auction records available.				

Benjamin Franklin Tercentenary
Founding Father Silver Dollar (2006)

Designer: *Don Everhart (obverse), Donna Weaver (reverse).* **Weight:** *26.73 grams.*
Composition: *.900 silver, .100 copper (net weight .7736 oz. pure silver).*
Diameter: *38.1 mm.* **Edge:** *Reeded.* **Mint:** *Philadelphia.*

The bill authorizing the issue of this silver dollar and its counterpart (see previous coin) took note of many of his accomplishments, stating he was "the only Founding Father to sign all of our Nation's organizational documents," who printed "official currency for the colonies of Pennsylvania, Delaware, New Jersey and Maryland," and helped design the Great Seal of the United States.

Designs. *Obverse:* Head and shoulders portrait of Franklin facing forward slightly to the viewer's right, with his signature reproduced below. *Reverse:* Copy of a 1776 Continental dollar within a frame of modern lettering. The mottoes on this coin were suggested by Franklin.

Mintage Data. Authorized by Public Law 104-463, the Benjamin Franklin Tercentenary Act, and signed by President George W. Bush on December 21, 2004. *Maximum authorized—250,000. Number minted*—58,000 Uncirculated, 142,000 Proof.

Original Cost. Sale prices $33 (Uncirculated, pre-issue) and $35 (Proof, pre-issue); Uncirculated later raised to $35, and Proof later raised to $39. The surcharge of $10 per coin went to the Franklin Institute.

Key to Collecting. Superb gems are easily found in the marketplace.

	Distribution	Cert	Avg	%MS	MS-67
					PF-67
2006-P	58,000	8,232	69.8	100%	$35
	Auctions: $90, MS-70, April 2013				
2006-P, Proof	142,000	10,164	69.7		$45
	Auctions: $96, PF-70DCam, January 2013; $103, PF-70DCam, April 2013				

SAN FRANCISCO OLD MINT CENTENNIAL SILVER DOLLAR (2006)

Designer: *Sherl J. Winter (obverse), Joseph Menna after George T. Morgan (reverse).*
Weight: *26.73 grams.* **Composition:** *.900 silver, .100 copper (net weight .7736 oz. pure silver).*
Diameter: *38.1 mm.* **Edge:** *Reeded.* **Mint:** *San Francisco.*

This coin and the five-dollar gold coin issued alongside it celebrated the 100th anniversary of the second San Francisco Mint surviving the 1906 Bay Area earthquake and fire.

Designs. *Obverse:* The Second San Francisco Mint as viewed from off the left front corner. *Reverse:* Copy of the reverse of a standard Morgan silver dollar of the era 1878–1921, said to have been taken from a 1904-S.

Mintage Data. Authorized by Public Law 109-230, the San Francisco Old Mint Commemorative Act, signed by President George W. Bush in June 2006. *Maximum authorized—500,000. Number minted—67,100 Uncirculated and 160,870 Proof.*

Original Cost. Sale prices $33 (Uncirculated, pre-issue) and $35 (Proof, pre-issue); Uncirculated later raised to $35, and Proof later raised to $39. The surcharge of $10 per coin went to the "San Francisco Museum and Historical Society for rehabilitating the Historic Old Mint as a city museum and an American Coin and Gold Rush Museum."

Key to Collecting. Superb gems are easily found in the marketplace.

	Distribution	Cert	Avg	%MS	MS-67 PF-67
2006-S	67,100	4,570	69.6	100%	$37
Auctions: $94, MS-70, January 2013					
2006-S, Proof	160,870	8,491	69.2		$35
Auctions: No auction records available.					

SAN FRANCISCO OLD MINT CENTENNIAL $5 GOLD COIN (2006)

Designer: *Charles L. Vickers (obverse), Don Everhart after Christian Gobrecht (reverse).*
Weight: *8.359 grams.* **Composition:** *.900 gold, .100 copper (net weight .242 oz. pure gold).*
Diameter: *21.6 mm.* **Edge:** *Reeded.* **Mint:** *San Francisco.*

The designs of this coin and the corresponding silver dollar both had obverses showing the same subject (albeit from a different view), and reverses being copies of old coinage designs.

Designs. *Obverse:* Front view of the portico of the Second San Francisco Mint, with a portion of the building to each side. Modeled after an 1869 construction drawing by Supervising Architect A.B. Mullet. *Reverse:* Copy of the reverse of the Liberty Head half eagle with motto IN GOD WE TRUST, as regularly used from 1866 to 1907.

Mintage Data. Authorized by Public Law 109-230, the San Francisco Old Mint Commemorative Act, signed by President George W. Bush in June 2006. *Maximum authorized*—100,000. *Number minted*—17,500 Uncirculated and 44,174 Proof.

Original Cost. Sale prices $220 (Uncirculated, pre-issue) and $230 (Proof, pre-issue); Uncirculated later raised to $245, and Proof later raised to $255. The surcharge of $35 per coin went to the "San Francisco Museum and Historical Society for rehabilitating the Historic Old Mint as a city museum and an American Coin and Gold Rush Museum."

Key to Collecting. Superb gems are easily found in the marketplace.

	Distribution	Cert	Avg	%MS	MS-67 PF-67
2006-S	17,500	2,786	69.7	100%	$325
	Auctions: $329, MS-70, October 2014; $294, MS-70, July 2015; $306, MS-69, July 2015; $282, MS-69, October 2015				
2006-S, Proof	44,174	3,882	69.5		$325
	Auctions: $376, PF-70UCam, February 2015; $353, PF-70UCam, July 2015; $341, PF-70UCam, February 2015				

JAMESTOWN 400TH ANNIVERSARY SILVER DOLLAR (2007)

Designer: *Donna Weaver (obverse), Susan Gamble (reverse).* **Weight:** *26.73 grams.*
Composition: *.900 silver, .100 copper (net weight .7736 oz. pure silver).*
Diameter: *38.1 mm.* **Edge:** *Reeded.* **Mint:** *Philadelphia.*

Note that Jamestown was also honored on the 2000 Virginia State quarter.

Designs. *Obverse:* Captain John Smith is shown with an Indian man and woman. *Reverse:* Three sailing ships are shown, elements already seen from the 2000 State quarter, but differently arranged.

Mintage Data. Authorized by Public Law 108-289, the Jamestown 400th Anniversary Commemorative Coin Act, signed by President George W. Bush on August 6, 2004. *Maximum authorized*—500,000. *Number minted*—81,034 Uncirculated and 260,363 Proof.

Original Cost. Sale prices $33 (Uncirculated, pre-issue) and $35 (Proof, pre-issue); Uncirculated later raised to $35, and Proof later raised to $39. The surcharge of $20 per coin went to fund the public observance of the anniversary.

Key to Collecting. Superb gem coins are readily available.

	Distribution	Cert	Avg	%MS	MS-67 PF-67
2007-P	81,034	7,671	69.6	100%	$30
	Auctions: $90, MS-70, April 2013				
2007-P, Proof	260,363	10,829	69.5		$30
	Auctions: $100, PF-70DCam, April 2013				

JAMESTOWN 400TH ANNIVERSARY $5 GOLD COIN (2007)

Designer: *John Mercanti (obverse), Susan Gamble (reverse).* **Weight:** *8.359 grams.*
Composition: *.900 gold, .100 copper (net weight .242 oz. pure gold).*
Diameter: *21.6 mm.* **Edge:** *Reeded.* **Mint:** *West Point.*

Susan Gamble, who designed the reverse of both this coin and the silver dollar issued alongside it, was a participant in the Mint's Artistic Infusion Program, which was created to bring artists in from the private sector to upgrade the quality of coin designs.

Designs. *Obverse:* Captain John Smith is shown with Indian chief Powhatan, who holds a bag of corn. *Reverse:* Ruins of the old church at Jamestown.

Mintage Data. Authorized by Public Law 108-289, the Jamestown 400th Anniversary Commemorative Coin Act, signed by President George W. Bush on August 6, 2004. *Maximum authorized*—100,000. *Number minted*—18,623 Uncirculated and 47,123 Proof.

Original Cost. Sale prices $33 (Uncirculated, pre-issue) and $35 (Proof, pre-issue); Uncirculated later raised to $35, and Proof later raised to $39. The surcharge of $35 per coin went to fund the public observance of the anniversary.

Key to Collecting. Superb gem coins are readily available.

	Distribution	Cert	Avg	%MS	MS-67
					PF-67
2007-W	18,623	3,225	69.8	100%	$325
Auctions: $353, MS-70, April 2015; $329, MS-70, November 2014; $306, MS-70, July 2015; $294, MS-70, July 2015					
2007-W, Proof	47,123	4,152	69.6		$325
Auctions: $341, PF-70DCam, July 2014; $317, PF-70DCam, August 2014; $306, PF-70UCam, July 2015					

LITTLE ROCK CENTRAL HIGH SCHOOL DESEGREGATION SILVER DOLLAR (2007)

Designer: *Richard Masters (obverse), Don Everhart (reverse).* **Weight:** *26.73 grams.*
Composition: *.900 silver, .100 copper (net weight .7736 oz. pure silver).*
Diameter: *38.1 mm.* **Edge:** *Reeded.* **Mint:** *Philadelphia.*

This coin commemorated the 50th anniversary of the desegregation of Little Rock Central High School, which was the result of the landmark U.S. Supreme Court case *Brown v. the Board of Education.*

Designs. *Obverse:* The feet of the "Little Rock Nine" students are shown, escorted by a soldier. *Reverse:* Little Rock Central High School as it appeared in 1957.

Mintage Data. Authorized by Public Law 109-146, the Little Rock Central High School Desegregation 50th Anniversary Commemorative Coin Act, signed by President George W. Bush on December 22, 2005. *Maximum authorized*—500,000. *Number minted*—66,093 Uncirculated and 124,678 Proof.

Original Cost. Sale prices $33 (Uncirculated, pre-issue) and $35 (Proof, pre-issue); Uncirculated later raised to $35, and Proof later raised to $39. The surcharge of $10 per coin went toward improvements at the Little Rock Central High School National Historic Site.

Key to Collecting. Superb gem coins are readily available.

	Distribution	Cert	Avg	%MS	MS-67 PF-67
2007-P	66,093	2,652	69.7	100%	$28
	Auctions: $79, MS-70, October 2014; $90, MS-70, April 2013				
2007-P, Proof	124,678	3,058	69.5		$25
	Auctions: $80, PF-70DCam, July 2014; $113, PF-70DCam, April 2013				

BALD EAGLE RECOVERY AND NATIONAL EMBLEM HALF DOLLAR (2008)

Designer: *Susan Gamble (obverse), Donna Weaver (reverse).* **Weight:** *11.34 grams.*
Composition: *.9167 copper, .0833 nickel.* **Diameter:** *30.61 mm.* **Edge:** *Reeded.* **Mint:** *San Francisco.*

This copper-nickel half dollar, as well as the silver dollar and five-dollar gold coin issued alongside it, was issued to commemorate the recovery of the bald eagle species, the 35th anniversary of the Endangered Species Act of 1973, and the removal of the bald eagle from the Endangered Species List.

Designs. *Obverse:* Two eaglets and an egg in a bald eagle nest. *Reverse:* "Challenger," a non-releasable bald eagle in the care of the American Eagle Foundation and the first of his species to be trained to free-fly into major sporting events during the National Anthem.

Mintage Data. Authorized by Public Law 108-486, the Bald Eagle Commemorative Coin Act, signed by President George W. Bush on December 23, 2004. *Maximum authorized*—750,000. *Number minted*—120,180 Uncirculated and 220,577 Proof.

Original Cost. Sale prices $7.95 (Uncirculated, pre-issue) and $9.95 (Proof, pre-issue); Uncirculated later raised to $8.95, and Proof later raised to $10.95. The surcharge of $3 per coin went to the American Eagle Foundation of Tennessee for the purposes of continuing its work to save and protect bald eagles nationally.

Key to Collecting. Superb gem coins are readily available.

	Distribution	Cert	Avg	%MS	MS-67 PF-67
2008-S	120,180	6,797	69.8	100%	$15
	Auctions: $30, MS-70, April 2013				
2008-S, Proof	220,577	8,831	69.7		$17
	Auctions: No auction records available.				

BALD EAGLE RECOVERY AND NATIONAL EMBLEM SILVER DOLLAR (2008)

Designer: *Joel Iskowitz (obverse), Jim Licaretz (reverse).* **Weight:** *26.73 grams.*
Composition: *.900 silver, .100 copper (net weight .7736 oz. pure silver).*
Diameter: *38.1 mm.* **Edge:** *Reeded.* **Mint:** *Philadelphia.*

The bald eagle, selected in 1782 by the Second Continental Congress as the national emblem of the United States, was common at the time of the nation's establishment. Through the years, however, poaching, habitat destruction, pesticides, and food-source contamination reduced the number of nesting pairs from approximately 100,000 to just more than 400 in the early 1960s. Fortunately, conservationists have saved the species in the past five decades.

Designs. *Obverse:* Bald eagle in flight, mountains in background. *Reverse:* The Great Seal of the United States used from 1782 to 1841.

Mintage Data. Authorized by Public Law 108-486, the Bald Eagle Commemorative Coin Act, signed by President George W. Bush on December 23, 2004. *Maximum authorized—500,000. Number minted—119,204* Uncirculated and 294,601 Proof.

Original Cost. Sale prices $35.95 (Uncirculated, pre-issue) and $39.95 (Proof, pre-issue); Uncirculated later raised to $37.95, and Proof later raised to $43.95. The surcharge of $10 per coin went to the American Eagle Foundation of Tennessee for the purposes of continuing its work to save and protect bald eagles nationally.

Key to Collecting. Superb gem coins are readily available.

	Distribution	Cert	Avg	%MS	MS-67 PF-67
2008-P	119,204	9,088	69.7	100%	$28
	Auctions: $90, MS-70, April 2013				
2008-P, Proof	294,601	13,566	69.3		$25
	Auctions: $92, PF-70DCam, July 2014; $89, PF-70UCam, July 2015; $79, PF-70DCam, July 2014				

BALD EAGLE RECOVERY AND NATIONAL EMBLEM $5 GOLD COIN (2008)

Designer: *Susan Gamble (obverse), Don Everhart (reverse).* **Weight:** *8.359 grams.*
Composition: *.900 gold, .100 copper (net weight .242 oz. pure gold).*
Diameter: *21.6 grams.* **Edge:** *Reeded.* **Mint:** *West Point.*

Government entities, private organizations, and citizens were all part of the bald eagle's recovery from near-extinction in the middle of the 1900s. Bans on certain pesticides, protections granted under the Endangered Species Act of 1973, and captive-breeding and nest-watch programs have been crucial and have led to the removal of the national emblem from the Endangered Species List.

Designs. *Obverse:* Two bald eagles perched on a branch. *Reverse:* The current Great Seal of the United States.

Mintage Data. Authorized by Public Law 108-486, the Bald Eagle Commemorative Coin Act, signed by President George W. Bush on December 23, 2004. *Maximum authorized*—100,000. *Number minted*—15,009 Uncirculated and 59,269 Proof.

Original Cost. Sale prices $284.95 (Uncirculated, pre-issue) and $294.95 (Proof, pre-issue); Uncirculated later raised to $309.95, and Proof later raised to $319.95. The surcharge of $35 per coin went to the American Eagle Foundation of Tennessee for the purposes of continuing its work to save and protect bald eagles nationally.

Key to Collecting. Superb gem coins are readily available.

	Distribution	Cert	Avg	%MS	MS-67
					PF-67
2008-W	15,009	1,067	69.9	100%	$325
Auctions: $458, MS-70, January 2013					
2008-W, Proof	59,269	1,830	69.8		$325
Auctions: $442, PF-70DCam, March 2014; $427, PF-70DCam, September 2014; $306, PF-70UCam, July 2015					

ABRAHAM LINCOLN BICENTENNIAL SILVER DOLLAR (2009)

Designer: *Justin Kunz (obverse), Phebe Hemphill (reverse).* **Weight:** *26.73 grams.*
Composition: *.900 silver, .100 copper (net weight .7736 oz. pure silver).*
Diameter: *38.1 mm.* **Edge:** *Reeded.* **Mint:** *Philadelphia.*

These coins, issued to mark the 200th anniversary of President Abraham Lincoln's birth, were extremely popular with collectors. The 450,000 pieces allocated to individual coin sales sold out after a month. Note that this anniversary was also commemorated with the release of four different reverse designs for the 2009 Lincoln cents.

Designs. *Obverse:* A portrait of Abraham Lincoln in three-quarter view. *Reverse:* The final 43 words of President Lincoln's Gettysburg Address, surrounded by a laurel wreath.

Mintage Data. Authorized Public Law 109-285, the Abraham Lincoln Commemorative Coin Act, signed by President George W. Bush on September 27, 2006. *Maximum authorized*—500,000. *Number minted*—125,000 Uncirculated and 325,000 Proof.

Original Cost. Sale prices $31.95 (Uncirculated, pre-issue) and $37.95 (Proof, pre-issue); Uncirculated later raised to $33.95, and Proof later raised to $41.95. The surcharge of $10 per coin went to the Abraham Lincoln Bicentennial Commission.

Key to Collecting. Superb gem coins are readily available.

	Distribution	Cert	Avg	%MS	MS-67
					PF-67
2009-P	125,000	10,129	69.8	100%	$27
Auctions: $96, MS-70, February 2014; $60, MS-70, June 2015; $56, MS-70, July 2014					
2009-P, Proof	325,000	18,239	69.4		$25
Auctions: $353, PF-70DCam, November 2014; $90, PF-70DCam, August 2014; $74, PF-70DCam, June 2015					

LOUIS BRAILLE BICENTENNIAL SILVER DOLLAR (2009)

Designer: *Joel Iskowitz (obverse), Phebe Hemphill (reverse).* **Weight:** *26.73 grams.*
Composition: *.900 silver, .100 copper (net weight .7736 oz. pure silver).*
Diameter: *38.1 mm.* **Edge:** *Reeded.* **Mint:** *Philadelphia.*

The 200th anniversary of the birth of Louis Braille—the inventor of the eponymous system which is used by the blind to read and write—furnished the occasion for this commemorative. Fittingly, this was the first U.S. coin to feature readable Braille.

Designs. *Obverse:* A forward-facing portrait of Louis Braille. *Reverse:* The word Braille (in Braille code, abbreviated Brl) above a child reading a book in Braille.

Mintage Data. Authorized by Public Law 109-247, the Louis Braille Bicentennial–Braille Literacy Commemorative Coin Act, signed by President George W. Bush on July 27, 2006. *Maximum authorized*—400,000. *Number minted*—82,639 Uncirculated and 135,235 Proof.

Original Cost. Sale prices $31.95 (Uncirculated, pre-issue) and $37.95 (Proof, pre-issue); Uncirculated later raised to $33.95, and Proof later raised to $41.95. The surcharge of $10 per coin went to the National Federation of the Blind.

Key to Collecting. Superb gem coins are readily available.

	Distribution	Cert	Avg	%MS	MS-67
					PF-67
2009-P	82,639	3,438	69.4	100%	$30
	Auctions: $90, MS-70, April 2013				
2009-P, Proof	135,235	4,432	69.1		$35
	Auctions: $94, PF-70DCam, July 2014; $94, PF-70DCam, April 2013				

AMERICAN VETERANS DISABLED FOR LIFE SILVER DOLLAR (2010)

Designer: *Don Everhart.* **Weight:** *26.73 grams.*
Composition: *.900 silver, .100 copper (net weight .7736 oz. pure silver).*
Diameter: *38.1 mm.* **Edge:** *Reeded.* **Mint:** *West Point.*

This coin honored those members of the U.S. Armed Forces who have made extraordinary personal sacrifices in defense of the country.

Designs. *Obverse:* The legs and boots of three veterans, one of whom is using a pair of crutches. *Reverse:* The words "Take This Moment to Honor Our Disabled Defenders of Freedom," surrounded by a laurel wreath with a forget-me-not (widely known as a symbol for those who fought and became disabled in World War I) at its base.

Mintage Data. Authorized by Public Law 110-277, the American Veterans Disabled for Life Commemorative Coin Act, signed by President George W. Bush on July 17, 2008. *Maximum authorized*—350,000. *Number minted*—78,301 Uncirculated and 202,770 Proof.

Original Cost. Sale prices $33.95 (Uncirculated, pre-issue) and $39.95 (Proof, pre-issue); Uncirculated later raised to $35.95, and Proof later raised to $43.95. The surcharge of $10 per coin went to the Disabled Veterans' LIFE Memorial Foundation for the purpose of constructing the American Veterans' Disabled for Life Memorial in Washington, D.C.

Key to Collecting. Superb gem coins are readily available.

	Distribution	Cert	Avg	%MS	MS-67
					PF-67
2010-W	78,301	3,994	69.8	100%	$32
Auctions: $70, MS-70, May 2013					
2010-W, Proof	202,770	5,088	69.7		$32
Auctions: $78, PF-70DCam, May 2013; $42, PF-70DCam, September 2014					

BOY SCOUTS OF AMERICA CENTENNIAL SILVER DOLLAR (2010)

Designer: *Donna Weaver (obverse), Jim Licaretz from the universal logo of the Boy Scouts of America (reverse).*
Weight: *26.73 grams.* **Composition:** *.900 silver, .100 copper (net weight .7736 oz. pure silver).*
Diameter: *38.1 mm.* **Edge:** *Reeded.* **Mint:** *Philadelphia.*

The 100th anniversary of the establishment of the Boy Scouts of America was celebrated with this silver dollar. The design was somewhat controversial due to its inclusion of a female but was specifically requested by the organization itself so as to portray the evolution of the Boy Scouts over time to include all American youth.

Designs. *Obverse:* A Cub Scout, a female member of the Venturer Program, and a Boy Scout saluting. *Reverse:* The universal logo of the Boy Scouts of America, featuring an eagle bearing a shield on a fleur-de-lis.

Mintage Data. Authorized by Public Law 110-363, the Boy Scouts of America Centennial Commemorative Coin Act, signed by President George W. Bush on October 8, 2008. *Maximum authorized—*350,000. *Number minted—*105,020 Uncirculated and 244,693 Proof.

Original Cost. Sale prices $33.95 (Uncirculated, pre-issue) and $39.95 (Proof, pre-issue); Uncirculated later raised to $35.95, and Proof later raised to $43.95. The surcharge of $10 per coin went to the National Boy Scouts of America Foundation; the funds were then meant to be made available to local councils in the form of grants for the extension of Scouting in hard-to-serve areas.

Key to Collecting. Superb gem coins are readily available.

	Distribution	Cert	Avg	%MS	MS-67
					PF-67
2010-P	105,020	7,292	69.8	100%	$27
Auctions: $82, MS-70, March 2013					
2010-P, Proof	244,963	8,166	69.4		$30
Auctions: $82, PF-70DCam, March 2013					

U.S. Army Half Dollar (2011)

Designer: *Donna Weaver (obverse), Thomas Cleveland (reverse).* **Weight:** *11.34 grams.*
Composition: *.9167 copper, .0833 nickel.* **Diameter:** *30.61 mm.*
Edge: *Reeded.* **Mints:** *Denver (Uncirculated) and San Francisco (Proof).*

This copper-nickel half dollar was one of three commemoratives released in honor of the U.S. Army in 2011, by which time the entity had already defended the nation for 236 years. The reverse design was praised by the Citizens Coinage Advisory Committee (CCAC) and the Commission of Fine Arts.

Designs. *Obverse:* Three scenes split in a "storyboard" fashion (from left to right): a soldier surveying; two servicemen laying a flood wall; the Redstone Army rocket at takeoff. *Reverse:* A Continental with a musket, with 13 stars (representing the first states) in an arc above.

Mintage Data. Authorized by Public Law 110-450, the United States Army Commemorative Coin Act of 2008, signed by President George W. Bush on December 1, 2008. *Maximum authorized*—750,000. *Number minted*—2011-D: 39,442 Uncirculated; 2011-S: 68,332 Proof.

Original Cost. Sale prices $15.95 (Uncirculated, pre-issue) and $17.95 (Proof, pre-issue); Uncirculated later raised to $19.95, and Proof raised to $21.95. The surcharge of $5 went toward the yet-to-be-constructed National Museum of the United States Army.

Key to Collecting. Superb gem coins are readily available.

	Distribution	Cert	Avg	%MS	MS-67
					PF-67
2011-D	39,442	2,557	69.0	100%	$30
	Auctions: No auction records available.				
2011-S, Proof	68,332	2,459	69.5		$50
	Auctions: No auction records available.				

U.S. Army Silver Dollar (2011)

Designer: *Richard Masters (obverse), Susan Gamble (reverse).* **Weight:** *26.73 grams.*
Composition: *.900 silver, .100 copper (net weight .7736 oz. pure silver).* **Diameter:** *38.1 mm.*
Edge: *Reeded.* **Mints:** *San Francisco (Uncirculated) and Philadelphia (Proof).*

The act authorizing this silver dollar (as well as the related copper-nickel half dollar and five-dollar gold coin) called for the coins to be "emblematic of the traditions, history, and heritage of the U.S. Army and its role in American society from the Colonial period to today."

Designs. *Obverse:* A male and female soldier back-to-back in front of a globe. *Reverse:* The Great Seal of the United States (which appears on Army uniforms) inside a ring that bears the seven core values of the Army (Loyalty, Duty, Respect, Selfless Service, Honor, Integrity, and Personal Courage).

Mintage Data. Authorized by Public Law 110-450, the United States Army Commemorative Coin Act of 2008, signed by President George W. Bush on December 1, 2008. *Maximum authorized*—500,000. *Number minted*—2011-S: 43,512 Uncirculated; 2011-P: 119,829 Proof.

Original Cost. Sale prices $49.95 (Uncirculated, pre-issue) and $54.95 (Proof, pre-issue); Uncirculated later raised to $54.95, and Proof later raised to $59.95. The surcharge of $10 per coin went toward the yet-to-be-constructed National Museum of the United States Army.

Key to Collecting. Superb gem coins are readily available.

	Distribution	Cert	Avg	%MS	MS-67 PF-67
2011-S	43,512	2,364	69.7	100%	$43
	Auctions: No auction records available.				
2011-P, Proof	119,829	3,869	69.5		$43
	Auctions: $80, PF-70DCam, April 2013				

U.S. ARMY $5 GOLD COIN (2011)

Designer: *Joel Iskowitz (obverse), Joseph Menna from the U.S. Army emblem (reverse).*
Weight: *8.359 grams.* **Composition:** *.900 gold, .100 copper (net weight .242 oz. pure gold).*
Diameter: *21.6 mm.* **Edge:** *Reeded.* **Mints:** *Philadelphia (Uncirculated) and West Point (Proof).*

By depicting soldiers from five distinct eras in U.S. history, the obverse of this five-dollar gold coin symbolizes the "continuity of strength and readiness" of the Army.

Designs. *Obverse:* Five U.S. Army soldiers representing various eras (from left to right): Revolutionary War, Civil War, modern era, World War II, and World War I. *Reverse:* The U.S. Army emblem, which features various items representative of home life and war time and the phrase "This We'll Defend" on a banner.

Mintage Data. Authorized by Public Law 110-450, the United States Army Commemorative Coin Act of 2008, signed by President George W. Bush on December 1, 2008. *Maximum authorized*—100,000. *Number minted*—2011-P: 8,052 Uncirculated; 2011-W: 17,148 Proof.

Original Cost. Sale prices $439.95 (Uncirculated, pre-issue) and $449.95 (Proof, pre-issue); Uncirculated later raised to $444.95, and Proof later raised to $454.95. The surcharge of $35 per coin went toward the yet-to-be-constructed National Museum of the United States Army.

Key to Collecting. Superb gem coins are readily available.

	Distribution	Cert	Avg	%MS	MS-67 PF-67
2011-P	8,052	442	69.9	100%	$350
	Auctions: $560, MS-70, September 2013				
2011-W, Proof	17,148	566	69.7		$350
	Auctions: $353, PF-69DCam, May 2014				

MEDAL OF HONOR SILVER DOLLAR (2011)

Designer: *Jim Licaretz (obverse), Richard Masters (reverse).* **Weight:** *26.73 grams.*
Composition: *.900 silver, .100 copper (net weight .7736 oz. pure silver).*
Diameter: *38.1 mm.* **Edge:** *Reeded.* **Mints:** *San Francisco (Uncirculated) and Philadelphia (Proof).*

The 150th anniversary of the creation of the Medal of Honor—the highest award for valor in action in the U.S. Armed Forces—was the impetus for this commemorative silver dollar, as well as a five-dollar gold coin.

Designs. *Obverse:* From left to right, the Medals of Honor of the Army, Navy, and Air Force. *Reverse:* An infantry soldier carrying a wounded soldier to safety on his back.

Mintage Data. Authorized by Public Law 111-91, the Medal of Honor Commemorative Coin Act of 2009, signed by President Barack Obama on November 6, 2009. *Maximum authorized*—500,000. *Number minted*—2011-S: 44,752 Uncirculated; 2011-P: 112,833 Proof.

Original Cost. Sale prices $49.95 (Uncirculated, pre-issue) and $54.95 (Proof, pre-issue); Uncirculated later raised to $54.95, and Proof later raised to $59.95. The surcharge of $10 per coin went to the Congressional Medal of Honor Foundation to help finance its educational, scholarship, and outreach programs.

Key to Collecting. Superb gem coins are readily available.

	Distribution	Cert	Avg	%MS	MS-67
					PF-67
2011-S	44,752	2,842	69.6	100%	$45
	Auctions: $100, MS-70, April 2013				
2011-P, Proof	112,833	2,221	69.3		$45
	Auctions: $123, PF-70DCam, March 2013				

MEDAL OF HONOR $5 GOLD COIN (2011)

Designer: *Joseph Menna (obverse), Joel Iskowitz (reverse).* **Weight:** *8.359 grams.*
Composition: *.900 gold, .100 copper (net weight .242 oz. pure gold).* **Diameter:** *21.6 mm.*
Edge: *Reeded.* **Mints:** *Philadelphia (Uncirculated) and West Point (Proof).*

This coin and the silver dollar issued alongside it were created in recognition of the Medal of Honor, the Navy's greatest personal award, first authorized by Congress in 1861. Though counterparts are now given in the Army and Air Force as well, fewer than 3,500 Medals of Honor have ever been awarded to date.

Designs. *Obverse:* The original Medal of Honor, the Navy's highest individual decoration. *Reverse:* Minerva, holding a shield and the U.S. flag on a staff, in front of munitions and a Civil War–era cannon.

Mintage Data. Authorized by Public Law 111-91, the Medal of Honor Commemorative Coin Act of 2009, signed by President Barack Obama on November 6, 2009. *Maximum authorized*—100,000. *Number minted*—2011-P: 8,233 Uncirculated; 2011-W: 17,999 Proof.

Original Cost. Sale prices $439.95 (Uncirculated, pre-issue) and $449.95 (Proof, pre issue); Uncirculated later raised to $444.95, and Proof later raised to $454.95. The surcharge of $35 per coin went to the Congressional Medal of Honor Foundation to help finance its educational, scholarship, and outreach programs.

Key to Collecting. Superb gem coins are readily available.

	Distribution	Cert	Avg	%MS	MS-67
					PF-67
2011-P	8,233	491	69.8	100%	$375
	Auctions: $470, MS-70, November 2014; $470, MS-70, August 2014; $400, MS-70, January 2015; $400, MS-69, January 2015				
2011-W, Proof	17,999	523	69.6		$325
	Auctions: $646, PF-70DCam, February 2015; $646, PF-70DCam, November 2014; $558, PF-70DCam, July 2014				

INFANTRY SOLDIER SILVER DOLLAR (2012)

Designer: *Joel Iskowitz (obverse), Ronald D. Sanders (reverse).* **Weight:** *26.73 grams.*
Composition: *.900 silver, .100 copper (net weight .7736 oz. pure silver).*
Diameter: *38.1 mm.* **Edge:** *Reeded.* **Mint:** *West Point.*

This coin recognizes the long history and crucial role of the U.S. Army Infantry. The infantry has accounted for more than half of all the Medals of Honor awarded, despite being just one of many branches of the Army.

Designs. *Obverse:* An infantry soldier advancing and motioning for others to follow. *Reverse:* The infantry insignia of two crossed rifles.

Mintage Data. Authorized by Public Law 110-357, the National Infantry Museum and Soldier Center Commemorative Coin Act, signed by President George W. Bush on October 8, 2008. *Maximum authorized*—350,000. *Number minted*—44,352 Uncirculated and 161,218 Proof.

Original Cost. Sale prices $44.95 (Uncirculated, pre-issue) and $49.95 (Proof, pre-issue); Uncirculated later raised to $49.95, and Proof later raised to $54.95. The surcharge of $10 per coin went to an endowment to support the maintenance of the National Infantry Museum and Solider Center in Columbus, Georgia.

Key to Collecting. Superb gem coins are readily available.

	Distribution	Cert	Avg	%MS	MS-67
					PF-67
2012-W	44,348	2,004	69.8	100%	$40
	Auctions: $69, MS-70, April 2013				
2012-W, Proof	161,151	2,923	69.2		$50
	Auctions: $74, PF-70DCam, April 2013				

STAR-SPANGLED BANNER SILVER DOLLAR (2012)

Designer: *Joel Iskowitz (obverse), William C. Burgard II (reverse).* **Weight:** *26.73 grams.*
Composition: *.900 silver, .100 copper (net weight .7736 oz. pure silver).*
Diameter: *38.1 mm.* **Edge:** *Reeded.* **Mint:** *Philadelphia.*

The 200th anniversary of the War of 1812—particularly the Battle of Baltimore, which is recounted in the U.S. National Anthem—was commemorated with this silver dollar, as well as a five-dollar gold coin issued alongside it.

Designs. *Obverse:* Miss Liberty waving the 15-star version of the U.S. flag with Fort McHenry in the background. *Reverse:* A waving modern U.S. flag.

Mintage Data. Authorized by Public Law 111-232, the Star-Spangled Banner Commemorative Coin Act, signed by President Barack Obama on August 16, 2010. *Maximum authorized*—500,000. *Number minted*—41,686 Uncirculated and 169,065 Proof.

Original Cost. Sale prices $44.95 (Uncirculated, pre-issue) and $49.95 (Proof, pre-issue); Uncirculated later raised to $49.95, and Proof later raised to $54.95. The surcharge of $10 per coin went to the Maryland War of 1812 Bicentennial Commission for the purpose of supporting bicentennial activities, educational outreach activities, and preservation and improvement activities pertaining to the sites and structures relating to the War of 1812.

Key to Collecting. Superb gem coins are readily available.

	Distribution	Cert	Avg	%MS	MS-67 PF-67
2012-P	41,686	2,057	69.8	100%	$40
Auctions: $100, MS-70, April 2013; $94, MS-70, October 2014					
2012-P, Proof	169,065	3,212	69.4		$40
Auctions: $94, PF-70DCam, April 2013; $153, PF-69DCam, November 2014					

STAR-SPANGLED BANNER $5 GOLD COIN (2012)

Designer: *Donna Weaver (obverse), Richard Masters (reverse).* **Weight:** *8.359 grams.*
Composition: *.900 gold, .100 copper (net weight .242 oz. pure gold).*
Diameter: *21.6 mm.* **Edge:** *Reeded.* **Mint:** *West Point.*

The reverse of this commemorative coin features the first five words of the Star-Spangled Banner in the handwriting of Francis Scott Key, the man who penned it. On September 7, 1814, Key visited the British fleet in the Chesapeake Bay to secure the release of his friend Dr. William Beanes. Key secured Beanes's release, but the two were held by the British during the bombardment of Fort McHenry. It was on the morning of September 14, 1814, that the shelling stopped and Key saw through the smoke the massive American flag, flying above the U.S. fort, that would inspire his song.

Designs. *Obverse:* A naval battle, with a U.S. ship in the foreground and a British vessel in the background. *Reverse:* The words "O say can you see" over an arrangement of 13 stripes and 15 stars, representing the U.S. flag.

Mintage Data. Authorized by Public Law 111-232, the Star-Spangled Banner Commemorative Coin Act, signed by President Barack Obama on August 16, 2010. *Maximum authorized*—100,000. *Number minted*—7,027 Uncirculated and 18,313 Proof.

Original Cost. Sale prices $519.30 (Uncirculated, pre-issue) and $529.30 (Proof, pre-issue); both prices later increased by a base of $5 plus the change in gold market value. The surcharge of $35 per coin went to the Maryland War of 1812 Bicentennial Commission for the purpose of supporting bicentennial activities, educational outreach activities, and preservation and improvement activities pertaining to the sites and structures relating to the War of 1812.

Key to Collecting. Superb gem coins are readily available.

	Distribution	Cert	Avg	%MS	MS-67
					PF-67
2012-W	7,027	645	69.9	100%	$400
Auctions: $618, MS-70, September 2013					
2012-W, Proof	18,313	497	69.8		$350
Auctions: $470, PF-70DCam, April 2014					

GIRL SCOUTS OF THE U.S.A. CENTENNIAL SILVER DOLLAR (2013)

Designer: *Barbara Fox (obverse), Chris Costello (reverse).* **Weight:** *26.73 grams.*
Composition: *.900 silver, .100 copper (net weight .7736 oz. pure silver).*
Diameter: *38.1 mm.* **Edge:** *Reeded.* **Mint:** *West Point.*

This commemorative silver dollar was issued as part of the celebration of the Girl Scouts of the United States of America's 100th anniversary of establishment. The Citizens Coinage Advisory Committee was particularly enthusiastic about this beautiful design.

Designs. *Obverse:* Three Girl Scouts of varying ages and ethnicities. The three girls are meant to reflect the organization's diversity. *Reverse:* The iconic Girl Scouts trefoil symbol.

Mintage Data. Authorized by Public Law 111-86, the 2013 Girl Scouts of the USA Centennial Commemorative Coin Program, signed by President Barack Obama on October 29, 2009. *Maximum authorized*—350,000. *Number minted*—31,714 Uncirculated and 86,353 Proof.

Original Cost. Sale prices $50.95 (Uncirculated, pre-issue) and $54.95 (Proof, pre-issue); Uncirculated later raised to $55.95, and Proof later raised to $59.95. The surcharge of $10 per coin went to the Girl Scouts of the United States of America.

Key to Collecting. Superb gem coins are readily available.

	Distribution	Cert	Avg	%MS	MS-67
					PF-67
2013-W	37,462	1,010	69.9	100%	$40
	Auctions: No auction records available.				
2013-W, Proof	86,355	1,756	69.3		$45
	Auctions: No auction records available.				

5-STAR GENERALS HALF DOLLAR (2013)

Designer: *Phebe Hemphill.* **Weight:** *11.34 grams.* **Composition:** *.9167 copper, .0833 nickel.*
Diameter: *30.61 mm.* **Edge:** *Reeded.* **Mints:** *Denver (Uncirculated) and San Francisco (Proof).*

The 5-star generals of the U.S. Army—as well as the institution that they each graduated from, the U.S. Army Command and General Staff College—were commemorated with this half dollar, as well as a silver dollar and five-dollar gold coin issued as part of the program.

Designs. *Obverse:* Side-by-side portraits of General Henry "Hap" Arnold and General Omar N. Bradley, 5-star insignia at center.

Reverse: Heraldic crest of Fort Leavenworth, home of the U.S. Army Command and General Staff College.

Mintage Data. Authorized by Public Law 111-262, the 5-Star Generals Commemorative Coin Act, signed by President Barack Obama on October 8, 2010. *Maximum authorized*—750,000. *Number minted*—2013-D: 38,191 Uncirculated; 2013-P: 47,337 Proof.

Original Cost. Sale prices $16.95 (Uncirculated, pre-issue) and $17.95 (Proof, pre-issue); Uncirculated later raised to $20.95, and Proof later raised to $21.95. The surcharge of $5 per coin went to the Command and General Staff College Foundation.

Key to Collecting. Superb gem coins are readily available.

	Distribution	Cert	Avg	%MS	MS-67
					PF-67
2013-D	38,095	1,057	69.0	100%	$22
	Auctions: No auction records available.				
2013-S, Proof	47,326	2,296	69.4		$35
	Auctions: No auction records available.				

5-STAR GENERALS SILVER DOLLAR (2013)

Designer: *Richard Masters (obverse), Barbara Fox (reverse).* **Weight:** *26.73 grams.*
Composition: *.900 silver, .100 copper (net weight .7736 oz. pure silver).*
Diameter: *38.1 mm.* **Edge:** *Reeded.* **Mints:** *West Point (Uncirculated) and Philadelphia (Proof).*

Each of the 5-star generals was given one appearance across this series of three commemoratives. Note that Dwight Eisenhower, who is featured on this silver dollar along with George C. Marshall, had previously appeared on another commemorative silver dollar that marked the centennial of his birth in 1990.

Designs. *Obverse:* Side-by-side portraits of General George C. Marshall and General Dwight D. Eisenhower against a striped background, 5-star insignia at top center. *Reverse:* The Leavenworth Lamp, a symbol of the Command and General Staff College.

Mintage Data. Authorized by Public Law 111-262, the 5-Star Generals Commemorative Coin Act, signed by President Barack Obama on October 8, 2010. *Maximum authorized*—500,000. *Number minted*—2013-W: 34,639 Uncirculated; 2013-P: 69,290 Proof.

Original Cost. Sale prices $50.95 (Uncirculated, pre-issue) and $54.95 (Proof, pre-issue); Uncirculated later raised to $55.95, and Proof later raised to $59.95. The surcharge of $10 per coin went to the Command and General Staff College Foundation.

Key to Collecting. Superb gem coins are readily available.

	Distribution	Cert	Avg	%MS	MS-67 PF-67
2013-W	34,638	1,665	69.9	100%	$55
	Auctions: No auction records available.				
2013-P, Proof	69,283	2,669	69.7		$55
	Auctions: No auction records available.				

5-STAR GENERALS $5 GOLD COIN (2013)

Designer: *Ronald D. Sanders (obverse), Barbara Fox (reverse).* **Weight:** *8.359 grams.*
Composition: *.900 gold, .100 copper (net weight .242 oz. pure gold).*
Diameter: *21.6 mm.* **Edge:** *Reeded.* **Mints:** *Philadelphia (Uncirculated) and West Point (Proof).*

The Leavenworth Lamp, seen on the reverse of this coin as well as that of the silver dollar in this series, is a symbol of the Command and General Staff College. The institution celebrated its 132nd anniversary in the year these coins were released.

Designs. *Obverse:* A portrait of General Douglas MacArthur and the 5-star insignia to the right. *Reverse:* The Leavenworth Lamp, a symbol of the Command and General Staff College.

Mintage Data. Authorized by Public Law 111-262, the 5-Star Generals Commemorative Coin Act, signed by President Barack Obama on October 8, 2010. *Maximum authorized*—100,000. *Number minted*—2013-P: 5,674 Uncirculated; 2013-W: 15,949 Proof.

Original Cost. Sale prices $480.50 (Uncirculated, pre-issue) and $485.50 (Proof, pre-issue); both prices later increased by a base of $5 plus the change in gold market value. The surcharge of $35 per coin went to the Command and General Staff College Foundation.

Key to Collecting. Superb gem coins are readily available.

	Distribution	Cert	Avg	%MS	MS-67 PF-67
2013-P	5,667	518	69.9	100%	$500
	Auctions: No auction records available.				
2013-W, Proof	15,844	565	69.8		$425
	Auctions: $499, PF-70DCam, September 2014				

NATIONAL BASEBALL HALL OF FAME HALF DOLLAR (2014)

Designer: *Cassie McFarland (obverse), Don Everhart (reverse).* **Weight:** *11.34 grams.*
Composition: *.9167 copper, .0833 nickel.* **Diameter:** *30.61 mm.* **Edge:** *Reeded.*
Mints: *Denver (Uncirculated) and San Francisco (Proof).*

This half dollar and the silver dollar and five-dollar gold coin issued alongside it were the first "curved" coins to be produced by the U.S. Mint—that is, the obverse is concave, and the reverse is convex. The three commemorated the 75th anniversary of the National Baseball Hall of Fame in Cooperstown, New York.

Designs. *Obverse:* A baseball glove, concave. *Reverse:* A baseball, convex.

Mintage Data. Authorized by Public Law 112-152, the National Baseball Hall of Fame Commemorative Coin Act, signed by President Barack Obama on August 3, 2012. *Maximum authorized*—750,000. *Number minted*—2014-D: 147,934 Uncirculated; 2014-S: 258,643.

Original Cost. Sale prices $18.95 (Uncirculated, pre-issue) and $19.95 (Proof, pre-issue); Uncirculated later raised to $22.95, and Proof later raised to $23.95. The surcharge of $5 per coin went to the National Baseball Hall of Fame.

Key to Collecting. Superb gem coins are readily available.

	Distribution	Cert	Avg	%MS	MS-67 PF-67
2014-D ††	*142,405*	*9,868*	*69.5*	*100%*	$30
2014-S, Proof ††	*249,049*	*35,164*	*69.6*		$24

†† All 2014 National Baseball Hall of Fame Commemorative coins (in all denominations and finishes) are ranked in the *100 Greatest U.S. Modern Coins* (fourth edition), as a single entry.

NATIONAL BASEBALL HALL OF FAME SILVER DOLLAR (2014)

Designer: *Cassie McFarland (obverse), Don Everhart (reverse).* **Weight:** *26.73 grams.*
Composition: *.900 silver, .100 copper (net weight .7736 oz. pure silver).*
Diameter: *38.1 mm.* **Edge:** *Reeded.* **Mint:** *Philadelphia.*

Coins shaped like this silver dollar (as well as the corresponding half dollar and five-dollar gold coin) had previously been minted by Monnaie de Paris in commemoration of the 2009 International Year of Astronomy. The National Baseball Hall of Fame coins were the first curved issues for the U.S. Mint.

Designs. *Obverse:* A baseball glove, concave. *Reverse:* A baseball, convex.

Mintage Data. Authorized by Public Law 112-152, the National Baseball Hall of Fame Commemorative Coin Act, signed by President Barack Obama on August 3, 2012. *Maximum authorized*—400,000. *Number minted*—137,909 Uncirculated and 268,076 Proof.

Original Cost. Sale prices $47.95 (Uncirculated, pre-issue) and $51.95 (Proof, pre-issue); Uncirculated later raised to $52.95, and Proof later raised to $56.95. The surcharge of $10 per coin went to the National Baseball Hall of Fame.

Key to Collecting. Superb gem coins are readily available.

	Distribution	Cert	Avg	%MS	MS-67
					PF-67
2014-P ††	*131,910*	*19,896*	*69.7*	100%	$50
2014-P, Proof ††	*267,847*	*4,332*	*69.9*		$48

†† All 2014 National Baseball Hall of Fame Commemorative coins (in all denominations and finishes) are ranked in the *100 Greatest U.S. Modern Coins* (fourth edition), as a single entry.

NATIONAL BASEBALL HALL OF FAME $5 GOLD COIN (2014)

Designer: *Cassie McFarland (obverse), Don Everhart (reverse).* **Weight:** *8.359 grams.*
Composition: *.900 gold, .100 copper (net weight .242 oz. pure gold).*
Diameter: *21.6 mm.* **Edge:** *Reeded.* **Mint:** *West Point.*

The common obverse design for these coins was selected through a national competition, and the Department of the Treasury chose California artist Cassie McFarland's submission after input from the National Baseball Hall of Fame, the U.S. Commission of Fine Arts, and the Citizens Coinage Advisory Committee.

Designs. *Obverse:* A baseball glove, concave. *Reverse:* A baseball, convex.

Mintage Data. Authorized by Public Law 112-152, the National Baseball Hall of Fame Commemorative Coin Act, signed by President Barack Obama on August 3, 2012. *Maximum authorized*—50,000. *Number minted*—18,000 Uncirculated and 32,495 Proof.

Original Cost. Sale prices $431.90 (Uncirculated, pre-issue) and $436.90 (Proof, pre-issue); Uncirculated later raised to $436.90, and Proof later raised to $441.90. The surcharge of $35 per coin went to the National Baseball Hall of Fame.

Key to Collecting. Superb gem coins are readily available.

	Distribution	Cert	Avg	%MS	MS-67
					PF-67
2014-W ††	*17,674*	*2,282*	*69.9*	100%	$350
2014-W, Proof ††	*32,428*	*4,539*	*69.9*		$350

†† All 2014 National Baseball Hall of Fame Commemorative coins (in all denominations and finishes) are ranked in the *100 Greatest U.S. Modern Coins* (fourth edition), as a single entry.

CIVIL RIGHTS ACT OF 1964 SILVER DOLLAR (2014)

Designer: *Justin Kunz (obverse), Donna Weaver (reverse).* **Weight:** *26.73 grams.*
Composition: *.900 silver, .100 copper (net weight .7736 oz. pure silver).*
Diameter: *38.1 mm.* **Edge:** *Reeded.* **Mint:** *Philadelphia.*

This silver dollar commemorated the 50th anniversary of the Civil Rights Act of 1964, which greatly expanded American civil rights protections; outlawed racial segregation in public places and places of public accommodation; and funded federal programs.

Designs. *Obverse:* Three people holding hands at a Civil Rights march; man on left holding sign that reads WE SHALL OVERCOME. *Reverse:* Three intertwined flames representing freedom of education, freedom to vote, and freedom to control one's own destiny. Inspired by a quote by Dr. Martin Luther King Jr.

Mintage Data. Authorized by Public Law 110-451, the Civil Rights Act of 1964 Commemorative Coin Act, signed by President George W. Bush on December 2, 2008. *Maximum authorized*—350,000. *Number minted*—24,720 Uncirculated and 61,992 Proof.

Original Cost. Sale prices $44.95 (Uncirculated, pre-issue) and $49.95 (Proof, pre-issue); Uncirculated later raised to $49.95, and Proof later raised to $54.95. The surcharge of $10 per coin went to the United Negro College Fund, which has provided scholarships and internships for minority students for the past 70 years.

Key to Collecting. Superb gem coins are readily available.

	Distribution	Cert	Avg	%MS	MS-67
					PF-67
2014-P	24,720	830	69.6	100%	$50
2014-P, Proof	61,992	935	69.4		$55

U.S. MARSHALS SERVICE 225TH ANNIVERSARY HALF DOLLAR (2015)

Designer: *Joel Iskowitz (obverse), Susan Gamble (reverse).* **Weight:** *11.34 grams.*
Composition: *.9167 copper, .0833 nickel.* **Diameter:** *30.61 mm.*
Edge: *Reeded.* **Mints:** *Denver (Uncirculated) and San Francisco (Proof).*

The 225th anniversary of the establishment of the U.S. Marshals Service was commemorated with the release of a series including this half dollar as well as a silver dollar and five-dollar gold coin. The actual anniversary—September 24, 2014—was marked with a celebration in Washington, D.C., and the issuance of 35 special preview sets to employees of the Service.

Designs. *Obverse:* An Old West marshal and his horse at left, and a modern marshal in tactical gear at right. *Reverse:* Lady Justice holding scales and the U.S. Marshals Service star and standing over a copy of the Constitution, a stack of books, handcuffs, and a whiskey jug, each representing areas of responsibility of the Service in the past or present.

Mintage Data. Authorized by Public Law 112-104, the United States Marshals Service 225th Anniversary Commemorative Coin Act, signed into law by President Barack Obama on April 2, 2012. *Maximum authorized*—750,000. *Number minted*—2015-D: 29,400 Uncirculated; 2015-S: 60,763 Proof (as of press time).

Original Cost. Sale prices $13.95 (Uncirculated, pre-issue) and $14.95 (Proof, pre-issue); Uncirculated later raised to $17.95, and Proof later raised to $18.95. The surcharge of $3 per coin went to the U.S. Marshals Museum.

Key to Collecting. Superb gem coins are readily available.

	Distribution	Cert	Avg	%MS	MS-67		
					PF-67		
2015-D	30,231	1,462	69.2	100%	$20		
2015-S, Proof	76,549	2,029	69.2		$22		

U.S. Marshals Service 225th Anniversary Silver Dollar (2015)

Designer: *Richard Masters (obverse), Frank Morris (reverse).* **Weight:** *26.73 grams.*
Composition: *.900 silver, .100 copper (net weight .7736 oz. pure silver).*
Diameter: *38.1 mm.* **Edge:** *Reeded.* **Mint:** *Philadelphia.*

The first federal law-enforcement officers of the United States, the U.S. Marshals were created under section 27 of the Act of Congress entitled "Chapter XX—An Act to Establish the Judicial Courts of the United States." The original 13 men to serve were confirmed on September 26, 1789.

Designs. *Obverse:* U.S. marshals riding on horseback under the U.S. Marshals Service star. *Reverse:* A U.S. marshal of the frontier era holding a "wanted" poster.

Mintage Data. Authorized by Public Law 112-104, the United States Marshals Service 225th Anniversary Commemorative Coin Act, signed into law by President Barack Obama on April 2, 2012. *Maximum authorized*—500,000. *Number minted*—37,588 Uncirculated and 107,847 Proof (as of press time).

Original Cost. Sale prices $43.95 (Uncirculated, pre-issue) and $46.95 (Proof, pre-issue): Uncirculated later raised to $48.95, and Proof later raised to $51.95. The surcharge of $10 went to the U.S. Marshals Museum.

Key to Collecting. Superb gem coins are readily available.

	Distribution	Cert	Avg	%MS	MS-67		
					PF-67		
2015-P	38,149	2,531	69.7	100%	$47		
2015-P, Proof	124,329	3,738	69.1		$52		

U.S. Marshals Service 225th Anniversary $5 Gold Coin (2015)

Designer: *Donna Weaver (obverse), Paul C. Balan (reverse).* **Weight:** *8.359 grams.*
Composition: *.900 gold, .100 copper (net weight .242 oz. pure gold).*
Diameter: *21.6 mm.* **Edge:** *Reeded.* **Mint:** *West Point.*

The U.S. Marshals officially became the U.S. Marshals Service in 1969 by order of the Department of Justice. The Service achieved Bureau status in 1974 and today is the primary agency for fugitive operations, as well as protection of officers of the court and court buildings.

Designs. *Obverse:* The U.S. Marshals Service star superimposed on a mountain range. *Reverse:* An eagle, shield on chest, holding a banner and draped flag.

Mintage Data. Authorized by Public Law 112-104, the United States Marshals Service 225th Anniversary Commemorative Coin Act, signed into law by President Barack Obama on April 2, 2012. *Maximum authorized*—100,000. *Number minted*—6,592 Uncirculated and 9,671 Proof (as of press time)

Original Cost. Sale prices $395.45 (Uncirculated, pre-issue) and $400.45 (Proof, pre-issue): Uncirculated later raised to $400.45, and Proof later raised to $405.45. The surcharge of $35 per coin went to the U.S. Marshals Museum.

Key to Collecting. Superb gem coins are readily available.

	Distribution	Cert	Avg	%MS	MS-67 / PF-67
2015-W	6,743	588	69.9	100%	$400
2015-W, Proof	24,959	948	69.8		$400

MARCH OF DIMES 75TH ANNIVERSARY SILVER DOLLAR (2015)

Designer: *Paul C. Balan (obverse), Don Everhart (reverse).* **Weight:** *26.73 grams.*
Composition: *.900 silver, .100 copper (net weight .7736 oz. pure silver).*
Diameter: *38.1 mm.* **Edge:** *Reeded.* **Mints:** *Philadelphia (Uncirculated) and West Point (Proof).*

Inspired by his own struggle with polio, President Franklin Delano Roosevelt created the National Foundation for Infantile Paralysis, now known as the March of Dimes, on January 3, 1938. This coin celebrated the organization's 75th anniversary (despite coming out after the actual date of said event) and recognized its accomplishments, which included the funding of research which resulted in Dr. Jonas Salk and Dr. Albert Sabin's polio vaccines.

Designs. *Obverse:* A profile view of President Franklin Delano Roosevelt and Dr. Jonas Salk. *Reverse:* A sleeping baby cradled in its parent's hand.

Mintage Data. Authorized by Public Law 112-209, the March of Dimes Commemorative Coin Act of 2012, signed into law by President Barack Obama on December 18, 2012. *Maximum authorized*—500,000. *Number minted*—2015-D: 24,387 Uncirculated; 2015-W: 56,718 Proof (as of press time)

Original Cost. Sale prices $43.95 (Uncirculated, pre-issue) and $46.95 (Proof, pre-issue): Uncirculated later raised to $48.95, and Proof later raised to $51.95. The surcharge of $10 per coin went to the March of Dimes to help finance research, education, and services aimed at improving the health of women, infants, and children.

Key to Collecting. Superb gem coins are readily available.

	Distribution	Cert	Avg	%MS	MS-67 / PF-67
2015-P	24,742	1,135	69.8	100%	$47
2015-W, Proof	32,030	6,713	69.6		$45

MARK TWAIN SILVER DOLLAR (2016)

Designer: *Chris Costello (obverse), Patricia Lucas-Morris (reverse).* **Weight:** *26.73 grams.*
Composition: *.900 silver, .100 copper (net weight .7736 oz. pure silver).*
Diameter: *38.1 mm.* **Edge:** *Reeded.* **Mint:** *Philadelphia.*

Samuel Langhorne Clemens—better known by his pen name, Mark Twain—is among the most celebrated authors in U.S. history. His *Adventures of Huckleberry Finn*, originally published in 1885, is often referred to as "The Great American Novel."

Designs. *Obverse:* A portrait of Mark Twain holding a pipe, with the smoke forming a silhouette of Huck Finn and Jim on their raft. *Reverse:* Depictions of several characters from Mark Twain's works, including the knight and horse from *A Connecticut Yankee in King Arthur's Court*, the frog from *The Celebrated Jumping Frog of Calaveras County*, and Huck and Jim from *Adventures of Huckleberry Finn*.

Mintage Data. Authorized by Public Law 112-201, the Mark Twain Commemorative Coin Act, signed into law by President Barack Obama on December 4, 2012. *Maximum authorized—350,000. Number minted—*To be determined.

Original Cost. Sale prices $44.95 (Uncirculated, pre-issue) and $45.95 (Proof, pre-issue). Uncirculated later raised to $49.95, and Proof later raised to $50.95. The surcharge of $10 per coin is to be distributed evenly between the Mark Twain House & Museum in Hartford, Conn.; the University of California, Berkeley, for the benefit of the Mark Twain Project at the Bancroft Library; Elmira College in New York; and the Mark Twain Boyhood Home and Museum in Hannibal, Missouri.

Key to Collecting. Superb gem coins are readily available.

	Distribution	Cert	Avg	%MS	MS-67
					PF-67
2016-P	26,281	2,452	69.8	100%	$40
2016-P, Proof	78,536	2,678	69.8	100%	$45

MARK TWAIN $5 GOLD COIN (2016)

Designer: *Benjamin Sowers (obverse), Ronald D. Sanders (reverse).* **Weight:** *8.359 grams.*
Composition: *.900 gold, .100 copper (net weight .242 oz. pure gold).*
Diameter: *21.6 mm.* **Edge:** *Reeded.* **Mint:** *West Point.*

The designs for the Mark Twain commemorative coins were unveiled two days before the 180th anniversary of his birth, November 30, 2015. Interestingly, Twain was born shortly after a visit by Halley's Comet, and he later predicted that he would "go out with it," too. He passed away two days after the comet returned.

Designs. *Obverse:* A portrait of Mark Twain. *Reverse:* A steamboat on the Mississippi River.

Mintage Data. Authorized by Public Law 112-201, the Mark Twain Commemorative Coin Act, signed into law by President Barack Obama on December 4, 2012. *Maximum authorized*—100,000. *Number minted*—To be determined.

Original Cost. Sale prices $359 (Uncirculated, pre-issue) and $364 (Proof, pre-issue). Uncirculated later raised to $364, and Proof later raised to $369. The surcharge of $35 per coin is to be distributed evenly between the Mark Twain House & Museum in Hartford, Conn.; the University of California, Berkeley, for the benefit of the Mark Twain Project at the Bancroft Library; Elmira College in New York; and the Mark Twain Boyhood Home and Museum in Hannibal, Missouri.

Key to Collecting. Superb gem coins are readily available.

	Distribution	Cert	Avg	%MS	MS-67
					PF-67
2016-W	5,695	395	70.0	100%	$400
2016-W, Proof	13,266	501	69.8	100%	$400

NATIONAL PARK SERVICE 100TH ANNIVERSARY HALF DOLLAR (2016)

Designer: *Barbara Fox (obverse), Thomas Hipschen (reverse).* **Weight:** *11.34 grams.*
Composition: *.9167 copper, .0833 nickel.* **Diameter:** *30.61 mm.*
Edge: *Reeded.* **Mints:** *Denver (Uncirculated) and San Francisco (Proof).*

The National Park Service was created through the National Park Service Organic Act, signed into law by President Woodrow Wilson on August 25, 1916. Today the agency employs approximately 20,000 people and operates on a budget of nearly $3 billion.

Designs. *Obverse:* A hiker taking in a mountain landscape above a child observing a frog. *Reverse:* The National Park Service logo.

Mintage Data. Authorized by Public Law 113-291, signed into law by President Barack Obama on December 19, 2014. *Maximum authorized*—750,000. *Number minted*—To be determined.

Original Cost. Sale prices $20.95 (Uncirculated, pre-issue) and $21.95 (Proof, pre-issue). Uncirculated later raised to $24.95, and Proof later raised to $25.95. The surcharge of $5 per coin is assigned to the National Park Foundation.

Key to Collecting. Superb gem coins are readily available.

	Distribution	Cert	Avg	%MS	MS-67
					PF-67
2016-D	21,019	465	69.4	100%	$40
2016-S, Proof	54,844	653	69.6	100%	$32

NATIONAL PARK SERVICE 100TH ANNIVERSARY SILVER DOLLAR (2016)

Designer: *Joseph Menna (obverse), Chris Costello (reverse).* **Weight:** *26.73 grams.*
Composition: *.900 silver, .100 copper (net weight .7736 oz. pure silver).*
Diameter: *38.1 mm.* **Edge:** *Reeded.* **Mint:** *Philadelphia.*

The United States' National Parks range from Alaska's Gates of the Arctic National Park—an expanse of pristine wilderness devoid of any actual park facilities—to American Samoa National Park, which features coral reefs, rainforests, and volcanic mountains.

Designs. *Obverse:* Yellowstone National Park's Old Faithful geyser with a bison in the foreground. *Reverse:* A Latina Folklórico dancer and the National Park Service logo.

Mintage Data. Authorized by Public Law 113-291, signed into law by President Barack Obama on December 19, 2014. *Maximum authorized*—500,000. *Number minted*—To be determined.

Original Cost. Sale prices $44.95 (Uncirculated, pre-issue) and $45.95 (Proof, pre-issue). Uncirculated later raised to $49.95, and Proof later raised to $50.95. The surcharge of $10 per coin is assigned to the National Park Foundation.

Key to Collecting. Superb gem coins are readily available.

	Distribution	Cert	Avg	%MS	MS-67 PF-67
2016-P	*20,994*	756	69.7	100%	$50
2016-P, Proof	*77,309*	1,148	69.4	100%	$52

NATIONAL PARK SERVICE 100TH ANNIVERSARY $5 GOLD COIN (2016)

Designer: *Don Everhart.* **Weight:** *8.359 grams.* **Composition:** *.900 gold, .100 copper (net weight .242 oz. pure gold).* **Diameter:** *21.6 mm.* **Edge:** *Reeded.* **Mint:** *West Point.*

The National Park Service acts as the steward of 409 official "units," which includes the 59 National Parks as well as the country's National Monuments, National Preserves, National Historic Sites, and more.

Designs. *Obverse:* Profiles of John Muir and Theodore Roosevelt with Yosemite National Park's Half Dome in the background. *Reverse:* The National Park Service logo.

Mintage Data. Authorized by Public Law 113-291, signed into law by President Barack Obama on December 19, 2014. *Maximum authorized*—100,000. *Number minted*—To be determined.

Original Cost. Sale prices to be determined. The surcharge of $35 per coin is assigned to the National Park Foundation.

Key to Collecting. Superb gem coins are readily available.

	Distribution	Cert	Avg	%MS	MS-67
					PF-67
2016-W ††	5,150	275	70.0	100%	$375
2016-W, Proof	19,506	536	69.8	100%	$370

†† Ranked in the *100 Greatest U.S. Modern Coins* (fourth edition).

LIONS CLUB INTERNATIONAL CENTURY OF SERVICE SILVER DOLLAR (2017)

Designer: *Joel Iskowitz (obverse), Patricia Lucas-Morris (reverse).* **Weight:** *26.73 grams.*
Composition: *.900 silver, .100 copper (net weight .7736 oz. pure silver).*
Diameter: *38.1 mm.* **Edge:** *Reeded.* **Mints:** *Philadelphia.*

In 1917, Melvin Jones founded the Lions Clubs International as a service club organization with the simple guiding principle of "We Serve." The organization empowers its volunteers to serve their communities, meet humanitarian needs, encourage peace, and promote international understanding. Services participated in include community, environmental, youth, health programs, and disaster relief work.

Designs. *Obverse:* The portrait of founder Melvin Jones is paired with the Lions Clubs International logo. *Reverse:* A male and female lion with a lion cub superimposed over a globe.

Mintage Data. Authorized by Public Law 112-181, the Lions Clubs International Century of Service Commemorative Coin Act, signed into law by President Barack Obama on October 5, 2012 to commemorate the organization's centennial in 2017. *Maximum authorized—400,000. Number minted—*To be determined.

Original Cost. Sale prices $46.95 (Uncirculated, pre-issue) and $47.95 (Proof, pre-issue): Uncirculated later raised to $51.95, and Proof later raised to $52.95. The surcharge of $10 per coin was paid to the Lions Clubs International Foundation to further its programs for the blind and visually impaired, invest in adaptive technologies for the disabled, and invest in youth and those affected by major disaster.

Key to Collecting. Superb gem coins are readily available.

	Distribution	Cert	Avg	%MS	MS-67
					PF-67
2017-P	17,250				$50
2017-P, Proof	68,525				$48

BOYS TOWN CENTENNIAL HALF DOLLAR (2017)

Designer: *Chris Costello.* **Weight:** *11.34 grams.* **Composition:** *.9167 copper, .0833 nickel.*
Diameter: *30.61 mm.* **Edge:** *Reeded.* **Mints:** *San Francisco and Denver.*

Through its Boys Town National Hotline, Boys Town National Research Hospital, and other community services, Boys Town provides treatment for the behavioral, emotional, and physical problems of children and families in 11 regions across the country. Boys Town programs impact the lives of more than two million children and families each year.

Designs. *Obverse:* Two brothers from 1917 walk toward Father Flanagan's Boys Home and a pylon erected at the facility in the 1940s, symbolizing what the home would grow into. *Reverse:* A present-day Boys Town neighborhood of homes overlooked by the profiles of Boys Town graduates.

Mintage Data. Authorized by Public Law 114-30, the Boys Town Centennial Commemorative Coin Program Act of 2015, signed into law by President Barack Obama on July 6, 2015. *Maximum authorized*—300,000. *Number minted*—To be determined.

Original Cost. Sale prices to be determined. The surcharge of $5 per coin went to Boys Town to carry out its cause of caring for and assisting children and families in underserved communities across America.

Key to Collecting. Superb gem coins are readily available.

	Distribution	Cert	Avg	%MS	MS-67
					PF-67
2017-S	15,549				$30
2017-D, Proof	23,213				$32

BOYS TOWN CENTENNIAL SILVER DOLLAR (2017)

Designer: *Emily Damstra.* **Weight:** *26.73 grams.* **Composition:** *.900 silver, .100 copper (net weight .7736 oz. pure silver).* **Diameter:** *38.1 mm.* **Edge:** *Reeded.* **Mints:** *Philadelphia.*

Father Edward Flanagan, a young parish priest, founded Boys Town on the maxim: "Every child could be a productive citizen if given love, a home, an education, and a trade." From the beginning boys of all races and religions were welcomed, and eventually the institution grew to support girls and families as well.

Designs. *Obverse:* A young girl sitting under a tree alone, looking up plaintively. *Reverse:* A family holding hands and playing under the same tree with the same girl.

Mintage Data. Authorized by Public Law 114-30, the Boys Town Centennial Commemorative Coin Program Act of 2015, signed into law by President Barack Obama on July 6, 2015. *Maximum authorized*—350,000. *Number minted*—To be determined.

Original Cost. Sale prices to be determined. The surcharge of $10 per coin went to Boys Town to carry out its cause of caring for and assisting children and families in underserved communities across America.

Key to Collecting. Superb gem coins are readily available.

	Distribution	Cert	Avg	%MS	MS-67
					PF-67
2017-P	12,256				$42
2017-P, Proof	31,644				$50

Boys Town Centennial $5 Gold Coin (2017)

Designer: *Donna Weaver.* **Weight:** *8.359 grams.* **Composition:** *.900 gold, .060 silver, .040 copper (net weight .242 oz. pure gold).* **Diameter:** *21.6 mm.* **Edge:** *Reeded.* **Mint:** *West Point.*

Father Flanagan's Home for Boys, or "Boys Town" as it became known, was founded in rented a boarding house with $90 he had borrowed. It has grown exponentially since its founding in 1917. Today it is one of the largest non-profit organizations in the country, dedicated to serving at-risk children and families of all backgrounds and religions.

Designs. *Obverse:* A portrait of Father Flanagan. *Reverse:* An outstretched hand holding a sprouting acorn.

Mintage Data. Authorized by Public Law 114-30, the Boys Town Centennial Commemorative Coin Program Act of 2015, signed into law by President Barack Obama on July 6, 2015. *Maximum authorized*—50,000. *Number minted*—To be determined.

Original Cost. Sale prices to be determined. The surcharge of $35 per coin went to Boys Town to carry out its cause of caring for and assisting children and families in underserved communities across America.

Key to Collecting. Superb gem coins are readily available.

	Distribution	Cert	Avg	%MS	MS-67
					PF-67
2017-W	2,947				$375
2017-W, Proof	7,370				$390

WORLD WAR I CENTENNIAL SILVER DOLLAR (2018)

Designer: *LeRoy Transfield (obverse and reverse).* **Weight:** *26.73 grams.*
Composition: *.900 silver, .100 copper (net weight .7736 oz. pure silver).*
Diameter: *38.1 mm.* **Edge:** *Reeded.* **Mint:** *Philadelphia.*

This silver dollar commemorates the centennial of America's involvement in World War I (April 1917 to November 1918) and honors the more than four million men and women from the United States who served during the war. In support of the coin program, the Mint created special companion silver medals honoring each of the five branches of the U.S. Armed Forces that were active during the war. Each set included a Proof silver dollar and a Proof medal.

Designs. *Obverse:* "Soldier's Charge" depicts a doughboy gripping a rifle, with twines of barbed wire in the lower right. *Reverse:* "Poppies in the Wire" features abstract poppies—symbols of war remembrance—mixed in with barbed wire continued from the obverse.

Mintage Data. Authorized by Public Law 113-212, the World War I American Veterans Centennial Commemorative Coin Act, and signed by President Barack Obama on December 16, 2014. *Maximum authorized*—350,000 total. *Number minted*—15,979 Uncirculated, 39,956 individual Proofs, 62,660 Proofs in coin-and-medal sets (mintages as of February 2018; not final).

Original Cost. Sale prices $48.95 (Uncirculated, introductory) and $51.95 (Proof, introductory); later raised to $53.95 and $56.95. A surcharge of $10 went to the United States Foundation for the Commemoration of the World Wars, a non-profit organization that supports the U.S. World War I Centennial Commission in public outreach and education about American involvement in the war. The surcharge is expected to be used to help create a new National World War I Memorial at Pershing Park, a block from the White House.

The coin and medal sets were limited to 100,000 units across all five options; their issue price was $99.95.

Key to Collecting. Superb gems are easily found in the marketplace.

	Distribution	Cert	Avg	%MS	MS-67
					PF-67
2018-P					$50
2018-P, Proof					$51

BREAST CANCER AWARENESS HALF DOLLAR (2018)

Designer: *Emily Damstra.* **Weight:** *11.34 grams.* **Composition:** *.9167 copper, .0833 nickel.*
Diameter: *30.61 mm.* **Edge:** *Reeded.* **Mints:** *Denver and San Francisco.*

This suite of three coins commemorates the role of awareness and education in funding cancer research to improve outcomes and save lives. All three coins share the same designs.

Designs. *Obverse:* A butterfly flies above two women. The older woman has her hands on her chest and a relieved expression on her face. The younger, with a scarf on her head, holds one hand over her chest and the other raised in a fist as if she is ready to fight. *Reverse:* A tiger swallowtail butterfly in flight, symbolic of hope.

Mintage Data. Authorized by Public Law 114-148, the Breast Cancer Awareness Commemorative Coin Act, and signed by President Barack Obama on April 29, 2016. *Maximum authorized*—750,000 total. *Number minted*—To be determined.

Original Cost. Sale prices to be determined. A surcharges of $5 is assigned to the Breast Cancer Research Foundation.

	Distribution	Cert	Avg	%MS	MS-67
					PF-67
2018-D					$21
2018-S, Proof					$22

BREAST CANCER AWARENESS SILVER DOLLAR (2018)

Designer: *Emily Damstra.* **Weight:** *26.73 grams.* **Composition:** *.900 silver, .100 copper (net weight .7736 oz. pure silver).* **Diameter:** *38.1 mm.* **Edge:** *Reeded.* **Mint:** *Philadelphia.*

This suite of three coins commemorates the role of awareness and education in funding cancer research to improve outcomes and save lives. All three coins share the same designs.

Designs. *Obverse:* A butterfly flies above two women. The older woman has her hands on her chest and a relieved expression on her face. The younger, with a scarf on her head, holds one hand over her chest and the other raised in a fist as if she is ready to fight. *Reverse:* A tiger swallowtail butterfly in flight, symbolic of hope.

Mintage Data. Authorized by Public Law 114-148, the Breast Cancer Awareness Commemorative Coin Act, and signed by President Barack Obama on April 29, 2016. *Maximum authorized*—400,000 total. *Number minted*—To be determined.

Original Cost. Sale prices to be determined. A surcharges of $10 is assigned to the Breast Cancer Research Foundation.

	Distribution	Cert	Avg	%MS	MS-67	
					PF-67	
2018-P					$50	
2017-P, Proof					$50	

BREAST CANCER AWARENESS $5 GOLD COIN (2017)

Designer: *Emily Damstra.* **Weight:** *8.359 grams.* **Composition:** *.900 gold, .060 silver, .040 copper (net weight .242 oz. pure gold).* **Diameter:** *21.6 mm.* **Edge:** *Reeded.* **Mint:** *West Point.*

This suite of three coins commemorates the role of awareness and education in funding cancer research to improve outcomes and save lives. The $5 gold coin, with slightly more copper and zinc than the standard alloy, has a pink hue, symbolizing breast cancer awareness. All three coins share the same designs.

Designs. *Obverse:* A butterfly flies above two women. The older woman has her hands on her chest and a relieved expression on her face. The younger, with a scarf on her head, holds one hand over her chest and the other raised in a fist as if she is ready to fight. *Reverse:* A tiger swallowtail butterfly in flight, symbolic of hope.

Mintage Data. Authorized by Public Law 114-148, the Breast Cancer Awareness Commemorative Coin Act, and signed by President Barack Obama on April 29, 2016. *Maximum authorized*—50,000 total. *Number minted*—To be determined.

Original Cost. Sale prices to be determined. A surcharges of $35 is assigned to the Breast Cancer Research Foundation.

	Distribution	Cert	Avg	%MS	MS-67	
					PF-67	
2018-W	2,947				$375	
2018-W, Proof	7,370				$370	

APOLLO 11 50TH ANNIVERSARY HALF DOLLAR (2019)

Designer: *Gary Cooper.* **Weight:** *11.34 grams.* **Composition:** *.9167 copper, .0833 nickel.* **Diameter:** *30.61 mm.* **Edge:** *Reeded.* **Mints:** *San Francisco and Denver.*

This program commemorates the historic Apollo 11 Moon landing on July 20, 1969. All three domed-format coins share common designs, which include, on the concave reverse, the words MERCURY, GEMINI, and APOLLO separated by moon-phase emblems, indicating the three NASA missions that culminated with the world's first manned Moon landing. The coins are "curved"—that is, the obverse is concave, and the reverse is convex, the second series struck in such a fashion by the U.S. Mint.

Designs. *Obverse:* The footprint of Neil Armstrong on the Moon, with the names of NASA missions MERCURY, GEMINI, and APOLLO above. *Reverse:* A close-up of the famous "Buzz Aldrin on the Moon" photo centered on the astronaut's visor, which reflects the landing scene.

Mintage Data. Authorized by the Apollo 11 50th Anniversary Commemorative Coin Act (P.L. 114-282), signed by President Barack Obama on December 16, 2016. *Maximum authorized—*750,000. *Number minted —*To be determined.

Original Cost. Sale prices $25.95 (Uncirculated, pre-issue) and $27.95 (Proof, pre-issue); Uncirculated later raised to $30.95 and Proof to $32.95. The surcharge of $5 goes to the Smithsonian Institution's National Air and Space Museum's "Destination Moon" exhibit, the Astronauts Memorial Foundation, and the Astronaut Scholarship Foundation.

Key to Collecting. Superb gem coins are readily available.

	Distribution	Cert	Avg	%MS	MS-67
					PF-67
2019-D					$26
2019-S, Proof					$28

APOLLO 11 50TH ANNIVERSARY SILVER DOLLAR (2019)

Both Varieties: Designer: *Gary Cooper.* **Edge:** *Reeded.* **Mints:** *Philadelphia.* **Standard Issue: Diameter:** *38.1 mm.* **Weight:** *26.73 grams.* **Composition:** *.999 silver (net weight .8594 oz. pure silver).* **Five-Ounce Proof: Diameter:** *76.2 mm.* **Weight:** *155.52 grams.* **Composition:** *.999 silver (net weight 5 oz. pure silver).*

The common reverse depicts the footprint of Neil Armstrong on the Moon's surface, as photographed by the astronaut to demonstrate the depth to which his boot could penetrate the lunar soil.

The silver dollar was produced in two sizes: the normal 38.1 mm and a large, 5-ounce size measuring 76.2 mm in diameter (struck only in Proof format). Except for the size, the designs are identical in every respect.

The coins are "curved"—that is, the obverse is concave, and the reverse is convex, the second series struck in such a fashion by the U.S. Mint.

Designs. *Obverse:* The footprint of Neil Armstrong on the Moon, with the names of NASA missions MERCURY, GEMINI, and APOLLO above. *Reverse:* A close-up of the famous "Buzz Aldrin on the Moon" photo centered on the astronaut's visor, which reflects the landing scene.

Mintage Data. Authorized by the Apollo 11 50th Anniversary Commemorative Coin Act (P.L. 114-282), signed by President Barack Obama on December 16, 2016. *Maximum authorized—*Standard size, 400,000; 5-ounce size, 100,000. *Number minted—*Standard size, to be determined; 5-ounce size, *100,000.*

Original Cost. Normal size, sale prices $51.95 (Uncirculated, pre-issue) and $54.95 (Proof, pre-issue); Uncirculated later raised to $56.95 and Proof to $59.95. 5-ounce size, sale price $224.95 (pre-issue) later raised to $229.95. The surcharges of $10 (normal size) and $50 (5-ounce size) go to the Smithsonian Institution's National Air and Space Museum's "Destination Moon" exhibit, the Astronauts Memorial Foundation, and the Astronaut Scholarship Foundation.

Key to Collecting. Superb gem coins are readily available.

	Distribution	Cert	Avg	%MS	MS-67
					PF-67
2019-P					$52
2019-P, Proof					$55
2019-P, 5-oz. Proof					$225

APOLLO 11 50TH ANNIVERSARY $5 GOLD COIN (2019)

Designer: *Gary Cooper.* **Weight:** *8.359 grams.* **Composition:** *.900 gold, .060 silver, .040 copper (net weight .242 oz. pure gold).* **Diameter:** *21.6 mm.* **Edge:** *Reeded.* **Mint:** *West Point.*

The convex reverse depicts one of the most famous images in U.S. history—the helmet of astronaut Buzz Aldrin, its visor reflecting Aldrin's shadow; astronaut Neil Armstrong, holding the camera; the lunar module *Eagle*; and the American flag the mission placed on the Moon. The design was mandated by the authorizing legislation. The coins are "curved" —that is, the obverse is concave, and the reverse is convex, the second series struck in such a fashion by the U.S. Mint.

Designs. *Obverse:* The footprint of Neil Armstrong on the Moon, with the names of NASA missions MERCURY, GEMINI, and APOLLO above. *Reverse:* A close-up of the famous "Buzz Aldrin on the Moon" photo centered on the astronaut's visor, which reflects the landing scene.

Mintage Data. Authorized by the Apollo 11 50th Anniversary Commemorative Coin Act (P.L. 114-282), signed by President Barack Obama on December 16, 2016. *Maximum authorized*—50,000. *Number minted*—To be determined.

Original Cost. Sale prices $421 (Uncirculated, pre-issue) and $431 (Proof, pre-issue); Uncirculated later raised to $426 and Proof to $436. The surcharge of $35 goes to the Smithsonian Institution's National Air and Space Museum's "Destination Moon" exhibit, the Astronauts Memorial Foundation, and the Astronaut Scholarship Foundation.

Key to Collecting. Superb gem coins are readily available.

	Distribution	Cert	Avg	%MS	MS-67
					PF-67
2019-W					
2019-W, Proof					

AMERICAN LEGION 100TH ANNIVERSARY HALF DOLLAR (2019)

Designer: *Richard Masters.* **Weight:** *11.34 grams.* **Composition:** *.9167 copper, .0833 nickel.* **Diameter:** *30.61 mm.* **Edge:** *Reeded.* **Mints:** *San Francisco and Denver.*

With divisions ranging from the national to the local levels, the American Legion focuses on service to veterans, their families, and the community. Among other efforts, the Legion runs civic programs for both boys and girls, and has awarded millions of dollars in Child Welfare Foundation grants and college scholarships.

Designs. *Obverse:* Two children recite the Pledge of Allegiance with their hands over their hearts, the little girl wearing her grandfather's old American Legion hat. *Reverse:* A flag on a flagpole is depicted from a low angle, as if from a child's point of view, with the American Legion's emblem above.

Mintage Data. Authorized by the American Legion 100th Anniversary Commemorative Coin Act (P.L. 115-65), signed by President Donald Trump on October 6, 2017. *Maximum authorized*—750,000. *Number minted*—To be determined.

Original Cost. Sale prices $25.95 (Uncirculated, pre-issue) and $27.95 (Proof, pre-issue); Uncirculated later raised to $30.95 and Proof to $32.95. The surcharge of $5 goes to the American Legion for costs related to promoting the welfare of veterans and servicemembers, and to promoting patriotic values, strong families, and the importance of assistance for at-risk children.

Key to Collecting. Superb gem coins are readily available.

	Distribution	Cert	Avg	%MS	MS-67
					PF-67
2019-D					$26
2019-S, Proof					$28

AMERICAN LEGION 100TH ANNIVERSARY SILVER DOLLAR (2019)

Designer: *Paul C. Balan (obverse), Patricia Lucas-Morris (reverse).* **Weight:** *26.73 grams.* **Composition:** *.999 silver (net weight .8594 oz. pure silver).* **Diameter:** *38.1 mm.* **Edge:** *Reeded.* **Mints:** *Philadelphia.*

Founded on March 15, 1919, in Paris, France, the American Legion was concerned with the welfare of U.S. soldiers and the communities they returned to after World War I. Today the Legion focuses on four areas: Veterans Affairs and Rehabilitation, Children and Youth, National Security, and Americanism— the "Four Pillars" of American Legion service.

Designs. *Obverse:* The emblem of the American Legion adorned by oak leaves and a lily, commemorating the Legion's founding in March 1919. *Reverse:* The founding of the American Legion in Paris, France, is represented by crossed U.S. and Legion flags below a fleur de lis and the legend 100 YEARS OF SERVICE.

Mintage Data. Authorized by the American Legion 100th Anniversary Commemorative Coin Act (P.L. 115-65), signed by President Donald Trump on October 6, 2017. *Maximum authorized—400,000. Number minted—*To be determined.

Original Cost. Sale prices $51.95 (Uncirculated, pre-issue) and $54.95 (Proof, pre-issue); Uncirculated later raised to $56.95 and Proof to $59.95. The surcharge of $10 goes to the American Legion for costs related to promoting the welfare of veterans and servicemembers, and to promoting patriotic values, strong families, and the importance of assistance for at-risk children.

Key to Collecting. Superb gem coins are readily available.

	Distribution	Cert	Avg	%MS	MS-67 PF-67
2017-P	12,256				$50
2017-P, Proof	31,644				$51

AMERICAN LEGION 100TH ANNIVERSARY $5 GOLD COIN (2019)

Designer: *Chris Costello (obverse), Paul C. Balan (reverse).* **Weight:** *8.359 grams.*
Composition: *.900 gold, .060 silver, .040 copper (net weight .242 oz. pure gold).*
Diameter: *21.6 mm.* **Edge:** *Reeded.* **Mint:** *West Point.*

The non-partisan American Legion is the nation's largest veterans' group, with nearly two million members in more than 12,000 posts throughout the United States. Men and women of any ethnic background or religious affiliation may join. The GI Bill, which provides educational assistance to veterans, servicemembers, and their children, has been among the Legion's many efforts.

Designs. *Obverse:* A "V" for "Victory" is superimposed over the Eiffel Tower. *Reverse:* An eagle soars from right to left, with the emblem of the American Legion in the field.

Mintage Data. Authorized by the American Legion 100th Anniversary Commemorative Coin Act (P.L. 115-65), signed by President Donald Trump on October 6, 2017. *Maximum authorized—50,000. Number minted—*To be determined.

Original Cost. Sale prices to be determined. The surcharge of $35 goes to the American Legion for costs related to promoting the welfare of veterans and servicemembers, and to promoting patriotic values, strong families, and the importance of assistance for at-risk children.

Key to Collecting. Superb gem coins are readily available.

	Distribution	Cert	Avg	%MS	MS-67	
					PF-67	
2019-W						
	Auctions: No auction records available.					
2019-W, Proof						
	Auctions: No auction records available.					

GOVERNMENT COMMEMORATIVE SETS

	Value
(1983–1984) LOS ANGELES OLYMPIAD	
1983 and 1984 Proof silver dollars	$50
1983 and 1984 6-coin set. One each of 1983 and 1984 silver dollars, both Proof and Uncirculated gold $10 (a)	$1,500
1983 3-piece collector set. 1983 P, D, and S Uncirculated silver dollars	$70
1984 3-piece collector set. 1984 P, D, and S Uncirculated silver dollars	$75
1983 and 1984 gold and silver Uncirculated set. One each of 1983 and 1984 Uncirculated silver dollars and one 1984 Uncirculated gold $10	$775
1983 and 1984 gold and silver Proof set. One each of 1983 and 1984 Proof silver dollars and one 1984 Proof gold $10	$775
(1986) STATUE OF LIBERTY	
2-coin set. Proof silver dollar and clad half dollar	$30
3-coin set. Proof silver dollar, clad half dollar, and gold $5	$400
2-coin set. Uncirculated silver dollar and clad half dollar	$35
2-coin set. Uncirculated and Proof gold $5	$675
3-coin set. Uncirculated silver dollar, clad half dollar, and gold $5	$400
6-coin set. One each of Proof and Uncirculated half dollar, silver dollar, and gold $5 (a)	$725
(1987) CONSTITUTION	
2-coin set. Uncirculated silver dollar and gold $5	$375
2-coin set. Proof silver dollar and gold $5	$410
4-coin set. One each of Proof and Uncirculated silver dollar and gold $5 (a)	$725
(1988) SEOUL OLYMPIAD	
2-coin set. Uncirculated silver dollar and gold $5	$350
2-coin set. Proof silver dollar and gold $5	$410
4-coin set. One each of Proof and Uncirculated silver dollar and gold $5 (a)	$750
(1989) CONGRESS	
2-coin set. Proof clad half dollar and silver dollar	$35
3-coin set. Proof clad half dollar, silver dollar, and gold $5	$400
2-coin set. Uncirculated clad half dollar and silver dollar	$35
3-coin set. Uncirculated clad half dollar, silver dollar, and gold $5	$400
6-coin set. One each of Proof and Uncirculated clad half dollar, silver dollar, and gold $5 (a)	$850
(1991) MOUNT RUSHMORE	
2-coin set. Uncirculated clad half dollar and silver dollar	$50
2-coin set. Proof clad half dollar and silver dollar	$45
3-coin set. Uncirculated clad half dollar, silver dollar, and gold $5	$400
3-coin set. Proof half dollar, silver dollar, and gold $5	$400
6-coin set. One each of Proof and Uncirculated clad half dollar, silver dollar, and gold $5 (a)	$900
(1992) XXV OLYMPIAD	
2-coin set. Uncirculated clad half dollar and silver dollar	$45
2-coin set. Proof clad half dollar and silver dollar	$35
3-coin set. Uncirculated clad half dollar, silver dollar, and gold $5	$400
3-coin set. Proof half dollar, silver dollar, and gold $5	$400
6-coin set. One each of Proof and Uncirculated clad half dollar, silver dollar, and gold $5 (a)	$900

a. Packaged in cherrywood box.

	Value
(1992) CHRISTOPHER COLUMBUS	
2-coin set. Uncirculated clad half dollar and silver dollar	$45
2-coin set. Proof clad half dollar and silver dollar	$40
3-coin set. Uncirculated clad half dollar, silver dollar, and gold $5	$400
3-coin set. Proof half dollar, silver dollar, and gold $5	$400
6-coin set. One each of Proof and Uncirculated clad half dollar, silver dollar, and gold $5 (a)	$900
(1993) BILL OF RIGHTS	
2-coin set. Uncirculated silver half dollar and silver dollar	$60
2-coin set. Proof silver half dollar and silver dollar	$50
3-coin set. Uncirculated silver half dollar, silver dollar, and gold $5	$400
3-coin set. Proof half dollar, silver dollar, and gold $5	$400
6-coin set. One each of Proof and Uncirculated silver half dollar, silver dollar, and gold $5 (a)	$900
"Young Collector" set. Silver half dollar	$35
Educational set. Silver half dollar and James Madison medal	$35
Proof silver half dollar and 25-cent stamp	$20
(1993) WORLD WAR II	
2-coin set. Uncirculated clad half dollar and silver dollar	$55
2-coin set. Proof clad half dollar and silver dollar	$45
3-coin set. Uncirculated clad half dollar, silver dollar, and gold $5	$400
3-coin set. Proof clad half dollar, silver dollar, and gold $5	$400
6-coin set. One each of Proof and Uncirculated clad half dollar, silver dollar, and gold $5 (a)	$900
"Young Collector" set. Clad half dollar	$30
Victory Medal set. Uncirculated clad half dollar and reproduction medal	$40
(1993) THOMAS JEFFERSON	
"Coinage and Currency" set (issued in 1994). Silver dollar, "frosted" Uncirculated Jefferson nickel, and $2 note	$110
(1994) WORLD CUP SOCCER	
2-coin set. Uncirculated clad half dollar and silver dollar	$50
2-coin set. Proof clad half dollar and silver dollar	$45
3-coin set. Uncirculated clad half dollar, silver dollar, and gold $5	$400
3-coin set. Proof clad half dollar, silver dollar, and gold $5	$400
6-coin set. One each of Proof and Uncirculated clad half dollar, silver dollar, and gold $5 (a)	$900
"Young Collector" set. Uncirculated clad half dollar	$20
"Special Edition" set. Proof clad half dollar and silver dollar	$50
(1994) U.S. VETERANS	
3-coin set. Uncirculated POW, Vietnam, and Women in Military Service silver dollars	$150
3-coin set. Proof POW, Vietnam, and Women in Military Service silver dollars	$125
(1995) SPECIAL OLYMPICS	
2-coin set. Proof Special Olympics silver dollar, 1995-S Kennedy half dollar	$75
(1995) CIVIL WAR BATTLEFIELD PRESERVATION	
2-coin set. Uncirculated clad half dollar and silver dollar	$90
2-coin set. Proof clad half dollar and silver dollar	$90
3-coin set. Uncirculated clad half dollar, silver dollar, and gold $5	$500
3-coin set. Proof clad half dollar, silver dollar, and gold $5	$420
6-coin set. One each of Proof and Uncirculated clad half dollar, silver dollar, and gold $5 (a)	$950
"Young Collector" set. Uncirculated clad half dollar	$50
2-coin "Union" set. Clad half dollar and silver dollar	$125
3-coin "Union" set. Clad half dollar, silver dollar, and gold $5	$485
(1995–1996) CENTENNIAL OLYMPIC GAMES	
4-coin set #1. Uncirculated clad half dollar (Basketball), silver dollars (Gymnastics, Paralympics), gold $5 (Torch Bearer)	$700
4-coin set #2. Proof clad half dollar (Basketball), silver dollars (Gymnastics, Paralympics), gold $5 (Torch Bearer)	$650
4-coin set #3. Proof half dollar (Baseball), dollars (Cyclist, Track Runner), gold $5 (Olympic Stadium)	$650
2-coin set #1: Proof silver dollars (Gymnastics, Paralympics)	$70

a. Packaged in cherrywood box.

	Value
(1995–1996) CENTENNIAL OLYMPIC GAMES	
"Young Collector" set. Uncirculated Basketball clad half dollar	$35
"Young Collector" set. Uncirculated Baseball clad half dollar	$35
"Young Collector" set. Uncirculated Swimming clad half dollar	$200
"Young Collector" set. Uncirculated Soccer clad half dollar	$175
1995–1996 16-coin Uncirculated set. One each of all Uncirculated coins (a)	$4,600
1995–1996 16-coin Proof set. One each of all Proof coins (a)	$2,000
1995–1996 8-coin Proof silver dollars set	$400
1995–1996 32-coin set. One each of all Uncirculated and Proof coins (a)	$6,750
(1996) NATIONAL COMMUNITY SERVICE	
Proof silver dollar and Saint-Gaudens stamp	$100
(1996) SMITHSONIAN INSTITUTION 150TH ANNIVERSARY	
2-coin set. Proof silver dollar and gold $5	$400
4-coin set. One each of Proof and Uncirculated silver dollar and gold $5 (a)	$900
"Young Collector" set. Proof silver dollar	$100
(1997) U.S. BOTANIC GARDEN	
"Coinage and Currency" set. Uncirculated silver dollar, "frosted" Uncirculated Jefferson nickel, and $1 note	$250
(1997) JACKIE ROBINSON	
2-coin set. Proof silver dollar and gold $5	$500
4-coin set. One each of Proof and Uncirculated silver dollar and gold $5 (a)	$1,300
3-piece "Legacy" set. Baseball card, pin, and gold $5 (a)	$650
(1997) FRANKLIN D. ROOSEVELT	
2-coin set. One each of Proof and Uncirculated gold $5	$800
(1997) NATIONAL LAW ENFORCEMENT OFFICERS MEMORIAL	
Insignia set. Silver dollar, lapel pin, and patch	$200
(1998) ROBERT F. KENNEDY	
2-coin set. RFK silver dollar and JFK silver half dollar	$200
2-coin set. Proof and Uncirculated RFK silver dollars	$110
(1998) BLACK REVOLUTIONARY WAR PATRIOTS	
2-coin set. Proof and Uncirculated silver dollars	$125
"Young Collector" set. Uncirculated silver dollar	$125
Black Revolutionary War Patriots set. Silver dollar and four stamps	$150
(1999) DOLLEY MADISON	
2-coin set. Proof and Uncirculated silver dollars	$75
(1999) GEORGE WASHINGTON DEATH	
2-coin set. One each of Proof and Uncirculated gold $5	$720
(1999) YELLOWSTONE NATIONAL PARK	
2-coin set. One each of Proof and Uncirculated silver dollars	$100
(2000) LEIF ERICSON MILLENNIUM	
2-coin set. Proof silver dollar and Icelandic 1,000 kronur	$100
(2000) MILLENNIUM COIN AND CURRENCY SET	
3-piece set. Uncirculated 2000 Sacagawea dollar; Uncirculated 2000 Silver Eagle; George Washington $1 note, series 1999	$100
(2001) AMERICAN BUFFALO	
2-coin set. One each of Proof and Uncirculated silver dollars	$300
"Coinage and Currency" set. Uncirculated American Buffalo silver dollar, face reprint of 1899 $5 Indian Chief Silver Certificate, 1987 Chief Red Cloud 10¢ stamp, 2001 Bison 21¢ stamp	$200
(2001) U.S. CAPITOL VISITOR CENTER	
3-coin set. Proof clad half dollar, silver dollar, and gold $5	$400
(2002) SALT LAKE OLYMPIC GAMES	
2-coin set. Proof silver dollar and gold $5	$400
4-coin set. One each of Proof and Uncirculated silver dollar and gold $5	$900
(2003) FIRST FLIGHT CENTENNIAL	
3-coin set. Proof clad half dollar, silver dollar, and gold $10	$800

a. Packaged in cherrywood box.

	Value
(2003) LEGACIES OF FREEDOM	
Uncirculated 2003 $1 American Eagle silver bullion coin and an Uncirculated 2002 £2 Silver Britannia coin	$75
(2004) THOMAS A. EDISON	
Edison set. Uncirculated silver dollar and light bulb	$85
(2004) LEWIS AND CLARK	
Coin and Pouch set. Proof silver dollar and beaded pouch	$200
"Coinage and Currency" set. Uncirculated silver dollar, Sacagawea golden dollar, two 2005 nickels, replica 1901 $10 Bison note, silver-plated Peace Medal replica, three stamps, two booklets	$100
(2004) WESTWARD JOURNEY NICKEL SERIES	
Westward Journey Nickel Series™ Coin and Medal set. Proof Sacagawea golden dollar, two 2004 Proof nickels, silver-plated Peace Medal replica	$60
(2005) WESTWARD JOURNEY NICKEL SERIES	
Westward Journey Nickel Series™ Coin and Medal set. Proof Sacagawea golden dollar, two 2005 Proof nickels, silver-plated Peace Medal replica	$40
(2005) CHIEF JUSTICE JOHN MARSHALL	
"Coin and Chronicles" set. Uncirculated silver dollar, booklet, BEP intaglio portrait	$60
(2005) AMERICAN LEGACY	
American Legacy Collection. Proof Marine Corps silver dollar, Proof John Marshall silver dollar, 11-piece Proof set	$100
(2005) MARINE CORPS 230TH ANNIVERSARY	
Marine Corps Uncirculated silver dollar and stamp set	$100
(2006) BENJAMIN FRANKLIN	
"Coin and Chronicles" set. Uncirculated "Scientist" silver dollar, four stamps, *Poor Richard's Almanack* replica, intaglio print	$75
(2006) AMERICAN LEGACY	
American Legacy Collection. Proof 2006-P Benjamin Franklin, Founding Father silver dollar; Proof 2006-S San Francisco Old Mint silver dollar; Proof cent, nickel, dime, quarter, half dollar, and dollar	$90
(2007) AMERICAN LEGACY	
American Legacy Collection. 16 Proof coins for 2007: five state quarters; four Presidential dollars; Jamestown and Little Rock Central High School Desegregation silver dollars; Proof cent, nickel, dime, half dollar, and dollar	$140
(2007) LITTLE ROCK CENTRAL HIGH SCHOOL DESEGREGATION	
Little Rock Coin and Medal set. Uncirculated 2007-P silver dollar, bronze medal	$175
(2008) BALD EAGLE	
3-piece set. Proof clad half dollar, silver dollar, and gold $5	$400
Bald Eagle Coin and Medal Set. Uncirculated silver dollar, bronze medal	$70
"Young Collector" set. Uncirculated clad half dollar	$18
(2008) AMERICAN LEGACY	
American Legacy Collection. 15 Proof coins for 2008: cent, nickel, dime, half dollar, and dollar; five state quarters; four Presidential dollars; Bald Eagle silver dollar	$150
(2009) LOUIS BRAILLE	
Uncirculated silver dollar in tri-folded package	$50
(2009) ABRAHAM LINCOLN COIN AND CHRONICLES	
Four Proof 2009-S cents and Abraham Lincoln Proof silver dollar	$150
(2012) STAR-SPANGLED BANNER	
2-coin set. Proof silver dollar and gold $5	$400
(2013) 5-STAR GENERALS	
3-coin set. Proof clad half dollar, silver dollar, and gold $5	$550
Profile Collection. Uncirculated half dollar and silver dollar, replica of 1962 General MacArthur Congressional gold medal	$80
(2013) THEODORE ROOSEVELT COIN AND CHRONICLES	
Theodore Roosevelt Proof Presidential dollar, silver Presidential medal, National Wildlife Refuge System Centennial bronze medal, and Roosevelt print	$60
(2013) GIRL SCOUTS OF THE U.S.A.	
"Young Collector" set. Uncirculated silver dollar	$60
(2014) FRANKLIN D. ROOSEVELT COIN AND CHRONICLES	
Franklin D. Roosevelt Proof dime and Presidential dollar, bronze Presidential medal, silver Presidential medal, four stamps, information booklet	$100

	Value
(2014) NATIONAL BASEBALL HALL OF FAME	
"Young Collector" set. Uncirculated silver dollar	$30
(2014) AMERICAN $1 COIN AND CURRENCY SET	
2014-D Native American—Native Hospitality Enhanced Uncirculated dollar and $1 Federal Reserve Note	$50
(2015) HARRY S. TRUMAN COIN AND CHRONICLES	
Harry S. Truman Reverse Proof Presidential dollar, silver Presidential medal, one stamp, information booklet	$300
(2015) DWIGHT D. EISENHOWER COIN AND CHRONICLES	
Dwight D. Eisenhower Reverse Proof Presidential dollar, silver Presidential medal, one stamp, information booklet	$150
(2015) JOHN F. KENNEDY COIN AND CHRONICLES	
John F. Kennedy Reverse Proof Presidential dollar, silver Presidential medal, one stamp, information booklet	$100
(2015) LYNDON B. JOHNSON COIN AND CHRONICLES	
Lyndon B. Johnson Reverse Proof Presidential dollar, silver Presidential medal, one stamp, information booklet	$100
(2015) MARCH OF DIMES SPECIAL SILVER SET	
Proof dime and March of Dimes silver dollar, Reverse Proof dime	$80
(2015) AMERICAN $1 COIN AND CURRENCY SET	
2015-W Native American—Mohawk Ironworkers Enhanced Uncirculated dollar and $1 Federal Reserve Note	$25
(2016) NATIONAL PARK SERVICE 100TH ANNIVERSARY	
3-piece set. Proof clad half dollar, silver dollar, and gold $5	$550
(2016) RONALD REAGAN COIN AND CHRONICLES	
Ronald Reagan Reverse Proof Presidential dollar, 2016-W American Eagle silver Proof dollar, Ronald and Nancy Reagan bronze medal, engraved Ronald Reagan Presidential portrait, information booklet	$125
(2016) AMERICAN $1 COIN AND CURRENCY SET	
2016-S Native American—Code Talkers Enhanced Uncirculated dollar and $1 Federal Reserve Note	$25
(2017) BOYS TOWN CENTENNIAL	
3-piece set. Proof clad half dollar, silver dollar, and gold $5	$460
(2018) BREAST CANCER AWARENESS COIN AND STAMP SET	
Breast Cancer Awareness commemorative Proof half dollar and Proof silver Breast Cancer Awareness stamp	$100
(2018) WORLD WAR I CENTENNIAL SILVER DOLLAR AND AIR SERVICE MEDAL SET	
World War I Centennial commemorative Proof silver dollar and Proof silver Air Service medal	$100
(2018) WORLD WAR I CENTENNIAL SILVER DOLLAR AND ARMY MEDAL SET	
World War I Centennial commemorative Proof silver dollar and Proof silver Army medal	$100
(2018) WORLD WAR I CENTENNIAL SILVER DOLLAR AND COAST GUARD MEDAL SET	
World War I Centennial commemorative Proof silver dollar and Proof silver Coast Guard medal	$100
(2018) WORLD WAR I CENTENNIAL SILVER DOLLAR AND MARINE CORPS MEDAL SET	
World War I Centennial commemorative Proof silver dollar and Proof silver Marine Corps medal	$100
(2018) WORLD WAR I CENTENNIAL SILVER DOLLAR AND NAVY MEDAL SET	
World War I Centennial commemorative Proof silver dollar and Proof silver Navy medal	$100
(2019) APOLLO 11 50TH ANNIVERSARY HALF DOLLAR SET	
Apollo 11 50th Anniversary commemorative uncirculated and Proof clad half dollars	
(2019) AMERICAN LEGION 100TH ANNIVERSARY THREE-COIN PROOF SET	
American Legion 100th Anniversary commemorative Proof clad half dollar, silver dollar, and gold $5	
(2019) AMERICAN LEGION 100TH ANNIVERSARY SILVER DOLLAR AND AMERICAN VETERANS MEDAL SET	
American Legion 100th Anniversary commemorative Proof silver dollar and American Veterans medal	
(2019) NATIVE AMERICAN $1 COIN & CURRENCY SET	
2019-W Native American–Indians in Space Enhanced Uncirculated dollar and $1 Federal Reserve Note	
(2019) AMERICAN INNOVATION UNCIRCULATED COIN SET	
Four Uncirculated American Innovation $1 coins	
(2019) AMERICAN INNOVATION $1 PROOF SET	
Four Proof American Innovation $1 coins	

Proof and Mint Sets
1936 to Date

AN OVERVIEW OF PROOF AND MINT SETS

PROOF COINS AND SETS

A Proof is a specimen coin struck for presentation, souvenir, exhibition, or numismatic purposes. Before 1968, Proofs were made only at the Philadelphia Mint, except in a few rare instances in which presentation pieces were struck at branch mints. Today Proofs are made at the San Francisco and West Point mints.

The term *Proof* refers not to the condition of a coin, but to its method of manufacture. Regular-production coins (struck for circulation) in Mint State have coruscating, frosty luster; soft details; and minor imperfections. A Proof coin can usually be distinguished by its sharpness of detail, high wire edge, and extremely brilliant, mirrorlike surface. All Proofs are originally sold by the Mint at a premium.

Very few Proof coins were made prior to 1856. Because of their rarity and infrequent sales, they are not all listed in the regular edition of the *Guide Book of United States Coins*. However, here, in the *Deluxe Edition*, you will find them listed individually within their respective denominations.

Frosted Proofs were issued prior to 1936 and starting again in the late 1970s. These have a brilliant, mirrorlike field with contrasting dull or frosted design.

Matte Proofs have a granular, "sandblast" surface instead of the mirror finish. Matte Proof cents, nickels, and gold coins were issued from 1908 to 1916; a few 1921 and 1922 silver dollars and a 1998-S half dollar were also struck in this manner.

Brilliant Proofs have been issued from 1936 to date. These have a uniformly brilliant, mirrorlike surface and sharp, high-relief details.

Reverse Proofs were first struck for bullion coins in 2006, and regularly denominated, silver-struck coins have also been made with this finish since 2014. As their name implies, the devices, not the field, have a brilliant, mirrorlike finish, while the field has a matte finish.

"Prooflike" coins are occasionally seen. These are examples struck from dies that were lightly polished, often inadvertently during the removal of lines, contact marks, and other marks in the fields. In other instances, such as with certain New Orleans gold coins of the 1850s, the dies were polished in the machine shop of the mint. They are not true Proofs, but may have most of the characteristics of a Proof coin and generally command a premium. Collectors should beware of coins that have been buffed to look like Proofs; magnification will reveal polishing lines and loss of detail.

After a lapse of some 20 years, Proof coins were struck at the Philadelphia Mint from 1936 to 1942, inclusive. During these years the Mint offered Proof coins to collectors for individual sale, rather than in officially packaged sets, as such.

In 1942, when the composition of the five-cent piece was changed from copper-nickel to copper-silver-manganese, there were two Proof types of this denomination available to collectors.

The striking of all Proof coins was temporarily suspended from 1943 through 1949, and again from 1965 through 1967; during the latter period, Special Mint Sets were struck (see page 1202). Proof sets were resumed in 1968.

Sets from 1936 through 1972 included the cent, nickel, dime, quarter, and half dollar; from 1973 through 1981 the dollar was also included, and again from 2000 on. Regular Proof sets issued from 1982 to 1998 contain the cent through the half dollar. Specially packaged Prestige sets containing commemorative coins were sold from 1983 through 1997 at an additional premium. From 1999 to 2009, sets contain five different Statehood or Territorial quarters, and from 2010 to 2021, different National Parks quarters. In 1999 Proof dollars were sold separately. Four-piece Presidential dollar sets have been issued since 2007.

As part of a memorial John F. Kennedy half dollar set released in 2014, Reverse Proofs struck in silver at West Point were introduced. The Philadelphia mint first struck Reverse Proofs in 2015, also in silver, for inclusion in the March of Dimes commemorative set. Additionally, Coin and Chronicles sets of 2015 include Philadelphia-struck Reverse Proofs of the Presidential dollars of the year.

With the recent State and Territorial quarters programs, as well as the ongoing National Park quarters and Presidential dollars programs, the U.S. Mint has offered Proof sets featuring each of the designs issued for a particular year.

From time to time the Mint issues special Proof sets. One recent example is the four-piece 2009-S Lincoln Bicentennial set, which included each of the special cent designs issued that year, but coined in 95% copper (the Lincoln cent's original 1909 alloy).

Collectors are encouraged to consult David W. Lange's *Guide Book of Modern United States Proof Coin Sets* for detailed coverage and illustrations of Proof sets from 1936 to date.

How Modern Proof Coins Are Made

Selected dies are inspected for perfection and are highly polished and cleaned. They are again wiped clean or polished after every 15 to 25 impressions and are replaced frequently to avoid imperfections from wear. Coinage blanks for Proof coins are polished and cleaned to ensure high quality in striking. They are then hand fed into the coinage press one at a time, each blank receiving two or more blows from the dies to bring up sharp, high-relief details. The coinage operation is done at slow speed with extra pressure. Finished Proofs are individually inspected and are handled with gloves or tongs. They also receive a final inspection by packers before being sonically sealed in special plastic cases.

Mint Sets

Official Uncirculated Mint sets are specially packaged by the government for sale to collectors. They contain Uncirculated examples of each year's coins for every denomination issued from each mint. Before 2005, the coins were the same as those normally intended for circulation and were not minted with any special consideration for quality. From 2005 to 2010, however, Mint sets were made with a satin finish rather than the traditional Uncirculated luster. As in the past, coins struck only as Proofs are not included.

Uncirculated Mint sets sold by the Treasury from 1947 through 1958 contained two examples of each regular-issue coin. These were packaged in cardboard holders that did not protect the coins from tarnish. Nicely preserved early sets generally command a 10 to 20% premium above average values. Since 1959, sets have been sealed in protective plastic envelopes.

Privately assembled Mint sets, and Souvenir sets produced for sale at the Philadelphia or Denver mints for special occasions, are valued according to the individual pieces they contain. Only the official, government-packaged full sets are included in the following list. No Mint Sets were produced in 1950, 1982, or 1983, though Souvenir sets were sold in the latter two years (see the final section of this overview).

From time to time the Mint issues special Mint sets. One recent example is the 1996-P-D Mint set, which also included a 1996-W dime (released only in those sets).

Special Mint Sets

In mid-1964 the Treasury department announced that the Mint would not offer Proof sets or Mint sets the following year. This was prompted by a nationwide shortage of circulating coins, which was wrongly blamed on coin collectors.

In 1966 the San Francisco Assay Office began striking coins dated 1965, for inclusion in so-called United States Special Mint Sets. These were issued in pliofilm packaging similar to that of recent Proof sets. The coins in early 1965 Special Mint Sets are semi-brilliant or satiny (distinctive, but not equal in quality to Proofs); the coins in later 1965 sets feature very brilliant fields (but again not reaching Proof brilliance).

The San Francisco Assay Office started striking 1966-dated coins in August of that year, and its Special Mint Sets were packaged in rigid, sonically sealed plastic holders. The coins were struck once on unpolished planchets, unlike Proof coins (which are struck at least twice on polished planchets). Also unlike Proofs, the SMS coins were allowed to come into contact with each other during their production, which accounts for minor contact marks and abrasions. To achieve a brilliant finish, Mint technicians overpolished the coinage dies. The result was a tradeoff: most of the coins have prooflike brilliance, but many are missing polished-off design details, such as Frank Gasparro's initials on the half dollar.

All 1967-dated coinage was struck in that calendar year. Nearly all SMS coins of 1967 have fully brilliant, prooflike finishes. This brilliance was achieved without overpolishing the dies, resulting in coins that approach the quality of true Proofs. Sales of the 1967 sets were lackluster, however. The popularity of coin collecting had dropped from its peak in 1964. Also, collectors and speculators did not anticipate much secondary-market profit from the sets, which had an issue price of $4.00, compared to $2.10 for a 1964 Proof set. As a result, fewer collectors bought multiples of the 1967 sets, and today they are generally worth more than those of 1965 and 1966.

Similar SMS coins dated 1964 exist as single pieces and in sets. Like the 1965 through 1967 SMS coins, they have a semi-brilliant or satiny finish but are not equal in quality to Proofs. They are referred to as SP (Special Strike) coins and command much higher prices than their regular SMS counterparts.

SOUVENIR SETS

Uncirculated Souvenir sets were packaged and sold in gift shops at the Philadelphia and Denver mints in 1982 and 1983 in place of the "official Mint sets," which were not made in those years. A bronze Mint medal is packaged with each set. Similar sets were also made in other years.

1936 Proof Set
Liberty Walking half dollar, Washington quarter dollar, Mercury or Winged Liberty dime, Buffalo nickel, and Lincoln cent with Wheat Ears reverse.

1938 Proof Set
Buffalo nickel replaced with the new Jefferson nickel.

1950 Proof Set
There was a seven-year hiatus (1943–1949) before Proof sets were issued again after World War II. By 1950 the Liberty Walking half dollar had been replaced by the Franklin half dollar (introduced 1948), and the Mercury dime by the Roosevelt dime (introduced 1946).

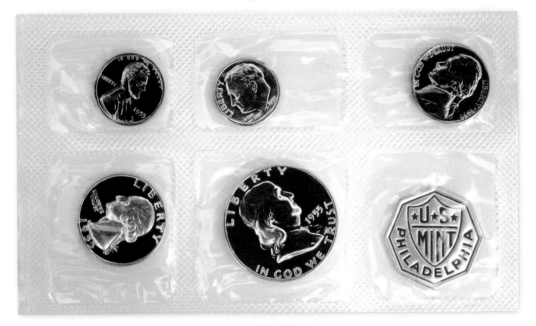

1955 Proof Set
Issued in traditional individual envelopes, or in the new pliofilm package (pictured), with a Philadelphia Mint embossed paper seal with a metallic finish.

MODERN PROOF SETS (1936 TO DATE)

	Mintage	Issue Price	Face Value	Current Value
1936	3,837	$1.89	$0.91	$6,000
1937	5,542	$1.89	$0.91	$2,750
1938	8,045	$1.89	$0.91	$1,100
1939	8,795	$1.89	$0.91	$1,050
1940	11,246	$1.89	$0.91	$900
1941	15,287	$1.89	$0.91	$825
1942, Both nickels	21,120	$1.89	$0.96	$950
1942, One nickel	(a)	$1.89	$0.91	$825
1950	51,386	$2.10	$0.91	$525
1951	57,500	$2.10	$0.91	$475
1952	81,980	$2.10	$0.91	$240

a. Included in 1942, Both nickels, mintage figure.

	Mintage	Issue Price	Face Value	Current Value
1953	128,800	$2.10	$0.91	$190
1954	233,300	$2.10	$0.91	$100
1955, Box pack	378,200	$2.10	$0.91	$100
1955, Flat pack	**(b)**	$2.10	$0.91	$120
1956	669,384	$2.10	$0.91	$65
1957	1,247,952	$2.10	$0.91	$30
1958	875,652	$2.10	$0.91	$32
1959	1,149,291	$2.10	$0.91	$30
1960, With Large Date cent	1,691,602	$2.10	$0.91	$25
1960, With Small Date cent	**(c)**	$2.10	$0.91	$30
1961	3,028,244	$2.10	$0.91	$22
1962	3,218,019	$2.10	$0.91	$22
1963	3,075,645	$2.10	$0.91	$22
1964	3,950,762	$2.10	$0.91	$22
1968-S	3,041,506	$5	$0.91	$7
1968-S, With No S dime	**(d)**	$5	$0.91	$15,000
1969-S	2,934,631	$5	$0.91	$7
1970-S	2,632,810	$5	$0.91	$11
1970-S, With Small Date cent	**(e)**	$5	$0.91	$85
1970-S, With No S dime *(estimated mintage: 2,200)*	**(e)**	$5	$0.91	$900
1971-S	3,220,733	$5	$0.91	$4
1971-S, With No S nickel *(estimated mintage: 1,655)*	**(f)**	$5	$0.91	$1,200
1972-S	3,260,996	$5	$0.91	$5
1973-S	2,760,339	$7	$1.91	$8
1974-S	2,612,568	$7	$1.91	$10
1975-S, With 1976 quarter, half, and dollar	2,845,450	$7	$1.91	$9
1975-S, With No S dime	**(g)**	$7	$1.91	$250,000
1976-S	4,149,730	$7	$1.91	$9
1976-S, Silver clad, 3-piece set	3,998,621	$15	$1.75	$24
1977-S	3,251,152	$9	$1.91	$7
1978-S	3,127,781	$9	$1.91	$7
1979-S, Type 1	3,677,175	$9	$1.91	$8
1979-S, Type 2	**(h)**	$9	$1.91	$50
1980-S	3,554,806	$10	$1.91	$5
1981-S, Type 1	4,063,083	$11	$1.91	$5
1981-S, Type 2 (all six coins in set)	**(i)**	$11	$1.91	$275
1982-S	3,857,479	$11	$0.91	$5
1983-S	3,138,765	$11	$0.91	$5
1983-S, With No S dime	**(j)**	$11	$0.91	$700
1983-S, Prestige set (Olympic dollar)	140,361	$59	$1.91	$42
1984-S	2,748,430	$11	$0.91	$6
1984-S, Prestige set (Olympic dollar)	316,680	$59	$1.91	$26
1985-S	3,362,821	$11	$0.91	$4
1986-S	2,411,180	$11	$0.91	$6
1986-S, Prestige set (Statue of Liberty half, dollar)	599,317	$48.50	$2.41	$28
1987-S	3,792,233	$11	$0.91	$5
1987-S, Prestige set (Constitution dollar)	435,495	$45	$1.91	$26
1988-S	3,031,287	$11	$0.91	$5
1988-S, Prestige set (Olympic dollar)	231,661	$45	$1.91	$30

b. Included in 1955, Box pack, mintage figure. **c.** Included in 1960, With Large Date cent, mintage figure. **d.** Included in 1968-S mintage figure. **e.** Included in 1970-S mintage figure. **f.** Included in 1971-S mintage figure. **g.** Included in 1975-S, With 1976 quarter, half, and dollar, mintage figure. **h.** Included in 1979-S, Type 1, mintage figure. **i.** Included in 1981-S, Type 1, mintage figure. **j.** Included in 1983-S mintage figure.

	Mintage	Issue Price	Face Value	Current Value
1989-S	3,009,107	$11	$0.91	$5
1989-S, Prestige set (Congressional half, dollar)	211,807	$45	$2.41	$30
1990-S	2,793,433	$11	$0.91	$5
1990-S, With No S cent	3,555	$11	$0.91	$4,250
1990-S, With No S cent (Prestige set)	(k)	$45	$1.91	$4,750
1990-S, Prestige set (Eisenhower dollar)	506,126	$45	$1.91	$30
1991-S	2,610,833	$11	$0.91	$5
1991-S, Prestige set (Mt. Rushmore half, dollar)	256,954	$59	$2.41	$45
1992-S	2,675,618	$11	$0.91	$5
1992-S, Prestige set (Olympic half, dollar)	183,293	$56	$2.41	$48
1992-S, Silver	1,009,586	$11	$0.91	$22
1992-S, Silver Premier set	308,055	$37	$0.91	$24
1993-S	2,409,394	$12.50	$0.91	$6
1993-S, Prestige set (Bill of Rights half, dollar)	224,045	$57	$2.41	$36
1993-S, Silver	570,213	$21	$0.91	$28
1993-S, Silver Premier set	191,140	$37.50	$0.91	$35
1994-S	2,308,701	$12.50	$0.91	$5
1994-S, Prestige set (World Cup half, dollar)	175,893	$57	$2.41	$35
1994-S, Silver	636,009	$21	$0.91	$28
1994-S, Silver Premier set	149,320	$37.50	$0.91	$36
1995-S	2,010,384	$12.50	$0.91	$10
1995-S, Prestige set (Civil War half, dollar)	107,112	$57	$2.41	$80
1995-S, Silver	549,878	$21	$0.91	$50
1995-S, Silver Premier set	130,107	$37.50	$0.91	$52
1996-S	1,695,244	$12.50	$0.91	$8
1996-S, Prestige set (Olympic half, dollar)	55,000	$57	$2.41	$325
1996-S, Silver	623,655	$21	$0.91	$28
1996-S, Silver Premier set	151,366	$37.50	$0.91	$32
1997-S	1,975,000	$12.50	$0.91	$8
1997-S, Prestige set (Botanic dollar)	80,000	$57	$1.91	$60
1997-S, Silver	605,473	$21	$0.91	$34
1997-S, Silver Premier set	136,205	$37.50	$0.91	$38
1998-S	2,086,507	$12.50	$0.91	$10
1998-S, Silver	638,134	$21	$0.91	$24
1998-S, Silver Premier set	240,658	$37.50	$0.91	$28
1999-S, 9-piece set	2,543,401	$19.95	$1.91	$9
1999-S, 5-piece quarter set	1,169,958	$13.95	$1.25	$5
1999-S, Silver 9-piece set	804,565	$31.95	$1.91	$90
2000-S, 10-piece set	3,082,572	$19.95	$2.91	$6
2000-S, 5-piece quarter set	937,600	$13.95	$1.25	$5
2000-S, Silver 10-piece set	965,421	$31.95	$2.91	$38
2001-S, 10-piece set	2,294,909	$19.95	$2.91	$11
2001-S, 5-piece quarter set	799,231	$13.95	$1.25	$5
2001-S, Silver 10-piece set	889,697	$31.95	$2.91	$45
2002-S, 10-piece set	2,319,766	$19.95	$2.91	$8
2002-S, 5-piece quarter set	764,479	$13.95	$1.25	$5
2002-S, Silver 10-piece set	892,229	$31.95	$2.91	$35
2003-S, 10-piece set	2,172,684	$19.95	$2.91	$6
2003-S, 5-piece quarter set	1,235,832	$13.95	$1.25	$5
2003-S, Silver 10-piece set	1,125,755	$31.95	$2.91	$35
2004-S, 11-piece set	1,789,488	$22.95	$2.96	$11
2004-S, 5-piece quarter set	951,196	$15.95	$1.25	$5

k. Included in 1990-S mintage figure.

	Mintage	Issue Price	Face Value	Current Value
2004-S, Silver 11-piece set	1,175,934	$37.95	$2.96	$35
2004-S, Silver 5-piece quarter set	593,852	$23.95	$1.25	$24
2005-S, 11-piece set	2,275,000	$22.95	$2.96	$5
2005-S, 5-piece quarter set	987,960	$15.95	$1.25	$4
2005-S, Silver 11-piece set	1,069,679	$37.95	$2.96	$38
2005-S, Silver 5-piece quarter set	608,970	$23.95	$1.25	$24
2006-S, 10-piece set	2,000,428	$22.95	$2.91	$8
2006-S, 5-piece quarter set	882,000	$15.95	$1.25	$4
2006-S, Silver 10-piece set	1,054,008	$37.95	$2.91	$36
2006-S, Silver 5-piece quarter set	531,000	$23.95	$1.25	$24
2007-S, 14-piece set	1,702,116	$26.95	$6.91	$16
2007-S, 5-piece quarter set	672,662	$13.95	$1.25	$7
2007-S, 4-piece Presidential set	1,285,972	$14.95	$4	$6
2007-S, Silver 14-piece set	875,050	$44.95	$6.91	$42
2007-S, Silver 5-piece quarter set	672,662	$25.95	$1.25	$24
2008-S, 14-piece set	1,405,674	$26.95	$6.91	$28
2008-S, 5-piece quarter set	672,438	$13.95	$1.25	$28
2008-S, 4-piece Presidential set	869,202	$14.95	$4	$12
2008-S, Silver 14-piece set	763,887	$44.95	$6.91	$45
2008-S, Silver 5-piece quarter set	429,021	$25.95	$1.25	$24
2009-S, 18-piece set	1,482,502	$29.95	$7.19	$25
2009-S, 6-piece quarter set	630,976	$14.95	$1.50	$6
2009-S, 4-piece Presidential set	629,585	$14.95	$4	$9
2009-S, Silver 18-piece set	697,365	$52.95	$7.19	$53
2009-S, Silver 6-piece quarter set	299,183	$29.95	$1.50	$30
2009-S, 4-piece Lincoln Bicentennial set	201,107	$7.95	$0.04	$10
2010-S, 14-piece set	1,103,815	$31.95	$6.91	$35
2010-S, 5-piece quarter set	276,296	$14.95	$1.25	$13
2010-S, 4-piece Presidential set	535,397	$15.95	$4	$15
2010-S, Silver 14-piece set	585,401	$56.95	$6.91	$52
2010-S, Silver 5-piece quarter set	274,034	$32.95	$1.25	$24
2011-S, 14-piece set	1,098,835	$31.95	$6.91	$36
2011-S, 5-piece quarter set	152,302	$14.95	$1.25	$14
2011-S, 4-piece Presidential set	299,853	$19.95	$4	$28
2011-S, Silver 14-piece set	574,175	$67.95	$6.91	$60
2011-S, Silver 5-piece quarter set	147,901	$39.95	$1.25	$28
2012-S, 14-piece set	794,002	$31.95	$6.91	$125
2012-S, 5-piece quarter set	148,498	$14.95	$1.25	$15
2012-S, 4-piece Presidential set	249,265	$18.95	$4	$65
2012-S, Silver 14-piece set	395,443	$67.95	$6.91	$235
2012-S, Silver 8-piece Limited Edition set	44,952	$149.95	$2.85	$235
2012-S, Silver 5-piece quarter set	162,448	$41.95	$1.25	$30
2013-S, 14-piece set	802,460	$31.95	$6.91	$35
2013-S, 5-piece quarter set	128,377	$14.95	$1.25	$14
2013-S, 4-piece Presidential set	266,677	$18.95	$4	$18
2013-S, Silver 14-piece set	419,720	$67.95	$6.91	$70
2013-S, Silver 8-piece Limited Edition set	47,791	$139.95	$2.85	$120
2013-S, Silver 5-piece quarter set	138,451	$41.95	$1.25	$30
2014-S, 14-piece set	680,977	$31.95	$6.91	$35
2014-S, 5-piece quarter set	109,423	$14.95	$1.25	$16
2014-S, 4-piece Presidential set	218,976	$18.95	$4	$18
2014-S, Silver 14-piece set	387,310	$67.95	$6.91	$58
2014-S, Silver 8-piece Limited Edition set	41,609	$139.95	$2.85	$160

	Mintage	Issue Price	Face Value	Current Value
2014-S, Silver 5-piece quarter set	103,311	$41.95	$1.25	$35
2015-S, 14-piece set	662,854	$32.95	$6.91	$38
2015-S, 5-piece quarter set	99,466	$14.95	$1.25	$14
2015-S, 4-piece Presidential set	222,068	$18.95	$4	$20
2015-S, Silver 14-piece set	387,460	$53.95	$6.91	$60
2015-S, Silver 5-piece quarter set	103,369	$31.95	$1.25	$32
2016-S, 13-piece set	595,184	$31.95	$5.91	$48
2016-S, 5-piece quarter set	91,754	$14.95	$1.25	$14
2016-S, 3-piece Presidential set	231,559	$17.95	$3	$18
2016-S, Silver 13-piece set	369,849	$52.95	$5.91	$65
2016-S, Silver 8-piece Limited Edition set	49,407	$139.95	$2.85	$135
2016-S, Silver 5-piece quarter set	95,649	$31.95	$1.25	$28
2017-S, 10-piece set	544,759	$26.95	$2.91	$30
2017-S, 5-piece quarter set	85,238	$14.95	$1.25	$15
2017-S, Silver 10-piece set	333,547	$47.95	$2.91	$48
2017-S, Silver 5-piece quarter set	84,258	$31.95	$1.25	$33
2017-S, Silver 8-piece Limited Edition set	48,906	$139.95	$2.85	$175
2018-S, 10-piece set		$27.95		$28
2018-S, 5-piece quarter set		$15.95		$15
2018-S, Silver 10-piece set		$49.95		$50
2018-S, Silver 5-piece quarter set		$33.95		$33
2018-S, 50th Anniversary Silver 10-piece Reverse Proof set		$54.95		$60
2018-S, Silver 8-piece Limited Edition set		$144.95		$175
2019-S, 14-piece set				
2019-S, 5-piece quarter set		$15.95		
2019-S, Silver 14-piece set				
2019-S, Silver 5-piece quarter set				
2019-S, Silver 8-piece Limited Edition set				

UNCIRCULATED MINT SETS (1947 TO DATE)

	Mintage	Issue Price	Face Value	Current Value
1947 P-D-S	5,000	$4.87	$4.46	$2,250
1948 P-D-S	6,000	$4.92	$4.46	$1,450
1949 P-D-S	5,000	$5.45	$4.96	$1,750
1951 P-D-S	8,654	$6.75	$5.46	$1,450
1952 P-D-S	11,499	$6.14	$5.46	$1,350
1953 P-D-S	15,538	$6.14	$5.46	$1,000
1954 P-D-S	25,599	$6.19	$5.46	$650
1955 P-D-S	49,656	$3.57	$2.86	$400
1956 P-D	45,475	$3.34	$2.64	$450
1957 P-D	34,324	$4.40	$3.64	$675
1958 P-D	50,314	$4.43	$3.64	$425
1959 P-D	187,000	$2.40	$1.82	$55
1960 P-D	260,485	$2.40	$1.82	$45
1961 P-D	223,704	$2.40	$1.82	$45
1962 P-D	385,285	$2.40	$1.82	$45
1963 P-D	606,612	$2.40	$1.82	$40
1964 P-D	1,008,108	$2.40	$1.82	$30
1968 P-D-S	2,105,128	$2.50	$1.33	$8
1969 P-D-S	1,817,392	$2.50	$1.33	$8
1970 P-D-S, With Large Date cent	2,038,134	$2.50	$1.33	$20
1970 P-D-S, Small Date cent	(a)	$2.50	$1.33	$55

a. Included in 1970 P-D-S, With Large Date cent, mintage figure.

	Mintage	Issue Price	Face Value	Current Value
1971 P-D-S (no Ike dollar)	2,193,396	$3.50	$1.83	$5
1972 P-D-S (no Ike dollar)	2,750,000	$3.50	$1.83	$5
1973 P-D-S	1,767,691	$6	$3.83	$12
1974 P-D-S	1,975,981	$6	$3.83	$8
1975 P-D, With 1976 quarter, half, dollar	1,921,488	$6	$3.82	$10
1976, Silver clad, 3-piece set	4,908,319	$9	$1.75	$20
1976 P-D	1,892,513	$6	$3.82	$8
1977 P-D	2,006,869	$7	$3.82	$8
1978 P-D	2,162,609	$7	$3.82	$8
1979 P-D (b)	2,526,000	$8	$3.82	$8
1980 P-D-S	2,815,066	$9	$4.82	$8
1981 P-D-S	2,908,145	$11	$4.82	$10
1984 P-D	1,832,857	$7	$1.82	$5
1985 P-D	1,710,571	$7	$1.82	$5
1986 P-D	1,153,536	$7	$1.82	$8
1987 P-D	2,890,758	$7	$1.82	$5
1988 P-D	1,646,204	$7	$1.82	$5
1989 P-D	1,987,915	$7	$1.82	$5
1990 P-D	1,809,184	$7	$1.82	$5
1991 P-D	1,352,101	$7	$1.82	$5
1992 P-D	1,500,143	$7	$1.82	$5
1993 P-D	1,297,431	$8	$1.82	$5
1994 P-D	1,234,813	$8	$1.82	$5
1995 P-D	1,038,787	$8	$1.82	$5
1996 P-D, Plus 1996-W dime	1,457,949	$8	$1.92	$20
1997 P-D	950,473	$8	$1.82	$5
1998 P-D	1,187,325	$8	$1.82	$5
1999 P-D (18 pieces) (c)	1,243,867	$14.95	$3.82	$10
2000 P-D (20 pieces)	1,490,160	$14.95	$5.82	$10
2001 P-D (20 pieces)	1,116,915	$14.95	$5.82	$10
2002 P-D (20 pieces)	1,139,388	$14.95	$5.82	$10
2003 P-D (20 pieces)	1,001,532	$14.95	$5.82	$10
2004 P-D (22 pieces)	842,507	$16.95	$5.92	$10
2005 P-D (22 pieces)	1,160,000	$16.95	$5.92	$10
2006 P-D (20 pieces)	847,361	$16.95	$5.82	$10
2007 P-D (28 pieces)	895,628	$22.95	$13.82	$20
2008 P-D (28 pieces)	745,464	$22.95	$13.82	$50
2009 P-D (36 pieces)	784,614	$27.95	$14.38	$25
2010 P-D (28 pieces)	583,897	$31.95	$13.82	$25
2011 P-D (28 pieces)	533,529	$31.95	$13.82	$25
2012 P-D (28 pieces)	392,224	$27.95	$13.82	$80
2013 P-D (28 pieces)	376,844	$27.95	$13.82	$25
2014 P-D (28 pieces)	327,969	$27.95	$13.82	$25
2015 P-D (28 pieces)	314,029	$28.95	$13.82	$25
2016 P-D (26 pieces)	296,579	$26.95	$11.82	$27
2017 P-D (20 pieces)	271,686	$20.95	$5.82	$25
2017-S, 225th Anniversary Enhanced Uncirculated set (10 pieces)	210,402	$29.95	$2.91	$30
2018 P-D (20 pieces)			$5.82	
2019 P-D (28 pieces)			$13.82	

b. S-mint dollar not included. c. Dollar not included.

SPECIAL MINT SETS (1965–1967)

	Mintage	Issue Price	Face Value	Current Value
1965 ††	2,360,000	$4	$0.91	$10
1966 ††	2,261,583	$4	$0.91	$10
1967 ††	1,863,344	$4	$0.91	$11

Note: See page 1202 for details on the similar 1964 Special Strike coins. Values for these coins are approximately $13,000 for each denomination. †† All 1965–1967 Special Mint Set coins graded Ultra Cameo are ranked in the *100 Greatest U.S. Modern Coins* (fourth edition), as a single entry.

SOUVENIR SETS (1982–1983)

	Issue Price	Face Value	Current Value
1982-P	$4	$0.91	$60
1982-D	$4	$0.91	$60
1983-P	$4	$0.91	$80
1983-D	$4	$0.91	$80

POPULAR DIE VARIETIES FROM MINT SETS

As noted in the *Cherrypickers' Guide to Rare Die Varieties*, "Beginning with those modern Mint sets from 1947 . . . there are many years of one or the other that are absent of a significant variety. Not all of the known varieties are significant." The following are some popular die varieties from Mint sets; for more information and additional examples, consult the *Cherrypickers' Guide*.

DIE VARIETIES IN MINT SETS

Year	Denomination	Variety	Year	Denomination	Variety
1949	5¢	D/S—over mintmark (**a**)	1970	50¢	D—doubled-die reverse (**d**)
1954	25¢	doubled-die reverse (**b**)	1971	5¢	D/D—repunched mintmark
1960	5¢	(P)—doubled-die obverse (**c**)	1971	10¢	D/D—repunched mintmark
1960	25¢	(P)—doubled-die obverse (**c**)	1971	10¢	D—doubled-die reverse
1961	50¢	D/D—repunched mintmark	1971	50¢	D—doubled-die obverse
1963	10¢	(P)—doubled-die obverse	1971	50¢	D—doubled-die reverse
1963	25¢	(P)—doubled-die obverse	1972	1¢	(P)—doubled-die obverse
1963	25¢	(P)—doubled-die reverse	1972	5¢	D—doubled-die reverse
1963	50¢	(P)—doubled-die obverse	1972	50¢	D—doubled-die reverse
1963	50¢	(P)—doubled-die reverse	1973	50¢	(P)—doubled-die obverse
1968	10¢	(P)—doubled-die obverse	1973	50¢	D—doubled-die obverse
1968	25¢	D—doubled-die reverse	1974	50¢	D—doubled-die obverse
1969	5¢	D/D—repunched mintmark	1981	5¢	D—doubled-die reverse
1969	10¢	D/D—repunched mintmark	1984	50¢	D/D—repunched mintmark
1969	25¢	D/D—repunched mintmark	1987	5¢	D/D—repunched mintmark
1969	50¢	D—doubled-die reverse	1987	10¢	D/D—repunched mintmark
1970	1¢	D/D—repunched mintmark	1989	5¢	D—doubled-die reverse
1970	1¢	D—doubled-die obverse	1989	10¢	P—doubled-die reverse
1970	10¢	D—doubled-die reverse	1989	50¢	D/D—repunched mintmark
1970	25¢	D—doubled-die reverse	1991	5¢	D—doubled-die obverse

a. Although known, most have already been removed from their Mint-packaged sets. **b.** Small Date. **c.** Found in sets labeled as Small Date. **d.** Small Date.

U.S. Mint Bullion Coins

AN OVERVIEW OF U.S. MINT BULLION COINS

The United States' bullion-coin program was launched in 1986. Since then, American Eagle and other silver, gold, platinum, and palladium coins have provided investors with convenient vehicles to add physical bullion to their portfolios. They also have value as numismatic collectibles.

In addition to regular investment-grade strikes, the U.S. Mint offers its bullion coins in various collectible formats. Proofs are created in a specialized minting process: a polished coin blank is manually fed into a press fitted with special dies; the blank is struck multiple times "so the softly frosted yet detailed images seem to float above a mirror-like field" (per Mint literature); a white-gloved inspector scrutinizes the coin; and it is then sealed in a protective plastic capsule and mounted in a satin-lined velvet presentation case along with a certificate of authenticity. Members of the public can purchase Proofs directly from the Mint, at fixed prices.

Burnished (called Uncirculated by the Mint) coins are also sold directly to the public. These coins have the same design as other bullion coins, but are distinguished from regular bullion strikes by a W mintmark (for West Point), and by their distinctive finish (the result of burnished coin blanks). Their blanks are individually fed by hand into specially adapted coining presses. After striking, each Burnished specimen is carefully inspected, encapsulated in plastic, and packaged in a satin-lined velvet presentation case, along with a certificate of authenticity.

In recent years the Mint has also broadened its collectible bullion offerings with Reverse Proof and Enhanced Uncirculated formats. Various bullion coins have been offered in collector sets, as well.

Since the inception of the bullion-coin program in 1986, the Mint has marked several anniversaries with special issues and sets.

Regular bullion-strike coins are bought in bulk by Mint-authorized purchasers (wholesalers, brokerage companies, precious-metal firms, coin dealers, and participating banks). These authorized purchasers in turn sell them to secondary retailers, who then make them available to the general public. Authorized purchasers are required to meet financial and professional criteria, attested to by an internationally accepted accounting firm. They must be an experienced and established market-maker in bullion coins; provide a liquid two-way market for the coins; be audited annually; have an established and broad retail-customer base for distribution; and have a tangible net worth of $5 million (for American Silver Eagles) or $25 million (for gold and platinum American Eagles). Authorized purchasers of gold, platinum, and palladium must have sold 100,000 or more ounces of those metals (bullion, or bullion coins) in any 12-month period since 1990. For gold, the initial order must be for at least 1,000 ounces, with reorders in increments of 500 ounces; for platinum/palladium, 100 ounces for both the initial order and reorders; and for silver, a minimum order of 25,000 ounces. For American Eagles, an authorized purchaser's cost is based on the market value of the bullion, plus a premium to cover minting, distribution, and other overhead expenses. For ASEs, the premium is $2 per coin. For gold, the premiums are 3% (for the one-ounce coin), 5% (1/2 ounce), 7% (1/4 ounce), and 9% (1/10 ounce). For platinum the premium is 4% for the one-ounce coin; for palladium, 6.25%.

Note that the U.S. Mint does not release bullion mintage data on a regular basis; the numbers given herein reflect the most recently available official data.

The listed values of uncertified, average Mint State coins have been based on bullion prices of silver ($17 per ounce), gold ($1,300), platinum ($999), and palladium ($1,050).

For more detailed coverage of these coins, readers are directed to *American Silver Eagles: A Guide to the U.S. Bullion Coin Program* (Mercanti), *American Gold and Platinum Eagles: A Guide to the U.S. Bullion Coin Programs* (Moy), and *American Gold and Silver: U.S. Mint Collector and Investor Coins and Medals, Bicentennial to Date* (Tucker).

AMERICAN SILVER EAGLES (1986 TO DATE)

Designers: *Adolph A. Weinman (obverse) and John Mercanti (reverse).*
Weight: *31.101 grams.* **Composition:** *.999 silver, .001 copper (net weight 1 oz. pure silver).*
Diameter: *40.6 mm.* **Edge:** *Reeded.* **Mints:** *Philadelphia, San Francisco, and West Point.*

Regular Finish

Burnished Finish

Reverse Lettering Style of 1986–2007
Note the lack of spur or stem at bottom right of U.

Enhanced Uncirculated Finish
This special format incorporates elements with a brilliant mirrored finish, a light frosted finish, and a heavy frosted finish.

Reverse Lettering Style of 2008 to Date
Note the spur at bottom right of U.

Proof
Finish

Reverse
Proof Finish

History. The American Silver Eagle (face value $1, actual silver weight one ounce) is a legal-tender bullion coin with weight, content, and purity guaranteed by the federal government. It is one of the few silver coins allowed in individual retirement accounts (IRAs). The obverse design features Adolph A. Weinman's Liberty Walking, as used on the circulating half dollar of 1916 to 1947. Weinman's initials appear on the hem of Miss Liberty's gown. The reverse design, by John Mercanti, is a heraldic eagle.

From 1986 to 1999 all American Silver Eagles were struck at the Philadelphia and San Francisco mints (with the exception of the 1995 West Point Proof). In 2000 they were struck at both Philadelphia (Proofs) and the U.S. Mint's West Point facility (bullion strikes). From 2001 to 2010, West Point was their sole producer (with one exception in 2006), making regular bullion strikes (without mintmarks) and Proof and "Burnished" specimens (with mintmarks). (The exception is the 2006 Reverse Proof, which was struck in Philadelphia.) In 2011, for the 25th anniversary of the American Eagle bullion program, the mints at West Point, San Francisco, and Philadelphia were all put into production to make several collectible formats of the coins. Since 2012, West Point has been their main production mint, with Philadelphia and San Francisco helping when demand is high.

In addition to the individually listed coins, American Silver Eagles were issued in two 2006 "20th Anniversary" sets and in several other special bullion coin sets.

Striking and Sharpness. Striking is generally sharp. The key elements to check on the obverse are Miss Liberty's left hand, the higher parts and lines of her skirt, and her head. On the reverse, the eagle's breast is a main focal point.

Availability. The American Silver Eagle is one of the most popular silver-investment vehicles in the world. Between the bullion coins and various collectible formats, more than 400 million have been sold since 1986. The coins are readily available in the numismatic marketplace and from some banks, investment firms, and other non-numismatic channels.

MS-60 to 70 (Mint State). *Obverse and Reverse:* At MS-60, some abrasion and contact marks are evident on the higher design areas (Miss Liberty's left arm, her hand, and the areas of the skirt covering her left leg). Luster may be dull or lifeless at MS–60 to 62, but there should be deep frost at MS-63 and better, particularly in the lower-relief areas. At MS-65 and above, the luster should be full and rich. These guidelines are more academic than practical, as American Silver Eagles are not intended for circulation, and nearly all are in high Mint State grades.

PF-60 to 70 (Proof). *Obverse and Reverse:* Proofs that are extensively cleaned and have many hairlines are lower level, such as PF–60 to 62. Those with fewer hairlines or flaws are deemed PF–63 to 65. (These exist more in theory than actuality, as nearly all Proof ASEs have been maintained in their original high condition by collectors and investors.) Given the quality of modern U.S. Mint products, even PF–66 and 67 are unusually low levels for ASE Proofs.

AMERICAN SILVER EAGLES

	Mintage	MS / PF	MS-69 / PF-69	MS-70 / PF-70
1986 †† (a,b)	5,393,005	$40	$55	$800
1986-S, Proof	1,446,778	$60	$80	$500
1987 (a,c)	11,442,335	$25	$35	$1,700
1987-S, Proof	904,732	$60	$80	$800
1988 (a,d)	5,004,646	$28	$38	$2,500
1988-S, Proof	557,370	$60	$80	$550
1989 (a)	5,203,327	$28	$37	$1,500
1989-S, Proof	617,694	$60	$80	$325
1990 (a)	5,840,210	$28	$40	$1,500
1990-S, Proof	695,510	$60	$80	$250
1991 (a,e)	7,191,066	$28	$40	—
1991-S, Proof	511,925	$60	$80	$500
1992 (a,f)	5,540,068	$28	$40	$1,600
1992-S, Proof	498,654	$60	$80	$400
1993 (a,g)	6,763,762	$28	$40	$2,900
1993-P, Proof (h)	405,913	$90	$125	$1,500
1994 (a,i)	4,227,319	$38	$50	$4,000
1994-P, Proof †† (j)	372,168	$180	$195	$1,600
1995 (a)	4,672,051	$35	$47	$1,100
1995-P, Proof	438,511	$75	$90	$400
1995-W, Proof †† (k)	30,125	$3,800	$4,750	—
1996 †† (a,l)	3,603,386	$65	$100	—
1996-P, Proof	500,000	$75	$95	$450
1997 (a)	4,295,004	$32	$42	$900
1997-P, Proof	435,368	$80	$95	$500
1998 (a)	4,847,549	$30	$38	$1,700
1998-P, Proof	450,000	$65	$85	$250
1999 (a,m)	7,408,640	$30	$40	—
1999-P, Proof	549,769	$65	$85	$375
2000 (n,o)	9,239,132	$28	$38	$3,500
2000-P, Proof	600,000	$65	$75	$425
2001 (n)	9,001,711	$28	$37	$800
2001-W, Proof	746,398	$65	$80	$175
2002 (n)	10,539,026	$26	$30	$250
2002-W, Proof	647,342	$65	$80	$150
2003 (n)	8,495,008	$25	$32	$150
2003-W, Proof	747,831	$65	$80	$120
2004 (n)	8,882,754	$25	$32	$135
2004-W, Proof	801,602	$65	$80	$125
2005 (n)	8,891,025	$25	$32	$160
2005-W, Proof	816,663	$65	$80	$125

Note: For more information, consult *American Silver Eagles: A Guide to the U.S. Bullion Coin Program*, 3rd edition (Mercanti). MS values are for uncertified Mint State coins of average quality, in their complete original U.S. Mint packaging. PF values are for uncertified Proof coins of average quality, in their complete original U.S. Mint packaging. †† Ranked in the *100 Greatest U.S. Modern Coins* (fourth edition). **a.** Minted at Philadelphia, without mintmark. **b.** Auction: $1,028, MS-70, September 2015. **c.** Auction: $999, MS-70, August 2015. **d.** Auction: $1,704, MS-70, August 2015. **e.** Auction: $3,760, MS-70, August 2015. **f.** Auction: $1,528, MS-70, June 2015. **g.** Auction: $3,760, MS-70, June 2015. **h.** Auction: $1,528, PF-70UCam, March 2015. **i.** Auction: $4,700, MS-70, June 2015. **j.** Auction: $1,293, PF-70DCam, September 2015. **k.** Auction: $14,100, PF-70UCam, June 2015. **l.** Auction: $5,640, MS-70, August 2015. **m.** Auction: $4,935, MS-70, June 2015. **n.** Minted at West Point, without mintmark. **o.** Auction: $1,293, MS-70, July 2015.

	Mintage	MS	MS-69	MS-70
		PF	PF-69	PF-70
2006 (n)	10,676,522	$25	$32	$160
2006-W, Burnished †† (p)	468,020	$75	$85	$190
2006-W, Proof	1,092,477	$65	$80	$125
2006-P, Reverse Proof †† (q,r,s)	248,875	$160	$185	$325
2007 (n)	9,028,036	$25	$30	$95
2007-W, Burnished	621,333	$30	$38	$75
2007-W, Proof	821,759	$65	$80	$100
2008 (n)	20,583,000	$25	$30	$95
2008-W, Burnished	533,757	$48	$65	$100
2008-W, Burnished, Rev of 2007 †† (t,u)	47,000	$450	$550	$1,250
2008-W, Proof	700,979	$65	$80	$100
2009 (n)	30,459,000	$24	$30	$95
2010 (n)	34,764,500	$24	$28	$85
2010-W, Proof (v)	849,861	$65	$80	$100
2011 (n,w)	40,020,000	$24	$28	$95
2011-W, Burnished	409,776	$38	$45	$115
2011-W, Proof	947,355	$65	$80	$100
2011-P, Reverse Proof †† (r,x)	99,882	$255	$280	$450
2011-S, Burnished †† (y)	99,882	$225	$275	$325
2012 (n,w)	33,121,500	$24	$29	$80
2012-W, Burnished	226,120	$65	$85	$100
2012-W, Proof	869,386	$65	$85	$95
2012-S, Proof	285,184	$75	$90	$165
2012-S, Reverse Proof †† (r)	224,981	$125	$140	$175
2013 (n,w)	42,675,000	$24	$28	$80
2013-W, Burnished	222,091	$50	$75	$95
2013-W, Enhanced Uncirculated ††	281,310	$90	$115	$150
2013-W, Proof	934,812	$65	$85	$95
2013-W, Reverse Proof	281,310	$115	$140	$145
2014 (n,w)	44,006,000	$24	$29	$80
2014-W, Burnished	253,169	$50	$75	$80
2014-W, Proof	944,757	$65	$80	$95
2015 (n,w)	47,000,000	$24	$29	$80
2015-W, Burnished	223,879	$50	$75	$80
2015-W, Proof	707,518	$65	$80	$100
2016 (n,w)	37,701,500	$24	$29	$80
2016-W, Burnished †† (z)	216,501	$50	$75	$80
2016-W, Proof ††	595,483	$65	$80	$100
2017 (n,w)	18,065,500	$24	$29	$70
2017-W, Burnished	176,739	$50	$75	$85
2017-W, Proof	440,596	$65	$80	$100
2017-S, Proof (aa)	123,799	$100	$150	$200

Note: For more information, consult *American Silver Eagles: A Guide to the U.S. Bullion Coin Program*, 3rd edition (Mercanti). MS values are for uncertified Mint State coins of average quality, in their complete original U.S. Mint packaging. PF values are for uncertified Proof coins of average quality, in their complete original U.S. Mint packaging. †† Ranked in the *100 Greatest U.S. Modern Coins* (fourth edition). **n.** Minted at West Point, without mintmark. **p.** In celebration of the 20th anniversary of the Bullion Coinage Program, in 2006 the W mintmark was used on bullion coins produced in sets at West Point. **q.** The 2006-P Reverse Proof coins were issued to mark the 20th anniversary of the Bullion Coinage Program. **r.** Reverse Proofs have brilliant devices, and their background fields are frosted (rather than the typical Proof format of frosted devices and mirror-like backgrounds). **s.** Auction: $329, PF-70, February 2015. **t.** Reverse dies of 2007 and earlier have a plain U in UNITED. Modified dies of 2008 and later have a small spur at the bottom right of the U. **u.** Auction: $940, MS-70, August 2015. **v.** The U.S. Mint did not strike any Proof American Silver Eagles in 2009. **w.** Minted at San Francisco, without mintmark. **x.** Auction: $376, PF-70, September 2015. **y.** Auction: $306, MS-70, October 2015. **z.** In celebration of the 30th anniversary of the Bullion Coinage Program, in 2016 special edge lettering was used on bullion coins sold directly to the public. **aa.** Issued in the 2017 Congratulations Set.

| | Mintage | MS | MS-69 | MS-70 |
		PF	PF-69	PF-70
2018 (n,w)	15,700,000	$24	$29	$70
2018-W, Burnished	131,935	$50	$75	$85
2018-W, Proof	361,192	$65	$80	$100
2018-S, Proof	158,791	$65	$80	$100
2019 (n,w)		$24	$29	$70
2019-W, Burnished		$50	$75	$85
2019-W, Proof		$65	$80	$100
2019-S, Proof		$65	$80	$100

Note: For more information, consult *American Silver Eagles: A Guide to the U.S. Bullion Coin Program*, 3rd edition (Mercanti). MS values are for uncertified Mint State coins of average quality, in their complete original U.S. Mint packaging. PF values are for uncertified Proof coins of average quality, in their complete original U.S. Mint packaging. **n.** Minted at West Point, without mintmark. **w.** Minted at San Francisco, without mintmark.

AMERICAN SILVER EAGLE COIN SETS

	Uncertified	69	70
1997 Impressions of Liberty set (a)	$3,300	$3,400	$6,200
2006 20th Anniversary Three-Coin Set. Silver dollars, Uncirculated, Proof, Reverse Proof	$325	$400	$800
2006-W 20th Anniversary 1-oz. Gold- and Silver-Dollar Set. Uncirculated	$1,600	$1,700	$2,100
2011 25th Anniversary Five-Coin Set	$650	$750	$1,100
2012-S 75th Anniversary of San Francisco Mint Two-Coin Set. Proof, Reverse Proof	$200	$240	$340
2013-W 75th Anniversary of West Point Depository Two-Coin Set. Reverse Proof, Enhanced Uncirculated	$175	$225	$270

Note: Uncertified values are for uncertified sets of average quality, in their complete original U.S. Mint packaging. **a.** This set contains a $100 platinum, $50 gold, and a $1 silver piece.

AMERICA THE BEAUTIFUL 5-OUNCE SILVER BULLION COINS (2010–2021)

Designers: *See image captions on pages 739–743 for designers.* **Weight:** *155.517 grams.* **Composition:** *.999 silver, .001 copper (net weight 5 oz. pure silver).* **Diameter:** *76.2 mm.* **Edge:** *Lettered.* **Mint:** *Philadelphia.*

Bullion Strike

History. In conjunction with the National Park quarter dollars, the U.S. Mint issues silver-bullion coins based on each of the "America the Beautiful" program's circulation-strike coins. The coinage dies are cut on a CNC milling machine, bypassing a hubbing operation, which results in finer details than seen on the smaller quarter dollars. The bullion coins are made of .999 fine silver, have a diameter of three inches, weigh five ounces, and carry a face value of 25 cents. The fineness and weight are incused on

Specimen
Strike

**Mintmark location is
on the obverse, to the
right of the hair ribbon.**

Details of the incused edge markings.

**Details on 2014 Great Smoky Mountains
National Park 5-ounce silver bullion coin (left)
and quarter dollar (right). Note differences
on window, cabin, and grass in foreground.**

each coin's edge. The Mint's German-made Gräbener press strikes 22 coins per minute, with two strikes per coin at 450 to 500 metric tons of pressure. In December 2010, the Mint announced it would produce Specimen versions (called *Uncirculated* by the Mint) for collectors. Detailed information on each issue is in *American Gold and Silver: U.S. Mint Collector and Investor Coins and Medals, Bicentennial to Date* (Tucker).

Striking and Sharpness. Striking is generally sharp.

Availability. The National Park silver bullion coins are distributed through commercial channels similar to those for the Mint's American Silver Eagle coins. Production of the 2010 coins was delayed (finally starting September 21) as the Mint worked out the technical details of striking such a large product. Production and distribution have been smoother since then.

MS-65 to 70 (Mint State). *Obverse and Reverse:* At MS-65, some abrasion and contact marks are evident on the higher design areas. Luster may be dull or lifeless at MS–65 to 66, but there should be deep frost at MS-67 and better, particularly in the lower-relief areas. At MS-68 and above, the luster should be full and rich. These guidelines are more academic than practical, as these coins are not intended for circulation, and nearly all are in high Mint State grades.

SP-68 to 70 (Specimen). *Obverse and Reverse:* These pieces should be nearly perfect and with full luster, in their original Mint packaging. Any with imperfections due to careless handling or environmental damage are valued lower.

The U.S. Mint produces the America the Beautiful™ 5-ounce silver coins in bullion and numismatic versions. The bullion version, which lacks the P mintmark, has a brilliant finish and is sold only through dealers. The numismatic version, with the mintmark, has a matte or burnished finish. These coins are designated "Specimens" (SP) by most collectors and grading services. They are sold directly to the public by the Mint.

25¢ AMERICA THE BEAUTIFUL 5-OUNCE SILVER BULLION COINS

	Mintage	MS / SP	MS-69 / SP-69	MS-70 / SP-70
2010, Hot Springs National Park	33,000	$135	$250	—
2010-P, Hot Springs National Park, Specimen	26,788	$155	$200	$600
2010, Yellowstone National Park	33,000	$135	$170	—
2010-P, Yellowstone National Park, Specimen	26,711	$155	$185	$270
2010, Yosemite National Park	33,000	$145	$250	—
2010-P, Yosemite National Park, Specimen	26,716	$155	$185	$325
2010, Grand Canyon National Park	33,000	$135	$250	—
2010-P, Grand Canyon National Park, Specimen	25,967	$155	$185	$270
2010, Mt. Hood National Forest	33,000	$155	$250	—
2010-P, Mt. Hood National Forest, Specimen	26,637	$155	$195	$270
2011, Gettysburg National Military Park	126,700	$135	$275	—
2011-P, Gettysburg National Military Park, Specimen (a)	24,625	$255	$290	$550
2011, Glacier National Park	126,700	$135	$250	—
2011-P, Glacier National Park, Specimen (b)	20,805	$170	$205	$350
2011, Olympic National Park	104,900	$120	$250	—
2011-P, Olympic National Park, Specimen (c)	18,345	$155	$190	$350
2011, Vicksburg National Military Park	58,100	$125	$250	—
2011-P, Vicksburg National Military Park, Specimen (d)	18,528	$155	$200	$400
2011, Chickasaw National Recreational Area	48,700	$120	$250	—
2011-P, Chickasaw National Recreational Area, Specimen (e)	16,746	$215	$250	$450
2012, El Yunque National Forest	24,000	$215	$350	—
2012-P, El Yunque National Forest, Specimen (f)	17,314	$400	$435	$600
2012, Chaco Culture National Historical Park	24,400	$235	$270	—
2012-P, Chaco Culture National Historical Park, Specimen (g)	17,146	$355	$390	$600
2012, Acadia National Park	25,400	$350	$385	—
2012-P, Acadia National Park, Specimen (h)	14,978	$550	$585	$875
2012, Hawai'i Volcanoes National Park	20,000	$350	$850	—
2012-P, Hawai'i Volcanoes National Park, Specimen (i)	14,863	$650	$700	$1,500
2012, Denali National Park and Preserve	20,000	$235	$350	—
2012-P, Denali National Park and Preserve, Specimen	15,225	$475	$515	$700
2013, White Mountain National Forest	35,000	$125	$210	—
2013-P, White Mountain National Forest, Specimen	20,530	$180	$215	$250
2013, Perry's Victory and International Peace Memorial	30,000	$125	$210	—
2013-P, Perry's Victory and International Peace Memorial, Specimen	17,707	$165	$215	$250
2013, Great Basin National Park	30,000	$125	$210	—
2013-P, Great Basin National Park, Specimen	17,792	$165	$200	$250
2013, Ft. McHenry Nat'l Mon & Historic Shrine	30,000	$125	$210	—
2013-P, Ft. McHenry Nat'l Mon & Historic Shrine, Specimen	19,802	$165	$200	$250
2013, Mount Rushmore National Monument	35,000	$125	$210	—
2013-P, Mount Rushmore National Monument, Specimen	23,547	$165	$200	$250
2014, Great Smoky Mountains National Park	33,000	$130	$180	—
2014-P, Great Smoky Mountains National Park, Specimen	24,710	$125	$160	$210
2014, Shenandoah National Park	25,000	$130	$165	—
2014-P, Shenandoah National Park, Specimen	28,276	$125	$160	$210
2014, Arches National Park	22,000	$130	$165	—
2014-P, Arches National Park, Specimen	28,183	$130	$165	$210
2014, Great Sand Dunes National Park	22,000	$130	$165	—
2014-P, Great Sand Dunes National Park, Specimen	22,262	$130	$165	$210

Note: MS values are for uncertified Mint State coins of average quality, in their complete original U.S. Mint packaging. SP values are for uncertified Specimen coins of average quality, in their complete original U.S. Mint packaging. **a.** Auction: $341, SP-70, May 2015. **b.** Auction: $376, SP-70, September 2014. **c.** Auction: $188, SP-69, December 2015. **d.** Auction: $212, SP-69, October 2014. **e.** Auction: $353, SP-70, September 2014. **f.** Auction: $206, SP-69, December 2015. **g.** Auction: $306, SP-70, December 2014. **h.** Auction: $529, SP-70, September 2014. **i.** Auction: $776, SP-70, December 2014.

| | Mintage | MS | MS-69 | MS-70 |
		SP	SP-69	SP-70
2014, Everglades National Park	34,000	$130	$165	—
2014-P, Everglades National Park, Specimen	19,772	$125	$160	$210
2015, Homestead National Monument of America	35,000	$130	$165	—
2015-P, Homestead National Monument of America, Specimen	21,286	$160	$165	$210
2015, Kisatchie National Forest	42,000	$130	$165	—
2015-P, Kisatchie National Forest, Specimen	19,449	$160	$165	$210
2015, Blue Ridge Parkway	45,000	$130	$165	—
2015-P, Blue Ridge Parkway, Specimen	17,461	$160	$165	$210
2015, Bombay Hook National Wildlife Refuge	45,000	$130	$165	—
2015-P, Bombay Hook National Wildlife Refuge, Specimen	17,309	$160	$165	$210
2015, Saratoga National Historic Park	45,000	$130	$165	—
2015-P, Saratoga National Historic Park, Specimen	17,563	$160	$165	$210
2016, Shawnee National Forest	105,000	$130	$165	—
2016-P, Shawnee National Forest, Specimen	18,781	$160	$165	$210
2016, Cumberland Gap National Historical Park	75,000	$130	$165	—
2016-P, Cumberland Gap National Historical Park, Specimen	18,713	$160	$165	$210
2016, Harpers Ferry National Historical Park	75,000	$130	$165	—
2016-P, Harpers Ferry National Historical Park, Specimen	18,896	$160	$160	$210
2016, Theodore Roosevelt National Park	40,000	$130	$165	—
2016-P, Theodore Roosevelt National Park, Specimen	18,917	$160	$165	$210
2016, Fort Moultrie (Fort Sumter National Monument)	35,000	$130	$165	—
2016-P, Fort Moultrie (Fort Sumter National Monument), Specimen	17,882	$160	$165	$210
2017, Effigy Mounds National Monument	35,000	$130	$165	—
2017-P, Effigy Mounds National Monument, Specimen	17,251	$130	$165	$210
2017, Frederick Douglass National Historic Site	20,000	$130	$165	—
2017-P, Frederick Douglass National Historic Site, Specimen	17,678	$125	$160	$210
2017, Ozark National Scenic Riverways	20,000	$130	$165	—
2017-P, Ozark National Scenic Riverways, Specimen	17,694	$125	$160	$210
2017, Ellis Island (Statue of Liberty National Monument)	40,000	$130	$165	—
2017-P, Ellis Island (Statue of Liberty National Monument), Specimen	17,670	$130	$165	$210
2017, George Rogers Clark National Historical Park	35,000	$130	$165	—
2017-P, George Rogers Clark National Historical Park, Specimen	14,731	$130	$165	$210
2018, Pictured Rocks National Lakeshore	30,000	$130	$165	—
2018-P, Pictured Rocks National Lakeshore, Specimen	17,773	$130	$165	$210
2018, Apostle Islands National Lakeshore	30,000	$130	$165	—
2018-P, Apostle Islands National Lakeshore, Specimen	16,801	$125	$160	$210
2018, Voyageurs National Park	30,000	$130	$165	—
2018-P, Voyageurs National Park, Specimen	16,225	$125	$160	$210
2018, Cumberland Island National Seashore	52,500	$130	$165	—
2018-P, Cumberland Island National Seashore, Specimen	15,437	$130	$165	$210
2018, Block Island National Wildlife Refuge	80,000	$130	$165	—
2018-P, Block Island National Wildlife Refuge	15,152	$130	$165	$210
2019, Lowell National Historical Park		$130	$165	—
2019-P, Lowell National Historical Park, Specimen		$130	$165	$210
2019, American Memorial Park		$130	$165	—
2019-P, American Memorial Park, Specimen		$130	$165	$210
2019, War in the Pacific National Historical Park		$130	$165	—
2019-P, War in the Pacific National Historical Park, Specimen		$130	$165	$210
2019, Frank Church River of No Return Wilderness		$130	$165	—
2019-P, Frank Church River of No Return Wilderness, Specimen		$130	$165	$210

Note: MS values are for uncertified Mint State coins of average quality, in their complete original U.S. Mint packaging. SP values are for uncertified Specimen coins of average quality, in their complete original U.S. Mint packaging.

	Mintage	MS	MS-69	MS-70
		SP	SP-69	SP-70
2019, San Antonio Missions National Historical Park		$130	$165	—
2019-P, San Antonio Missions National Historical Park, Specimen		$130	$165	$210

Note: MS values are for uncertified Mint State coins of average quality, in their complete original U.S. Mint packaging. SP values are for uncertified Specimen coins of average quality, in their complete original U.S. Mint packaging.

AMERICAN GOLD EAGLES (1986 TO DATE)

Designers: *Augustus Saint-Gaudens (obverse) and Miley Busiek (reverse).* **Weight:** *$5 1/10 oz.— 3.393 grams; $10 1/4 oz.—8.483 grams; $25 1/2 oz.—16.966 grams; $50 1 oz.—33.931 grams.* **Composition:** *.9167 gold, .03 silver, .0533 copper.* **Diameter:** *$5 1/10 oz.—16.5 mm; $10 1/4 oz.— 22 mm; $25 1/2 oz.—27 mm; $50 1 oz.—32.7 mm.* **Edge:** *Reeded.* **Mints:** *Philadelphia and West Point.*

Regular Finish
Obverse design common to all denominations.

Burnished Finish

Proof Finish

Reverse Proof Finish

Mintmark location is on the obverse, below the date.

History. American Eagle gold bullion coins are made in four denominations: $5 (1/10 ounce pure gold), $10 (1/4 ounce), $25 (1/2 ounce), and $50 (1 ounce). Each shares the same obverse and reverse designs: a modified rendition of Augustus Saint-Gaudens's famous Liberty (as depicted on the double eagle of 1907 to 1933), and a "family of eagles" motif by sculptor Miley Tucker-Frost (nee Busiek). From 1986 to 1991 the obverse bore a Roman numeral date, similar to the first Saint-Gaudens double eagles of 1907; this was changed to Arabic dating in 1992. The coins are legal tender—with weight, content, and purity guaranteed by the federal government—and are produced from gold mined in the United States. Investors can include them in their individual retirement accounts.

"American Eagles use the durable 22-karat standard established for gold circulating coinage over 350 years ago," notes the U.S. Mint. "They contain their stated amount of pure gold, plus small amounts of alloy. This creates harder coins that resist scratching and marring, which can diminish resale value."

Since the Bullion Coin Program started in 1986, these gold pieces have been struck in Philadelphia and West Point, in various formats similar to those of the American Silver Eagles—regular bullion strikes, Burnished, Proof, and Reverse Proof. Unlike their silver counterparts, none of the American Gold Eagles have been struck at San Francisco.

In addition to the individual coins listed below, American Eagle gold bullion coins have been issued in various sets (see pages 1243–1244).

Striking and Sharpness. Striking is generally sharp. The key elements to check on the obverse are Liberty's chest and left knee, and the open fields.

Availability. American Gold Eagles are the most popular gold-coin investment vehicle in the United States. The coins are readily available in the numismatic marketplace as well as from participating banks, investment firms, and other non-numismatic channels.

MS-60 to 70 (Mint State). *Obverse and Reverse:* At MS-60, some abrasion and contact marks are evident on the higher design areas (in particular, Miss Liberty's chest and left knee) and the open fields. Luster may be dull or lifeless at MS–60 to 62, but there should be deep frost at MS-63 and better, particularly in the lower-relief areas. At MS-65 and above, the luster should be full and rich. Contact marks and abrasion are less and less evident at higher grades. These guidelines are more academic than practical, as these coins are not intended for circulation, and nearly all are in high Mint State grades.

PF-60 to 70 (Proof). *Obverse and Reverse:* Proofs that are extensively cleaned and have many hairlines are lower level, such as PF–60 to 62. Those with fewer hairlines or flaws are deemed PF–63 to 65. (These exist more in theory than actuality, as nearly all Proof American Eagle gold bullion coins have been maintained in their original high condition by collectors.) Given the quality of modern U.S. Mint products, even PF–66 and 67 are unusually low levels for these Proofs.

$5 1/10-Ounce
American Gold Eagles

| | Mintage | MS | MS-69 | MS-70 |
		PF	PF-69	PF-70
$5 MCMLXXXVI (1986)	912,609	$170	$200	$700
$5 MCMLXXXVII (1987)	580,266	$180	$195	$1,300
$5 MCMLXXXVIII (1988) (a)	159,500	$175	$225	$3,500
$5 MCMLXXXVIII (1988)-P, Proof	143,881	$205	$225	$325
$5 MCMLXXXIX (1989) (b)	264,790	$180	$200	$2,600
$5 MCMLXXXIX (1989)-P, Proof	84,647	$195	$210	$375
$5 MCMXC (1990) (c)	210,210	$190	$200	$4,000
$5 MCMXC (1990)-P, Proof	99,349	$195	$210	$350
$5 MCMXCI (1991) (d)	165,200	$190	$220	$1,400
$5 MCMXCI (1991)-P, Proof	70,334	$195	$210	$400
$5 1992	209,300	$185	$200	$1,400
$5 1992-P, Proof	64,874	$185	$200	$450
$5 1993	210,709	$175	$195	$1,500
$5 1993-P, Proof	58,649	$185	$200	$450
$5 1994	206,380	$175	$195	$400
$5 1994-W, Proof	62,849	$185	$200	$350
$5 1995	223,025	$170	$195	$975
$5 1995-W, Proof	62,667	$185	$200	$450
$5 1996	401,964	$165	$195	$600
$5 1996-W, Proof	57,047	$185	$200	$450
$5 1997	528,266	$155	$185	$450
$5 1997-W, Proof	34,977	$185	$200	$550
$5 1998	1,344,520	$170	$195	$300

Note: MS values are for uncertified Mint State coins of average quality, in their complete original U.S. Mint packaging. PF values are for uncertified Proof coins of average quality, in their complete original U.S. Mint packaging. **a.** Auction: $159, MS-69, October 2014. **b.** Auction: $141, MS-69, October 2014. **c.** Auction: $141, MS-69, October 2014. **d.** Auction: $2,115, MS-70, January 2016.

| | Mintage | MS | MS-69 | MS-70 |
		PF	PF-69	PF-70
$5 1998-W, Proof	39,395	$185	$200	$450
$5 1999	2,750,338	$165	$185	$275
$5 1999-W, Unc made from unpolished Proof dies †† (e,f)	14,500	$900	$1,100	$4,000
$5 1999-W, Proof	48,428	$185	$200	$400
$5 2000	569,153	$165	$185	$275
$5 2000-W, Proof	49,971	$185	$205	$400
$5 2001	269,147	$165	$185	$245
$5 2001-W, Proof	37,530	$185	$200	$400
$5 2002	230,027	$180	$190	$375
$5 2002-W, Proof	40,864	$185	$200	$400
$5 2003	245,029	$165	$185	$250
$5 2003-W, Proof	40,027	$185	$200	$350
$5 2004	250,016	$165	$185	$250
$5 2004-W, Proof	35,131	$185	$200	$400
$5 2005	300,043	$155	$175	$220
$5 2005-W, Proof	49,265	$185	$200	$375
$5 2006	285,006	$155	$175	$200
$5 2006-W, Burnished	20,643	$190	$210	$240
$5 2006-W, Proof	47,277	$175	$195	$250
$5 2007	190,010	$155	$175	$200
$5 2007-W, Burnished	22,501	$195	$210	$250
$5 2007-W, Proof	58,553	$175	$195	$250
$5 2008	305,000	$155	$175	$240
$5 2008-W, Burnished (g)	12,657	$325	$350	$450
$5 2008-W, Proof	28,116	$175	$195	$300
$5 2009	270,000	$155	$175	$210
$5 2010	435,000	$155	$175	$190
$5 2010-W, Proof	54,285	$185	$205	$300
$5 2011	350,000	$155	$175	$190
$5 2011-W, Proof	42,697	$175	$195	$300
$5 2012	290,000	$155	$175	$190
$5 2012-W, Proof	20,637	$175	$195	$250
$5 2013	555,000	$155	$175	$190
$5 2013-W, Proof	21,738	$175	$195	$235
$5 2014	565,500	$155	$175	$190
$5 2014-W, Proof	22,725	$175	$195	$250
$5 2015	980,000	$155	$175	$190
$5 2015, Narrow Reeding	(h)			
$5 2015-W, Proof	16,851	$175	$195	$250
$5 2016	925,000	$155	$175	$190
$5 2016-W, Proof	38,788	$175	$195	$250
$5 2017	395,000	$155	$175	$190
$5 2017-W, Proof	11,158	$175	$195	$250
$5 2018	230,000	$155	$175	$190
$5 2018-W, Proof	21,343	$175	$195	$250
$5 2019		$155	$175	$190
$5 2019-W, Proof		$175	$195	$250

Note: MS values are for uncertified Mint State coins of average quality, in their complete original U.S. Mint packaging. PF values are for uncertified Proof coins of average quality, in their complete original U.S. Mint packaging. †† Ranked in the *100 Greatest U.S. Modern Coins* (fourth edition). **e.** Unpolished Proof dies were used to mint some 1999 $5 gold coins, resulting in a regular bullion-strike issue bearing a W mintmark (usually reserved for Proofs). A similar error exists in the $10 (1/4-ounce) series. The mintage listed is an estimate. Other estimates range from 6,000 to 30,000 pieces. **f.** Auction: $764, MS-69, July 2015. **g.** Auction: $352, MS-70, November 2014. **h.** Included in mintage for $5 2015.

$10 1/4-OUNCE AMERICAN GOLD EAGLES

	Mintage	MS	MS-69	MS-70
		PF	PF-69	PF-70
$10 MCMLXXXVI (1986) (a)	726,031	$450	$500	$1,550
$10 MCMLXXXVII (1987) (b)	269,255	$450	$550	—
$10 MCMLXXXVIII (1988) (c)	49,000	$600	$700	$3,250
$10 MCMLXXXVIII (1988)-P, Proof	98,028	$420	$450	$900
$10 MCMLXXXIX (1989) (d)	81,789	$600	$675	$1,700
$10 MCMLXXXIX (1989)-P, Proof	54,170	$420	$450	$850
$10 MCMXC (1990) (e)	41,000	$725	$775	$4,000
$10 MCMXC (1990)-P, Proof	62,674	$420	$450	$600
$10 MCMXCI (1991) (f)	36,100	$725	$775	$2,250
$10 MCMXCI (1991)-P, Proof	50,839	$420	$450	$700
$10 1992 (g)	59,546	$550	$600	$2,000
$10 1992-P, Proof	46,269	$420	$450	$750
$10 1993 (h)	71,864	$550	$600	$2,250
$10 1993-P, Proof	46,464	$420	$450	$750
$10 1994 (i)	72,650	$550	$600	$2,500
$10 1994-W, Proof	48,172	$420	$450	$700
$10 1995 (j)	83,752	$550	$600	$2,000
$10 1995-W, Proof	47,526	$420	$450	$700
$10 1996 (k)	60,318	$550	$600	$2,100
$10 1996-W, Proof	38,219	$420	$450	$550
$10 1997	108,805	$400	$425	$2,000
$10 1997-W, Proof	29,805	$420	$450	$700
$10 1998	309,829	$400	$425	$2,500
$10 1998-W, Proof	29,503	$420	$450	$900
$10 1999	564,232	$400	$425	$2,500
$10 1999-W, Unc made from unpolished Proof dies †† (l,m)	10,000	$1,800	$2,000	—
$10 1999-W, Proof	34,417	$420	$450	$750
$10 2000	128,964	$425	$475	$900
$10 2000-W, Proof	36,036	$420	$450	$750
$10 2001	71,280	$550	$600	$700
$10 2001-W, Proof	25,613	$420	$450	$750
$10 2002	62,027	$550	$600	$700
$10 2002-W, Proof	29,242	$420	$450	$575
$10 2003	74,029	$400	$450	$500
$10 2003-W, Proof	30,292	$420	$450	$575
$10 2004	72,014	$375	$400	$500
$10 2004-W, Proof	28,839	$420	$450	$600
$10 2005	72,015	$375	$400	$500
$10 2005-W, Proof	37,207	$420	$450	$550
$10 2006	60,004	$375	$400	$500

Note: MS values are for uncertified Mint State coins of average quality, in their complete original U.S. Mint packaging. PF values are for uncertified Proof coins of average quality, in their complete original U.S. Mint packaging. †† Ranked in the *100 Greatest U.S. Modern Coins* (fourth edition). **a.** Auction: $1,058, MS-70, January 2016. **b.** Auction: $306, MS-68, November 2015. **c.** Auction: $3,290, MS-70, August 2014. **d.** Auction: $3,290, MS-70, October 2015. **e.** Auction: $16,450, MS-70, October 2015. **f.** Auction: $1,293, MS-70, October 2014. **g.** Auction: $9,400, MS-70, September 2015. **h.** Auction: $3,055, MS-70, June 2014. **i.** Auction: $5,640, MS-70, February 2015. **j.** Auction: $505, MS-69, March 2014. **k.** Auction: $306, MS-68, October 2015. **l.** Unpolished Proof dies were used to mint some 1999 $10 gold coins, resulting in a regular bullion-strike issue bearing a W mintmark (usually reserved for Proofs). A similar error exists in the $5 (1/10-ounce) series. The mintage listed is an estimate. Other estimates range from 6,000 to 30,000 pieces. **m.** Auction: $1,763, MS-69, July 2015.

	Mintage	MS PF	MS-69 PF-69	MS-70 PF-70
$10 2006-W, Burnished (n)	15,188	$650	$675	$700
$10 2006-W, Proof	36,127	$420	$450	$550
$10 2007	34,004	$550	$600	$800
$10 2007-W, Burnished (o)	12,766	$700	$750	$800
$10 2007-W, Proof	46,189	$420	$450	$600
$10 2008	70,000	$370	$390	$415
$10 2008-W, Burnished (p)	8,883	$1,600	$1,650	$1,700
$10 2008-W, Proof	18,877	$500	$530	$700
$10 2009	110,000	$370	$390	$415
$10 2010	86,000	$370	$390	$475
$10 2010-W, Proof	44,507	$450	$500	$550
$10 2011	80,000	$370	$390	$415
$10 2011-W, Proof	28,782	$450	$500	$550
$10 2012	90,000	$370	$390	$415
$10 2012-W, Proof	13,926	$450	$500	$550
$10 2013	114,500	$370	$390	$415
$10 2013-W, Proof	12,782	$450	$500	$550
$10 2014	90,000	$370	$390	$415
$10 2014-W, Proof	14,790	$450	$500	$550
$10 2015	158,000	$370	$390	$415
$10 2015-W, Proof	15,775	$450	$500	$550
$10 2016	152,000	$370	$390	$415
$10 2016-W, Proof	24,405	$450	$500	$550
$10 2017	64,000	$370	$390	$415
$10 2017-W, Proof	14,516	$450	$500	$550
$10 2018	62,000	$370	$390	$415
$10 2018-W, Proof	11,961	$450	$500	$550
$10 2019		$370	$390	$415
$10 2019-W, Proof		$450	$500	$550

Note: MS values are for uncertified Mint State coins of average quality, in their complete original U.S. Mint packaging. PF values are for uncertified Proof coins of average quality, in their complete original U.S. Mint packaging. **n.** Auction: $646, MS-70, October 2015. **o.** Auction: $376, MS-70, October 2015. **p.** Auction: $1,528, MS-70, July 2015.

$25 1/2-OUNCE AMERICAN GOLD EAGLES

	Mintage	MS PF	MS-69 PF-69	MS-70 PF-70
$25 MCMLXXXVI (1986) (a)	599,566	$800	$850	$1,500
$25 MCMLXXXVII (1987) (b)	131,255	$950	$1,200	$2,000
$25 MCMLXXXVII (1987)-P, Proof	143,398	$800	$850	$2,000
$25 MCMLXXXVIII (1988) (c)	45,000	$1,650	$2,000	$5,000
$25 MCMLXXXVIII (1988)-P, Proof	76,528	$800	$850	$1,600
$25 MCMLXXXIX (1989) (d)	44,829	$1,800	$2,150	$4,000
$25 MCMLXXXIX (1989)-P, Proof	44,798	$950	$1,000	—
$25 MCMXC (1990) (e)	31,000	$2,200	$2,500	$5,000

Note: MS values are for uncertified Mint State coins of average quality, in their complete original U.S. Mint packaging. PF values are for uncertified Proof coins of average quality, in their complete original U.S. Mint packaging. **a.** Auction: $646, MS-68, October 2015. **b.** Auction: $999, MS-69, January 2016. **c.** Auction: $1,528, MS-69, October 2015. **d.** Auction: $9,400, MS-70, September 2015. **e.** Auction: $9,694, MS-70, September 2015.

| | Mintage | MS | MS-69 | MS-70 |
		PF	PF-69	PF-70
$25 MCMXC (1990)-P, Proof	51,636	$850	$900	—
$25 MCMXCI (1991) †† (f)	24,100	$3,300	$3,550	—
$25 MCMXCI (1991)-P, Proof	53,125	$850	$900	$1,500
$25 1992 (g)	54,404	$1,100	$1,400	$3,800
$25 1992-P, Proof	40,976	$850	$900	$1,500
$25 1993 (h)	73,324	$900	$1,100	$3,500
$25 1993-P, Proof	43,819	$850	$900	—
$25 1994 (i)	62,400	$900	$1,100	—
$25 1994-W, Proof	44,584	$850	$900	$1,500
$25 1995 (j)	53,474	$1,300	$1,650	$1,750
$25 1995-W, Proof	45,388	$850	$900	$1,500
$25 1996 (k)	39,287	$1,350	$1,500	$3,800
$25 1996-W, Proof	35,058	$850	$900	$1,500
$25 1997 (l)	79,605	$900	$1,100	$2,800
$25 1997-W, Proof	26,344	$850	$900	$1,500
$25 1998	169,029	$750	$808	—
$25 1998-W, Proof	25,374	$850	$900	$1,500
$25 1999 (m)	263,013	$900	$1,100	$3,000
$25 1999-W, Proof	30,427	$850	$900	$1,500
$25 2000	79,287	$900	$1,050	—
$25 2000-W, Proof	32,028	$800	$850	$1,500
$25 2001 (n)	48,047	$1,250	$1,500	$1,800
$25 2001-W, Proof	23,240	$800	$850	$1,500
$25 2002	70,027	$900	$1,050	—
$25 2002-W, Proof	26,646	$800	$850	$1,500
$25 2003	79,029	$800	$850	$900
$25 2003-W, Proof	28,270	$800	$850	$1,500
$25 2004	98,040	$800	$850	$900
$25 2004-W, Proof	27,330	$800	$850	$1,500
$25 2005	80,023	$750	$800	$900
$25 2005-W, Proof	34,311	$800	$850	$1,500
$25 2006	66,005	$750	$800	$900
$25 2006-W, Burnished (o)	15,164	$775	$850	$1,150
$25 2006-W, Proof	34,322	$800	$850	$1,500
$25 2007	47,002	$775	$850	$1,150
$25 2007-W, Burnished †† (p)	11,455	$1,100	$1,200	$1,700
$25 2007-W, Proof	44,025	$800	$850	$1,500
$25 2008	61,000	$750	$800	$900
$25 2008-W, Burnished (q)	15,682	$875	$925	$1,100
$25 2008-W, Proof	22,602	$1,000	$1,050	$1,200
$25 2009	110,000	$750	$800	$900
$25 2010	81,000	$750	$800	$900
$25 2010-W, Proof	44,527	$850	$900	$1,000
$25 2011	70,000	$750	$800	$900
$25 2011-W, Proof	26,781	$800	$850	$950
$25 2012	43,000	$750	$800	$900
$25 2012-W, Proof	12,919	$800	$850	$1,000

Note: MS values are for uncertified Mint State coins of average quality, in their complete original U.S. Mint packaging. PF values are for uncertified Proof coins of average quality, in their complete original U.S. Mint packaging. †† Ranked in the *100 Greatest U.S. Modern Coins* (fourth edition). **f.** Auction: $2,820, MS-69, October 2015. **g.** Auction: $3,966, MS-70, July 2014. **h.** Auction: $4,964, MS-70, January 2015. **i.** Auction: $705, MS-68, October 2015. **j.** Auction: $5,875, MS-70, August 2015. **k.** Auction: $1,293, MS-69, September 2015. **l.** Auction: $1,293, MS-69, September 2015. **m.** Auction: $646, MS-69, November 2014. **n.** Auction: $1,763, MS-69, July 2014. **o.** Auction: $705, MS-70, October 2015. **p.** Auction: $646, MS-69, October 2015. **q.** Auction: $1,175, MS-70, November 2015.

| | Mintage | MS | MS-69 | MS-70 |
		PF	PF-69	PF-70
$25 2013	57,000	$750	$800	$900
$25 2013-W, Proof	12,716	$800	$850	$1,000
$25 2014	35,000	$750	$800	$900
$25 2014-W, Proof	14,693	$800	$850	$1,000
$25 2015	78,000	$750	$800	$900
$25 2015-W, Proof	15,287	$800	$850	$1,000
$25 2016	71,000	$750	$800	$900
$25 2016-W, Proof	23,585	$800	$850	$1,000
$25 2017	37,000	$750	$800	$900
$25 2017-W, Proof	12,717	$800	$850	$1,000
$25 2018	32,000	$850	$1,000	$2,500
$25 2018-W, Proof	9,204	$800	$850	$1,000
$25 2019		$750	$800	$900
$25 2019-W, Proof		$800	$850	$1,000

Note: MS values are for uncertified Mint State coins of average quality, in their complete original U.S. Mint packaging. PF values are for uncertified Proof coins of average quality, in their complete original U.S. Mint packaging.

$50 1-Ounce
American Gold Eagles

| | Mintage | MS | MS-69 | MS-70 |
		PF	PF-69	PF-70
$50 MCMLXXXVI (1986) (a)	1,362,650	$1,425	$1,475	$5,500
$50 MCMLXXXVI (1986)-W, Proof	446,290	$1,700	$1,700	$2,200
$50 MCMLXXXVII (1987) (b)	1,045,500	$1,425	$1,500	$5,000
$50 MCMLXXXVII (1987)-W, Proof	147,498	$1,650	$1,700	$2,200
$50 MCMLXXXVIII (1988) (c)	465,000	$1,425	$1,500	$11,000
$50 MCMLXXXVIII (1988)-W, Proof	87,133	$1,650	$1,700	$2,200
$50 MCMLXXXIX (1989)	415,790	$1,425	$1,500	—
$50 MCMLXXXIX (1989)-W, Proof	54,570	$1,700	$1,750	$2,200
$50 MCMXC (1990) (d)	373,210	$1,425	$1,500	$5,500
$50 MCMXC (1990)-W, Proof	62,401	$1,700	$1,750	$2,200
$50 MCMXCI (1991) (e)	243,100	$1,425	$1,500	$5,500
$50 MCMXCI (1991)-W, Proof	50,411	$1,700	$1,750	$3,000
$50 1992	275,000	$1,425	$1,450	$2,100
$50 1992-W, Proof (f)	44,826	$1,700	$1,750	$3,000
$50 1993	480,192	$1,425	$1,450	$2,600
$50 1993-W, Proof (g)	34,369	$1,700	$1,750	$3,500
$50 1994 (h)	221,633	$1,425	$1,450	$6,500
$50 1994-W, Proof	46,674	$1,650	$1,750	$2,500
$50 1995	200,636	$1,425	$1,450	—
$50 1995-W, Proof	46,368	$1,700	$1,750	$2,500
$50 1996	189,148	$1,425	$1,450	—

Note: MS values are for uncertified Mint State coins of average quality, in their complete original U.S. Mint packaging. PF values are for uncertified Proof coins of average quality, in their complete original U.S. Mint packaging. **a.** Auction: $2,585, MS-70, June 2015. **b.** Auction:$1,351, MS-68, August 2014. **c.** Auction: $1,303, MS-68, December 2013. **d.** Auction: $1,469, MS-69, March 2014. **e.** Auction: $1,293, MS-69, July 2015. **f.** Auction: $2,056, PF-70UCam, July 2015. **g.** Auction: $2,233, PF-70UCam, June 2015. **h.** Auction: $2,820, MS-69, April 2014.

	Mintage	MS	MS-69	MS-70
		PF	PF-69	PF-70
$50 1996-W, Proof	36,153	$1,700	$1,750	$2,500
$50 1997 (i)	664,508	$1,425	$1,450	$5,000
$50 1997-W, Proof	32,999	$1,700	$1,750	$2,500
$50 1998	1,468,530	$1,425	$1,450	$2,300
$50 1998-W, Proof (j)	25,886	$1,700	$1,750	$4,000
$50 1999	1,505,026	$1,425	$1,450	$2,300
$50 1999-W, Proof	31,427	$1,700	$1,750	$3,000
$50 2000	433,319	$1,425	$1,450	$2,500
$50 2000-W, Proof	33,007	$1,700	$1,750	$2,500
$50 2001 (k)	143,605	$1,425	$1,450	$3,000
$50 2001-W, Proof †† (l)	24,555	$1,700	$1,700	$5,000
$50 2002	222,029	$1,425	$1,450	$2,800
$50 2002-W, Proof	27,499	$1,700	$1,750	$2,200
$50 2003	416,032	$1,425	$1,450	$2,500
$50 2003-W, Proof	28,344	$1,700	$1,750	$2,200
$50 2004	417,019	$1,425	$1,450	$2,500
$50 2004-W, Proof	28,215	$1,700	$1,750	$2,150
$50 2005	356,555	$1,425	$1,450	$2,000
$50 2005-W, Proof	35,246	$1,675	$1,725	$2,150
$50 2006	237,510	$1,425	$1,450	$1,700
$50 2006-W, Burnished	45,053	$1,600	$1,700	$1,900
$50 2006-W, Proof	47,092	$1,675	$1,725	$2,100
$50 2006-W, Reverse Proof †† (m,n)	9,996	$2,900	$3,050	$3,400
$50 2007	140,016	$1,425	$1,450	$1,950
$50 2007-W, Burnished	18,066	$1,500	$1,550	$1,750
$50 2007-W, Proof	51,810	$1,675	$1,725	$2,100
$50 2008	710,000	$1,425	$1,450	$1,950
$50 2008-W, Burnished (o)	11,908	$1,900	$1,950	$2,200
$50 2008-W, Proof	30,237	$1,675	$1,725	$2,500
$50 2009	1,493,000	$1,425	$1,450	$1,750
$50 2010	1,125,000	$1,425	$1,450	$1,550
$50 2010-W, Proof	59,480	$1,675	$1,725	$2,100
$50 2011	857,000	$1,425	$1,450	$1,550
$50 2011-W, Burnished (p)	8,729	$2,200	$2,250	$2,450
$50 2011-W, Proof	48,306	$1,675	$1,725	$2,100
$50 2012	675,000	$1,425	$1,450	$1,550
$50 2012-W, Burnished (q)	6,118	$2,200	$2,250	$2,500
$50 2012-W, Proof	23,805	$1,700	$1,750	$2,100
$50 2013	758,500	$1,425	$1,450	$1,600
$50 2013-W, Burnished	7,293	$1,500	$1,550	$1,900
$50 2013-W, Proof	24,709	$1,700	$1,750	$2,100
$50 2014	425,000	$1,425	$1,450	$1,500
$50 2014-W, Burnished	7,902	$1,700	$1,750	$1,900
$50 2014-W, Proof	28,703	$1,700	$1,750	$2,100
$50 2015	594,000	$1,425	$1,450	$1,500
$50 2015-W, Burnished	6,533	$1,700	$1,750	$1,900

Note: MS values are for uncertified Mint State coins of average quality, in their complete original U.S. Mint packaging. PF values are for uncertified Proof coins of average quality, in their complete original U.S. Mint packaging. †† Ranked in the *100 Greatest U.S. Modern Coins* (fourth edition). **i.** Auction: $1,645, MS-69, April 2014. **j.** $2,233, PF-70UCam, September 2015. **k.** Auction: $1,351, MS-69, October 2014. **l.** Auction: $2,820, PF-70UCam, January 2015. **m.** The 2006-W Reverse Proof coins were issued to mark the 20th anniversary of the Bullion Coinage Program. They have brilliant devices, and their background fields are frosted (rather than the typical Proof format of frosted devices and mirror-like backgrounds). **n.** Auction: $4,935, PF-70, September 2015. **o.** Auction: $1,293, MS-69, July 2015. **p.** Auction: $1,998, MS-70, June 2015. **q.** Auction: $2,585, MS-70, February 2015.

| | Mintage | MS | MS-69 | MS-70 |
		PF	PF-69	PF-70
$50 2015-W, Proof	40,004	$1,700	$1,750	$2,100
$50 2016	817,500	$1,425	$1,450	$1,500
$50 2016-W, Burnished		$1,700	$1,750	$3,000
$50 2016-W, Proof	24,352	$1,700	$1,750	$2,100
$50 2017	228,500	$1,425	$1,450	$1,500
$50 2017-W, Burnished	5,800	$2,200	$2,500	$3,500
$50 2017-W, Proof	9,245	$1,700	$1,750	$2,100
$50 2018	191,000	$1,425	$1,450	$1,500
$50 2018-W, Burnished	7,913	$1,700	$1,750	$3,000
$50 2018-W, Proof	13,806	$1,700	$1,750	$2,000
$50 2019		$1,425	$1,450	$1,500
$50 2019-W, Burnished		$1,700	$1,750	$3,000
$50 2019-W, Proof		$1,700	$1,750	$2,000

Note: MS values are for uncertified Mint State coins of average quality, in their complete original U.S. Mint packaging. PF values are for uncertified Proof coins of average quality, in their complete original U.S. Mint packaging. †† Ranked in the *100 Greatest U.S. Modern Coins* (fourth edition).

AMERICAN GOLD EAGLE PROOF COIN SETS

	PF	PF-69	PF-70
1987 Gold Set. $50, $25	$2,400	$2,500	$4,200
1988 Gold Set. $50, $25, $10, $5	$3,000	$3,150	$5,400
1989 Gold Set. $50, $25, $10, $5	$3,200	$3,350	—
1990 Gold Set. $50, $25, $10, $5	$3,150	$3,300	—
1991 Gold Set. $50, $25, $10, $5	$3,100	$3,250	$5,600
1992 Gold Set. $50, $25, $10, $5	$3,100	$3,250	$5,700
1993 Gold Set. $50, $25, $10, $5	$3,100	$3,250	—
1993 Bicentennial Gold Set. $25, $10, $5, Silver Eagle, and medal (a)	$1,400	$1,500	—
1994 Gold Set. $50, $25, $10, $5	$3,100	$3,250	$5,000
1995 Gold Set. $50, $25, $10, $5	$3,100	$3,250	$5,600
1995 Anniversary Gold Set. $50, $25, $10, $5, and Silver Eagle (b)	$6,800	$7,900	—
1996 Gold Set. $50, $25, $10, $5	$3,100	$3,250	$5,000
1997 Gold Set. $50, $25, $10, $5	$3,300	$3,450	$5,600
1997 Impressions of Liberty Set. $100 platinum, $50 gold, Silver Eagle (c)	$3,200	$3,250	$6,200
1998 Gold Set. $50, $25, $10, $5	$3,200	$3,350	$6,850
1999 Gold Set. $50, $25, $10, $5	$3,100	$3,250	$5,600
2000 Gold Set. $50, $25, $10, $5	$3,100	$3,250	$5,100
2001 Gold Set. $50, $25, $10, $5	$3,100	$3,250	$7,700
2002 Gold Set. $50, $25, $10, $5	$3,100	$3,250	$4,450
2003 Gold Set. $50, $25, $10, $5	$3,100	$3,250	$4,450
2004 Gold Set. $50, $25, $10, $5	$3,100	$3,250	$4,800
2005 Gold Set. $50, $25, $10, $5	$3,100	$3,250	$3,800
2006 Gold Set. $50, $25, $10, $5	$3,100	$3,250	$3,800
2007 Gold Set. $50, $25, $10, $5	$3,100	$3,250	$3,800
2008 Gold Set. $50, $25, $10, $5	$3,100	$3,250	$4,700
2010 Gold Set. $50, $25, $10, $5 (d)	$3,100	$3,250	$3,800
2011 Gold Set. $50, $25, $10, $5	$3,100	$3,250	$3,800
2012 Gold Set. $50, $25, $10, $5	$3,100	$3,250	$3,800
2013 Gold Set. $50, $25, $10, $5	$3,100	$3,250	$3,800

Note: PF values are for uncertified Proof sets of average quality, in their complete original U.S. Mint packaging. **a.** The 1993 set was issued to commemorate the bicentennial of the first coins struck by the U.S. Mint in Philadelphia. **b.** The 1995 set marked the 10th anniversary of the passage of the Liberty Coin Act, which authorized the nation's new bullion coinage program. **c.** The Impressions of Liberty set was issued in the first year that platinum coins were added to the Mint's bullion offerings. **d.** The U.S. Mint did not issue a 2009 gold set.

	PF	PF-69	PF-70
2014 Gold Set. $50, $25, $10, $5	$3,100	$3,250	$3,800
2015 Gold Set. $50, $25, $10, $5	$3,100	$3,250	$3,800
2016 Gold Set. $50, $25, $10, $5	$3,100	$3,250	$3,800
2017 Gold Set. $50, $25, $10, $5	$3,100	$3,250	$3,800
2018 Gold Set. $50, $25, $10, $5	$3,100	$3,250	$3,800
2019 Gold Set. $50, $25, $10, $5	$3,100	$3,250	$3,800

Note: PF values are for uncertified Proof sets of average quality, in their complete original U.S. Mint packaging. **a.** The 1993 set was issued to commemorate the bicentennial of the first coins struck by the U.S. Mint in Philadelphia.

2006 American Gold Eagle 20th-Anniversary Coin Sets

	Uncertified	69	70
2006-W $50 Gold Set. Uncirculated, Proof, and Reverse Proof	$5,900	$6,400	$6,800
2006-W 1-oz. Gold- and Silver-Dollar Set. Uncirculated	$1,800	$1,900	$2,000

Note: Uncertified values are for uncertified sets of average quality, in their complete original U.S. Mint packaging.

Gold Bullion Burnished Sets

	Uncertified	69	70
2006-W Burnished Gold Set. $50, $25, $10, $5	$3,700	$4,000	$5,000
2007-W Burnished Gold Set. $50, $25, $10, $5 ††	$4,000	$4,250	$5,500
2008-W Burnished Gold Set. $50, $25, $10, $5	$5,450	$5,600	$7,000

Note: Uncertified values are for uncertified sets of average quality, in their complete original U.S. Mint packaging. †† Ranked in the *100 Greatest U.S. Modern Coins* (fourth edition).

AMERICAN BUFFALO .9999 FINE
GOLD BULLION COINS (2006 TO DATE)

Designer: *James Earle Fraser.* **Weight:** *$5 1/10 oz.—3.393 grams; $10 1/4 oz.—8.483 grams; $25 1/2 oz.—16.966 grams; $50 1 oz.—31.108 grams.* **Composition:** *.9999 gold.* **Diameter:** *$5 1/10 oz.—16.5 mm; $10 1/4 oz.—22 mm; $25 1/2 oz.—27 mm; $50 1 oz.—32.7 mm.* **Edge:** *Reeded.* **Mint:** *West Point.*

Regular Finish

Burnished Finish

Mintmark location is on the obverse, behind the neck.

Proof Finish

Reverse Proof Finish

History. American Buffalo gold bullion coins, authorized by Congress in 2005 and produced since 2006, are the first 24-karat (.9999 fine) gold coins made by the U.S. Mint. They are coined, by mandate, of gold derived from newly mined sources in America. They feature an adaptation of James Earle Fraser's iconic Indian Head / Buffalo design, first used on circulating five-cent pieces of 1913 to 1938.

Only 1-ounce ($50 face value) coins were struck in the American Buffalo program's first two years, 2006 and 2007. For 2008, the Mint expanded the coinage to include fractional pieces of 1/2 ounce ($25), 1/4 ounce ($10), and 1/10-ounce ($5), in various finishes, individually and in sets.

The coins are legal tender, with weight, content, and purity guaranteed by the federal government. Investors can include them in some individual retirement accounts. Proofs and Burnished (*Uncirculated*, in the Mint's wording) pieces undergo special production processes, similar to the American Eagle gold-bullion coinage, and can be purchased directly from the Mint. As with other products in the Mint's bullion program, regular bullion-strike pieces are distributed through a network of authorized distributors.

All American Buffalo gold bullion coins (Proofs, Burnished, and regular bullion pieces) are struck at the U.S. Mint's West Point facility.

Striking and Sharpness. Striking is generally sharp.

Availability. American Buffalo .9999 fine gold bullion coins are a popular way to buy and sell 24-karat gold. The coins are readily available in the numismatic marketplace as well as from participating banks, investment firms, and other non-numismatic channels.

MS-60 to 70 (Mint State). *Obverse and reverse:* At MS-60, some abrasion and contact marks are evident on the higher design areas and the open areas of the design. Luster may be dull or lifeless at MS–60 to 62, but there should be deep frost at MS-63 and better, particularly in the lower-relief areas. At MS-65 and above, the luster should be full and rich. Contact marks and abrasion are less and less evident at higher grades. These guidelines are more academic than practical, as these coins are not intended for circulation, and nearly all are in high Mint State grades, as struck.

PF-60 to 70 (Proof). *Obverse and reverse:* Proofs that are extensively cleaned and have many hairlines are lower level, such as PF–60 to 62. Those with fewer hairlines or flaws are deemed PF–63 to 65. (These exist more in theory than actuality, as nearly all Proof American Buffalo gold coins have been maintained in their original high condition by collectors.) Given the quality of modern U.S. Mint products, even PF–66 and 67 are unusually low levels for these Proofs.

AMERICAN BUFFALO *.9999 FINE GOLD BULLION COINS*

$5 1/10-oz. $10 1/4-oz. $25 1/2-oz. $50 1-oz.

| | Mintage | MS | MS-69 | MS-70 |
		PF	PF-69	PF-70
$5 2008-W, Burnished (a)	17,429	$450	$485	$600
$5 2008-W, Proof (b)	18,884	$450	$485	$600
$10 2008-W, Burnished †† (c)	9,949	$1,000	$1,050	$1,400
$10 2008-W, Proof (d)	13,125	$1,100	$1,200	$1,500
$25 2008-W, Burnished (e)	16,908	$1,150	$1,200	$1,500
$25 2008-W, Proof (f)	12,169	$1,600	$1,650	$2,000
$50 2006	337,012	$1,425	$1,450	$1,500
$50 2006-W, Proof	246,267	$1,450	$1,500	$1,600
$50 2007	136,503	$1,425	$1,450	$1,500
$50 2007-W, Proof	58,998	$1,450	$1,500	$1,600
$50 2008	214,058 **(g)**	$1,425	$1,450	$1,500
$50 2008-W, Burnished (h)	9,074	$2,350	$2,400	$2,850
$50 2008-W, Proof †† (i)	18,863	$2,750	$2,850	$3,200
$50 2009	200,000	$1,425	$1,450	$1,500
$50 2009-W, Proof	49,306	$1,450	$1,500	$1,600
$50 2010	209,000	$1,425	$1,450	$1,500
$50 2010-W, Proof	49,263	$1,450	$1,500	$1,600
$50 2011	250,000	$1,425	$1,450	$1,500
$50 2011-W, Proof	28,693	$1,500	$1,550	$1,700
$50 2012	100,000	$1,425	$1,450	$1,500
$50 2012-W, Proof	19,765	$1,650	$1,700	$2,000
$50 2013	198,500	$1,425	$1,450	$1,500
$50 2013-W, Proof	18,594	$1,600	$1,650	$2,100
$50 2013-W, Reverse Proof ††	47,836	$1,500	$1,550	$1,800
$50 2014	180,500	$1,425	$1,450	$1,500
$50 2014-W, Proof	20,557	$1,450	$1,500	$1,600
$50 2015	223,500	$1,425	$1,450	$1,500
$50 2015-W, Proof	16,591	$1,425	$1,500	$1,600
$50 2016	211,000	$1,425	$1,450	$1,500
$50 2016-W, Proof		$1,425	$1,500	$1,600
$50 2017	99,500	$1,425	$1,450	$1,500
$50 2017-W, Proof	15,810	$1,425	$1,500	$1,600
$50 2018	121,500	$1,425	$1,450	$1,500
$50 2018-W, Proof	15,283	$1,425	$1,500	$1,600
$50 2019		$1,425	$1,450	$1,500
$50 2019-W, Proof		$1,425	$1,500	$1,600

Note: MS values are for uncertified Mint State coins of average quality, in their complete original U.S. Mint packaging. PF values are for uncertified Proof coins of average quality, in their complete original U.S. Mint packaging. †† Ranked in the *100 Greatest U.S. Modern Coins* (fourth edition). **a.** Auction: $447, MS-70, September 2015. **b.** Auction: $705, PF-70DCam, June 2015. **c.** Auction: $1,116, MS-70, August 2015. **d.** Auction: $823, PF-70DCam, January 2015. **e.** Auction: $764, MS-69, November 2015. **f.** Auction: $1,528, PF-70UCam, August 2015. **g.** 24,558 sold as Lunar New Year Celebration coins. **h.** Auction: $2,703, MS-70, June 2015. **i.** Auction: $3,525, PF-70DCam, July 2015.

AMERICAN BUFFALO *.9999* FINE GOLD BULLION COIN SETS

| | Uncertified | MS-69 | MS-70 |
		PF-69	PF-70
2008-W Four-coin set ($5, $10, $25, $50), Proof	$5,900	$6,100	$7,200
2008-W Four-coin set ($5, $10, $25, $50), Burnished	$4,900	$5,100	$6,300
2008-W Double Prosperity set (Unc. $25 American Buffalo gold and $25 American Gold Eagle coins)	$2,000	$2,100	$2,600

Note: Uncertified values are for uncertified sets of average quality, in their complete original U.S. Mint packaging.

FIRST SPOUSE $10 GOLD BULLION COINS
(2007–2016)

Designers: *See image captions for designers.* **Weight:** *8.483 grams.*
Composition: *.9999 gold.* **Diameter:** *26.5 mm.* **Edge:** *Reeded.* **Mint:** *West Point.*

Burnished Finish
The first coin in the series,
featuring Martha Washington.

Mintmark location is on the
obverse, below the date.

Proof Finish

History. The U.S. Mint's First Spouse bullion coins were struck in .9999 fine (24-karat) gold. Each weighs one-half ounce and bears a face value of $10. The coins honor the nation's first spouses and were struck on the same schedule as the Mint's Presidential dollars program. Each features a portrait on the obverse, and on the reverse a unique design symbolic of the spouse's life and work. In cases where a president held office widowed or unmarried, the coin bears "an obverse image emblematic of Liberty as depicted on a circulating coin of that era and a reverse image emblematic of themes of that president's life." All First Spouse gold bullion coins (Proofs and Burnished pieces) were struck at the U.S. Mint's West Point facility.

Note that the Mint does not release bullion mintage data on a regular basis; the numbers given herein reflect the most recently available official data.

Striking and Sharpness. Striking is generally sharp.

Availability. These coins are readily available in the numismatic marketplace. They could be purchased by the public, in both Burnished and Proof formats, directly from the U.S. Mint. Sales of later issues were low, leading to some issues being ranked among the 100 Greatest U.S. Modern Coins.

MS-60 to 70 (Mint State). *Obverse and Reverse:* At MS-60, some abrasion and contact marks are evident on the higher design areas and the open areas of the design. Luster may be dull or lifeless at MS–60 to 62, but there should be deep frost at MS-63 and better, particularly in the lower-relief areas. At MS-65 and above, the luster should be full and rich. Contact marks and abrasion are less and less evident at higher grades. These guidelines are more academic than practical, as these coins are not intended for circulation, and nearly all are in high Mint State grades, as struck.

PF-60 to 70 (Proof). *Obverse and Reverse:* Proofs that are extensively cleaned and have many hairlines are lower level, such as PF–60 to 62. Those with fewer hairlines or flaws are deemed PF–63 to 65. (These exist more in theory than actuality, as nearly all Proof First Spouse gold coins have been maintained in their original high condition by collectors.) Given the quality of modern U.S. Mint products, even PF–66 and 67 are unusually low levels for these Proofs.

FIRST SPOUSE $10 GOLD BULLION COINS

Martha Washington	Abigail Adams	Jefferson's Liberty	Dolley Madison
Designers:	*Designers:*	*Designers: obverse—*	*Designers:*
obverse—Joseph Menna;	*obverse—Joseph Menna;*	*Robert Scot / Phebe Hemphill;*	*obverse—Don Everhart;*
reverse—Susan Gamble.	*reverse—Thomas Cleveland.*	*reverse—Charles Vickers.*	*reverse—Joel Iskowitz.*

	Mintage	MS / PF	MS-69 / PF-69	MS-70 / PF-70
$10 2007-W, M. Washington	17,661	$700	$725	$775
$10 2007-W, M. Washington, Proof	19,167	$700	$725	$775
$10 2007-W, A. Adams	17,142	$700	$725	$775
$10 2007-W, A. Adams, Proof	17,149	$700	$725	$775
$10 2007-W, Jefferson's Liberty ††	19,823	$700	$725	$775
$10 2007-W, Jefferson's Liberty, Proof ††	19,815	$700	$725	$775
$10 2007-W, D. Madison	12,340	$700	$725	$775
$10 2007-W, D. Madison, Proof	17,943	$700	$725	$775

Note: MS values are for uncertified Mint State coins of average quality, in their complete original U.S. Mint packaging. PF values are for uncertified Proof coins of average quality, in their complete original U.S. Mint packaging. †† All First Spouse Gold Bullion with "Liberty" Designs, in all finishes, are ranked in the *100 Greatest U.S. Modern Coins* (fourth edition), as a single entry.

Elizabeth Monroe	Louisa Adams	Jackson's Liberty	Van Buren's Liberty
Designers:	*Designers:*	*Designers:*	*Designer:*
obverse—Joel Iskowitz;	*obverse—Susan Gamble;*	*obverse—John Reich;*	*obverse—Christian Gobrecht;*
reverse—Donna Weaver.	*reverse—Donna Weaver.*	*reverse—Justin Kunz.*	*reverse—Thomas Cleveland.*

	Mintage	MS / PF	MS-69 / PF-69	MS-70 / PF-70
$10 2008-W, E. Monroe	4,462	$750	$775	$1,000
$10 2008-W, E. Monroe, Proof	7,800	$800	$1,250	$1,250
$10 2008-W, L. Adams	3,885	$725	$775	$1,000
$10 2008-W, L. Adams, Proof	6,581	$850	$1,250	$1,250

Note: MS values are for uncertified Mint State coins of average quality, in their complete original U.S. Mint packaging. PF values are for uncertified Proof coins of average quality, in their complete original U.S. Mint packaging.

	Mintage	MS	MS-69	MS-70
		PF	PF-69	PF-70
$10 2008-W, Jackson's Liberty ✝✝ (a)	4,609	$850	$1,400	$1,400
$10 2008-W, Jackson's Liberty, Proof ✝✝	7,684	$900	$1,250	$1,400
$10 2008-W, Van Buren's Liberty ✝✝	3,826	$850	$1,400	$1,450
$10 2008-W, Van Buren's Liberty, Proof ✝✝ (b)	6,807	$1,000	$1,250	$1,600

Note: MS values are for uncertified Mint State coins of average quality, in their complete original U.S. Mint packaging. PF values are for uncertified Proof coins of average quality, in their complete original U.S. Mint packaging. ✝✝ All First Spouse Gold Bullion with "Liberty" Designs, in all finishes, are ranked in the *100 Greatest U.S. Modern Coins* (fourth edition), as a single entry. **a.** Auction: $999, MS-69, February 2015. **b.** Auction: $1,058, PF-70DCam, January 2015.

Anna Harrison
Designers:
obverse—Donna Weaver;
reverse—Thomas Cleveland.

Letitia Tyler
Designers:
obverse—Phebe Hemphill;
reverse—Susan Gamble.

Julia Tyler
Designer:
obverse and reverse—
Joel Iskowitz.

Sarah Polk
Designer: obverse and
reverse—Phebe Hemphill.

Margaret Taylor
Designers: obverse—Phebe Hemphill;
reverse—Mary Beth Zeitz.

	Mintage	MS	MS-69	MS-70
		PF	PF-69	PF-70
$10 2009-W, A. Harrison	3,645	$800	$850	$1,300
$10 2009-W, A. Harrison, Proof (c)	6,251	$900	$950	$1,200
$10 2009-W, L. Tyler	3,240	$900	$950	$1,450
$10 2009-W, L. Tyler, Proof (d)	5,296	$1,000	$1,050	$1,200
$10 2009-W, J. Tyler (e)	3,143	$900	$950	$1,500
$10 2009-W, J. Tyler, Proof (f)	4,844	$1,000	$1,050	$1,200
$10 2009-W, S. Polk	3,489	$925	$975	$1,250
$10 2009-W, S. Polk, Proof	5,151	$800	$850	$1,000
$10 2009-W, M. Taylor	3,627	$750	$800	$1,025
$10 2009-W, M. Taylor, Proof	4,936	$750	$800	$1,050

Note: MS values are for uncertified Mint State coins of average quality, in their complete original U.S. Mint packaging. PF values are for uncertified Proof coins of average quality, in their complete original U.S. Mint packaging. **c.** Auction: $646, PF-69DCam, June 2015. **d.** Auction: $881, PF-70DCam, June 2015. **e.** Auction: $1,293, MS-70, June 2015. **f.** Auction: $764, PF-69DCam, June 2015.

Abigail Fillmore
Designers:
obverse—Phebe Hemphill;
reverse—Susan Gamble.

Jane Pierce
Designer:
obverse and reverse—
Donna Weaver.

Buchanan's Liberty
Designers:
obverse—Christian Gobrecht;
reverse—David Westwood.

Mary Lincoln
Designers:
obverse—Phebe Hemphill;
reverse—Joel Iskowitz.

	Mintage	MS	MS-69	MS-70
		PF	PF-69	PF-70
$10 2010-W, A. Fillmore	3,482	$750	$800	$1,100
$10 2010-W, A. Fillmore, Proof	6,130	$900	$950	$1,050
$10 2010-W, J. Pierce	3,338	$750	$800	$1,100
$10 2010-W, J. Pierce, Proof	4,775	$950	$1,000	$1,350
$10 2010-W, Buchanan's Liberty ††	5,162	$800	$850	$1,050
$10 2010-W, Buchanan's Liberty, Proof ††	7,110	$900	$950	$1,050
$10 2010-W, M. Lincoln	3,695	$800	$850	$1,100
$10 2010-W, M. Lincoln, Proof	6,861	$900	$950	$1,250

Note: MS values are for uncertified Mint State coins of average quality, in their complete original U.S. Mint packaging. PF values are for uncertified Proof coins of average quality, in their complete original U.S. Mint packaging. †† All First Spouse Gold Bullion with "Liberty" Designs, in all finishes, are ranked in the *100 Greatest U.S. Modern Coins* (fourth edition), as a single entry.

Eliza Johnson
Designers:
obverse—Joel Iskowitz;
reverse—Gary Whitley.

Julia Grant
Designers:
obverse—Donna Weaver;
reverse—Richard Masters.

Lucy Hayes
Designers:
obverse—Susan Gamble;
reverse—Barbara Fox.

Lucretia Garfield
Designers:
obverse—Barbara Fox;
reverse—Michael Gaudioso.

	Mintage	MS	MS-69	MS-70
		PF	PF-69	PF-70
$10 2011-W, E. Johnson	800	$800	$850	$1,300
$10 2011-W, E. Johnson, Proof	950	$950	$1,000	$1,100
$10 2011-W, J. Grant	800	$800	$850	$1,150
$10 2011-W, J. Grant, Proof	950	$950	$1,000	$1,200
$10 2011-W, L. Hayes (g)	950	$950	$1,000	$1,600

Note: MS values are for uncertified Mint State coins of average quality, in their complete original U.S. Mint packaging. PF values are for uncertified Proof coins of average quality, in their complete original U.S. Mint packaging. **g.** Auction: $1,763, MS-70, January 2015.

| | Mintage | MS | MS-69 | MS-70 |
		PF	PF-69	PF-70
$10 2011-W, L. Hayes, Proof	1,100	$1,100	$1,150	$1,500
$10 2011-W, L. Garfield	950	$950	$1,000	$1,600
$10 2011-W, L. Garfield, Proof	900	$900	$950	$1,300

Note: MS values are for uncertified Mint State coins of average quality, in their complete original U.S. Mint packaging. PF values are for uncertified Proof coins of average quality, in their complete original U.S. Mint packaging.

Alice Paul	**Frances Cleveland (Type 1)**	**Caroline Harrison**	**Frances Cleveland (Type 2)**
Designers:	*Designers:*	*Designers:*	*Designers:*
obverse—Susan Gamble;	*obverse—Joel Iskowitz;*	*obverse—Frank Morris;*	*obverse—Barbara Fox;*
reverse—Phebe Hemphill.	*reverse—Barbara Fox.*	*reverse—Donna Weaver.*	*reverse—Joseph Menna.*

| | Mintage | MS | MS-69 | MS-70 |
		PF	PF-69	PF-70
$10 2012-W, Alice Paul	2,798	$850	$900	$1,100
$10 2012-W, Alice Paul, Proof	3,505	$875	$925	$1,350
$10 2012-W, Frances Cleveland, Variety 1	2,454	$850	$900	$950
$10 2012-W, Frances Cleveland, Variety 1, Proof	3,158	$925	$975	$1,100
$10 2012-W, Caroline Harrison	2,436	$850	$900	$1,100
$10 2012-W, Caroline Harrison, Proof	3,046	$925	$975	$1,150
$10 2012-W, Frances Cleveland, Variety 2	2,425	$850	$900	$950
$10 2012-W, Frances Cleveland, Variety 2, Proof	3,104	$925	$975	$1,150

Note: MS values are for uncertified Mint State coins of average quality, in their complete original U.S. Mint packaging. PF values are for uncertified Proof coins of average quality, in their complete original U.S. Mint packaging.

Ida McKinley	**Edith Roosevelt**	**Helen Taft**
Designers:	*Designers:*	*Designers:*
obverse—Susan Gamble;	*obverse—Joel Iskowitz;*	*obverse—William C. Burgard;*
reverse—Donna Weaver.	*reverse—Chris Costello.*	*reverse—Richard Masters.*

Ellen Wilson
Designers: obverse—Frank Morris;
reverse—Don Everhart.

Edith Wilson
Designers: obverse—David Westwood;
reverse—Joseph Menna.

	Mintage	MS	MS-69	MS-70
		PF	PF-69	PF-70
$10 2013-W, I. McKinley	2,008	$825	$875	$950
$10 2013-W, I. McKinley, Proof	2,724	$900	$950	$1,300
$10 2013-W, E. Roosevelt	2,027	$825	$875	$950
$10 2013-W, E. Roosevelt, Proof	2,840	$900	$950	$1,050
$10 2013-W, H. Taft	1,993	$825	$875	$950
$10 2013-W, H. Taft, Proof	2,598	$900	$950	$1,050
$10 2013-W, Ellen Wilson	1,980	$825	$875	$950
$10 2013-W, Ellen Wilson, Proof	2,511	$900	$950	$1,050
$10 2013-W, Edith Wilson	1,974	$825	$875	$950
$10 2013-W, Edith Wilson, Proof	2,464	$900	$950	$1,050

Note: MS values are for uncertified Mint State coins of average quality, in their complete original U.S. Mint packaging. PF values are for uncertified Proof coins of average quality, in their complete original U.S. Mint packaging.

Florence Harding
Designer:
obverse and reverse—
Thomas Cleveland.

Grace Coolidge
Designers:
obverse—Joel Iskowitz;
reverse—Frank Morris.

Lou Hoover
Designers:
obverse—Susan Gamble;
reverse—Richard Masters.

Eleanor Roosevelt
Designer:
obverse and reverse—
Chris Costello.

	Mintage	MS	MS-69	MS-70
		PF	PF-69	PF-70
$10 2014-W, F. Harding	1,944	$825	$875	$950
$10 2014-W, F. Harding, Proof	2,372	$875	$925	$1,250
$10 2014-W, G. Coolidge	1,949	$825	$875	$950
$10 2014-W, G. Coolidge, Proof	2,315	$900	$950	$1,500
$10 2014-W, L. Hoover	1,936	$825	$875	$950
$10 2014-W, L. Hoover, Proof	2,392	$900	$950	$1,600
$10 2014-W, E. Roosevelt	1,886	$1,600	$1,700	$2,200
$10 2014-W, E. Roosevelt, Proof	2,377	$1,400	$1,500	$2,400

Note: MS values are for uncertified Mint State coins of average quality, in their complete original U.S. Mint packaging. PF values are for uncertified Proof coins of average quality, in their complete original U.S. Mint packaging.

Bess Truman
Designer:
obverse and reverse—
Joel Iskowitz.

Mamie Eisenhower
Designers:
obverse—Richard Masters;
reverse—Barbara Fox.

Jacqueline Kennedy
Designers:
obverse—Susan Gamble;
reverse—Benjamin Sowards.

Claudia "Lady Bird" Johnson
Designers:
obverse—Linda Fox;
reverse—Chris Costello.

	Mintage	MS	MS-69	MS-70
		PF	PF-69	PF-70
$10 2015-W, B. Truman	1,946	$825	$850	$950
$10 2015-W, B. Truman, Proof	2,747	$900	$925	$1,000
$10 2015-W, M. Eisenhower	2,102	$825	$850	$950
$10 2015-W, M. Eisenhower, Proof	2,704	$900	$925	$1,000
$10 2015-W, J. Kennedy	6,771	$825	$850	$950
$10 2015-W, J. Kennedy, Proof	11,222	$900	$925	$1,000
$10 2015-W, Lady Bird Johnson	1,927	$825	$850	$950
$10 2015-W, Lady Bird Johnson, Proof	2,653	$900	$925	$1,000

Note: MS values are for uncertified Mint State coins of average quality, in their complete original U.S. Mint packaging. PF values are for uncertified Proof coins of average quality, in their complete original U.S. Mint packaging.

Patricia Nixon
Designer:
obverse and reverse—
Richard Masters.

Betty Ford
Designers:
obverse—Barbara Fox;
reverse—Chris Costello.

Nancy Reagan
Designers:
obverse—Benjamin Sowards;
reverse—Joel Iskowitz.

	Mintage	MS	MS-69	MS-70
		PF	PF-69	PF-70
$10 2016-W, P. Nixon	1,839	$825	$850	$950
$10 2016-W, P. Nixon, Proof	2,645	$900	$925	$1,000
$10 2016-W, B. Ford	1,824	$825	$850	$950
$10 2016-W, B. Ford, Proof	2,471	$900	$925	$1,000
$10 2016-W, N. Reagan	2,009	$825	$850	$950
$10 2016-W, N. Reagan, Proof	3,548	$900	$925	$1,000

Note: MS values are for uncertified Mint State coins of average quality, in their complete original U.S. Mint packaging. PF values are for uncertified Proof coins of average quality, in their complete original U.S. Mint packaging.

AMERICAN PLATINUM EAGLES
(1997 TO DATE)

Designers: *John M. Mercanti (obverse), Thomas D. Rogers Sr. (original reverse) (see image captions for other reverse designers).* **Weight:** *$10 1/10 oz.—3.112 grams; $25 1/4 oz.—7.780 grams; $50 1/2 oz.—15.560 grams; $100 1 oz.—31.120 grams.* **Composition:** *.9995 platinum.* **Diameter:** *$10 1/10 oz.—16.5 mm; $25 1/4 oz.—22 mm; $50 1/2 oz.—27 mm; $100 1 oz.—32.7 mm.* **Edge:** *Reeded.* **Mints:** *Philadelphia and West Point.*

Regular Finish

Burnished Finish
Burnished coins of all denominations feature the year's Proof reverse design. Mintmark location varies by design.

Proof Finish
First-year Proof coins featured the original reverse design, which is still in use on bullion strikes. See pages 1274–1276 for illustrations of Proof reverse designs from 1998 to date.

Reverse Proof Finish
Reverse Proofs were only struck in 2007, and only in the $50 1/2-oz. denomination.

Frosted FREEDOM
This variety is seen, very rarely, for 2007 Proof coins of the $25, $50, and $100 denominations.

History. Platinum American Eagles (face values of $10 to $100) are legal-tender bullion coins with weight, content, and purity guaranteed by the federal government. They were added to the U.S. Mint's program of silver and gold bullion coinage in 1997.

In their debut year, Proofs had the same reverse design as regular bullion strikes. Since then, the regular strikes have continued with the 1997 reverse, while the Proofs have featured new reverse designs each year. From 1998 through 2002, these special Proof designs comprised a "Vistas of Liberty" subset, with eagles flying through various American scenes. Since 2003, they have featured patriotic allegories and symbolism. From 2006 to 2008 the reverse designs honored "The Foundations of Democracy"—the nation's legislative branch (2006), executive branch (2007), and judicial branch (2008). In 2009 the Mint introduced a new six-year program of reverse designs, exploring the core concepts of American democracy as embodied in the preamble to the Constitution. The designs—which were based on narratives by John Roberts, chief justice of the United States—began with *To Form a More Perfect Union* (2009), which features four faces representing the nation's diversity, with the hair and clothing interweaving symbolically. The tiny eagle privy mark is from an original coin punch from the Philadelphia Mint's archives. This design is followed by *To Establish*

Justice (2010), *To Insure Domestic Tranquility* (2011), *To Provide for the Common Defence* (2012), *To Promote the General Welfare* (2013), and *To Secure the Blessings of Liberty to Ourselves and Our Posterity* (2014). In 2015, the Mint issued the first of a two-year series of new reverse designs emblematic of the core values of liberty and freedom called *Liberty Nurtures Freedom*. In 2017 the Proof reverse returned to the original 1997 design for the program's 20th anniversary. One-ounce Proofs of 2018 through 2020 feature new obverse designs in the theme of Life, Liberty, and the Pursuit of Happiness, and also share a new common reverse design. Beginning in 2021 the Mint will issue a new five-year series of one-ounce Proofs, for the five freedoms guaranteed under the First Amendment of the U.S. Constitution.

The Philadelphia Mint strikes regular bullion issues, which are sold to the public by a network of Mint-authorized precious-metal firms, coin dealers, banks, and brokerages. The West Point facility strikes Burnished pieces (called *Uncirculated* by the Mint, and featuring the reverse design of the Proof coins), which are sold directly to collectors. Proofs are also struck at West Point and, like the Burnished coins, are sold by the Mint to the public, without middlemen. Similar to their gold-bullion cousins, the platinum Proofs and Burnished coins bear a W mintmark and are specially packaged in plastic capsules and fancy presentation cases.

In addition to the individual coins listed below, platinum American Eagles were issued in the 1997 "Impressions of Liberty" bullion coin set; in 2007 "10th Anniversary" sets; and in annual platinum-coin sets.

Striking and Sharpness. Striking is generally sharp.

Availability. The platinum American Eagle is one of the most popular platinum-investment vehicles in the world. The coins are readily available in the numismatic marketplace and through some banks, investment firms, and other non-numismatic channels.

MS-60 to 70 (Mint State). *Obverse and Reverse:* At MS-60, some abrasion and contact marks are evident on the higher design areas. Luster may be dull or lifeless at MS–60 to 62, but there should be deep frost at MS-63 and better, particularly in the lower-relief areas. At MS-65 and above, the luster should be full and rich. These guidelines are more academic than practical, as platinum American Eagles are not intended for circulation, and nearly all are in high Mint State grades.

PF-60 to 70 (Proof). *Obverse and Reverse:* Proofs that are extensively cleaned and have many hairlines are lower level, such as PF–60 to 62. Those with fewer hairlines or flaws are deemed PF–63 to 65. (These exist more in theory than actuality, as nearly all Proof American Eagle platinum bullion coins have been maintained in their original high condition by collectors.) Given the quality of modern U.S. Mint products, even PF–66 and 67 are unusually low levels for these Proofs.

$10 1/10-Ounce
American Platinum Eagles

	Mintage	MS	MS-69	MS-70
		PF	PF-69	PF-70
$10 1997 (a)	70,250	$160	$185	$1,300
$10 1997-W, Proof	36,993	$195	$220	$275
$10 1998 (b)	39,525	$165	$190	$1,450
$10 1998-W, Proof (c)	19,847	$250	$275	$550
$10 1999 (d)	55,955	$160	$185	$800
$10 1999-W, Proof (c)	19,133	$205	$230	$300
$10 2000	34,027	$160	$185	$600
$10 2000-W, Proof (c)	15,651	$220	$245	$400

Note: MS values are for uncertified Mint State coins of average quality, in their complete original U.S. Mint packaging. PF values are for uncertified Proof coins of average quality, in their complete original U.S. Mint packaging. **a.** Auction: $4,230, MS-70, January 2015. **b.** Auction: $223, MS-69, January 2013. **c.** Burnished and Proof coins from 1998 on featured the designs illustrated on pages 1258–1259.

| | Mintage | MS | MS-69 | MS-70 |
		PF	PF-69	PF-70
$10 2001	52,017	$160	$185	$375
$10 2001-W, Proof (c)	12,174	$200	$225	$425
$10 2002	23,005	$165	$190	$300
$10 2002-W, Proof (c)	12,365	$200	$225	$400
$10 2003	22,007	$165	$190	$300
$10 2003-W, Proof (c,e)	9,534	$195	$220	$290
$10 2004	15,010	$170	$195	$300
$10 2004-W, Proof (c,f)	7,161	$350	$375	$490
$10 2005	14,013	$170	$195	$300
$10 2005-W, Proof (c,g)	8,104	$225	$250	$375
$10 2006	11,001	$190	$215	$300
$10 2006-W, Burnished (c,h)	3,544	$410	$435	$550
$10 2006-W, Proof (c)	10,205	$190	$215	$350
$10 2007 (i)	13,003	$170	$195	$325
$10 2007-W, Burnished (c,j)	5,556	$200	$225	$280
$10 2007-W, Proof (c)	8,176	$190	$215	$350
$10 2008	17,000	$165	$190	$300
$10 2008-W, Burnished (c,k)	3,706	$335	$370	$425
$10 2008-W, Proof (c,l)	5,138	$325	$350	$450

Note: MS values are for uncertified Mint State coins of average quality, in their complete original U.S. Mint packaging. PF values are for uncertified Proof coins of average quality, in their complete original U.S. Mint packaging. **c.** Burnished and Proof coins from 1998 on featured the designs illustrated on pages 1258–1259. **d.** Auction: $170, MS-69, August 2014. **e.** Auction: $176, PF-69DCam, December 2014. **f.** Auction: $447, PF-69DCam, February 2015. **g.** Auction: $212, PF-70UCam, February 2015. **h.** Auction: $441, MS-70, June 2013. **i.** Auction: $153, MS-70, September 2015. **j.** Auction: $364, MS-70, May 2015. **k.** Auction: $282, MS-69, September 2015. **l.** $376, PF-70UCam, January 2015.

$25 1/4-OUNCE AMERICAN PLATINUM EAGLES

| | Mintage | MS | MS-69 | MS-70 |
		PF	PF-69	PF-70
$25 1997 (a)	27,100	$310	$335	$3,000
$25 1997-W, Proof	18,628	$390	$415	$575
$25 1998	38,887	$310	$335	$1,400
$25 1998-W, Proof (b)	14,873	$390	$415	$700
$25 1999 (c)	39,734	$310	$335	$2,750
$25 1999-W, Proof (b)	13,507	$390	$415	$700
$25 2000	20,054	$310	$335	$800
$25 2000-W, Proof (b)	11,995	$390	$415	$700
$25 2001 (d)	21,815	$310	$335	$2,300
$25 2001-W, Proof (b)	8,847	$390	$415	$750
$25 2002	27,405	$310	$335	$575
$25 2002-W, Proof (b)	9,282	$390	$415	$750
$25 2003	25,207	$310	$335	$550
$25 2003-W, Proof (b)	7,044	$390	$415	$750
$25 2004	18,010	$310	$335	$550
$25 2004-W, Proof (b,e)	5,193	$850	$900	$1,250
$25 2005	12,013	$340	$365	$600

Note: MS values are for uncertified Mint State coins of average quality, in their complete original U.S. Mint packaging. PF values are for uncertified Proof coins of average quality, in their complete original U.S. Mint packaging. **a.** Auction: $7,638, MS-70, January 2015. **b.** Burnished and Proof coins from 1998 on featured the designs illustrated on pages 1258–1259. **c.** Auction: $411, MS-68, October 2012. **d.** Auction: $374, MS-68, June 2012. **e.** Auction: $764, PF-70DCam, July 2015.

	Mintage	MS	MS-69	MS-70
		PF	PF-69	PF-70
$25 2005-W, Proof (b,f)	6,592	$550	$600	$950
$25 2006	12,001	$340	$365	$600
$25 2006-W, Burnished (b,g)	2,676	$600	$650	$800
$25 2006-W, Proof (b)	7,813	$390	$415	$750
$25 2007	8,402	$345	$370	$650
$25 2007-W, Burnished (b,h)	3,690	$550	$600	$700
$25 2007-W, Proof (b)	6,017	$390	$415	$750
$25 2007-W, Frosted FREEDOM, Proof †† (b)	21	—		
$25 2008	22,800	$310	$335	$575
$25 2008-W, Burnished (b,i)	2,481	$850	$900	$1,250
$25 2008-W, Proof (b,j)	4,153	$700	$750	$1,000

Note: MS values are for uncertified Mint State coins of average quality, in their complete original U.S. Mint packaging. PF values are for uncertified Proof coins of average quality, in their complete original U.S. Mint packaging. †† All Proof 2007-W Platinum Eagles with Frosted FREEDOM, in all denominations, are ranked in the *100 Greatest U.S. Modern Coins* (fourth edition), as a single entry. **b.** Burnished and Proof coins from 1998 on featured the designs illustrated on pages 1258–1259. **f.** Auction: $564, PF-70DCam, January 2015. **g.** Auction: $306, MS-69, November 2015. **h.** Auction: $598, MS-70, August 2014. **i.** Auction: $764, MS-70, September 2015. **j.** Auction: $470, PF-70UCam, June 2015.

$50 1/2-OUNCE AMERICAN PLATINUM EAGLES

	Mintage	MS	MS-69	MS-70
		PF	PF-69	PF-70
$50 1997 (a)	20,500	$625	$675	$5,000
$50 1997-W, Proof	15,431	$725	$750	$925
$50 1998 (b)	32,415	$625	$675	$3,500
$50 1998-W, Proof (c)	13,836	$725	$750	$900
$50 1999 (d)	32,309	$625	$675	$3,500
$50 1999-W, Proof (c)	11,103	$725	$750	$900
$50 2000 (e)	18,892	$625	$675	$4,000
$50 2000-W, Proof (c)	11,049	$725	$750	$900
$50 2001 (f)	12,815	$625	$675	$3,750
$50 2001-W, Proof (c)	8,254	$725	$750	$900
$50 2002	24,005	$625	$675	$1,700
$50 2002-W, Proof (c)	8,772	$725	$750	$900
$50 2003	17,409	$625	$675	$1,100
$50 2003-W, Proof (c)	7,131	$725	$750	$900
$50 2004	13,236	$625	$675	$1,100
$50 2004-W, Proof (c,g)	5,063	$1,100	$1,150	$1,550
$50 2005	9,013	$675	$725	$1,100
$50 2005-W, Proof (c,h)	5,942	$950	$1,000	$1,400
$50 2006	9,602	$700	$750	$950
$50 2006-W, Burnished (c)	2,577	$850	$900	$1,300
$50 2006-W, Proof (c)	7,649	$725	$750	$1,250
$50 2007	7,001	$700	$750	$950
$50 2007-W, Burnished (c)	3,635	$825	$875	$1,000

Note: MS values are for uncertified Mint State coins of average quality, in their complete original U.S. Mint packaging. PF values are for uncertified Proof coins of average quality, in their complete original U.S. Mint packaging. **a.** Auction: $870, MS-69, July 2014. **b.** Auction: $881, MS-68, October 2012. **c.** Burnished and Proof coins from 1998 on featured the designs illustrated on pages 1258–1259. **d.** Auction: $823, MS-69, April 2014. **e.** Auction: $823, MS-69, November 2012. **f.** Auction: $796, MS-69, July 2014. **g.** Auction: $1,058, PF-70DCam, July 2015. **h.** Auction: $705, PF-70UCam, February 2015.

	Mintage	MS	MS-69	MS-70
		PF	PF-69	PF-70
$50 2007-W, Proof (c)	25,519	$725	$750	$900
$50 2007-W, Reverse Proof (c)	19,583	$800	$850	$1,000
$50 2007-W, Frosted FREEDOM, Proof †† (c)	21	—		
$50 2008	14,000	$625	$675	$1,000
$50 2008-W, Burnished †† (c,i)	2,253	$1,200	$1,300	$2,500
$50 2008-W, Proof †† (c,j)	4,020	$1,200	$1,250	$1,600

Note: MS values are for uncertified Mint State coins of average quality, in their complete original U.S. Mint packaging. PF values are for uncertified Proof coins of average quality, in their complete original U.S. Mint packaging. †† Ranked in the *100 Greatest U.S. Modern Coins* (fourth edition); all Proof 2007-W Platinum Eagles with Frosted FREEDOM, in all denominations, are as a single entry. **c.** Burnished and Proof coins from 1998 on featured the designs illustrated on pages 1258–1259. **i.** Auction: $1,528, MS-70, October 2015. **j.** Auction: $1,234, PF-70UCam. October 2015.

$100 1-OUNCE AMERICAN PLATINUM EAGLES

Proof Reverse, 1998:
Eagle Over New England.
Vistas of Liberty series.
Designer: John Mercanti.

Proof Reverse, 1999:
Eagle Above
Southeastern Wetlands.
Vistas of Liberty series.
Designer: John Mercanti.

Proof Reverse, 2000:
Eagle Above
America's Heartland.
Vistas of Liberty series.
Designer: Alfred Maletsky.

Proof Reverse, 2001:
Eagle Above
America's Southwest.
Vistas of Liberty series.
Designer: Thomas D. Rogers Sr.

Proof Reverse, 2002:
Eagle Fishing in
America's Northwest.
Vistas of Liberty series.
Designer: Alfred Maletsky.

Proof Reverse, 2003.
Designer: Alfred Maletsky.

Proof Reverse, 2004.
Designer: Donna Weaver.

Proof Reverse, 2005.
Designer: Donna Weaver.

Proof Reverse, 2006:
Legislative Branch.
Foundations of
Democracy series.
Designer: Joel Iskowitz.

Proof Reverse, 2007:
Executive Branch.
Foundations of
Democracy series.
Designer: Thomas Cleveland.

Proof Reverse, 2008:
Judicial Branch.
Foundations of
Democracy series.
Designer: Joel Iskowitz.

Proof Reverse, 2009:
"To Form a More
Perfect Union."
Preamble to the
Constitution series.
Designer: Susan Gamble.

Proof Reverse, 2010:
"To Establish Justice."
Preamble to the
Constitution series.
Designer: Donna Weaver.

Proof Reverse, 2011:
"To Insure Domestic
Tranquility."
Preamble to the
Constitution series.
Designer: Joel Iskowitz.

Proof Reverse, 2012:
"To Provide for the
Common Defence."
Preamble to the
Constitution series.
Designer: Barbara Fox.

Proof Reverse, 2013:
"To Promote the
General Welfare."
Preamble to the
Constitution series.
Designer: Joel Iskowitz.

Proof Reverse, 2014:
"To Secure the
Blessings of Liberty
to Ourselves and
Our Posterity."
Preamble to the
Constitution series.
Designer: Susan Gamble.

Proof Reverse, 2015:
Liberty Nurtures
Freedom.
Designer: Joel Iskowitz.

Proof Reverse, 2016:
Portrait of Liberty.
Designer: John Mercanti.

New Common
Reverse, "Preamble
to the Declaration of
Independence" series.
Designer: Patricia
Lucas-Morris.

Proof Obverse, 2018:
"Life."
Preamble to the
Declaration of
Independence series.
Designer: Justin Kunz.

Proof Obverse, 2019:
"Liberty."
Preamble to the
Declaration of
Independence series.
Designer: Justin Kunz.

	Mintage	MS	MS-69	MS-70
		PF	PF-69	PF-70
$100 1997 (a)	56,000	$1,250	$1,350	—
$100 1997-W, Proof	20,851	$1,450	$1,500	$2,900
$100 1998 (b)	133,002	$1,250	$1,350	—
$100 1998-W, Proof	14,912	$1,450	$1,500	$2,800
$100 1999 (c)	56,707	$1,250	$1,350	—
$100 1999-W, Proof (d)	12,363	$1,450	$1,500	$3,750

Note: MS values are for uncertified Mint State coins of average quality, in their complete original U.S. Mint packaging. PF values are for uncertified Proof coins of average quality, in their complete original U.S. Mint packaging. **a.** *Auction: $1,821, MS-69, July 2014.* **b.** *Auction: $1,704, MS-68, October 2012.* **c.** *Auction: $1,660, MS-69, November 2012.* **d.** *Auction: $1,645, PF69-UCam, March 2015.*

	Mintage	MS	MS-69	MS-70
		PF	PF-69	PF-70
$100 2000 (e)	10,003	$1,250	$1,350	—
$100 2000-W, Proof (f)	12,453	$1,450	$1,500	$2,300
$100 2001 (g)	14,070	$1,250	$1,350	—
$100 2001-W, Proof	8,969	$1,450	$1,500	$3,900
$100 2002 (h)	11,502	$1,250	$1,350	—
$100 2002-W, Proof (i)	9,834	$1,450	$1,500	$3,900
$100 2003	8,007	$1,250	$1,350	$3,750
$100 2003-W, Proof (j)	8,246	$1,450	$1,500	$3,900
$100 2004	7,009	$1,250	$1,350	$2,500
$100 2004-W, Proof (k)	6,007	$2,100	$2,150	$3,400
$100 2005	6,310	$1,250	$1,350	$2,500
$100 2005-W, Proof (l)	6,602	$2,300	$2,350	$3,000
$100 2006	6,000	$1,250	$1,350	$2,200
$100 2006-W, Burnished †† (m)	3,068	$2,100	$2,200	$2,400
$100 2006-W, Proof	9,152	$1,450	$1,500	$2,000
$100 2007	7,202	$1,250	$1,350	$2,100
$100 2007-W, Burnished	4,177	$1,900	$2,000	$2,200
$100 2007-W, Proof	8,363	$1,450	$1,500	$2,500
$100 2007-W, Frosted FREEDOM, Proof ††	12	—		
$100 2008	21,800	$1,250	$1,350	$1,950
$100 2008-W, Burnished (n)	2,876	$2,200	$2,300	$2,500
$100 2008-W, Proof (o)	4,769	$1,900	$1,950	$3,500
$100 2009-W, Proof ††	7,945	$1,800	$1,850	$2,000
$100 2010-W, Proof	14,790	$1,800	$1,850	$2,000
$100 2011-W, Proof	14,835	$1,550	$1,600	$1,750
$100 2012-W, Proof	10,084	$1,550	$1,600	$1,750
$100 2013-W, Proof	5,745	$1,950	$2,000	$2,500
$100 2014	16,900	$1,250	$1,350	$1,800
$100 2014-W, Proof	4,596	$2,300	$2,400	$2,900
$100 2015-W, Proof	3,881	$2,500	$2,600	$3,000
$100 2016	20,000	$1,000	$1,100	$1,400
$100 2016-W, Proof	9,151	$1,200	$1,250	$1,600
$100 2017	20,000	$1,000	$1,100	$1,400
$100 2017-W, Proof	8,892	$1,300	$1,350	$1,600
$100 2018	30,000	$1,000	$1,100	$1,400
$100 2018-W, Proof	12,411	$1,250	$1,300	$1,500
$100 2019		$950	$1,050	$1,200
$100 2019-W, Proof		$1,250	$1,300	$1,500

Note: MS values are for uncertified Mint State coins of average quality, in their complete original U.S. Mint packaging. PF values are for uncertified Proof coins of average quality, in their complete original U.S. Mint packaging. †† Ranked in the *100 Greatest U.S. Modern Coins* (fourth edition); all Proof 2007-W Platinum Eagles with Frosted FREEDOM, in all denominations, are as a single entry. **f.** Auction: $1,410, PF-70UCam, April 2015. **g.** Auction: $4,994, MS-69, April 2014. **h.** Auction: $1,645, MS-69, September 2012. **i.** Auction: $1,880, PF-70DCam, February 2015. **j.** Auction: $1,880, PF-70DCam, April 2015. **k.** Auction: $2,291, PF-70UCam, January 2015. **l.** Auction: $1,998, PF-70UCam, October 2015. **m.** Auction: $1,351, MS-69, November 2015. **n.** Auction: $1,880, MS-70, October 2015. **o.** Auction: $2,291, PF-70UCam, October 2015.

AMERICAN PLATINUM EAGLE BULLION COIN SETS

	MS	MS-69	MS-70
1997 Platinum Set. $100, $50, $25, $10	$2,350	$2,550	—
1998 Platinum Set. $100, $50, $25, $10	$2,350	$2,550	—
1999 Platinum Set. $100, $50, $25, $10	$2,350	$2,550	—
2000 Platinum Set. $100, $50, $25, $10	$2,350	$2,550	—

Note: MS values are for uncertified Mint State sets of average quality, in their complete original U.S. Mint packaging.

	MS	MS-69	MS-70
2001 Platinum Set. $100, $50, $25, $10	$2,350	$2,550	—
2002 Platinum Set. $100, $50, $25, $10	$2,350	$2,550	—
2003 Platinum Set. $100, $50, $25, $10	$2,350	$2,550	$5,700
2004 Platinum Set. $100, $50, $25, $10	$2,450	$2,650	$4,450
2005 Platinum Set. $100, $50, $25, $10	$2,400	$2,600	$4,450
2006 Platinum Set. $100, $50, $25, $10	$2,400	$2,600	$4,000
2006-W Platinum Burnished Set. $100, $50, $25, $10	$3,900	$4,200	$4,900
2007 Platinum Set. $100, $50, $25, $10	$2,400	$2,600	$3,900
2007-W Platinum Burnished Set. $100, $50, $25, $10	$3,400	$3,600	$4,000
2008 Platinum Set. $100, $50, $25, $10	$2,300	$2,500	$3,800
2008-W Platinum Burnished Set. $100, $50, $25, $10	$4,500	$4,800	$6,500

Note: MS values are for uncertified Mint State sets of average quality, in their complete original U.S. Mint packaging.

AMERICAN PLATINUM EAGLE PROOF COIN SETS

	PF	PF-69	PF-70
1997-W Platinum Set. $100, $50, $25, $10	$2,700	$2,850	$4,600
1998-W Platinum Set. $100, $50, $25, $10	$2,800	$2,950	$4,900
1999-W Platinum Set. $100, $50, $25, $10	$2,700	$2,850	$5,600
2000-W Platinum Set. $100, $50, $25, $10	$2,700	$2,900	$4,300
2001-W Platinum Set. $100, $50, $25, $10	$2,700	$2,900	$5,900
2002-W Platinum Set. $100, $50, $25, $10	$2,700	$2,900	$5,900
2003-W Platinum Set. $100, $50, $25, $10	$2,700	$2,900	$5,800
2004-W Platinum Set. $100, $50, $25, $10	$4,000	$4,200	$6,000
2005-W Platinum Set. $100, $50, $25, $10	$3,800	$4,000	$5,300
2006-W Platinum Set. $100, $50, $25, $10	$2,750	$2,900	$4,350
2007-W Platinum Set. $100, $50, $25, $10	$2,700	$2,850	$4,500
2008-W Platinum Set. $100, $50, $25, $10	$3,800	$4,000	$6,100

Note: PF values are for uncertified Proof sets of average quality, in their complete original U.S. Mint packaging. The Proof $100 American Platinum Eagle of 1997 is also included in the 1997 Impressions of Liberty set, listed on pages 1231 and 1243.

2007 AMERICAN PLATINUM EAGLE 10TH-ANNIVERSARY PROOF COIN SETS

	PF	PF-69	PF-70
2007 Two-Coin Set (a)	$1,500	$1,600	$1,900

a. This two-coin set, housed in a mahogany-finish hardwood box, includes one half-ounce Proof (with the standard cameo-finish background and frosted design elements) and one half-ounce Reverse Proof (with frosted background fields and mirrored raised elements) dated 2007-W.

AMERICAN PALLADIUM EAGLES
(2017 TO DATE)

Designer: *Adolph A. Weinman.* **Weight:** *31.120 grams (1 oz. pure palladium).* **Composition:** *.9995 palladium.* **Diameter:** *32.7 mm.* **Edge:** *Reeded.* **Mints:** *Philadelphia (bullion) and West Point (Proof).*

A side view showing the coin's high relief.

History. In 2017 palladium was added to the U.S. Mint's American Eagle bullion programs, becoming the fourth precious metal in the lineup.

The American Palladium Bullion Act of 2010 (Public Law 111-303) required the secretary of the Treasury to mint and issue .9995 fine palladium bullion coins weighing one troy ounce and with a face value of $25, "in such quantities as the secretary determines appropriate to meet demand." Only coins in the one-ounce size are permitted; fractional sizes are not authorized. Title 31 U.S.C. Section 5112(v) authorizes the secretary to mint and issue Proof and Burnished ("Uncirculated") versions for collectors.

The American Palladium Eagle's designs were mandated by law. The obverse is a high-relief allegorical portrait derived from artist Adolph Weinman's Winged Liberty dime of 1916 to 1945. The reverse is a high-relief version of Weinman's 1907 American Institute of Architects gold medal reverse, showing an eagle grasping a branch. To develop the coin, the Mint was able to use the original reverse plaster of the AIA gold medal.

Although largely symbolic, the palladium coin's denomination of $25 provides proof of its authenticity as official U.S. coinage.

Bullion-strike coins are minted in Philadelphia on an annual basis, and distributed through the Mint's network of authorized purchasers. A Proof version was struck at the West Point Mint in 2018, and sold by the Mint directly to collectors.

Striking and Sharpness. Striking is generally sharp.

Availability. The American Palladium Eagle is a readily available bullion and collector coin. The coins are easily acquired in the numismatic marketplace and through some banks, investment firms, and other non-numismatic channels.

MS-60 to 70 (Mint State). *Obverse and Reverse:* Grading guidelines are more academic than practical for this program, since American Palladium Eagles are not intended for circulation, and nearly all are in high Mint State grades.

PF-60 to 70 (Proof). *Obverse and Reverse:* Impaired, cleaned, and otherwise low-level Proofs exist more in theory than in actuality for this series, as nearly all Proof American Palladium Eagle coins have been maintained in their original high condition by collectors. Given the quality of modern U.S. Mint products, even PF-66 or 67 would be unusually low for these Proofs.

	Mintage	Value
2017	15,000	$1,900
2018-W, Proof	14,986	$2,200
2019-W		
2019-W, Reverse Proof		

Significant U.S. Patterns

Pattern coins are a fascinating part of numismatics that encompass thousands of designs and experimental pieces made by the U.S. Mint to test new motifs, alloys, coin sizes, and other variables. Most were official creations—products of the research-and-development process that takes a coin from congressionally authorized concept to finished pocket change. Some were made in secret, outside the normal day-to-day work of the Mint. The book *United States Pattern Coins*, by J. Hewitt Judd, gives extensive details of the history and characteristics of more than 2,000 different pattern varieties from 1792 to the present era.

Patterns provide students and collectors a chronology of the continuing efforts of engravers and artists to present their work for approval. Throughout the 220-plus years of federal coinage production, concepts meant to improve various aspects of circulating coins have been proposed and given physical form in patterns. In some instances, changes have been prompted by an outcry for higher aesthetics, a call for a more convenient denomination, or a need to overcome striking deficiencies. In many other instances, workers or officials at the Mint simply created special coins for the numismatic trade—often controversial in their time, but enthusiastically collected today. Certain patterns, bearing particular proposed designs or innovations, provided tangible examples for Mint and Treasury Department officials or members of Congress to review and evaluate. If approved and adopted, the pattern design became a familiar regular-issue motif; those that were rejected have become part of American numismatic history.

The patterns listed and illustrated in this section are samples from a much larger group. Such pieces generally include die and hub trials, off-metal Proof strikings of regular issues, and various combinations of dies that were sometimes struck at a later date. Certain well-known members of this extended pattern family historically have been included with regular issues in many popular, general-circulation numismatic reference books. The four-dollar gold Stellas of 1879 and 1880; certain Gobrecht dollars of 1836, 1838, and 1839; the transitional half dimes and dimes of 1859 and 1860; and the Flying Eagle cents of 1856 are examples. No official mintage figures of patterns and related pieces were recorded in most instances, and the number extant of each can usually only be estimated from auction appearances and from those found in museum holdings and important private collections. Although most patterns are very rare, the 2,000-plus distinct varieties make them unexpectedly collectible—not by one of each, but by selected available examples from favorite types or categories. Curiously, the most common of all patterns is the highly sought and expensive 1856 Flying Eagle cent!

Unlike regular coin issues that were emitted through the usual channels of commerce, and Proofs of regular issues that were struck expressly for sale to collectors, patterns were not intended to be officially sold. Yet as a matter of Mint practice, often against stated policy and law, countless patterns were secretly and unofficially sold and traded to favorite dealers (most notably William K. Idler and his son-in-law John W. Haseltine) and collectors, disseminated to government officials, and occasionally made available to numismatic societies. Not until mid-1885 did an incoming new director of the Mint enforce stringent regulations prohibiting their sale and distribution, although there had been many misleading statements to this effect earlier. In succeeding decades the Mint, while not making patterns available to numismatists, did place certain examples in the Mint Collection, now called the National Numismatic Collection, in the Smithsonian Institution. On other occasions, selected patterns were obtained by Mint and Treasury officials, or otherwise spared from destruction. Today, with the exception of certain cents and five-cent pieces of 1896, all pattern coins dated after 1885 are extremely rare.

The private possession of patterns has not been without its controversy. Most significant was the 1910 seizure by government agents of a parcel containing some 23 pattern pieces belonging to John W. Haseltine, a leading Philadelphia coin dealer with undisclosed private ties to Mint officials. The government asserted that the patterns had been removed from the Mint without authority, and that they remained the property of the United States. Haseltine's attorney successfully used the Mint's pre-1887 policies in his defense, and recovered the patterns a year after their confiscation. This set precedent for ownership, at least for the patterns minted prior to 1887, as all of the pieces in question predated that year. Today pattern coins can be legally held, and, in fact, they were inadvertently made legal tender (as was the earlier demonetized silver trade dollar) by the Coinage Act of 1965.

Among the grandest impressions ever produced at the U.S. Mint are the two varieties of pattern fifty-dollar gold pieces of 1877. Officially titled half unions, these large patterns were created at the request of certain politicians with interests tied to the gold-producing state of California. Specimens were struck in copper, and one of each variety was struck in gold. Both of the gold pieces were purchased around 1908 by numismatist William H. Woodin (who, years later, in 1933, served as President Franklin D. Roosevelt's first secretary of the Treasury). The sellers were John W. Haseltine and Stephen K. Nagy, well known for handling many rarities that few others could obtain from the Mint. The Mint desired to re-obtain the pieces for its own collection, and through a complex trade deal for quantities of other patterns, did so, adding them to the Mint Collection. Now preserved in the Smithsonian Institution, these half unions are regarded as national treasures.

The following resources are recommended for additional information, descriptions, and complete listings:

United States Pattern Coins, 10th edition, J. Hewitt Judd, edited by Q. David Bowers, 2009.

United States Patterns and Related Issues, Andrew W. Pollock III, 1994. (Out of print)

www.harrybassfoundation.org

www.uspatterns.com

Judd-52

J-67

	PF-60	PF-63	PF-65
1836 Two-cent piece (J-52, billon) (a)	$3,000	$5,000	$8,500
Auctions: $8,625, PF-65, January 2009			
1836 Gold dollar (J-67, gold) (b)	$7,500	$12,500	$30,000
Auctions: $24,725, PF-65, November 2010			

a. This proposal for a two-cent coin is one of the earliest collectible patterns. It was designed by Christian Gobrecht. An estimated 21 to 30 examples are known. b. Gobrecht styled the first gold dollar pattern after the familiar "Cap and Rays" design used on Mexican coins, which at the time were legal tender in the United States. An estimated 31 to 75 pieces are known.

J-164   J-177

	PF-60	PF-63	PF-65
1854 Cent (J-164, bronze) (a)	$1,750	$3,500	$7,500
Auctions: $16,100, PF-67BN, March 2005			
1856 Half cent (J-177, copper-nickel) (b)	$2,500	$4,500	$5,500
Auctions: $6,038, PF-64, January 2006			

a. Beginning in 1850, the Mint produced patterns for a reduced-weight cent. Among the designs were ring-style, Liberty Head, and Flying Eagle motifs. These experiments culminated with the 1856 Flying Eagle cent. An estimated 31 to 75 examples of J-164 are known. Those with red mint luster are worth more than the values listed here. **b.** Before producing copper-nickel small-size cents in 1856, the Mint experimented with that alloy using half-cent dies. An estimated 31 to 75 examples are known.

J-204   J-239

	PF-60	PF-63	PF-65
1858 Cent (J-204, copper-nickel) (a)	$1,600	$2,500	$4,000
1859 Half dollar (J-239, silver) (b)	$1,500	$2,000	$3,750

a. This pattern cent's flying eagle differs from the one adopted for regular coinage of the one-cent piece. An estimated 31 to 75 pieces are known. **b.** This design proposal for a new half dollar features James Longacre's French Liberty Head design. An estimated 76 to 200 pieces are known.

J-305

	PF-60	PF-63	PF-65
1863 Washington two-cent piece (J-305, copper) (a)	$1,500	$2,250	$4,000

a. Before the two-cent coin was introduced to circulation, two basic designs were considered. If this George Washington portrait design had been adopted, it would have been the first to depict a historical figure. An estimated 76 to 200 pieces are known.

J-349

J-407

J-470

	PF-60	PF-63	PF-65
1863 Eagle (J-349, gold) (a)		$450,000	
1865 Bimetallic two-cent piece (J-407, silver and copper) (b)	$6,000	$11,000	$19,500
1866 Five-cent piece (J-470, nickel) (c)	$1,650	$2,500	$4,500

a. This unique gold eagle features IN GOD WE TRUST on a scroll on the reverse. This feature would not appear on regular eagle coinage until 1866. The obverse is from the regular 1863 die. b. This experimental piece is the first "clad" coin. It consists of an irregular and streaky layer of silver fused to copper. The experiment was unsuccessful. An estimated 4 to 6 pieces are known. c. Another of George Washington's early pattern appearances was on five-cent pieces of 1866. An estimated 21 to 30 are known.

J-486

J-611

	PF-60	PF-63	PF-65
1866 Lincoln five-cent piece (J-486, nickel) (a)	$5,000	$11,000	$25,000
1868 Cent (J-611, copper) (b)	$17,500	$30,000	$36,000
Auctions: $36,800, PF-66BN, March 2005			

a. A number of pattern nickels were produced in 1866, including one designed to depict the recently assassinated President Abraham Lincoln. An estimated 7 to 12 examples are known. b. There is no known reason for the minting of this unusual piece, which mimics the original large cents that had last been made in 1857. There was no intent to resume the coinage of old-style copper "large" cents in 1868. Accordingly, this variety is regarded as a rarity created for collectors. Fewer than 15 examples are believed to exist.

J-1195

J-1235

	PF-60	PF-63	PF-65
1872 Amazonian quarter (J-1195, silver) (a)	$17,500	$30,000	$65,000
Auctions: $80,500, PF-66Cam, January 2009			
1872 Amazonian gold $3 (J-1235, gold) † (b)	—	—	$1,250,000

† All 1872 Amazonian Gold Patterns are ranked in the *100 Greatest U.S. Coins* (fourth edition), as a single entry. a. Many of the most popular patterns have been given colorful nicknames by collectors in appreciation of their artistry. This design is by Chief Engraver William Barber. An estimated 7 to 12 examples are known. b. This unique piece was contained in the Mint's only uniform gold set using the same design from the gold dollar to the double eagle.

J-1373

	PF-60	PF-63	PF-65
1874 Bickford eagle (J-1373, gold) † (a)	—	$550,000	$1,500,000

† Ranked in the *100 Greatest U.S. Coins* (fourth edition). **a.** Dana Bickford, a New York City manufacturer, proposed a ten-dollar gold coin that would be exchangeable at set rates with other world currencies. Patterns were made, but the idea proved impractical. 2 examples are known.

J-1392

	PF-60	PF-63	PF-65
1875 Sailor Head twenty-cent piece (J-1392, silver) (a)	$3,000	$5,500	$9,500

a. Chief Engraver William Barber's "Sailor Head" is one of the most elegant of several rejected designs for a twenty-cent coin. The same head was used on other patterns, including proposals for trade dollars. An estimated 21 to 30 examples of J-1392 are known.

J-1507

J-1512   J-1528

	PF-60	PF-63	PF-65
1877 Morgan half dollar (J-1507, copper) (a)	$18,000	$29,000	$50,000
1877 Morgan half dollar (J-1512, silver) (b)	$15,000	$28,000	$45,000
1877 Half dollar (J-1528, silver) (c)	$17,000	$33,000	$50,000

a. A year before his famous and eponymous dollar design was adopted for regular coinage, engraver George Morgan's Liberty Head appeared on several varieties of pattern half dollars, all of which are rare today. J-1507 pairs the well-known obverse with an indented shield design. 2 examples are known. **b.** The half dollar pattern cataloged as J-1512 pairs Morgan's "silver dollar style" obverse with a dramatic "Defiant Eagle" reverse. 6 examples are known. **c.** This is one of several 1877 pattern half dollars by Chief Engraver William Barber. 4 are known.

J-1549

	PF-60	PF-63	PF-65
1877 Half union (J-1549, copper) (a)	$115,000	$215,000	$350,000
Auctions: $575,000, PF-67BN, January 2009			

a. This famous fifty-dollar pattern by Chief Engraver William Barber would have been the highest denomination ever issued by the Mint up to that time. The gold impression (J-1548) is unique and resides in the Smithsonian's National Numismatic Collection, but copper specimens (J-1549, which are priced here and are sometimes gilt) occasionally come to the market. Varieties exist with a somewhat larger or smaller head. The gold impression is ranked in the *100 Greatest U.S. Coins* (fourth edition).

J-1590

	PF-60	PF-63	PF-65
1879 Quarter dollar (J-1590, silver) (a)	$4,500	$8,000	$16,500
Auctions: $34,500, PF-68, January 2007			

a. Referred to as the "Washlady" design, this was Charles Barber's first attempt at a uniform silver design. An estimated 13 to 20 examples are known.

J-1609

	PF-60	PF-63	PF-65
1879 Dollar (J-1609, copper) (a)	$12,500	$17,500	$45,000
Auctions: $74,750, PF-66RB, September 2006			

a. The "Schoolgirl" design by George T. Morgan is a widespread favorite among pattern collectors. Examples are rare, with only 7 to 12 known.

J-1643

	PF-60	PF-63	PF-65
1879 Metric double eagle (J-1643, gold) (a)	$325,000	$600,000	$1,000,000

a. James Longacre's Liberty Head design was the same as that used on regular-issue double eagles, but with an added inscription indicating the coin's specifications in metric units. 5 are known.

J-1667   J-1669   J-1673

	PF-60	PF-63	PF-65
1881 One-cent piece (J-1667, aluminum) (a)	$2,025	$3,780	$6,440
1881 Three-cent piece (J-1669, copper) (a)	$2,000	$3,750	$6,000
1881 Five-cent piece (J-1673, aluminum) (a)	$2,300	$4,800	$9,000

a. These patterns by Chief Engraver Charles Barber represent an attempt at a uniform set of minor coins; if adopted, they would have been struck in nickel for circulation. An estimated 7 to 20 examples are known of each of the illustrated patterns.

J-1698

	PF-60	PF-63	PF-65
1882 Quarter dollar (J-1698, silver) (a)	$17,500	$34,000	$55,000

a. George Morgan's "Shield Earring" design was made in patterns of quarter, half, and dollar denominations. 7 to 12 of the quarter dollar patterns are known.

J-1761   J-1770

	PF-60	PF-63	PF-65
1891 Barber quarter (J-1761, silver) (a)	—	—	—
1896 Shield nickel (J-1770, nickel) (b)	$1,500	$2,750	$4,000

a. Charles Barber prepared various pattern dimes, quarters, and half dollars in 1891. The quarter illustrated is similar to the design adopted for regular coinage in 1892. Two pieces are known, both in the Smithsonian's National Numismatic Collection. **b.** In 1896 the Mint struck experimental cents and nickels with similar designs, by Charles Barber. 21 to 30 examples of J-1770 are known.

J-1905

	PF-60	PF-63	PF-65
MCMVII (1907) Indian Head double eagle (J-1905, gold) † (a)			$15,000,000

† Ranked in the *100 Greatest U.S. Coins* (fourth edition). **a.** Designed by Augustus Saint-Gaudens, this pattern is unique and extremely valuable. A variation of the reverse of this design was used on the double eagles struck for circulation from 1907 through 1933.

J-1992

	PF-60	PF-63	PF-65
1916 Liberty Walking half dollar (J-1992, silver) (a)	$25,000	$50,000	$100,000
Auctions: $115,000, PF-65, July 2008			

a. Various pattern Mercury dimes, Standing Liberty quarters, and Liberty Walking half dollars were struck, all dated 1916. All are extremely rare, but a few found their way into circulation.

J-2063

	PF-60	PF-63	PF-65
1942 Experimental cent (J-2051 through J-2069, several metallic and other compositions) (a)	$1,500	$2,750	$4,500

a. Before settling on the zinc-coated steel composition used for the Lincoln cents of 1943, the Mint considered various alternative compositions, including plastics. Most were struck by outside contractors using specially prepared dies provided by the Mint. An estimated 7 to 12 examples are known of most types and colors.

Private and Territorial Gold

The expression *private gold*, used with reference to coins struck outside the United States Mint, is a general term. In the sense that no state or territory had authority to coin money, *private gold* simply refers to those necessity pieces of various shapes, denominations, and degrees of intrinsic worth that were coined by facilities other than official U.S. mints and circulated in isolated areas of the United States by assayers, bankers, and other private individuals and organizations. Some numismatists use the terms *territorial gold* and *state gold* to cover certain issues because they were coined and circulated in a territory or state. While the state of California properly sanctioned the ingots stamped by F.D. Kohler as state assayer, in no instance (except for the Mormon issues of Salt Lake City) were any of the gold pieces struck by authority of any of the territorial governments.

The stamped fifty-dollar and other gold coins, sometimes called *ingots*, but in coin form, were made by Augustus Humbert, the United States Assayer of Gold, but were not receivable at face value for government payments, despite the fact that Humbert was an official agent selected by the Treasury Department. However, such pieces circulated widely in commerce.

Usually, private coins were circulated due to a shortage of regular federal coinage. In the Western states particularly, official money became so scarce that gold itself—the very commodity the pioneers had come so far to acquire—was converted into a local medium of exchange.

Ephraim Brasher's New York doubloons of 1786 and 1787 are also private American gold issues and are described on page 125.

TEMPLETON REID

GEORGIA GOLD, 1830

The first private gold coinage in the 19th century was struck by Templeton Reid, a jeweler and gunsmith, in Milledgeville, Georgia, in July 1830. To be closer to the mines he moved some 120 miles northwest to Gainesville, where most of his coins were made. Although their weights were accurate, Reid's assays were not and his coins were slightly short of their claimed value. He was severely attacked in the newspapers by a determined adversary, and soon lost the public's confidence. He closed his mint before the end of October in 1830; his output had amounted to only about 1,600 coins. Denominations struck were $2.50, $5, and $10. All are great rarities today.

	VF	EF	AU	Unc.
1830 $2.50	$150,000	$185,000	$300,000	$425,000
1830 $5 (a)	$400,000	$575,000	$725,000	

a. 7 examples are known.

	VF	EF
1830 TEN DOLLARS (a)	$700,000	$975,000
(No Date) TEN DOLLARS (b)	—	

a. 6 examples are known. **b.** 3 examples are known.

CALIFORNIA GOLD, 1849

The enigmatic later issues of Templeton Reid, dated 1849 and marked CALIFORNIA GOLD, were probably made from California gold late in that year when bullion from California arrived in quantity in the East. Reid, who never went to California, was by then a cotton-gin maker in Columbus, Georgia (some 160 miles southwest of his former location of Gainesville), where he would die in 1851. The coins were in denominations of ten and twenty-five dollars. Struck copies of both exist in various metals.

The only example known of the twenty-five–dollar piece was stolen from the cabinet of the U.S. Mint on August 16, 1858. It was never recovered.

1849 TEN DOLLAR CALIFORNIA GOLD	*(unique, in Smithsonian collection)*
1849 TWENTY-FIVE DOLLARS CALIFORNIA GOLD	*(unknown)*

THE BECHTLERS, RUTHERFORD COUNTY, NORTH CAROLINA, 1831–1852

A skilled German metallurgist, Christopher Bechtler, assisted by his son August and his nephew, also named Christopher, operated a private mint in Rutherford County, North Carolina. Rutherford County and other areas in the Piedmont region of North Carolina and Georgia (from the coastal plain to the mountains of north Georgia) were the principal sources of the nation's gold supply from the early 1800s until the California gold strikes in 1848.

The coins minted by the Bechtlers were of only three denominations, but they covered a wide variety of weights and sizes. Rotated dies are common throughout the series. In 1831, the Bechtlers produced the first gold dollar in the United States. (The Philadelphia Mint made patterns in 1836 and struck its first circulating gold dollar in 1849.) Bechtler coins were well accepted by the public and circulated widely in the Southeast without interference from the government.

The legend AUGUST 1. 1834 on several varieties of five-dollar pieces has a special significance. The secretary of the Treasury recommended to the director of the U.S. Mint that gold coins of the reduced weight introduced in 1834 bear the authorization date. This ultimately was not done on federal gold coinage, but the elder Christopher Bechtler evidently acted on the recommendation to avoid potential difficulty with Treasury authorities.

CHRISTOPHER BECHTLER

	VF	EF	AU	Unc.
ONE GOLD DOLLAR N. CAROLINA, 30.G., Star		$4,500	$7,000	$15,000
ONE GOLD DOLLAR N. CAROLINA, 28.G Centered, No Star	$5,000	$6,000	$11,500	$26,000
ONE GOLD DOLLAR N. CAROLINA, 28.G High, No Star	$9,000	$15,000	$23,000	$35,000

	VF	EF	AU	Unc.
ONE DOLLAR CAROLINA, 28.G, N Reversed	$2,600	$3,200	$4,750	$8,250
2.50 NORTH CAROLINA, 20 C. Without 75 G.	$28,000	$38,500	$57,500	$120,000

	VF	EF	AU	Unc.
2.50 NORTH CAROLINA, 75 G., 20 C. RUTHERFORD in a Circle. Border of Large Beads	$26,000	$36,000	$52,500	$115,000
2.50 NORTH CAROLINA, 20 C. Without 75 G., CAROLINA above 250 instead of GOLD (a)				—
2.50 NORTH CAROLINA, 20 C. on Obverse, 75 G. and Star on Reverse. Border Finely Serrated	—	—	—	

a. This piece is unique.

	VF	EF	AU	Unc.
2.50 CAROLINA, 67 G., 21 CARATS	$8,000	$13,000	$17,500	$33,000
2.50 GEORGIA, 64 G., 22 CARATS (Uneven "22")	$7,500	$12,500	$16,500	$32,000
2.50 GEORGIA, 64 G., 22 CARATS (Even "22")	$9,000	$15,000	$20,000	$40,000
2.50 CAROLINA, 70 G., 20 CARATS	$7,500	$12,500	$16,500	$32,000

	VF	EF	AU	Unc.
5 DOLLARS NORTH CAROLINA GOLD, 150 G., 20.CARATS	$28,000	$40,000	$72,000	$120,000
Similar, Without 150.G. (a)		—	—	

a. 1 or 2 examples are known.

CHRISTOPHER BECHTLER, CAROLINA

	VF	EF	AU	Unc.
5 DOLLARS CAROLINA, RUTHERFORD, 140 G., 20 CARATS, Plain Edge	$6,000	$8,500	$12,500	$26,000
5 DOLLARS CAROLINA, RUTHERFORD, 140 G., 20 CARATS, Reeded Edge	$20,000	$30,000	$45,000	$70,000
5 DOLLARS CAROLINA GOLD, RUTHERF., 140 G., 20 CARATS, AUGUST 1, 1834	$11,000	$18,000	$30,000	$50,000
Similar, but "20" Distant From CARATS	$6,500	$10,000	$15,000	$27,500
5 DOLLARS CAROLINA GOLD, 134 G., 21 CARATS, With Star	$6,000	$8,000	$12,000	$24,000

CHRISTOPHER BECHTLER, GEORGIA

	VF	EF	AU	Unc.
5 DOLLARS GEORGIA GOLD, RUTHERFORD, 128 G., 22 CARATS	$8,500	$12,000	$16,500	$33,000
5 DOLLARS GEORGIA GOLD, RUTHERFORD, 128 G:, 22 CARATS, With Colon After G	$16,000	$26,000	$38,500	
5 DOLLARS GEORGIA GOLD, RUTHERF., 128 G., 22 CARATS	$8,000	$11,500	$15,000	$32,000

AUGUST BECHTLER, CAROLINA

	VF	EF	AU	Unc.
1 DOL:, CAROLINA GOLD, 27.G., 21.C	$1,800	$2,400	$3,200	$5,500
5 DOLLARS, CAROLINA GOLD, 134.G:, 21 CARATS	$6,000	$8,750	$15,000	$36,000
5 DOLLARS, CAROLINA GOLD, 134 G:, 21 CARATS, Reverse of C. Bechtler as Shown Above	—	—		

	VF	EF	AU	Unc.
5 DOLLARS, CAROLINA GOLD, 128.G., 22 CARATS	$15,000	$18,000	$27,500	$45,000
5 DOLLARS, CAROLINA GOLD, 141.G., 20 CARATS	$12,500	$17,000	$25,000	$40,000

Note: Restrikes in "Proof" of this type using original dies were made about 1920.

NORRIS, GREGG & NORRIS, SAN FRANCISCO, 1849

Collectors consider this piece the first of the California private gold coins. A newspaper account dated May 31, 1849, described a five-dollar gold coin, struck at Benicia City, though with the imprint of San Francisco. It mentioned the private stamp of Norris, Gregg & Norris, the California branch of a New York City plumbing and hardware firm.

	F	VF	EF	AU	Unc.
1849 Half Eagle, Plain Edge	$4,750	$7,000	$12,000	$17,000	$37,000
1849 Half Eagle, Reeded Edge	$4,750	$7,000	$12,000	$17,000	$37,000
1850 Half Eagle, With STOCKTON Beneath Date (a)		—			

a. This unique piece is housed in the Smithsonian's National Numismatic Collection.

MOFFAT & CO., SAN FRANCISCO, 1849–1853

The firm of Moffat & Co. (principals John Little Moffat, Joseph R. Curtis, Philo H. Perry, and Samuel H. Ward) was the most important of the California private coiners. The assay office they conducted became semi-official in character starting in 1851. The successors to this firm, Curtis, Perry, and Ward, later sold their coining facility to the Treasury Department, which in March 1854 reopened it as the branch mint of San Francisco.

In June or July 1849, Moffat & Co. began to issue small, rectangular ingots of gold in response to lack of coin in the locality, in values from $9.43 to $264. The $9.43, $14.25, and $16.00 varieties are the only types known today.

$9.43 Ingot (a)	—
$14.25 Ingot (a)	—
$16.00 Ingot	$225,000

a. This unique piece is housed in the Smithsonian's National Numismatic Collection..

The dies for the five-dollar and ten-dollar Moffat & Co. pieces were cut by a Bavarian engraver, Albrecht Küner, who had moved to the United States in October 1848. On the coronet of Miss Liberty appear the words MOFFAT & CO., instead of the word LIBERTY as in regular U.S. issues.

	F	VF	EF	AU	Unc.
1849 FIVE DOL. (a)	$2,200	$3,300	$4,700	$7,000	$15,000
1850 FIVE DOL. (a)	$2,200	$3,500	$5,000	$7,500	$17,500
1849 TEN DOL.	$4,000	$6,500	$12,500	$22,500	$38,000
1849 TEN D.	$5,000	$7,000	$13,500	$25,000	$45,000

a. Multiple varieties exist.

UNITED STATES ASSAY OFFICE
AUGUSTUS HUMBERT, UNITED STATES ASSAYER OF GOLD, 1851

Augustus Humbert, a New York watchcase maker, was appointed United States assayer by the Treasury Department in 1850 and arrived in California in early 1851. He placed his name and the government stamp on the ingots of gold issued by Moffat & Co., but without the Moffat imprint. The assay office, a provisional government mint, was a temporary expedient to accommodate the Californians until the establishment of a permanent federal branch mint.

The fifty-dollar gold piece was accepted by most banks and merchants as legal tender on a par with standard U.S. gold coins and was known variously as a *slug*, *quintuple eagle*, *five-eagle piece*, or *adobe* (the latter a type of construction brick). It was officially termed an *ingot*.

LETTERED-EDGE VARIETIES

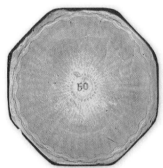

	F	VF	EF	AU	Unc.
1851 50 D C 880 THOUS., No 50 on Reverse. Sunk in Edge: AUGUSTUS HUMBERT UNITED STATES ASSAYER OF GOLD, CALIFORNIA 1851 †	$25,000	$36,000	$60,000	$90,000	$200,000
Auctions: $546,250, MS-63, August 2010					
1851 50 D C 880 THOUS., Similar to Last Variety, but 50 on Reverse †	$50,000	$60,000	$90,000	$160,000	$300,000
1851 50 D C, 887 THOUS., With 50 on Reverse †	$30,000	$50,000	$75,000	$115,000	$250,000

† All U.S. Assay Office $50 Gold Slugs are ranked in the *100 Greatest U.S. Coins* (fourth edition), as a single entry.

REEDED-EDGE VARIETIES

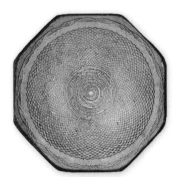

	F	VF	EF	AU	Unc.
1851 FIFTY DOLLS, 880 THOUS., "Target" Reverse †	$16,500	$25,000	$40,000	$52,000	$150,000
Auctions: $460,000, MS-65, September 2008					
1851 FIFTY DOLLS, 887 THOUS., "Target" Reverse †	$16,500	$25,000	$40,000	$52,000	$150,000
1852 FIFTY DOLLS, 887 THOUS., "Target" Reverse †	$17,000	$27,000	$50,000	$95,000	$200,000

† All U.S. Assay Office $50 Gold Slugs are ranked in the *100 Greatest U.S. Coins* (fourth edition), as a single entry.

MOFFAT-HUMBERT

In 1851, certain issues of the Miners' Bank, Baldwin, Pacific Company, and others were discredited, some unfairly, by newspaper accounts stating they were of reduced gold value. This provided an enhanced opportunity for Moffat and the U.S. Assay Office of Gold. Supplementing privately struck gold pieces and federal issues, coins of almost every nation were being pressed into service by the Californians, but the supply was too small to help to any extent. Moffat & Co. proceeded in January 1852 to issue a new ten-dollar gold piece bearing the stamp MOFFAT & CO.

Close Date   **Wide Date**

	F	VF	EF	AU	Unc.
1852 TEN D. MOFFAT & CO., Close Date	$4,200	$7,000	$25,000	$65,000	
1852 TEN D. MOFFAT & CO., Wide Date	$4,200	$7,000	$15,000	$35,000	$77,500
Auctions: $940,000, SP-63, January 2014					

1852, Normal Date   **1852, 2 Over 1**

	F	VF	EF	AU	Unc.
1852 TEN DOLS.	$2,750	$4,250	$7,500	$12,000	$27,500
Auctions: $1,057,500, MS-68, April 2013					
1852 TEN DOLS. 1852, 2 Over 1	$2,850	$5,250	$9,500	$20,000	$50,000

	F	VF	EF	AU	Unc.
1852 TWENTY DOLS., 1852, 2 Over 1	$8,250	$14,000	$27,500	$45,000	$140,000
Auctions: $211,500, MS-64, April 2014					

UNITED STATES ASSAY OFFICE OF GOLD, 1852

The firm of Moffat & Co. was dissolved in 1852 and a newly reorganized company known as the United States Assay Office of Gold took over the contract. Principals in the firm were Joseph Curtis, Philo Perry, and Samuel Ward.

 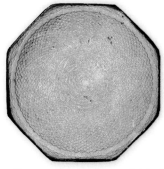

	F	VF	EF	AU	Unc.
1852 FIFTY DOLLS., 887 THOUS.	$16,500	$25,000	$40,000	$65,000	$150,000
1852 FIFTY DOLLS., 900 THOUS.	$17,500	$27,000	$42,000	$55,000	$125,000

	F	VF	EF	AU	Unc.
1852 TEN DOLS., 884 THOUS.	$2,500	$3,500	$5,250	$9,500	$22,500
1853 TEN D., 884 THOUS.	$10,000	$20,000	$30,000	$45,000	$125,000
1853 TEN D., 900 THOUS.	$4,500	$6,500	$10,000	$16,000	$25,000

	F	VF	EF	AU	Unc.
1853 TWENTY D., 884 THOUS.	$7,800	$11,500	$19,000	$32,000	$75,000

	F	VF	EF	AU	Unc.
1853 TWENTY D., 900 THOUS.	$2,400	$3,500	$5,000	$8,000	$13,000

Note: Modern prooflike forgeries exist.

Moffat & Co. Gold, 1853

The last Moffat & Co. issue, an 1853 twenty-dollar piece, is very similar to the U.S. double eagle of that period. It was struck after John L. Moffat retired from the Assay Office. The circumstances of its issue are unclear, but many were coined.

	F	VF	EF	AU	Unc.
1853 TWENTY D.	$4,750	$7,000	$11,000	$20,000	$65,000

J.H. BOWIE, 1849

Joseph H. Bowie joined his cousins in San Francisco in 1849 and possibly produced a limited coinage of gold pieces. A trial piece of the dollar denomination is known in copper, but may never have reached the coinage stage. Little is known about the company or the reason for considering these pieces.

1849 1 DOL., copper pattern	—

CINCINNATI MINING & TRADING CO., 1849

The origin and location of this company are unknown.

	EF	Unc.
1849 FIVE DOLLARS (a)		
1849 TEN DOLLARS (b)	$750,000	—

Note: Beware of spurious specimens cast in base metal with the word TRACING in place of TRADING. **a.** This piece is unique. **b.** 5 examples are known.

MASSACHUSETTS AND CALIFORNIA COMPANY, 1849

This company was organized in Northampton, Massachusetts, in May 1849. Years later fantasy and copy dies were made and coins struck in various metals including gold. Pieces with the denomination spelled as 5D are not genuine.

	VF	EF
1849 FIVE D. (a)	$185,000	$475,000

a. 5 to 7 examples are known.

MINERS' BANK, SAN FRANCISCO, 1849

The institution of Wright & Co., exchange brokers located in Portsmouth Square, San Francisco, was known as the Miners' Bank. The firm issued a ten-dollar gold piece in the autumn of 1849, and it saw wide use in commerce. However, the firm's coinage was ephemeral, and it was dissolved on January 14, 1850. Unlike the gold in most California issues, the gold in these coins was alloyed with copper.

	VF	EF	AU	Unc.
(1849) TEN D.	$19,000	$34,000	$50,000	$110,000

J.S. ORMSBY, SACRAMENTO, 1849

The initials J.S.O., which appear on certain issues of California privately coined gold pieces, represent the firm of J.S. Ormsby & Co., located in Sacramento. They struck five- and ten-dollar denominations, all undated.

	VF
(1849) 5 DOLLS, Plain Edge (a)	—
(1849) 5 DOLLS, Reeded Edge (b)	—
(1849) 10 DOLLS (c)	$650,000

a. This piece may be unique. **b.** This unique piece is housed in the Smithsonian's National Numismatic Collection. **c.** 4 examples are known.

PACIFIC COMPANY, SAN FRANCISCO, 1849

The origin of the Pacific Company is very uncertain. All data regarding the firm are based on conjecture.

Edgar H. Adams wrote that he believed that the coins bearing the stamp of the Pacific Company were produced by the coining firm of Broderick and Kohler. The coins were probably hand struck with the aid of a sledgehammer. Trial pieces exist in silver. All are rarities today.

	EF	AU	Unc.
1849 1 DOLLAR (a)			$300,000
1849 5 DOLLARS (b)	$500,000	$750,000	
Auctions: $763,750, AU-58, April 2014			
1849 10 DOLLARS (c)	$600,000	$800,000	$1,000,000

a. 2 examples are known. b. 4 examples are known. c. 4 examples are known.

F.D. KOHLER, CALIFORNIA STATE ASSAYER, 1850

The State Assay Office was authorized on April 12, 1850. That year, Governor Peter Burnett appointed to the position of state assayer Frederick D. Kohler, who thereupon sold his assaying business to Baldwin & Co. Kohler served at both the San Francisco and Sacramento offices. The State Assay Offices were discontinued at the time the U.S. Assay Office was established, on February 1, 1851.

Ingots issued ranged from $36.55 to $150. An Extremely Fine specimen sold in the Garrett Sale, 1980, for $200,000. Each is unique.

$36.55 Sacramento	—
$37.31 San Francisco	—
$40.07 San Francisco	—
$45.34 San Francisco	—
$50.00 San Francisco	—
$54.00 San Francisco	—

Note: A $40.07 ingot was stolen from the Mint Cabinet in 1858 and never recovered.

DUBOSQ & COMPANY, SAN FRANCISCO, 1850

Theodore Dubosq Sr., a Philadelphia jeweler, took melting and coining equipment to San Francisco in 1849 and minted five-dollar gold pieces.

	VF
1850 FIVE D. (a)	—
1850 TEN D. (b)	$300,000
Auctions: $329,000, MS-60, April 2014	

a. 3 to 5 examples are known. **b.** 8 to 10 examples are known.

BALDWIN & CO., SAN FRANCISCO, 1850–1851

George C. Baldwin and Thomas S. Holman were in the jewelry business in San Francisco and were known as Baldwin & Co. They were the successors to F.D. Kohler & Co., taking over its machinery and other equipment in May 1850. The firm ceased minting coins in early 1851, at which time newspaper accounts stated that its coins fell short of their stated gold value. The 1850 Vaquero or Horseman ten-dollar design is one of the most famous of the California gold issues.

	F	VF	EF	AU	Unc.
1850 FIVE DOL.	$7,500	$13,000	$25,000	$35,000	$75,000
1850, TEN DOLLARS, Horseman Type	$45,000	$80,000	$125,000	$175,000	$350,000

	F	VF	EF	AU	Unc.
1851 TEN D.	$16,000	$34,000	$50,000	$85,000	$225,000

The Baldwin & Co. twenty-dollar piece was the first of that denomination issued in California. Baldwin coins are believed to have contained about 2% copper alloy.

	EF	Unc.
1851 TWENTY D. (a)	$650,000	—
Auctions: $646,250, EF-45, April 2014		

a. 4 to 6 examples are known.

SCHULTZ & COMPANY, SAN FRANCISCO, 1851

The firm of Schultz & Co., a brass foundry, was operated by Judge G.W. Schultz and William T. Garratt. The surname is misspelled as SHULTZ on the coins.

	F	VF	EF	AU	Unc.
1851 FIVE D.	—	$75,000	$130,000	$235,000	$350,000

DUNBAR & COMPANY, SAN FRANCISCO, 1851

Edward E. Dunbar operated the California Bank in San Francisco. He later returned to New York City and organized the famous Continental Bank Note Co.

	VF	EF	Unc.
1851 FIVE D. (a)	$400,000	$550,000	$750,000

a. 4 to 6 examples are known.

WASS, MOLITOR & CO., SAN FRANCISCO, 1852–1855

The gold-smelting and assaying plant of Wass, Molitor & Co. was operated by two Hungarian patriots exiled after the Revolution of 1848, Count Samu Wass and A.P. Molitor. They maintained an excellent laboratory and complete apparatus for analysis and coinage of gold.

The company struck five-, ten-, twenty-, and fifty-dollar coins. In 1852 they produced a ten-dollar piece similar in design to the five-dollar denomination. The difference is in the reverse legend, which reads: S.M.V. [Standard Mint Value] CALIFORNIA GOLD TEN D.

No pieces were coined in 1853 or 1854, but they brought out the twenty- and fifty-dollar pieces in 1855. A considerable number of the fifty-dollar coins were made. There was a ten-dollar piece issued in 1855 also, with the Liberty Head design and small close date.

Small Head, Rounded Bust

Large Head, Pointed Bust

	F	VF	EF	AU	Unc.
1852 FIVE DOLLARS, Small Head, With Rounded Bust	$5,500	$11,000	$22,500	$40,000	$80,000
1852 FIVE DOLLARS, Large Head, With Pointed Bust	$5,000	$10,000	$20,000	$36,000	$70,000

Large Head

Small Head   **Small Date**   **1855**

	F	VF	EF	AU	Unc.
1852 TEN D., Large Head	$2,750	$4,750	$8,250	$14,500	$32,500
1852 TEN D., Small Head	$6,200	$8,000	$19,000	$32,000	$80,000
1852 TEN D., Small Close Date	$12,500	$28,000	$47,000	$90,000	
1855 TEN D.	$9,500	$16,000	$22,000	$29,000	$52,500

Large Head   **Small Head**

	F	VF	EF	AU	Unc.
1855 TWENTY DOL., Large Head (a)	—	—	$550,000	$675,000	—
Auctions: $558,125, AU-53, April 2014					
1855 TWENTY DOL., Small Head	$12,000	$25,000	$35,000	$75,000	$165,000

a. 4 to 6 examples are known. A unique piece with the Large Head obverse and the reverse used on the Small Head coins (which differs in the position of the eagle's left wing) also exists.

	F	VF	EF	AU	Unc.
1855 50 DOLLARS	$25,000	$36,000	$55,000	$85,000	$180,000

KELLOGG & CO., SAN FRANCISCO, 1854–1855

John G. Kellogg went to San Francisco on October 12, 1849, from Auburn, New York. At first he was employed by Moffat & Co., and remained with that organization when control passed to Curtis, Perry, and Ward. When the U.S. Assay Office was discontinued, December 14, 1853, Kellogg became associated with George F. Richter, who had been an assayer in the U.S. Assay Office of Gold. These two set up business as Kellogg & Richter on December 19, 1853.

When the U.S. Assay Office ceased operations, a period ensued during which no private firm was striking gold. The new San Francisco branch mint did not produce coins for some months after Curtis & Perry took the contract for the government (Ward having died). The lack of coin was again keenly felt by businessmen, who petitioned Kellogg & Richter to "supply the vacuum" by issuing private coin. Their plea was soon answered: on February 9, 1854, Kellogg & Co. placed their first twenty-dollar piece in circulation.

The firm dissolved late in 1854 and reorganized as Kellogg & Humbert. The latter partner was Augustus Humbert, for some time identified as U.S. assayer of gold in California. Regardless of the fact that the San Francisco branch mint was then producing coins, Kellogg & Humbert issued twenty-dollar coins in 1855 in a quantity greater than before. On September 12, 1857, hundreds of the firm's rectangular gold ingots in transit to New York City were lost in the sinking of the SS *Central America*. They were the most plentiful of bars aboard the ill-fated ship from several different assayers.

	F	VF	EF	AU	Unc.
1854 TWENTY D.	$3,250	$4,750	$6,500	$10,000	$25,000

The 1855 Kellogg & Co. twenty-dollar piece is similar to that of 1854. The letters on the reverse are larger and the arrows longer on one 1854 variety. There are die varieties of both.

	F	VF	EF	AU	Unc.
1855 TWENTY D.	$3,500	$5,000	$7,000	$12,000	$27,500

In 1855, Ferdinand Grüner cut the dies for a round-format fifty-dollar gold coin for Kellogg & Co., but coinage seems to have been limited to presentation pieces in Proof format. Only 10 to 12 pieces are known to exist. A "commemorative restrike" was made in 2001 using transfer dies made from the original and gold recovered from the SS *Central America*. These pieces have the inscription S.S. CENTRAL AMERICA GOLD, C.H.S. on the reverse ribbon.

	PF
1855 FIFTY DOLLS. (a)	$600,000
Auctions: $763,750, PF-64Cam, April 2014; $747,500, PF-64, January 2007	

a. 13 to 15 examples are known.

OREGON EXCHANGE COMPANY, OREGON CITY, 1849

THE BEAVER COINS OF OREGON

Upon the discovery of gold in California, a great exodus of Oregonians joined in the hunt for the precious metal. Soon, gold seekers returned with their gold dust, which became an accepted medium of exchange. As in other Western areas at that time, the uncertain qualities of the gold and weighing devices tended to irk tradespeople, and petitions were made to the legislature for a standard gold coin issue.

On February 16, 1849, the territorial legislature passed an act providing for a mint and specified five- and ten-dollar gold coins without alloy. Oregon City, the largest city in the territory with a population of about 1,000, was designated as the location for the mint. At the time this act was passed, Oregon had been brought into the United States as a territory by act of Congress. When the new governor arrived on March 2, he declared the coinage act unconstitutional.

The public-spirited people, however, continued to work for a convenient medium of exchange and soon took matters into their own hands by starting a private mint. Eight men of affairs, whose names were Kilborne, Magruder, Taylor, Abernethy, Willson, Rector, Campbell, and Smith, set up the Oregon Exchange Company.

The coins struck were of virgin gold as specified in the original act. Ten-dollar dies were made slightly later.

	F	VF	EF	AU	Unc.
1849 5 D.	$32,000	$50,000	$75,000	$125,000	$275,000

	F	VF	EF	AU	Unc.
1849 TEN.D.	$80,000	$145,000	$270,000	$350,000	—

MORMON GOLD PIECES,
SALT LAKE CITY, UTAH, 1849–1860

The first name given to the organized Mormon Territory was the "State of Deseret," the last word meaning "honeybee" in the Book of Mormon. The beehive, which is shown on the reverse of the five-dollar 1860 piece, was a favorite device of the followers of Joseph Smith and Brigham Young. The clasped hands appear on most Mormon coins and exemplify strength in unity. HOLINESS TO THE LORD was an inscription frequently used.

Brigham Young was the instigator of the coinage system and personally supervised the mint, which was housed in a little adobe building in Salt Lake City. The mint was inaugurated late in 1848 as a public convenience and to make a profit for the church. Each coin had substantially less gold than the face value stated.

	F	VF	EF	AU	Unc.
1849 TWO.AND.HALF.DO.	$12,500	$23,000	$35,000	$57,000	$90,000
1849 FIVE.DOLLARS	$9,500	$18,500	$30,000	$40,000	$75,000

	F	VF	EF	AU
1849 TEN.DOLLARS	$375,000	$550,000	$700,000	$800,000
Auctions: $705,000, AU-58, April 2014				

	F	VF	EF	AU	Unc.
1849 TWENTY.DOLLARS (a)	$95,000	$175,000	$275,000	$375,000	$525,000
Auctions: $558,125, MS-62, April 2014					

a. The first coin of the twenty-dollar denomination to be struck in the United States.

	F	VF	EF	AU	Unc.
1850 FIVE DOLLARS	$13,000	$22,000	$34,000	$47,500	$85,000

	F	VF	EF	AU	Unc.
1860 5.D.	$20,000	$32,000	$42,000	$65,000	$90,000

COLORADO GOLD PIECES

CLARK, GRUBER & CO., DENVER, 1860–1861

Clark, Gruber & Co. was a well-known private minting firm in Denver, Colorado, in 1860 and 1861, formed by bankers from Leavenworth, Kansas Territory. In 1862 their operation was purchased by the Treasury Department and thenceforth operated as an assay office.

	F	VF	EF	AU	Unc.
1860 2 1/2 D.	$1,900	$3,000	$4,200	$5,700	$13,500
1860 FIVE D.	$2,200	$3,000	$4,500	$6,250	$14,500

	F	VF	EF	AU	Unc.
1860 TEN D.	$9,000	$15,000	$21,000	$30,000	$55,000
1860 TWENTY D.	$70,000	$135,000	$250,000	$385,000	$650,000
Auctions: $690,000, MS-64, January 2006					

The $2.50 and $5 pieces of 1861 follow closely the designs of the 1860 issues. The main difference is found in the legends. The reverse side now has CLARK GRUBER & CO. DENVER. On the obverse, PIKES PEAK now appears on the coronet of Miss Liberty.

	F	VF	EF	AU	Unc.
1861 2 1/2 D.	$1,900	$3,000	$4,400	$7,500	$14,000
1861 FIVE D.	$2,300	$3,700	$5,750	$11,500	$37,500
1861 TEN D.	$2,400	$4,200	$6,750	$11,500	$28,500

	F	VF	EF	AU	Unc.
1861 TWENTY D.	$20,000	$40,000	$60,000	$100,000	$235,000

JOHN PARSONS & COMPANY, TARRYALL MINES, COLORADO, 1861

Very little is known regarding the mint of John Parsons and Co., although it is reasonably certain that it operated in the South Park section of Park County, Colorado, near the original town of Tarryall, in the summer of 1861.

	VF	EF
(1861) Undated 2 1/2 D. (a)	$200,000	$300,000
(1861) Undated FIVE D. (b)	$275,000	$375,000

a. 6 to 8 examples are known. **b.** 5 or 6 examples are known.

J.J. CONWAY & CO., GEORGIA GULCH, COLORADO, 1861

Records show that the Conway mint operated for a short while in 1861. As in all gold-mining areas the value of gold dust caused disagreement among the merchants and the miners. The firm of J.J. Conway & Co. solved this difficulty by bringing out its gold pieces in August 1861.

	VF	EF	AU
(1861) Undated 2 1/2 DOLL'S (a)		$450,000	$650,000
(1861) Undated FIVE DOLLARS (b)	$475,000	$650,000	

a. 8 to 12 examples are known. **b.** 5 to 8 examples are known.

(1861) Undated TEN DOLLARS (a)	—

a. 3 examples are known.

CALIFORNIA SMALL-DENOMINATION GOLD

There was a scarcity of small coins during the California gold rush. Starting in 1852, quarter, half, and dollar coins were privately minted from native gold to alleviate the shortage. The commercial acceptability of these hard-to-handle, underweight coins was always limited, but they soon became popular as souvenirs. Early coins contained up to 85% of face value in gold. The amount and quality of gold in the coins soon decreased, and some later issues are merely gold plated.

The Coinage Act of April 22, 1864, made private coinage illegal, but the law was not fully enforced until 1883. In compliance with the law, non-denominated tokens were made, and from 1872 until 1883 both coins and tokens were produced. After 1883, most of the production was tokens. To circumvent the law, and to make them more acceptable, some pieces made after 1881 were backdated to the 1850s or 1860s.

Early issues have Liberty heads; later issues have Indian heads and often are prooflike. Most have a wreath on the reverse, but some have original designs. About 35,000 pieces are believed to exist. Numismatists have identified more than 570 different varieties, many of them very rare. The quality of strike and edge treatment is inconsistent. Many bear their makers' initials: D, DERI, DERIB, DN, FD, G, GG, GL, H, L, N, or NR. Major denominated coins are listed below; values are for the most common variety of each type. Non-denominated tokens are not included in these listings. They are much less valuable. ***Beware of extremely common modern replicas*** (often having a bear in the design), which have little numismatic value.

The values in the following charts are only for coins made before 1883 with the denomination on the reverse expressed as CENTS, DOL., DOLL., or DOLLAR.

QUARTER DOLLAR, OCTAGONAL

	EF	AU	Unc.
Large Liberty Head / Value and Date in Wreath	$175	$250	$450
Large Liberty Head / Value and Date in Beaded Circle	$175	$275	$470
Large Liberty Head / Value and CAL in Wreath	$175	$230	$350
Small Liberty Head / Value and Date in Wreath	$170	$230	$320
Small Liberty Head / Value and Date in Beaded Circle	$175	$250	$340
Small Liberty Head / Value in Shield, Date in Wreath	$175	$250	$375
Small Liberty Head / Value and CAL in Wreath	$175	$250	$425
Small Liberty Head, date below / Value in Wreath	$175	$230	$320
Large Indian Head / Value in Wreath	$215	$310	$475
Large Indian Head / Value and CAL in Wreath	$200	$280	$450
Small Indian Head / Value and CAL in Wreath	$500	$625	$975
Washington Head 1872 / Value and CAL in Wreath	$775	$1,350	$2,000

QUARTER DOLLAR, ROUND

	EF	AU	Unc.
Liberty Head / Value in Wreath	$150	$250	$425
Large Liberty Head / Value and Date in Wreath	$190	$310	$450
Large Liberty Head / Value and CAL in Wreath	$150	$250	$400
Small Liberty Head / 25 CENTS in Wreath	$320	$500	$800
Small Liberty Head / Value and Date in Wreath	$180	$300	$435
Small Liberty Head / Value in Shield, Date in Wreath	$180	$315	$550
Small Liberty Head / Value and CAL in Wreath	$180	$225	$400
Large Indian Head / Value in Wreath	$350	$520	$825
Large Indian Head / Value and CAL in Wreath	$300	$400	$675
Small Indian Head / Value and CAL in Wreath	$375	$525	$850
Washington Head 1872 / Value and CAL in Wreath	$725	$1,000	$1,600

HALF DOLLAR, OCTAGONAL

	EF	AU	Unc.
Large Liberty Head / Value and Date in Wreath	$300	$370	$690
Large Liberty Head / Value and Date in Beaded Circle	$170	$210	$450
Large Liberty Head / Value and CAL in Wreath	$210	$425	$650
Large Liberty Head / Legend Surrounds Wreath	$400	$600	$1,000
Small Liberty Head / Value and Date in Wreath	$200	$375	$575
Small Liberty Head / Value and CAL in Wreath	$185	$320	$475
Small Liberty Head / Small Eagle With Rays	$1,300	$2,000	$3,250
Small Liberty Head / Large Eagle With Raised Wings	$1,500	$2,200	$3,250
Large Indian Head / Value in Wreath	$210	$400	$675
Large Indian Head / Value and CAL in Wreath	$235	$350	$575
Small Indian Head / Value in Wreath	$250	$425	$700
Small Indian Head / Value and CAL in Wreath	$450	$585	$975

HALF DOLLAR, ROUND

	EF	AU	Unc.
Liberty Head / Value in Wreath	$180	$325	$500
Liberty Head / Value and Date in Wreath	$180	$325	$500
Liberty Head / Value and CAL in Wreath	$225	$350	$575
Liberty Head / CALIFORNIA GOLD Around Wreath	$225	$375	$600
Large Indian Head / Value in Wreath	$210	$325	$525
Large Indian Head / Value and CAL in Wreath	$200	$300	$465
Small Indian Head / Value and CAL in Wreath	$200	$330	$525

DOLLAR, OCTAGONAL

	EF	AU	Unc.
Liberty Head / Value and Date in Wreath	$500	$750	$1,350
Liberty Head / Value and Date in Beaded Circle	$500	$800	$1,500
Liberty Head / Legend Around Wreath	$500	$825	$1,550
Liberty Head / Large Eagle	$2,150	$3,150	$5,250
Large Indian Head / Value in Wreath	$725	$1,150	$2,100
Small Indian Head / Value and CAL in Wreath	$725	$1,150	$2,100

DOLLAR, ROUND

	EF	AU	Unc.
Liberty Head / CALIFORNIA GOLD. Value and Date in Wreath	$1,750	$2,600	$4,500
Liberty Head / Date Beneath Head	$2,300	$3,200	$5,100
Indian Head / Date Beneath Head	$2,000	$3,100	$5,000

COINS OF THE GOLDEN WEST

Small souvenir California gold pieces were made by several manufacturers in the early 20th century. A series of 36 pieces, in the size of 25¢, 50¢, and $1 coins, was sold by the M.E. Hart Company of San Francisco to honor Alaska and various Western states. The Hart Company also marketed the official commemorative Panama-Pacific gold coins from the 1915 Exposition and manufactured plush copper cases for them. Similar cases were acquired by Farran Zerbe, who mounted 15 complete sets of what he termed "Coins of the Golden West." Intact, framed 36-piece sets are rare; individual specimens are among the most popular of all souvenir pieces of that era.

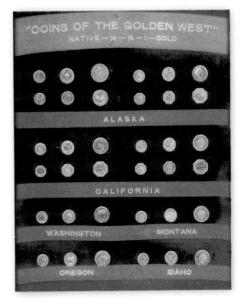

	AU	MS-63
Alaska Pinch, 25¢, octagonal, 1902	$300	$550
Alaska Pinch, 50¢, octagonal, 1900	$300	$600
Alaska Pinch, $1, octagonal, 1898	$400	$750
Alaska Pinch, 25¢, round, 1901	$300	$550
Alaska Pinch, 50¢, round, 1899	$350	$600
Alaska Pinch, $1, round, 1897	$400	$750
Alaska Parka, 25¢, round, 1911	$1,200	$1,900
Alaska Parka, 50¢, round, 1911	$1,300	$2,250
Alaska Parka, $1, round, 1911	$1,500	$2,650
Alaska AYPE, 25¢, round, 1909	$200	$300
Alaska AYPE, 50¢, round, 1909	$225	$350
Alaska AYPE, $1, round, 1909	$300	$450
California Minerva, 25¢, octagonal, 1915	$200	$400
California Minerva, 50¢, octagonal, 1915	$250	$400
California Minerva, $1, octagonal, 1915	$300	$550
California Minerva, 25¢, round, 1915	$250	$400
California Minerva, 50¢, round, 1915	$250	$450
California Minerva, $1, round, 1915	$300	$550
California 25¢, octagonal, 1860 or 1902	$500	$1,200
California 50¢, octagonal, 1900	$600	$1,350
California $1, octagonal, 1898	$700	$1,600
California 25¢, round, 1849, 1860, 1871, or 1901	$450	$1,250
California 50¢, round, 1849 or 1899	$550	$1,500
California $1, round, 1849	$700	$1,750
Idaho, 25¢, round, 1914	$700	$1,250
Idaho, 50¢, round, 1914	$800	$1,350
Idaho, $1, round, 1914	$850	$1,550
Montana, 25¢, round, 1914	$550	$1,050
Montana, 50¢, round, 1914	$650	$1,150
Montana, $1, round, 1914	$750	$1,400
Oregon, 25¢, round, 1914	$500	$1,200
Oregon, 50¢, round, 1914	$600	$1,250
Oregon, $1, round, 1914	$700	$1,450
Washington, 25¢, round, 1914	$500	$1,150
Washington, 50¢, round, 1914	$600	$1,250
Washington, $1, round, 1914	$700	$1,450

CALIFORNIA GOLD INGOT BARS

During the Gold Rush era, gold coins, ingots, and "dust" (actually flakes and nuggets) were sent by steamship from San Francisco to other ports, most importantly to New York City and London, where the gold was sold or, in some instances, sent to mints for conversion into coins. The typical procedure in the mid-1850s was to send the gold by steamship from San Francisco to Panama, where it was transported across 48 miles of territory by small water craft and pack animals from 1849 until the Panama Railroad opened in 1855, then loaded aboard another ship at the town of Aspinwall on the Atlantic side. On September 12, 1857, the SS *Central America*, en route from Aspinwall to New York City with more than 475 passengers, over 100 crew members, and an estimated $2.6 million in gold (in an era in which pure gold was valued at $20.67 per ounce) was lost at sea. Miraculously, more than 150 people, including all but one of the women and children, were rescued by passing ships. The *Central America* went to the bottom of the Atlantic Ocean off the Carolina coast.

In the 1980s a group of researchers secured financing to search for the long-lost ship. After much study and many explorations, they discovered the wreck of the *Central America* 7,200 feet below the surface. They used the robotic *Nemo*, a sophisticated device weighing several tons, to photograph the wreck and to carefully bring to the surface many artifacts. A king's ransom in gold ingots was found, along with more than 7,500 coins, the latter mostly consisting of Mint State 1857-S double eagles.

The 500-plus gold ingots furnished a unique opportunity to study specimens that, after conservation, were essentially in the same condition as they had been in 1857. These bore the imprints of five different California assayers, who operated seven offices. With few exceptions, each ingot bears individual stamps, indicating its maker, a serial number, the weight in ounces, the fineness (expressed in thousandths, e.g., .784 indicating 784/1000 pure gold), and the 1857 value in dollars. The smallest bar found was issued by Blake & Co., weighed 4.95 ounces, was .795 fine, and was stamped with a value of $81.34. The largest ingot, dubbed the "Eureka bar," bore the imprint of Kellogg & Humbert, and was stamped with a weight of 933.94 ounces, .903 fine, and a value of $17,433.57.

Blake & Co., Sacramento, California: From December 28, 1855, to May 1858, Blake & Co. was operated by Gorham Blake and W.R. Waters. • 34 ingots recovered. Serial numbers in the 5,100 and 5,200 series. Lowest weight and value: 4.95 ounces, $81.34. Highest weight and value: 157.40 ounces, $2,655.05. These bars have beveled or "dressed" edges and may have seen limited use in California commerce.

Harris, Marchand & Co., Sacramento and Marysville: This firm was founded in Sacramento in 1855 by Harvey Harris and Desiré Marchand, with Charles L. Farrington as the "& Co." The Marysville office was opened in January 1856. Serial numbers in the 6000 series are attributed to Sacramento, comprising 36 bars; a single bar in the 7000 series (7095) is attributed to Marysville. The Marchand bars each have a circular coin-style counterstamp on the face. Lowest weight and value (Sacramento): 9.87 ounces, $158.53. Highest weight and value (Sacramento): 295.20 ounces, $5,351.73. • Unique Marysville bar: 174.04 ounces, $3,389.06.

Henry Hentsch, San Francisco: Hentsch, a Swiss, was an entrepreneur involved in banking, real estate, assaying, and other ventures. In February 1856, he opened an assay office as an annex to his bank. It is likely that many of his ingots were exported to Europe, where he had extensive banking connections. • 33 ingots recovered. Lowest weight and value: 12.52 ounces, $251.82. Highest weight and value: 238.84 ounces, $4,458.35.

Justh & Hunter, San Francisco and Marysville: Emanuel Justh, a Hungarian, was a lithographer in San Francisco in the early 1850s. In 1854 and 1855 he worked as assistant assayer at the San Francisco Mint. Solomon Hillen Hunter came to California from Baltimore. The Justh & Hunter partnership was announced in May 1855. • Although study is continuing, the 60 ingots in the 4000 series are tentatively attributed to San Francisco, and the 26 ingots in the 9000 series are attributed to Marysville. • San Francisco—Lowest weight and value: 5.24 ounces, $92.18. Highest weight and value: 866.19 ounces, $15,971.93. • Marysville—Lowest weight and value: 19.34 ounces, $356.21. Highest weight and value: 464.65 ounces, $8,759.90.

Kellogg & Humbert, San Francisco: John Glover Kellogg and Augustus Humbert, two of the most famous names in the minting of California gold coins, formed the partnership of Kellogg & Humbert in spring 1855. The firm was one of the most active of all California assayers during the mid-1850s. • 346 ingots recovered, constituting the majority of those found. • Lowest weight and value: 5.71 ounces, $101.03. Highest weight and value: 933.94 ounces, $17,433.57.

A selection of gold ingots from the SS *Central America* treasure (with an 1857-S double eagle shown for scale, near lower left). (1) Harris, Marchand & Co., Marysville office, serial number 7095, 174.04 ounces, .942 fine, $3,389.06 (all values as stamped in 1857). (2) Henry Hentsch, San Francisco, serial number 3120, 61.93 ounces, .886 fine, $1,134.26. (3) Kellogg & Humbert, San Francisco, serial number 215, .944 fine, $1,045.96. (4) Blake & Co., Sacramento, 19.30 ounces, .946 fine, $297.42. (5) Another Blake & Co. ingot, serial number 5216, .915 fine, $266.12. (6) Justh & Hunter, Marysville office, serial number 9440, 41.79 ounces, $761.07. (7) Justh & Hunter, San Francisco office, serial number 4243, 51.98 ounces, .916 fine, $984.27. (8) Harris, Marchand & Co., Sacramento office, serial number 6514, 35.33 ounces, .807 fine, $589.38. (9) Harris, Marchand & Co., Sacramento office, serial number 6486, 12.64 ounces, .950 fine, $245.00.

Private Tokens

Privately issued tokens are by no means an American invention. They were common to most capitalist nations in the 1800s (and known even earlier), created and circulated by businessmen and others in periods of economic weakness or uncertainty, during financial panics, depressions, and times of war. Sometimes they were handed out as advertising trinkets or political propaganda pieces; more often they passed as makeshift currency when few real coins were available to make small change. Unlike real coins, which are government-issued as legal tender, tokens are minted by private citizens and companies. Commonly made of metal, usually round in shape, coins and tokens are very similar in appearance, but a token lacks a coin's official status as government-backed currency. Typically it would only have trade value, and then only in the vicinity in which it was issued (if, for example, a local merchant was prepared to redeem it in goods or services).

This section describes several of the more commonly encountered American tokens of the 1800s.

HARD TIMES TOKENS (1832–1844)

Hard Times tokens, as they are called, are pieces of Americana dating from the era of presidents Andrew Jackson and Martin Van Buren. They are mostly the size of a contemporary large copper cent. Privately minted from 1832 to 1844, they display diverse motifs reflecting political campaigns and satire of the era as well as carrying advertisements for merchants, products, and services. For many years these have been a popular specialty within numismatics, helped along with the publication of *Hard Times Tokens* by Lyman H. Low (1899; revised edition, 1906) and later works, continuing to the present day (see the *Guide Book of Hard Times Tokens*, 2015). In 1899 Low commented (adapted) that "the issues commonly called Hard Times tokens . . . had no semblance of authority behind them. They combine the character of political pieces with the catch-words of party cries; of satirical pieces with sarcastic allusions to the sentiments or speeches of the leaders of opposing parties; and in some degree also of necessity pieces, in a time when, to use one of the phrases of the day, 'money was a cash article,' hard to get for daily needs."

Although examples from the earlier 1830s are designated as Hard Times tokens, the true Hard Times period started in a serious way on May 10, 1837, when banks began suspending specie payments and would no longer exchange paper currency for coins. This date is memorialized on some of the token inscriptions. Difficult economic conditions continued through 1843; the first full year of recovery was 1844. From March 1837 to March 1841, President Martin Van Buren vowed to "follow in the steps of my illustrious predecessor," President Andrew Jackson, who had been in office from March 1829 until Van Buren's inauguration. Jackson was perhaps the most controversial president up to that time. His veto in 1832 of the impending (1836) recharter of the Bank of the United States set off a political firestorm, and the flames were fanned when his administration shifted deposits to favored institutions, derisively called "pet banks."

The Jackson era was one of unbridled prosperity. Due to sales of land in the West, the expansion of railroads, and a robust economy, so much money piled up in the Treasury that distributions were made in 1835 to all of the states. Seeking to end wild speculation, Jackson issued the "Specie Circular" on July 11, 1836, mandating that purchases of Western land, often made on credit, by paper money of uncertain worth, or by non-cash means, had to be paid in silver or gold coins. Almost immediately, the land boom settled and prices stabilized. A chill began to spread across the economy, which worsened in early 1837. Finally, many banks ran short of ready cash, causing the specie suspension.

After May 10, 1837, silver and gold coins completely disappeared from circulation. Copper cents remained, but were in short supply. Various diesinkers and others produced a flood of copper tokens. These were sold at discounts to merchants and banks, with $6 for 1,000 tokens being typical. Afterward, they were paid out in commerce and circulated for the value of one cent.

The actions of Jackson, the financial tribulations that many thought he precipitated, and the policies of Van Buren inspired motifs for a class of Hard Times tokens today known as "politicals." Several hundred other varieties were made with the advertisements of merchants, services, and products and are known as "store cards" or "merchants' tokens." Many of these were illustrated with elements such as a shoe, umbrella, comb, coal stove, storefront, hotel, or carriage.

One of the more famous issues depicts a slave kneeling in chains, with the motto "Am I Not a Woman & a Sister?" This token was issued in 1838, when abolition was a major rallying point for many Americans in the North. The curious small-size Feuchtwanger cents of 1837, made in Feuchtwanger's Composition (a type of German silver), were proposed to Congress as a cheap substitute for copper cents, but no congressional action was taken. Lewis Feuchtwanger produced large quantities on his own account and circulated them extensively (see page 1300).

As the political and commercial motifs of Hard Times tokens are so diverse, and reflect the American economy and political scene of their era, numismatists have found them fascinating to collect and study. Although there are major rarities in the series, most of the issues are very affordable. Expanded information concerning more than 500 varieties of Hard Times tokens can be found in Russell Rulau's *Standard Catalog of United States Tokens, 1700–1900* (fourth edition). Collectors and researchers are also encouraged to consult *A Guide Book of Hard Times Tokens* (Bowers). A representative selection is illustrated here.

L1, HT1   L57, HT76

L4, HT6   L56, HT75

	VF	EF	AU
L1, HT1. Andrew Jackson. Copper	$5,000	$8,500	—
L57, HT76. Van Buren, facing left. Brass	$2,200	$3,250	$4,250
L4, HT6. Jackson President of the U.S. Brass	$135	$275	$750
L56, HT75. Van Buren facing left. Copper	$80	$160	$375

L66, HT24

L54, HT81

L55, HT63

L31, HT46

L8, HT9

L18, HT32

L51, HT70

L47, HT66

L60, HT18

L44, HT69

	VF	EF	AU
L66, HT24. Agriculture. Copper	$225	$350	$650
L54, HT81. A Woman & A Sister. Copper ‡	$180	$275	$400
L55, HT63. Loco Foco, 1838. Copper ‡	$55	$160	$275
L31, HT46. Not One Cent, Motto. Copper ‡	$45	$60	$135
L8, HT9. My Victory / Jackson. Copper ‡	$30	$90	$125
L18, HT32. Executive Experiment. Copper ‡	$25	$65	$110
L51, HT70. Roman Firmness. Copper ‡	$35	$70	$125
L47, HT66. Phoenix / May Tenth. Copper ‡	$25	$65	$110
L60, HT18. Ship/Lightning. Copper ‡	$25	$65	$110
L44, HT69. Ship/Jackson. Copper ‡	$25	$70	$125

‡ Ranked in the *100 Greatest American Medals and Tokens*; L54, HT81 as its own entry, the other listings as a single entry for Satirical Hard Times Tokens.

L59, HT17   L65, HT23

	VF	EF	AU
L59, HT17. Ship / Wreath Border. Copper	$25	$65	$110
L65, HT23. Ship / Liberty Head. Copper	$100	$200	$350

FEUCHTWANGER TOKENS (1837–1864)

Lewis Feuchtwanger, a German-born chemist, moved to the United States in 1829 and settled in New York City. He produced a variety of German silver (an alloy of metals not including any actual silver) consisting of nickel, copper, and some zinc. Feuchtwanger suggested to Congress as early as 1837 that his metal be substituted for copper in U.S. coinage, and he made one-cent and three-cent trial pieces that circulated freely during the coin shortage of 1836 through 1844.

	VF	EF	AU	Unc.
1837 One Cent, Eagle ‡	$135	$210	$300	$500
1837 Three-Cent, New York Coat of Arms ‡	$750	$1,600	$2,750	$5,250
1837 Three-Cent, Eagle ‡	$1,700	$3,600	$5,500	$13,000
1864 Three-Cent, Eagle	$1,300	$2,800	$3,800	$7,500

‡ All 1837 Feuchtwanger Tokens are ranked in the *100 Greatest American Medals and Tokens*, as a single entry.

CIVIL WAR TOKENS (1860s)

Early Friday morning, April 12, 1861, the Confederate States Army fired shells from 10-inch siege mortars into the Union's Fort Sumter in Charleston Bay, South Carolina, touching off the American Civil War. The ensuing turmoil would bring many changes to America's financial and monetary systems, including a dramatic reworking of the banking structure, federalization of paper money, bold innovations in taxation, tariffs, and land grants, and radical government experiments in new kinds of currency. For the man on the street, one daily noticeable development of the war was the large-scale hoarding of coins, which began in late 1861 and early 1862—people squirreled away first their gold, then silver coins, and finally, as the war dragged on that summer, even small copper-nickel cents. This caused trouble for day-to-day commerce. There were no coins to buy a newspaper or a glass of soda, to get a haircut, or tip a doorman. The situation gave birth to the humble but ubiquitous Civil War token.

Tokens were a familiar sight on the American scene by the time the Civil War was ignited. In fact, Americans had been using tokens as monetary substitutes since the colonial era, during the early days of the new nation, and throughout the 1800s. Two main kinds of tokens entered into American commerce during the war: *patriotics,* so called for their political and nationalistic themes; and *store cards*, or merchant tokens. An estimated 50 million or more were issued—more than two for every man, woman, and child in the Union. Civil War tokens were mostly a Northern phenomenon; not surprising, considering that New York State alone produced four times as much manufacturing as the entire Confederacy at the start of the war. Southerners had to make do with weak government-backed paper money, which quickly depreciated in value; Yankee tradesmen had the industrial base and financial means to produce a hard-money substitute that at least *looked* like money, even if it was backed by nothing more substantial than a local grocery store's promise to accept it at the value of one cent.

Most Civil War tokens were made of copper, some were brass, and rare exceptions were struck in copper-nickel or white metal. In addition to patriotics and store cards, some issuers crafted *numismatic* tokens during the war. These were struck for collectors rather than for day-to-day commerce, and made in the typical alloys as well as (rarely) in silver and other metals. Some were overstruck on dimes or copper-nickel cents.

Many kinds of tokens and medals were issued during the war. This sometimes leads to the question, "What, exactly, counts as a *Civil War token?*" How about the small hard-rubber checks and tickets, in various shapes, of that era? Or encased postage stamps, another small-change substitute of the war years? Or sutler tokens, issued by registered vendors who supplied the Union Army and traveled with the troops? These and more are sometimes collected along with the main body of about 10,000 varieties of store cards and patriotics. There is a long tradition of collecting Civil War tokens, dating back to even before the end of the war, and the hobby community has developed various habits and traditions over the years. Ultimately what to include in a collection is up to the individual collector. The Civil War Token Society (www.cwtsociety.com), the preeminent club for today's collector, suggests that to be "officially" considered a Civil War token, a piece must be between 18 and 25 mm in diameter. (Most of the copper tokens issued to pass as currency during the war were 18 or 19 mm, the size of the federal government's relatively new Flying Eagle and Indian Head cents, introduced in the late 1850s.)

Civil War tokens can be collected by state and by city, by type of issuer (druggist, saloonkeeper, doctor, etc.), or by any number of designs and themes. If you live in New York City and would like to study store cards issued by local shops and businesses, you have hundreds to choose from. You might hail from a small town and still be able to find a Civil War token from where you grew up. In 1863 in Oswego, New York, M.L. Marshall—a general-store seller of the unlikely combination of toys, fancy goods, fishing tackle, and rare coins—issued a cent-sized copper token featuring a fish! Undertakers issued store cards with tiny coffins advertising their services. Booksellers, bootmakers, beer brewers, hat dealers, and hog butchers all pictured their products on small copper tokens. On the patriotic side, Civil War tokens show Abraham Lincoln, various wartime presidential candidates, national heroes, cannons at the ready, unfurled flags, defiant eagles, and soldiers on horseback. They shout out the slogans of the day, warning the South of the strength of THE ARMY & NAVY, urging Americans to STAND BY THE FLAG, and insisting that THE FEDERAL UNION MUST AND SHALL BE PRESERVED.

Many tokens were more or less faithful imitations of the federal copper-nickel Indian Head cent. A few of this type have the word NOT in small letters above the words ONE CENT. For a time the legal status of the Civil War tokens was uncertain. Mint Director James Pollock thought they were illegal; however, there was no law prohibiting the issue of tradesmen's tokens or of private coins not in imitation of U.S. coins. Finally a law was passed April 22, 1864, prohibiting the private issue of any one- or two-cent coins, tokens, or devices for use as money, and on June 8 another law was passed that abolished private coinage of every kind. By that summer the government's new bronze Indian Head cents, minted in the tens of millions, were plentiful in circulation.

Today, Civil War tokens as a class are very accessible for collectors. Store-card tokens of Illinois, Massachusetts, Michigan, New York, Ohio, Pennsylvania, and Wisconsin are among those most frequently seen. A collector seeking special challenges will hunt for tokens from Iowa, Kansas, Maryland,

and Minnesota—and, on the Confederate side, from Alabama, Louisiana (a counterstamped Indian Head cent), and Tennessee.

Three pieces of advice will serve the beginning collector. First, read the standard reference books, including *Patriotic Civil War Tokens* and *U.S. Civil War Store Cards*, both classics by George and Melvin Fuld, and the *Guide Book of Civil War Tokens*, by Q. David Bowers. These books lay the foundation and offer inspiration for building your own collection. Second, join the Civil War Token Society. This will put you in touch with other collectors who offer mentoring, friendship, and information. Third, visit a coin show and start looking for Civil War tokens in the inventories of the dealers there. Above all, enjoy the hobby and the many paths and byways it can lead you on through this important and turbulent era of American history.

Values shown are for the most common tokens in each composition.

	F	VF	EF	MS-63
Copper or brass	$15	$25	$35	$125
Nickel or German silver	$55	$75	$130	$290
White metal	$80	$125	$150	$275
Copper-nickel	$75	$125	$175	$325
Silver	$200	$300	$500	$1,200

PATRIOTIC CIVIL WAR TOKENS

Patriotic Civil War tokens feature leaders such as Abraham Lincoln; military images such as cannons or ships; and sociopolitical themes popular in the North, such as flags and slogans. Thousands of varieties are known.

	F	VF	AU	MS-63
Lincoln ‡	$35	$70	$150	$300
Monitor ‡	$30	$50	$125	$225
"Wealth of the South" ‡ (a)	$200	$400	$600	$1,000
Various common types ‡	$15	$25	$45	$125

‡ Ranked in the *100 Greatest American Medals and Tokens*; "Wealth of the South" as its own entry, the other listings as a single entry for Patriotic Civil War Tokens. **a.** Dated 1860, but sometimes collected along with Civil War tokens.

CIVIL WAR STORE CARDS

Tradesmen's tokens of the Civil War era are often called store cards. These are typically collected by geographical location or by topic. The Fuld text (see bibliography) catalogs store cards by state, city, merchant, die combination, and metal. Values shown below are for the most common tokens for each state. Tokens from obscure towns or from merchants who issued only a few can be priced into the thousands of dollars and are widely sought.

	VG	VF	AU	MS-63
Alabama ‡	$1,500	$3,000	$4,000	$6,500
Connecticut ‡	$10	$25	$50	$125
Washington, D.C. ‡	—	$1,000	$1,400	$2,000
Idaho ‡	$400	$700	$1,300	—
Illinois ‡	$10	$25	$50	$125
Indiana ‡	$10	$25	$50	$135
Iowa ‡	$150	$450	$550	$1,250
Kansas ‡	$900	$2,500	$3,500	$5,500
Kentucky ‡	$50	$125	$200	$350
Louisiana ‡	$2,000	$3,500	$4,500	—
Maine ‡	$50	$100	$175	$275
Maryland ‡	$150	$350	$550	$1,000
Massachusetts ‡	$15	$35	$60	$140
Michigan ‡	$10	$25	$50	$125
Minnesota ‡	$150	$450	$550	$750
Missouri ‡	$40	$100	$150	$250
New Hampshire ‡	$80	$130	$175	$275
New Jersey ‡	$10	$25	$50	$135
New York ‡	$10	$25	$50	$125
Ohio ‡	$10	$25	$50	$125
Pennsylvania ‡	$10	$25	$50	$125
Rhode Island ‡	$10	$25	$50	$135
Tennessee ‡	$300	$650	$1,200	$1,750
Virginia ‡	$250	$500	$1,000	—
West Virginia ‡	$45	$100	$175	$400
Wisconsin ‡	$15	$30	$60	$130
Sutlers' ‡ (a)	$185	$375	$500	$700

‡ Ranked in the *100 Greatest American Medals and Tokens*; Sutlers' Store Cards as its own entry, the other listings as a single entry for Civil War Store Cards. **a.** Sutler tokens were issued by registered contractors who operated camp stores that traveled with the military. These were made by coiners who also produced Civil War tokens, including John Stanton, Shubael Childs, and Francis X. Koehler. Each had a denomination, typically 5 cents to 50 cents. Some used on one side a die also used on Civil War tokens.

DC500A-1h

IN190D-3a

	VG	VF	AU	MS-63
DC500a-1h. H.A. Hall, Washington, D.C.	—	$1,000	$1,400	$2,200
IN190D-3a. J.L. & G.F. Rowe, Corunna, IN, 1863	$15	$40	$75	$175

MI865A-1a

MN980A-1a

MO910A-2a

NY630AQ-4a

NY630Z-1a

OH165M-1a

NY630BJ-1a

WI510M-1a

PA750F-1a

WV890D-4a

	VG	VF	AU	MS-63
MI865A-1a, W. Darling, Saranac, MI, 1864	$7,500	$12,000	$15,000	—
MN980A-1a. C. Benson, Druggist, Winona, MN	$300	$700	$900	$1,500
MO910A-4a. Drovers Hotel, St. Louis, MO, 1863	$125	$300	$600	$1,250
NY630AQ-4a. Gustavus Lindenmueller, New York, 1863	$15	$25	$50	$125
NY630Z-1a. Fr. Freise, Undertaker, New York, 1863	$20	$35	$85	$135
OH165M-1a. B.P. Belknp., "Teeth Extracted Without Pain"	$125	$250	$400	$600
NY630BJ-1a. Sanitary Commission, New York, 1864	$400	$850	$1,100	$1,750
WI510M-1a. Goes & Falk Malt House & Brewery, Milwaukee, WI, 1863	$25	$65	$100	$175
PA750F-1a. M.C. Campbell's Dancing Academy, Philadelphia, PA	$20	$35	$50	$130
WV890D-4a. R.C. Graves, News Dealer, Wheeling, WV, 1863	$45	$100	$175	$400

LESHER REFERENDUM DOLLARS (1900–1901)

Distributed in 1900 and 1901 by Joseph Lesher of Victor, Colorado, these private tokens manufactured in Denver were used in trade to some extent, and stocked by various merchants who redeemed them in goods. Lesher was an Ohio-born Civil War veteran and, after the war, an early pioneer of Colorado's mining fields. His coins, octagonal in shape, were numbered and a blank space left at bottom of 1901 issues, in which were stamped names of businessmen who bought them. All are quite rare; many varieties are extremely rare. Their composition is .950 fine silver (alloyed with copper).

	VF	EF	AU	Unc.
1900 First type, no business name	$2,900	$3,500	$4,200	$6,750
1900 A.B. Bumstead, with or without scrolls (Victor)	$1,600	$2,500	$2,900	$4,000
1900 Bank type	$15,000	$22,000	$35,000	—
1901 Imprint type, no name	$1,800	$2,200	$3,300	$4,800
1901 Imprint type, Boyd Park. Denver	$1,800	$2,200	$3,300	$4,800
1901 Imprint type, Slusher. Cripple Creek	$2,000	$2,600	$3,600	$5,500
1901 Imprint type, Mullen. Victor	$3,000	$4,200	$7,000	$12,000
1901 Imprint type, Cohen. Victor	$5,000	$7,500	$11,000	$16,000
1901 Imprint type, Klein. Pueblo	$7,000	$9,500	$14,000	$20,000
1901 Imprint type, Alexander. Salida	$7,500	$10,000	$16,000	$23,000
1901 Imprint type, White. Grand Junction	$13,000	$21,000	$30,000	—
1901 Imprint type, Goodspeeds. Colorado Springs	$27,000	$37,000	$47,000	—
1901 Imprint type, Nelson. Holdrege, Nebraska	$22,500	$33,000	$45,000	—
1901 Imprint type, A.W. Clark (Denver) (a)			$42,000	

‡ All Lesher Referendum Tokens are ranked in the *100 Greatest American Medals and Tokens*, as a single entry. **a.** This piece is unique.

Confederate Issues

The Confederate States of America proclaimed itself in February 1861, a few weeks after Abraham Lincoln was elected president of the United States in November 1860. The newly formed nation based its monetary system on the Confederate dollar. Its paper currency was backed not by hard assets (such as gold) but by the promise to pay the bearer after the war was over—assuming Southern victory and independence. In addition to paper money, the Confederacy also explored creating its own coinage for day-to-day circulation. While this goal never came to fruition, interesting relics remain as testaments to the effort.

CONFEDERATE CENTS

Facts about the creation of the original Confederate cents are shrouded in mystery. However, a plausible storyline has developed based on research and recollections, through telling and retelling over the years. An order to make cents for the Confederacy is said to have been placed with Robert Lovett Jr., an engraver and diesinker of Philadelphia, through Bailey & Co., a jewelry firm of that city. Fearing arrest by the United States government for assisting the enemy, Lovett decided instead to hide the coins and the dies in his cellar. Captain John W. Haseltine, well known for finding numismatic rarities unknown to others, claimed that a bartender had received one of the coins over the counter and sold it to him. Haseltine recognized it as the work of Lovett, called on him, learned that he had struck 12 of the coins, and bought the remaining 11 and the dies. In 1874 Haseltine made restrikes in copper, silver, and gold.

Circa 1961, the dies were copied and additional pieces made by New York City coin dealer Robert Bashlow. These show prominent die cracks and rust marks that distinguish them from earlier examples.

	Mintage	Unc. PF
1861 Cent, Original, Copper-Nickel, Unc.	*13–16*	$135,000
1861 Cent, Haseltine Restrike, Copper, Proof	55	$15,000
1861 Cent, Haseltine Restrike, Gold, Proof	7	$45,000
1861 Cent, Haseltine Restrike, Silver, Proof	12	$12,500

CONFEDERATE HALF DOLLARS

According to records, only four original Confederate half dollars were struck (on a hand press). Regular silver planchets were used, as well as a regular federal obverse die. One of the coins was given to Secretary of the Treasury Christopher G. Memminger, who passed it on to President Jefferson Davis for his approval. Another was given to Professor John L. Riddell of the University of Louisiana. Edward Ames of New Orleans received a third specimen. The last was kept by chief coiner Benjamin F. Taylor. Lack of bullion prevented the Confederacy from coining more pieces.

The Confederate half dollar was unknown to collectors until 1879, when a specimen and its reverse die were found in Taylor's possession in New Orleans. E. Mason Jr., of Philadelphia, purchased both and later sold them to J.W. Scott and Company of New York. J.W. Scott acquired 500 genuine 1861-O half dollars, routed or otherwise smoothed away the reverses, and then restamped them with the Confederate die. Known as restrikes, these usually have slightly flattened obverses. Scott also struck some medals in white metal using the Confederate reverse die and an obverse die bearing this inscription: 4 ORIGINALS STRUCK BY ORDER OF C.S.A. IN NEW ORLEANS 1861 / ******* / REV. SAME AS U.S. (FROM ORIGINAL DIE•SCOTT)

Confederate Reverse   **Scott Obverse**

	Mintage	VF-20	EF-40	Unc.
1861 HALF DOL. (a)		—	$1,000,000	—
	Auctions: $881,250, VF, January 2015			
1861 HALF DOL., Restrike	500	$6,500	$7,500	$15,000
1861 Scott Obverse, Confederate Reverse	500	$3,000	$4,000	$6,500

a. 4 examples are known.

Hawaiian and Puerto Rican Issues

Although the following issues of Hawaii and Puerto Rico were not circulating U.S. coins, they have political, artistic, and sentimental connections to the United States. Generations of American numismatists have sought them for their collections.

HAWAIIAN ISSUES

Five official coins were issued for the Kingdom of Hawaii. These include the 1847 cent issued by King Kamehameha III and the 1883 silver dimes, quarters, halves, and dollars of King Kalakaua I. The silver pieces were all designed by U.S. Mint chief engraver Charles E. Barber and struck at the San Francisco Mint. The 1883 eighth-dollar piece is a pattern. The 1881 five-cent piece is an unofficial issue.

The Hawaiian dollar was officially valued equal to the U.S. dollar. After Hawaii became a U.S. territory in 1900, the legal-tender status of these coins was removed and most were withdrawn from circulation and melted.

1847, One Cent

1883, Ten Cents

1881, Five Cents
Unofficial issue.

1883, Eighth Dollar

1883, Quarter Dollar

1883, Half Dollar

1883, Dollar

	Mintage	F-12	VF-20	EF-40	AU-50	MS-60	MS-63
							PF-63
1847 Cent (a)	100,000	$350	$450	$650	$850	$1,000	$1,600
	Auctions: $2,585, MS-64BN, August 2014; $3,056, MS-64BN, November 2014; $2,350, MS-63RB, August 2014						
1881 Five Cents		$7,000	$10,000	$11,000	$12,000	$15,000	$22,000
	Auctions: $14,688, MS-63, August 2014						
1881 Five Cents, Proof (b)							$7,000
	Auctions: $2,185, PF-62, June 2001						
1883 Ten Cents	249,974	$55	$100	$275	$400	$900	$2,000
	Auctions: $1,528, MS-63, July 2014; $823, MS-62, September 2014; $282, AU-55, September 2014; $206, EF-45, July 2014						
1883 Ten Cents, Proof	26						$15,000
	Auctions: $12,690, PF-64, August 2014; $11,750, PF-63, November 2014						
1883 Eighth Dollar, Proof	20						$40,000
	Auctions: $8,800, PF-50, July 1994						
1883 Quarter Dollar	499,974	$55	$90	$150	$175	$250	$400
	Auctions: $9,400, MS-67, July 2014; $1,293, MS-66, August 2014; $823, MS-65, August 2014; $646, MS-65, August 2014						
1883 Quarter Dollar, Proof	26						$15,000
	Auctions: $11,750, PF-62, November 2014						
1883 Half Dollar	699,974	$100	$150	$300	$450	$900	$1,900
	Auctions: $17,625, MS-66, August 2014; $5,875, MS-65, August 2014; $2,350, MS-64, August 2014; $2,115, MS-64, August 2014						
1883 Half Dollar, Proof	26						$20,000
	Auctions: $14,100, PF-63, November 2014						
1883 Dollar	499,974	$350	$500	$750	$1,200	$3,750	$9,000
	Auctions: $10,575, MS-64, July 2014; $6,463, MS-63, August 2014; $1,087, AU-55, July 2014; $823, EF-45, August 2014						
1883 Dollar, Proof	26						$35,000
	Auctions: $22,325, PF-61, November 2014						

a. Values shown are for the most common of the six known varieties. b. All Proofs were made circa 1900.

PLANTATION TOKENS

During the 1800s, several private firms issued tokens for use as money in Hawaiian company stores. These are often referred to as Plantation tokens. The unusual denomination of 12-1/2 cents was equivalent to a day's wages in the sugar plantations, and was related to the fractional part of the Spanish eight-reales coin.

(1860) Undated, Waterhouse Token

**(1871) Undated,
Wailuku Plantation**

**1880, Wailuku
Plantation**

1882, Haiku Plantation

1891, Kahului Railroad

	F-12	VF-20	EF-40	AU-50
Waterhouse / Kamehameha IV, ca. 1860	$1,500	$3,000	$4,500	$7,000
Wailuku Plantation, 12-1/2 (cents), (1871), narrow starfish	$750	$2,000	$3,750	$6,200
Similar, broad starfish	$900	$2,400	$4,500	$7,500
Wailuku Plantation, VI (6-1/4 cents), (1871), narrow starfish	$1,800	$4,750	$7,000	$9,500
Similar, broad starfish	$2,200	$5,500	$7,500	$10,500
Thomas H. Hobron, 12-1/2 (cents), 1879 (b)	$600	$850	$1,100	$1,400
Similar, two stars on both sides	$1,600	$3,000	$6,000	$10,000
Thomas H. Hobron, 25 (cents), 1879 (a)			$55,000	$70,000
Wailuku Plantation, 1 Real, 1880	$750	$1,800	$3,750	$8,000
Wailuku Plantation, Half Real, 1880	$2,200	$5,000	$8,500	$11,500
Haiku Plantation, 1 Rial, 1882	$800	$1,250	$1,750	$2,250
Grove Ranch Plantation, 12-1/2 (cents), 1886	$1,500	$3,000	$5,000	$7,000
Grove Ranch Plantation, 12-1/2 (cents), 1887	$3,000	$4,500	$8,000	$10,500
Kahului Railroad, 10 cents, 1891	$3,000	$6,000	$11,000	$13,500
Kahului Railroad, 15 cents, 1891	$3,000	$6,000	$11,000	$13,500
Kahului Railroad, 20 cents, 1891	$3,000	$6,000	$11,000	$13,500
Kahului Railroad, 25 cents, 1891	$3,000	$6,000	$11,000	$13,500
Kahului Railroad, 35 cents, 1891	$3,000	$6,000	$11,000	$13,500
Kahului Railroad, 75 cents, 1891	$3,000	$6,000	$11,000	$13,500

a. 3 examples are known. b. Rare varieties exist.

PUERTO RICAN ISSUES

Puerto Rico, the farthest east of the Greater Antilles, lies about 1,000 miles southeast of Florida between the Atlantic Ocean and the Caribbean Sea. Settled by Spain in 1508, the island was ceded to the United States after the Spanish-American War in 1898. Puerto Ricans were granted U.S. citizenship in 1917. Today Puerto Rico is a self-governing territory of the United States with commonwealth status.

The Puerto Rican coins of 1895 and 1896 were minted at the Casa de Moneda de Madrid, in Spain. The peso was struck in .900 fine silver, and the others were .835 fine. The portrait is of King Alfonso XIII, and the arms are of the Bourbons, the royal house of Spain. These coins were in circulation at the time of the Spanish-American War of 1898, which ended with U.S. victory and with Spain's loss of sovereignty over Cuba (along with its cession of the Philippine Islands, Puerto Rico, and Guam to the United States for $20 million). Puerto Rico's Spanish coins continued to circulate after the war.

Collectors of United States coins often include Puerto Rican coins in their collections, even though they are not U.S. issues. After the Spanish-American War, exchange rates were set for these coins relative to the U.S. dollar, and the island transitioned to a dollar-based currency. Today in Puerto Rico the dollar is still popularly referred to as a "peso."

1896, 5 Centavos

1896, 10 Centavos

1895, 20 Centavos

1896, 40 Centavos

1895, One Peso

	Mintage	F-12	VF-20	EF-40	AU-50	Unc.
1896 5 Centavos	600,000	$30	$50	$100	$150	$200
Auctions: $56, EF-45, September 2014						
1896 10 Centavos	700,000	$40	$85	$135	$200	$300
Auctions: $170, AU-55, September 2014; $212, AU-55, January 2014						
1895 20 Centavos	3,350,000	$45	$100	$150	$250	$400
Auctions: No auction records available.						
1896 40 Centavos	725,002	$180	$300	$900	$1,700	$2,900
Auctions: $705, AU-55, January 2015; $352, EF-45, January 2015						
1895 1 Peso	8,500,021	$200	$400	$950	$2,000	$3,250
Auctions: $3,819, MS-63, September 2014; $1,380, AU-55, June 2006						

Philippine Issues

In April 1899, control of the Philippine Islands was officially transferred from Spain to the United States, as a condition of the treaty ending the Spanish-American War. The U.S. military suppressed a Filipino insurgency through 1902, and partway through that struggle, in July 1901, the islands' military government was replaced with a civilian administration led by American judge William Howard Taft. One of its first tasks was to sponsor a new territorial coinage that was compatible with the old Spanish issues, but also legally exchangeable for American money at the rate of two Philippine pesos to the U.S. dollar. The resulting coins—which bear the legend UNITED STATES OF AMERICA but are otherwise quite different in design from regular U.S. coins—today can be found in many American coin collections, having been brought to the States as souvenirs by service members after World War II or otherwise saved. The unusual designs, combined with the legend, have sometimes caused them to be confused with standard federal United States coins.

The coins, introduced in 1903, were designed by Filipino silversmith, sculptor, engraver, and art professor Melecio Figueroa, who had earlier worked for the Spanish *Casa de Moneda*, in Manila. They are sometimes called "Conant coins" or "Conants," after Charles Arthur Conant, an influential American journalist and banking expert who served on the commission that brought about the Philippine Coinage Act of March 2, 1903. "Both in the artistic quality of the designs and in perfection of workmanship, they compare favorably with anything of the kind ever done in America," wrote Secretary of War Elihu Root in his annual report to President Theodore Roosevelt. Figueroa died of tuberculosis on July 30, 1903, age 61, shortly after seeing his coins enter circulation.

Following Spanish custom, the dollar-sized peso was decimally equivalent to 100 centavos. Silver fractions were minted in denominations of fifty, twenty, and ten centavos, and minor coins (in copper-nickel and bronze) included the five-centavo piece, the centavo, and the half centavo.

In addition to the name of the United States, the coins bear the Spanish name for the islands: FILIPINAS. The silver coins feature a female personification of the Philippines, holding in one hand a hammer that she strikes against an anvil, and in the other an olive branch, with the volcanic Mount Mayon (northeast of the capital city of Manila) visible in the background. The minor coinage shows a young Filipino man, barechested and seated at an anvil with a hammer, again with Mount Mayon seen in the distance. The first reverse design, shared across all denominations, shows a U.S. federal shield surmounted by an eagle with outstretched wings, clutching an olive branch in its right talon and a bundle of arrows in its left. This reverse design was changed in 1937 to a new shield emblem derived from the seal of the 1936 Commonwealth.

Dies for the coins were made at the Philadelphia Mint by the U.S. Mint's chief engraver, Charles E. Barber. Mintmarks were added to the dies, as needed, at the branch mints. From 1903 to 1908 the coins were struck at the Philadelphia Mint (with no mintmark) and the San Francisco Mint (with an S mintmark). From

1909 through 1919, they were struck only at San Francisco. In the first part of 1920, one-centavo coins were struck in San Francisco; later in the year a new mint facility, the Mint of the Philippine Islands, was opened in Manila, and from that point into the early 1940s Philippine coins of one, five, ten, twenty, and fifty centavos were struck there. The coins produced at the Manila Mint in 1920, 1921, and 1922 bore no mintmark. No Philippine coins were struck in 1923 or 1924. The Manila Mint reopened in 1925; from then through 1941 its coinage featured an M mintmark. The Denver and San Francisco mints would be used for Philippine coinage in the final years of World War II, when the islands were under Japanese occupation.

Rising silver prices forced reductions in the fineness and weight for each Philippine silver denomination beginning in 1907, and subsequent issues are smaller in diameter. The new, smaller twenty-centavo piece was very close in size to the five-centavo piece (20.0 mm compared to 20.5 mm), resulting in a mismatching of dies for these two denominations in 1918. A small number of error coins were minted from this accidental combination, with some finding their way into circulation (often with the edge crudely reeded to induce them to pass as twenty-centavo coins). A solution was found by reducing the diameter of the five-centavo piece beginning in 1930.

It should be noted that, in addition to normal coins and paper currency, special token money in the form of coins and printed currency was made for use in the Culion Leper Colony. The token coinage saw six issues from 1913 to 1930, some produced at the Manila Mint. The leper colony was set up in May 1906 on the small island of Culion, one of the more than 7,000 islands comprising the Philippines, and the coinage was intended to circulate only there.

In 1935 the United States, responding to popular momentum for independence, approved the establishment of the Commonwealth of the Philippines, with the understanding that full self-governing independence would be recognized after a ten-year transition period. In 1936 a three-piece set of silver commemorative coins was issued to mark the transfer of executive power.

An adaptation of the new commonwealth's seal, introduced on the 1936 commemorative coins, was used for the reverse design of all circulating Philippine issues beginning in 1937. For their obverses, the Commonwealth coins retained the same Figueroa designs as those struck from 1903 to 1936. (A final transitional issue of more than 17 million 1936-dated one-centavo coins was minted using the federal-shield reverse design, rather than the new Commonwealth shield.)

After the bombing of Pearl Harbor, Japanese military forces advanced on the Philippines in late 1941 and early 1942, prompting the civil government to remove much of the Philippine treasury's bullion to the United States. Nearly 16 million pesos' worth of silver remained, mostly in the form of one-peso pieces of 1907 through 1912. These coins were hastily crated and dumped into Manila's Caballo Bay to prevent their capture by Japan. The Japanese occupied the Philippines, learned of the hidden treasure, and managed to recover some of the sunken coins (probably fewer than half a million). After the war, over the course of several years, more than 10 million of the submerged silver pesos were retrieved under the direction of the U.S. Treasury and, later, the Central Bank of the Philippines. Most of them show evidence of prolonged salt-water immersion, with dark corrosion that resists cleaning. This damage to so many coins has added to the scarcity of high-grade pre-war silver pesos.

Later during World War II, in 1944 and 1945, the U.S. Mint struck coins for the Philippines at its Philadelphia, Denver, and San Francisco facilities. These coins were brought over and entered circulation as U.S. and Philippine military forces fought to retake the islands from the Japanese.

After the war, the Commonwealth of the Philippines became an independent republic, on July 4, 1946, as had been scheduled by the Constitution of 1935. Today the Philippine coins of 1903 to 1945, including the set of commemoratives issued in 1936, remain significant mementos of a colorful and important chapter in U.S. history and numismatics. They are a testament to the close ties and special relationship between the United States of America and the Republic of the Philippines.

PHILIPPINES UNDER U.S. SOVEREIGNTY (1903–1936)

The Philippine Islands were governed under the sovereignty of the United States from 1899 until early 1935. (In the latter year a largely self-governing commonwealth was established, followed by full independence in 1946.) Coinage under U.S. sovereignty began in 1903. There was a final issue of centavos dated 1936, minted in the style of 1903–1934, after which the design of all circulating coins changed to the new Commonwealth style.

BRONZE COINAGE

HALF CENTAVO (1903–1908)

Designer: *Melecio Figueroa.* **Weight:** *2.35 grams.* **Composition:** *.950 copper, .050 tin and zinc.* **Diameter:** *17.5 mm.* **Edge:** *Plain.* **Mint:** *Philadelphia.*

History. In 1903 and 1904 the United States minted nearly 18 million half centavos for the Philippines. By March of the latter year, it was obvious that the half centavo was too small a denomination, unneeded in commerce despite the government's attempts to force it into circulation. The recommendation of Governor-General Luke Edward Wright—that the coin be discontinued permanently—was approved, and on April 18, 1904, a new contract was authorized to manufacture one-centavo blanks out of unused half-centavo blanks. In April 1908, Governor-General James Francis Smith received permission to ship 37,827 pesos' worth of stored half centavos (7,565,400 coins) to the San Francisco Mint to be re-coined into one-centavo pieces. Cleared from the Philippine Treasury's vaults, the coins were shipped to California in June 1908, and most of them were melted and made into 1908 centavos.

Striking and Sharpness. Half centavos typically are well struck, except for the 1903 issue, of which some coins may show weak numerals in the date. Reverses sometimes show light flattening of the eagle's wing tips.

Half Centavo, 1903–1908

High Points of Wear. *Obverse Checkpoints:* 1. Figure's left hand. 2. Figure's right hand. 3. Face and frontal hair just above ear. 4. Edge of anvil. *Reverse Checkpoints:* 1. Eagle's wing tips. 2. Eagle's breast feathers. 3. Upper points of shield. 4. Eagle's right leg.

Proofs. The Philadelphia Mint struck small quantities of Proof half centavos for collectors throughout the denomination's existence, for inclusion in Proof sets (except for 1907, when no Proof sets were issued).

| | Mintage | EF | MS-60 | MS-63 |
		PF-60	PF-63	PF-65
1903	12,084,000	$2.25	$20	$40
	Auctions: $138, MS-65RD, September 2012; $247, MS-65RB, September 2013; $103, MS-65RB, September 2012			
1903, Proof	2,558			$150
	Auctions: $447, PF-67RB, October 2014; $282, PF-66RD, October 2014			
1904	5,654,000	$3.50	$25	$60
	Auctions: $270, MS-65RD, July 2013; $200, MS-65BN, January 2013; $65, MS-64RB, July 2013			
1904, Proof	1,355			$175
	Auctions: $382, PF-66RB, November 2014			
1905, Proof (a)	471	$175	$300	$550
	Auctions: $253, PF-64RB, June 2007; $207, PF-62BN, January 2012			
1906, Proof (a)	500	$150	$250	$500
	Auctions: $323, PF-65BN, January 2012; $374, PF-64RB, June 2007			
1908, Proof (a)	500	$150	$250	$500
	Auctions: $282, PF-64RB, April 2014; $230, PF-64RB, January 2012			

Note: The half centavo was unpopular in circulation. More than 7,500,000 were withdrawn and melted to be recoined as one-centavo pieces in 1908. **a.** Proof only.

ONE CENTAVO (1903–1936)

Designer: *Melecio Figueroa.* **Weight:** *4.7 grams.* **Composition:** *.950 copper, .050 tin and zinc.* **Diameter:** *24 mm.* **Edge:** *Plain.* **Mints:** *Philadelphia, San Francisco, and Manila.*

Mintmark location is on the reverse, to the left of the date.

History. Unlike the half centavo, the bronze centavo was a popular workhorse of Philippine commerce from the start of its production. Nearly 38 million coins were minted in the denomination's first three years. In 1920 the centavo was struck for circulation by two different mints (the only year this was the case). San Francisco produced the coins during the first part of 1920; later in the year, the coins were struck at the Manila Mint, after that facility opened. From that point forward all centavos struck under U.S. sovereignty were products of the Manila Mint. Those dated 1920, 1921, and 1922 bear no mintmark identifying their origin. Manila produced no coins (of any denomination) in 1923 and 1924.

Coin collectors, notably educator, writer, and American Numismatic Association member Dr. Gilbert S. Perez, urged Manila Mint officials to include an M mark on their coinage—similar to the way that, for example, San Francisco coins were identified by an S—and this change was made starting with the coinage of 1925.

Coinage of the centavo continued through the late 1920s and early 1930s. U.S. sovereignty was significantly altered in 1935 with the establishment of the Commonwealth of the Philippines, and this change was reflected in all Philippine currency. A final mintage of 1936-dated centavos (17,455,463 pieces) was struck using the federal-shield reverse of the denomination's 1903–1934 coinage. The coin then switched over to the Commonwealth shield design in 1937.

Several centavo die varieties exist to give the specialist a challenge. Among them is the 1918-S, Large S, whose mintmark appears to be the same size and shape of that used on fifty-centavo pieces of the era.

Striking and Sharpness. On the obverse, the figure's right hand (holding the hammer) is almost always found flatly struck. The reverse, especially of later-date centavos, often shows flattening of the eagle's breast and of the left part of the shield. Issues of the Manila Mint, especially of 1920, often are lightly struck. Those of San Francisco typically are better struck, with only occasional light strikes. On centavos of 1929 to 1936, the M mintmark often is nearly unidentifiable as a letter.

One Centavo, 1903–1936

High Points of Wear. *Obverse Checkpoints:* 1. Figure's left hand. 2. Frontal hair just above ear. 3. Head of hammer. 4. Left part of anvil. *Reverse Checkpoints:* 1. Eagle's breast feathers. 2. Upper points of shield. 3. Eagle's right leg.

Proofs. One-centavo Proofs were struck at the Philadelphia Mint for annual Proof sets in 1903, 1904, 1905, 1906, and 1908. Proof centavos of 1908 bear a date with numerals noticeably larger than those of circulation-strike 1908-S coins.

1908-S, S Over S

	Mintage	VF	EF	MS-60 PF-60	MS-63 PF-63
1903	10,790,000	$1.25	$3	$15	$35
Auctions: $247, MS-66BN, January 2014					
1903, Proof	2,558			$60	$120
Auctions: $408, PF-65RB, April 2010; $212, PF-65RB, October 2015					
1904	17,040,400	$1.25	$3	$25	$45
Auctions: $94, MS-65BN, July 2015					
1904, Proof	1,355			$75	$125
Auctions: $217, PF-65RD, August 2013; $141, PF-64RB, April 2014					
1905	10,000,000	$1.25	$3.50	$30	$45
Auctions: $76, MS-64BN, June 2014					
1905, Proof	471			$175	$275
Auctions: $441, PF-65RB, April 2014; $805, PF-65RB, April 2010; $235, PF-64RD, August 2013					
1906, Proof (a)	500			$150	$250
Auctions: $423, PF-64RD, February 2014					
1908, Proof (a)	500			$150	$275
Auctions: $411, PF-66RD, October 2014; $499, PF-65RB, January 2014; $400, PF-65RB, August 2015					
1908-S	2,187,000	$4	$8	$40	$100
Auctions: $141, MS-65RB, April 2014; $129, MS-65RB, February 2014; $84, MS-64RB, December 2015					
1908-S, S Over S	(b)	$30	$50	$135	$300
Auctions: $558, MS-64RB, January 2014					

a. Proof only. **b.** Included in 1908-S mintage figure.

1918-S, Normal S   **1918-S, Large S**

	Mintage	VF	EF	MS-60	MS-63
1909-S	1,737,612	$10	$20	$110	$225
	Auctions: $317, MS-65RB, August 2014; $153, MS-64RB, December 2015; $62, MS-64BN, March 2014				
1910-S	2,700,000	$4.50	$9	$35	$60
	Auctions: $881, MS-66RD, April 2015; $118, MS-65RB, April 2014; $80, MS-64RB, April 2014				
1911-S	4,803,000	$2.50	$5	$25	$60
	Auctions: $90, MS-65RB, April 2014; $64, MS-64RB, March 2014				
1912-S	3,001,000	$7.50	$15	$75	$125
	Auctions: $118, MS-65BN, March 2014; $90, MS-64BN, June 2014				
1913-S	5,000,000	$4	$7	$35	$75
	Auctions: $270, MS-65BN, November 2014; $79, MS-63BN, January 2014; $62, MS-63BN, April 2015				
1914-S	5,000,500	$3.50	$5	$35	$70
	Auctions: $84, MS-64BN, November 2014; $113, MS-64BN, May 2014				
1915-S	2,500,000	$40	$90	$525	$1,250
	Auctions: $805, MS-63BN, June 2011; $647, MS-62BN, January 2014				
1916-S	4,330,000	$7.50	$12.50	$90	$150
	Auctions: $135, MS-64BN, July 2014; $159, MS-63RB, June 2014				
1917-S	7,070,000	$4	$10	$75	$150
	Auctions: $176, MS-65RD, February 2014; $53, MS-62BN, September 2014				
1917-S, 7 Over 6	(c)	$50	$160	$500	
	Auctions: No auction records available.				
1918-S	11,660,000	$5	$12	$100	$200
	Auctions: $212, MS-65BN, January 2015; $229, MS-64RB, June 2014				
1918-S, Large S	(d)	$150	$250	$1,000	$1,900
	Auctions: $2,585, MS-62BN, January 2016; $306, EF-45, January 2014				
1919-S	4,540,000	$5	$15	$75	$125
	Auctions: $110, MS-64BN, June 2014; $128, MS-64BN, January 2014				
1920	3,552,259	$8	$20	$125	$225
	Auctions: $259, MS-65RB, January 2014; $353, MS-65BN, June 2014				
1920-S	2,500,000	$3.50	$20	$50	$175
	Auctions: $236, MS-64BN, January 2014; $90, MS-62BN, March 2014				
1921	7,282,673	$2.50	$5	$35	$85
	Auctions: $153, MS-65RB, January 2014				
1922	3,519,100	$3	$6	$30	$70
	Auctions: $223, MS-65RB, January 2014; $52, MS-64BN, March 2014				
1925-M	9,325,000	$3	$7	$35	$65
	Auctions: $68, MS-64BN, May 2014				
1926-M	9,000,000	$2.50	$5	$30	$55
	Auctions: $89, MS-65BN, January 2015; $30, MS-64RB, March 2014				
1927-M	9,279,000	$2	$4	$25	$45
	Auctions: $212, MS-66RD, April 2014; $165, MS-66RB, January 2014				
1928-M	9,150,000	$2	$5	$30	$75
	Auctions: $141, MS-65RD, October 2015; $75, MS-64RD, April 2014; $50, MS-64RB, May 2014				
1929-M	5,657,161	$3	$6	$40	$85
	Auctions: $141, MS-65RD, January 2014; $106, MS-65RB, October 2015; $43, MS-63BN, March 2014				

c. Included in 1917-S mintage figure. **d.** Included in 1918-S mintage figure.

	Mintage	VF	EF	MS-60	MS-63
1930-M	5,577,000	$2	$4.50	$30	$50
	Auctions: $69, MS-65BN, January 2014; $75, MS-64RD, August 2014				
1931-M	5,659,355	$2.25	$5	$40	$60
	Auctions: $100, MS-65RB, December 2015; $40, MS-65RB, March 2014; $89, MS-65RB, January 2014				
1932-M	4,000,000	$3	$7	$50	$75
	Auctions: $112, MS-65RD, April 2014; $95, MS-65RD, January 2014				
1933-M	8,392,692	$2	$3	$20	$50
	Auctions: $147, MS-66RD, January 2014; $80, MS-66RB, March 2014; $141, MS-65RB, December 2015				
1934-M	3,179,000	$2.50	$4.50	$50	$75
	Auctions: $200, MS-66RD, April 2014; $112, MS-65RB, January 2014				
1936-M	17,455,463	$2.50	$4	$35	$65
	Auctions: $37, MS-64BN, March 2014				

COPPER-NICKEL COINAGE

FIVE CENTAVOS (1903–1935)

Designer: *Melecio Figueroa.* **Weight:** *1903–1928, 5 grams; 1930–1935, 4.75 grams.*
Composition: *.750 copper, .250 nickel.* **Diameter:** *1903–1908, 20.5 mm; 1930–1935, 19 mm.*
Edge: *Plain.* **Mints:** *Philadelphia, San Francisco, and Manila.*

Five Centavos, Large Size | *Mintmark location is on the* | **Five Centavos, Reduced Size**
(1903–1928, 20.5 mm) | *reverse, to the left of the date.* | (1930–1935, 19 mm)

History. Five-centavo coins were minted under U.S. sovereignty for the Philippines from 1903 to 1935, with several gaps in production over the years. Circulation strikes were made in Philadelphia in 1903 and 1904, then coinage resumed in 1916, this time at the San Francisco Mint. The newly inaugurated Manila Mint took over all five-centavo production starting in 1920, continuing through the end of direct U.S. administration, and under the Commonwealth government beginning in 1937.

The Manila Mint coins of 1920 and 1921 bore no mintmark indicating their producer, a situation noticed by coin collectors of the day. Gilbert S. Perez, superintendent of schools for Tayabas in the Philippines (and a member of the American Numismatic Association), wrote to Assistant Insular Treasurer Salvador Lagdameo in June 1922: "Several members of numismatic societies in Europe and America have made inquiries as to why the Manila mint has no distinctive mint mark. Some do not even know that there is a mint in the Philippine Islands and that the mint is operated by Filipinos." He recommended the letter M be used to identify Manila's coins. Lagdameo replied later that month, thanking Perez and informing him: "It is now being planned that the new dies to be ordered shall contain such mark, and it is hoped that the coins of 1923 and subsequent years will bear the distinctive mint mark suggested by you." Coinage would not resume at the Manila facility until 1925, but from that year forward the mintmark would grace the coins struck in the Philippines.

The diameter of the five-centavo coin was 20.5 mm diameter from 1903 to 1928. This was very close to the 20 mm diameter of the twenty-centavo coin of 1907 to 1929. By 1928 there had been two separate instances where a reverse die of one denomination was "muled" to an obverse of the other. In 1918 this occurred by accident when a small quantity of five-centavo pieces was struck in combination with the reverse die of the twenty centavos (identifiable by its wider shield and a smaller date, compared to the normal five-centavo reverse). This error was known to numismatists by 1922, by which time it was recognized as a scarce variety. The second instance of muling, in 1928, is discussed under twenty-centavo pieces. In 1930, to clearly differentiate the sizes of the coins, the diameter of the five-centavo piece was reduced from 20.5 to 19.0 mm.

Five-centavo coinage under U.S. sovereignty continued to 1935. From 1937 on, the Manila Mint's production of five-centavo coins would use the new Commonwealth shield design on the reverse.

Striking and Sharpness. The obverse of the 1918 and 1919 San Francisco Mint issues often is weakly struck, with considerable loss of detail. The Manila Mint started production in 1920, and many five-centavo coins from that year lack sharpness in the rims and have weak details overall.

Five Centavos, 1903–1928

High Points of Wear. *Obverse Checkpoints:* 1. Figure's right hand. 2. Frontal hair just above ear. 3. Figure's left hand. *Reverse Checkpoints:* 1. Eagle's breast feathers. 2. Eagle's wing tip (to viewer's right). 3. Upper points of shield.

Five Centavos, 1930–1935

High Points of Wear. *Obverse Checkpoints:* 1. Figure's right hand. 2. Frontal hair just above ear. 3. Edge of anvil. *Reverse Checkpoints:* 1. Eagle's breast feathers. 2. Eagle's wing tip (to viewer's right).

Proofs. Five-centavo Proofs were struck at the Philadelphia Mint for annual Proof sets in 1903, 1904, 1905, 1906, and 1908.

	Mintage	VF	EF	MS-60 / PF-60	MS-63 / PF-63
1903	8,910,000	$1.25	$2.50	$20	$35
	Auctions: $247, MS-66, July 2013; $200, MS-65, August 2013; $242, MS-65, December 2012; $123, MS-65, January 2015				
1903, Proof	2,558			$75	$130
	Auctions: $270, PF-66, August 2013; $223, PF-65, October 2015; $200, PF-65, November 2013				

| | Mintage | VF | EF | MS-60 | MS-63 |
				PF-60	PF-63
1904	1,075,000	$2.50	$3	$20	$40
Auctions: $82, MS-64, June 2013; $76, MS-64, May 2013					
1904, Proof	1,355			$90	$150
Auctions: $235, PF-65, August 2013; $153, PF-64, October 2014; $153, PF-64, August 2013					
1905, Proof (a)	471			$200	$300
Auctions: $952, PF-67, August 2012; $476, PF-65, August 2013; $382, PF-64, August 2013					
1906, Proof (a)	500			$175	$250
Auctions: $617, PF-66, October 2014; $670, PF-66, August 2013; $400, PF-65, August 2013					
1908, Proof (a)	500			$200	$300
Auctions: $505, PF-66, October 2014; $969, PF-66, August 2013; $500, PF-66, August 2013					
1916-S	300,000	$85	$150	$800	$1,700
Auctions: $4,465, MS-65, January 2016; 240, MS-62, January 2014; $235, MS-62, February 2014					
1917-S	2,300,000	$5	$12	$160	$350
Auctions: $423, MS-65, April 2014; $447, MS-64, August 2014					
1918-S	2,780,000	$8	$15	$140	$300
Auctions: $306, MS-63, August 2014; $188, MS-62, January 2014					
1918-S, S Over S	(c)	$20	$150	$600	$1,250
Auctions: No auction records available.					
1918-S, Mule (c)	(c)	$575	$1,750	$4,750	$9,750
Auctions: $14,100, MS-61, January 2016; $544, VF-30, April 2014					
1919-S	1,220,000	$15	$30	$200	$450
Auctions: $588, MS-64, September 2014; $499, MS-63, January 2014					
1920	1,421,078	$8.50	$20	$175	$375
Auctions: $141, MS-63, January 2014; $200, MS-63, July 2013					
1921	2,131,529	$9	$15	$125	$300
Auctions: $212, MS-63, August 2013; $212, MS-63, July 2013; $153, MS-63, August 2014					
1925-M	1,000,000	$12	$30	$175	$300
Auctions: $575, MS-64, November 2011; $423, MS-63, December 2015; $217, MS-63, January 2014					
1926-M	1,200,000	$5	$25	$140	$250
Auctions: $112, MS-62, January 2014					
1927-M	1,000,000	$5	$10	$90	$150
Auctions: $259, MS-65, January 2014; $129, MS-64, June 2014					
1928-M	1,000,000	$7	$14	$75	$150
Auctions: $259, MS-65, January 2014; $259, MS-63, November 2015; $96, MS-63, June 2014					
1930-M	2,905,182	$2.50	$6	$50	$100
Auctions: $353, MS-65, September 2014; $71, MS-64RD, July 2014; $153, MS-64, August 2013					
1931-M	3,476,790	$2.50	$6	$75	$150
Auctions: $108, MS-64, June 2014; $74, MS-64, October 2015; $86, MS-63, June 2014					
1932-M	3,955,861	$2	$6	$50	$130
Auctions: $143, MS-64, June 2014; $65, MS-62, January 2014					
1934-M	2,153,729	$3.50	$10	$100	$300
Auctions: $306, MS-64, September 2014; $170, MS-63, June 2014; $88, MS-63, July 2013					
1934-M, Recut 1	(d)	$10	$35	$125	$300
Auctions: No auction records available.					
1935-M	2,754,000	$2.50	$8	$85	$225
Auctions: $282, MS-64, September 2014; $100, MS-63, January 2014					

a. Proof only. b. Included in 1918-S mintage figure. c. Small Date Reverse of twenty centavos. d. Included in 1934-M mintage figure.

SILVER COINAGE
TEN CENTAVOS (1903–1935)

Designer: *Melecio Figueroa.* **Weight:** *1903–1906, 2.7 grams (.0779 oz. ASW);
1907–1935, 2 grams (.0482 oz. ASW).* **Composition:** *1903–1906, .900 silver, .100 copper;
1907–1935, .750 silver, .250 copper.* **Diameter:** *1903–1906, 17.5 mm; 1907–1935, 16.5 mm.*
Edge: *Reeded.* **Mints:** *Philadelphia, San Francisco, and Manila.*

Ten Centavos, Large Size
(1903–1906, 17.5 mm)

*Mintmark location is on the
reverse, to the left of the date.*

Ten Centavos, Reduced Size
(1907–1935, 16.5 mm)

History. The Philippine ten-centavo coin was minted from 1903 to 1935, in several facilities and with occasional interruptions in production.

In 1907 the silver ten-centavo coin's fineness was reduced from .900 to .750, and at the same time its diameter was decreased. This was in response to the rising price of silver, with the goal of discouraging exportation and melting of the silver coins. The net effect was nearly 40 percent less silver, by actual weight, in the new ten-centavo piece. The older coins continued to be removed from circulation, and by June 30, 1911, it was reported that only 35 percent of the ten-centavo pieces minted from 1903 to 1906 still remained in the Philippines.

The Manila Mint took over ten-centavo production from San Francisco in 1920. The ten-centavo coins of 1920 and 1921 bear no mintmark identifying them as products of Manila (this was the case for all Philippine coinage of those years, and of 1922). The efforts of Philippine numismatists, including American Numismatic Association member Gilbert S. Perez, encouraged mint officials to add the M mintmark when the facility reopened in 1925 after a two-year hiatus for all coinage.

Ten-centavo production after 1921 consisted of 1 million pieces struck in 1929 and just less than 1.3 million in 1935. The next ten-centavo mintage would be under the Commonwealth, not U.S. sovereignty.

Die varieties include a 1912-S with an S Over S mintmark, and date variations of the 1914-S.

Striking and Sharpness. The ten-centavo coins of 1903 to 1906 generally are well struck, although some show slight weakness of features. Those of 1907 to 1935 also are generally well struck; some obverses may have slight flattening of the hair just above the ear and on the upper part of the figure. On the reverse, check the eagle's breast feathers for flatness.

Ten Centavos, 1903–1906

High Points of Wear. *Obverse Checkpoints:* 1. Figure's left bosom. 2. Figure's right knee. 3. Figure's left knee. 4. Edge of anvil. *Reverse Checkpoints:* 1. Eagle's breast feathers. 2. Upper points of shield. 3. Eagle's wing tips. 4. Eagle's right leg.

Ten Centavos, 1907–1935

High Points of Wear. *Obverse Checkpoints:* 1. Figure's left thigh. 2. Figure's left bosom. 3. Figure's left hand. *Reverse Checkpoints:* 1. Eagle's breast feathers. 2. Upper points of shield. 3. Eagle's right leg.

Proofs. Ten-centavo Proofs were struck at the Philadelphia Mint for annual Proof sets in 1903, 1904, 1905, 1906, and 1908.

	Mintage	VF	EF	MS-60 PF-60	MS-63 PF-63
1903	5,102,658	$4	$5	$35	$75
Auctions: $188, MS-65, January 2015; $100, MS-64, October 2014; $76, MS-64, July 2013
1903, Proof	2,558			$100	$150
Auctions: $270, PF-65, May 2014; $153, PF-63, September 2015; $70, PF-60, June 2013
1903-S	1,200,000	$20	$45	$350	$1,000
Auctions: $1,645, MS-62, January 2014
1904	10,000	$20	$50	$120	$250
Auctions: $397, MS-66, September 2014; $223, MS-65, July 2013; $100, MS-64, November 2014
1904, Proof	1,355			$110	$150
Auctions: $388, PF-66, October 2014; $259, PF-64, April 2015; $153, PF-64, October 2014; $88, PF-62, June 2014
1904-S	5,040,000	$4	$9	$65	$120
Auctions: $92, MS-64, June 2014; $59, MS-62, November 2014
1905, Proof (a)	471			$225	$350
Auctions: $259, PF-63, June 2004; $299, PF-62, April 2011
1906, Proof (a)	500			$150	$250
Auctions: $470, PF-65, April 2014; $212, PF-61, January 2014
1907	1,500,781	$4	$7.50	$60	$135
Auctions: $223, MS-65, April 2014; $188, MS-65, January 2014; $118, MS-65, August 2013
1907-S	4,930,000	$2	$5	$40	$70
Auctions: $170, MS-64, June 2014; $90, MS-63, May 2014
1908, Proof (a)	500			$175	$250
Auctions: $617, PF-66, October 2014; $353, PF-65, January 2014; $207, PF-63, January 2012
1908-S	3,363,911	$2	$5	$40	$70
Auctions: $306, MS-65, September 2014; $112, MS-64, January 2014
1909-S	312,199	$30	$65	$450	$1,200
Auctions: $2,350, MS-65, April 2015; $752, MS-62, May 2014; $382, MS-61, January 2014
1911-S	1,000,505	$10	$15	$250	$600
Auctions: $588, MS-63, January 2014

a. Proof only.

1912-S, S Over S   **1914-S, Short Crossbar**   **1914-S, Long Crossbar**

	Mintage	VF	EF	MS-60 / PF-60	MS-63 / PF-63
1912-S	1,010,000	$6	$12	$150	$300
Auctions: $306, MS-63, April 2014					
1912-S, S Over S	(b)		$85	$200	$500
Auctions: $646, MS-63, September 2014					
1913-S	1,360,693	$4.25	$13	$140	$250
Auctions: $558, MS-65, September 2014; $270, MS-63, June 2014					
1914-S (c)	1,180,000	$6	$12	$175	$375
Auctions: $411, MS-63, May 2014; $374, MS-63, April 2010					
1915-S	450,000	$25	$40	$350	$750
Auctions: $1,234, MS-64, January 2014; $200, AU-58, January 2014					
1917-S	5,991,148	$2	$3	$20	$65
Auctions: $247, MS-65, June 2014; $447, MS-64, July 2014; $129, MS-64, October 2015					
1918-S	8,420,000	$2	$3	$20	$75
Auctions: $188, MS-65, December 2015; $129, MS-65, January 2013; $306, MS-63, July 2014					
1919-S	1,630,000	$2.50	$3.50	$30	$110
Auctions: $182, MS-64, June 2014					
1920	520,000	$6	$16	$105	$300
Auctions: $494, MS-64, June 2014					
1921	3,863,038	$2	$3	$25	$50
Auctions: $182, MS-65, June 2014; $153, MS-63, July 2014					
1929-M	1,000,000	$2	$3	$25	$45
Auctions: $176, MS-65, December 2015; $123, MS-65, June 2014					
1935-M	1,280,000	$2	$4	$30	$50
Auctions: $182, MS-65, June 2014					

b. Included in 1912-S mintage figure. **c.** Varieties exist with a short or long crossbar in the 4 of 1914. The Long Crossbar is scarcer.

Twenty Centavos (1903–1929)

Designer: *Melecio Figueroa.* **Weight:** *1903–1906, 5.385 grams (.1558 oz. ASW);*
1907–1929, 4 grams (.0964 oz. ASW). **Composition:** *1903–1906, .900 silver, .100 copper;*
1907–1929, .750 silver, .250 copper. **Diameter:** *1903–1906, 23 mm; 1907–1929, 20 mm.*
Edge: *Reeded.* **Mints:** *Philadelphia, San Francisco, and Manila.*

Twenty Centavos, Large Size (1903–1906, 23 mm)   *Mintmark location is on the reverse, to the left of the date.*   **Twenty Centavos, Reduced** Size (1907–1929, 20 mm)

History. In the early 1900s the rising value of silver was encouraging exportation and melting of the Philippines' silver twenty-centavo coins. As was the case with the ten-centavo piece, in 1907 the diameter of the twenty-centavo coin was reduced and its silver fineness decreased from .900 to .750. The net effect was about 40 percent less silver, by actual weight, in the new smaller coins. Attrition continued to draw the older coins out of circulation and into the melting pot, as their silver value exceeded their face value. A report of June 30, 1911, held that only about 25 percent of the twenty-centavo coins minted from 1903 to 1906 still remained in the Philippines.

Circulation strikes were made at the Philadelphia and San Francisco mints through 1919. In July 1920, a new "Mint of the Philippine Islands," located in Manila, started production. Its output during the period of U.S. sovereignty included twenty-centavo pieces in 1920, 1921, 1928, and 1929. (Production of the coins later continued under the Commonwealth, with a slightly modified design.) The first two years of coinage did not feature a mintmark identifying Manila as the producer of the coins. This was noticed by collectors of Philippine coins; they protested the oversight, and later coinage dies had an M mintmark added.

In 1928 a rush order for twenty-centavo coins was received at the Manila Mint—by that time the only producer of the denomination. Manila had not minted the coins since 1921, and the Philadelphia Mint had not shipped any new reverse dies (which would have featured their 1928 date). Under pressure to produce the coins, workers at the Manila Mint married a regular twenty-centavo obverse die with the 1928-dated reverse die of the five-centavo denomination, which was only .5 mm larger. As a result, the entire mintage of 100,000 1928 twenty centavos consists of these "mule" (mismatched-die) coins. The reverse of the 1928 coins, compared with others of 1907 to 1929, has a narrower shield and a larger date.

Striking and Sharpness. Most twenty centavos of 1903 to 1906 are well struck. The 1904-S usually shows weak striking on the figure's left bosom, the frontal hair just above her ear, and her left hand. Most of the coins of 1907 to 1929 show flattening of the figure's hair, sometimes extending into the area of her left bosom and her left hand.

Twenty Centavos, 1903–1906

High Points of Wear. *Obverse Checkpoints:* 1. Figure's left thigh and knee. 2. Figure's left bosom. 3. Figure's left hand. *Reverse Checkpoints:* 1. Eagle's breast feathers. 2. Upper points of shield. 3. Eagle's right leg.

Twenty Centavos, 1907–1929

High Points of Wear. *Obverse Checkpoints:* 1. Figure's left thigh. 2. Edge of anvil. 3. Figure's left bosom. 4. Figure's left hand. *Reverse Checkpoints:* 1. Eagle's breast feathers. 2. Eagle's right leg. 3. Upper points of shield.

Proofs. Twenty-centavo Proofs were struck at the Philadelphia Mint for annual Proof sets in 1903, 1904, 1905, 1906, and 1908.

	Mintage	VF	EF	MS-60 PF-60	MS-63 PF-63
1903	5,350,231	$3.50	$15	$45	$100
Auctions: $88, MS-64, July 2014; $86, AU-55, July 2014
1903, Proof	2,558			$125	$200
Auctions: $482, PF-66, October 2014; $129, PF-63, September 2014; $123, PF-63, September 2014
1903-S	150,080	$25	$50	$600	$1,900
Auctions: $447, AU-58, May 2014
1904	10,000	$45	$60	$125	$200
Auctions: $529, MS-66, June 2014; $194, MS-64, May 2014; $200, MS-63, January 2016; $188, MS-62, January 2015
1904, Proof	1,355			$150	$225
Auctions: $200, PF-65, July 2014; $153, PF-63, May 2014; $200, PF-61, January 2014
1904-S	2,060,000	$7.50	$11	$110	$200
Auctions: $223, MS-64, January 2015; $211, MS-64, March 2014; $411, MS-63, January 2014
1905, Proof (a)	471			$250	$450
Auctions: $470, PF-64, January 2013; $282, PF-61, January 2014
1905-S	420,000	$20	$35	$425	$1,250
Auctions: No auction records available.
1906, Proof (a)	500			$225	$375
Auctions: $541, PF-66, October 2014; $564, PF-64, April 2015; $329, PF-62, November 2014; $329, PF-62, October 2014
1907	1,250,651	$6	$12	$200	$450
Auctions: $881, MS-63, April 2015; $558, MS-63, September 2014
1907-S	3,165,000	$4.50	$10	$75	$200
Auctions: $3,525, MS-65, April 2015; $374, MS-63, January 2010; $247, MS-62, June 2014
1908, Proof (a)	500			$200	$325
Auctions: $397, PF-64, January 2014; $299, PF-63, January 2012
1908-S	1,535,000	$3.50	$10	$100	$300
Auctions: $1,880, MS-64, September 2015; $2,233, MS-63, September 2014
1909-S	450,000	$12.50	$50	$600	$1,500
Auctions: $5,640, MS-66, April 2015; $4,113, MS-64, April 2014; $1,528, MS-64, January 2013
1910-S	500,259	$25	$60	$400	$1,200
Auctions: $9,988, MS-66, April 2015; $3,450, MS-64, April 2012; $2,070, MS-63, April 2012
1911-S	505,000	$25	$45	$400	$1,000
Auctions: $2,350, MS-64, September 2013
1912-S	750,000	$10	$30	$200	$400
Auctions: $294, MS-63, July 2014
1913-S	795,000	$10	$15	$175	$300
Auctions: $235, MS-63, July 2014; $247, MS-62, June 2014
1914-S	795,000	$12.50	$30	$300	$750
Auctions: $353, MS-63, January 2014
1915-S	655,000	$20	$50	$500	$1,800
Auctions: $1,116, MS-63, January 2014; $270, AU-58, May 2014
1916-S (b)	1,435,000	$10	$17.50	$225	$725
Auctions: No auction records available.
1917-S	3,150,655	$5	$8	$75	$200
Auctions: $1,293, MS-66, September 2014; $646, MS-65, September 2014
1918-S	5,560,000	$4	$6	$50	$125
Auctions: $188, MS-64, January 2014; $66, MS-63, June 2014
1919-S	850,000	$6	$15	$125	$225
Auctions: $1,880, MS-66, January 2014; $106, MS-61, November 2014

a. Proof only. **b.** Tilted 6 and Straight 6 varieties exist.

	Mintage	VF	EF	MS-60	MS-63
1920	1,045,415	$8	$20	$135	$225
	Auctions: $411, MS-63, September 2014				
1921	1,842,631	$2	$7	$50	$90
	Auctions: $79, MS-63, January 2014; $48, AU-58, May 2014				
1928-M, Mule (c)	100,000	$15	$50	$900	$1,800
	Auctions: $3,055, MS-65, April 2014; $3,525, MS-64, January 2016; $2,233, MS-64, January 2013				
1929-M	1,970,000	$3	$5	$40	$100
	Auctions: $92, MS-64, June 2014; $21, AU-55, May 2014				
1929-M, 2 Over 2 Over 2	(d)		$75	$250	$400
	Auctions: No auction records available.				

c. Reverse of 1928 five centavos. **d.** Included in 1929-M mintage figure.

FIFTY CENTAVOS *(1903–1921)*

Designer: *Melecio Figueroa.* **Weight:** *1903–1906, 13.48 grams (.3900 oz. ASW);
1907–1921, 10 grams (.2411 oz. ASW).* **Composition:** *1903–1906, .900 silver, .100 copper;
1907–1921, .750 silver, .250 copper.* **Diameter:** *1903–1906, 30 mm; 1907–1921, 27 mm.*
Edge: *Reeded.* **Mints:** *Philadelphia, San Francisco, and Manila.*

Fifty Centavos, Large Size
(1903–1906, 30 mm)

*Mintmark location is
on the reverse, to
the left of the date.*

Fifty Centavos, Reduced Size
(1907–1921, 27 mm)

History. After four years of fifty-centavo coinage, in 1907 the denomination's silver fineness was lowered from .900 to .750, and its diameter was reduced by ten percent. This action was in response to rising silver prices. The new smaller coins contained 38 percent less silver, by actual weight, than their 1903–1906 forebears, making them unprofitable to melt for their precious-metal content. Gresham's Law being what it is ("Bad money will drive out good"), the older, heavier silver coins were quickly pulled from circulation; by June 30, 1911, it was officially reported that more than 90 percent of the 1903–1906 coinage had disappeared from the Philippines.

The reduced-size coins of the U.S. sovereignty type were minted from 1907 to 1921. The Manila Mint took over their production from the Philadelphia and San Francisco mints in 1920, using coinage dies shipped from Philadelphia. The fifty centavos was the largest denomination produced at the Manila Mint. Neither the 1920 nor the 1921 coinage featured a mintmark identifying Manila as its producer.

Production of the fifty-centavo denomination would again take place, in 1944 and 1945, in San Francisco, using the Commonwealth design introduced for circulating coins in 1937.

Striking and Sharpness. On fifty-centavo coins of 1903 to 1906, many obverses show slight flattening of the frontal hair just above the figure's ear. The reverses sometimes show slight flattening of the eagle's breast feathers. On the reverse, a high spot on the shield is the result of an unevenness in striking. The coins of 1907 to 1921 often show notable flatness of strike in the figure's hair just above her ear, and sometimes on her left hand. A flat strike on the abdomen and left leg should not be mistaken for circulation wear. The reverses are quite unevenly struck; observe the top part of the shield, which has a depressed middle and raised sides. The right side is slightly higher than the left and may show some flattening.

Fifty Centavos, 1903–1906

High Points of Wear. *Obverse Checkpoints:* 1. Edge of anvil. 2. Figure's left thigh and knee. 3. Figure's right knee. 4. Figure's right bosom. *Reverse Checkpoints:* 1. Part of shield just to left of lower-right star. 2. Eagle's breast feathers. 3. Eagle's right leg and claws.

Fifty Centavos, 1907–1921

High Points of Wear. *Obverse Checkpoints:* 1. Figure's left thigh and lower leg. 2. Mid-drapery. 3. Figure's left bosom. 4. Edge of anvil. *Reverse Checkpoints:* 1. Eagle's breast feathers. 2. Eagle's right leg. 3. Part of shield just to left of lower-right star.

Proofs. Fifty-centavo Proofs were struck at the Philadelphia Mint for annual Proof sets in 1903, 1904, 1905, 1906, and 1908. Proofs of 1908 often are found with considerable flatness in the frontal hair above Miss Liberty's hair and sometimes with flatness in her left hand.

	Mintage	VF	EF	MS-60 PF-60	MS-63 PF-63
1903	3,099,061	$7.50	$10	$75	$150
	Auctions: $259, MS-64, May 2014; $165, MS-64, September 2013; $129, MS-62, January 2014				
1903, Proof	2,558			$150	$275
	Auctions: $764, PF-66, January 2016; $734, PF-66, October 2014; $189, PF-64, September 2014; $411, PF-64, January 2014				
1903-S (a)			$30,000		
	Auctions: No auction records available.				
1904	10,000	$35	$75	$150	$300
	Auctions: $1,234, MS-66+, June 2014; $329, MS-64, September 2015; $223, MS-63, November 2014; $247, MS-63, May 2014				
1904, Proof	1,355			$175	$350
	Auctions: $476, PF-65, September 2012; $470, PF-64, April 2015; $247, PF-63, February 2014				
1904-S	216,000	$12	$15	$125	$225
	Auctions: $881, MS-65, September 2014; $443, MS-64, May 2014				
1905, Proof (b)	471			$275	$625
	Auctions: $3,760, PF-65, January 2016; $764, PF-63, January 2015; $411, PF-63, April 2014				
1905-S	852,000	$20	$75	$700	$2,100
	Auctions: $1,058, MS-62, April 2014; $206, AU-55, June 2014				

a. 2 examples are known. **b.** Proof only.

	Mintage	VF	EF	MS-60 PF-60	MS-63 PF-63
1906, Proof (b)	500			$325	$575
Auctions: $2,820, PF-67, October 2014; $940, PF-65, April 2014; $353, PF-61, November 2014					
1907	1,200,625	$15	$40	$250	$475
Auctions: $1,763, MS-64, April 2014; $427, MS-62, September 2014					
1907-S	2,112,000	$12.50	$30	$225	$450
Auctions: $5,640, MS-66, August 2015; $499, MS-63, September 2014; $427, MS-62, September 2014					
1908, Proof (b)	500			$300	$525
Auctions: $1,645, PF-66, January 2016; $499, PF-64, April 2014; $499, PF-64, January 2014					
1908-S	1,601,000	$15	$40	$500	$1,800
Auctions: $2,820, MS-63, January 2014; $823, MS-62, September 2014					
1909-S	528,000	$17.50	$60	$450	$1,400
Auctions: $4,230, MS-65, April 2015; $1,645, MS-64, April 2014; $1,528, MS-63, January 2014					
1917-S	674,369	$15	$35	$200	$550
Auctions: $541, MS-63, December 2015; $294, MS-63, January 2014; $411, MS-62, September 2014					
1918-S	2,202,000	$7.50	$15	$125	$220
Auctions: $129, MS-62, June 2014; $176, MS-61, January 2014					
1918-S, S Over Inverted S	(c)	$7.50	$15	$185	$600
Auctions: No auction records available.					
1919-S	1,200,000	$7.50	$15	$100	$225
Auctions: $353, MS-64, July 2014; $129, MS-62, January 2015					
1920	420,000	$7.50	$12.50	$120	$180
Auctions: $211, MS-64, January 2014; $212, MS-62, July 2014					
1921	2,316,763	$5	$11	$70	$110
Auctions: $588, MS-65, January 2016; $62, MS-63, October 2014; $94, MS-63, July 2014; $82, MS-63, July 2013					

b. Proof only. **c.** Included in 1918-S mintage figure.

ONE PESO (1903–1912)

Designer: *Melecio Figueroa.* **Weight:** *1903–1906, 26.96 grams (.7800 oz. ASW); 1907–1912, 20 grams (.5144 oz. ASW).* **Composition:** *1903–1906, .900 silver, .100 copper; 1907–1912, .800 silver, .200 copper.* **Diameter:** *1903–1906, 38 mm; 1907–1912, 35 mm.* **Edge:** *Reeded.* **Mints:** *Philadelphia and San Francisco.*

Peso, Large Size
(1903–1906, 38 mm)

Peso, Reduced Size
(1907–1912, 35 mm)

Mintmark location is on the
reverse, to the left of the date.

History. The Philippine silver peso was struck under U.S. sovereignty from 1903 to 1912. The key date among those struck for circulation is the issue of 1906-S. Although the San Francisco Mint produced more than 200,000 of the coins that year, nearly all of them were held back from circulation. They were instead stored and then later sold as bullion.

By 1906 natural market forces were driving the Philippine silver pesos out of commerce and into the melting pot: the rising price of silver made the coins worth more as precious metal than as legal tender. In 1907 the U.S. Mint responded by lowering the denomination's silver fineness from .900 to .800 and reducing its diameter from 38 mm to 35. The resulting smaller coins had about one-third less silver, by actual weight, than those of 1903 to 1906, guaranteeing that they would stay in circulation. The older coins, meanwhile, were still profitable to pull aside and melt for their silver value. An official report of June 30, 1911, disclosed that less than ten percent of the heavier silver coins still remained in the Philippines.

The new smaller pesos were minted every year from 1907 to 1912, with the San Francisco Mint producing them for commerce and the Philadelphia Mint striking a small quantity of Proofs in 1907 and 1908. Millions of the coins were stored as backing for Silver Certificates (and, later, Treasury Certificates) in circulation in the Philippines. Although the Manila Mint started operations in 1920, the silver peso was never part of its production for circulation.

In December 1941, Imperial Japan, immediately after attacking Pearl Harbor, began a fierce assault on the Philippines. Manila fell on January 2, 1942, and General Douglas MacArthur, commander of U.S. Army Forces in the Far East, fell back to the Bataan Peninsula. In late February President Franklin Roosevelt ordered him to leave the Philippines for Australia, prompting the general's famous promise to the Philippine people: "I shall return!" Not long after the fighting erupted it had become apparent that the Japanese would overtake the islands, and early in 1942 the U.S. military dumped crates holding 15,700,000 silver pesos, mostly of 1907–1912 coinage, into the sea near Corregidor, to avoid their seizure. Many millions of these coins were salvaged by the U.S. Treasury and the Central Bank of the Philippines after the war, with all but about five million pieces being reclaimed by 1958. Today a great majority of the salvaged "war pesos" show clear evidence of their prolonged submersion in saltwater. A typical effect is a dark corrosion strongly resistant to any manner of cleaning or conservation.

Striking and Sharpness. The silver pesos of 1903 to 1906 generally have well-struck obverses, but occasionally with some flattening of the figure's frontal hair above her ear, and sometimes her left bosom and hand. On the reverse, the feathers on the eagle's breast are indistinctly cut, and the wing tips can sometimes be found slightly flatly struck. Of the silver pesos of 1907 to 1912, some but not all exhibit flattened frontal hair, and sometimes a flattened left hand. On the reverse, the eagle's breast feathers are not clearly defined. On some examples the reverses are quite unevenly struck; check the top part of the shield, which has a depressed middle and raised sides, and the right side, which is slightly higher than the left and may show some flattening.

One Peso, 1903–1906

High Points of Wear. *Obverse Checkpoints:* 1. Figure's upper-left leg and knee. 2. Figure's right knee. 3. Figure's left bosom. 4. Frontal hair just above ear. *Reverse Checkpoints:* 1. Eagle's breast feathers. 2. Eagle's right leg. 3. Eagle's wing tips.

One Peso, 1907–1912

High Points of Wear. *Obverse Checkpoints:* 1. Figure's upper-left leg and knee. 2. Figure's lower-left leg. 3. Figure's left hand. 4. Frontal hair just above ear. *Reverse Checkpoints:* 1. Eagle's breast feathers. 2. Eagle's right leg.

Proofs. Proof pesos were struck at the Philadelphia Mint for annual Proof sets in 1903, 1904, 1905, 1906, and 1908. Unlike the smaller denominations, Proof pesos of 1907 also are known—but only to the extent of two examples.

1905-S, Curved Serif on "1"   1905-S, Straight Serif on "1"

	Mintage	VF	EF	MS-60 / PF-60	MS-63 / PF-63
1903	2,788,901	$35	$45	$250	$550
Auctions: $3,290, MS-64, January 2016; $552, MS-63, October 2014					
1903, Proof	2,558			$350	$650
Auctions: $3,525, PF-67, October 2014; $999, PF-65, January 2016; $200, PF-62, September 2014					
1903-S	11,361,000	$35	$40	$150	$325
Auctions: $690, MS-63, March 2011; $188, MS-60, January 2014; $129, AU-58, September 2015					
1904	11,355	$90	$110	$300	$625
Auctions: $3,995, MS-65, January 2016; $705, MS-64, January 2014; $329, MS-63, August 2013					
1904, Proof	1,355			$450	$750
Auctions: $7,050, PF-67, January 2016; $3,525, PF-67, October 2014; $3,290, PF-67, October 2014; $881, PF-64, September 2014					
1904-S	6,600,000	$35	$50	$175	$375
Auctions: $440, MS-63, September 2014; $282, MS-62, May 2015; $188, MS-62, January 2015					
1905, Proof (a)	471			$750	$2,400
Auctions: $11,163, PF-67, January 2013; $5,875, PF-65, January 2016; $911, PF-63, October 2014					
1905-S, Curved Serif on "1"	6,056,000	$40	$60	$350	$750
Auctions: $764, MS-61, January 2014					
1905-S, Straight Serif on "1"	(b)	$50	$75	$900	$3,500
Auctions: $3,819, MS-63, September 2014					
1906, Proof (a)	500			$700	$1,800
Auctions: $3,819, PF-67, October 2014; $3,525, PF-67, October 2014; $6,463, PF-66, January 2016; $1,880, PF-63, April 2014					
1906-S	201,000	$1,500	$3,900	$17,500	$32,500
Auctions: $7,050, AU-55, October 2014; $7,638, AU-55, April 2014					

Note: Philippine silver pesos of 1907–1912 that were corroded from submersion in Caballo Bay during World War II are worth considerably less than their problem-free counterparts, but are avidly collected for their historical value. **a.** Proof only. **b.** Included in 1905-S, Curved Serif on "1," mintage figure.

	Mintage	VF	EF	MS-60 / PF-60	MS-63 / PF-63
1907, Proof (a,c)					$160,000
Auctions: $189,750, PF, June 2012					
1907-S	10,278,000	$10	$20	$250	$450
Auctions: $940, MS-64, October 2014; $447, MS-63, March 2015; $188, MS-62, December 2014; $112, MS-60, January 2014					
1908, Proof (a)	500			$700	$1,300
Auctions: $2,585, PF-66, January 2016; $1,763, PF-64, January 2015; $940, PF-64, August 2014; $999, PF-64, January 2014					
1908-S	20,954,944	$10	$20	$225	$425
Auctions: $881, MS-64, January 2016; $852, MS-64, January 2015; $705, MS-64, September 2014					
1909-S	7,578,000	$15	$24	$275	$500
Auctions: $4,935, MS-65, April 2015; $1,058, MS-64, October 2014; $235, MS-62, January 2014					
1909-S, S Over S	(d)	$35	$100	$325	$750
Auctions: No auction records available.					
1910-S	3,153,559	$24	$35	$350	$700
Auctions: $5,170, MS-65, April 2015; $489, MS-63, January 2010					
1911-S	463,000	$45	$75	$1,050	$4,250
Auctions: $5,875, MS-62, January 2016					
1912-S	680,000	$100	$220	$4,000	$7,000
Auctions: $9,988, MS-63, October 2014; $5,875, MS-61, April 2014; $999, AU-58, April 2014					

Note: Philippine silver pesos of 1907–1912 that were corroded from submersion in Caballo Bay during World War II are worth considerably less than their problem-free counterparts, but are avidly collected for their historical value. **a.** Proof only. **c.** 2 examples are known. **d.** Included in 1909-S mintage figure.

Manila Mint Opening Medal (1920)

Designer: *Clifford Hewitt.* **Composition:** *bronze; silver; gold.*
Diameter: *38 mm.* **Edge:** *Plain.* **Mint:** *Manila.*

Bronze

Silver

Gold

History. During U.S. sovereignty, much of the civilian government of the Philippines was administered by the Bureau of Insular Affairs, part of the War Department. Most heads or secretaries of Philippine government departments were appointed by the U.S. governor general, with the advice and consent of the Philippine Senate. In 1919, the chief of the Bureau of the Insular Treasury (part of the Department of Finance) was Insular Treasurer Albert P. Fitzsimmons, formerly a mayor of Tecumseh, Nebraska, and member of the municipal board of Manila. Fitzsimmons, a surgeon who had served in the U.S. Army Medical Corps in Cuba and the Philippines, was active in civil affairs, and had been in charge of U.S. government bond issues in the Philippines during the Great War. On May 20, 1919, he was named director ad interim of the Mint of the Philippine Islands, which was then being organized.

The genesis of this new mint started on February 8, 1918, when the Philippine Legislature passed an appropriations bill for construction of its machinery. The war in Europe was interfering with shipments from the San Francisco Mint, where Philippine coinage was produced, and a local mint was seen as more expedient and economical. In addition, a mint in Manila would serve the United States' goal of preparing the Philippines for its own governance and infrastructure.

The mint was built in Manila in the Intendencia Building, which also housed the offices and hall of the Senate, and the offices and vaults of the Philippine Treasury. Its machinery was designed and built in Philadelphia under the supervision of U.S. Mint chief mechanical engineer Clifford Hewitt, who also oversaw its installation in Manila. The facility was opened, with formalities and machine demonstrations, on July 15, 1920. The fanfare included the production of an official commemorative medal, the first example of which was struck by Speaker of the House of Representatives Sergio Osmeña.

The medal has since come to be popularly known as the "Wilson Dollar" (despite not being a legal-tender coin), because of its size and its bold profile portrait of Woodrow Wilson on the obverse, surrounded by the legend PRESIDENT OF THE UNITED STATES. The reverse features the ancient Roman goddess Juno Moneta guiding a youth—representing the fledgling mint staff of the Philippines—in the art of coining. She holds a pair of metallurgical scales. The reverse legend is TO COMMEMORATE THE OPENING OF THE MINT / MANILA P.I., along with the date, 1920. The medal was designed by Hewitt, the mint's supervising engineer from Philadelphia. Its dies were made by U.S. Mint chief engraver George T. Morgan, whose initial, M, appears on the obverse on President Wilson's breast and on the reverse above the goddess's sandal.

The issue was limited to 2,200 silver medals (2,000 of which were struck on the first day), sold to the public at $1 apiece; and 3,700 in bronze, sold for 50¢. In addition, at least five gold specimens were reportedly struck. These included one for presentation to President Wilson and one for U.S. Secretary of War Newton Baker. The other gold medals remained in the Philippines and were lost during World War II. Of the medals unsold and still held by the Treasury in the early 1940s, some or all were dumped into Caballo Bay in April 1942 along with millions of silver pesos, to keep them from the approaching Japanese forces. The invaders learned of the coins and in May attempted to recover the sunken silver coins using the labor of Filipino divers. Although skilled divers, the Filipinos were not experienced in deep-sea diving, and the coins were at the bottom of the bay, 120 feet below the surface. After three deaths the Filipinos refused to participate in further recovery efforts. The Japanese then forced U.S. prisoners of war who were experienced deep-sea divers to recover the coins and medals. The American divers conspired to salvage only small quantities of the sunken treasure. They repeatedly sabotaged the recovery process, and smuggled a significant number of recovered silver coins to the Philippine guerrillas. Only about 2 to 3 percent of the dumped coinage was recovered before the Japanese ceased recovery operations. Following the war the United States brought up much of the coinage that had been dumped into the sea. Many of the recovered silver and bronze Wilson dollars in grades VF through AU bear evidence of saltwater corrosion.

The Manila Mint Opening medal is popular with collectors of Philippine coins and of American medals. It is often cataloged as a *So-Called Dollar*, a classification of historic dollar-sized souvenir medals, some of which were struck by the U.S. Mint and some produced privately. The Manila Mint Opening medal is valued for its unique connections to the United States and to American numismatics.

	Mintage	VF-20	EF-40	AU-50	MS-60	MS-63	MS-65
Manila Mint medal, 1920, bronze	3,700	$50	$125	$235	$785	$1,350	$4,500
Manila Mint medal, 1920, silver	2,200	$100	$250	$350	$600	$1,850	$3,200

Note: VF, EF, and AU examples in bronze and silver often show signs of saltwater corrosion. The values above are for problem-free examples.

	Mintage	AU-55	MS-62
Manila Mint medal, 1920, gold	5	$44,000	$75,000

COMMONWEALTH ISSUES FOR CIRCULATION (1937–1945)

The Philippine Islands were largely self-governed, as a commonwealth of the United States, from 1935 until full independence was recognized in 1946. Coinage under the Commonwealth began with three commemorative coins in 1936 (see next section). Circulating issues were minted from 1937 to 1941 (in Manila) and in 1944 and 1945 (in Philadelphia, Denver, and San Francisco).

The Commonwealth coinage retained the obverse motifs designed by Melecio Figueroa and used on the coinage of 1903 to 1936. Its new reverse design featured a shield derived from the official seal of the government of the Philippines, with three stars symbolizing Luzon, Mindanao, and the Visayas, the islands' three main geographical regions. In the oval set in the shield's center is a modification of the colonial coat of arms of the City of Manila: a fortress tower above with a heraldic crowned *morse* or sea-lion (half dolphin, half lion) below. An eagle with outstretched wings surmounts the entirety of the shield design, and beneath is a scroll with the legend COMMONWEALTH OF THE PHILIPPINES.

World War II forced the Commonwealth government to operate in exile during the Japanese occupation of 1942 to 1945. A pro-Japan puppet government was set up in Manila in 1943; it issued no coins of its own, and in fact during the Japanese occupation many coins were gathered from circulation to be melted and remade into Japanese coins. Barter and low-denomination emergency paper money took their place in day-to-day commerce. (Much of the money used in the Philippines during World War II consisted of hastily printed "guerrilla" currency.) The United States military knew of the local need for circulating coins, and the U.S. and Philippine governments included new coinage in the plans to liberate the islands. The U.S. Treasury Department used its Philadelphia, San Francisco, and Denver mints to produce brass, copper-nickel-zinc, and silver coins in 1944 and 1945, to be shipped to the Philippines during and after the liberation.

Note that mintage figures given for 1938, 1939, 1940, and 1941 are estimates, as many Manila Mint records were lost during the war.

BRONZE AND BRASS COINAGE
ONE CENTAVO (1937–1944)

Designer: *Melecio Figueroa (obverse).* **Weight:** *5.3 grams.*
Composition: *.950 copper, .050 tin and zinc (except for 1944-S: .950 copper, .050 zinc).*
Diameter: *24 mm.* **Edge:** *Plain.* **Mints:** *Manila and San Francisco.*

Bronze Alloy (1937–1941)

Mintmark location is on the reverse, to the left of the date.

Brass Alloy (1944)

History. The Manila Mint struck one-centavo coins for the Commonwealth of the Philippines every year from 1937 through 1941. This production was brought to an end by the Japanese invasion that started in December 1941, immediately after the bombing of Pearl Harbor. Part of the United States–Commonwealth plan to retake the islands included the San Francisco Mint's 1944 striking of 58 million one-centavo coins—a quantity greater than all of Manila's centavo output since 1937. Like the federal Lincoln cents of 1944 to 1946, these coins were made of *brass* rather than bronze—their alloy was derived in part from recycled cartridge cases, and their composition included copper and zinc, but no tin (a vital war material). The coins were transported to the islands to enter circulation as U.S. and Philippine military forces fought back the Japanese invaders. This would be the final mintage of centavos until the Republic of the Philippines, created on July 4, 1946, resumed the denomination's production in 1958.

The centavo was a popular coin that saw widespread circulation. As a result, many of the coins today are found with signs of wear or damage, exacerbated by corrosion and toning encouraged by the islands' tropical climate.

Striking and Sharpness. Well-struck examples are uncommon. Obverses of the Commonwealth centavos usually have very flat or depressed strikes in the left shoulder of the seated figure, and part of the face and chest. His right hand is better struck than in the coins struck under U.S. sovereignty. The left side of the anvil's edge is slightly rounded. On the reverse, many Uncirculated coins have flatness on the lower and central sections of the coat of arms, and some or most of the words COMMONWEALTH OF THE PHILIPPINES are unreadable.

On a perfectly struck coin, the eagle surmounting the Commonwealth shield would have a pattern of feathers visible on its breast; this level of detail is rarely evident, with the breast instead appearing smooth or flat.

Many 1937-M centavos have a barely readable mintmark. Issues of 1938 to 1941 used a narrow M mintmark, rather than a square version of the letter, resulting in better legibility.

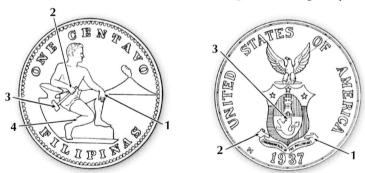

One Centavo, 1937–1944

High Points of Wear. *Obverse Checkpoints:* 1. Figure's left hand. 2. Figure's right hand. 3. Head of hammer. 4. Figure's right calf. *Reverse Checkpoints:* 1. Inner-right fold of ribbon. 2. Outer-left fold of ribbon. 3. Center of coat of arms.

	Mintage	VF	EF	MS-60	MS-63
1937-M	15,790,492	$2	$3	$15	$50
	Auctions: $153, MS-65RD, December 2015				
1938-M	10,000,000	$1.50	$2.50	$15	$35
	Auctions: $66, MS-65RB, March 2014; $94, MS-64RB, January 2014				
1939-M	6,500,000	$2.50	$3.50	$17.50	$55
	Auctions: $223, MS-66RD, April 2014				

	Mintage	VF	EF	MS-60	MS-63
1940-M	4,000,000	$1.25	$3	$15	$25
	Auctions: $50, MS-65RB, May 2014; $30, MS-64RD, March 2014				
1941-M	5,000,000	$3	$7.50	$20	$45
	Auctions: $59, MS-65RD, March 2014				
1944-S	58,000,000	$0.25	$0.50	$2	$4
	Auctions: $32, MS-65RD, March 2014				

COPPER-NICKEL AND COPPER-NICKEL-ZINC COINAGE
FIVE CENTAVOS (1937–1945)

Designer: *Melecio Figueroa (obverse).* **Weight:** *1937–1941, 4.8 grams; 1944–1945, 4.92 grams.*
Composition: *1937–1941, .750 copper, .250 nickel; 1944–1945, .650 copper, .230 zinc, .120 nickel.*
Diameter: *19 mm.* **Edge:** *Plain.* **Mints:** *Manila, Philadelphia, and San Francisco.*

Copper-Nickel
(1937–1941)

Mintmark location is on the reverse, to the left of the date (Manila and San Francisco issues only; Philadelphia issues have no mintmark).

Copper-Nickel-Zinc
(1944–1945)

Manila mintmark style of 1937 and 1941 (wide, with midpoint not extending to baseline).

Manila mintmark style of 1938 (narrow, with midpoint extending to baseline).

History. The Manila Mint switched its coinage of five-centavo pieces to the Commonwealth reverse design in 1937. Production of the coins increased in 1938, then skipped two years. The 1941 output would be Manila's last for the type; the Japanese invasion at year's end stopped all of its coinage.

Philippine commerce was starved for coins during the war. As part of the broader strategy for liberating the Philippines from Japanese occupation, the U.S. Treasury Department swung its mints into production of five-centavo coins in 1944 (Philadelphia and San Francisco) and 1945 (San Francisco alone). This effort dwarfed that of the Commonwealth's late-1930s coinage, producing in those two years more than ten times the combined output of 1937, 1938, and 1941. In order to help save copper and nickel for military use, the U.S. Mint reduced the proportions of those metals in the five-centavo coinage, making up for them with the addition of zinc. This substitution saved more than 4.2 million pounds of nickel and 3.2 million pounds of copper for the war effort. The Philadelphia and San Francisco coins were shipped to the islands during the combined American-Filipino military operations against Japan.

Striking and Sharpness. Most pre-war five-centavo coins are poorly struck. On the obverse, the seated figure's left hand is flat, and the left shoulder can be as well. The left side of the pedestal and the right side of Mount Mayon can be poorly detailed. The obverse rim typically lacks sharpness. On the reverse, the ribbon usually is flat, with its wording partially or completely illegible, and the coat of arms can lack detail especially at the top-left side. On a perfectly struck coin, the eagle surmounting the Commonwealth shield would have a pattern of feathers visible on its breast; this level of detail is rarely evident, with the breast instead appearing smooth or flat.

The mintmark style of 1937 and 1941—a wide M, with the middle point not descending to the letter's baseline—usually did not strike clearly, making it difficult to read. The mintmark style of 1938 was narrower, with the middle point descending to the base, and typically is more legible.

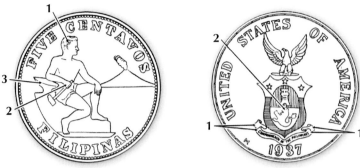

Five Centavos, 1937–1945

High Points of Wear. *Obverse Checkpoints:* 1. Frontal hair just above ear. 2. Figure's right hand. 3. Edge of anvil. *Reverse Checkpoints:* 1. Inner and outer folds of ribbon. 2. Center of coat of arms.

	Mintage	VF	EF	MS-60	MS-63
1937-M	2,493,872	$5	$7	$50	$75
	Auctions: $188, MS-65, September 2013				
1938-M	4,000,000	$1	$2.25	$25	$55
	Auctions: $92, MS-65, July 2014; $112, MS-65, September 2013				
1941-M	2,750,000	$4	$8	$55	$150
	Auctions: $282, MS-65, January 2014; $88, MS-64, September 2013				
1944 (a)	21,198,000	$0.50	$1	$2	$3
	Auctions: $46, MS-65, June 2013; $29, MS-64, April 2013				
1944-S (a)	14,040,000	$0.25	$0.50	$1	$2
	Auctions: $165, MS-67, September 2013; $200, MS-67, August 2013; $188, MS-67, August 2013				
1945-S (a)	72,796,000	$0.25	$0.50	$1	$2
	Auctions: No auction records available.				

a. Copper-nickel-zinc alloy.

SILVER COINAGE
TEN CENTAVOS (1937–1945)

Designer: *Melecio Figueroa.* **Weight:** *2 grams (.0482 oz. ASW).* **Composition:** *.750 silver, .250 copper.* **Diameter:** *16.5 mm.* **Edge:** *Reeded.* **Mints:** *Manila and Denver.*

Mintmark location is on the
reverse, to the left of the date.

History. As with its production of other denominations, the Manila Mint under Commonwealth governance struck ten-centavo coins in 1937 and 1938, followed by a hiatus of two years, and a final coinage in 1941. Normal mint functions were interrupted in 1941 when Imperial Japan invaded the Philippines as part of its war with the United States. The Japanese puppet government of 1943–1945 would not produce any of its own coins, and the Manila Mint, damaged by bombing during the Japanese assault, was later used as part of the invaders' defensive fortifications on the Pasig River.

Japan's wartime exportation of Philippine coins resulted in scarcity of coinage in day-to-day commerce. The U.S. Treasury geared up the Denver Mint for a massive production of Philippine ten-centavo coins in 1944 and 1945, to be shipped overseas and enter circulation as American and Philippine troops liberated the islands. The 1945 coinage was particularly heavy: more than 130 million ten-centavo coins, compared to the Denver Mint's production of just over 40 million Mercury dimes that year. This large mintage of silver coins continued to circulate in the Philippines into the 1960s.

Striking and Sharpness. Well-struck examples of the Commonwealth ten-centavo coin are unusual. Part of the figure's bust is nearly always flatly struck, especially along the left side. The hair and left arm may also be poorly struck. On the reverse, the coat of arms usually lacks detail, and COMMONWEALTH OF THE PHILIPPINES, on the ribbon, often is only partly legible. On a perfectly struck coin, the eagle surmounting the Commonwealth shield would have a pattern of feathers visible on its breast; this level of detail is rarely evident, with the breast instead appearing smooth or flat.

The Denver coinage of 1944 and 1945 often is weakly struck on the obverse, with loss of detail. The reverse typically is weakly struck on the ribbon, with indistinct lettering.

The mintmark style of 1937 and 1941—a wide M, with the middle point not descending to the letter's baseline—usually did not strike clearly, making it difficult to read. The mintmark style of 1938 was narrower, with the middle point descending to the base, and typically is more legible.

Ten Centavos, 1937–1945

High Points of Wear. *Obverse Checkpoints:* 1. Figure's left leg. 2. Edge of anvil. 3. Mid-drapery area. *Reverse Checkpoints:* 1. Inner and outer folds of ribbon. 2. Center of coat of arms.

	Mintage	VF	EF	MS-60	MS-63
1937-M	3,500,000	$2.25	$3.50	$15	$45
	Auctions: $500, MS-67, January 2013				
1938-M	3,750,000	$1.75	$2.25	$12	$20
	Auctions: $36, MS-63, August 2009				
1941-M	2,500,000	$1.50	$2	$7	$12.50
	Auctions: $36, MS-65, August 2009				
1944-D	31,592,000	$1	$2	$2.50	$3.50
	Auctions: No auction records available.				
1945-D	137,208,000	$1	$2	$2.50	$3.50
	Auctions: No auction records available.				
1945-D, D Over D	(a)	$8.50	$15	$25	$50
	Auctions: $470, AU-50, April 2014				

a. Included in 1945-D mintage figure.

Twenty Centavos (1937–1945)

Designer: *Melecio Figueroa (obverse).* **Weight:** *4 grams (.0964 oz. ASW).*
Composition: *.750 silver, .250 copper.* **Diameter:** *20 mm.*
Edge: *Reeded.* **Mints:** *Manila and Denver.*

Mintmark location is on the reverse, to the left of the date.

History. The twenty-centavo piece was the largest circulating coin struck by the Commonwealth of the Philippines at the Manila Mint. Production commenced in 1937 and 1938, followed by a hiatus of two years, and a final year of output in 1941 before Japan's December invasion put a halt to all coinage. During their occupation, the Japanese pulled many twenty-centavo pieces out of circulation and melted them as raw material for new imperial coins.

Anticipating driving the Japanese military out of the islands, the United States and Commonwealth governments planned an impressive production of coinage for the Philippines in 1944 and 1945. The Denver Mint was the source for twenty-centavo pieces, and its output was immense, in 1945 exceeding even the Philadelphia Mint's production of Washington quarters for domestic use. 111 million of the coins were shipped overseas to accompany the U.S. military as Americans and Filipinos fought to liberate the islands. The need was great, as legal-tender coins had largely disappeared from circulation. Most day-to-day commerce was transacted with small-denomination scrip notes and paper money issued by guerrilla military units, local governments, or anti-Japanese military and civilian currency boards.

Striking and Sharpness. Well-struck twenty-centavo Commonwealth coins are a challenge to locate. Nearly all obverses have flattened hair on the figure's head. On the reverse, the coat of arms usually lacks detail, and COMMONWEALTH OF THE PHILIPPINES, on the ribbon, often is only partly legible. The Denver coins typically lack sharp details on the obverse and have the same reverse weakness as earlier Manila issues.

On a perfectly struck coin, the eagle surmounting the Commonwealth shield would have a pattern of feathers visible on its breast; this level of detail is rarely evident, with the breast instead appearing smooth or flat.

The mintmark style of 1937 and 1941—a wide M, with the middle point not descending to the letter's baseline—usually did not strike clearly, making it difficult to read. The mintmark style of 1938 was narrower, with the middle point descending to the base, and typically is more legible.

Twenty Centavos, 1937–1945

High Points of Wear. *Obverse Checkpoints:* 1. Figure's left thigh and knee. 2. Figure's left hand. 3. Edge of anvil. *Reverse Checkpoints:* 1. Inner folds of ribbon. 2. Center of coat of arms.

1944-D, D Over S

	Mintage	VF	EF	MS-60	MS-63
1937-M	2,665,000	$3	$5	$35	$40
	Auctions: No auction records available.				
1938-M	3,000,000	$3	$5	$15	$20
	Auctions: $40, MS-64, August 2009; $32, MS-64, August 2009				
1941-M	1,500,000	$3	$3.50	$15	$20
	Auctions: No auction records available.				
1944-D	28,596,000	$2	$2.75	$3	$5
	Auctions: No auction records available.				
1944-D, D Over S	(a)	$5	$9	$25	$50
	Auctions: $403, MS-66, January 2010				
1945-D	82,804,000	$2	$2.75	$3	$5
	Auctions: No auction records available.				

a. Included in 1944-D mintage figure.

FIFTY CENTAVOS (1944–1945)

Designer: *Melecio Figueroa.* **Weight:** *10 grams (.2411 oz. ASW).*
Composition: *.750 silver, .250 copper.* **Diameter:** *27 mm.*
Edge: *Reeded.* **Mint:** *San Francisco.*

Mintmark location is on the reverse, to the left of the date.

History. No fifty-centavo coins were struck at the Manila Mint for the Commonwealth of the Philippines. The denomination's first issue was a wartime production of the San Francisco Mint, in 1944, to the extent of some 19 million coins, or double that facility's production of Liberty Walking half dollars for the year. This was followed by a similar mintage in 1945. These coins were intended to enter circulation after being shipped overseas with the U.S. military during the liberation of the Philippines from Imperial Japan's 1942–1945 occupation. They were readily accepted in the coin-starved wartime economy and continued to circulate in the islands into the 1960s.

Striking and Sharpness. Many Commonwealth fifty-centavo coins are lightly struck, but they typically show flattening less severe than that of the 1907–1921 issues struck under U.S. sovereignty. On the reverse, the coat of arms usually is weakly struck, with COMMONWEALTH OF THE PHILIPPINES rarely completely legible. On a perfectly struck coin, the eagle surmounting the Commonwealth shield would have a pattern of feathers visible on its breast; this level of detail is rarely evident, with the breast instead appearing smooth or flat.

Fifty Centavos, 1944–1945

High Points of Wear. *Obverse Checkpoints:* 1. Figure's left thigh and lower leg. 2. Mid-drapery area. 3. Figure's left bosom. 4. Edge of anvil. *Reverse Checkpoints:* 1. Inner folds of ribbon. 2. Center of coat of arms.

1945-S, S Over S

	Mintage	VF	EF	MS-60	MS-63
1944-S	19,187,000	$5	$6	$8	$10
	Auctions: $94, MS-66, July 2015; $44, MS-64, March 2013				
1945-S	18,120,000	$5	$6	$8	$10
	Auctions: $100, MS-66, January 2014				
1945-S, S Over S	(a)	$12	$25	$80	$180
	Auctions: $306, MS-66, May 2014; $118, MS-62, October 2015				

a. Included in 1945-S mintage figure.

COMMONWEALTH COMMEMORATIVE ISSUES

The American territory of the Philippines was governed by the U.S. military from 1899 to mid-1901. Its executive branch was managed by the Bureau of Insular Affairs (part of the War Department) from mid-1901 to 1935. In the latter year the Philippines' status was changed to that of a commonwealth—a type of organized but unincorporated dependent territory, self-governed (except in defense and foreign policy) under a constitution of its own adoption, whose right of self-government would not be unilaterally withdrawn by Congress. This was a step in the direction of complete independence, scheduled to be recognized after an additional ten years of "nation building."

To celebrate this transfer of government, the Manila Mint in 1936 produced a set of three silver commemorative coins—one of the fifty-centavo denomination, and two of the one-peso. These were designed by Ambrosio Morales, professor of sculpture at the University of the Philippines School of Fine Arts.

The fifty-centavo coin and one of the set's pesos feature busts of Philippine president Manuel L. Quezon and the last U.S. governor-general, Frank Murphy, who served (largely ceremonially) as the first U.S. high commissioner to the Commonwealth of the Philippines. On the fifty-centavo piece the two men face each other with the rising sun between them; on the peso, they appear jugate (in conjoined profile portraits). The other peso has busts of Quezon and U.S. president Franklin D. Roosevelt. This was a rare instance of a living American president appearing on a coin, the only precedent being the 1926 Sesquicentennial commemorative half dollar, which showed President Calvin Coolidge.

On each of the three coins appears the date November 15, 1935, when the new commonwealth's government was inaugurated on the steps of the Legislative Building in Manila, witnessed by 300,000 people in attendance.

The set's issue price was $3.13, or about 2.5 times the coins' face value expressed in U.S. dollars. Commemorative coins were popular in the United States at the time, but still these sets sold poorly, and thousands remained within the Philippine Treasury at the onset of World War II. In early 1942 many if not all of the remainders were crated and thrown into Caballo Bay, to keep them (along with millions of older silver pesos) from being captured by the approaching forces of Imperial Japan. Today many of the coins are found with corrosion caused by their long exposure to saltwater before being salvaged.

FIFTY CENTAVOS (1936)

Designer: *Ambrosio Morales (obverse).* **Weight:** *10 grams (.2411 oz. ASW).*
Composition: *.750 silver, .250 copper.* **Diameter:** *27.5 mm.* **Edge:** *Reeded.* **Mint:** *Manila.*

Striking and Sharpness. This issue typically is found well struck.

	Mintage	VF	EF	MS-60	MS-63
1936-M, Silver fifty centavos	20,000	$30	$50	$100	$155
	Auctions: $1,528, MS-66, January 2016; $206, MS-64, January 2014; $112, MS-63, December 2014				

ONE PESO (1936)

Designer: *Ambrosio Morales (obverse).* **Weight:** *20 grams (.5144 oz. ASW).*
Composition: *.800 silver, .200 copper.* **Diameter:** *35 mm.* **Edge:** *Reeded.* **Mint:** *Manila.*

One Peso, Busts of Murphy and Quezon   **One Peso, Busts of Roosevelt and Quezon**

Striking and Sharpness. Sharply struck gems of the Murphy/Quezon peso can be a challenge to locate. Weak strike is evident on the reverse in particular, where the sea-lion can be softly detailed. On some pieces, tiny bubbles resulting from improper fabrication of the planchet can be observed among the letters surrounding the rim.

The Roosevelt/Quezon peso typically is found well struck.

	Mintage	VF	EF	MS-60	MS-63
1936-M, Silver one peso, busts of Murphy and Quezon	10,000	$70	$85	$200	$325
	Auctions: $940, MS-66, October 2014; $764, MS-66, October 2014; $176, MS, May 2015				
1936-M, Silver one peso, busts of Roosevelt and Quezon	10,000	$70	$85	$200	$300
	Auctions: $823, MS-66, January 2016; $359, MS-65, August 2013; $329, MS-65, January 2013				

Alaska Tokens

ALASKA RURAL REHABILITATION CORPORATION TOKENS OF 1935

Before the Roosevelt Administration's dramatic New Deal response to the Great Depression, it was the states themselves, rather than the federal government, that organized and funded the relief of their citizens in need. This changed with the Federal Emergency Relief Act of 1933, by which Congress appropriated $250 million for states to use in their relief efforts, with the same amount funded for federal programs. Other relief acts would follow. The states were to use their 1933 FERA grant money "to aid in meeting the costs of furnishing relief and in relieving the hardship and suffering caused by unemployment in the form of money, service, materials, and/or commodities to provide the necessities of life to persons in need as a result of the present emergency, and/or their dependents, whether resident, transient, or homeless," as well as to "aid in assisting cooperative and self-help associations for the barter of goods and services."

Americans living in cities benefited from direct relief grants as well as employment in work-relief projects. Those in rural areas, however, had a stronger need for *rehabilitation* programs rather than relief as such. In April 1934 a special Rural Rehabilitation Division was set up. This helped establish rural camps where people made homeless by the Depression could find shelter and assistance until conditions improved. Nonprofits called *rural rehabilitation corporations* were devised to carry this effort forward. One function of the corporations was to buy large expanses of farmland to divide into 40- or 60-acre plots. These would be mortgaged to displaced farm families who agreed to develop and farm the land in exchange for low-interest loans and other assistance. One community developed under this plan was the Matanuska Valley Colony at Palmer, about 45 miles northeast of Anchorage, in the territory of Alaska. For the Alaska program some 203 families were recruited from Michigan, Minnesota, and Wisconsin. Those states were targeted not only because they had a very high percentage of displaced farmers on social-assistance relief, but also because their cold-weather climates were similar to Alaska's.

A suite of (undated) 1935 tokens was issued by the U.S. government for the use of the Midwesterners who relocated to the colonization project. These aluminum and brass tokens (nicknamed "bingles") would supply the settlers with much-needed federal aid, being paid out for work at the rate of 50¢ per hour. In theory this wage payment in tokens, rather than regular coinage, would also discourage the workers from spending their money unwisely, as the bingles were redeemable only at Alaska Rural Rehabilitation Corporation stores. In addition to use as wages, the tokens were issued based on immediate need and according to the size of the family. A family of two would receive a monthly allowance of $45; a family of three, $55; a family of four, $75; and a family of five, $85. The bingles were in use only about six months, during the winter of 1935 and 1936. The colony's managers were unable to restrict their use to the purchase of necessities in corporation-run stores—other merchants, including the local saloon, realized they could also accept them as currency. Eventually the tokens were recalled and redeemed for regular U.S. money. Practically all of the circulated tokens were destroyed after redemption.

Of the $23,000 face value minted, about $18,000 worth of tokens were issued in the months they were in active use. The unissued tokens were later made into souvenir sets for collectors. Some 250 complete sets were thus preserved in unused condition, in addition to about 100 "short" sets consisting of the one-cent, five-cent, and ten-cent pieces.

Each token is similar in size to the corresponding U.S. coin of the same denomination (one cent through ten dollars), with the exception of the one-cent piece, which is octagonal. The design is the same on both sides of each denomination.

Even after leaving hardship in the Midwest, and even with this federal aid, the Alaska colonists faced ongoing challenges. Potatoes and other crops were successfully grown, but the farming seasons were short, markets were far away, and the expense of shipping was high. More than half of the Alaska colonists left the Matanuska Valley within five years, and thirty years later only twenty of the original families were still farming there. Still, the New Deal colony helped the Matanuska Valley to slowly grow into Alaska's most productive agricultural region.

For more information on these and other Alaska-related coins and tokens, see *Alaska's Coinage Through the Years*, by Maurice Gould, Kenneth Bressett, and Kaye and Nancy Dethridge.

ALUMINUM

	Mintage	EF	Unc.
One Cent	5,000	$90	$160
Five Cents	5,000	$90	$160
Ten Cents	5,000	$90	$160
Twenty-Five Cents	3,000	$135	$265
Fifty Cents	2,500	$135	$265
One Dollar	2,500	$225	$265

BRASS

	Mintage	EF	Unc.
Five Dollars	1,000	$225	$350
Ten Dollars	1,000	$250	$400

APPENDIX A

Misstrikes and Errors

With the production of millions of coins each year, it is natural that a few abnormal pieces escape inspection and are inadvertently released for circulation, usually in original bags or rolls of new coins. These are not considered regular issues because they were not made intentionally. They are all eagerly sought by collectors for the information they shed on minting techniques, and as a variation from normal date and mint series collecting.

MISSTRUCK COINS AND ERROR PIECES

Nearly every misstruck or error coin is unique in some way, and prices may vary from coin to coin. They may all be classified in general groups related to the kinds of errors or manufacturing malfunctions involved. Collectors value these pieces according to the scarcity of each kind of error for each type of coin. Non-collectors usually view them as curios, and often believe that they must be worth much more than normal coins because they look so strange. In reality, the value assigned to various types of errors by collectors and dealers reflects both supply and demand, and is based on recurring transactions between willing buyers and sellers.

The following listings show current average values for the most frequently encountered kinds of error coins. In each case, the values shown are for coins that are unmarred by serious marks or scratches, and in Uncirculated condition for modern issues, and Extremely Fine condition for obsolete types. Exceptions are valued higher or lower. Error coins of rare-date issues generally do not command a premium beyond their normal values. In most cases each of these coins is unique in some respect and must be valued according to its individual appearance, quality, and eye appeal.

There are many other kinds of errors and misstruck coins beyond those listed in this guide book. Some are more valuable, and others less valuable, than the most popular pieces that are listed here as examples of what this interesting field contains. The pieces illustrated are general examples of the types described.

Early in 2002 the mints changed their production methods to a new system designed to eliminate deformed planchets, off-center strikes, and similar errors. They also changed the delivery system of bulk coinage, and no longer shipped loose coins in sewn bags to be counted and wrapped by banks or counting rooms, where error coins were often found and sold to collectors. Under the new system, coins are packaged in large quantities and go directly to automated counters that filter out deformed coins. The result has been that very few error coins have entered the market since late 2002, and almost none after that date. The values shown in these listings are for pre-2002 coins; those dated after that, with but a few exceptions, are valued considerably higher.

For additional details and information about these coins, the following books are recommended:

Margolis, Arnold, and Fred Weinberg. *The Error Coin Encyclopedia* (4th ed.). 2004.

Herbert, Alan. *Official Price Guide to Minting Varieties and Errors.* New York, 1991.

Fivaz, Bill, and J.T. Stanton. *The Cherrypickers' Guide to Rare Die Varieties.* Atlanta, GA, updated regularly.

The coins discussed in this section must not be confused with others that have been mutilated or damaged after leaving the mint. Examples of such pieces include coins that have been scratched, hammered, engraved, impressed, acid etched, or plated by individuals to simulate something other than a normal coin. Those pieces have no numismatic value, and can only be considered as altered coins not suitable for a collection.

TYPES OF ERROR COINS

Clipped Planchet—**An incomplete coin, missing 10 to 25% of the metal.** Incomplete planchets result from accidents when the steel rods used to punch out blanks from the metal strip overlap a portion of the strip already punched. There are curved, straight, ragged, incomplete, and elliptical clips. Values may be greater or less depending on the nature and size of the clip. Coins with more than one clip usually command higher values.

Multiple Strike—**A coin with at least one additional image from being struck again off center.** Value increases with the number of strikes. These minting errors occur when a finished coin goes back into the press and is struck again with the same dies. The presence of a date can bring a higher value.

No Rim　　　**With Rim**

Blank or Planchet—**A blank disc of metal intended for coinage but not struck with dies.** In the process of preparation for coinage, the blanks are first punched from a strip of metal and then milled to upset the rim. In most instances, first-process pieces (blanks without upset rims) are slightly more valuable than the finished planchets. Values shown are for the most common pieces.

Defective Die—**A coin showing raised metal from a large die crack, or small rim break.** Coins that show evidence of light die cracks, polishing, or very minor die damage are generally of little or no value. Prices shown here are for coins with very noticeable, raised die-crack lines, or those for which the die broke away, producing an unstruck area known as a *cud*.

Off Center—**A coin that has been struck out of collar and incorrectly centered, with part of the design missing.** Values are for coins with approximately 10 to 20% of design missing from obsolete coins, or 20 to 60% missing from modern coins. These are misstruck coins that were made when the planchet did not enter the coinage press properly. Coins that are struck only slightly off center, with none of the design missing, are called broadstrikes (see the next category). Those with nearly all of the impression missing are generally worth more, but those with a readable date and mint are the most valuable.

Broadstrike—**A coin that was struck outside the retaining collar.** When coins are struck without being contained in the collar die, they spread out larger than normal pieces. All denominations have a plain edge.

Lamination—**A flaw whereby a fragment of metal has peeled off the coin's surface.** This defect occurs when a foreign substance, such as gas oxides or dirt, becomes trapped in the strip as it is rolled out to the proper thickness. Lamination flaws may be missing or still attached to the coin's surface. Minor flaws may only decrease a coin's value, while a clad coin that is missing the full surface of one or both sides is worth more than the values listed here.

Brockage—**A mirror image of the design impressed on the opposite side of the same coin.** These errors are caused when a struck coin remains on either die after striking, and impresses its image into the next blank planchet as it is struck, leaving a negative or mirror image. Off-center and partial brockage coins are worth less than those with full impression. Coins with negative impressions on both sides are usually mutilated pieces made outside the mint by the pressing together of coins.

Wrong Planchet—**A coin struck on a planchet intended for another denomination or of the wrong metal.** Examples of these are cents struck on dime planchets, nickels on cent planchets, or quarters on dime planchets. Values vary depending on the type of error involved. Those struck on coins of a different denomination that were previously struck normally are of much greater value. A similar kind of error occurs when a coin is struck on a planchet of the correct denomination but wrong metal. One famous example is the 1943 cent struck in bronze (pictured), rather than in that year's new steel composition. (Fewer than three dozen are thought to exist.) Such errors presumably occur when an older planchet is mixed in with the normal supply of planchets and goes through the minting process.

MINT-CANCELED COINS

In mid-2003, the U.S. Mint acquired machines to eliminate security concerns and the cost associated with providing Mint police escorts to private vendors for the melting of scrap, substandard struck coins, planchets, and blanks. Under high pressure, the rollers and blades of these machines cancel the coins and blanks in a manner similar in appearance to the surface of a waffle, and they are popularly known by that term. This process has effectively kept most misstruck coins produced after 2003 from becoming available to collectors. Waffled examples are known for all six 2003-dated coin denominations, from the Lincoln cent through the Sacagawea dollar. The Mint has not objected to these pieces' trading in the open market because they are not considered coins with legal tender status.

MISSTRUCK AND ERROR PIECES

	Clipped Planchet	Multiple Strike	Blank, No Raised Rim	Planchet, Raised Rim	Defective Die	Off Center	Broadstrike	Lamination	Brockage
Large Cent	$50	$1,000	$200	$275	$25	$600	$100	$25	$1,000
Indian Head 1¢	$15	$600	—	—	$25	$150	$50	$15	$400
Lincoln 1¢ (95% Copper)	$3	$50	$4	$3	$12	$10	$8	$3	$35
Steel 1¢	$20	$250	$55	$75	$15	$60	$35	$15	$250
Lincoln 1¢ (Zinc)	$4	$35	$3	$2	$15	$8	$5	$15	$35
Liberty 5¢	$20	$700	—	$250	$35	$250	$110	$20	$450
Buffalo 5¢	$20	$2,500	—	$600	$40	$500	$300	$30	$850
Jefferson 5¢	$3	$40	$15	$10	$15	$12	$10	$10	$40
Wartime 5¢	$8	$400	$400	$350	$25	$200	$70	$15	$200
Barber 10¢	$40	$750	—	—	$75	$300	$85	$12	$400
Mercury 10¢	$18	$800	—	—	$35	$175	$55	$15	$300
Roosevelt 10¢ (Silver)	$7	$250	$50	$40	$35	$150	$45	$12	$100
Roosevelt 10¢ (Clad)	$3	$50	$3	$4	$15	$12	$10	$16	$40

	Clipped Planchet	Multiple Strike	Blank, No Raised Rim	Planchet, Raised Rim	Defective Die	Off Center	Broadstrike	Lamination	Brockage
Washington 25¢ (Silver)	$18	$400	$175	$160	$25	$350	$200	$15	$300
Washington 25¢ (Clad)	$5	$150	$8	$7	$12	$70	$20	$25	$50
Bicentennial 25¢	$35	$350	—	—	$65	$150	$50	$50	$250
State 25¢	$20	$500	—	—	$25	$75	$35	$200	$325
Franklin 50¢	$35	$1,800	—	—	$150	$1,800	$500	$25	$750
Kennedy 50¢ (40% Silver)	$20	$1,000	$185	$150	$70	$450	$200	$40	$450
Kennedy 50¢ (Clad)	$15	$600	$135	$100	$50	$250	$75	$25	$300
Bicentennial 50¢	$40	$700	—	—	$90	$300	$95	$40	$550
Silver $1	$40	$5,000	$1,600	$1,500	$950	$2,200	$775	$50	$550
Eisenhower $1	$30	$1,000	$150	$100	$500	$600	$150	$50	$950
Bicentennial $1	$45	$1,500	$135	—	$750	$750	$200	$50	$1,100
Anthony $1	$25	$600	$200	$110	$100	$250	$75	$30	$300
Sacagawea $1	$85	$1,950	$250	$60	$50	$1,500	$275	$50	$450

WRONG PLANCHETS

	Zinc 1¢	Copper 1¢	Steel 1¢	5¢	Silver 10¢	Copper-Nickel Clad 10¢	Silver 25¢	Copper-Nickel Clad 25¢	Copper-Nickel Clad 50¢
Indian Head 1¢	(a)	—	(a)	(a)	$9,500	(a)	(a)	(a)	(a)
Lincoln 1¢	—	—	—	(a)	$1,000	$350	(a)	(a)	(a)
Buffalo 5¢	(a)	$4,000	(a)	—	$6,000	(a)	(a)	(a)	(a)
Jefferson 5¢	$300	$250	$2,500	—	$450	$375	(a)	(a)	(a)
Wartime 5¢	(a)	$2,500	$3,500	—	$2,000	(a)	(a)	(a)	(a)
Washington 25¢ (Silver)	(a)	$900	$7,000	$450	$1,500	—	—	—	(a)
Washington 25¢ (Clad)	—	$750	(a)	$225	—	$350	—	—	(a)
Bicentennial 25¢	(a)	$3,000	(a)	$2,500	—	$3,500	—	—	(a)
State 25¢ (b)	$4,500	(a)	(a)	$600	(a)	$4,000	(a)	—	(a)
Walking Liberty 50¢	(a)	—	—	—	—	(a)	$25,000	(a)	(a)
Franklin 50¢	(a)	$5,500	(a)	$5,000	$6,000	(a)	$1,500	(a)	(a)
Kennedy 50¢ (c)	(a)	$3,000	(a)	$1,250	—	$2,000	—	$650	—
Bicentennial 50¢	(a)	$4,000	(a)	$2,750	—	—	—	$1,200	—
Eisenhower $1	(a)	$10,000	(a)	$9,000	—	$10,000	—	$6,000	$2,500
Anthony $1	—	$3,500	(a)	$5,000	(a)	—	—	$1,000	(a)
Sacagawea $1	$10,000	(a)	(a)	$10,000	(a)	$10,000	(a)	$3,500	(a)

Note: Coins struck over other coins of different denominations are usually valued three to five times higher than these prices. Coins made from mismatched dies (State quarter obverse combined with Sacagawea dollar reverse) are extremely rare. **a.** Not possible. **b.** Values for State quarter errors vary with each type and state, and are generally much higher than for other quarters. **c.** The Kennedy fifty-cent piece struck on an Anthony one-dollar planchet is very rare.

A GALLERY OF SIGNIFICANT U.S. MINT ERROR COINS

Every high-production manufacturing facility makes a certain percentage of "factory irregulars." The U.S. Mint—which for decades has produced billions of coins annually—is no exception. Today's Mint, though, has cutting-edge machinery and quality-control procedures that keep errors and misstruck coins to a minimum. When such coins *do* come into being, the Mint's sophisticated safeguards (such as riddlers that filter aside odd-shaped coins) prevent nearly all of them from leaving its facilities. Over the course of its 220-plus years of making and issuing coins, however, the Mint has produced some amazing and unusual coins that have made their way into collectors' hands. This gallery highlights a selection of collectible, significant, and valuable errors and misstruck coins.

Some early U.S. Mint coins might appear to be misstrikes when in fact they simply illustrate the standard operating procedures of the time. For example, many 1795 and 1797 half cents show faint evidence of the design of Talbot, Allum & Lee tokens. These are not highly prized double-denominations, but rather regular federal coins intentionally struck on planchets made from cut-down tokens. Other examples exist, such as "spoiled" (misstruck) large cents salvaged and cut down into planchets for half cents.

The introduction of steam-driven coining presses in the 1830s ushered in what today's collector might consider a golden age of misstruck coins. Two competing factors were at work: improved minting techniques and quality control helped curb (or at least catch) most errors and misstrikes, but dramatically increasing mintages naturally led to a greater quantity of such mistakes.

The 1900s and 2000s saw continuing modernization of the mints and a gradual conversion from older presses to new higher-speed presses, eventually capable of striking up to 750 coins per minute. In addition to their speed, today's presses strike coins horizontally, allowing highly efficient and consistently accurate production. As discussed earlier, major misstrikes and coinage errors from 2002 to the present are very rare. Currently, only a handful of new significant pieces enter the market each year.

Error and misstruck coins are a growing specialty in the rare-coin market. Their appeal and value lie in their rarity, their unusual appearance, and the insight they provide into the minting process. When major specimens appear at auction, they bring excitement and active bidding. While no misstrike or error coin has yet sold for a million dollars, several have sold for six-figure sums.

This gallery illustrates a variety of such pieces not typically seen. Some of the featured coins reside in museums or other permanent collections. Each is a classic representation of its type (e.g., wrong planchet or double strike). In many cases, they are unique; for the rest, only a few such pieces are known. The valuations are approximate, based on recent sales and market conditions. For misstruck and error coins, the grade, type, and eye appeal are important factors in market pricing.

Special credit is due to Nicholas P. Brown, David J. Camire, and Fred Weinberg, authors of *100 Greatest U.S. Error Coins*, for contributing to this feature.

1904 Lewis and Clark Exposition gold dollar (partial collar with reverse brockage). This specimen, part of the Smithsonian's National Numismatic Collection, is unique among commemorative gold coinage. It was created when a struck coin failed to fully eject from the press. A new planchet entered and came to rest partially atop the coin; when they were struck together, a reverse image was transferred to the error coin. The obstruction also prevented the planchet from being fully enclosed by the collar. *Value:* $25,000 or more.

1943 Lincoln cent struck over a struck 1943 Mercury dime (double denomination). This piece is unique for the date, and one of only a handful known in silver for the series. It occurred when 1943-dated cent dies struck a 1943 dime instead of a steel cent planchet. *Value:* $16,000 or more.

1999-P Anthony dollar struck on a 2000 Sacagawea planchet (wrong planchet–transitional). About six examples of this kind are known, most acquired from Mint rolls and bags. During transitions in a coin series (e.g., in metal content or design), wrong planchets may accidentally be used in production. This transitional error shows a "golden dollar" planchet that was used to strike an Anthony dollar. *Value:* $16,000 or more.

1863 Indian Head cent (obverse capped die). This dramatic piece is unique for the date and the series. The coin was struck multiple times by the obverse die against a planchet that rested atop the reverse die. Since the planchet was not properly seated in the collar, the force of the strike spread the planchet (cracking it in the process) until it was larger than a quarter dollar. *Value:* $55,000 or more.

1906 Indian Head cent struck on a quarter eagle planchet (wrong planchet). This error is unique for the date, and one of perhaps four known in the series. Somehow a gold quarter-eagle planchet made its way into the coining chamber for cent production. Some theorize that this and similar specimens were intentionally struck, but most show light to moderate wear that suggests they entered circulation. *Value:* $150,000 or more.

1860 Liberty Seated quarter struck on a cent planchet (wrong planchet). This specimen is unique for the date and the series. Its bright bronze color (from the copper-nickel Indian Head cent planchet) and Mint State grade give it great visual appeal. *Value:* $50,000 or more.

1837 Capped Bust half dollar struck on a struck large cent (double denomination). This misstrike is unique for the date and the series. It was made when the steam press had been in use for half dollars only a little more than a year. The coin appears to have circulated for a while before being placed into a collection. Much detail still shows from both strikes. *Value:* $50,000 or more.

Peace dollar struck on a Standing Liberty quarter planchet (wrong planchet). This error is unique for the date and the series. Judging from its Mint State grade, it was probably placed into a collection after being found in a bag or roll of coins. *Value:* $75,000 or more.

1909 Indian Head cent struck on a struck 1906 Barber dime (double denomination). This piece is unique for the date and the series. Considerable detail shows from both strikes. *Value:* $25,000 or more.

1976-D Eisenhower dollar (obverse die cap). This specimen is unique for the date, and one of only a couple known in the series. It occurred when a struck coin adhered to the die, essentially becoming a die itself. Each subsequent strike caused the planchet to bend around the die, forming a deep, bottle cap–shaped coin. *Value:* $25,000 or more.

1976-D Washington quarter (double strike). A few such specimens are known, in varying degrees of off-center double striking. This misstrike has a second strike 40% off center from the first, and is die-struck on both sides. *Value:* $2,750 or more.

1923 Peace dollar (double strike). This misstrike is unique for the date and the series. Apparently the coin was struck about 45% off center, then repositioned and struck a second time, centered normally. *Value:* $75,000 or more.

1977 Jefferson nickel struck on a 1976 Lincoln cent (double denomination–dual date). Two examples of this error are known for the date, among a half dozen in the series. Both dates are clearly visible. *Value:* $8,000 or more.

(1976 or 1977) Lincoln cent struck off center on a Philippine five-sentimos planchet (wrong planchet–multiple error). This error is unique for the series as an off center; several are known struck on center. The Philadelphia Mint struck almost 99 million five-sentimo coins for the Philippines in 1976, and more than 1 million in 1977. Only a few U.S. coins are known accidentally struck on their planchets. *Value:* $2,750 or more.

(1960) Jefferson nickel struck on a 1960 Peruvian five-centavos coin (double denomination–dual country). This error is unique for the date and the series. Interestingly, Mint records do not indicate any coins of Peru were struck at the Philadelphia Mint in 1960. *Value:* $10,000 or more.

Lincoln cent struck off center on a Roosevelt dime (double denomination–off center). Only a few off-center double denominations are known for this series. This is a full dime that was struck off-center by cent dies. *Value:* $5,500 or more.

1943 Lincoln cent struck on a bronze planchet (wrong planchet–transitional). About a dozen of these well-known errors have been confirmed. They came about when bronze planchets left over from 1942 cent production were mixed with the regular 1943 steel planchets. All but one were found in circulation. This error was voted among the *100 Greatest U.S. Coins* (Garrett and Guth). *Value:* $100,000 or more.

(2000) Washington quarter obverse muled with a Sacagawea dollar reverse (mule). About two dozen of these dramatic errors are known to have been struck at Philadelphia, in three die pairings. They have received nationwide publicity in the mainstream press. *Value:* $100,000 or more.

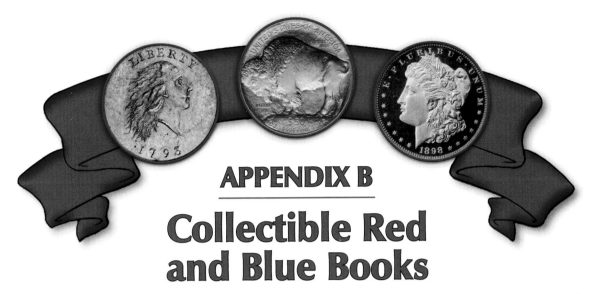

APPENDIX B
Collectible Red and Blue Books

The book you are reading is the *Deluxe Edition* of a classic hobby reference, the *Guide Book of United States Coins*, popularly known as the "Red Book." More than 23 million copies of the Red Book have been sold since 1946, making it one of the best-selling nonfiction titles in American publishing history. By 1959 more than 100,000 copies were being printed annually. The 1965 (18th) edition, published in 1964, reached a peak of 1,200,000 copies. That year the Red Book was ranked fifth on the list of best-selling nonfiction—ahead of Dale Carnegie's classic *How to Win Friends and Influence People* (at number 6) and John F. Kennedy's *Profiles in Courage* (at number 9).

The idea for the Red Book started in the 1940s with R.S. Yeoman. Employed by Whitman Publishing Company (part of Western Publishing), Yeoman at first created the "Blue Book" (official title, the *Handbook of United States Coins With Premium List*), which gave hobbyists an overview of American coinage and a detailed guide to the prices that dealers were paying for collectible coins. The first edition was published in 1942. Yeoman saw that collectors wanted even more information, and he began compiling data and records for an expanded *retail* version of the Blue Book (showing how much a collector could expect to pay a dealer for coins). After World War II ended, Yeoman and his team introduced the new volume, the *Guide Book of United States Coins*, soon nicknamed the Red Book because of its distinctive cover color.

Numismatist Kenneth E. Bressett joined the Red Book in 1956 as a freelance editor. He has continued to work on the annually published book, and other Whitman projects, ever since. He took a full-time editorial position with Whitman Publishing in 1959, and assumed full editorship of the Red Book in 1975. Today Bressett serves as the Red Book's editor emeritus, with Jeff Garrett as senior editor, Q. David Bowers as research editor, and a panel of more than 100 coin dealers, researchers, and other specialists.

THE RED BOOK AS A COLLECTIBLE

The *Guide Book of United States Coins* holds the record as the longest-running annual retail coin-price guide. It has passed its 65th anniversary, and collectors seem to be almost as interested in assembling sets of old Red Books as of old coins. The demand for old Red Books has created a solid market. Some who collect these old editions maintain reference libraries of all kinds of coin publications. To them, having one of each edition is essential, because that is the way old books are collected. Others are speculators who believe that the value of old editions will go up as interest and demand increase. Many people who save old Red Books do so to maintain a record of coin prices going back further than any other source.

Following price trends in old Red Books is a good indicator of how well individual coins are doing in comparison to each other. The price information published in each year is an average of what collectors are paying for each coin. It is a valuable benchmark, showing how prices have gone up or down over the years. Information like this often gives investors an edge in predicting what the future may hold.

Old Red Books are also a handy resource on collecting trends. They show graphically how grading has changed over the years, what new coins have been discovered and added to the listings, and which areas are growing in popularity. Studying these old books can be educational as well as nostalgic. It's great fun to see what your favorite coins sold for 15 or 25 years ago or more—and a bit frustrating to realize what might have been if we had only bought the right coins at the right time in years past.

Many collectors have asked about the quantities printed of each edition. That information has never been published, and now no company records exist specifying how many were made. The original author, R.S. Yeoman, told inquirers that the first press run in November 1946 was for 9,000 copies. In February 1947 an additional 9,000 copies were printed to satisfy the unexpected demand.

There was a slight but notable difference that can be used to differentiate between the first and second printings. The wording in the first printing at the bottom of page 135 reads, "which probably accounts for the scarcity of *this* date." Those last few words were changed to "the scarcity of *1903 O*" in the second printing.

The second edition had a press run of 22,000. The printing of each edition thereafter gradually increased, with the highest number ever being reached with the 18th edition, dated 1965 and published in 1964. At the top of a booming coin market, a whopping 1,200,000 copies were produced. Since that time the numbers have decreased, but the Red Book still maintains a record of being the world's largest-selling coin publication each year.

In some years a very limited number of Red Books were made for use by price contributors. Those were interleaved with blank pages. No more than 50 copies were ever made for any one year. Perhaps fewer than 20 were made in the first few years. Three of these of the first edition, and one of the second edition, are currently known. Their value is now in four figures. Those made in the 1960s sell for about $300–$500 today.

There are other unusual Red Books that command exceptional prices. One of the most popular is the 1987 special edition that was made for, and distributed only to, people who attended the 1986 American Numismatic Association banquet in Milwaukee. Only 500 of those were printed with a special commemorative cover.

Error books are also popular with collectors. The most common is one with double-stamped printing on the cover. The second most frequently seen are those with an upside-down cover. Probably the best known of the error books is the 1963 16th edition with a missing page. For some uncanny reason, page 239 is duplicated in some of those books, and page 237 is missing. The error was corrected on most of the printing.

The terminology used to describe book condition differs from that utilized in grading coins. A "Very Fine" book is one that is nearly new, with minimal signs of use. Early editions of the Red Book are rarely if ever found in anything approaching "New" condition. Exceptionally well-preserved older editions command a substantial premium and are in great demand. Nice used copies that are still clean and in good shape, but slightly worn from use, are also desirable. Only the early editions are worth a premium in badly worn condition.

For a more detailed history and edition-by-edition study of the Red Book, see Frank J. Colletti's *A Guide Book of The Official Red Book of United States Coins* (Whitman, 2009).

VALUATION GUIDE FOR PAST EDITIONS OF THE RED BOOK
CLASSIC HARDCOVER BINDING
See page 1357 for special editions in the classic hardcover binding.

Year/Edition	Issue Price	VG	F	VF	New
1947 (1st ed.), 1st Printing	$1.50	$275	$475	$775	$1,500
1947 (1st ed.), 2nd Printing	$1.50	$225	$425	$775	$1,200
1948 (2nd ed.)	$1.50	$60	$125	$200	$450
1949 (3rd ed.)	$1.50	$60	$135	$300	$500
1951/52 (4th ed.)	$1.50	$50	$100	$165	$300
1952/53 (5th ed.)	$1.50	$110	$200	$385	$1,200
1953/54 (6th ed.)	$1.75	$40	$60	$85	$100
1954/55 (7th ed.)	$1.75	$35	$55	$80	$100
1955 (8th ed.)	$1.75	$30	$40	$70	$80
1956 (9th ed.)	$1.75	$20	$35	$45	$70
1957 (10th ed.)	$1.75	$10	$15	$35	$50
1958 (11th ed.)	$1.75		$8	$12	$20
1959 (12th ed.)	$1.75		$8	$10	$20
1960 (13th ed.)	$1.75		$7	$9	$20
1961 (14th ed.)	$1.75		$4	$6	$20
1962 (15th ed.)	$1.75		$4	$6	$15
1963 (16th ed.)	$1.75		$4	$6	$15
1964 (17th ed.)	$1.75		$3	$4	$10
1965 (18th ed.)	$1.75		$3	$4	$10
1966 (19th ed.)	$1.75		$3	$4	$10
1967 (20th ed.)	$1.75		$2	$3	$8
1968 (21st ed.)	$2		$2	$3	$8
1969 (22nd ed.)	$2		$2	$3	$8
1970 (23rd ed.)	$2.50		$2	$3	$8
1971 (24th ed.)	$2.50		$2	$3	$7
1972 (25th ed.)	$2.50		$2	$3	$7
1973 (26th ed.)	$2.50		$2	$3	$7
1974 (27th ed.)	$2.50		$2	$3	$7
1975 (28th ed.)	$3			$3	$6
1976 (29th ed.)	$3.95			$3	$6
1977 (30th ed.)	$3.95			$3	$6
1978 (31st ed.)	$3.95			$3	$6
1979 (32nd ed.)	$3.95			$3	$6
1980 (33rd ed.)	$3.95			$3	$6
1981 (34th ed.)	$4.95			$2	$5
1982 (35th ed.)	$4.95			$2	$5
1983 (36th ed.)	$5.95			$2	$5
1984 (37th ed.)	$5.95			$2	$5
1985 (38th ed.)	$5.95			$2	$5
1986 (39th ed.)	$5.95			$2	$5
1987 (40th ed.)	$6.95			$2	$5
1988 (41st ed.)	$6.95			$2	$5
1989 (42nd ed.)	$6.95			$2	$5
1990 (43rd ed.)	$7.95			$2	$5
1991 (44th ed.)	$8.95			$2	$5
1992 (45th ed.)	$8.95			$2	$5

Note: Values are for unsigned books. Those signed by R.S. Yeoman are worth substantially more. **a.** Values are for books in Near Mint condition, as truly New copies are effectively nonexistent.

Year/Edition	Issue Price	VG	F	VF	New
1993 (46th ed.)	$9.95				$5
1994 (47th ed.)	$9.95				$3
1995 (48th ed.)	$10.95				$3
1996 (49th ed.)	$10.95				$3
1997 (50th ed.)	$11.95				$3
1998 (51st ed.)	$11.95				$2
1999 (52nd ed.)	$11.95				$2
2000 (53rd ed.)	$12.95				$2
2001 (54th ed.)	$13.95				$2
2002 (55th ed.)	$14.95				$2
2003 (56th ed.)	$15.95				$2
2004 (57th ed.)	$15.95				$2
2005 (58th ed.)	$15.95				$2
2006 (59th ed.)	$16.95				$2
2007 (60th ed.)	$16.95				$2
2008 (61st ed.)	$16.95				$2
2009 (62nd ed.)	$16.95				$2
2010 (63rd ed.)	$16.95				$2
2011 (64th ed.)	$16.95				$2
2012 (65th ed.)	$16.95				$2
2013 (66th ed.)	$16.95				$2
2014 (67th ed.)	$16.95				$2
2015 (68th ed.)	$16.95				$2
2016 (69th ed.)	$16.95				$2
2017 (70th ed.)	$16.95				$2
2018 (71st ed.) (b)	$16.95				$2
2019 (72nd ed.) (c)	$16.95				

Note: Values are for unsigned books. Those signed by R.S. Yeoman are worth substantially more. **b.** The 2018 hardcover features a back-cover gold-foil portrait of David Rittenhouse, first director of the United States Mint, in celebration of 225 years of U.S. coinage at Philadelphia. **c.** The 2019 Red Book (in every format) includes a 10-page illustrated tribute to Editor Emeritus Kenneth Bressett. The back of the hardcover features a gold-foil portrait of Bressett.

SOFTCOVERS (1993–2007)

The first softcover (trade paperback) Red Book was the 1993 (46th) edition. The softcover binding was offered (alongside other formats) in the 1993, 1994, 1995, and 1996 editions; again in the 1998 edition; and from 2003 through 2007. All are fairly common and easily collectible today. Values in New condition range from $2 up to $3–$4 for the earlier editions.

SPIRALBOUND SOFTCOVERS (1997 TO DATE)

The first spiralbound softcover Red Book was the 1997 (50th) edition. The spiralbound softcover format was next available in the 1999 edition, and it has been an annually offered format every edition since then. Today the spiralbound softcovers all are easily collectible. The 1997 edition is worth $4 in New condition, and later editions are valued around $2.

SPIRALBOUND HARDCOVERS (2008 TO DATE)

The first spiralbound hardcover Red Book was the 2008 (61st) edition. The format has been available (alongside other formats) every edition since. All spiralbound hardcovers are readily available to collectors, and are valued from $2 to $4.

JOURNAL EDITION (2009)

The large-sized Journal Edition, featuring a three-ring binder, color-coded tabbed dividers, and removable pages, was issued only for the 2009 (62nd) edition. Today it is valued at $5 in VF and $30 in New condition.

LARGE PRINT EDITIONS (2010 TO DATE)

The oversized Large Print format of the Red Book has been offered annually since the 2010 (63rd) edition. All editions are readily available to collectors and are valued at $5 in New condition.

LEATHER LIMITED EDITIONS (2005 TO DATE)

Year/Edition	Print Run	Issue Price	New
2005 (58th ed.)	3,000	$69.95	$75
2006 (59th ed.)	3,000	$69.95	$75
2007 (60th ed.)	3,000	$69.95	$75
2007 1947 Tribute Edition	500	$49.95	$125
2008 (61st ed.)	3,000	$69.95	$75
2008 (61st ed.), Numismatic Literary Guild (a)	135 (b)		$650
2008 (61st ed.), American Numismatic Society (c)	250 (b)		$500
2009 (62nd ed.)	3,000	$69.95	$75
2010 (63rd ed.)	1,500	$69.95	$75
2011 (64th ed.)	1,500	$69.95	$75
2012 (65th ed.)	1,000	$69.95	$75
2013 (66th ed.)	1,000	$69.95	$75
2014 (67th ed.)	1,000	$69.95	$75
2015 (68th ed.)	500	$99.95	$100
2016 (69th ed.)	500	$99.95	$100
2017 (70th ed.)	250	$99.95	$100
2018 (71st ed.)	250	$99.95	$100
2019 (72nd ed.)	250	$99.95	$100

a. One hundred thirty-five imprinted copies of the 2008 leather Limited Edition were created. Of these, 125 were distributed to members of the NLG at its 2007 literary awards ceremony; the remaining 10 were distributed from Whitman Publishing headquarters in Atlanta. b. Included in total print-run quantity. c. Two hundred fifty copies of the 2008 leather Limited Edition were issued with a special bookplate honoring the 150th anniversary of the ANS. They were distributed to attendees of the January 2008 celebratory banquet in New York.

SPECIAL EDITIONS

Year/Edition	Print Run	Issue Price	VF	New
1987 (40th ed.), American Numismatic Association 95th Anniversary	500		$600	$750
1992 (45th ed.), American Numismatic Association 100th Anniversary	600		$120	$225
1997 (50th ed.), Red Book 50th Anniversary	1,200	$24.95	$50	$100
2002 (55th ed.), American Numismatic Association "Target 2001"	500	$100	$25	$50
2002 (55th ed.), SS *Central America*		$35	$20	$30
2005 (58th ed.), FUN (Florida United Numismatists) 50th Anniversary	1,100		$50	$100
2007 (60th ed.), American Numismatic Association 115th Anniversary	500		$50	$100
2007 (60th ed.), Michigan State Numismatic Society 50th Anniversary	500		$50	$100
2007 (1st ed.), 1947 Tribute Edition		$17.95	$5	$20
2008 (61st ed.), ANA Milwaukee World's Fair of Money	1,080		$25	$50
2008 (61st ed.), Stack's Rare Coins			$5	$15
2010 (63rd ed.), Hardcover, Philadelphia Expo (a)		$24.95	$20	$40
2011 (64th ed.), Boston Numismatic Society		$85	$45	$90
2012 (65th ed.), American Numismatic Association	800	$100	$30	$60
2013 (66th ed.), American Numismatic Society (b)	250		$100	$250
2015 (68th ed.), Central States Numismatic Society	500	$15	$25	$60
2016 (69th ed.), American Numismatic Association 125th Anniversary		$100	$40	$75
2018 (71st ed.), NGC 30th Anniversary			$60	$100
2020 (73rd ed.), Chicago Coin Club 100th Anniversary	250		$50	$125

a. Two thousand and nine copies of a special 2010 hardcover edition were made for distribution to dealers at the premiere Whitman Coin and Collectibles Philadelphia Expo (September 2009). Extra copies were sold at $50 apiece with proceeds benefiting the National Federation for the Blind. b. Two hundred fifty copies of the 2013 hardcover were issued with a special bookplate honoring ANS Trustees' Award recipient (and Red Book research contributor) Roger Siboni.

THE BLUE BOOK AS A COLLECTIBLE

The precursor to the Red Book was the *Handbook of United States Coins With Premium List*, popularly known as the "Blue Book." Its mastermind was R.S. Yeoman, who had been hired by Western Publishing as a commercial artist in 1932. He distributed Western's Whitman line of "penny boards" to coin collectors, promoting them through department stores, along with children's books and games. He eventually arranged for Whitman to expand the line into other denominations, giving them the reputation of a numismatic endeavor rather than a "game" of filling holes with missing coins. He also developed these flat boards into a line of popular folders.

Yeoman began to compile coin-mintage data and market values to aid collectors. This research grew into the Blue Book: now collectors had a coin-by-coin guide to the average prices dealers would pay for U.S. coins. The first two editions were both published in 1942.

In the first edition of the Red Book, Whitman Publishing would describe the Blue Book as "a low-priced standard reference book of United States coins and kindred issues" for which there had been "a long-felt need among American collectors."

The Blue Book has been published annually (except in 1944 and 1950) since its debut. Past editions offer valuable information about the hobby of yesteryear as well as developments in numismatic research and the marketplace. Old Blue Books are collectible; most editions after the 12th can be found for a few dollars in VF or better condition. Major variants were produced for the third, fourth, and ninth editions, including perhaps the only "overdate" books in American numismatic publishing. Either to conserve the previous years' covers or to correct an error in binding, the cloth on some third-edition covers was overstamped "Fourth Edition," and a number of eighth-edition covers were overstamped "Ninth Edition." The third edition was produced in several shades of blue ranging from light to dark. Some copies of the fourth edition were also produced in black cloth—the only time the Blue Book was bound in other than blue.

VALUATION GUIDE FOR SELECT PAST EDITIONS OF THE BLUE BOOK

Edition	Date (a)		VF	New
	Title Page	Copyright		
1st	1942	1942	$100	$250
2nd	1943	1942	40	60
3rd	1944	1943	25	60
4th	none	1945	25	50
5th	none	1946	20	50
6th	1948	1947	15	30
7th	1949	1948	12	25
8th	1950	1949	10	20
9th	1952	1951	5	10
10th	1953	1952	5	10

a. During its early years of production, the Blue Book's date presentation was not standardized. Full information is given here to aid in precise identification of early editions.

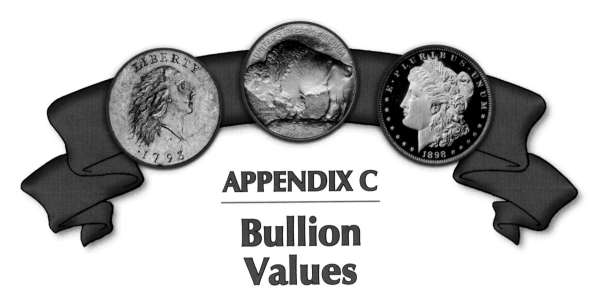

APPENDIX C

Bullion Values

These charts show the bullion values of silver and gold U.S. coins. These are intrinsic values and do not reflect any numismatic premium a coin might have. The weight listed under each denomination is its actual silver weight (ASW) or actual gold weight (AGW).

In recent years, the bullion price of silver has fluctuated considerably. You can use the following chart to determine the approximate bullion value of many 19th- and 20th-century silver coins at various price levels—or you can calculate the approximate value by multiplying the current spot price of silver by the ASW for each coin, as indicated. Dealers generally purchase common silver coins at around 15% below bullion value, and sell them at around 15% above bullion value.

Nearly all U.S. gold coins have an additional premium value beyond their bullion content, and thus are not subject to minor bullion-price variations. The premium amount is not necessarily tied to the bullion price of gold, but is usually determined by supply and demand levels in the numismatic marketplace. Because these factors can vary significantly, there is no reliable formula for calculating "percentage below and above bullion" prices that would remain accurate over time. The gold chart lists bullion values based on AGW only; consult a coin dealer to ascertain current buy and sell prices.

BULLION VALUES OF SILVER COINS

Silver Price Per Ounce	Wartime Nickel .05626 oz.	Dime .07234 oz.	Quarter .18084 oz.	Half Dollar .36169 oz.	Silver Clad Half Dollar .14792 oz.	Silver Dollar .77344 oz.
$8.00	$0.45	$0.58	$1.45	$2.89	$1.18	$6.19
$8.50	$0.48	$0.61	$1.54	$3.07	$1.26	$6.57
$9.00	$0.51	$0.65	$1.63	$3.26	$1.33	$6.96
$9.50	$0.53	$0.69	$1.72	$3.44	$1.41	$7.35
$10.00	$0.56	$0.72	$1.81	$3.62	$1.48	$7.73
$10.50	$0.59	$0.76	$1.90	$3.80	$1.55	$8.12
$11.00	$0.62	$0.80	$1.99	$3.98	$1.63	$8.51
$11.50	$0.65	$0.83	$2.08	$4.16	$1.70	$8.89
$12.00	$0.68	$0.87	$2.17	$4.34	$1.78	$9.28
$12.50	$0.70	$0.90	$2.26	$4.52	$1.85	$9.67
$13.00	$0.73	$0.94	$2.35	$4.70	$1.92	$10.05
$13.50	$0.76	$0.98	$2.44	$4.88	$2.00	$10.44

Note: The U.S. bullion coins first issued in 1986 are unlike the older regular issues. They contain the following amounts of pure metal: silver $1, 1 oz.; gold $50, 1 oz.; gold $25, 1/2 oz.; gold $10, 1/4 oz.; gold $5, 1/10 oz.

Silver Price Per Ounce	Wartime Nickel .05626 oz.	Dime .07234 oz.	Quarter .18084 oz.	Half Dollar .36169 oz.	Silver Clad Half Dollar .14792 oz.	Silver Dollar .77344 oz.
$14.00	$0.79	$1.01	$2.53	$5.06	$2.07	$10.83
$14.50	$0.82	$1.05	$2.62	$5.24	$2.14	$11.21
$15.00	$0.84	$1.09	$2.71	$5.43	$2.22	$11.60
$15.50	$0.87	$1.12	$2.80	$5.61	$2.29	$11.99
$16.00	$0.90	$1.16	$2.89	$5.79	$2.37	$12.38
$16.50	$0.93	$1.19	$2.98	$5.97	$2.44	$12.76
$17.00	$0.96	$1.23	$3.07	$6.15	$2.51	$13.15
$17.50	$0.98	$1.27	$3.16	$6.33	$2.59	$13.54
$18.00	$1.01	$1.30	$3.26	$6.51	$2.66	$13.92
$18.50	$1.04	$1.34	$3.35	$6.69	$2.74	$14.31
$19.00	$1.07	$1.37	$3.44	$6.87	$2.81	$14.70
$19.50	$1.10	$1.41	$3.53	$7.05	$2.88	$15.08
$20.00	$1.13	$1.45	$3.62	$7.23	$2.96	$15.47
$20.50	$1.15	$1.48	$3.71	$7.41	$3.03	$15.86
$21.00	$1.18	$1.52	$3.80	$7.60	$3.11	$16.24
$21.50	$1.21	$1.56	$3.89	$7.78	$3.18	$16.63
$22.00	$1.24	$1.59	$3.98	$7.96	$3.25	$17.02
$22.50	$1.27	$1.63	$4.07	$8.14	$3.33	$17.40
$23.00	$1.29	$1.66	$4.16	$8.32	$3.40	$17.79
$23.50	$1.32	$1.70	$4.25	$8.50	$3.48	$18.18
$24.00	$1.35	$1.74	$4.34	$8.68	$3.55	$18.56
$24.50	$1.38	$1.77	$4.43	$8.86	$3.62	$18.95
$25.00	$1.41	$1.81	$4.52	$9.04	$3.70	$19.34
$25.50	$1.43	$1.84	$4.61	$9.22	$3.77	$19.72
$26.00	$1.46	$1.88	$4.70	$9.40	$3.85	$20.11
$26.50	$1.49	$1.92	$4.79	$9.58	$3.92	$20.50
$27.00	$1.52	$1.95	$4.88	$9.77	$3.99	$20.88
$27.50	$1.55	$1.99	$4.97	$9.95	$4.07	$21.27
$28.00	$1.58	$2.03	$5.06	$10.13	$4.14	$21.66
$28.50	$1.60	$2.06	$5.15	$10.31	$4.22	$22.04
$29.00	$1.63	$2.10	$5.24	$10.49	$4.29	$22.43
$29.50	$1.66	$2.13	$5.33	$10.67	$4.36	$22.82
$30.00	$1.69	$2.17	$5.43	$10.85	$4.44	$23.20
$30.50	$1.72	$2.21	$5.52	$11.03	$4.51	$23.59
$31.00	$1.74	$2.24	$5.61	$11.21	$4.59	$23.98
$31.50	$1.77	$2.28	$5.70	$11.39	$4.66	$24.36
$32.00	$1.80	$2.31	$5.79	$11.57	$4.73	$24.75
$32.50	$1.83	$2.35	$5.88	$11.75	$4.81	$25.14
$33.00	$1.86	$2.39	$5.97	$11.94	$4.88	$25.52
$33.50	$1.88	$2.42	$6.06	$12.12	$4.96	$25.91
$34.00	$1.91	$2.46	$6.15	$12.30	$5.03	$26.30
$34.50	$1.94	$2.50	$6.24	$12.48	$5.10	$26.68
$35.00	$1.97	$2.53	$6.33	$12.66	$5.18	$27.07
$35.50	$2.00	$2.57	$6.42	$12.84	$5.25	$27.46
$36.00	$2.03	$2.60	$6.51	$13.02	$5.33	$27.84
$36.50	$2.05	$2.64	$6.60	$13.20	$5.40	$28.23
$37.00	$2.08	$2.68	$6.69	$13.38	$5.47	$28.62
$37.50	$2.11	$2.71	$6.78	$13.56	$5.55	$29.00
$38.00	$2.14	$2.75	$6.87	$13.74	$5.62	$29.39

Note: The U.S. bullion coins first issued in 1986 are unlike the older regular issues. They contain the following amounts of pure metal: silver $1, 1 oz.; gold $50, 1 oz.; gold $25, 1/2 oz.; gold $10, 1/4 oz.; gold $5, 1/10 oz.

BULLION VALUES OF GOLD COINS

Gold Price Per Ounce	$5.00 Liberty Head 1839–1908 Indian Head 1908–1929 .24187 oz.	$10.00 Liberty Head 1838–1907 Indian Head 1907–1933 .48375 oz.	$20.00 1849–1933 .96750 oz.
$850	$205.59	$411.19	$822.38
$875	$211.64	$423.28	$846.56
$900	$217.68	$435.38	$870.75
$925	$223.73	$447.47	$894.94
$950	$229.78	$459.56	$919.13
$975	$235.82	$471.66	$943.31
$1,000	$241.87	$483.75	$967.50
$1,025	$247.92	$495.84	$991.69
$1,050	$253.96	$507.94	$1,015.88
$1,075	$260.01	$520.03	$1,040.06
$1,100	$266.06	$532.13	$1,064.25
$1,125	$272.10	$544.22	$1,088.44
$1,150	$278.15	$556.31	$1,112.63
$1,175	$284.20	$568.41	$1,136.81
$1,200	$290.24	$580.50	$1,161.00
$1,225	$296.29	$592.59	$1,185.19
$1,250	$302.34	$604.69	$1,209.38
$1,275	$308.38	$616.78	$1,233.56
$1,300	$314.43	$628.88	$1,257.75
$1,325	$320.48	$640.97	$1,281.94
$1,350	$326.52	$653.06	$1,306.13
$1,375	$332.57	$665.16	$1,330.31
$1,400	$338.62	$677.25	$1,354.50
$1,425	$344.66	$689.34	$1,378.69
$1,450	$350.71	$701.44	$1,402.88
$1,475	$356.76	$713.53	$1,427.06
$1,500	$362.81	$725.63	$1,451.25
$1,525	$368.85	$737.72	$1,475.44
$1,550	$374.90	$749.81	$1,499.63
$1,575	$380.95	$761.91	$1,523.81
$1,600	$386.99	$774.00	$1,548.00
$1,625	$393.04	$786.09	$1,572.19
$1,650	$399.09	$798.19	$1,596.38
$1,675	$405.13	$810.28	$1,620.56
$1,700	$411.18	$822.38	$1,644.75
$1,725	$417.23	$834.47	$1,668.94
$1,750	$423.27	$846.56	$1,693.13
$1,775	$429.32	$858.66	$1,717.31
$1,800	$435.37	$870.75	$1,741.50
$1,825	$441.41	$882.84	$1,765.69
$1,850	$447.46	$894.94	$1,789.88
$1,875	$453.51	$907.03	$1,814.06
$1,900	$459.55	$919.13	$1,838.25
$1,925	$465.60	$931.22	$1,862.44
$1,950	$471.65	$943.31	$1,886.63
$1,975	$477.69	$955.41	$1,910.81
$2,000	$483.74	$967.50	$1,935.00

Note: The U.S. bullion coins first issued in 1986 are unlike the older regular issues. They contain the following amounts of pure metal: silver $1, 1 oz.; gold $50, 1 oz.; gold $25, 1/2 oz.; gold $10, 1/4 oz.; gold $5, 1/10 oz.

APPENDIX D

Top 250 U.S. Coin Prices Realized at Auction

Rank	Price	Coin	Grade	Firm	Date
1	$10,016,875	$1(s), 1794	PCGS SP-66	Stack's Bowers	Jan-13
2	$7,590,020	$20, 1933	Gem BU	Sotheby's/Stack's	Jul-02
3	$4,993,750	$1(s), 1794	PCGS MS-66+	Sotheby's / Stack's Bowers	Sep-15
4	$4,582,500	Prefed, 1787, Brasher dbln, EB on Wing	NGC MS-63	Heritage	Jan-14
5	$4,560,000	5¢, 1913, Liberty Head	PCGS PF-66	Stack's Bowers	Aug-18
6	$4,140,000	$1(s), 1804, Class I	PCGS PF-68	B&M	Aug-99
7	$3,960,000	$1 Trade, 1885	NGC PF-66	Heritage	Jan-19
8	$3,877,500	$1(s), 1804, Class I	PCGS PF-62	Heritage	Aug-13
9	$3,737,500	5¢, 1913, Liberty Head (A)	NGC PF-64	Heritage	Jan-10
10	$3,737,500	$1(s), 1804, Class I	NGC PF-62	Heritage	Apr-08
11	$3,290,000	$1(s), 1804, Class I	PCGS PF-65	Sotheby's / Stack's Bowers	Mar-17
12	$3,290,000	5¢, 1913, Liberty Head (A)	NGC PF-64	Heritage	Jan-14
13	$3,172,500	5¢, 1913, Liberty Head	PCGS PF-63	Heritage	Apr-13
14	$2,990,000	$20, MCMVII, Ultra HR, LE (B)	PCGS PF-69	Heritage	Nov-05
15	$2,990,000	Prefed, 1787, Brasher, EB on Breast (C)	NGC EF-45	Heritage	Jan-05
16	$2,820,000	$1(s), 1794	PCGS MS-64	Stack's Bowers	Aug-17
17	$2,760,000	$20, MCMVII, Ultra HR, LE (B)	PCGS PF-69	Stack's Bowers	Jun-12
18	$2,640,000	$1(s), 1804, Class I	PCGS PF-62	Heritage	Jun-18
19	$2,585,000	$10, 1795, 13 Leaves, BD-4	PCGS MS-66+	Sotheby's / Stack's Bowers	Sep-15
20	$2,585,000	Pattern 1¢, 1792, Birch Cent, LE, J-4	NGC MS-65RB	Heritage	Jan-15
21	$2,574,000	$4, 1880, Coiled Hair (D)	NGC PF-67 Cam	Bonhams	Sep-13
22	$2,415,000	Prefed, 1787, Brasher, EB on Wing	NGC AU-55	Heritage	Jan-05
23	$2,350,000	$2.50, 1808	PCGS MS-65	Sotheby's / Stack's Bowers	May-15
24	$2,350,000	1¢, 1793, Chain AMERICA, S-4	PCGS MS-66BN	Heritage	Jan-15
25	$2,300,000	$1(s), 1804, Class III	PCGS PF-58	Heritage	Apr-09
26	$2,232,500	Pattern 25¢, 1792, copper, J-12	NGC MS-63BN	Heritage	Jan-15
27	$2,185,000	$10, 1907, Rounded Rim	NGC Satin PF-67	Heritage	Jan-11
28	$2,160,000	$5, 1854-S	NGC EF-45	Heritage	Aug-18
29	$2,115,000	$20, MCMVII, Ultra HR, LE	PCGS PF-68	Heritage	Jan-15
30	$1,997,500	10¢, 1894-S	PCGS PF-66	Heritage	Jan-16
31	$1,997,500	Pattern 1¢, 1792 Silver Center, J-1	PCGS MS-64BN	Heritage	Aug-14
32	$1,997,500	$20, 1927-D	NGC MS-66	Heritage	Jan-14

Rank	Price	Coin	Grade	Firm	Date
33	$1,897,500	$20, 1927-D	PCGS MS-67	Heritage	Nov-05
34	$1,880,000	Pattern $20, 1879 Quintuple Stella, J-1643	PCGS PF-64Dcam	Legend	May-16
35	$1,880,000	$1(s), 1804, Class III	NGC PF-55	Stack's Bowers	Aug-14
36	$1,840,000	10¢, 1873-CC, No Arrows	PCGS MS-65	Stack's Bowers	Aug-12
37	$1,840,000	5¢, 1913, Liberty Head	NGC PF-66	Superior	Mar-08
38	$1,840,000	$20, MCMVII, Ultra HR, LE	PCGS PF-68	Heritage	Jan-07
39	$1,840,000	$1(s), 1804, Class I (E)	PCGS PF-64	Stack's	Oct-00
40	$1,821,250	$4, 1880, Coiled Hair	NGC PF-67	Heritage	Apr-15
41	$1,815,000	$1(s), 1804, Class I	PF-63	B&M/Stack's	Apr-97
42	$1,740,000	Pre-Fed, 1792, Washington $10, M-31	NGC EF-45*	Heritage	Aug-18
43	$1,725,000	$2.50, 1796, No Stars (F)	PCGS MS-65	Heritage	Jan-08
44	$1,725,000	$10, 1920-S	PCGS MS-67	Heritage	Mar-07
45	$1,645,000	$20, 1861, Paquet Reverse (G)	PCGS MS-61	Heritage	Aug-14
46	$1,610,000	$10, 1839/8, Type of 1838, Lg Letters (H)	NGC PF-67 Ucam	Heritage	Jan-07
47	$1,610,000	$20, 1861, Paquet Reverse (G)	PCGS MS-61	Heritage	Aug-06
48	$1,552,500	10¢, 1894-S	PCGS PF-64	Stack's	Oct-07
49	$1,527,500	25¢, 1796, B-2	PCGS MS-66	Sotheby's / Stack's Bowers	May-15
50	$1,527,500	50¢, 1797, O-101a	PCGS MS-66	Sotheby's / Stack's Bowers	May-15
51	$1,527,500	Prefed, 1776, Cont. $1 Silver, N-3D	NGC MS-62	Heritage	Jan-15
52	$1,527,500	Prefed, 1776, Cont. $1 Silver, N-1C	NGC EF-40	Heritage	Jan-15
53	$1,527,500	25¢, 1796, B-2	NGC MS-67+	Heritage	Nov-13
54	$1,500,000	1¢, 1793, Chain, S-1	PCGS MS-64BN+	Heritage	Jan-19
55	$1,495,000	$20, 1927-D	PCGS MS-66	Heritage	Jan-10
56	$1,495,000	$20, 1921	PCGS MS-63	B&M	Aug-06
57	$1,485,000	5¢, 1913, Liberty Head	Gem PF-66	B&M/Stack's	May-96
58	$1,437,500	$20, 1856-O	NGC SP-63	Heritage	May-09
59	$1,410,000	Prefed, 1776, Cont. $1 Silver, N-3D	NGC MS-63	Heritage	May-14
60	$1,410,000	Pattern 1¢, 1792, Silver Center, J-1	NGC MS-63BN+	Heritage	May-14
61	$1,410,000	Pattern half disme, 1792, J-7 (I)	PCGS SP-67	Heritage	Jan-13
62	$1,380,000	$5, 1829, Large Date	PCGS PF-64	Heritage	Jan-12
63	$1,380,000	1¢, 1793, Chain AMERICA, S-4	PCGS MS-65BN	Heritage	Jan-12
64	$1,380,000	50¢, 1797, O-101a (J)	NGC MS-66	Stack's	Jul-08
65	$1,380,000	$2.50, 1796, No Stars (F)	PCGS MS-65	Stack's (ANR)	Jun-05
66	$1,351,250	$5, 1833, BD-1	PCGS PF-67	Sotheby's / Stack's Bowers	May-16
67	$1,322,500	$3, 1855-S	NGC PF-64 Cam	Heritage	Aug-11
68	$1,322,500	Pattern half disme, 1792, J-7 (I)	PCGS SP-67	Heritage	Apr-06
69	$1,322,500	$20, 1927-D	NGC MS-65	Heritage	Jan-06
70	$1,322,500	10¢, 1894-S	NGC PF-66	DLRC	Mar-05
71	$1,292,500	Pattern half disme, 1792, J-7 (I)	PCGS SP-67	Heritage	Aug-14
72	$1,292,500	50¢, 1797, O-101a	PCGS MS-65+	Heritage	Aug-14
73	$1,265,000	Pattern $10, 1874, Bickford, J-1373	PCGS PF-65 DCam	Heritage	Jan-10
74	$1,265,000	1¢, 1795, Reeded Edge, S-79 (K)	PCGS VG-10	Goldberg	Sep-09
75	$1,265,000	$1(s), 1795, Flowing Hair, B-7, BB-18	V Ch Gem MS	Bullowa	Dec-05
76	$1,210,000	$20, MCMVII, Ultra HR, LE (L)	PCGS PF-67	Goldberg	May-99
77	$1,207,500	$1(s), 1794	NGC MS-64	B&M	Aug-10
78	$1,207,500	$1(s), 1866, No Motto	NGC PF-63	Stack's (ANR)	Jan-05
79	$1,207,500	$1(s), 1804, Class III (M)	PCGS PF-58	B&M	Jul-03
80	$1,175,000	$5, 1798, Small Eagle, BD-1	PCGS AU-55	Sotheby's / Stack's Bowers	Sep-15
81	$1,175,000	Pattern 1¢, 1792, Birch Cent, LE, J-4	PCGS AU-58	Stack's Bowers	Mar-15
82	$1,175,000	Prefed, 1783, quint, T-II, Nova Const.	PCGS AU-53	Heritage	Apr-13
83	$1,175,000	$1(s), 1796, Sm Dt, Sm Ltrs, B-2, BB-63	NGC MS-65	Heritage	Apr-13
84	$1,150,000	1/2¢, 1794, C-7 (G)	PCGS MS-67RB	Goldberg	Jan-14

Rank	Price	Coin	Grade	Firm	Date
85	$1,150,000	Pattern 1¢, 1792, Silver Center Cent, J-1	PCGS MS-61BN	Heritage	Apr-12
86	$1,150,000	$1(s), 1794	NGC MS-64	Stack's (ANR)	Jun-05
87	$1,145,625	Pattern half disme, 1792, J-7	NGC MS-68	Stack's Bowers	Jan-13
88	$1,140,000	$1 Trade, 1884	NGC PF-66	Heritage	Jan-19
89	$1,121,250	1/2¢, 1811, C-1	PCGS MS-66RB	Goldberg	Jan-14
90	$1,116,250	$4, 1880, Coiled Hair	PCGS PF-65	Heritage	Jun-15
91	$1,092,500	$20, 1921	PCGS MS-66	Heritage	Nov-05
92	$1,092,500	$1(s), 1870-S	BU PL	Stack's	May-03
93	$1,057,500	$1(s), 1795 Draped Bust, BB-51	PCGS SP-66	Sotheby's / Stack's Bowers	May-16
94	$1,057,500	$10, 1795, 9 Leaves, BD-3	PCGS MS-63+	Sotheby's / Stack's Bowers	Sep-15
95	$1,057,500	Pattern disme, 1792, copper, J-11	NGC MS-64RB	Heritage	Jan-15
96	$1,057,500	Terr, 1852, Humbert, $10, K-10	NGC MS-68	Heritage	Apr-13
97	$1,057,500	$20, MCMVII, Ultra HR, LE of 06	PCGS PF-58	Heritage	Aug-12
98	$1,050,000	$4, 1879, Coiled Hair	NGC PF-66 Cam	Heritage	Jan-19
99	$1,041,300	$4, 1879, Coiled Hair (**N**)	NGC PF-67 Cam	Bonhams	Sep-13
100	$1,035,000	10¢, 1894-S	PCGS PF-65	Heritage	Jan-05
101	$1,012,000	$20, 1921 (**O**)	PCGS MS-65 PQ	Goldberg	Sep-07
102	$1,006,250	$2.50, 1796, Stars, Bass-3003, BD-3 (**P**)	NGC MS-65	Heritage	Jan-08
103	$1,006,250	$1 Trade, 1885	NGC PF-62	DLRC	Nov-04
104	$998,750	1/2¢, 1811, C-1	PCGS-MS66RB	Sotheby's / Stack's Bowers	Mar-17
105	$998,750	Pattern disme, 1792, J-9	PCGS AU-50	Heritage	Apr-16
106	$998,750	1¢, 1793, Chain, S-3	PCGS MS-65RB	Sotheby's / Stack's Bowers	Feb-16
107	$998,750	Pattern disme, 1792, J-9	NGC AU-50	Heritage	Jan-15
108	$998,750	$1 Trade, 1884	PCGS PF-65	Heritage	Jan-14
109	$998,750	1¢, 1793, Chain, S-2	PCGS MS-65BN	Stack's Bowers	Jan-13
110	$990,000	1¢, 1793, Chain, AMERICA, S-4 (**T**)	PCGS MS-65BN	Heritage	Jun-18
111	$990,000	$1(s), 1804, Class I (**E**)	Choice Proof	Rarcoa	Jul-89
112	$977,500	1¢, 1799, S-189	NGC MS-62BN	Goldberg	Sep-09
113	$977,500	$4, 1880, Coiled Hair (**D**)	NGC PF-66 Cam	Heritage	Jan-05
114	$977,500	$5, 1833, Large Date	PCGS PF-67	Heritage	Jan-05
115	$966,000	50¢, 1797, O-101a (**J**)	NGC MS-66	Stack's (ANR)	Mar-04
116	$962,500	5¢, 1913, Liberty Head	Proof	Stack's	Oct-93
117	$960,000	Confed, 1861, Original 50¢	NGC PF-40	Heritage	Nov-17
118	$959,400	$4, 1880, Flowing Hair	NGC PF-67	Bonhams	Sep-13
119	$948,750	Terr, 1852, Moffat & Co., $10, Wide Date, K-9	PCGS SP-67	Stack's (ANR)	Aug-06
120	$940,000	1¢, 1793, Liberty Cap, S-13, B-20	PCGS AU-58	Sotheby's / Stack's Bowers	Mar-17
121	$940,000	$5, 1825, Over 4, BD-2	PCGS MS-64	Sotheby's / Stack's Bowers	May-16
122	$940,000	1/2¢, 1794, C-7 (**G**)	PCGS MS-67RB	Sotheby's / Stack's Bowers	Feb-16
123	$940,000	Terr, 1852, Moffat & Co., $10, Wide Date, K-9	PCGS SP-63	Heritage	Jan-14
124	$920,000	1/2¢, 1793, C-4	PCGS MS-66BN	Goldberg	Jan-14
125	$920,000	$1(s), 1802, Restrike	PCGS PF-65 Cam	Heritage	Apr-08
126	$920,000	$20, 1907, Small Edge Letters	PCGS PF-68	Heritage	Nov-05
127	$920,000	$1 Trade, 1885	NGC PF-61	Stack's	May-03
128	$910,625	$1(s), 1794	PCGS AU-58+	Stack's Bowers	Mar-17
129	$910,625	$1(s), 1795, Draped, Off-Ctr, B-14, BB-51	NGC MS-66+	Heritage	Nov-13
130	$907,500	$1 Trade, 1885	Gem PF-65	B&M/Stack's	Apr-97
131	$900,000	Pattern 1¢, 1792 Silver Center, J-1	PCGS MS-61BN	Stack's Bowers	Nov-17
132	$891,250	1/2¢, 1796, No Pole, C-1	PCGS MS-65BN	Goldberg	Jan-14
133	$891,250	10¢, 1873-CC, No Arrows (**R**)	NGC MS-65	B&M	Jul-04
134	$882,500	$5, 1815, BD-1	PCGS MS-65	Sotheby's / Stack's Bowers	Feb-16
135	$881,250	$10, 1933	PCGS MS-66	Goldberg	Jun-16
136	$881,250	$5, 1829, Small Date, BD-2	PCGS MS-65+	Sotheby's / Stack's Bowers	May-16

Rank	Price	Coin	Grade	Firm	Date
137	$881,250	$4, 1879, Coiled Hair	PCGS PF-65	Heritage	Apr-15
138	$881,250	Confed, 1861, Original 50¢	NGC PF-30	Heritage	Jan-15
139	$881,250	25¢, 1796, B-1	PCGS SP-66	Heritage	Aug-14
140	$881,250	$10, 1795, BD-5	PCGS MS-65	Heritage	Aug-14
141	$881,250	10¢, 1796, JR-1	PCGS MS-67	Heritage	Jun-14
142	$881,250	$1(s), 1889-CC	PCGS MS-68	Stack's Bowers	Aug-13
143	$881,250	1¢, 1794, Head of 93, S-18b	PCGS MS-64BN	Stack's Bowers	Jan-13
144	$874,000	$1(s), 1804, Class III **(M)**	PCGS PF-58	B&M	Nov-01
145	$862,500	1¢, 1793, Strawberry Leaf, NC-3	NGC F-12	Stack's	Jan-09
146	$862,500	Pattern $4, 1879, Quintuple Stella, J-1643	PCGS PF-62	Heritage	Jan-07
147	$862,500	$2.50, 1796, Stars, Bass-3003, BD-3 **(P)**	NGC MS-65	Heritage	Jan-07
148	$851,875	$4, 1879, Coiled Hair	PCGS PF-66	Heritage	Jan-14
149	$851,875	$1(s), 1803, Restrike	PCGS PF-66	Heritage	Jan-13
150	$851,875	$1(s), 1802, Restrike	PCGS PF-65 Cam	Heritage	Aug-12
151	$825,000	$20, MCMVII, Ultra HR, LE	Proof	Sotheby's	Dec-96
152	$824,850	Pattern half disme, 1792, copper, J-8	NGC AU-55	Heritage	Jan-15
153	$822,500	$10, 1795, 13 Leaves, BD-1	PCGS MS-64+	Legend	Mar-19
154	$822,500	$5, 1832, 12 Stars, BD-12	PCGS MS-63	Sotheby's / Stack's Bowers	May-16
155	$822,500	$5, 1835, McM-5	PCGS PF-67+ DCam	Sotheby's / Stack's Bowers	May-16
156	$822,500	$1(s), 1795, Flowing Hair, B-7, BB-18	PCGS MS-66	Sotheby's / Stack's Bowers	Sep-15
157	$822,500	50¢, 1796, 16 Stars, O-102	PCGS MS-66	Sotheby's / Stack's Bowers	May-15
158	$822,500	$2.50, 1796, No Stars, BD-2	PCGS MS-62	Sotheby's / Stack's Bowers	May-15
159	$822,500	$10, 1933	PCGS MS-65	Heritage	Apr-15
160	$822,500	$1(s), 1795, Flowing Hair, B-2, BB-20	NGC SP-64	Stack's Bowers	Aug-14
161	$822,500	$1(s), 1799, B-5, BB-157	NGC MS-67	Heritage	Nov-13
162	$822,500	Pattern 1¢, 1792, Silver Center Cent, J-1 **(T)**	NGC MS-61BN+	Heritage	Apr-13
163	$805,000	$1(s), 1870-S	NGC EF-40	Heritage	Apr-08
164	$805,000	$20, 1921	PCGS MS-65	Heritage	Nov-05
165	$793,125	10¢, 1796, JR-6	PCGS MS-68	Heritage	Aug-14
166	$793,125	Pattern half disme, 1792, J-7	PCGS MS-66	Stack's Bowers	Aug-13
167	$780,000	$1(s), 1794	NGC AU-58	Heritage	Aug-18
168	$763,750	$1(s), 1795, Draped Bust, BB-51	PCGS MS-66	Sotheby's / Stack's Bowers	May-16
169	$763,750	$5, 1829, Large Date, BD-1	PCGS MS-66+	Sotheby's / Stack's Bowers	May-16
170	$763,750	1/2¢, 1796, No Pole, C-1	PCGS MS-67RB	Sotheby's / Stack's Bowers	Feb-16
171	$763,750	50¢, 1794, O-101a	PCGS MS-64	Sotheby's / Stack's Bowers	May-15
172	$763,750	$2.50, 1798, BD-1	PCGS MS-65	Sotheby's / Stack's Bowers	May-15
173	$763,750	Terr, 1849, Pacific Company, $5, K-1	PCGS AU-58	Heritage	Apr-14
174	$763,750	Terr, 1855, Kellogg & Co., $50	PCGS PF-64 Cam	Heritage	Apr-14
175	$763,750	50¢, 1838-O	NGC PF-64	Heritage	Jan-14
176	$763,750	$1(s), 1870-S	PCGS EF-40	Heritage	Jan-14
177	$763,750	$5, 1826, BD-2	PCGS MS-66	Heritage	Jan-14
178	$750,000	Pattern, 1792, Silver Center Cent, J-1	PCGS SP-58BN+	Heritage	Jan-19
179	$750,000	$4, 1880, Flowing Hair	NGC PF-67 Cam	Heritage	Jan-18
180	$747,500	1¢, 1793, Chain, S-3	NGC MS-66BN	Stack's Bowers	Aug-12
181	$747,500	$20, 1921	PCGS MS-66	Heritage	Jan-12
182	$747,500	Terr, 1855, Kellogg & Co., $50	PCGS PF-64	Heritage	Jan-07
183	$747,500	$1(s), 1794	NGC MS-61	Heritage	Jun-05
184	$734,375	50¢, 1838-O	PCGS PF-64	Heritage	Jan-13
185	$725,000	Prefed, 1787, Brasher, EB on Wing	MS-63	B&R	Nov-79
186	$718,750	1/2¢, 1793, C-3	PCGS MS-65BN	Goldberg	Jan-14
187	$718,750	1/2¢, 1796, With Pole, C-2	PCGS MS-65RB+	Goldberg	Jan-14
188	$718,750	$10, 1933	Unc	Stack's	Oct-04

Rank	Price	Coin	Grade	Firm	Date
189	$705,698	$1(s), 1870-S	VF-25	B&M	Feb-08
190	$705,000	1¢, 1796, Liberty Cap, S-84	PCGS MS-66RB+	Sotheby's / Stack's Bowers	Mar-17
191	$705,000	Pattern disme, 1792, copper, RE, J-10	PCGS SP-64BN	Heritage	Apr-16
192	$705,000	$1(s), 1795, Flowing Hair, B-7, BB-18	PCGS MS-65+	Sotheby's / Stack's Bowers	Sep-15
193	$705,000	$10, 1798/7, 7x6 Stars, BD-2	PCGS MS-61	Sotheby's / Stack's Bowers	Sep-15
194	$705,000	25¢, 1827, Original	PCGS PF-66+ Cam	Sotheby's / Stack's Bowers	May-15
195	$705,000	50¢, 1794, O-109	NGC VF-25	Heritage	Apr-15
196	$705,000	Pattern 1¢, 1792, Silver Center Cent, J-1 **(T)**	NGC MS-61BN+	Heritage	Sep-14
197	$705,000	Prefed, 1783, Nova Const., PE Bit, W-1820	NGC AU-55	Heritage	May-14
198	$705,000	Terr, 1849, Mormon, $10, K-3	NGC AU-58	Heritage	Apr-14
199	$705,000	$1(s), 1803, Large 3, B-6, BB-255	NGC MS-65+	Heritage	Nov-13
200	$690,300	$5, 1836	NGC PF-67 UCam	Bonhams	Sep-13
201	$690,000	$5, 1909-O **(S)**	PCGS MS-66	Heritage	Jan-11
202	$690,000	1¢, 1796, Liberty Cap, S-84	PCGS MS-66RB	Goldberg	Sep-08
203	$690,000	Pattern disme, 1792, copper, RE, J-10	NGC PF-62BN	Heritage	Jul-08
204	$690,000	$5, 1825, 5 Over 4	NGC AU-50	Heritage	Jul-08
205	$690,000	$20, MCMVII, Ultra HR, LE of 06	NGC PF-58	Stack's	Jul-08
206	$690,000	Terr, 1860, Clark, Gruber & Co., $20	NGC MS-64	Heritage	Jan-06
207	$690,000	Prefed, 1742 (1786), Lima Brasher	NGC EF-40	Heritage	Jan-05
208	$690,000	$5, 1835	PCGS PF-67	Heritage	Jan-05
209	$690,000	$1(g), 1849-C, Open Wreath	NGC MS-63 PL	DLRC	Jul-04
210	$690,000	$20, MCMVII, Ultra HR, LE	Proof	Sotheby's/Stack's	Oct-01
211	$690,000	$10, 1839, 9/8, Type of 1838, Lg Letters **(H)**	NGC PF-67	Goldberg	Sep-99
212	$687,500	$3, 1870-S	EF-40	B&R	Oct-82
213	$687,500	$5, 1822	VF-30/EF-40	B&R	Oct-82
214	$675,525	$10, 1795, BD-5	NGC MS-65	Heritage	Aug-13
215	$672,750	$1(s), 1803, Restrike	PF-66	B&M	Feb-07
216	$661,250	1¢, 1804, S-266c	PCGS MS-63BN	Goldberg	Sep-09
217	$661,250	1/2 dime, 1870-S	NGC MS-63 PL	B&M	Jul-04
218	$660,000	Pattern, 1792, Birch Cent, PE, J-3	PCGS AU-58	Stack's Bowers	Oct-18
219	$660,000	$20, MCMVII, Ultra HR, LE **(L)**	PF-67	B&M	Jan-97
220	$660,000	$20, 1861, Paquet Reverse	MS-67	B&M	Nov-88
221	$655,500	$4, 1879, Coiled Hair **(N)**	NGC PF-67 Cam	Heritage	Jan-05
222	$655,200	$20, 1891	NGC PF-68 UCam	Bonhams	Sep-13
223	$646,250	$1(s), 1795, Draped Bust, BB-52	MS-66	Sotheby's / Stack's Bowers	May-16
224	$646,250	$5, 1831, Small 5D, BD-1	MS-67	Sotheby's / Stack's Bowers	May-16
225	$646,250	$5, 1795, Small Eagle, BD-3	PCGS MS-65	Sotheby's / Stack's Bowers	Sep-15
226	$646,250	50¢, 1838-O	NGC PF-64	Heritage	May-15
227	$646,250	Confed, 1861, Original 50¢	NGC EF-40	Stack's Bowers	Mar-15
228	$646,250	$1(s), 1893-S	PCGS MS-65	Legend	Oct-14
229	$646,250	Prefed, (1652), NE 6 Pence, N-1-A, S-1-A	NGC AU-58	Heritage	May-14
230	$646,250	Terr, 1851, Baldwin & Co., $20, K-5	PCGS EF-45	Heritage	Apr-14
231	$646,250	1¢, 1795, Reeded Edge, S-79 **(K)**	PCGS VG-10	Heritage	Jan-14
232	$646,250	$5, 1909-O **(S)**	PCGS MS-66	Heritage	Jan-14
233	$646,250	$1(s), 1795, 3 Leaves, B-5, BB-27	NGC MS-65	Heritage	Nov-13
234	$646,250	$4, 1879, Coiled Hair	PCGS PF-64 Cam	Stack's Bowers	May-13
235	$632,500	$5, 1828, 8 Over 7	NGC MS-64	Heritage	Jan-12
236	$632,500	$1(s), 1870-S	PCGS EF-40	B&M	Aug-10
237	$632,500	10¢, 1804, 14 Star Reverse, JR-2	NGC AU-58	Heritage	Jul-08
238	$632,500	1¢, 1793, Liberty Cap, S-13, B-20	PCGS AU-55	Heritage	Feb-08
239	$632,500	1¢, 1794, Starred Reverse, S-48, B-38	PCGS AU-50	Heritage	Feb-08
240	$632,500	50¢, 1838-O	PCGS PF-63 BM	Heritage	Feb-08

Rank	Price	Coin	Grade	Firm	Date
241	$632,500	Prefed, 1652, Willow Tree Threepence, N-1A	VF	Stack's	Oct-05
242	$632,500	50¢, 1838-0	PCGS PF-64 BM	Heritage	Jun-05
243	$632,500	Confed, 1861, Original 50¢	VF	Stack's	Oct-03
244	$632,500	10¢, 1873-CC, No Arrows **(R)**	PCGS MS-64	Heritage	Apr-99
245	$630,000	1/2¢, 1796, With Pole, C-2	PCGS MS-66+	Heritage	Aug-18
246	$625,000	Prefed, 1787, Brasher, EB on Breast **(C)**	VF	B&R	Mar-81
247	$618,125	$4, 1880, Coiled Hair	NGC PF-63	Superior	Jul-05
248	$605,000	$2.50, 1796, No Stars	Choice BU	Stack's	Nov-95
249	$603,750	1/2¢, 1852, Large Berries	PCGS PF-65RD	Goldberg	Jan-14
250	$603,750	$20, 1854-0	PCGS AU-55	Heritage	Oct-08

KEY

Price: The sale price of the coin, including the appropriate buyer's fee.

Coin: The denomination/classification, date, and description of the coin, along with pertinent catalog or reference numbers. B = Baker (for pre-federal), Bolender (for silver dollars), Breen (for gold), or Browning (for quarter dollars); BB = Bowers/Borckardt; BD = Bass-Dannreuther; Confed = Confederate States of America issue; dbln = doubloon; HR = High Relief; J = Judd; JR = John Reich Society; LE = Lettered Edge; N = Newman; NC = Non-Collectible; O = Overton; P = Pollock; Pattern = a pattern, experimental, or trial piece; Prefed = pre-federal issue; S = Sheldon; T = Taraskza; Terr = territorial issue. Letters in parentheses, **(A)** through **(T)**, denote instances in which multiple sales of the same coin rank within the Top 250.

Grade: The grade of the coin, plus the name of the grading firm (if independently graded). BM = branch mint; NGC = Numismatic Guaranty Corporation of America; PCGS = Professional Coin Grading Service; PQ = premium quality.

Firm: The auction firm (or firms) that sold the coin. ANR = American Numismatic Rarities; B&R = Bowers & Ruddy; DLRC = David Lawrence Rare Coins; Stack's Bowers = Stack's Bowers Galleries (name under which Stack's and B&M merged in 2010; also encompasses the merger of Stack's and ANR in 2006).

Date: The month and year of the auction.

Auction records compiled and edited by P. Scott Rubin.

APPENDIX E

Conditions of Coins and Grading Standards

ESSENTIAL ELEMENTS OF THE AMERICAN NUMISMATIC ASSOCIATION GRADING STANDARDS

Proof—A specially made coin distinguished by sharpness of detail and usually with a brilliant, mirrorlike surface. *Proof* refers to the method of manufacture and is not a grade. The term implies superior condition unless otherwise noted.

> **Gem Proof (PF-65)**—Surfaces are brilliant, with no noticeable blemishes or flaws. A few scattered, barely noticeable marks or hairlines.

> **Choice Proof (PF-63)**—Surfaces are reflective, with only a few blemishes in secondary focal places. No major flaws.

> **Proof (PF-60)**—Surfaces may have several contact marks, hairlines, or light rubs. Luster may be dull and eye appeal lacking.

Mint State—The terms *Mint State (MS)* and *Uncirculated (Unc.)* are interchangeable and refer to coins showing no trace of wear from circulation. Such coins may vary slightly because of minor surface imperfections, as described in the following subdivisions:

> **Perfect Uncirculated (MS-70)**—Perfect new condition, showing no trace of wear. The finest quality possible, with no evidence of scratches, handling, or contact with other coins. Very few circulation-issue coins are ever found in this condition.

> **Gem Uncirculated (MS-65)**—An above-average Uncirculated coin that may be brilliant or lightly toned and that has very few contact marks on the surface or rim.

> **Choice Uncirculated (MS-63)**—A coin with some distracting contact marks or blemishes in prime focal areas. Luster may be impaired.

> **Uncirculated (MS-60)**—A coin that has no trace of wear, but which may show a number of marks from contact with other coins during minting, storage, or transportation, and whose surface may be spotted or lack some luster.

Choice About Uncirculated (AU-55)—Evidence of friction on high points of design. Most of the mint luster remains.

About Uncirculated (AU-50)—Traces of light wear on many of the high points. At least half of the mint luster is still present.

Choice Extremely Fine (EF-45)—Light overall wear on the highest points. All design details are very sharp. Some of the mint luster is evident.

Extremely Fine (EF-40)—Light wear on the design throughout, but all features are sharp and well defined. Traces of luster may show.

Choice Very Fine (VF-30)—Light, even wear on the surface and highest parts of the design. All lettering and major features are sharp.

Very Fine (VF-20)—Moderate wear on design high points. All major details are clear.

Fine (F-12)—Moderate to considerable even wear. The entire design is bold with an overall pleasing appearance.

Very Good (VG-8)—Well worn with main features clear and bold, although rather flat.

Good (G-4)—Heavily worn, with the design visible but faint in areas. Many details are flat.

About Good (AG-3)—Very heavily worn with portions of the lettering, date, and legend worn smooth. The date may be barely readable.

Important: Undamaged coins are worth more than bent, corroded, scratched, holed, nicked, stained, or mutilated ones. Flawless Uncirculated coins are generally worth more than values quoted in this book. Slightly worn coins ("sliders") that have been cleaned and conditioned ("buffed") to simulate Uncirculated luster are worth considerably less than perfect pieces.

Unlike damage inflicted after striking, manufacturing defects do not always lessen values. Examples include colonial coins with planchet flaws or weakly struck designs; early silver or gold coins with weight-adjustment "file marks" (parallel cuts made on the planchet prior to striking); and coins with "lint marks" (surface marks due to the presence of dust or other foreign matter during striking).

Note that while grading *standards* strive to be precise, interpretations are subjective and can vary among collectors, dealers, and certification services.

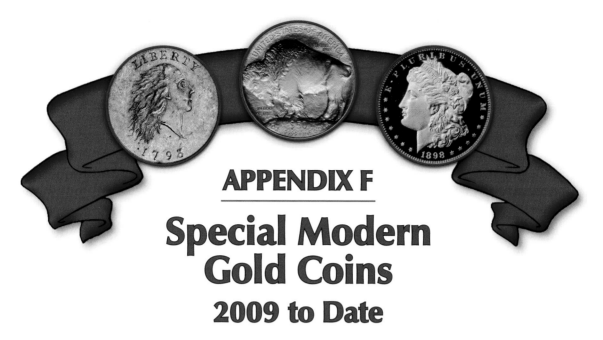

APPENDIX F

Special Modern Gold Coins

2009 to Date

AN OVERVIEW OF SPECIAL MODERN GOLD COINS

In recent years, the U.S. Mint has introduced several innovative new gold coins. These coins showcase the Mint's technological and creative abilities in impressive and often surprising ways.

Chapter 31, section 5112, of the United States Code gives the secretary of the Treasury considerable leeway in the specifics of the nation's gold bullion coins. Without needing to get congressional orders or approval, the secretary can change coinage designs, denominations, and other details in coins of that precious metal (similar changes in silver bullion coins would require Congress to get involved).

The Mint has used this authority to create such modern marvels as the MMIX Ultra High Relief gold double eagle (2009), a gold Kennedy half dollar (2014), and a series of American Liberty high-relief gold coins (2015 to date). Authority for 2016 gold coins struck with the designs of the Mercury dime, the Standing Liberty quarter, and the Liberty Walking half dollar, to celebrate the 100th anniversary of their debut, derives from the same legislation.

These gold coins are focused on collectors, using the U.S. Mint's 40 years of modern experience to determine what collectors and investors want (and don't want) in terms of gold. While these gold–collector coin programs would have been impossible for much of the 20th century under the gold laws legislated in the 1930s, it was made legal for private citizens to own gold again in 1974. The minting of the gold National Bicentennial Medals and the Colorado Centennial Medal was followed by the minting of the American Arts gold medallions of the early 1980s, which ramped up to the globally popular American Gold Eagles, and the subsequent American Buffalo and First Spouse bullion programs have also met with success. Special modern gold coins represent the culmination of the Mint's experience with each of these series, and at the same time they promise new innovations in the coming years.

The American Liberty gold coin's packaging.

MMIX ULTRA HIGH RELIEF $20 GOLD COIN (2009)

In 2009 the U.S. Mint produced a modern collector's version of the first Augustus Saint-Gaudens double eagle. When the original debuted in 1907, the Mint had been unable to strike large quantities for circulation—the ultra high relief design was artistic, but difficult to coin. (It was modified later in 1907 to a lower relief suitable for commercial production.) Just over 100 years later, the 2009 version was a showcase coin: a tangible demonstration of the Mint's 21st-century ability to combine artistry and technology to make an outstanding numismatic treasure.

Like its predecessor, the new coin was dated in Roman numerals (with 2009 as MMIX). The Mint digitally mapped Saint-Gaudens's original plasters and used the results in the die-making process. The date was changed, and four additional stars were inserted, to represent the nation's current 50 states. Augustus Saint-Gaudens's striding Liberty occupied the obverse. On the reverse was his flying eagle, with the addition of IN GOD WE TRUST, a motto not used in the original design. The 2009 version, struck in Philadelphia, was made in a smaller diameter (27 mm instead of 34), with a thickness of 4 mm, and composed of 24-karat (.9999 fine) gold, thus making it easier to strike and stay true to the ultra high-relief design. Its weight is one ounce.

As with other coins of the U.S. Mint, these are legal tender and their weight, content, and purity are guaranteed by the federal government. They were packaged in a fancy mahogany box and sold directly to the public, instead of through a network of distributors.

Note that the Mint does not release bullion mintage data on a regular basis; the number given here reflects the most recently available official data.

	Mintage	MS	MS-69	MS-70
MMIX (2009) Ultra High Relief $20 Gold Coin †† (a)	114,427	$2,000	$2,100	$2,550

Note: MS values are for uncertified Mint State coins of average quality, in their complete original U.S. Mint packaging. †† Ranked in the *100 Greatest U.S. Modern Coins* (fourth edition) **a.** Auction: $2,820, MS-70, October 2015.

KENNEDY 50TH ANNIVERSARY HALF DOLLAR GOLD COIN (2014)

Following the assassination of President John F. Kennedy on November 22, 1963, the Kennedy half dollar was authorized. The first coins were made available to the public on March 24, 1964. The new half dollars were immediately hoarded by the public who were eager to obtain a memento of the late president.

The 50th anniversary Kennedy gold half dollar was struck as a tribute to the original issue as part of a year-long numismatic celebration that included two other coin sets (one Uncirculated set and one silver set). The gold coin, struck at West Point, features a restored obverse portrait of President Kennedy, which brings out the original details of the coin, and it is dual dated as "1964–2014". On the reverse an indication of the precious metal weight and purity appears: .9999 gold weighing 3/4 of an ounce. Otherwise the specifications match those of a standard half dollar.

The release of this coin caused a collector frenzy, but prices and collector interest soon stabilized.

	Mintage	PF-65	PF-67Cam	PF-68DC
2014-W, Kennedy 50th Anniversary Half Dollar Gold Coin, Proof	73,772	$900	$1,000	$1,200

AMERICAN LIBERTY HIGH-RELIEF $100 GOLD COINS

2015-W   1792–2017-W   2018-W, Tenth-Ounce

The first American Liberty high-relief .9999-fine gold coin, with a weight of one troy ounce and a face value of $100, was minted at West Point in 2015. The coin was not congressionally mandated, instead being created under authority granted to the secretary of the Treasury by federal law—31 U.S.C. Section 5112 (i)(4)(C).

The design was strongly influenced by the Citizens Coinage Advisory Committee, who, according to a Mint spokesperson, "emphasized creating a 'modern' Liberty that reflects the nation's diversity." The U.S. Commission of Fine Arts also reviewed designs and made recommendations.

Of the 2015 American Liberty's eagle reverse the designer, Paul C. Balan, commented, "My reverse design for the American Liberty High Relief gold coin was created with inspiration from the Great Seal of the United States and its depiction of an American bald eagle clutching an olive branch. The soaring eagle is a symbol of strength, freedom and bravery, and the 13 olives on the branch represent the original 13 colonies, which epitomize the power and solidarity of our nation. I want people to feel a sense of pride and integrity as Americans when they see my design." Balan also shares that his design was initially submitted for the U.S. Marshals Service commemorative but was chosen for the American Liberty high-relief coin instead.

The designs for the American Liberty high-relief gold coins are created to take full advantage of the same high-relief techniques used to create the MMIX Ultra High Relief gold coin.

The design of the 2015 American Liberty high-relief gold coin was adapted for a silver medal in 2016, but in 2017 the Mint continued the series with a 1792–2017 American Liberty high-relief gold coin. The series is slated to continue biennially, with a new design being issued every two years. In the years between gold issues, silver medals featuring the same designs will be issued.

	Mintage	Unc.	PF
$100, 2015-W, 1 ounce	49,325	$1,950	
$100, 1792–2017-W, 1 ounce	27,886		$2,000
$10, 2018-W, one-tenth ounce			$245
$100, 2019-W, one ounce			$1,800

1916 CENTENNIAL GOLD COINS (2016)

In 2016 the Mint celebrated the 100th anniversary of the Mercury dime, Standing Liberty quarter, and Walking Liberty half dollar designs by issuing gold versions of the three classic coins, all struck at West Point. The gold coins are reduced in diameter from the original silver coins. They are composed of .9999-fine gold and weigh, respectively, 1/10 oz., 1/4 oz, and 1/2 oz. The dime was struck at 16.5 mm; the quarter, at 22 mm; and the half dollar, 27 mm. Some discussion at the Mint had centered around issuing similar commemorative coins in silver, but that would require congressional action. The gold Mercury dime sold out within 45 minutes of its release, but the two larger gold coins have seen much slower sales.

	Mintage	SP-67	SP-70
2016-W, Mercury Dime Centennial Gold Coin	124,885	$250	$300
2016-W, Standing Liberty Quarter Centennial Gold Coin	91,752	$450	$550
2016-W, Liberty Walking Half Dollar Centennial Gold Coin	65,509	$850	$1,000

APPENDIX G

So-Called Dollars

The contents of this section are based on the work and research of Jeff Shevlin.

AN OVERVIEW OF SO-CALLED DOLLARS

So-Called Dollars are U.S. medals approximately the size of a silver dollar that were struck to commemorate a historical subject. A collection of So-Called Dollars is strikingly different from a typical collection of U.S. coins assembled by date and mintmark, in that each piece in the collection has a uniquely different design. There are more than 750 different design types, and when different metal compositions are considered, there are more than 1,500 varieties to consider collecting. So-Called Dollars were struck in virtually every metal composition conceivable, including gold, silver, copper, bronze, brass, aluminum, nickel, white metal, German silver, gutta-percha, gold-plated, and silver-plated.

These collectibles were cataloged in the illustrated standard reference book *So-Called Dollars*, authored by Harold Hibler and Charles Kappen and published in 1963. This book, which is widely considered as the most definitive reference on So-Called Dollars, was revised and edited by Tom Hoffman, Dave Hayes, Jonathan Brecher, and John Dean in 2008.

So-Called Dollars were struck by the U.S. Mint as well as by private mints (and one was struck by the Manila Mint while the Philippines was an American territory). Many of the most famous engravers of U.S. coins also engraved So-Called Dollars, including William and Charles Barber, George T. Morgan, Augustus Saint-Gaudens, and others. Some of the designs and artwork on these pieces match or surpass these artists' other work in coin and medal design.

Historical medals come in all sizes. To be classified as a So-Called Dollar one must be approximately the size of a silver dollar, between 33 and 45 mm in diameter (a silver dollar is 38.1 mm), although collectors traditionally include a few specific exceptions such as the 1939 Charbneau medals (see the gallery, which follows).

From national events and celebrations to local anniversaries, from great successes to major disasters, bits and pieces of the history of the United States are chronologically depicted on these fascinating historical medals.

About half of the So-Called Dollars are related to a Fair or Exposition with the other half commemorating important events in U.S. history. Expositions played a significant part in the development of the United States. Local communities, often with federal funding support, would begin to plan years ahead of time and build enormous halls and buildings for their expositions, which would last anywhere from a few months to a few years. Millions of people would travel to attend these grand events and see things they had never seen before, often visiting for days, sometimes weeks.

Throngs of tourists entering the Electrical Building at the World's Columbian Exposition.

When the city of Chicago hosted the World's Columbian Exposition in 1893, its population was slightly greater than a million people. More than five years were spent in the exposition's planning and construction on a 700-acre site on the shore of Lake Michigan. President Benjamin Harrison invited all of the nations of the earth to take part by sending exhibits that most fully illustrated their resources, their industries, and their progress in civilization. Every state and territory of the United States and more than 50 foreign countries were represented, many erecting their own buildings. Exhibits exceeded 50,000, including one set up by the U.S. Mint. Attendance at the exposition was 27,500,000, and by the end of the 1890s Chicago's population had grown to 1,700,000, making it one of the fastest-growing cities in the history of mankind and the fifth or sixth largest city in the world. More than 100 So-Called Dollars were struck commemorating the World's Columbian Exposition, its events, and its structures—the last remaining of which, originally called the "Palace of Fine Arts," now serves as Chicago's Museum of Science and Industry.

When Philadelphia hosted the Centennial Exposition in 1876, the first United States International Exhibition of the arts, manufacturers, and products, the country was showing the world the progress it had made in the past 100 years. The United States was, for the first time being recognized as one of the leading nations in the world. Until then, the young nation had focused on material problems, with art playing a less significant part in American life. Approximately 10,000,000 people attended the exposition and were not only exposed to the latest machines, mechanical progress, and industrial expansion, but also electrified by displays of art by the world's greatest artists throughout time. After the exposition numerous art schools and societies were formed, and there was a rush of American students to art schools in Paris. The impact on the emphasis for the arts in American culture was dramatic and everlasting. There are close to 50 different So-Called Dollars related to the 1876 Centennial Exposition.

The U.S. Mint had a presence at many of the expositions, often setting up presses and striking souvenir medals to sell to the attendees. The medals produced by the Mint were always designated as the official exposition medal and were usually struck in a variety of metals including silver.

Outside of fairs and expositions, the other half of the series of So-Called Dollars covers a broad range of topics. From the completion of the Erie Canal in 1826 and the completion of the first Transcontinental Railroad in 1869 through the centennial of the Pony Express in 1961, So-Called Dollars celebrate and remember hundreds of national, regional, and local events.

FOR THE COLLECTOR AND INVESTOR: SO-CALLED DOLLARS AS A SPECIALTY

So-Called Dollars as a specialty can be exciting, fascinating, and controversial, and they are collected in hundreds of different ways. Some collectors aspire to collect the entire series, and some collect specific metal compositions. Many collectors have an interest in one or more of the major expositions or other significant events in U.S. history that are portrayed on these medals. Some collect medals from local or regional areas, while others have an interest in those with a U.S. Mint relationship, which includes a broad area of different designs. In addition to marking battles of the Revolutionary War and the Civil War, as well as other military events, So-Called Dollars were struck that address the gold-versus-silver political controversy of the late 1800s and early 1900s. Lesher dollars; silver Bryan dollars; Pedley-Ryan dollars; and others struck by professor Montroville Dickeson, coin dealer Thomas Elder, numismatic historian Q. David Bowers, and other famous personalities are all popular collector categories.

So-Called Dollars range in rarity from very common to exceptionally rare. For many types only one example or very few are known to exist; for others there are thousands. Many So-Called Dollars are considerably rarer than U.S. coins. One of the most common So-Called Dollars is the 1931 McCormick Reaper Centennial Dollar, of which there were possibly as many as 5,000 struck. Compare that to the 1909-S V.D.B. Lincoln cent, of which 484,000 were minted. While the Lincoln cent in MS-63 would sell for $1,500, the McCormick Reaper in the same grade sells for around $20 despite being 100 times rarer. The following rarity scale is used for So-Called Dollars in this appendix:

R-1	More than 5000 known
R-2	2001–5000 known
R-3	501–2000 known
R-4	201–500 known
R-5	76–200 known
R-6	21–75 known
R-7	11–20 known
R-8	5–10 known
R-9	2–4 known
R-10	1 known (unique)

Hundreds of different So-Called Dollars in MS-63 can be purchased for less than $100. All of the major third-party grading firms, including NGC, PCGS, ANACS, and ICG, grade So-Called Dollars. Professional grading and slabbing of So-Called Dollars has had a significant impact on collector interest and prices realized when they appear in auction. Many of today's advanced collectors want the finer and higher-grade pieces, and if the medals are certified by a major grading firm, their confidence in the value goes up. Higher prices paid today for rare So-Called Dollars are a direct result of this increase in buyers' confidence.

So-Called Dollars have a broad appeal to today's collectors. Similar to most series of U.S. coinage, there are many interesting and historically significant pieces available to the beginning collector at relatively low introductory prices. There are literally hundreds of different types available in Uncirculated and Choice Uncirculated grades in the $25 to $75 range. There are also many highly desired rare varieties from the 1800s that are beautiful pieces of art, struck in bronze and with high relief, that the more advanced collectors appreciate. At the upper end of the So-Called Dollar market—those that sell for $1,000 or more—collectors are treated to exceptionally rare and significant pieces.

1826, Erie Canal Completion

1826, U.S. Semicentennial

1857, Dr. Elisha Kent Kane

1859, Nassau Water Works

| | Rarity | HK# | VF-20 | EF-40 | AU-50 | MS-60 | MS-63 | MS-65 |
						PF-60	PF-63	PF-65
1826, Erie Canal Completion. Gold Proof ‡	R-9	1001		$63,000		$200,000		
1826, Erie Canal Completion. Silver	R-6	1000	$900	$1,100	$1,850	$3,500	$6,900	$9,500
1826, Erie Canal Completion. Bronze	R-10	UNL				—		
1826, Erie Canal Completion. White Metal	R-6	1	$250	$575	$950	$2,300	$5,300	
1826, Erie Canal Completion. Gold-Plated	R-8	UNL	$425	$625	$1,750	$2,900	$5,800	—
1826, U.S. Semicentennial. Silver	R-9	2	$3,450	$4,800	$6,000	—	—	—
1826, U.S. Semicentennial. Copper	R-9	3	$3,000	$3,800	$4,450	—	—	—
1826, U.S. Semicentennial. White Metal	R-8	4	$2,800	$3,950	$4,500	$5,200	—	—
1857, Dr. Elisha Kent Kane. Bronze	R-7	756	—	—	$575	$800	$1,150	$1,400
1857, Dr. Elisha Kent Kane. White Metal	R-7	757	—	—	$600	$850	$1,250	$1,550
1859, Nassau Water Works. Silver	R-8	589C	—	—	$2,000	$2,850	$5,250	$6,750
1859, Nassau Water Works. Silver Proof	R-8	589C				$3,300	$5,750	—
1859, Nassau Water Works. Bronze	R-7	589A	$500	$625	$800	$950	$1,250	$2,300
1859, Nassau Water Works. Bronze Proof	R-8	589A						$2,600
1859, Nassau Water Works. White Metal	R-6	589B	$185	$225	$395	$575	$825	—
1859, Nassau Water Works. White Metal Proof	R-8	589B				$1,050	$1,450	—

UNL = Unlisted. ‡ Ranked in the *100 Greatest American Medals and Tokens*.

1826, Erie Canal Completion (HK–1, 1000, and 1001): This piece was struck to celebrate the completion of the Erie Canal, the greatest and most expensive U.S. engineering achievement yet undertaken. Pan and Neptune appear with cornucopias on the obverse; an eagle on the reverse sits atop the New York State coat of arms. Engraved by Charles Cushing Wright. **1826, U.S. Semicentennial (HK–2 to 4):** Struck to commemorate the 50th anniversary of the Declaration of Independence. An eagle perches on a shield on the obverse; the reverse legend refers to the Declaration of Independence dramatically stating; "For the support of this we pledge to each other our lives, our fortunes and our sacred honor." **1857, Dr. Elisha Kent Kane (HK–756 to 757):** The bust of Elisha Kent Kane, commander of the Second Grinnell Expedition, is on the obverse. In the early 1800s the British encouraged attempts to find the Northwest Passage, an ocean route hoped to connect the Atlantic and Pacific oceans via the Arctic. Kane commanded an unsuccessful recovery effort in 1850 to rescue two vessels that were lost in an attempt to find the passage. **1859, Nassau Water Works (HK–589A to 589C):** Neptune moves a lever with his right arm, which causes water to gush out of a vase or pipe held in his left. In July of 1858 public water was first introduced to Brooklyn, New York, and celebrated in April of 1859, at which time this medal was struck. Engraved by F.B. Smith & Hartmann.

1861, Bombardment
of Fort Sumter

1869, Grant
Transcontinental
Railway Completion

1873, San Francisco
Mint Coining Press

1875, Battle of
Lexington Centennial

	Rarity	HK#	VF-20	EF-40	AU-50	MS-60	MS-63	MS-65
						PF-60	PF-63	PF-65
1861, Bombardment of Fort Sumter. Copper	R-7	11C	$450	$650	$975	$1,650	$2,650	$3,680
1861, Bombardment of Fort Sumter. Brass	R-8	11B	—	—	—	—	$3,200	—
1861, Bombardment of Fort Sumter. White Metal	R-7	11	$200	$350	$550	$1,150	$1,800	$2,600
1869, Grant Transcontinental Railway Completion. Silver Proof	R-7	12A	$600	$950	$1,500	$2,800	$5,250	$6,750
1869, Grant Transcontinental Railway Completion. Bronze	R-6	12	$85	$175	$400	$600	$900	$1,750
1869, Grant Transcontinental Railway Completion. Gilt Bronze	R-9	12B	—	—	$2,500	$3,500	—	—
1869, Grant Transcontinental Railway Completion. Yellow Bronze. Restrike	R4	UNL	$25	$40	$65	$85	$120	$160
1873, San Francisco Mint Coining Press. Silver Proof	R-9	1003	—	—	$3,800	$5,200	$7,500	$7,800
1873, San Francisco Mint Coining Press. Copper	R-9	1003A	—	$1,100	$1,900	$2,300	—	—
1875, Battle of Lexington Centennial. Gold	R-9	1004					—	
1875, Battle of Lexington Centennial. Silver	R-9	16					$3,800	$6,200
1875, Battle of Lexington Centennial. Silver Proof	R-7	16				$2,600	$4,100	$6,200
1875, Battle of Lexington Centennial. Bronze	R-5	17	$200	$250	$375	$475	$575	$675
1875, Battle of Lexington Centennial. Bronze Proof	R-7	17				$700	$850	
1875, Battle of Lexington Centennial. White Metal	R-6	18				$135	$350	$475	$575
1875, Battle of Lexington Centennial. White Metal not holed	R-8	18	—	—	$500	$1,100	$1,700	—
1875, Battle of Lexington Centennial. White Metal Proof	R-7	18				$195	$425	$500	$750

UNL = Unlisted.

1861, Bombardment of Fort Sumter (HK–11 to 11C): A battle scene on the obverse depicts exploding bombs and smoke as Fort Sumter is attacked by the South Carolina Rebels—the initial engagement of the Civil War. The reverse legend elaborates how 75 men in the fort held off 8,000 Southern Confederate Rebels for 30 hours. **1869, Grant Transcontinental Railway Completion (HK–12 to 12B):** The completion of the first transcontinental railroad was a major technological accomplishment. Only 20 years after the California Gold Rush there was now an economical way to transport people and goods from coast to coast. Dies made by William Barber and struck at the Philadelphia Mint. **1873, San Francisco Mint Coining Press (HK–1003 and 1003A):** The mint in San Francisco dropped the word "Branch" from its title to become the United States Mint at San Francisco on April 1, 1873. On October 14, 1873, this medal was struck to celebrate the delivery of the largest and most powerful coining press in the world to the San Francisco Mint. **1875, Battle of Lexington Centennial (HK–16 to 18 and 1004):** "What a glorious morning for America," Samuel Adams exclaimed after the Battle of Lexington, April 19, 1775, which marked the beginning of the Revolutionary War. The gold, silver, and bronze medals were struck at the Philadelphia Mint; the white-metal pieces were privately minted later. Dies by Henry Mitchell from designs by Edward Griffin Porta.

1876, Centennial Exposition Nevada

1876, Centennial Exposition Official Medal

1876, Centennial Exposition Liberty Bell / Independence Hall

1876, Centennial Exposition Liberty Seated / Colonial Soldiers

	Rarity	HK#	VF-20	EF-40	AU-50	MS-60	MS-63	MS-65
						PF-60	PF-63	PF-65
1876, Centennial Exposition Nevada. Silver	R-5	19	$300	$495	$550	$950	$1,200	$1,350
1876, Centennial Exposition Nevada. Silver Proof	R-6	19				$975	$1,350	$1,450
1876, Centennial Exposition Nevada. Copper	R-9	19A				—	—	—
1876, Centennial Exposition Nevada. White Metal	R-9	UNL				—	—	—
1876, Centennial Exposition Official Medal. Silver ‡	R-4	20	$65	$120	$195	$425	$675	$1,250
1876, Centennial Exposition Official Medal. Silver Proof	R-6	20				$500	$850	$1,500
1876, Centennial Exposition Official Medal. Copper	R-6	UNL	$60	$85	$125	$225	$325	$475
1876, Centennial Exposition Official Medal. Bronze	R-4	21	$55	$85	$140	$210	$300	$450
1876, Centennial Exposition Official Medal. Bronze Proof	R-7	21				$250	$375	$575
1876, Centennial Exposition Official Medal. White Metal	R-9	22A					$2,500	
1876, Centennial Exposition Official Medal. Gilt	R-4	22	$25	$50	$70	$115	$265	$535
1876, Centennial Exposition Liberty Bell/Independence Hall. Silver Proof	R-9	23					$6,900	
1876, Centennial Exposition Liberty Bell/Independence Hall. Copper	R-6	25	$25	$45	$75	$145	$245	$425
1876, Centennial Exposition Liberty Bell/Independence Hall. Bronze	R-6	24	$35	$60	$90	$200	$350	$500
1876, Centennial Exposition Liberty Bell/Independence Hall. White Metal	R-5	26	$20	$40	$80	$185	$375	$525
1876, Centennial Exposition Liberty Bell/Independence Hall. Gold-Plated	R-9	UNL	—	—	$1,500	$2,500	$3,500	$4,500
1876, Centennial Exposition Liberty Seated/Colonial Soldiers. Silver	R-9	56	—	—	$1,500	$2,750	$5,800	$7,800
1876, Centennial Exposition Liberty Seated/Colonial Soldiers. Copper	R-9	57	—	—	$650	$900	—	—
1876, Centennial Exposition Liberty Seated/Colonial Soldiers. White Metal	R-7	59	—	—	—	$950	$1,300	—
1876, Centennial Exposition Liberty Seated/Colonial Soldiers. Gold-Plated	R-6	58	$175	$275	$450	$700	$1,100	$1,375

UNL = Unlisted. ‡ Ranked in the *100 Greatest American Medals and Tokens*.

1876, Centennial Exposition Nevada (HK–19 and 19A): Made of pure silver crushed from Nevada ores at the Nevada quartz mill located in the Centennial Exposition and later refined and struck at the Philadelphia Mint and sold at the 1876 Centennial Exposition. Dies engraved by William Barber. **1876, Centennial Exposition Official Medal (HK–20 to 22A):** This medal depicts the United States rising in importance to be recognized as a world power, grasping a sword in her right hand to enforce her demands. The medal was designed and engraved by William Barber, struck at the Philadelphia Mint, and sold at the 1876 Centennial Exposition. **1876, Centennial Exposition Liberty Bell / Independence Hall (HK–23 to 26):** The Centennial Exposition held in Philadelphia had the Liberty Bell on display, as depicted on the obverse. Independence Hall is on the reverse. The medal was engraved by William H. Key, assistant engraver to William Barber, 1864–1885. **1876, Centennial Exposition Liberty Seated / Colonial Soldiers (HK–56 to 59):** A seated woman, similar to James Longacre's one-dollar patterns, represents America. The reverse depicts an interesting scene of colonial soldiers preparing for battle. This is one of many So-Called Dollars engraved by George B. Soley, who was an engraver for the U.S. Mint from 1859 until his death in 1908.

1876, Centennial Exposition Washington Bust / Declaration of Independence

1876, Centennial Exposition Lovett Battle of Moores Creek Bridge

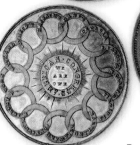

1876, Dickeson Continental Dollar

1876, Dickeson Perseverando / Confederation

	Rarity	HK#	VF-20	EF-40	AU-50	MS-60 PF-60	MS-63 PF-63	MS-65 PF-65
1876, Centennial Expo Declaration of Independence/Washington. Silver	R-9	75A	—	—	$2,500	$4,500	—	—
1876, Centennial Expo Declaration of Independence/Washington. Bronze	R-7	75	—	—	—	$325	$625	$975
1876, Centennial Expo Declaration of Independence/Washington. White Metal	R-7	76	—	—	—	$625	$875	$1,100
1876, Centennial Exposition Lovett Battle of Moores Creek Bridge. Silver	R-9	90			$2,000	$2,900	$4,500	$5,900
1876, Centennial Exposition Lovett Battle of Moores Creek Bridge. Bronze	R-8	91	$200	$400	$750	$1,250	$2,500	$2,800
1876, Centennial Exposition Lovett Battle of Moores Creek Bridge. White Metal	R-6	92	$50	$110	$160	$275	$475	$800
1876, Dickeson Continental Dollar. Gold, struck on gold $20	R-10	852B					—	
1876, Dickeson Continental Dollar. Silver	R-8	852					$4,200	$5,000
1876, Dickeson Continental Dollar. Silver, struck on silver $1	R-10	UNL					$6,000	
1876, Dickeson Continental Dollar. Copper	R-7	853	$350	$500	$650	$1,200	$1,400	$1,900
1876, Dickeson Continental Dollar. White Metal	R-6	854	$125	$250	$375	$950	$1,250	$1,650
1876, Dickeson Continental Dollar. Lead	R-9	856	—	—	—	—	—	—
1876, Dickeson Continental Dollar. Bowers White Metal	R-4	854A	$15	$20	$30	$60	$115	$185
1876, Dickeson Continental Dollar. Bashlow Silver	R-5	852A	$50	$20	$85	$115	$180	$245
1876, Dickeson Continental Dollar. Bashlow Bronze	R-4	853A	$15	$20	$40	$55	$85	$120
1876, Dickeson Continental Dollar. Bashlow Goldine	R-4	856A	$15	$20	$35	$50	$80	$110
1876, Dickeson Perseverando/Confederation. Copper	R-8	866B				$1,200	$1,500	
1876, Dickeson Perseverando/Confederation. White Metal	R-9	UNL				$1,250	$1,600	

UNL = Unlisted.

1876, Centennial Exposition Washington Bust / Declaration of Independence (HK–75 to 77): The obverse by George Hampden Lovett features a naked bust of George Washington with an ornamental border depicting cavalry and infantry. Abraham Demarest's reverse features a copy of John Trumbull's painting of the 1776 Congress Committee of Five making its report on the Declaration of Independence. **1876, Centennial Exposition Lovett Battle of Moores Creek Bridge (HK–90 to 92):** The first in a series of eight medals engraved and issued by George Hampden Lovett to commemorate the Revolutionary Battles of 1776. On February 27, 1776, the American victory ended British authority in North Carolina and greatly boosted patriotic morale. Less than two months later North Carolina became the first colony to vote in favor of independence from Britain. **1876, Dickeson Continental Dollar and Modern Restrikes (HK–852 to 856A):** Prominent numismatist Professor Montroville Dickeson, publisher of the *American Numismatic Manual of 1859,* had dies made and struck copies of the Continental Dollar as souvenirs for the 1876 Centennial Exposition. In the 20th century Robert Bashlow used the Dickeson dies to restrike medals. **1876, Dickeson Perseverando / Confederation (HK–866B):** For the obverse, Dickeson adopted a vignette from the Perseverando $6 bills issued by the 1775–1778 Continental Congress: the all-seeing eye above casts rays down upon a flaming altar surrounded by 13 stars. A vignette depicting a beaver gnawing on what is likely a palmetto tree, from the Confederation $40 bills issued by the 1778–1779 Continental Congress, was adopted for the reverse.

**1878, Wyoming Battle
and Massacre Centennial**

**1878, Washington Valley
Forge Centennial**

**1881, Battle of Groton
Heights Centennial**

**1882, William Penn
Pennsylvania Bicentennial
Official Medal**

	Rarity	HK#	VF-20	EF-40	AU-50	MS-60	MS-63	MS-65
						PF-60	PF-63	PF-65
1878, Wyoming Battle & Massacre Centennial. Gold	R-9	120D			—	—	—	—
1878, Wyoming Battle & Massacre Centennial. Silver	R-8	120A	$350	$550	$1,725	$2,650	$4,850	
1878, Wyoming Battle & Massacre Centennial. Bronze	R-6	120	$75	$160	$250	$450	$850	$1,050
1878, Wyoming Battle & Massacre Centennial. Brass	R-9	120B	—	—	—	$850	—	—
1878, Wyoming Battle & Massacre Centennial. White Metal	R-6	121	$50	$95	$175	$350	$475	$825
1878, Wyoming Battle & Massacre Centennial. White Metal Proof	R-7	121				$425	$550	$950
1878, Wyoming Battle & Massacre Centennial. Gold-Plated	R-7	120C	$100	$220	$350	$1,050	$1,650	—
1878, Washington Valley Forge Centennial. Silver	R-7	136			$1,800	$3,800	$5,200	$7,800
1878, Washington Valley Forge Centennial. Silver Proof	R-7	136				$3,800	$5,200	$7,800
1878, Washington Valley Forge Centennial. Bronze	R-6	137	$200	$325	$425	$600	$825	$1,200
1878, Washington Valley Forge Centennial. Yellow Bronze. Restrike	R-5	UNL	$20	$35	$45	$60	$75	$145
1881, Battle of Groton Heights Centennial. Silver Proof	R-8	125C					$4,200	
1881, Battle of Groton Heights Centennial. Bronze	R-6	125B	$75	$140	$195	$325	$700	$1,250
1881, Battle of Groton Heights Centennial. White Metal	R-6	125	$75	$135	$185	$320	$650	$900
1881, Battle of Groton Heights Centennial. White Metal Proof	R-6	125				$440	$750	$1,050
1882, William Penn Pennsylvania Bicentennial Official Metal. Gold-Plated Brass	R-7	138	$90	$150	$235	$425	$650	$850

UNL = Unlisted.

1878, Wyoming Battle and Massacre Centennial (HK–120 to 121): The scene on the obverse depicts Indians, with tomahawks raised in their hands, attacking a family of settlers. On the reverse is a memorial monument with the legend "Dulce et decorum est pro patria mori," which translated means: "It is a sweet and noble thing to die for one's country." Dies engraved by George T. Morgan. **1878, Washington Valley Forge Centennial (HK–136 and 137):** Engraved by William Barber, the medal commemorates the departure of the Continental Army from Valley Forge on June 19, 1778. A large naked bust of George Washington adorns the obverse. Struck originally in 1880 at the Philadelphia Mint, this is one of the medals in the U.S. Mint Medal Series. **1881, Battle of Groton Heights Centennial (HK–125, 125B, and 125C):** The obverse shows two American soldiers reloading and firing their muskets while being attacked by the British at the Fort Griswold Massacre. Their determination echoes the legend: "We will not give up the fort, let the consequence be what they may." The outline of Fort Griswold is displayed on the piece's reverse. **1882, William Penn Pennsylvania Bicentennial Official Medal (HK-138):** This medal celebrates the 200th anniversary of the founding of Pennsylvania and the landing of William Penn. A bust of William Penn is on the obverse, and anniversary dates are on the reverse. Engraved by George T. Morgan.

1884, World's Industrial and Cotton Centennial Exposition Official Medal

1891, South Carolina General Assembly Centennial

1893, World's Columbian Exposition Official Medal, Large Letters

1893, World's Columbian Exposition, by Saint-Gaudens

	Rarity	HK#	VF-20	EF-40	AU-50	MS-60 / PF-60	MS-63 / PF-63	MS-65 / PF-65
1884, World's Industrial & Cotton Centennial Expo Official Metal. Copper	R-8	142A						
1884, World's Industrial & Cotton Centennial Expo Official Metal. White Metal	R-7	142	$125	$210	$300	$450	$695	$850
1884, World's Industrial & Cotton Centennial Expo Official Metal. Gold-Plated	R-8	UNL					$750	
1891, South Carolina General Assembly Centennial. Silver, struck on silver $1	R-10	UNL					$3,800	
1891, South Carolina General Assembly Centennial. Copper	R-8	621				$750	$950	$1,250
1891, South Carolina General Assembly Centennial. White Metal	R-8	622				$1,500	$2,000	
1893, World's Columbian Expo Official Medal Large Letters. Silver Proof	R-9	154B					$4,800	
1893, World's Columbian Expo Official Medal Large Letters. Struck on silver $1	R-10	UNL					$2,500	
1893, World's Columbian Expo Official Medal Large Letters. Brass (a)	R-5	UNL	$20	$30	$60	$70	$150	$195
1893, World's Columbian Expo Official Medal Large Letters. Aluminum Proof	R-9	154A					$5,600	
1893, World's Columbian Expo Official Medal Large Letters. Gilted Brass	R-3	154	$9	$13	$15	$30	$80	$130
1893, World's Columbian Expo Official Medal Large Letters. Silver-Plated	R-6	UNL	$65	$125	$225	$375	$825	—
1893, World's Columbian Expo Official Medal Large Letters. Struck on Large Cent	R-10	UNL					$2,800	
1893, World's Columbian Exposition Saint-Gaudens. Copper C. Emmerich ‡	R-5	223	$35	$60	$90	$175	$300	$450
1893, World's Columbian Exposition Saint-Gaudens. Copper Chas Emmerich	R-7	223	$60	$90	$125	$265	$375	$550
1893, World's Columbian Exposition Saint-Gaudens. White Metal	R-10	223A						$4,200
1893, World's Columbian Exposition Saint-Gaudens. Gold-Plated	R-10	UNL						$2,800

UNL = Unlisted. ‡ Ranked in the *100 Greatest American Medals and Tokens*. **a.** Originally issued in Brass, replaced with the more common Gilted Brass.

1884, World's Industrial and Cotton Centennial Exposition Official Medal (HK–142 and 142A): Engraved by George T. Morgan and struck in the U.S. Mint Exhibit at the exposition. The Cotton Centennial Exposition was held in 1884 and 1885 to commemorate the first shipment of cotton exported to England and to promote the cotton industry. **1891, South Carolina General Assembly Centennial (HK–621 and 622):** This piece celebrates the centennial of the "Start of South Carolina," which occurred in 1791 with the first meeting of the General Assembly (legislature) of the state. The state's seal is on the obverse, and the reverse legend describes the date and location of the meeting. **1893, World's Columbian Exposition Official Medal, Large Letters (HK–154 and 154A):** This is the official medal from the Columbian Exposition held to commemorate the 400th anniversary of the discovery of America by Columbus and to tell the story of the world's progress for the past four centuries. On the obverse, large letters are found in the legend U.S. GOVT BUILDING. Engraved by George T. Morgan and struck at the Exposition. **1893, World's Columbian Exposition, by Saint-Gaudens (HK–223 and 223A):** The obverse portrays a smaller version of the Official Award Medal engraved by Augustus Saint-Gaudens, featuring Columbus wearing a cloak and armor; his head is upraised and arms spread as if giving thanks for finding land. The obverse was designed by Saint-Gaudens, and the detailed reverse by Charles Barber. Struck at the Philadelphia Mint.

1894, California Midwinter Exposition Official Medal

1894, California Midwinter Exposition Grizzly Bear / Exposition View

1895, Cotton States and International Exposition Official Medal

1897, Tennessee Centennial Exposition Official Medal

	Rarity	HK#	VF-20	EF-40	AU-50	MS-60 PF-60	MS-63 PF-63	MS-65 PF-65
1894, California Midwinter Exposition Official Medal. Copper	R-9	UNL	$85	$125	$175	$300	$450	$600
1894, California Midwinter Exposition Official Medal. Brass	R-5	245	$35	$45	$60	$120	$210	$325
1894, California Midwinter Exposition Official Medal. Gold-Plated	R-7	UNL	$45	$80	$225	$375	$495	$750
1894, California Midwinter Exposition Official Medal. Silver-Plated	R-8	UNL	$50	$90	$275	$425	$550	$800
1894, California Midwinter Exposition Grizzly Bear/Expo View. Aluminum	R-6	259	$65	$120	$190	$290	$475	$750
1895, Cotton States & International Exposition Official Medal. Gold-Plated Brass	R-4	268	$25	$40	$60	$95	$150	$210
1897, Tennessee Centennial Exposition Official Medal. Gold-Plated Brass	R-5	274	$35	$45	$60	$125	$190	$300

UNL = Unlisted.

1894, California Midwinter Exposition Official Medal (HK-245): The exposition official medal was struck in the Mechanics Building at the exposition under contract by agent J.W. Ewing of the U.S. Department of the Interior. The exposition's purpose was to showcase to the world the great wealth and riches of California. Dies were engraved by Charles E. Barber and produced by the Philadelphia Mint. Gold-plated medals were struck on opening day. **1894, California Midwinter Exposition Grizzly Bear / Exposition View (HK-259):** The obverse shows a California grizzly bear on a crag high atop a mountain looking down over a detailed bird's-eye view of the exposition grounds. The reverse legend expounds the numerous benefits of aluminum, a popular metal that could now be produced inexpensively due to the invention of electricity. Engraved, struck, and signed by Noble Chicago along the lower rim on the reverse. **1895, Cotton States and International Exposition Official Medal (HK-268):** Designed by Philip Martinez and struck at the Philadelphia Mint. The medal symbolizes that Atlanta and the South had "risen from its fires and ashes" after the Civil War. **1897, Tennessee Centennial Exposition Official Medal (HK-274):** The official medal designed by Charles E. Barber was struck and sold in the U.S. Mint Exhibit at the Exposition. The exposition celebrated the 100th anniversary of statehood for Tennessee and was meant to attract business to the state and increase its population.

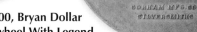

1898, Trans-Mississippi and International Exposition Official Medal

1900, Bryan Dollar Cartwheel With Legend

1901, Pan-American Exposition Official Medal

1901, South Carolina Exposition Official Medal

| | Rarity | HK# | VF-20 | EF-40 | AU-50 | MS-60 | MS-63 | MS-65 |
						PF-60	PF-63	PF-65
1898, Trans-Mississippi & International Expo Official Medal. Gold	R-9	UNL	$60	$85	$195	$340	$575	$925
1898, Trans-Mississippi & International Expo Official Medal. Silver	R-5	281				—	—	$2,000
1898, Trans-Mississippi & International Expo Official Medal. Silver Proof	R-9	281	$90	$140	$225	$300	$380	$475
1898, Trans-Mississippi & International Expo Official Medal. Bronze (a)	R-7	282	$30	$50	$70	$125	$175	$275
1898, Trans-Mississippi & International Expo Official Medal. Gold-Plated Brass	R-4	283				—	—	—
1898, Trans-Mississippi & International Expo Official Medal. White Metal Proof	R-9	UNL	$400	$625	$710	$1,100	$1,350	$1,800
1900, Bryan Dollar Cartwheel with Legend. Silver	R-6	782	$235	$295	$360	$495	$635	$1,150
1901, Pan-American Exposition Official Medal. Silver	R-6	287	$100	$250	$495	$850	$1,600	$2,500
1901, Pan-American Exposition Official Medal. Copper	R-8	288	$15	$55	$75	$90	$115	$185
1901, Pan-American Exposition Official Medal. Gold-Plated Copper	R-4	289	—	—	—	—	—	—
1901, South Carolina Exposition Official Medal. Silver	R-8	294A	—	—	—	—	—	—
1901, South Carolina Exposition Official Medal. Nickel	R-8	295A	—	—	—	$1,800	$2,500	—
1901, South Carolina Exposition Official Medal. White Metal	R-8	295	$125	$210	$285	$390	$600	$950
1901, South Carolina Exposition Official Medal. Gold-Plated Bronze	R-5	294	$125	$210	$285	$495	$950	$1,250

UNL = Unlisted. **a.** Reported copper strikings appear to be bronze.

1898, Trans-Mississippi and International Exposition Official Medal (HK–281 to 283A): On the obverse, a composite picture of the most beautiful women in the Trans-Mississippi county portion of the country celebrates past 50 years of expansion west of the Mississippi since the discovery of gold in California in 1848. T.R. Kimball proposed the use of the well-known picture "The Wild Huntsman" as inspiration for the reverse. The medal was designed and the models were prepared by Emil Fuchs. The official medal was struck in the U.S. Mint Exhibit at the exposition from dies made at the Philadelphia Mint. **1900, Bryan Dollar Cartwheel With Legend (HK–782):** A satirical piece struck to discredit Democratic congressman William Jennings Bryan during his 1900 presidential campaign. Bryan ran unsuccessfully against William McKinley on the Free Silver platform, supporting the coining of silver and gold at the legal ratio of sixteen to one. The cartwheel is the size of a silver dollar, and its oversize shows how unmanageably large a silver dollar would have to be to have the silver value Bryan proposed. **1901, Pan-American Exposition Official Medal (HK–287 to 289):** Designed by G.T. Brewster, the dies were engraved at the Philadelphia Mint, and the medals were struck in Buffalo, New York, in the U.S. Mint Exhibit at the exposition. The purpose of the exposition was to promote trade and social relations with our Pan-American neighbors. Tragedy overtook the nation when President McKinley was assassinated while greeting citizens in the Temple of Music at the exposition. **1901, South Carolina Exposition Official Medal (HK–294 to 295A):** The winged female standing on a globe with ships, trains, buildings, and agriculture in the background promotes Charleston's well-situated shipping port and the potential for trade with the West Indies, Central America, and South America. Designed by George T. Morgan and struck in the U.S. Mint Exhibit at the Exposition.

1902, Wells Fargo Semicentennial

1904, Louisiana Purchase Exposition Official Medal

1904, Louisiana Purchase Exposition Napoleon and Jefferson / Good Luck

1905, Louis and Clark Centennial Exposition Official Medal

| | Rarity | HK# | VF-20 | EF-40 | AU-50 | MS-60 | MS-63 | MS-65 |
						PF-60	PF-63	PF-65
1902, Wells Fargo Semicentennial. Silver	R-5	296	$450	$600	$900	$1,200	$1,500	$2,350
1902, Wells Fargo Semicentennial. Brown leatherette box of issue	R-6	UNL	$250	$350	$500			
1904, Louisiana Purchase Exposition Official Medal. Gold	R-10	299A				—	—	—
1904, Louisiana Purchase Exposition Official Medal. Silver (a)	R-4	299	$50	$70	$110	$170	$240	$385
1904, Louisiana Purchase Exposition Official Medal. Copper	R-6	301	$30	$60	$120	$165	$250	$290
1904, Louisiana Purchase Exposition Official Medal. Bronze	R-4	303	$15	$40	$55	$95	$275	$290
1904, Louisiana Purchase Exposition Official Medal. Yellow Bronze (Brass)	R-3	302	$15	$35	$50	$100	$140	$250
1904, Louisiana Purchase Exposition Official Medal. Gold-Plated Bronze (b)	R-3	300/304	$15	$30	$45	$95	$125	$225
1904, Louisiana Purchase Exposition Napoleon & Jefferson/Good Luck. Gold	R-10	310B	$7,250					
1904, Louisiana Purchase Exposition Napoleon & Jefferson/Good Luck. Silver	R-9	311A			$1,450	$2,200	$4,500	
1904, Louisiana Purchase Exposition Napoleon & Jefferson/Good Luck. Brass	R-5	310	$20	$35	$50	$125	$170	$240
1904, Louisiana Purchase Exposition Napoleon & Jefferson/Good Luck. Aluminum	R-6	311	$25	$40	$55	$135	$175	$250
1905, Louis and Clark Centennial Exposition Official Medal. Silver	R-5	325	$225	$300	$375	$575	$750	$895
1905, Louis and Clark Centennial Exposition Official Medal. Bronze (c)	R-5	327	$45	$65	$135	$180	$225	$450
1905, Louis and Clark Centennial Exposition Official Medal. Gold-Plated Bronze	R-6	326	$50	$90	$160	$240	$350	$550

UNL = Unlisted. **a.** There is a rare "no star reverse" variety that is found in several different compositions and is considerably more valuable. **b.** Gold-Plated Bronze and Gilt are combined. **c.** Reported brass strikings appear to be bronze.

1902, Wells Fargo Semicentennial (HK–296 and 296A): Struck in silver in 1902, the medal was given to each employee of Wells Fargo who had worked there for one year or more. The obverse displays a fascinating design of a stagecoach with guns firing at robbers above and a Pony Express rider being attacked by Indians below. The reverse depicts ships, trains, and various symbols of industry and progress. **1904, Louisiana Purchase Exposition Official Medal (HK–299 to 304):** The design depicts and commemorates the 100th anniversary of the Louisiana Purchase by Thomas Jefferson from Napoleon Bonaparte: 1,000,000 square miles for $15,000,000. Designed by George T. Morgan and struck in the U.S. Mint Exhibit at the exposition. **1904, Louisiana Purchase Exposition Napoleon and Jefferson / Good Luck (HK–310 to 311B):** Conjoined busts of Napoleon and Jefferson are depicted on the obverse with an inscription around, stating, "– NAPOLEON SOLD IT – APRIL 30th – JEFFERSON BOUGHT IT – 1803." For good luck, a horseshoe with entwined ribbon and a four-leaf clover are shown together on the reverse. **1905, Lewis and Clark Centennial Exposition Official Medal (HK–325 to 327):** In the arms of a female figure representing America, captains Meriwether Lewis and William Clark sight the Pacific Ocean at the western termination of their Northwest Expedition. Westward the course of the empire takes its way. On the reverse is a topographical map of the American West showing the states, major cities, and shipping routes from Seattle, Portland, and San Francisco. Designed by George T. Morgan and struck in the U.S. Mint Exhibit at the Exposition.

1905, Louis and Clark Centennial Expo, Conjoined Busts

1905, Denver Mint Opening

1906, Pike's Peak Southwest Centennial Exposition Official Medal

1907, Jamestown Tercentennial Exposition Official Medal

	Rarity	HK#	VF-20	EF-40	AU-50	MS-60	MS-63	MS-65
						PF-60	PF-63	PF-65
1905, Louis and Clark Centennial Expo Conjoined Busts, 34 mm. Silver	R-7	UNL	$45	$80	$150	$295	$370	$550
1905, Louis and Clark Centennial Expo Conjoined Busts, 34 mm. Silver antiqued	R-5	328	$30	$70	$135	$275	$350	$510
1905, Louis and Clark Centennial Expo Conjoined Busts, 34 mm. Bronze	R-6	329	$30	$60	$95	$190	$250	$375
1905, Louis and Clark Centennial Expo Conjoined Busts, 34 mm. Gold-Plated Bronze	R-7	330	$45	$70	$120	$220	$300	$425
1905, Denver Mint Opening. Silver	R-9	876A	—	—	—	$4,500	$6,500	
1905, Denver Mint Opening. Bronze	R-6	876	$300	$450	$950	$1,100	$1,500	$2,025
1906, Pike's Peak Southwest Centennial Exposition Official Medal. Silver	R-6	UNL	$90	$190	$270	$350	$500	$625
1906, Pike's Peak Southwest Centennial Exposition Official Medal. Silver oxidized	R-5	336	$30	$50	$75	$115	$195	$395
1906, Pike's Peak Southwest Centennial Exposition Official Medal. Silver Proof	R-6	335	$90	$150	$225	$325	$625	$800
1906, Pike's Peak Southwest Centennial Exposition Official Medal. Bronze	R-4	338	$15	$30	$50	$60	$85	$150
1906, Pike's Peak Southwest Centennial Exposition Official Medal. Gold-Plated	R-8	337	$175	$350	$850	$1,150	$1,750	$2,530
1907, Jamestown Tercentennial Exposition Official Medal. Silver	R-5	344	$95	$150	$195	$325	$495	$725
1907, Jamestown Tercentennial Exposition Official Medal. Bronze	R-4	346	$35	$50	$75	$125	$225	$350
1907, Jamestown Tercentennial Exposition Official Medal. Gold-Plated Bronze	R-4	347	$30	$45	$60	$95	$175	$275
1907, Jamestown Tercentennial Exposition Official Medal. Silver-Plated Bronze	R-7	345	$85	$140	$180	$285	$595	$895

UNL = Unlisted.

1905, Lewis and Clark Centennial Exposition, Conjoined Busts, 34 mm (HK–328 to 331B): Captain Meriwether Lewis and Captain William Clark grace this unofficial medal struck by Joseph Mayer & Brothers of Seattle. This issue was struck in several sizes as well as different die varieties and metal compositions. A view of the Government Building at the exposition is shown on the reverse. **1905, Denver Mint Opening (HK–876 and 876A):** As the first product of the Denver Mint, this type was struck to test the new machinery and, some believe, new dies for a $20 gold piece. It was issued as a souvenir at the official opening ceremonies of the mint in early 1906. **1906, Pike's Peak Southwest Centennial Exposition Official Medal (HK–335 to 338):** Designed by Charles E. Barber and struck at the Philadelphia Mint, this medal commemorates the 100th anniversary of the discovery of Pike's Peak by Lt. Zebulon Montgomery Pike during his Southwest Expedition of 1806–1807, which followed the Louisiana Purchase and Lewis and Clark's expedition with the Corp of Discovery. **1907, Jamestown Tercentennial Exposition Official Medal (HK–344 to 347):** With Pocahontas on the obverse and Captain John Smith's ship on the reverse, this medal commemorates the 300th anniversary of the Jamestown settlement in North America by English-speaking people. Designed by George T. Morgan and struck in the U.S. Mint Exhibit at the Exposition.

**1909, Alaska-Yukon-Pacific
Exposition Official Medal**

1908, Bryan the Great Commoner, by Thomas Elder

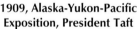

**1909, Alaska-Yukon-Pacific
Exposition, President Taft**

1910, Brian Boru

	Rarity	HK#	VF-20	EF-40	AU-50	MS-60 PF-60	MS-63 PF-63	MS-65 PF-65
1908, Bryan the Great Commoner by Thomas Elder. Silver	R-9	805						$3,500
1908, Bryan the Great Commoner by Thomas Elder. Copper	R-9	807						$2,530
1908, Bryan the Great Commoner by Thomas Elder. Brass	R-9	808						$2,780
1908, Bryan the Great Commoner by Thomas Elder. Aluminum	R-9	809						$1,610
1908, Bryan the Great Commoner by Thomas Elder. German-silver	R-9	806						$3,300
1909, Alaska-Yukon-Pacific Exposition Official Medal. Silver	R-5	353	$80	$95	$130	$150	$300	$525
1909, Alaska-Yukon-Pacific Exposition Official Medal. Copper	R-5	355	$25	$35	$65	$75	$110	$245
1909, Alaska-Yukon-Pacific Exposition Official Medal. Bronze	R-4	354	$25	$35	$60	$95	$145	$265
1909, Alaska-Yukon-Pacific Exposition Official Medal. Bronze sandblast finish	R-7	UNL	$45	$65	$115	$180	$235	$295
1909, Alaska-Yukon-Pacific Exposition Official Medal. Gold-Plated	R-7	356	$140	$200	$250	$360	$435	$475
1909, Alaska-Yukon-Pacific Exposition President Taft. Gold-Plated Silver	R-8	361					$7,800	
1910, Brian Boru. Silver	R-6	390	$275	$465	$800	$1,450	$2,500	$3,250
1910, Brian Boru. Bronze	R-9	391						$6,400
1910, Brian Boru. Aluminum	R-5	392	$150	$200	$270	$350	$575	$750

UNL = Unlisted.

1908, Bryan the Great Commoner, by Thomas Elder (HK–805 to 809): William Jennings Bryan, who virtually controlled the Democratic Party for 30 years, ran unsuccessfully for the U.S. presidency in 1896, 1900, and 1908. After his unsuccessful campaign in 1900 against William McKinley, Bryan edited a weekly political journal, The Commoner, after which he became known as "The Great Commoner." Thomas L. Elder, a coin dealer in New York City, struck this satirical Bryan medal. **1909, Alaska-Yukon-Pacific Exposition Official Medal (HK–353 to 356):** The exposition and official medal were designed to promote the "enormous value of Alaska" and the "greatness" of Seattle's sea port. U.S. Mint die engraver George T. Morgan designed the official medal based on Adelaide Hanscomb's official logo for the exposition and the Seattle City seal. The medals were struck at the exposition by the U.S. Mint and sold through Joseph Mayer & Brothers of Seattle. **1909, Alaska-Yukon-Pacific Exposition, President Taft (HK-361):** The visit of President William H. Taft to Seattle on September 30, 1909, is commemorated on this gold-plated, .900-fine silver medal designed and produced by Joseph Mayer & Brothers Jewelry Company in Seattle. A variation of the exposition logo surrounded by an ornate wreath is depicted on the obverse. The reverse has commemorative text with an olive branch, a Mayer signature, and .900 indicating the piece's composition along with SILVER imprinted on the edge. **1910, Brian Boru (HK–390 to 392):** Brian Boru was king of Ireland from 1002–1014 A.D. Considered the George Washington of Ireland, at the age of 88 he broke Danish power over Ireland at the Battle of Clontart, where he was slain. The medal was issued by Thomas Elder, a coin dealer in New York City, to pay "tribute to the indomitable spirit of the Irish race."

1910, Ohio Valley Exposition Official Medal

1915, Panama Pacific International Exposition Official Medal

1915, Panama-California Exposition Official Medal

1920, Manila Mint Opening ("Wilson Dollar")

	Rarity	HK#	VF-20	EF-40	AU-50	MS-60 / PF-60	MS-63 / PF-63	MS-65 / PF-65
1910, Ohio Valley Exposition Official Medal. Silver	R-6	393	$175	$225	$300	$425	$500	$625
1910, Ohio Valley Exposition Official Medal. Copper	R-6	394	$75	$105	$145	$200	$325	$595
1910, Ohio Valley Exposition Official Medal. Bronze	R-6	395	$75	$100	$135	$210	$325	$540
1910, Ohio Valley Exposition Official Medal. Gold-Plated	R-8	UNL	$175	$225	$300	$425	$500	$625
1915, Panama Pacific International Exposition Official Medal. Silver ‡	R-5	399	$50	$110	$225	$500	$750	$1,800
1915, Panama Pacific International Exposition Official Medal. Bright Bronze	R-5	400	$25	$55	$70	$90	$225	$375
1915, Panama Pacific International Exposition Official Medal. Statuary Bronze	R-6	UNL	$30	$60	$85	$120	$275	$485
1915, Panama Pacific International Exposition Official Medal. Antiqued Bronze	R-7	UNL	$30	$60	$90	$135	$310	$500
1915, Panama Pacific International Exposition Official Medal. Oxidized Bronze	R-7	UNL	$30	$60	$90	$135	$310	$500
1915, Panama Pacific International Exposition Official Medal. Gold-Plated Bronze	R-5	401	$40	$55	$90	$175	$325	$475
1915, Panama Pacific International Exposition Official Medal. Silver-Plated Bronze	R-6	UNL	$125	$175	$250	$325	$475	$595
1915, Panama-California Exposition Official Medal. Silver	R-5	426	$75	$125	$225	$275	$425	$675
1915, Panama-California Exposition Official Medal. Bronze	R-5	427	$35	$80	$110	$160	$295	$460
1915, Panama-California Exposition Official Medal. Gold-Plated Bronze	R-4	428	$30	$70	$95	$130	$195	$275
1915, Panama-California Exposition Official Medal. Silver-Plated Bronze	R-6	UNL	$55	$110	$140	$185	$320	$450
1920, Wilson Dollar Manila Mint Opening. Gold	R-8	1031			$44,000	$60,000	$75,000	
1920, Wilson Dollar Manila Mint Opening. Silver (a)	R-4	449	$85	$250	$525	$875	$1,850	$3,200
1920, Wilson Dollar Manila Mint Opening. Bronze (a)	R-5	450	$35	$125	$600	$1,000	$1,750	$4,500
1920, Wilson Dollar Manila Mint Opening. Brass no "M" Morgan signature	R-10	450						$6,000

UNL = Unlisted. ‡ Ranked in the *100 Greatest American Medals and Tokens*. **a.** VF and EF show signs of sea salvage.

1910, Ohio Valley Exposition Official Medal (HK–393 to 395): The exposition and official medal promoted the "industrial prowess of Ohio Valley," a century of "steamboat navigation on Ohio River," and the "commercial strength of South." Designed by George T. Morgan and struck in the U.S. Mint Exhibit at the exposition. **1915, Panama-Pacific International Exposition Official Medal (HK–399 to 401):** The official medal celebrates the opening of the Panama Canal. Winged Mercury opens the canal locks with the ship Argo, the symbol of navigation, passing through. Two women, entwined around the globe holding cornucopias, represent the two hemispheres on the reverse. Designed by Robert Aitken, who also designed the official $50 gold commemorative coins for the exposition, the medal was struck in the U.S. Mint Exhibit at the exposition. **1915, Panama-California Exposition Official Medal (HK–426 to 428):** On the obverse Uncle Sam, in front of North and Central America, holds a shovel with its handle overlaying the Panama Canal. Designed by *Washington Star* cartoonist C.K. Berryman, engraved by Charles E. Barber, and struck in the U.S. Mint Exhibit at the exposition. **1920, Manila Mint Opening ("Wilson Dollar") (HK–449, 450, and 1031):** This medal was struck at the opening of the Manila Mint in the Philippines. President Woodrow Wilson's bust is on the obverse; the goddess Juno Moneta guides a child striking medals in a coining press on the reverse—an apparent reference to the relationship between the United States and the Philippines. Many examples were dumped into Manila Bay just days prior to the Japanese invasion of the Philippines during WWII. Design concept by Clifford Hewitt and dies engraved by George T. Morgan.

1933, Century of Progress Exposition Official Medal

1926, U.S. Sesquicentennial Exposition

1939, Golden Gate International Exposition, by Charbneau (shown at 200%)

1950, Washington, D.C., Sesquicentennial

	Rarity	HK#	VF-20	EF-40	AU-50	MS-60	MS-63	MS-65
						PF-60	PF-63	PF-65
1926, U.S. Sesquicentennial Exposition. Bronze	R-5	451/452	$20	$45	$65	$95	$140	$195
1926, U.S. Sesquicentennial Exposition. Bronze high relief antiqued	R-6	UNL	$45	$80	$120	$165	$265	$350
1926, U.S. Sesquicentennial Exposition. Nickel	R-4	454	$15	$45	$67	$75	$190	$265
1926, U.S. Sesquicentennial Exposition. Gold-Plated Bronze	R-4	453	$15	$45	$65	$75	$195	$285
1933, Century of Progress Exposition Official Medal. Bronze	R-4	463	$15	$20	$40	$50	$95	$125
1933, Century of Progress Exposition Official Medal. Bronze antiqued	R-6	UNL	$20	$35	$65	$95	$150	$245
1939, Golden Gate International Expo Charbneau. J1 Gold 1 D SOLID GOLD	R-6	488			$1,780	$2,185	$2,350	$2,950
1939, Golden Gate International Expo Charbneau. J14 Gold 1 D SOLID GOLD stamped 10K & 40	R-9	UNL			$2,400	$2,700	$2,950	$3,300
1939, Golden Gate International Expo Charbneau. J2 Gold 1 D 10K SOLID GOLD	R-8	UNL			$1,850	$2,300	$2,450	$2,950
1939, Golden Gate International Expo Charbneau. J3 Gold 1 * 10K SOLID GOLD	R-7	UNL			$1,900	$2,350	$2,600	$3,000
1939, Golden Gate International Expo Charbneau. J4 Gold 1 * 22 over 10K SOLID GOLD	R-8	UNL			$2,100	$2,750	$3,350	$3,600
1939, Golden Gate International Expo Charbneau. J5 Gold 1 D 10K SOLID GOLD stamped 40	R-8	UNL			$2,100	$2,400	$2,600	$2,750
1939, Golden Gate International Expo Charbneau. J6 STERLING	R-6	487			$1,200	$1,495	$1,975	$2,400
1939, Golden Gate International Expo Charbneau. J7 STERLING Gold-Plated	R-7	487C			$1,300	$1,550	$2,100	$2,600
1939, Golden Gate International Expo Charbneau. J8 STERLING stamped 40	R-8	487B			$1,900	$2,400	$2,650	$2,750
1939, Golden Gate International Expo Charbneau. J9 Copper	R-9	UNL			$2,500	$2,700	$3,000	$3,600
1939, Golden Gate International Expo Charbneau. J10 Copper Gold-Plated	R-6	490			$850	$975	$1,450	$2,250
1940, Golden Gate International Expo Charbneau. J11 Gold 1 * 10K SOLID GOLD	R-8	489			$1,800	$1,950	$2,350	$2,750
1940, Golden Gate International Expo Charbneau. J12 Gold 1 * 22 over 10K SOLID GOLD	R-8	UNL			$1,650	$1,700	$2,100	$2,300
1940, Golden Gate International Expo Charbneau. J13 STERLING	R-6	487A			$1,350	$1,650	$2,100	$2,550

§ Ranked in the *100 Greatest American Medals and Tokens*. **UNL** = Unlisted.

1926, U.S. Sesquicentennial Exposition Official Medal (HK–451 to 454): For the 150th anniversary of the Declaration of Independence. The obverse displays a bust of George Washington, with Liberty riding a Pegasus and holding a torch on the reverse. Designed by Albin Polasek and struck in the U.S. Mint Exhibit at the exposition. **1933, Century of Progress Exposition Official Medal (HK-463):** A semi-nude male stretches his arms over Research and Industry on the obverse, with a topographical map of Chicago fairgrounds on the reverse. Designed by Emil Robert Zettler, dies made by Medallic Art Company, and struck in the U.S. Mint Exhibit at the exposition. **1939–1940, Golden Gate International Exposition, by Charbneau (HK-488):** Designed by Jules Charbneau and sold as souvenirs. Fourteen varieties were struck in gold, silver, and copper. All are the size of a U.S. gold dollar. The exposition statue Pacifica adorns the obverse, with the Tower of the Sun edifice, Portals of the Pacific, and the Golden Gate Bridge on the reverse.

	Rarity	HK#	VF-20	EF-40	AU-50	MS-60	MS-63	MS-65
						PF-60	PF-63	PF-65
1950, Washington, D.C. Sesquicentennial. Silver oxidized	R-5	507	$50	$65	$95	$275	$325	$485
1950, Washington, D.C. Sesquicentennial. Copper oxidized	R-4	508	$10	$20	$30	$50	$80	$120
1950, Washington, D.C. Sesquicentennial. Gold-Plated Copper	R-8	UNL	—	—	—	—	—	—

UNL = Unlisted.

1950, Washington, D.C., Sesquicentennial (HK–507 and 508): For the 150th anniversary of Washington, D.C., as the seat of the federal government. The obverse displays the Statue of Freedom on the dome of the U.S. Capitol. On the reverse President John Adams addresses the 6th Congress, resulting in the city becoming the permanent capital. Designed by Thomas Hudson Jones and struck at the Philadelphia Mint.

1954, Cradle of the Union Celebration

1959, Nevada Silver Centennial

**1959, Colorado Rush
to the Rockies Centennial**

**1959, Oregon Statehood Centennial /
Buchanan-Eisenhower**

	Rarity	HK#	VF-20	EF-40	AU-50	MS-60	MS-63	MS-65
						PF-60	PF-63	PF-65
1954, Cradle of the Union Celebration. Gold Proof	R-7	511				$3,500	$4,000	$5,600
1954, Cradle of the Union Celebration. Silver oxidized	R-5	510	$65	$125	$275	$325	$380	$545
1954, Cradle of the Union Celebration. Bronze oxidized	R-4	512	$10	$25	$40	$55	$65	$90
1959, Nevada Silver Centennial. Silver	R-5	552	$110	$125	$150	$225	$345	$425
1959, Nevada Silver Centennial. Nickel holed	R-6	552A	$30	$45	$70	$115	$165	$195
1959, Colorado Rush to the Rockies Centennial. Silver	R-3	542	$15	$20	$35	$50	$65	$95
1959, Oregon Statehood Centennial Buchanan-Eisenhower. Gold Proof	R-8	554				—	$5,000	$8,000
1959, Oregon Statehood Centennial Buchanan-Eisenhower. Silver antiqued	R-9	553	$250	$360	$500	$625	$750	$1,200
1959, Oregon Statehood Centennial Buchanan-Eisenhower. Aluminum	R-6	555	—	—	—	—	—	—
1959, Oregon Statehood Centennial Buchanan-Eisenhower. Uniface Gold-Plated	R-9	UNL				$700	$950	$1,500

UNL = Unlisted.

1954, Cradle of the Union Celebration (HK–510 to 512): This medal honors the 200th anniversary of the Albany, New York, Congress of 1754—historically the First American Congress—where Benjamin Franklin presented his plan for a federal union. Albany's first public building, known as the Stadt Huys, later to be City Hall and the Courthouse, is depicted on the obverse. The reverse design is based on Franklin's famous cartoon, first published in 1754, of a segmented serpent representing the Colonies with a message "Join, or Die." Dies were engraved by Gilroy Roberts and struck at the Philadelphia Mint. **1959, Nevada Silver Centennial (HK–552 and 552A):** The State Seal of Nevada with a mining scene, train, and agricultural implements, is depicted on the obverse. The legend on the reverse mentions Virginia City, which was a boomtown in 1859 due to the Comstock Lode (the first major silver-deposit discovery in the United States) bestowing Virginia City the title of "Richest City in America." **1959, Colorado Rush to the Rockies Centennial (HK–542):** Oxen pulling a covered wagon heading west, being escorted by a cowboy on horseback, adorn the obverse. The reverse depicts the U.S. Air Force Academy logo in tribute to its First Commencement and Official Dedication by President Dwight Eisenhower. Designed by Arthur Roy Mitchell, modeled by Frank Gasparro, and struck at the Philadelphia Mint. **1959, Oregon Statehood Centennial / Buchanan-Eisenhower (HK–553 to 555):** The conjoined busts of the 15th president, James Buchanan, and the 34th president, Dwight D. Eisenhower, grace the obverse. The official Oregon Centennial emblem is depicted on the reverse. Issued by Northwestern Specialty Sales Co.

1960, Pony Express Centennial

1961, Kansas Statehood Centennial

1961, Mobile, Alabama 250th Anniversary

1961, Pony Express Termination Centennial

| | Rarity | HK# | VF-20 | EF-40 | AU-50 | MS-60 | MS-63 | MS-65 |
						PF-60	PF-63	PF-65
1960, Pony Express Centennial. Silver	R-3	582	$25	$30	$35	$50	$60	$75
1960, Pony Express Centennial. Bronze	R-2	583	$5	$7	$10	$12	$25	$70
1961, Kansas Statehood Centennial. Silver	R-3	586	$25	$30	$35	$50	$60	$85
1961, Mobile, Alabama 250th Anniversary. Silver	R-3	587	$25	$30	$35	$55	$70	$90
1961, Pony Express Termination Centennial. Silver	R-3	588	$25	$30	$35	$50	$65	$85
1961, Pony Express Termination Centennial. Silver	R-2	589	$5	$7	$10	$12	$25	$50

1960, Pony Express Centennial (HK–582 and 583): This piece was struck to commemorate the 100th anniversary of the famed Pony Express, which delivered mail from St. Joseph, Montana, to Sacramento, California, from April 3, 1860, to October 24, 1861. The medal displays busts of the Pony Express founders Russel, Majors, and Waddell on the obverse. The reverse depicts the famous painting by Herman Hansen depicting a Pony Express rider on horseback. **1961, Kansas Statehood Centennial (HK-586):** Issued for the Kansas Centennial, the medal's obverse shows a covered-wagon train being pulled by oxen, with mountains and a setting sun in the background. Its reverse depicts a vertical stalk of wheat over a sunflower. With its design a composite resulting from the work of Topeka artists and Treasury Department experts, this medal was struck at the Philadelphia Mint. **1961, Mobile, Alabama, 250th Anniversary (HK-587):** A bust of Sieur de Bienville, who founded the city in 1711 as the French capital of Louisiana, graces the obverse. The official seal of the anniversary is shown on the reverse along with six flags, representing the six countries that ruled Mobile. **1961, Pony Express Termination Centennial (HK-588 and 589):** The Pony Express was discontinued when the transcontinental telegraph was completed in late 1861. President Abraham Lincoln characterized the Pony Express as "an immortal service to the Union." A telegraph key and a riderless horse are on the obverse. The reverse depicts a dismounted Pony Express rider leading his horse away, walking with his back to us, with telegraph wires in the background.

APPENDIX H

Advertising Counterstamps on U.S. Quarters

In the nineteenth century various merchants counterstamped many coins, including quarters, with advertisements and notices. Carried place to place in pocket change, these coins were a free way to promote goods and services widely. Converse to normal numismatic practice, well-worn coins display counterstamps more sharply than do high-grade ones. Today, it is an interesting exercise to track down information about issuers by looking on the Internet.

In 1824 Lafayette, French hero of the American Revolution, returned to spend a year in America. Congress designated him as "The Nation's Guest." Many coins were counterstamped with his image. Most were cents; an exception is this 1818 quarter, the only one seen.

"The Landing of General Lafayette at Castle Garden, New York, August 1824."

The hallmark of jeweler
C.S. Ball on an 1836 quarter.

An advertisement of Cairns & Bro. on a
quarter. Well-worn coins such as this
permitted clearer counterstamping.

F. Bolton of Chatham, Connecticut,
counterstamped this 1854-dated
quarter, probably in the same year.

J.D. Crane, artist (daguerreotype photographer), counterstamped
both sides of this 1858 quarter, an unusual practice.

The stamp of Benedict & Barnes
on an 1841-O quarter.

McKenney, a Biddeford, Maine,
gunsmith, counterstamped many
coins, but nearly all were cents. This
1854 quarter is the only one seen.

Sage's Candy Coin was advertised by counterstamping quarters,
half dollars, and trade dollars. "Despite much searching," says
Q. David Bowers, "I have learned nothing about the issuer."

A counterstamp of Stelling, 51 Old Slip,
New York City, on an 1857 quarter.

A counterstamp of J.M. Taylor on an
1818 quarter. With different stamps and
various addresses he also advertised on
Spanish-American two-reales coins.

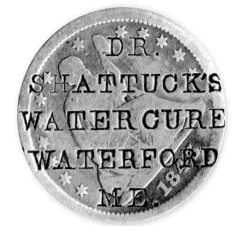

The VOTE THE LAND FREE political slogan of the National Reform Party is on an 1843 quarter. This counterstamp was usually placed on copper cents.

Shattuck's Water Cure was advertised on an 1843 quarter. In 1992 *The Waterford Water Cure* (Bowers) told the story of this cure-all hydropathic establishment.

J.L. Polhemus, a Sacramento druggist, counterstamped this 1855-S quarter, the first San Francisco coin of this denomination. He was a prolific issuer of his stamp on quarters, half dollars, foreign coins, and even gold double eagles.

What was the business at Knight's at 5 Beaver Street in Albany, New York, the counterstamper of this 1854 quarter?

A little mystery here: Who at 407 Broadway, New York City, counterstamped this 1857 quarter?

Prepared solely from Vegetable Matter,

By JACOB HOUCK, Baltimore,

Which may be taken with perfect safety by all ages and in all diseases; Its cures are for the following diseases—Dyspepsia, Loss of Appetite, Indigestion, Inflamation of the Stomach, Heart Burn, Diarrhea, Dysentary or Flux, Piles, Fistula, Obstructed Menstruation, Ague and Fever, Billious or Remittent Fever, Typus Fever, Scarlet Fever, Small Pox, Erysipelous of St. Anthony's Fire, Asthma. Pleurisy, Measels, Yellow Fever, Costiveness, Wind on the Stomach or Bowels, Cholera Morbus, Consumption, Influenza, Colds, Coughs, Inflammation of the chest, Palsey, Gout, Rheumatism, Inflammatory Sore Throat or Quinsey, Whooping Cough, Thrush or Sore Mouth, Putrid Sore Throat, Croup, Inflammation of the Heart, Dropsy, Rickets, Diseases of the Liver, Jaundice, Difficulty of making Urine, Gleet, Histerics, Nervous & Scrofulous Affections of the Members and Ligaments, Mercurial and Venereal Diseases, Ulcers, Sores, Affections of the Skin, and all diseases arising from Impure Blood, &c.

Price per Bottle $1 50.

The above medicine can be obtained at No. 121 Market street, opposite the Museum, with proper directions for using. A liberal discount made to persons who buy to sell.

Houck's Panacea, a cure-all patent medicine made in Baltimore, was extensively advertised on half dollars. This 1818 quarter is the only one seen on this denomination.

Goodwin's Grand Greasejuice and Goodwin's Grand Glittering Globules were patent medicines advertised on many coins, including this 1853-O quarter. The products were widely familiar and most Americans would have known what "G.G.G." and "G.G.G.G." stood for.

CHARLES H. GOODWIN,
DRUGGIST & MANUFACTURING CHEMIST.
DEALER IN
Drugs, Medicines, Dye Stuffs, Perfumery and Fancy Goods.

Inventor, Manufacturer, and Proprietor of the following Preparations:

G. G. G., or Q. of F., GOODWIN'S GRAND GREASEJUICE, OR QUINTESSENCE OF FAT,

The great AMERICAN Compound for the embellishment, preservation, growth, and beauty of the Human Hair.

The unrivalled Breath Perfume,

G. G. G. G., GOODWIN'S GRAND GLITTERING GLOBULES, or AMBROSIAL AROMATIC YANKEE CACHOUS.

G. G. T., and Q. of Q., Goodwin's Grand Tobaccojuice, and Quintessence of Quicksilver,

The great American Remedy for the *Cimex Lectularius*, or common Bed Bug.

Also of **Goodwin's Flavoring Extracts**, and **Madame Delectable's Handkerchief Perfume.**

All orders to be addressed to CHARLES H. GOODWIN, Chemist, at

GOODWIN'S GRAND GREASEJUICE DEPOT,

No. 49 Water Street, Exeter, N. H.

APPENDIX I

Advertising Counterstamps on Two-Reales Coins

Spanish-American two-reales coins or "two bits" circulated as legal tender in the United States from the 1700s until late 1859. In commerce after the establishment of the U.S. Mint these were usually valued at the same as a federal quarter dollar. In the early 1850s there were far more two-reales coins in circulation, many dating back to the previous century, than federal quarter dollars. As most were worn smooth they were an ideal canvas for impressing counterstamp messages clearly, often at length. New York City was the epicenter of such issues. Historical details of many of these issuers can be researched on the Internet. Examples are shown here.

A Hutchings at 395 Broadway, New York City, advertisement on an 1807 coin. Various city directories available on the Internet can yield information on many counterstamp advertisers, as can old newspapers. Generally, a person or business that advertised on a coin also advertised elsewhere.

An advertisement of Meschutt's Metropolitan Coffee Room on a 1785 coin. The typical coffee room catered to temperance advocates and offered coffee, food including oysters served in multiple styles, and desserts, and newspapers and magazines to read. Meschutt's counterstamped many coins, mostly copper cents.

A counterstamp by James S. Bradley, a gilder and frame maker, on a 1780 coin.

A counterstamp of J.M. Taylor on a 1798 coin with the separate unrelated mark of Wm. A. Dodge.

The hallmark of I.W. & C. Forbes on a 1790 coin.

An advertisement of Horsley's Knickerbocker Daguerreotype Gallery in New York City, applied with five different punches on an 1800 coin.

A ticket to George Christy and Wood's Minstrels, with the figure of a minstrel player, on a 1787 coin.

An extensive advertisement on the reverse (an unusual position) of an 1826 coin.

Cooper's Coffee House advertised
on a well-worn coin of King Charles III.

An advertisement of R. Lundy
of New York City on a 1776 coin.

An early Miller's advertisement using
several single-line punches on a 1780s
coin, before the single multi-line punch
seen on the 1821 coin below was made.

L. Miller's Hair Invigorator,
advertised with a multiple-
line punch on an 1821 coin.

The hallmark of
I.W. Whitcomb & Adam
on a 1793 coin.

The entertainer
Wyman the Wizard
advertised on this 1782 coin.

Many people with similar punches stamped both
sides of this 1790s coin, but why, and who were they?

A Wood's Minstrels admission ticket as stamped on both
sides of a two-reales coin of King Charles IV of Spain.

Louis Hof, a Rochester, New York
brewer, advertised on this early
eighteenth-century coin. He also
stamped U.S. coins, but not in quantity.

An unnamed locksmith was at
No. 3 Mott Street in New York City.

An admission ticket to the
Model Artists in New York City
on a 1797 coin. On stage were
nude women in various poses.

An admission ticket to
Broadway Varieties, a
New York City show.

An advertisement for
Ebling's Columbian Gardens,
a New York City beer garden.

A Potter & Bassett
of Elmira, New York,
advertisement on a 1795 coin.

This counterstamp of
C.C. Tracy on a 1790 coin
gives details of his business.

An advertisement of the
Washington Lunch
on a 1796 coin.

APPENDIX J

Two Special Quarter-Related Hard Times Tokens

Hard Times tokens form a popular specialty in American numismatics. They consist of various tokens, mostly the size of a large copper cent and struck in copper or brass, that were issued for political or advertising reasons from 1832 to 1844. In the American economy the Hard Times period of bank and financial difficulties began in early 1837 and ended early in 1843. Hundreds of banks closed their doors and thousands of businesses failed. Fearful of the current events, citizens hoarded silver and gold coins to the extent that all disappeared by late spring of 1837, and most copper cents disappeared as well. To facilitate commerce private citizens and businesses issued Hard Times tokens, as well as paper scrip notes.

As to the category's start and end dates of 1832 to 1844, these were assigned by Lyman H. Low, who in the late nineteenth century published *Hard Times Tokens*, which became the standard reference with "Low numbers" assigned to the different varieties. Nearly a century later, Russell Rulau assigned HT numbers. In the *Guide Book of Hard Times Tokens* (Bowers), published by Whitman Publishing, historical information never before published in a single volume is given together with Whitman numbers cross-referenced to Low and Rulau numbers.

There are two Hard Times tokens that are part of the quarter dollar tradition. The first is a silver strike made by using the dies normally intended for copper issues to overstrike Capped Bust quarters. The issue celebrates the Whig Party victory of 1834. The second is a token inscribed "American Silver" with a denomination of 25 cents, dated 1837, struck in a composition metal by Dr. Lewis Feuchtwanger of New York City.

THE 1834 WHIG VICTORY TOKEN

The *Guide Book of Hard Times Tokens* gives this description for the standard issue in brass:

Whitman-08-10b PE • Ship / Whigs of N. York • Low-6 • Rulau HT-14A • R-5 • 25 mm • Brass. Plain edge. Dies by George Lovett Sr. • Obverse with FOR THE CONSTITUTION HURRA. • Reverse with inscription FLOURISH COMMERCE, FLOURISH INDUSTRY around with center celebrating the GLORIOUS Whig victory at the three-day elections of New York, April 8 to 10, 1834. The newly named Whig party envisioned this as the first step to a nationwide movement to counter the policies of Andrew Jackson. Usually seen in worn grades.

The 1834 Whig Victory token overstruck on a quarter.

For the silver issue:

W-08-10f RE • Dies as preceding • Low-6 • HT-14C • R-8 • 27 mm • Silver. Three known: One struck over an 1833 Capped Bust quarter dollar, reeded edge from the quarter dollar, Tanenbaum Collection; overstrike on a quarter, Robert A. Schuman Collection; Fine, holed, ANS. • HT-014C: Ford (Stack's 2004) Gem Unc $17,250

History. Beginning in early 1834 there were many midterm elections of state and local officials. This set the scene for several varieties of copper and brass tokens, some picturing President Andrew Jackson, others with different messages, reflecting hopes, policies, and contentions of the 1832 presidential election, the veto of the Bank of the United States charter, not to overlook a softening of commerce and scattered failures of businesses.

The Whig Party made gains in the states of Connecticut and New York. The city papers proclaimed the event, such as this in the *New York Courier & Enquirer*, April 11: "We subjoin the result of the election, as far as ascertained, and it will be perceived that we have indeed achieved a GLORIOUS VICTORY." In New York City, Robert Lovett engraved dies for the related token.

THE 1837 AMERICAN SILVER TOKEN

The *Guide Book of Hard Times Tokens* gives this description:

NY-480-80j • American Silver / 1837 25 Cents Token • Feuchtwanger's Composition • Low-50 • HT-74 • R-8 • 26 mm • One is Miller to Bowers to Partrick and the second is the Ford Collection example sold in 2004 for $126,500, setting a Hard Times token record.

In *An Arrangement of Tradesmen's Cards, Political Tokens, also, Election Medals, Medalets, &c.*, 1858, Charles I. Bushnell seems to have introduced this variety; at least, no earlier mention of it has been found: "No. 24, Ob: An Eagle, with expanded wings, facing to the left, holding an olive branch in one talon, and three barbed arrows in the other. The shield of the United States upon his breast. *'American Silver.'* Rev: *'Token. 25 Cents. 1837.'* Edge, milled. Metal, Silver. Size, 7." This listing would seem to indicate that Bushnell did not associate the token with Feuchtwanger, nor did he seem to be aware that "American Silver" was Feuchtwanger's term for his compound of German silver (although "American Silver" could have had other meanings as well). Lyman H. Low looked askance at the token and suggested it might have been made to the order of Bushnell himself, an idea agreed upon by no other scholar earlier or later.

The 1837 American Silver 25 Cents token.

History. Of all issuers of Hard Times tokens, Dr. Lewis Feuchtwanger was the most prominent of his era and is one of the more widely studied today. Born in Fürth, Bavaria, Germany, January 11, 1805, the son of a mineralogist, he developed an interest in science at an early age. In 1827 he graduated as a medical doctor from the University of Jena, Germany, an institution with which he kept in contact for years thereafter. Seeking expanded opportunities, Feuchtwanger emigrated to America in 1829 and settled in New York City, where in time he opened the first German pharmacy. From this period onward he imported medicines, apparatus, chemicals, and other items from his native country.

In the year of his arrival in the United States, Feuchtwanger introduced an alloy he had compounded, later widely known as Feuchtwanger's Composition, a version of German silver, intended to imitate silver through an alloy of other metals, typically nickel, copper, and tin, sometimes with a trace of silver. To differentiate his alloy from the German silver of others—a common alloy at the time—and to build a trade for it, he called his compound not only Feuchtwanger's Composition, but also suggested that it be referred to as American Silver. This alloy was recommended as being ideal as a substitute for silver in many uses and for copper in coinage.

By 1831 he set up a drugstore, curiosity shop, and museum at 377 Broadway, near the corner of White Street, where he would remain until 1837. In addition to his business as a druggist and chemist, "he also sold natural curiosities, such as rare minerals, gems, preserved reptiles, etc., a large collection of which he placed on exhibition at Peale's Museum and Gallery of Fine Arts at 252 Broadway, and at a later time (in the 1850s) at the New York Lyceum of Natural History. At his Broadway store, 'one door below White Street,' he advertised 'Nuremburgh Salve' and 'Kreosote . . . a recent German discovery for preventing toothache.' These nostrums seem to have been highly esteemed in their time" (*American Journal of Numismatics*, July 1899).

At the annual fair of the American Institute in 1834 Lewis Feuchtwanger was awarded a silver medal for the display of his special alloy and products made from it, including tableware and implements. In 1837 he commissioned Bale & Smith to strike a large quantity of small-diameter reeded-edge tokens. The obverse had an eagle killing a rattlesnake and the date 1837 below. The reverse had FEUCHT-WANGER'S COMPOSITION and ONE CENT. These circulated widely in their time, as evidenced by the fact that they are common today and nearly all show wear, sometimes extensive.

The American Silver 25 Cents token is much more rare, with only two or three pieces estimated to exist.

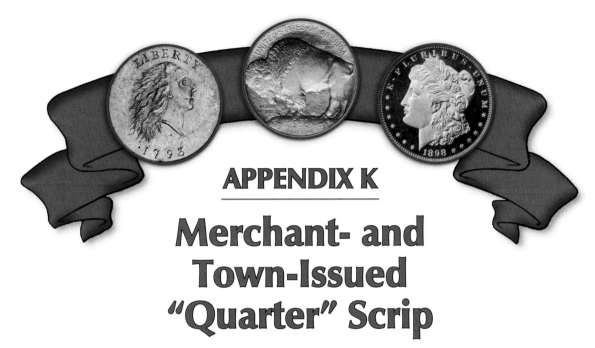

APPENDIX K

Merchant- and Town-Issued "Quarter" Scrip

In the early nineteenth century in the era before the Civil War various merchants and other entities issued 25¢ scrip notes in times when silver coins were scarce, or simply to facilitate trade. In addition, after the war merchants issued various scrip notes for promotional purposes. No detailed study has ever been made of these series. Selected examples are shown here.

A note dated March 3, 1853, by D. Parmely of Pittsford, either in New York or Vermont. The engraver was W.L. Ormsby, one of the most famous currency engravers and printers of that decade.

A note issued in Bridgeport, Ohio, in 1837, redeemable by D. Murry of Wheeling, Virginia, who was located not far away across the Ohio River. This was in the Hard Times era.

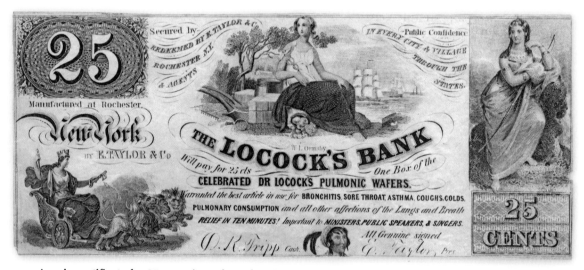

A scrip certificate for 25 cents issued to advertise Dr. Locock's Pulmonic Wafers, a worthless patent medicine sold for much of the nineteenth century in America and Europe. It was made under agreement in several different locations. This says Rochester, New York. Ornately engraved by W.L. Ormsby.

Unissued note of the Oil Creek Mills, Oil Creek, Pennsylvania, 1837, redeemable
one year after issue at the store of Chase, Newton & Co. This is another note
from the Hard Times era when silver coins were absent from circulation.

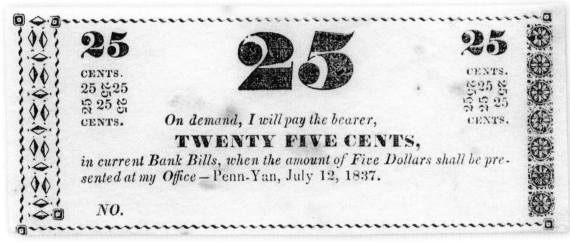

A generic note for Penn Yan, New York, merchants, July 12, 1837, early in the Hard Times era.

An unissued set of Pinconning Bay Company notes, Michigan. A
generic note of Fort Wayne, Indiana, 1853. Engraved by W.L. Ormsby.

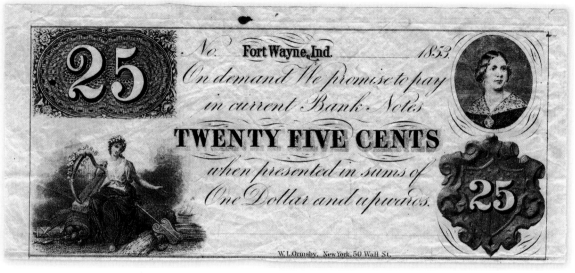

A generic note of Fort Wayne, Indiana, 1853. Engraved by W.L. Ormsby.

A note issued in Lansingburgh, New York, dated December 1, 1852. This note was signed in ink by the issuer and also has two other signatures. This could be used by various merchants.

This note dated February 11, 1838, is signed by J.W. Peirce, a grocer and dry-goods merchant of Grand Rapids, Michigan, who issued Civil War tokens. These notes were redeemable at the Kent Book Store. This was the second year of the Hard Times era, and all silver coins had disappeared from circulation.

This note dated November 20, 1857, is a later issue of J.W. Peirce.

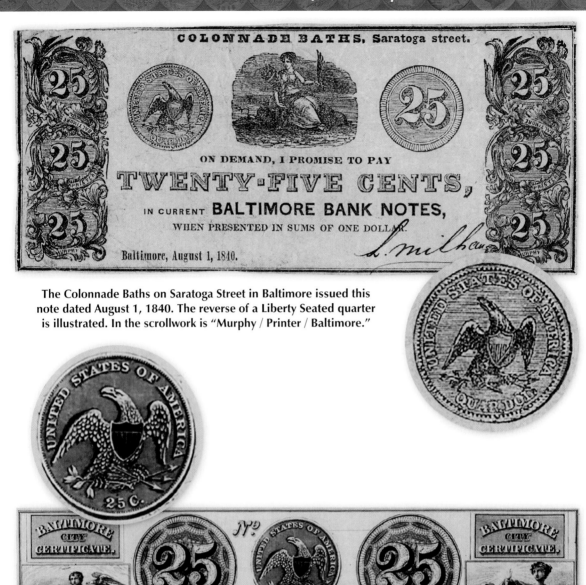

The Colonnade Baths on Saratoga Street in Baltimore issued this note dated August 1, 1840. The reverse of a Liberty Seated quarter is illustrated. In the scrollwork is "Murphy / Printer / Baltimore."

The mayor and City of Baltimore issued this note dated May 16, 1857, to be signed and circulated. The reason for this would make a nice research inquiry. Illustrated is the reverse of a quarter of the old Capped Bust type last coined in 1838.

APPENDIX L

Civil War "Quarter" Store Cards

The story of Civil War tokens is summarized in the "Private Tokens" section of this book.

The vast majority of Civil War store cards issued by merchants were valued at 1¢ each, making them convenient small-change substitutes when federal coins were scarce or absent from circulation. There were a few, however, that were redeemable for 25¢. These stood in for the nation's silver quarters, which were gone from circulation by the summer of 1862. All range from scarce to rare today.

A sampling of "quarter" tokens are illustrated here. Many of these were struck in brass and nickel. For more information regarding varieties, see the *Guide Book of Civil War Tokens* (Bowers) and *U.S. Civil War Store Cards*, published by the Civil War Token Society. Attributions are to Fuld numbers listed in both references.

White & Swann, Huntsville, Alabama. Fuld AL-425-A-6. Despite extensive research nothing definite is known about this issuer.

S.W. Cunning, wholesale liquors, Portsmouth, Ohio. Fuld OH-745-B-6a.

D. Carlile, dealer in oysters, confectionery, cigars, &c. in Warsaw, Indiana. Fuld IN-950-Ab. This token was payable in bank bills, but presumably useful as well for buying oysters.

Henry Porter, 95 Fifth Street, Cincinnati. Fuld OH-165-EO-4b. Henry D. Porter was an ambrotype photographer.

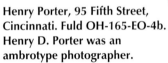

Walter & Smith, Alton, Illinois. Fuld IL-10-A-2b. This is another mystery token. It is thought Walter & Smith might have been sutlers. Their tokens are extreme rarities with only a few known. The reverse is a backstamp of the John Stanton die and minting shop in Cincinnati.

William McDonald, drayage, Memphis, Tennessee. Fuld TN-600-D-3a. This token was used for drayage or carting goods to and from the sidewheel steamships at the Memphis levee landing. McDonald received his business license on August 1, 1862.

APPENDIX M

Civil War Sutlers' "Quarter" Tokens

During the Civil War the Union Army licensed retailers known as sutlers to travel with troops and supply them with goods. Typically a sutler would set up in a tent, or, if located in an occupied town, in a storefront. Offered for sale would be magazines, newspapers, books, games, playing cards, clothing, gift items, bitters and other quasi-medical preparations, and more.

Sutlers issued tokens in copper or brass, in denominations from 5¢ to $1. Soldiers bought the tokens with their pay and could redeem them for goods. Most of the sutler tokens were made by shops that also issued Civil War patriotic tokens and store cards, the most important being John Stanton and William K, Lanphear of Cincinnati and Shubael D. Childs of Chicago. Some sutlers' tokens shared the same reverse dies as Civil War tokens. A selection of 25¢ tokens, substitutes for quarters, is illustrated here. The inscription side is the obverse. Attributions are to Schenkman numbers.

Token for the 21st Kentucky Volunteer Infantry. Schenkman KY-A-25C. The reverse die by F.W. Lutz was also used on Civil War tokens. Struck by the William K. Lanphear shop in Cincinnati.

A sutler camp scene.

Token of J.M. Kerr, sutler of the Simmonds Battery
unit of Kentucky. Schenkman KY-C-25C.

Token of J.W. Cruikshank, sutler of the 21st Regiment of Ohio Volunteers.
Schenkman OH-AF-25C. The reverse was also used on Civil War tokens.

Token of G.W. Forbes, sutler of the 23rd Ohio Regiment. Schenkman OH-N-25C.

Token of J.B. Spitzer, sutler of the 55th Ohio Volunteer Infantry.
Schenkman OH-V-25C. The reverse was also used on Civil War tokens

APPENDIX N

Quarter Dollar Scrip of the Civil War

Fear about the outcome of the Civil War, and what effects it would have on the nation's economy, led everyday citizens to hoard first their gold coins, then silver, and finally even copper-nickel cents. With coins gone from circulation, Americans had to come up with creative substitutes for day-to-day commerce. In 1862 and 1863 merchants and towns issued hundreds of varieties of paper scrip. Values typically ranged from 3¢ to 50¢. A sampling of notes that substituted for hoarded quarter dollars is shown here.

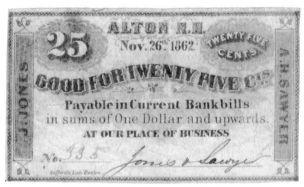

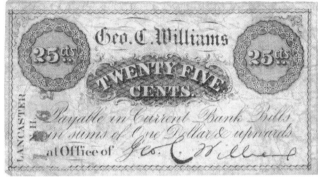

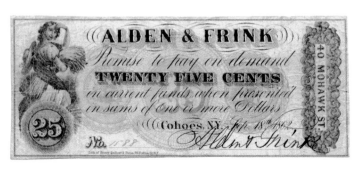

APPENDIX O

"Paper Quarters" From the Treasury Department

Silver coins were hoarded by the public and disappeared from circulation in late spring 1862 and did not reappear until after April 20, 1876. To fill the public need for legal tender in small-change amounts, in August 1862 the U.S. Treasury Department issued Postage Currency fractional bills. At first they were distributed to Army paymasters, then in September to the general public.

These small paper notes, made in denominations of 5¢, 10¢, 25¢, and 50¢, bore the designs of contemporary postage stamps printed within a border, and with added inscriptions. Similar to stamps, the Postage Currency notes were issued in perforated sheets, to be torn apart by the recipients. By early 1863 about $100,000 of these notes reached circulation per day, but the demand remained unsatisfied.

A lively trade developed in the making and selling of small cardboard and leather wallets for the storage of these little bills.

An informational sheet issued by the Treasury Department describing a specimen set of Fractional Currency sold by the government in the 1870s.

TREASURY OF THE UNITED STATES.

Specimen Set of Fractional Currency.

Comprising all the Varieties and Denominations as originally issued.

POSTAGE CURRENCY—With Perforated Edges.	
50's, 25's, 10's, 5's.........................	90
POSTAGE CURRENCY—With Plain Edges.	
50's, 25's, 10's, 5's.........................	.90
FRACTIONAL CURRENCY—Second Issue.	
50's, 25's, 10's, 5's.........................	.90
FRACTIONAL CURRENCY—Third Issue.	
50's. Vignette Goddess of Liberty.......	.50
Same, with red back...............	.50
Same, with autographic signatures......	.50
25's. Vignette head of Fessenden.......	.25
Same, with red back...............	.25
10's. Vignette head of Washington.....	.10
Same, with red back...............	.10
Same, with autographic signatures.....	.10
5's. Vignette head of Clark..........	.05
Same, with red back...............	.05
3's. Vignette head of Washington.....	.03
50's. Vignette head of Spinner.......	.50
Same, with red back...............	.50
Same, with altered green back......	.50
Same, with autographic signatures....	.50
	$4.43
FRACTIONAL CURRENCY—Fourth Issue.	
50's. Vignette head of Lincoln......	.50
Vignette head of Stanton.....	.50
25's, 15's, 10's......	.50
	1.50
Thirty-two pieces, amounting to	8.63
Stationery expenses............	.02
	$8.65

The Act of March 3, 1863, provided for a new small-denomination series, Fractional Currency. Distribution of such notes—5¢, 10¢, 25¢, and 50¢—began in October of the same year. In late autumn 1864, a new Fractional Currency denomination, the 3¢ note, reached circulation, but it never became popular. In summer 1869 another Fractional Currency denomination, 15¢, was added to the Fractional Currency lineup, but it, too, was never widely used. Face and back colors varied over a period of time as did the notes' sizes.

Fractional bills were created from 1862 to 1876. A selection of 25¢ issues is illustrated here. Attributions are by Friedberg numbers, from *Paper Money of the United States*, and to Whitman numbers, from the *Whitman Encyclopedia of U.S. Paper Money* (which also has extensive historical information on the series).

As shown in the other appendices of this edition of *Mega Red*, 25¢ scrip notes were issued by banks, merchants, and other entities, but mainly in 1862 and 1863 and in no long series, in contrast with the Treasury Department's "paper quarters" and other small-change notes.

Postage Currency, first issue. Friedberg-1279, Whitman-6143. The face, printed in brown, depicts five standard 5¢ postage stamps with the portrait of Thomas Jefferson, each slightly overlapped except for the rightmost.

Fractional Currency, third issue. F-1291, W-6365, with a bronze overprint design on the face and 25 on the back. The portrait is of William P. Fessenden, secretary of the Treasury.

F-1294, W-6351, with a bronze overprint
design on the face and 25 on the back.

Fractional Currency, fourth issue. F-1301,
W-6621. George Washington portrait.

Fractional Currency, fifth issue. F-1308,
W-6661. Portrait of Robert J. Walker, who served
as secretary of the Treasury from 1845 to 1848.

FRACTIONAL CURRENCY SHIELDS

To aid in the identification of counterfeits and to provide bills for display to banks and others interested, the Treasury Department created Fractional Currency Shields. These consisted of a shield outline printed in gray (a few are in green or pink, which are much rarer) surmounted by an eagle and stars. On the shield, 39 specimens of Fractional Currency, consisting of 20 faces and 19 backs, were pasted by hand. These were of the First, Second, and Third issues.

The shields were sold for $4.50 each, beginning in 1867. Purchasers mounted many of them under glass in a wooden frame with a gilt inner frame next to the glass, and backed by thin wooden slats. Most of these today have slight water stains along the bottom (especially to the right) from slight flooding in the Treasury Department basement, where they were stored.

As to how many were issued, no records have been found, but the figure was certainly in the high hundreds or perhaps even far more than a thousand. Perhaps 300 are known to exist today, most with a gray background. About 20 with the pink background are estimated to exist, and about 10 with the green background.

Among all the numismatic items produced in American history, the Fractional Currency Shield is no doubt the most "displayable" in its original form. Indeed, this is one of only a few such 19th-century items originally intended for this purpose.

Fractional Currency shields displaying
various issues and varieties were sold by
the Treasury Department starting in 1867. Most
purchasers had them framed, as shown here.

APPENDIX P

The 1893 Isabella Quarter

**The 1893 Isabella quarter, the only classic
U.S. commemorative coin of this denomination.**

Of the hundreds of commemorative coin designs struck in the United States from 1892 to date, only one is of the twenty-five–cents denomination. Dated 1893, these were made for and placed on sale at the World's Columbian Exposition in Chicago. The event was the second world's fair in America, following the 1876 Centennial Exhibition held in Philadelphia.

In 1890, plans were made to stage a fair in 1892 to commemorate the 400th anniversary of Christopher Columbus's landing in the New World in 1492. Competition was intense as St. Louis, New York City, Washington, D.C., and Chicago desired to host an event that would attract millions of visitors. Congress made the decision on April 25, 1890, naming Chicago.

An ideal 686-acre undeveloped site on the shore of Lake Michigan beckoned, and in January 1891 a group of architects met in the city to lay out specifications. In time, many buildings were erected in classical style reflecting Greek and Roman influences, and with exteriors made of an artificial composition called "staff," resembling marble, giving rise to the name "White City" for the structures. In November that year Dr. George F. Heath called a meeting in Chicago for interested coin collectors, and the American Numismatic Association was formed. The attendees visited the construction site.

Work proceeded, and on October 20, 1892, a dedication ceremony was held. Many exhibits were not in place, winter was approaching, and opening for the public was postponed. In the meantime Columbian souvenir (as they were labeled) half dollars were sold for $1 each, America's first commemorative coins. Nationwide interest was intense, almost completely eclipsing the launch of the new dimes, quarters, and half dollars of 1892, designed by Mint chief engraver Charles E. Barber. Similar half dollars dated 1893 were also made.

**An admission ticket to the
World's Columbian Exposition.**

President Grover Cleveland pushes a telegraph key to open the exposition.

Part of the crowd on opening day. (*Harper's Weekly*, June 10, 1893)

Finally, at noon on May 1, 1893, President Grover Cleveland officiated at a ceremony and pushed a telegraph key that signaled the opening of the Exposition grounds to the public. Strains of the *Hallelujah Chorus* greeted the estimated 300,000 individuals who had come to attend the opening-day festivities.

The Exposition was intended to showcase American progress in art, architecture, technology, science, agriculture, and other endeavors. No expense was spared to create a virtual city, complete with 160 buildings (many of which were connected by canals plied by gondolas and small steam-powered craft) and 65,000 exhibits devoted to commercial, national, artistic, and other subjects. Separate structures showcased the attractions and products of different states and a number of foreign countries. Sculptures and other works of art decorated many of the open spaces as well as building interiors. Ultimately the event cost an estimated $30 million to stage and attracted 28 million visitors. Attending the Exposition was the aim of citizens all across America, and to oblige them the various railroads ran special cars and excursions to Chicago. Many individuals made hometown-newspaper headlines by walking or bicycling to the Exposition from distant locations.

Almost as an afterthought, well after the 1892 half dollars were in distribution, Mrs. Potter Palmer, well-known Chicago socialite, patron of the arts, and grande dame of the Exposition, suggested to the Appropriations Committee of the House of Representatives in Congress that $10,000 of the money earmarked for the Board of Lady Managers of the Exposition be used to make souvenir quarters. This was approved on March 3, 1893, limiting the production to 40,000, which fit the amount allowed.

The Board of Lady Managers took complete charge of the quarter dollar project and stated that the coins were to have female motifs. Kenyon Cox, a well-known illustrator, was commissioned to prepare sketches, apparently furnishing motifs that were eventually modified by Charles E. Barber at the Mint. For the obverse, a depiction of Queen Isabella of Spain was suggested, for King Ferdinand and Queen Isabella furnished the financing for Columbus's voyage of discovery, Isabella vowing to pledge her crown and jewels if necessary (according to popular legend).

In April 1893 the Treasury Department responded by submitting its own two obverse designs to the Board of Lady Managers, one sketch showing Isabella as a young queen (this was eventually chosen) and the other with a facing head of Isabella as an adult. Thus the Isabella quarter, as it was soon to be designated, became the first legal-tender United States coin to depict a foreign monarch.

Kenyon Cox, designer of the Isabella quarter.

A birds-eye view of
the Exposition grounds.

The Ferris Wheel was
the fair's main attraction.

The sketch for the reverse design depicted a woman kneeling, holding a distaff, showing woman's industry. The models and dies for the Isabella quarter were prepared by Barber. The quarters were set to be available for distribution on May 1. The low mintage in comparison to the authorized mintage of well over a million coins for the half dollars would certainly make them attractive.

Production of the quarters began at the Philadelphia Mint on June 13, 1893, well past the May 1 date.

Yawn. The newspapers already had their fill of news about the Exposition and the commemorative half dollars. There

The Woman's Building where the
commemorative quarters were sold.

was hardly any interest in the quarters. The coins were only for sale in the Woman's Building. Priced at $1 each, the same price as the half dollars, they were viewed as unreasonably expensive. Not surprisingly, sales were poor.

Probably no more than 15,000 Isabella quarters were sold at the Exposition and by mail to collectors and dealers in 1893, a minuscule quantity compared to the Columbian half dollar coins distributed. The biggest buyer is believed to have been the Scott Stamp & Coin Company, America's largest rare-coin dealer, which purchased several thousand Isabella quarters late in the year 1893.

After the fair ended the Board of Lady Managers still had about 25,000 unsold pieces on hand. 10,000 of these were bought for face value by Mrs. Potter Palmer and several of her friends and were parceled out through coin dealers and others through the mid-1920s at prices ranging from 40 cents per coin to slightly more. Returned to the Mint for remelting were 15,809 unwanted coins.

Thousands of the Isabella quarters
went unsold at the time of their issue.

Today as you read these words, nearly all known Isabella quarters are in Mint State, although some show friction from evidence of mishandling by those who purchased them as souvenirs. Very few specimens show actual wear. Most are very well struck. An example makes a nice addition to any coin collection or grouping of Exposition memorabilia.

An elongated 1892 Barber quarter. Several vendors had mechanical roller presses into which a visitor could insert a coin, usually a cent or nickel, and have it rolled out in elongated form with an exposition notice on one side. Quarters with this impression are rare today.

The Treasury Department exhibited coins and medals from the Mint Cabinet at the exposition.

APPENDIX Q

Pattern Quarter Dollars,
or What Might Have Been But Wasn't

From 1792, continuing into modern times, there have been many proposals for changes in circulating coins. Different metal compositions and different designs for the first century of coins, to 1892, comprised more than 1,000 different varieties known as patterns. Some were adopted, after which motifs in circulating coinage changed. Most, however, were similar to faces on the cutting-room floor—created, but never used.

Most patterns were of higher denominations. In silver series new designs were often tried out on half dollars and dollars, rarely on quarters. An exception might be the 1792 pattern that may have been for a quarter or a half eagle; documents have not been found to explain it with certainty. In some later instances a pattern motif was made to include lower denominations as well, including the dime. For example, in 1879 William Barber's "Washlady" obverse motif was made in the form of dimes, quarters, half dollars, and dollars, to create sets for numismatists. George T. Morgan's beautiful "Shield Earring" design of 1882 was used on quarters, half dollars, and dollars.

Often sets were made in multiple metals, again for collectors. Copper, silver, and, sometimes, aluminum were employed. To create numismatic rarities some sets of regular-design Proofs were made in other metals. Hence, there are a number of different Liberty Seated dimes that were struck in copper and aluminum. From spring 1859 until the summer of 1885, most patterns were secretly made, with few records kept, and were privately sold by Mint officials for their own profit. This practice accounts for an estimated 90 percent or more of the patterns in existence today.

We offer a photographic gallery of selected pattern quarters here, with the date and Judd catalog number for each, as described in *United States Pattern Coins*, by J. Hewitt Judd, a Whitman title that is the standard reference on the subject.

1792, J-12. This pattern may have been intended as a prototype for the quarter dollar. Its dies are by an unknown engraver. Copper and white-metal versions were made, in addition to uniface impressions.

1857, J-188. This interesting pattern was made with a regular obverse die for the Liberty Seated quarter, plus an incomplete reverse die with letters around the border (smaller than those used on the regular-issue coin).

1858, J-221. Anthony Paquet's tall-letter legends grace the reverse of this pattern, along with a Perched Eagle motif.

1865, J-426. This is a transitional pattern, its obverse featuring the regular Liberty Seated design. The reverse is similar to the regular die of the year, but with IN GOD WE TRUST on a scroll above the eagle (as would be adopted in 1866).

1868, J-650. The U.S. Mint struck many patterns and experimental pieces in 1868, including this trial produced in aluminum from regular Proof dies.

1869, J-722. Several types of Standard Silver patterns were struck in the quarter dollar denomination in 1869. This example in silver shows Miss Liberty capped with a headband of three stars.

1869, J-727 and J-733. These Standard Silver obverses show Miss Liberty
with variations in her head-covering: a tiara with no stars, and a starred band.

1870, J-895 and J-917. Two reverse varieties of the 1870 Standard Silver pattern quarter
dollar: one with an open agricultural wreath, and one with a wreath of oak and laurel.

1871, J-1093. In 1871 several experiments were made in the quarter dollar diameter in various
alloys including copper, silver, and aluminum. This pattern used James Longacre's Indian
Princess design with a plain (starless) field, combined with the year's regular reverse die.

1871, J-1097. Another 1871 quarter pattern, this one struck in copper, set Longacre's Indian Princess within an arc of stars. On the reverse is an open agricultural wreath.

1872, J-1197. Chief Engraver William Barber's famous Amazonian design shows Miss Liberty seated, facing left, with her right hand touching the head of a perched eagle, and her left arm resting on a shield. She holds a sword. United States Pattern Coins describes this as "certainly among his finest productions from the standpoint of art and classicism."

1877, J-1500. William Barber developed this pleasing obverse pattern design with Miss Liberty facing left, wearing a pearl-bordered coronet and with her hair tied back in a ribbon. The portrait is affectionately known as the Sailor Head.

1879, J-1590. Charles Barber's Society Lady portrait of Miss Liberty—popularly called the Washlady design—was used on several patterns, including this quarter dollar.

1879, J-1593. Another 1879 pattern features George T. Morgan's Liberty Head (used on the silver dollar of 1878 to 1921), and a large perched eagle.

1882, J-1698. A well-known pattern design is George Morgan's Shield Earring motif, named for the shield-shaped ornament dangling from Miss Liberty's ear.

1891, J-1761. In 1891 various patterns were minted to test options for the new coinage envisioned by Charles Barber to replace the time-worn Liberty Seated design. Two specimens are known of this quarter dollar, featuring a portrait of Miss Liberty similar to what would debut in 1892. On the reverse, the heraldic eagle resembles what would be adopted for regular coinage, but with clouds above, and other variations.

1916, J-1998. Hermon MacNeil's full-length figure of Miss Liberty is somewhat different in this 1916 pattern than the one ultimately used for regular coinage. The reverse, too, is similar to the final design, though with noticeable differences (including olive branches and different positioning for the eagle).

1965, J-2116. The Mint in 1965 experimented with various metals to replace the .900 fine silver used in circulating coinage. Fantasy designs featuring Martha Washington were created, with no connection to current coin motifs, in order to avoid creating rarities using regular dies. Copper-nickel–clad versions in a quarter-sized diameter are confirmed to exist

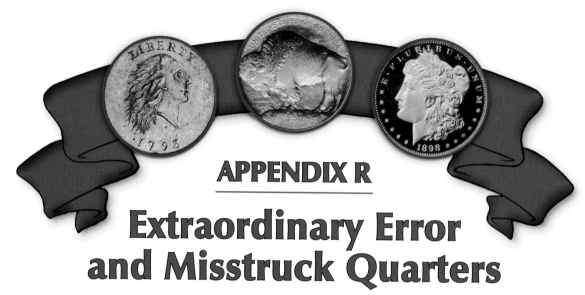

APPENDIX R

Extraordinary Error and Misstruck Quarters

This appendix is based on the work of Nicholas P. Brown, David J. Camire, and Fred Weinberg.

"*Errare humanum est,*" wrote Richard G. Doty, curator of the Smithsonian's National Numismatic Collection, in his foreword to *100 Greatest U.S. Error Coins.* "To err is human. Errors on coins have been around as long as coinage itself. The reason is simple. Coinage is an industrial process, and coins were the first mass-produced objects in human history. Mass production of anything involves a number of simple, repetitive steps. During each of these steps, something can go wrong. Given the nature of human endeavor as summed up by Murphy's Law, something *will* go wrong, even if the manufacturing process is simple, requiring few steps for its completion. And the more sophisticated production becomes, the more individual steps it involves, the greater the potential for error. This is as true for coinage as it is for any other human product."

This appendix explores some of the most fascinating error and misstruck quarter dollars. As outlandish as many of them seem, they are all real coins—each was personally examined by error-coin experts Nicholas Brown, David Camire, and Fred Weinberg as they wrote their book *100 Greatest U.S. Error Coins.* "In selecting the 100 greatest error coins for this book," they said, "we felt it was crucial to have each coin in our possession to be able to confirm that it actually exists, to ensure the authenticity of each error coin being considered, and to capture high-resolution photographs of the selected coins."

THE IMPORTANCE OF CERTIFICATION

With the advent of grading services like Professional Coin Grading Service (PCGS) and Numismatic Guaranty Corporation of America (NGC), even novice hobbyists can now easily collect error coins. This is because the grading services offer four valuable services: authentication of the coin; attribution (i.e., verification of its die characteristics); grading; and protection through encapsulation, ensuring safe long-term storage. This standardized assessment process has helped propel error coins to the mainstream market, attracting an even larger audience. After certification, the only variable the buyer needs to determine is how much to pay for the coin. Years ago, some seeming "error" coins were fabricated outside of the mint by private individuals; the only error was in buying them!

GRADING ERROR COINS

Grading mint errors is generally the same as grading normal coins, with a few exceptions. First, an extensive understanding of the minting process is a must. Grading a mint error has a lot to do with knowing how the coin was made. For instance, when an off-center coin is assessed, a grade is determined not only by the features of the portion of the coin that was struck but also by the area that was not struck. Why is that? Because such after-coining defects as scratches, wheel marks, post-strike mechanical damage, and environmental damage have to be taken into consideration—just as they must be on a normal coin. However, because mint errors occur from a malfunction in the minting process, there are times when there is "allowable damage" (although this is usually damage that occurred before striking). For instance, on an off-center Roosevelt dime, a scratch on the planchet (pre-striking) that can still be seen after striking will generally not affect the grade of the coin. If the scratch occurred after the coin was struck, then it would matter.

Moreover, there are times when error coins can be attributed but not graded. One instance is blanks and planchets: since they were never struck, these items cannot be assessed a numerical grade. Another such example is die-adjustment strikes: since these pieces are used to adjust the amount of detail on a coin, many show very little detail. Again, no grade can be assigned to such coins.

Mint-error grading employs the same system, the Sheldon scale (which grades numerically from Poor-1 to MS-70), as does non-error grading. Most dimes and other coins minted before the advent of the steam press show considerable wear, because in the early years of the Philadelphia Mint, economics dictated what went out the door—that is, nearly everything. For this reason, most mint errors from the late 1700s and early 1800s survive in a low state of preservation. In many cases they circulated as money. True Mint State *gems* of this era are genuinely rare and highly prized. In contrast, many mint errors from the 1980s to the present are found in brilliant Uncirculated condition.

PRICING ERROR COINS

It is challenging to price error coins, since many are considered to be unique and many trade privately. The factors in determining error-coin values are similar to those that determine the price for non-error coins, with some important distinctions.

- The first is referred to as the "wow" factor. How excited does someone get viewing the coin? Error coins are often dramatic. The more dramatic an error, the higher the price usually is for the coin. It bodes well when someone says, "I have never seen this coin before." Even better is when someone says, "I never knew a coin like this existed"—which leads us to the second variable:
- Rarity. How rare is the error? How many coins are known of its type and of the series? Is it the only known of that date? Does it even have a date? Is it the farthest off center? The list of qualities that can make an error coin unique is nearly endless. Rarity definitely plays a key role in determining the price.
- Third, what is the condition of the coin? How much detail can be seen, and how well preserved is it? This is no less important a consideration for an error coin than for a regular coin.
- The popularity of a series is also an important factor in determining the price of an error coin.

These four factors are just a few of the variables that determine an error coin's price. Brown, Camire, and Weinberg used auction records, fixed-price lists, known private transactions, and their experience as professional numismatists to determine the value of each error coin ranked in the 100 Greatest.

Until recently, a question many collectors asked was, "Which error coin will be the first to pass the $1,000,000 threshold?" Among non-error coins, it took quite a while for this barrier to be surmounted. Once the threshold was breached, however—when Bowers and Merena Galleries sold the Eliasberg specimen 1913 Liberty Head nickel at auction for $1,485,000 on May 21, 1996—it suddenly became more common to hear of coins selling for this price or higher. The same is true for error coins, as bronze 1943 cents have crossed the $1,000,000 mark in recent years.

For error coins, values continue to rise as the market continues to mature. "Looking back, it is almost unbelievable that error-coin prices have reached these levels," wrote Brown, Camire, and Weinberg in 2010. "In fact, when researching for the *100 Greatest U.S. Error Coins* we were amazed at the prices of mint errors in the 1980s. It was hard to find an error coin then that sold in the high four figures, never mind high five figures! Fast-forward to today, and it is a whole different story. Many major error coins are now trading in the high five figures, with some in the high six figures. Who would have guessed?"

A GALLERY OF EXTRAORDINARY QUARTER ERRORS

Peace dollar struck on a quarter dollar planchet.

No. 5—(1922–1935) Peace Dollar Struck on a Quarter Dollar Planchet. A unique wrong-planchet Peace dollar, this undated low-relief dollar could have been struck only between 1922 and 1935. It is a breathtaking example of a wrong planchet on a high-denomination U.S. coin.

This error resulted when a quarter dollar planchet was somehow fed into the striking chamber and collar setup used to produce Peace dollars. The planchet was centered when struck, unfortunately causing the omission of the date at the bottom of the coin.

Because of the large size of silver dollars, error coins such as this were easily spotted by the mint personnel who inspected coins after striking. The fact that there are no other Peace dollar (or Morgan dollar, for that matter) off-metal or wrong-planchet errors in existence is a testimony to the effectiveness of the Mint's inspection process for silver dollar coins.

This error is in choice brilliant Uncirculated condition, but there are no early records or reports of when it was discovered. It is the top Peace dollar error coin, and first appeared in the November 1985 Bowers and Merena sale of the Abe Kosoff collection, as lot number 4200. It sold for $8,250 (with buyer's premium), which, at the time, was a lot of money for a mint error. It has remained in the same collection ever since then—more than three decades now!

The unique piece was valued at $10,000 to $15,000 in 2000, and $75,000 to $100,000 in 2010.

1860 Liberty Seated quarter dollar struck on a cent planchet.

No. 18—1860 Liberty Seated Quarter Struck on a Cent Planchet. Probably plucked right out of the coining chamber, this choice Uncirculated Liberty Seated quarter dollar was struck on an Indian Head cent planchet of copper-nickel (the composition used from 1859 to 1864). Because the Indian Head cent planchet is only 19 mm in diameter and the quarter is 24.3 mm, there was enough room in the collar for the cent planchet to expand nicely, making it a broadstrike, as well. The metal flowing outward from the design elements shows this effect well. It is the only known example of a Liberty Seated quarter struck on any other planchet size or composition. It has survived in gem Uncirculated condition for more than 150 years and grades MS-66.

The unique piece was valued at $5,000 to $10,000 in 2000, and $50,000 to $75,000 in 2010.

1920 Standing Liberty quarter struck on a Mercury dime planchet.

No. 25—1920 Standing Liberty Quarter Struck on a Mercury Dime Planchet. This specimen is one of only a handful known of wrong-planchet, off-metal strikes in the Standing Liberty quarter dollar series. It is the result of a dime planchet finding its way to the Philadelphia Mint's quarter presses and being struck by those dies.

The Standing Liberty quarter series has always been known for having the fewest error coins (clips, off-metal coins, even die cracks!) of any design issued in the twentieth century. There are also two quarters known on nickel planchets (one is also off center). Another Standing Liberty quarter, this one also dated 1920, is known struck on a copper-nickel planchet for a Peruvian 20-centavo piece; that mint error was last sold by Stack's in January 2006. One of the two known specimens struck on a nickel planchet was part of the Bolt Collection, which sold in 1974. It currently resides in what is considered to be one of the best off-metal mint-error collections known.

After 100 years, it's quite a statement to say that there are only three wrong-planchet, off-metal striking errors that have ever surfaced for this series.

This piece was valued at $10,000 to $15,000 in 2000, and $35,000 to $50,000 in 2010.

2000-P Maryland quarter mule.

No. 30—2000-P Maryland Quarter Mule. Although a true mule is considered to be a coin having mismatched obverse and reverse dies, this example is a mule of both dies: that is, *neither* die is correct for the planchet. It was struck on a press set up to strike dollars. The planchet is that of a dollar, and the collar (the "third die") is correct for dollars, but quarter dollar dies were used for both obverse and reverse (a Washington obverse and Maryland reverse).

How could this have happened? Well, consider this: during 2000 several coining presses were often used to strike different denominations, routinely switching between striking quarters and dollars (two higher-mintage denominations made that year). It can be speculated that this coin was struck in a press that was in transition from striking quarters to dollars or vice versa. It is unknown if this was an oversight or a worker's prank. What we do know is that two or three of these made it out of the Mint. The coin shown is the finer of the two confirmed examples (the other is scratched). It was purchased by a dealer and sold to a customer in California, but its whereabouts are unknown today.

This error was valued at $10,000 to $15,000 in 2000, and $50,000 to $75,000 in 2010.

Double-struck (1916–1946)-S Liberty Walking half dollar on a quarter planchet.

No. 35—Double-Struck (1916–1946)-S Liberty Walking Half Dollar on a Quarter Planchet. First appearing in a collection of pedestrian error coins in 2005, this piece combines two rare errors not only for the Liberty Walking series, but for the entire denomination. This undated San Francisco Mint half dollar was first struck on a silver quarter dollar planchet. Then, instead of being ejected into the tote bin like other coins, it was struck a second time with a newly fed planchet lying on top of its obverse. Due to the presence of this new planchet, the coin's second strike is uniface on its obverse, with a distorted image of the right side of Lady Liberty's leg and skirt showing underneath the indented area. There is a full second strike on the reverse side (which also shows the S mintmark). This is the only dual-error Liberty Walking half dollar known.

The unique piece was valued at $20,000 to $30,000 in 2000, and $75,000 to $95,000 in 2010.

1944 Washington quarter struck on a steel Lincoln cent or Belgian 2-franc planchet.

No. 46—1944 Washington Quarter Struck on a Steel Lincoln Cent or Belgian 2-Franc Planchet. This is a most interesting error. It is a Washington quarter dollar struck not only on a cent planchet, but a steel cent planchet at that! The quarter is dated 1944, one year after America's steel-cent coinage. This would be classified as a wrong-planchet transitional error, and it's a nice problem-free example.

Somehow a steel cent planchet was fed into the striking chamber for quarters during 1944 and struck. The remaining zinc-plated steel planchets were also used in 1944 to strike 25 million Belgian 2-franc coins at the Philadelphia Mint, and it's quite possible that the error occurred at that time.

The piece, one of fewer than a half dozen known of the type, was valued at $5,000 to $7,000 in 2000, and $15,000 to $30,000 in 2010.

2000-P Sacagawea dollar struck on a 2000-P Massachusetts quarter.

No. 59—2000-P Sacagawea Dollar Struck on a 2000-P Massachusetts Quarter. Although there are more than a dozen Sacagawea dollars struck on *Maryland* quarters, this one struck over a 2000 Massachusetts quarter is the only example known for this state. It was first reported in the January 22, 2001, issue of *Coin World*.

At the Philadelphia Mint in 2000 the presses used to strike both quarters and dollars were, at times, within close distance to each other (if not interchangeable). There are, therefore, several scenarios that can apply to the creation of this coin. The most likely cause of this double-denomination error coin was that a tote bin was not fully emptied of struck quarters, and this coin remained stuck in the groove or seam of the release door. If that bin was then used to hold dollar planchets, the struck quarter would fall out as well when those planchets were fed into the dollar press, and it would get struck a second time as a dollar coin. It's possible, though less likely, that a mint employee picked up a struck quarter lying on the floor and threw it into a nearby bin of unstruck planchets intended for the Sacagawea dollar. Again there are numerous possibilities—especially for conspiracy theorists who adhere to the principal that all errors are deliberately made and taken out of the mints!

This is one of the best double-denomination dollars, as far as detail is concerned. The dollar obverse was struck on the obverse of the quarter and shows the 2000 date of the dollar and the mintmarks of each denomination fully, as well as a tremendous number of other details. The reverse shows the Minuteman from the quarter under the eagle design of the dollar, along with the 1788 and 2000 dates for the quarter. Most of the detail of the dollar's reverse is also visible.

There are other states known to have been struck a second time by Sacagawea dollar dies, but the most common state (if it can be called "common," with only around a dozen known) is Maryland. It appears that a number of struck quarters got mixed in with dollar planchets. The detail visible on most coins is far lesser than on this Massachusetts example. The key to identifying these coins and others of this error type is the reeding visible on their edges, which proves that the coins were struck as quarters before being overstruck with dollar dies.

The unique error was valued at $15,000 to $20,000 in 2010.

1983-P Washington quarter struck on an amusement token.

No. 65—1983-P Washington Quarter Struck on an Amusement Token. Coined at the Philadelphia Mint, this 1983 Washington quarter is one of a very small number of federally issued coins struck on a non–legal tender token. Over the years there have been numerous examples, mostly from the San Francisco and Philadelphia mints, of U.S. coins struck on a previously struck world coin. These error types have occurred due to our mints having contractual agreements to strike coinage for other countries. As part of the minting process, a struck world coin could find itself back in a U.S. coinage press and then be overstruck by U.S. dies.

In this case, a brass amusement token struck for private use found its way into the Philadelphia Mint and was overstruck by dies used to make Washington quarters. The words THIS IS MY LUCKY DAY can very easily been seen underneath the obverse of the Washington quarter strike, giving it a most unusual appearance. It certainly was a lucky day in 1983 when a rolling-room employee found it and offered it for sale to a then-prominent error-coin dealer for $500.

We can speculate, but we will never know exactly how and why this brass token came to be struck by Washington quarter dies in Philadelphia. Either a series of accidents must have led to its striking, or, more likely, a mint employee had it in his pocket or lunch box and decided on a whim to strike the piece again inside the Mint, thereby befuddling and exciting error-coin collectors forever!

Such an item would have been almost expected to have come from the San Francisco Mint in the late 1960s through the mid-1970s, so the fact that it is from Philadelphia makes this a most unusual issue. It is also interesting to note that this coin is a regular Mint issue and not a Proof, as are the others of this type from the 1960s and 1970s. It has changed hands just a few times in more than 35 years, and it now resides in a prominent error-coin collection.

This unique piece was valued at $5,000 to $7,500 in 2000, and $10,000 to $15,000 in 2010.

2000-P Connecticut quarter struck on a 2000-P Roosevelt dime.

No. 72—2000-P Connecticut Quarter Struck on a 2000-P Roosevelt Dime. About a half dozen State quarters in total are known to have been struck on previously struck dimes. This example shows good detail of the original dime strike. It was created when a struck dime somehow found its way into the coining chamber for a Connecticut quarter and was struck again, making a double-denomination "35-cent" piece. Much of the Roosevelt dime's detail is still visible beneath the Connecticut quarter strike.

This error coin was valued at $3,500 to $5,000 in 2000, and $12,000 to $15,000 in 2010.

1979-P Susan B. Anthony dollar struck on a 1979 Washington quarter.

No. 75—1979-P Susan B Anthony Dollar Struck on a 1979 Washington Quarter. Here is an error coin that relates to the problem the Mint faced from 1979 to 1981, and again in 1999, with the minting of the Susan B. Anthony dollar. The biggest problem, and a common public complaint about the coin, was that it was, with a quick glance or cursory handling, very similar to a Washington quarter. With the same composition as the quarter (outer copper-nickel layers bonded to an inner core of pure copper) and just slightly larger (a mere 2 mm wider in diameter), the dollar coin was not quickly distinguishable from the smaller denomination. Moreover, apparently most of the public could not immediately spot the difference between George Washington and Susan B. Anthony!

At some point at the Philadelphia Mint, a normally struck 1979 quarter found its way into the Anthony dollar press area (probably tossed into a bin of dollar planchets by accident) and was soon struck again by the dollar dies. The coin was fed into the dollar collar upside down and received a strong strike by the dollar dies, showing the full date of the 1979 dollar and much of the underlying type of the quarter. It is in gem condition and is unique for the series.

This unique piece was valued at $2,500 to $3,500 in 2000, and $10,000 to $12,500 in 2010.

1968-S Washington quarter struck on a 1968-S Lincoln cent.

No. 78—1968-S Washington Quarter Struck on a 1968-S Lincoln Cent. Found in a large group of major error coins that were in a closed safe-deposit box, the contents of which were authorized to be auctioned by the state of California, this was one of the most eye-catching double-denomination coins in the group of 235-plus pieces. A 1968-S Proof quarter was struck over a previously struck 1968-S cent, with the strikes rotated 180 degrees in relationship to each other. This is the first year of the returning S mintmark on the cent since 1955, and because all of the other coins in the safe-deposit-box hoard had the S mintmark and were dated 1968 and 1969, we can safely say that the quarter was struck on the cent at the San Francisco Mint.

A handful of such errors are known; valued at $1,500 to $2,000 in 2000, and $7,500 to $10,000 in 2010.

1985-P off-center Washington quarter struck on a 1985 Lincoln cent.

No. 79—1985-P Off-Center Washington Quarter Struck on a 1985 Lincoln Cent. Different from almost all other double-denomination coins, here is a 1985 Lincoln cent that was struck again by dies for the Washington quarter. The quarter strike is about 25 percent off center, with a uniface second strike on the reverse from another planchet lying underneath the cent. It's one of the ultimate "26-cent" pieces known.

This unique piece was valued at $3,500 to $5,000 in 2000, and $6,000 to $9,000 in 2010.

1999-P Georgia quarter struck on a Lincoln cent planchet.

No. 91—1999-P Georgia Quarter Struck on a Lincoln Cent Planchet. Because of how the presses were set up on the floor of the Philadelphia Mint (at least since 1999), it is a wonder this coin was ever struck. All cent planchets are supplied by an outside vendor (as has been the case since the Mint switched to copper-plated zinc planchets in 1982), shipped in large plastic bags within wooden crates. These planchets are then unloaded by forklift into the waiting bins of the presses used to strike Lincoln cents. This cent planchet was somehow diverted to a different line (the Philadelphia Mint uses rows or lines of presses for each denomination), mixed in with the quarter planchets, and struck. It also could have been lying on the floor and simply tossed into a bin—of quarter planchets, that is.

During the 10 years in which State quarters were struck, only three or four escaped the Mint struck on cent planchets, including this unique Georgia piece and two North Carolina quarters.

This error was valued at $3,000 to $5,000 in 2000, and $12,500 to $15,000 in 2010.

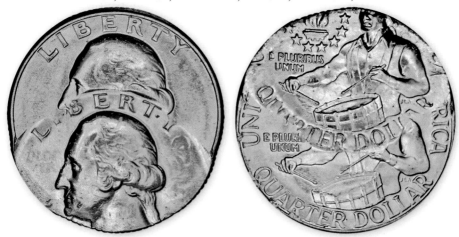

1976-D double-struck Bicentennial quarter.

No. 95—1976-D Double-Struck Bicentennial Quarter. An error on a special, one-year-only issue, minted to commemorate the 200th anniversary of the Declaration of Independence, this Bicentennial quarter is an almost perfect 50 percent off-center, double-struck coin. It was struck normally the first time, but instead of being ejected into the box of newly minted coinage it was only partially ejected. Half of the struck coin remained over the collar when it was struck again. A very eye-catching error, it is just one of a few dated 1976 that are double struck, with this being the finest and most dramatic.

This error coin, one of only a few known of the type, was valued at $750 to $1,200 in 2000, and $2,500 to $3,000 in 2010.

APPENDIX S

Carson City Mint Quarters

Carson City quarter dollars are the rarest of the rare, as a group, when compared to quarters from the other mints of their era: Philadelphia, New Orleans, San Francisco, and Denver.

HISTORY OF THE CARSON CITY MINT

What was often referred to as the Mint at Carson, later the Carson City Mint, was established by the Act of March 3, 1863, which provided also for the appointment of a superintendent at a salary of $2,000 and an assayer, a melter-refiner, and a coiner for $1,800 each annually.

The Comstock Lode, which was discovered in June 1859, was located approximately 15 miles away and for a time was America's richest silver bonanza. In addition, large quantities of gold were extracted from the earth in the district. Today the Silver State, as Nevada is familiarly known, is more remembered for the white metal. In terms of value (not ounces), gold production often rivaled that of silver.

The Carson City Mint was ready to commence business in December 1869. Coinage dies dated 1869 were sent by the Philadelphia Mint and were received at Carson City by October 21, 1869. How many were sent is not known; no inventory listing of 1869 and 1870 dies has been found. The 1869-dated dies were not used; the reverses were probably held for 1870 and later use.

The first Carson City Mint coins were 3,747 silver dollars struck from 1870-dated dies on February 10, 1870. All were minted using a press made in Philadelphia by Morgan & Orr. Other coins and denominations then and later were shipped by horse-drawn wagon 30 miles over very rough roads to the railhead in Reno. Stored in cloth bags, the coins were extensively marked by the time they arrived at Reno, more so at their final destinations. Among silver denominations dimes, quarters, and half dollars were made until 1878. Twenty-cent pieces were struck with CC mintmarks in 1875 and 1876. Liberty Seated silver dollars were made from 1870 to 1873, after which there was a lapse for this denomination until Morgan dollars were coined in 1878. In the meantime trade dollars were struck continuously from 1873 to 1878. In 1870 the minting of gold commenced, limited to the higher $5, $10, and $20 denominations. For the first several years most gold coins were circulated locally and regionally, which remained true for later $5 and $10 (but not $20) coins. Many double eagles were shipped overseas.

The Carson City Mint struck silver coins from dimes to trade dollars from 1870 to 1878. From 1879 onward the only coins made in this metal were Morgan dollars. Gold $5, $10, and $20 coins were made from 1870 to 1885, after which the presses became still. No coins were struck at Carson City from 1885 to 1888. The mint was closed after coinage in the early part of 1893. There were two main reasons:

1. Coinage costs were significantly cheaper at the San Francisco Mint, more than 200 miles away, even considering the railroad express charges.

2. The first director of the mint was Abram Curry, a partner in the Gould & Curry mine and refinery, a situation not appreciated by some of his competitors.

An undated architect's drawing of the front elevation of the United States Mint on Carson Street, Carson City, Nevada.

From the standpoint of care and minting, a special nod must be given to the coiners at Carson City, for their silver dollars in particular, but certain other issues as well, are usually better struck, with finer detail, than are those from other minting institutions.

There was thought of additional coinage later, but that did not happen. In 1900 officials were sure that Carson City's days of coining silver and gold had ended, and dies and certain equipment were shipped to the Philadelphia Mint. In 1911 quantities of bagged silver dollars were sent to the Treasury Building in Washington for storage. In 1942 the mint building became the Nevada State Museum, which today is a prime attraction.

For a comprehensive history of the Carson City Mint see *The Mint on Carson Street: A Tribute to the City Mint & Guide to a Complete Collection of "CC" Coins*, by Rusty Goe. See also *Carson City Morgan Dollars: Featuring the Coins of the GSA Hoard*, by Adam Crum, Selby Ungar, and Jeff Oxman.

CARSON CITY MINT QUARTERS IN THE ELIASBERG COLLECTION (1997)

The Louis Eliasberg Collection sold by Bowers and Merena Galleries that crossed the block in 1997 was the first in numismatic history to have all Carson City quarter varieties in Mint State.

Since their sale, most of these coins have been upgraded by the third-party grading services. Certain of the Eliasberg coins later appeared in the Battle Born Collection formed by Rusty Goe and sold by Stack's Bowers Galleries in 2013. Others have appeared elsewhere. The Eliasberg pedigree is one of the most coveted in American numismatics.

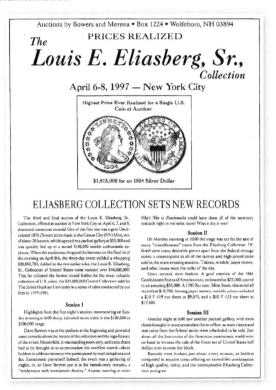

The original catalog descriptions are given here, lightly edited, with the prices realized.

Lot 1495 • 1870-CC • MS-64 PL • Sold for $187,000. For starters, Larry Briggs mentions that not only is the 1870-CC "considered to be the rarest date in the series," but that it is "unknown in Uncirculated grade." Larry did not have the opportunity to examine the Eliasberg Collection and did not know of this piece.

In 1893, when the 1870-CC was scarcely 23 years old, Augustus G. Heaton reflected that "It has the smallest coinage of the CC series and is exceedingly rare." The reference was to the 1870-CC in *any* grade, never mind Uncirculated.

The obverse and reverse of the Eliasberg Collection 1870-CC are both highly prooflike. In fact, if the piece did not bear a CC mintmark one could readily assign it the *Proof* designation. Most probably this issue was struck for presentation or to observe the initial coinage of this denomination at the newly opened Carson City Mint. Production of the variety commenced on April 20, 1870, when 3,540 were made. As no 1870-CC dimes were struck this year, the quarter dollar represented the smallest denomination. Just 8,340 were made during the year.

The obverse of the present piece displays lightly mottled gold toning with splashes of electric blue at the rims. The reverse is similar but somewhat lighter at the centers. In the left obverse field the Proof surface is the result of highly polishing the dies, including within the shield stripes. Under high-powered magnification some die striae can be seen as artifacts from the process.

Among quarter dollars the Carson City issues of this era are all seemingly rare. Front row center is, of course, the remarkable 1873-CC Without Arrows at Date. However, in terms of rarity at the gem level, the present 1870-CC far eclipses its more famous cousin! In fact, the highest coin certified by either NGC (AU-53) or PCGS (EF-40) falls far short of even minimum Mint State.

If the term "once in a lifetime opportunity" is appropriate, and few would argue that it can be used multiple times in the Eliasberg Collection, it certainly can be used with the present coin. This 1870-CC, remarkable in its quality and rarity, is certainly one of the most important pieces in the present sale and will forever be a highlight in the collection of its next owner.

Pedigree: Harlan P. Smith Collection, S.H. and Henry Chapman, May 8–11, 1906; John H. Clapp; Clapp estate, 1942, to Louis E. Eliasberg Sr.

Lot 1497 • 1871-CC • MS-65 PL • Sold for $165,000. Sharply struck. A cameo showpiece. One of just three report to exist in Mint State. Obverse and reverse with delicate lilac and heather toning with splashes of blue and gold.

Here is another landmark Carson City Liberty Seated quarter, a piece that will attract great excitement and enthusiasm when it crosses the auction block. It may be many years before an example of comparable quality is offered. To our knowledge, only three coins in this grade league are known to exist.

The two other Mint State pieces are believed to be the coin we offered in March 1988 as the Norweb Collection (lot 1640) and the Giacomo Opezzo to James A. Stack to Reed Hawn coin, sold by Stack's, which we have not seen, so we cannot compare it to the present specimen. We do know, however, that the presently offered coin is of nearly flawless quality and would be exceedingly difficult to match.

The 1871-CC quarter is one of the great rarities in the Liberty Seated series. Even worn specimens are very difficult to find. In grades above Extremely Fine there is no price indication in *A Guide Book of United States Coins*. Here is one of the most remarkable coins in the present offering, a legendary piece which will be forever remembered by specialists in the series.

Pedigree: Purchased by Louis E. Eliasberg Sr., in the Numismatic Gallery's sale of the "World's Greatest Collection" (Frederick C.C. Boyd Collection), 1945, and in the Eliasberg Collection since that time.

Lot 1500 • 1872-CC • MS-66 or finer • Sold for $99,000. A landmark specimen. Outranks, outflanks the famous 1871-CC in this regard, and *in gem Mint State is even rarer than the legendary 1873-CC Without Arrows!*

Partially prooflike obverse. Frosty reverse. Brilliant and satiny, virtual perfection. Delicate toning is just beginning to form. On the reverse to the left of the Q in QUAR there is a darker spot.

Only 22,850 examples were minted of the 1872-CC quarter dollar. All of these were put into the channels of commerce, so far as is known, and none were saved for numismatic cabinets. Over a period of time most became worn or lost. Today, the 1872-CC is a major rarity in any grade, and even an EF-40 piece would be a prize. The present coin is believed to be far and away the finest known. The finest known to Larry Briggs was our Norweb lot 1643 which was graded by the present cataloger as AU-55 or finer (since that time PCGS has graded it as MS-62), while NGC has mustered an EF-45 as its finest. Each of these two coins is, of course, very desirable.

Here, indeed, in the Eliasberg Collection 1872-CC is a Liberty Seated coin for the ages. Again the prospective bidder is confronted with what may truly be a once-in-a-lifetime opportunity.

Pedigree: Isaac Excell, August 1905; John H. Clapp; Clapp estate, 1942, to Louis E. Eliasberg, Sr.

Lot 1503 • 1873-CC, No Arrows at date • MS-62/65 PL • Sold for $187,000. Close 3 in date, as always. Lightly mottled gold, gray, and brown toning over mostly brilliant surfaces. Obverse well struck except for star points on right side of obverse, as normal. Reverse well struck. A very pleasing specimen of this landmark quarter dollar, *the* rarity in the Liberty Seated quarter series and, indeed, the entire denomination.

**A 1972 view of the East Façade, which served as
the front of the mint building. (Library of Congress).**

The mintage of the 1873-CC Without Arrows quarter dollar is believed to have been only 4,000 coins. Apparently, most were melted (after April 1, 1873, and by July 10, 1873) as being obsolete; the Coinage Act of 1873 had specified a slightly increased authorized weight, and later 1873-CC (With Arrows) quarters were made under this new standard.

The Eliasberg Collection specimen is one of only three Mint State specimens confirmed to exist. In addition, two worn pieces are known. This equals a total population of five specimens, ranking the issue among the rarest of all American coins.

Neither J.M. Clapp nor John H. Clapp ever owned an 1873-CC Without Arrows quarter dollar. Circa the 1890s J.M. Clapp was in touch with DeWitt S. Smith, who acted as a consultant concerning which mintmarked coins were minted or which existed, and which were never made or for which no pieces were known. Smith told Clapp that Augustus G. Heaton owned a specimen, and that New York City dealer and collector Harlan P. Smith had sold it to him. "Want this" Clapp wrote in his notebook, but the opportunity to acquire one never happened. In this era very little was known about the 1873 mintmark coinage.

In 1997 we are in a "grand era" of appreciation of nineteenth-century coins. More truly valuable and interesting information has been published in the past decade or two than in the entire century before. The oft-mentioned *Gobrecht Journal* has been the flagship publication for much of this knowledge, but reference books, articles in general-interest coin periodicals, exhibits and displays, the certification services (which have broadened the market and, seemingly, have removed some of the arcane aspects of grading), auction appearances, and other factors have all played a part.

Today, we not only *appreciate* a rarity such as the 1873-CC Without Arrows quarter dollar, we *understand* it as well. And, doubtless, as more old auction catalogs are studied and as more people become interested, our horizons will expand.

Coins such as the Eliasberg Collection 1873-CC Without Arrows quarter dollar will play a part in this growth and will be secure as the Rembrandts of numismatics.

Pedigree: Most recently from the Frederick C.C. Boyd "World's Greatest Collection" sale, 1945.

Lot 1505 • 1873-CC Arrows at Date • MS-63/65 PL • Sold for $88,000. A splendid example, one of the very finest known to exist. The obverse is prooflike and has a few contact marks, giving rise to the MS-63 designation. The reverse is satiny, frosty, and virtually perfect. Both surfaces are brilliant with just a whisper of toning.

The 1873-CC With Arrows was struck just to the extent of 14,462 pieces. Examples are very rare in all grades, with both Walter Breen and Larry Briggs echoing the sentiment that the issue is "prohibitively rare" in EF or better. Of course, Mint State is another category entirely, and whatever the next level above "prohibitively rare" is, this coin qualifies! The Eliasberg Collection will be forever remembered as comprising a truly unbelievable, breathtaking, incredible offering of Carson City and San Francisco quarter dollars of this era, a holding unmatched in quality in any other cabinet. These pieces are the *crème de la crème* of the Liberty Seated quarter dollar series.

Lot 1510 • 1875-CC • MS-64 PL • Sold for $5,720. A splendid specimen, with the obverse closely resembling a Philadelphia Mint Proof and even exceeding it from the standpoint of die preparation. However, the Proof finish was *inadvertent.* There are patches of Proof surface near the center of Liberty including in the three upper-right spaces between the vertical shield stripes. Clearly, someone polished this die with great determination! As such, it is one of the most distinctive we have seen in the entire series.

Pedigree: Richard B. Winsor Collection, S.H. and H. Chapman, December 1895: J.M. Clapp; John H. Clapp; Clapp estate, 1942 to Louis E. Eliasberg Sr.

Lot 1515 • 1876-CC • MS-64/65 • Sold for $6,380. Coarsely spaced edge reeding (in contrast to the next piece offered). A splendid specimen of exquisite quality. Light gold and champagne hues mingled with delicate blue and gray, all over deeply mirrored fields. Light blue borders. A splendid example which may have been a presentation striking of some sort or, in any event, is much finer than normally seen. Called a *Proof* by the Chapman brothers.

Pedigree: Richard B. Winsor Collection, S.H. and H. Chapman, December 1895: J.M. Clapp; John H. Clapp; Clapp estate, 1942 to Louis E. Eliasberg Sr.

Lot 1516 • 1876-CC • MS-62/65. Somewhat prooflike. Very possibly a presentation piece. Larger CC mintmark than on the preceding. Very finely spaced edge reeding. Champagne and lilac toning. A very attractive example.

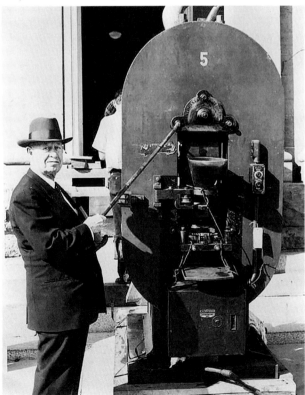

The founder of the Nevada State Museum, Judge Clark J. Guild, points to the old coining press, 1958.

Concerning reeding: The interested reader is referred to a significant article, "A Study of Seated Quarter Reeding," by John W. McCloskey, appearing in *The Gobrecht Journal*, November 1977. The author mentions that the reeding observed among Liberty Seated quarters ranges from 110 reeds used on certain New Orleans quarter dollars and certain San Francisco issues, which would be described as "coarse," to 153 reeds, "used only the 1876-CC quarter and reported as the Fine Reeding variety in the literature." Of course, not every numismatist has the patience to count reeding, and what with the great popularity of "slabs" the counting of reeding will become increasingly difficult, if not impossible! However, the Eliasberg pieces, not encapsulated, do provide examination of the reeding and may be of special interest.

Lot 1520 • 1877-CC • MS-63 • Sold for $1,100. Heather and light gold toning with some splashes of blue, over satiny fields. A couple tiny marks are seen near star 2, and on the reverse there is a scratch at U of UNITED. These are mostly hidden by toning, and without them the coin would be an easy MS-65 if not 66.

Pedigree: Henry Blair Collection sale, Charles Steigerwalt, October 14, 1896; J.M. Clapp; John H. Clapp; Clapp estate, 1942, to Louis E. Eliasberg Sr.

Lot 1521 • 1877-CC • MS-66 • Sold for $3,960. A prooflike gem, quite possibly a presentation piece. Delicate heather and gold toning over surfaces struck from a highly polished die. Simply gorgeous! Not rare as a date-and-mintmark combination, especially in lower grades, but certainly beautiful to behold. As MS-66, this is one the finest known.

Lot 1526 • 1878-CC • MS-61 • Sold for $990. Mottled light gray toning. Fairly scarce in Mint State, despite the generous mintage. At the time, Virginia City, Nevada (close by Carson City), was experiencing an economic downturn as the price of silver was dropping on domestic as well as international markets. However, during the general years 1875–1877, and to a lesser extent 1878, generous numbers of Carson City coins were struck in the dime, quarter dollar, and half dollar denominations. After 1878—the present 1878-CC quarter being the last of its kind—mintages of denominations lower than the dollar were discontinued at the Carson City facility.

The historic Coin Press No. 1, refurbished and on display at the Nevada State Museum today.

The vault door in the basement of the Carson City Mint, November 1972.

A night view of the Nevada State Museum, which incorporates the old Carson City Mint, August 2009.

APPENDIX T

Modern U.S. Mint Medals

This appendix is based on the research of Dennis Tucker, including extracts from American Gold and Silver: U.S. Mint Collector and Investor Coins and Medals, Bicentennial to Date.

During the American Revolution, the Continental Congress authorized official medals to be designed and struck (often in Paris) to honor heroes of the emerging new nation. One famous example is the Washington Before Boston medal, awarded in 1776 to thank General George Washington, his officers, and his soldiers after their victorious bombardment of Boston and the British evacuation of the city.

The national mint of the United States was established in 1792, and since the early 1800s it has issued medals for commemorative and historical purposes. These have celebrated everything from acts of heroic lifesaving to famous entertainers and wildlife conservation. "The United States Mint produces a variety of national medals to commemorate significant historical events or sites and to honor those whose superior deeds and achievements have enriched U.S. history or the world," the Mint says. "Some of these are bronze duplicates of Congressional Gold Medals authorized by Congress under separate public laws, while others are produced under the secretary of the Treasury's authority to strike national medals."

The following is a sampling of medals struck by the U.S. Mint since the early 1970s. Many of these, and others, are studied in detail in *American Gold and Silver* (Tucker). A number of the Mint's modern medals are available for sale to collectors at catalog.usmint.gov.

American Revolution Bicentennial Medals (1972–1976)

Congress passed a law on February 15, 1972, to authorize national medals to commemorate the bicentennial of the American Revolution and "historical events . . . in the continuing progress of the United States of America toward life, liberty, and the pursuit of happiness." Medals were issued each year from 1972 to 1976, in various bronze, silver, and gold formats.

	Distribution*	Value
1972, G. Washington, Liberty Tree, bronze, dated	672,200	$4
(1972) G. Washington, Liberty Tree, bronze, undated (a)	791,000	$6
1973, P. Henry and S. Adams, Committees of Correspondence, bronze, dated	237,790	$4
(1973) P. Henry and S. Adams, Committees of Correspondence, bronze, undated (a)	475,812	$6
1973, P. Henry and S. Adams, Committees of Correspondence, silver	208,120	$25
1974, J. Adams, First Continental Congress, bronze, dated	188,308	$4
(1974) J. Adams, First Continental Congress, bronze, undated (a)	511,428	$6
1974, J. Adams, First Continental Congress, silver	150,428	$25
1975, P. Revere, Lexington/Concord, bronze, dated	327,677	$4
(1975) P. Revere, Lexington/Concord, bronze, undated (a)	668,419	$6
1975, P. Revere, Lexington/Concord, silver	212,542	$25
1976, T. Jefferson, Declaration of Independence, bronze, dated	98,408	$4
(1976) T. Jefferson, Declaration of Independence, bronze, undated (a)	446,939	$6
1976, T. Jefferson, Declaration of Independence, silver (pictured)	98,677	$25
1976, Statue of Liberty, We the People, 1.5-inch, bronze	438,971	$5
1976, Statue of Liberty, We the People, 1.5-inch, gilt bronze	45,163	$9
1976, Statue of Liberty, We the People, 1.5-inch, silver	211,772	$24
1976, Statue of Liberty, We the People, 3-inch, silver	8,824	$300
1976, Statue of Liberty, We the People, .906-inch, gold (pictured)	29,468	$750
1976, Statue of Liberty, We the People, 1.31-inch, gold	5,396	$1,900
1976, Statue of Liberty, We the People, 3-inch, gold	423	$25,500

* There are discrepancies in Mint and other government records as to the exact mintages and quantities sold of some medals. **a.** Issued as part of a Philatelic-Numismatic Combination or PNC (medal, postage stamp, and first-day cover).

Colorado Statehood Centennial Medal (1976)

Colorado was the only state to join the Union in the national centennial year of 1876 (before it, Nebraska had joined in 1867; after it, the Dakotas, Montana, and Washington would join in 1889), and therefore was the only one to celebrate its 100th anniversary during the national Bicentennial in 1976. Congress authorized a medal—struck in various alloys at the Denver Mint—to mark the anniversary.

	Mintage	Value
1976, Colorado Centennial, bronze	41,000	$6
1976, Colorado Centennial, bronze, mule (a)	*	$6
1976, Colorado Centennial, gilt bronze	5,000	$8
1976, Colorado Centennial, silver	20,200	$32
1976, Colorado Centennial, gold (pictured)	100	$5,100
1976, Colorado Centennial, three-piece set (b)	1,876	$48

* Included in number above. **a.** The mule variety has the standard centennial logo reverse combined with a Denver Mint obverse (showing the mint building). **b.** Issued in a hard plastic case containing one each of the bronze, gilt bronze, and silver medals.

Valley Forge Medal (1978)

Congress authorized this medal to be struck for the United States Capitol Historical Society. It was designed by Chief Engraver Frank Gasparro and struck in several formats at the Philadelphia Mint.

	Mintage	Value
1978, Valley Forge, 3-inch, bronze	2,500	$35
1978, Valley Forge, 1.5-inch, gilt bronze	5,000	$15
1978, Valley Forge, 1.5-inch, silver	1,999	$50
1978, Valley Forge, 3-inch, silver (pictured)	1,000	$600
1978, Valley Forge, 1.31-inch, gold	339	$5,000

Young Astronauts Medals (1988)

Three different designs were created for bronze, silver, and gold medals by students in the Young Astronauts program (a White House initiative that encouraged proficiency and interest in science, math, and technology). The medals were executed by U.S. Mint sculptor-engravers and struck in Philadelphia in 1988.

| **Common Reverse** | **Bronze** | **Silver** | **Gold** |

	Mintage	Value
1988, Young Astronauts, bronze, Unc.	28,700	$9
1988, Young Astronauts, bronze, Proof	17,250	$14
1988, Young Astronauts, silver, 1.5-inch, Unc.	15,400	$40
1988, Young Astronauts, silver, 1.5-inch, Proof	33,250	$45
1988, Young Astronauts, silver, 3-inch, 6-ounce, Unc.	1,075	$345
1988, Young Astronauts, silver, 3-inch, 12-ounce, Unc.	3,700	$575

	Mintage	Value
1988, Young Astronauts, gold, .875-inch, Unc.	13,000	$600
1988, Young Astronauts, gold, .875-inch, Proof	3,400	$700
1988, Young Astronauts, gold, 3-inch	38	$20,000
1988, Young Astronauts, three-piece set, Unc. (a)		$675

a. Bronze, small silver, and small gold medals in Unc. format in a blue box. Other two- and three-medal sets were issued as well; each is worth about the combined retail value of the medals it contains.

Benjamin Franklin Firefighters Medal (1993)

This medal was authorized as part of the Benjamin Franklin National Memorial Commemorative Medal and Fire Service Bill of Rights Act. Franklin organized the country's first fire company in Philadelphia in 1736. The medals were struck at the Philadelphia Mint on American Silver Eagle planchets (40.6 mm in diameter, with one ounce of .999 fine silver), and each bears a P mintmark.

	Mintage	Value
1993, Franklin Firefighters, Unc.	26,011	$37
1993, Franklin Firefighters, Proof	89,311	$42

National Wildlife Refuge System Centennial Medals (2003)

In 2003 the U.S. Mint released its first-ever series of silver national medals, to celebrate the 100th anniversary of the National Wildlife Refuge System. Their shared obverse features a standing portrait of President Theodore Roosevelt, who designated Florida's Pelican Island as the nation's first wildlife refuge in 1903.

Sales started with the Bald Eagle variety, available in bronze and .900 fine silver formats. The Salmon, Elk, and Canvasback Duck varieties, in silver only, were released successively every few weeks after that.

The bronze Bald Eagle had no mintage limit, and in fact since then has been reissued in 2008 in the Bald Eagle Coin and Medal Set, and in 2013 in the Theodore Roosevelt Coin and Chronicles Set. The four silver medals all sold out their mintage limits (35,000 for the Bald Eagle and 25,000 for the others).

The silver medals were the first U.S. Mint products made using laser technology to texture their dies. They feature distinctive matte-finish frosted devices on mirror-finish fields. All were struck at the Philadelphia Mint without a mintmark.

Some early strikes of the silver medals were not as heavily frosted as later issues, with less pronounced cameo contrast between the fields and the design devices. This transition was caused by the Mint experimenting with its laser technology (as opposed to traditional sandblasting) for texturing the dies. The laser technique would later be used in the Mint's annual Proof sets and various commemorative coins.

A portion of the proceeds from the sale of the medals (10 percent of each silver medal and 5 percent of each bronze) benefited the National Fish and Wildlife Foundation and its conservation efforts.

Common
Obverse

	Mintage	Value
2003, National Wildlife Refuge System Centennial, Bald Eagle, bronze	(a)	$6
2003, National Wildlife Refuge System Centennial, Bald Eagle, silver	35,000	$28.50
2003, National Wildlife Refuge System Centennial, Salmon	25,000	$30
2003, National Wildlife Refuge System Centennial, Elk	25,000	$30
2003, National Wildlife Refuge System Centennial, Canvasback Duck	25,000	$29

a. The Mint established no production limit for the bronze medal. Mintage was ongoing into the early 2010s. At least 22,000 were distributed as part of the Mint's 2008 Bald Eagle Coin and Medal Set, and at least 15,000 in the 2013 Theodore Roosevelt Coin and Chronicles Set.

September 11, 2011, National Medal (2011)

This silver medal was authorized to mark the 10th anniversary of the September 11, 2001, terror attacks in New York City; Washington, D.C.; and Shanksville, Pennsylvania. A surcharge from each sale benefited the National September 11 Memorial & Museum at the World Trade Center site in New York.

	Distribution*	Value
2011-P, September 11	67,928	$50
2011-W, September 11	109,365	$45

* Quantities sold by the end of sale in December 2012.

Silver Presidential Medals (2013–2015)

In 2013, 2014, and 2015 the Mint issued restrikes, in silver, of several historic Presidential medals from its archives. These were packaged in Coin and Chronicles sets along with Presidential golden dollars (in Proof or Reverse Proof) and other collectibles related to each of six chief executives. The medals were struck on American Silver Eagle planchets, marking the first time the Mint offered its Presidential medals in .999 fine silver. They were made in a regular-strike format, not Burnished or Proof. Their designs are by Mint chief engravers Charles E. Barber (Theodore Roosevelt), John R. Sinnock (Franklin Roosevelt, Harry Truman), and Gilroy Roberts (Dwight Eisenhower, John F. Kennedy, and Lyndon Johnson obverses), and sculptor-engraver Frank Gasparro (Eisenhower, Kennedy, and Johnson reverses).

Theodore Roosevelt   Franklin D. Roosevelt   Harry S. Truman

Dwight D. Eisenhower   John F. Kennedy   Lyndon B. Johnson

	Distribution	Value
(2013) Theodore Roosevelt	15,144	$50
(2014) Franklin D. Roosevelt	20,000	$65
(2015) Harry S. Truman	17,000	$55
(2015) Dwight D. Eisenhower	17,000	$55
(2015) John F. Kennedy	50,000	$45
(2015) Lyndon B. Johnson	25,000	$45

Centennial of World War I Silver Medals (2018)

In 2018 the United States Mint issued five silver medals as part of its World War I Centennial commemorative program. This marked the 100th anniversary of the end of the war, and honored the involvement of more than 4 million men and women in America's Army, Navy, Marine Corps, Coast Guard, and Air Service. The medals were struck in West Point (Army), San Francisco (Marines), Philadelphia (Navy and Coast Guard), and Denver (Air Service) on silver dollar–sized planchets (1.5 inches in diameter), in .900 fine silver, in Proof format, with a plain edge. Each medal was issued in a two-piece set that also included a Proof example of the World War I Centennial silver commemorative dollar. The sets were limited to 100,000 units across all five medal product options.

The early-order issue price of each two-piece set was $99.95. The Mint has not yet audited its final mintage figures for each medal.

	Distribution*	Value
2018, U.S. Army	*15,621*	$50
2018, U.S. Navy	*12,253*	$65
2018, U.S. Marines	*12,648*	$55
2018, U.S. Air Service	*12,520*	$55
2018, U.S. Coast Guard	*9,813*	$45

* As of March 30, 2019.

Congressional Gold Medals

The legislation that authorizes a Congressional Gold Medal will often permit the U.S. Mint to strike duplicates in bronze (90 percent copper, 10 percent zinc) for sale to the public. These medals, minted in Philadelphia, are typically offered in three-inch format for $39.95, and/or 1.5-inch format for $6.95. Here is a small sampling of recent Congressional Gold Medals available in bronze for collectors. More of the Mint's catalog of modern medals is online at catalog.usmint.gov.

MOTHER TERESA OF CALCUTTA (AUTHORIZED 1997)

A Congressional Gold Medal was authorized in 1997 to recognize the worldwide humanitarian influence of Mother Teresa of Calcutta: "She greatly impacted the lives of people from all walks of life in every corner of the world through her love and her selfless charitable works for nearly 70 years."

CODE TALKERS (AUTHORIZED 2000, 2008)

Code Talkers were Native Americans who used their tribal languages as a means of secret communication during wartime. The Code Talkers Recognition Act of 2008 authorized Congressional Gold Medals recognizing the valor of Native American Code Talkers and their dedication to the U.S. Armed Services during World War I and World War II.

On November 20, 2013, in the U.S. Capitol's Emancipation Hall, 33 tribes were officially recognized, and 25 were presented with their Congressional Gold Medals. Unique gold medals were struck for each tribe that had a member who served as a Code Talker. Silver duplicate medals were presented to the surviving Code Talkers, their next of kin, or other personal representatives. In addition, bronze duplicates are available for sale to the public.

The Navajo Nation had been awarded a Congressional Gold Medal in 2001. The following are the tribes and nations honored by the 2008 legislation.

Cherokee Nation
Cheyenne and Arapaho Tribes
Cheyenne River Sioux Tribe
Choctaw Nation
Comanche Nation
Crow Creek Sioux Tribe
Crow Nation
Fond du Lac Band of Lake Superior Chippewa Tribe

Fort Peck Assiniboine and Sioux Tribes
Ho-Chunk Nation
Hopi Tribe
Kiowa Tribe
Lower Brule Sioux Tribe
Menominee Nation
Meskwaki Nation
Muscogee (Creek) Nation
Oglala Sioux Tribe

Oneida Nation
Osage Nation
Pawnee Nation
Ponca Tribe
Pueblo of Acoma Tribe
Pueblo of Laguna Tribe
Rosebud Sioux Tribe
Santee Sioux Nation
Seminole Nation

Sisseton Wahpeton Oyate (Sioux) Tribe
St. Regis Mohawk Tribe
Standing Rock Sioux Tribe
Tlingit Tribe
Tonto Apache Tribe
White Mountain Apache Tribe
Yankton Sioux Tribe

St. Regis Mohawk Tribe

Kiowa Tribe

Oneida Nation

Rosebud Sioux Tribe

NEW FRONTIER (AUTHORIZED 2011)

America's historic achievements in space were celebrated with the New Frontier Congressional Gold Medal featuring Apollo 11 astronauts John Glenn, Neil A. Armstrong, Michael Collins, and Edwin E. "Buzz" Aldrin. The men were awarded the gold version of the medal at a ceremony in the U.S. Capitol Building on November 16, 2011. The bronze version is available in small and large formats.

"John Glenn became the first American to orbit the Earth on February 20, 1962, helping pave the way for the first lunar landing," the Mint noted in a press release. "As mission commander for Apollo 11, Neil Armstrong gained the distinction of being the first astronaut to land a spacecraft on the moon and the first to step on its surface on July 21, 1969. Buzz Aldrin joined Armstrong in piloting the lunar module, *Eagle*, to the surface of the moon and became the second person to walk on the lunar surface. Michael Collins piloted the command module, *Columbia*, in lunar orbit and helped his fellow Apollo 11 astronauts complete their mission on the moon."

New Frontier

9/11 FALLEN HEROES (AUTHORIZED 2011)

A suite of three Congressional Gold Medals—and their bronze duplicates—honor those who lost their lives in the terrorist attacks of September 11, 2001. With unique designs, each medal marks one of three sites: the World Trade Center in New York, the Pentagon, and rural Pennsylvania.

| Fallen Heroes of New York | Fallen Heroes of Pennsylvania | Fallen Heroes of the Pentagon |

WORLD WAR II (AUTHORIZED VARIOUS YEARS)

Many Congressional Gold Medals have been awarded to honor service, bravery, and sacrifices in World War II. These are popular among students of military history; veterans and their families; current service members; and medal collectors and hobbyists.

The Tuskegee Airmen medal, authorized in 2006, recognizes the unique military record of the Tuskegee Airmen, who inspired revolutionary reform in the U.S. armed forces.

The Women Airforce Service Pilots medal was authorized in 2009 in honor of the pioneering military service and exemplary record of the WASPs.

The Doolittle Tokyo Raiders medal was authorized in 2014 to honor the extraordinary service of the 80 U.S. airmen who flew a mission into Japan on April 18, 1942.

The Monuments Men medal, also authorized in 2014, recognizes the heroic role played in the preservation, protection, and restitution of monuments, works of art, and culturally important artifacts during and following the war.

The Filipino Veterans of World War II medal, authorized in 2016, acknowledges the debt owed by the United States for the bravery, valor, and dedication that Filipinos and Filipino-Americans displayed during the war. The medal is shown here in its three-inch bronze format.

These and other World War II commemorative medals are available in both small and large sizes directly from the U.S. Mint.

Tuskegee Airmen

Doolittle
Tokyo Raiders

Women Airforce
Service Pilots

Monuments Men

Filipino Veterans of World War II
Shown in the three-inch size.

APPENDIX U

The "Liberty" Subset of First Spouse Gold Coins

This appendix is excerpted and condensed from chapter 6 of **American Gold and Silver: U.S. Mint Collector and Investor Coins and Medals, Bicentennial to Date,** *by Dennis Tucker.*

By 2007 the United States was more than 20 years into its successful modern gold-bullion programs. Collectors and investors were buying hundreds of thousands of ounces of American Gold Eagles annually. The American Buffalo 24-karat coins had been introduced the year before and were off to a galloping start. Next in the lineup was a gold-coinage series designed as a companion to the Mint's soon-to-roll-out Presidential dollars. The new bullion program's 24-karat coins would honor and commemorate the nation's First Ladies.

DETAILS OF THE PRESIDENTIAL $1 COIN ACT

The Presidential $1 Coin Act of 2005 (Public Law 109-145) was the legislation that authorized the U.S. Mint's First Spouse gold bullion coins. It was enacted "to require the secretary of the Treasury to mint coins in commemoration of each of the nation's past presidents and their spouses, respectively, to improve circulation of the $1 coin, to create a new bullion coin, and for other purposes." The act was considered and passed in the Senate on November 18, 2005; considered and passed in the House on December 13; and signed into law by President George W. Bush on December 22.

Relevant to the First Spouse coins, the text of the act noted the following:

First Spouses have not generally been recognized on American coinage.

Although the Congress has authorized the Secretary of the Treasury to issue gold coins with a purity of 99.99 percent, the Secretary has not done so. [This was in 2005, when the American Buffalo 24-karat gold coins had yet to be released.]

Bullion coins are a valuable tool for the investor and, in some cases, an important aspect of coin collecting.

The 2005 act ordered that, starting in 2007 to coincide with the debut of the Presidential dollar coins, "the Secretary shall issue bullion coins . . . that are emblematic of the spouse of [each] President." It spelled out the coins' specifications: they would have the same diameter as the Presidential dollars

[26.5 mm]; they would weigh 1/2 ounce; and they would contain 99.99% pure gold. In terms of designs, the obverse of each coin would feature:

the name and likeness of the spouse of each president during the president's period of service,

the years during which she was the spouse of the president during the president's period of service, and

a number indicating the order of the period of service in which such president served.

On each coin's reverse:

images emblematic of the life and work of the First Spouse whose image is borne on the obverse,

the inscription "United States of America," and

an inscription of the nominal denomination of the coin, $10.

The legislation's focus on *First Spouses* rather than *First Ladies* avoided any confusion over cases where a president was widowed or unmarried and the usual ceremonial functions of First Lady were carried out by a daughter or other relative; or if he was married but someone other than his wife performed some or all of the duties typically assigned to the First Lady (as was the case when various presidential wives were too sick or frail).

In cases where a president served without a spouse, the act ordered that "the image on the obverse of the bullion coin corresponding to the $1 coin relating to such President shall be an image emblematic of the concept of 'Liberty'"—

as represented on a United States coin issued during the period of service of such President; or

as represented, in the case of President Chester Alan Arthur, by a design incorporating the name and likeness of Alice Paul, a leading strategist in the suffrage movement, who was instrumental in gaining women the right to vote upon the adoption of the 19th amendment and thus the ability to participate in the election of future Presidents, and who was born on January 11, 1885, during the term of President Arthur; and

the reverse of such bullion coin shall be of a design representative of themes of such President, except that in the case of [the Alice Paul coin] the reverse of such coin shall be representative of the suffrage movement.

The act further specified that if two presidential spouses served during an executive term (in the case of death of one and remarriage to another), a separate coin would be designed and issued for each.

The four First Spouse gold pieces issued with historical coin images "emblematic of the concept of Liberty as represented on a United States coin" make up a popular subset of the series. They are: Thomas Jefferson's Liberty; Andrew Jackson's Liberty; Martin Van Buren's Liberty; and James Buchanan's Liberty.

THOMAS JEFFERSON'S LIBERTY (2007)

Designer: *Robert Scot (obverse); Charles L. Vickers (reverse).* **Sculptor:** *Phebe Hemphill (obverse); Charles L. Vickers (reverse).* **Composition:** *.9999 gold.* **Actual Gold Weight:** *1/2 ounce.* **Diameter:** *26.49 mm.* **Edge:** *Reeded.* **Mint:** *West Point.* **Issue Price:** *$410.95 (Burnished); $429.95 (Proof).* **Release Date:** *August 30, 2007.*

Mintage: 19,823 Burnished; 19,815 Proof

Draped Bust half cent (1800–1808).

2007 Thomas Jefferson's Liberty, Burnished format.

Hobby observers anticipated a hot market for the third coin of the First Spouse series. This issue was the first of four that would feature an allegorical Miss Liberty rather than an actual First Lady. Thomas Jefferson's wife, Martha, had died some 19 years before he won the presidency, and he never remarried, so the nation had no First Lady during his two terms in office.

The image for Jefferson's coin is Mint Medallic Sculptor Phebe Hemphill's resculpted version of Miss Liberty from Chief Engraver Robert Scot's Draped Bust half cent of 1800 to 1808. "This beautiful coin captures a classic image of Liberty from Jefferson's time," said Mint director Ed Moy, "connecting us to the history of our coinage."

There are special elements of appeal for the four Liberty designs. Viewed by collectors as a self-contained "short set," they make a more attainable (less expensive) goal than acquiring one of every type in the First Spouse gold series. On top of that the Liberty coins recreate the classic designs of popular older coins. For these reasons, enthusiasts in 2007 expected strong demand for the Jefferson's Liberty coins. By mid-September, market-makers in modern coins were advertising buy prices up to $550 per raw coin (which would yield a quick $100-plus profit for the seller), and retailing 70-graded coins for up to $900. Sellers on eBay advertised the coins at prices above their official Mint issue price, even before they were delivered.

As predicted, Jefferson's Liberty did garner the series' highest mintages up to that point, in both Proof and Burnished formats—a distinction they still maintain, as mintages never again got close to their first-year highs.

Not long after their August 30 release, it became evident that the Jefferson's Liberty coins would not enjoy a repeat of the sustained strong secondary markets of their Washington and Adams predecessors. The Mint placed an order limit of one coin of each format per household, which allowed for broader, more equitable distribution—speculators had a harder time grabbing up large quantities. "The Mint got out its bulldozer and leveled the playing field," is how one collector put it. Once the coins were in collectors' and dealers' hands, they started to flow in to the professional third-party grading firms for certification. The Jefferson coin had the largest certified population of First Strike 70s. This combination of factors—broad distribution throughout the collector base, and a large quantity of perfect First Strike coins—dampened the secondary market. Everyone who wanted a nice example of the coin had one.

Rare-coin dealer Wayne Herndon made this observation in November 2007: "The real question is not what happened to the Jefferson, but what happened to the Washington and Adams. The Jefferson did exactly what it should have done based on the mintage, interest, etc. Somehow, some way, a lot of people got it into their heads that is would be a great series and the first two sold out quickly. Slow delivery contributed to the apparent lack of supply vs. demand. As a result, the first two ended up being the exceptions, not Jefferson." Presciently, Herndon went on: "I predict this series will see some pieces with mintages in the low four figures. Those are the ones that will have some potential."

Scott Schechter and Jeff Garrett, too, have noted the potential of the Liberty gold coins. "Collectors like them because of the way they honor numismatic history, recasting old designs in a new way," they wrote in *100 Greatest U.S. Modern Coins*. As a set, the First Spouse Liberty gold coins are ranked in the fourth edition of the *100 Greatest* book at number 58. Their ranking will undoubtedly climb closer to number 1 if the now-concluded program grows in popularity. Eric Jordan and John Maben wrote in *Top 50 Most Popular Modern Coins*: "One of the best things that can happen to a series is to have a large population of good-looking common dates in the hands of the public to get them started without the intimidating hurdle of a high collector premium. Jefferson's Liberty is this coin in the four-coin Liberty gold subset."

Regarding the aesthetics of the Jefferson's Liberty coin, collectors were charmed by the Mint's use of the early-1800s half-cent portrait of Miss Liberty. America's copper half cents and large cents have been popular collectibles since they went obsolete in the late 1850s. Today a solid and growing collector base benefits from the educational and fraternal missions of hobby groups such as Early American Coppers, whose members keep the series alive with ongoing research (they publish new findings regularly, and were instrumental in sharing their scholarship in Q. David Bowers's *Guide Book of Half Cents and Large Cents*, 2015). EAC nationwide has more than 1,200 members who congregate at coin shows and online at www.eacs.org. Undoubtedly many of these enthusiasts bought this First Spouse "Liberty" coin to complement their half cent and large cent collections.

The *reverse* of the coin, on the other hand, won few kudos with its text-heavy design. U.S. Mint Sculptor-Engraver Charles Vickers depicted Thomas Jefferson's grave monument, located on the grounds of his Monticello estate, in minutely textured detail. He overset the obelisk with the president's self-penned epitaph: "Here was buried Thomas Jefferson, author of the declaration of American independence, of the statute of Virginia for religious freedom and father of the University of Virginia. Born April 2, 1743, O.S. Died July 4, 1826." Surrounding this well-balanced but lengthy inscription are the standard legends UNITED STATES OF AMERICA and E PLURIBUS UNUM, plus the denomination of $10, the weight of 1/2 OZ., and the purity of .9999 FINE GOLD. "Enjoy the obverse," remarked some hobby wags, "but don't flip the coin over"—no offense to the very talented Mr. Vickers, who was tasked with fitting nearly 50 words into a one-inch–diameter circle of gold.

ANDREW JACKSON'S LIBERTY (2008)

Designer: *John Reich (obverse); Justin Kunz (reverse).* **Sculptor:** *Don Everhart (reverse).*
Composition: *.9999 gold.* **Actual Gold Weight:** *1/2 ounce.* **Diameter:** *26.49 mm.* **Edge:** *Reeded.*
Mint: *West Point.* **Issue Price:** *$599.95 (Burnished); $619.95 (Proof).* **Release Date:** *August 28, 2008.*

Mintage: 4,609 Burnished; 7,684 Proof

**Capped Bust half dollar
(1807–1836).**

**2008 Andrew Jackson's Liberty,
Burnished format.**

On August 21, 2008, the Mint announced that it would begin accepting orders for its next First Spouse gold coin on August 28. Mintage was set at a maximum of 40,000 coins across both product options, Burnished and Proof, with customer demand determining the quantity produced of each format. The household limit, previously capped at one coin of each format for the first week of sales, was raised to 10 coins of each format for the first week in an effort to stimulate purchasing.

Once again the provisions of the Presidential $1 Coin Act of 2005 were invoked due to a president having served without a spouse. Andrew Jackson's wife Rachel died shortly before he took office, leaving him grief-stricken and the nation without an official First Lady from 1829 to 1837. The gold coin for the seventh presidency featured "an obverse design emblematic of Liberty as represented on a United States coin issued during the president's period of service and a reverse image emblematic of that president." The figure of Miss Liberty was derived from Mint engraver John Reich's Capped Bust, Lettered Edge, silver half dollar of 1807 to 1836. The reverse design by Artistic Infusion Program Master Designer Justin Kunz shows a military equestrian portrait of Jackson as "Old Hickory"—the moniker by which he became known for leading American forces against the British Army in the War of 1812. Don Everhart's sculpting of Kunz's design has remarkable depth and nuanced detail.

The hobby community's reaction to the coin was mixed. Why did collectors *not* buy Jackson's Liberty in droves? Some in 2008 were saving their hobby money for the upcoming 2009 Ultra High Relief gold coin. Some were disgruntled with the issue price of the latest First Spouse coin—about 50 percent above gold's spot value. Some collectors found the prospect of completing the set of First Spouse coins too daunting to continue (or begin), especially with the uncertainty of gold's value fluctuating. Collectors of modern issues felt the pressure of many other Mint products competing for their discretionary income. And the interest of some hobbyists had cooled after the market couldn't sustain the initial firestorm of excitement over the program's first two coins the year before.

Even with this chill, Andrew Jackson's Liberty was appealing enough to gin up total sales about 20 percent higher than the preceding Louisa Adams issue. The attractive designs of the Jackson coin, with a classic American coinage motif of Miss Liberty and the dramatic horseback portrait of the famous war hero, strengthened its appeal. So did its status as one of only four members of the subset of Liberty coins in the First Spouse series.

All of the 2007 coins and half of the preceding 2008 issues had sold more Proofs than did Jackson's Liberty, but none after it (until 2015) would reach its level of 7,684 Proof coins. Its Burnished mintage level would not be exceeded by a predecessor until nine coins down the line—another in the Liberty subset, James Buchanan's Liberty, in 2010.

MARTIN VAN BUREN'S LIBERTY (2008)

Designer: *Christian Gobrecht (obverse); Thomas Cleveland (reverse).* **Sculptor:** *Jim Licaretz (reverse).*
Composition: *.9999 gold.* **Actual Gold Weight:** *1/2 ounce.* **Diameter:** *26.49 mm.* **Edge:** *Reeded.*
Mint: *West Point.* **Issue Price:** *$524.95 (Burnished); $549.95 (Proof).* **Release Date:** *November 25, 2008.*

Mintage: 3,826 Burnished; 6,807 Proof

Liberty Seated silver dollar (1840–1873).

2008 Martin Van Buren's Liberty, Burnished format.

The U.S. Mint started accepting orders for the Martin Van Buren First Spouse gold coin at 12 noon on November 25, 2008. The issue price was set about $75 lower than that of its predecessor coin, following gold's activity in the bullion markets. As with the Andrew Jackson coin that had debuted three months earlier, the Mint set an order limit of 10 coins per format (Burnished and Proof) per household for the first week, reserving the right to evaluate sales and either extend, adjust, or eliminate the limit after that. The total mintage was capped at 40,000 pieces, to be distributed between the Burnished and Proof coins according to buyers' demand.

Collector interest waned a bit for this issue, the third in the First Spouse program's four-coin Liberty subset, despite its attractive engraving of Christian Gobrecht's classic Liberty Seated design. This motif had been used on the silver dime from 1837 to 1891, and on other U.S. silver coins in various time spans of the same era. The reason the 2008 gold bullion coin for Van Buren's presidency featured no First Lady is that his wife, Hannah, had died of tuberculosis in 1819, early in his political career, when he was a member of the New York State Senate. Van Buren never remarried. Their son's wife, Sarah Angelica Singleton Van Buren, performed many of the hostess functions for the White House during her father-in-law's presidency.

The reverse tableau shows Martin Van Buren as a youth reading a book outside the Kinderhook, New York, tavern run by his father, with a traveler on horseback in the background. When Martin was growing up, the tavern, situated along a post road, was a meeting place for conversation, debate, and voting. Politicians traveling between New York City and the state capital of Albany stopped there. From this exposure young Van Buren developed a taste for politics and the philosophy of law. The coin's richly detailed scene, with its well-balanced blend of natural, architectural, and human elements, was designed by Artistic Infusion Program Master Designer Thomas Cleveland and sculpted by Mint Sculptor-Engraver Jim Licaretz.

Numismatics offers many opportunities to cross-pollinate a sophisticated coin collection. No doubt more than just a few of Van Buren's Liberty gold coins are kept company by much older silver half dimes, dimes, quarters, half dollars, and silver dollars that date back to the presidency of "The Red Fox of Kinderhook." Consider the Liberty Seated Collectors Club ("Uniting Collectors of Liberty Seated Coinage Since 1973," online at www.lsccweb.org). That particular hobby group is very active, and proved its numismatic chops in sharing information, research, and insight for Q. David Bowers's *A Guide Book of Liberty Seated Silver Coins* (2016). How many of its 600-plus members treated themselves to one or more of these artful gold pieces? New members will undoubtedly feel the same attraction.

Due to its low mintage, and ongoing collector demand for the four coins of the Liberty subset, Van Buren's Liberty has emerged as the aftermarket winner among the First Spouse issues of 2007 and 2008. In both Burnished and Proof format it typically carries a premium of 25 to 50 percent over the other coins of those years. Eric Jordan and John Maben gave Van Buren's Liberty an overall score of 4.0 in their book *Top 50 Most Popular Modern Coins*, calling it "the undisputed king of the Liberty subset," with "classic good looks that attract both classic and modern collectors."

JAMES BUCHANAN'S LIBERTY (2010)

Designer: *Christian Gobrecht (obverse); David Westwood (reverse).* **Sculptor:** *Joseph F. Menna (reverse).*
Composition: *.9999 gold.* **Actual Gold Weight:** *1/2 ounce.* **Diameter:** *26.49 mm.* **Edge:** *Reeded.*
Mint: *West Point.* **Issue Price:** *$766 (Burnished); $779 (Proof).* **Release Date:** *September 2, 2010.*
Mintage: 5,162 Burnished; 7,110 Proof

Liberty Head quarter eagle (1840–1907).

2010 James Buchanan's Liberty, Burnished format.

The design of the 2010 James Buchanan's Liberty gold bullion coin was unveiled in Washington, D.C., on December 21, 2009. On June 29, 2010, the U.S. Mint announced that the coin would be released for sale on September 2. As with other recent issues, the combined mintage for Burnished and Proof pieces was capped at 15,000, with customer demand determining the quantities of each format. No household ordering limits were set.

This was the fourth and final First Spouse gold coin in the Liberty subset. "Because President James Buchanan did not have a spouse," the Mint announced, "the obverse of his corresponding First Spouse Gold Coin features a design emblematic of Liberty as it appeared on a U.S. coin issued during his time in office." It features a reproduction of the Liberty Head design by Christian Gobrecht, minted on the quarter eagle ($2.50 gold piece) from 1840 through 1907.

In an interesting case of "what might have been," the Citizens Coinage Advisory Committee, which advises the Treasury Department on coin designs, had leaned toward using the Flying Eagle cent of 1856 to 1858.

The Liberty Head motif was the dominant obverse element of U.S. gold coins minted from the late 1830s to the early 1900s. Undoubtedly Gobrecht's elegant and popular design attracted a share of collector interest above and beyond that of First Spouse specialists and bullion investors. Writing about the Proof format in particular, Jordan and Maben have noted, "This attractive $10 Proof gold coin is the last issue of an affordable four-coin set that is in some ways a tour of the great designs of the 1800s that can't be acquired in a cameo Proof format any other way. . . . It's the *only* option if you like the look of high-grade antique Proof gold but have to live within a reasonable budget."

As to why there was no First Spouse in James Buchanan's life, modern historians and biographers support the idea that the Pennsylvania politician was gay. For whatever reason, he is the only U.S. president to have remained a lifelong bachelor. Unrelated to his personal life, many presidential historians rank Buchanan as one of the nation's worst chief executives. Despite grand ideas he proved unable to map out a plan for peace as the country became more and more split by the slavery question. The Southern states seceded in the waning months of his presidency, and the Civil War erupted shortly after. Avoiding these political failings, the reverse design of the Buchanan's Liberty coin focuses not on his presidential tenure but on his early life. Artistic Infusion Program Associate Designer David Westwood envisioned Buchanan as a young man keeping a ledger in his father's country store in Pennsylvania. It is a scene of quiet work and dedication—the boy who would grow up to be an "incorruptible statesman" (as honored on his congressionally approved memorial in Washington, D.C.), rather than the beleaguered president overwhelmed by national events.

Buchanan's Liberty was the most popular of the First Spouse gold coins of 2010 in each format, and one of the last of the program's issues to exceed a mintage of 10,000. In the first three days of sales, the Mint sold more than 6,000 pieces total, nearing the halfway point of the issue's maximum coinage. Collector interest continued to be strong, and the Mint announced a second round of minting just weeks into the sales period. Ultimately more than 12,000 coins were purchased before the Mint closed its sales of the Proof version on February 8, 2011, and of the Burnished version on April 11.

Demand for the Liberty subset keeps the secondary-market prices of this issue relatively high, despite its larger-than-average mintage.

THE FIFTH LIBERTY COIN THAT WASN'T: ALICE PAUL

Designer: *Susan Gamble (obverse); Phebe Hemphill (reverse).* **Sculptor:** *Phebe Hemphill (obverse and reverse).* **Composition:** *.9999 gold.* **Actual Gold Weight:** *1/2 ounce.* **Diameter:** *26.49 mm.* **Edge:** *Reeded.* **Mint:** *West Point.* **Issue Price:** *$1,041 (Burnished); $1,054 (Proof).* **Release Date:** *October 11, 2012.*

Mintage: 2,798 Burnished; 3,505 Proof

2012 Alice Paul, Burnished format.

In December 2011, Secretary of the Treasury Timothy Geithner directed that the U.S. Mint suspend minting and issuing Presidential dollars for circulation. "Regular circulating demand for the coins will be met through the Federal Reserve Bank's existing inventory of circulating coins minted prior to 2012," the Mint announced, noting that it would still offer various products and packages containing the dollar coins. Although the Presidential $1 Coin Act of 2005 tied the First Spouse coins to the Presidential dollars, this change had no effect on the issuance of the gold pieces.

On April 23, 2012, the U.S. Mint announced the Alice Paul design of the year's first First Spouse gold coin. The mintage limit for the Alice Paul coin was lowered from the previous year's 15,000 to 13,000, with customer demand determining how many would be Burnished and how many Proof.

Complications in striking the coins delayed their release until late in the year. They finally went on sale October 11, 2012. Initial demand was strong, perhaps with some buyers anticipating a short sales period and therefore a low mintage. Nearly a quarter of the mintage limit was ordered in the first week.

As with the prior year's issues, the 2012 First Spouse coins were priced by the Mint's sliding scale based on the fluctuating market value of gold. They started out higher than $1,000 per coin, but a decline in the spot value led to prices as low as $840 for the Proof format and $820 for the Burnished. The Proof coins remained on sale into the summer of 2013, with the Mint declaring them sold out on July 16. The final Proof mintage, after an official audit accounting for returned and melted coins, was 3,505. The Burnished version remained in the Mint's product catalog until December 31, 2013, with a final mintage of 2,798.

Some collectors bemoaned the U.S. Mint's "political correctness" in depicting suffragist Alice Paul instead of a coinage-inspired Miss Liberty to represent the presidency of widower Chester Alan Arthur. This complaint mischaracterizes the source of the design: the U.S. Congress, not the Mint. Alice Paul was written into the First Spouse program's authorizing legislation.

The coin's obverse design departs from others in the series with the word SUFFRAGIST underneath Alice Paul's portrait, instead of the ordinal of Arthur's presidency (21st) and the year-date range of his term (1881–1885). The portrait, designed by Susan Gamble and sculpted by Phebe Hemphill, has Alice facing the viewer with a steady and determined gaze that embodies her strength and courage. Alice was born in New Jersey in 1885 and raised in the Quaker traditions of public service and gender equality. She studied social work but soon realized that "I was never going to be a social worker, because I could see that social workers were not doing much good in the world. . . . you couldn't change the situation by social work." The "situation" was the inequality endured by women worldwide. In England in her early 20s Alice developed a more militant advocacy for women's rights, taking part in protests and being jailed for voicing her beliefs. She returned to the United States energized and well known. She publicized the cause of equal rights—in particular the right of women to vote—on a national scale, organizing a 1913 parade march in Washington, D.C., the day before Woodrow Wilson's inauguration as president. The lead banner in the march read, "We Demand an Amendment to the United States Constitution Enfranchising the Women of the Country." Alice Paul and other suffragists pushed the right-to-vote agenda for several more years, facing arrest, harassment, and even brutal confinement to psychiatric wards, which only fueled popular support for their cause. Finally in June 1919 the U.S. Senate passed the Constitution's 19th amendment, which was ratified in August 1920, guaranteeing women the right to vote. The reverse of the Alice Paul First Spouse gold coin, designed and sculpted by Phebe Hemphill, shows Alice in action, marching for equality with an American flag and a sash reading VOTES FOR WOMEN. Her stride is bold, and the energy of the motif, with the flag and the sash in motion, captures the suffragist's forward movement.

The Alice Paul gold coin is something of an anomaly in the First Spouse series, illustrating neither a First Lady nor a purely symbolic coinage-inspired representation of Liberty. However, no other suffragist embodies the ideals of American liberty—and the human urge to fight and to endure personal suffering for the liberty of others—more so than Alice Paul. Yes, there are coins from the era of Chester Arthur's presidency that depict Liberty and could have been used, making this the fifth in the series' Liberty subset. The Morgan dollar, the Indian Head cent, the Liberty Head nickel, and the Indian Princess Head $3 gold piece come to mind. But as a *living* symbol of American liberty, Alice Paul fits the First Spouse gold coin quite nicely.

THE FUTURE OF THE FIRST SPOUSES

"When I became Mint director in 2006," recalls Ed Moy, "one of the key issues on my plate was making sure of the successful launch of the Presidential dollar coins and their companion First Spouse gold bullion coins."

Today, whether they're collected for sentimental reasons or hoarded as hedges against inflation, the First Spouse coins have found their niche among gold buyers. The audience for the coins is diverse. It includes hobbyists who add one or two of each issue to keep their collections complete and up to date; precious-metal investors seeking 24-karat gold in coin form; and people who don't consider themselves numismatists but are attracted to the occasional design that interests them. The first issues in 2007 established a "field population" of tens of thousands of coins, while low-mintage issues of later years added a limited-supply challenge to assembling a complete collection. After slow activity in the early 2010s, popular mainstream sales skyrocketed in 2015 with the Jackie Kennedy coin. This introduced (or re-introduced) many Americans to the First Spouse coins. Over time, the expanded audience might bring additional mainstream interest to earlier issues. Many collectors enjoy the Liberty subset of four coins discussed in this appendix, with their classic U.S. coinage designs of Miss Liberty.

From the start of the series, many specialists have sought the finest grades (MS-70 and PF-70) not only for their personal aesthetic satisfaction but also to compete with other collectors in the NGC and PCGS set registries. Some pay a premium for "First Strike" or "Early Release" coins—those pieces acknowledged by the grading firms as coming from the earliest Mint production (usually the first 30 days) for each type. As noted, several of the First Spouse gold coins have been ranked in the *100 Greatest U.S. Modern Coins* and also among the *100 Greatest Women on Coins* (by Ron Guth). As more collectors work to assemble collections based on those popular books, demand for the included coins will increase. And as the First Spouse coinage matures from "modern" to "classic," the coins will continue to capture the imaginations and appreciation of history buffs and numismatists.

APPENDIX V

Coin Clubs

Joining a coin club is an important part of your hobby fulfillment. Membership brings many advantages, most important of which are camaraderie and the accumulation of knowledge. We all need both.

Even if you can't travel to meeting locations and shows, most clubs produce newsletters that are highly educational and encourage members to contribute articles. This is one of the best ways to learn about a specific numismatic subject. With every article you write, you'll travel new avenues of research and add to your numismatic knowledge. It never fails.

Many specialized coin clubs have been born in the virtual environment of the Internet. These clubs often are interactive, offering all members a great opportunity to ask questions of specialists, share knowledge, and meet others with similar interests.

This appendix lists numismatic organizations dedicated to subjects that should interest most of our readers. The information noted, including membership fees and addresses, is as accurate as possible at the time of publication. A visit to a group's Web site can provide the latest information.

NATIONWIDE CLUBS AND GROUPS

The American Numismatic Association. This is the largest coin-collecting group in the world. The monthly magazine, *The Numismatist*, contains articles submitted by members on a wide array of topics. Additionally, the ANA's library is second to none and is available to all members. Other great benefits are also included as a part of your membership.

American Numismatic Association
818 N. Cascade Ave.
Colorado Springs, CO 80903-3279
Phone: 800-367-9723
Fax: 719-634-4085
E-mail: ana@money.org
Web site: www.money.org

CONECA (Combined Organizations of Numismatic Error Collectors of America). CONECA is a worldwide organization that specializes in the study of errors and varieties. Its bimonthly newsletter, *ErrorScope*, is filled with educational topics. Additionally, CONECA's Web site has a huge listing with descriptions of several thousand repunched mintmarks and doubled dies. And access to that is free to all! Finally, there are also members-only sections with still more for your error and variety education.

CONECA
c/o Rachel Irish
3807 Belmont Rd.
Coeur d'Alene, ID 83815
Web site: www.conecaonline.org

SPECIALIZED CLUBS AND GROUPS

Barber Coin Collectors' Society. Serving collectors of the many U.S. coins designed by Charles Barber, chief engraver of the Mint from 1879 to 1917, this group offers myriad resources for the interested numismatist. It publishes the *Journal of the Barber Coin Collectors' Society* on a quarterly basis. A membership application is available via its Web site.

> Dave Earp
> BCCS Membership
> P.O. Box 1723
> Decatur, IL 62525

Early American Coppers. Founded in 1967, this not-for-profit numismatic organization serves as a point of contact for collectors of early U.S. copper coins, including colonial issues and Hard Times tokens in addition to U.S. half cents and large cents. The group's publication, *Penny-Wise*, is renowned as a great source of information. A membership application is available via its Web site.

> EAC
> P.O. Box 2462
> Heath, OH 43056
> Web site: www.eacs.org

Fly-In Club. This specialty group, formed in 1991, is for collectors of Flying Eagle and Indian Head small cents. *Longacre's Ledger* is the group's award-winning publication. A membership application is available via its Web site.

> Fly-In Club
> P.O. Box 559
> Sandwich, IL 60548
> Web site: www.fly-inclub.org

John Reich Collectors Society. The purpose of the John Reich Collectors Society is to encourage the study of numismatics, particularly United States gold and silver coins minted before the introduction of the Liberty Seated design, and to provide technical and educational information concerning such coins. JRCS has a great newsletter and conducts meetings at various times throughout the year.

> John Reich Collectors Society
> Attn: Stephen A. Crain
> P.O. Box 1680
> Windham, ME 04062
> Web site: http://logan.com/jrcs

Liberty Seated Collectors Club. LSCC is one of the strongest groups dedicated to any coin design or series. LSCC members receive the quarterly *Gobrecht Journal*, which is filled with some of the most educational numismatic articles available anywhere.

> LSCC
> Dennis Fortier
> LSCC New Member Dues
> P.O. Box 1841
> Pawtucket, RI 02862
> Web site: www.lsccweb.org

Lincoln Cent Forum. An active online community for Lincoln cent collectors to discuss America's smallest circulating denomination, this forum also provides various resources for Lincoln cent collectors, including detailed explanation of the series and various aspects of the design, a glossary, and tips on coin photography. Creating an account is free.

> Web site: www.lincolncentforum.com

Shield Nickels. This is another excellent online group, this one for enthusiasts of Shield nickels. Like many of the others, the discussion groups are filled with excellent information. There is no better discussion group available for the variety enthusiast. And best of all, you can join free!

> Web site: groups.yahoo.com/group/
> Shield_Nickels

Notes

The History of Coins in America, 1607 to Date

1. Decades ago James F. Kelly, a leading Ohio dealer, demonstrated this to the editor. On June 24, 1922, Sanford Saltus, a well-to-do numismatist and benefactor of the American Numismatic Society, died while using cyanide to clean ancient silver coins (widely reported at the time).

2. Narrative by Q. David Bowers. Certain information and text provided by Kenneth E. Bressett, Dennis Tucker, Christopher McDowell, Ray Williams, and the late Dr. Richard Doty was particularly valuable in the compilation and editing of this narrative.

3. An example is provided by the ledgers of Henry Rust, who operated a general store in Wolfeboro, New Hampshire, and took in goods as pay as late as the 1840s.

4. *American Journal of Numismatics*, April 1874.

5. Per a comment from Edward D. Cogan in the *American Journal of Numismatics*, March 1868. Cogan had no firsthand knowledge of the activities of the Mint in the 1820s and 1830s, for he did not become involved in numismatics until the late 1850s.

6. The $285 figure is from R.W. Julian (letter, December 27, 1998); another source states $290. No doubt exchange rates varied from city to city and from broker to broker.

7. Certain commemorative information is adapted from the editor's "Joys of Collecting" column in *Coin World*.

8. Extensive details of all commemorative prices in 1989 and 1990 can be found in *Commemorative Coins of the United States: A Complete Encyclopedia*, Q. David Bowers, 1993.

9. As of August 2018 PCGS had certified 102 and NGC 43. Including resubmissions likely nets to about 100 different.

10. The 1976 convention in New York City was posted at over 20,000, but examination revealed that some attendees were counted twice (information from Edward C. Rochette).

11. Clifford Mishler stated he came up with a similar estimate years ago when he reviewed this comment (letter to the editor, August 30, 2018).

12. The PCGS Population Report of August 29, 2018, listed one coin, the same as years ago, but 93 in PF-69 DC and 273 in PF-68 DC.

13. An example is the story, "Limited Supply—How to Sell Coins and Frustrate People," by Tom DeLorey, *COINage*, May 2005.

14. *Coin World*, April 4, 2015.

15. Editorial in *Numismatic News*, April 26, 2005, and many other articles of the era.

16. David C. Harper editorial in *Numismatic News*, August 16, 2005; lengthy letter from collector R. Mittelbach, *Coin World*.

17. Details were given by Debbie Bradley in "Poor Quality Coin Designs Lamented," *Numismatic News*, June 3, 2010.

18. Ibid.

19. Partly adapted from Steve Roach, "Stickers and Plus Signs—Markets Multiply, Heads Spin," *Coin World*, July 12, 2010.

20. 2011 Annual Report to the Congress on the Presidential $1 Coin Program.

21. Paul Gilkes, *Coin World*, December 12, 2011.

22. Written by Clifford Mishler and Q. David Bowers at the request of the ANA.

23. Reports by Harry Miller in *Numismatic News*, September 13, 2011, and November 28, 2011.

24. The extensively detailed scenario was given by William T. Gibbs and Paul Gilkes in *Coin World*, August 25, 2014. When the ANA was asked if it would publish this information in *The Numismatist* or censure the arrangement, the "unofficial" comment was that the names were "too big" to criticize.

25. Connor Falk provided details in *Numismatic News*, October 14, 2014.

26. Proofs struck at the West Point Mint were offered in September 2018, in limited quantity. The offering was sold out in a matter of just a few minutes, to the disappointment of many loyal Mint customers who received "sold out" notices.

Quarter Dollars

1. This had been compiled by J. Colvin Randall of Philadelphia and was either bought by Haseltine, who assumed ownership, or was plagiarized. Randall received no credit. Randall also created a manuscript on early gold coin varieties, but it was never published and is lost today.

2. This and selected other comments for early quarters are used or adapted from text mostly created by John Kraljevich for use in the Stack's Bowers Galleries sales of the D. Brent Pogue Collection.

3. Another account has the amount as $14,371.

4. Certain information about the deliveries is from R. W. Julian, "1815 Quarter, First of the Capped Bust Series," *Coins Magazine*, December 2013.

5. *American Journal of Numismatics*, October 1875; 1806 date of an unattributed newspaper clipping from the scrapbook of J. J. Mickley.

6. Interestingly, most Mint engravers were also associated in one way or another with bank-note engraving. Robert Scot furnished testimonials and may have engraved plates (none have been seen by the author). John Reich in 1810 worked on the side with Murray & Draper. Before coming to the Mint, William Kneass engraved and signed bank notes. Christian Gobrecht engraved notes (no signed vignettes have been seen by the author, however). James B. Longacre was a principal of Draper, Toppan, Longacre & Co., one of the leading bank-note companies of the 1830s.

7. *American Journal of Numismatics*, vol. 18–19, July 1883.

8. Karl Moulton (in a communication to Q. David Bowers, August 31, 1996), noted that the four thousand 1827 quarters listed for the calendar year 1827 are probably the 1828 B-3.

9. A very lengthy account of the fraud was later published in the issue of September 27, 1834, and includes more details.

10. From an exchange item in the *Newark Daily Advertiser* on November 11, 1835; this notice was widely published.

11. The complete Friesner catalog is available online at the Newman Numismatic Portal, Washington University (https://nnp.wustl.edu/).

12. Greg Johnson, communication, May 10, 2015; Larry Briggs, communication, May 19, 2015.

13. Details in Bowers, *American Coin Treasures and Hoards* (1987) and *Lost and Found Coin Hoards and Treasures* (2015).

14. Larry Briggs, communication, May 19, 2015.

15. Greg Johnson, communication, May 10, 2015.

16. Larry Briggs, communication, May 19, 2015.

17. Ibid.

18. Modern comment by Mark Borckardt, June 2, 2015. Also see P. Scott Rubin, "Three Rare Quarters," *The Gobrecht Journal*, April 1975; and Eliasberg sale catalog, 1997, lot 1428 for registry.

19. Ibid.

20. Rich Uhrich, communication, May 7. 2015.

21. John W. McCloskey, "The 1847-O Quarter," *The Gobrecht Journal*, November 1981.

22. Greg Johnson, communication, May 10, 2015.

23. Larry Briggs, communication, May 19, 2015.

24. Communication, May 19, 2015.

25. Also see John W. McCloskey, "The 1849-O Quarter,"*The Gobrecht Journal*, March 1980. The present author notes that the issue is a key date and is very seldom offered for sale either at auction or in coin shows.

26. Population reports may exaggerate the number known.

27. Larry Briggs, communication, May 19, 2015.

28. Ibid.

29. Greg Johnson, communication, May 10, 2015.

30. Ibid.

31. From Tom DeLorey, communication, May 14, 2015: "I have a theory that the Mint may have backdated an 1854 die in order to pair it with a now-obsolete Without Rays reverse die that would otherwise have to be discarded. This may have happened in early 1853, if indeed it happened."

32. John W. McCloskey, "An 1853-O Arrows Quarter with Circular Die Defects," *The Gobrecht Journal*, November 1982; the nature of lathe marks was not known at the time. Since then they have been seen on other coins in various denominations.

33. Larry Briggs, communication, May 19, 2015.

34. Communication, May 31, 2015.

35. Larry Briggs, communication, May 19, 2015.

36. Ibid.

37. John W. McCloskey, "A Rarity Study for Early San Francisco Quarters 1855-S to 1862-S," *The Gobrecht Journal*, July 2014.

38. Larry Briggs, communication, May 19, 2015.

39. Population reports may exaggerate the number known.

40. Larry Briggs, communication, May 19, 2015.

41. Of interest may be an article by James C. Gray, "The 1860-S Quarter, the Most Underrated Seated Coin," *The Gobrecht Journal*, November 1990, and another by John W. McCloskey, "A Rarity Study for Early San Francisco Quarters 1855-S to 1862-S," *The Gobrecht Journal*, July 2014.

42. Larry Briggs, communication, May 19, 2015.

43. Communication, May 19, 2015.

44. Larry Briggs, communication, May 19, 2015.

45. For further reading: Larry Briggs in *The Gobrecht Journal*, November 1983, "Die Characteristics of the 1870-CC Quarter," which illustrated die-finish lines and gave other technical information. Also see "The Underpriced 1870-CC Quarter," by Bob Foster, in the March 1983 edition of the same periodical. He notes that this is "one of the most underrated and underpriced coins in the Liberty Seated quarter series."

46. Sold by Heritage Auctions in August 2001 for $276,000; resold by Heritage in August 2013 for $176,250.

47. Larry Briggs, communication, May 19, 2015.

48. If you are interested in technical aspects of this series you would do well to examine the motto IN GOD WE TRUST on various issues of this era, to determine common use of reverse dies. Here, more than in any other area, there are numerous die-finish lines, strengthenings, repunchings, etc. Also, the depth at which the motto and ribbon are impressed into the die varies, with some dies showing parts of the ribbon missing, particularly in the distant fold near the left side. Die studies in *The Gobrecht Journal* are very helpful.

49. Larry Briggs, communication, May 12, 2015.

50. Ibid.

51. Larry Briggs, communication, May 19, 2015.

52. Ibid.

53. Population reports may exaggerate the number known.

54. Ibid.

55. Larry Briggs, communication, May 31, 2015.

56. Andy Lustig, communication, May 27, 2015.

57. Larry Briggs, communication, May 19, 2015.

58. Greg Johnson, communication, May 10, 2015.

59. Certain information is from R. W. Julian, "A Cut Above the Rest," *Coins* magazine, December 1998; other information is from Mint correspondence and contemporary published accounts.

60. From *Aesop's Fables*.

61. *Liberty Enlightening the World*, a.k.a. the Statue of Liberty, dedicated in 1886.

62. Although the World's Columbian Exposition was scheduled to open in 1892, construction delays occurred, and it did not open to the public until the spring of 1893.

63. *Numismatic Art in America: Aesthetics of the United States Coinage.*

64. *Boston Herald*, January 5, 1892, with January 4 dispatch from Washington.

65. R.W. Julian, "Barber Design Reigned on Quarters for 25 Years," *Journal of the BCCS*, 2010 (no. 4), adapted from his article in *Numismatic News*, September 20, 2005.

66. For a detailed discussion see Steve Hustad, "Barber Quarter Design Varieties," *Journal of the BCCS*, 2011 (no. 4).

67. These differences were first described in detail by George W. Rice in "United States Quarter Dollar of 1892," *The Numismatist*, May 1899.

68. John Frost, letter, January 28, 2015.

69. Ibid.

70. Letter, January 28, 2015. His comment demonstrates the wisdom of not relying on grades marked on holders.

71. Discovery reported by John A. Wexler, "Major Barber Quarter Doubled Die Discovered," *Journal of the BCCS*, Fall 1997.

72. From research by David W. Lange.

73. John Frost, letter, January 28, 2015.

74. The BCCS website, www.barbercoins.org, has the diagnostics of the dies used to strike the 1901-S quarter.

75. Letter, January 28, 2015.

76. John Frost, letter, January 28, 2015.

77. Ibid.

78. Details on authenticating the 1913-S Barber quarter can be found on the BCCS website, www.barbercoins. org.

79. Mint State Barber coins by the roll are hardly ever seen. Stacks sale of August 10, 1990, has an original roll of 40 1916-D quarters.

80. Roger W. Burdette's *Renaissance of American Coinage 1916–1921* (pp. 14–31) gives correspondence and extensive details and is recommended as a source for additional information.

81. Booker T. Washington is said to have suggested the theme of the film. It was a counter to D.W. Griffith's racist *The Birth of a Nation*, 1915, and endeavored to show the equality of various races.

82. For details see the author's 2015 Whitman *Guide Book* on the 1916 coinage.

83. Sent to the author on March 20, 2007, as a contribution to educate coin buyers beyond "conventional wisdom" and grading-service labels.

84. Figures from NGC and PCGS population reports of July 2018. There have been some increases since then, but the proportions remain close to the same.

85. Merkin, an accomplished clarinetist, entered professional numismatics in 1958.

86. NGC and PCGS figures are closer on this than on any other quarter of the type.

87. Act of September 26, 1890, sec. 3510.

88. The three medals mentioned in this paragraph are critiqued by Cornelius Vermeule in *Numismatic Art in America*, pp. 124 and 125.

89. One of the great controversies in scientific circles in the early 20th century was the Smithsonian's strong endorsement of Langley as the inventor of powered flight; he was said to have preceded the accomplishments of the Wright brothers. This stance was finally dropped.

90. Years later, in 1975, quarters dated 1776–1976 (or, more literally, "1776 • 1976"—with a bullet) were prestruck at the Philadelphia, Denver, and San Francisco mints.

91. Comments to the author, December 19, 2005.

92. Communication to the author, December 14, 2005.

93. David W. Lange, "The 1937-S Washington Quarter," *USA Coin Album*, July 2002.

94. *Coin World*, November 14, 2005.

95. David W. Lange, "The 'Anonymous' Coins of 1965–67," *USA Coin Album*, November 2002.

96. Ibid.

97. For detailed information on coin-market price cycles see Bowers, *The Expert's Guide to Collecting and Investing In Rare Coins*, 2005. Few if any of these investment peaks and valleys surprised long-time *numismatists*. 92. David W. Lange, *The Complete Guide to Mercury Dimes* (second ed., 2005).

Glossary

Over the years coin collectors have developed a special jargon to describe their coins. The following list includes terms that are used frequently by coin collectors or that have a special meaning other than their ordinary dictionary definitions. You will find them useful when you want to discuss or describe your coins.

alloy—A combination of two or more metals.

altered date—A false date on a coin; a date altered to make a coin appear to be one of a rarer or more valuable issue.

bag mark—A surface mark, usually a small nick, acquired by a coin through contact with others in a mint bag.

billon—A low-grade alloy of silver (usually less than 50%) mixed with another metal, typically copper.

blank—The formed piece of metal on which a coin design will be stamped.

bronze—An alloy of copper, zinc, and tin.

bullion—Uncoined gold or silver in the form of bars, ingots, or plate.

cast coins—Coins that are made by pouring molten metal into a mold, instead of in the usual manner of striking blanks with dies.

cent—One one-hundredth of the standard monetary unit. Also known as a *centavo*, *centimo*, or *centesimo* in some Central American and South American countries; *centime* in France and various former colonies in Africa; and other variations.

certified coin—A coin that has been graded, authenticated, and encapsulated in plastic by an independent (neither buyer nor seller) grading service.

cherrypicker—A collector who finds scarce and unusual coins by carefully searching through unattributed items in old accumulations or dealers' stocks.

circulation strike—An Uncirculated coin intended for eventual use in commerce, as opposed to a Proof coin.

clad coinage—Issues of the United States dimes, quarters, halves, and some dollars made since 1965. Each coin has a center core of pure copper and a layer of copper-nickel or silver on both sides.

collar—The outer ring, or die chamber, that holds a blank in place in the coinage press while the coin is impressed by the obverse and reverse dies.

contact marks—Minor abrasions on an Uncirculated coin, made by contact with other coins in a bag or roll.

countermark—A stamp or mark impressed on a coin to verify its use by another government or to indicate revaluation.

crack-out—A coin that has been removed from a grading service holder.

crown—Any dollar-size coin (c. 38 mm in diameter) in general, often struck in silver; specifically, one from the United Kingdom and some Commonwealth countries.

cud—An area of raised metal at the rim of a coin where a portion of the die broke off, leaving a void in the design.

designer—The artist who creates a coin's design. An engraver is the person who cuts a design into a coinage die.

die—A piece of metal, usually hardened steel, with an incuse reverse image, engraved with a design and used for stamping coins.

die crack—A fine, raised line on a coin, caused by a broken die.

die defect—An imperfection on a coin, caused by a damaged die.

die variety—Any minor alteration in the basic design of a coin.

dipped, dipping—Refers to chemical cleaning of a coin to remove oxidation or foreign matter.

double eagle—The United States twenty-dollar gold coin.

doubled die—A die that has been given two misaligned impressions from a hub; also, a coin made from such a die.

doubloon—Popular name for a Spanish gold coin originally valued at $16.

eagle—A United States ten-dollar gold coin; also refers to U.S. silver, gold, and platinum bullion pieces made from 1986 to the present.

edge—Periphery of a coin, often with reeding, lettering, or other decoration.

electrotype—A reproduction of a coin or medal made by the electrodeposition process. Electrotypes are frequently used in museum displays.

electrum—A naturally occurring mixture of gold and silver. Some of the world's first coins were made of this alloy.

encapsulated coins—Coins that have been authenticated, graded, and sealed in plastic by a professional service.

engrailed edge—A coin edge marked with small curved notches.

engraver—The person who engraves or sculpts a model for use in translating to a coin die.

error—A mismade coin not intended for circulation.

exergue—That portion of a coin beneath the main design, often separated from it by a line, and typically bearing the date.

field—The background portion of a coin's surface not used for a design or inscription.

filler—A coin in worn condition but rare enough to be included in a collection.

fineness—The purity of gold, silver, or any other precious metal, expressed in terms of one thousand parts. A coin of 90% pure silver is expressed as .900 fine.

flan—A blank piece of metal in the size and shape of a coin; also called a *planchet*.

gem—A coin of exceptionally high quality, typically considered MS-65 or PF-65 or better.

gripped edge—An edge with irregularly spaced notches.

half eagle—The United States five-dollar gold coin minted from 1795 to 1929.

hub—A positive-image punch to impress the coin's design into a die for coinage.

incuse—The design of a coin that has been impressed below the coin's surface. A design raised above the coin's surface is in relief.

inscription—The legend or lettering on a coin.

intrinsic value—Bullion or "melt" value of the actual precious metal in a numismatic item.

investment grade—Promotional term; generally, a coin in grade MS-65 or better.

junk silver—Common-date silver coins taken from circulation; worth only bullion value.

key coin—One of the scarcer or more valuable coins in a series.

laureate—Head crowned with a laurel wreath.

legal tender—Money that is officially issued and recognized for redemption by an authorized agency or government.

legend—A principal inscription on a coin.

lettered edge—The edge of a coin bearing an inscription, found on some foreign and some older United States coins, modern Presidential dollars, and the MMIX Ultra High Relief gold coin.

luster—The brilliant or "frosty" surface quality of an Uncirculated (Mint State) coin.

milled edge—The raised rim around the outer surface of a coin, not to be confused with the reeded or serrated narrow edge of a coin.

mint error—Any mismade or defective coin produced by a mint.

mint luster—Shiny "frost" or brilliance on the surface of an Uncirculated or Mint State coin.

mintmark—A small letter or other mark on a coin, indicating the mint at which it was struck.

Mint set—A set of Uncirculated coins packaged and sold by the Mint. Each set contains one of each of the coins made for circulation at each of the mints that year.

motto—An inspirational word or phrase used on a coin.

mule—A coin struck from two dies not originally intended to be used together.

obverse—The front or face side of a coin.

overdate—Date made by superimposing one or more numerals on a previously dated die.

overgraded—A coin in poorer condition than stated.

overstrike—An impression made with new dies on a previously struck coin.

patina—The green or brown surface film found on ancient copper and bronze coins, caused by oxidation over a long period of time.

pattern—Experimental or trial coin, generally of a new design, denomination, or metal.

pedigree—The record of previous owners of a rare coin.

planchet—The blank piece of metal on which a coin design is stamped.

Proof—Coins struck for collectors by the Mint using specially polished dies and planchets.

Proof set—A set of each of the Proof coins made during a given year, packaged by the Mint and sold to collectors.

quarter eagle—The United States $2.50 gold coin.

raw—A coin that has not been encapsulated by an independent grading service.

reeded edge—The edge of a coin with grooved lines that run vertically around its perimeter, as seen on modern United States silver and clad coins.

regula—The bar separating the numerator and the denominator in a fraction.

relief—Any part of a coin's design that is raised above the coin's field is said to be in relief. The opposite of relief is incuse, meaning sunk into the field.

restrike—A coin struck from genuine dies at a later date than the original issue.

reverse—The back side of a coin.

rim—The raised portion of a coin that protects the design from wear.

round—A round one-ounce silver medal or bullion piece.

series—A set of one coin of each year of a specific design and denomination issued from each mint. For example, Lincoln cents from 1909 to 1959.

slab—A hard plastic case containing a coin that has been graded and encapsulated by a professional service.

spot price—The daily quoted market value of precious metals in bullion form.

token—A privately issued piece, typically with an exchange value for goods or services, but not an official government coin.

trade dollar—Silver dollar issued especially for trade with a foreign country. In the United States, trade dollars were first issued in 1873 to stimulate commerce with the Orient. Many other countries have also issued trade dollars.

truncation—The sharply cut-off bottom edge of a bust or portrait.

type—A series of coins defined by a shared distinguishing design, composition, denomination, and other elements. For example, Barber dimes or Franklin half dollars.

type set—A collection consisting of one representative coin of each type, of a particular series or period.

Uncirculated—A circulation-strike coin that has never been used in commerce, and has retained its original surface and luster; also called Mint State.

unique—An item of which only one specimen is known to exist.

variety—A coin's design that sets it apart from the normal issue of that type.

wheaties—Lincoln cents with the wheat ears reverse, issued from 1909 to 1958.

year set—A set of coins for any given year, consisting of one of each denomination issued that year.

Bibliography

A note from Q. David Bowers on the bibliography:

From the time that the first numismatically important book was published in America by Joseph B. Felt in 1839 to the present day, books have been the key to knowledge. A basic library of useful volumes is essential to the collecting and enjoyment of coins.

The following list includes the most important titles published over a long period of years. "Standard References" are ones that are essential today and include many updates of past writing and research. "References of Historical Interest" include titles from the past that for the most part have been made obsolete by later writing and research. Some of these remain valuable as a window into the state of the art years ago: they often contain anecdotal and narrative text not included in later works. Quality, usefulness, and desirability can vary widely, so before spending a large sum it is advisable to seek further information.

Beyond this listing, auction catalogs and price lists issued by various firms contain much interesting and valuable information. Countless articles in numismatic publications are valuable. The Numismatic Bibliomania Society (www.coinbooks.org) is the key to information on publications of the past and present. The Newman Numismatic Portal (www.nnp.wustl.edu) offers thousands of auction catalogs, magazine issues, and books free of charge; an incredible treasury for research and enjoyment.

The Whitman Publishing Web site (www.whitman.com) offers publications on coins, tokens, medals, and paper money currently available for purchase.

COLONIAL AND STATE COINAGE

STANDARD REFERENCES:

Bowers, Q. David. *Whitman Encyclopedia of Colonial and Early American Coins.* Second edition. Pelham, AL: 2019.

Breen, Walter. *Walter Breen's Complete Encyclopedia of U.S. and Colonial Coins.* New York, NY: 1988.

Carlotto, Tony. *The Copper Coins of Vermont.* Chelsea, MI: 1998.

Crosby, S.S. *The Early Coins of America.* Boston, MA: 1875 (reprinted 1945, 1965, 1974, 1983).

Demling, Michael. *New Jersey Coppers.* 2011.

Maris, Edward. *A Historic Sketch of the Coins of New Jersey.* Philadelphia, PA: 1881 (reprinted 1965, 1974, 1987).

Martin, Sydney F. *The Hibernia Coinage of William Wood (1722–1724).* n.p., 2007.

——— *The Rosa Americana Coinage of William Wood.* Ann Arbor, MI: 2011.

——— *French Coinage Specifically for Colonial America.* Ann Arbor, MI: Colonial Coin Collectors Club, 2015.

McDowell, Christopher. *Abel Buell and the History of the Connecticut and Fugio Coppers.* Ann Arbor, MI: 2015.

Miller, Henry C., and Hillyer C. Ryder. *The State Coinages of New England.* New York, NY: 1920.

Musante, Neil. *Medallic Washington* (2 vols.). London and Boston, MA: 2016.

Newman, Eric P. *Coinage for Colonial Virginia.* New York, NY: 1956.

——— *The United States Fugio Copper Coinage of 1787.* Ypsilanti, MI: 2007.

Newman, Eric P., and Richard G. Doty. *Studies on Money in Early America*. New York, NY: 1976.

Nipper, Will. *In Yankee Doodle's Pocket: The Myth, Magic, and Politics of Early America*. Conway, AR: 2008.

Noe, Sydney P. *The New England and Willow Tree Coinage of Massachusetts*. New York, NY: 1943.

—— *The Oak Tree Coinage of Massachusetts*. New York, NY: 1947.

—— *The Pine Tree Coinage of Massachusetts*. New York, NY: 1952.

—— *The Silver Coins of Massachusetts (Combined Reprint)*. New York, NY: 1973.

Rulau, Russell, and George Fuld. *Medallic Portraits of Washington*. Iola, WI: 1999.

Salmon, Christopher J. *The Silver Coins of Massachusetts*. New York, NY: 2010.

Siboni, Roger; John Howes; and A. Buell Ish. *New Jersey State Coppers. History. Description. Collecting*. New York, NY: 2013.

REFERENCES OF HISTORICAL INTEREST:

Anton, William T., Jr., and Bruce Kesse. *The Forgotten Coins of the North American Colonies*. Published by William T. Anton: 1990.

Atkins, James. *Coins and Tokens of the Possessions and Colonies of the British Empire*. London: 1889.

Baker, W.S. *American Engravers and Their Works*. Philadelphia, PA: 1875.

—— *The Engraved Portraits of Washington*. Philadelphia, PA: Lindsay & Baker, 1880.

—— *Medallic Portraits of Washington*. Philadelphia, PA: Robert M. Lindsay, 1885. An annotated reprint with updated information was prepared by George J. Fuld in 1965 and issued by Krause Publications.

Betts, C. Wyllys. *Counterfeit Half Pence Current in the American Colonies and Their Issue from the Mints of Connecticut and Vermont*. New York, NY: American Numismatic and Archaeological Society, 1886. Transcript of speech given to the Society.

Bressett, Kenneth E. "The Vermont Copper Coinage," part of *Studies on Money in Early America*. New York, NY: 1976.

Dalton, R., and S.H. Hamer. *English Provincial Token Coinage of the 18th Century*. London: 1910–1922. Issued in parts.

Douglas, Damon G. Manuscript notes on James Jarvis and Fugio coppers. Notes on New Jersey coppers. Excerpts published in *The Colonial Newsletter* and elsewhere. Loose copies made.

Felt, Joseph B. *An Historical Account of Massachusetts Currency*. Boston, MA: 1839.

Freidus, Daniel. "The History and Die Varieties of the Higley Coppers." *The Token: America's Other Money*. Coinage of the Americas Conference, 1994; New York, NY: 1995.

Guth, Ronald J. "The Copper Coinage of Vermont," *America's Copper Coinage 1783–1857*. Coinage of the Americas Conference, 1984; New York, NY: 1985.

Hull, John. "The Diaries of John Hull, Mint-Master and Treasurer of the Colony of Massachusetts Bay." *Archæologica Americana: Transactions and Collections of the American Antiquarian Society*. Vol. III. Cambridge, MA: 1850.

Jordan, Louis E., Robert H. Gore Jr., Numismatic Endowment, University of Notre Dame, Department of Special Collections, Website compiled maintained by Louis E. Jordan. Anthology of published information on various series.

Kenney, Richard D. *Struck Copies of Early American Coins*. New York, NY: 1952.

—— *Early American Medalists and Die-Sinkers Prior to the Civil War*. New York, NY: 1954.

Kessler, Alan. *The Fugio Cents*. Newtonville, MA: 1976.

Maris, Edward. *A Historical Sketch of the Coins of New Jersey*. Philadelphia, PA: 1881.

Mossman, Philip L. *Money of the American Colonies and Confederation: A Numismatic, Economic & Historical Correlation*. New York, NY: 1993.

—— "The American Confederation: The Times and Its Money." *Coinage of the American Confederation Period*. New York, NY: 1996.

—— *From Crime to Punishment: Counterfeit and Debased Currencies in Colonial and Pre-Federal America*. American Numismatic Society, 2013.

Musante, Neil E. *The Medallic Works of John Adams Bolen, Die Sinker &c.* Springfield, MA: 2002.

Nelson, Philip. *The Coinage of William Wood, 1722–1733*. London: 1959. Reprint.

Peck, C. Wilson. *English Copper, Tin and Bronze Coins in the British Museum 1558–1958*. London: 1960.

Prattent, Thomas, and M. Denton. *The Virtuoso's Companion and Coin Collector's Guide*. 8 volumes. London: 1795–1797.

Richardson, John M. "The Copper Coins of Vermont," published in *The Numismatist*: May 1947.

Ryder, Hillyer C. "The Colonial Coins of Vermont." Part of *State Coinages of New England*. New York, NY: 1920.

Slafter, Edmund F. "The Vermont Coinage." Essay in *Proceedings of the Vermont Historical Society*. Volume 1. Montpelier, VT: 1870.

Smith, Pete. "Vermont Coppers: *Coinage of an Independent Republic.*" *Coinage of the American Confederation Period*. New York, NY: 1996.

Snelling, T. *A View of the Silver Coin and Coinage of England, From the Norman Conquest to the Present Time, Considered with Regard to Type, Legend, Sorts, Rarity, Weight, Fineness and Value, with Copper-Plates.* London: 1762.

Vlack, Robert A. *A. Catalog of Early American Coins.* Anaheim, CA: 1963.

—— *Early American Coins.* Johnson City, NY: Windsor Research Publications, Inc., 1965.

Williams, Malcolm E., Peter T. Sousa, and Edward C. Harris. *Coins of Bermuda 1616–1996.* Hamilton, Bermuda: 1997.

Wroth, Lawrence C. *Abel Buell of Connecticut: Silversmith, Type Founder & Engraver.* Middletown, CT: Acorn Club of Connecticut,1958.

HALF CENTS

STANDARD REFERENCES:

Bowers, Q. David. *A Guide Book of Half Cents and Large Cents.* Atlanta, GA: 2015.

Breen, Walter. *Walter Breen's Encyclopedia of United States Half Cents 1793–1857.* South Gate, CA: 1983.

Cohen, Roger S., Jr. *American Half Cents–The "Little Half Sisters."* Second edition. 1982.

Manley, Ronald P. *The Half Cent Die State Book, 1793–1857.* United States, 1998.

REFERENCES OF HISTORICAL INTEREST:

Frossard, Ed. *Monograph of United States Cents and Half Cents Issued Between the Years 1793 and 1857.* Irvington-on-Hudson, NY: 1879.

Gilbert, Ebenezer. *The United States Half Cents from the First Year of Issue, in 1793, to the Year When Discontinued.* New York, NY: 1916.

LARGE CENTS

STANDARD REFERENCES:

Bowers, Q. David. *A Guide Book of Half Cents and Large Cents.* Atlanta, GA: 2015.

Breen, Walter. *Walter Breen's Encyclopedia of Early United States Cents 1793–1814.* Wolfeboro, NH: 2001.

Grellman, J.R., Jr. *The Die Varieties of United States Large Cents 1840–1857.* Lake Mary, FL: 1991.

—— *Attribution Guide for United States Large Cents 1840–1857.* Third edition. Bloomington, MN: 2002.

Neiswinter, Jim. *The Aristocrat: The Story of the 1793 Sheldon 1.* Printed by the author, 2013.

Newcomb, H.R. *United States Copper Cents 1816–1857,* New York, NY: 1944 (reprinted 1983).

Noyes, William C. *United States Large Cents, 1793–1857.* Six volumes. Ypsilanti, MI: 2006–2015.

—— *United States Large Cents 1793–1814.* Bloomington, MN: 1991.

—— *United States Large Cents 1816–1839.* Bloomington, MN: 1991.

Penny-Wise, official publication of Early American Coppers, Inc.

Sheldon, William H. *Penny Whimsy (1793–1814),* New York, NY: 1958 (reprinted 1965, 1976).

Smith, Pete. *The Story of the Starred Reverse Cent.* Minneapolis, MN: Printed by the author.

Wright, John D. *The Cent Book 1816–1839.* Bloomington, MN: 1992.

REFERENCES OF HISTORICAL INTEREST:

Adams, John W. (editor). *Monographs on Varieties of United States Large Cents, 1793–1794.* Lawrence, MA: 1976.

Chapman, S. Hudson. *The United States Cents of the Year 1794.* Second edition. Philadelphia, PA: 1926.

Clapp, George H. *The United States Cents of the Years 1798–1799.* Sewickley, PA: 1931.

—— *The United States Cents 1804–1814.* The Coin Collector Series Number Eight. New York, NY: 1941.

Clapp, George H., and Howard R. Newcomb. *The United States Cents of the Year 1795, 1796, 1797 and 1800.* New York, NY: The American Numismatic Society, 1947.

Crosby, Sylvester S. *The United States Coinage of 1793——Cents and Half Cents.* Boston, MA: 1897.

Frossard, Ed. *Monograph of United States Cents and Half Cents Issued Between the Years 1793 and 1857.* Irvington-on-Hudson, NY: 1879.

Frossard, Ed., and W.W. Hays. *Varieties of United States Cents of the Year 1794: Described and Illustrated.* New York, NY: 1893.

Lapp, Warren A., and Herbert A. Silberman (editors). *United States Large Cents 1793–1857.* Lawrence, MA: 1975.

Loring, Denis W. (editor). *Monographs on Varieties of United States Large Cents, 1795–1803.* Lawrence, MA: 1976.

Maris, Edward. *Varieties of the Copper Issues of the United States Mint in the Year 1794.* Philadelphia, PA: 1869 and 1870.

McGirk, Charles E. "United States Cents and Die Varieties, 1793–1857," *The Numismatist,* October 1913 to December 1914.

Noyes, William C., Del Bland, and Dan Demeo. *The Official Condition Census for U.S. Large Cents 1793–1839.* 2005.

Sheldon, William H. *Early American Cents.* New York, NY: 1949.

Smith, Pete. *Names with Notes.* Minneapolis, MN: 1992.

SMALL CENTS
STANDARD REFERENCES:
Bowers, Q. David. *A Guide Book of Lincoln Cents.* Second edition. Atlanta, GA: 2016.

Lange, David W. *The Complete Guide to Lincoln Cents.* Wolfeboro, NH: 1996.

Schein, Allan. *The Gold Indians of Bela Lyon Pratt.* Published by the author, 2016.

Snow, Richard. *A Guide Book of Flying Eagle and Indian Head Cents.* Third edition. Atlanta, GA: 2016.

REFERENCES OF HISTORICAL INTEREST:
Anderson, Shane M. *The Complete Lincoln Cent Encyclopedia.* Iola, WI: 1996.

Bowers, Q. David. *A Buyer's and Enthusiast's Guide to Flying Eagle and Indian Cents.* Wolfeboro, NH: 1996.

Daughtrey, Charles D. *Looking Through Lincoln Cents: Chronology of a Series.* Second edition. Irvine, CA: 2005.

Lange, David W. *The Complete Guide to Lincoln Cents.* Wolfeboro, NH: 1996.

Manley, Stephen G. *The Lincoln Cent.* Muscatine, IA: 1981.

Steve, Larry, and Kevin Flynn, *Flying Eagle and Indian Cent Die Varieties.* Jarrettville, MD: 1995.

Taylor, Sol. *The Standard Guide to the Lincoln Cents.* Fourth Edition. Anaheim, CA: 1999.

Tomaska, Rick Jerry, *Cameo and Brilliant Proof Coinage of the 1950 to 1970 Era.* Encinitas, CA: 1991.

Wexler, John and Kevin Flynn. *The Authoritative Reference on Lincoln Cents.* Rancocas, NJ: 1996.

TWO-CENT PIECES AND THREE CENT PIECES
Bierly, William. In God We Trust. Pelham, AL: 2019.

Bowers, Q. David. *United States Three-Cent and Five-Cent Pieces.* Wolfeboro, NH: 2005.

Kliman, Myron. *The Two Cent Piece and Varieties.* South Laguna, CA: 1977.

Leone, Frank. *Longacre's Two Cent Piece Die Varieties & Errors.* College Point, NY: 1991.

NICKEL FIVE-CENT PIECES
STANDARD REFERENCES:
Bowers, Q. David. *United States Three-Cent and Five-Cent Pieces.* Wolfeboro, NH: 2005.

—— *A Guide Book of Buffalo and Jefferson Nickels.* Atlanta, GA: 2007.

—— *A Guide Book of Shield and Liberty Head Nickels.* Atlanta, GA: 2006.

Fletcher, Edward L., Jr. *The Shield Five Cent Series.* Ormond Beach, FL: 1994.

Flynn, Kevin, and Bill Van Note. *Treasure Hunting Liberty Head Nickels.* Second edition. Brooklyn, NY: 2005.

Lange, David W. *The Complete Guide to Buffalo Nickels.* Virginia Beach, VA: 2006.

Nagengast, Bernard. *The Jefferson Nickel Analyst.* Second edition. Sidney, OH: 1979.

REFERENCES OF HISTORICAL INTEREST:
Montgomery, Paul, Mark Borckardt, and Ray Knight. *Million Dollar Nickels: Mysteries of the Illicit 1913 Liberty Head Nickels Revealed.* Irvine, CA: 2005.

Peters, Gloria, and Cynthia Mahon. *The Complete Guide to Shield and Liberty Head Nickels.* Virginia Beach, VA: 1995.

Spindel, Howard. "The Shield Nickel Viewer." Computerized reference on the series published by Howard Spindel, 2005. Information available at www.shieldnickels.net.

Wescott, Michael. *The United States Nickel Five-Cent Piece: A Date-by-Date Analysis and History.* Wolfeboro, NH: 1991.

Young, Richard G., and Wade J. Wilkin. *Racketeer Nickel and Its Many Mysteries.* Published by the authors, 2004.

HALF DIMES
STANDARD REFERENCES:
Bowers, Q. David. *A Guide Book of Liberty Seated Silver Coins.* Second edition. Pelham, AL: 2019.

Blythe, Al. *The Complete Guide to Liberty Seated Half Dimes.* Virginia Beach, VA: 1992.

Logan, Russell, and John McCloskey. *Federal Half Dimes 1792–1837.* Manchester, MI: 1998.

Smith, Pete, Joel J. Orosz, and Leonard Augsburger. *1792: Birth of a Nation's Coinage.* Dallas, TX: 2017.

REFERENCES OF HISTORICAL INTEREST:
Amato, Jon. *Numismatic Background and Census of 1802 Half Dimes.* Dallas, TX: 2017.

Breen, Walter. *United States Half Dimes: A Supplement.* New York, NY: 1958.

Newlin, H.P. *The Early Half-Dimes of the United States.* Philadelphia, PA: 1883 (reprinted 1933).

Valentine, D.W. *The United States Half Dimes.* New York, NY: 1931 (reprinted 1975).

DIMES AND TWENTY-CENT PIECES
STANDARD REFERENCES:
Bowers, Q. David. *A Guide Book of Barber Silver Coins.* Atlanta, GA: 2015.

—— *A Guide Book of Liberty Seated Silver Coins.* Second edition. Pelham, AL: 2019.

—— *A Guide Book of Mercury Dimes, Standing Liberty Quarters, and Liberty Walking Half Dollars*. Atlanta, GA: 2015.

Brunner, Lane J., and John M. Frost. *Double Dime: The United States Twenty-Cent Piece*. 2014.

Davis, David, Russell Logan, Allen Lovejoy, John McCloskey, and William Subjack. *Early United States Dimes 1796–1837*. Ypsilanti, MI: 1984.

Flynn, Kevin. *The Authoritative Reference on Roosevelt Dimes*. Brooklyn, NY: 2001.

—— *The Authoritative Reference on Twenty Cent.*, Lumberton, NJ: 2013.

Fortin, Gerry. *Liberty Seated Dimes Web-Book*. www.seateddimevarieties.com.

Greer, Brian. *The Complete Guide to Liberty Seated Dimes*. Virginia Beach, VA: 2005.

Lange, David W. *The Complete Guide to Mercury Dimes*. Second edition. Virginia Beach, VA: 2005.

Lawrence, David. *The Complete Guide to Barber Dimes*. Virginia Beach, VA: 1991.

REFERENCES OF HISTORICAL INTEREST:
Ahwash, Kamal M. *Encyclopedia of United States Liberty Seated Dimes 1837–1891*. Kamal Press, 1977.

Lawrence, David. *The Complete Guide to Barber Dimes*. Virginia Beach, VA: 1991.

Wexler, John A., and Kevin Flynn. *Treasure Hunting Mercury Dimes*. Savannah, GA: 1999.

QUARTER DOLLARS
STANDARD REFERENCES:
Bowers, Q. David. *A Guide Book of Barber Silver Coins*. Atlanta, GA: 2015.

—— *A Guide Book of Liberty Seated Silver Coins*. Second edition. Pelham, AL: 2019.

—— *A Guide Book of Mercury Dimes, Standing Liberty Quarters, and Liberty Walking Half Dollars*. Atlanta, GA: 2015.

—— *A Guide Book of Washington Quarters*. Second edition. Pelham, AL: 2017.

Bressett, Kenneth. *The Official Whitman Statehood Quarters Collector's Handbook*. New York, NY: 2000.

Briggs, Larry. *The Comprehensive Encyclopedia of United States Seated Quarters*. Lima, OH: 1991.

Cline, J.H. *Standing Liberty Quarters*. Third edition. 1996.

Knauss, Robert H. *Standing Liberty Quarter Varieties & Errors*. Second edition. Published by the author, 2014.

Rea, Rory, Glenn Peterson, Bradley Karoleff, and John Kovach. *Early Quarter Dollars of the U.S. Mint, 1796–1838*. 2010.

Tompkins, Steve M. *Early United States Quarters, 1796–1838*. 2008.

REFERENCES OF HISTORICAL INTEREST:
Browning, A.W. *The Early Quarter Dollars of the United States 1796–1838*. New York, NY: 1925 (reprinted 1992).

Duphorne, R. *The Early Quarter Dollars of the United States*. 1975.

Haseltine. J.W. *Type Table of United States Dollars, Half Dollars and Quarter Dollars*. Philadelphia, PA: 1881 (reprinted 1927, 1968).

Lawrence, David. *The Complete Guide to Barber Quarters*. Virginia Beach, VA: 1989.

HALF DOLLARS
STANDARD REFERENCES:
Ambio, Jeff. *Collecting and Investing Strategies for Walking Liberty Half Dollars*. Irvine CA: 2008.

Bowers, Q. David. *A Guide Book of Barber Silver Coins*. Atlanta, GA: 2015.

—— *A Guide Book of Liberty Seated Silver Coins*. Second edition. Pelham, AL: 2019.

—— *A Guide Book of Mercury Dimes, Standing Liberty Quarters, and Liberty Walking Half Dollars*. Atlanta, GA: 2015.

Overton, Al C. *Early Half Dollar Die Varieties 1794–1836*. Fifth edition. Murietta, CA: 2014.

Peterson, Glenn R. *The Ultimate Guide to Attributing Bust Half Dollars*. Rocky River, OH: 2000.

Tomaska, Rick. *A Guide Book of Franklin and Kennedy Half Dollars*. Second edition. Atlanta, GA: 2012.

Wiley, Randy, and Bill Bugert. *The Complete Guide to Liberty Seated Half Dollars*. Virginia Beach, VA: 1993.

REFERENCES OF HISTORICAL INTEREST:
Amato, Jon. *The Draped Bust Half Dollars of 1796–1797*. Dallas, TX: 2015.

Beistle, M.L. *A Register of Half Dollar Die Varieties and Sub-Varieties*. Shippensburg, PA: 1929.

Haseltine. J.W. *Type Table of United States Dollars, Half Dollars and Quarter Dollars*. Philadelphia, PA: 1881 (reprinted 1927, 1968).

Howe, Dean F. *Walking Liberty Half Dollars, an In-Depth Study*. Sandy, UT: 1989.

Lawrence, David. *The Complete Guide to Barber Halves*. Virginia Beach, VA: 1991.

Swiatek, Anthony. *Walking Liberty Half Dollars*. New York, NY: 1983.

SILVER AND RELATED DOLLARS
STANDARD REFERENCES:
Bolender, M.H. *The United States Early Silver Dollars From 1794 to 1803*. Fifth edition. Iola, WI: 1987.

Bowers, Q. David. *The Encyclopedia of United States Silver Dollars 1794–1804*. Wolfeboro, NH: 2013.

—— *The Rare Silver Dollars Dated 1804*. Wolfeboro, NH: 1999.

—— *Silver Dollars and Trade Dollars of the United States: A Complete Encyclopedia*. Wolfeboro, NH: 1993.

—— *A Guide Book of Liberty Seated Silver Coins*. Second edition. Pelham, AL: 2019.

—— *A Guide Book of Modern United States Dollar Coins*. Atlanta, GA: 2016.

—— *A Guide Book of Morgan Silver Dollars*. Fifth edition. Atlanta, GA: 2016.

Burdette, Roger W. *A Guide Book of Peace Dollars*. Fourth edition. Pelham, AL: 2019.

Crum, Adam, Selby Ungar, and Jeff Oxman. *Carson City Morgan Dollars*. Third edition. Pelham, AL: 2019.

Fey, Michael S., and Jeff Oxman. *The Top 100 Morgan Dollar Varieties*. Morris Planes, NJ: 1997.

Logies, Martin A. *The Flowing Hair Silver Dollars of 1794*. 2004.

Newman, Eric P., and Kenneth E. Bressett. *The Fantastic 1804 Dollar*, Racine, WI: 1962 (tribute edition 2009).

Standish, Michael "Miles," with John B. Love. *Morgan Dollar: America's Love Affair With a Legendary Coin*. Atlanta, GA: 2014.

Van Allen, Leroy C., and A. George Mallis. *Comprehensive Catalogue and Encyclopedia of U.S. Morgan and Peace Silver Dollars*. New York, NY: 1997.

REFERENCES OF HISTORICAL INTEREST:

Carter, Mike. *The 1921 Morgan Dollars: An In-Depth Study*. Beverly Hills, CA: 1986.

Coinage of Gold and Silver. Collection, amounting to 491 printed pages, of documents, testimonies, etc., before the House of Representatives, Committee on Coinage, Weights, and Measures, 1891. The silver question, the silver-gold ratio, international monetary situations, financial panics, and more are debated. Washington, D.C.: Government Printing Office, 1891.

Haseltine. J.W. *Type Table of United States Dollars, Half Dollars and Quarter Dollars*. Philadelphia, PA: 1881 (reprinted 1927, 1968).

Highfill, John W. *The Comprehensive U.S. Silver Dollar Encyclopedia*. Broken Arrow, OK: 1992.

Osburn, Dick, and Brian Cushing. *A Register of Liberty Seated Dollar Varieties*. www.seateddollarvarieties.com.

Wexler, Crawford, and Kevin Flynn, *The Authoritative Reference on Eisenhower Dollars*. Rancocas, NJ: 1998.

Willem, John M. *The United States Trade Dollar*. Second edition. Racine, WI: 1965.

GOLD COINS ($1 THROUGH $20)

STANDARD REFERENCES:

Akers, David W. *Gold Dollars (and Other Gold Denominations)*. Englewood, OH: 1975–1982.

Bowers, Q. David. *United States Gold Coins: An Illustrated History*. Second edition. Wolfeboro, NH: 2011.

—— *Harry W. Bass, Jr. Museum Sylloge*, Wolfeboro, NH: 2002.

—— *A Guide Book of Gold Dollars*. Atlanta, GA: 2008.

—— *A Guide Book of Double Eagle Gold Coins*. Second edition. Pelham, AL: 2019.

—— *A Guide Book of Quarter Eagle and Half Eagle Gold Coins*. Pelham, AL: 2019.

—— *U.S. Liberty Head Double Eagles: The Gilded Age of Coinage*. Wolfeboro, NH: 2015.

Bowers, Q. David, and Douglas Winter, *The United States $3 Gold Pieces 1854–1889*. Wolfeboro, NH: 2005.

Dannreuther, John W., and Harry W. Bass Jr. *Early U.S. Gold Coin Varieties*. Atlanta, GA: 2006.

Fivaz, Bill. *United States Gold Counterfeit Detection Guide*. Atlanta, GA: 2005.

Garrett, Jeff, and Ron Guth. *Encyclopedia of U.S. Gold Coins, 1795–1933*. Second edition. Atlanta, GA: 2008.

Schein, Allan. *The $2 1/2 and $5 Gold Indians of Bela Lyon Pratt*. 2016.

Winter, Douglas. *Gold Coins of the Charlotte Mint, 1838–1861*. Wolfeboro, NH: 1987.

—— *New Orleans Mint Gold Coins*. Wolfeboro, NH: 1992.

—— *Gold Coins of the Dahlonega Mint 1838–1861*. Dallas, TX: 1997.

Winter, Douglas, and Lawrence E. Cutler, M.D., *Gold Coins of the Old West: The Carson City Mint 1870–1893*. Wolfeboro, NH: 1994.

REFERENCES OF HISTORICAL INTEREST:

Augsburger, Leonard D. *Treasure in the Cellar: A Tale of Gold in Depression-Era Baltimore*. Baltimore, MD: 2008.

Breen, Walter. *Major Varieties of U.S. Gold Dollars*. Chicago, IL: 1964.

Gilliland, Cory. *Sylloge of the United States Holdings in the National Numismatic Collection of the Smithsonian Institution. Volume 1: Gold Coins, 1785–1834*. Washington, D.C.: 1992.

Miller, Robert W., Sr., *U.S. Half Eagle Gold Coins*. Elmwood Park, NJ: 1997.

Schein, Allan. *The Gold Indians of Bela Lyon Pratt*. 1997.

Taglione, Paul F. *Federal Gold Coinage: Volume I, An Introduction to Gold Coinage & the Gold Dollars*. Boston, MA: 1986.

—— *A Reference to United States Federal Gold Coinage: Volume II, The Quarter Eagles.* Boston, MA: 1986.

—— *A Reference to United States Federal Gold Coinage: Volume III, The Three Dollar Pieces.* Boston, MA: 1986.

—— *A Reference to United States Federal Gold Coinage: Volume IV, An Investment Philosophy for the Prudent Consumer.* Boston, MA: 1986.

Taraskza, Anthony J. *United States Ten Dollar Gold Eagles.* Portage, MI: 1999.

Tripp, David E. *Illegal Tender: Gold, Greed, and the Mystery of the Lost 1933 Double Eagle.* New York, NY: 2004.

COMMEMORATIVE COINS
STANDARD REFERENCES:
Bowers, Q. David. *A Guide Book of United States Commemorative Coins.* Second edition. Atlanta, GA: 2016.

Swiatek, Anthony J. *Encyclopedia of the Commemorative Coins of the United States.* Chicago, IL: 2012.

REFERENCES OF HISTORICAL INTEREST:
Bullowa, David M. *The Commemorative Coinage of the United States 1892–1938.* New York, NY: 1938.

Mosher, Stuart. *United States Commemorative Coins.* New York, NY: 1940.

Swiatek, Anthony and Walter H, Breen. *The Encyclopedia of United States Silver and Gold Commemorative Coins 1892–1954.* New York, NY: 1981.

Taxay, Don. *An Illustrated History of U.S. Commemorative Coinage.* New York, NY: 1967.

BULLION COINS
Mercanti, John M., with Michael Standish. *American Silver Eagles: A Guide to the U.S. Bullion Coin Program.* Third edition. Atlanta, GA: 2016 (reprint, Pelham, AL, 2018).

Moy, Edmund. *American Gold and Platinum Eagles: A Guide to the U.S. Bullion Coin Programs.* Atlanta, GA: 2013.

Tucker, Dennis. *American Gold and Silver: U.S. Mint Collector and Investor Coins and Medals, Bicentennial to Date.* Atlanta, GA: 2016.

Whitman Publishing. *Precious Metal: Investing and Collecting in Today's Silver, Gold, and Platinum Markets.* Second edition. Pelham, AL: 2019.

PATTERN COINS
STANDARD REFERENCES:
Judd, J. Hewitt. *United States Pattern Coins.* Tenth edition. Atlanta, GA: 2008. Updated by Q. David Bowers.

REFERENCES OF HISTORICAL INTEREST:
Adams, Edgar H., and William H. Woodin. *United States Pattern, Trial, and Experimental Pieces.* New York, NY: 1913.

Cassel, David. *United States Pattern Postage Currency.* Miami, FL: 2000.

Davis, Robert Coulton. "Pattern and Experimental Issues of the United States Mint." *The Coin Collector's Journal.* September 1885.

Pollock, Andrew W., III. *United States Patterns and Related Issues.* Wolfeboro, NH: 1994.

PRIVATE AND TERRITORIAL GOLD
STANDARD REFERENCES:
Adams, Edgar H. *Private Gold Coinage of California 1849–1855.* Brooklyn, NY: 1913.

Bowers, Q. David. *A California Gold Rush History Featuring Treasure from the S.S. Central America.* Wolfeboro, NH: 2001.

Breen, Walter H., and Ronald Gillio. *California Pioneer Fractional Gold.* Second edition. Santa Barbara, CA: 1983.

Kagin, Donald H. *Private Gold Coins and Patterns of the United States.* New York, NY: 1981.

Leonard, Robert D., Jr., *California Pioneer Fractional Gold.* Wolfeboro, NH: 2003.

Moulton, Karl. *John J. Ford, Jr. and the Franklin Hoard.* Congress, AZ: 2003.

Owens, Dan. *California Coiners and Assayers.* Wolfeboro, NH; and New York, NY: 2000.

REFERENCES OF HISTORICAL INTEREST:
Adams, Edgar H. *Official Premium Lists of Private and Territorial Gold Coins.* Brooklyn, NY: 1909.

—— *Private Gold Coinage of California 1849–1855.* Brooklyn, NY: 1913.

Conrad, Judy (editor). Preface by Barry Schatz. *Story of an American Tragedy. Survivors' Accounts of the Sinking of the Steamship Central America.* Columbus, OH: 1988.

Griffin, Clarence. *The Bechtlers and Bechtler Coinage and Gold Mining in North Carolina 1814–1830.* Spindale, NC: 1929.

Lee, Kenneth W. *California Gold—Dollars, Half Dollars, Quarter Dollars.* Santa Ana, CA: 1979.

TOKENS, MEDALS, AND EXONUMIA
STANDARD REFERENCES:
Betts, C. Wyllys. *American Colonial History Illustrated by Contemporary Medals.* New York, NY: 1894.

Bowers, Q. David. *A Guide Book of Civil War Tokens.* Second edition. Atlanta, GA: 2015.

—— *A Guide Book of Hard Times Tokens.* Atlanta, GA: 2015.

Brunk, Gregory G. *American and Canadian Counter-marked Coins.* Rockford, IL: 1987.

Coffee, John M., and Harold V. Ford, *The Atwood-Coffee Catalogue of United States and Canadian Transportation Tokens.* Fifth edition. Boston, MA: 1996.

Fuld, George, and Melvin Fuld (edited by John Ostendorf, Q. David Bowers, Evelyn R. Mishkin, and Susan Trask). *U.S. Civil War Store Cards.* Third edition. Civil War Token Society, 2015.

Fuld, George, and Melvin Fuld (edited by John Mark Glazer, Q. David Bowers, and Susan Trask). *Patriotic Civil War Tokens.* Sixth edition. Civil War Token Society. 2016.

Hibler, Harold E., and Charles V. Kappen. *So-Called Dollars.* Second edition. Clifton, NJ: 2008.

Hodder, Michael, and Q. David Bowers. *The Standard Catalogue of Encased Postage Stamps.* Wolfeboro, NH: 1989.

Jaeger, Katherine. *A Guide Book of United States Tokens and Medals.* Atlanta, GA: 2008.

Jaeger, Katherine, and Q. David Bowers. *100 Greatest American Medals and Tokens.* Atlanta, GA: 2007.

Julian, R.W. *Medals of the United States Mint: The First Century 1792–1892.* El Cajon, CA: 1977.

Leonard, Robert D., Jr., Ken Hallenbeck, and Adna G. Wilde Jr. *Forgotten Colorado Silver: Joseph Lesher's Defiant Coins.* Charleston, SC: 2017.

Musante, Neil. *Medallic Washington* (2 volumes). London and Boston, MA: 2016.

Rulau, Russell. *Standard Catalog of U.S. Tokens 1700–1900.* Fourth edition. Iola, WI: 2004.

Schenkman, David E. *Civil War Sutler Tokens and Cardboard Scrip.* Bryans Road, MD: 1983.

Schuman, Robert A., M.D. *The True Hard Times Tokens.* M&G Publications, 2000.

Sullivan, Edmund. *American Political Badges & Medals.* Lawrence, MA: 1981.

REFERENCES OF HISTORICAL INTEREST:

Adams, Edgar H. *United States Store Cards.* New York, NY: Edgar H. Adams and Wayte Raymond, 1920.

Appleton, William Sumner, *Description of Medals of Washington in the Collection of W.S. Appleton.* Boston, MA: 1873.

Bushnell, Charles I. *An Arrangement of Tradesmen's Cards, Political Tokens, also Election Medals, Medalets, &c. Current in the United States of America for the Last Sixty Years, Described from the Originals, Chiefly in the Collection of the Author.* Published by the author, 1858.

Collett, Mark W., J. Ledyard Hodge, and Alfred B. Taylor. *Catalogue of American Store Cards & c.* Philadelphia, PA: 1859.

DeWitt, J. Doyle. *A Century of Campaign Buttons 1789–1889.* Hartford, CT: 1959.

Doty, Richard G. (editor), *The Token: America's Other Money.* New York, NY: American Numismatic Society and Coinage of the Americas Conference, 1994.

Loubat, J.F. *The Medallic History of the United States of America, 1776–1876.* New York, NY: 1878.

Low, Lyman H. *Hard Times Tokens.* New York, NY: 1899.

Miller, Donald M. *A Catalogue of U.S. Store Cards or Merchants' Tokens.* Indiana, PA: 1962.

Rulau, Russell. *Hard Times Tokens: A Complete Revision and Enlargement of Lyman H. Low's 1899 Classic Reference.* Iola, WI: Krause Publications, 1987.

Rulau Russell, and George Fuld, *Medallic Portraits of Washington.* Iola, WI: 1985 and later editions.

Satterlee, Alfred H. *An Arrangement of The Medals and Tokens Struck in Honor of the Presidents of the United States and of the Presidential Candidates From the Administration of John Adams to That of Abraham Lincoln, Inclusive.* New York, NY: Printed for the author, 1862.

Snowden, James Ross. *A Description of the Medals of Washington.* Philadelphia, PA: 1861.

Woodward, W. Elliot. *A List of Washington Memorial Medals.* Boston, MA: 1865.

GENERAL COVERING MULTIPLE AMERICAN COIN SERIES

STANDARD REFERENCES:

Bowers, Q. David. *The History of United States Coinage as Illustrated by the Garrett Collection.* Los First printing. Los Angeles, CA: Published for The Johns Hopkins University.

—— *American Coin Treasures and Hoards.* Wolfeboro, NH: 1997.

—— *The History of American Numismatics Before the Civil War, 1760–1860.* Wolfeboro, NH: 1998.

—— *A Guide Book of United States Type Coins.* Second edition. Atlanta, GA: 2008.

Breen, Walter H. *Walter Breen's Encyclopedia of U.S. and Colonial Proof Coins, 1792–1977.* Albertson, NY: 1977; updated, Wolfeboro, NH: 1989.

——"Secret History of the Gobrecht Coinages." *Coin Collectors Journal,* 157–158. New York, NY: Wayte Raymond, Inc., 1954.

—— *Walter Breen's Encyclopedia of U.S. and Colonial Proof Coins, 1792–1977.* Albertson, NY: FCI Press, 1977.

—— *Walter Breen's Complete Encyclopedia of U.S. and Colonial Coins.* New York, NY: 1988.

Burdette, Roger W. *The Renaissance of American Coinage 1905–1908.* Great Falls, VA: 2006.

—— *The Renaissance of American Coinage 1909–1915.* Great Falls, VA: 2007.

—— *The Renaissance of American Coinage 1916–1921.* Great Falls, VA: 2005.

Carothers, Neil. *Fractional Money.* New York, NY: John Wiley & Sons, Inc., 1930.

Fivaz, Bill, and J.T. Stanton. *The Cherrypickers' Guide to Rare Die Varieties.* Atlanta, GA: various editions and volumes.

Garrett, Jeff, and Ron Guth. *100 Greatest U.S. Coins.* Fourth edition. Atlanta, GA: 2014.

Guth, Ron, and Jeff Garrett. *United States Coinage: A Study by Type.* Atlanta, GA: 2005.

Lange, David W. *A Guide Book of Modern United States Proof Coin Sets.* Second edition. Atlanta, GA: 2010.

Tucker, Dennis. *American Gold and Silver: U.S. Mint Collector and Investor Coins and Medals, Bicentennial to Date.* Atlanta, GA: 2016.

REFERENCES OF HISTORICAL INTEREST:

Alexander, David T., Thomas K. DeLorey, and Brad Reed. *Coin World Comprehensive Catalog & Encyclopedia of United States Coins.* Sidney, OH: Coin World, 1995.

Eckfeldt, Jacob R., and William E. DuBois. *A Manual of Gold and Silver Coins of All Nations, Struck Within the Past Century.* Philadelphia, PA: Assay Office of the Mint, 1842.

Scott Stamp & Coin Co., Ltd., also Scott & Co. and J.W. Scott Co., Ltd. *Standard Catalogue* (various titles). 1878–1913.

Taxay, Don. *Counterfeit, Mis-Struck and Unofficial U.S. Coins.* New York, NY: 1963.

—— *U.S. Mint and Coinage.* New York, NY: Arco Publishing, 1966.

—— *Scott's Comprehensive Catalogue of United States Coinage.* New York, NY: Scott Publications, 1970 (cover date 1971).

Tomaska, Rick Jerry. *Cameo and Brilliant Proof Coinage of the 1950 to 1970 Era.* Encinitas, CA: 1991.

Vermeule, Cornelius. *Numismatic Art in America.* Cambridge, MA: 1971.

Witham, Stewart. *Johann Matthaus Reich, Also Known as John Reich.* Canton, OH: November 1993.

WORLD ISSUES RELATED TO THE UNITED STATES

Allen, Lyman L. *U.S. Philippine Coins.* Oakland Park, FL: 1998.

Medcalf, Donald, and Russell, Ronald. *Hawaiian Money Standard Catalog.* Second edition. Mill Creek, WA: 1991.

Schilke, Oscar G., and Raphael E. Solomon. *America's Foreign Coins: An Illustrated Standard Catalogue with Valuations of Foreign Coins with Legal Tender status in the United States, 1793–1857.* New York, NY: 1964.

Shafer, Neil. *United States Territorial Coinage for the Philippine Islands.* Racine, WI: 1961.

HISTORY OF THE U.S. MINTS AND THE MINT COLLECTION

STANDARD REFERENCES:

Augsburger, Leonard D., and Orosz, Joel J. *The Secret History of the First U.S. Mint.* Atlanta, GA: 2011.

Bierly, William. *In God We Trust.* Pelham, AL: 2019.

Bowers, Q. David. *Guide Book of the United States Mint.* Pelham, AL: 2016.

Goe, Rusty. *The Mint on Carson Street.* Reno, NV: 2003.

Lange, David W. *History of the United States Mint and Its Coinage.* Atlanta, GA: 2005.

Mishler, Clifford. *Coins: Questions and Answers.* Sixth edition. Pelham, AL: 2019.

Smith, Pete, Joel Orosz, and Leonard Augsburger. *1792: Birth of a Nation's Coinage.* Birmingham, UK: 2017.

Taxay, Don. *The United States Mint and Coinage.* New York, NY: 1966.

REFERENCES OF HISTORICAL INTEREST:

Comparette, T.L. *Catalogue of Coins, Tokens and Medals in the Numismatic Collection of the Mint of the United States at Philadelphia, Pa.* Washington, D.C.: 1914.

Dubois, William E. *Pledges of History: A Brief Account of the Collection of Coins Belonging to the Mint of the United States, More Particularly of the Antique Specimens.* First edition. Philadelphia, PA: C. Sherman, 1846; Second edition. New York, NY: George P. Putnam, 1851.

Evans, George. *Illustrated History of the U.S. Mint* (various eds.), Philadelphia, PA: 1885–1901.

Hickson, Howard. *Mint Mark CC: The Story of the United States Mint at Carson City, Nevada.* Carson City, NV: The Nevada State Museum, 1972 and 1990.

Johnston, Elizabeth B. *A Visit to the Cabinet of the United States Mint, at Philadelphia.* Philadelphia, PA: 1876.

McClure, R.A. *An Index to the Coins and Medals of the Mint of the United States at Philadelphia*. Philadelphia, PA: 1891.

Moulton, Karl. *Henry Voigt and Others Involved in Early American Coinage*. Congress, AZ: 2003.

Smith, A.M. *Illustrated History of the U.S. Mint*. Philadelphia, PA: 1881.

Snowden, James Ross. *A Description of Ancient and Modern Coins in the Cabinet of the Mint of the United States*. Philadelphia, PA: 1860. (Mostly researched and written by George Bull [then curator of the Mint Cabinet] and William Ewing Dubois.)

Stewart, Frank. *History of the First United States Mint, Its People and ItsOperations*. 1924 (reprinted 1974).

Treasury Department, United States Mint, *et al. Annual Report of the Director of the Mint*. Philadelphia (later, Washington), 1795 onward.

Young, James Rankin. *The United States Mint at Philadelphia*. Philadelphia, PA: Capt. A.J. Andrews (agent, not publisher), 1903.

PUBLICATIONS ABOUT BOOKS, COINAGE, MONEY, AND NUMISMATICS

Adams, John W. *United States Numismatic Literature. Volume I. Nineteenth Century Auction Catalogs*. Mission Viejo, CA: 1982.

—— *United States Numismatic Literature. Volume II. Twentieth Century Auction Catalogues*. Crestline, CA: 1990.

Adelson, Howard. *The American Numismatic Society 1858–1958*. New York, NY: 1958.

American Journal of Numismatics. New York, NY, and Boston, MA: Various issues 1866 to 1912.

Attinelli, Emmanuel J. *Numisgraphics, or A List of Catalogues, Which Have Been Sold by Auction in the United States*. New York, NY: 1876.

Augsburger, Leonard D., Roger W. Burdette, and Joel J. Orosz. *Truth Seeker: The Life of Eric P. Newman*. Dallas, TX: 2015.

Baker, W.S. *American Engravers and Their Works*. Philadelphia, PA: 1875.

Becker, Thomas W. *The Coin Makers*. Garden City, NY: Doubleday & Company, 1969.

Bowers, Q. David. *Adventures with Rare Coins*. Los Angeles, CA: 1979, and later editions.

——*Abe Kosoff: Dean of Numismatics*. Wolfeboro, NH: 1985.

——*American Numismatics Before the Civil War, 1760–1860: Emphasizing the Story of Augustus B. Sage*. Wolfeboro, NH: 1998.

——*More Adventures with Rare Coins*. Wolfeboro, NH: 2001.

Breen, Walter H. *A Coiner's Caviar: Walter Breen's Encyclopedia of U.S. and Colonial Proof Coins*. Albertson, New York: 1977; reprint and update Wolfeboro, NH: 1989.

Bressett, Kenneth E. and A. Kosoff; introduction by Q. David Bowers. *The Official American Numismatic Association Grading Standards for United States Coins*. Seventh edition. Atlanta, GA: American Numismatic Association, 2013.

Brown, Martin R., and John W. Dunn. *A Guide to the Grading of United States Coins*. Oklahoma City, OK: Published by the authors, 1963.

Burdette, Roger. *From Mine to Mint: American Coinage Operations and Technology, 1833 to 1837*. Great Falls, VA: 2013.

Coin Collector's Journal, The. New York City, NY: J.W. Scott & Co.,1870s and 1880s.

Coin World Almanac. Sidney, OH: Coin World, 1976 and later editions.

Coinage Laws of the United States 1792–1894. Modern foreword to reprint by David L. Ganz. Wolfeboro, NH: 1991.

Cooper, Denis R. *The Art and Craft of Coinmaking, A History of Minting Technology*. London, England: 1988.

Davis, Charles E. *American Numismatic Literature: An Annotated Survey of Auction Sales 1980–1991*. Lincoln, MA: 1992.

Del Mar, Alexander. *The History of Money in America from the Earliest Times to the Establishment of the Constitution*. Reprint. Hawthorne, CA: 1966.

Dickeson, Montroville W. *American Numismatical Manual*. Philadelphia, PA: J.B. Lippincott & Co., 1859, also editions of 1860 and 1866.

Doty, Richard G. *America's Money, America's Story*. Iola, WI: 1998.

Durst, Lorraine S. *United States Numismatic Auction Catalogs: A Bibliography*. New York, NY: 1981.

Eckfeldt, Jacob Reese, and William Ewing DuBois. *A Manual of Gold and Silver Coins of All Nations, Struck Within the Past Century*. Philadelphia, PA: 1842.

Gengerke, Martin. *American Numismatic Auctions*. Woodside, NY: printed by the author, 1990.

Groce, George C., and David H. Wallace. *New York Historical Society's Dictionary of Artists in America*. New Haven, CT: 1957.

Heaton, Augustus G. *A Treatise on the Coinage of the United States Branch Mints*. Washington, D.C.: Published by the author, 1893.

Hepburn, A. Barton. *A History of Currency in the United States.* New York, NY: 1915.

Hickcox, John H. *An Historical Account of American Coinage.* Albany, NY: 1858.

Hodder, Michael J., and Q. David Bowers. *The Norweb Collection: An American Legacy.* Wolfeboro, NH: 1987.

Jaeger, Katherine M., and Q. David Bowers. *The 100 Greatest American Medals and Tokens.* Atlanta, GA: 2007.

Jones, George F. *The Coin Collector's Manual: A Guide Book for Coin Collectors.* Philadelphia, PA: 1860.

Kenney, Richard D. *Early American Medalists and Die-Sinkers Prior to the Civil War.* New York, NY: 1954.

Kleeberg, John M. "The Shipwreck of the *Faithful Steward:* A 'Missing Link' in the Exports of British and Irish Halfpence." New York, NY: 1996.

Linderman, Henry R. *Money and Legal Tender.* New York, NY: G.P. Putnam's Sons, 1877.

Lupia, John N. III. *American Numismatic Auctions to 1875, Volume 1, 1738–1850.* 2013.

Moulton, Karl. *United States Numismatic Catalogues, 1990–2000.* Congress, AZ: 2001.

Orosz, Joel J. *The Eagle That Is Forgotten: Pierre Eugène Du Simitière, Founding Father of American Numismatics.* Wolfeboro, NH: 1988.

Prime, W.C. *Coins, Medals, and Seals.* New York, NY: 1861.

Raymond, Wayte. *Standard Catalogue of United States Coins and Paper Money* (titles vary). New York, NY: Scott Stamp & Coin Co. (and others), 1934 to 1957 editions.

Ruddy, James F. *Photograde.* Nineteenth edition. Racine, WI: Western Publishing Co., 1990.

Rulau, Russell. *Standard Catalogue of United States Tokens 1700–1900.* Fourth edition. Iola, WI: 2004.

Shippee, Robert W. *Pleasure & Profit: 100 Lessons for the Building and Selling of a Collection of Rare Coins.* Atlanta, GA: 2015.

Smith, A.M. *Coin Collectors' of the United States, Illustrated Guide.* Philadelphia, PA: January 1886.

Stauffer, David McNeely. *American Engravers Upon Copper and Steel.* New York, NY: 1907.

Sumner, William Graham. *A History of American Currency.* New York, NY: 1874.

Taxay, Don. *Counterfeit, Mis-Struck, and Unofficial U.S. Coins.* New York, NY: 1963.

—— *U.S. Mint and Coinage.* New York, NY: 1966.

—— *Scott's Comprehensive Catalogue of United States Coinage.* New York, NY.

Wright, Benjamin P. "The American Store or Business Cards." Published serially in *The Numismatist,* 1898–1901. Reprinted by the Token and Medal Society, 1963.

Image Credits

PHOTO CREDITS

Note: Images are credited by page number and by location on the page, starting with number 1 at upper left and reading left to right. Obverse-reverse pairs are counted as a single image and are noted in italic type.

Roger W. Burdette shared the following images: 620.2.

Jeff Garrett shared the following images: 543.2.

Heritage Auctions shared the following images: 77.2; 82.2; 88.1; 123.1; 138.5; 141.4; 141.5; 143.3; 147.5; 150.1; 155.1; 155.2; 155.3; 155.4; 166.1; 168.2; 168.3; 177.2; 178.1; 178.3; 180.2; 181.2; 181.5; 182.4; 188.1; 191.1; 191.2; 191.3; 194.1; 195.1; 195.5; 196.4; 197.1; 198.1; 199.3; 203.1; 203.2; 203.3; 205.6; 205.7; 206.1; 206.2; 207.3; 209.1; 213.1; 214.2; 214.3; 216.2; 217.1; 219.1; 219.2; 219.3; 222.1; 222.2; 222.3; 223.1; 223.3; 223.4; 224.2; 224.3; 228.2; 229.1; 232.1; 232.2; 232.5; 234.3; 235.3; 235.4; 238.2; 249.3; 257.3; 258.1; 258.2; 260.1; 264.1; 279.1; 279.2; 286.4; 286.5; 286.7; 288.1; 294.1; 294.2; 294.3; 294.4; 294.5; 294.6; 294.7; 294.8; 294.9; 294.10; 295.1; 296.1; 297.1; 297.2; 297.3; 297.3; 298.1; 298.1; 298.2; 298.3; 298.4; 301.1; 302.1; 302.2; 302.3; 302.4; 303.1; 309.1; 310.2; 314.1; 315.2; 320.2; 321.1; 321.2; 323.1; 323.2; 327.1; 327.2; 328.4; 356.1; 361.2; 362.1; 362.2; 362.3; 363.1; 363.2; 365.2; 367.3; 368.2; 370.1; 372.3; 372.4; 372.5; 374.2; 375.1; 375.3; 377.3; 378.2; 381.3; 381.4; 381.5; 381.6; 386.1; 386.2; 393.1; 394.2; 395.1; 395.2; 395.3; 396.1; 396.2; 396.30; 396.40; 397.1; 401.8; 403.2; 409.1; 409.2; 409.5; 410.8; 410.9; 413.3; 413.4; 414.70; 418.1; 420.30; 420.40; 421.10; 421.20; 424.3; 440.1; 440.3; 440.6; 441.1; 449.1; 460.2; 461.1; 461.2; 461.3; 461.4; 462.1; 462.2; 465.1; 465.2; 465.3; 466.1; 466.2; 467.2; 469.5; 470.1; 480.5; 481.1; 481.3; 495.4; 496.1; 499.1; 499.4; 500.2; 501.5; 501.6; 501.7; 501.8; 501.9; 501.10; 501.11; 502.1; 502.2; 502.4; 514.2; 515.1; 516.2; 517.2; 517.3; 518.3; 518.40; 520.4; 521.1; 524.20; 525.1; 526.1; 527.4; 531.2; 532.1; 532.2; 543.3; 546.2; 546.3; 547.1; 547.2; 549.3; 550.1; 551.2; 551.30; 554.2; 555.1; 555.2; 555.4; 556.1; 556.2; 558.1; 558.3; 559.1; 561.2; 562.2; 563.2; 563.4; 564.2; 565.1; 565.3; 566.2; 566.3; 567.3; 568.2; 568.3; 569.1; 569.3; 576.10; 576.20; 577.3; 579.1; 579.20; 579.3; 579.40; 580.1; 580.20; 580.3; 580.40; 581.1; 581.20; 581.3; 581.40; 583.1; 583.3; 584.1; 584.2; 585.1; 585.2; 585.3; 587.2; 588.2; 589.3; 590.1; 591.2; 593.1; 593.3; 594.1; 594.2; 596.1; 597.1; 598.1; 598.2; 599.1; 599.3; 600.2; 601.1; 601.2; 601.3; 603.2; 604.1; 604.2; 604.3; 606.3; 608.3; 609.3; 611.1; 611.3; 612.2; 613.1; 614.1; 614.30; 614.4; 627.1; 650.30; 652.40; 652.60; 652.70; 655.10; 668.2; 668.30; 680.3; 686.2; 707.1; 707.2; 718.1; 718.2; 720.1; 720.2; 720.3; 721.10; 721.50; 732.1; 732.2; 738.1; 738.2; 753.1; 757.1; 760.3; 765.3; 766.1; 775.8; 777.5; 781.1; 781.3; 782.1; 802.3; 802.4; 809.3; 816.1; 849.4; 858.2; 862.1; 862.3; 886.1; 888.2; 922.1; 922.1; 930.1; 934.3; 944.1; 946.1; 957.1; 970.1; 977.1; 980.1; 980.2; 980.4; 982.3; 982.4; 985.2; 985.3; 986.3; 986.4; 986.5; 986.6; 986.7; 989.1; 989.2; 991.4; 992.2; 1010.3; 1013.1; 1013.2; 1013.3; 1013.4; 1014.1; 1014.2; 1014.3; 1014.4; 1016.3; 1016.4; 1034.2; 1073.1; 1158.1; 1258.1; 1278.4; 1278.7; 1314.1; 1315.1; 1316.2; 1317.1; 1317.2; 1318.1; 1318.2; 1318.3; 1321.1; 1321.2; 1321.3; 1323.1; 1323.2; 1323.3; 1323.4; 1323.5; 1323.6; 1326.1; 1326.2; 1326.3; 1328.1; 1328.2; 1328.3; 1330.1; 1330.2; 1331.1; 1331.2; 1331.3; 1333.1; 1333.2; 1333.3; 1335.1; 1335.2; 1335.3; 1335.4; 1335.5; 1336.1; 1336.2; 1339.1; 1339.2; 1339.3; 1340.1; 1341.1; 1341.2; 1341.3; 1371.3; 1419.1; 1425.4; 1430.1; 1430.2; 1432.2; 1449.1; 1452.1.

The **Library Company of Philadelphia** shared the following images: 504.10; 505.10; 505.2.

Harry Miller shared the following images: 322.2; 322.3.

Tom Mulvaney photographed the following coins: 184.2; 186.1; 276.3; 288.2; 309.3; 310.1; 315.3; 315.4; 316.1; 355.1; 841.1; 879.1; 886.1; 886.2; 888.1; 975.3; 977.3; 977.5; 978.1; 987.3; 1010.2; 1019.1; 1037.2; 1037.3; 1038.1; 1041.1; 1110.1; 1112.1; 1113.2; 1114.1; 1115.1; 1115.2; 1116.1; 1117.1; 1118.1; 1119.1; 1120.1; 1121.1; 1121.2; 1122.1; 1123.1; 1123.2; 1124.1; 1125.1;

1125.2; 1127.1; 1127.2; 1128.1; 1129.1; 1129.2; 1130.1; 1131.1; 1131.2; 1132.1; 1133.1; 1134.1; 1135.1; 1135.2; 1136.1; 1137.1; 1137.2; 1138.1; 1150.2; 1151.1; 1152.1; 1152.2; 1154.1; 1155.1; 1155.2; 1156.1; 1157.1; 1157.2; 1159.1; 1160.1; 1160.2; 1161.1; 1162.1; 1162.2; 1163.1; 1164.1; 1164.2; 1165.1; 1166.1; 1166.2; 1167.1; 1169.1; 1169.2; 1170.1; 1171.1; 1171.2; 1172.1.

The **National Numismatic Collection** at the Smithsonian Institution shared the following images: 947.3; 963.2; 963.3; 648.1.

The **Nevada State Museum** shared the following images: 1451.1; 1452.2.

Newman-Heritage Auctions shared the following images: 147.3; 147.6.

NGC shared the following images: 491.5; 491.60; 495.1; 495.20; 670.3; 675.2; 676.4; 678.1; 681.3; 682.4; 684.1; 685.1; 689.4; 691.3; 692.2; 694.1; 696.1; 697.4; 698.1; 698.3; 698.4; 699.1; 699.2; 700.1; 700.3; 701.1; 701.3; 702.1; 702.3; 703.1; 703.3; 703.4; 704.2; 704.3; 705.2; 705.3; 708.1; 708.2; 708.4; 708.5; 708.7; 708.8; 709.3; 709.4; 709.6; 709.7; 709.8; 709.10; 710.1; 710.3; 710.4; 710.6; 710.7; 710.9; 710.10; 711.2; 711.3; 711.5; 711.6; 711.8; 711.9; 712.1; 712.2; 712.4; 712.5; 712.7; 712.8; 712.10; 713.1; 713.3; 713.4; 713.6; 713.7; 713.9; 713.10; 714.2; 714.3; 714.5; 714.6; 714.8; 714.9; 1436.1; 1437.1; 1437.2; 1438.1; 1439.2; 1440.1; 1441.1; 1444.1.

PCGS shared the following images: 500.3.

Ken Potter shared the following image: 683.3.

Scott Schrantz shared the following image: 1453.2.

Jeff Shevlin shared the following images: 1377.1; 1377.2; 1377.3; 1377.4; 1378.1; 1378.2; 1378.3; 1378.4; 1379.1; 1379.2; 1379.3; 1379.4; 1380.1; 1380.2; 1380.3; 1380.4; 1381.1; 1381.2; 1381.3; 1381.4; 1382.1; 1382.2; 1382.3; 1382.4; 1383.1; 1383.2; 1383.3; 1383.4; 1384.1; 1384.2; 1384.3; 1384.4; 1385.1; 1385.2; 1385.3; 1385.4; 1386.1; 1386.2; 1386.3; 1386.4; 1387.1; 1387.2; 1387.3; 1387.4; 1388.1; 1388.2; 1388.3; 1388.4; 1389.1; 1389.2; 1389.3; 1389.4; 1390.1; 1390.2; 1390.3; 1390.4; 1391.1; 1391.2; 1391.3; 1391.4.

Roger Siboni shared the following images: 125.3; 125.4; 126.3; 160.3; 160.5; 160.6; 161.2; 161.3; 161.7; 161.8; 161.9; 162.3; 162.5; 163.9; 171.1; 259.3; 259.4; 260.3; 260.5; 260.6.

Stack's Bowers Galleries shared the following images: 125.1; 125.2; 134.2; 140.5; 141.1; 141.2; 141.3; 142.2; 142.4; 142.5; 143.1; 143.2; 144.3; 146.1; 146.4; 146.5; 147.7; 162.1; 162.4; 165.1; 172.2; 173.3; 182.2; 182.3; 183.4; 184.3; 188.2; 189.1; 189.2; 190.1; 190.2; 190.3; 193.1; 193.2; 193.3; 194.2; 194.3; 195.2; 195.4; 196.1; 197.2; 198.2; 198.3; 199.1; 199.2; 200.6; 200.7; 201.8; 201.9; 202.1; 202.2; 203.4; 204.1; 204.2; 204.3; 206.3; 207.1; 207.2; 208.1; 208.2; 208.3; 209.2; 214.1; 215.1; 215.2; 215.3; 216.1; 217.2; 218.1; 218.2; 218.3; 221.1;

221.2; 221.3; 223.2; 225.2; 226.1; 226.2; 227.1; 227.2; 227.3; 228.1; 234.1; 234.2; 235.1; 237.2; 237.4; 237.5; 238.1; 239.1; 239.2; 239.3; 240.1; 240.2; 242.2; 247.2; 248.1; 248.2; 249.1; 249.2; 249.4; 254.1; 255.2; 256.1; 256.2; 257.1; 257.2; 257.4; 258.3; 260.2; 260.4; 262.1; 262.2; 262.3; 263.1; 263.2; 263.3; 263.4; 264.2; 272.1; 272.2; 272.3; 272.4; 272.5; 274.1; 274.2; 274.3; 275.1; 275.2; 275.3; 275.4; 276.1; 276.2; 285.1; 286.6; 287.1; 288.3; 297.2; 300.1; 300.2; 300.3; 301.3; 307.1; 307.2; 307.3; 307.4; 307.5; 307.6; 308.1; 309.2; 310.3; 313.1; 313.2; 314.2; 314.3; 315.1; 316.2; 322.1; 322.4; 323.3; 326.2; 327.3; 327.4; 328.1; 328.2; 328.3; 329.1; 334.1; 334.2; 335.1; 335.2; 335.3; 336.1; 336.2; 336.3; 336.4; 342.1; 343.1; 343.2; 343.3; 343.4; 357.4; 357.5; 366.1; 366.2; 366.3; 367.1; 367.2; 368.1; 369.1; 369.2; 370.2; 370.3; 371.1; 371.2; 371.3; 373.1; 373.2; 373.3; 374.1; 375.2; 376.4; 377.1; 377.2; 378.1; 378.4; 379.2; 381.2; 381.7; 381.8; 381.12; 383.1; 383.2; 383.3; 384.1; 384.2; 384.3; 385.2; 394.1; 394.3; 397.2; 398.1; 398.2; 398.3; 399.1; 399.2; 399.3; 400.1; 401.5; 401.7; 402.1; 403.1; 403.3; 404.1; 404.2; 405.1; 405.2; 406.10; 406.20; 407.40; 407.50; 407.60; 410.2; 410.5; 411.1; 412.1; 412.2; 412.3; 413.1; 413.2; 414.1; 415.40; 424.1; 424.4; 425.1; 426.1; 426.2; 426.3; 426.4; 431.3; 432.1; 432.2; 433.1; 433.2; 433.3; 433.4; 434.1; 434.2; 434.3; 440.20; 440.50; 440.7; 441.3; 457.1; 457.2; 459.1; 460.1; 462.3; 463.1; 463.2; 466.3; 467.1; 467.3; 467.4; 468.2; 468.3; 469.1; 469.2; 469.3; 469.4; 470.2; 470.3; 470.4; 471.1; 471.2; 476.1; 476.2; 477.1; 477.2; 477.3; 478.1; 478.2; 478.3; 478.4; 479.1; 479.2; 479.30; 480.1; 480.2; 480.3; 480.4; 481.2; 481.4; 482.1; 482.20; 482.3; 482.4; 482.50; 483.1; 483.20; 483.3; 483.4; 483.5; 484.1; 484.20; 484.3; 484.4; 485.1; 485.2; 485.3; 485.4; 486.1; 486.2; 487.1; 487.20; 487.3; 487.40; 488.1; 488.20; 488.3; 488.40; 489.1; 489.2; 489.30; 489.4; 489.50; 489.60; 490.1; 490.20; 490.30; 490.4; 491.1; 491.20; 491.3; 491.40; 492.1; 492.2; 492.3; 492.4; 492.50; 493.1; 493.20; 493.3; 493.4; 493.5; 494.1; 494.2; 494.3; 495.3; 495.5; 496.2; 496.3; 496.4; 497.1; 497.2; 497.3; 497.4; 497.5; 498.1; 498.2; 498.3; 498.40; 498.50; 498.6; 499.2; 499.3; 500.1; 500.4; 501.1; 501.20; 501.3; 501.4; 502.3; 503.1; 506.1; 506.2; 506.3; 506.4; 507.1; 507.2; 507.3; 507.4; 507.5; 511.1; 512.1; 512.2; 512.3; 512.4; 513.1; 513.2; 513.3; 513.4; 514.1; 514.3; 515.2; 516.1; 516.3; 517.1; 518.1; 518.20; 519.1; 519.20; 519.3; 519.40; 519.5; 520.1; 520.2; 521.2; 521.3; 522.1; 522.2; 522.3; 522.4; 523.3; 523.4; 524.1; 524.3; 524.4; 525.2; 525.3; 526.2; 526.3; 527.1; 527.2; 527.30; 528.1; 528.2; 528.3; 529.2; 530.1; 530.2; 530.3; 530.40; 531.1; 531.3; 532.3; 533.1; 533.2; 533.3; 533.40; 534.1; 534.3; 534.4; 535.1; 535.2; 535.3; 536.1; 536.2; 536.3; 537.1; 537.2; 537.3; 537.4; 538.1; 538.2; 538.3; 539.1; 539.2; 539.3; 540.1; 540.2; 540.3; 541.1; 541.2; 541.3; 541.4; 542.1; 542.2; 542.3; 543.1; 544.1; 544.2; 544.3; 545.1; 545.2; 545.3; 546.1; 546.4; 547.3; 548.1; 548.2; 549.1; 549.2; 550.2; 550.3; 551.1; 552.1; 552.2; 552.30; 552.4; 553.1; 553.2; 553.3; 554.1; 554.3; 555.3; 557.1; 557.2; 557.3; 558.2; 559.3; 559.4; 560.1; 560.2; 560.3; 561.1; 561.3; 561.4; 562.1; 562.3;

562.4; 563.1; 563.3; 564.1; 564.3; 565.2; 566.1; 566.4;
567.1; 567.2; 568.1; 576.3; 576.4; 577.1; 577.2; 577.4;
578.1; 578.2; 578.3; 582.1; 582.20; 582.4; 582.50; 583.2;
584.3; 586.1; 586.2; 586.3; 587.10; 587.3; 587.4; 588.1;
589.1; 589.2; 590.2; 590.3; 591.1; 592.1; 592.3; 592.4;
593.2; 594.3; 595.1; 595.2; 596.2; 596.3; 596.4; 597.2;
597.3; 598.3; 598.4; 599.2; 600.1; 600.3; 602.1; 602.2;
602.3; 603.1; 603.3; 605.1; 605.2; 605.3; 606.1; 606.2;
607.1; 607.2; 607.3; 607.4; 608.1; 608.2; 609.1; 609.2;
610.1; 610.2; 610.3; 611.2; 612.1; 612.3; 613.2; 613.3;
614.2; 617.10; 623.10; 623.20; 623.30; 623.40; 625.1;
625.2; 625.3; 626.1; 626.2; 626.3; 626.4; 627.2; 629.1;
629.20; 630.1; 630.20; 630.3; 630.40; 631.1; 631.20;
631.3; 631.4; 632.1; 632.20; 633.1; 633.2; 633.3; 634.1;
634.2; 635.1; 635.2; 635.3; 636.1; 636.2; 637.1; 637.2;
638.1; 638.2; 638.3; 639.1; 640.1; 640.2; 641.1; 641.2;
642.1; 642.2; 642.3; 643.2; 644.1; 644.2; 645.1; 645.2;
655.2; 656.1; 656.2; 656.3; 656.4; 657.1; 657.2; 657.4;
658.1; 658.2; 659.1; 659.2; 660.10; 660.20; 661.10;
661.20; 661.3; 661.40; 662.10; 662.2; 662.3; 662.4;
663.1; 663.20; 663.3; 663.4; 664.1; 664.2; 665.2; 665.3;
666.1; 666.2; 667.1; 667.2; 667.3; 667.4; 668.1; 668.4;
669.1; 669.2; 669.3; 670.4; 671.2; 671.3; 671.5; 672.1;
672.2; 672.4; 673.3; 673.4; 674.1; 674.3; 675.1; 675.3;
676.1; 676.3; 677.1; 677.2; 677.4; 678.2; 678.3; 679.1;
679.2; 679.3; 680.1; 680.2; 681.1; 681.2; 682.1; 682.2;
683.1; 683.2; 683.4; 684.2; 684.3; 684.4; 685.2; 685.3;
686.4; 686.5; 687.1; 687.2; 687.3; 688.1; 688.2; 688.3;
688.4; 689.1; 689.2; 690.1; 690.2; 690.3; 691.1; 691.2;
691.4; 692.1; 692.3; 693.1; 693.2; 693.3; 694.2; 694.3;

695.1; 695.2; 695.3; 696.2; 696.3; 697.1; 699.3; 700.2;
701.2; 702.2; 703.2; 704.1; 705.1; 706.1; 706.2; 706.3;
707.3; 708.3; 708.6; 709.1; 709.2; 709.5; 709.9; 710.2;
710.5; 710.8; 711.1; 711.4; 711.7; 711.10; 712.3; 712.6;
712.9; 713.2; 713.5; 713.8; 714.1; 714.4; 714.7; 714.10;
754.1; 760.2; 760.4; 777.6; 783.1; 795.4; 802.2; 831.2;
849.1; 849.2; 855.1; 897.1; 916.1; 916.2; 930.2; 946.2;
947.2; 952.3; 952.4; 953.1; 953.1; 957.3; 957.4; 958.1;
958.4; 964.1; 968.1; 970.3; 970.4; 971.1; 971.2; 972.1;
972.2; 974.9; 974.10; 974.11; 974.12; 976.1; 976.2;
983.1; 983.3; 986.1; 987.1; 987.2; 988.2; 992.5; 992.7;
1001.2; 1001.3; 1002.1; 1009.1; 1015.1; 1015.2; 1016.2;
1028.1; 1028.4; 1028.5; 1028.6; 1029.1; 1029.2; 1034.1;
1034.4; 1034.5; 1035.1; 1036.1; 1037.1; 1039.1; 1047.1;
1047.2; 1048.1; 1057.1; 1058.1; 1059.1; 1060.1; 1061.1;
1062.1; 1064.1; 1064.2; 1065.1; 1065.2; 1068.2; 1069.1;
1069.2; 1069.3; 1070.1; 1070.2; 1071.1; 1071.2; 1072.1;
1072.2; 1073.2; 1074.1; 1075.1; 1078.1; 1079.1; 1080.1;
1081.1; 1082.1; 1083.1; 1084.1; 1084.2; 1086.1; 1087.1;
1089.1; 1089.2; 1090.1; 1091.1; 1092.1; 1093.1; 1093.2;
1094.1; 1095.1; 1096.1; 1096.2; 1097.1; 1098.1; 1098.2;
1099.1; 1100.1; 1101.1; 1101.2; 1103.1; 1103.2; 1104.1;
1105.1; 1105.2; 1107.1; 1119.2; 1269.2; 1403.1; 1404.1;
1450.1.

Richard Stinchcomb shared the following images:
746.1; 1373.1; 1373.2; 1373.3.

Fred Weinberg shared the following images: 1439.1.

John Wexler shared the following image: 592.2.

Index
General Index

INDEX

Alphabetical Index of Dates for Commemoratives